LIST OF SECTIONS

Alphabetical

	SECTION
Charting and Graphic Methods	10
Electronic Computers	16
Inspection	7
Machinery and Equipment Economics	22
Manufacturing Processes	20
Materials Control and Standardization	4
Materials Handling	23
Motion and Methods Study	13
Operations Research	18
Plant Layout and Location	19
Plant Maintenance	24
Plant Organization	1
Process Charts	11
Production Control Systems and Procedures	3
Production Planning and Control	2
Purchasing	5
Quality Control	8
Research and Development	17
Safety and Fire Prevention	25
Statistical Methods	9
Storeskeeping	6
Tools, Jigs, and Fixtures	21
Wage Plans and Controls	15
Work Measurement and Time Study	12
Work Simplification	14

PRODUCTION HANDBOOK

Edited by

GORDON B. CARSON
M.S. in M.E., M.E., D. Eng.

PROFESSOR OF INDUSTRIAL ENGINEERING
DEAN OF THE COLLEGE OF ENGINEERING, AND
DIRECTOR OF THE ENGINEERING EXPERIMENT STATION
THE OHIO STATE UNIVERSITY

SECOND EDITION

NEW YORK
THE RONALD PRESS COMPANY
1967

Library of Congress Catalog Card Number: 58–6733

PRINTED IN THE UNITED STATES OF AMERICA

iii

To Leon Pratt Alford (1877–1942)

Creative engineer, editor, author, and educator, who gave unsparingly of his judgment and wisdom toward the evolution of modern industrial management, and especially for his contributions in developing Management's Handbook, *the* Cost and Production Handbook, *and the First Edition of the* Production Handbook, *this Second Edition is respectfully dedicated.*

PUBLISHERS' PREFACE

The PRODUCTION HANDBOOK has, for many years, served the industrial community with distinction and has become the standard source of authoritative information on the diverse and complex aspects of production management and control.

Broad in scope and thoroughly detailed in its explanation of all phases of production, the Handbook has been widely accepted by seasoned managers, engineers, supervisors, and foremen for bringing their knowledge into sharper focus and giving practical answers to their questions ranging from policy formation to operating procedures. To consultants, controllers, accountants, personnel workers, marketing men, finance men, and others whose work or interests call for an accurate understanding of industrial production and management, it has proved an essential source of information. Those developing toward greater responsibility in industry, as well as those studying it in business, technical, and engineering schools and colleges, have found the Handbook of continual value in broadening and maturing their knowledge of the component production facilities and functions.

It has ever been the purpose of the PRODUCTION HANDBOOK to synthesize from the vast literature of the field the important facts, accepted principles, and tested procedures upon which efficient cost-saving manufacturing operations are based; to present this information in clear, concise terms, appropriately supplemented with examples and illustrations of successful application to production; and to integrate the whole in logically organized form for quick, easy reference. That it fulfils this purpose dependably is amply confirmed by its wide acceptance and constant use the world over.

This eminently practical concept was pioneered by the late L. P. Alford with MANAGEMENT'S HANDBOOK in 1924 and further developed by him in the succeeding volume, COST AND PRODUCTION HANDBOOK. To Dr. Alford, to John R. Bangs who with him added further refinements in editing the First Edition of the PRODUCTION HANDBOOK, and to the hundreds of contributors who have helped to establish the high standards set in these predecessor volumes, much is owed.

While fundamental principles endure, recent advances in the field of production management and engineering have been dramatic. Rapidly expanding knowledge in science, technology, and the management of men has not only given rise to new systems and practices but has also brought about countless refinements in the old. Through accurate analysis and rigorous testing many of yesterday's theories have become proven realities today, often reducible to formulas for immediate application.

These developments, coming over a period of years, are recorded in thousands of scattered sources, including books, magazines, technical journals and transactions, institutional bulletins, and company reports. To search this wealth of literature, much of which is not readily accessible, for significant and enduring fact, and to check the standard books for basic principles is an exacting research job. Add to this the work of evaluating, organizing, and presenting the information thus gleaned in terms that all can readily use and the task becomes truly herculean. The Publishers are indeed fortunate to have secured the services of Gordon B. Carson and his staff of contributing and consulting editors for its accomplishment.

Under the incisive leadership of Dean Carson, the Contributing Editors have not merely brought the facts up to date, but have modernized the presentation. While fully recognizing the value of the older empirical approach, they have reflected the current trend in industry and in management and engineering education by the addition of a complete treatment of analytical tools and methods. These have been carefully integrated and cross-referenced for maximum utility.

To this excellence of editorial skill and technical judgment, the Publishers have added their experience gained in nearly half a century of handbook publishing. The Second Edition of the PRODUCTION HANDBOOK is, therefore, presented with the utmost confidence in its usefulness and dependability.

THE RONALD PRESS COMPANY
Publishers

EDITOR'S PREFACE

EDITOR'S PREFACE

Addressed to all who are engaged in or involved with production, the PRODUC-TION HANDBOOK describes and analyzes every phase and function of the planning, organizing, operation, and control of industry in our economy today.

The interlocking forces of management, engineering, and science are ever active in our dynamic economy. The unceasing drive toward greater productivity and reduced costs has resulted in a multitude of changes in production in the last few years. The lines of demarcation between company functions and departments are constantly shifting as production evolves and new materials, machines, and processes are developed. This new edition of the Handbook has been redesigned and completely revised to synthesize and reflect these developments accurately and comprehensively and to integrate them with enduring fundamental principles. Thus, while much of the basic subject matter of the earlier edition has been retained, all sections have been rewritten and many new sections have been added.

For every production function analyzed in this Handbook, the basic concepts are formulated, the principles explained, planning and designing described, and systems, methods, and operating practices concretely detailed and implemented with cases, forms, tables, and charts. The Handbook fully recognizes that the ultimate purpose of the production phase of industry is to satisfy a healthy, competitive market efficiently and economically. Thus, the inseparable roles of management and engineering in the direction and operation of an industrial enter-prise are analyzed and integrated. The control techniques most directly deriving from mathematics, such as quality control, statistical methods, and charting and graphic methods are explained and exemplified in practice. The work improve-ment and simplification procedures employed in industrial engineering are com-prehensively treated, as well as the powerful new tools for efficient production furnished by operations research, electronic computers, and research and develop-ment. Such recent developments as the use of radioactive materials and its attendant problems to industry are appropriately reflected. Specialized fields of production in industry, including plant location and layout, manufacturing tooling and processing, materials handling, and plant maintenance, are fully detailed and the best modern methods described.

Each section of the Handbook in turn represents a synthesis of the tested knowledge of the field selected by the contributors through a comprehensive evaluation of the literature and company experience on the subject, including countless books, articles, pamphlets, manuals, and reports on outstanding com-pany practices. The Handbook reflects throughout such basic influences on production management and engineering as financing and accounting, materials, type and design of product, automation, transportation, employee relations, dis-tribution, and research. Whatever the production level or problems of the reader, progressive policies, standard practices, a diversity of workable organization, im-plementation, and control procedures, and validated criteria for evaluating results are provided.

Much credit must be shared with the former editors, L. P. Alford and John R. Bangs, and all of the prior contributors for their work in preparing the previous edition of the Handbook. This Second Edition is again the joint product of the thoughtful planning and expert authorship of many men. The contributing editors must be given full credit for their great share in the accomplishment of the revision and the effectiveness of its coverage. While the writing and the thinking of each are reflected throughout the Handbook, their names and the sections to which their major contributions were made are listed below:

George H. Amber ....Electronic Computers
Paul S. Amber ....Electronic Computers
B. H. Amstead ....Manufacturing Processes
James M. Apple ....Plant Layout and Location
Myron L. Begeman ....Manufacturing Processes
Kenneth L. Block ....Materials Control
Francis J. Bradley................................Plant Maintenance
John S. Crout ....Research and Development
William J. Darmody ....Inspection
John W. Enell ....Quality Control
J. W. Gavett ....Work Measurement and Time Study
Henry P. Goode ....Statistical Methods
Herbert F. Goodwin ....⎰Process Charts
                                              ⎱Work Simplification
Robert E. Greenlee ....Research and Development
Thomas T. Holme ....Plant Organization
George D. Hudelson ....Plant Layout and Location
George E. Kane ....Tools, Jigs, and Fixtures
Clyde H. Kearns ....Charting and Graphic Methods
O. D. Lascoe ....Machinery and Equipment Economics
K. A. Lifson ....Statistical Methods
H. P. Losely ....Plant Maintenance
John F. Magee.....................................Operations Research
Frank W. McBee, Jr. ....Manufacturing Processes
Gerald Nadler ....⎰Motion and Methods Study
                                            ⎱Process Charts
Eugene Richman ....Storeskeeping
William E. Ritchie ....⎰Production Control Systems and Procedures
                             ⎱Production Planning and Control
H. Barrett Rogers ....Wage Plans and Controls
Albert Romeo ....Machinery and Equipment Economics
E. Ralph Sims, Jr. ....Materials Handling
Joseph K. Walkup ....Safety and Fire Prevention
W. B. Wight ....Purchasing

For the work of the other members of the Board of Contributing and Consulting Editors, whose functions ranged from rendering advice and counsel to providing additional significant material of great value to those charged with the preparation of this edition, I am very grateful. Special thanks must be given also to Albert Romeo for his assistance in the work of revision and proofing. Finally, the Editor wishes to express his deep gratitude for the enthusiasm with which countless companies, professional societies, and individuals provided materials for the Handbook. Specific acknowledgment is given elsewhere for the many publications referred to in the preparation of this book.

GORDON B. CARSON

CONTENTS

	SECTION
PLANT ORGANIZATION	1
PRODUCTION PLANNING AND CONTROL	2
PRODUCTION CONTROL SYSTEMS AND PROCEDURES	3
MATERIALS CONTROL AND STANDARDIZATION	4
PURCHASING	5
STORESKEEPING	6
INSPECTION	7
QUALITY CONTROL	8
STATISTICAL METHODS	9
CHARTING AND GRAPHIC METHODS	10
PROCESS CHARTS	11
WORK MEASUREMENT AND TIME STUDY	12
MOTION AND METHODS STUDY	13
WORK SIMPLIFICATION	14
WAGE PLANS AND CONTROLS	15
ELECTRONIC COMPUTERS	16
RESEARCH AND DEVELOPMENT	17
OPERATIONS RESEARCH	18
PLANT LAYOUT AND LOCATION	19
MANUFACTURING PROCESSES	20
TOOLS, JIGS, AND FIXTURES	21
MACHINERY AND EQUIPMENT ECONOMICS	22
MATERIALS HANDLING	23
PLANT MAINTENANCE	24
SAFETY AND FIRE PREVENTION	25
ACKNOWLEDGMENTS	A
INDEX	

CONTENTS

SECTION

1. Plant Organization . . . .
2. Production Planning and Control . . .
3. Production Control Systems and Procedures
4. Materials Control and Standardization .
5. Purchasing . . . .
6. Storekeeping . . . . . .
7. Inspection . . . . . .
8. Quality Control . . . .
9. Statistical Methods . . .
10. Charting and Graphic Methods .
11. Process Charts . . . .
12. Work Measurement and Time Study
13. Motion and Methods Study . .
14. Work Simplification . . . .
15. Wage Plans and Controls . .
16. Electronic Computers . . .
17. Research and Development .
18. Operations Research . . .
19. Plant Layout and Location .
20. Manufacturing Processes .
21. Tools, Jigs and Fixtures .
22. Machinery and Equipment Economics
23. Materials Handling . . .
24. Plant Maintenance . . .
25. Safety and Fire Prevention .
A. Acknowledgments . . . .
    Index

PLANT ORGANIZATION

CONTENTS

Nature of Organization

PAGE

Scope of organization 1
Purpose of organization 1
The element of objective 1
Framework of organization 1
Aspects of industrial organization 2
Factors or components 2
Functions and activities 2
Structural relationships 2
Definitions of organization 2
Administration 3
Management 3
Organization 3

Policies and Organization

Relation of policies and organization 4
The policy manual 4
Policy enforcement 4

Development of a Plan of Organization

Determination of fundamentals 5
Authority 5
Responsibility 5
Duties 6
Principles of organization 6
Industrial organization design 7
Lines of authority and response in an industrial organization (f. 1) 7
Degrees of responsibility and corresponding duties in an industrial organization (f. 2) 8
Work division in industrial organization 8
Coordination in organization 9
Ideal for an industrial organization 10
Functions of organization and their assignment, as compared with the functioning of the human body (f. 3) 9

Types of Organization

Line organization 10
Requirements for command 10
Features of line organization 10
Advantages and disadvantages of line control 11
Taylor system of functional foremanship .. 11
Taylor plan of functional foremanship (f. 4) 12
Evaluation of Taylor's functional organization 12
Importance of the functional idea 13

PAGE

Line and staff organization 14
Separation of operating authority and advisory service 14
Illustration of line and staff relationship (f. 5) 15
Advantages and disadvantages 15
Staff plan of coordination 16
Staff assistants 16
Duties of staff assistants 16
Committee organization 17
Classification of types 17
Principles of operation 17
Committee functions 18
Advantages and disadvantages 18
Examples of committees 19
General executive committee 19
Joint labor-management committees 19
Shop conference committee 19
Equipment committee 20
Plant safety committee 20
Grievance committee 20
Criticism of committees 20
Multiple management 21
The four boards 21
Operation of the boards 21
Benefits to employees and company 22

Factors in Planning an Organization

Allotment of duties in an organization 23
The ladder or bridge of Fayol 23
Cross contacts or relationships illustrated by the "ladder" or "bridge" of Fayol (f. 6) 23
Essentials for maintaining intersecting relationships 24
Span of control 24
Increase in interrelationships as number of subordinates increases under the span of control (f. 7) 26
Graphical analysis of the span of control (f. 8) 27
Geometric increase in number of primary operative employees and number of operative executives with increasing size of line organization (f. 9)......... 27
Executive levels 28
Determining the levels 28
The five important levels 28
Top executives 29
Senior executives 29
Intermediate executives 29
Junior executives 30
Supervisors and foremen 31

CONTENTS (*Continued*)

PAGE

Intercommunication between levels 31
Qualifications of a top executive 31
Qualifications of other executives 32

Organization Charts and Manuals

Fundamental considerations 33
Organization charts 35
  Drawing organization charts 35
    Four typical ways of drawing organiza-
    tion charts (*f.* 10) 36
  Examples of organization charts 36
    Organization chart of a typical manu-
    facturing company (*f.* 11) 38–39
    The organization approach 36
    Organization chart of the General Elec-
    tric Co. (*f.* 12) 40–41
  Organization chart constructed horizontally 42
  Organization reporting to the vice-presi-
  dent—The Chesapeake & Potomac
  Telephone Co. (*f.* 13) 43
  Organization reporting to the chief en-
  gineer—The Chesapeake & Potomac
  Telephone Co. (*f.* 14) 43

PAGE

Aircraft engineering department chart 44
  General plan of organization of the
  engineering department in representa-
  tive aircraft companies (*f.* 15) 44
A comprehensive system of company
  charts 45
  Organization of the Sperry Gyroscope
  Co. (*f.* 16) 45
  Chart of a typical Sperry Gyroscope
  division (*f.* 17) 46
The organization manual 46
Administration of a company manual 47
  Typewritten organization chart from
  organization manual (*f.* 18) 48
Position descriptions 49
Standard practice instructions 53

Analysis of Organization and Procedures

Organization analysis 54
Inspection of policy and organization 54
Effect of organization on operating results.. 55

PLANT ORGANIZATION

Nature of Organization

SCOPE OF ORGANIZATION. The subject of organization, in its broadest definition, includes (1) the persons who man a company, (2) the respective places they occupy, (3) the range of authority and responsibility they individually exercise, (4) the framework of relations through which they contact and deal with one another, and (5) the mechanisms through which they operate and coordinate their activities in the enterprise. It is upon the basis of persons, positions, authority, contacts, operations, and coordination that successful production work is carried on.

PURPOSE OF ORGANIZATION. Rabbe (Mechanical Engineering, vol. 63) states that:

Organization concerns itself with the classification or grouping of the activities of an enterprise for purposes of administering them. Organization is to business what the nervous system is to the human body. Its purpose is to send instructions (impulses) to the operating members and to receive and transmit to top management (the brain) information which will enable it to function intelligently.

Spriegel and Lansburgh (Industrial Management) observe that:

There is a wide range of opinion regarding the relative importance of organization. One executive will claim that almost any type of organization will work so long as the right people are operating it. Other administrators lay great stress on organization charts, procedures, and techniques, and adapt the human factor to this framework. Perhaps a compromise between these two views is the best plan, giving due consideration to the human side of organization and using certain proved charts and guides, procedures and techniques.

Good management concerns itself with the development of people as well as the direction of things. Proper selection, training, and upgrading form the very basis of morale building, and morale can make or break an organization.

Organizing is for the purpose of creating relationships that will minimize friction, focus on the objective, clearly define the responsibilities of all parties, and facilitate the attaining of the objective. A sound organizational structure creates an atmosphere in which both personal and group satisfactions may be realized, cooperation is encouraged, morale and the "will to do" are substituted for detailed orders, and the group moves smoothly and resolutely towards its goal.

THE ELEMENT OF OBJECTIVE. Whenever two or more persons unite to attain a common purpose an organization is formed. Organization, the framework within which individuals unite, is an essential in reaching toward a **common objective.** In spite of this fact, successful and adequately functioning organizations are rare. Most organizations are short-lived, at any rate in their original form, and those that have had uninterrupted success are exceptions. The types of organizations set up in industrial enterprises are discussed here.

FRAMEWORK OF ORGANIZATION. The structure of industrial organization under usual conditions of operation is the result of growth. Concerns start in a small way and gradually expand. One or two men have authority and all responsibilities at first and, by force of circumstances, operation centers in and around them. As growth continues, this method of operation and control becomes ineffective and a **planned or formal framework of organization** becomes imperative. Determining the organizational structure to satisfy this demand is not a one-time decision but rather a continuing consideration.

With the passage of time, any fixed organization will degenerate under mechanical and routinized operation and hence the organizational structure must be **continuously studied** and periodically revamped to prevent stagnation or stunted growth.

ASPECTS OF INDUSTRIAL ORGANIZATION.

The industrial organization like the proverbial elephant studied and described by the three blind men, takes on an apparent form depending upon the angle from which it is viewed. In order that a true picture may be obtained it is necessary to study an industrial organization from at least **three different viewpoints.**

Factors or Components. Certainly the initial viewpoint should be of the factors and components which go to make up an industrial organization, such as men, money, machines, materials, methods, and ideas. If one is to understand the whole he must have knowledge of the parts.

Functions and Activities. Contrasted to the properties of an industrial organization are its processes, its functions and activities, studies of work flow, authority, reward and penalty, evaluation, and perpetuation. Coordination, communication, and control can, when integrated, present probably the most valuable viewpoint of all. Of course, implied here under functions, is that undesirable feature of malfunctions.

Structural Relationships. Most common of all studies or viewpoints of organization is that of the structural relationships of the factors involved in the enterprises. In reality it is the study of the **delegation of responsibility,** which may be made along the lines of product, subproducts, territory, function, or some other rational basis. Besides the factor of viewpoint, **timing** is a most important aspect in the study of an industrial organization. Like the athletic organization it is dynamic in character and thus its true picture can only be captured by the equivalent of the motion picture camera. Just as it is possible, however, to take a still picture of a football team with each man in position, so too it is possible to picture or to chart an industrial organization as of some moment. Such a record is useful but certainly not essential. It is the organization which comes first, not the picture, and it would be as foolish to reverse the process as it would be to hold up a picture before a group of individuals and say, "Look like this!"

There is another aspect of organization always present in an industrial concern, unseen and intangible but none the less real and existent. This aspect is sometimes known as the **informal organization.** It comprehends the endowments, character, and personality of the individuals who form the organization personnel. If the informal organization is good, it will function with less friction. Many of the activities of industrial managers are concerned with this informal organizaton, the interaction of persons, and the endless chain of effects that arise from human associations.

DEFINITIONS OF ORGANIZATION.

The literature of industrial organization and management is probably the most confusing of all disciplines since it contains such a conflict of terminology. The same word can mean two different things, even diametrically opposed concepts, and different words can stand for one and the same. The word "therblig" is probably the only term concerning which there can be no doubt as to meaning. Even the new contributors to the field have developed a jargon which intermingles the old terms with new to define new concepts or redefine old. Besides the over-all term of **organization** there are two other principal terms which are victims of this confusion: **management** and **administration**. Each of these terms is applied to a function as well as to the personnel group responsible for that function. Probably the principal difference in use of these terms occurs between British and United States usage. In the United States, the predominant support is for "that function of an enterprise which concerns itself with over-all determination of policies and major objectives" to be called administration, while the term management is reserved for "that function which concerns itself with the direction and control of the various activities to attain the business objectives." Definitions of administration, management, and organization given by authorities in these areas follow.

Administration. Sheldon (The Philosophy of Management) has defined administration as "the function in industry concerned in the determination of the corporate policy, the coordination of finance, production, and distribution, the settlement of the compass of the organization, and the ultimate control of the executive." Holden *et al.* (Top-Management Organization and Control) indicate that: "The administrative function includes the active planning, direction, coordination, and control of the business as a whole, within the scope of basic policies established and authority delegated by the board. In other words, this function involves the determination of objectives, of operating policies, and of results."

Management. The Management Division of A.S.M.E. has defined management as the "art and science of preparing, organizing, and directing human effort applied to control the forces and to utilize the materials of nature for the benefit of man." Sheldon (The Philosophy of Management) states that: "Management proper is the function in industry concerned in the execution of policy, within the limits set up by administration, and the employment of the organization for the particular objects set before it."

Organization. Alford defines organization as: "Division of work to be done into defined tasks and assignment of these tasks to individuals qualified by training and natural characteristics for their efficient accomplishment." Brown (Organization of Industry) states that: "Organization defines the part that each member of an enterprise is expected to perform and the relations among those members, to the end that their concerted endeavor shall be most effective for the purposes of the enterprise." Sheldon defines organization as "the process of so combining the work which individuals or groups have to perform with the faculties necessary for its execution that the duties so formed provide the best channels for the efficient, systematic, positive, and coordinated application of the available effort."

Sheldon also presents one of the best summaries defining these terms in relation to one another:

Organization is the formation of an effective machine; management of an effective executive; administration of an effective direction. Administration determines the organization; management uses it. Administration defines the goal; management strives toward it. Organization is the machine of management in its achievement of the ends determined by administration.

Policies and Organization

RELATION OF POLICIES AND ORGANIZATION. A necessary preliminary to all activity in an industrial enterprise is a clear, complete statement of the object of the activity, formulated as a policy or set of instructions. In this connection an **industrial policy** can be thought of as a code or general rule which states the established procedure to follow in a recurring situation. Policies considered here are those set up by production executives as part of the managerial procedure of operating the plant to produce the product. A policy of this kind establishes objectives and formulates plans for achieving them. Thus all rules, regulations, and systems should be explicit expressions of formulated policies.

Determination of policies is an important step; if policies are wrong, the subsequent results may bring confusion and losses. Policies must be based on (1) thorough investigation and analysis and (2) a full appreciation of consequences, both good and bad. **Adoption of a policy** requires on the part of managers both ability and courage, for fundamentally a policy at the time of its adoption is intended to initiate a change, to improve conditions, to correct ineffectiveness, or to eliminate inefficiencies.

THE POLICY MANUAL. The policy manual or "policy book" is a valuable management device, but one that is not widely used except for personnel relations. It can be employed for any one or all of the several kinds of policies found in a production organization—managerial or supervisory, long range, general, or departmental. Its advantages are: (1) it avoids misunderstandings, friction, lost motion and expense, for the policies are written down; (2) it facilitates a check on compliance; (3) it aids in indoctrinating or inculcating throughout the executive and supervisory personnel the principles and procedures necessary to put the policies into effect.

Mooney and Reiley (The Principles of Organization) emphasize the importance of **indoctrination** if freedom of action is to be secured in a production organization:

Industrial indoctrination simply means thorough definition of the principles governing the industrial policy. It includes the application of the principles through line delegation of authority, the staff function, the duties and responsibilities of each in relation to the others, the place and purpose of rules and procedures, and the comprehension of this doctrine throughout the organization.

POLICY ENFORCEMENT. Inasmuch as a policy is a statement of procedure, of something to be done and how to do it, it has within itself no force to bring results. **Executive action** is needed to make any policy effective. The stronger and more effective the leadership exerted, the greater the probability that policies will be adequately enforced and predetermined results realized. In other words, achievements in manufacturing enterprises come from decisions put into effect by the will of the one who is responsible for policy enforcement and who exercises leadership. It is a familiar saying that any institution is but the shadow of a man, of a creative mind, and that statement is particularly true of industrial plants.

Whatever an organization accomplishes by way of achievement or economic results depends upon the **quality of leadership** that organizes, directs, and manages the efforts of every individual, from president to laborer. A plant cannot attain sound objectives or achieve adequate results if its leaders are deficient in ethics, abilities, or volition. The capacity of an individual for leadership appears to be the net sum of all his powers.

Development of a Plan of Organization

DETERMINATION OF FUNDAMENTALS. In setting up a plan of organization, the first step is the determination of the fundamentals that are to enter into the design, and their relationships. These fundamentals are: policies, authorities, responsibilities, and duties or activities. Policies have been presented in preceding paragraphs; authorities, responsibilities, and duties are discussed in those immediately following.

Authority. The term authority may be defined as follows: In an organizational sense, authority is the right of one person to require another person to perform certain duties.

Authority is the right to act, decide, and command. In a corporation it emanates from the stockholders, flows to the elected board of directors, whence it is delegated to designated persons who issue orders and instructions to subordinates. Authority may be classified as either (1) direct or (2) delegated. **Direct** authority exists where the line between the issuer and acceptor is unbroken; **delegated** authority exists where an intermediate agency is between the issuer and acceptor.

Authority may have one or more of these aspects:

1. It may be **formal,** that is, conferred by law or delegated within an organization.
2. It may be **functional** or intrinsic, because it is based on special knowledge or skill.
3. It may be **personal,** that is, accorded because of seniority, popularity, or outstanding qualities of leadership.

While authority is the right to require performance of duties by another, nevertheless authority rests upon the **acceptance** of the orders or instructions by the person to whom they are addressed. Barnard (The Functions of the Executive) has this to say:

The necessity of the assent of the individual to establish authority for him is inescapable. A person can and will accept a communication as authoritative only when four conditions simultaneously obtain: (1) he can and does understand the communication; (2) at the time of his decision he believes it is not inconsistent with the purpose of the organization; (3) at the time of his decision he believes it to be compatible with his personal interest as a whole; and (4) he is able mentally and physically to comply with it.

Responsibility. A clear conception of the significance of the term responsibility is presented in the following definition: "In an organizational sense, responsibility is accountability for the performance of assigned duties."

Responsibility is a moral attribute. It implies fulfillment of a task, duty, or obligation according to orders given or promises made. Authority is commonly delegated only to persons of proven responsibility.

Organizational design calls for setting up **limits of responsibility** for each activity and effort; otherwise shortcoming or failure cannot be traced to its source and cause. Executives of weak responsibility cannot carry the burden of many simultaneous obligations or make the multitude of decisions necessary in the operation of an industrial concern. Barnard (The Functions of the Executive) supports this statement:

Executive positions (1) imply a complex morality, and (2) require a high capacity of responsibility, (3) under conditions of activity, necessitating (4) commensurate general and specific technical abilities as a moral factor—in addition there is required (5) the faculty of creating morals for others.

Duties. The activities assigned to a person in an organization are best specified in the form of duties, a term which may be thus defined: "In an organizational sense, the duties allotted to an individual are the activities he is required to perform because of the place he occupies in the organization."

A duty is that which a person is bound by obligation to do. In a factory it is often called "a piece of work," a job, a task, or a **work assignment.** In an organizational sense it is a contribution to the goal or objective, and an organization can be thought of as a system of coordinated contributions, or a system of coordinated activities.

PRINCIPLES OF ORGANIZATION. Urwick (Notes on The Theory of Organization) presents the following "Ten Principles of Organization":

1. The Principle of the **Objective:** Every organization and every part of every organization must be an expression of the purpose of the undertaking concerned or it is meaningless and therefore redundant. You cannot organize in a vacuum; you must organize for something.
2. The Principle of **Specialization:** The activities of every member of any organized group should be confined, as far as possible, to the performance of a single function.
3. The Principle of **Coordination:** The purpose of organizing per se, as distinguished from the purpose of the undertaking, is to facilitate coordination; unity of effort.
4. The Principle of **Authority:** In every organized group the supreme authority must rest somewhere. There should be a clear line of authority from the supreme authority to every individual in the group.

    This principle has also been called "The Scalar Principle" (Mooney and Reiley, Onward Industry), "The Hierarchical Principle" (Henri Fayol, Administration Industrielle et Générale) and "The Chain of Command" (military writers, *passim*).

5. The Principle of **Responsibility:** The responsibility of the superior for the acts of his subordinate is absolute.
6. The Principle of **Definition:** The content of each position—the duties involved, the authority and responsibility contemplated, and the relationships with other positions should be clearly defined in writing and published to all concerned.
7. The Principle of **Correspondence:** In every position the responsibility and the authority should correspond.
8. The **Span of Control:** No person should supervise more than five, or at the most six, direct subordinates whose work interlocks.
9. The Principle of **Balance:** It is essential that the various units of an organization should be kept in balance.
10. The Principle of **Continuity:** Reorganization is a continuous process; in every undertaking specific provisions should be made for it.

In contrast to Urwick's "Ten Principles of Organization," Spriegel and Lansburgh (Industrial Management) list primary and operating fundamentals of organization. "Primary fundamentals deal with those phases of management which include policy formulation and organization structure. The operating fundamentals deal almost entirely with the operating phase of management."

The Primary Fundamentals

1. Regard for the aim and objectives of the enterprise.
2. The establishment of definite lines of supervision within the organization structure.
3. The placing of fixed responsibility among the various persons and departments within the organization.
4. Regard for the personal equation.

The Operating Fundamentals

1. The development of an adequate system.
2. The establishment of adequate records to implement the system and to use as a basis of control.
3. The laying down of proper operating rules and regulations within the established organization in keeping with the established policies.
4. The exercise of effective leadership.

The express purpose of organization is to develop coordination and morale, yet certain features or organizational building may result in counter effects.

INDUSTRIAL ORGANIZATION DESIGN. Industrial organization design recognizes: (1) levels of authority and (2) degrees of responsibility. The **line of authority** (line of command, or line of instruction) goes down from a higher to a lower level of authority. The **line of response** (line of performance, or line of accountability) comes up from a lower to a higher level of authority. These lines are also called **lines of communication,** and may be used to ask questions directed up or down the lines. In addition to these principal lines there is another function in the functional, or expert, staff.

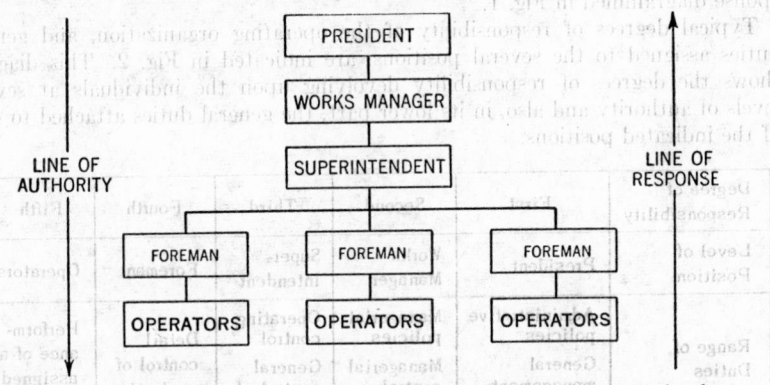

Fig. 1. Lines of authority and response in an industrial organization.

A typical line of industrial authority is shown in Fig. 1, wherein titular positions are indicated as president, works manager, superintendent, foreman, and operators giving five **levels of authority.** This number of levels is seldom exceeded except in very large organizations. The arrow at the left of the diagram indicates the flow of authority and issuing of orders from the president down, level by level, until the operators are reached. The arrow at the right indicates the line of response whereby reports and returns flow upward from operators to whatever level these reports are directed. This line of response should be open for operators to send suggestions, make complaints, and ask for adjustment of grievances in such a way that these communications will reach the level of authority and responsibility at which action can be taken. These lines of communication hold the organization together and make a coordinated operating unit. They make possible the enforcement of policies and execution of orders with economy and dispatch.

Methods, procedures, and techniques of communication are an important factor in carrying on an industrial organization, and their excellence and effectiveness of use mean much to the efficiency of organizational performance. In this connection Barnard (The Functions of the Executive) says:

In an exhaustive theory of organization, communication would occupy a central place, because the structure, extensiveness, and scope of organization are almost entirely determined by communication techniques.

Certain **controlling factors** are essential to frictionless operation of organizational lines of communication. Barnard recognizes seven subfactors:

1. The channels of communication should be definitely known.
2. A definite, formal channel of communication is required to every member of an organization.
3. The line of communication must be as direct or short as possible.
4. The complete line of communication should usually be used.
5. The competence of the persons serving as communication centers, that is, officers, supervisory heads, must be adequate.
6. The line of communication should not be interrupted during the time when the organization is to function.
7. Every communication transmitted along the line of communication should be authenticated.

There are many variations from the simple, typical lines of authority and response diagrammed in Fig. 1.

Typical degrees of responsibility of the operating organization, and general duties assigned to the several positions, are indicated in Fig. 2. This diagram shows the degrees of responsibility devolving upon the individuals at several levels of authority and also, in its lower part, the general duties attached to each of the indicated positions.

Degree of Responsibility	First	Second	Third	Fourth	Fifth
Level of Position	President	Works Manager	Super-intendent	Foreman	Operators
Range of Duties	Administrative policies General management	Managerial policies Managerial control	Operating control General control of production	Detail control of production	Performance of an assigned job

Fig. 2. Degrees of responsibility and corresponding duties in an industrial organization.

WORK DIVISION IN INDUSTRIAL ORGANIZATION. Work division is the foundation of the approach to determine the relation of duties to be performed and the selection of individuals to whom duties are to be assigned in a production organization. Assignment of separate duties is necessary because of: (1) volume or amount of work to be done in an industrial plant; (2) differences in nature, capability, and skill of men; and (3) range of knowledge required in an organization which is so vast that one individual can command only a fraction of it.

Although work division is the foundation of organization, there are **limitations** beyond which it should not be carried. (1) No advantage is gained by subdividing work so minutely that the resulting task is less than that which a man can perform when working continuously. (2) Technology and custom make it impractical to subdivide certain kinds of work, although the influence of these factors is subject to change. (3) Subdivision must not be carried to the point of organic subdivision.

COORDINATION IN ORGANIZATION. When duties and activities are subdivided and allotted throughout a production organization, means must be provided to have all of them performed and all the product turned out on time; that is, everything must be completed according to a predetermined schedule. This process of timing activities and reuniting subdivided work in a factory is called **coordination.** The mechanism, or normal routine, through which coordination is achieved is the **system.**

The necessity for timing the doing of work, or coordinating efforts, is apparent by observing a gang of men hauling on a rope, or moving a heavy object. Members of the group must pull together, or heave together, if the work is to be done. Otherwise their efforts are wasted. An even simpler illustration is that of two men carrying a table or bench. They must lift together and walk in step in the same direction if they are to move the piece of furniture from one place to another.

Coordination means to combine activity into a consistent and harmonious action. It is exhibited in the highest degree of perfection in the functioning of the human

Function	Human Body	Business as a Whole	Manufacturing	Selling
Direction	Brain and "sixth sense"	Executive heads, "assistants to" executive heads	Works Manager	Sales Manager
Expert Advice	Five senses	Professional auditors, appraisers, consulting engineers, lawyers patent attorneys	Industrial engineers, research and development engineers	Marketing specialist
Control and Coordination	Cerebellum	Controller, financial control	Production and planning engineers	Sales Planning and Control
Service and Facilitation	Involuntary organs	Service departments	Maintenance, Purchasing, Personnel	Sales Promotion and Advertising
Performance	Voluntary organs	Manufacturing and Selling	Operating departments, workers	Sales Department, salesmen

(C. E. Knoeppel)

Fig. 3. Functions of organization and their assignment, as compared with the functioning of the human body.

body. Coordination of the kind which exists between mind and muscles of the human body is the ideal of an industrial organization. The highest form of coordination in industry is that in which an entire group consciously accepts the objectives and policies laid down by the leader and consciously acquiesces in disciplines which are necessary to achieve the purpose. This type of coordination is possible only in a carefully selected, well-trained organization.

Barnard (The Functions of the Executive) lays emphasis on the willingness of persons to contribute their efforts as an indispensable factor in the successful operation of organization. All of the components and forces of organization must work in harmony and unison. Activities must be kept in balance and properly timed at each level of authority.

Ideal for an Industrial Organization. An ideal industrial organization would be one that functioned as perfectly as does a **normal, healthy human body** (see Fig. 3). Another apt comparison is to a well-trained and coordinated football team, knowing thoroughly every play and signal, quick to diagnose and offset opponents' tactics, snapping into action instantaneously, and running every play with perfect teamwork.

Types of Organization

LINE ORGANIZATION. Line of authority, or command, in its simple form is often referred to as the **military type of organization.** Its prototype is the organization of an army in its line or operational activities, apart from the present-day staff or planning and strategy functions, and probably it is as old as the combining of individuals for a joint activity, such as hunting or war. In its simple, typical form it is not so extensively used as formerly in industry, except in small shops. In larger companies it is now usually combined with the functional or expert staff.

Requirements for Command. Because of the ancient origin and continued use of line organization, its relations are well defined. Henri Fayol, the French industrialist, laid down the requirements of command for the functioning of a line organization as follows:

1. There must be a thorough knowledge of the working force.
2. Incompetence must be eliminated.
3. There must be a sound knowledge of the agreements between the management and its employees.
4. Those in authority must set a good example to the working force.
5. The organization must be periodically examined with the help of charts.

Features of Line Organization. A business controlled under the line form of organization may act more quickly and effectively in changing its direction and policy than any other form of organization. Authority is passed down from the owners through a board of directors to a general manager, to whom report the heads of the various departments. Each department in most instances is a complete self-sustaining unit, its head being responsible for the performance of its particular process, product, or function. This means that the foreman must (1) direct its techniques, (2) formulate the necessary work specifications, (3) sometimes purchase materials, (4) plan and schedule the work, (5) oversee the necessary materials handling, and (6) keep the necessary shop cost and production records. This same procedure would be repeated in all other departments with complete control centered in each head, subject only to the will of the general manager. What little research, planning, or central record-keeping is absolutely required falls upon the general manager. Fig. 1 is a partial presentation of such a plan in diagrammatic form.

The line organization is very stable and ideas and orders travel strictly according to the line of authority. There is never any question as to who is boss. Each division, department, or section is under a supervisor or foreman who is completely responsible for the work of his unit, except for those particular items which the general manager reserves for his own attention. The only interrelationship between the various departments is such as the general manager may establish. In short, he must be in constant touch with all the details of the business, and make decisions constantly, based upon, and involving, these details. It is obvious that this plan of organization grows more unwieldy and inefficient the larger the company becomes.

Advantages and Disadvantages of Line Control. The advantages and disadvantages of line control may be summarized briefly as follows:

Advantages:
1. It is simple.
2. There is a clear-cut division of authority and responsibility.
3. It is extremely stable.
4. It makes for quick action.
5. Discipline is easily maintained.

Disadvantages:
1. The organization is rigid and inflexible.
2. Being an autocratic system, it may be operated on an arbitrary, opinionated, and dictatorial basis.
3. Department heads carry out orders independently and often in accordance with their own whims and desires.
4. As division of labor is only incidental, crude methods may prevail because of lack of expert advice.
5. There is undue reliance upon the skill and personal knowledge of operators.
6. Foremen may offer resistance to much-needed changes.
7. Key men are loaded to the breaking point.
8. The loss of one or two capable men may cripple the entire organization.
9. Difficulty of operation occurs in large or complex enterprises.

The line relationship in modern industry is extremely important, although because of its obvious limitations, as stated previously, there are perhaps few companies, except small shops, that operate entirely by line organization control.

TAYLOR SYSTEM OF FUNCTIONAL FOREMANSHIP. In the process of his investigations, Frederick W. Taylor, who developed what became known as "scientific management," made an analysis of the duties of a first-class foreman as found in the organization of his day. In his writings he states that such a foreman must:

1. Be a good machinist.
2. Be able to read drawings readily.
3. Plan the work of his department and see that it is properly prepared.
4. See that each man keeps his machine clean and in good order.
5. See that each man turns out work of the proper quality.
6. See that the men work steadily and fast.
7. See that the work flows through the work centers in the proper sequence.
8. In a general way, supervise timekeeping and rate setting.
9. Maintain discipline and adjust wages.

Since men possessing three, four, or five of these qualities were readily obtainable, he assigned them to specialized duties in harmony with their characteristics and training, such that they would act as **functional** rather than **all-round** foremen. He gave this explanation of his idea: "Functional management consists in so dividing the work of management that each man from the assistant superintendent down shall have as few functions as possible to perform."

The plan really means loading each man to capacity. Taylor discovered, moreover, that the typical foreman of his day was loaded with much clerical duty as well as operating responsibility. He found it necessary to remove the **planning activities** from the shop, where they were performed at low efficiency and hampered production, into the hands of men who could specialize in such work. Thus production could be speeded up and costs radically reduced.

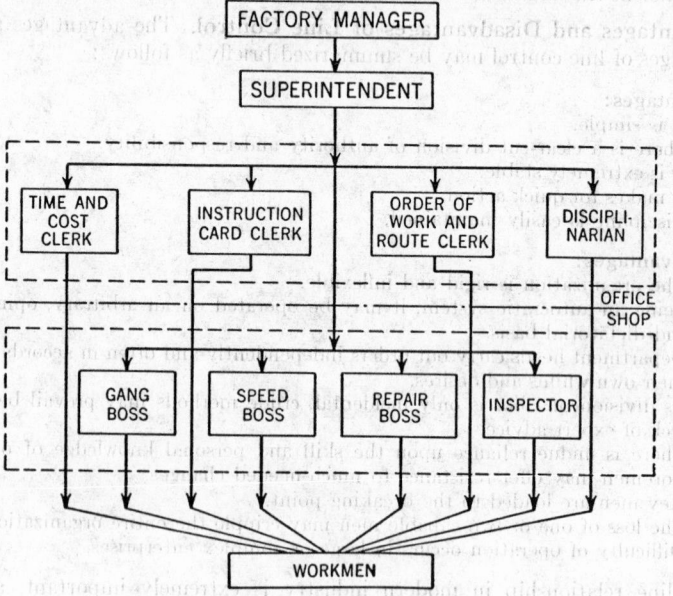

Fig. 4. Taylor plan of functional foremanship.

The **separation of the functions** was made as shown in Fig. 4. The time and cost clerk, instruction card clerk, and order-of-work and route clerk attended to the mental and clerical functions of production, while the gang boss, speed boss, repair boss, and inspector looked after the actual production in the shop. A disciplinarian was appointed to look after the disciplinary functions of the whole plant.

The duties of the gang boss were to see that machines were set up for jobs and that work was moved efficiently from machine to machine. The speed boss served as an instructor to the workmen and saw that they maintained the specified rates of production. The repair boss and the inspector performed the duties that their titles indicate.

Evaluation of Taylor's Functional Organization. The marked advantage of this type of organization was that each function was administered by specialists. Expert advice was available to each individual worker, and division of labor was carefully planned. In fact, functional organization was highly instructional. The specialists in the various fields served as instructors, with suitable authority.

The marked disadvantage of Taylor's functional plan of organization was that it gave eight foremen or supervisors, in turn as occasion arose, direct authority or temporary supervision of some form over the individual workmen, whereas it is now clearly recognized that no man can work satisfactorily for, or obey, the instructions of more than one foreman or executive. The plan, however, called for so many interrelationships and such integrated coordination that it became cumbersome and topheavy.

An analysis of the advantages and disadvantages of this system of organization are:

Advantages

1. Functional organization is based on expert knowledge.
2. Division of labor is planned, not incidental.
3. The highest functional efficiency of each person is maintained.
4. The manual work is separated from the mental—a separation initiated by Taylor.

Disadvantages

1. A relative lack of stability is manifest.
2. The coordinating influences needed to insure a smoothly functioning organization may involve heavy overhead expenses.
3. The inability to locate and fix responsibility may seriously affect the discipline and morale of the workers through apparent or actual contradiction of orders.
4. Overlapping authority may give rise to friction between foremen and supervisors.
5. The initiative of supervisors may become stifled. Men may become mere automatons and routine may become very complicated.

Importance of the Functional Idea. The functional foremanship plan or organization was applied to plants mainly by Taylor, the group of men who were associated with him as consultants, and certain executives who saw the importance of Taylor's work and early adopted his principles and methods. Experience, however, showed the seriousness of its disadvantages as a physical arrangement, and as such it had gradually disappeared by about 1920. It did provide for specialists to do all the preliminary planning of work in the shop offices, leaving the foremen free to become highly efficient in their four major responsibilities—getting work done according to plan and schedule, setting standards for work, training workers for higher proficiency and gradually increased earnings, and directly handling grievances and all other immediate personnel problems with their workers. This was one of the most progressive steps in the entire field of industrial management.

Some concept of the influence of functional foremanship is gained by examining closely any modern organization chart. Therein, to one familiar with the Taylor plan, it is clearly evident that the functions are all provided for in the following manner:

1. The gang boss is now usually two men—the set-up man, and the move man, trucker, or craneman.
2. The speed boss is the assistant foreman.
3. The repair boss has become a maintenance engineer.
4. The inspector heads the inspection organization. There is now often a supervisor of quality control.
5. The time and cost clerk is replaced by two men—the payroll clerk and the cost accountant.
6. The instruction card man has become the time-and-motion-study engineer.

7. The order-of-work and route clerk has developed into two men—one scheduling work and doing machine loading, and the other the methods engineer or individual who plans procedures and prepares operation lists for the parts and assemblies.

Taylor's developments along the above lines became the basis of the present-day **line and staff plan of organization**, in which the recognition of functions, and the corresponding assignment of specialized advisory and facilitation duties to staff individuals who give their attention solely to such work, has tremendously aided and increased the efficiency of line performance in the industrial plant.

Without the staff function modern industry and business could not operate except at tremendous disadvantages. Every industrial organization gets its real work done by action according to a preplanned program set up and operated by the line organization. The aim is **accomplishment**—quickly, efficiently, and at reasonable cost. The basis of the most successful action, however, is **preplanning** to set up goals which inspire men to accomplishment and then devise the ways for attaining the objectives. Those who work out and recommend these ways are the **specialists** in the organization. They are appointed by the operating executives to concentrate their thinking and to develop their funds of information and their analytical skills so as to become experts or authorities upon the respective special subjects to which they have been assigned. Executives who actively operate the organization to get the work actually done then take the suggestions and recommendations of the various specialists, modify them where necessary, and convert them from possibilities into actualities by translating the ideas into practical forms of action to attain the goals. Ideas and information from several or all the specialists are pooled and **translated from sound theory into practical workable plans.** The line executives know how to build up such plans from the information provided them and know what means and which individuals to use for getting action under the plans and achieving objectives.

LINE AND STAFF ORGANIZATION. In the line and staff organization, the line serves to maintain discipline and stability; the staff serves to bring in expert information. The staff function is strictly advisory and carries no power or authority to put its knowledge into operation.

The **staff officers** or services of an organization provide such advice and their duties are as follows:

1. Research into technical, operating, or managerial problems.
2. Determination and recommendation of the various standards of performance.
3. Keeping of records and statistics on the above activities as a measuring stick of performance.
4. Advice and aid in the carrying out of plans and programs.

Separation of Operating Authority and Advisory Service. Line and staff control makes a clear distinction between doing and thinking—between the actual work of getting things done in the operating and other line departments, and the work of analyzing, testing, researching, investigating, and recording carried on by the staff. It permits specialization by desirable functions but at the same time maintains the integrity of the principle of undivided responsibility and authority throughout the line organization. A simple diagrammatic illustration of the idea is given in Fig. 5, where the line executives are listed at the left and the staff experts who may assist them with advice are at the right.

Here at the level of president is shown his legal counsel; at the level of works manager, a management consultant, who may be either an outside engineer or a resident industrial engineer; at the level of superintendent, a standards committee; and at the level of foreman, a tool expert. The relation of each one of these staff experts is shown at only one level. However, it is evident that advice from the legal counsel may be given not only to the president but also to any other individual in the line of authority. Similarly, the management consultant may advise not only the works manager but also the superintendent or foreman. Again, the shop standards committee may advise the superintendent and also the foreman, while the tool expert, whose primary responsibility is to advise the foreman, may also assist the operators. That is, Fig. 5, which puts in relationship the line of authority and expert staff, indicates that there are **cross relationships in the line and staff organization** for the purpose of more immediate contact without breaking down the line authority or scattering control.

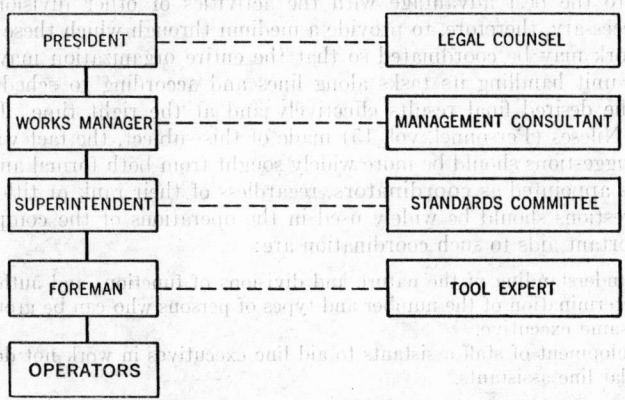

Fig. 5. Illustration of line and staff relationship.

Advantages and Disadvantages. The advantages and disadvantages of the line and staff organization may be summarized as follows:

Advantages:
1. It is based upon planned specialization.
2. It brings expert knowledge to bear upon management and operating problems.
3. It provides more opportunity for advancement for able operators, in that a greater variety of responsible jobs are available.
4. It makes possible the principle of undivided responsibility and authority, and at the same time permits staff specialization.
5. It repays its added costs many times over through the savings resulting from increased efficiency of operations.

Disadvantages:
1. Unless the duties and responsibilities of the staff members are clearly indicated by charts and manuals, there may be considerable confusion throughout the organization as to the functions and positions of staff members with relation to the line supervisors.
2. The staff may be ineffective for lack of authority to carry out its functions or intelligent backing in the application of its recommendations.
3. The inability to see each other's viewpoint may cause difficulty and friction between the line supervisors and staff members.
4. Although expert information and advice is available, it reaches the operators through line officers and thus runs the risk of misunderstanding and misinterpretation.

5. Line supervisors sometimes may resent the activities of staff members, feeling that the prestige and influence of line men suffers from the presence of the specialists.

STAFF PLAN OF COORDINATION. Apart from the line and staff provisions for extending advisory aid to operating executives by means of staff specialists assigned to specific fields of activity which concern several of the individual divisions or departments of the enterprise, there is further need of coordination throughout an industrial organization. In large organizations especially, the divisions or departments are often so extensive as to demand the concentrated attention of the division heads to the exclusion of their cooperative participation in each other's activities. There are fewer men, moreover, who have such a general grasp of the business that they can line up their individual activities to the best advantage with the activities of other divisions. It has become necessary, therefore, to provide a medium through which these diversified lines of work may be coordinated so that the entire organization may team up, with each unit handling its tasks along lines and according to schedules which produce the desired final results effectively and at the right time. In a study which the Nileses (Personnel, vol. 15) made of this subject, the fact was brought out that suggestions should be more widely sought from both formal and informal individuals appointed as **coordinators,** regardless of their rank or title, and that these suggestions should be widely used in the operations of the company. The three important aids to such coordination are:

1. An understanding of the nature and divisions of functions and authority.
2. A determination of the number and types of persons who can be grouped under the same executive.
3. Development of staff assistants to aid line executives in work not delegated to regular line assistants.

Staff Assistants. Further, the division heads need additional aid within their own areas of operation, and the appointment of staff assistants to the division heads may provide the required help. The practice of having assistant superintendents, assistant chief inspectors, etc., is well recognized, but these men have line authority under their executive directors. The staff assistant, however, would not manage any of the work, and his rank would be junior to his chief's leading line assistants. He would serve as contact man between his chief and the other members of the department. In this capacity he would translate the decisions of his superior into a working program and correlate the work of the various sections of the division. He would fulfill both planning and personnel functions. The only line authority he would have, however, would be that delegated to him in carrying out his chief's direct orders. Administrative officers would similarly have assistants to aid them in discharging administrative functions.

Duties of Staff Assistants. The Nileses in their writings outline the duties of staff assistants as follows:

1. Prepare information and recommendations:
    a. Compile appropriate information.
    b. Make recommendations for action.
    c. Investigate proposals from other sources.
    d. Check on results obtained.
2. Aid in formulating instructions and making decisions:
    a. Give out orders for the chief.
    b. Make decisions in certain cases where policies and procedures are established.

3. Assist in contact work:
   a. Interview individuals for the chief.
   b. Save the chief's time.
   c. Arrange interviews between individuals and the chief.
   d. Make reports on activities.
   e. Settle minor complaints.
   f. Disseminate information.
   g. Coordinate the division's activities and correlate its work with that of other divisions.

Among the **things which a staff assistant should not do** are to:

1. Take over line duties.
2. Give advice as a specialist.
3. Merely make investigations without recommendations.
4. Only make suggestions instead of taking some action.
5. Assume authority over subordinate line men.
6. Be guided by his own personal opinions.
7. Exceed his authority.
8. Talk too much or reveal matters which should be kept confidential.

By serving as staff assistants men are trained for promotion to executive duties and are tried out as candidates for such advancement. If they do not make out well in the staff assignment, they will be limited to subordinate positions. Those who demonstrate capability may develop into successful management prospects.

COMMITTEE ORGANIZATION. Supplementary to both line and line and staff organization is the committee form of organization. "In general," according to Dutton (Principles of Organization), "a group may be considered as interchangeable with an individual, for organizing purposes, although not necessarily of the same effectiveness." It is conceivable therefore that the committee form of **joint or multiple control** could run from the top to the bottom of an enterprise, but such is not the case except perhaps in cooperative institutions. In reality this form of organization with its meetings or conferences is used for the most part in addition to rather than in lieu of line and staff organization. The **primary functions** of committees are to define and solve complex problems, to facilitate execution of decisions, and to improve coordination, cooperation, and control throughout the entire organization.

Classification of Types. Committee types may be classified in numerous ways, such as by authority or power, by responsibility or function, by objective or purpose, by organizational level(s) represented, or by degree of permanence. In general, committees are considered to be of four principal types when considering the major classifications of **power and function**:

1. Committees with full power, such as the administrative or executive.
2. Committees with limited or partial power, such as functional committees with power to act but subject to possible veto.
3. Advisory or staff committees which are empowered only to recommend.
4. Educational committees, the purposes of which are discussion, contact, information, or instruction.

Principles of Operation. Alford and Beatty (Principles of Industrial Management) indicate that: "For a committee to be effective, certain fundamental principles must be adhered to." These principles are as follows:

1. The number of individuals on a committee should be the minimum that will function effectively. Generally, this is not more than three to five persons.

Too many members will result in much wasted time in lengthy discussions and delayed decisions.

2. The chairman of the committee should prepare the material to be discussed in advance of the meeting and circulate it among the members of the committee so that they will have time to think about it before the meeting.

3. The chairman should control the behavior of the members of his committee while it is in session so that there will be a minimum of wasted time and thought.

4. Committee meetings should be operated on a time schedule, should begin on time and end on time, and should be conducted from an agenda containing those things which require attention, arranged in the order of their importance.

5. All participants in committee meetings should be made to realize that more time can be wasted and less accomplished in committee than in any other human activity unless each member cooperates to conserve the time of the others.

According to Harold Guetzkow (Public Administration Review, vol. X), "Only four factors were found to be directly related to committee effectiveness: frequency and length of meeting, the preciseness of the agenda, and the type of secretarial service provided the committee."

Committee Functions. The real functions of a committee are to:

1. Interchange ideas.
2. Secure a meeting of minds.
3. Supply important information to the members or through them to the departments and the organization.
4. Receive and act on reports from committee members or departments which have been asked for data or information.
5. Assemble facts from many sources and put them together into a combined plan.
6. Assay the results of operations, arrive at conclusions, and formulate reports or suggestions.
7. Make intelligent and expert studies of important factors, activities, or problems.
8. Develop and recommend procedures of operation.
9. Coordinate, or set up, time relationships between the operations of different departments.
10. Correlate or associate together the activities of different departments.
11. Provide for cooperation—or special efforts in performance—between the different departments.
12. Formulate and set up standards of various kinds.
13. Act as a clearing house for matters for which no other channel has been provided.

Advantages and Disadvantages. The major advantages and disadvantages of committee activities may be summarized as follows:

Advantages

1. Under a strong executive chairman, a committee may quickly marshal many valuable points of view, since "two heads are better than one."
2. In conducting investigations, the several phases of the various questions may be quickly assigned to responsible members, with a reasonable assurance of speedy action if a time schedule and proper follow-up are instituted.
3. There is a stimulus toward cooperative action.
4. The members of the committee know better what is going on in the plant so that they can spread the information and team up with other individuals or departments.

Disadvantages

1. Committees may be too large for constructive action. The number of members should seldom exceed three.
2. Committees are expensive in time and usually have to be prodded to prevent delays.
3. Important executives may be called so frequently from their work for meetings that the operations of the enterprise slow down.
4. The members of the committee often are unfamiliar with important details of questions at issue and therefore may make wrong or ineffective decisions.
5. Action may often be superficial because of lack of time or the uninterestedness of committee members.
6. Committees weaken individual responsibility and make for compromise instead of clear-cut decisions.
7. The decisions often are made to conform with what it is assumed some executive wants, or to enable the members to avoid direct responsibility for any bad results.
8. Aggressive and outspoken members may dominate committee meetings and unduly influence the action, often adversely.

EXAMPLES OF COMMITTEES. A few of the typical industrial committees are explained in the paragraphs which follow.

General Executive Committee. An excellent example of the need for a committee is shown at the level of authority which includes the sales manager, works manager, controller, chief engineer, and director of industrial relations. These men, with the general manager, represent the various **functions of the executive power.** No one of them alone can intelligently decide difficult major questions of policy. But when the five men are assembled, each as an executive thoroughly familiar with his own field, the discussions are authoritative, and the decisions have every chance of being sound.

The general manager is logically the chairman of such a committee, and the matters that usually come before the committee pertain to the **general policy** of operating the factory. Thus, the committee might decide the character and size of the articles to be manufactured. It might approve all manufacturing orders for either stock or special products. It would decide all questions of extraordinary expenditures and would consider all economic problems.

Joint Labor-Management Committees. In connection with efforts to increase production and settle matters of mutual interest joint labor-management committees (LMC) were introduced into many plants during World War II. The plan followed was to set up a committee composed of representatives of both groups, whose work would be to find out ways in which productive energies could be more efficiently applied and ways of **eliminating wastes and losses** could be developed. Workers were known to have ideas which could be turned to good account, but even in plants with suggestion systems already in effect, it was found that many such ideas were not brought to the attention of the management. Although these committees thrived under the wartime efforts to increase production, they have declined since 1945 except for those which have been outstandingly successful in supporting a formal methods improvement program.

Shop Conference Committee. Under some conditions, a committee composed of a few of the shop foremen and a representative from the order department, with the superintendent of manufacturing as chairman, is most effective in solving **production problems.** Such a committee would discuss all matters pertaining to the operation of the factory and the status of production orders, and the discussion would bring to light any portion of a given production order that was behind schedule, together with the reasons for the delays. The findings of such a committee, in fact, may constitute a **progress report** of all work in process, and thus put into the hands of the superintendent first-hand information as to what should be done to speed up the work. Committees of this kind, composed of men who are actually in touch with the work, are of great value if they are properly conducted.

Equipment Committee. The equipment committee is made up of men drawn from different ranks and may consist of a representative of the shop superintendent's office, the foreman of the tool design and tool-making department, the methods engineer, and any other men from the production control, production engineering, or shop departments who may be of service. The chief engineer or his representative may also be included with advantage in this committee. If the plant is large enough to employ an equipment manager, he would be logically the chairman of the committee.

Such a committee would discuss all problems concerning **new tools** or **improvement of existing equipment.** When ways and means of reducing the cost of manufacture of any particular line of goods are under discussion, the engineer who is familiar with the line should always sit with the committee. An engineer, a good foreman toolmaker, and a good manufacturing foreman together can often reduce costs to an extent which would be beyond the power of any one of them singly. A committee of this kind—when no other specific committees exist—is also very valuable in **establishing standards** and in advising the executive committee regarding the standardization of products.

Plant Safety Committee. The plant safety committee, with the works manager as chairman, is the form that the safety organization usually takes in the small concern. This committee is charged with making the work force "safety conscious," but the actual safety work is the responsibility of the operating organization.

Grievance Committee. The grievance committee is mainly a minor instrument. It serves to represent the employee who has a grievance against his company in the second step of the grievance procedure. There are some companies without unions which make use of a grievance committee, but these are rare, for as a general principle most companies prefer to deal directly with the individual involved.

CRITICISM OF COMMITTEES. Committee organization has been the target for much abuse and the subject of many caustic remarks. For instance, one "standard" definition of a committee is "A group of individuals who know nothing and get together to agree to do nothing." Committees have been a particularly useful tool for those who wish to avoid decision: "Let's refer it back to committee."

Urwick is severely critical of committee operation. He states that better results by far can be secured in most cases when an executive himself obtains the necessary information and advice and acts on questions within his field of authority. Conferences among executives are necessary to obtain information and find out how the problem affects other departments, but then the executive should take action. Most frequently, matters are referred to committees when individual executives wish to dodge responsibility or avoid friction. The committee decision is a makeshift or compromise worked out by persons who may have only a remote idea of the matter at stake and very little ability to give even an opinion of value on the subject. Yet such persons are often most insistent in expressing themselves. Finally, the committee may state its conclusions in a manner to avoid committing itself to anything which may be held against it later. In short, much committee activity, from start to finish, may be merely "passing the buck."

MULTIPLE MANAGEMENT. In any company with more than approximately 100 employees, the problem arises of maintaining close relationships between management and employee. Important questions are: How can employees be given a feeling of participating in the company? How can management keep employees informed? How can management be extended down to the intermediate levels of authority as the company grows?

An executive plan now tested through depression, prosperity, and war was put into operation at McCormick & Company by its president, Charles P. McCormick, in 1932 and has been in successful operation ever since. The plan has been described and has had wide publicity (McCormick, The Power of People). Multiple management has been adopted with variations for changing circumstances by approximately 500 business firms of all types in the United States, England, and Australia.

The Four Boards. Under this plan in the McCormick Company, management has extended to approximately 50 executive and supervisory men in the company through a system of four boards.

The senior board is comparable to the board of directors in any company, is elected by the stockholders, sets up and controls company policy, and acts through its members as a clearing house for final decision on all recommendations from the other boards.

The junior board is a group of approximately 15 younger executives representing the office and executive group. It meets regularly once a week to consider any matters dealing with company affairs it cares to investigate. Its recommendations must be unanimous, and become final only upon approval of the senior board member concerned with the suggestion. In its first five years the junior board made 2,109 unanimous suggestions to the senior board, and of this number only 6 were rejected.

The factory board, composed of 15 active members and 3 associate members, represents the factory, warehouse, and shipping department unit of the business. Problems concerning production schedules, stock control and shipping, machinery, and maintenance are discussed at regular weekly meetings. Recommendations must be unanimous and approved by the senior board member concerned.

The sales board is composed of 10 active and 5 associate members chosen from the outside sales force actually calling on the trade, plus 5 inside sales executives. This board, because of the distance to be traveled by its members, meets only twice a year, usually for a week at a time. The committees secure cross-section opinion of the sales force between meetings, and resolutions passed unanimously for senior board approval at sales board meetings represent the opinion of the salesmen on merchandising, advertising, sales training, and similar subjects.

Operation of the Boards. Provision is made to give eligible men in the company an opportunity to be elected to the boards through an arrangement that at each semi-annual election of the junior, factory, and sales boards three members must be dropped from each board and replaced with three new men. Over a 10-year period 87 men served at one time or another on the factory board and 65 on the junior board. Elections are handled by a merit-rating system whereby each board member rates on a rating chart the abilities of every other member.

The three members who are lowest on the semi-annual rating chart on each board are dropped off and replaced.

The employees do not elect the members of the board, because the tendency would be to select on popularity rather than on merit. However, the employees have a feeling of participation in that men they know and work with in their departments every day are actually directors in management. For example, a girl on a factory machine feels free to present her ideas or problems or suggestions to the young man who comes around as a mechanic on that machine, who is a member of the factory board, whereas she would never have a similar opportunity to talk things over with a top executive on the ordinary board of directors of the company. Thus management is actually extended down to every employee through a representation system.

Benefits to Employees and Company. Many claims are made by both company and employees concerning the benefits to be derived from the multiple management system. McCormick (The Power of People) analyzes the workings and benefits of multiple management and includes the following appraisal from a worker's viewpoint:

It's more than just good personnel policies. Sure, we have a lot of nice things in the way of wages and benefits. Our pay has climbed way up from the old days and matches anything we could get in the same kind of job anywhere around town. In addition to that we've got a pension plan for everybody that the company pays all the premiums on. We've got security because the firm gives forty-eight weeks of work a year to the top 90 percent of the organization, based on merit and length of service. And we've got profit sharing so that when we all do a good job we share in the rewards of it. Our vacations are good and we have rest periods twice a day so with lunch nobody has to work more than two hours without a break from their machines.

But most important of all, we're part of the whole show. Working here, you get the idea that people really want to listen to you and have you join in things instead of just being part of the machinery around the place.

McCormick, himself, states:

Our sponsorship plan is closely allied to a firm policy of promoting from within. Nothing is more devastating to worker morale than a constant influx of outsiders into desirable jobs. . . .

In addition to all these advantages, the board system produces another great asset, a willingness to seek and value the knowledge and opinions of others. . . . By establishing a concept of group or team accomplishment, rather than individual competition, the board system encourages cooperative thinking and quells the natural tendency to seek recognition and promotion through individual efforts. It is another tool in the emancipation of man from "the tyranny of his own ego."

Therefore, the success of the entire system depends on the maintenance of esprit de corps and individual morale and good will. . . .

Here, then, is one of the real secrets of Multiple Management. For the board system not only throws together men of diverse talents, but in operation it causes them to recognize their interdependence. Again, this feeling, acquired in board meetings, carries over into the entire managerial atmosphere. Our supervisors are not practicing clever psychology when they look to their people for help and suggestions. They have come to realize that we can all learn something from each other—and the man on the job is often the man best fitted to give advice about it. In such an atmosphere of security and mutual trust, our workers feel completely free to release the constructive talents inherent in them. How great that latent power can be, once released from brooding over management's unfairness, is one of the great revelations of the coming decade—the power of people.

Factors in Planning an Organization

ALLOTMENT OF DUTIES IN AN ORGANIZATION. Duties of activities in an industrial organization are allotted to individuals by several different methods, of which the following are the most important:

1. By persons. An executive or supervisor is given authority over, and made responsible for, certain subordinates.
2. Within physical boundaries. An executive or supervisor is given supervision over a room, a department, or a production center.
3. By production. An executive or supervisor is given supervision over the manufacture of a particular item of product, or a certain line of product.
4. By process. An executive or supervisor is given supervision over a particular manufacturing process, or over a series of such processes.
5. By equipment. An executive is given supervision over a particular group of machines or class of equipment.

The above allotments are in the nature of **vertical subdivisions** where each executive's or supervisor's authority is exercised within his determined sphere of control but subject to higher line authority and to functional or expert staff advice.

THE LADDER OR BRIDGE OF FAYOL. However, in addition to vertical, there are **horizontal relations** which have received but little study and managerial attention. In this connection there is a nearly unexplored field, where the vertical lines of authority cross and conflict with the horizontal lines of relations. This situation is made plain from a consideration of Fig. 6.

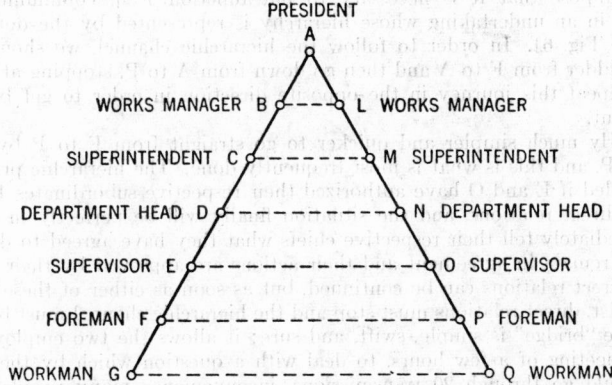

Fig. 6. Cross contacts or relationships illustrated by the "ladder" or "bridge" of Fayol.

This diagram represents two lines of authority apexing in the president and in each case following through a works manager, superintendent, department head, supervisor, and foreman to the operator. It is evident that, to perform duties assigned to each line—assuming that they are in the same industrial organization—there must be some contact, communication, and relationship between individuals at each level of authority in the two converging lines. Such **cross relations** may be concerned with: (1) jurisdiction, that is, a determination of which line is to do certain work; (2) coordination of policies and operation methods needful to secure uniform operating results; (3) review and criticism of work, which may occur where work is transferred from one line of authority to another in order to complete succeeding operations; and (4) division of overlapping duties. The points where vertical authority and cross relations meet are illustrated by the small circles in the diagram. In practice these relations are real and continuing, and give rise to **points of possible friction and conflict.**

Essentials for Maintaining Intersecting Relationships. Fayol, whose "requirements for command" have been previously mentioned, set up the essentials for establishing and maintaining these intersecting relationships on a frictionless and properly managed basis. Essentially his solution is a **process of self-adjustment.** He pointed out that executives at any level in line of authority may contact one another, reach decisions, and initiate action, provided these requirements are satisfied:

1. Contact or relationship should be initiated only with the consent of the immediate line superiors.
2. Before any action is taken, it must be approved by the immediate line superiors.

Fayol's statement of his method (Industrial and General Administration) is:

The need for a **hierarchic channel** arises both from the need for safe transmission of information and orders and from unity of command, but it is not always the quickest channel, and in very big enterprises, the State in particular, it is sometimes disastrously long. As, however, there are many operations whose success depends on rapid execution, we must find a means of reconciling respect for the hierarchic channel with the need for quick action. This can be done in the following way:

Let us suppose that it is necessary to put function F in communication with function P, in an undertaking whose hierarchy is represented by the double ladder G-A-Q [see Fig. 6]. In order to follow the hierarchic channel, we should have to climb the ladder from F to A and then go down from A to P, stopping at each rung, and then repeat this journey in the opposite direction in order to get back to our starting point.

It is clearly much simpler and quicker to go straight from F to P by using the "bridge" F-P, and this is what is most frequently done. The hierarchic principle will be safeguarded if E and O have authorized their respective subordinates F and P to enter into direct relations, and the situation finally will be perfectly in order if F and P immediately tell their respective chiefs what they have agreed to do. So long as F and P remain in agreement and their actions are approved by their immediate superiors, direct relations can be continued, but as soon as either of these conditions ceases to exist, direct relations must stop and the hierarchic channel must be resumed.

Use of the "bridge" is simple, swift, and sure; it allows the two employees F and P, in one meeting of a few hours, to deal with a question which by the hierarchic channel would go through 20 transmissions, inconvenience many people, entail an enormous amount of writing, and waste weeks or months in arriving at a solution, which would probably not be so good as the one obtained by putting F in direct contact with P.

SPAN OF CONTROL. By the term "span of control" is meant the number of subordinates who can be successfully directed by a supervisor or superior. In the direction and control of industrial enterprise it has long been apparent that delay, friction, and confusion can be traced to the fact that too many subordinates are assigned to one superior.

The theory of Graicunas states that in an organization there are **three kinds of relationship:** direct single, direct group, and cross.

In almost every instance a supervisor measures his responsibility by the number of direct single relationships between himself and his subordinates. He thinks of a group of 12 employees as requiring twice as much work of supervision as a group of 6. However, there are direct group and cross relationships to be considered as well as the simple direct. To illustrate:

Designate the supervisor as A, and assume that he has only two subordinates, B and C. It is evident that A can deal individually with B and with C, or he can deal with them as a pair. The behavior of B in the presence of C will differ from his behavior if he alone is with his superior, A. Furthermore, the attitude of B toward C, and C toward B, constitute cross relationships which A must keep in mind in arranging the work of B and C. It is evident that B and C might have widely different racial, political, or trade union affiliations, which would have no influence upon either as a good workman working alone, but which might prevent them from working together harmoniously. Then again, some individuals, the so-called "lone wolf type," cannot work well with others, no matter who they may be.

The relations among a supervisor, A, and two subordinates, B and C, are:

Kind of Relationships	Minimum Basis	Maximum Basis
Direct single relationships:		
A to B, and A to C....................................	2	2
Cross relationships:		
B and C	1	
B to C, and C to B..		2
Direct group relationships:		
A to B and C	1	
A to B with C, and A to C with B.........................		2
	4	6

It is evident, then, that in this simplest unit or organization there are from 4, on a minimum basis, to 6 relations, on a maximum basis, demanding A's attention, instead of only two. It is evident, further, that direct single relationships increase in the same proportion as the number of subordinates assigned to a supervisor. The number of direct group and cross relationships, however, increases more rapidly than the increase in number of subordinates as more are assigned to a supervisor. On a minimum basis these relationships are counted once for each combination of subordinates. The **direct group relationships** can be conveniently shown by the following analysis:

Number of Subordinates Reporting to One Supervisor A	Number of Direct Group Relationships
Two subordinates B, C:	
Direct group relationships ABC...	1
Three subordinates B, C, D:	
Direct group relationships ABC, ABD, ACD, ABCD...............	4
Four subordinates B, C, D, E:	
Direct group relationships ABC, ABD, ABE, ACD, ACE, ADE, ABCD, ABCE, ABDE, ACDE, ABDE..........................	11
Five subordinates B, C, D, E, F:	
Direct group relationships ABC, ABD, ABE, ABF, ACD, ACE, ACF, ADE, ADF, AEF, ABCD, ABCE, ABCF, ABDE, ABDF, ABEF, ACDE, ACDF, ACEF, ABCDE, ABCDF, ABCEF, ABDEF, ACDEF, ABCDEF	26

The process of extending the diagram beyond this point is self-evident. On a minimum basis—used in the diagram above—the number of direct group relationships for 6 subordinates is 57; for 7 subordinates, 120; and so on.

On a minimum basis the increase in total number of relationships between a supervisor and his subordinates, as the number of subordinates increases, can be determined mathematically from the following formulas:

$$\text{Let } N = \text{number of subordinates}$$
$$A = \text{number of direct single relationships}$$
$$B = \text{number of cross relationships}$$
$$C = \text{number of direct group relationships}$$
$$F = A + B + C$$

$$\text{Then } A = N$$
$$B = \frac{N}{2}\,(N-1)$$
$$C = (2)^N - (N+1)$$

Solving the above formulas for the number of subordinates from 1 to 10 yields the tabulation shown in Fig. 7.

Factor in Formulas	Number of Subordinates									
	1	2	3	4	5	6	7	8	9	10
Values of A	1	2	3	4	5	6	7	8	9	10
Values of B	0	1	3	6	10	15	21	28	36	45
Values of C	0	1	4	11	26	57	120	247	502	1013
Values of F	1	4	10	21	41	78	148	283	547	1068

Fig. 7. Increase in interrelationships as number of subordinates increases under the span of control.

Graicunas assumes that it is possible for one supervisor to give adequate attention to a **maximum of only 12 cross and 28 direct group relationships**, from which comes the conclusion that, in cases other than the simplest of routine work, the number of cross and direct group relationships governs the number of subordinates to place under a supervisor. A strict application of this conclusion indicates that the span of control should be restricted to a maximum of 5 subordinates.

This theoretical conclusion, that the number of subordinates reporting to a superior should be few, has ample support from practice. The smallest organizational unit in an army is the squad, made up of a corporal, or supervisor, and 7 privates, or subordinates. Many factories limit the number of employees under a supervisor to some 8 or 10. Practically, a supervisor can probably direct 10 to 12 workers before there is a considerable falling off in his directive efficiency.

Turning to higher levels in the line of authority, Swope has said that 4 or 5 subordinates reporting to a chief executive are a sufficient number for good organization. However, the nature of the relationship between superior and subordinate at any level in the line of authority should govern the extent of responsibilities of the superior. It is true here, as in many other relationships in industry, that no hard and fast rule can be laid down.

Davis (The Influence of the Unit of Supervision and the Span of Executive Control on the Economy of Line Organization Structure) has made a study of the

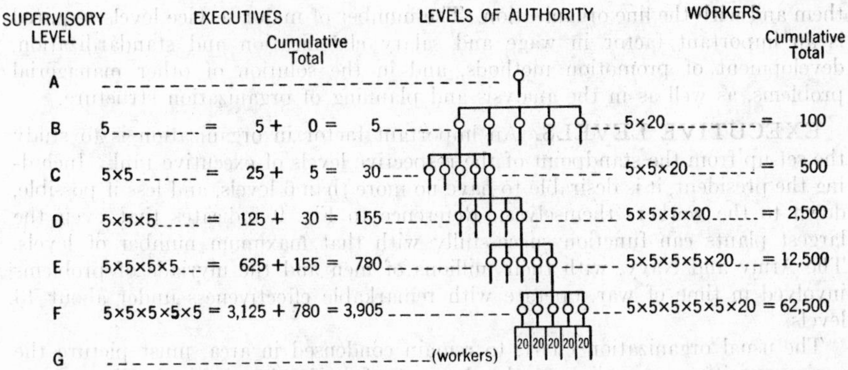

Constructed by assuming the several successive executive levels indicated below chief executive A (5 subordinates for each subexecutive, in turn), and calculating the number of subexecutives and finally the number of workers (20 per foreman) in turn for the successive assumptions. (See also Fig. 9.)

Fig. 8. Graphical analysis of the span of control.

span of control, assuming at successive levels that each executive has 5 subexecutives under him, and that, at the workers' level, there are 20 employees reporting to each foreman. The analysis has been graphed for present purposes in Fig. 8 and the Davis tabulation, rearranged, is given in Fig. 9.

Level	Service Levels Required *	Span of Executive Control	The Unit of Supervision	Number of Operating Executives	Number of Primary Workers Who Can Be Supervised
A	—	—	—	—	—
B	1	5	20	5	100
C	2	5	20	30	500
D	3	5	20	155	2,500
E	4	5	20	780	12,500
F	5	5	20	3,905	62,500

* Between workers and the head of the line.

Fig. 9. Geometric increase in number of primary operative employees and number of operative executives with increasing size of line organization. (See also Fig. 8.)

Davis explains his terms in this way:

A **major service level** may be defined as one that represents a major change in the kind or type of employee service that is required. It may be broken down, of course, into a number of minor service levels. While **minor service levels** are important in such problems as wage and salary classification, they are not important in this problem. When the term "service level" is used, it refers to major service levels only. A major service level is an important organizational factor, affecting the number of high-salaried executives who will be required and the complexity of organizational relationships. In general, the larger the number of major service levels required, the greater the number of staff organization units that must be set up and the greater the complexity of the relationship between them and with the line organization. The number of major service levels required is an important factor in wage and salary classification and standardization, development of promotion methods, and in the solution of other managerial problems, as well as in the analysis and planning of organization structure.

EXECUTIVE LEVELS. An important factor in organization is to study the set-up from the standpoint of the respective levels of executive rank. Including the president, it is desirable to have no more than 6 levels, and less if possible, down to the workers themselves. Reference to Fig. 9 indicates that even the largest plants can function successfully with that maximum number of levels. The Army and Navy, with their millions of men and the myriads of problems involved in time of war, operate with remarkable effectiveness under about 13 levels.

The usual organization chart, to remain condensed in area, must picture the various positions according to the **descent of authority** down the line. Some divisions and departments have few levels between the top executive in charge, who reports to the president, and the supervisors who have the final titles just above the rank of worker. Other departments have several such levels. Hence it is not customary to try to show across the chart, horizontally, the respective levels or ranks of positions among the different departments. Merely the descent of authority for each department, independently, is shown. Neither is it easily possible to picture the evaluation of the various positions horizontally across the chart. The rates of salary vary between departments, irrespective of relative rank or level. Some kinds of work require much higher remuneration because of their nature, and seniority of service—accompanied by demonstrated ability —usually brings with it a larger salary than is paid to others of approximately equal rank but less experience. Likewise, the number of persons over whom the executive or supervisor has charge may be a factor in settling his relative rank. Even the organization manual in which the duties and responsibilities of each position are written up cannot indicate clearly the relative levels or ranks of jobs horizontally throughout the organization.

DETERMINING THE LEVELS. In spite of the difficulties of determining levels and ranks, it has been done in the armed forces and should be done in industry. This step involves more than a determination of respective duties and responsibilities; it covers the general sphere of influence which the individual governs and the relative rating of his position as compared with other jobs throughout the entire company. If a good job evaluation plan is in effect in the organization, the basis for rating positions on their relative levels is well established. In fact, this is one of the elements in job evaluation. Fine shades of distinction in rank are unnecessary as well as impossible.

Probably the best approach to the problem—with or without a job evaluation plan in effect—is to set up three or four general ranges of rank or levels under which the respective positions will be grouped. The Nileses have recognized the importance of this method in their book on Middle Management, which discusses the subject mainly in the field of office organization. It is of equal importance from the plant viewpoint.

THE FIVE IMPORTANT LEVELS. There are five important levels into which members of the executive and supervisory employees may be classed. These levels are:

1. Top executives.
2. Senior executives.

3. Intermediate executives (often divided into two, or even three, ranks according to the nature and size of company).
4. Junior executives.
5. Supervisors and foremen.

Top Executives. In the ranks of top executives are the officers of the company. Typical titles are:

1. President.
2. Vice-President in Charge of Engineering.
3. Vice-President in Charge of Manufacturing.
4. Vice-President in Charge of Sales.
5. Vice-President in Charge of Industrial Relations.
6. Secretary.
7. Treasurer.
8. General Manager.

These men discharge **major responsibilities** and exercise a **wide range of authority.** They are directly concerned with the application of the basic policies of the company and the direction of its respective major lines of activity. Likewise they establish the central coordination between the principal activities and should have delegated to them practically full authority—subject to company policies and the responsibilities of, and relationships with, other activities—to carry on their work according to plans which they themselves largely develop.

Since there is no definite standardization of titles of positions among industrial organizations, the titles employed here are descriptive and indicative rather than specific and exact. Thus, where there is a general manager, he presumably would exercise immediate direction over the activities of engineering, manufacturing, sales, and accounting, and perhaps over industrial relations. There might be a vice-president, but his position, and those of treasurer and secretary, might cover corporate duties of a special nature, rather than operating responsibilities, although the vice-president might also be the general manager.

Senior Executives. In the class of senior executives may be men such as the chief engineer, factory manager, sales manager, purchasing agent, controller, personnel director, and two or three others with related titles. While these men do not have the official rank entitling them to the designation of top executives, they carry heavy responsibilities and exercise full authority in their respective areas of action. They are rated as executive heads of the divisions or departments of which they have charge. Their tasks are to break down the company's **basic policies,** particularly the ones governing their lines of work, into directive regulations and to develop the **fundamental procedures** for their respective divisions or departments.

Intermediate Executives. In moderate-sized and large companies the senior executives have immediate assistants who are qualified in some cases to take over the work of the division or department in the absence of their chiefs, or to aid them by performing certain of their duties or handling special assignments. Such men usually are chosen to succeed their chiefs if the latter leave or are promoted to higher responsibilities. Reporting to the chief engineer, for example, would be an assistant chief engineer or perhaps an executive engineer; to the factory manager such men as a manufacturing manager, production control superintendent or manager, chief inspector, works engineer, and perhaps others with corresponding duties. Under the sales manager would be an assistant sales manager; under the purchasing agent, an assistant purchasing agent; under the controller, a chief accountant cost accountant. statistician or budget director and office manager; and under the personnel director, an employment manager, training director, employee-service manager, a specialist in industrial relations and bargaining with workers and perhaps a safety director.

To these first-rank intermediate executives are often assigned **particular areas of work** in the division or department. They become, in effect, specialists in such lines and usually assume practically full direction of the activities which they supervise. They are responsible for the direct application of the immediate policies of the company, the development of specific procedures for the performance of the work, and direct supervision over assistants carrying more detailed assignments.

In the second rank of intermediate executives are classed important subexecutives who work under the direction of those in the first rank. The assistant chief engineer would have reporting to him perhaps a chief draftsman, in some cases project engineers, and engineering specialists who are chiefs of other sections, notably, chief of structures and chief of weights in the aircraft industry. The manufacturing manager may have superintendents who head departments. The planning superintendent would have a methods engineer, a chief time study engineer. a chief of planning, and related heads of units under his jurisdiction. Under the assistant sales manager might be an advertising manager, a field sales manager, etc. Under the assistant purchasing agent would be buyers and others in responsible positions connected with purchasing; and under the employment manager, a director of employee tests, and a chief of shop training, and heads of other personnel sections. The chief accountant would have assistants specializing in specific phases of accounting, such as accounts receivable and accounts payable.

In all cases these subexecutives would be in charge of **detailed sections of work** which, in large companies, would be still further subdivided into units to be handled by junior executives. Certain decisions are required of the intermediate executives, and they are responsible for the development and improvement of various techniques and procedures. They have direct control over their assistants and are held responsible for the proper performance of the work.

Junior Executives. The level of junior executives includes those who have begun their progress through the organization because of experience or training which qualifies them to head a **smaller unit of the enterprise** and direct the work of a few assistants or supervisors. Under the chief draftsman may be a chief checker who may direct the work of drawing inspection and checking; under the superintendents would be assistant superintendents; under chief of planning there may be a schedule man who lays out the program for factory work. The field sales manager often has branch managers. Buyers sometimes have assistant buyers. The chief of shop training may have a head instructor in machine-tool work, and a head safety-training instructor.

Junior executives in some cases would direct the work of subexecutives in the ranks of supervisors or foremen, especially in the factory departments. Assistant superintendents, for example, may have general shop foremen covering particular units of the plant engaged in distinctive kinds of work such as foundry, forge-shop, machine-shop, etc. In other cases the junior executive may head a unit of workers, sometimes operating under group leaders, who are performing some definite kind of work, especially in the office, engineering department, or laboratory. His responsibilities include the making of decisions, giving of advice, and the development of procedures. He is therefore doing an executive class of work rather than conducting an operation. Consequently he should be rated in the executive category rather than as a supervisor or foreman.

The junior rank involves activities in many of which the individual is on his own, but in which he has the ready aid of some chief close enough to his work to guide him in his decisions and procedures. At the junior level, therefore, the executive applies on his own responsibility many of the things he learned as a worker and supervisor, but at the same time he is on the "proving ground," being tested in his ability to use what he knows, to train others, and to be a leader in getting work done and in commanding not only the obedience but also the respect, high regard, and loyalty of his subordinates. No man who demonstrates mere "drive" for accomplishment but fails to continue his own training and lacks the power of building his assistants into a loyal and efficient team should be promoted into the intermediate or higher ranks.

Supervisors and Foremen. In immediate charge of employees are supervisors and foremen. Many companies distinguish between these two terms, implying by the title of "supervisor" that such men have **semi-advisory or assisting duties** included in their range of activity. The term "foreman" is then used to indicate that the holder of this title actually **directs employees** in their work. The designation "foreman" is likewise used with different implications in different plants. Sometimes a foreman heads only a small group of workers. In other cases an individual with this title may head a department of one or two hundred, or more, workers, in which case he would be aided by assistant foremen, under whom subforemen or group or squad leaders would work. Each person immediately in charge of the performance of the work, therefore, would have perhaps from 5 to 20 workers under him.

Persons in supervisory or foreman ranks are responsible mainly for four important functions:

1. Getting work done in the time, and of the quality, set by careful and coordinated planning.
2. Setting standards for the work in conjunction with the special units (methods, time study, inspection, etc.) particularly concerned with such problems.
3. Training workers to perform their tasks better so that spoilage will be cut down, quality maintained, and output increased, thus enabling employees to add to their earnings.
4. Handling grievances in the department, thus eliminating causes of dissatisfaction as soon as they arise and thereby maintaining good labor relations.

INTERCOMMUNICATION BETWEEN LEVELS. A good organization functions with freedom of communication among its executives regardless of their respective positions. In well-run companies a junior executive may ask for advice or aid from some senior executive in another department by direct approach, when his problem concerns, or is affected by, some element under the senior's control. Senior executives may likewise secure the aid of junior executives. There is no violation of line control in such contacts, and they improve the efficiency and speed with which work is done.

QUALIFICATIONS OF A TOP EXECUTIVE. Considerable discussion has been devoted to the question as to what are the important qualifications of a competent top executive. Coes has suggested the following (Mechanical Engineering, vol. 65):

1. Character, that is, honesty, integrity, loyalty, truthfulness, fairness, tolerance, firmness.
2. Orderliness in mind and in action.

3. Poise and control of temper.
4. Respect for time, its value, and its use.
5. Ability to assume responsibility.
6. Ability to cooperate.
7. Ability to take and to give constructive criticism.
8. Ability to compromise when necessary.
9. A sense of humor.
10. Broadmindedness.
11. Action without procrastination.
12. Wisdom to understand that it is no sign of weakness to seek help from competent sources.
13. Clarity of thought—the ability to reason from the facts, draw sound conclusions, and then act.
14. Good judgment, acting intuitively at times without the aid of logical reasoning. In fact, with only the facts at hand at the time the decision must be made, logical reasoning from the facts frequently will produce a conclusion at direct variance with what judgment dictates.

Barnard (Organization and Management) conceives the fundamental active qualities of leaders, in the order of their importance, as:

1. Vitality and endurance.
2. Decisiveness.
3. Persuasiveness.
4. Responsibility.
5. Intellectual capacity.

In contrast to the desirable executive qualities, Alford and Beatty (Principles of Industrial Management) present "certain failings of individuals which affect their ability to lead others." They say that of the individuals with failings in leadership:

1. Some are not close enough to their followers to know or anticipate their reactions when new conditions must be met.
2. Some are emotionally immature, resulting in loss of temper or other forms of emotional instability when under pressure.
3. Some lack human understanding, and therefore build antagonism instead of friendship into their relations with others.
4. Some lack foresight, the ability to look ahead, to anticipate problems and to plan the work of the group.
5. Some are not big enough for their jobs and attempt to compensate for their feelings of inferiority by a superior attitude toward their followers.
6. Some fail to reveal their attitudes and intentions to their subordinates or to invite expressions of opinion from them.
7. Some depend too much on punishment and financial reward as motivating forces, and overlook praise, recognition, self-expression, and pride in accomplishment.
8. Some fail to be consistent in their behavior toward others, thus making it impossible for subordinates to know what to expect and to have the resulting sense of security.
9. Some fail to cooperate with others in working for the common good of all.

QUALIFICATIONS OF OTHER EXECUTIVES. It is important that executives from the senior down to the supervisory and foremanship levels be trained so that they may acquire, at least to some degree, the characteristics desirable in the top executive. In addition, there is need for emphasis on specific characteristics or qualifications of a more detailed nature in each case.

For **senior and intermediate executives,** the factors of initiative, integrity, dependability, and coordinative ability are particularly important. Such characteristics indicate the ability to forward and carry through the ideas and plans of top executives.

In the case of **junior executives,** the list may include qualities such as:

1. Adequate training and experience.
2. Ability to contribute new ideas.
3. Willingness to learn.
4. Adaptability.
5. Capacity for detail.
6. Teamwork.
7. Loyalty.
8. Ability to follow instructions.
9. Leadership.

A still more specific list may be given for the qualifications of **supervisors and foremen** concerning their four fields of activity stated in a previous paragraph (Johnson, Business and the Man):

1. For directing or handling work:
   a. Mechanical ability.
   b. Versatility and ingenuity.
   c. Knowledge of equipment.
   d. Familiarity with modern practices.
   e. Ability to correlate activities.
   f. A cooperative spirit.
   g. Understanding of costs.
   h. Safety consciousness.
2. For setting standards:
   a. Engineering sense.
   b. Knowledge of job requirements.
   c. Sense of relativity.
3. For training:
   a. Teaching ability.
   b. Knowledge of crafts or subjects taught.
   c. Patience.
   d. Perseverance.
   e. Ability to develop men.
4. For handling human relations:
   a. Sympathetic understanding of human nature.
   b. Trustworthiness.
   c. Fairness.
   d. Tact.
   e. Discernment.
   f. Self-control.
   g. Freedom from prejudice.
   h. Ability to translate company policies into practical terms.

Organization Charts and Manuals

FUNDAMENTAL CONSIDERATIONS. In planning an organization and developing the charts, manual, and standard practice instructions which graph and formulate its set-up—whether the procedure is for a new organization or for readjustment of an existing organization along more effective lines—it is necessary to keep in mind the basic requirements already stated, which may be summarized as follows:

1. The first fundamental is that **the organization must be built around functions,** not individuals. The activities or tasks which must be carried on should be blocked out following a typical or representative chart which carries the major functions normally necessary in most manufacturing enterprises. Modifications may be introduced at any point to adapt the chart to the particular company. There is no such thing as a standard chart of organization and no organization chart can be copied in whole from any other company, although it may be in the same industry or even in another plant of the same company. There are chart patterns but none which can be applied directly without alteration.

The **main functions** in a manufacturing concern are those of engineering, manufacturing, selling, purchasing, industrial relations, accounting, and financing.

2. **Functions which are closely related** must come under the same head.

3. When the major and related functions are thus distinguished and identified, they should be arranged so that each activity will be definitely provided for and all necessary duties may be properly performed.

4. In smaller companies—or in cases where the extent or the amount of work in some duties is limited—some such **duties may be combined with others** as closely related as possible, so that each such group can be handled by one person.

5. Only after such considerations have been settled should the question of persons enter into the picture. Since it is obviously impossible to secure in all cases individuals who are ideally qualified to handle the various functions or tasks, those who have most of the necessary qualifications are selected or engaged to take over the individual assignments. At this point it may be necessary to **readjust the setup** so that the best results may be secured in performance. While some realignments may be necessary and certain usually unassociated activities may be delegated to the same individual, two points should be **rigidly** adhered to:

  a. The functions and subfunctions must be clearly identified and retained in the framework.
  b. No assignments should be made which allow any two individuals to cross lines of authority and come into conflict. The authority and responsibility accompanying each function and subfunction, therefore, should be definitely delimited in the organization manual.

6. No more than 5 or 6 persons, in general, should report to an individual on executive or subexecutive level, where these subordinates, in turn, direct the work of others. Departments should be broken down into sections and the sections into units or groups, each headed by capable assistants. Where immediate direction of workers enters, the limit to the number of subordinates reporting to the supervisor or foreman should be 10 to 15 in most cases. If work is highly routine or a large number of workers are engaged in repetitive work, the limit may be raised to about 20. It is better to break up any larger units into two or three groups, each headed by a leader who reports to the supervisor or foreman (Principle of Graicunas).

7. While it is desirable to limit the number of executives, supervisors, and foremen in a company for reasons of efficiency and economy, no executive should be unduly overloaded with contacts and work. Especially in a growing organization, each executive should have some time for **constructive planning** and for growing in his job.

8. The organization plan should be developed with the idea of **future expansion** in mind, so that major reorganizations at a later period may be avoided.

9. All persons in executive capacity should have copies of the charts and manual and everyone in the organization should have access to these items at all times. There is nothing secret about the information. It is advisable to change all copies of charts and manuals, or at least issue change notifications, as soon as such shifts occur. At least the master copies should be altered promptly to keep them up to date.

10. **Freedom of contact** among all members of the organization for quick interchange of information and arriving at prompt decisions (Fayol's Principle) should be provided for in developing the charts and writing the organization manual.

11. Since no organization stays in a permanent form, it should be realized that frequent changes in the charts and manual will become necessary, beginning shortly after the original setup is made.

The **functions** of organization chart, organization manual, and standard practice instructions which are discussed below are related by Alford and Beatty (Principles of Industrial Management) as follows: "The chart is used to tell **where** in the organization a function is performed and by **whom**; the manual explains **what** the nature of the function is and the duties and responsibilities involved; and the standard practice instructions describe **how** and **when** it is to be performed. These constitute the tools through which coordination is achieved."

ORGANIZATION CHARTS. It is advisable, even in small companies, to draw up and post organization charts so that all persons may know how the various duties and activities are assigned and can find out where they fit into the setup. While workers are not indicated in such charts, they know for which supervisor or foreman they work and therefore can see the relationship of their units or groups to the remainder of the company. In large companies it is necessary to draw a **series of charts,** starting with that of the top organization, which shows the relationships among officers and senior executives and the breakdown into divisions. A succession of charts then may show the organization of the respective departments and sections, in which intermediate and junior executives appear. A further breakdown then may graph the individual sections and units to indicate how authority and responsibility are carried down to supervisors, foremen, and group leaders.

In the **breakdown charts** it is helpful in each case to include a skeleton outline of the top organization to point out how authority from the president is delegated to the divisions, and then how the chain follows through the particular department, section, unit, and group down to the individuals to whom the workers report. If the spectator at a football game is interested in the organization of the teams he sees playing and the position that each man plays, how much more interested will the workman in a company be in knowing how the industrial team of which he is a member, and in which he earns his living, is organized and the positions which he and his boss play in the enterprise!

Drawing Organization Charts. The drawing and revising of organization charts requires considerable work and involves expense, but the trouble and cost are many times repaid by the benefits secured through broadcasting the information. It is likely that if a poll were taken of the workers in most plants, not 1 percent of them would know anything worthwhile about the organization setup of their companies and the responsibilities of the executives, supervisors, and foremen. It is small wonder that, when the professional labor organizer vividly pictures the worker's position in the union and shows him what man heads the union and carries on the union's relationships with the company, the employee feels himself closer to the union and more a member of it than he is of the company. The top executive himself, in a large company, unfortunately often has only a hazy conception of the interrelationships, and sometimes very little of the detailed breakdown, in his organization; but at least he knows the fundamental setup and responsibilities, and he directs the enterprise, so that he can work through its channels. The worker, conceiving little of the importance of organization, usually is left completely at sea.

There are **four typical ways** in which organization charts may be drawn, as shown in Fig. 10. In this illustration, example (a) is most common and (c) is a variant sometimes useful for saving space. Example (b) is seldom used, while (d) is common in telephone companies—the blocks surrounding the titles and names often being omitted—and is often accompanied by a statement of the total number under the direction of each executive at the successive levels.

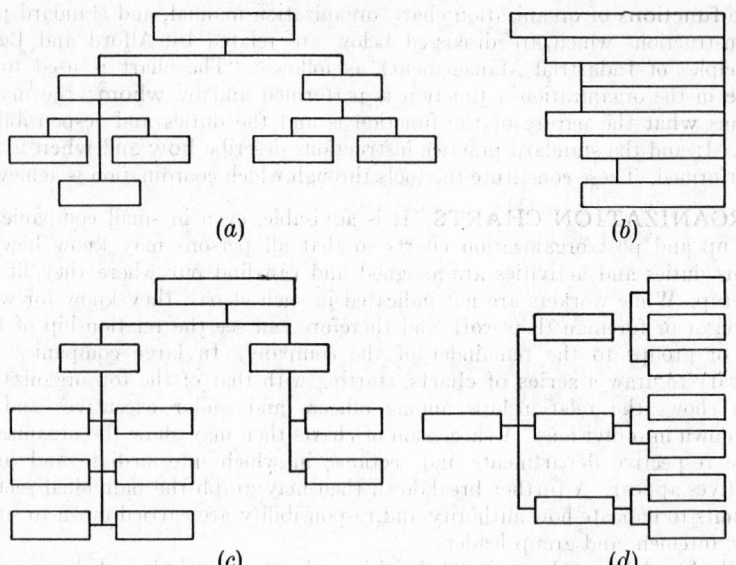

Fig. 10. Four typical ways of drawing organization charts.

Examples of Organization Charts. The chart shown in Fig. 11 is a typical organization chart for manufacturing plants in that it shows the principal functions and subfunctions usually provided for, and the range of work covered by the various departments and sections. As stated before, there are no standard organization charts, but merely representative charts which serve as guides in individual cases. This chart, however, merits careful study because of its comprehensive coverage of functions and the descriptive nature of its titles and the kinds of work indicated for the respective departments. The charts which follow may be compared with this representative set-up and will then be more clearly comprehended. It is seen that the names of individuals are not important in the building up of a chart, and have been omitted in the examples because obviously there will be changes occurring constantly in the personnel of the respective companies. In individual companies, for internal use, the names of persons make the charts clearer to the members of the entire organization.

The Organization Approach. Fig. 12 shows an organization chart, in condensed form, of the General Electric Co. The General Electric Co. produces diverse electrical end products and components for defense, industry, commerce, and the home. It is engaged also in a wide variety of business operations ranging from raw material processing, through fabrication and manufacture, to widespread distribution, installation, and product-servicing on both a national and an international scale.

As Cordiner states in explaining the organization approach of General Electric (Bulletin No. 159, American Management Association), the concept of **decentralization** in General Electric envisages decentralization not only of products, geographic districts, and functions, but also of the actual authority for making decisions in the interests of the enterprise, its customers, its shareowners, its employees, its suppliers, and the public (see Fig. 12). Under this philosophy of genuine decentralization, **operating divisions** and **departments** each have their own product or salable-service responsibility, their own markets, and so their own natural autonomy. Top managerial personnel can correct unsatisfactory conditions by replacing the people managing such a business but not by taking away their authority. In turn, the organization as a whole makes a logical and coordinated business enterprise, with common economic factors influencing its future and bearing on the company-wide decisions required. The fundamental **objectives** of the executive management under this philosophy are essentially to determine what business fields the enterprise is to enter or continue in and then to organize its human and capital resources so as to operate within them well, competitively, and profitably.

Decentralization in General Electric includes true decentralization of decision-making. Thus, irrespective of the circumstances or context in which an incumbent of a position may exercise his decision-making authority and responsibility, he is considered to be exercising it individually and personally. The fact that specific decisions may be made by an individual while in contact with other members of the organzation, or while participating in a group or other meeting, does not alter the personal nature of the authority and responsibility involved in decision-making. On the other hand, while the organization structure and organization chart define the lines of responsibility and authority (and of accountability)—especially as to such personal responsibility for decision-making—they do not indicate or limit channels of contact or flow of information among members of the organization. Contacts and flow of information between people and components of the organization are to be carried out in the simplest and most direct way practicable. But it is the duty of each party to a contact to keep his manager promptly informed if he gets into matters that involve: accountability by his manager to others, disagreement or controversy, requirement of advice from others or coordination by his manager with others, or changes in, or variance from, established policies.

Management's authority and responsibilities flow from the shareowners through the board of directors, who represent them, to the three following distinct **management organization components:**

1. Executive management—comprising the president, who is the chief executive officer, and any senior officers who assist him in determining the company's over-all objectives, in leadership, planning, organizing, and performance appraisals.
2. Services management—made up of people skilled in specialist functions and subfunctions, who render expert technical service within the limits of their respective functions on a company-wide basis, that is, to all operating divisions and departments. These men thus assist in the formulation of over-all objectives, policies, plans, and programs, and provide specialized functional service and recommendations for carrying them out.
3. Operating management—made up of general managers and managers responsible for the successful conduct of their respective decentralized businesses within the framework of the company's over-all policies and programs. These men not only carry out over-all company objectives, policies, plans, and programs but also formulate and determine the goals and activities of their respective operating components.

The large box on the organization chart (Fig. 12) just below that of the directors is entitled "executive office." Within this box are individual boxes for the president, the chairman of the board, and the group executives, who carry on executive management and for whom there are no other boxes on the chart. In addition, in

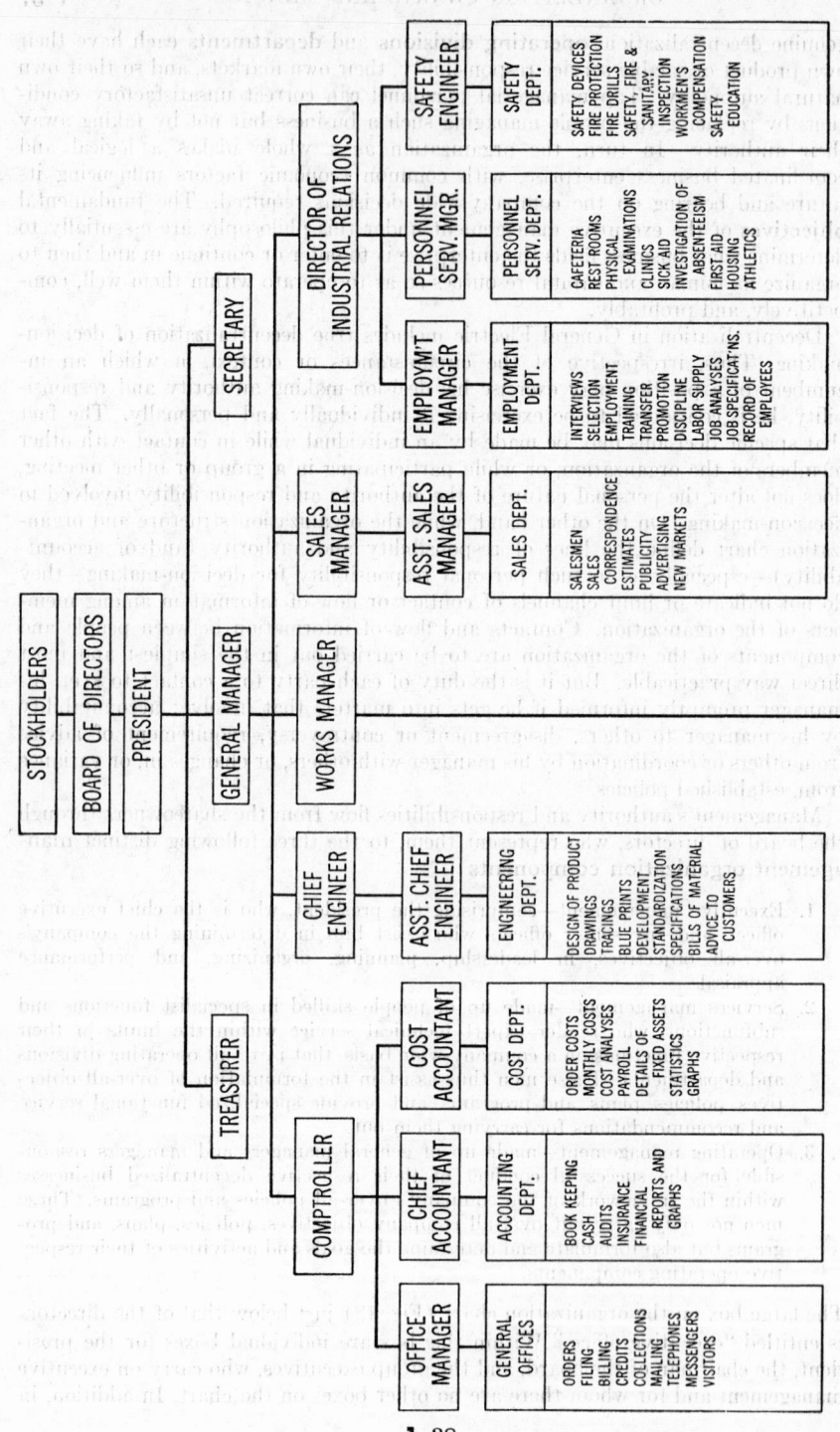

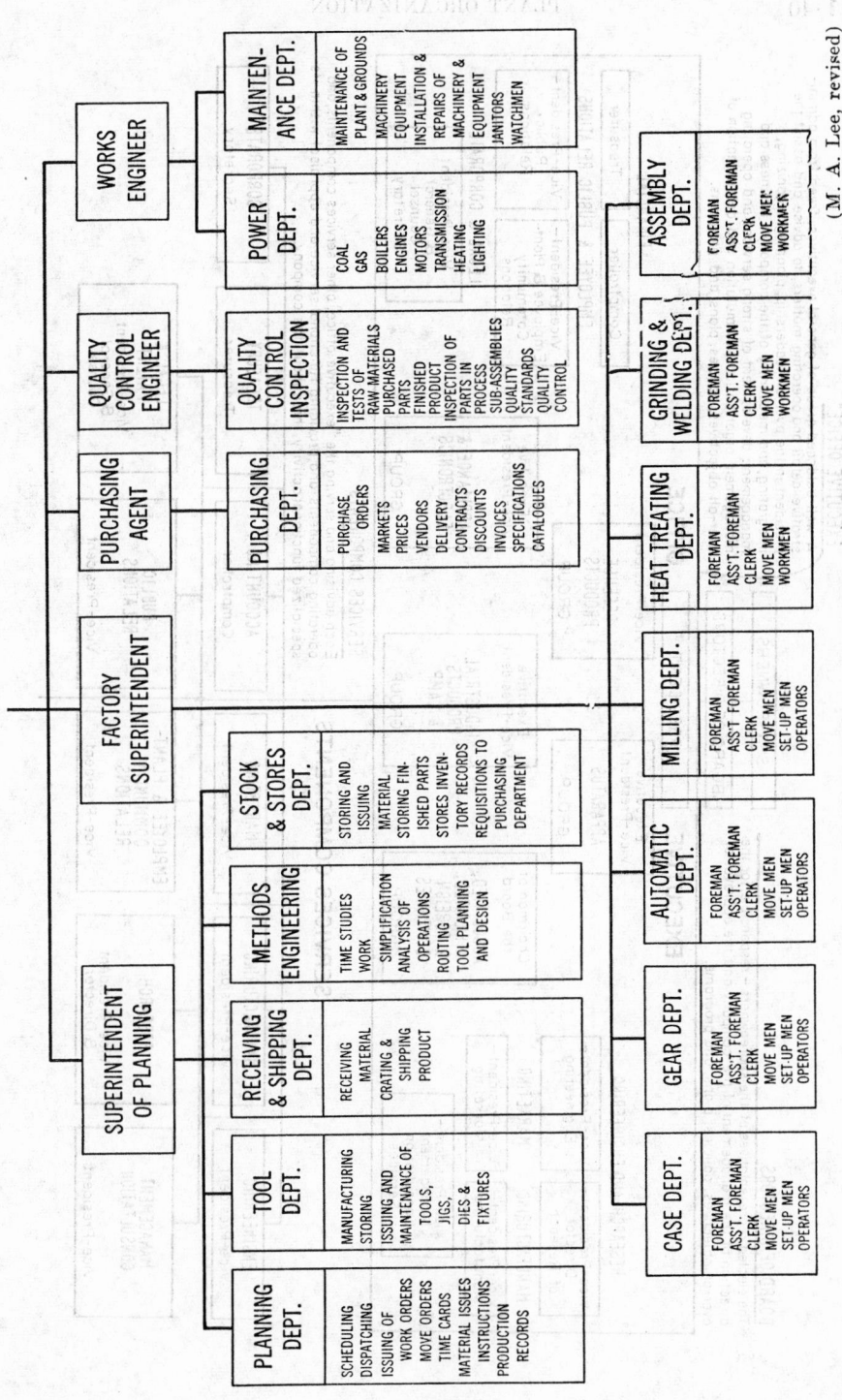

Fig. 11. Organization chart of a typical manufacturing company.

(M. A. Lee, revised)

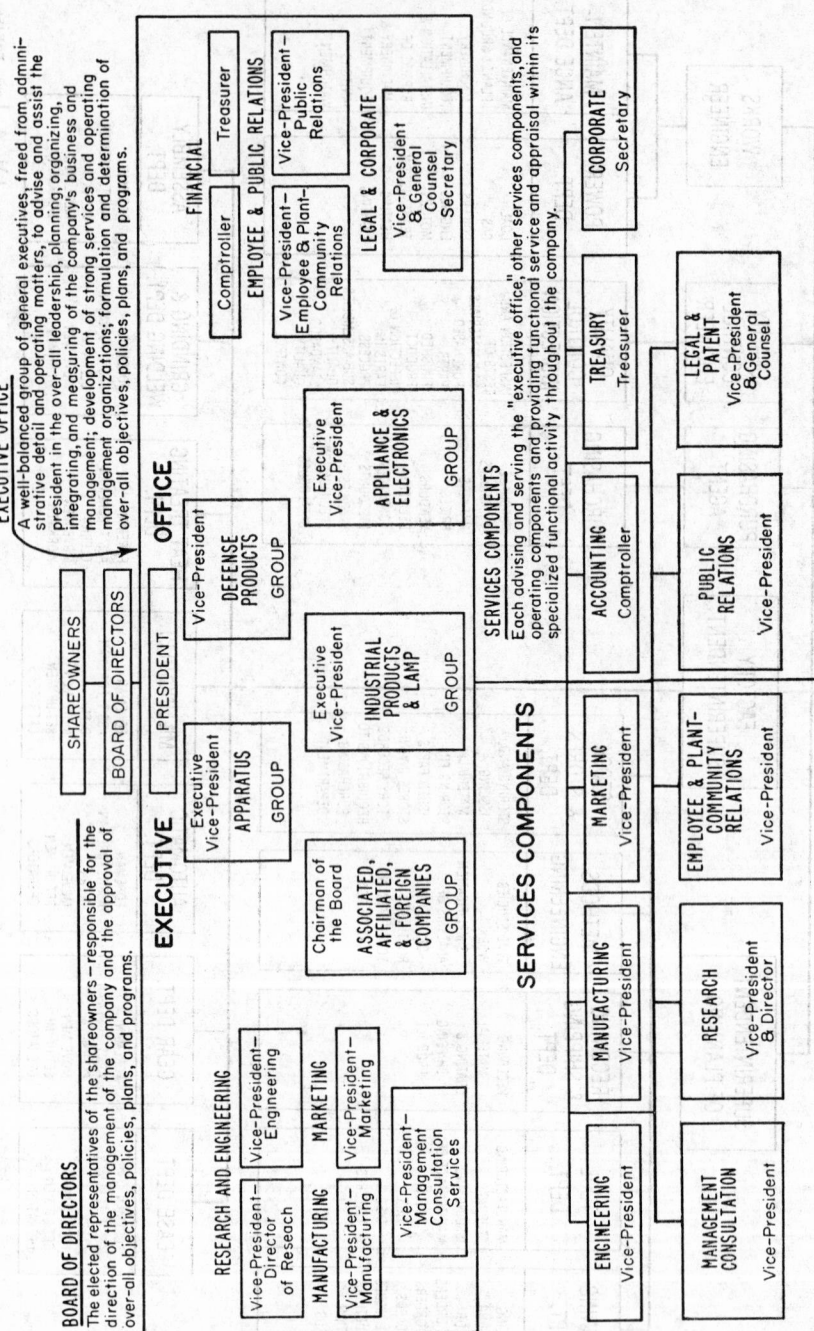

BOARD OF DIRECTORS
The elected representatives of the shareowners — responsible for the direction of the management of the company and the approval of over-all objectives, policies, plans, and programs.

"EXECUTIVE OFFICE"
A well-balanced group of general executives, freed from administrative detail and operating matters, to advise and assist the president in the over-all leadership, planning, organizing, integrating, and measuring of the company's business and management; development of strong services and operating management organizations; formulation and determination of over-all objectives, policies, plans, and programs.

SERVICES COMPONENTS
Each advising and serving the "executive office," other services components, and operating components and providing functional service and appraisal within its specialized functional activity throughout the company.

EXECUTIVE OFFICE

SHAREOWNERS

BOARD OF DIRECTORS

PRESIDENT

Chairman of the Board

FINANCIAL

Comptroller

Treasurer

EMPLOYEE & PUBLIC RELATIONS

Vice-President — Public Relations

Vice-President — Employee & Plant-Community Relations

LEGAL & CORPORATE

Vice-President & General Counsel

Secretary

Executive Vice-President

APPARATUS GROUP

Vice-President

DEFENSE PRODUCTS GROUP

Executive Vice-President

INDUSTRIAL PRODUCTS & LAMP GROUP

Executive Vice-President

APPLIANCE & ELECTRONICS GROUP

ASSOCIATED, AFFILIATED, & FOREIGN COMPANIES GROUP

RESEARCH AND ENGINEERING

Vice-President — Director of Research

Vice-President — Engineering

MANUFACTURING

Vice-President — Manufacturing

MARKETING

Vice-President — Marketing

Vice-President — Management Consultation Services

SERVICES COMPONENTS

ENGINEERING
Vice-President

MANUFACTURING
Vice-President

MARKETING
Vice-President

ACCOUNTING
Comptroller

TREASURY
Treasurer

CORPORATE
Secretary

MANAGEMENT CONSULTATION
Vice-President

RESEARCH
Vice-President & Director

EMPLOYEE & PLANT-COMMUNITY RELATIONS
Vice-President

PUBLIC RELATIONS
Vice-President

LEGAL & PATENT
Vice-President & General Counsel

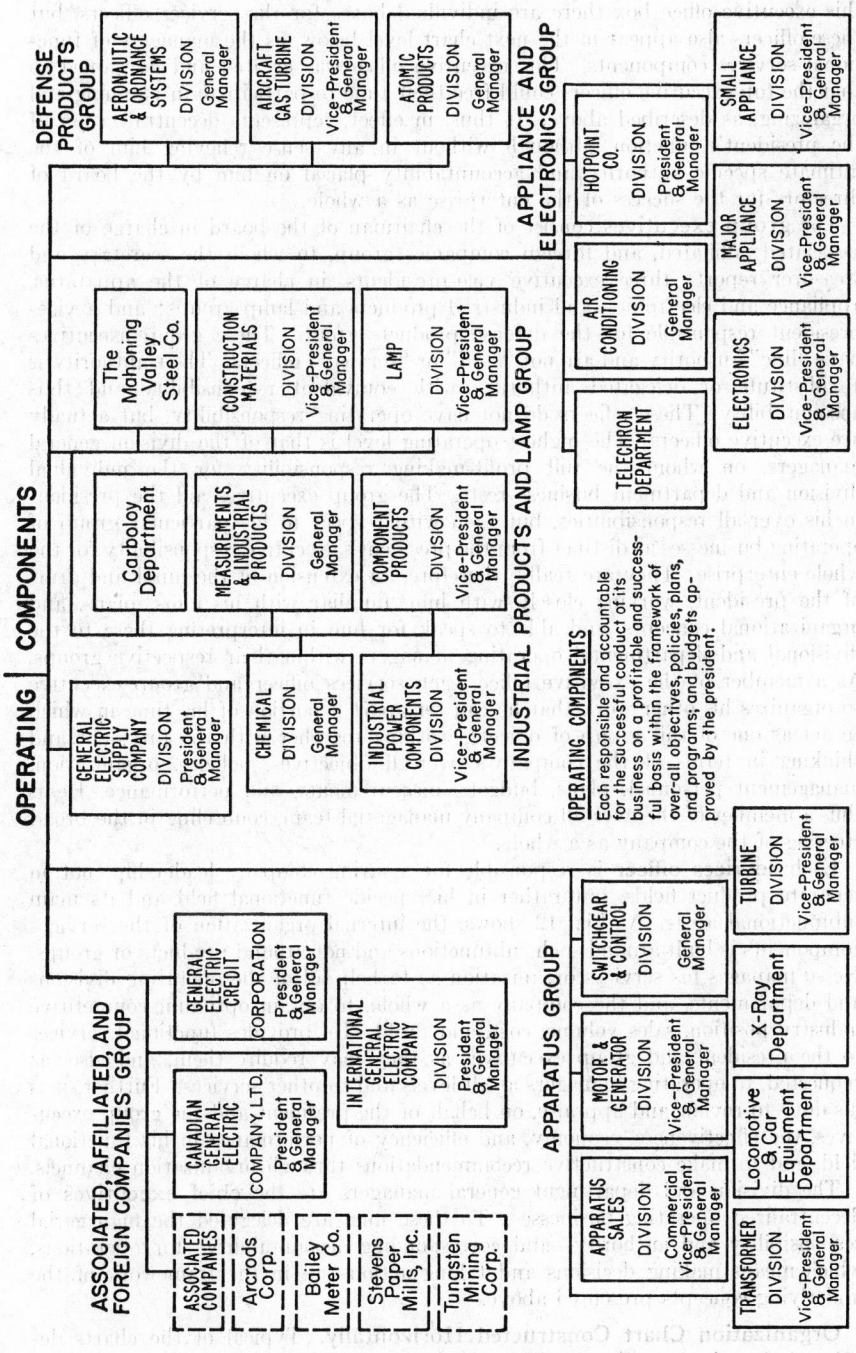

Fig. 12. Organization chart of the General Electric Co.

this executive office box there are individual boxes for the services officers, but these officers also appear in the next chart level below, as the managers of functional services components. This executive office was created and developed so that the top executive officers could free their time to participate in planning and organizing, as described above. It thus, in effect, represents decentralization of the president's function, although without in any sense relieving him of the ultimate specific authority and accountability placed on him by the board of directors for the success of the enterprise as a whole.

The **group executives** consist of the chairman of the board in charge of the associated, affiliated, and foreign companies group, to whom the secretary and treasurer report; three executive vice-presidents, in charge of the apparatus, appliance and electronics, and industrial products and lamp groups; and a vice-president responsible for the defense products group. These group executives have "line" authority and are not "staff" or "services" officers. Their authority is a substitute or delegated authority, with equivalent responsibility and thus accountability. These officers do not have operating responsibility, but actually are executive officers. The highest operating level is that of the division general managers, on whom the full profit-making responsibility for the individual division and department business rests. The group executives aid the president in his over-all responsibilities, but each with respect to his particular group of operating businesses as distinct from the president's executive responsibility for the whole enterprise. They are really, therefore, an extension of the mind and arms of the president, working closely with him, familiar with his aims, plans, and organizational concepts, and able to speak for him in interpreting these to the divisional and departmental operating managers within their respective groups. As a member of the executive office, each services officer and group executive so organizes his other work that he can set apart a portion of his time in which to act as one of this group of officers, working together with the president and thinking in terms of the company's over-all objectives, policies, organization, management personnel, plans, budgets, measurements, and performance. He is thus a member of the over-all company managerial team, counseling in the broad steering of the company as a whole.

Each **services officer** is responsible for assuring company leadership, not in separate product fields, but rather in his specific functional field and its main subfunctional areas. As Fig. 12 shows, the internal organization of the services components is built around such subfunctions and not around products or groups. He so manages his services organization as to help all of the operating divisions and departments, and the company as a whole, to obtain optimum competitive industry position, sales volume, cost, and profit. He provides functional services to the president and group executives as they may require them, and also, as requested, to operating managers at all levels and to other services. Further, it is his duty to review and appraise, on behalf of the president and the group executives, the effectiveness, economy, and efficiency of performance in his functional field, and to make constructive recommendations through organization channels.

The division and department general managers are the **chief executives** of decentralized operating businesses. To these men are delegated the managerial responsibility and authority—and corresponding accountability—for operations, which means making decisions and taking action—all in the framework of the underlying concepts presented above.

Organization Chart Constructed Horizontally. Typical of the charts developed along horizontal instead of vertical lines, which are used to a considerable

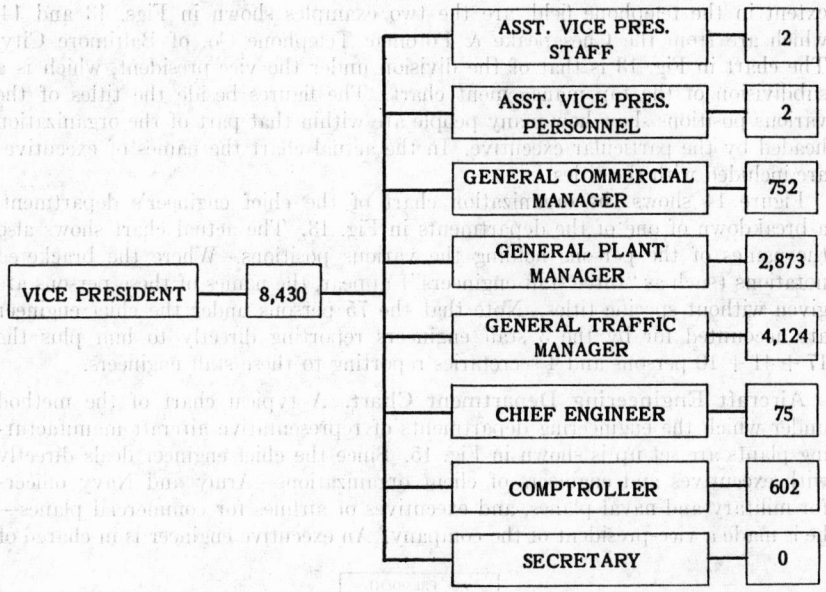

Fig. 13. Organization reporting to the vice-president—The Chesapeake & Potomac Telephone Co.

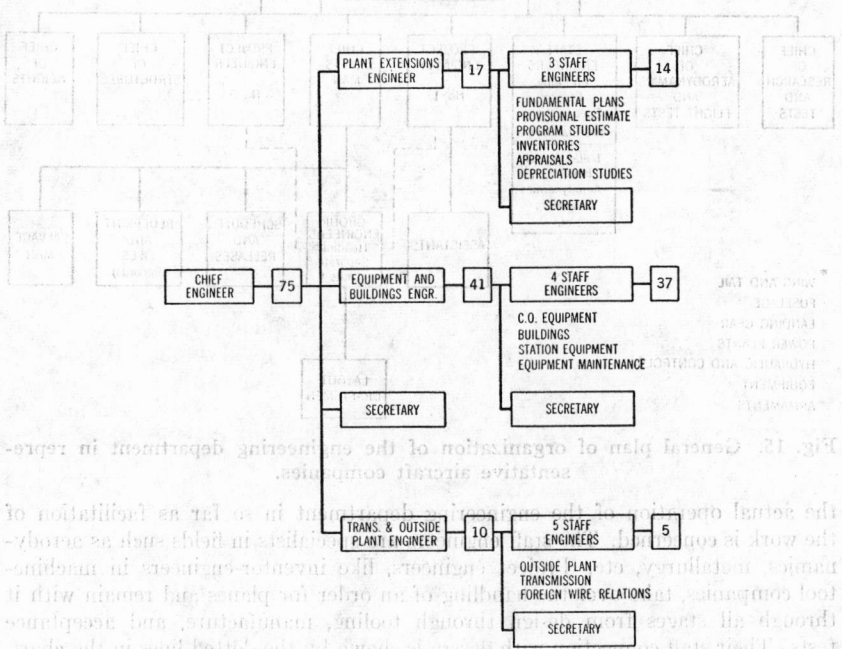

Fig. 14. Organization reporting to the chief engineer—The Chesapeake & Potomac Telephone Co.

extent in the telephone field, are the two examples shown in Figs. 13 and 14, which are from the Chesapeake & Potomac Telephone Co. of Baltimore City. The chart in Fig. 13 is that of the division under the vice-president, which is a subdivision of the top management chart. The figures beside the titles of the various positions show how many people are within that part of the organization headed by the particular executive. In the actual chart the names of executives are included with the titles.

Figure 14 shows the organization chart of the chief engineer's department, a breakdown of one of the departments in Fig. 13. The actual chart shows also the names of the persons holding the various positions. Where the bracketed notations (such as "three staff engineers") appear, the names of these persons are given without specific titles. Note that the 75 persons under the chief engineer are accounted for by the 3 staff engineers reporting directly to him plus the 17 + 41 + 10 persons and 4 secretaries reporting to these staff engineers.

Aircraft Engineering Department Chart. A typical chart of the method under which the engineering departments of representative aircraft manufacturing plants are set up is shown in Fig. 15. Since the chief engineer deals directly with executives and engineers of client organizations—Army and Navy officers for military and naval planes, and executives of airlines for commercial planes—he is made a vice-president of the company. An executive engineer is in charge of

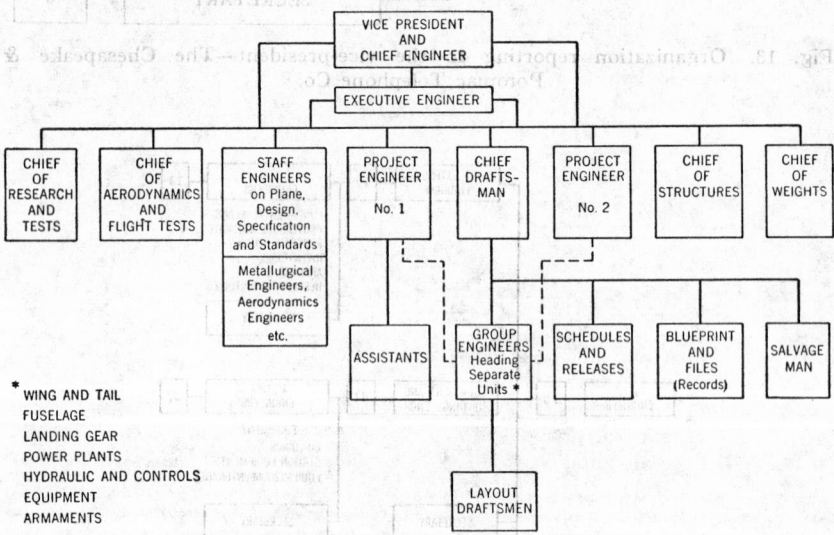

Fig. 15. General plan of organization of the engineering department in representative aircraft companies.

the actual operation of the engineering department in so far as facilitation of the work is concerned. The staff engineers are specialists in fields such as aerodynamics, metallurgy, etc. Project engineers, like inventor-engineers in machine-tool companies, take over the handling of an order for planes and remain with it through all stages from design through tooling, manufacture, and acceptance tests. Their staff connection with design is shown by the dotted lines in the chart.

The chief draftsman is the operating executive in charge of the design section, in which there are usually about seven large groups—wing and tail, etc.—as shown. The chief of structures must approve all airplane structural features and the chief of weights must check all designs to hold down weights and maintain proper weight balance in the planes.

A Comprehensive System of Company Charts. An interesting example of modern industrial organization is the Sperry Gyroscope Co. A part of Sperry Rand Corporation, this company has some 23,000 employees occupying more than 3.5 million sq. ft. of facilities. Its research and engineering activities are carried on by more than 2,700 graduate engineers and scientists who, in turn, are supported by an equal number of engineering personnel, such as aides, technicians, and draftsmen. The Sperry Gyroscope Co. itself consists of a group of divisions.

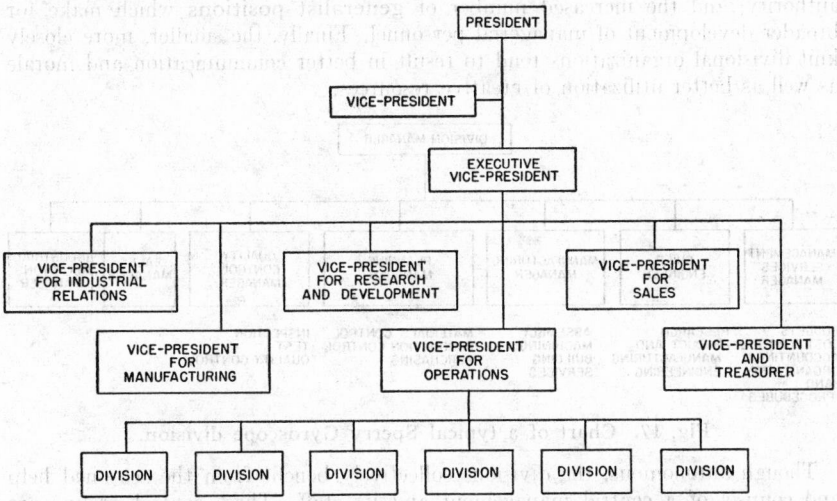

Fig. 16. Organization of the Sperry Gyroscope Co.

Its structure, shown in Fig. 16, is the result of a reorganization accomplished recently. This realignment has been based on the principles of **decentralization** and **divisionalization** which have become the prevalent pattern of most large and many medium-sized American corporations. Dividing the large organization into relatively autonomous and self-sufficient units, the company achieved a combination of the administrative and social advantages which make for small-plant efficiency and the advantages of economic strength and specialization which are inherent in the larger organization. Each division has its own sales, engineering, and manufacturing components and, in many cases, its own industrial relations and finance group. Fig. 17 shows the organization chart of a typical division. Generally speaking, each division manager has full responsibility and authority to run his own business within his particular product area subject only to the general policies established by top management. He is fully accountable for the profit or loss of his division. The responsibilities and functions of a typical division manager are specified in the **position description** below. Among the advantages of this scheme of organization are the creation of relatively small, closely knit and flexible **product teams,** shorter channels of communication, and the capability of responding quickly to market demands. Since each division manager may make all decisions pertinent to his operation, decisions are made closer to the point of actual operation and problems and policies can be resolved more speedily. Since such over-all **decision-making centers** are thus established for each division, a great many decisions which formerly had to be channeled to the top can now be resolved at the division manager's level. As a result, top management is free to concentrate on planning, policy development, and long-term guidance.

Divisional teams tend to be oriented more toward their product, its cost, delivery, and profitability, rather than toward their specialty, as is the case in large, functional organizations. This pattern also facilitates the generation of costs in each area and, subsequently, the accurate control of profit and loss. It facilita'es comparability among divisions and promotes management development. The latter is the direct result of both increased delegation of responsibility and authority, and the increased number of **generalist positions** which make for broader development of managerial personnel. Finally, the smaller, more closely knit divisional organizations tend to result in better communication and morale as well as better utilization of creative resources.

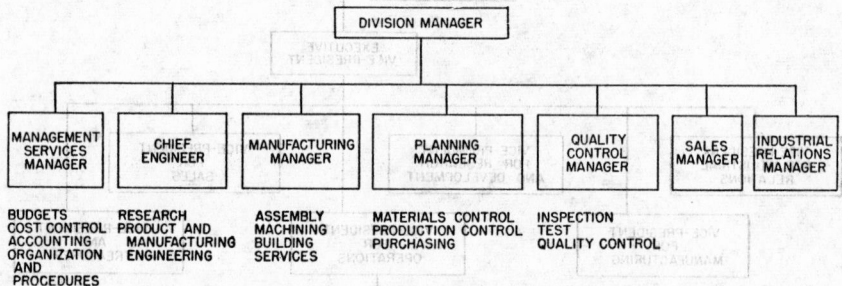

Fig. 17. Chart of a typical Sperry Gyroscope division.

Though autonomous, the divisions collectively benefit from the seasoned help and counsel of a central management and its staff. These central groups are headed by several senior vice-presidents who form the **Management Committee.** Their functions, as well as the general philosophy which guides the relationship between top management and divisional operations are perhaps best characterized by the position description of the Management Committee given below. It is the purpose of this headquarters group to preserve the experience of the entire organization and to make sure that the best available knowledge and techniques are brought to bear where they will do the most good. Broadly speaking, all operating responsibilities are vested in the product divisions and the headquarters group is charged with rendering service and consultation to the former.

THE ORGANIZATION MANUAL. Organization charts give merely a picture of the organization and show the position of each individual in respect to others in the structure. Titles may indicate the nature of the work carried on by each person, but often they are misleading as to his real functions because there is no general agreement among industries on the meaning of specific titles nor any attempt made in most companies to develop definitions for the various titles. A foreman in one company would rank as a superintendent in some other company, or in one case he might be over 5 men and in another over 200 but still be called a foreman. An organization chart, moreover, is static. It requires an additional medium to bring in the dynamic factor setting the organization in motion.

It is necessary, therefore, to develop an organization manual stating definitely the nature and extent of the authority and responsibility assigned to each position, so that the person filling it may know his duties, exactly what relationship he has to those above and below him, and the connection of his work with that of men in other divisions or departments of the company. Even an organization manual cannot so specifically draw the borderlines that there will be no questions on the above points. In addition, the continual shifting of the organization to take care of changes, and the new problems of operation which constantly come up, call for further explanations or some changes in the write-ups of the positions from time to time. Nevertheless, in the absence of an organization manual, even the smaller companies find that the various positions overlap, two or more persons are trying to handle some particular kinds of work, and certain other work is neglected, each person concerned with it leaving it to someone else to attend to.

The **function** of the organization manual is to set forth clearly the purposes which the manual is intended to fulfill, describe the general framework of the organization, state how it is broken down into divisions, departments, etc., state in general the different ranks or levels of authority—officers, division heads, department heads, etc.—indicate the difference between line authority and the staff function, define the terms used in the above explanations, and to give, for each division down through its successive breakdowns, the titles of the different positions together with their relationships to the immediately superior and subordinate positions and the range of responsibility, authority, and duties carried under the title. It thus defines the lines of authority and responsibility but cannot directly show the many crisscrossing channels of contact between individuals in different parts of the organization. These are provided for according to Fayol's principle, given in a previous portion of this section, in a general statement authorizing all individuals to secure aid or information from any proper source within the company.

Administration of a Company Manual. The Sperry Gyroscope Co. has one of the oldest and most comprehensive systems of company manuals. This consists of an Organization Manual and a Standard Practice Instructions Manual covering the entire company, as well as Standard Practice Instructions Manuals for each division. In addition there are a number of technical manuals originating from various specialized departments.

The company-wide manuals are administered by the Organization and Procedures Department in the office of the Executive Vice-President. The Organization Manual is revised constantly to keep it up to date. Changes and additions are announced by means of pink bulletins and authorized by the appropriate division head as soon as an appointment or transfer has been made. These bulletins are followed as quickly as possible by the revised pages of the manual.

In order to facilitate the mechanics of issuing and maintaining organization pages, Sperry has departed from the conventional block-type of presentation of organization charts which it uses only for the top, over-all company chart. The manual itself is set up on the basis of **typewritten organization charts.** Levels of organization are indicated by indentations. Alongside each position is shown the department number, the name of the incumbent, and an **approval code.** This code denotes the general range and degree of authorizations which the incumbent of this particular position may approve. Such authorizations may be in such areas as budgets and expenses, personnel hiring and transfer, timecards, and capital equipment. This format of organization pages allows the handling of the entire manual by means of typewriter and avoids time-consuming drafting. It also makes for a considerable reduction in volume. A typical page is shown in Fig. 18

	Dept. No.	Names of Incumbents	Approval Code	Night Shift
(MANAGER, AERONAUTICAL EQUIPMENT DIVISION)..................	(3100	———	D)	
(MANUFACTURING MANAGER)	(3400	———	C)	
GENERAL FOREMAN, FLIGHT INSTRUMENT ASSEMBLY-MECHANICAL....	3401	———	C	
FOREMAN, S-3 GYROSYN ASSEMBLY..............................	3475	———	B	
SECTION FOREMAN, GYRO ASSEMBLY	3473	———	A	
ASST. FOREMAN, GYRO ASSEMBLY	3473	———	A	
ASST. FOREMAN, GYRO ASSEMBLY	3473			——— A
ASST. FOREMAN, GYRO ASSEMBLY..............................	3473			
SECTION FOREMAN, S-3 GYROSYN ASSEMBLY.....................	3475	———	A	
ASST. FOREMAN, GYRO HORIZON ASSEMBLY......................	3482	———	A	
ASST. FOREMAN, FLIGHT INSTRUMENT PREPARATION..............	3439	———	A	
FOREMAN, MECHANICAL ASSEMBLY FOR AUTOMATIC PILOTS.........	3465	———	B	
ASST. FOREMAN, MOTOR & SYNCHRO ASSEMBLY..................	3425	———	A	
SECTION FOREMAN, C-5-C ASSEMBLY...........................	3451	———	A	
ASST. FOREMAN, FLIGHT INSTRUMENT ASSEMBLY.................	3472	———	A	
SECTION FOREMAN, MECHANICAL ASSEMBLY FOR AUTOMATIC PILOTS	3465	———	A	
ASST. FOREMAN, MECHANICAL ASSEMBLY FOR AUTOMATIC PILOTS	3465	———	A	
ASST. FOREMAN, FLIGHT INSTRUMENT REPAIR	3483	———	A	
ASST. FOREMAN, MECHANICAL ASSY. FOR AUTOMATIC PILOTS.	3465	———	A	
GENERAL FOREMAN, FLIGHT INSTRUMENT ASSEMBLY-ELECTRICAL....	3402	———	C	
FOREMAN, ELECTRONIC EQUIPMENT ASSEMBLY....................	3434	———	B	
ASST. FOREMAN, A-12 MODIFICATION..........................	3484	———	A	
SECTION FOREMAN, ELECTRONIC EQUIPMENT ASSEMBLY........	3434	———	A	
ASST. FOREMAN, ELECTRONIC EQUIPMENT ASSEMBLY........	3434	———	A	
SECTION FOREMAN, ELECTRONIC EQUIPMENT ASSEMBLY........	3434	———	A	
ASST. FOREMAN, ELECTRONIC EQUIPMENT ASSEMBLY........	3434	———	A	
ASST. FOREMAN, ELECTRONIC EQUIPMENT ASSEMBLY........	3434	———	A	
SECTION FOREMAN, ELECTRONIC EQUIPMENT ASSEMBLY.........	3434			——— A
ASST. FOREMAN, ELECTRONIC EQUIPMENT ASSEMBLY.........	3434			——— A

AERONAUTICAL EQUIPMENT DIVISION CHART
Issue Date: June 7, 19—
Page: 7

Signed ———————
Manager, Aeronautical Equipment Division

Fig. 18. Typewritten organization chart from organization manual.

Position Descriptions. Sperry Gyroscope has developed position descriptions for most managerial and specialist personnel which appear in the organization manual with the organization charts. These descriptions specify the title, the objectives, the specific duties and responsibilities, and special relationships, if any, of each position. In order to stress the nature of managerial responsibilities inherent in all supervisory jobs, and in order to economize on space for individual descriptions, a listing of common duties and responsibilities **applicable to all management positions** precedes all position descriptions in the Sperry manual:

It is the responsibility of every executive and supervisor:
To **plan, execute,** and **review** the operations under his jurisdiction, and to **feed back** the results of the review in order to improve the planning of the next phase.

Notes: 1. Organization charts, position descriptions, schedules, budgets, and other management tools are to be relied upon as guides for decisions; they do not relieve any supervisor of the obligation to exercise common sense and good judgment in the accomplishment of his mission.

2. The functions listed below apply only to the degree required in a given position. The scope of their applicability is stated in the "specific" section of the position description of which this "common" section constitutes a part.

A. PLANNING

1. **To Formulate Policy**
   a. To formulate policy relative to his position.
   b. To establish short and long term objectives and to develop programs to implement these objectives.
   c. To be guided by the applicable Divisional and General SPI (Standard Practice Instructions) in regard to objectives, policies, procedures, forms, organization, etc.

2. **To Forecast Requirements**
   a. To forecast personnel, machine, material, space, financial and other requirements pertinent to his function.
   b. To prepare estimates, as required, on such matters as cost of work, delivery date, etc.

3. **To Keep Abreast**
   a. To keep abreast of developments in the field of management, of the technical areas under his supervision, and of developments within the Company.

4. **To Establish an Organization**
   a. To insure that each subordinate has a clean-cut responsibility to a single superior only.
   b. To clarify and define the objectives, functions, responsibilities, and relationships inherent in the positions under his jurisdiction; to make no change in responsibilities without notifying all parties concerned; to insure that his subordinates understand how they fit into the over-all picture of the Division.
   c. To delegate responsibility (with commensurate authority) to the greatest possible extent in order to get decisions made as close to the point of operation as possible; in order to utilize effectively the talents and capabilities under his jurisdiction; and in order to develop them to assume the fullest possible responsibilities for the Division's as well as their own benefit.
   d. To designate one subordinate to act in his absence or to meet this requirement by rotation among his subordinates.
   e. To develop at least one potential successor.
   f. To appoint all personnel under his immediate jurisdiction with the approval of his superior.

    5. **To Establish Internal Controls**
      a. To insure optimum utilization of men, machines, and materials.
      b. To develop procedures, standards, methods, internal controls, budgets, and schedules pertinent to his function.
      c. To insure that management controls are governed by a philosophy of "prevention" and good planning, rather than merely by "after-the-fact control."

B. EXECUTING

    1. **To Integrate Activities Under His Jurisdiction**
      a. To operate in accordance with the above objectives and policies.
      b. To disseminate to his subordinates all possible general information, plans, and policies for their guidance.
      c. To encourage suggestions and complaints.
      d. To direct, motivate, integrate, and coordinate all personnel under his jurisdiction. To assign work, to promote the closest possible teamwork, and to insure appropriate quality and quantity.
      e. To assure the safety of his subordinates.
      f. To insure compliance with Company and Division policies and regulations, as well as labor and other laws, etc.
      g. To approve all authorizations as prescribed for his position.
      h. To initiate, maintain, and dispose of appropriate records.
      i. To maintain and protect Company assets under his jurisdiction.

    2. **To Achieve Cost and Delivery Objectives**
      a. To operate within the approved budget.
      b. To insure that individuals under his jurisdiction make responsible commitments and promises regarding costs, schedules, etc., and that they live up to these commitments.
      c. To promote cost-consciousness to the utmost, but not to promote short-term economies at the expense of long-term growth.
      d. To maintain and promote a questioning and experimental attitude toward his operations.

    3. **To Coordinate His Activities with Those of Other Supervisors**
      a. To work out problems relevant to his position directly with other supervisors affected, but to keep his principal informed in regard to matters:
        (1) For which his superior may be properly held accountable by others.
        (2) Which are likely to cause disagreements or controversy.
        (3) Which require the superior's advice or his coordination with other components of the organization.
        (4) Which involve recommendations for change of, or in variance from, established policies.
      To present (in the event that such problems cannot be resolved without a higher level decision) complete recommendations to his principal, rather than merely appeal for a decision.
      b. To promote management "by exception" wherever possible. (This entails that each supervisor use a maximum of discretion within the authority delegated to him, and within the established plans, policies, budgets, schedules, etc., and bring to his principal's attention only those matters which deviate from and are exceptions to these established plans.)
      c. To coordinate his activity with those of other departments not under his control.
      d. To insure that operations and services not under his control are brought to bear effectively on his operation.

    4. **To Promote Sound Human Relations**
      a. To build positive, productive human relations. To consider the dignity and well-being of the individual employee as a principal factor governing management decisions. To promote meaningful job contents and constructive

relationships down the line. To treat subordinates as individuals. To promote a team spirit and feeling of loyalty and "belonging" on the part of employees. To maintain effective two-way communication with his subordinates and superior.

   b. To direct the selection, hiring, placing, evaluating, transferring, promoting, disciplining, training, developing, and discharging of personnel, with emphasis on proper placement and development of employees.

C. REVIEW
1. To Review Performance
   a. To review and evaluate continuously the performance of his function, and to make recommendations for any action whose need arises from this review.

2. To Improve Performance
   a. To develop a habit for continuous self-criticism; to improve his job; to seek, accept, and transmit suggestions; and to make suitable recommendations; and to coach and counsel his subordinates constructively in the performance of their work.

3. To Report Performance
   a. To render a periodic account of progress to his superior; to insure that the benefits of the above reviews are "fed back" into the planning of the next phase of operations.

In general, position descriptions are intended to **define the mission** of the incumbent of a particular position. They specify what he is expected to accomplish and the functions he is to perform. They do not include the "how" of the job. The manner in which it is to be accomplished is left for procedural write-ups contained in the Standard Practice Instructions. Thus, by preceding the position descriptions with a common section and by limiting them to the mission of the job, the individual descriptions can be held relatively brief. The specific position description of **division manager** at Sperry Gyroscope follows:

TITLE:
> Division Manager

OBJECTIVE:
> To operate the division within the objectives and policies specified by the Vice President for Operations; to attain an optimum profit at the highest possible quality level, and at competitive cost and delivery, consistent with good customer service and good human relations practice.

DUTIES AND RESPONSIBILITIES:
The following are in addition to the statement of "Duties and Responsibilities Common to all Management Positions" which constitutes a part of this position description:

   1. To be fully responsible for the operations and, inasmuch as possible, for the profitability of his division within the limits of policies established by the Vice President for Operations.

     Note: All authority not retained specifically by top management (as specified in the Gyro Group Policy Manual, or in other written or verbal directives) shall be vested in Division Managers. Policies, standards, and procedures which are not stated specifically by the Gyro Group Manual as mandatory, may be taken exception to by divisional SPI. However, such policies, standards, and procedures, as developed by central groups or even by other divisions, shall be used to the fullest possible extent consistent with the objectives of the division.

2. To develop long- and short-term sales, engineering, manufacturing, financial, and industrial relations goals and policies for the division in consultation with the members of the Management Committee.

3. To develop, productize, manufacture, price, and sell the product line assigned to his division.

4. To conduct public, employee, customer, and vendor relations pertinent to the division; to represent the Company locally (if the division is removed geographically from the parent plant) and to participate in local affairs for the purpose of promoting the welfare of the division and its environment.

5. To review continuously the division's performance, with particular emphasis on its profit and loss position.

SPECIAL RELATIONSHIPS:

1. **Other Division and Plant Managers**
   To cooperate with the managers of other divisions and plants of the Company on all matters of mutual interest and concern.

2. **The Management Committee**
   To consult with the members of the Management Committee on all matters in which they might be of assistance by virtue of their specialized experience, and to utilize to the extent necessary the centralized, specialized services available. To bring to the attention of the Vice President for Operations only those problems which cannot be resolved satisfactorily at the above level, and to present to him, in such exceptional cases, complete recommendations for his decision.

The description of the duties, responsibilities, and membership of the **management committee** at Sperry Gyroscope, cited above, follows:

TITLE:
                    Management Committee
OBJECTIVE:
                    A. As a Committee: To assist the Executive Vice President in planning and appraising Gyro Group performance.
                    B. As Individuals: To assist in preserving corporate know-how and experience and in bringing the best possible information relative to specialized skills to bear throughout all corporate groups and divisions. To make the experience of the whole corporation available to all groups and divisions.

DUTIES AND RESPONSIBILITIES

A. **As a Committee:**

1. To develop long-range goals and objectives for the Gyro Group and to recommend policies and programs for their implementation.
2. To keep abreast of the Gyro Group's general competitive and profit positions.
3. To appraise the performance of the Gyro Group and to make recommendations for improvement.
4. To maintain balance among, and recommend growth rates of, the divisions of the Gyro Group.
5. To recommend the location, size, nature, and product areas of all plants and facilities.
6. To resolve policies relating to compensation and status.
7. To resolve problems referred to it by Divisional Management.

B. **As Individuals:**

1. To generate long-range objectives and programs within their individual fields of specialization and to coordinate programs of mutual interest among corporate groups and divisions.

2. To monitor and audit divisional performance relative to their individual fields of specialization and to make recommendations for improvement.
3. To offer consultation within their specialty.
4. To issue technical manuals within their field of specialization, if necessary and desirable.
5. To keep abreast of current developments within their field, both within the Corporation and outside, and to act as a clearinghouse in disseminating this information.
6. To operate specialized central services for the benefit of the Gyro Group and its divisions.
7. To undertake special studies and projects within their field of specialty.
8. To relieve the President, the Executive Vice President and the Management Committee, through consultation with Division Managers, of all decisions which can be resolved by virtue of their specialized individual know-how and experience and to bring to the attention of the Gyro Group's top management only those problems which cannot be resolved satisfactorily at this level; to present in such exceptional cases complete recommendations for decision.

MEMBERSHIP:
1. Executive Vice President (Chairman)
2. Vice President for Operations
3. Vice President for Sales
4. Vice President for Industrial Relations
5. Vice President and Treasurer
6. Vice President for Manufacturing
7. Vice President for Research and Development
8. Assistant to the Executive Vice President (Secretary)
9. President (Ex officio)

SPECIAL RELATIONSHIPS:
Close liaison with Patent Committee.

STANDARD PRACTICE INSTRUCTIONS. An organization is further implemented by what are known as standard practice instructions, which constitute write-ups of established procedures for the carrying out of various activities or the performance of certain kinds of work. Such write-ups constitute the "system" of the enterprise, but should not be allowed to degenerate into the class of unnecessarily complicated routines commonly called "red tape." It is readily seen that the organization chart tells "where" in the company a function is placed, the organization manual tells "what" the detailed nature of the function or position is and indicates its relationships to other functions and positions, while the standard practice instruction tells "how" the functions are to be carried on and the duties and responsibilities are to be discharged.

It is necessary to have such procedures written up not only for the guidance of employees performing the work—so that it is all done according to instructions —and the training of new employees, but also because many of the important procedures cover several sections and departments some of which are feeders-in of information that others must then compile and use in carrying on their work. Thus the procedure of handling time tickets covers not only getting the workers' time on jobs but also the checking off of completed work from production schedules, the making up of the payroll to pay workers, the charging of time to jobs or kinds of product to get current costs and record data for future estimating, and the posting of entries in the general accounts. In addition these time tickets form the basis for social security payroll deductions and taxation and for reports to workers and to the government on earnings and withholdings. The time tickets are only one of hundreds of items for which standard procedures are not only helpful but also imperative.

The various divisions and departments may have **handbooks** in which these standard procedures are kept on file for frequent reference, copies being placed in the hands of executives and supervisors who are concerned with phases of such standard practices. Like charts and manuals, these write-ups must also be frequently checked and revised to keep them up-to-date.

Analysis of Organization and Procedures

ORGANIZATION ANALYSIS. An organization, whether existing or in process of being designed, and particularly its procedures, can be submitted to detailed analysis. The methods used lead to simplification and standardization of duties or activities, methods, and procedures. The end result is elimination of conflict and friction, reduction of waste time and energy, quicker action in performing work, and lower costs.

The analytic procedures involved are identical to those used in methods analysis or work simplification (see sections on Motion and Methods Study and Work Simplification).

In brief, organization analysis involves:

1. Selecting the procedure to be improved.
2. Securing and recording facts. Recording all details of procedure exactly as at present with process charts (see section on Process Charts).
3. Questioning each and every detail. Using the "five prompters":
   a. What is done? Why?
   b. Where is it done? Why?
   c. When is it done? Why?
   d. Who does it? Why?
   e. How is it done? Why?
4. Developing new procedure. This requires using the four principal tools of methods improvement; elimination, combination, change in sequence, and simplification.
5. Applying new procedure. It is human nature to resent criticism and to resist change, therefore "selling" the new method to those who must work with it becomes of paramount importance in the improvement of a procedure. Before any new procedure can be made to work, it must be accepted and understood by those whom it affects. Participation is a means to cooperation and therefore it is most desirable that those who must live with the new procedure be consulted in its birth. Those who understand the reason and need for a change and have been able to participate in the development of a new procedure will have a paternalistic feeling toward its success. A change in procedure by fiat has little chance of survival.

INSPECTION OF POLICY AND ORGANIZATION. The production organization of a plant employing a large number of workers is complex and made up of many individuals, each with numerous duties. It is estimated that out of every 100 individuals in a typical factory organization, 4 are major executives, 12 are supervising executives, and 84 are workers or wage earners. Because of this complexity, continual changes in projects, methods, and procedures, and the developments and evaluations which come about with passage of time, it is easy for an organization to depart from the policies, authorities, responsibilities, and duties as they have been established. For this reason it is good practice to set up the function of **policy and organization inspection.** That is, someone should be assigned the duty of continually watching and observing the policies and organization structure to determine when changes should be made and recorded and whether departures from the original plans need to be corrected. This function of inspection is no different in principle from the inspection of product. In the latter case the inspector determines the degree of conformance between the product as produced and the specifications for it; in the former case, the inspector determines the degree of conformance of operation with established policies, delegation of authority and responsibility, and allotment of duties as originally laid out.

EFFECT OF ORGANIZATION ON OPERATING RESULTS. Fixing definite tasks and responsibilities in an organization is a requirement for satisfactory production control. Such determination likewise is a prerequisite to the personal efficiency of every industrial executive, supervisor, and foreman. Only by removing all uncertainties and conflicts of responsibility and authority can a smooth-running organization be set up. Once established and maintained it must constantly be renewed to operate with a minimum of executive effort and to yield the lowest obtainable manufacturing costs. In this way the most can be made of both human and physical resources. The former include the personalities, strong points, training, and experience of every member. The latter comprehend the practical work of bringing together and directing the use of materials, tools, machines, equipment, working space, power, and all other physical agencies of production. Thus organization affects every activity in industrial operation, and is a powerful aid in obtaining economic results.

PRODUCTION PLANNING AND CONTROL

CONTENTS

PAGE

Nature and Organization

Definition 1
Functions of production control 1
Factors determining control procedures 2
Varied and repetitive operation 2
Nature of manufacturing 3
Magnitude of operations 4
Costs and benefits of production control 4
Production control organization 5
Control functions 6
Variations according to conditions 7
Representative organization forms 7
Representative production control organ-
ization in terms of functions performed
(f. 1) 8
Centralized production control organiza-
tion (f. 2) 8
Combination of centralized and decen-
tralized production control organization
(f. 3) 8

Production Planning

Importance of organized planning 9
Types of production plans 10
Plans which prescribe quantities 10
Plans which prescribe method 10
Plans which prescribe timing 10
Production planning: quantities 11
Establishing relationships 11
Analyzing trends 11
Adjusting production to seasonal sales
(f. 4) 12
Sales forecasts 13
Influence of guaranteed annual wages on
planning and control 13
Past performance data 13
Data, formulas, and cumulative chart of
sales with control limits and trends
(f. 5) 14-15
Cumulative chart of percentage of sales
volume vs. percentage of number of
items (f. 6) 16
Production plans 17
Plan based on forecasts 17
Sales forecast of tool manufacturer (f. 7) 17
Production and inventory schedule based
on sales forecast (f. 8) 18
Control chart plotting forecasted sales,
inventories, and production (f. 9) 18
Production planning: timing 19
Analysis of capacity 19
Preparation for the job 20

PAGE

Total capacity in terms of time 20
Units of capacity 20
Process industries 21
Simplified flow chart of petrochemical
production and distribution (f. 10).... 22
Simultaneous operations 23
Graphic presentation of single-purpose
and automatic machine productivity
(f. 11) 23
Simultaneous performance and operating
efficiency 23
Preliminary scheduling 25
Master schedule for manufacture and
assembly of a product (f. 12) 24

Mathematical Planning Techniques

Economical manufacturing quantity 25
Costs affecting economic lot size (f. 13) 26
Setup costs 26
Cost of shop orders 27
Analytic calculation of economic quantity 27
Data for computation of economic manu-
facturing quantity (f. 14) 27
Cost comparisons for manufacturing
quantities of various sizes (f. 15) 28
Norton formula 28
Davis formula 29
Other types of formulas 30
Slope of economic lot quantity curve
(f. 16) 31
Use of nomographs and slide rules 32
Modifications in economic order quantity
theory 32
Optimal machine loading 32

Production Control

Elements of control 32
Manufacturing or production orders 33
Subsidiary orders 33
Combined production and job order
where routing is fixed (f. 17) 34
Production order combined with schedule
(f. 18) 35
Production order authorizing weekly out-
puts (f. 19) 36
Production order and progress record
(f. 20) 37
Control of manufacturing 36

Routing

The routing function 38

PAGE

Scheduling

Definition 39
Effect of manufacturing methods on sched-
uling 39
Components of a schedule 39
   Departmental and cumulative time cover-
ing the cycle of a production order
(*f.* 21) 40
   Time cycle of the production order of
Fig. 21 in Gantt chart form (*f.* 22)... 41
   Preliminaries to manufacturing 42
   Production planning time 42
   Procurement cycle 42
   Tooling 43
   Factory processing cycle 43
   Transit time 43
   Subassembly 43
   Final assembly, testing, and shipping 44
Machine loading 44
   Collection of load data 45

Dispatching

Definition 46
Principal factors 46
Dispatching: intermittent manufacture 46
   Sequence of dispatching operations (*f.* 23) 47
Dispatching: continuous manufacture 48
   Position of dispatching in automobile
assembly operations (*f.* 24) 48
Job orders 49
   Job order tabulating card (*f.* 25) 50
   Job order combined with inspection re-
port (*f.* 26) 50

PAGE

Inspection and release of work 51
Follow-up 51

Control of Down Time and Machine Utilization

Idleness losses 51
   Crossover chart illustrating idleness losses
(*f.* 27) 53
Clerical control 54
   Machine time report (*f.* 28) 54
   Time, productivity, and yield report
(*f.* 29) 56–57
Waste and scrap control 58
Instrumentation 58
   Chronolog for down time control (*f.* 30) 59
   Chronolog record tape (*f.* 31) 60

Procedural Analysis

Procedure flow charts 61
   Procedure flow chart with form repre-
sentations (*f.* 32) 62
   Tabular presentation of control proce-
dure (*f.* 33) 63
Procedure analysis 61
Standard practice instructions 64
   Sample page of standard practice in-
structions manual (*f.* 34) 64

Measuring Effectiveness of Production Control

Criteria for effectiveness 65
Formulas indicating effectiveness 65

PRODUCTION PLANNING AND CONTROL

Nature and Organization

DEFINITION. Production planning and control involves generally the organization and planning of the manufacturing process. Specifically, it consists of the planning of routing, scheduling, dispatching, and inspection coordination, and the control of materials, methods, machines, tooling, and operation times. The ultimate **objective** is the organization of the supply and movement of materials and labor, machine utilization, and related activities, in order to bring about the desired manufacturing results in terms of quantity, quality, time, and place.

FUNCTIONS OF PRODUCTION CONTROL. Since no two plants are organized alike, it is necessary first to define specifically what functions belong in the category of production control and require provisions for proper handling. The names assigned to production control departments differ; the kinds of work allotted to them vary among different plants; and the titles applied to different positions or kinds of work carried on are not the same throughout industry. In many cases there is often no clear distinction between production control and actual manufacturing; i.e., both utilize the same personnel. A further set of complicating factors arises from the mistaken impression that, first, there are numerous varieties of production control systems; second, that there are definitely standard systems which apply directly to certain types of industries and, third, that setups can be copied bodily from other factories and, when introduced, will work with corresponding success. Organized production control is necessary for the most successful operation, but the methods installed must be definitely adapted to the particular plant in which they are to be used.

Production control is a **facilitating service to manufacturing.** It coordinates all of the necessary production information and production aids, including methods, times, materials, and tools; it directs and checks on the course and progress of work, and closes the records when work on an order has been completed. It has sometimes been called the "paper work" of manufacturing, although this term is too limited to cover all its duties. In general, it relieves the manufacturing superintendent of nonoperating responsibilities and removes from the foreman the burden of preliminary planning and recording duties.

The **spread of production control department functions** will depend (1) on the nature of the business and (2) on the way in which organization activities are divided. In some industries an engineering department prepares fundamental data; drawings, blueprints, specifications of material and of operations on each piece, lists of parts, inspection standards, and similar technical data are usually prepared by this department where there is one. Sometimes a process development department is maintained, continually studying improvements in processes. In other industries the starting point is the pattern or model, such as printer's copy or a foundry pattern. It may also be merely a sketch or drawing from which a model or pattern is prepared. Plants making stamped, pressed, or molded parts, foundries, and concerns handling small repetitive work for customers, come into this category. In chemical processes, the starting point is a formula or series of formulas with data on materials, purity, quality, quantity, temperatures of processing, and other control data.

How much of this work falls to the production control department will depend on the **method of organization.** Properly, such design work should be entrusted to the special department corresponding to the engineering department; if it is not assigned there, the production control department will have to deal with it. In one department or another, someone must analyze the proposed product into its components, determine the quality and quantity of material, specify standards of quality for the product, and provide all the necessary technical data on which accurate planning must rest. So-called "simple" systems are not infrequently described; on examination it is often found either that the product is one requiring but little planning, or, more often, that some of the planning and control functions are being performed by other departments under other names On the other hand, preparation of technical data and even the layout of machines and conveying systems are sometimes called planning.

FACTORS DETERMINING CONTROL PROCEDURES. Control procedures are determined by several conditioning factors:

1. Varied or repetitive character of operations.
2. Nature of manufacturing processes.
3. Magnitude of operations.

Although there is a basic pattern for developing a production control organization and a basic line of procedure which all production control activities must follow, both have to be adapted, not only to the **kind of industry,** but to the **specific plant.** This is true whether the planning and control is all mental and unrecorded, or whether it involves a most elaborate system. The apparently wide difference between the method of planning and operation in one company and another arises solely from the way in which the production control activities are necessarily carried on, not from fundamental variations in the "what, why, when, where, and how" of such activities. The various systems of production control represent adaptations and should not be regarded as totally different conceptions of the control functions and procedures.

Varied and Repetitive Operation. In general, variety of operations complicates the problem of planning and control, whereas repetitive operations, since they reduce variety, tend to simplify the problem. In practice, there are all sorts of variants between these two extremes. These may be represented by the continuous production of a **single standardized product** on the one hand and the completely **special-order business** on the other. Some of the principal variants are:

1. **Manufacturing to order,** which may or may not be repeated at regular intervals. Examples: Jobbing foundries, printing plants, bleaching and dyeing, jobbing and repair machine shop, manufacturers of locomotives, conveying machinery, large special machines in general, and machine shops that contract for batches of products for other plants.
2. **Manufacturing for stock, under repetitive or mass production,** with some choice between processes and with assembly. Examples: Automobiles, watches, clocks, and typewriters. Custom orders may be intermingled with repetitive work, but this is not considered good practice if it can be avoided.

3. **Manufacturing for stock, where the product is made up of parts but the processes are not optional.** Examples: Shoe manufacture, garments, and many other nonmachine shop type of industries. Custom orders may be intermingled.

4. **Manufacturing for stock, under continuous process manufacturing.** Examples: Many chemical and food products, glass, soap, paper pulp, and synthetic yarn.

Factors tending to a **complex control system** are:

1. Number of ultimate parts in the product.
2. Number of different operations on each part.
3. Extent to which processes are dependent, that is, processes which cannot be performed until previous operations have been completed.
4. Variations in capacity of machines for different classes of work. In many industries speed of machines varies according to the nature of the material being worked on.
5. Degree to which subassembly exists.
6. Degree to which customers' orders with specific delivery dates occur.
7. Receipt of orders for many small lots.

Factors tending to **simplicity of planning and control** are:

1. Degree to which repetitive work occurs, that is, when the same work is done over and over again in the same way, preferably in cycles.
2. Absence of special dates for special items, as when everything is made for stock.
3. Fixed capacity of machines or processes.
4. Invariable method of operation of machines or processes.
5. Absence of discreet parts and assembly.
6. Completely balanced production in which capacity of every process is strictly proportional to flow of work.

Nature of Manufacturing. The degree to which production control is developed varies with different industries. It is at a minimum where a **single homogeneous product is treated by a fixed sequence of processes in a continuous flow.** Modern examples on a vast scale are afforded in paper, pulp, and petrochemical industries. Flow sheets in these industries exhibit a continuous stream of production in which many operations are performed, materials added, and by-products or wastes eliminated, but without break in flow or exceptions in work or processes. Very little production control is required in such industries, since it has already been embodied in the equipment itself. On the other hand, quality control is highly developed and long-range planning for raw materials, finished inventory levels, and markets is extremely important.

In contrast to the continuous industries are **repetitive operations** in plants making automobiles, typewriters, sewing machines, and similar complex mechanisms. Here a great variety of material is used in many ways and for many purposes. There are hundreds and even thousands of parts, on each of which one or many processes take place on a diversity of machines. To bring together in proper sequence and at the right time and place the results of such complex activities, taxes planning and control functions to the utmost. The situation is yet more difficult if custom orders are intermingled with manufacturing for stock.

In **custom manufacturing** less accurate planning is possible than when manufacturing for stock. In many cases, however, it is possible to forecast probable business rather closely, based on past experience and known trade conditions. While definite scheduling is not possible, the raw material situation can be surveyed in the light of probable demands. Custom orders usually require a certain time, over and above actual operating time, to pass through the plant. This time lag gives opportunity for planning, scheduling being effected immediately on receipt of order. In some industries, such as in certain textile industries, orders are taken on **samples** made up in advance of the season, each sample being ac- cepted by many customers in varying quantities. When the bulk of such orders are in, a consolidation is made and the yardage of each pattern found. These orders are then treated as being manufactured for stock.

In **mixed stock and custom manufacturing,** either stock or custom orders may be the main feature. The routine will vary somewhat. If (1) the stock manufacturing situation prevails, surplus machine capacity is ascertained from machine load charts and custom orders are scheduled to absorb it. If (2) the custom manufacture predominates, the reverse is true; stock manufacturing is fitted into whatever machine capacity is left over from custom work. Course (1) above may mean slow delivery of custom orders; course (2) an uncertain output of stock. A middle course is generally advisable, stock production being inter- rupted at times convenient for custom orders, yet not so often or at such moments as to hinder efficient output. A certain amount of stock manufacturing to fill gaps in machine loading is a useful accompaniment of custom work.

Magnitude of Operations. Scale of operations has an important bearing on the nature of the problem. In the small-scale enterprise, control may be more informal because it is more personal and direct. As an enterprise increases in size, new techniques must be devised.

The degree to which the performance of any activity must be decentralized depends upon the **scope of operations** and the **convenience of their location.** In large factories, activities associated with storeskeeping, processing operations, and custody of finished goods must of necessity be carried on in numerous loca- tions. The issue then becomes one of determining whether authority and control over these various operations shall be centralized or decentralized. **Coordination** is most effective when authority is centralized. When performance must be de- centralized, however, centralized authority has to be buttressed with supporting forms of organization and procedures for rapid two-way communication, if it is to provide effective control.

COSTS AND BENEFITS OF PRODUCTION CONTROL. In evalu-
ating the costs and benefits of production control, it is necessary to recognize that, in every production organization, someone is performing the planning and control functions. Koepke (Plant Production Control) says:

In any manufacturing enterprise, someone must perform the various functions of production control; whether it is done by a group of specialists or whether it is done by the superintendents, foremen, and workmen is a matter for each organization to decide, after a consideration of the costs of each method as related to the results obtained.

Therefore, since production control is being paid for, either as a specialist function or a hidden cost, it is necessary to decide which method is most efficient.

Although no standard method for budgeting the cost of a production control group is available, a simple **budgeting method** that limits the cost is reported by Moore (Production Control). He uses a ratio of factory man-hours to production control hours on a weekly basis. This ratio is further modified by acknowledging that the **production control work load** varies in proportion to the number of orders it processes rather than the hours of production load. Moore points out further that the

... most important offset to the costs of production control, however, is the reduction in manufacturing costs. The costs of poor production control can be summed up as low rates of production, high costs, high inventory of materials in process, poor morale and disappointed customers.

MacNiece (Production Forecasting, Planning, and Control) classifies the **benefits and advantages** of production control as exerting influence on five segments of society. He summarizes these segments and their benefits as follows:

1. The consumers:
   a. Increased productivity.
   b. Better values.
   c. Deliveries at proper times.
2. The producers:
   a. Adequate wages.
   b. Stable employment.
   c. Job security.
   d. Improved working conditions.
   e. Increased personal satisfaction.
3. The investors:
   a. Security of investment.
   b. Adequacy of return.
4. The community:
   a. Economic and social stability.
5. The nation:
   a. Security.
   b. Prosperity.

Schleusener and Maddox (Factory Management, vol. 114) report these specific advantages of production control at the Mueller Brass Company. ". . . Better schedules mean better use of men and machines for higher efficiency. . . . Set-up costs cut by [proper] scheduling. . . . In-process inventory minimized by [proper] scheduling." MacNiece points out that good control procedures can direct the attention of the sales department to the areas of the plant where the work load is lowest and, therefore, encourage the sales division to concentrate their efforts on products that utilize these areas.

A unique advantage of production control is used by the Aeroquip Radio Manufacturing Company in the training of personnel for supervisory and lower level executive positions. Betley (Factory Management, vol. 111) points out that the company wants its trainees productive, and since a good control system has a relatively stable routine, the trainee fits into the production control group easily. The advantages he cites in this procedure are:

1. The trainee acquires an over-all picture of the plant operation in a short time.
2. The trainee develops his abilities in human relations, because his duties require close cooperation with other personnel.

PRODUCTION CONTROL ORGANIZATION. The size and character of a production control organization will depend on:

1. The duties specifically delegated to the production control group.
2. The degree of control required.
3. The size of the company involved.

In general, successful production control depends on the satisfactory perform-ance of several types of functions. These are:

1. Forecasting and planning.
2. Inventory control.
3. Control of production operations.
4. Process engineering.

As far as quantities are concerned, **forecasting and planning** are usually joint activities with sales and general management. The position of **inventory control** depends on the relative importance of material value and material availability. In those situations where wide fluctuations in the price, usage, or availability of materials are the rule, and where these materials make up a large percentage of the cost of the finished product, inventories are usually controlled by the group responsible for purchasing. If the size of inventories is extremely large, and if they involve a wide variety of items, it is not unusual to find a separate group, ranking with or above production control, responsible for them. In the majority of cases, the availability of materials as they are needed to meet production sched-ules is the most important criterion, and inventory control is delegated to the production control group.

Control of production operations is, by definition, one of the most important production control functions. The position of **process engineering** in the pro-duction control department is not nearly so clear cut. The functions involved here are usually those of determining manufacturing methods, tooling, and equip-ment and of developing operation sheets, instruction cards, and time standards. Where these functions demand a delicate balance between the requirements of functional design and ease of manufacture, they are handled better by an **engi-neering group**. Where product specification sharply limits process choice, or where the problems involved are usually those of production rather than engi-neering, these functions may be handled in the **production control group**. The development of time standards, for instance, is usually one of the duties of an industrial engineering department.

Control Functions. The list below covers all the important **production con-trol positions** which might be found in a central department:

1. Chief of production control department.
2. Planner or production man in charge of orders, who ascertains quantities con-cerned in each order, is responsible for progress of orders and deliveries, authorizes replacement of spoiled work, and supervises preparation of purchase requisitions for materials or parts bought outside.
3. Materials control or stores record clerk, who keeps in close touch with stores records, makes reservations of material on orders being planned for produc-tion, prepares purchase requisitions for material to be bought for replenish-ment of stores, and prepares or supervises preparation of stores, requisitions, and move orders.
4. Methods engineer, who studies drawings, bills of material and/or specifications to determine methods of manufacturing, tooling, equipment changes, or machine relayouts, etc. He prepares operations lists, tool orders, and plans for relayout.
5. Time study and work simplification engineer. He sets time standards on opera-tions and develops instruction cards. He develops improved methods for performing jobs and better work place layouts.
6. Rate setter, who sets wage rates on operations according to class of work and standard times established.

7. Routing man, who makes out route sheets for each part or component in order, specifying sequence of operations, machines, time allowances, and (after scheduling) due dates for each stage of the work, and supervises preparation of work orders and time tickets.
8. Order-writing clerk, who writes work or operation orders, material issue slips, tool issue slips, time cards, inspection orders, move orders, purchase requisitions for items bought outside, etc.
9. Scheduler, who keeps machine load charts; posts loads from route sheets; ascertains dates for each operation; keeps production schedule; posts progress data to production schedule.
10. Dispatchers. Central dispatcher in production control office and perhaps local dispatchers in shops. He keeps dispatching boards or charts for the shop; files all papers to be issued in releasing orders; frequently acts as time and cost clerk; and reports all completed jobs, idle machines, shortages, and replacements to the production control department.
11. Traffic man, who controls intraplant movement of materials, schedules pick-ups and deliveries, and may control and follow up interplant shipments.

Variations According to Conditions. Titles given in the list of positions are descriptive and may vary among different companies. Because of local conditions, also, the duties may be split up under different combinations for more successful handling under the particular circumstances. **Qualifications of individuals** may cause variations in the assignment of duties. In other words, the functions may be consolidated, subdivided, or assigned elsewhere, according to the nature of the operation. The relative amount of detail covered in each case will also vary according to industry and individual plant.

In any case, however, the work involved under the titles given here must be provided for somewhere. When, as in standard repetitive manufacturing, for example, the preliminary work of analyzing the product into its ultimate parts, listing material, making operation instruction sheets showing operations in sequence and the necessary tools, fixtures, and time allowances, has already been done, and these data are in properly classified files, the work of the production department is confined to planning and control of routine operation on orders. **Staff functions** will then be fulfilled by the following personnel:

1. Chief of production control.
2. Planner or production man.
3. Materials clerk.
4. Scheduler.
5. Dispatcher.

The relative proportion of **persons engaged specifically in production control** to total number of persons on the payroll varies from about 1 in 30 to 1 in 70 or more under good systems. Since the amount of work required for control does not necessarily vary directly with the size of the company, larger concerns should have a ratio at least near 1 in 70 and, in some cases, may show an even more favorable one.

Representative Organization Forms. The varied ways in which different companies set up production control activities are demonstrated by any group of organization charts. A few examples are shown in Figs. 1, 2, and 3.

There are **three basic organization forms for production control activities.** These are:

1. Control through line foremen or other line personnel.
2. Control through expediters.
3. Control through a central production planning group and its representatives.

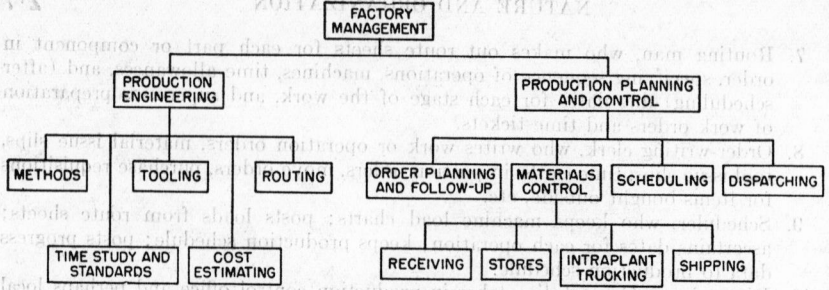

Fig. 1. Representative production control organization in terms of functions performed.

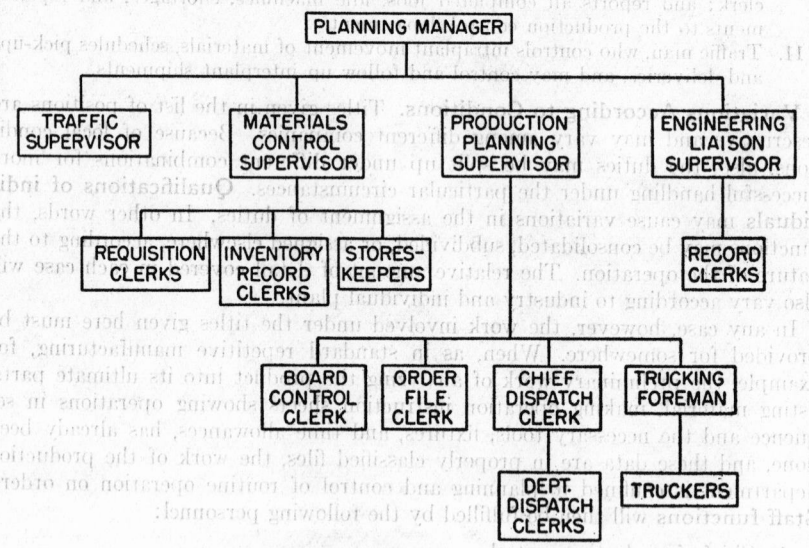

Fig. 2. Centralized production control organization.

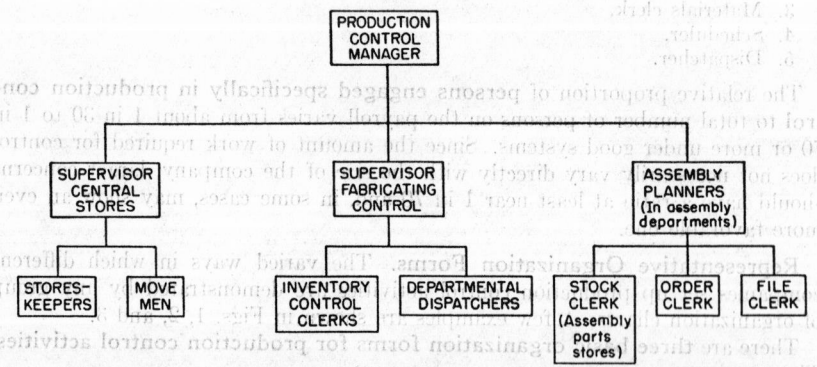

Fig. 3. Combination of centralized and decentralized production control organization. (Each assembly department assembles a different type of instrument. Its production is controlled by its own assembly planner and many required parts come from its own stockroom.)

2·8

Each of these forms has certain advantages and disadvantages associated with its use. These may be outlined as follows:

1. Foreman control
   a. Advantages:
      (1) Intimate knowledge of current capabilities and limitations of men and machines in his department.
      (2) Knowledge of the best sequence of jobs for most effective operation of the department as a whole.
      (3) Complete control over work assignments, building up the importance of the foreman's job in his own and workers' estimation.
      (4) No added overhead.
   b. Disadvantages:
      (1) Best sequence of orders in one department may be worst in another.
      (2) No accurate picture of shop load available.
      (3) Follow-up difficult.
      (4) Little opportunity for effective over-all planning and coordination.
      (5) Overworked foremen.
2. Expediter control
   a. Advantages:
      (1) Flexibility.
      (2) Low overhead cost.
      (3) Opportunity to move some orders through the plant very rapidly.
   b. Disadvantages:
      (1) Indirect costs (broken setups, etc.) may be high.
      (2) No central picture of shop load usually available.
      (3) Limited opportunity for over-all planning and coordination.
      (4) Extreme stress placed on the system when plant operations approach capacity.
3. Central office control
   a. Advantages:
      (1) Possibility of an accurate picture of present and future load.
      (2) Evaluation of the effect of each new order on the shop.
      (3) A basis for accurate delivery commitments.
      (4) Central evaluation of delays.
      (5) Centralized collection of data on which corrective action may be based.
      (6) Central coordination of production and supporting activities.
   b. Disadvantages:
      (1) Tendency for central office personnel to lose contact with actual shop conditions.
      (2) High installation and operating costs.
      (3) Risk of inflexibility.
      (4) Danger of encroaching on areas of line authority.

In practice, production control organizations usually include more than one of these forms in order to capitalize on inherent advantages and minimize the disadvantages of one form alone. Combinations of centralized and decentralized control are good examples of this kind of organization.

Production Planning

IMPORTANCE OF ORGANIZED PLANNING. The necessity for careful planning of production operations arises from four important factors:

1. The increased complexity of production and distribution systems.
2. The need for careful timing of interrelated activities.
3. The necessity for anticipation of changes and orderly reaction to them.
4. The desire to achieve the most economical combination of resources.

TYPES OF PRODUCTION PLANS. Types of production plans include:

1. Those relating to quantities and synchronization of production operations with sales requirements.
2. Those relating to methods.
3. Those relating to timing of individual production operations or processes, and to establishing the proper relationship among them.

Plans Which Prescribe Quantities. Actual production must be reconciled with estimated sales requirements in coming periods. This implies a **manufacturing program,** extending weeks or months ahead, which correlates expected demand with production and inventory capacities.

Sales estimates should be expressed in quantities as well as values. Estimates should reach a level of detail useful for production planning purposes. Variations from period to period should be shown.

Plans Which Prescribe Method. Operation planning and routing fall under the heading of methods planning or process engineering. It is important to note that the division between mass production control and custom order control begins here. In mass production, operation and routing plans are frequently inherent in the plant design. This is true in many chemical operations. In any case, they are standard and fixed by the process until the process is modified. Data on operations and operating sequences are available as soon as the process is fully engineered. These data remain valid until some change in process becomes advisable.

In custom work, on the contrary, every new order requires its own special **operation** and **sequence study.** Nothing can be done until the order is received. Work when done cannot be utilized directly a second time unless it happens that the precise order is duplicated at some future date. This implies that a more extensive organization must be maintained to handle operations study and sequence planning for each new order as it comes in. Data to be assembled will be much the same as for repetitive work; but, as the data may be used only once, less elaborate time study is indicated. Use of **past records** and **synthetic time standards** should be substituted wherever practicable. (See section on Work Measurement and Time Study.)

Operation planning, it will be noted, prescribes time allowances for each operation or process. Operation times and sequences provide the basic information for establishing production rates and operating plans. Other sections of this book deal with the detail of methods planning. With the knowledge that it must be accomplished in order to provide essential production planning data, no further reference will be made to process engineering or operations planning in this section.

Plans Which Prescribe Timing. While it is true that machine analysis and operation study have made by-products of value, their main objective from the standpoint of production control is to set up a **working timetable of shop operations.** The objective is the same in all plants, large or small—to distribute physical materials to various processes so that:

1. Every order is executed in the shortest possible time.
2. Promised dates of deliveries are based on definite information.
3. A constant supply of work is kept ahead of each process or machine.

In planning production an important point, requiring the most careful coordination, is the **establishment of delivery dates** which fit both the requirements of the sales department and the capacity of the manufacturing department.

PRODUCTION PLANNING: QUANTITIES. The relative complexity of modern production is caused chiefly by the division of labor, or specialization, both at the executive level and in the factory. Division of labor, within limits, promotes economy through increased productivity per man-hour, but is always attended by correspondingly increased difficulty of coordination. Efficient production is rarely achieved by the voluntary cooperation of specialists acting on their own initiative. It must be brought about through the operation of a **preconceived plan.**

Establishing Relationships. Production planning must establish the basic relationships among production capacity, inventory levels, and sales rates for some period in the future. The length of this period ranges from one or two months to twelve or eighteen months. Its exact extent depends on the type of business and the scale of operation involved. In any case, plans which extend much more than a year and a half ahead are usually better classified as **general operations planning** or investment planning. This type of planning is not fundamentally different from production planning; it is simply not the area of planning with which we are principally concerned here.

Within an area properly classified as "production" planning, the outward appearance of the problems dealt with can vary widely. However, there is no basic difference between the problem of balancing the raw material output of one division with the supply requirements of a second and the problem of balancing the output of three fabricating departments with the parts requirements of an assembly department.

Although the physical facilities available for production are usually fixed for the interval of the planning cycle, output can often be varied through a considerable range. Changes in the number of shifts or the length of the work week, for example, can have a marked effect. Inventory levels also can fluctuate from practically nothing to the upper limit of permanent storage capacity—and, in some cases, beyond. The relationships between production rates and inventory levels can be established quite exactly as soon as sales rates are known. In most cases, however, the level and composition of future demand are uncertain. Despite this uncertainty, the objective of production planning is to strike the most economic **balance** possible **between production rates** and **inventory levels.** This involves:

1. Evaluation of the uncertainty involved in the sales estimate; determination of expected levels of demand and the probable range of error on each side of these levels.
2. Establishment of production rates and inventory levels which offer the best probability of meeting estimated sales requirements with the most economic combination of labor, facilities, materials, and working capital.
3. Determination in advance of the changes needed in these relationships if actual demand begins to vary by predetermined amounts from expected demand.

Analyzing Trends. Continually changing demand makes the task of planning difficult. The factor of change manifests itself in a variety of ways. Sometimes it occurs with sufficient regularity and frequency to show an underlying rhythm. Sometimes **long-term trends** can be discovered and therefore predicted with a reasonable degree of certainty. Often qualitative as well as quantitative changes in demand are important.

Secular changes are upward or downward trends over long periods of time, often traceable to some profound technological or competitive disturbance. They may affect the interests of the enterprise adversely or favorably. They play a large part in the long-run investment plans of industry, but their impact on shorter-range production plans is generally limited. Insofar as cyclical changes are concerned, the problem of production planning is one of foreseeing significant turns in business activity with sufficient accuracy to avoid serious maladjustments.

Seasonal fluctuations may often be predicted with reasonable accuracy since the causes lie in the regularly changing seasons. Fig. 4 shows the way in which current production may be adjusted to provide for seasonal demands. The production line is held uniform at three hundred units per month. Sales vary from two hundred at the beginning and end of the period to a maximum of five

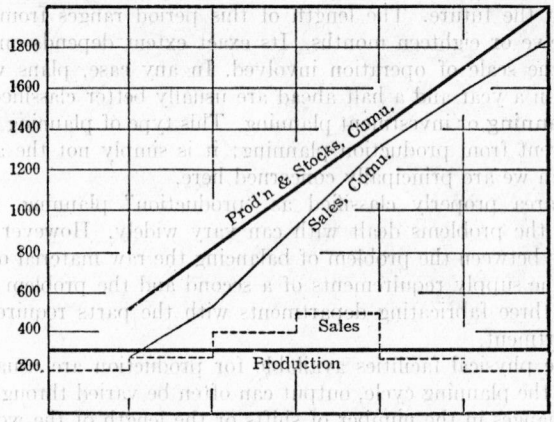

Fig. 4. Adjusting production to seasonal sales.

hundred units toward the middle of the period. There are in stock two hundred units at the beginning of the period, and cumulative lines show the relation of production and stocks to products sold. Production begins and ends with two hundred in stock and keeps ahead of sales, although at the end of the peak period, only fifty units are in stock. This margin might or might not be considered safe. If not, overtime would probably be indicated as the peak period was being passed.

The dependence of steady production on **reliable forecasts of sales** is shown by Fig. 4. When the nature of the business prevents reasonably accurate forecasts of sales, the risks involved in a steady rate of production for twelve months may be too great for a manufacturer to assume. Firms producing highly stylized products or products whose sales depend on weather conditions at some season fall in this category. Here, too, are many contract manufacturers and companies with perishable products. Considerably greater fluctuations in production levels than shown in Fig. 4 are usually found in these firms.

Weekly and daily fluctuations are important chiefly in industries producing very perishable products or services which must be supplied at the instant demand develops. This situation presents a highly specialized problem of planning in public utilities such as power, light, and gas companies. The problem of planning and control in such instances consists chiefly of maintaining suitable **standby equipment** which may be cut in when required and cut out when peak-demand periods are passed.

Sales Forecasts. There are two general approaches to the preparation of sales forecasts. The first tries to build a picture of **total sales** at some future period by summing up and combining estimates drawn from the sources of the company's business. The second relates general economic trends to particular industries and then works back to the **company's share of an industry's business.** Wherever possible, a **sales forecast** or **budget** should form the basis for production plans. Such a forecast is an attempt to predict what changes in demand will occur during a coming period. The Accountants' Handbook states that:

A carefully prepared sales budget affords the opportunity to apply the principles of budgetary control, in their fullest sense, to the other operations of the organization. It permits, for example, the planning of purchases on the most economical basis, and the assurance of adequate inventories. It permits the planning of manpower requirements to avoid frequent layoffs, and subsequent rehiring, with the attendant problems of employee training and personnel relations. It makes possible the planning and scheduling of production for longer runs and the better utilization of equipment. It permits the planning of inventories so as to obtain better utilization of space, lower handling and storage costs, and lower working capital requirements. In the area of distribution costs, it provides for the improved control of the costs of order getting and order filling.

Influence of Guaranteed Annual Wages on Planning and Control. The use of good production control procedures in stabilizing employment is well recognized. Three of the eight **stabilization devices** recommended by Latimer (Guaranteed Wages, Report to the President) are from the area of production control. These three devices are:

1. Manufacture for stock.
2. Train employees for a variety of jobs and make transfers as production requirements change.
3. Make intensive analyses of product demand in order to make reasonable forecasts of demand and to schedule production accurately.

These devices require good control procedures to minimize costs. For instance, in scheduling employees, a **man load chart** can be utilized effectively not only to control total hours per individual, but also to use their respective abilities most effectively.

A major influence of stabilized employment is cited by Davenport (Fortune, vol. 40) in which he points out that Procter and Gamble have eliminated excess plant capacity by good planning and production control. Procter and Gamble estimate that 100 million dollars of capital investment were saved in 22 years due to good planning and control for stabilized employment.

The most common and immediate result of stabilized employment is that the production planning group acts as the safety valve for management in that they can predict when the shop load or backlog will be low. Any decision management makes as to a future course of action obviously depends on good control procedures.

Past Performance Data. Adequate records of past performance are essential to production planning. These will certainly include data on production, shipments, and inventory for each item manufactured. They may also cover quality or other factors pertinent to a particular business. Detail should usually be available by weeks as well as for summary periods.

Various methods of **market analysis** can provide estimates of future sales; similar estimates can be derived by extrapolating data on past performance. Complete reliance on past statistics forces a company to "back into the future." On the other hand, failure to use such statistics properly deprives production planners of an extremely valuable tool and a useful check on estimates arrived at by entirely different methods. Finally, at some level of product detail, trends developed from past data frequently provide the only practical method of estimating for future periods.

Three points are most important for **effective handling of data** on past performance:

1. Records must be reasonably accurate and available as soon as possible after the period covered.
2. Data recording, correlation, and extraction procedures should be simple, rapid, and as automatic as the economics of a given situation will permit.
3. Information must be presented in forms which highlight significant factors and promote decisions.

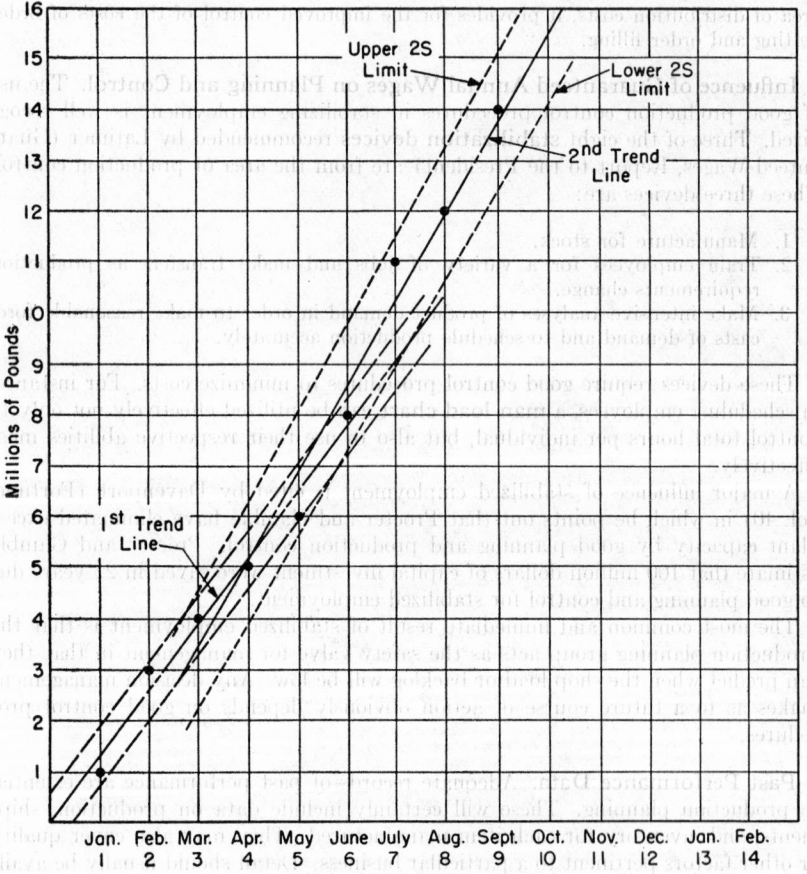

Fig. 5. Data, formulas, and cumulative chart of sales with control limits and trends (continued on next page).

One of the commonest failings of systems for the collection and presentation of production planning data is that planning personnel are forced to work with information that is so voluminous and so unimaginatively presented as to confuse planning decision processes rather than simplify them. The exact method of presentation must of course be selected to fit the requirements of a given situation. The "best way" will vary from one firm to another.

One company has used an interesting adaptation of statistical control techniques to meet its needs. Fig. 5 illustrates the theory as applied there. A trend line is established on cumulative monthly product shipments and extended into the future along with $2S$ control limits. (See section on Quality Control.) In practice, this trend would be based on more data than the four months used in this example.

Cumulative sales for January, February, March, and April are available. These months are used as the X coordinates and are numbered 1, 2, 3, and 4. The Y coordinates are cumulative monthly sales. Substitution in Equations 1, 2, and 3 (Fig. 5) gives:

$$13 = 4a + 10b \qquad\qquad a = 0$$
$$39 = 10a + 30b \qquad\qquad b = 1.3$$
$$S^2 = \frac{51 - 0 - 50.7}{4} = 0.075 \qquad \therefore y = 1.3x$$
$$S = 0.274 \qquad\qquad 2S = \pm 0.55$$

The trend line, $y = 1.3x$, and the $2S$ control limits around that line ± 0.55, are plotted as shown in Fig. 5. In May and June further plots are made and these points stay within established limits. By the end of July, however, it is evident that the old trend line no longer applies. The probability is quite small that the July plot 11 million pounds, is simply a chance variation from the January-June trend. Thus, if any monthly plot falls outside a control limit, or if 6 successive plots approach the same limit, a new trend line is established together with

Month	Sales	X	Y	XY	X²	Y²	Yc	d*	XY	X²	Y²
Jan.	1	1	1	1	1	1	1.3	+0.3			
Feb.	2	2	3	6	4	9	2.6	−0.4			
Mar.	1	3	4	12	9	16	3.9	−0.1	12	9	16
Apr.	1	4	5	20	16	25	5.2	+0.2	20	16	25
		10	13	39	30	51					
May	1	5	6				6.5	+0.5	30	25	36
June	2	6	8				7.8	−0.2	48	36	64
July	3	7	11				9.1	−1.9	77	49	121
		25	34						187	135	262
Aug.	1	8	12								
Sept.	2	9	14				*d = Yc − Y				

$$\text{Eq. 1: } \Sigma(y) = Na + b\Sigma(X)$$
$$\text{Eq. 2: } \Sigma(xy) = a\Sigma(x) + b\Sigma(X^2)$$

S_y = standard error of estimate $\qquad\qquad N$ = no. of items

$$\text{Eq. 3: } S_y{}^2 = \frac{\Sigma(y^2) - a\Sigma(y) - b\Sigma(xy)}{N}$$

Fig. 5. (Concluded.)

its control limits. The number "6" above is an arbitrary selection, chosen simply because it worked well in this company's application. Other products and markets might well require other choices. The number of points selected in calculating the second trend line is that number between 4 and 12 which gives the smallest total difference between values of y computed on the old trend line and actual values of y. Again this rule is empirical and based on this company's situation.

Calculations for the second set of lines in Fig. 5 are:

$$\sum_{x=7}^{x=3} d = -1.5 \qquad \sum_{x=7}^{x=2} d = -1.9 \qquad \sum_{x=7}^{x=1} d = -1.6$$

∴ 2d Trend based on March–July ($x = 7$ to $x = 3$) plots

$$34 = 5a + 25b \qquad\qquad a = -1.7$$
$$187 = 25a + 135b \qquad\qquad b = +1.7$$
$$S^2 = \frac{262 + 57.8 - 318}{5} = 0.36 \qquad ∴ y = -1.7 + 1.7x$$
$$S = 0.6 \qquad\qquad 2S = \pm 1.2$$

August and September sales remain within the new limits. The company in question found that a trend line usually lasted from 5 to 14 months before out-of-limit plots required a new one.

In this particular case, the charts were confined to a relatively few major products. Analyzing its shipments as shown in Fig. 6, the company determined that about 10 percent of the items accounted for 80 percent of shipments. Charts

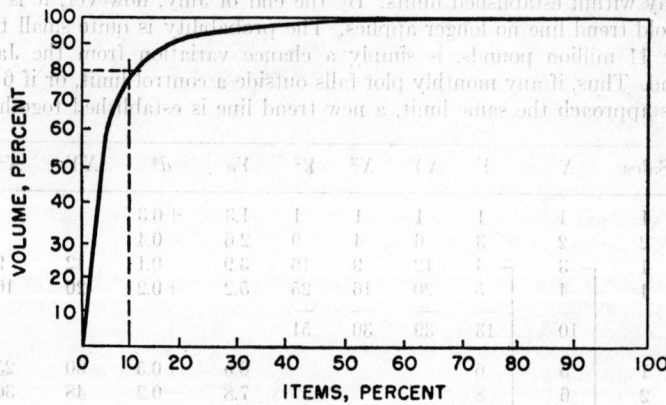

Fig. 6. Cumulative chart of percentage of sales volume vs. percentage of number of items.

were applied only to these items, since manual calculations and charting of more items at monthly intervals would quickly have grown too cumbersome. Since the arithmetic involved is quite simple, the system can be adapted to punched cards with elimination of manual calculating and the need for charts. This will allow additional coverage. Computers open an even wider range.

It should be emphasized that historical data are not the sole bases for an estimate of future shipments. They provide a check on the forecasts supplied by sales, and they direct planning attention to the items which need attention most. Properly presented, they minimize the risk of overcontrolling production operations.

Production Plans. To the production department, the sales forecast is a statement of desired results. If it is to serve as the basis for production, the figures in the forecast must be translated into **specific production requirements** at specific periods of time. The resulting production plan will establish relationships between end products, required quantities of parts and materials, necessary lead times for manufacture or procurement of each item, the load on the plant's facilities, and the capacity available to meet this load. It will also determine the extent and timing of the contributions which all other groups in the company must make to implement the plan successfully. These considerations are readily developed once the amount of each product to be produced and the times when these quantities will be required have been determined. Some of the details involved will be discussed in the section dealing with plans for production timing.

The most useful production plans are those which are **reviewed and changed at frequent intervals.** No one can guarantee that a given forecast is completely accurate. The occasional forecast which does check exactly with actual developments is more the result of chance than of technique. The intervals between revisions of forecasts and plans vary among different companies. Plans may be reviewed monthly, quarterly, semi-annually, or merely once a year. Annual review would be adequate only in a company whose market was very stable; monthly changes of significant scope would be too frequent for most businesses. The majority of firms, whose markets permit detailed planning and forecasting of production, review and alter established requirements either quarterly or semi-annually.

Those companies, for example, that prepare a new forecast every quarter always have at hand a year's forecast which is never more than three months old. The general accuracy of each forecast is constantly checked by the actual rate of sales during the first quarter of its life. Succeeding forecasts may be carbon copies of the first, but it is more likely that they will vary from it as they make use of actual sales data during the early quarters and of evidences of new trends in the economy. Production plans, of course, are also changed to reflect revisions in the sales forecasts. The companies which follow this pattern of planning always have a general plan of operations extending a year in the future and a fairly accurate idea of operations during the next few months.

Plan Based on Forecasts. A manufacturer of tools and shop equipment developed planning procedures based on quarterly sales forecasts. Fig. 7 shows the

Second Quarter Forecast						Page 4	
Product	Month of:						
	April	May	June	July	uary	February	March
Pliers: (Total)	7,500	7,000	5,100	420	500	7,300	7,800
Ignition	800	600	300	10	00	900	1,000
Long Nose	1,000	800	500	20	00	1,300	1,500
Diag. Cut	600	300	100	2	00	600	800
Pt. Nose	1,400	1,250			0	1,000	1,200
Lineman's							000
S.J. Side							00
Bat							

Fig. 7. Sales forecast of tool manufacturer.

form in which each quarter's forecast appears. At the left are listed all the products in the company's line. The columns at the right provide space for monthly sales estimates by product classes and individual items. These sheets are prepared in the sales department and are passed on to the production group and top management about four weeks before the start of the new quarter. The second quarter forecast shown in Fig. 7 would be released around March 1.

After discussion of the new forecast, and any necessary revisions, the production planning group translates it into the **production** and **inventory schedule** illustrated in Fig. 8. Based on the sales forecast for each item for each month;

Production and Inventory Schedule									
Second Quarter Forecast									
	April		May		June		July		Au
	End. Inv.	Sched. Prod.	End. Inv.	Sched. Prod.	End. Inv.	Sched. Prod.	End. Inv.	Sched. Prod.	End. Inv.
Pliers: (Total)	4,000	6,000	2,800	5,800	3,300	5,600	4,000	4,900	
Ignition	500	700	400	500	600	500	900	400	
Long Nose	700	900	600	700	800	700	1,100	500	
Diag. Cut									

Fig. 8. Production and inventory schedule based on sales forecast.

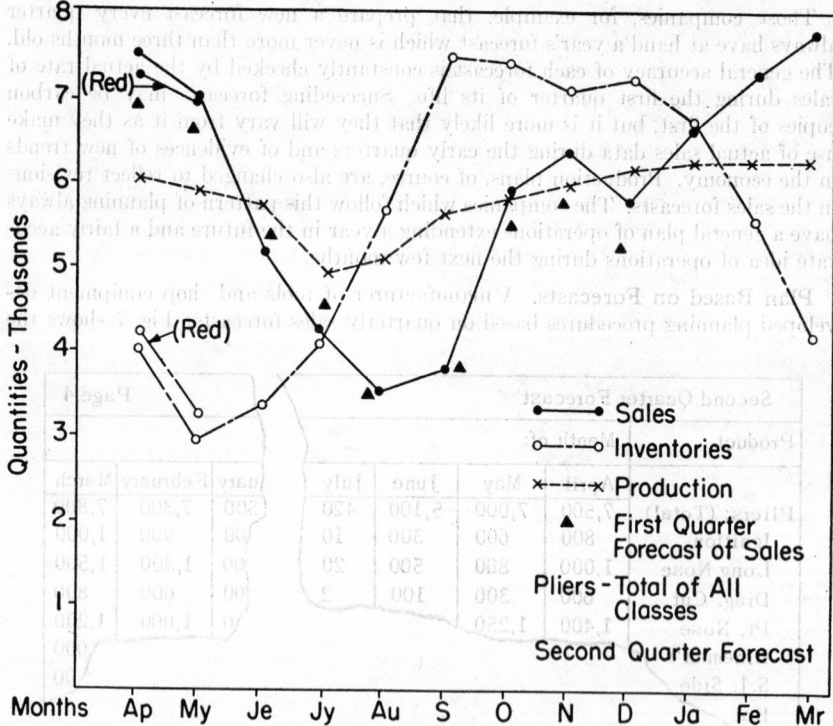

Fig. 9. Control chart plotting forecasted sales, inventories, and production.

this plan takes account of such factors as equipment loading, availability of materials, vacation schedules, economic lots, desired average inventory levels, and the like. The planner sets down production totals and estimates of closing inventories for each month for every item and product class.

The final results of the production and inventory schedule are charted as shown in Fig. 9 for control purposes. Note that **variations in production** range roughly between 5,000 and 6,000, while sales and inventories vary much more sharply. In addition to plots of current estimates for sales, inventories, and production, the chart includes the sales estimate from preceding forecasts of the current year. Since only one other forecast has been prepared so far, only one appears here. The old estimates are indicated by the triangles (▲) and were generally lower than those of the second quarter forecast. Although these charts are prepared only for product classes, the inventory control group, of course, follows the figures for each individual item in each class and gives warning if changes in product mix have left total inventories of a class about as predicted but have made individual item inventories out of balance.

The process described here is repeated every quarter. Actual results are also plotted (Fig. 9) during the intervening months, and changes can be made if sales depart sharply from estimated levels.

PRODUCTION PLANNING: TIMING. Whether they are based on sales forecasts or specific customer's orders, production plans must be related to the **actual productive capacity** of the plant and to technical requirements of sequence and timing. The former may be accomplished through analysis of capacity, the latter through preliminary scheduling and knowledge of process limitations.

Although the objectives are the same, production planning problems and procedures in this phase vary considerably from industry to industry and from one type plant to another. In many chemical plants, for example, questions of timing relate to raw material supplies, inventory tank capacities, bulk transport schedules, and geographic availability of finished inventories in future periods. Planning problems emphasize inventory planning and transportation economics to a much greater degree than factors inherent in the production process itself. In a custom machine shop, on the other hand, machine capacity, alternative routing, and process balance occupy the planner's attention. Between the extremes lies a whole range of industrial situations which mix these elements in varying proportions.

Analysis of Capacity. When the necessary information on materials and methods of manufacture has been developed, the next step is to acquire equally accurate data on the capacity of the machine which will operate on the material. In considering a machine, the first question likely to arise is:

1. How long will this machine take to perform its operation on a unit quantity of material?

This question can be answered either (a) by actual experiment and trial, or (b) by reference to records of past performance. Though this appears a simple enough procedure, it is not infrequently complicated by the fact that **speed** of **operation** varies according to the nature of material and according to the degree of finish or accuracy required.

In machining operations, for instance, the cutting speed varies as hard steel, cast iron, brass, copper, aluminum, etc., are worked on. The condition of castings may cause wide variations in possible operating time. Greater speed may be expected in coarse work than in finely finished work. In working near the **limit** of **capacity** of a machine, insufficient power may be available, or the awkward character of the job may prevent power being applied in the right amount. In textile manufacture operation speeds vary with the nature of yarn or fabric. In many paper plants the particular material being worked on is a controlling factor in operating speed. On the other hand, many industries, working on uniform material, can answer the above question easily.

Preparation for the Job. Actual time consumed on a job is made up of two factors in all machine tool work and in many other cases. It takes time to get the equipment ready to do the job. This is called **"setup"** or **"make-ready"** **time.** It is frequently difficult to determine accurately, since it varies with the nature of the job.

In the "make-ready" of a large press for printing a three-color job, long and tedious work is sometimes necessary. The amount of such work may be wholly unexpected and may be due to some slight peculiarity in plates, speed, pressure, ink, or paper. Once these are mutually adjusted the operation proceeds at an expected speed; but, if the run is not a long one, the cost of the job may be affected unfavorably. In setting up machine tools, proper work holding is frequently a problem that can be solved only by the design of a special fixture or jig. Cutting speeds and feeds have to be determined and much preliminary work done before the job is actually started. In other industries, no such preparation is necessary; material is placed in a hopper or fed into grips to be drawn into the machine without further attention. Where preparation time is considerable, the question of the economic size of lots to be worked on at one setting becomes important.

In machine tool and similar work, question 1 should be extended to read:

1a. How long does it take to set up this machine for a new job?
1b. How long does this machine take to perform the actual operation on a unit quantity of material, once it has been set up?

From what has already been said it will be seen that the first of these new questions can be answered only in an average way. It may be assumed that an average job takes n minutes for setup. But, when it comes to the consideration of a specific job, this factor requires careful scrutiny to make sure that there are no exceptional difficulties inherent in it. In many cases only experiment will disclose the proper **time allowance.** This phase of the problem may require **operation analysis,** inasmuch as it is a characteristic of specific jobs.

The answer to question 1b can be determined quite accurately, either by careful study or from records of past performance.

Total Capacity in Terms of Time. The second question in machine analysis is:

2. How many units of each variety of material can be processed on this machine per unit of time?

Summation of the number of units which can be processed by similar machines gives the **total plant capacity** in units of product for one process. When all processes have been analyzed and tabulated, a third question can be answered:

3. What is the maximum plant capacity for each process on each variety of material per unit of time?

Units of Capacity. Units of product in which capacity may be expressed vary necessarily according to industry. In textile and other fabric industries, poundage of yarn and yardage of fabric are usual. In foundries, a tonnage basis may be expected. In machine shops, the problem is, generally, more difficult. **Machine tool analysis** implies determination of the interaction of several factors: spindle speed, torque, maximum chip area, length of piece that can be operated on, swing-over, and available feeds. All these variables must be taken into account before actual performance can be determined. (See section on Tools, Jigs, and Fixtures.) The capacity of machine tools, therefore, cannot be stated accurately in general terms, except in cases where long runs of identical pieces allow output to be stated as dozens or hundreds per hour. It can, however, be reduced to tables which aid in the solution of any particular problem.

Machine analysis, therefore, has two important objectives:

1. To determine approximate maximum capacity of each process, and hence of all processes, and the plant as a whole.
2. In machine shops and industries where several factors enter into machine capacity, to provide a basis for calculating the time of operation on specific jobs.

This calculation is usually effected by embodying the results of machine analysis in tabular or in graphic form. When both setup and operating time requirements are determined for a job, the period during which the machines will be occupied by such jobs will be proportional to the size of the lots going through. **Machine loading** for all planned jobs can then be determined easily. The amount of work ahead of each machine, expressed in working hours, becomes a known quantity.

It is generally recognized that "bottlenecks" are a serious obstacle to economical production. When the output of each process for each variety of material has been charted or tabulated, **flow sheets** can be drawn which will show at once if excess capacity, or insufficient capacity, exists at any point.

Process Industries. Analysis of capacity in terms of machine analysis and preparation times is of slight interest in many process industries. The physical relationships and problems of timing which concern the planners here are apt to revolve around raw material supplies, physical limitations on finished inven-tories, shipping schedules, and transportation economics.

Fig. 10 illustrates one case at this end of the spectrum of planning problems. In this example of a **petrochemical operation,** these points should be under-stood:

1. The process is entirely enclosed within a system of pipes, towers, and tanks. Acetic acid, formaldehyde, acetone, and other alcohols and ketones are the end products derived from mixed feed gases.
2. Within certain limits, the mix of end products can be altered by changes in the proportions of gases in the feedstock.
3. Feedstock of a specified composition must be contracted for two to three months in advance of processing in order to assure supply and to buy eco-nomically. Spot purchases can usually be made only in limited quantities to achieve small variations in feedstock composition.
4. With the plant built, the process is established. Information on capacity is immediately available. The primary products must be made; their volume may be altered somewhat by production of secondary products, but they will always be present in large amounts.
5. Storage capacity is expensive and limited. Some tanks can be used for different products, some cannot.
6. Bulk movements to the terminal must fit the tanker schedule. Inventories of products shipped in bulk must be high at the plant when the tanker is to be

loaded; similarly, tanks at the terminal must be almost empty when the tanker arrives there to unload.

7. Freight economics determine whether a customer is served from the plant or the terminal. Inventories of various products at each point must therefore meet the demands of specific groups of customers.

In the case illustrated by Fig. 10, **production planning** involves:

1. Estimates, by periods, of inventory requirements for each product at each storage location so that forecast customer requirements can be met most economically.
2. Establishment of plant operating rates at a level for each period which will:
   a. Maintain inventories at planned levels.
   b. Promote stable plant operations and minimize fluctuations from period to period.
   c. Take into account tanker schedules for bulk movements to the terminal.
3. Indication of the quantity and composition of feedstock required for each period.
4. Establishment of operating periods for secondary operations which produce several products alternately from the same facilities. This must be accomplished in such a way that operating and cleaning cycles are economic but physical limitations on product storage are not exceeded.
5. Preservation of maximum flexibility to meet sudden surges or drops in demand for specific products.

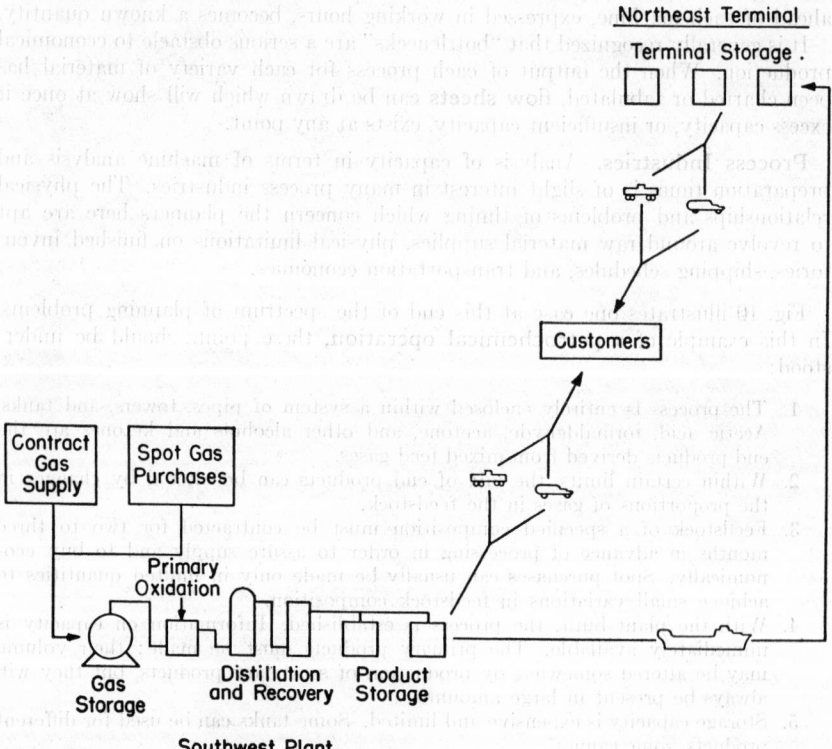

Fig. 10. Simplified flow chart of petrochemical production and distribution.

Simultaneous Operations. In repetitive work and in any work in which single operations last a considerable time (as in large machining work), it becomes worth while to study how far two or more operations may be performed simultaneously on the same piece, or alternatively, how two or more pieces may be passed through different phases of one operation simultaneously.

Alford (Laws of Management Applied to Manufacturing) has stated the principles governing this situation as follows:

1. The minimum over-all production time for a group of operations or for the operations on an item of product is obtained by the maximum overlapping or simultaneous performance of the several work units.
2. The minimum over-all production time for a group of simultaneous operations tends to approach the time of the longest work unit as its limit.

Fig. 11 has four graphs showing the proportion of actual productive time to total operating time in four different machine tools.

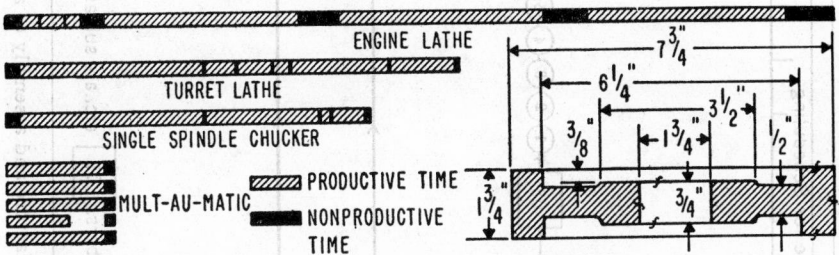

Fig. 11. **Graphic presentation of single-purpose and automatic machine productivity.**

Simultaneous Performance and Operating Efficiency. When several operations are performed at the same time, it does not necessarily follow that each one is performed with maximum efficiency. Blanchard has pointed out that the secondary or tertiary operations—performed simultaneously with the primary operation by which the rate of performance is set—may be permitted to lag in certain points of efficiency, provided that the work is accomplished within the time limits set by the primary operation. In other words, the problem is to obtain a **net advantage on the whole series** even though particular operations might be more efficient if conducted singly. An example of simultaneous operation is afforded by a baking oven through which the product moves slowly on a conveyor. Such an operation may be adjusted to any rate of flow within reasonable limits and, as long as the material is in the oven just long enough to be completely baked, dried, or ripened, the required results are accomplished. At any one time, individual pieces may be at all stages of drying, but the net cost is far below that of small batches handled in individual ovens.

Simultaneous operations in assembly work are now common practice. Assembly operations are divided into units capable of being handled by single operators. A belt or rotary conveyor carries the product forward, each operator performing his unit task simultaneously with all the others. Thus, in drug and similar industries, bottles are loaded on a conveyor, filled, labeled, sealed, and then removed from the table. The five successive operations overlap. A further stage is reached when some or all of the steps are performed automatically.

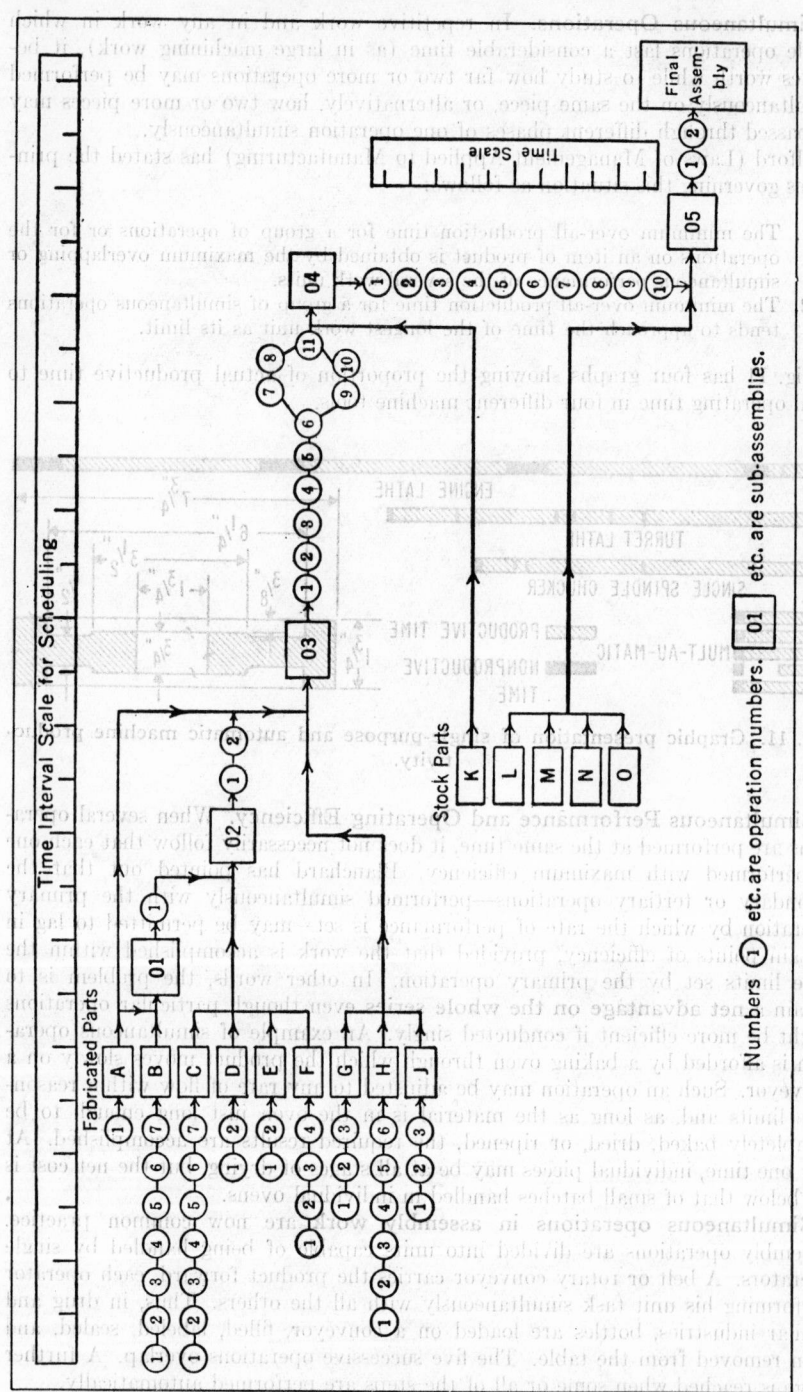

Fig. 12. Master schedule for manufacture and assembly of a product.

Numbers ① etc. are operation numbers.   01 etc. are sub-assemblies.

Simultaneous production can also be effected in the case of lots, containing a large number of pieces, without special tools or devices. As soon as one day's product is free from machine A, it is passed to machine B for the next process. A and B are thus working on the same job at the same time, though on different individual pieces of it. This procedure does not economize labor or machine time, but it does speed the passage of the job through the plant. It is better described as **overlapping** or **telescoping** rather than as simultaneous production. From the control viewpoint, simultaneous operations on the same unit of product simply shorten the time during which the machine is occupied by the job. When the process is applied to different units, control boards and route sheets must be so arranged as to permit grouping of these units for simultaneous processing.

Preliminary Scheduling. Sales forecasts or sales orders state desired end results. The production planner must work from these to determine the steps necessary to achieve them and the interrelation of these steps with one another. In order to do this, some form of general production plan or preliminary schedule is desirable. The objective of preliminary scheduling is to determine, from the quantities of each variety of product to be made in a future period, the correlation of this call on manufacturing capacity with the normal manufacturing capacity available. The **order or sequence of different items,** that is, approximate periods in which specific quantities are to be manufactured, is also an essential feature. In preparation for this determination, **master schedules** should be available for each separate line of product. These schedules should show, at least approximately, the time required to process each item and hence carry a unit quantity of products through all stages of manufacture. With this relation between quantity of product and time, the question whether the proposed program is above or below productive capacity of the plant can be settled with reasonable accuracy.

Preliminary scheduling should be general in character and not immediately pinned down to specific dates. The more standardized the product and the plant's manufacturing procedures, the more definite these production plans can be. The plans developed by many automobile assembly plants provide good illustrations of this point. These plans, based on repeatedly revised sales forecasts, lay out daily and weekly **production quotas** for the coming months for each model, body style, and all important accessories. In practice, plans are developed for the three succeeding months; although cars are produced generally for specific dealers' orders, the first month's plan is usually very close to the final schedule of production during that month. As time passes and actual sales trends become more apparent, the plan for the second month is usually revised somewhat and that for the third month is subject to even sharper revisions. This planning process is repeated each month as the second month in the original plan becomes the "firm" first month in the new one, and another third month is added at the end.

Fig. 12 shows the master schedule for a highly standardized and purely repetitive type of manufacture. The **sequence** and **relative date** of each operation are carefully set out. Such a plan becomes a schedule when definite dates and quantities are assigned for actual production in the shop.

Mathematical Planning Techniques

ECONOMICAL MANUFACTURING QUANTITY. Many production planning and control problems lend themselves to mathematical analysis. The sections devoted to Operations Research and to Statistical Methods deal with the details of many of these techniques. The discussion which follows simply indicates a few of the areas in which this type of analysis can promote more effective planning.

The economical manufacturing quantity is the quantity of any one item which should be manufactured at any one time to realize the lowest unit cost.

There is a balance of costs as there is in the computation of economical purchasing quantities. (See section on Purchasing for a discussion of most economic purchase and storage lots.) Some of the factors involved are as follows:

1. Costs which tend to decrease as the size of the manufacturing order is increased.
   a. Setup and make-ready costs in the shop.
   b. Costs associated with the issuance and control of shop orders.
2. Costs which tend to increase as the size of the order is increased.
   a. Inventory storage charges.
   b. Inventory carrying charges.

The inventory costs, which tend to increase, are discussed in the section on Materials Control and Standardization. The same considerations hold true for storing and carrying manufactured items as for purchased items.

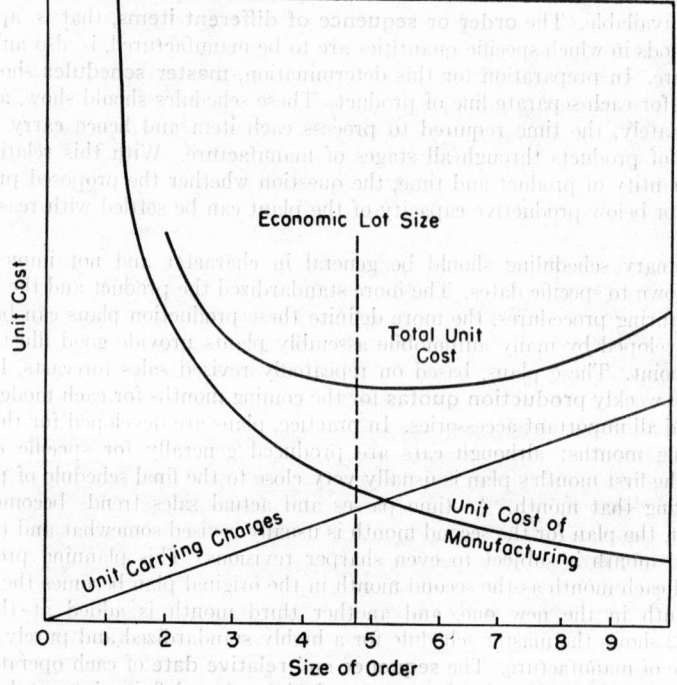

Fig. 13. Costs affecting economic lot size.

Fig. 13 illustrates the manner in which manufacturing costs decrease as a greater quantity of an item is ordered at one time and how the carrying charges increase as a greater quantity is manufactured at one time. The best quantity to manufacture is shown as the lowest point of the total cost curve.

Setup Costs. Setup costs may range from less than $1.00 to hundreds of dollars each time a manufacturing order is processed in the shop. Hoehing (AMA

Special Report No. 4) suggests that "a reasonable assumption for the job order and job lot type of mechanical production is that about 5 percent of productive time in the factory is consumed in preparing and setting up for the job." He cites a case of a plant with a thousand workers having about two million productive hours per year. One hundred thousand of these hours are consumed in making setups so that if setup men are paid $2.00 an hour, the annual bill for setups is two hundred thousand dollars. While setups cannot be eliminated entirely, they can usually be reduced by better planning and by producing in economic lot quantities. The industrial engineering department often sets a **standard setup time** for each type of job. Multiplying this by an average setup rate per hour gives the setup cost for that part. If no time standards are available, the foreman can usually estimate the setup time for each job rather closely.

Cost of Shop Orders. The costs of planning and initiating shop orders together with the handling and make-ready costs involved in issuing and processing an order through the shop are hard to estimate because of the many variables involved. However, it is certain that not only production control people, but foremen, cost accounting, inspection, timekeeping, and other functions are affected adversely by a larger number of orders. Some companies use the rule of thumb of about $5.00 to $10.00 per order in computing savings. Other companies neglect this factor in computing savings because they say that a decrease in the number of shop orders will not result in any reduction in work force.

Analytic Calculation of Economic Quantity. Alford and Beatty (Principles of Industrial Management) give an example of a calculation to determine the economic quantity for a part that is to be manufactured in the plant and will be stored.

Assume these data:

Preparation cost: $15.00.
Storage charges per piece per year: $.001.
Manufacturing cost per piece: $.25.
Desired annual return on capital: 10 percent.
Manufacturing capacity per year: 1,000,000.
Demand for pieces per year: 960,000.

Further data for the computation are arranged in Fig. 14. Quantities studied range from one lot to seven lots per year; the corresponding sizes of the lots range up to 960,000. This table also gives the maximum inventory in pieces, computed from a production per week of 20,000 pieces, and a demand per week of 19,200 pieces. The difference, 800 pieces, is carried to inventory for each of 48 weeks, the time required to make 960,000 pieces when one lot is made per year, giving a maximum inventory of 38,400 pieces. The **investment in inventory** is the number of pieces multiplied by the manufacturing cost per piece.

Number of lots per year	1	2	3	4	5	6	7
Number of pieces per lot	960,000	480,000	320,000	240,000	192,000	160,000	137,000
Maximum inventory in pieces	38,400	19,200	12,800	9,600	7,680	6,400	5,600
Maximum investment in inventory	$9,600	$4,800	$3,200	$2,400	$1,920	$1,600	$1,400

Fig. 14. Data for computation of economic manufacturing quantity.

Fig. 15 gives the costs that vary with the size of manufacturing lot—the preparation and storage costs—and the interest on the investment in inventory. Examination shows that the lowest annual cost for the sum of these three charges is when six lots are made per year. However, there is no practical difference in the costs for five, six, and seven lots per year, showing that there is a considerable range for the economic number of pieces per lot.

Number of lots per year	1	2	3	4	5	6	7
Preparation cost per year. $15 × No. of lots	$ 15.00	$ 30.00	$ 45.00	$ 60.00	$ 75.00	$ 90.00	$105.00
Storage cost per year. One-half the maximum number in inventory	19.20	9.60	6.40	4.80	3.80	3.20	2.80
Interest charge per year. One-half investment in inventory × .10...	480.00	240.00	160.00	120.00	96.00	80.00	70.00
	$514.20	$279.60	$211.40	$184.80	$174.80	$173.20	$177.80

Fig. 15. Cost comparisons for manufacturing quantities of various sizes.

Analytic calculation of standard quantities, as described above, takes considerable time and the method is not widely used. Formulas have been devised, therefore, to make quicker calculations. Examples of these formulas and their application follow. Results from the analytic method and the formulas do not always agree. Both should be used wherever convenient as a means of either checking on quantities which have been selected tentatively by judgment and experience, to see whether the selection seems correct, or, conversely, to make a calculation and then judge or modify it in the light of experience and reason. Many authorities do not favor the use of such methods, but they are presented here because of their availability at least as checks.

Norton Formula. Norton has devised the following method involving the equation given below. His symbolization is:

$Q =$ economic lot size (pieces per lot).

$S =$ total preparation cost per lot in dollars. (Included is the cost of preparing manufacturing orders, setting up machines, and other costs that are independent of the number of pieces in the lot.)

$A =$ cost of storing one piece for one year, in dollars.

$B =$ annual charges for taxes, insurance, etc., in percent of the inventory investment, used as a decimal.

$C =$ manufacturing cost per piece in dollars. (Included are costs of material, direct labor, and overhead.)

$I =$ desired annual return on capital in percent, used as a decimal.

$N =$ number of days worked per year.

$P =$ number of pieces manufactured per day.

$U =$ number of pieces used (or shipped) per day.

Then,

$$Q = \sqrt{\dfrac{S}{\dfrac{(B + I)\, C + 2A\left(1 - \dfrac{U}{P}\right)}{2NU}}}$$

Example. A worked-out example shows how the formula is used, and the difference in the result obtained when the rate for the desired return on capital is used instead of the rate for simple interest.

Assume the following data:

$$S = \$10.00 \qquad I = 20 \text{ percent}$$
$$A = \$.001 \qquad N = 300$$
$$B = 3 \text{ percent} \qquad P = 1,000$$
$$C = \$.10 \qquad U = 100$$

Substituting in the formula,

$$Q = \sqrt{\dfrac{10}{\dfrac{(.03 + .20) \times .1 + 2\,(.001)\,1 - \left(\dfrac{100}{1,000}\right)}{2(300)\,(100)}}}$$

$$= \sqrt{\dfrac{10}{\dfrac{.0248}{60,000}}} = \sqrt{\dfrac{10}{.41\,(10 - 6)}} = 4,940 \text{ pieces}$$

If a simple interest rate of 6 percent were used as the value of I, the answer would be:

$$Q = \sqrt{\dfrac{10}{.16\,(10 - 6)}} = 7,900 \text{ pieces}$$

Davis Formula. The Davis formula for economic manufacturing lot sizes (Purchasing and Storing) is built up from the following factors symbolized as indicated:

$Q =$ The quantity to be manufactured in a single run that will give the lowest unit cost.

$A =$ The preparation cost of manufacturing, expressed in dollars.

$M =$ The equivalent annual rate of manufacturing, expressed in the same units as Q.

$S =$ The equivalent annual rate of consumption, expressed in the same units as Q.

$C' =$ The standard cost of the particular item, expressed in dollars per piece.

$Z =$ The desired rate of profit on working capital, expressed in percent and used as a decimal value.

$B =$ The number of square feet of net storage space required to store one unit of the item.

$E =$ The annual unit charge for storage space, expressed in dollars per square foot of storage space.

$k =$ The lot factor, expressing the influence of lot or batch production on the economy of manufacturing, $k = 2F - 1$, approximately.

$F =$ The ratio R/R_1 or the ratio of quantity at order point to quantity used while awaiting delivery.

$$Q = \sqrt{\dfrac{2AMS}{(M + kS)\,(C'Z + 2BE)}}$$

Example. Using the same values as in the Norton equation and assuming that the ratio of R/R_1, reorder point to consumption while getting the new stock into the storeroom, is 1.1 (that is, 10 percent of the "consumption while replenishing" is assumed to be sufficient as a cushion stock), the following figures apply in determining the economic manufacturing lot:

> $A = \$10$, preparation cost.
> $M = 300 \times 1,000$, equivalent annual rate of manufacture.
> $S = 300 \times 100$, equivalent annual rate of consumption.
> $C' = \$.10$, standard cost per piece.
> $Z = 20$ percent, rate of profit on working capital.
> $B \times E = \$.001$, sq. ft. storage space per unit $\times$ annual storage cost per sq. ft.

$$k = 2F - 1 = 2 \times \frac{R}{R_1} - 1 = 2 \times 1.1 - 1 = 2.2 - 1 = 1.2, \text{ the lot factor}$$

$$Q = \sqrt{\frac{2 \times 10 \times 300,000 \times 30,000}{(300,000 + 1.2 \times 30,000)(.10 \times .20 + 2 \times .001)}}$$

$$= \sqrt{\frac{20 \times 300,000 \times 30,000}{30,000 \,(10 + 1.2)\,(.02 + .002)}}$$

$$= \sqrt{\frac{6,000,000}{11.2 \times .022}} = 4,935 \text{ parts in the economic manufacturing lot}$$

The difference in results between the two formulas is caused by the basis of certain of the assumptions, for example, the ratio of reorder point to cushion stock.

Other Types of Formulas. Another common **simplified formula** for computing economic lot manufacturing sizes mentioned by Spriegel (Industrial Management), is as follows:

$$Q = \sqrt{\frac{2PR}{CI}}$$

> $Q = $ Economic lot quantity in units.
> $P = $ Preparation cost in dollars consisting of the clerical cost of preparing, recording and supervising the order as well as setup and dismantling costs.
> $R = $ Requirements in units on an annual basis.
> $C = $ Cost of the part in dollars per unit.
> $I = $ Carrying charge in percentage per year.

This simplified formula, which yields nearly the same result as the more complex ones, is probably the most commonly utilized.

Moore (Production Control) points out that "if the economic lot size is increased or decreased by less than 25 percent of the optimum or economic lot size, the unit cost is affected very little." This is due to the flatness of the curve at this point and is shown by Fig. 16.

Because of this feature it is unnecessary to process goods in exact economic lots in order to attain the exact minimum cost, but a computation should be made wherever possible in order to indicate the area in which the order should be placed.

Applying operations research techniques to problems of machine tool production, R. L. Ackoff (Advanced Management, vol. 20) developed this approach to find the number of lots that **minimize production costs:**

> $c_1 = $ Setup and take-down cost per lot (including both shop and office operations).
> $c_2 = $ Raw material cost plus process cost per part.
> $P = $ Inventory carrying cost expressed as a percent per month of the value of the part.

L = Required number of parts per scheduling period.

M = Number of scheduling periods.

$N = ML$ = Number of parts required per planning period.

$N' = ML/n$ = Number of parts per lot.

K = Total incremental production cost per planning period (i.e., total cost less raw material inventory cost and in-process inventory cost).

K' = Total incremental production cost per lot.

n = The number of equal-sized lots per planning period.

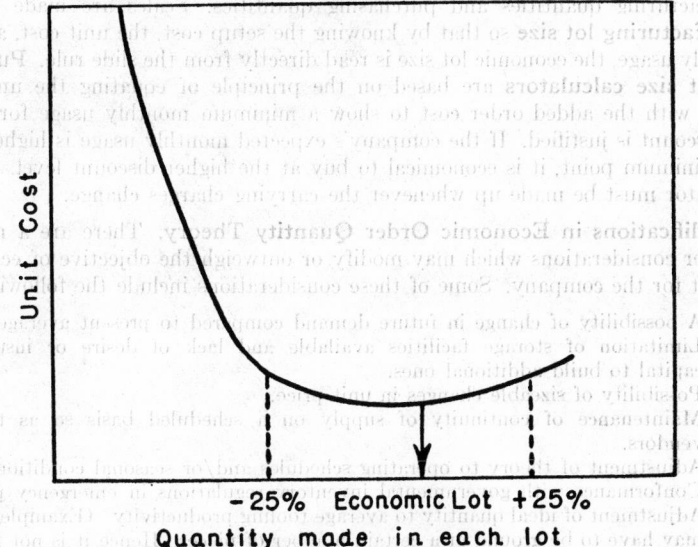

Fig. 16. Slope of economic lot quantity curve.

The **planning period** was assumed to be one year. Relating the variables yields:

$$K = nc_1 - MLc_2 n - \frac{nPc_1}{2}\left(\frac{M}{n} - 1\right) - \frac{Pc_2 LM}{2}\left(\frac{M}{n} - 1\right) \tag{1}$$

For any part, values of c_1, c_2, P, L, and M can be determined. The optimum value of n (n_o) is that which minimizes K. Developing this minimum gives:

$$n_o = M\sqrt{\frac{LPc_2}{c_1(2 - P)}} \tag{2}$$

Algebraic translation of terms yields the following equation for the optimum value of N' (N_o'):

$$N_o' = \frac{L}{\sqrt{\dfrac{LPc_2}{c_1(2 - P)}}} \tag{3}$$

Equation (1) is exact only if an integral number of months' requirements are made per lot run, but it is possible to work around this limitation. (See section on Operations Research for other techniques involved in the solution of industrial problems.)

Use of Nomographs and Slide Rules. Many companies have developed nomographs or use slide rules to speed up the computation of economic manufacturing quantities or economic purchasing quantities. These nomographs show the economic lot quantities to be produced if the setup cost and the rate of consumption are known. Each nomograph is based on a particular **inventory carrying charge,** and if the carrying charge changes, a new nomograph must be made up. (See section on Charting and Graphic Methods.)

Slide rules are also manufactured commercially for computing both economic manufacturing quantities and purchasing quantities. Scales are made up for **manufacturing lot size** so that by knowing the setup cost, the unit cost, and the monthly usage, the economic lot size is read directly from the slide rule. **Purchasing lot size calculators** are based on the principle of equating the unit cost saving with the added order cost to show a minimum monthly usage for which the discount is justified. If the company's expected monthly usage is higher than this minimum point, it is economical to buy at the higher discount level. A new calculator must be made up whenever the carrying charges change.

Modifications in Economic Order Quantity Theory. There are a number of other considerations which may modify or outweigh the objective of economic lot cost for the company. Some of these considerations include the following:

1. A possibility of change in future demand compared to present average usage.
2. Limitation of storage facilities available and lack of desire or insufficient capital to build additional ones.
3. Possibility of sizeable changes in unit price.
4. Maintenance of continuity of supply on a scheduled basis so as to help vendors.
5. Adjustment of theory to operating schedules and/or seasonal conditions.
6. Conformance with governmental inventory regulations in emergency periods.
7. Adjustment of ideal quantity to average tooling productivity. (Example: A die may have to be ground at a certain number of pieces. Hence it is not feasible to specify a larger number of pieces.)
8. Changes in business policy which demand an increase in inventory where larger quantities must be ordered without reference to economic lot sizes. If business conditions are generally declining or there is a possibility of a lower price level, it is often wise to reduce inventory or to limit investment even though purchases are not made in economic lot sizes.
9. Limitation of working capital with consequent necessity of operating with a higher unit cost of goods than optimum because of lack of capital.

OPTIMAL MACHINE LOADING. M. E. Salveson (Management Science, vol. 2) describes a method for determining optimal production programs for a given set of manufacturing facilities. This example covers the fabrication and scheduling of large sheet metal parts on a group of heavy presses, ranging in capacity from 60 tons to 300 tons. It is a straightforward mathematical programming problem.

Salveson's paper continues with a discussion of methods for computing optimal **cycle length** and for determining the optimum level of **average reserve inventory** of parts to be carried between fabrication and assembly. (See section on Operations Research.)

Production Control

ELEMENTS OF CONTROL. Production control depends for success on procedures which quickly relate actual progress to previously established plans and schedules, give notice of incipient trouble or delays, and provide facts for analysis and prompt executive action. Some of the elements in successful **control procedures** are:

1. Control of activities: Release of orders setting plans in motion at assigned times by means of dispatching.
2. Control of materials: Checks on materials, on relations between planned and actual times of delivery, on issues to and movements within shop.
3. Control of tooling: Checks on progress of tool design, if necessary, on tool manufacture or tool purchase, and on issue of tools to the shop departments from the tool cribs.
4. Control of due dates: Observation of machine loading and recognition of delays or stoppages which interfere with due dates of work assigned to each machine.
5. Control of quality and quantity: Observation of work in process at predetermined stages to determine:
   a. If the right quantity has been processed.
   b. If the work done is in accordance with standards of quality.
6. Control of replacements: Observation of the quantity of raw materials and work in process that fails to pass each stage of inspection and issuance of orders for replacing such material or work.
7. Adjustment of ideal quantity to average tooling productivity. (Example: A die of items 4, 5, and 6) and checkoff of completed work on production schedules and route sheets.
8. Control of materials handling: Observation of movement of work by cranes, trucks, and other means of interdepartmental transportation.

MANUFACTURING OR PRODUCTION ORDERS. Authorization to start production is given by manufacturing or production orders. Manufacturing orders may be actual or virtual. In custom work they are always **actual**. Each production order deals with a specific sales order received from the customer. In mass production and in continuous process industries they may be **virtual**, that is, simply an understanding that a certain output is to be maintained over a coming period. Even in the latter case, some device must be adopted to distinguish production of one period from that of another. **Monthly outputs** are frequently used in this way. Instead of charging production to a specific order number, the charges are made to each month's production.

Objectives in issuing manufacturing or production orders are:

1. To convey information on the customer, his specifications, and promised time of delivery.
2. To serve as a nucleus for cost collection, either for the order as a whole or for individual components and processes on components.
3. To form a starting point for the control mechanism.

Subsidiary Orders. In machine shop work, a production order initiates a whole series of subsidiary orders, among which are pattern and casting orders, tool, fixture, and jig orders, processing or job orders, all of which are extensions of the productive process. A particular control system may require, in addition, material requisitions, stores issue orders, tool issue orders, move orders, inspection orders, and replacement orders.

In small plants and in industries with fixed processes, manufacturing orders are sometimes **consolidated** with the routing and even the scheduling procedures. Fig. 17 illustrates this type of form. Stubs are detached and sent to the planning department as soon as each operation is performed. The top stub represents the manufacturing order and the lower ones process or job orders. The first to be detached (the bottom stub) serves as a material issue slip.

Date _____ To be shipped on _____

Customer _____ 7963

Shipping instructions _____

Order for _____ Pieces _____ Pattern
Material _____
Finish _____

Customer's Order No. _____ Dated _____

FINISHING   7963

Man _____ Machine _____

Begun _____ Fin. _____ Time _____

Pieces Rec'd _____ Spoiled _____

Pieces Good _____ Insp. _____

MOLDING   7963

Man _____ Machine _____

Begun _____ Fin. _____ Time _____

Pieces Rec'd _____ Spoiled _____

Pieces Good _____ Insp. _____

MATERIAL   7963

_____
_____
_____
_____

Rec'd by _____ Time _____

Fig. 17. Combined production and job order where routing is fixed.

Fig. 18 shows a production order for mirror manufacture. The right-hand portion serves to schedule the order. Symbols A, B, and C indicate first, second, and third periods into which monthly production is divided. Fig. 19 illustrates a production order based on a different idea. Here it is not a question of specific customers' orders but of authorizing production of so much of each size and kind of fabric during one week. In most cases this authorization is based on a consolidation of orders from customers, or on anticipated demands. Such a procedure amounts to manufacture of goods for stock, after which they are divided up into lots as ordered by each customer.

KNITTING ORDER

ORDER NO. 6000	LOT: 5		
CUST. NO. 4001			
CHARGE TO: John Widdecomb & Co.			
SHIP TO: Grand Rapids, Mich.			
VIA:			
SOLD BY: J. L.			

	MO	DAY	YR
RECEIVED	Oct.	1	19—
WANTED PROMISED	Oct.	31	19—

SIZE	BEV.	SILV.	PATTERN	QUAL.	PLATES	REMARKS	DATE CUT	ACID	POL.	BEV.	PE	MIT.	SILV.
18" x 30"	∨	—	plain	I	50		3		A-50				A-50
12" x 20"	∨	—	"	I	200		4,5 &6	A-50	B-50				B-100
22" x 40"	∨	—	"	I	150		8 & 9		B-150				B-150
15" x 28"	∨	—	"	III	100		10 & 11		B-100	C-10	C-10		C-100
36" x 60"	—	1"	342-a		10	See previous order #3562							

(SCHEDULING: ACID, POL., BEV., PE, MIT., SILV.)

Fig. 18. Production order combined with schedule.

FABRIC	7½	8	8½	9	9½	10	10½	11	12	12½	13	14	15	16	17	18	19	20	21	22	23	24	25	26	GRAND TOTAL
1639 — Machine Numbers / Cloth Order													2-16 / 600	3-5 / 700	7-10 / 700	8-11 / 1700	9-12 / 240	14-17 / 300	16 / 300	17 / 360					4900
1940 — Machine Numbers / Cloth Order											18-1 / 400	24-26 / 500	28-30 / 600	30-40 / 700	42-41 / 700	46-47 / 700	49-60 / 800	68-66 / 400	67-65 / 400	63-61 / 400	79-78 / 400				6000

KNITTING ORDER for   Serial No. 46   Mill No. 6   Week of 10/10/ to 10/17/   Date 10/11

Fig. 19. Production order authorizing weekly outputs.

In engineering work and in assembly industries of similar character, the manufacturing order sometimes is more in the nature of a **memorandum of identification,** together with a record of the **successive steps** in filling the order. It may provide for (1) customer's name, address, order number, and shipping instructions; (2) date of promised delivery; and (3) descriptions of goods to be made. These brief particulars must be supplemented by parts lists providing columns for: (1) pattern order numbers; (2) casting order numbers; (3) tool, jig, and fixture order numbers if required; and (4) process or job order numbers. In repair work or any work of few components, all these particulars may be listed on the order itself. The actual form of such orders varies from plant to plant and their number is legion. Fig. 20 shows one type used by a machinery manufacturer.

Production orders are usually **manifolded,** with copies distributed to all departments working on the order, and to any staff departments affected. This plan is usually followed as a means of reference and identification even though all definite working instructions are contained in other documents.

The receipt of a manufacturing order by the planning department sets the activities of that department in motion. The **material situation** receives first attention. Stock is reserved on a stores record, requisitions for purchases are made, and the question of making or buying outside is settled. The times at which purchased materials will be available are ascertained as closely as possible. The way is then open for the specific **control work.** If the engineering department has not already completed operation studies, these must now be made. With machines and fixed operations sequences specified, route sheets may be set up while time allowances are being established.

CONTROL OF MANUFACTURING. Control of operating procedure in the manufacturing departments includes:

1. Determining where the work is to be done.
2. Determining when the work is to be done.
3. Seeing that the work is done by providing mechanisms and procedures for issuing and receiving the orders in the shop. Also, collecting information on progress, and revising specified places and times when changes in the original plans become necessary.

The first of these tasks is known as routing, the second as scheduling, and the third as dispatching.

B82

PRODUCTION ORDER

CHARGED TO / ORDERED BY: John Doe

SHIP. ORDER NO. 38700

SHIP PREPAID / COLLECT TO: John Doe

New York

C

WEIGHT ______ HOW PACKED ______

VIA: Express

F. O. B.: Providence SERIAL NO.

TERMS: Net 30 Days

CUSTOMER'S ORDER NO. 40 REQ. 750

DATE ORDERED BY CUSTOMER			SHIPPING ORDER ISSUED			SHIPMENT DUE		
MONTH	DAY	YEAR	MONTH	DAY	YEAR	MONTH	DAY	YEAR
4	15		4	15		4	17	

Item	Quantity	Description	Drawing No.	Check	Pattern No.	Stock M'f'g. Purch.	Symbol	On Hand	Ship-ped
1	100	#2 Change Gears 72T. 16P. 7/16" F.	11701-D-72			WM	Rav. 11701-72 G2R	/ /	
						PM		– –	
						P		– –	

CUSTOMER'S ORDER REC'D		SHEET WRITTEN AND APPROVED		ORDER WRITTEN		DRAWINGS AND DATA CHECKED		ISSUES WRITTEN		MATERIAL APPORT'ND		PASSED	SHIPMENT COMPLETE		BILLED		ENTERED ON RECORD	
GL		CSB		MM		CSB		RT		JS		FG	RH		DH		JH	
DAY	HOUR	DAY	HOUR	DAY	HOUR	DAY	HOUR	DAY	HOUR	DAY	HOUR	INSPECTOR	DAY	HOUR	DAY	HOUR	DAY	HOUR
4/15	1	4/15	2	4/15	3	4/15	2	4/15	3	4/15	3	4/15 – 3	4/15	4	4/15	5	4/15	5

WM = worked material. *PM* = plant foundry material. *P* = purchased material. The two checks in the "On Hand" column indicate that material is on hand and ready to ship.

Fig. 20. Production order and progress record.

Routing

THE ROUTING FUNCTION. The implications of the term "routing" are rather indefinite. The word is occasionally used to include every step from machine analysis through analysis into parts, operation studies, and the preparation of orders for production. It is sometimes applied to the flow of materials through the process; conveyor assembly systems as developed in automobile plants are sometimes cited as examples of good "routing." Such uses of the term have little in common with the definite steps required to get an order into production. The term as used here applies to the **actual preparation of route sheets.**

In engineering and machine shop practice, the steps needed to prepare for production occur as follows:

1. The future product exists only as an idea, possibly embodied in sketches.
2. The more important or novel details of the idea are studied at length and drawings are prepared and developed.
3. When these features have been approved, working drawings of the whole product are prepared.
4. Detail drawings of parts and assemblies are made, blueprints are run off, and all necessary technical data are assembled.

Where standardized or repetitive work is concerned, the best practice demands that the foregoing design of parts and details shall have been simultaneous with consideration of:

1. The operations and processes by which the part is to be made.
2. The most suitable material in light of the use of the part and the exigencies of manufacture.

In this case the completed design, as received from the engineering division by the production control office, will include:

1. List of parts and assemblies.
2. Working drawings (blueprints of each part and assembly).
3. Specification of kind and quality of material for each part.
4. Inspection data (limits and tolerances) on each part.
5. Specification of machine processes by which a part is to be made.
6. Sequence in which these processes are to be performed.
7. Time allowances for each process subdivided into:
   a. Setup time.
   b. Operation time.

In custom work and less standardized manufacture, design sometimes ends at item 4 in this list. Detailed drawings (supplied in many cases by the customer) simply give form dimensions and leave the decision on methods of manufacture to the production control department. Since custom work is the most complicated, it is the kind of work that will be described in the following discussion.

In nonengineering industries, the route of the work is often fixed. In some cases (e.g., shoe manufacture), breakdown of a pattern or model provides a list of separate parts and indicates the kind and quantity of material required. There is little choice, however, as to the way in which it is to be made. In continuous industries, processes and their sequences are wholly fixed, although successive batches of product may vary in composition.

A detailed description of routing, scheduling, and dispatching procedures will be found in the section on Production Control Systems and Procedures.

Scheduling

DEFINITION. Scheduling may be defined as the fitting of specific jobs into a general timetable so that orders may be manufactured in accordance with contractual liabilities, or, in mass production, so that each component may arrive at and enter into assembly in proper order and time.

EFFECT OF MANUFACTURING METHODS ON SCHEDULING. Proper scheduling procedures in a given plant are determined by its methods of production and the degree of control required. Four general situations may be distinguished:

1. **Intermittent or lot manufacture** in which the product is routed through the plant in lots or job orders. Under this general heading there are two general methods of procedure:
   a. **Manufacturing to order,** where orders go through shops for individual parts. Parts may be single pieces or multiples. Each part passes through one to several processes. Assembly is dependent on all parts being ready simultaneously. Examples are simple products, such as castings or stampings, finished or unfinished, both requiring assembly.

   Orders are not necessarily individual customers' orders; they may represent consolidations of several such orders for identical styles or patterns. Manufacturing orders may also represent estimated stock or sales requirements of a particular item or product, such as 120 pairs of a certain style of shoe, 50,000 yards of a certain pattern of fabric, or 12 dozen of a single catalog item, such as a particular window stand in a shop-fitting manufacturer's line.
   b. **Stock manufacturing.** This differs from (a) principally in that very large numbers of pieces are involved, so that it is more convenient to make parts in large quantities and put them into stock to be withdrawn for assembly as required. Parts are put through in separate lots at predetermined intervals over a period. Assembly is an independent operation. It can go on as long as stock parts are available.
2. **Continuous manufacture,** which is also divided into two general kinds:
   a. **Single-product continuous manufacture,** where a single product goes through a fixed series of processes without assembly. Output is usually reckoned in weeks or months instead of by orders. The only variation is increased or diminished output as demand indicates.
   b. **Multi- or assembly-product continuous manufacture,** where parts, or the more important parts, are made continuously, each operation having a given output per day, all being proportionately increased or diminished together as demand indicates. From a scheduling standpoint this is equivalent to several separate streams of continuous manufacture, but subassemblies, assembly, and simultaneous end processes increase or diminish with the output of parts.

COMPONENTS OF A SCHEDULE. For a product that consists of individual parts grouped into subassemblies the subassemblies then being assembled into the final product, the schedule covering the complete cycle from receipt of customers' orders to delivery of finished products will be divided into several steps or periods as shown in Figs. 21 and 22. The times used in these figures are assumed and may be modified by specific conditions for individual orders as explained in the following paragraph:

In cases where the product and production processes are standardized, the planning procedure outlined below will occur only once, when production is first

Division of Procedure	For Individual Units within Divisions	Gross (If there were no overlapping among divisions)	Net for Division (Subtracting overlap of previous divisions)†	Saved by Overlapping of Divisions	Delay Allowances Added* (net)	Total Cumulative Time up to Start of Next Operation	Starting Days Ahead of Delivery
1. Credit checking	1	1	1	0		1	154
2. Sales dept. preparation of production order.......	1	1	1	0		2	153
3. Engineering..............	48	48	48	0		0	152
4. Production planning ..... (Use over-all time)	60	60	12	48		42	152 (start) 116 (finish)
5. Procurement (including receiving and inspection) ...							
a. Raw materials	30						
b. Purchased parts	36	38	18	20		50	112
(Use over-all time)							
6. Raw materials storage (net)‡	(12)	(12)	–	–		72	82
7. Tooling	32	32	2	30		48	104
8. Processing in factory Dept. 1...................	20						
" 2...................	26						
" 3...................	35						
" 4	32						
" 5....................	24						
" 6....................	21	56	22	34		58	106
(Use over-all time)							
9. Component parts storage‡							
a. Purchased parts	(40)						
b. Manufactured parts.....	(46)	(50)	–	–		86	92
(Use over-all time)							
10. Subassembly Group A..................	18						
" B..................	20						
" C	22						
" D	12	46	28	18		86	68
(Use over-all time)							
11. Final assembly of finished product	28	28	10	18		114	40
12. Tests or final working inspections	18	18	8	10		132	22
13. Packing and shipping	10	10	4	6		144	10
14. Over-all time	–	338	154	184		154	154

† Represented in Fig. 22 by shaded portions of bars.

* Allowances would take into account possible machine breakdowns, materials shortages, processing interruptions, unduly long time lapses in transporting materials and parts between departments, etc. Values have been omitted here for simplicity.

‡ Storage is considered here as merely incidental to take care of materials and parts until they are needed in manufacturing, and does not delay or add to the time of the actual manufacturing cycle.

Fig. 21. Departmental and cumulative time covering the cycle of a production order (see Fig. 22).

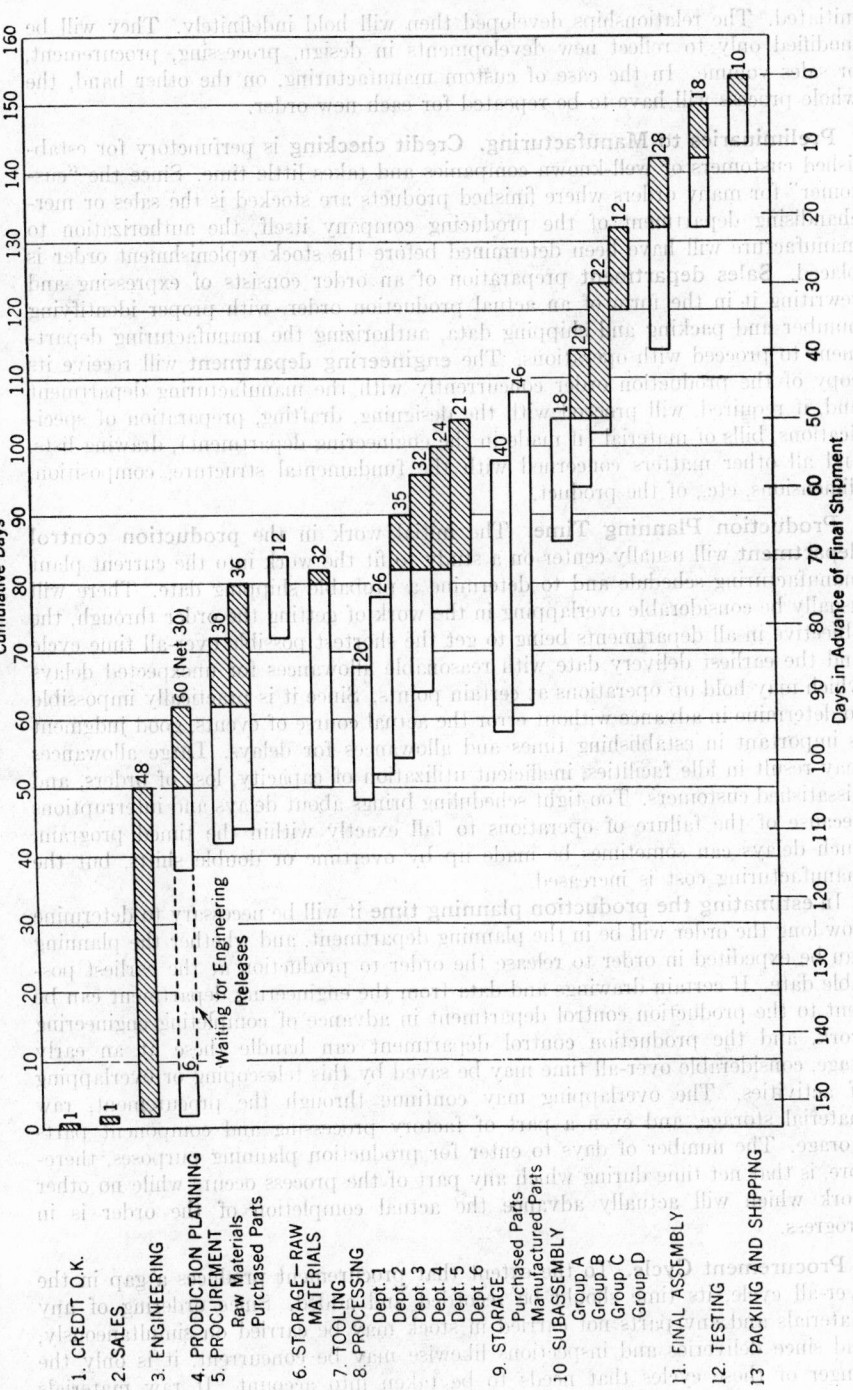

Fig. 22. Time cycle of the production order of Fig. 21 in Gantt chart form (shaded areas represent the net cumulative time in divisions, white areas the time saved by divisions through overlapping of work).

initiated. The relationships developed then will hold indefinitely. They will be modified only to reflect new developments in design, processing, procurement, or sales volume. In the case of custom manufacturing, on the other hand, the whole process will have to be repeated for each new order.

Preliminaries to Manufacturing. **Credit checking** is perfunctory for established customers or well-known companies and takes little time. Since the "customer" for many orders where finished products are stocked is the sales or merchandising department of the producing company itself, the authorization to manufacture will have been determined before the stock replenishment order is placed. **Sales department** preparation of an order consists of expressing and rewriting it in the form of an actual production order, with proper identifying number and packing and shipping data, authorizing the manufacturing department to proceed with operations. The **engineering department** will receive its copy of the production order concurrently with the manufacturing department and, if required, will proceed with the designing, drafting, preparation of specifications, bills of material (if made in the engineering department), drawing lists, and all other matters concerned with the fundamental structure, composition, dimensions, etc., of the product.

Production Planning Time. The initial work in the **production control department** will usually center on a study to fit the work into the current plant manufacturing schedule and to determine a probable shipping date. There will usually be considerable overlapping in the work of getting the order through, the objective in all departments being to get the shortest possible over-all time cycle and the earliest delivery date with reasonable allowances for unexpected delays which may hold up operations at certain points. Since it is practically impossible to determine in advance without error the actual course of events, good judgment is important in establishing times and allowances for delays. Large allowances may result in idle facilities, inefficient utilization of capacity, loss of orders, and dissatisfied customers. Too tight scheduling brings about delays and interruptions because of the failure of operations to fall exactly within the timed program. Such delays can sometimes be made up by overtime or double shifts, but the manufacturing cost is increased.

In **estimating the production planning time** it will be necessary to determine how long the order will be in the planning department, and whether the planning can be expedited in order to release the order to production at the earliest possible date. If certain drawings and data from the engineering department can be sent to the production control department in advance of completing engineering work, and the production control department can handle these at an early stage, considerable over-all time may be saved by this telescoping or overlapping of activities. The overlapping may continue through the procurement, raw material storage, and even a part of factory processing and component parts storage. The number of days to enter for production planning purposes, therefore, is that net time during which any part of the process occurs while no other work which will actually advance the actual completion of the order is in progress.

Procurement Cycle. To the extent that procurement produces a gap in the over-all cycle, its time should be recorded and added. Since ordering of any materials and any parts not carried in stock may be carried on simultaneously, and since deliveries and inspections likewise may be concurrent, it is only the longer of these cycles that needs to be taken into account. If raw materials already in storage can be withdrawn to start manufacture of the parts with the longest production cycle, the fact that other materials, arriving later and having short cycles, go temporarily into storage would affect the over-all time of the whole order only if such storage held up processing or subassembly.

Tooling. Tooling is often a cause of delay unless planned early by the methods engineer. Designs and tool production should follow promptly once manufacturing methods and the need for new types of tools, jigs, or fixtures are determined. Methods and tooling studies can parallel procurement and sometimes that part of planning which is concerned with the material situation. They may be delayed by the engineering work, if the parts which require new tooling are among the last designed. The total and the net time can be estimated, and the latter will be the time that the whole production cycle will be held up or lengthened by tools and fixture procurement.

In many cases the necessary tools may be available, but their condition should be ascertained, and any required adjustments and repairs should be made at the time the order is being prepared for production.

Factory Processing Cycle. Factory processing should be planned and scheduled to give the shortest over-all cycle time commensurate with existing load and the most economic utilization of equipment capacity. If it is known that the processing of parts and assemblies for other orders will delay the new order at any point, where the effect will be to hold up the whole order, this time should be added as part of the time for factory processing. Since the operation orders for parts and processes will be scheduled according to (1) available and open machine capacity, (2) times when material can be obtained, (3) sequence in which parts will be needed, and (4) coordination of subassembly and final assembly program, there will be considerable overlapping or **telescoping of jobs** so that a large number of parts will usually be in process at the same time. The chart or schedule covering production of the entire order will give the net over-all processing time from the start of the first part to completion of the last part. If this processing time overlaps component parts storage or subassembly, the net time of whichever is affected can be reduced by that much, or the net time of factory processing can be reduced by the overlap. It is probably better in most cases to schedule the processing in full and component storage or subassembly in net time (overlapping processes deducted).

Component parts storage may exist only to the extent that parts are most conveniently finished or delivered ahead of actual need and therefore must await withdrawal until required for subassembly or assembly. In such cases the time factor for this period drops out. It is only when subassembly must be postponed because of other orders—where it has been convenient to get all parts of the order cleared through in advance because of availability of machines—that component parts storage is a significant factor in over-all production time.

Transit Time. The time consumed in moving the work from station to station in the department or between departments is an important part of the schedule. It is futile to set close times on machining operations to get work done rapidly only to have it lie idle or be in transit an unduly long time. Sometimes, however, a "safety factor" is provided by allowing, say, a day, between operations for transit. If operations are late the parts may be handled more quickly to make up for lost time.

Subassembly. Subassembly time frequently overlaps with both factory processing (and component parts storage) time and final assembly time. The time of the **longest subassembly group** or longest assembly series is usually the determining factor, less any overlaps backward or forward, provided this group can be started early during the subassembly cycle. If, however, the long subassembly operations must await several preliminary subassemblies, which in turn follow on deliveries from some of the longest parts manufacturing cycles, then there will usually be little overlapping.

On an order for a number of identical or very similar items, final assembly may overlap subassembly to a considerable degree. One typical example is in the assembly plants of the automotive industry. In other cases, as in the building of special individual machine tools, the relative degree of overlapping is reduced. It is probably better to take the overlapping from subassembly time and obtain a net for that, because final assembly is the crux of the entire program. If that can begin and end on time, the whole order will be finished on schedule.

Final Assembly, Testing, and Shipping. Testing, or final working inspection time, must be totaled only if each unit of product is tested. Otherwise, the overall time of testing the lot, or the specified number of samples, will constitute the period. Units often undergo tests in groups or successive steps in the test may be applied simultaneously as the units pass through the cycle. The net time from start to finish is the time to include.

If the single unit is packed and shipped, the time for this purpose is the over-all time taken. **Disassembly time** and the time taken by special provisions for protecting against damage, rust, the elements, etc., must also be included. Where a number of items are to be sent out, the **sequential** packing and shipping operations often may overlap final assembly so that a net time is determinable.

MACHINE LOADING. Every job allotted to a machine decreases its capacity for additional work in a given period. It is therefore essential to know how far the work on hand will occupy the machines and, as each new order comes in, what time it will require for processing in each operation to be performed on it. **Machine analysis** has been indicated as the procedure by which the productive capacity of machines is ascertained. **Machine loading** is the process of compiling the "load" or quantity of work assigned to each machine for a given period. The unit in which machine load is expressed will depend on:

1. Whether capacity can be expressed in terms of product output—pounds, numbers, yardage, etc., per hour.
2. Whether it can be expressed only in hours of work.

In the first case, operation study is not required. Dividing the number, weight, or yardage in a lot on order by the capacity of the machine or process gives the "load." Different grades of material may take different speeds, but for a given kind of material the time of processing is easily ascertained. Thus a printing press or a dyeing machine has a known output, although this will vary with different papers or fabrics and other factors in a particular lot.

In the second case, which includes practically all machine tools not specialized for particular work, **operation study** must first determine the time allowance for the unit of product to be processed. The machine load for a specific order can then be ascertained by multiplying the unit time allowance by the number of pieces in the lot. In most machine tool work an additional setup time allowance must be made. **Machine load control** has two main objectives: (1) to keep machines continuously at work, and (2) to assign dates for processing each unit of a product so that production in the shortest possible time results. A by-product of this control is observation of the degree to which overload or underload occurs on particular machines or classes of machines.

Overload may be temporary or persistent. If temporary, relief can be had (1) by working overtime, or (2) by rerouting jobs to other machines, if available. Persistent overload must be met by additional equipment, alteration of the method of production, or procurement through purchasing or subcontracting.

Underload may arise from insufficient work. In custom manufacturing underload may easily occur, unless a certain amount of stock manufacturing can be used to balance out the load. Underload of certain departments may also arise from poor planning, in which case the remedy is to plan more closely.

Collection of Load Data. In collecting load data two factors must be considered: (1) the units in which the load is to be measured, and (2) the size of the work center against which load data will be collected. Two types of load data have already been mentioned. These apply where an accurate picture of load is desired.

Even in machining operations, **shop load** may be expressed in terms of time, money, weight, or other units. Expressed in terms of time, it will take the form of machine-hours or man-hours. Dollar load figures will usually be based on the sales value of shipments or some combination of manufacturing costs. In certain types of plants, the relationship between capacity and orders can be stated in terms of other units, such as pounds of raw material involved, or the total weight of finished product. Units other than time are really translations of production time requirements into figures which can be collected more easily. While figures on shop load in terms of production hours are the most accurate, other units of measure are frequently very useful. If, for example, a plant finds from experience that the total pounds of machinery which it produces or the total value of sales order in the shop consistently form an accurate enough picture for the amount of control required, there is no reason to shift the standard of measurement. Generally, figures not based on time are most useful in giving an **over-all load picture.** This is partly because errors in one department may cancel those in another and partly because errors which would be large in relation to one machine or one department's capacity are small in relation to plant capacity as a whole.

Considerable variation is also possible in the size of the production units against which the load is figured. These may be individual machines or operators, batteries of similar machines, departments or work centers, or the entire shop. With the larger units, load figures are easier to collect and schedules based on them are more flexible. On the other hand, the degree of control that can be achieved is reduced.

The most accurate type of loading stems from calculations of the time required for a machine or operator to perform each operation. These calculations are based on time studies or built up from good tables of **synthetic element times.** This type of data is required if individual machines are to be scheduled effectively, by hours or in some cases even by shifts. Operating times based on a summation of estimates are likely to be inaccurate unless the estimator has had many years of experience on the same type of order in a particular shop. As the size of the scheduled production unit increases from one machine to a battery of machines or to a department as a whole, the shortest practical schedule interval also increases. When this interval reaches the day or week, the finer gradations of load measurement are no longer necessary. If, for example, schedules consist of weekly production quotas for a whole department, it is unnecessary to calculate loads from the elemental times required to do each operation on every order in that department. An over-all estimate of the time needed by each order will probably be sufficient.

The character of a production schedule is closely related to the accuracy and fineness of the load data on which it is based. A **schedule** is simply a method of relating facilities, orders, and time. The manufacturing unit to which the schedule applies may range from one machine up to the entire capacity of the plant; orders may take the form of a variety of individual assignments or a single production order running for an extended period; the time unit of the schedule may be anywhere from an hour to a period of a month or more. In general, the longer time units are used in schedules which apply to the larger producing units and which are not designed to give tight control. Schedules which apply to the smaller production units and make use of the short time intervals are necessary when very close control is desired.

Dispatching

DEFINITION. Dispatching may be defined as "the routine of setting productive activities in motion through release of orders and instructions and in accordance with previously planned times and sequences as embodied in route sheets and loading schedules." The more complete and centralized the planning, the more dispatching tends toward a mechanical routine.

PRINCIPAL FACTORS. The principal factors or activities included in dispatching are:

1. Movement of material from stores to the first process and from process to process.
2. Issue of tool orders instructing tool department to collect and make ready tools, jigs, and fixtures and to furnish them to the using department in advance of the time at which the operation will commence.
3. Issue of job orders authorizing operations in accordance with dates and times previously planned and entered on machine loading charts, route sheets, and progress and control sheets or boards.
4. Issue of time tickets, instruction cards, drawings and any other necessary items to the workers who are to perform the various operations.
5. Issue of inspection orders after each operation to determine the result and number of good and bad pieces and causes of any excessive spoilage.
6. Clean-up on jobs, collecting time tickets, recovering blueprints and instruction cards and returning them to production control department.
7. Seeing that work is forwarded to the next department, storeroom, or stockroom.
8. Recording time of beginning and completing job and calculating duration, forwarding time tickets to payroll department and records on jobs to production control department.
9. Recording and reporting idle time of machines and of operators and requesting action on delays.

DISPATCHING: INTERMITTENT MANUFACTURE. Dispatching stations, cages, or offices are usually the local outposts of the planning department. In smaller companies, however, or in those where the day-to-day control is decentralized, dispatching may be handled by the foreman or his assistant. In either case, the routine of dispatching will be the same.

It has been explained that **manufacturing orders** form the starting point of a series of subsidiary orders and that preparation of these working papers should be taken in hand as soon as route sheets have reached the necessary stage of completion. Fig. 23 shows in diagram form the relation of subsidiary orders (1) to operations on a part, (2) to separate parts, and (3) to the whole order. This diagram applies to the routine of dispatching in intermittent manufacture.

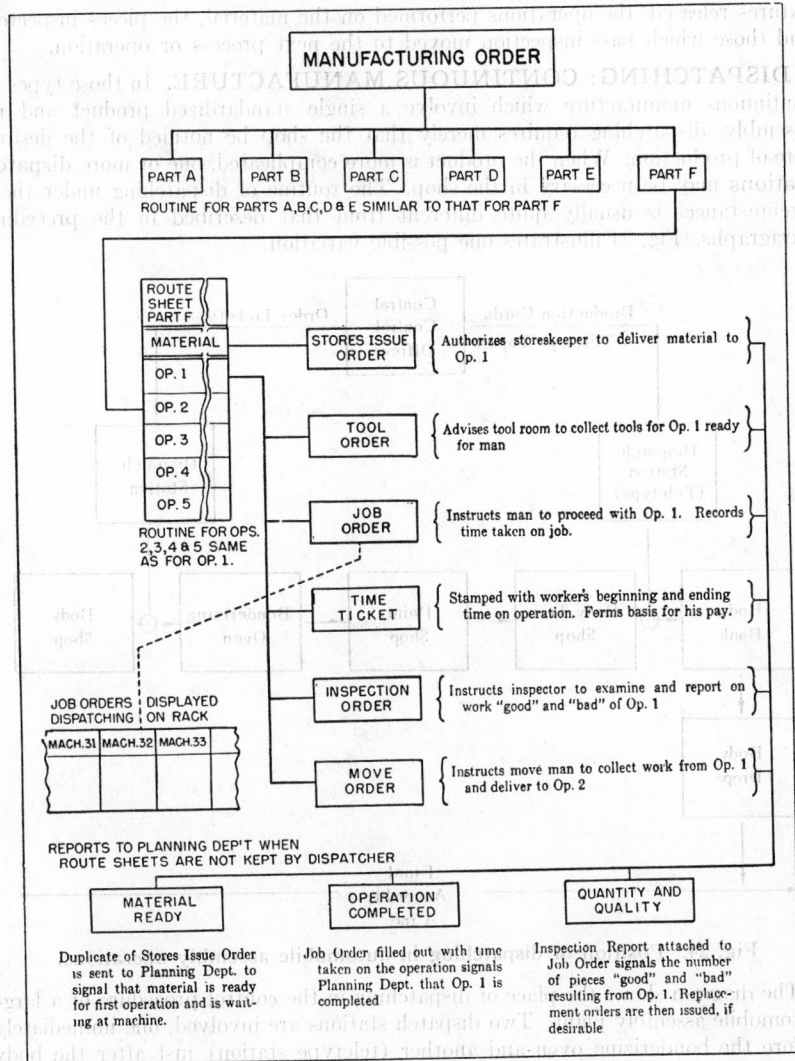

Fig. 23. Sequence of dispatching operations.

The manufacturing order is first broken down into **parts** and **assemblies**. Route sheets are made out for each part and assembly. The route sheets indicate materials to be used, operations to be performed, and their sequence. Against each operation are entered the time allowance, the date when it should begin and end, and the tools and fixtures required. The corresponding blueprint gives data for inspection limits and tolerances. To give effect to this information, material, tool, job, inspection, and move orders are made out as soon as dates assigned for operations are known. All these **working papers** are filed until a day or two before the job should start. They are then issued by the dispatcher to the various persons concerned. The material will be delivered at the machine, tools and fixtures released, the operations performed on the material, the pieces inspected, and those which pass inspection moved to the next process or operation.

DISPATCHING: CONTINUOUS MANUFACTURE. In those types of continuous manufacture which involve a single standardized product and no assembly, dispatching requires merely that the shop be notified of the desired rate of production. When the product is more complicated, one or more **dispatch stations** may be necessary in the shop. The routine of dispatching under these circumstances is usually quite different from that described in the preceding paragraphs. Fig. 24 illustrates one possible variation.

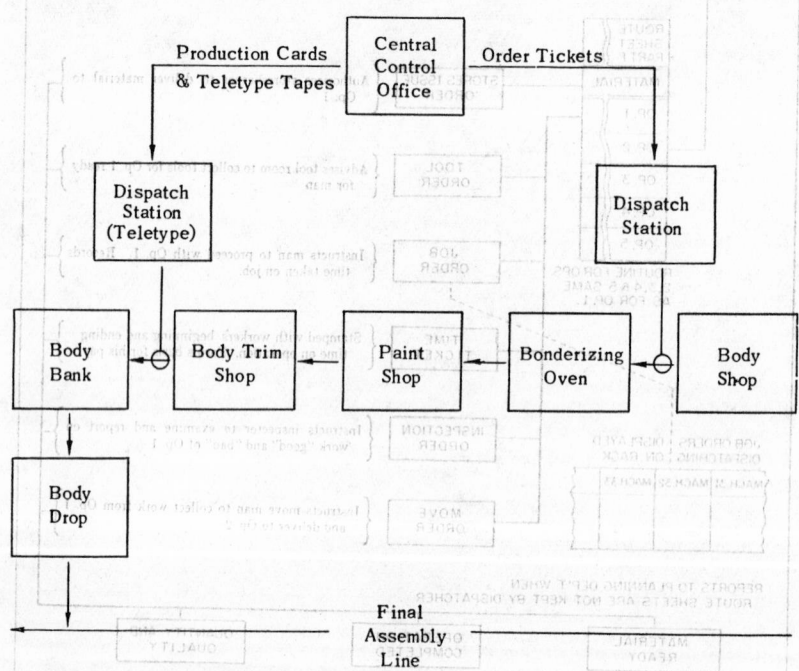

Fig. 24. **Position of dispatching in automobile assembly operations.**

The diagram shows the place of dispatching in the control procedure of a large automobile assembly plant. Two dispatch stations are involved, one immediately before the bonderizing oven and another (teletype station) just after the body trim shop.

Working within the framework of the month's production schedule and the instructions of the car distributor, the central control department in the plant makes out an order ticket for each car scheduled. These order tickets include all the information necessary to build a car exactly as specified on some original order from a dealer. At the same time a **serial number** is assigned to the car and a **teletype tape** is prepared. The control department arranges the order tickets in proper sequence for work in the body shop and notes this sequence on a list sent down to the body shop foreman. Each group of order tickets goes to the first dispatch station, and a similar group of production cards is sent to the teletype dispatch station.

As the rough bodies come off the body jigs and approach the bonderizing oven, the first dispatcher assigns an **order ticket,** referring to a specific dealer's order, to each body. At this point the assignment can be made only on the basis of the body style involved. The ticket and the teletype tape associated with it are attached to the dash in a metal holder. The dispatcher at this station thus controls the paint-and-trim operations which follow.

At the end of the body trim shop, the bodies pass the teletype dispatch station. This station controls the sequencing activities at a variety of points on lines which feed the final assembly line. As the bodies come through, the dispatcher takes the precut teletype tape from the holder on the dash and uses it to transmit the data on style, color, accessories, etc., to all the scattered feeder points involved. This dispatch station contributes a great deal of flexibility to the plant's control system. Almost any desirable changes in sequence can be made here without serious consequences. Once the sequence is established and flashed to other areas in the shop, the sequence number is chalked on the car's windshield and it enters the body bank before the body drop to the final assembly line.

JOB ORDERS. With materials and tools available, the operation may proceed as scheduled. Final release of the work to an operator is usually accomplished by some form of job order. The amount of detail on job orders varies greatly. In some cases, particularly in repair work, the job is described in as much detail as necessary, but ordinarily actual instructions are obtained from blueprints and instruction cards. The usual information on the job order includes:

1. Order number and part number or symbol.
2. Operation and operation number.
3. Machine and man number.
4. Number of pieces to be processed.
5. Date at which jobs should start.
6. Time allowed for operation; price if any.
7. Space for recording starting, finishing, and elapsed time on the job.

Job orders are made out at the same time as the route sheets. If assigned to a group of like machines, only the assignment to the group should be made in the first instance. Final machine assignment is made by the dispatcher at the time he releases the order.

Combinations of job orders with other forms are often used. Inspection reports are sometimes provided for on the reverse side. Move coupons are frequently attached. Sometimes the job order is used as the time record, sometimes this record is separate. Fig. 25 shows a job order combined with a tabulating card, which when punched is used for costing, payroll, and other purposes. Fig. 26 shows a job order, here termed a production card, as used in a large plant manufacturing automobile bodies. The job order itself is duplicated, one copy, as already explained, being kept in the dispatch rack. The lower portion of the form is an inspector's report where provision is made for half-hourly inspection checks.

The job order is time-stamped and handed to the workman, who uses it as authority to collect his tools and fixtures for the job. When the job is complete, the job order is again presented at the dispatch office where it is time-stamped

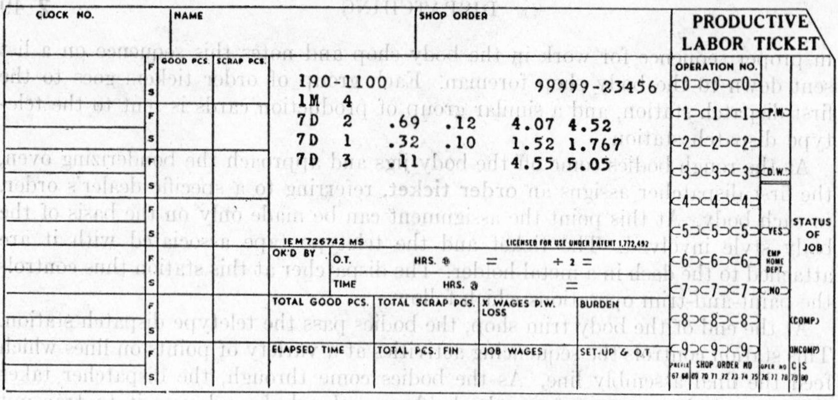

CLOCK NO. | NAME | SHOP ORDER

PRODUCTIVE LABOR TICKET

OPERATION NO.

F S | GOOD PCS. | SCRAP PCS.

190-1100 99999-23456
1M 4
7D 2 .69 .12 4.07 4.52
7D 1 .32 .10 1.52 1.767
7D 3 .11 4.55 5.05

IEM 726742 MS LICENSED FOR USE UNDER PATENT 1,772,492

OK'D BY | O.T. | HRS. ⑨ = ÷ 2 =
TIME | HRS. ⑩ =

TOTAL GOOD PCS. | TOTAL SCRAP PCS. | X WAGES P.W. LOSS | BURDEN

ELAPSED TIME | TOTAL PCS. FIN | JOB WAGES | SET-UP & O.T.

P.W. D.W. YES STATUS OF JOB EMP HOME DEPT NO COMP UNCOMP

PREFIX | SHOP ORDER NO | OPER NO | C/S

Fig. 25. Job order tabulating card.

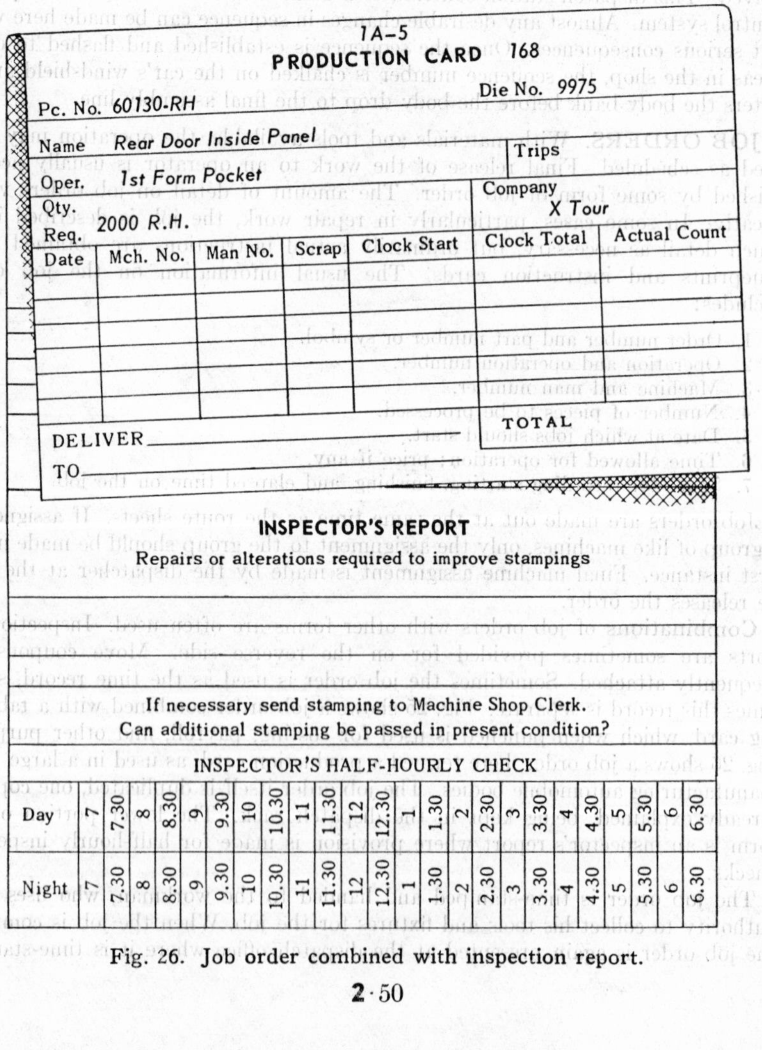

1A-5

PRODUCTION CARD 168

Die No. 9975

Pc. No. 60130-RH

Name Rear Door Inside Panel | Trips

Oper. 1st Form Pocket | Company X Tour

Qty. Req. 2000 R.H.

Date	Mch. No.	Man No.	Scrap	Clock Start	Clock Total	Actual Count
					TOTAL	

DELIVER

TO

INSPECTOR'S REPORT

Repairs or alterations required to improve stampings

If necessary send stamping to Machine Shop Clerk.

Can additional stamping be passed in present condition?

INSPECTOR'S HALF-HOURLY CHECK

Day	7	7.30	8	8.30	9	9.30	10	10.30	11	11.30	12	12.30	1	1.30	2	2.30	3	3.30	4	4.30	5	5.30	6	6.30
Night	7	7.30	8	8.30	9	9.30	10	10.30	11	11.30	12	12.30	1	1.30	2	2.30	3	3.30	4	4.30	5	5.30	6	6.30

Fig. 26. Job order combined with inspection report.

again and a new one handed to the workman. The original and the duplicate of the completed job order are then forwarded to the planning department and to the cost and payroll offices for use in making entries on their records.

INSPECTION AND RELEASE OF WORK. Two further steps have to be taken by the dispatcher before the job is disposed of. Inspection must be arranged unless it is being carried on continuously, and completed work must be moved to the next operation. **Instruction forms** for this purpose are frequently combined (see Fig. 26). Inspection orders are usually arranged to specify: (1) order and part, (2) operation, and (3) man's number for identification purposes. Spaces are also provided for the report which must indicate: (1) number of good pieces, (2) number of bad pieces, and (3) number capable of repair. Move orders are sometimes separate slips, but more usually take the form of additional lines at the foot of the job order or inspection order. In Fig. 26 the words "deliver" and "to" on the upper part of the form are moving instructions. Inspection and move orders are time-stamped on their return to the dispatcher and are then sent to the planning department for entry on route sheets and control boards. The question of replacing parts that have failed to pass inspection is also taken up by this department. **Replacement orders** are issued when the shortage is greater than the allowance made for this purpose.

FOLLOW-UP. The regular routine of dispatching ends with methods of control similar to those discussed in regard to individual operations. It is simply repeated in all details for the next operation. Exceptions to routine must be taken care of; this necessity applies particularly to lots behind schedule.

Effective follow-up procedures require:

1. Recognition of a delay as such.
2. Evaluation of its consequences.
3. Action to remove its causes or at least to minimize their effects.

Progress reports from the shop form the basis for intelligent comparisons of schedules and progress. The routine of dispatching must provide means for rapidly transmitting information on progress and delays to the control group. Exactly how this is accomplished—tear-off tickets, copies of completed job tickets or route sheets, copies of move orders, special reports—will depend on the particular control system in use. In any case, whoever sets the operating schedules must be supplied constantly with up-to-date progress data. Such data are vital for successful recognition and evaluation of delays. Action is then required to eliminate each delay or minimize its effects. In some plants, lots behind schedule are listed daily by the planning department and copies are sent to the dispatchers and foremen concerned. Job orders for such parts or lots are often distinguished by a colored sticker signifying that they are to receive precedence over other lots where possible. It is sometimes the practice to affix a brightly colored tag to the work itself. Where large numbers of parts are being processed and where assembly work is required on most orders, **expediters** are frequently used to locate a delayed parts order, follow its courses through the shop, and see that it is handled with all possible speed.

Control of Down Time and Machine Utilization

IDLENESS LOSSES. Idle equipment is a considerable problem in many plants. To keep within the scope of this section, the term "idle" will be used to denote facilities which are ostensibly prepared for and needed in production but are not turning out any product or are producing at an abnormally low rate. The problem of excess plant capacity, that is, facilities which have been idle and will continue so because of a receding level of demand, is not involved here. That calls primarily for a change in management policy which will either eliminate the excess or expand the company's markets.

Even in well-run machine shops, idleness of 20 to 60 percent is not unusual. The factor on continuous process equipment is usually lower, but even here it may run up to 20 or 30 percent. In general, this idleness does not occur at any single time, but rather as an accumulation of short delays and stoppages throughout the shift.

The fundamental importance of **idleness control** is brought out in the concept of a "pool of waste." The analogy to a leaky faucet is a good one. If it should happen that the idleness on each machine in the course of a day added up to 20 percent, it would mean that available plant capacity had in effect been reduced 20 percent without any corresponding reduction in overhead. This would lead to a reduction in the plant's earning potential of 20 percent, and would also cause one-fifth of the normal overhead expense to be wasted. With selling price relatively inflexible, this lost expense could be charged only against profits. Thus potential earnings would be reduced and at the same time an actual loss would be incurred. The former is serious enough; the latter is even more critical.

Up to now the discussion has centered on overhead expense and no mention has been made of the **direct charges to production.** Idleness, and the lowered productive capacity which follows it, lead naturally to the production of fewer units in the course of the shift. Since material charges vary directly with the number of units produced, no expense is incurred here when the stoppages occur. This may or may not be true in the case of direct labor.

If an employee's wage is figured on the basis of a straight piece rate, his incentive pay stops when production stops and does not start again until production is resumed. While appreciable idleness under these conditions may lead to all types of labor difficulties, it is, nevertheless, true that a portion of the direct expense is reduced. Going to the other extreme, consider the operator who is paid a straight hourly rate. It is obvious here that a daily production rate, whether of 10 units or a 1,000 units, will have no effect on the amount of money paid him. If the direct labor charge to a unit of product is to be uniform, it is equally obvious that idleness in this case results in an increment of expense which must be charged against profit.

The importance of idleness control is shown graphically by the crossover chart in Fig. 27. In this chart **costs** and **income** are plotted at various percentages of **plant capacity.** Material costs have been left out since they would merely complicate the picture. The income shown is an adjustment from actual income, omitting the direct material costs at each point. The chart gives the data for one month's operation of one machining department in the plant.

Points 1 and 2 in Fig. 27 show operation at 80 percent and 100 percent capacity, respectively. If the plant is actually at a planned operation level of 80 percent capacity, this department's share of fixed and variable overhead will be $13,000, its direct labor $4,500, and its income $4,500. If plant operations are at point 2, 100 percent of capacity, the department would operate with an overhead charge of $14,400, direct labor of $5,600, and income of $8,000. The point of immediate interest is the case where the backlog of orders calls for operation at the 100 percent level, but total idleness during the month amounts to 20 percent. With 20 percent idleness, the department is actually operating at

80 percent of capacity. If the plant's operations had been planned at that capacity, that is if only enough sweepers, move men, clerks, secretaries, supervisors, etc., had been at hand for operations at that level, income from the department's operations would have been $4,500. The lost capacity of 20 percent would have lowered that potential income by $3,500. However, reference to

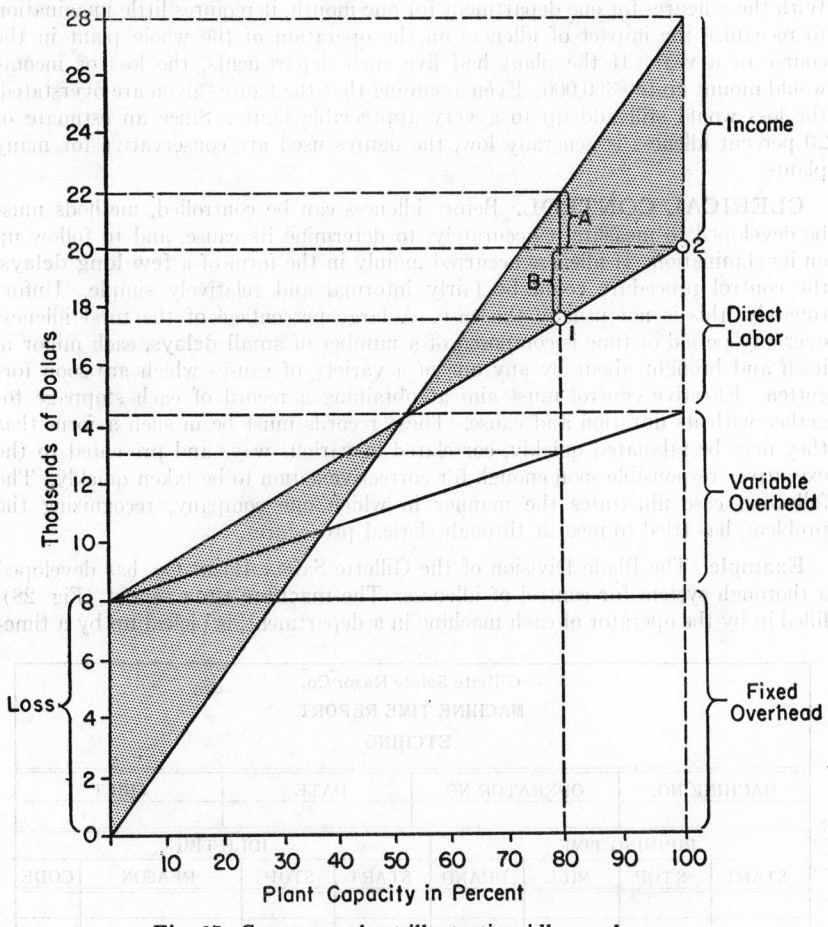

Fig. 27. Crossover chart illustrating idleness losses.

points 1 and 2 of the diagram shows that this is only part of the picture. With operations and overhead planned for 100 percent capacity, department charges are much nearer point 2 than point 1. Depending on how much direct labor expense and how much variable overhead expense, such as power, is saved, the department has to absorb additional charges up to amount B, $2,500. The remaining $2,000 (A) is the actual income from the month's operation. To summarize these facts, 20 percent idleness in this department during the month would result in the loss of departmental income shown in the following tabulation.

| Potential income at 100 percent..................................... | $8,000 |
| Potential income at 80 percent..................................... | 4,500 |

| 1. Reduction of potential income............................. | $3,500 |
| 2. Loss from potential income at 80 percent capacity............ | 2,500 |

| 3. Total loss .... | $6,000 |

With these figures for one department for one month, it requires little imagination to recognize the impact of idleness on the operation of the whole plant in the course of a year. If the plant had five such departments, the loss of income would mount up to $360,000. Even assuming that the figures given are overstated, the loss would still add up to a very appreciable figure. Since an estimate of 20 percent idleness is generally low, the figures used are conservative for many plants.

CLERICAL CONTROL. Before idleness can be controlled, methods must be developed to measure it accurately, to determine its cause, and to follow up on its elimination. If idleness occurred mainly in the form of a **few long delays,** the control procedure could be fairly informal and relatively simple. Unfortunately, this is not usually the case. A large percentage of the total idleness over any period of time is composed of a number of **small delays,** each minor in itself and brought about by any one of a variety of causes which are soon forgotten. Effective control must aim at obtaining a record of each stoppage together with its duration and cause. These records must be in such a form that they may be tabulated quickly, correlated in various ways and presented to the executives responsible soon enough for corrective action to be taken quickly. The following case illustrates the manner in which one company, recognizing the problem, has tried to meet it through clerical procedures.

Example. The Blade Division of the Gillette Safety Razor Co. has developed a thorough system for control of idleness. The **machine time report** (Fig. 28), filled in by the operator of each machine in a department, is picked up by a time-

Gillette Safety Razor Co. MACHINE TIME REPORT ETCHING							
MACHINE NO.		OPERATOR NO.		DATE		SHIFT	
RUNNING TIME				IDLE TIME			
START	STOP	MILL	BRAND	START	STOP	REASON	CODE

Fig. 28. Machine time report.

keeper at the end of the shift and sent to the tabulating section. Here the information on these reports is punched onto cards and run through tabulating machines. The figures assembled in this manner are given to the control section where they are posted to the time, productivity, and yield reports, and then final calculations are made. Copies of this time, productivity, and yield report are then distributed to the executives concerned with such problems.

A blank machine time report (Fig. 28) is attached to each machine in the department. Besides being identified as to operator, machine, day, and shift, this report provides a complete record of all **running** and **idle time.** An operator starts his machine, glances at the clock, and notes the time in the "start" column under running time. From information on the tag attached to the roll of steel, he also identifies the steel mill from which the strip came and the coded brand of the razor blade which is being manufactured from it. When the machine is forced to stop for any reason, the operator writes the time in the "stop" column under "running time" and the "start" column under "idle time." When operations are resumed, he records the time in the "stop" column of the idleness section and indicates the reason for the delay. A **code** must be applied to each of these delays so that the information may be transferred to the tabulating card.

The **time, productivity,** and **yield report** (Fig. 29) is a summary of the machine time reports for one department over the shift and period indicated at the top left and right of the sheet. Differentiation between **operational** and **nonoperational delays** is made on the basis of whether or not they may be controlled by the foreman. While some of the delays listed under either heading are obviously borderline cases, the majority fit into the definition fairly well. The foreman has little control over most of the nonoperational delays.

To understand this report, certain terms must be grasped as they are defined by the Gillette Co. **Running time** is that time during which the machine actually turns out units of product; time during which materials are available for production is called **operating time; scheduled capacity** is the operating capacity planned for the day or week in question; **maximum capacity** is the full capacity of the department with that number of shifts actually in use. In other words, if three shifts are used, maximum capacity is figured on the basis of three shifts; if only one shift is planned, then maximum capacity calculations are based on one shift. The total time expended under each of these headings is summarized in the **disposition of capacity** section in the upper left of the page (Fig. 29).

The two sections of the time, productivity, and yield report which deal with operational and nonoperational delays give the detailed record of how much lost time may be attributed to each of the reasons presented for such delays. (All the reasons are not shown.) These figures are expressed in hours and as percentages of the total operational or nonoperational idleness.

The production rate of each machine in the department, expressed in pounds per hour of operating time for each stock thickness, is listed on the right-hand side of the report. Averages of these figures are compared with the standard production rate of 100 percent utilization to arrive at the actual percentage of **machine utilization** for that department.

Yields are determined for each thickness of stock worked. The difference between the original and final weight gives the loss of weight. **Rejections** refer to the amount of material discarded as imperfect during the operation, not the material which does not pass later inspection. Loss through perforations is a standard percentage determined in advance by the engineering department. The sum of rejections and perforations subtracted from the loss of weight gives the percentage of scrap unaccounted for.

As a check on the amount of delay time reported by the operator, running time is multiplied by the standard machine production rate in lb. per hr. for the particular thickness of material in use. The result is compared with the actual

TIME, PRODUCTIVITY, AND YIELD REPORT

1st Shift	
2d Shift	
3d Shift	Date _____
All Shifts	

Disposition of Capacity	Hours	%
Running time		
Operational delays		
Operating time		
Non-operational delays		
Scheduled capacity		
Capacity in excess prod. requirements		
Maximum capacity		100.00

Operating Ratio	Hours	%
Running time		
Operational delays		
Operating time		100.00

Analysis of Operational Delays		
Reasons	Hours	%
1. Changing, checking, adjusting dies		
2. Changing pads		
3. Changing thickness		
4. No dies available		
5. Off center – sink die		
6. Burrs		
7. Nicks		
8. Stripper marks		
9. Section marks		
10. Screw-head marks		
11. Pawl marks		
12. Roller marks		
13. Miscellaneous		
14. Out of time		
15. Jams		
16. Welding breaks		
17. Pounding		
18. Loose slugs		
19. Checking inspection tools		
20. Cutting samples		
21. Changing coils		
22. Dirt in dies		
23. Changing fluid		
24. Warmup		

Unrecorded miscellaneous delays		
Total operational delays		100.00

Fig. 29. Time, productivity,

Analysis of Non-operational Delays			Remarks
	Hours	%	Weighting Factors
50. Operator late or quit early			
51. Operator absent			
52. Operator relief time			
53. Operator working elsewhere			
54. Inspect, oil, check machine			
55. Waiting for repair man			
56. Machine repairs			
57. No material			
58. No power			
59. Bad steel			
60. Experimental			
61. No inspector available			
62. Electrical repairs			
63. Cleanup			
Total non-operational delays		100.00	

Rates of Production Lb. (Finished Wt.) per Hr. (Operating Time)	Thickness			Weighted Total
Press No. 1				
2				
3				
4				
5				
6				
7				
13				
14				
15				
16				
17				
18				
19				
20				
Averages				
100% machine utilization, lb. per hr.				
% machine utilization				

Yields	Thickness			Total
Weight started				
Weight finished				
Loss in weight				
Rejections				
Perforations				
Scrap by diff.				

and yield report.

number of pounds of finished product produced. Since the machine rate is fixed, any difference between the two figures indicates **unreported delay time.** This difference in pounds is divided by the standard production rate to give the additional delay time which is entered as unrecorded miscellaneous delays under the analysis of operational delays on the time, productivity, and yield report.

These reports highlight productivity and machine utilization in each department. They provide management with a yardstick to measure:

1. The operating efficiency of each department.
2. The efficiency of certain service functions, such as inspection, repairs, and materials control.
3. The amount of idle time in comparison to the operating time.
4. Seriousness and frequency of each type of delay.
5. The effectiveness of the foreman in holding the idleness to a minimum.
6. The ability, skill, and effort of the operator.
7. The necessity for corrective action and the points where such action may best be applied.

Operational delays have been reduced by 20 to 30 percent since this system was installed.

WASTE AND SCRAP CONTROL. It is obvious that good control procedures can reduce the losses from **material waste** and scrap. Two areas in which attention should be concentrated are: (1) proper material utilization, and (2) scrap and waste disposal. The problem in **material utilization** is in specifying the minimum material for the specific product. For example, since the weight of a round bar varies as square of the diameter, the use of stock larger than needed is more wasteful than is apparent. For instance, if a part requires 1 in. diameter stock and 1¹⁄₁₆ in. is used, the material converted to scrap is roughly 10 percent higher although the diameter is only about 6 percent greater.

In **scrap** and **waste disposal** two conditions must be considered:

1. Does the **scrap generated** have any value?
2. Is the value significant enough to warrant **in-process classification?**

For example, copper scrap has a high market value. At times it has approached 80 percent of the selling price of the base product. Obviously, it is economically sound to classify this scrap and prevent its contamination.

Production control should coordinate the final scrap disposal; the advantage being that the measure of scrap being generated might be utilized by management in rating the efficiency of the process. For instance, in a machine shop the weight of new material should equal the sum of the weight of the finished product and the scrap generated. The percentage of scrap generated can then furnish an index of **production efficiency.**

INSTRUMENTATION. Instruments to aid in controlling idleness and down time are not new. Many attempts have been made to develop instruments which will effectively aid control of machine utilization and a large number of them are now available. If the desirable features and advantages of these instruments were all combined into one instrument, a list of **ideal features in a recorder** for effective control of idleness might run as follows:

1. A continuous, graphic, and automatic record throughout the shift of the productive and idle periods of each machine.

2. An indication on this record of the reasons for each period of idleness shown.
3. These reasons recorded semi-automatically in such a way that the wrong reason or no reason could not result merely from inattention or indifference on the part of the operator.
4. A switch on the machine which could be counted on to differentiate positively between those times when the machine was actually producing and those times when it was merely turning over.
5. Some form of cycling or timing arrangement which could be set at a predetermined standard and would record as idleness, and necessitate an explanation for, any productive time in excess of the standard.
6. An indication of the number of productive cycles, and piece count.
7. All records easily tabulated and correlated for control purposes.
8. Simplicity of design and operation.
9. Low-cost installation and maintenance.

Description of one of the recording instruments will serve to show how these units can be used.

Example. The Chronolog is designed by the National Acme Co. specifically for **down time control.** It is an electrically controlled device which may be attached to any machine or operation that is subject to production interruptions. Basically, it records **when, why,** and **how long** the production unit is idle. In many applications this information serves to fix responsibility, save arguments, and increase production 10 to 25 percent.

Fig. 30. Chronolog for down time control.

Extra Key	Operator's Key Number	Clock Time	Symbol For Dialed Idle Time	Dialed Idle Time Min. & Tenths	Undialed Idle Time Min. & Tenths	Units Produced
	716	7:00		0.0	0.0	00000
	716	7:05	S	0.0	5.2	00000
		7:10	S	5.0	5.2	00000
		7:20	S	15.0	5.2	00000
		7:30	S	25.3	5.2	00000
		7:40		25.3	5.2	00010
		7:50		25.3	6.1	00019
	716	7:58	E	25.3	7.1	00026
		8:00	E	27.0	7.1	00026
		8:10		32.7	7.1	00030
		8:20		32.7	7.1	00040
		8:30		32.7	7.1	00050
		8:40		32.7	7.1	00060
		8:50		32.7	9.0	00068
		9:00		32.7	12.3	00075
INSP.	716	9:02		32.7	12.3	00077
		9:10		32.7	12.3	00085
		9:20		32.7	15.0	00092
FOR.	716	9:21	M	32.7	15.9	00092
		9:30	M	42.0	15.9	00092
		9:40	M	52.0	15.9	00092
		9:50		52.0	15.9	00102
		10:00		52.0	15.9	00112
	716	10:01		52.1	15.9	00113

Recap. of the Above Section of a Chart Gives the Following Information:

Elapsed time .... 181 minutes
Dialed idle time .... 52.1 minutes
Undialed idle time 15.9   68

Deducting total idle time from
elapsed time leaves:
Production time................... 113 minutes
Units produced—113
Machine speed: One minute per unit produced.

Note: Explanatory recap and column headings are not printed on
Chronolog tape.

Fig. 31. Chronolog record tape.

A picture of the unit is shown in Fig. 30. The major components are a continuously moving tape, a printing head, a dial (similar to a telephone dial), and a switch on the machine. This switch is located so that it can be closed only when one unit of product is produced. The instrument automatically prints a record of clock time, undialed idle time, and accumulated count of units produced at intervals of ten minutes. When a delay occurs, the operator dials the coded reason and, as soon as production is resumed, the duration of the delay, together with this coded reason, is registered on the tape. An illustration of such a tape is shown in Fig. 31. Special keys inserted in the instrument print the operator's number or indicate that an inspector or foreman has checked in at the machine.

Delays and productive time are both shown in relation to clock time. Provision is made for recording at least nine reasons for down time. The Chronolog will record as idleness all time in excess of a predetermined cycle. As a quick check on the accuracy of the dialed idle time, in addition to that provided by piece count and standard time, undialed delays are also recorded as such.

Procedural Analysis

PROCEDURE FLOW CHARTS. Production control systems usually involve a great amount of detail. Information must pass from one group in the plant to another; decisions must be made and action taken; multiple forms must be made out, filed, distributed, and posted by a number of different people. In designing or evaluating such systems, the analyst must visualize each element of the procedure in relation to the system as a whole and the major objectives of control. With complex systems, this is not easy. Written descriptions by themselves tend to be overcomplicated and confusing. Pure memory is often unreliable. A very useful tool in this situation is a **procedure flow chart**, sometimes known as a flow-of-information or movement-of-papers chart. This chart, properly drawn, gives an over-all picture of the system as well as the relationships among the different functions involved. The construction and use of procedure flow charts are discussed in the section on Process Charts.

Procedure flow charts, such as Fig. 32, illustrating only a few steps in a production control procedure (9, 10, 11, and 12) can be set up with the actual forms themselves, or with **small-scale representations** of these forms. The latter procedure is the one followed here. Use of the actual forms with posting shown is sometimes practical in a large-sized exhibit used to explain or sell the system. If much photographic reduction in over-all size is necessary, actual forms become illegible and are better replaced by blocks with printed titles. Some realism is preserved if the shapes and relative sizes of the blocks are the same as those of the forms they represent.

Fig. 33 shows a type of **tabular chart** which, while it is less graphic than the others, is very useful in gathering information on a system. It helps get details down accurately and in orderly fashion and is simpler to prepare quickly than some of the other charts. Steps 9, 10, 11, and 12 correspond to those in Fig. 32.

Procedure Analysis. Procedure flow charts are useful supplements to written descriptions of control procedures. Their most important contribution, however, can be made when established systems are reviewed or new systems analyzed. Combining on one sheet both the general flow and the control procedures at each step, they allow the analyst to grasp and evaluate the control offered by the system and the effectiveness of its operation. They make it unnecessary to leaf back and forth through many pages of written material and

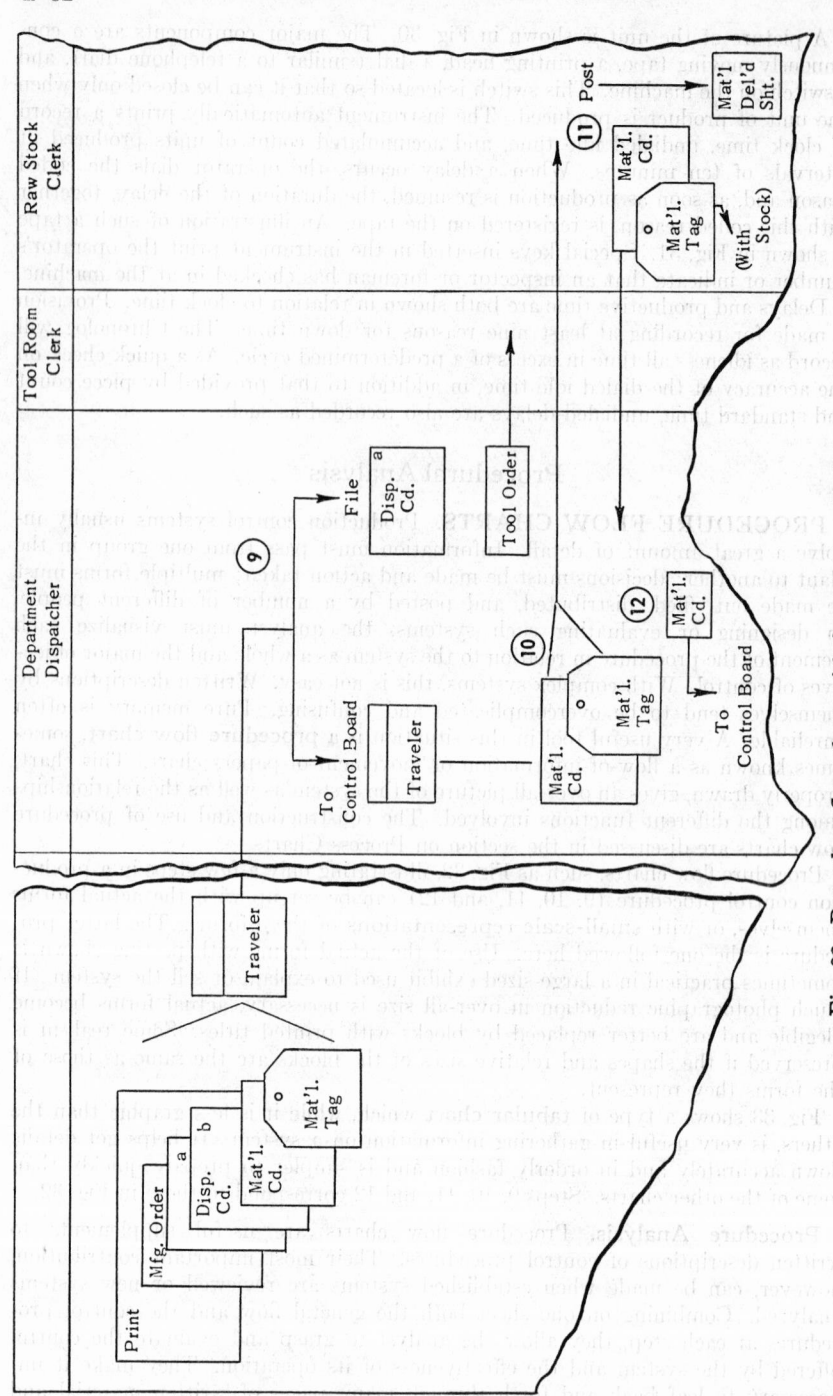

Fig. 32.   Procedure flow chart with form representations.

ANALYSIS OF PROCEDURE:									Page 2 of 2 Pages	

Production and Inventory
Control Procedures

o By or From x To Paper or Information	Inspection	Planner	File Clerk	Finished Parts Stock Clerk	Department Dispatcher	Tool Room Clerk	Raw Stock Clerk	Operator	Next Operating Department	
9. Traveler on control board					o					
9.1 File Disp. Cd. (a)					o					
10. Tool Order					o	x				
10.1 Mat'l. Cd. & Tag					o		x			
11. Post Mat'l Delivered Sheet							o			
11.1 Mat'l Tag on stock							o			
11.2 Mat'l. Cd.					x		o			
12. Mat'l. Cd. on control bd.					o					
13. Mfg. Order, etc.					o		x			
14. Mfg. Order, etc.					x		o			
15. Mfg. Order, etc.					o				x	
15.1 File Disp. Cd. (a)					o					
15.2 Disp. Cd. (b)		x			o					
16. Post Master Schedule Cd.		o								
17. Mfg. Order, etc.	o			x						
18. Mfg. Order, etc.			x	o						
19. Post Stock Cd.			o							

Fig. 33. Tabular presentation of control procedure.

they provide a graphic tool of analysis. The charts bring into sharp focus such points as:

1. The level in the organization at which important control decisions are made. One company found on analysis that decisions on the relative priority of orders were being made by a clerk in the control office. The clerk's position in the organization and the information available to her left too many important decisions in this area to chance.
2. The amount of information available at each step. Analysis of one system showed that an important scheduling step in the central office procedure had to be taken before adequate information was available from the shop.
3. The complexity of the system. In one case, further investigation of an apparently complicated routine in one phase of the system led to changes in control forms which simplified procedures considerably.
4. The presence of excess paper work. Tracing the course and use of multiple copy forms, the analyst frequently finds some which no longer fill any control needs.
5. The build-up of dead files. Study of the chart leads to questions about the final disposition of documents which have apparently served their purpose and yet appear to be held indefinitely in temporary files.
6. The opportunity for further decentralization of control. Analysis of one chart showed many minor decisions being made, with considerable effort, in the central office, which could be made easily and more effectively in the shop.

While this list is far from exhaustive, it shows the kind of questions which studies of this type of chart may suggest. Moreover, the mere act of collecting data and drawing the chart is often beneficial in focusing attention on the system, clearing up misunderstandings, and indicating minor gaps existing in control procedures.

STANDARD PRACTICE INSTRUCTIONS. These charts, and the written outlines keyed to them, can form the basis for standard practice instructions on the operation and procedures of the production control system. The use of such written standards has spread in recent years. Where they were once largely confined to big companies and complex systems, one now finds them employed in many progressive smaller companies. (See section on Motion and Methods Study.)

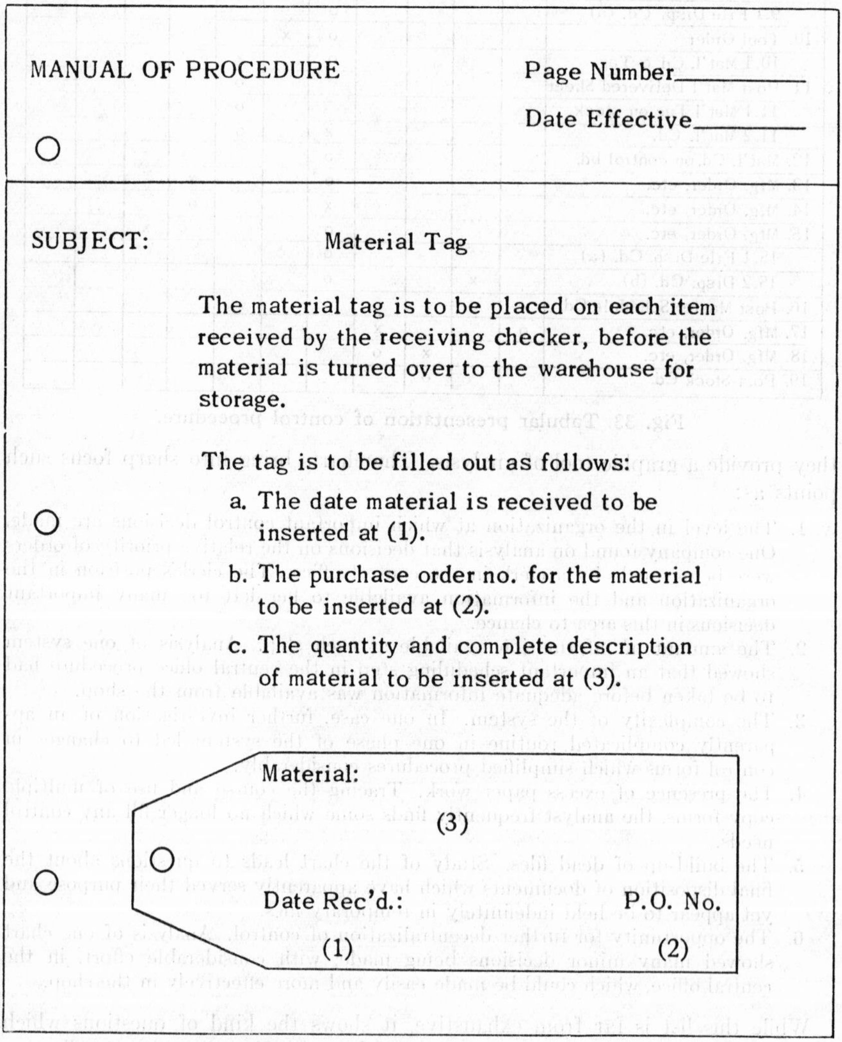

MANUAL OF PROCEDURE   Page Number_____

                                       Date Effective_____

○

SUBJECT: Material Tag

The material tag is to be placed on each item received by the receiving checker, before the material is turned over to the warehouse for storage.

The tag is to be filled out as follows:

○   a. The date material is received to be inserted at (1).

b. The purchase order no. for the material to be inserted at (2).

c. The quantity and complete description of material to be inserted at (3).

○   Material:

                          (3)

○   Date Rec'd.:   P.O. No.

              (1)   (2)

Fig. 34. Sample page of standard practice instructions manual.

Complete and well-written standard practice instructions can repay their preparation costs many times over by:

1. Benefits gained through the organized analysis of the system which is required to prepare or revise them.
2. The tremendous assistance they can give as training aids.
3. Their use as references by more experienced personnel, and the view which they give each person concerned with the system of other jobs which depend on, or support, his own.

Standard practice instructions will contain more detailed information on the posting of the various forms than is usually necessary in the write-up accompanying a flow chart used for system analysis. Fig. 34 shows a sample page from a set of these instructions and the form to which this part of the procedure applies.

It is best to print instructions on loose-leaf paper so that the manuals in which they are bound can be revised partially as necessary. Each page should carry a heading which shows the procedure to which it applies and the date of the latest revision of this page. A central file should show the distribution of every copy of the manual. This file is checked each time a revision is made to make sure that all old copies are called in and changed.

Measuring Effectiveness of Production Control

CRITERIA FOR EFFECTIVENESS. Since a production planning department does not contribute directly to the value of the product, it is advantageous to measure the **effectiveness** of the department. The two obvious measures are:

1. A periodic comparison of dollar volume produced.
2. A periodic comparison between planned production (scheduling) and actual production.

FORMULAS INDICATING EFFECTIVENESS. However, MacNiece (Production Forecasting, Planning, and Control) suggests empirical formulas for **planning effectiveness.** For stock production his formula is:

$$\text{Planning Effectiveness (percent)} = \frac{[(\text{Number of items on back order}) + (\text{Number of items over stock maximum})]100}{\text{Number of items planned}}$$

For job-order production he suggests this formula:

$$\text{Planning Effectiveness (percent)} = \left(\frac{\text{Number of deliveries on time}}{\text{Total deliveries}}\right) 100$$

Another measure of effectiveness is the inventory turnover ratio. The formula is:

$$\text{Inventory Turnover} = \frac{\text{Cost of annual sales}}{\text{Average annual inventory}}$$

This measure evaluates the efficient use of inventory investment, on which the planning and control department exerts the greatest influence.

Another measure, which may indicate inefficient planning, is the machine utilization ratio. It is computed as follows:

$$\text{Machine Utilization Ratio} = \frac{\text{Total idle machine time}}{\text{Available machine operating time}}$$

Obviously this index is not always reliable because there are other factors which can influence machine operating time.

PRODUCTION CONTROL SYSTEMS AND PROCEDURES

CONTENTS

PAGE

Functions and Systems

Production planning and control 1
Routing 1
  Preparation of route sheets 2
  Spoilage and stock allowances 3
  Use of route sheets 3
    Route sheet for a plant order (f. 1) 4
    Combination route sheet and progress
    record (f. 2) 5
Loading and scheduling 4
  Loading and scheduling procedures 6
  Procedures for intermittent manufacture .. 6
  Production for stock 6
    Machine loading and scheduling control
    forms (f. 3) 8–9
  Procedures for continuous manufacture .. 7
    Departmental operating conditions report
    (f. 4) 10–11
    Weekly schedule for parts production
    (f. 5) 11
    Control board for parts fabrication (f. 6) 11
Dispatching 12
  Methods of filing working papers 12
    Order-of-work form controlling produc-
    tion sequence (f. 7) 13
  Assignment to machines 14
  Materials 14
  Tools 15
    Tool order form (f. 8) 15
Systems for production control 15

Control Charts

Varieties 16
Graphs 16
  Scheduled vs. actual progress 16
    Scheduled vs. actual progress on ship
    construction (f. 9) 17
  Component schedules 17
    Scheduled production of tractors (f. 10) 18
    Monthly component schedules and pro-
    duction (f. 11) 18
Assembly charts 19
  Assembly chart: tractor production (f.
  12) 19
Gantt charts 20
  Machine load 20
    Central planning and shop control of
    operations (f. 13) 21
  Control of manufacture of parts on order 20
    Gantt progress chart for a fuse (f. 14) .. 22

Summary progress chart 23
Control of manufacture of parts for stock 23
Mechanized Gantt charts 23
Modified Gantt charts 24
  Control of development operations 24
    Target and commitment schedule (f. 15) 24

Control Boards

Types of boards 25
Pocket racks; hook boards 26
    Typical hook-type dispatch rack (f. 16) 26
    Operation control board (f. 17) 27
  Planning 26
    Planning department copy of manufac-
    turing order (face) (f. 18a) 28
    Reverse side of Fig. 18a (f. 18b) 29
    Diagram illustrating use of control board
    in Fig. 17 (f. 19) 29
  Control 29
    Time card used with production control
    system (f. 20) 30
  Results secured 30
Pocket or grooved-strip boards 31
  Operation record system 31
    Machine loader cards used with flexible
    machine loading chart (f. 21a) 32
    Flexible machine loading chart (f. 21b) 33
  Continuous operation control 34
    Control of a continuous process (f. 22)..36–37
  Order control system 35
Spring-clip panel boards 36
    Typical manufacturing order (spring-clip
    panels) (f. 23) 38
    Schedule ticket for board (f. 24) 38
  Production order control board 37
    Production order control board (spring-
    clip type) (f. 25) 39
    Time tickets and work orders posted on
    board (f. 26) 41
  Machine load scheduling and dispatching
  control 40
Tape or peg boards 42
    Order schedule control board (f. 27) 43
Index-Visible boards 45
    Index-Visible production control board
    with removable cards (f. 28) 44
Pictorial boards 45

Card Files

Varieties of systems 45

CONTENTS (*Continued*)

PAGE

Vertical card files 46
  Load summary and order list (*f. 29*) ... 46
Visible index files, vertical overlapping 47
  Applications of visible index 47
  Form for controllng and recording the
    progress of complete order (*f. 30*).....48–49
  Card for recording the manufacture of
    parts for order shown in Fig. 30
    (*f. 31*) 50–51
  Record to control progress on an order
    (*f. 32*) 52
Visible index files, horizontal overlapping... 53
  Card with visible triple margins (*f. 33*) . 53
Rotary or wheel-type files 55
  Desk-model rotary file (*f. 34*) 54
  Revolving desk files (*f. 35*).............. 55

Electromechanical Punched-Card Systems

Elements of the system 55
Application to assembly operations 56
  Application of punched-card system to
    production and inventory control (*f. 36*) 56
  Planning plant output 57
  Material and inventory planning 57
  Stock status summary report (*f. 37*) 57
  Inventory and authorization ledger re-
    port (*f. 38*) 58
  Facility and manpower planning 59
  A manufacturing order (*f. 39*) 59
  A material requisition card (*f. 40*) 60
  A machine tool load summary (*f. 41*) ... 61
  Relation to other records 59
Application to custom molding 61
  Application of punched-card system to
    custom molding production control
    (*f. 42*) 62
  Master specification file 64
  Material master and material issue card
    (*f. 43*) 63
  Scheduling card (*f. 44*) 65
  Loading and scheduling 64
  Scheduling report (*f. 45*) 66
  Material requirements 64
  Detail press load report (*f. 46*) 67
  Factory order 70
  Piecework ticket (*f. 47*) 68
  Report of parts pressed (*f. 48*) 69

Automatic Data Processing

Electronic computers 70
  Sales estimates 70
  Operation models 70
  Loading and scheduling 71

PAGE

  Flow chart of computer loading and
    scheduling process (*f. 49*) 71

Marginally Punched Card Systems

Keysort system 72
  Work-in-process control 75
  Load card (*f. 50*) 73
  Work load summary chart (*f. 51*) 74

Duplication and Communication Systems

Duplication of information 75
Continuous forms 75
  Procedure flow chart (*f. 52*) 76–77
  Line setting ticket (*f. 53*) 78
Ditto masters 78
  Parts order system 78
  Production order master form (*f. 54*) .. 79
  Unit cards reproduced in sets for each
    operation (*f. 55*) 79
  Group bonus record form (*f. 56*) 80
  Assembly and subassembly order system.. 83
  Assembly order master form (*f. 57*) 80
  Production office and scheduling depart-
    ment copies (*f. 58*) 81
  Unit requisitions (*f. 59*) 82
Addressograph duplicating plates 83
  Bills of material and parts lists 83
  Bill of material and parts list (*f. 60*)....84–85
  Production control for manufacturing parts
    to stock 83
  Production order duplicating master with
    overlay (*f. 61*) 86
  Reverse side of cost copy (*f. 62*) 88
  Reverse side of control point or traveler
    copy (*f. 63*) 89
Communication systems 89
  Teletype 89
  TelAutograph telescriber 90
  Temporator 90
  Pneumatic-tube systems 91
  Closed-circuit television 91
  Two-way radio communication 92
Integrated data processing 92
  Common-language media 92
  Tape storage 93
  Integrated data-processing systems........ 93
  Flow chart of integrated order-invoice
    processing system (*f. 64*) 94
  Plant invoice form (*f. 65*) 95
Forms design 93
Functional coding 96
Error control 96
System design and installation 97

PRODUCTION CONTROL SYSTEMS AND PROCEDURES

Functions and Systems

PRODUCTION PLANNING AND CONTROL. There are certain basic elements or functions in any system of production planning and control. These functions may be listed and defined as follows:

1. **Production planning** coordinates the production department with other departments of the business. Considering future sales requirements, it determines what the production department must produce, the quantities involved, when the products must be available, and the time and quantity requirements for materials, parts, labor, and facilities. It presents these data to inventory control, purchasing, personnel, engineering, and administrative groups in the manner which most effectively synchronizes their contribution to production activities.

2. **Production control** promotes effective shop operation through its control of activities within the production department itself. This control may involve routing, the decision on facilities and sequence for each operation; loading and scheduling, the relationship between available capacity and current and future orders; dispatching, the final placement of the order at a work station with all the materials, tools, and instructions necessary to perform required operations; and follow-up, the comparison of progress with plans to discover incipient delays and to promote action which prevents or minimizes them.

The importance of the **control functions**, routing, loading and scheduling, and dispatching, and the procedures through which they are effected, will vary from plant to plant. This variation stems from differences in:

1. The degree of control required.
2. The control organization form.
3. The size of the company.
4. The market served.
5. The manufacturing process.
6. The product complexity.

Once the general form of production control requirements has been outlined, it is necessary to develop the detailed procedures through which control can be achieved. These procedures will involve both operating routines and forms, and supporting mechanisms—files, control boards, etc.

ROUTING. There are many factors that may be involved in routing:

1. A study of the product to determine the possible methods of processing and to select the best method.
2. A study of methods to determine what, if any, special equipment is necessary to carry them out.
3. An analysis of the capacity of the machines and equipment available for the process.
4. The establishment of the sequence of operations.
5. A decision as to speeds at which operations shall be performed.

3·1

6. The determination of time required for each operation. The factors covered include machine setup time, machine operating time, allowances for process operations (heat treating, metal finishing, etc.), bench work time, inspection time and handling time of work in process.

7. The preparation of route sheets listing the sequence of operations. It is often desirable to incorporate on such route sheets detailed information regarding some of the decisions arrived at under factors (1) to (5).

8. The grouping of route sheets into subassemblies and major assemblies to insure that the components will be started in process at such times as will insure their being completed simultaneously.

9. The preparation of work orders for the purpose of carrying into effect the details of routing.

10. The adapting of procedures to the dispatching systems in use—centralized or decentralized.

Because of the overlap of the first six functions with process engineering, the last four will be considered as distinctly the responsibility of the production control department. From the viewpoint of production control mechanics, **routing decisions** must be made on:

1. The form of the route sheet.
2. The need for duplicating methods.
3. The choice of a filing system.
4. The possibility of applying mechanical sorting and tabulating methods.

Preparation of Route Sheets. Route sheets deal with specific manufacturing orders (actual or virtual). One sheet is required for each part or component of the order. On such a sheet are assembled working data for controlling the passage of the piece through the shop. In large plants, route sheets are sometimes departmental; operations in each department are listed separately. The **data usually included on a route sheet** are as follows:

1. Number and other identification of order.
2. Symbol and other identification of part.
3. Number of pieces to be made.
4. If put through in lots, the number in each lot.
5. Operation data including:
   a. List of operations on the part.
   b. Departments in which the work is to be done.
   c. Machine to be used for each operation.
   d. Fixed sequence in any of the operations.
6. Rate at which the job (or first lot) must be completed. The data for this entry will be obtained from the standard time per piece or lot as noted on the operation sheet.

Routing really begins at the determination of the **sequence of operations.** Methods of work and machine analysis are preliminary to it. Routing can be performed properly only by some person who is thoroughly familiar with the character of the work to be done and with the processes available for doing it. The sequence of operations adopted for any class of work may have a noticeable effect on the time and cost of production. Changing the position of a single operation in the sequence often facilitates the performance of all other operations on the part. Thus, for a certain piece, a number of surfaces may be located at different distances from the center of a drilled hole. It is important to determine whether the hole should be drilled first and surfaces finished in relation to it or whether the surfaces should be finished and the hole located with reference to them. In the first method a plug might be dropped into the hole and the surfaces located from it by means of gages or distance pieces; in the second method, if the surfaces are first machined, the piece may be put into a drilling jig which will locate the hole. If the piece is to be made in quantities sufficient to warrant the expense of the jig, the second method will probably prove more accurate and cheaper.

When the sequence of operations has been determined, this sequence is listed on the route sheet, or operation sheet. The route sheet shows every operation that is to be performed. If a special adjustment of the machine is required for an operation, or if special tools or fixtures must be placed on a machine, each of these factors should be listed. The time required is shown opposite each operation together with the machine or workplace at which the operations are to be performed. Time should be stated in hours or minutes for a single piece or a standard lot. Time for setups or adjustments should be given separately as the total time for each job or lot. Multiplying time per piece by number of pieces in the lot and adding setup time or adjustment time give the **time required per lot** for each operation. This procedure furnishes a basis for ascertaining when production should start. To the time required for each operation is added **time necessary for movement of material** between operations. Usually, where the work is not conveyorized, it is advisable to allow one day between successive operations for the handling of the material, especially when the work passes from one department to another. Where materials handling is scheduled, the time can be accurately assigned.

In certain classes of manufacturing, particularly those involving subassemblies and major assemblies, it is common practice to deliver the various parts to a storeroom, worked material stores, or finished parts stores. It is advisable to indicate, for each operation on the route sheets, when the work should be started, i.e., the number of working days before the time when the parts are due in worked material stores.

Spoilage and Stock Allowances. A spoilage allowance is always required. A waste allowance is needed if the part is to be made from raw materials. In many cases the opportunity is taken to make extra pieces for stock or for sale as spares or replacements. In repetitive work the two allowances may be combined into a single percentage. **Stock allowances** should be reviewed at intervals and revised up or down to reflect current capabilities of the process.

Stores-issue orders, time cards, and other working papers may also be prepared at this time, but often are written in a separate section of the production control department.

Use of Route Sheets. Route sheets serve as histories of the progress of a part through a cycle of operations. They are also used (1) to check on subsequent steps of control and shop procedure, and (2) to register progress of the part from stock to completion and delivery to stores or assembly. In filling out a route sheet, the time allowances for each operation cannot be entered until operation sheets are available. Similarly, due dates for beginning and completing each operation cannot be inserted until such dates have been determined by scheduling.

Fig. 1 illustrates a route sheet used for repair orders. In this case the route covers several departments. The sheet is attached to the **identification tag** of the lot and accompanies it from one department to the next. Ritchie (Production and Inventory Control) shows a routing card which details operations throughout the plant and also serves as a progress record (Fig. 2).

ROUTE SHEET	Name				Price Number				
	14" H.S. Apron				25–A–224				
	Date Started	Material	No. of Sheets	No. of Pcs.		Lot No.			
Order No. 6192			Sheet No.						
Op. No.	Operation	Dept.	Mach.	Tool List	S.U.T.	S.T.	INSPECTOR'S REPORT			
							O.K.	Spoil	Date	Sign
1	Rgh. & Fin. Plane	24								
2	Rgh. & Fin. Mill Pads & Bosses	22								
3	Rgh. & Fin. Mill for Rack Pinion Gear	22								
4	Scrape Apron Seat to Plate	78								
5	Drill & Tap for Carriage	26								
6	Drill & Tap for Pinion, Handwheel & Clutch	26								
7	File Burrs & Round Corners	88								
8	File, Rub & Shellac	14								
	Move to Stock #85									

Fig. 1. Route sheet for a plant order.

The same objective will be found in all these sheets, however different the rulings or methods of use. Identification of different operations on a single component, with some provision for checking off each as completed, is the minimum requirement. In a fully developed sheet, such as Fig. 2, **times** and **quantities** are included and such sheets form an important element of the control system.

LOADING AND SCHEDULING. Loading and scheduling are concerned with the flow of work to the shop and the relationship between the time required by production orders and available shop capacity. The loading and scheduling functions may be set up to give any desired degree of control over plant operations. However, it is impossible to establish a realistic schedule without some knowledge of the **shop load.** It is in this area of loading and scheduling procedures that the widest variety of mechanical aids and control forms exists. In line with the type and amount of control desired, **loading decisions** must be reached on:

1. The units and required accuracy of loading data.
2. The use of graphic controls—charts or boards—and the form they should take.
3. The design of control records.
4. Duplicating requirements.
5. Possible applications of mechanical or electronic sorting and tabulating methods.
6. Filing procedures.
7. The manner in which shop-office communication should be handled.

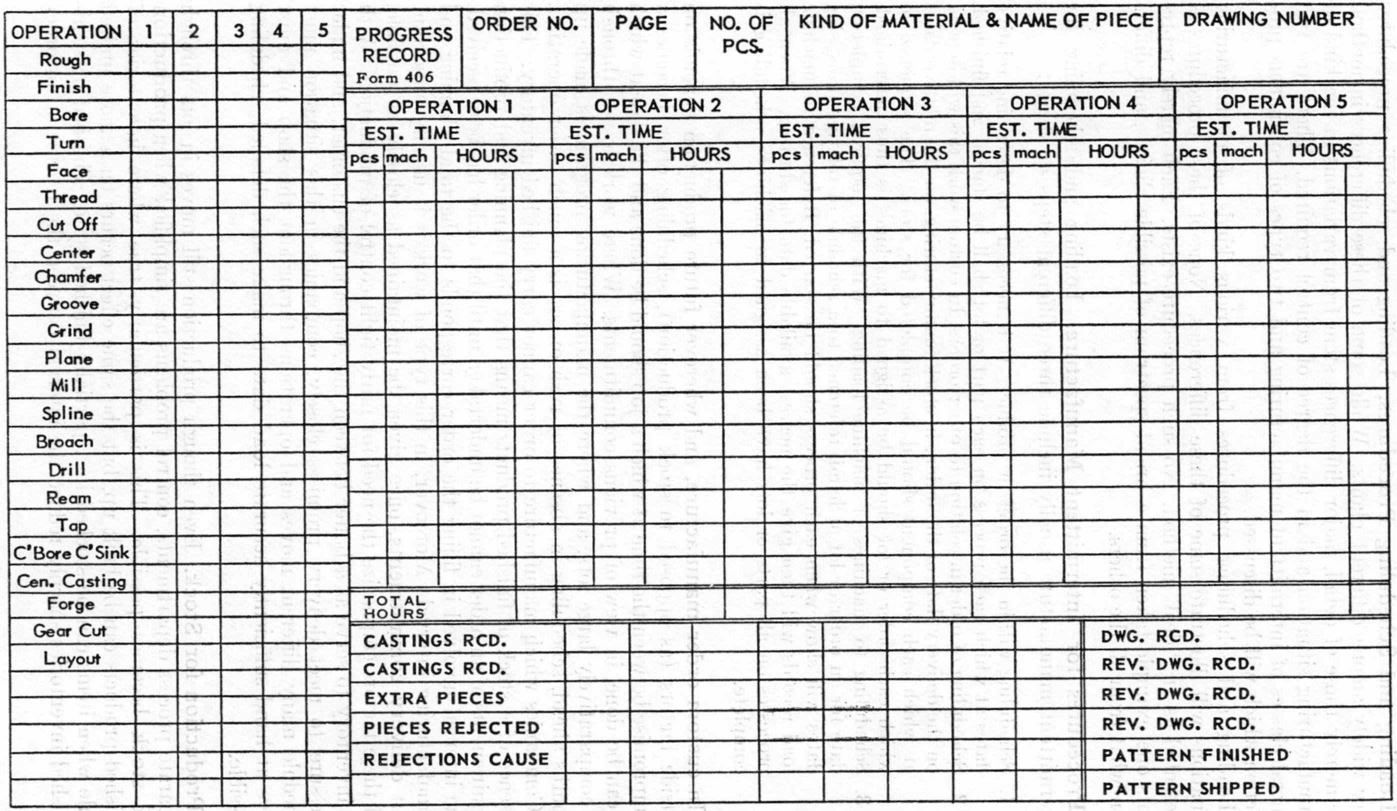

PROGRESS RECORD
Form 406

	ORDER NO.	PAGE	NO. OF PCS.	KIND OF MATERIAL & NAME OF PIECE	DRAWING NUMBER

OPERATION	1	2	3	4	5	OPERATION 1 EST. TIME (pcs / mach)	HOURS	OPERATION 2 EST. TIME (pcs / mach)	HOURS	OPERATION 3 EST. TIME (pcs / mach)	HOURS	OPERATION 4 EST. TIME (pcs / mach)	HOURS	OPERATION 5 EST. TIME (pcs / mach)	HOURS
Rough															
Finish															
Bore															
Turn															
Face															
Thread															
Cut Off															
Center															
Chamfer															
Groove															
Grind															
Plane															
Mill															
Spline															
Broach															
Drill															
Ream															
Tap															
C'Bore C'Sink															
Cen. Casting															
Forge															
Gear Cut															
Layout															
TOTAL HOURS															

CASTINGS RCD.	DWG. RCD.
CASTINGS RCD.	REV. DWG. RCD.
EXTRA PIECES	REV. DWG. RCD.
PIECES REJECTED	REV. DWG. RCD.
REJECTIONS CAUSE	PATTERN FINISHED
	PATTERN SHIPPED

Fig. 2. Combination route sheet and progress record.

Loading and Scheduling Procedures. Loading and scheduding procedures vary widely among different plants. While some of these differences in method are merely those of detail, major differences stem from variations in the kind of manufacturing situation and in the degree of control required. There are two general classes of intermittent manufacturing and two types of continuous production which will be discussed.

Loading and scheduling procedures from various kinds of manufacturing situations will illustrate some of these differences. None of these procedures is presented as an "ideal" method. No such procedure exists. Each merely represents one example taken from a broad spectrum of possible choices, and differs somewhat from all the others.

Procedures for Intermittent Manufacture. Loading and scheduling for intermittent manufacture usually include three different steps or stages:

1. Scheduling within the order or product. It is necessary to determine relative dates at which each process on each part or lot shall be started and finished.
2. Scheduling of order in relation to other orders. In custom work this will depend on the delivery date of the order; in stock manufacturing, on the relative dates at which each component should be completed for stock. The sequence in which each order or lot should be assigned to machines is thus determined.
3. Scheduling to machines or machine loading. With the required completion date for an order or lot at hand, reference to a schedule of relative processing dates will show when each process should be started. Reference to machine load records will then give the nearest available date for starting. When all processes on all parts or lots have been assigned to machines, scheduling is complete.

In **custom order manufacture,** and wherever future production depends on outside factors (as opposed to stock production), scheduling often becomes a compromise between the time at which a job should be done and the day at which it can be done, in view of previous commitments. Where work is put through in comparatively large lots, and where the manufacturing program is made up months ahead, scheduling in absence of rush orders is a much easier operation.

Companies which manufacture to order cannot carry finished inventory. This absence of a stock of finished products means that the planning and production requirements of an order cannot be undertaken until that order has been received. The interval involved in filling the order corresponds to the total planning and manufacturing interval. Moreover, in this type of work it is usually important that **delivery commitments,** once given, be maintained as closely as possible. All these factors emphasize the need for fairly tight control of production. With no inventory to serve as a buffer between the shop and the customer, and under pressure to meet delivery promises closely, companies in this situation must schedule many different moves and operations throughout the shop and must have at hand sufficiently accurate **load data** to make such detailed scheduling possible.

Production for Stock. Even though production still moves in lots through separate process departments, control problems are simplified when **production for stock** becomes possible. This is particularly true where inventories of finished products can be built up, but the same effect occurs on a more limited scale when items can be stocked in a partially finished state. Finished or semi-finished inventories sharply reduce the interval between the receipt of an order and its delivery to the customer. When the production departments operate to replenish inventories, some of the pressure on them is eased. Although schedules must still be maintained to avoid shortages and unbalanced stocks, short delays are not likely to be as serious as they are when they hold up final delivery dates. For these reasons, somewhat looser control may be perfectly adequate when production for stock is possible.

Machine loading and scheduling are controlled at the Eaton Manufacturing Co. by a system combining an **equipment record card** in the top holder in each pocket of a visible record system and a **machine load record** in the lower holder (Fig. 3). Cards for machines of a similar kind are grouped together. As each job is scheduled to a machine, the data are entered on the card. An orange Graph-A-Matic movable signal (shaded in Fig. 3) is set on the visible margin at the right over a scale of the 24-hr. day to show the estimated hours per day the machine will be run. When time studies are completed, the green Graph-A-Matic signal (dark pointer in Fig. 3) is moved to show the number of machine-hours required to produce the total quantity of pieces scheduled for the day. From this record the machines available for additional work can be picked as new jobs are scheduled.

Under this system, since cards for similar machines are grouped, salmon-colored **machine load summary cards** are used to separate the groups, and on these cards in each case the total load-hours per day, both estimated and actual for the group, are accumulated. A green signal at the right of each summary card shows the percentage of capacity which is in production for that class of machine.

Gantt charts are often used to give the detailed picture of the load and schedule of plants or departments. See the discussion of Gantt charts below.

Procedures for Continuous Manufacture. Loading and scheduling procedures for continuous manufacture are simpler than those required for intermittent manufacture. On the other hand, the careful planning required to coordinate production with sales, inventory levels, purchasing, engineering, and financing operations becomes extremely important because of the high and continuous rate of production.

The simplest case is that of **continuous manufacture of a single product,** which involves no assembly. One company manufacturing sulfuric acid establishes a quarterly production rate based on sales forecasts for that period. This rate remains unchanged unless market conditions change unexpectedly. Variations in the rate of production are accomplished by activating or shutting down separate units. Control is in the hands of the superintendent, who daily passes information along to sales, purchasing, and top management. These production reports show the amount and concentration of acid produced, stored, and shipped, sulfur used and on hand, and estimated sulfur requirements.

With **more complicated product lines** the detail involved in loading and scheduling procedures increases. A tabular form of the type shown in Fig. 4 is frequently used in repetitive work. Total operating capacity for the period appears above the name and number of each machine. Each horizontal line takes care of one lot. The quantity of each part to be manufactured in the period is converted into machine-hours from recorded data. The resulting figure is entered under the proper type of equipment. The upper figure represents hours on the job, the lower figure the cumulative loading for the period as far as posting has gone. The cumulative total in any column when balanced against the total capacity shown at the top of the column reflects any over- or underload.

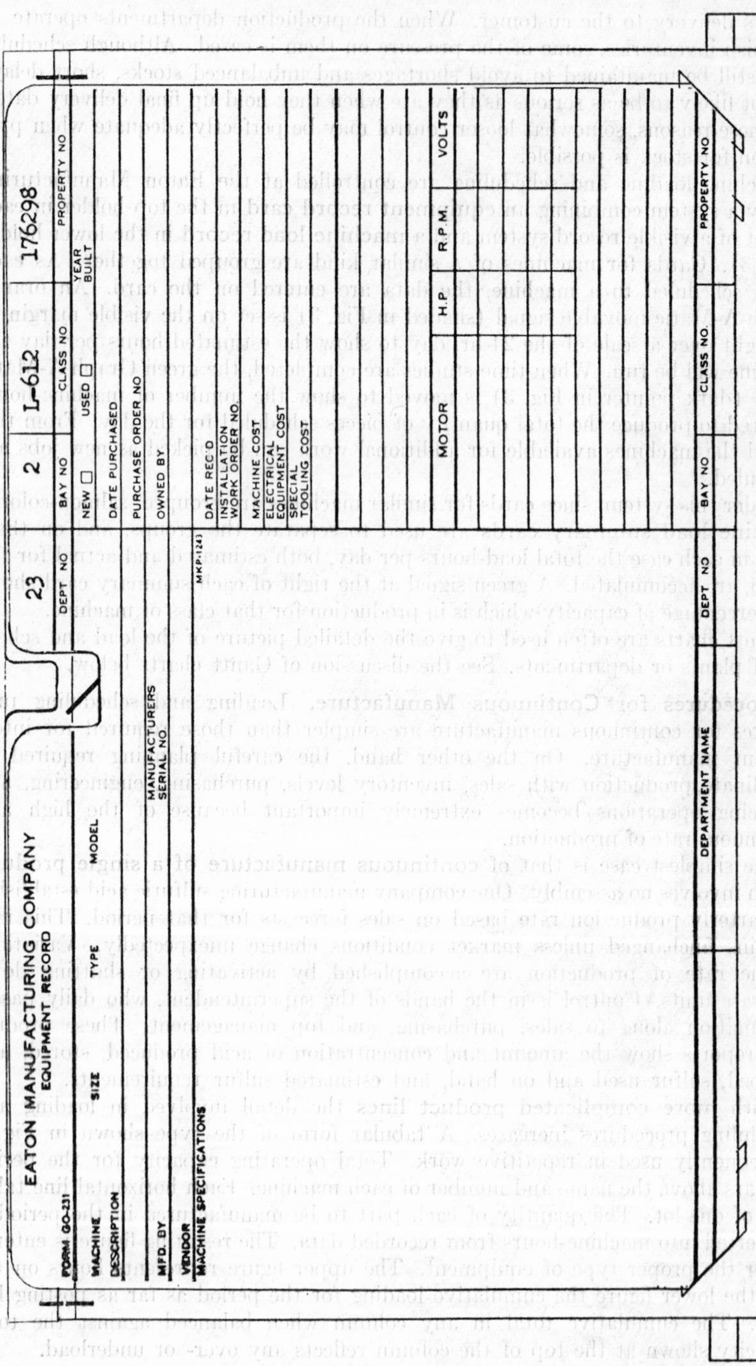

FORM GO-231

EATON MANUFACTURING COMPANY
EQUIPMENT RECORD

DEPT NO	BAY NO	CLASS NO	PROPERTY NO
23	2	L-612	176298

MACHINE
SIZE
TYPE
MODEL
DESCRIPTION
MFD. BY
MANUFACTURERS SERIAL NO
VENDOR
MACHINE SPECIFICATIONS

NEW ☐   USED ☐   YEAR BUILT
DATE PURCHASED
PURCHASE ORDER NO
OWNED BY

DATE REC'D
INSTALLATION WORK ORDER NO.
MACHINE COST
ELECTRICAL EQUIPMENT COST
SPECIAL EQUIPMENT COST
TOOLING COST

MOTOR   H.P   R.P.M.   VOLTS

DEPARTMENT NAME

DEPT NO	BAY NO	CLASS NO	PROPERTY NO

MKP-1243

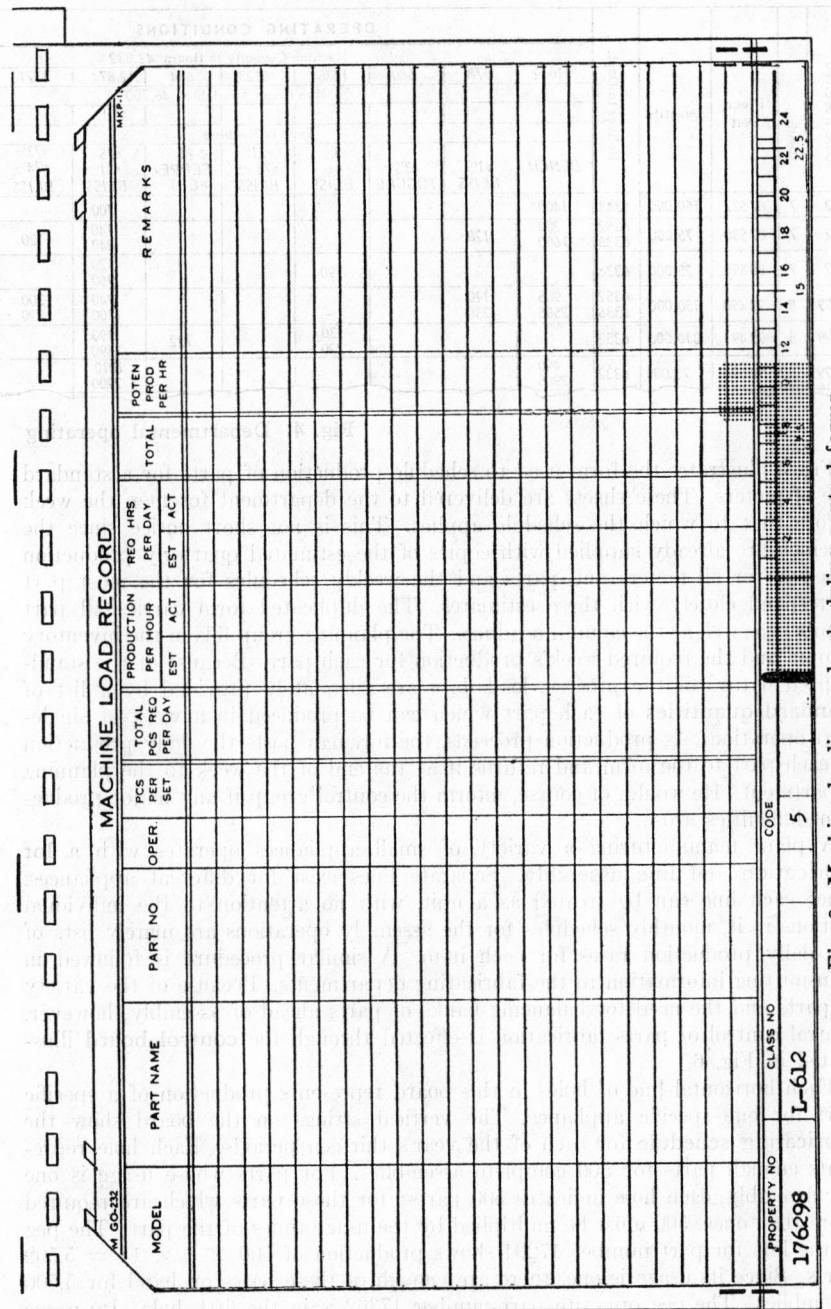

Fig. 3. Machine loading and scheduling control forms.

Date Received	Month	Piece Part	Quantity	Deliver to Dept.	OPERATING CONDITIONS								
					Machine Capacity in Hours 42,832								
					11032	978	580	1296	6123	604	12,874	3171	190
					Man Hours Available 46,700								
					Type of Machine								
					BENCH	#1½ BLISS	#3½ TOGGLE	#3½ #4 BLISS	#21½ #76 #5 BLISS	#6 FERRE-CUT	#75 #21 BLISS	#73½ #74½ BLISS	FOO PRE
7-2	7	87 527	150,000	6343	1400						700		
7-2	7	87 530	75,000	6352 6336	200 1600	120					140 840	120	
7-2	7	88 598	25,000	6338				90			120 960		
7-29	8	93 490	150,000	6352 6336	905 2505	110 230					740 1700	300 420	116
7-29	8	93 491	310,000	6352				130 220		122	190 1890		
7-29	8	94 594	75,000	6332	400 2905						1010 2900		

Fig. 4. Departmental operating

Fig. 5 illustrates the form used to schedule production of parts for a standard line of meters. These sheets are delivered to the department foremen the week before that to which the schedule applies. This is not short notice since the foremen are already supplied with copies of the estimated quarterly production schedule for all meters and parts and the weekly schedules for the most part correspond closely with these estimates. The duplicated form carries all part numbers as well as the column headings. The planning group fills in the inventory column and the required week's production for each part. Because of the standardized nature of the process, load data are adequately provided by a list of **standard quantities** of each part which can be produced in a week of single-shift operation. As production proceeds, the foreman posts the daily production of each part to the form and returns it at the end of the week to the planning department. He would, of course, inform the control group if any major production difficulties arose.

A plant manufacturing a variety of small appliances operates with a **lot fabrication** and **line assembly**. Separate lines exist for different appliances. Since each line can be treated as a unit, with no attention to the individual stations in it, monthly schedules for the assembly operations are merely lists of the daily production rates for each item. A similar procedure is followed in transmitting information to the fabricating departments. Because of the variety of parts and the need for balancing banks of parts ahead of assembly, however, central control of parts fabrication is effected through the **control board** illustrated in Fig. 6.

Each horizontal line of holes in this board represents production of a specific part for one specific appliance. The vertical strings on the board show the **fabricating schedule** for each of the year's thirteen periods. Each hole represents enough parts for 500 complete assemblies. For parts whose usage is one per assembly, each hole indicates 500 parts; for those parts which are required more than once, 500 must be multiplied by the usage times of the part. The peg in the line for part number 17204 shows production of $500 \times 1 \times 11 = 5,500$ parts. Since its usage is one, there are enough of these bases on hand for 5,500 assemblies. The peg opposite part number 17362 is in the fifth hole. Its usage is 4. Ten thousand ($500 \times 4 \times 5 = 10,000$) of these brackets, or enough for 2,500 assemblies, have been produced. The board is kept up to date by reports from the

Tools	R. M.	From Dept.	Mach. Repair	M. F. Parts	Help	Complaint	Date Promised	Date Completed	REMARKS
			HELD FOR						Dept._____ Month_____
5473									Held for tool on Change Order W-745364
							9–20		Daily 4000
							9–22	9–21	Completed
							9–22		Daily 5000
							10–2		
							9–21		Daily 5000

conditions report.

shop. A glance at it at any time will show how closely production is following the schedule, whether or not there are sufficient banks of parts available to support assembly schedules, and whether inventories of these parts are in balance.

Part No.	Inventory		Scheduled Prod.	Daily Production						Total Prod.	Remarks
	Qty.	Wks.		1	2	3	4	5	6		

Department Number_____   Week of _____

Fig. 5. Weekly schedule for parts production.

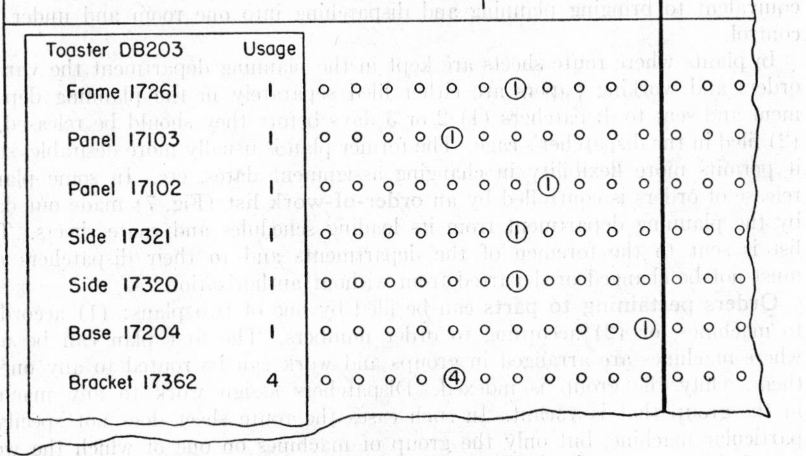

Fig. 6. Control board for parts fabrication.

DISPATCHING. Dispatching is concerned with the smooth introduction of work to the shop and the collection of information on progress. It can vary from a very simple procedure to a highly organized and complex routine. Dispatching of an order implies that **prints and instructions** necessary for its performance are released. The dispatcher may be responsible for a final check on the **availability of materials, tools, gages,** etc., required for each job, and he may be the one who supervises their delivery to a work center when the product order is ready for processing. Since dispatching can involve considerable **direction and recording of departmental production,** many of the mechanisms and procedures connected with central scheduling will have a direct effect on the operation of the dispatching function. It will be necessary to determine:

1. Communication procedures.
2. Requirements for duplicating information.
3. Filing procedures.
4. Methods of record-keeping and follow-up.
5. Possible use and form of control boards or charts.

Methods of Filing Working Papers. An important problem in dispatching is the filing of working papers so that they may be found quickly, either for alteration in the program or for release to the shop. As every operation on every part demands several documents and an order may contain a considerable number of parts, a large accumulation of working papers results. At one time such papers were not made out until the time came to make use of them. This course involved hurry and confusion, probable delay, and certainly much greater risk of error than when, as in modern practice, they are made out in sets at leisure and under conditions where attention can be concentrated on the many details they contain. Two main methods are followed in filing working papers: (1) route sheets are kept in dispatch cages or offices, or (2) route sheets are kept in the central planning office.

Modern practice tends to confine **dispatching** to the actual handing out and recording of working papers, leaving the **control of progress on route sheets and control boards and schedules** to be done by the planning department. Pneumatic communication between the planning department and various dispatching stations is frequently used. For all practical purposes this method is equivalent to bringing planning and dispatching into one room and under one control.

In plants where route sheets are kept in the planning department the various orders and working papers are either filed separately in the planning department and sent to dispatchers (1) 2 or 3 days before they should be released, or (2) filed in the dispatcher's cage. The former plan is usually more desirable, since it permits more flexibility in changing assignment dates, etc. In some plants, release of orders is controlled by an **order-of-work list** (Fig. 7) made out daily by the planning department from its loading schedules and route sheets. This list is sent to the foremen of the departments and to their dispatchers and must not be changed or departed from without authorization.

Orders pertaining to parts can be filed by one of two plans: (1) according to machines, or (2) according to order numbers. The first plan can be used where machines are arranged in groups and work can be routed to any one of them. Only the group is indexed. Dispatchers assign work to any machine in the group that is vacant. In such cases the route sheet does not specify a particular machine, but only the group of machines on one of which the work is to be done.

THE IMPERIAL ELECTRIC CO.
PLANNING DEPARTMENT   Issued _____ 19____

Order of Work in Dept. No._____   LOT NO._____

FRAME SIZE_____

SEQUENCE_____

Mach. or Stat. No.	Route Tag No. Order No.	Name of Item	No. of Pc's	Pattern No. or Style	Drawing No.	Working Sequence	PERCENTAGE OF WORK DONE
							10 20 30 40 50 60 70 80 90 100

NOTE — Foreman must receive through his General Foreman specific authority from Planning Department before any deviation is made from the order of work laid down above.

NOTE — Make out this report in Triplicate for Department Foreman, General Foreman, File.

FOR USE IN PLANNING DEPT. ONLY

Fig. 7. Order-of-work form controlling production sequence.

The second plan, filing according to order numbers, subdivided into parts or lots, has the disadvantage that it is no guide to sequence unless manufacturing orders must be taken up in sequence of their numbers, which is rarely the case. On the other hand, where an order-of-work list is sent down by the planning department daily, filing by manufacturing order number is probably the safest and quickest method.

Another method **combines these two systems.** Orders are filed under manufacturing numbers, but, when advice is received from the stores department that material is ready in the shop, the corresponding operation papers are withdrawn and placed in a file classified by machine numbers. It may be said, in fact, that no uniformity in plan exists. The method adopted should permit the papers next in sequence to be found quickly.

Assignment to Machines. The central feature of many dispatch offices is the **dispatch board** or rack, which provides visual control. A certain space is allotted to each machine in a department. This space is usually subdivided into three compartments:

1. For job actually on machine. A duplicate of the job order actually being worked on occupies this space.
2. For next job in sequence. This space is occupied by a job order and its duplicate which will be transferred to space number 1 as soon as the current order is completed.
3. For several jobs ahead. Job orders are filed one behind another as far as possible in the order in which they will later be transferred first to (2) and then finally to (1).

A glance at the board shows: (1) whether all machines are actually engaged in jobs; (2) whether any machine lacks a next job; (3) whether each machine has a fair supply of work in reserve after the next job has been disposed of. Approaching shortage of work for any machine is reported to the planning department, where it is either confirmed or, if caused by an error, rectified. Opportunity may be taken to reroute jobs to idle machines and relieve pressure on other equipment.

Methods used to display job orders vary. Taylor used **double hooks,** order or operation slips being punched and hung on these hooks. Modern practice tends to use **pocket racks** similar to those used for time cards. Orders do not require punching and are more easily handled by this method. Display racks may be made of wood or metal, and the three subdivisions may be placed side by side or in front of one another in successively lower levels. The principal consideration is to preserve visibility so that a single glance can take in the whole series and detect any machine where shortage of work is threatening.

Materials. Two different methods of initiating the movement of materials are in use. In some plants the **stores-issue order,** made out at the same time as the corresponding route sheet and marked with the date at which it should be delivered to the shop, is filed with the storeskeeper in a tickler in the order of due date. When this date arrives, the material is sent to the shop and a duplicate of the issue order is forwarded to the planning department and thence to the dispatcher to signal arrival of material. Another method is to file a duplicate stores-issue order with the other working papers pertaining to the part and to hand it with these papers to the dispatcher for release at the appointed time, a day before the operation is due to start. The storeskeeper readies the material for issue but does not actually move it into the shop before getting authority to do so.

Of the two methods the latter is more flexible. It permits changes in the program up to the last minute. Should the operation be canceled or the routing changed, the alteration can be made on the stores-issue order, or the order may be held up without having to pick it out of the storeskeeper's file. The choice between these methods will depend on the nature of work. In stock production the former practice may serve, whereas in custom manufacturing, with its comparatively disturbed routine, the latter plan may be preferred. The essential point is to get the material where it is needed, neither too early nor too late for the operation. (See section on Storeskeeping.)

Tools. Where operations and tooling are not completely standardized, it is customary to **specify cutting tools** for the job as well as to list all jigs, fixtures, gages, etc., which will be required. These particulars are listed in a **tool order.** One possible form this information may take is shown in Fig. 8, as used in a

TOOL ORDER							
Date 3–3							
No. Req'd	Tools and Gages	Sect.	Bin	No. Req'd	Tools and Gages	Sect.	Bin
1	Set of 18-38 Vise Jaws	10	28	1	x-467	6A	28
	VF160			1	7/16" Plug Gage		
1	3" dia. x 7/16" face x 1"						
	hole Side Milling						
	Cutter						
1	#50 Vise	1E	54				
1	1" Dia. Arbor	Rack					
				1	Drwg. E-97		
Name				Oper.			
Rocker Arm for Operating Distributing Roll				Mill inner surface in vise jaws.			
Part No. 18-33	Oper. No. 6	Dept. 4		Mach Hand Miller.		Equip. No. 981	

Fig. 8. Tool order form.

plant making small machines. A tool order is prepared from the **operation study sheets** at the time of making up the route sheets and is filed with the other working papers until wanted. As soon as the material is in place, the tool order is released. The tool room collects the tools and holds them until asked for by the man on the operation specified. Authority is given by presentation of the job order or time ticket for the operation in question. (See section on Tools, Jigs, and Fixtures.)

SYSTEMS FOR PRODUCTION CONTROL. There are seven general classes of mechanisms which may be used for the purposes of production control.

The controls and records required for effective routing, loading and scheduling, and dispatching under a particular system are maintained by selecting and applying some of these mechanisms. The seven classes, each of which is discussed in detail below, are:

1. Control charts.
2. Control boards.
3. Card record systems.
4. Mechanical sorting and tabulating equipment.
5. Electronic data-processing equipment.
6. Duplicating mechanisms.
7. Communication systems.

Control Charts

VARIETIES. Control charts offer condensed and effective means of correlating control information. Charts commonly used in production control take many forms. The more important are:

1. Graphs.
2. Assembly charts.
3. Gantt charts.
4. Modified Gantt charts.

The idea behind the use of any of these forms is that relationships among several factors are most easily portrayed and understood through graphic presentation. Each type has its own particular application and certain advantages favoring its use.

GRAPHS. Simple graphs are often used to show the relationship between two or more factors and to record variations in this relationship. They are best used to present a **general picture** and are not well adapted for control of a host of details. For this reason they are most often used in connection with **planning activities** or as **over-all controls and reports.** Figs. 9, 10, and 11 illustrate some of the forms that these graphs may take.

Scheduled vs. Actual Progress. Fig. 9 illustrates a chart used by the manager of a shipyard to check progress on different contracts. The axes represent percent completion of work on the contract against the number of weeks before the scheduled delivery date. The solid line is set down at the time construction plans become definite and shows the planned rate of activity. The chart is kept up to date by the planning department through biweekly postings. These take the form of a dotted line as shown. The relation between the solid and dotted lines indicates whether progress is ahead of or behind schedule. The relative slope of the two lines shows whether or not the rate of progress is satisfactory. Although this chart does not show results in detail, it does convey a general picture of work in the yard. It is designed as a control report for the yard manager. He can quickly note, for any contract, discrepancies between progress and plan which appear to be serious. The planning department can then supply any desired data on the nature of the delays, the reasons for them, and any follow-up information.

While they would not be satisfactory as working schedules, these charts do serve adequately as **general controls.** One point in their construction is worth noting. The definitions of various **percentages of completion** must be established when the schedule line is drawn and then rigidly adhered to in the progress postings.

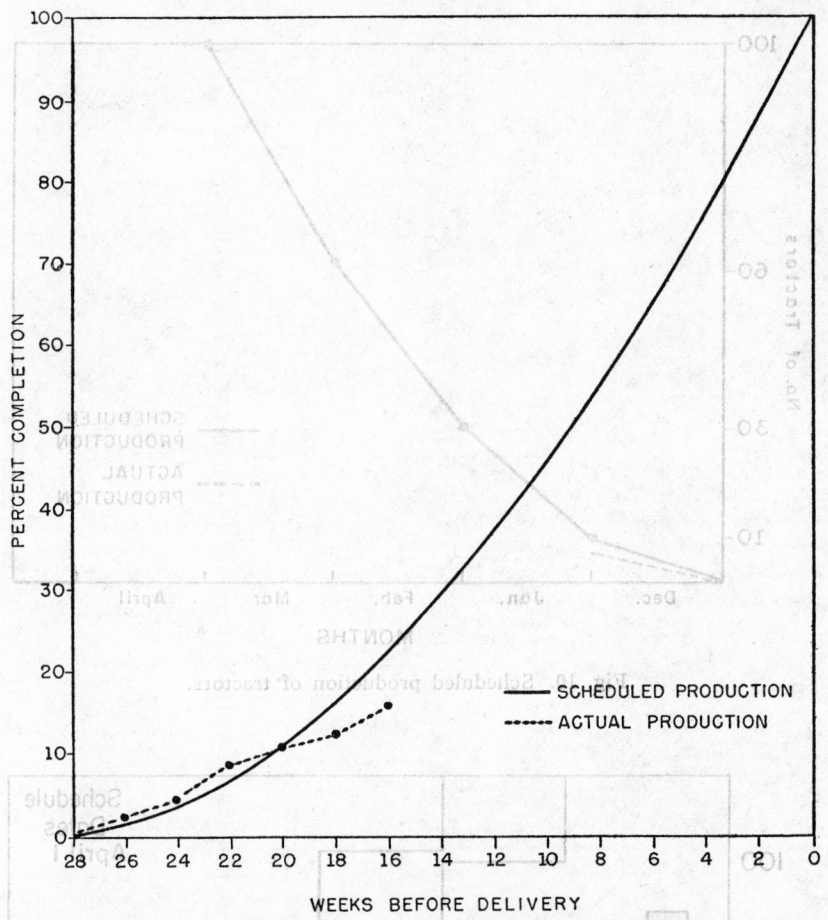

Fig. 9. Scheduled vs. actual progress on ship construction.

Component Schedules. In Fig. 10 the same type of graph is used to picture scheduled production of 100 tractors. The solid schedule line shows that cumulative deliveries of tractors should be 10 by January 1, 30 by February 1, 60 by March 1, and 100 by April 1. The slope of the solid **cumulative delivery line** indicates a steadily increasing rate of scheduled production through April. The extension of this line beyond March would have a constant slope to represent the **planned production rate** of 40 tractors per month. The dotted **progress line** has been posted to January 1 and shows cumulative deliveries of 8 tractors, 2 below the scheduled goal.

Fig. 11, another type of control graph, indicates the reason for the shortage. This chart shows cumulative production of each of the tractor's main components and assemblies, A, B, C, D, etc. It has been posted through January 1. The heavy solid lines which step down across the graph indicate quantities scheduled for production by January 1, February 1, and March 1. The chart shows only 8 tractors, 2 below the schedule, produced by January 1. Looking back, we now

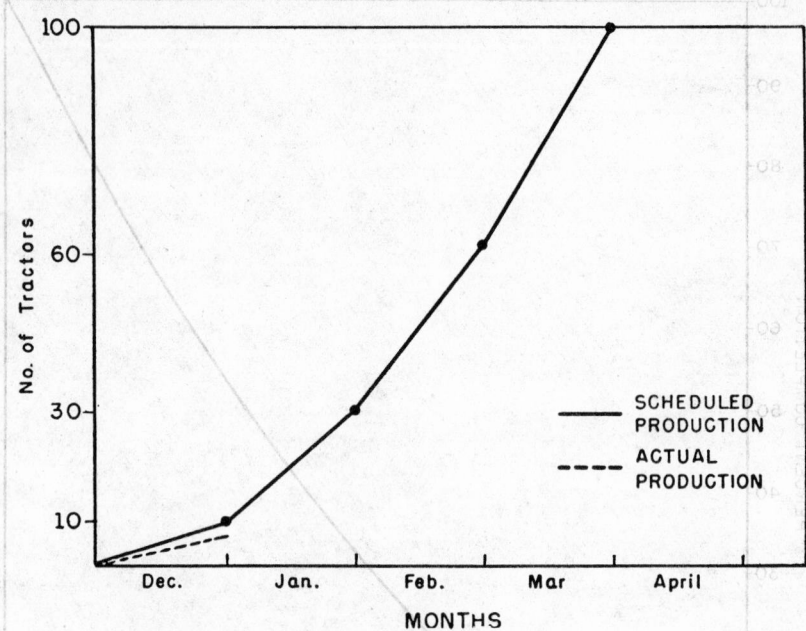

Fig. 10. Scheduled production of tractors.

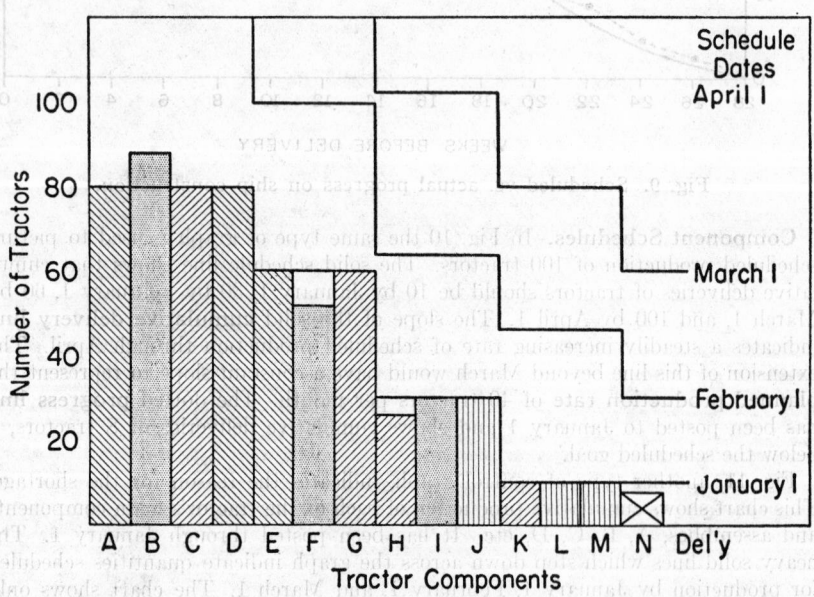

Fig. 11. Monthly component schedules and production.

see why. Some difficulty was encountered with the production of steering-gear assemblies (F), and this work is still 8 assemblies behind schedule. The delay here is also reflected in the progress of the station (H) where these assemblies are installed in the chassis. Production of differential assemblies (B) is ahead of schedule.

ASSEMBLY CHARTS. Charts are often aids in planning and control of **assembly operations.** A type that has proved useful in practice is illustrated in Fig. 12. A few components of a tractor have been used as the example.

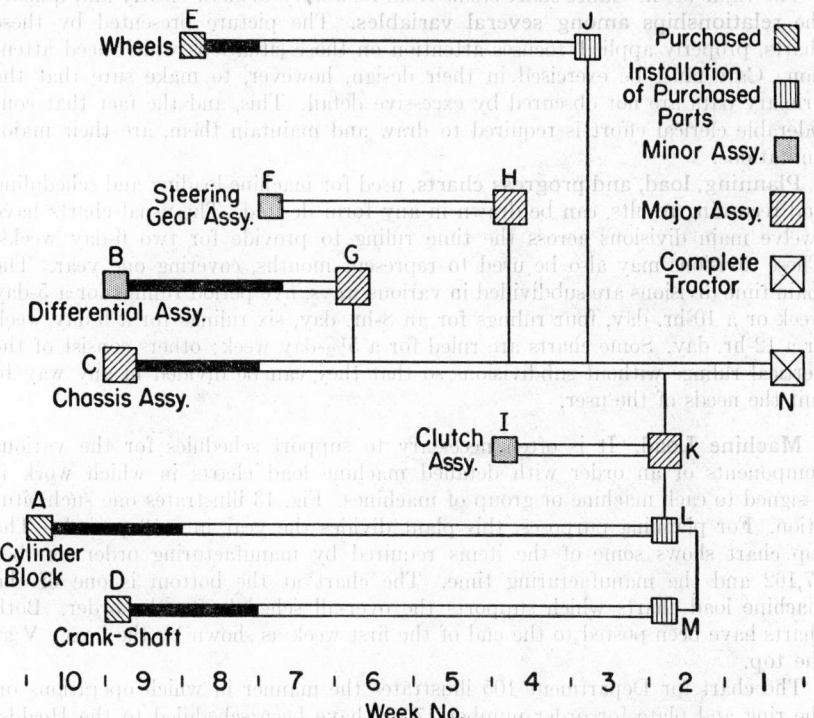

Fig. 12. Assembly chart: tractor production.

The chart shows the **sequence of operations** on a tractor and the **intervals** involved. The different blocks represent manufacture or procurement of major components or assemblies or installation of these in the chassis. The double horizontal lines connecting different blocks show the lead times required. According to the chart, the total interval needed for a complete cycle is 10 weeks. The size and shading of the various blocks follow the code noted on the diagram.

In addition to its use as a guide to the required sequence of operations and the lead times involved, the chart can be posted to **follow progress** on each group of tractors released for production. On the basis of results reported to them, the control group fills in the space between the double horizontal lines to indicate whether progress is behind, ahead of, or on schedule. The chart in Fig. 12 has been posted to the beginning of Week 7. Procurement of cylinder blocks is behind schedule, production of differential assemblies is ahead of schedule, and all other work is proceeding as planned.

GANTT CHARTS. The charts devised by Henry L. Gantt on the basis of many years' experience in a wide range of industries make use of the two fundamental factors in scheduling, dispatching, and control: the **item or facility** under consideration, and the vital element of **time** against which all production is really carried on. It is customary to list the items in the left-hand column and to use the remainder of the sheet for the time ruling. Charts can be drawn up by the user, although printed charts are available. Generally, they are made up on 11 x 17 in. sheets.

The value of the Gantt chart stems from its ability to show clearly and quickly the **relationships among several variables.** The picture presented by these charts, properly applied, focuses attention on those situations which need attention. Care must be exercised in their design, however, to make sure that the primary data are not obscured by excessive detail. This, and the fact that considerable clerical effort is required to draw and maintain them, are their major limitations.

Planning, load, and progress charts, used for machine loading and scheduling and recording results, can be drawn in any form desired. The usual charts have twelve main divisions across the time ruling to provide for two 6-day weeks. These divisions may also be used to represent months, covering one year. The main time divisions are subdivided in various ways, five period rulings for a 5-day week or a 10-hr. day, four rulings for an 8-hr. day, six rulings for a 6-day week or a 12-hr. day. Some charts are ruled for a 5½-day week; others consist of the vertical rulings without subdivisions so that they can be divided in any way to suit the needs of the user.

Machine Load. It is often necessary to support schedules for the various components of an order with detailed machine load charts in which work is assigned to each machine or group of machines. Fig. 13 illustrates one such situation. For planning purposes, this plant divides the year into 13 periods. The top chart shows some of the items required by manufacturing order number 17,162 and the manufacturing time. The chart at the bottom is one of the machine load charts which supports the over-all schedule for the order. Both charts have been posted to the end of the first week as shown by the heavy **V** at the top.

The chart for Department 105 illustrates the manner in which operations on the ring and plate for order number 17,162 have been scheduled to the Healds, drills, and mills. The ring operation on the No. 2 Heald requires more time per piece than on the No. 16 B. and D. For this reason the latter is not scheduled to start until a sufficient bank has been built up to permit it to run continuously and complete all the parts. It is also apparent from the schedule that time requirements for the second, third, and fourth operations on the No. 16 B. and D., the No. 3 Heald, and the No. 4 Cincinnati are more nearly the same. Reference to the upper chart shows that the progress postings and the total span of operations in Department 105 correspond to the details shown in the lower chart.

Control of Manufacture of Parts on Order. A chart for controlling manufacturing to order where each customer's order involves a **high rate of output** is illustrated in Fig. 14. The illustration applies to a few selected components of a fuse.

The weekly columns are divided into six spaces to permit daily posting, and the system of marginal indentations is used to distinguish between components and assemblies. In the upper part of Fig. 14, the numerals on the bars stand for

manufacturing operations, and their location on the time field indicates days on which the operations should be started. A symbol (⌐) and a numeral (1) indicate the day on which the first operation is to start, and operations 2, 3, 4, etc., are to start on days designated by their locations in the daily spaces. When the first operation is started, the heavy progress line is drawn halfway across the daily space, and when the second operation is started, the bar is drawn halfway across the daily space indicated by the numeral 2. When all the operations have started, there is a series of broken bars whose lengths simply indicate that work has commenced on these operations. When the full number of pieces has passed through an operation, the bar is drawn through that space to connect with the next portion, so that ultimately when all operations are completed there is a continuous bar.

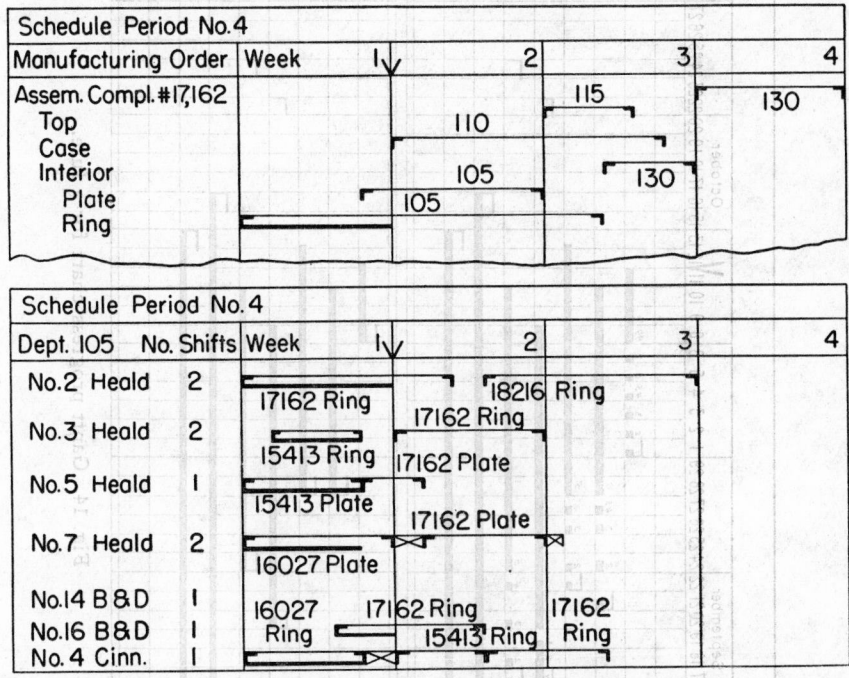

Fig. 13. Central planning and shop control of operations.

The **completion of parts** is shown by the solid portions of the bars which commence at the dates of the respective final operations and which are extended each day to record the amount of work done as measured by the daily schedule.

Assembly of the fuses as shown in the first line of the schedule calls for 1,000 per day. Delivery of completed units is planned to start on October 8, where the ninth and last operation in the assembly is recorded, and is to continue at the scheduled rate until the order is completed on November 7. Saturdays, if worked, are counted as half-days. Working back from the ninth operation, it is seen that assembly must be started on October 1; before the first operation can be started, two of the major components, the fuse body and the assembled detonator, must be ready, so their final operations are planned for September 28. This provision

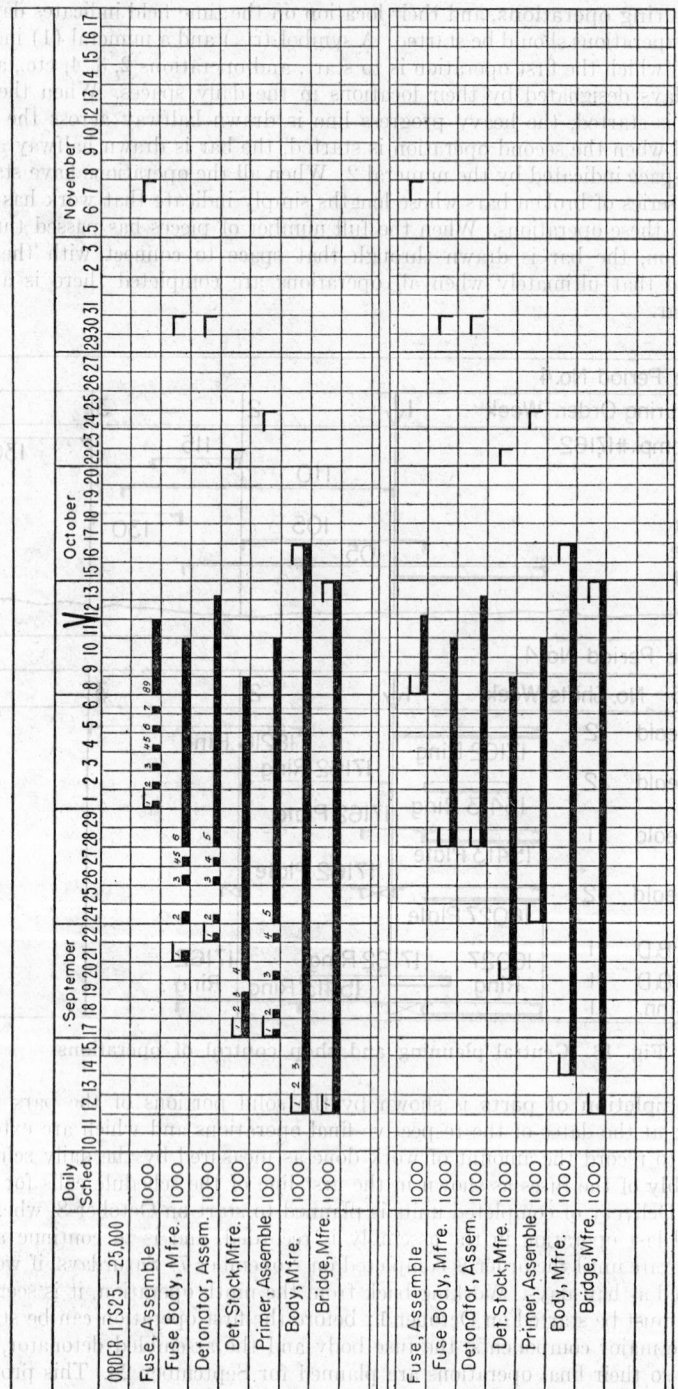

Fig. 14. Gantt progress chart for a fuse.

allows a leeway of 1½ working days for the accumulation of a reserve stock of these two parts before they are withdrawn for the fuse assembly. Since these are parts of the fuse, they are listed with a **marginal indentation** in the left-hand column. Similarly, the assembled detonator is made of a detonator stock and an assembled primer, so these two are given a further marginal indentation under the line "Detonator Assembly." No work may be performed on the detonator assembly until the stocks have been made, so the fourth and last operation on the stock is planned ahead of the first operation on the assembly and the primer is planned so that it will be ready when needed in the detonator assembly. In a similar manner the primer body is shown as a part of the assembled primer and the bridge as a part of the body. Such marginal indentations can be very helpful in pointing up the necessity for coordinating various elements in manufacturing.

Summary Progress Chart. The lower portion of Fig. 14 depicts a more **abbreviated method of showing progress,** where individual operations have been omitted and the initial brackets have been placed to show when deliveries from the final operation on each part or assembly are to begin.

Completion of fuse bodies must commence on September 28 if the assembling operations are to proceed on time and reach delivery of fuses on October 8. The fuse-body bar between these two days indicates two things: first, that the portion between October 1 and 8 represents the amount of bodies which is needed at a given time in the process of assembling the fuses; second, that the portion between September 28 and October 1 represents the amount which is considered necessary as a **reserve stock.**

The sum of these two portions, or that section of the bar appearing between the two starting brackets, represents the **minimum** quantity which is needed between the last operation on the fuse body **and** the last operation on the fuse assembly if **uninterrupted assembly** is to be maintained.

The total length of the body bar represents the number of bodies that have been made, and the fuse-assembly bar represents the number of completed fuses. Inasmuch as the completed fuses must have bodies in them, the difference between the length of these two bars represents the number of bodies which are actually in the assembly process and in stores. Consequently, in reading the chart it is necessary only to compare the relative positions of the ends of the two related bars in order to determine the number of days behind or ahead of schedule the production of the component part may be. For **balanced operation,** all bars will be abreast of the assembly bar and, if production has been progressing at the scheduled rate, all will be abreast of the current date, October 12, indicated by the **V** on the time scale along the top of the chart.

Control of Manufacture of Parts for Stock. Continuous manufacture for stock presents a somewhat different problem. It is not a case of charting the future plans of parts and assembly dates to be made on order as described above, but it involves charting production of parts now being made for stores and the continuous production of the product now being assembled from stock parts. It must be a cross section of the **current manufacturing position.** Special Gantt charts have been devised for this situation.

Mechanized Gantt Charts. The "Chart-O-Matic" (Spiral Mfg. Corp.) is a mechanized Gantt chart. It consists of a metal case, a 50-yd. roll of chart paper, a motor drive, and motor controls. The chart is mounted on two rolls, and only a small portion of its surface is visible at one time. Postings are made directly on this exposed portion, which provides enough space for charts of more than a dozen items. When other items are to be consulted or worked on, movement of one of the controls is all that is required to roll the chart forward or backward to the desired item. The motor has slow and fast speeds in both forward and reverse. About 2,000 items can be charted on one roll of paper. A vertical panel at the top of the slanted face of the case holds a fixed **master chart.** This might be used, for example, to show a master schedule, while the rolling chart below would list all the item schedules involved in it. Two movable **reference markers,** extending over both the fixed and rolling charts, can be set to show the current date, completion dates, and the like.

MODIFIED GANTT CHARTS. A wide variety of charts embodying Gantt chart principles have been developed for special applications. The illustration discussed below shows the form which such adaptations can take.

Control of Development Operations. The modified Gantt chart illustrated in Fig. 15 was developed by E. A. Boyan for control of development work and

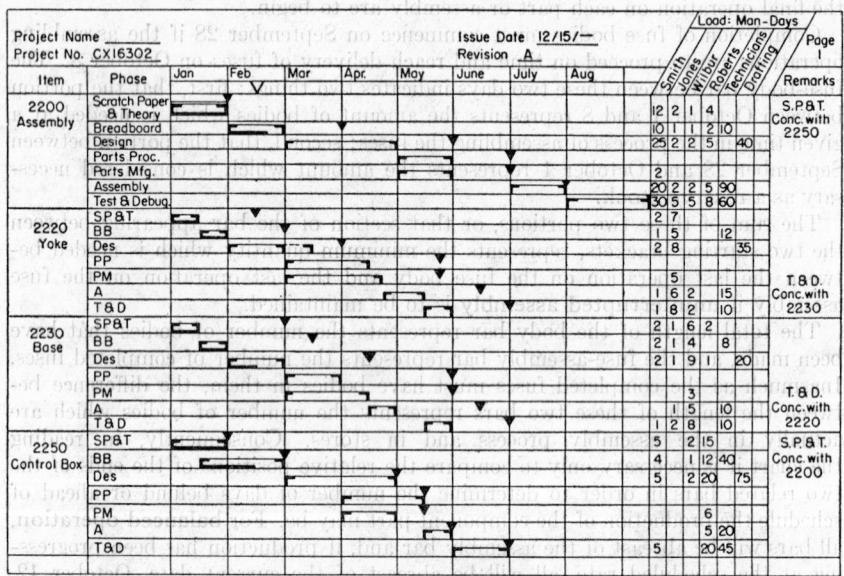

Fig. 15. Target and commitment schedule.

prototype production at the M.I.T. Radiation Laboratory. This chart shows the schedule and load involved for a few components of Assembly No. 2200. The schedule is laid out on the basis of estimates gathered by the planner from the engineers involved and on the basis of data on existing load. Estimates of man-days required on each phase also come from the engineers.

The **commitment schedule** (⌐¬) is prepared first and the load estimates are summarized. When this has been done for all parts, components, and assemblies, the **target schedule** (▼) is derived by working backward from the scheduled completion date of the project. Where limiting items, such as the control box, No. 2250, are concerned, target and commitment schedules are identical. For all other items where these are not identical, a **safety margin** appears between the two. As an example, the base, No. 2230, must be tested and ready when the final assembly starts at the first of July. However, this target date is a month beyond the test completion date (May) for 2230 in the commitment schedule. Targets for the preceding phases are set back from the test target date by the time interval required in each phase. The target on assembly of the base is half a month before the target for the test of the base. The same procedure is carried out for each of the other components. Note, however, that the target for "scratch paper" and theory on the assembly, No. 2200, does not follow this pattern. It is placed at the end of January rather than at the end of February, because scratch paper and theory on the assembly and the control box must proceed concurrently. This information was noted in the "remarks" column when the data for the commitment schedule were collected.

Progress postings are made in the usual manner. The chart shows the results of the last check made in the middle of February. The No. 2200 breadboard is 1 week ahead of schedule; design on No. 2220 has not yet started and is therefore 2 weeks behind. Since the end of the dotted extension of the commitment schedule is still 2 weeks ahead of the target for the No. 2220 design, the delay at this point has no effect on the project as a whole.

The purpose of this chart as applied here should not be misunderstood. It is not intended that the schedule will hold in the same sense as one which might be used in a machine shop. The major objective is to keep all phases of the project synchronized and to give early **warning of delays** which will affect the entire plan. Performance which is within 20 to 30 percent of that scheduled is considered good. The charts show each engineer how his work affects, and is affected by, the work of others; they indicate the different tasks which must be performed and the relationships among them; and they show clearly the seriousness of each delay. The estimates of load, although very rough, are important; without these the schedules do not take enough account of other projects in which the same personnel are involved or of the time they must spend on other parts of the same project. The target dates also make a major contribution to successful planning. They flag the key relationships and provide the means of keeping hundreds of separate jobs in line with the over-all dates and objectives of the project. They also make it unnecessary to redraw the entire schedule as the inevitable major delays come along; major changes in most of these cases require only **realignment of the targets.**

Control Boards

TYPES OF BOARDS. The various forms of control boards are quite closely related to the control charts discussed above. Again, control is based on a graphic method of highlighting exceptions and delays. Although some boards may be set up to show fairly complicated pictures, even their posting is generally much simpler than would be the case with charts of comparable complexity. The different types of control boards may be classified as:

1. Small three-pocket wooden racks.
2. Hook boards.
3. Pocket or grooved-strip boards.
4. Spring-clip panel boards.
5. Tape and peg boards.
6. Index-Visible boards.
7. Racks with movable data units.
8. Pictorial boards.

POCKET RACKS; HOOK BOARDS. Pocket racks and hook boards date back to Taylor's time but are still used in many applications. Both types are useful in visual dispatching systems in shop departments or in central dispatch offices of plants manufacturing a variety of products.

Fig. 16 shows a typical **hook-type dispatch rack.** Each machine or work space has three sets of hooks, one for the job in process, one for the next job ahead, and one for jobs assigned but not yet ready for work. The work-in-process hook carries a duplicate of the work order, the original being given to

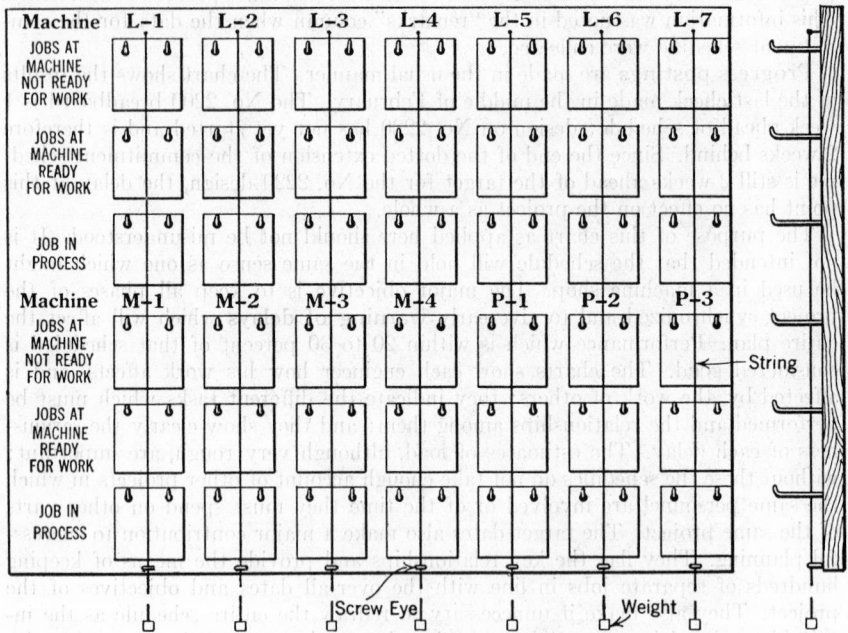

Fig. 16. Typical hook-type dispatch rack.

the operator. Other hooks either carry the duplicate work orders, the originals being in the route files, or both duplicates and originals, depending on the system of filing used. **Pocket racks** are used in exactly the same fashion except that the three sets of hooks for each machine are replaced by wooden racks which have three pockets.

A **hook-type production control board** used in the Brown Instrument Co., described by B. C. Carter, and pictured in Fig. 17, is one of the tools used for controlling manufacturing to insure that proper balances of all materials, supplies, and finished parts are maintained in the storeroom. In addition, it reflects the work record of all machines in the plant.

Planning. In creating a manufacturing order, the product planner, who is responsible for planning and ordering all component and detail parts required to assemble the instruments under his supervision, establishes quantities needed and the dates these quantities should be completed.

The order is then published on **route sheets** which go to various sections of the production control division for further handling. One copy (planning, Figs. 18a and 18b) is sent to the statistical group for insertion of machine numbers and travel times. One copy (material requisition) is sent to the **raw materials** or finished material stock record division for deduction. One copy (dispatching) is sent to the tool-checking division. The remaining copies go to the release desk. Each group receiving a copy of the order performs an individual job and forwards the copy to the release desk. When all copies of the order have been returned, the order is released by the scheduling group.

Upon receipt of the order, the scheduling group have **load tickets** prepared for all machine travel times. These tickets are made up from information supplied by the statistical group or the planning group regarding the types of machines and the travel time for each operation. A **color code** is used for operation identification, as noted in Fig. 19.

Fig. 17. Operation control board.

The orders are then scheduled to run in time to meet the date set by the planner according to the **travel time** involved and the **available machine capacity** on the various types of equipment needed. These tickets are then placed on the control board (Fig. 17) under the scheduled starting date, adjacent to the machine on which the operation is to be performed, as shown in Fig. 19. They are placed on the board with the front side of the ticket showing. All copies of scheduled orders except the planning copy, which is placed in the work-in-process file, are held at the scheduler's desk and filed according to the starting date of the first operation. One week in advance of the scheduled starting date, the orders are dispatched to the various group leaders. This procedure has been established to allow the raw materials storeroom and the tool crib to prepare and handle the obligations to have all materials, tooling, and equipment ready when needed.

Oper. No.	Operation Detail	Dept.	Machine	Tool No.	Sch. Date	Hrs/C	Hrs/Lot	S.U.	Mch. Ld.
1	Turn, burr, form, knurl and cut off.	1	#0 B&S A.S.M.	126	11/1	4.70	47.00	5.0	52.00
2	Drill and burr #55 hole	1	D. P.	22 78788	11/4	1.03	10.30	.5	10.80
3	Inspect	10							
4	Ferrocote	3			11/7				
5	Stock	14							

PRODUCTION ORDER — PLANNING — PRINTED IN U.S.A. — 1 — K. — E

Part No. 78788 Order No. OCT 2519- Date Due 11-10- Date Written

Quantity 1000 20'/C 7.5#/C

Part Name: Chassis Latch Stud
Material: 3/8" dia. C.R. Steel B-527 Die Size LOT 1

RELEASED NOV 1 19-

Total Pieces Run Total Salvaged Total Scrapped Total O. K.

Supersedes Master Dated Date of Master 6-28- Date Completed

Fig. 18a. Planning department copy of manufacturing order (face).

OPER. NO.	NO. PCS. WORKED	FIN. GOOD	NOT FIN.	NO. PCS. REJ.	EMPL. NO.	INSP. NO.	DATE	REMARKS

Fig. 18b. Reverse side of Fig. 18a.

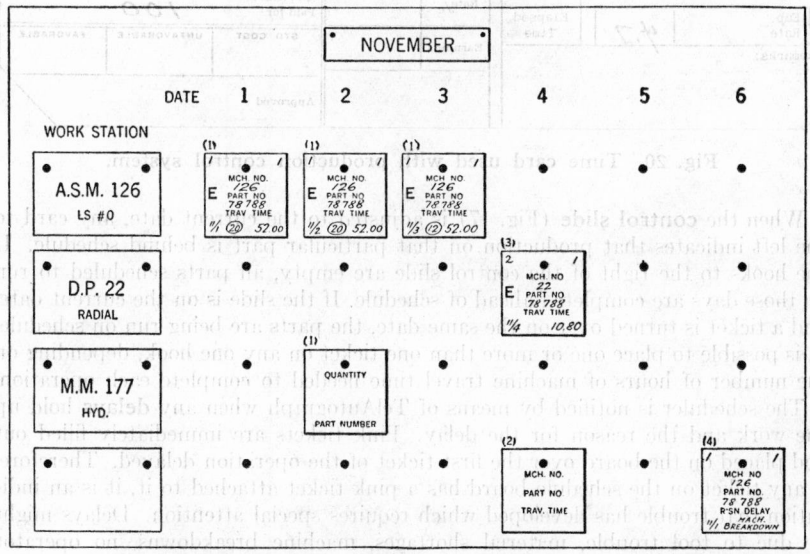

(Name plate is reversible. Dots represent brass hooks for tags.)

(1) **Green tickets:** used for first operation in machine shop. Entries are (upper left) operation number, (upper right) lot number, (letter) planning group, (center) machine number, part number, (bottom) scheduled starting date, machine load per day, total machine load in hours. Tickets are turned to reverse side when job is running, as shown in ticket on third row from top, entries being (top) quantity on order, (bottom) part number.

(2) **Yellow tickets:** Used for intermediate operations between first and last in machine shop. Entries same as on green tickets.

(3) **Blue tickets:** Used for last operation in machine shop. Entries same as on green tickets.

(4) **Pink tickets:** Used for jobs on which trouble is occurring. (Bottom) scheduled starting date, reasons for delay.

Fig. 19. Diagram illustrating use of control board in Fig. 17.

Control. As notification is received from the machine shop dispatcher that processing of any operation on a part has started, all tickets for that operation are turned over on hooks adjacent to the machine numbers, starting on the current date and extending for future days according to the number of hours required to complete the operation. Now the tickets are on the board with the reverse side of the ticket showing. This indicates that the part is running on that particular machine. Tickets representing the day's performance are removed by using the information from the time card (Fig. 20) which is sent from the machine shop each day.

Emp. No.	Name		Quantity on Order		Part Number	78788	
116	Joel Jones		Balance at Start of Job		Order Number	L-1	
Machine No. 126	126		Quantity Defective				
Dep't. No. 11/1			Set-Up Rate		Account Number		
Group No.		Stop	Allowance		Operation Number	1	
Nov. 2	21:50	Start	Rate/c		Quantity Paid for	100	
Nov. 2	16.80	Elapsed Time					
Emp. Rate	4.7		Earnings		STD. COST	UNFAVORABLE	FAVORABLE
Remarks:							
					Approved		

Fig. 20. Time card used with production control system.

When the **control slide** (Fig. 17) is adjusted to the current date, any card to the left indicates that production on that particular part is behind schedule. If the hooks to the right of the control slide are empty, all parts scheduled to run on those days are completed ahead of schedule. If the slide is on the current date, and a ticket is turned over on the same date, the parts are being run on schedule. It is possible to place one or more than one ticket on any one hook, depending on the number of hours of machine travel time needed to complete each operation.

The scheduler is notified by means of TelAutograph when any **delays** hold up the work and the reason for the delay. Pink tickets are immediately filled out and placed on the board over the first ticket of the operation delayed. Therefore, if any ticket on the schedule board has a pink ticket attached to it, it is an indication that trouble has developed which requires special attention. Delays might be due to tool trouble, material shortages, machine breakdowns, no operator available, etc. When a pink ticket is placed on the board, the proper person qualified to help or eliminate the condition is automatically notified.

By use of the control board, it is possible quickly to compute at any time the **hours of work ahead** of any machine or battery of machines. The board also shows a visible record of those parts which are behind schedule and, if a pink ticket is attached, the reason why the part is behind schedule and the group of instruments that will be affected by the delay. The board is also flexible enough to allow for inserting **rush orders** on any machine or group of machines at any time without creating too much disturbance in the shop or in the schedule.

Figs. 17, 18a, 18b. and 19 will clarify the method employed in posting tickets on the board, the different symbols and positions used to identify the parts, and the paper work used both to place the tickets and to remove them.

Results Secured. This master control board has been found to be the best means of planning and bringing about the movements of material, performance of machines and operations labor, no matter how subdivided, so that they will be controlled and coordinated as to quantity, time, place, and cost. In accomplishing these results the control board has the following **advantages**:

1. Permits scheduling to be posted for each production cycle (3 months).
2. Permits each productive machine in the plant to be loaded to its full operating capacity. This loading takes into consideration such basic features as production time, transportation time, setup time, cleaning, and maintenance.

3. Provides for an accurate and effective correction to be made in machine loading, a problem which is inevitable in a complicated kind of manufacture.
4. Enables such corrections to be made immediately, since it gives an over-all picture of plant operation.
5. Takes full advantage of economical operation by limiting setup costs and extending economical lot manufacture.
6. Provides a picture of the relationship of any correction to the rest of the program whether it concerns a part passing over a machine or the relationship of a machine to other operations.
7. Permits standardization of tooling setups and parts manufactured.
8. Allows inventories to be reduced to a minimum.
9. Aids in having theoretical schedules accomplished.
10. Accurately coordinates the planning operation with production cycles.
11. Makes available to all persons involved full knowledge concerning their objectives.
12. Permits more accurate planning and preparation.

A production control board will not automatically bring about such results, although there are features within its structure which go a long way toward realizing these advantages. For instance, it overcomes the tendency to offer excuses and alibis for failures, since it expresses what the manufacturing organization should do and how well it is doing it. The board does not argue or cause emotional upsets. It just stands in its place and displays evidence of any delays, or problems, and, as a result, these difficulties are recognized, understood, and solved.

POCKET OR GROOVED-STRIP BOARDS. Another form of board uses **pocket strips** or grooved metal **label-holders** across the board for the insertion of tickets or cards identifying the item posted. The boards may have part or product slips down the left column and a department or machine list horizontally across the top. The cards or tickets are moved to the right as work on the various parts progresses through the various departments or machines. A **time scale** may be used horizontally in place of the departmental or machine scale, in which case the identifying tickets should have their starting and completion dates noted on them. They may carry all the operations on one ticket or may require a separate ticket for each operation posted under its starting date. If a single ticket is used, it would have to be moved as the work progresses. **Separate tickets** enable scheduling to be shown on the board as well as progress of work, and they make the board much more useful.

Operation Record System. The **Sched-U-Graph system** (Kardex) illustrated in Figs. 21a and 21b uses pockets 40 in. long by 5 in. high. Four forms are used: an 8-in.-wide **index card** of the machine, placed at the left; a 32-in. **title insert** carrying the row of dates (1 to 31); a large-sized **operation card** (10 x 3 in.) divided along the bottom and top into inches and tenths for charting machine load in tenths of a day (100 periods) and having a red horizontal band above the bottom numbers; and a small **operation record card** 3 x 3 in., the right half (1 in.) of which is divided along the bottom and top into tenths of a day (15 periods) with a red band above the bottom numbers. These forms are placed in 40-in.-wide pockets with ⅜-in.-high Transloid tips along the bottom edges into which the forms are inserted. The pockets are fastened in overlapping series, leaving the Transloid edges visible, and are mounted in aluminum frames. The title insert is folded along the bottom to turn up the row of dates (1 through 31) and placed at the right in the pocket with these dates showing beneath the Transloid protector. The machine index card, carrying data identifying the

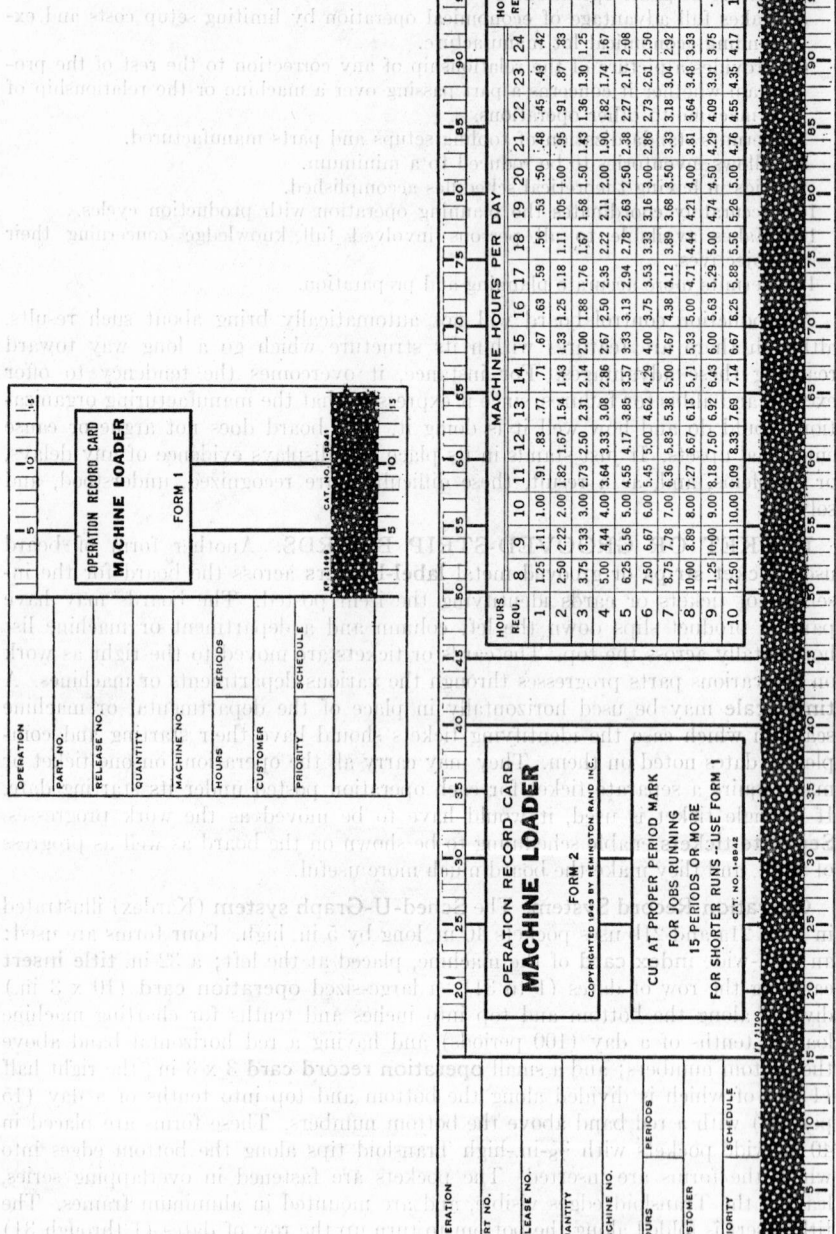

Fig. 21a. Machine loader cards used with flexible machine loading chart.

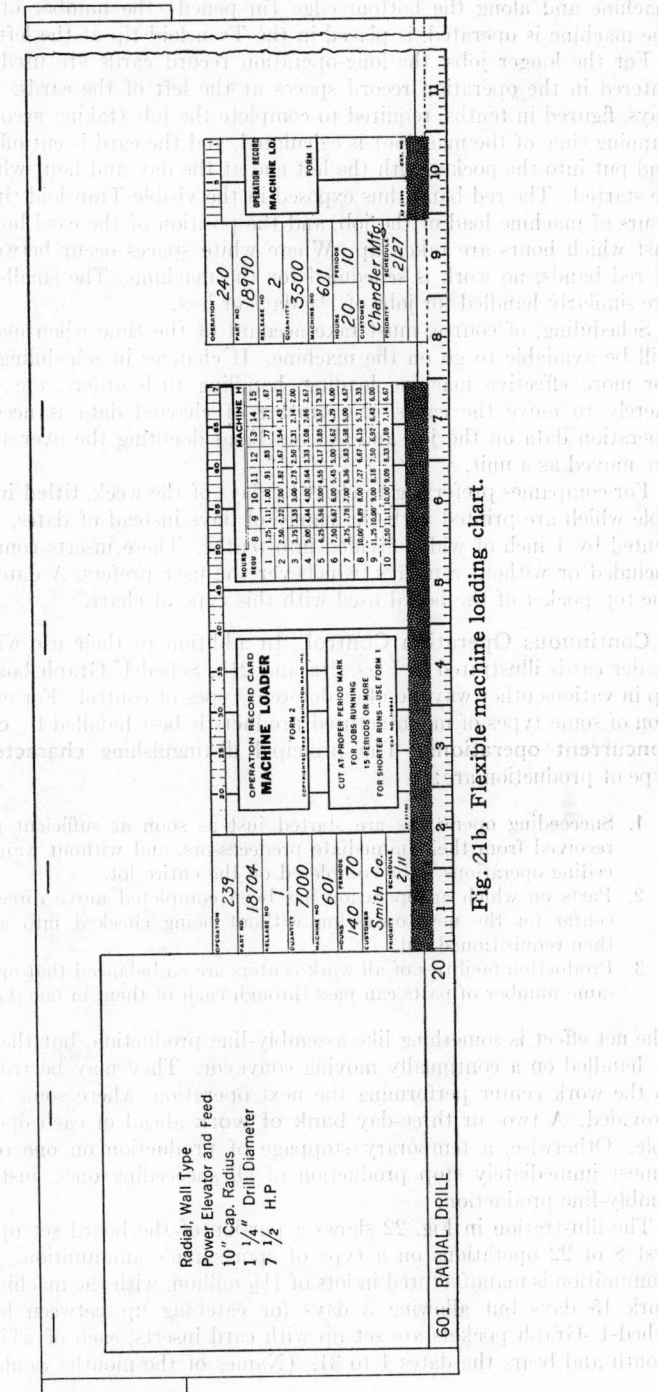

Fig. 21b. Flexible machine loading chart.

machine and along the bottom edge (in pencil) the number of hours per day the machine is operated, is placed in the Transloid tip at the left.

For the longer jobs, the long-operation record cards are used. **Job data** are entered in the operation record spaces at the left of the cards. The number of days, figured in tenths, required to complete the job (taking account of the daily running time of the machine) is calculated, and the card is cut off at this number and put into the pocket with the left end at the day and hour when the job is to be started. The red band thus exposed in the visible Transloid tip represents the hours of machine load of the job, and the position of the card horizontally shows just which hours are taken up. Where white spaces occur between the sections of red bands, no work is scheduled for the machine. The small-operation cards are similarly handled for jobs of 1½ days or less.

Scheduling, of course, must take account of the time when materials or parts will be available to go on the machine. If changes in scheduling must be made for more effective machine loading, handling rush orders, etc., it is necessary merely to move the cards. No erasing of charted data is necessary, and the operation data on the job and the red band denoting the over-all time required are moved as a unit.

For companies preferring to chart by days of the week, **titled inserts** are available which are printed with the names of days instead of dates, each day represented by 1 inch of width divided into tenths. These inserts come with Sundays included or without Sundays, whichever the user prefers. A date strip is put in the top pocket of the board used with this type of chart.

Continuous Operation Control. In addition to their use with the machine loader cards illustrated in Figs. 21a and 21b, Sched-U-Graph boards may be set up in various other ways to offer different types of control. For example, production of some types of manufactured products is best handled by **continuous and concurrent operations.** The principal distinguishing **characteristics** of this type of production are:

1. Succeeding operations are started just as soon as sufficient parts have been received from their immediate predecessors, and without waiting for the preceding operations to be completed on the entire lot.
2. Parts on which an operation has been completed move directly to the work center for the next operation without being checked into a storeroom and then requisitioned out.
3. Production facilities of all work centers are so balanced that approximately the same number of parts can pass through each of them in one day.

The net effect is something like assembly-line production, but the parts need not be handled on a continually moving conveyor. They may be trucked or carried to the work center performing the next operation, where some storage space is provided. A two- or three-day **bank of work** ahead of each operation is desirable. Otherwise, a temporary stoppage of production on one operation would almost immediately stop production of all succeeding ones, just as in true assembly-line production.

The illustration in Fig. 22 shows a portion of the board set up to control the first 8 of 22 operations on a type of sportsman's ammunition. This particular ammunition is manufactured in lots of 1½ million, with the machines scheduled to work 15 days but allowing 3 days for catching up between lots. The 40-in. Sched-U-Graph pockets are set up with card inserts, each of which represents a month and bears the dates 1 to 31. (Names of the months would be in the top pocket—not shown.) Four of these can be accommodated in the 40-in.-wide space, leaving space at the left for an 8 x 5-in. record card.

The scheduled starting and stopping times for each operation are graphed by the **red Span cards.** Three days are allowed between operations to care for transportation time and to provide a cushion in case production on one operation lags for a day or two. Even so, any lag over 3 days would stop all subsequent operations unless they themselves were behind and the time was used for catching up.

Production status is graphed by the **green Progress cards** which move to the right as daily reports of completions are received from the production departments. A daily production schedule has been typed in cumulative form on the card at the left in each pocket. Reports of completions are posted and accumulated. The cumulative production figure is then compared with the cumulative schedule, and the Progress card is set on the date where the cumulative production most nearly matches the cumulative schedule. On the illustration a glance at the **Today line** (blue) shows the first operation to be almost a full day behind, the second operation 2 days behind, the third on schedule, the fourth a day ahead, the fifth on schedule, and the rest not yet scheduled to start.

The Progress cards are cut to the same length as the Span cards. In addition, a **white Shield card** is used behind which the left portion of the Progress card hides. All three cards are tucked behind the turned-up stub of the insert. Note that, for convenience in handling, the cards toward the front in each pocket decrease in height. Also note that the span of the operation is always retained and indicated either by the Span card or by the Progress card.

As shown by the posting dates on the record card at the left, this plant works a 5-day week, Monday through Friday. It will be noted, though, that the inserts carry a scale which assumes 31 days in every month. At first thought it might appear that special inserts carrying only the days of the month on which work was scheduled to be performed should be used. This is unnecessary because the Span cards can be cut to fit, and they will indicate the starting and stopping dates which will, of course, always fall on working days. To avoid any possible confusion, however, the Saturday, Sunday, and holiday spaces can be indicated as on the illustration by placing crimped signals over them. The ½-in. signals will cover both Saturday and Sunday. The ¼-in. signals can be used for holidays. Signals placed over the Saturday, Sunday, and holiday spaces of every tenth pocket are generally sufficient, but they may be used in each pocket.

Order Control System. The Sched-U-Graph may also be used as the basis of an order follow-up system. In this case, the board is set up, and a copy of the **shop order** is inserted in the visible margin, with the order number showing through the acetate tip. Each order form has its own pocket, and all are filed in numerical order. Directly to the right of the order form a title insert is inserted with a ¼-in. numbered square showing through the visible margin. Each square represents a department. A colored ¼-in. signal is inserted to indicate the department the order has reached, and the Graph-A-Matic signal directly to the right shows the day on which the department is scheduled to complete its operation.

The Sched-U-Graph board is equipped to handle 3 months' orders. Another ¼-in. colored signal is used on the monthly chart to indicate the day the order is to be completed.

Like the Gantt chart, the Sched-U-Graph can show not only the load on each machine but also the exact time when this load occurs.

RECORD OF CONTINUOUS PRODUCTION BY OPERATION

TYPE Sportsman's			OPERATION NO. 1		OPERATION NAME Cut Off	
CALIBER .22 Long			TOTAL QUANTITY 1,500,000	DAYS 15	DAILY SCHEDULE 100,000	

DATE	CUMULATIVE SCHEDULED	DAILY PRODUCTION	CUMULATIVE PRODUCED	DATE	CUMULATIVE SCHEDULED	DAILY PRODUCTION	CUMULATIVE PRODUCED
Aug 15	100,000	90,000	90,000	Aug 29	1,100,000	75,000	1,050,000
16	200,000	100,000	190,000	30	1,200,000	70,000	1,120,000
17	300,000	95,000	285,000	31	1,300,000		
20	400,000	105,000	390,000	Sep 3	1,400,000		
21	500,000	110,000	500,000	4	1,500,000		
22	600,000	100,000	600,000				
23	700,000	98,000	698,000				
24	800,000	105,000	803,000				
27	900,000	92,000	895,000				
28	1,000,000	86,000	975,000				

OPERATION NO.	OPERATION NAME	
1	CUT OFF	1 2 3 4 5
OPERATION NO. 2	OPERATION NAME FIRST DRAW	1 2 3 4 5
OPERATION NO. 3	OPERATION NAME BENDING	1 2 3 4 5
OPERATION NO. 4	OPERATION NAME SECOND DRAW	1 2 3 4 5
OPERATION NO. 5	OPERATION NAME SEAMING	1 2 3 4 5
OPERATION NO. 6	OPERATION NAME HEAT TREAT	1 2 3 4 5
OPERATION NO. 7	OPERATION NAME BURRING	1 2 3
OPERATION NO. 8	OPERATION NAME THIRD DRAW	1 2 3 4 5

▧ Red: Span cards.
▨ Green: Progress cards.
▬ Blue: Today line.

Fig. 22. Control of

SPRING-CLIP PANEL BOARDS. The McCaskey Register "One-Writing and Visible Filing" systems have a long history of successful use for control of production, inventories, tools, and other factors in manufacturing. These systems employ spring-clip boards to present visually copies of the various forms required for control. A typical board has 10 vertical rows of clips with 10 horizontal columns down the board. The back of the board is similarly arranged, and panels are mounted in groups on brackets so that all but the one consulted can be swung back out of the way. The number of spring-clips varies with the size of the forms used.

Under typical **job-order production,** manufacturing orders (Fig. 23) are made out in the usual way, several copies being produced by means of one-writing,

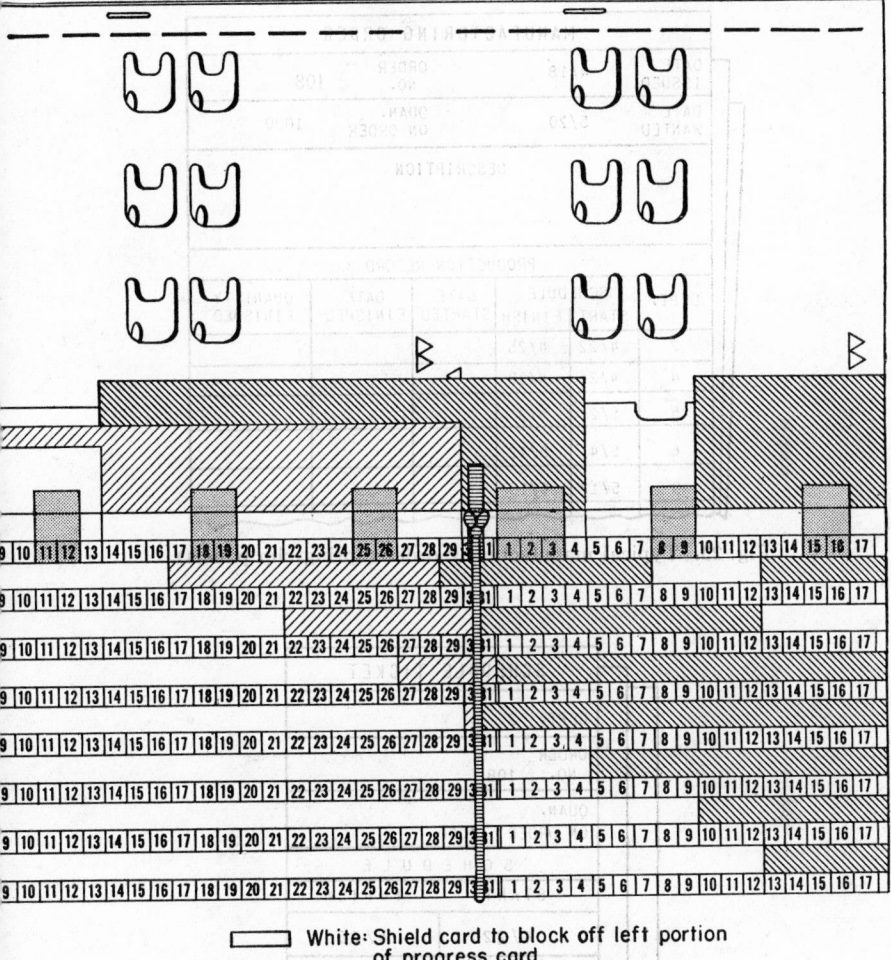

White: Shield card to block off left portion of progress card.

Buff: Crimped signal, 1/2 in. wide to block off Saturdays and Sundays and 1/4 in. to block off holidays.

a continuous process.

carbon-backed forms. A copy is kept in the central production or planning department, and other copies are sent to the various departments performing the operations on the order. Start and finish dates for the work to be done in each department are determined and listed. One set of **triplicate schedule tickets** (Fig. 24) on white, yellow, and pink forms is then made for each department to specify these start and finish dates.

Production Order Control Board. In the central control department, the manufacturing orders are filed on the production or order control board (Fig. 25), either consecutively or according to the last two digits of the number. On the central schedule boards for the various departments there are two vertical rows of clips for each day and date. One row is for orders to be **started** (S) that day,

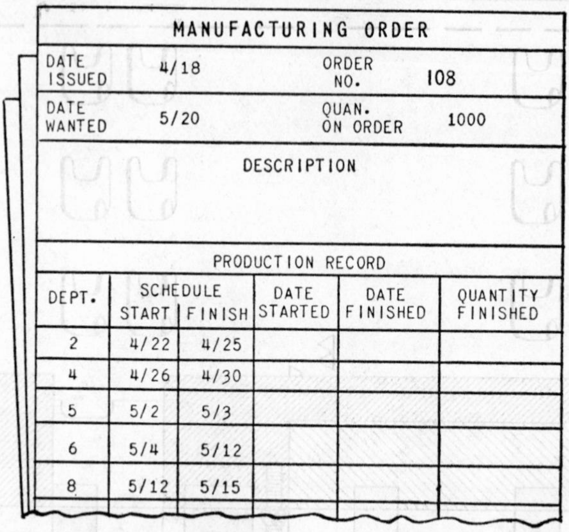

MANUFACTURING ORDER

DATE ISSUED	4/18		ORDER NO.	108
DATE WANTED	5/20		QUAN. ON ORDER	1000

DESCRIPTION

PRODUCTION RECORD

DEPT.	SCHEDULE		DATE STARTED	DATE FINISHED	QUANTITY FINISHED
	START	FINISH			
2	4/22	4/25			
4	4/26	4/30			
5	5/2	5/3			
6	5/4	5/12			
8	5/12	5/15			

Fig. 23. Typical manufacturing order (spring-clip panels).

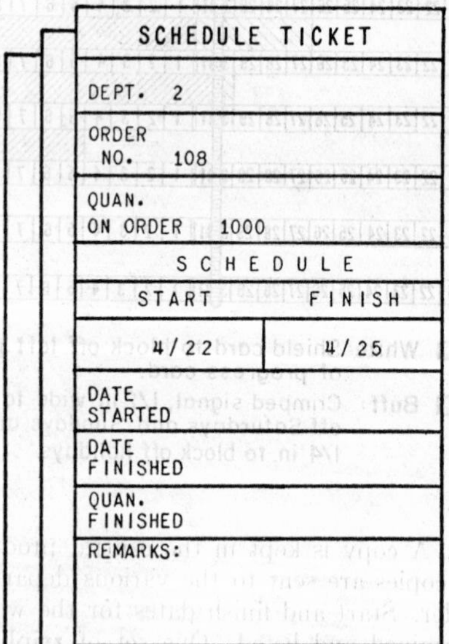

SCHEDULE TICKET

DEPT. 2

ORDER NO. 108

QUAN. ON ORDER 1000

SCHEDULE

START	FINISH
4/22	4/25

DATE STARTED

DATE FINISHED

QUAN. FINISHED

REMARKS:

FOREMAN

Fig. 24. Schedule ticket for board.

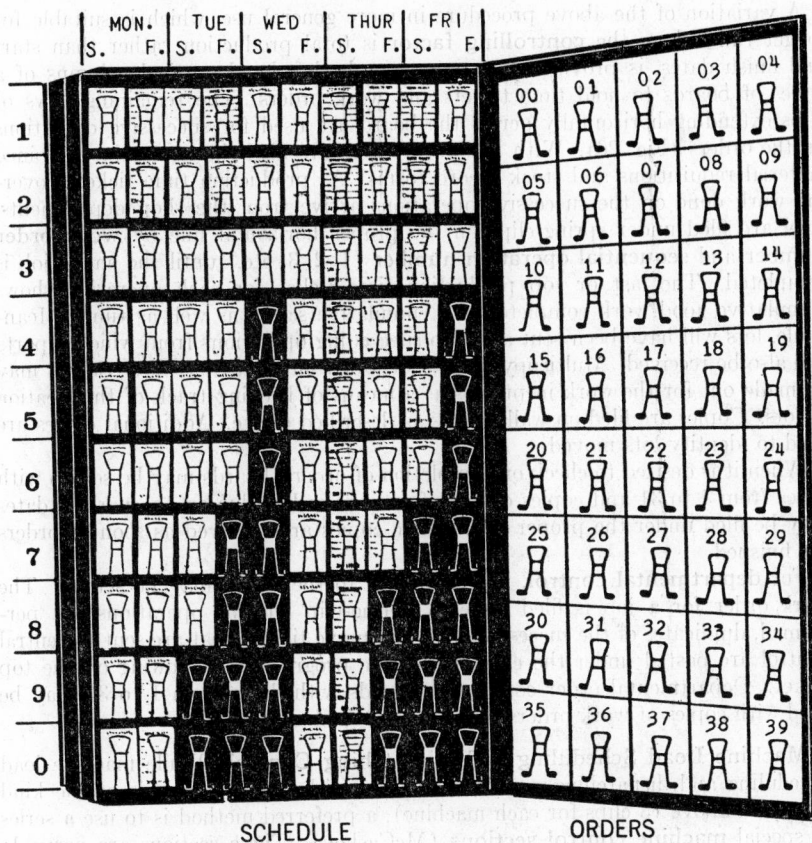

Fig. 25. Production order control board (spring-clip type).

and the other holds the tickets of orders to be **finished** (F) that day. The white copy of each schedule ticket is filed under its date in the "start" column. There are usually 10 clips down the date column, and the schedule tickets are filed under these according to the last digit of the order number. For example, Order 1683 would be under Clip No. 3. The corresponding yellow and pink copies of the schedule ticket go to the department doing the work and are there filed together in the start column on a similar schedule board under the scheduled starting date for the operation. When production is started, the yellow and pink copies are removed from the shop board, the starting date is put on them, the pink copy is filed under the finish date for the job, and the yellow copy is sent to central control where it is filed under the finish column of the corresponding date. The white ticket is removed from the start column and filed with the manufacturing order on which is entered the actual starting date. When the job is done, the pink ticket in the department is removed, the actual finishing date is entered on it, and the ticket is sent to central control. Here the pink ticket is removed from the board and filed with the manufacturing order upon which the finishing date is recorded. After all departments have finished their work, all tickets are removed from the order control board.

A variation of the above procedure in more general use, which is suitable for longer runs where the **controlling factor** is total production rather than start and finish dates, is provided by setting up the left-hand vertical columns of a series of boards to hold time tickets and work orders. The remaining rows of clips extending horizontally across the board are used for successive operations on the orders (Fig. 26). With the work orders are filed the necessary combined material requisitions and stock record forms. As production time tickets covering work done on the successive operations arrive from the shop departments, they are filed under spring-clips on the proper horizontal line by **work order number** and **sequential operation number** (1, 2, 3, etc.) until the entire job is completed. The last or top production time ticket for each operation shows cumulative good work completed and cumulative scrap, as well as time. Meanwhile, lots will have been sent along to succeeding operations from which reports will also be received. Multicopy move orders or combined time-move tickets may be made out for the work in process as a means of keeping track of the location of lots. Copies are filed on wall boards as described above. Additional copies are used to identify lots moved.

When it is desired to check on completion of orders, boards may be set up with dates from 1 to 31 and copies of manufacturing orders due on the various dates may be filed under the proper clip. These copies are removed as soon as orders are finished.

For **departmental control,** boards similar to the above may be set up. The work order for a job is filed under a spring-clip and, as operations are performed, duplicates of the successive time and move tickets that are sent to central control are posted under the clip, cumulative progress data showing on the top ticket. Departmental order completion boards with dates from 1 to 31 may be used with copies of work orders filed under their due dates.

Machine Load Scheduling and Dispatching Control. While machine load scheduling and dispatching can be carried on with separate boards of the kind described above (3 clips for each machine), a preferred method is to use a series of special **machine control sections** (McCaskey). These sections are vertical; they consist of seven units, each made up of two pockets with a spring-clip on the front. One unit, consisting of 3 filing positions, is assigned to each machine. The vertical units may be bolted together at the side to form as many rows of seven units each as desired. Labels beneath the clips identify the machines to which the pockets have been assigned.

The boards are mounted at the local dispatch center or in the foreman's office. Each installation has sufficient units for all machines or pieces of equipment in that manufacturing area. The work orders, job, time, or move tickets, representing operations to be performed, are sorted and filed on these boards in the pocket units for machines on which the operations will be done as jobs ahead, jobs next, jobs on the machine:

1. Back pocket: jobs for which material is not yet available arranged in sequence of order number or of expected performance.
2. Front pocket: jobs for which material is on hand and ready so that the work can be put into operation (next jobs ahead).
3. Under the spring-clip: the jobs currently on the respective machines and in operation.

If no tickets are filed in the "next job ahead" pocket for a machine, the dispatcher or foreman knows that the particular machine will be down unless some

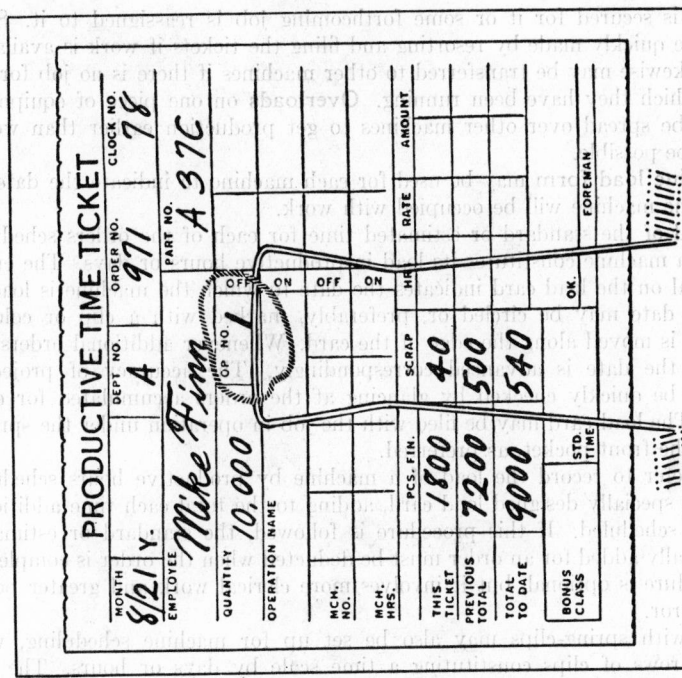

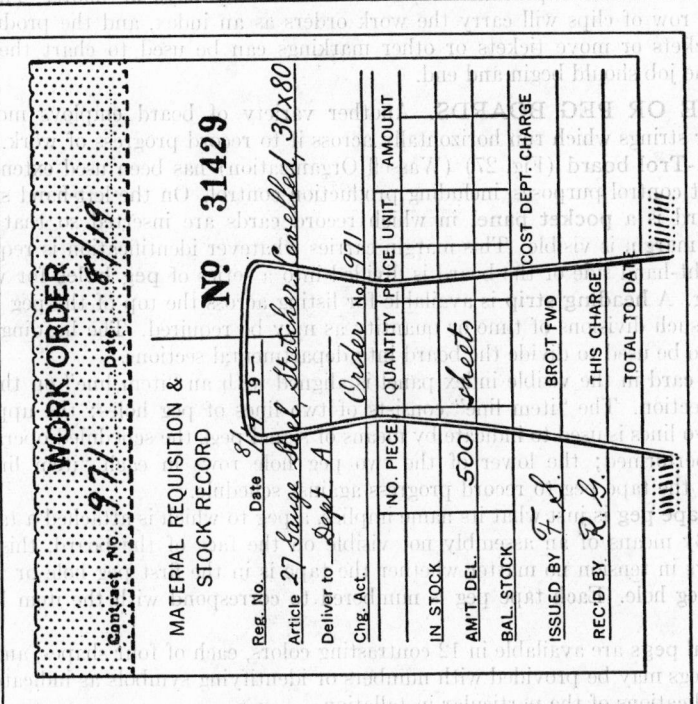

Fig. 26. Time tickets and work orders posted on board.

new work is secured for it or some forthcoming job is reassigned to it. Such changes are quickly made by resorting and filing the tickets if work is available. Workers likewise may be transferred to other machines if there is no job for the machine which they have been running. **Overloads** on one piece of equipment often can be spread over other machines to get production earlier than would otherwise be possible.

A **machine load form** may be used for each machine to indicate the date up to which the machine will be occupied with work.

The total of the standard or estimated time for each of the orders scheduled to run on a machine constitutes its load in productive hours or days. The entry of this total on the load card indicates the date to which the machine is loaded. The latest date may be circled or, preferably, marked with a clip or colored signal that is moved along the edge of the card. Whenever additional orders are scheduled, the date is advanced correspondingly. The accuracy of projected loads may be quickly checked by glancing at the orders accumulated for each machine. The load card may be filed with the job in operation under the spring-clip or in the front pocket, as preferred.

Some prefer to record the load of a machine by productive hours scheduled ahead on a specially designed load card, adding to the total each time additional orders are scheduled. If this procedure is followed, the standard or estimated time originally added for an order must be deducted when the order is completed. The procedure is optional, but it involves more clerical work and greater possibility of error.

Boards with spring-clips may also be set up for machine scheduling, with horizontal rows of clips constituting a time scale by days or hours. The left vertical row of clips will carry the work orders as an index, and the productive time tickets or move tickets or other markings can be used to chart the time when the job should begin and end.

TAPE OR PEG BOARDS. Another variety of board employs movable tapes or strings which run horizontally across it to record progress of work. This **Produc-Trol board** (Fig. 27) (Wassell Organization) has been used extensively for most control purposes, including production control. On the left-hand side of the board is a **pocket panel** in which record cards are inserted so that their bottom margin is visible. This margin carries whatever identification is required. The right-hand side of the board is divided into a series of **peg holes** for visible charting. A **heading strip** is available for listing across the top of the peg board section such divisions of time or quantity as may be required. The heading strip may also be used to divide the board into departmental sections.

Each card in the visible index panel is aligned with an "item line" on the peg board section. The "item line" consists of two lines of peg holes; the upper of these two lines is used to indicate by means of signal pegs the scheduled operations to be performed; the lower of the two peg hole rows in each "item line" is used by the tape peg to record progress against schedule.

The **tape peg** is just what its name implies, a peg to which is attached a tape or cord. By means of an assembly not visible on the face of the board, this cord is always in tension no matter whether the tape is in the first peg hole or in the 200th peg hole. Each tape peg is numbered to correspond with the item line it covers.

Signal pegs are available in 12 contrasting colors, each of four shapes, and any signal pegs may be provided with numbers or identifying symbols as indicated by the applications of the particular installation.

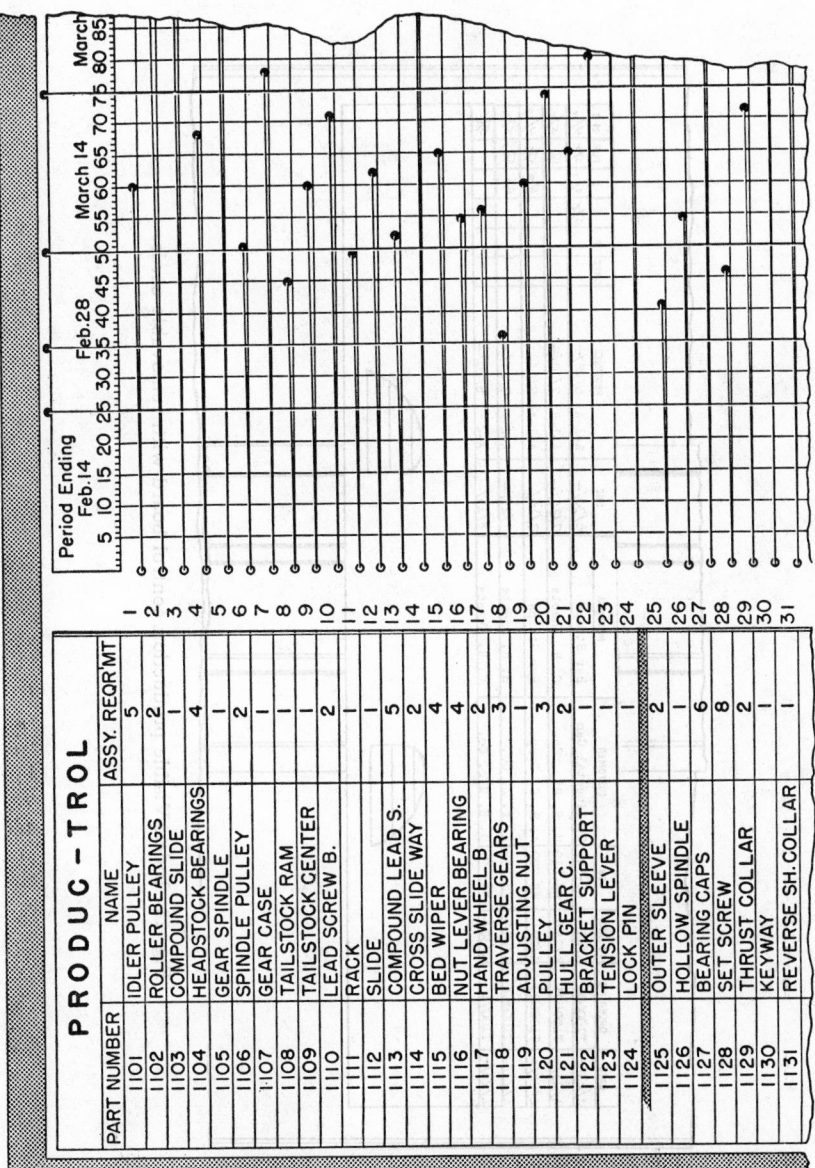

Fig. 27. Order schedule control board.

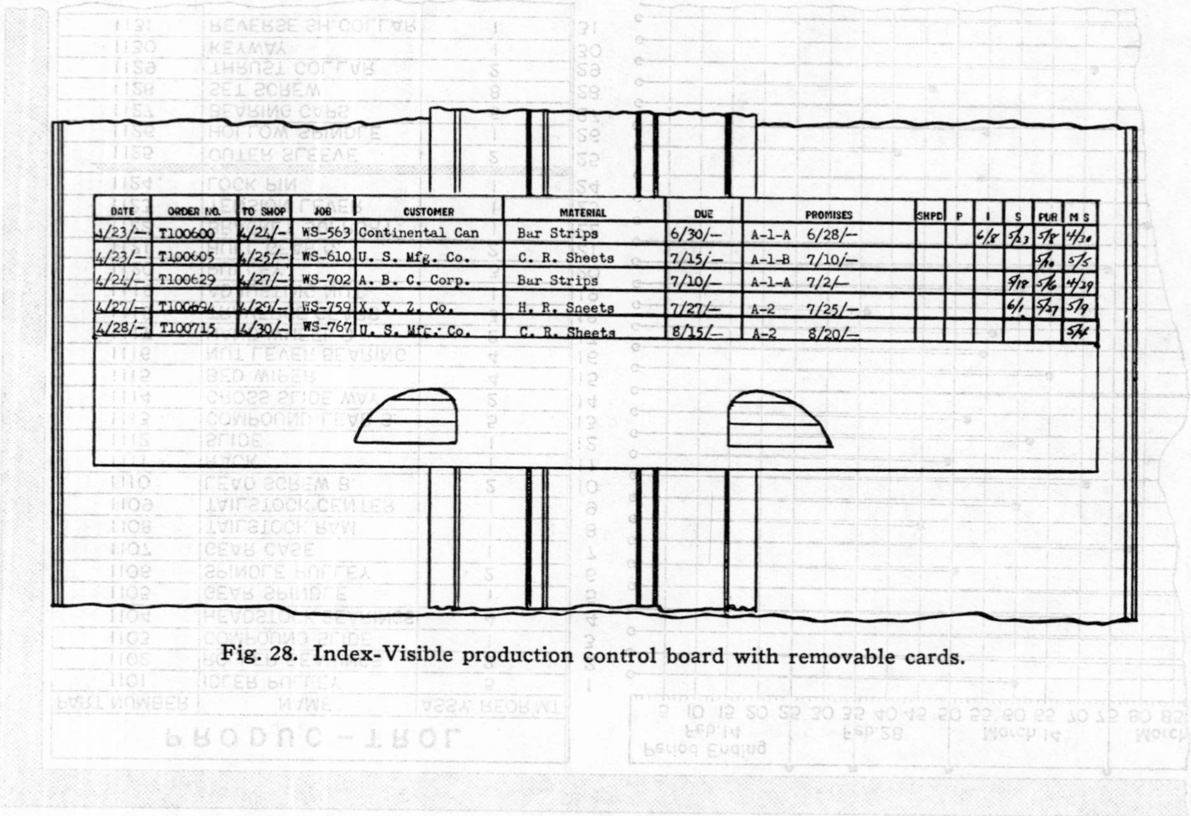

Fig. 28. Index-Visible production control board with removable cards.

DATE	ORDER NO.	TO SHOP	JOB	CUSTOMER	MATERIAL	DUE	PROMISES	SHPD	P	I	S	PUR	M	S
4/23/-	T100600	4/24/-	WS-563	Continental Can	Bar Strips	6/30/-	A-1-A 6/28/-		4/8	5/23	5/1		4/2
4/23/-	T100605	4/25/-	WS-610	U. S. Mfg. Co.	C. R. Sheets	7/15/-	A-1-B 7/10/-					5/6	5/5
4/24/-	T100629	4/27/-	WS-702	A. B. C. Corp.	Bar Strips	7/20/-	A-1-A 7/2/-			4/11	5/8		4/30
4/27/-	T100654	4/26/-	WS-759	X. Y. Z. Co.	H. R. Sheets	7/27/-	A-2 7/25/-			6/1	5/7		5/9
4/28/-	T100715	4/30/-	WS-767	U. S. Mfg. Co.	C. R. Sheets	8/15/-	A-2 8/20/-						5/4

By use of colored **vertical cords,** automatic control elements may be introduced. The relationship between these vertical cords and the signal and tape pegs indicates at a glance whether work is behind or ahead of schedule and by how much in terms of whatever divisions have been set up by the heading strip.

Fig. 27 shows one way in which these boards may be set up. The illustration applies to a series of orders for different customers. When an order is received, it is scheduled through all the departments which will do the work on it; completion dates are assigned for every stage. This and other necessary information on the order are noted on the record card. These cards are filed in the visible panel which runs down the left-hand side of the board. One line—2 horizontal rows of holes—on the board is used to reflect the data posted on the record card for that particular order.

INDEX-VISIBLE BOARDS. Typical of the index class is the production order control system maintained at the Treadwell Engineering Co. with listings on Index-Visible cards (Remington Rand) filed on special leaves housed in ring books. An illustration is shown in Fig. 28. The cards are blank except for the printed horizontal and vertical lines. A single **heading card** is used at the top of each leaf to identify the information. Any card may be unbuttoned quickly from the runway or simply slid up to expose any additional notations below the visible margin.

Cards are filed by order number and remain in place until the order is completely shipped. Inasmuch as some orders require much longer to process than others, the listing is in constant state of flux. All completed orders are instantly removed, leaving only orders in process in this record. Progress of the order through various steps is indicated in the squares at the right of the visible margin. The due date and promised shipping date are also shown, permitting visual reviews to be made frequently to check any orders on which expediting action is needed.

PICTORIAL BOARDS. Some companies have used pictorial boards for showing progress of work. One such board used in an aircraft plant carries a **layout diagram** of the assembly plant and location of the adjacent flight testing field. Preliminary operations departments are also noted. On the assembly lines, aircraft diagrams mark off the various assembly stations. Manufacture is controlled according to plane numbers in a lot going through. Spaces are left on the layout program so that each day, when the production report arrives, the plane numbers can be posted to the stations where these respective planes are on the subassembly or final assembly lines.

Card Files

VARIETIES OF SYSTEMS. One of the most widely used mechanisms for control of production is the card system. As compared with production boards, the card system occupies far less space, is highly accessible, brings pertinent information together in condensed form, offers greater facilities for checks and comparisons, and reduces the personnel required for record-keeping. It may be less costly to install and operate. The visual and graphic features of production boards and charts are lacking, however. These are often more useful because they are directly understandable and dynamic. Written or posted records, while necessary, are static, since they require interpretation into physical factors.

Card systems may be classified into the four main groups which are discussed below.

1. Vertical card files in standard sizes, 3 x 5 in., 4 x 6 in., 5 x 8 in., etc., with guides or markers dividing off and indexing the information.
2. Visible index systems with vertically overlapping pockets or envelopes containing cards showing their successive margins on which the indexing notations and often signals for control purposes are placed. These systems may be filed flat or mounted vertically.
3. Visible index systems with horizontally overlapping cards so that the side margin may be used for indexing notations and postings. Such cards are filed vertically, as in ordinary card systems, and are usually placed lengthwise instead of crosswise in file drawers to give more extensive top visibility. Long guides or markers index and divide off the various sections.
4. Rotary filing systems in which the cards are notched for mounting around the circumference of a large wheel or drum rotating within a cabinet and accessible for consultation or for the removal and replacement of cards on which typed or machine postings are made.

VERTICAL CARD FILES. Regular vertical card index systems can be set up for many production control purposes. They are often used in **purchasing departments** for quotations and bids, commodities, and other records or indexes. Frequently they are used in **stores records** or in storeroom location indexes. They may be used in **engineering departments** for indexing and cross-referencing parts and assembly drawings, bills of material, specifications, customers' orders, changes in drawings, patterns, pattern numbers, and other important data. In the **production control department** itself they are applicable to indexing and recording orders, operation sheets, route sheets, time study data, tooling for jobs, machine data, and other standard data sheets to which reference must be made. The extra time taken to locate information which must be consulted frequently, the extra work of removal for posting and refiling, and the danger of losing separate cards which are not attached or keyed into the file are among the factors which have led to the abandonment of such card files in favor of the visible index form of record in many production control installations.

Efforts to improve standard vertical files have led to such developments as **Simplafind** (Wheeldex Mfg. Co.), a motorized, automatic card file. The operator, pressing a button, can bring any desired record before her in less than 3 sec. File cards are set in light, easily removable trays and are presented in a series of 10-in. rows within comfortable reach and reading range of the operator. Simplafind handles any standard card size, a 12-sq.-ft. unit holding from 40,000 (8 x 5 in.) to 180,000 (2½ x 3 in.) cards. A minimum of 4,000 cards are open before the operator at all times.

LOAD SUMMARY AND ORDER LIST							MONTH OF:				
DEPARTMENT			100	200	300	400	PAGE OF PAGES				
MACHINE HRS. AVAILABLE			3240	5625	2910	4980					
CUSTOMER	ORDER NO.	DATE	IND / CUM	IND / CUM	IND / CUM	IND / CUM	PLANNED		ACTUAL		REMARKS
							QTY.	DATE	QTY.	DATE	
U.S.P.	12415	4/12	12 / 12	15 / 15	/	25 / 25	2000	5/15			
Lentro	11998	4/13	4 / 16	9 / 24	3 / 3	10 / 35	600	4/30			
Atlas	12431	4/15	100 / 116	78 / 102	84 / 87	180 / 215	4500	5/30			

Fig. 29. Load summary and order list.

Ritchie (Production and Inventory Control) gives an example of a control record form maintained in a **standard vertical file** (Fig. 29). This form is used by a machine shop to show the load on its various departments. The machine-hours available each month are indicated under the appropriate department heading. Each order is broken down into **estimated production time** in each department, and these figures are posted above the diagonal line in the appropriate columns. **Cumulative load figures** are noted below the diagonal. For example, Order No. 12431 will run on facilities in Department 200 for 78 hr., the figure shown above the line; this brings the total load in Department 200 up to 102 hr. Conditions of over- or underload are readily apparent.

VISIBLE INDEX FILES, VERTICAL OVERLAPPING. The vertically overlapping systems of visible indexes are typified by Kardex, Acme, and a number of other designs, each having special features adapting it to the purposes for which it is applied. These systems are in wide use and are high in economy of time and space, easy for reference and posting, safe from the standpoint of losing or misplacing cards or forms, durable, and effective for many kinds of production control work. The cards or forms are held in pockets which overlap one another in vertical rows.

The **vertically overlapping** pockets or cards have printed along their margins identifying data which place them in a proper position in a file which exposes these indexed or marked edges. The cards are carried in holders provided with flexible hinges. When it is necessary to consult a card, the proper card can be located and the covering cards can be thrown back to reveal the full surface of the card needed. Posting can be done by hand, or the card may be taken out and posted on a typewriter. In most cases the card is printed up specially for the company using the system and is designed to fit the special needs and purposes in view. **Control indexes** or **marker strips** can be printed along the bottom edge of the card showing items such as month of the year, days of the month, or any special entries such as follow-up, beginning operation, final delivery dates.

Cards of this kind are often provided with transparent coverings over the index section so that the cards are kept clean and do not become dog-eared or damaged. At the same time, by means of **colored transparent markers** of various types, such as the Kardex Graph-A-Matic signal, it is possible to provide checks or keys or other indications on important points. Such marking points might include markers to indicate reorder points, markers to indicate when internal manufacturing orders for parts carried in stock should be placed in production, dates for purchase follow-up, and so on.

Applications of Visible Index. The application of these cards to production control activities can be illustrated briefly by several examples of actual installations.

In the Parish Pressed Steel Co., a copy of the production order is prepared on the fold-over flap of an 11 x 9-in. buff Kardex form at the same time that the other necessary copies of this order are reproduced on a duplicating machine. The card (Fig. 30) is indexed by sales order (S.O. No.) and is signaled by day and month when assembly is scheduled to start. If change orders are issued, they are made out on pink sheets which show through a small hole punched under "Amount" in the visible margin of the card. Entries of completions and deliveries are made on the shipping record, and products scrapped or repaired are noted on the lower part of the card.

Blue cards (Fig. 31) placed below the order card are set up for each part needed to complete the order. If material is available, a signal is placed over the

FOLLOW UP RECORD

DATE	DEL'YD	BAL.	DATE	DEL'YD	BAL.	DATE	DEL'YD	BAL.

REMARKS

SHIPPING RECORD   PROM.

DATE	SHP'D	BAL.	DATE	SHP'D	BAL.	DATE	SHP'D	BAL.	DATE	SHP'D	BAL.

PREPLANNING SCHEDULE

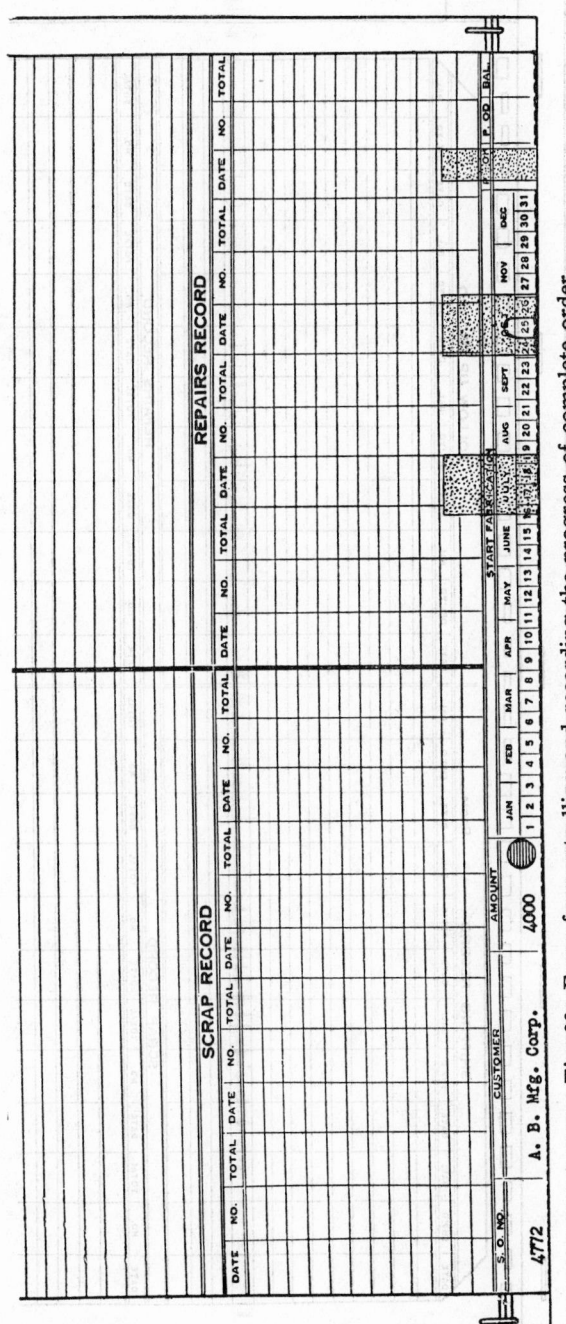

Fig. 30. Form for controlling and recording the progress of complete order.

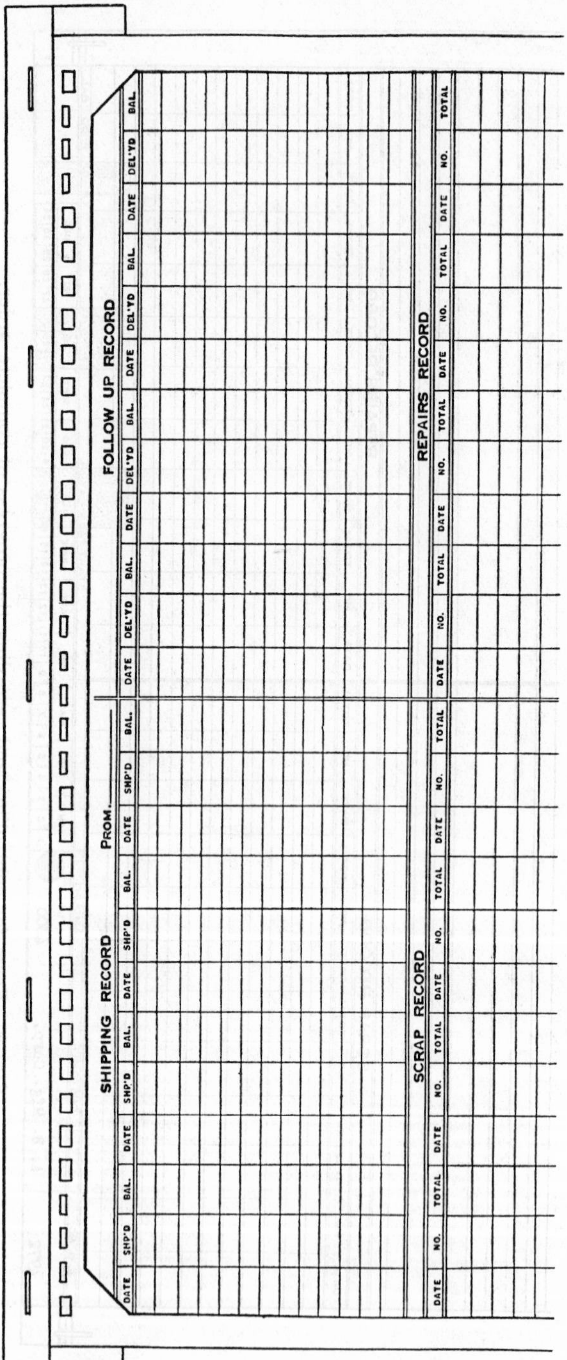

SHIPPING RECORD PROM.____ FOLLOW UP RECORD

DATE	SHP'D	BAL.	DATE	SHP'D	BAL.	DATE	SHP'D	BAL.	DATE	SHP'D	BAL.	DATE	DEL'YD	BAL.	DATE	DEL'YD	BAL.	DATE	DEL'YD	BAL.	DATE	DEL'YD	BAL.

SCRAP RECORD REPAIRS RECORD

DATE	NO.	TOTAL	DATE	NO.	TOTAL	DATE	NO.	TOTAL	DATE	NO.	TOTAL	DATE	NO.	TOTAL	DATE	NO.	TOTAL	DATE	NO.	TOTAL	DATE	NO.	TOTAL

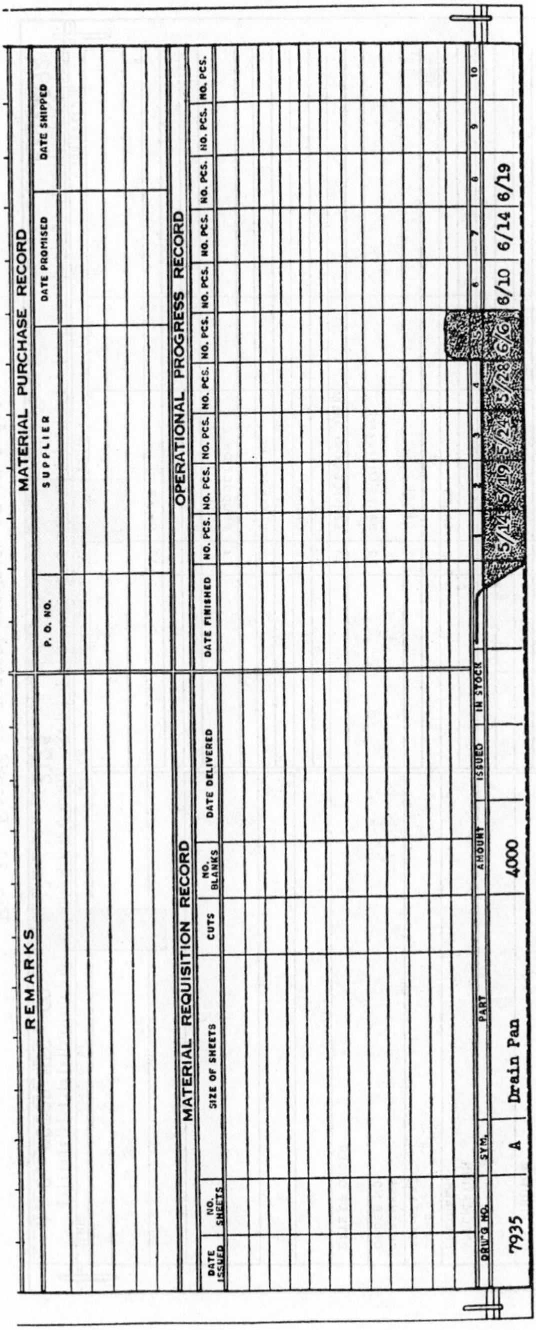

Fig. 31. Card for recording the manufacture of parts for order shown in Fig. 30.

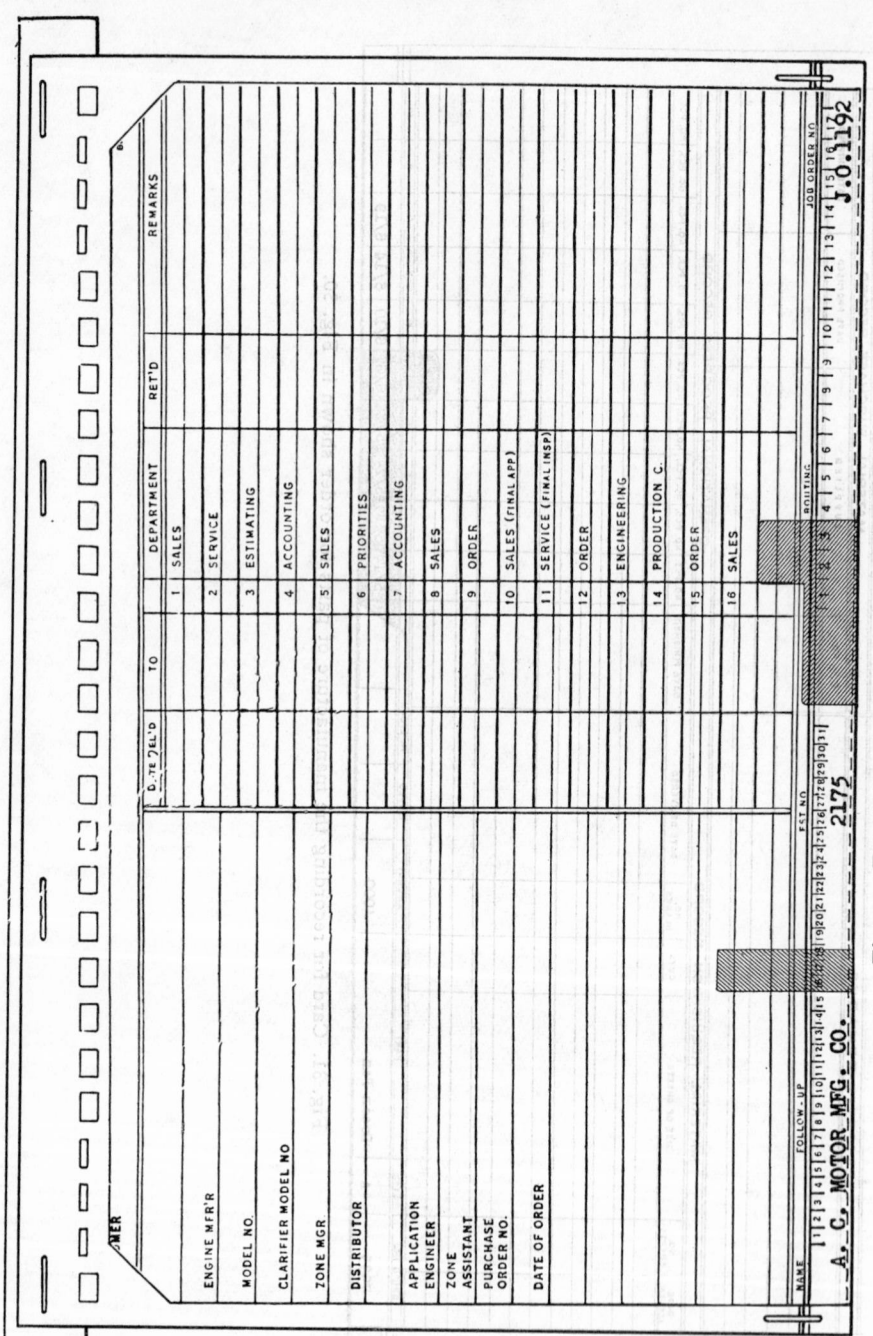

Fig. 32. Record to control progress on an order.

square marked "In Stock" and the production order for the part is released. If material must be bought, purchase record entries are made on the card and production orders are held until the material arrives. When the material is released to the first operation, the signal is moved to the square "Issued." Operation numbers appear along the right of the visible margin and the signal is moved over these numbers as the total quantity required is finished at each operation. The reports are entered in the operational progress record immediately above. Delivery of completed parts to the assembly line is entered in the upper left portion. Parts scrapped or repaired are reported below.

The record used by the Briggs Clarifier Co., shown in Fig. 32, is a basic instrument of production control because it charts the **progress of an order** from receipt through completion. In most plants, orders follow a definite flow line of procedure, and in this record the key points are printed on the form. The record is then indexed alphabetically by customer's name, which appears on a visible margin along with the estimate and job order numbers. A ¼-in. colored transparent movable signal over the left-hand 1 to 31 scale shows the date on which the current step is scheduled for completion. A glance down the slide each day spots any signals lagging behind current date, thus prompting attention. The **Graph-A-Matic** movable signal at the right shows by number the current operation, thus revealing the present status of the order.

VISIBLE INDEX FILES, HORIZONTAL OVERLAPPING. In the TraDex (Diebold, Inc.) or Visirecord systems, cards are filed vertically and overlap horizontally. For ease of reference, these cards are usually filed lengthwise instead of across the file drawers, particularly where they are kept in special large desks at which the record clerk sits. Index dividers and intermediate dividers are used to separate the different sections of cards where desired. Some 25,000 cards can be available within reach for consultation and posting without the operator moving from the desk chair. A desk telephone provides communication to and from operating departments which may receive and give information

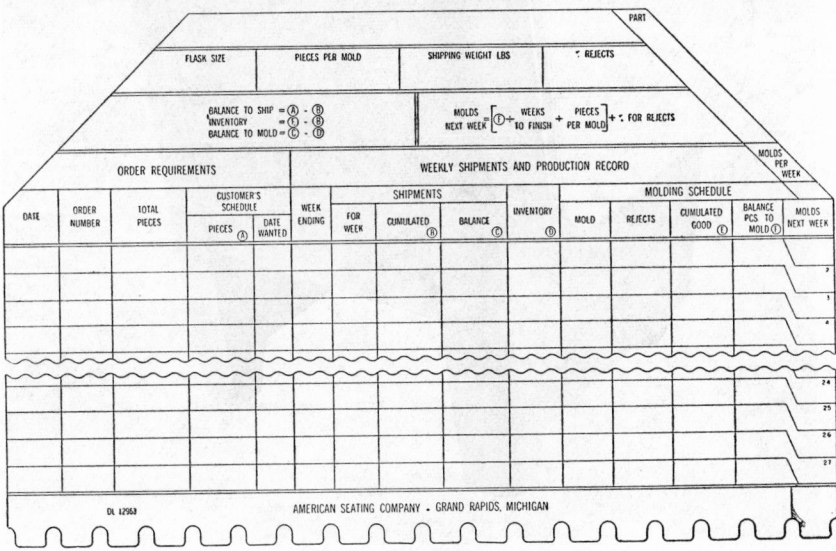

Fig. 33. Card with visible triple margins.

to go on the cards. Calculating machines enable the operator to figure any totals or values which are needed from the data.

The card illustrated in Fig. 33 has **visible triple margins.** In most cases, unless a numerical record is involved, the cards are diagonally cut at 45° on either or both upper corners for indexing. Wider margins are made by longer corner cuts. The upper horizontal edge is provided with a series of heavy signal blocks which automatically indicate when a card is out. The cards rest on a ribbed-corduroy base which gives them a footing. **Offsetting** of the individual cards is accomplished by a series of double notches on the bottom, fitting over spacer rods when the cards are down in place. **Temporary stuffing** is possible to bring like data on different cards together. Detailed data on operations, such as daily production quantities, can be posted to the columns normally covered on the card,

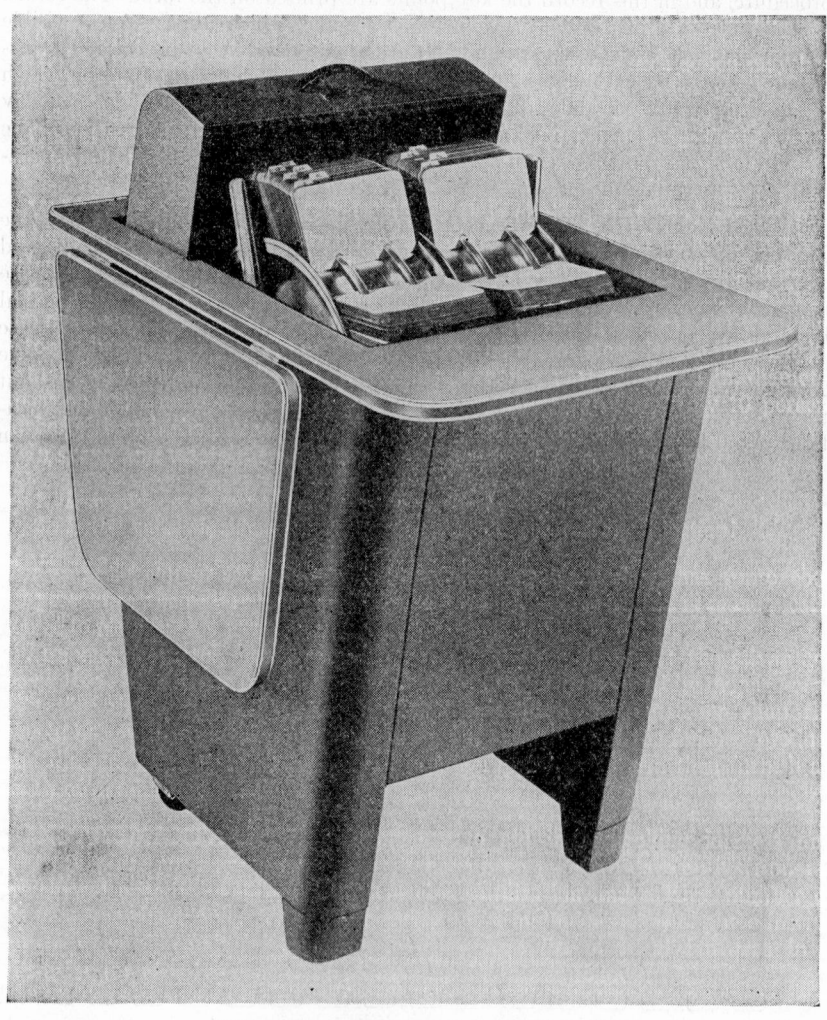

Fig. 34. Desk-model rotary file.

leaving the visible side margin for totals. Down the side margin, therefore, there may be a complete history of the status of the job in successive operations. This **progressive visible margin** is a unique feature of these cards. Various kinds of temporary and permanent signals can be applied to the card. Progressive signals can also be used on the diagonal or vertical margins.

The card can be used on both sides if printed front and back. This allows more than one operator at a time to work on a tray or drawer.

ROTARY OR WHEEL-TYPE FILES. To make large numbers of cards accessible in the shortest time and with the least wasted motion, devices have been developed which find considerable application in the work of production control.

Fig. 34 illustrates a rotary card file (Wheeldex). Cards are mounted by snapping the slot-punched holes over specially formed bars located around the circumference of a **drum.** The desired card is brought to reference position by simply revolving the drum. A special **stabilizing device** permits hand posting without holding the wheel or removing the card. Dividers separate and index the various segments of the file. The large file units come in movable metal cabinets, or they may be mounted in specially designed, semicircular work desks.

In the desk-model Cardineer (Diebold, Inc.) (Fig. 35), cards are filed in special trays with **double holding bars.** The trays, which may be thought of as segments of a drum, are mounted on a **rotor base** which revolves in a horizontal plane. Cards are easily taken out or may be posted while in the trays. The trays can be removed from the rotor for work distribution on peak load days.

Fig. 35. Revolving desk files.

Wheel-type or rotary files come in many different styles and sizes. Depending on their size, they can hold 1,000 to 120,000 cards per unit, all immediately accessible from one position.

Electromechanical Punched-Card Systems

ELEMENTS OF THE SYSTEM. Several electromechanical systems are available for producing the reports and documents essential to planning and controlling production, inventories, cost, and other elements of plant operation. The **elements** of these systems are:

1. The punched card itself, which records by proper perforations in predesignated positions on its surface the essential data (alphabetical or numerical) of a single transaction—sale, shipment, receipt, issue, etc.—as coded instructions for automatic machine operation.
2. Perforating devices for recording the data. Some models are manually operated by a keyboard similar to that of a typewriter or 10-key adding machine. Other devices punch cards automatically from other cards, result accumulators of calculating machines, or even from electronically sensed pencil marks.
3. Verifying machines for proving the accuracy of manually punched cards.
4. Processing machines in wide variety which, guided by instructions in the cards and in machine control units (adjustable at will by the operator), perform automatically an assortment of functions. These include physical arrangement of the cards in any required sequence; adding to or selecting from previously established files of cards; adding, subtracting, multiplying, or dividing several factors from the same or different cards and punching the results in cards which supply the data or in blank cards, or printing these results, together with any desired data from the cards themselves, to prepare a report or document. Most models incorporate large accumulating capacity so that a number of results may be accumulated simultaneously. All operate rapidly, later models using electronic tubes achieving almost unbelievable calculating speeds. Proof of accurate performance is easily obtained.

APPLICATION TO ASSEMBLY OPERATIONS. The International Business Machines system has been applied to a wide variety of industrial situations, including the planning and control of production. The following applications indicate the wide range of possibilities of this technique. A flow chart of a typical production and inventory control system is given in Fig. 36.

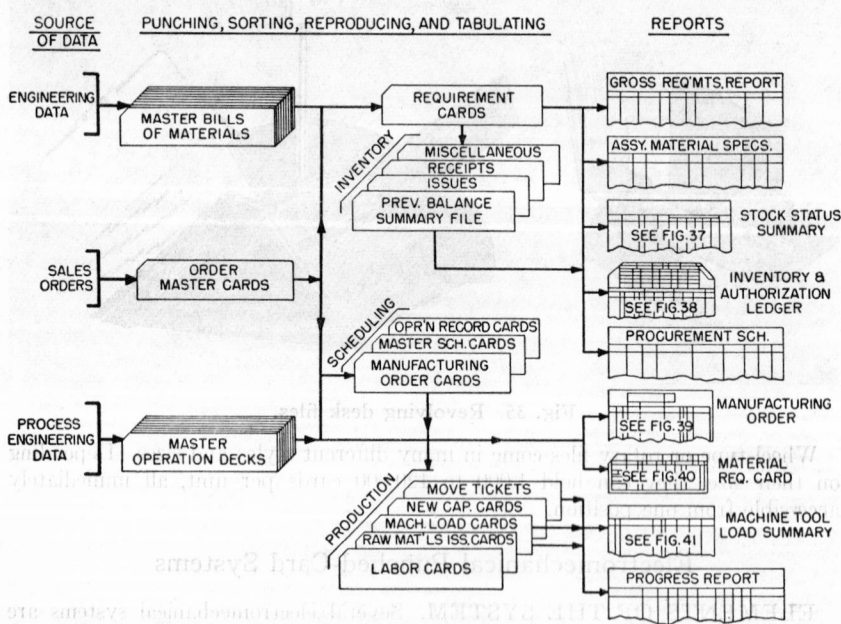

Fig. 36. Application of punched-card system to production and inventory control.

Planning Plant Output. Cards punched from sales orders, shipments, and other finished goods inventory transactions may be automatically processed as often as desired to provide **statistical and operating reports** that facilitate the preparation of product and service part schedules which balance supply to demand.

Material and Inventory Planning. The process by which a product schedule is expressed in terms of the supporting materials, facilities, and manpower required can be expedited by the use of punched-card methods. The basic record required is a permanent set of **bills of materials master cards** (see Fig. 36) for each product or subassembly thereof. One card is punched for each component item and records the symbol identifying the component, the product or assembly on which it is used, and the quantity of the component used. Other clarifying data may be included as needed.

When the production of a given product is authorized, the corresponding specification cards are selected and placed behind a card which records the quantity, order or lot number, date scheduled, etc.

A duplicate set of cards is then automatically reproduced to serve as **requirement cards** (Fig. 36) and the specification cards are returned to the file. A calculator automatically multiplies the number of products to be built by the item quantity per product to obtain the required quantity of each item. This is punched into each requirement card and checked for accuracy. **Accumulation lists** (bills of materials) may be automatically printed from these cards if desired (Fig. 36).

Usually the requirements for a number of products are developed simultaneously. Requirements for a given component are easily consolidated by machine-sorting the several sets of requirement cards to ascending component symbol sequence. In "to order" planning systems a report of the requirements for each component, in total and, if desired, subdivided by product, schedule period, source, or commodity class, may be automatically prepared. When parts are made in "lots" and distributed to assembly lines from stock, the requirement cards are usually merged with others recording actual and anticipated inventory

STOCK STATUS SUMMARY
HORIZONTAL TIME SERIES
DATE

PART NUMBER	PART DESCRIPTION	SCE	ON HAND	TRANS- ACTION	PERIOD						BALANCE TOTAL
					1	2	3	4	5	6	
27057	CONDENSER	2	1200	BALANCE							1200
				REQUIRED	400	410	420	450	410	420	2510−
				ORDERED			600		600		1200
				AVAIL.	800	390	570	120	310	110−	110−
27058	CONDENSER	2	1500	BALANCE							1500
				REQUIRED	450	480	500	500	510	520	2960−
				ORDERED			2000				2000
				AVAIL.	1050	570	2070	1570	1060	540	540
27069	PLATE	1	15000	BALANCE							15000
				REQUIRED	310	350	400	300	350	300	2010−
				ORDERED				5000			5000
				AVAIL.	14690	14340	13940	18640	18290	17990	17990

Fig. 37. Stock status summary report.

PART NUMBER	PART NAME	MFG. QTY.	SCRAP	STD. UNIT COST	ENG. CHG. NO.	NO.
5213	Clamp	400			9999	

PART NUMBER	DATE	REFERENCE NO.	QTY. AUTH.
5213	1-2-	44	400

TR. CODE UNPLANNED
- B = BALANCE OR SUM. CARD
- X = MISC. ISSUE
- W = CREDIT ISSUE
- A = INVTY ADJ. PLUS
- Z = INVTY ADJ. MINUS
- E = MISC. RECEIPT

TR. CODE PLANNED
- R = REQUIREMENT
- O = ON ORDER
- I = ISSUE
- D = RECEIPT
- K = CANC. REQMNT
- C = CANC. ON ORDER

REFERENCE DATA			ACTUAL TRANSACTIONS			PLANNED TRANSACTIONS		
PART NO.	U/M	ORDER OR REFERENCE NO.	DATE	T R	RECEIPTS	WITHDRAWALS	ON HAND	REQUIRED	ON ORDER	AVAILABLE
5213	PC	115418 14	101	B	130		130			130
5213	PC	119448 43	103	R				60		60-
5213	PC	115418 54	103	R				52		52-
5213	PC	119448 83	103	R				60		60-
5213	PC	115418 101	103	R				52		52-
5213	PC	119448 130	103	R				60		60-
5213	PC	179203 130	103	R				51		51-
5213	PC	115418 142	103	R				1		1-
5213	PC	119448 171	103	R				60		60-
5213	PC	179203 171	103	R				47		47-
5213	PC	5213 44	105	O				1	400	1-
					130		130	444	400	86 TOT

Fig. 38. Inventory and authorization ledger report.

transactions (balances, receipts, disbursements, and authorizations) so that a consolidated report may be obtained. A wide variety of **stock status reports** (Fig. 37) may be obtained, each designed to meet the needs of a particular situation. These may be simple periodic summaries relating requirements to present and anticipated supplies as a guide to further authorization of procurement or fabrication. A daily machine-posted ledger showing transaction detail (Fig. 38) is often required. In other cases, time distribution of net requirements may be more desirable in the form of a **procurement schedule.** Similar principles apply to the control of raw material inventories.

Facility and Manpower Planning. Punched cards are well suited to the preparation of authorization and control documents, as well as the resultant planning for facilities and manpower. **Labor specification cards** permanently record the pertinent data for each of the several steps in fabricating a part or

PART NO.	ORD.NO.	QUANTITY	DATE ISSUE		SHEET	MANUFACTURING ORDER
27002	125	325	5	12	1	

CHASSIS	PWR UNIT						

OPER. NO.	DEPT. NO.	GRP. NO.	DESCRIPTION OF OPERATION	TOOL NUMBER	SCE	COND	START DATE
1	500		RAW STORES	2110064 LB		5		115
3	500	122	SHEAR	TO FIT DIE			6	117
5	170	112	BLANK	PIERCE HOLES	1087	6	6	118
10	170	20	FORM		87603	6	6	119
20	190	810	SPOT WELD	CORNERS				120
25	030	201	CSK & BURR					122
35	010	142	FINISH	BRIGHT CADMIUM PLATE				124
40	830		STOCK					125
			ENG.CHG.	#4263				

Fig. 39. A manufacturing order.

assembly. These cards may automatically actuate machines which prepare in printed form or as punched cards such essential documents as **manufacturing orders** (Fig. 39), **material requisitions** (Fig. 40), move and dispatch cards, job cards, etc. Since all documents are prepared from a single verified source, accuracy is assured.

These cards also provide a means of calculating machine loads and operating schedules. Reports relating **capacity and load** (Fig. 41) form a basis for planning facility and manpower. Others reveal daily the progress of work to direct intelligent expediting effort.

Relation to Other Records. Of special interest is the re-use of information for other purposes; this is an inherent feature of the mobility of the punched-card system. For example, the same material requisition which is processed to reduce the quantities inventory record may be priced and extended to correct material valuation and control value accounts, charge work in process, and finally to transactions (balances, receipts, disbursements, and authorizations) so that a consolidated report may be obtained. A summary of several of these reports (Fig. 37) may be prepared for a particular area or for an entire plant situation. The present and anticipated requirements—to present and anticipated requirements of procurement or labor—may be obtained in detail (Fig. 38) is often expressed.

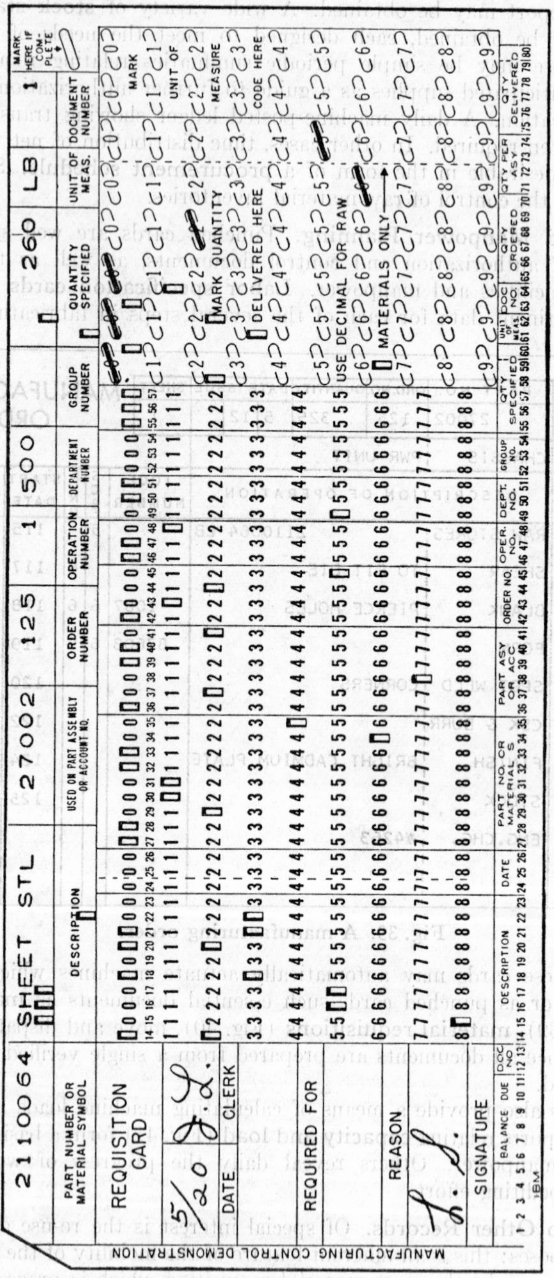

Facility and processes—

Fig. 40. A material requisition card.

MACHINE TOOL LOAD SUMMARY

MACHINE SHOP A

DEPT. NO.	GRP. NO.	DESCRIPTION	NO. OF MACHS.	EFFIC'Y	WK.	CAPACITY	LOAD	AVAILABLE CAPACITY	OVER-LOAD
1	1	BENCH MILLS	5	85%	1	136.0	130.0	6.0	
					2	170.0	160.0	10.0	
					3	170.0	165.5	4.5	
					4	170.0	179.0		9.0
					5	170.0	162.3	7.7	
					6	170.0	185.1		15.1
					7	170.0	150.0	20.0	
					8	170.0	162.8	7.2	
						1326.0*	1294.7*	55.4*	24.1*
1	3	SMALL HORZ MILLS	8	80%	1	204.8	198.0	6.8	
					2	256.0	250.0	6.0	
					3	256.0	251.9	4.1	
					4	256.0	269.5		13.5
					5	256.0	256.0		
					6	256.0	240.0	16.0	
					7	256.0	263.0		7.0
					8	256.0	248.0	8.0	
						1996.8*	1976.4*	40.9*	20.5*
1	5	MED HORZ MILLS	7	80%	1	179.2	178.1	1.1	
					2	224.0	221.0	3.0	
					3	224.0	222.0	2.0	
					4	224.0	225.6		1.6
					5	224.0	218.4	5.6	
					6	224.0	221.0	3.0	
					7	224.0	226.8		2.8
					8	224.0	223.0	1.0	
						1747.2*	1735.9*	15.7*	4.4*
1	7	LGE HORZ MILLS	6	80%	1	153.6	149.2	4.4	
					2	192.0	193.2		1.2
					3	192.0	194.1		2.1
					4	192.0	191.5	.5	
					5	192.0	187.2	4.8	
					6	192.0	191.0	1.0	
					7	192.0	193.2		1.2
					8	192.0	190.0	2.0	
						1497.6*	1489.4*	12.7*	4.5*

Fig. 41. A machine tool load summary.

establish the material cost of the order. Similar relationships between document needs exist in many areas wherein a coordinated record-keeping system may be developed.

APPLICATION TO CUSTOM MOLDING. Punched-card systems are not restricted to large assembly-type operations. The following procedures are typical for a plastics molding plant which does custom molding. The company has no product line of its own; all production is according to customers' specifications and the molds (tools) are owned by the customer. This example is taken from an actual Remington Rand punched-card accounting machine installation. Fig. 42 gives a flow chart of the production control procedures under this system

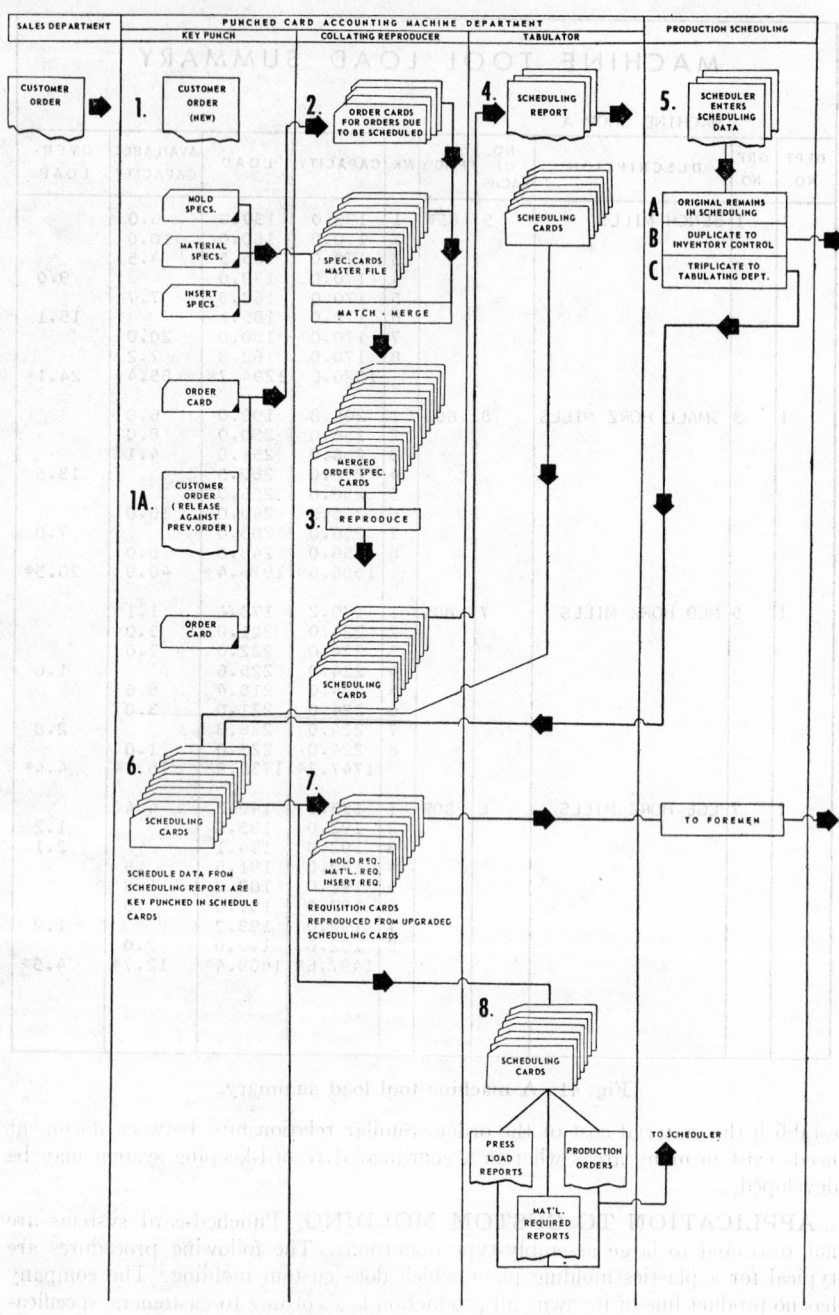

Fig. 42. Application of punched-card system to custom molding production control.

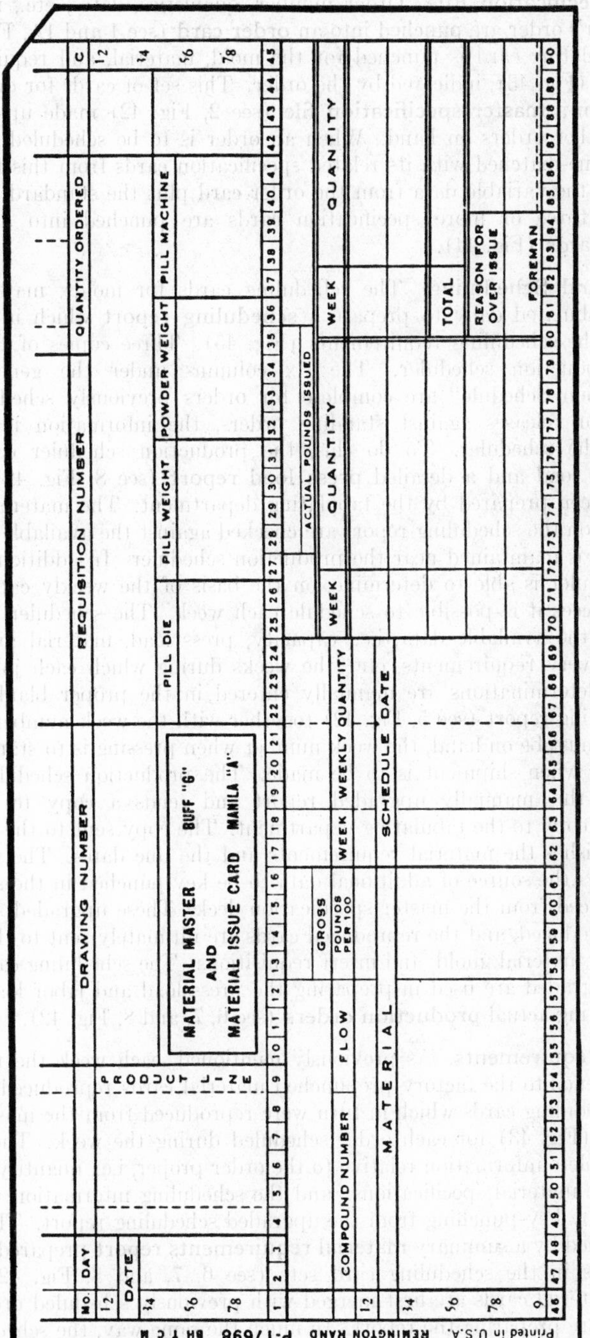

Fig. 43. Material master and material issue card.

Master Specification File. Order number, quantities, dates, etc., relative to each customer's order are punched into an **order card** (see 1 and 1A, Fig. 42). A separate tabulating card is punched for the mold, material, and required insert specifications (Fig. 43), indicated by the order. This set of cards for one order is then placed in a **master specification file** (see 2, Fig. 42) made up of similar sets for all other orders on hand. When an order is to be scheduled, the order card is machine-matched with its related specification cards from this file (see 3, Fig. 42), and the variable data from the order card plus the standard data from each of the three or more specification cards are punched into a series of **scheduling cards** (Fig. 44).

Loading and Scheduling. The scheduling cards for molds, materials, and inserts are tabulated daily to prepare a **scheduling report** which in its initial form shows the scheduling requirements (Fig. 45). Three copies of this report go to a production scheduler. The six columns under the general heading "Production Schedule" are complete for orders previously scheduled. For new orders or releases against standing orders, the information is manually entered by the scheduler. To do this, the production scheduler consults an over-all press load and a detailed **press load report** (see 8, Fig. 42), both of which have been prepared by the tabulating department. The material requirements shown on the scheduling report are checked against the available inventory record, which is maintained near the production scheduler. In addition, the production scheduler is able to determine, on the basis of the weekly capacity, the number of pieces it is possible to schedule each week. The scheduler can easily decide, from the available data, i.e., capacity, press load, material availability, customer delivery requirements, etc., the weeks during which each job is to be run. These determinations are manually entered in the proper blank columns of the scheduling report (see 5, Fig. 42) together with the week number in which the material must be on hand, the week number when pressing is to start, and the week number when shipment is to be made. The production scheduler retains one copy of this manually upgraded report and sends a copy to inventory control and a copy to the tabulating department. The copy sent to the inventory control establishes the material requirements and the due dates. The tabulating copy is used as the source of additional data to be key-punched in the scheduling cards reproduced from the master specification deck. These upgraded scheduling cards are reproduced, and the reproduced cards are ultimately sent to the factory for use as raw material, mold, and insert requisitions. The scheduling cards which have been upgraded are used in preparing the press load and labor load reports and in tabulating actual **production orders** (see 6, 7, and 8, Fig. 42).

Material Requirements. As previously mentioned, each week the tabulating department sends to the factory prepunched material cards reproduced from the upgraded scheduling cards which in turn were reproduced from the master specification deck (Fig. 43) for each order scheduled during the week. These copies contain: complete information relative to the order proper, i.e., quantity, delivery date, etc.; the material specifications; and the scheduling information which has been entered by key-punching from the upgraded scheduling report. These cards are accompanied by a summary **material requirements report** prepared from the material cards in the scheduling card sets (see 6, 7, and 8, Fig. 42). These scheduling material cards are first merged with previously scheduled order material cards before preparing the report. In much the same way, the schedule cards are prepared for tabulating the press load reports (Fig. 46). When a job is actually

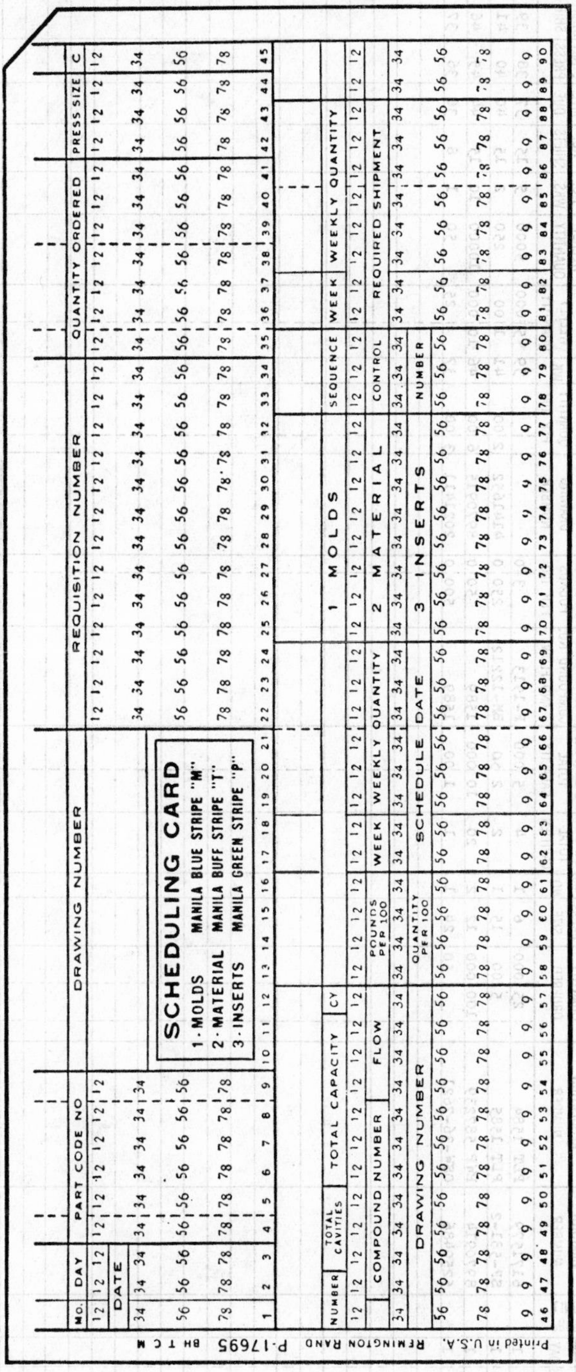

Fig. 44. Scheduling card.

SCHEDULING REPORT

SHEET NO. 1 OF 1
DATE PREPARED 9-1-
INITIALS WJC

DATE MO./DAY	PROD. LINE	DRAWING NUMBER	REQUISITION NUMBER	QUANTITY ORDERED	PRESS SIZE	MOLDS NO.	TOTAL CAVITIES	TOTAL CAPACITY	MATERIALS COMPOUND NO. AND FLOW	POUNDS PER 100	INSERTS DRAWING NUMBER	QUANTITY PER 100	REQ'D SHIP. WK.	REQ'D SHIP. WEEKLY QUANTITY	PROD. SCHED. WEEKLY QUANTITY	NO. WKS.	NO. SHIFTS	MTL. DUE	START PRESS	START SHIP
9 1		6171579	PLT 1584	25,000	6	1	4	5,000	P-1913	3 0	4141652		39	5,000	5000	5	15	37	38	39
9 1		SP-581-2	PLT 1585	5,100	15	1	2	2 50	BM-12212	250 0	8970915	2 00	41	1,100	250	2	15	40	40	41
9 1		8970914	PMP 587239	100,000	12	2	20	10,000	1589	50 0	2021411	6 00	46	10,000	10000	10	15	44	45	46
9 1		5250486	OSW-36-7621	50	24	1	1	1 00	1589	500 0		3 00	37	25	50	1	8	36	36	37

Fig. 45. Scheduling report.

DETAIL PRESS LOAD REPORT

PRODUCT CODE
PRODUCT LINE — 1 PHENOLIC   2 UREA   3 INJECTION   5 MYCALEX
PRESS SIZE 3"
NO. OF PRESSES 10

SHEET NO. _____ OF _____
DATE
INITIALS

SCHEDULED WEEKS: 1 2 3 4 5 6 7 8 9 10 11 12 13 14 15 16 17 18 19 20 21 22 23 24 25 26 27 28 29 30 31 32 33 34 35 36 37 38 39 40 41 42 43 44 45 46 47 48 49 50 51 52 53

DRAWING NUMBER	REQUISITION NUMBER	QUANTITY ORDERED	WEEKLY QUANTITY	SCHEDULED WEEKS
5520276	PLT-1446	10 000	1 000	X X X X X X X X X X X
14476-1	PLT-1375	5 00	5 00	X
4150360	SW-36-10711	110 000	25 000	X X X X X
SF-1589	PLT-1401	62 000	20 000	X X X X X X
5962360	FWP-690170	7 500	2 00	X X X X
414-SW-771	PLT-1392	50	25	X X
8920290-02	BPW-313160	10 000	2 000	X X X X X
18J576	EWR-6260	75 000	15 000	X X X X X
18J577	EWR-6261	75 000	15 000	X X X X X
2028360	EM-11136	5 000	5 00	X X X X X X X X
3160827	WL-15-1763	8 500	1 000	X X X X X X X

Fig. 46. Detail press load report.

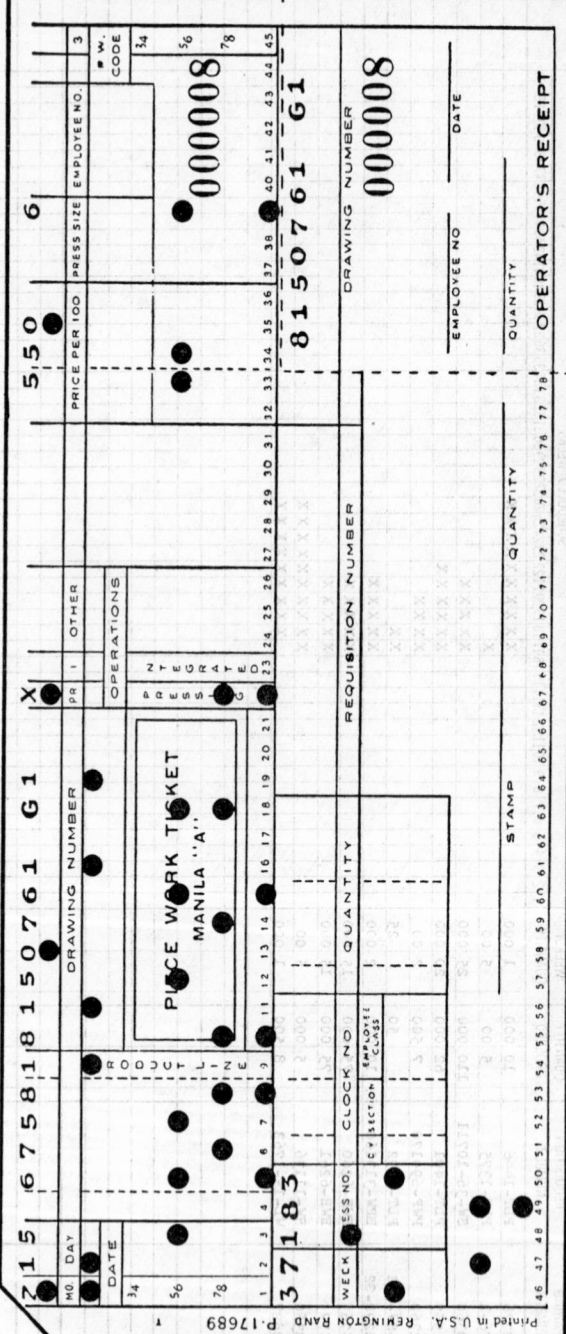

Fig. 47. Piecework ticket.

CDP 187 10-50 □

REPORT OF PARTS PRESSED

PRESS SIZE _____   FROM _____ TO _____   FOR PERIOD _____ TO _____

SHEET NO. _____ OF _____   WEEK ENDING _____   INITIALS _____

PROD. LINE	DRAWING NUMBER	PRESSED TODAY	WEEKLY SCHEDULE	WEEK TO DATE	DES.	TOTAL TO DATE	DES.	BALANCE DUE TO BE PRESSED	DES.	REMARKS
1	P 8300	2 808	20 000	13 565	T	127 800	T	108 200	T	
1	12600		1 500	1	T	1 273	T	12 127	T	
1	12928 3 1	32	750	93	T	407	T	793	T	
1	DP 52606 M	60	750	424	T	2 321	T	3 679	T	
1	DP 52609 M		250		T	1 208	T	1 292	T	
1	1290228 3	17	500	190	T	251	T	577	T	
1	4129309	392		2 261	T	9 528	T	10 472	T	
1	P4129375	14 355	75 000	83 255	T	982 740	T	2 817 260	T	
1	5229904	169		530	T	2 916	T	2 084	T	
1	5414952	572		3 739	T	4 736	T	45 264	T	
1	8907500 2	3 622	12 500	20 232	T	232 767	T	504 233	T	
1	8907500 3	502	2 800	3 680	T	41 782	T	62 218	T	
		22 529		127 969	G	1 407 729	G	3 568 199	G	

Fig. 48. Report of parts pressed.

released to the shop for production, the material cards, sent to the stock room as authority to issue material for the job, are used by the storeskeeper to enter the quantity delivered for production. These same cards are used to reduce the physical inventory balance and frequently are priced out and used in work-in-process and cost accounting.

Factory Order. Also from the scheduling cards at the time of preparing the material requisition cards, the tabulating department prepares the factory mold and insert requisition cards and sends them to scheduling. These are held by the production scheduler until, in accordance with the projected production line-up on the scheduling report, he releases them to a dispatcher. The dispatcher actually assigns the jobs to specific production centers in the factory. The requisition cards are sent to the foreman concerned, and the tabulating department supplies any required number of **piecework ticket cards** shown in Fig. 47. These tickets are designed to allow the operator to tear off the lower right-hand corner of the card as a receipt for work done. These cards, in addition to their use in payroll and cost accounting, are also used to tabulate the daily **production report** illustrated in Fig. 48.

Automatic Data Processing

ELECTRONIC COMPUTERS. The scope of automatic data processing has been greatly extended with the introduction of computers. In contrast to earlier punched-card equipment, these new machines are entirely electronic. This factor has so increased processing speeds that applications which would have been impractical with punched cards alone have become quite feasible. Computers range greatly in size and capacity and are dealt with in detail in the section on Electronic Computers. The following paragraphs outline a few of the production planning and control areas to which electronic computers may be applied effectively.

Sales Estimates. The application of computers to sales estimating offers a number of possible advantages:

1. **Quantity of data handled.** With operating speeds ranging from microseconds to a few milliseconds, computers can handle quantities of data which would be uneconomic with other methods. Previous practical limitations on the amount and coverage of sales data used in the estimating procedure can be revised sharply upward.
2. **Speed of reporting results.** Large quantities of data are of no value until they reach personnel responsible for decisions. Sales estimates characteristically are needed as soon as possible after the latest data become available and are subject to frequent changes. Until the advent of computers, these factors usually forced simplification and abbreviation of the data on which estimates were based.
3. **Application of mathematics.** Mathematical calculations that would take years by other methods are done in hours on a computer. This opens the way for the use of mathematical models of demand functions which need not be so simplified as to destroy the practical value.

Operation Models. Electronic computers further open the way for development of more precise **mathematical models** of industrial operations and for practical applications of such models. The many factors involved in planning the petrochemical operation discussed in the section on Production Planning and Control illustrate this point. The problems of balancing estimated sales, inventories, and production, establishing optimum operating rates and determining the most economic use of transportation and supply facilities all lend themselves to mathematical treatment. Since this type of treatment involves lengthy computations and large quantities of data, it is doubtful that it could be used in practice without a computer. This is particularly true if numerous runs, with somewhat altered data in each, are required to place alternative solutions, and their consequences, before planning personnel.

Loading and Scheduling. In situations which involve large numbers of machines, parts, and operations, loading and scheduling has always been a difficult and expensive job. It is particularly hard when new orders, cancellations, or delays are apt to call for frequent and comprehensive revisions of plans. With its stored program, stored constants, and high operating speed, a computer can handle problems of this type very quickly.

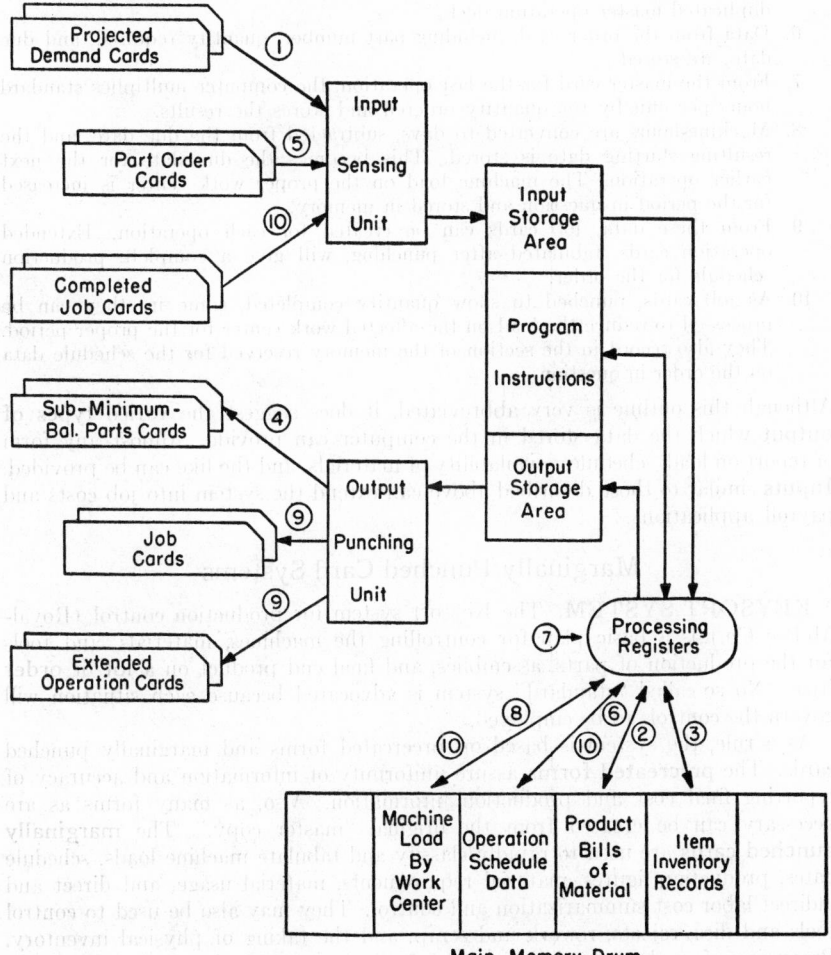

Fig. 49. Flow chart of computer loading and scheduling process.

Fig. 49 shows a simplified diagram of the way in which a computer can be applied to this kind of planning and control problem. Major steps in the computer procedure, numbered in the diagram, are described below:

1. Projected product demand is fed on cards into the computer.
2. For each product, computer explodes assembly and parts requirements based on bills of materials sorted in memory and arrives at total requirements for each part.
3. Computer compares parts requirements against parts availability by production periods through comparison with projected inventory plus production stored in memory.
4. On parts where this process causes available balance to drop below a predetermined minimum, card output is produced showing part number, on hand, on order, allocated, and available balances.
5. After planners determine how each of these exceptions should be handled, order cards for some or all of these parts are fed into the computer along with a duplicated master operation deck.
6. Data from the order card, including part number, quantity required, and due date, are stored.
7. From the master card for the last operation, the computer multiplies standard hours per unit by the quantity ordered and stores the results.
8. Machine-hours are converted to days, subtracted from the due date, and the resulting starting date is stored. This becomes the due date for the next earlier operation. The machine load on the proper work center is increased for the period in question and stored in memory.
9. From these data, job cards can be created for each operation. Extended operation cards, tabulated after punching, will give a complete production schedule for the order.
10. As job cards, punched to show quantity completed, come in, they can be processed to reduce the load on the affected work center for the proper period. They also record in the section of the memory reserved for the schedule data on the order in question.

Although this outline is very abbreviated, it does suggest the varied **types of output** which the data stored in the computer can provide. Almost any form of report on load, schedules, availability of materials, and the like can be provided. **Inputs** similar to those described above can extend the system into job costs and payroll applications.

Marginally Punched Card Systems

KEYSORT SYSTEM. The Keysort system for production control (Royal-McBee Co.) is a basic plan for controlling the machines, materials, and tools for the production of parts, assemblies, and final end product on a **lot** or **order** basis. No so-called "standard" system is advocated because each situation will govern the controls to be employed.

As a rule, the system is based on precreated forms and marginally punched cards. The **precreated forms** assure uniformity of information and accuracy of reporting final cost and production information. Also, as many forms as are necessary can be created from the original "master copy." The **marginally punched cards** are used to rapidly classify and tabulate machine loads, schedule dates, production figures, material requirements, material usage, and direct and indirect labor cost summarization and control. They may also be used to control tools and dies, rejects, rework and scrap, and the taking of physical inventory. Processing of cards and tabulation of information may be handled at a central location or at decentralized points throughout the plant.

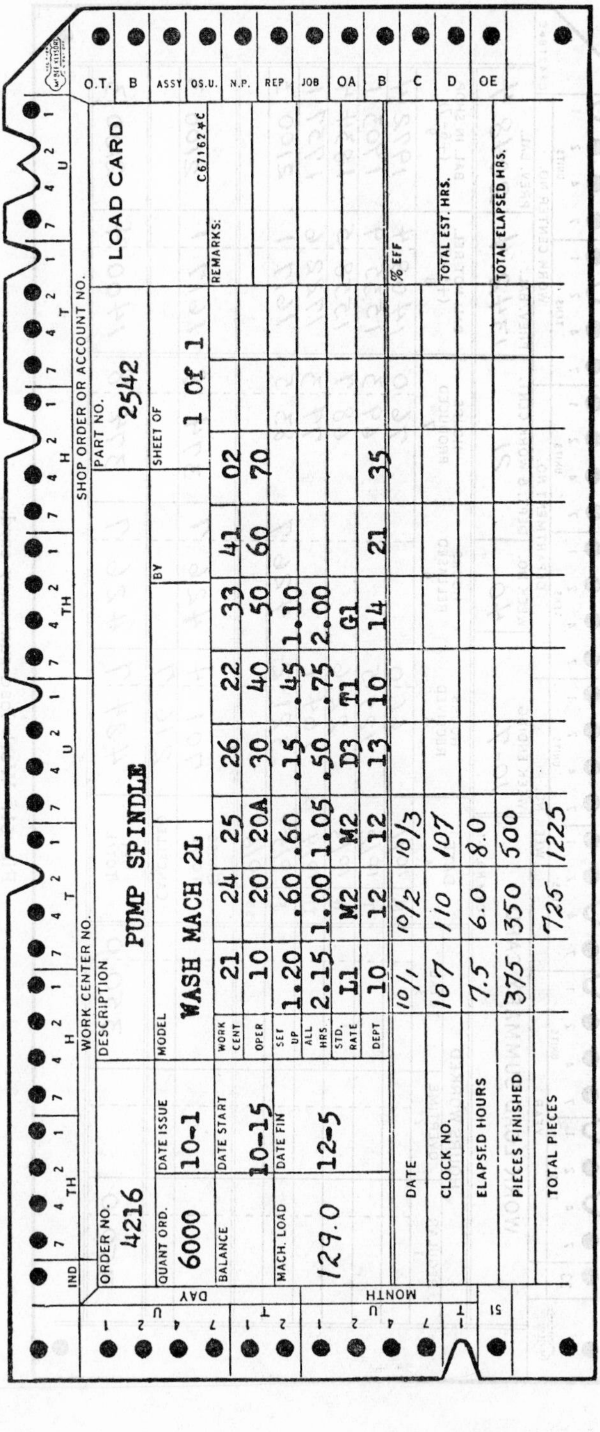
LOAD CARD
ORDER NO. 4216
QUANT ORD. 6000
BALANCE
MACH. LOAD 129.0
DATE ISSUE 10-1
DATE START 10-15
DATE FIN 12-5
WORK CENTER NO.
DESCRIPTION PUMP SPINDLE
MODEL WASH MACH 2L
SHOP ORDER OR ACCOUNT NO.
PART NO. 2542
SHEET OF 1 Of 1
BY
REMARKS:
C67162*C
WORK CENT 21 24 25 26 22 33 41 02
OPER 10 20 20A 30 40 50 60 70
SET UP 1.20 .60 .60 .15 .45 1.10
ALL HRS. 2.15 1.00 1.05 .50 .75 2.00
STD. RATE L1 M2 M2 D3 T1 G1
DEPT 10 12 12 13 10 14 21 35
% EFF
TOTAL EST. HRS.
TOTAL ELAPSED HRS.
DATE 10/1 10/2 10/3
CLOCK NO. 107 110 107
ELAPSED HOURS 7.5 6.0 8.0
PIECES FINISHED 375 350 500
TOTAL PIECES 725 1225
O.T. B ASSY OS.U. N.P. REP JOB OA B C D OE
IND
DAY
MONTH
TH H T U

Fig. 50. Load card.

WORK LOAD SUMMARY CARD

C84218*C

	WEEK NO.	WEEK ENDING	DEPARTMENT NO.	WORK CENTER NO.	PREV. BAL.
	40	10-7-	DEPT. & WORK CENT. 21	PREV. BAL. 1342.4	2048.4

FORM NO. X-149

HOURS WORKED: REGULAR 1 | OVERTIME 2 | TOTAL 3 — REGULAR 350.0, TOTAL 350.0

DATE 4	HOURS RECEIVED 5	HOURS RELEASED 6	HOURS PRODUCED 7	BAL. NOT REL. (+5-6) 8	BAL. IN SHOP (+6-7) 9
M 10/1	66.0		76.0	1408.4	1972.4
T 10/2	127.5		69.3	1535.9	1903.1
W 10/3	22.6		68.7	1558.5	1834.4
TH 10/4	164.1		71.3	1722.6	1757.1
F 10/5	321.2	426.7	83.5	1617.1	2100.3
S&S 10/6					
GROSS TOTAL	701.4	426.7	374.8	1617.1	2100.3
CANCELLED	216.7				
NET TOTAL	484.7	426.7	374.8	1400.4	2100.3

Fig. 51. Work load summary card.

Work-in-Process Control. The marginally punched labor cards, material requisitions, identification cards, and load cards provide the following:

1. Physical control of quantity of work in process—the quantity reported for both payroll and inventory is taken from the same source and is compared at various operational stages or when delivered to finished stores.
2. Financial summarization and control of work in process.
3. Identification of each item of work in process.
4. Positive location of work in process in the shop.
5. Systematic charting of work in process through the shop.
6. A preliminary check, in advance of actual needs, on the availability of materials to start work in process through the shop.

Figs. 50 and 51 demonstrate typical applications of the marginally punched cards.

Duplication and Communication Systems

DUPLICATION OF INFORMATION. Production control systems usually require considerable duplication of information and instructions. The number of forms and copies is often fairly high, even though every effort has been made to hold them to a minimum. Time and money are wasted and the chance of error is increased if control data are repeatedly recopied; for this reason, careful **form design** and choice of the proper **method of duplication** are very important.

The simplest method of duplication involves merely regular carbon paper. This method is limited by the number of clear copies which can be obtained from one typing and the clerical costs encountered in continually handling a number of separate sheets. It is employed most effectively where the number of copies is small and the same data are not required again and again. As standard data become more complex and the number of copies required increases, other duplicating methods usually prove more satisfactory.

CONTINUOUS FORMS. Typical of the numerous well-devised and efficient continuous-type forms available for production control are those made by the Standard Register Co., Moore Business Forms, Inc., and other well-known representative producers. Such forms find many applications in production control procedures. Standard Register products, for example, include continuous Kant-Slip forms, Zip-sets (unit combinations of forms and carbons), Form Flow Registers, Registrator Platens, and various types of auxiliary form-handling equipment such as carbon separators and bursters. The Formcraft Division of the company, like similar divisions in the other companies, assists customers in analyzing control procedures, writing methods, and form designs, and effecting improvements and simplifications wherever possible.

D. W. Onan and Sons, manufacturers of electric plants, use a 5-part Kant-Slip move order. The manner in which these **move orders** and the 3-part Kant-Slip **receiving report** fit into the control system is illustrated in the procedure flow chart, Fig. 52. (See section on Process Charts for a discussion of procedure flow and other charts.) When the material is received in the shop, a move order is made out on a Form Flow Kant-Slip Register. The move order provides both the production office and shop office with necessary information to trace material in process. This information has saved 30 man-hours of searching and checking per week.

By providing information concerning scrap and rework in addition to production flow, this move order becomes an important source record for both inventory

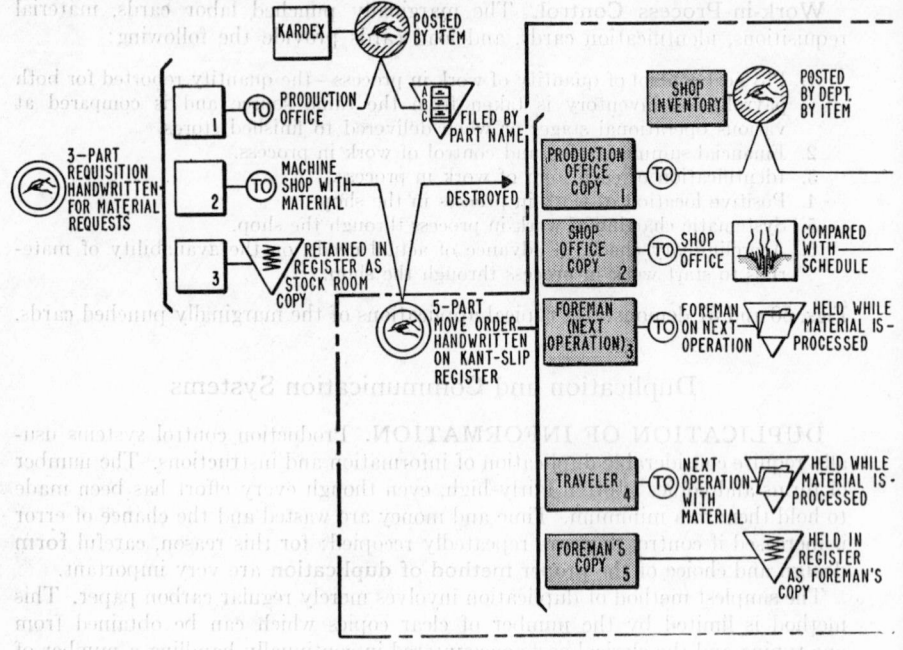

Fig. 52. Procedure

control and quality control, and insures the effectiveness of these controls since they are based on an accurate record.

In the production of International trucks at the Springfield works of International Harvester Co., the tabulating department produces a description of each truck's chassis, engine, axles, cab, and all other component parts about 10 days before that vehicle starts down the assembly line. This description, or group of specifications, is called a **line setting ticket** (Fig. 53) because it functions to get an assembly line "set" for a particular truck. Hundreds of these tickets, for as many vehicles, are run daily on an IBM alphabetic electric accounting machine. The cards used for writing them are pulled from a tub file of prepunched cards according to the requirements of the sales orders as they are released to the tabulating department by the production scheduling department.

The tabulating form is a Kant-Slip continuous **offset paper plate**—a master preprinted to reproduce the form together with the tabulated entries, on plain copy sheets, when it is operated on a lithographic-process type of duplicating machine.

Making about 45 copies of each tabulated ticket on a Multilith machine (the last one on heavy manila stock), Harvester distributes them to various key spots throughout the plant—at production control points and into the hands of department foremen. The tickets inform interested persons what trucks are coming up, the parts and assemblies each will require, and the approximate date for which completion is scheduled. In the cases of engines and axles, the tickets show the variables required for each and serve to guide these major subassembly lines the same as the truck assembly.

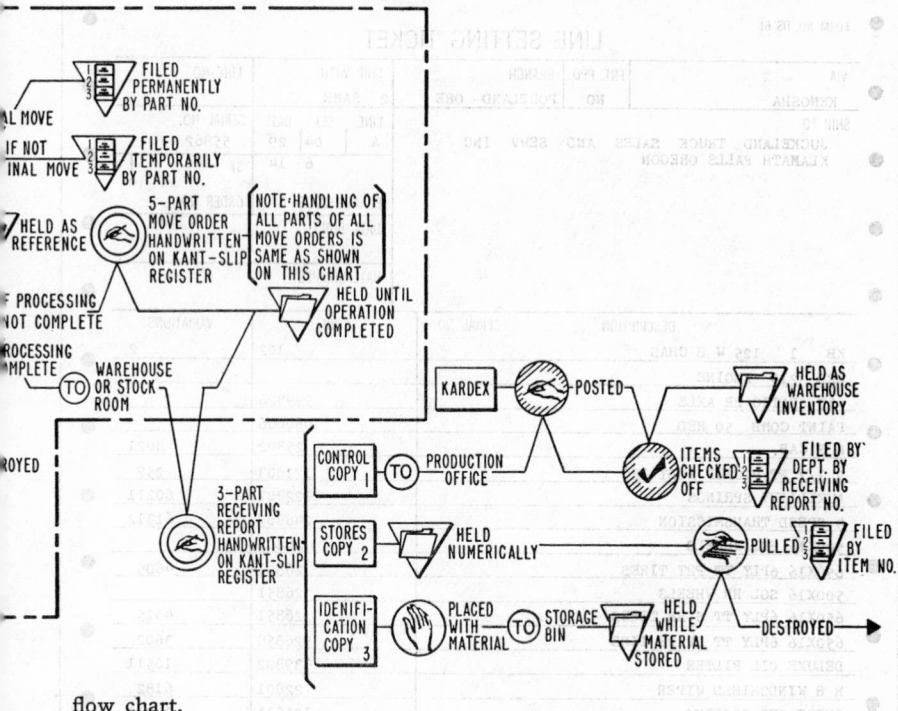

flow chart.

"Line No." is the significant entry on the ticket for the actual schedule. It will denote the position of the truck in sequence on the line. This is not put on in tabulating the master form. It is governed at the Springfield works by the limitation of manufacturing facilities. Two or three days before the "line set date" appearing on all copies, the production control department gives the **line number** to all points by TelAutograph, referring to the tabulated serial number of the ticket.

A copy of the line setting ticket accompanies each component assembly through its production to the final truck assembly. The heavy manila copy and several paper copies are attached to the chassis frame, the first item on the track. As it reaches each station, the part, identified by a ticket whose line and serial numbers match those of the manila copy, is assembled. As the frame passes the engine-mounting station, a chassis serial number is assigned and handwritten, with the engine number, on all copies of the ticket attached to the frame.

When the completely assembled truck has been tested and arrives at the shipping department, the heavy manila copy is pulled and forwarded to the billing department where an invoice number and shipping date are manually entered. This copy is then forwarded to the tabulating department.

After the preparation of the line setting ticket master, the IBM punched cards are held in a suspense file. These cards also contain all data required for billing, including price.

Upon receipt of the manila copy of the line setting ticket from the billing department, the tabulating department pulls the billing cards, punches invoice number and date, and tabulates a multiple-copy **invoice-bill of lading** on Kant-

FORM NO. DS 61

LINE SETTING TICKET

VIA	FRT. PPD.	BRANCH	SHIP WITH	LINE NO.
KENOSHA	NO	PORTLAND ORE	2 SAME	

SHIP TO
JUCKELAND TRUCK SALES AND SERV INC
KLAMATH FALLS OREGON

LINE	SET	DATE	SERIAL NO.
A	04	29	55862
	6	14	ST 160

BRANCH CODE   ORDER NO

DATE BUILT

DATE SHIPPED

DESCRIPTION	SERIAL NO.	CODE	VARIATIONS
KB 1 125 W B CHAS		102	2
GRD 214 ENGINE			
418 RATIO RR AXLE		999826	
PAINT COMB 50 RED		960006	
H P CAB		25802	8021
7 1/2 FT PICKUP BODY IHC		121803	257
AUXILIARY SPRINGS		122801	60211
4 SPEED TRANSMISSION		246807	61312
500X16 FRT WHEELS		26801	
650X16 6PLY TT FRT TIRES		26801	4605
500X16 SGL RR WHEELS		26851	
650X16 6PLY TT S RR TIRES		26851	4615
650X16 6PLY TT SPARE TIRE		926858	3602
DELUXE OIL FILTER		139802	10511
R H WINDSHIELD WIPER		22801	6182
INCREASED COOLING		101801	33011
HEATER AND DEFROSTER		370801	12311
R H REAR VIEW MIRROR		188801	14511
R H SUN VISOR		416801	6032
FULL LENGTH REAR BUMPER		414801	7812
SPEEDOMETER ADAPTER			90001

Fig. 53. Line setting ticket.

Slip continuous forms. The cards are then used to prepare various shipping and accounting reports.

DITTO MASTERS. Duplicating equipment has been used to advantage in cutting down the clerical labor required in production control systems. Reduction of 60 percent in labor and 90 percent in writing are not uncommon. Ditto systems are used with equal effectiveness in providing assembly, subassembly, and parts orders.

Parts Order System. In the Hamilton Manufacturing Co., among other plants, this system is employed for parts orders. A **production order master form** is prepared from the operations lists and routing for a part and is filed by part number. When the part is to be run, this master is used and, through Ditto carbon on a separate superimposed **variable master form**, there are written in longhand the necessary specific data, such as order number and quantity. These two masters are then reproduced to provide production orders to each department doing the work, and to the planning department (Kardex copy) and dispatcher. (See Fig. 54.)

Unit cards are then reproduced, without rewriting, for each single operation (only) plus the data from the head of the master. These cards constitute a move

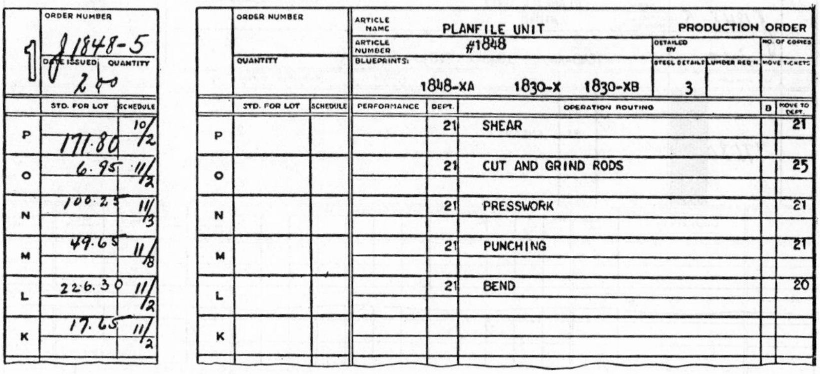

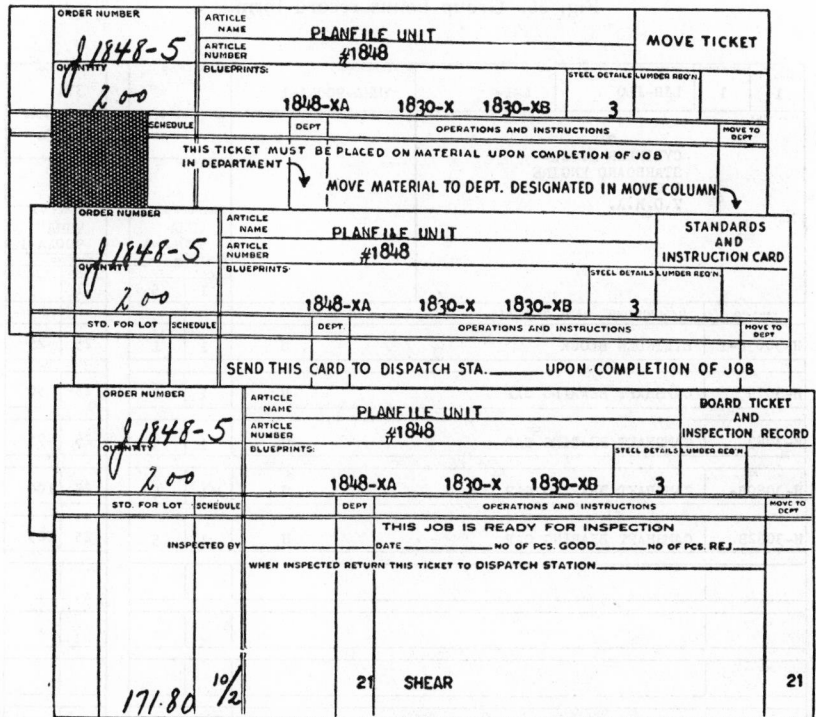

Fig. 54. Production order master form.

Fig. 55. Unit cards reproduced in sets for each operation.

ticket, standards and instruction card, board ticket and inspection record (Fig. 55) and a group bonus record (Fig. 56). The dispatcher receives a copy of the production order and the control copy of the board ticket and inspection record; he files the latter under the completion date for the department doing the operation.

Fig. 56. Group bonus record form.

Fig 57. Assembly order master form.

The department foreman receives a copy of the production order, a standards and instruction card, and a move ticket, filing the latter two in the "jobs not here" rack under the date when the preceding operation is scheduled to be completed. If the work does not come along on time, he sends the standards and instruction card to the dispatcher to get a new date for the operation. When the work does arrive, the cards are moved into the "jobs in process" rack under the stated completion date. After the job is done, the foreman sends the standards and instruction card to the dispatch station, where the dispatcher moves the board ticket and inspection record from the operation rack to the inspector's rack.

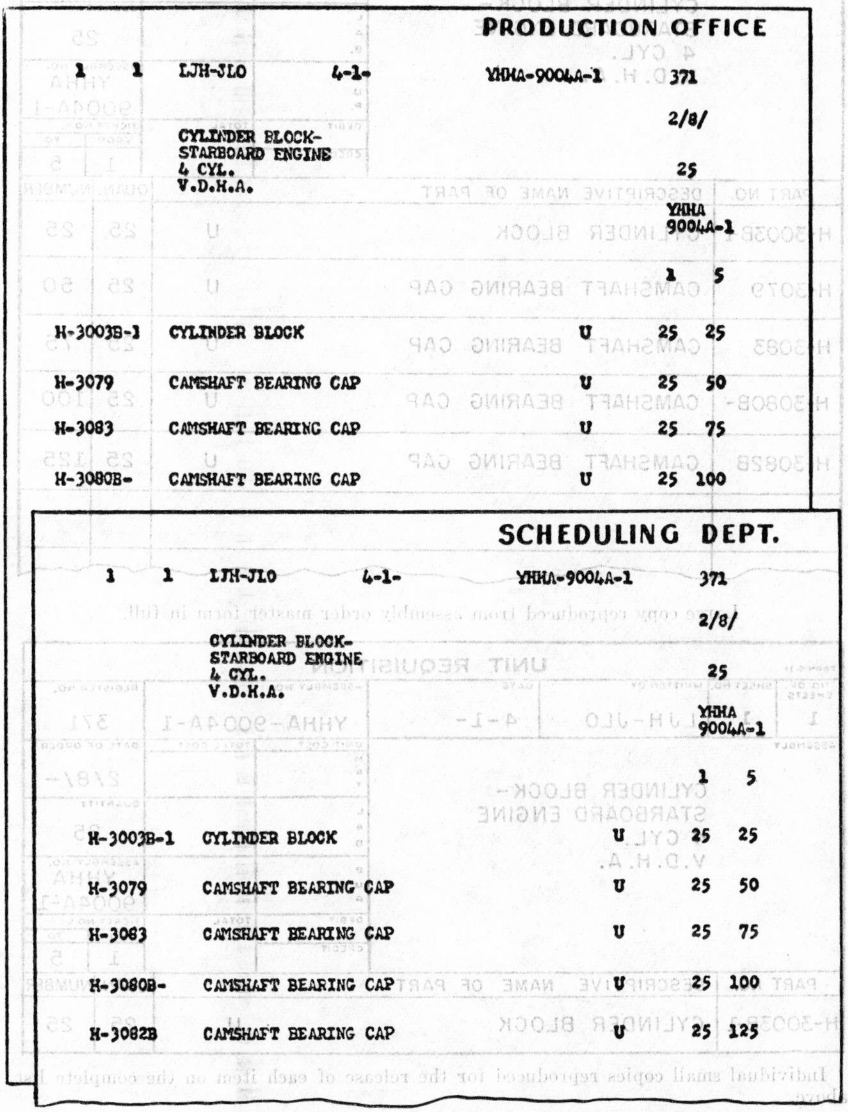

PRODUCTION OFFICE

1	1	LJH-JLO	4-1-	YHHA-9004A-1	371	
					2/8/	
		CYLINDER BLOCK- STARBOARD ENGINE 4 CYL. V.D.H.A.			25	
					YHHA 9004A-1	
					1	5
H-3003B-1	CYLINDER BLOCK			U	25	25
H-3079	CAMSHAFT BEARING CAP			U	25	50
H-3083	CAMSHAFT BEARING CAP			U	25	75
H-3080B-	CAMSHAFT BEARING CAP			U	25	100

SCHEDULING DEPT.

1	1	LJH-JLO	4-1-	YHHA-9004A-1	371	
					2/8/	
		CYLINDER BLOCK- STARBOARD ENGINE 4 CYL. V.D.H.A.			25	
					YHHA 9004A-1	
					1	5
H-3003B-1	CYLINDER BLOCK			U	25	25
H-3079	CAMSHAFT BEARING CAP			U	25	50
H-3083	CAMSHAFT BEARING CAP			U	25	75
H-3080B-	CAMSHAFT BEARING CAP			U	25	100
H-3082B	CAMSHAFT BEARING CAP			U	25	125

Fig. 58. Production office and scheduling department copies.

The inspector records on the inspection ticket the number of good pieces and rejects, and returns the card to the dispatcher, who forwards it to the planning department for entry on the production order. The work is sent to the next

FORM 9-31				UNIT REQUISITION				
NO. OF SHEETS	SHEET NO.	WRITTEN BY	DATE	ASSEMBLY NO.			REGISTER NO.	
1	1	LJH–JLO	4–1–	YHHA-9004A-1			371	
ASSEMBLY				UNIT COST	TOTAL COST		DATE OF ORDER	
				M A T.			2/8/–	
	CYLINDER BLOCK– STARBOARD ENGINE 4 CYL. V. D. H. A.			L A B.			QUANTITY 25	
				B U R.			ASSEMBLY NO. YHHA 9004A-1	
				DEBIT	TOTAL		TICKET NO'S.	
				CREDIT			FROM 1	TO 5
PART NO.	DESCRIPTIVE NAME OF PART						QUAN.	NUMBER
H-3003B-1	CYLINDER BLOCK				U		25	25
H-3079	CAMSHAFT BEARING CAP				U		25	50
H-3083	CAMSHAFT BEARING CAP				U		25	75
H-3080B–	CAMSHAFT BEARING CAP				U		25	100
H-3082B	CAMSHAFT BEARING CAP				U		25	125

Large copy reproduced from assembly order master form in full.

FORM 9-31				UNIT REQUISITION				
NO. OF SHEETS	SHEET NO.	WRITTEN BY	DATE	ASSEMBLY NO.			REGISTER NO.	
1	1	LJH–JLO	4–1–	YHHA-9004A-1			371	
ASSEMBLY				UNIT COST	TOTAL COST		DATE OF ORDER	
				M A T.			2/8/–	
	CYLINDER BLOCK– STARBOARD ENGINE 4 CYL. V. D. H. A.			L A B.			QUANTITY 25	
				B U R.			ASSEMBLY NO. YHHA 9004A-1	
				DEBIT	TOTAL		TICKET NO'S.	
				CREDIT			FROM 1	TO 5
PART NO.	DESCRIPTIVE NAME OF PART						QUAN.	NUMBER
H-3003B-1	CYLINDER BLOCK				U		25	25

Individual small copies reproduced for the release of each item on the complete list above.

Fig. 59. Unit requisitions.

operation with the move ticket. The **group bonus record form** (Fig. 56) is used for calculating the worker's earnings and bonus.

Assembly and Subassembly Order System. In the system of one company, a bill of materials master form is typed through Ditto carbon for each sub-assembly or assembly as it is set up, and is filed by assembly number. When an assembly order is to be put through, this master form, combined with a variable master, separately typed and superimposed (Fig. 57), is used to make a production office copy and scheduling department copy (Fig. 58) and unit requisitions gummed 15 to a set (Fig. 59). After separation, the unit requisitions are sent to the scheduling department, where they are filed by schedule date. On this date they are sent to the storeroom for delivery of parts to the assembly department.

The production office and scheduling copies of the order, reproduced on blank stock, are used for departmental records and follow-up.

ADDRESSOGRAPH DUPLICATING PLATES. A large number of combination uses of Addressograph-Multigraph equipment for preparing multigraph masters have been developed for the control and recording procedures connected with industrial operations. The following examples explain typical applications of this kind of equipment and show its wide range of uses.

Bills of Materials and Parts Lists. The mechanical preparation of bills of materials, listing component parts of a given assembly, is a common requirement in many kinds of manufacturing. Such listings may become even more complex when many parts have a common usage in similar end products. Often it is necessary to refer to master listings from which the detailed information regarding each part, including the number used in each assembly, is transcribed.

With the combination use of Addressograph **master plates** such listings can be written on Multigraph duplicating masters, which in turn can produce the required number of copies (Fig. 60). The master Addressograph plates are classified by means of tabs attached to the plates so that an **automatic selector** device on the Addressograph machine may be used to prepare a listing of the common parts plates which compose a given assembly.

Automatic Addressograph writing machines distribute this information across the bill of materials form and thus eliminate the typing and checking of these parts data.

The Multigraph duplicating master carries the bill of materials form in reproducing ink. When blank paper is run through the Multigraph duplicating machine, the completed form and all entries are duplicated simultaneously. Typed entries such as shown under "Notes" at the bottom of the illustration can be made to include special instructions not included on the Addressograph plate.

Production Control for Manufacturing Parts to Stock. An oil derrick construction company in Texas needs many different sizes of production forms carrying complete manufacturing instructions. The use of Multigraph duplicating machines and masters has provided a one-writing production control system which has brought about substantial savings.

Under the plan of work flow, the production-order-writing duplicating master (Fig. 61) is composed by typewriter from information furnished by the materials control department. Production orders are duplicated on 8½ x 11-in. and 5½ x 8½-in. paper card stock. The 8½ x 11-in. sheets receive the full image of the master, while the shorter 8½ x 5½-in. stock is duplicated from the upper portion of the duplicating master. After the copies required to produce parts for stock have been duplicated, the duplicating master is filed.

BILL OF MATERIAL AND PARTS LIST

PARTS LIST

ITEM	PARTS PURCHASED ADDED	PARTS PURCHASED DEDUCTED	PARTS NOT PURCHASED ADDED	PARTS NOT PURCHASED DEDUCTED	PART NAME	NOTE REFERENCE	ALL DRIVE	202A	202B	202C	202D	202E	202F	202G	202H
1															
2		3687086			Bracket-Pull Back Spring		L	2	2	2	2				2
3		442659			Rivet - Rd. Hd. 5/16x1 Chamfer Pt.	A	L	2	2	2	2				2
4															
5		3686002			Bracket-Pull Back Spring		L	1	2	2	1				1
6		442659			Rivet-Rd. Hd. 5/16x1 Chamfer Pt.	B	L	2	2	2	2				2
7															
8		3683932			Bracket-Pull Back Spring		L	1	2	2	1				1
9		442659			Rivet-Rd.Hd.5/16x1 Chamfer Pt.	C	L	2	2	2	2				2
10															
11		3685517			Bracket-Brake Pedal Pull Back Spring		L					1	1	1	
12		106286			Bolt-Hex.Hd. 3/8-24x1 1/8		L					1	1	1	
13		103321			Washer-Lock 3/8 Medium		L					1	1	1	

No.	Part No.	Description				
36						
37		Valve to Shifter Cylinder Front (Low)	L	1	1	1
38	3687062	Pipe Assy.-Rear Axle Vacuum Control Selector				
39		Valve to Shifter Cylinder Front (Low)	L			1
40	137399	Nut-Inverted Flared Tube 3/8 Cad, or Zo GH*	L	2	2	2
41		(Continued on next sheet)				
42						
43						
44						
45						
46						
47						
48						

NOTES *:-No drawing
A:-Used as brake pedal pull back spring bracket
B:-Used as clutch pedal pull back spring bracket
C:-Used as brake & clutch pedal pull back spring bracket
D:-Used as brake pedal pull back spring extension
E:-(1) Used with rear axle vac.cont.selector valve to shifter cyl.pipe assy. (high)
F:-(1) Used with rear axle vac.cont.selector valve to shifter cylinder pipe assy. (low)
G:-(1) Used with rear axle vacuum control selector valve to shifter cylinder front pipe assy. (high)
H:-(1) Used with rear axle vacuum control selector valve to shifter cylinder front pipe assy. (low)

REVISIONS

REGULAR PRODUCTION OPTION AT CUSTOMERS REQUEST

DATE ISSUED: 2-3-

REPLACES SHEET:

YEAR 19 -

SUBJECT: Two speed rear axle equipment

RPO 202   SHEET NO. 11

Fig. 60. Bill of material and parts list.

When the inventory of a finished part becomes low, a notification to manufacture is initiated. The appropriate duplicating master is removed from the file and a small **duplicating master overlay** (Fig. 61) is penciled with the date

● ● ● ● ● ● ● ● ● ● ● ●
─ ─ ─ ─ ─ ─ S LINE *Multilith* DupliMAT Master TRADE MARKS REG. U.S. PAT. OFF. PAT. PEND. **N E G I**

36   48 ▲   60   72   84   96

↓ WRITE BELOW THIS LINE ↓

DATE RELEASED 5-8-

PRODUCTION ORDER   SHEET 1 OF 4 REV. 6 CLASS 42

PROD ORDER NO. 6-78/0	SCHED. 3	QUAN. 50	ACCOUNT 1088-10	USED ON DD-58 DD-57	DESCRIPTION MAIN SKID	PART NO H-26264-B

CONTROL POINT NO.	OPER. NO.	DESCRIPTION	QUAN. COMP.	INSP. NO.	MACHINE NO.	TOOLS REQ'D.	STD. TIME	ACT. TIME
71	A	FURNISH GROUP 1						
14	1	COLD SAW			7467	*.30	.30	
	2	SHEAR			7666-S- 7462	*.30	.13	
	3	LAYOUT			FLOOR		.80	
	4	BURN			FLOOR		.30	
	5	PUNCH			7612-P	*.60	.55	
13S	6	STENCIL					.03	
	7	ASSEM. TO WELD				*.50	1.20	
	8	WELD					1.80	
	9	DRILL			7454	*.30	.60	
	10	CLEAN & GRIND					.80	
13S	11	INSPECTION					.10	
71	B	FURNISH GROUP II						
07	12	PAINT					.40	
71	C	STORE						

REV 12-5- E1
TOTAL RUNNING TIME 7.01
12-28- JVD TOTAL SET UP TIME * 2.00

EQUIPMENT COMPANY   * SET UP TIME ONLY

MATERIAL INVOLVED

QUAN. PER UNIT	PART NO.	DESCRIPTION	AMOUNT ISSUED	UNIT COST	WEIGHT	TOTAL COST	ACCOUNT NO.
		GROUP I					
1	H-26264-1B	10"CB@21# 10'-9-3/8"					
1	DO 2B	DO 10'-9-3/8"					
1	DO 3B	DO 3'-0"					
2	DO 5B	PL 5-3/4" x 1/4" 0-9-1/2"					
1	DO 4B	PL 9-1/2 x 1/2 1-9-1/4"					
6	DO 6B	PL 2-1/2 x 3/8 0'-9-3/16"					
1	DO 7B	L 1-1/2 x 1-1/2 x 3/16 1'-3-1/4					
		GROUP II					

(left margin, vertical) FOR 5 1/2 SHEET STOP HERE
(margin numbers) 6 12 18 24 30 36 42

Fig. 61. **Production order duplicating master with overlay.**

released, the production order number and schedule, and the quantity. The overlay is then positioned over the original duplicating master on a Multigraph duplicator and production order copies are again duplicated.

The production order (Fig. 61) is made up in seven basic copies with additional copies serving as the job ticket for each machine operation specified on the order. The seven basic **production order copies** are:

Title	Size, in.	Color and Stock	Function
1. Cost copy	8½ x 11	White card stock, preprinted on reverse side (see Fig. 62)	Used by the cost department to accumulate all charges against the order, and later used for cost analysis.
2. Material delivery copy	8½ x 11	Yellow paper stock	Serves as notification to the stock room to make ready the material required, and is sent to the control point to notify them when material has been issued.
3. Material requisition	8½ x 11	Green paper stock	Copy authorizing stock room to issue material required by the production order. This copy is then sent to the cost department for posting and cost accumulation.
4. Central control copy	8½ x 5½	Blue card stock	For production and materials control office to file for controlling this and subsequent production orders.
5. Control point copy	8½ x 5½	Pink card stock, preprinted on reverse side (see Fig. 63)	Used by production control points to control progress of order. Copy travels with materials between control points and then to the stock room with finished parts, where it is picked up and sent to the cost department to notify them that production on the order is completed.
6. Traveler copy	8½ x 5½	Buff card stock, preprinted on reverse side (see Fig. 63)	Remains with the order in a cellophane envelope to identify it from the raw material stage to the completion of the order. This copy is continually posted to show the manufacturing progress.
7. Job ticket	8½ x 5½	White card stock, preprinted on reverse side	To schedule each operation in proper sequence and to assign specific machines for each operation. Operators use this card as a time card of operations to record starting and finishing time on it by inserting in a time clock. One job ticket is duplicated for each operation on the order.

Four of the seven copies are preprinted on the reverse side. The **cost copy** contains a form for cumulative cost information on the reverse side (Fig. 62). The control point and **traveler copies** (identical except for color) have a form

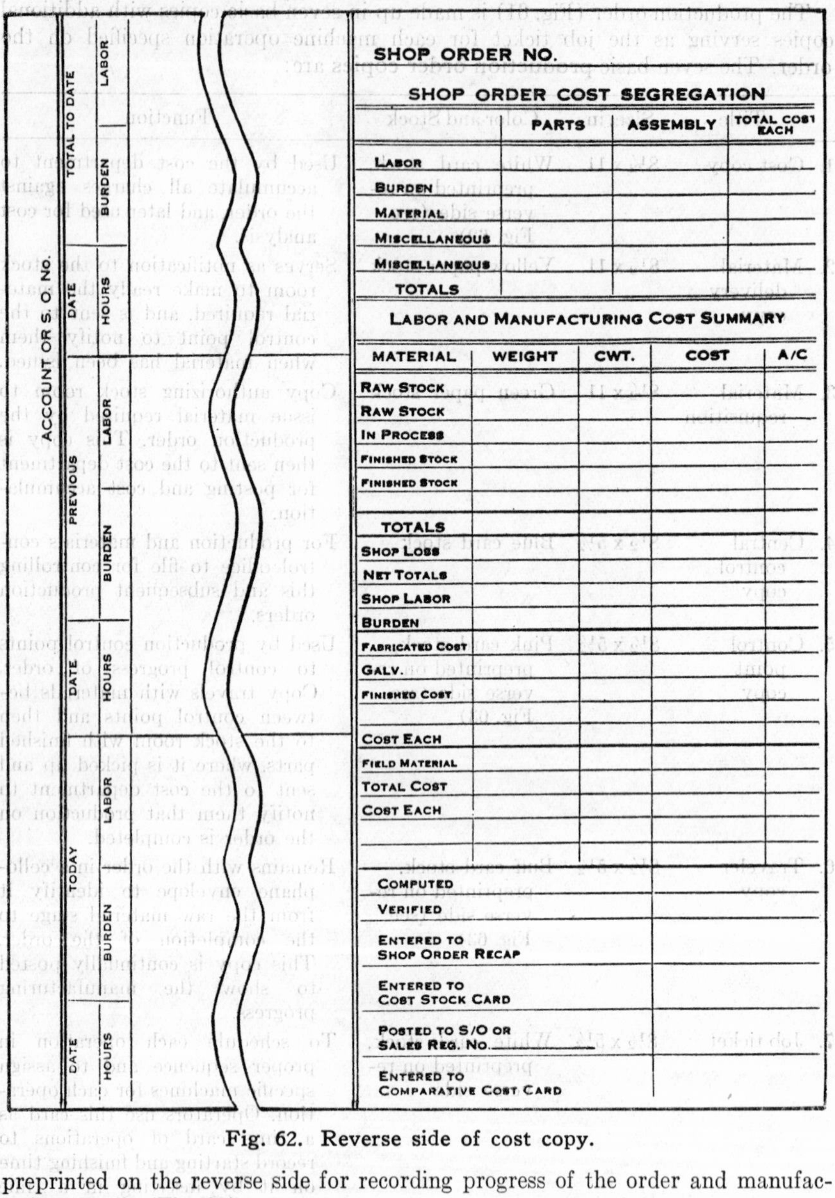

ACCOUNT OR S. O No.

TOTAL TO DATE		PREVIOUS			TODAY		
LABOR	BURDEN	DATE HOURS	LABOR	BURDEN	DATE HOURS	LABOR	BURDEN	DATE HOURS

SHOP ORDER NO.

SHOP ORDER COST SEGREGATION

	PARTS	ASSEMBLY	TOTAL COST EACH
LABOR			
BURDEN			
MATERIAL			
MISCELLANEOUS			
MISCELLANEOUS			
TOTALS			

LABOR AND MANUFACTURING COST SUMMARY

MATERIAL	WEIGHT	CWT.	COST	A/C
RAW STOCK				
RAW STOCK				
IN PROCESS				
FINISHED STOCK				
FINISHED STOCK				
TOTALS				
SHOP LOSS				
NET TOTALS				
SHOP LABOR				
BURDEN				
FABRICATED COST				
GALV.				
FINISHED COST				
COST EACH				
FIELD MATERIAL				
TOTAL COST				
COST EACH				
COMPUTED				
VERIFIED				
ENTERED TO SHOP ORDER RECAP				
ENTERED TO COST STOCK CARD				
POSTED TO S/O OR SALES REG. NO.				
ENTERED TO COMPARATIVE COST CARD				

Fig. 62. Reverse side of cost copy.

preprinted on the reverse side for recording progress of the order and manufacturing details (Fig. 63).

The **job ticket** is a production order with a clock card preprinted on the reverse side with columns to receive clock number, employee's signature, good parts finished, number of parts rejected, reason for rejection, setup time elapsed and time elapsed for piecework payment and control. A job ticket is duplicated for each operation on the order. If there are 12 operations, 12 job tickets will be duplicated in addition to the 6 other basic copies. A red arrow is then hand-stamped on the job ticket opposite the particular operation for which the ticket is to be used. The first copy of a job ticket will have an arrow stamped on it pointing to Operation No. 1, the second will have an arrow at Operation No. 2, and so on for the remaining operations.

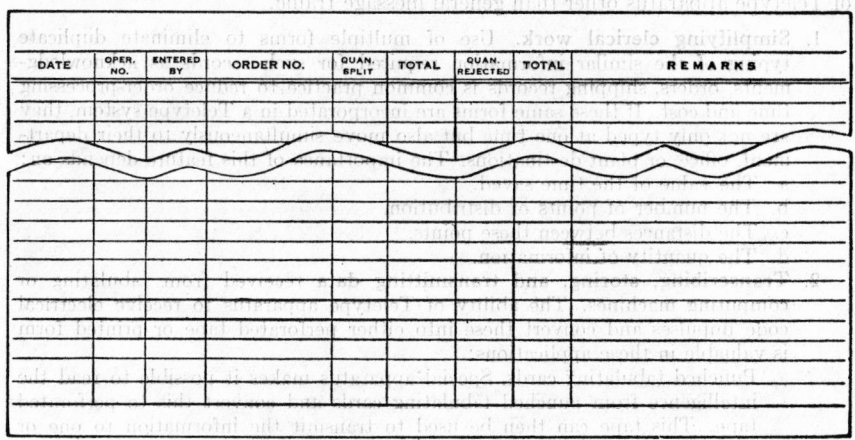

DATE	OPER. NO.	ENTERED BY	ORDER NO.	QUAN. SPLIT	TOTAL	QUAN. REJECTED	TOTAL	REMARKS

Fig. 63. Reverse side of control point or traveler copy.

Running, filing, and rerunning masters eliminate repetitive rewritings of the same information. Multigraph duplicating master overlays provide a simple and economical method of changing the variable production order data. Printing on various sizes, weights, and colors of stock permits easy copy identification and designation of purpose, and generally facilitates use. The duplicated production order forms control materials and the operations of men and machines.

COMMUNICATION SYSTEMS. Many production control systems rely heavily on a rapid exchange of information and instructions between separated points. These points may be scattered dispatch stations, a central office and decentralized plants, etc. In such situations, several types of communications equipment have proved useful.

Teletype. The teletypewriters and associated equipment manufactured by the Teletype Corp. have many business and industrial applications. The basic teletypewriter resembles an ordinary typewriter in that the operator actuates a similar keyboard. This converts each character into corresponding **telegraph code signals.** These are transmitted by wire or radio to one or more receiving machines. The incoming signals cause each receiver to record the message, character by character, exactly as sent. Messages may be transmitted manually by direct keyboarding, or automatically by **perforated tape.** The perforated tape for subsequent transmission may be prepared simultaneously with the original keyboarding.

Applied to production control, the system allows a central department to issue orders to different plants, modify schedules at widely separated plants at the same time, etc. These plants in turn can report back information on production, inventories, equipment loading, orders to be processed, and other data on the manufacturing situation. By this means, too, manufacturing orders can be sent by a sales office to the plant which will fill them at the same time that they are typed from the original customers' orders. Use of Teletype perforated tapes for transmission of production information to feeder lines in an automobile assembly plant is a common practice.

At the present time there are three fundamental types of industrial applications of Teletype apparatus other than general message traffic.

1. **Simplifying clerical work.** Use of multiple forms to eliminate duplicate typing of the similar information required for such records as acknowledgments, orders, shipping records is common practice to reduce order-processing time and cost. If these same forms are incorporated in a Teletype system, they are not only typed at one time but also move simultaneously to their department, office, or plant destinations. The importance of this feature depends on:
   a. The value of the time saved.
   b. The number of points of distribution.
   c. The distances between these points.
   d. The quantity of information.

2. **Transcribing, storing, and transmitting data** received from tabulating or computing machines. The ability of Teletype apparatus to receive electrical code impulses and convert these into either perforated tape or printed form is valuable in these applications:
   a. Punched tabulating cards. Special apparatus makes it possible to read the intelligence from punched tabulating cards and convert this to perforated tape. This tape can then be used to transmit the information to one or more distant stations where it may be received in printed tabulated form or converted back to punched cards.
   b. Electronic computers. Here again data may be removed and recorded directly in printed form or in the form of perforated tape which may be used to duplicate automatically the data in printed form.

3. **Remote control.** Standard Teletype printing apparatus, even in normal operation, performs certain mechanical operations in addition to printing. Some of these normal, remote-control functions include the return of the printing carriage, line feed, tabulating, and shifting the platen to print in the "figures" position. This ability may also be used to operate electric control devices on other equipment.

TelAutograph Telescriber. The TelAutograph Telescriber is an electrically operated instrument which transmits handwritten messages over wire from one point to one or more other points, many of which may be remotely located. The operation of the Telescriber is extremely simple. No specially trained personnel is needed, for anyone who can write can operate the machine.

Receiving instruments can be selectively written to, i.e., one Telescriber, a complete system, or any group in a system can be reached by the use of **selector keys.** The receiving instruments reproduce the same handwriting, diagrams, figures, etc., as are written on the transmitting Telescriber.

The Telescriber may be used in all types of business and industry. The four chief **operating functions** regulated by Telescriber communication are production control, quality control, materials handling, and sales control. Particularly valuable under noisy conditions, use of Telescriber messages eliminates the possibility of misunderstandings, which often occur through oral orders. The speed with which Telescriber messages are received at desired points is a vital factor in coordinating plant operation. Messages are received at the same time that they are being written.

Temporator. The Temporator is a dialing device operating by electromechanical means. Usually the control board is located in the production control department and visible and audible **annunciators** are located in the various departments of the plant. The system has two-way communication. The dials used by the workers to communicate, usually by code, with the central office, register letters and digits there and also at the local sending station.

Over the system from the central board go instructions to the local stations covering the methods and times of doing work, especially in case of changes, and requests for information on the status of certain jobs. In general, either the local dispatcher or the workers report on the completion of individual jobs, communicate delays, breakdowns of equipment, failures of material to arrive at work stations, and other interruptions of plans and schedules. Reports on completed jobs cover job numbers, station or machine numbers, operations started or finished, workers' clock numbers or names, quantities produced and amount of spoilage, time taken on jobs, and similar kinds of data. The facts and figures are dialed by means of letter symbols and numbers to the central station where production boards, charts, visible index systems, punched-card systems, or other production control systems are kept. As soon as any work is finished, the central production control office receives the information and can then bring its records up to date.

Pneumatic-Tube Systems. The use of pneumatic tubes by modern industry is essentially a function of the "time and place" requirements of paper work as a means of controlling the over-all operation of a plant. The value of such equipment is measured in terms of providing constantly available, fast, mechanical messenger service between departments and operations.

Pneumatic tubes are applicable to both large and small plants. Their need can be determined by an analysis of the **paper traffic** in the particular organization and the benefits to be derived through special handling of certain classes of paper. Such analysis usually indicates that a definite improvement in production can be secured through the rapidity of conveying information or instructions, blueprints, work orders, stores and stock reports, and other data, along with small tools, valuable small dies, etc., by pneumatic delivery. In addition, rapid amortization of investment in the tube system is often brought about through saving the valuable time of men in key positions who are called upon to make quick decisions and take prompt action on reports and other information transmitted to them through the system.

Closed-Circuit Television. There are indications that there will be wider industrial use of television to project in color, forms, sketches, drawings, parts, subassemblies, etc. It will also be adapted to production control so as to reduce the time required for personal contacts. Finally, it will speed up control and factory operations, reduce mistakes to a minimum, and speed up communication.

In the Chevrolet Motor Car Co. a television system was installed to control the loading of open freight cars with scrap steel from manufacturing operations. Trimmings from operations on car parts are delivered to a central baling station where they are put into a large press and formed into compressed blocks. These blocks are carried by a conveyor which takes them out over the cars into which they are dumped for shipment.

It was necessary formerly to keep in communication with the dumping station. A man stationed there moved the freight cars along as they were being filled to prevent piling up of the bales. He also advanced empty cars as fast as cars were filled. This operation has been replaced by a control station in the baling department from which the cars are moved as they are loaded. A television system permits control personnel to watch the loading and time car movements.

Two balers now carry on all these operations. The cost of the extra employee saved repaid the added investment within a short time.

Two-Way Radio Communication. Two-way communication by radio is used for **controlling the operation** of industrial electric or gasoline lift trucks or tractors and trailers handling materials within a plant storehouse or terminal. Trucks and trailer trains out on pickups or deliveries can be guided to and from other destinations so that they can carry on their work without returning to the central station to receive orders or instructions as to operations. An additional amount of handling work is promptly performed because of the opportunity of having loads to carry both in and going out from and returning to the central station from which the trucks radiate on their routes.

INTEGRATED DATA PROCESSING. The concepts of integrated data processing and **common-language machines** are not new. For many years tabulating machines have communicated with one another through the medium of punched cards; pieces of Teletype equipment have been linked together by means of the codes in 5-channel tape so that data recorded in one location could be reproduced automatically at another. In recent years, however, application of these concepts has been greatly extended.

Integrated data processing implies two things:

1. Data, recorded once at the point of origin, are transmitted and handled mechanically through all later processing stages.
2. Machines required by the data-handling process are able to communicate with one another through a "common language," usually punched tape or punched cards.

Almost any standard business machine can be equipped to meet the demands of an integrated system. Commercially available machines, which can be linked directly through 5-channel tape, for example, include the Flexowriter, accounting machine, automatic Graphotype, Computyper, and standard Teletype equipment. Through the use of tape-to-card and card-to-tape **converters,** tape-operated machines can communicate with card-operated machines, and vice versa. Machines such as the IBM Card-A-Type combine both media. It is also possible, with appropriate conversion equipment, to go in either direction from 5-channel to 8-channel tape or to magnetic tape. By means of the IBM Transceiver, information in one punched card can be transmitted directly to a second card at a remote location. Systematics, Inc., designs and manufactures conversion units which can be attached to certain office machines to provide data input or output in a second medium not standard for the machines in question. Adding machines and standard electric typewriters can also be equipped to produce punched tapes. Standard teletype units can be modified by the communication companies to perform many special functions tailored to meet the needs of an individual firm's data-processing system.

Common-Language Media. Common-language media include the following:

1. Five-channel punched tape.
2. Six-, seven-, and eight-channel punched tape.
3. Edge-punched cards.
4. Punched cards.
5. Magnetic tape.

Five-channel **punched tape** has the widest application, since it is the standard communications tape. Seven- and eight-channel tapes are used by many machines because they permit the use of more functional codes and also provide check channels for signaling errors in coding. However, these tapes must be converted to 5-channel if a wire communication system is involved.

Edge-punched cards replace tapes in many applications where standard data are used and filed over and over again. Although they can be combined with either, they should not be confused with standard punched cards for tabulating machines or with marginally punched cards of the Keysort variety. Edge-punched cards simply carry, along one or more of their outside edges, the punching that would normally go in a tape. The advantage of the cards lies in their being easier to file and handle than pieces of paper tape. On the other hand, the amount of information that can be stored on one card is limited. The **visible index card** comes in various sizes and can carry punched codes along either or both of its vertical edges. These cards are continuous and can be torn off after any required number of sections. A continuous strip of 5 or 6 cards will provide room for a considerable amount of data. Standard punching on either cards or tape is 10 characters per inch.

Magnetic tape uses magnetized spots rather than punched holes to record information. Data density is higher by a factor of at least 10 on magnetic tape, and tape-processing speeds are 2 to 3 times greater than for punched tape. Higher processing speed is one reason why magnetic tape is preferable as the input or output medium for high-speed computers.

Tape Storage. Long tapes are conveniently stored on reels. However, applications frequently require storage of many short paper tapes rather than a relatively few long ones. These short tapes may be filed in:

1. Pockets attached to standard file folders holding associated papers.
2. Pockets attached to standard file cards carrying data related to the tape application.
3. Divided envelopes which provide storage sections for 3 or more tapes. Envelopes are then indexed and filed in standard cabinets.
4. Channels in plastic dividers filed in standard visible index tub files.

Edge-punched cards may be filed in standard equipment designed for the size and shape of the cards used.

Integrated Data-Processing Systems. United States Steel, Alcoa, General Electric, and others have pioneered the development of integrated data-processing systems. Sylvania has established an integrated wire network linking its scattered operations with a large-scale computer center at Camillus, N. Y. Fig. 64 sketches the major flow lines of a typical system and principal pieces of equipment at the various locations. Fig. 65 shows an invoice form utilized in this system.

Forms Design. Forms design is particularly critical in such an integrated system. While all the visual principles of good design apply here, certain special problems also arise. With the form shown in Fig. 65 as an example, some of these are:

1. **Exact registration of all common data from form to form.** The first line of this form appears in exactly the same position on 5 sets of copies. The only link between the sets is 5-channel tape.
2. **Precise allocation of space to boxes carrying data for card punching.** Order number is a 5-digit field on the IBM cards. It must also appear as a 5-digit block on the form. There can be no extra spaces between it and the neighboring blocks—Delivery on the left and Point of Billing on the right—since these are also adjacent fields in the order card. "Fig. B," which does appear

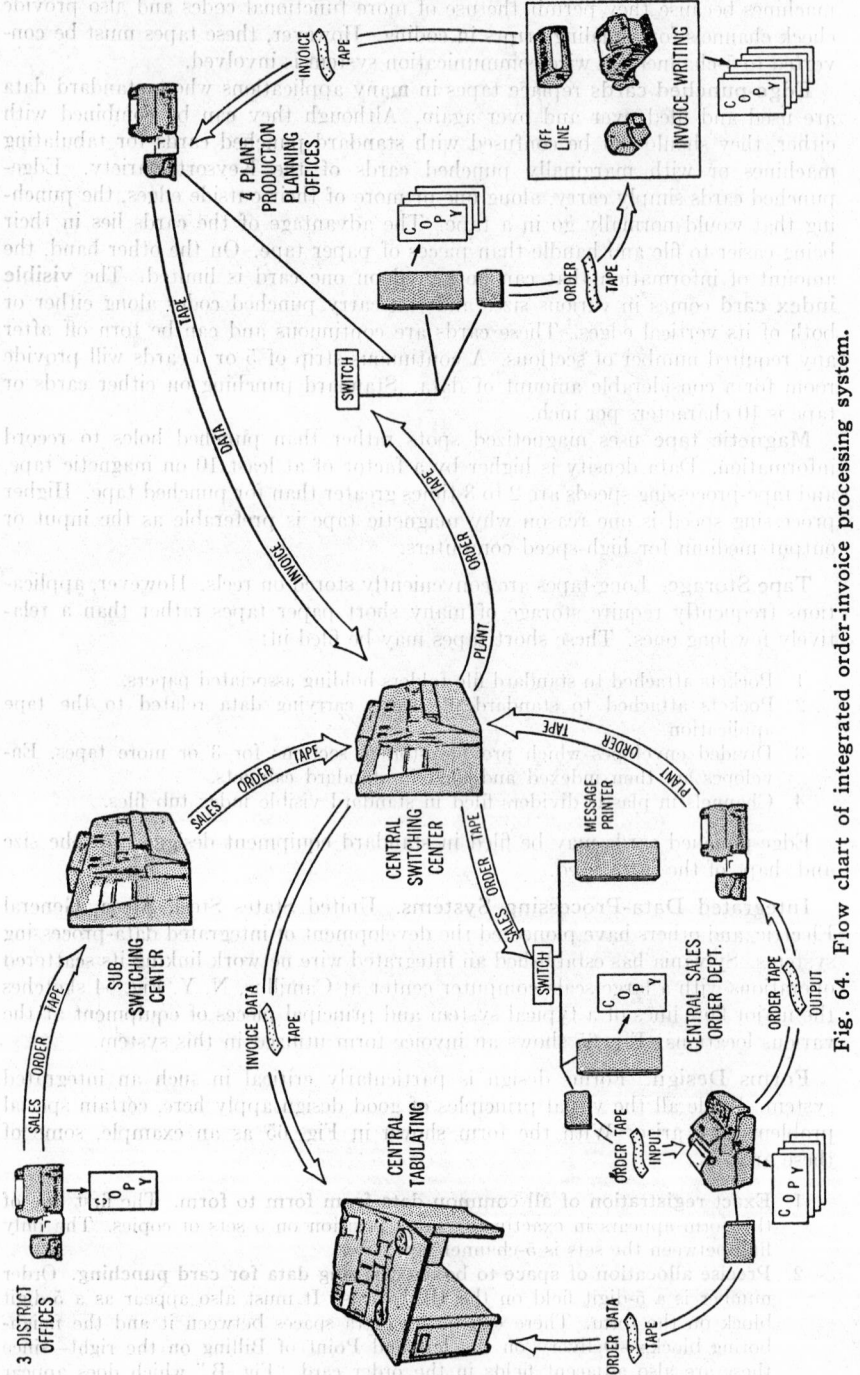

Fig. 64. Flow chart of integrated order-invoice processing system.

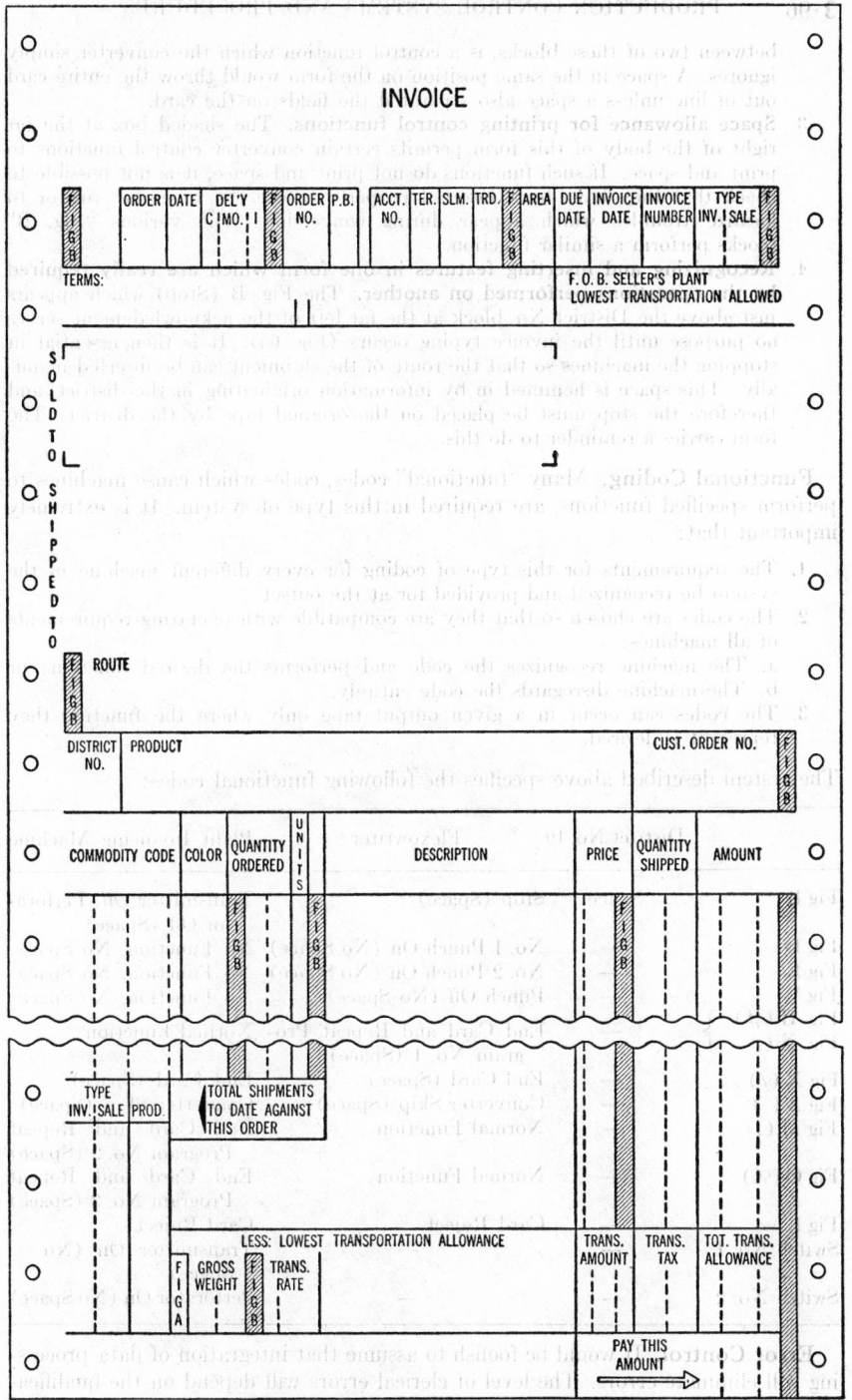

Fig. 65. Plant invoice form.

3·95

between two of these blocks, is a control function which the converter simply ignores. A space in the same position on the form would throw the entire card out of line unless a space also separated the fields on the card.

3. **Space allowance for printing control functions.** The shaded box at the far right of the body of this form permits certain converter control functions to print and space. If such functions do not print and space, it is not possible to check that they have been inserted properly before the tapes are run or to localize troubles which appear during conversion. The various "Fig. B" blocks perform a similar function.

4. **Recognizing and inserting features in one form which are really required by the operations performed on another.** The Fig. B (Stop) which appears just above the District No. block at the far left of the acknowledgment serves no purpose until the invoice typing occurs (Fig. 65). It is then essential in stopping the machines so that the route of the shipment can be inserted manually. This space is hemmed in by information originating in the district, and therefore the stop must be placed on the original tape by the district. The form carries a reminder to do this.

Functional Coding. Many "functional" codes, codes which cause machines to perform specified functions, are required in this type of system. It is extremely important that:

1. The requirements for this type of coding for every different machine in the system be recognized and provided for at the outset.
2. The codes are chosen so that they are compatible with operating requirements of all machines:
   a. The machine recognizes the code and performs the desired function; or
   b. The machine disregards the code entirely.
3. The codes can occur in a given output tape only where the function they represent is desired.

The system described above specifies the following functional codes:

	District No. 19	Flexowriter	Plant Invoicing Machine
Fig B	Space	Stop (Space)	Transmitter Off, Perforator Off (Space)
Fig D	—	No. 1 Punch On (No Space)	No Function, No Space
Fig K	—	No. 2 Punch On (No Space)	No Function, No Space
Fig V	—	Punch Off (No Space)	No Function, No Space
Fig. H (#) } Fig. N (,) }	—	End Card and Repeat Program No. 1 (Space)	Normal Function
Fig X (/)	—	End Card (Space)	End Card (Space)
Fig A (–)	—	Converter Skip (Space)	Converter Skip (Space)
Fig M (.)	—	Normal Function	End Card and Repeat Program No. 2 (Space)
Fig C (%)	—	Normal Function	End Card and Repeat Program No. 3 (Space)
Fig L	—	Card Reject	Card Reject
Switch No. 1	—	—	Transmitter On (No Space)
Switch No. 2	—	—	Perforator On (No Space)

Error Control. It would be foolish to assume that integration of data processing will eliminate errors. The level of clerical errors will depend on the qualifications and training of the personnel involved. The level of machine errors will usually be very low, but these errors will occur. The following kinds of **checks** have proved useful in controlling the incidence of undetected errors:

1. Careful proofing of data as they are entered into the system originally.
2. Repetition of key data.
3. Comparison of control totals with detail totals.
4. Comparison of identical data which have followed different routes to be sure that this identity has been preserved.
5. Printing of functional codes so that their absence from printed copy is immediately apparent.

The system illustrated uses many of these checks. For example, total pounds ordered is always repeated at the bottom of the acknowledgment to guard against transmission errors; after conversion, certain common areas in order and invoice cards are matched mechanically; daily totals of pounds and dollars invoiced follow the invoice transmission from the plants, and these figures are checked against the totals arrived at by mechanically tabulating the converted invoice cards for that day.

System Design and Installation. Problems involved in the design and installation of integrated data-processing systems are much the same as those encountered in any other type of system. However, careful study and planning at the outset are extremely important. Integrated systems leave little room for last-minute improvisation to work out unexpected difficulties or exceptions to planned routines. The critical importance of good forms design has already been stressed. Several additional points are also essential for **effective design** and smooth installation:

1. A complete, accurate picture of every detail of existing procedures which will be altered or affected by the new procedure; in particular, recognition of the need for thorough knowledge of every exception, its importance and frequency, and the way in which it should be handled.
2. Precise standardization of data and data entry procedures.
3. Early contact with equipment manufacturers and joint meetings with all of them. The machines involved will have to be entirely compatible. Keyboard design, functional coding, and many other questions should be settled simultaneously with all affected manufacturers as early in the program as possible.
4. Enough time for orderly planning and installation. Where ignorance of a simple detail may be serious, it does not pay to rush and hope for the best. For a system of the scope of that described above, 12 months would probably be a reasonable span from conception to installation with 2 to 3 men involved.
5. Planning of equipment and forms requirements as early as possible. Delivery intervals on major items generally used in these systems range from 4 to 9 months or more.
6. Preparation of a detailed manual of the new procedures and forms before installation. Such a manual will be useful for training, and its preparation will bring to light previously neglected elements in operating procedures.
7. Operator training and training aids.
8. Provision for adequate error control procedures.

MATERIALS CONTROL AND STANDARDIZATION

CONTENTS

PAGE

The Role of Materials in Industry

Definition and scope 1
Fundamental activities 1
Major phases of materials control 1
Inventory control 2
Reasons for inventories 2
Disadvantages in large inventories 2
Materials as a cost of manufacturing 3
Advantages of materials control 3

Planning for Materials Control

Planning policies 3
General policies 4
Factors affecting policies 4
"Normal" lead time quoted customers
for delivery from factory (f. 1) 5
Operating policies 5
Organization for materials control 6
Typical organization framework 6
Organization of a production control de-
partment (f. 2) 6
Other kinds of organization 8
Organization of a materials control group
(f. 3) 8
Establishing the bases for materials control 9
Grouping materials into classes 10
Determination of inventory status 10
Custom-made lines 10
Standard lines 11
Batch production 11
Production for stock 11
Using sales forecasts 11
Modified products 11
Speeding materials procurement 12
Optimum stock requirements 12
Relationship of stock policy to delivery
time (f. 4) 12
Materials control cycle 13

Records and Procedures for Materials Control

Determining material needs 13
Fixed order systems 14
Bin-tag methods 15
Bin tag (recording is done by hand)
(f. 5) 15
Bin tag with sections for addition or
subtraction to get new balance (f. 6) 16
Stores record card methods 17
Stores record card (f. 7) 17
Component parts stores record (f. 8) ... 18

Allocation methods 18
Stores record for allocation method
(f. 9) 20–21
Demand and supply methods 23
Demand and supply control card (f.
10) 24–25
Last bag method 26
Adjustment of reorder point 27
Determination of order point factor (f.
11) 28
Use of order point factors to order
material (f. 12) 29
Periodic reorder system 27
Parts required and in stock 27
Periodic reordering schedule (f. 13) 30
Modifying control methods according to
value of items 30
The A-B-C control method 31
Inventory analysis 31
Work sheet for making an A-B-C anal-
ysis of inventory (f. 14) 32
Recap of items from A-B-C work sheet
(f. 15) 32
Coordination of optimum inventory 33
Flow chart showing control of material
(f. 16) 33
Other types of stores records 34
Rotary drums 34
Inventory control card for use in a
rotary drum (f. 17) 35
Visible index cards 35
Commercial parts commitments and in-
tory record (f. 18) 36
Stores record card of the visible index
type (f. 19) 37
Stores record card used for control of
materials on manufacturing contracts
(f. 20) 38–39
Control boards 37
Spring-clip board for stores control (f.
21) 40
Permanent stores card for spring-clip
board system (f. 22) 41
Requisitions for new orders 41
Purchase requisitions 42
Purchase requisition (f. 23) 42
Repeating purchase requisitions 42
Repeating purchase requisition (f. 24)... 43
Blanket orders 44
Requests for shop order 44
Repeating request for shop order (f. 25) 45
Order requisition and low stock notice
(f. 26) 45

CONTENTS (*Continued*)

PAGE

Receiving and inspection 46
    Receiving report (*f.* 27) 46
Delivery to storeroom 47
    Finished goods report (*f.* 28) 47
Issuing from storeroom 48
    Stores requisitions 49
    Material issue, credit, or transfer slip
    (*f.* 29) 49
    Group stores issues 50
    Assembly bill of materials, "master" for
    group issue requisitions (*f.* 30) 50
    Material transfer 51
    Material deliveries 51
    Stores credits 51
    Entry in cost and accounting records 51
    Summary of materials issuing procedure .. 52
    Fundamental procedures in issuing stores
    (*f.* 31) 52
    Miscellaneous stores 53
    Other forms 54

Determining Economic Lot Sizes

Unit costs 54
Economic purchasing quantities 55
Inventory carrying charges 56
    Average inventory with one order per
    year (*f.* 32) 56
    Average inventory with ten orders per
    year (*f.* 33) 57
    Computing storage costs 56
    Carrying charges 57
    Total cost of carrying inventory 57
    Effect of economic climate 58
Inventory cost computation 59
    Data for inventory computation (*f.* 34).. 60
    Calculation of economical order 60
    Inventory cost computations for orders
    of varying sizes (*f.* 35) 61
Inventory turnover 61

Turnover ratio computation 61
Types of turnover ratios 61

Physical Inventories

Need for physical count 62
Methods of taking inventory 62
    Complete or once-a-year count 62
    Rotating physical counts 63
    Out-of-stock counts 63
Program for physical inventory 63
    Organization and personnel 64
    Programs, instructions, and forms 64
    Preparation of stock for counts 64
    Forms to be used 65
    Inventory tag (*f.* 36) 66
    Issues and receipts of inventory tags
    (*f.* 37) 66
    Record of missing tags (*f.* 38) 66
    Establishment of controls 67
    Listing of inventory adjustments (*f.* 39) 67

Simplification and Standardization of Materials

Definition 68
Results of standardization and simplification 69
    Inventory status before and after stand-
    ardization (*f.* 40) 69
    Results of standardization program (*f.*
    41) 70
Organization for standardization 70
    Materials standards committee 70
Procedure in standardizing materials 71
Materials specifications 72
    Development of specifications 72
    Sources of specifications 73
    Items covered by specifications 74
National and international standardization
and simplification 74

MATERIALS CONTROL AND STANDARDIZATION

The Role of Materials in Industry

DEFINITION AND SCOPE. **Materials control** is the process of providing the required quantity and quality of material which is needed in the manufacturing process at the required time and place and with the minimum feasible investment.

Inventory control refers to the process whereby the investment in materials and parts carried in stock is regulated within predetermined limits set in accordance with the inventory policy established by management. In this section only those concepts of inventory control which apply to raw material and parts are considered.

Materials control is limited in scope to the functions involved in supplying raw materials and parts to the shop. The handling and controlling of parts, assemblies, and finished items manufactured or processed in the shop is considered a part of **production control** rather than materials control and is discussed in the sections on Production Planning and Control, and on Production Control Systems and Procedures.

In general, then, materials control refers to all activities related to the ordering, procuring, receiving, and storing of raw materials and purchased parts and the issuing of these to the shop. Also considered a function of materials control is the ordering, storing, and issuing of the parts which are manufactured in the shop and sent to storerooms to be held until needed later in assemblies.

Fundamental Activities. In general, materials control may be considered to cover the following seven fundamental activities:

1. Planning what materials and parts are needed to fulfill customer orders or manufacturing schedules.
2. Ordering or requisitioning materials and parts from vendors and ordering parts from the shop.
3. Receiving and incoming inspection.
4. Storing and issuing raw materials and component parts.
5. Storing and issuing to the shop nonproductive items, or to the line.
6. Follow-up to determine the reasons for excessive material usage.
7. Material simplification, standardization, and substitution.

Its activities may include, depending on its relationship to the purchasing department: procurement or purchasing, and record-keeping to determine when and what to reorder.

Major Phases of Materials Control. There are two major phases of materials control:

1. **Clerical.** Primarily the determination of requirements; the keeping of records, together with several auxiliary procedures; and, when applicable, preparation of purchase and shop requisitions.

2. **Physical.** Primarily the receiving, storing and issuing of materials, and the checking of quantities by physical count to determine and adjust any discrepancies in stores records.

INVENTORY CONTROL. In the simplest manufacturing process, each item of material and each part required to manufacture a customer's order is purchased after the order has been received and the material requirements determined. When the material is received, it is used to produce the product ordered, and the assembly or end product is shipped to the customer.

Reasons for Inventories. In the usual manufacturing company, however, it would be prohibitively expensive and time-consuming to purchase each item of raw material and each part required for each customer's order. Most companies have found that it is to their advantage to order some types of raw material and purchased parts in advance and hold them in stock to be used when customer orders are received. There are several reasons why this is advisable:

1. Competitive customer delivery requirements are such that it is impossible to order raw material and parts after the customer order is received and still produce each part and assemble the end product in time to meet the required customer delivery date.
2. Substantial economies can often be achieved by buying or producing material in larger quantities than those which are required for a specific customer order. These economies derive from quantity discounts on purchased material, reduced set-up costs on manufactured items, and reduced clerical costs in placing orders less frequently.
3. Industry custom sometimes dictates that finished items will be available for sale to customers "off the shelf." Inventories of raw material and parts help to replace these shelf items faster once they are sold and shipped.
4. Sometimes difficulties are anticipated in procurement because of possible strikes or periods of high demand in relation to supply. In this case inventories may be built up on a temporary basis.
5. Sometimes higher prices or costs are anticipated because of price increases in raw material prices or labor rates.
6. Production schedules can be increased more rapidly when raw materials and parts are carried in stock.
7. The risk of not having raw materials and parts on hand when they are needed is reduced, thus minimizing the risk of shutting down production lines or not having work for production workers.

Disadvantages in Large Inventories. In contrast, however, there are a number of disadvantages in having too large a stock or too much inventory on hand. Most of these are concerned with the increased costs which may result from carrying large inventories. Some of these costs are as follows:

1. Interest on investment in inventory.
2. Storage or space charges.
3. Taxes.
4. Insurance.
5. Physical deterioration or its prevention.
6. Housekeeping.
7. Handling and distribution.
8. Record-keeping costs.
9. Obsolescence.
10. Repairs to product.

Therefore, it is necessary that close control be exercised over the inventory so that procurement and holding costs are the lowest possible consistent with the availability of **material** according to predetermined lead times, the availability of **capital** for investment in inventory, and the availability of **space** in which to store the inventory. As Magee points out (Harvard Business Review, vol. 34), the problem is "to balance conflicting objectives, such as those of minimum purchase or production costs, minimum inventory investment, minimum storage and distribution cost, and maximum service to customers." The purpose of this section is to discuss ways to achieve this objective.

MATERIALS AS A COST OF MANUFACTURING. The cost of the purchased raw materials and parts which go into a product being manufactured is always very important, and often it is the largest single item of cost in the manufacturing operation, according to Block (AMA Special Report No. 4). In manufacturing plants, 16 percent to 50 percent of the sales dollar often is spent for material, and in some processing plants as much as 75 percent of the sales dollar is so spent. Therefore, it is important that material costs be closely controlled, for this may mean the difference between a profit and a loss on operations.

The **investment in inventories** is often equivalent to 50 percent of the current assets of a company and may be the largest item on the balance sheet, with the exception of plant and equipment. In some cases it even exceeds this account. The most efficient utilization of inventory, therefore, is naturally an important factor in the success of any manufacturing plant.

ADVANTAGES OF MATERIALS CONTROL. There are many advantages for a company in properly providing for and controlling materials. Some of these are:

1. Reducing the possibility of nonaccomplishment of customer delivery promises. This is one of the most important factors in maintaining customer good will and sales position and therefore the ultimate profits of the Company. (Block, AMA Special Report No. 5.)
2. Reducing the possibility of shutting down production lines or other manufacturing activities by not having material on hand.
3. Reducing material waste due to theft, breakage, deterioration, spoilage, and obsolescence.
4. Reducing the cost of manufacturing by having proper parts on hand when needed so that it is not necessary to substitute other parts or material.

Companies which have established strong materials control activities under the direction of integrated production planning and control departments have usually reduced inventories, storage times, and handling costs, and have often increased their volume of output.

Planning for Materials Control

PLANNING POLICIES. In order to secure fully the advantages of proper materials and inventory control it is necessary to think through and set up policies, procedures, and a suitable organizational structure. Unless this is properly done, the various phases will not be coordinated into the most effective operation. Some of the steps necessary for an **effective system of materials control** are as follows:

1. Set policies necessary to guide the materials and inventory control program.
2. Determine the most appropriate organization structure to carry out these policies.

3. Establish the basis for materials control according to the method of manufacturing and the type of material.
4. Plan the availability status of each class of material and modify control methods to suit the value classification.
5. Set up procedures for planning, scheduling, and controlling production. (See section on Production Control Systems and Procedures.)
6. Set up records and procedures for properly ordering materials required and for controlling same.
7. Establish auxiliary procedures, including standardization of materials and parts.
8. Establish a procedure for physical verification of records.
9. Provide storage and physical handling facilities. (See the section on Materials Handling.)
10. Provide and train manpower for effective operation of the system.

GENERAL POLICIES. The responsibility for **material inventory policies** must rest with top management. Unless the broad and basic policies are laid down by top management, the detailed operating policies and procedures necessary for effective provision and control of materials cannot be developed properly by the manufacturing organization.

The establishment of inventory policies provides a guide for all operating personnel who have to make the day-to-day decisions regarding material and inventory. Such policies, therefore, should provide full flexibility to permit the operating people to exercise judgment in meeting new conditions as they arise.

Factors Affecting Policies. Policies set by top management will vary with the type of industry, type of company, characteristics of the product line, competitive practices, and the current state of business. The current financial condition of the particular company and the amount of capital available also may cause variations in policy.

For example, in some of the **process industries,** such as steel and chemicals, where the price of raw materials procured has a decided effect on the profit and loss statement, the company may engage in a certain amount of speculative or forward buying. Since this is a vital factor in the profit of the business, the decision as to when and how much raw material to buy is usually made by top management.

In **job shop operations,** on the other hand, the usual procedure is to do as little speculative or forward buying as possible. Although the policies of these companies often call for the maintenance of certain inventories of raw materials and parts in order to achieve purchasing and manufacturing economies and provide for availability of material, little attempt is made to try to outguess the market on price or to hedge against possible advances in prices.

Competitive practices in a particular industry often set limits on the delivery time that a company can quote to customers. Fig. 1 shows the normal lead time, exclusive of transportation, required for delivery from factory, as quoted to customers by companies in several different industries. In some industries, such as **appliances or foods,** it is customary to provide immediate shipment of finished items "off the shelf." In industries such as **elevator manufacturing or steel tank fabrication,** where substantially longer delivery times are quoted to customers, almost all manufacturing or production may be accomplished after the customer order is received. But even in these product lines with long delivery times there is an increasing tendency for one of the competitors to break the customary quoted delivery time and offer products on a more immediate basis. Usually other competitors are then forced to follow suit. The shorter the quoted delivery time, the greater the amount of inventory that has to be carried by the manufacturer; and this inventory must be processed closer to the finished goods stage.

Economic conditions or the general state of business often cause companies to change their inventory policy. During periods of high demand the steel industry traditionally produces to a large order backlog, and steel is started in the open hearths only after specific customer orders have been received for that "heat" of steel. During periods of low demand, however, the mills have found it necessary and advisable to produce certain standard specifications of steel for stock before receipt of customer orders. Thus, on many standard sizes, gauges, and specifications they are in a position to offer almost immediate shipment on customer orders.

	Days Required for Delivery Exclusive of Transportation	
Type of Industry	Standard Items	Special Items
Gas Ranges	3–4	28–35
Highway Trailers	14–21	35–42
Steel Sheets	28–35	
Furniture	35–42	
Gymnasium Equipment	30–45	
Steel Lockers	60–90	
Steel Tanks (glass-lined)	14–28	70–98
Cosmetics	2	
Powder Metal Products	14–21	28–42
Pianos	7–14	
Pumps	60–90	60–90
Valves	14	
Pipe—Seamless	90	
Pipe Fittings	7–14	30

Fig. 1. "Normal" lead time quoted customers for delivery from factory.

Seasonal businesses must accumulate material and inventory in expectation of high sales periods. Policies must be laid down concerning the production level or levels and the planned accumulation of inventory during periods of low sales activity. When new product lines or models are introduced, it may be desirable to build up certain quantities of inventories so as to be prepared for a **"surge" demand** due to promotional efforts and stocking by dealers.

In some industries, such as **automobiles and appliances,** where the policy is to keep stocks of raw materials and parts in the assembly plants as low as possible, schedules of authorized shipments from suppliers sometimes are changed as often as several times a week in order to reduce to an absolute minimum the amount of inventory which is carried on hand in the assembly plants.

OPERATING POLICIES. Policies set by top management cover a wide variety of subjects relative to materials control. The following are some of the areas in which the top management policies are most essential:

1. The delivery time quoted to customer for each product line.
2. The maximum amount of capital to be tied up in inventory.

3. The desired inventory turnover.
4. The degree of protection desired for normal manufacturing operations. Also the protection desired in case of threatened shortages due to strikes by suppliers, possible increases in prices of raw materials, etc.
5. The time lag on shipments of service parts to customers.

In a divisional organization structure, a **separate inventory policy** must be set for each of the divisions since policy may well differ in regard to the products and problems involved in each segment of the business.

ORGANIZATION FOR MATERIALS CONTROL. Providing raw materials and parts in proper quantities and when they are needed is one of the major concerns of any manufacturing business. Unless this is done properly people will be idle and delivery promises will not be met. Therefore, it is vitally important to provide proper delineation of authority and responsibility for this function and so to place it in the company's organization structure that it will function most effectively.

In **process industries** the procurement of raw materials and the follow-up to see that these materials arrive at the plant when they are needed is generally a responsibility of a vice-president of materials or director of purchases who reports to the president of the company. In these industries large quantities of material must be scheduled into the plant in ample time for production needs but without excessive accumulation in stock piles.

In most **manufacturing operations** the provision of materials is a function of the production control manager, who usually reports directly to the chief manufacturing executive. The **production planning and control manager** is responsible for planning the availability of manpower, materials, and production facilities in such a manner that predetermined product goals or objectives can be attained.

The responsibility of the production control manager in regard to materials is usually considerably greater than that of the **materials control manager** who is concerned only with raw materials and parts. The production control manager is responsible for seeing that all parts are produced in the plant according to schedule and that the finished product is brought through the plant to completion and shipped to the customer on time. Thus, placing materials control under the production department maintains the flow of materials into the plant through production and into finished products storage or into the shipping department. It is a completely centralized and integrated cycle.

Typical Organizational Framework. The following chart (Fig. 2) shows a production planning and control department with assignment of responsibility to five supervisors, who are in charge of the various phases of production and material control.

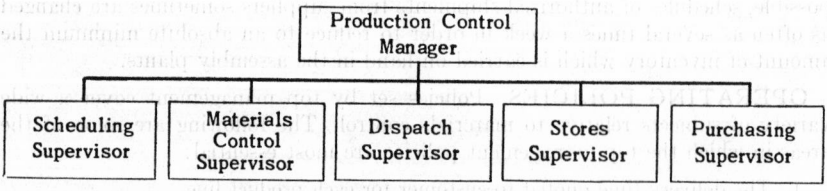

Fig. 2. **Organization of a production control department.**

The responsibilities of the various supervisors under this form of organization are as follows:

Scheduling Supervisor:

1. Initiates manufacturing schedules after reviewing sales forecasts and inventory position. Secures approval of chief manufacturing executives.
2. "Explodes" manufacturing schedules or analyzes drawings and bills of material to get detailed assembly and parts requirements by time periods.
3. Determines shop load and publishes estimates of manpower required in future periods to meet manufacturing schedules.
4. Furnishes material requirements to materials control manager for review and ordering of material.

Materials Control Supervisor:

1. Maintains perpetual inventory records by posting issues and receipts for raw material and parts.
2. Posts schedule requirements to perpetual inventory records and checks availability status of material and parts.
3. Gets information regarding economical lot quantities and lead times from purchasing and manufacturing departments and computes reorder points for each item.
4. Reorders when necessary by initiating purchase requisitions for raw material and purchased parts and by issuing shop orders for parts to be made in the shop.
5. Initiates change orders to be sent to vendors or to the shop for engineering or schedule changes.
6. Periodically audits and verifies perpetual inventory records.

Dispatch Supervisor:

1. Releases shop orders so that orders can be completed according to schedule.
2. Lines up orders so that shop will work on orders with earliest completion dates first.
3. Checks to see that materials, tools, and blueprints are available when work is to start.
4. Maintains machine load boards to show current status of load in relation to schedule.
5. Follows up to see that all parts are available in time to complete assembly schedules.

Stores Supervisor:

1. Receives material from vendors, issues receiving reports and checks material quantities against original purchase order to make certain that all material ordered is actually received.
2. Receives material into storage, records it on location cards, and properly protects it while in storage.
3. Issues material on authorized paper for delivery to the production lines or work stations.

Purchasing Supervisor:

1. Establishes contacts with vendors.
2. Secures competitive bids from vendors on all items requisitioned to secure lowest possible price consistent with quality requirements.
3. Writes and places purchase orders with appropriate vendor after receipt of requisition authorizing purchase. Advises vendors of changes in purchase orders and follows up to see that such changes are effected.
4. Places and releases blanket orders for repetitive purchases.
5. Follows up to make certain that materials are received according to schedule dates.
6. Deals with vendors on questions of quantity, quality, and price.

Under this organizational plan, the materials control function is carried out by the materials control supervisor, the purchasing supervisor, and the stores supervisor.

In some cases it is felt that the purchasing function is of sufficient importance to require that the purchasing agent or director of purchases report to the chief manufacturing executive, to the treasurer, or to the president. (See section on Purchasing.)

Other Kinds of Organization. A variation of this organization plan is described by Plitt (AMA Special Report No. 5), who details the functions of a production planning department. It includes a **planner group** "which is charged with forecasting the demand for all products, authorizing all production within the plant, and establishing production levels so as to provide inventories within the limits of policy outlined by the manager of production planning and inventory control." A **materials control group** is responsible for "acquiring and maintaining inventories of raw materials and supplies," and a **production coordination group** "is responsible for establishing the priority of each processing order."

A somewhat different type of organization in which the manager of materials reports directly to the general manager is described by Walter (AMA Special Report No. 5). In this case, the materials function was organized to take account of the need for:

1. Covering all necessary subfunctions.
2. Placing responsibility and accountability where they logically belong.
3. Eliminating overlap and unnecessary work effort.
4. Providing checks and balances compatible with the implementation of management-by-exception principles.
5. Placing the total materials function at a top reporting level commensurate with its significant position in business.

The organization chart for these functions appears in Fig. 3.

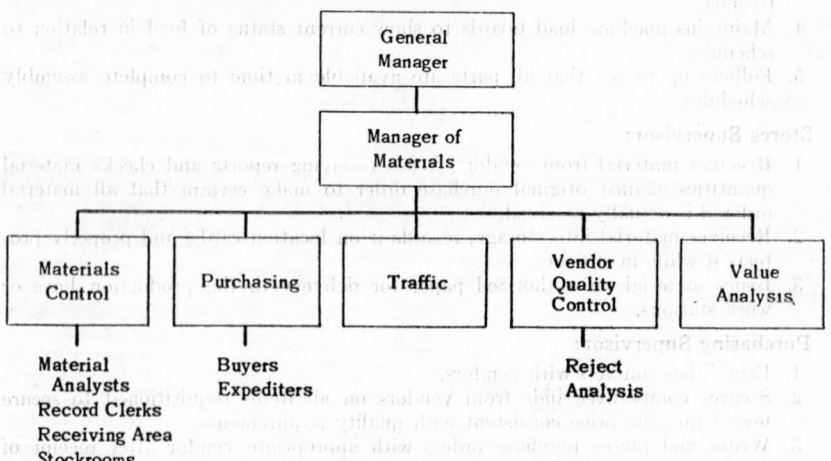

Fig. 3. Organization of a materials control group.

Walter explains that traffic and value analysis both are very important parts of the materials control function. He says that as far as purchasing is concerned, "all of its systems are based on keeping paper work and detail to an absolute minimum. Each functional buying section—with its senior buyer, junior buyer, expediter, and secretary—is the one and only contact with the suppliers from whom they purchase needed materials. All contacts by engineering or other departments must be made through this group."

In this organization, materials control is the center where complete records are kept by the material analyst and his clerk. They "convert manufacturing orders for finished sets into detail parts requirements both quantity- and time-wise and route these requirements to purchasing. Materials control also handles the receiving, stock keeping, and dispatching of materials to the manufacturing floor." Materials control specifies and schedules, and purchasing does the buying and is responsible for securing the right material, at the right price, at the right time. If it does not arrive on time or if it does not meet specifications, the materials control group immediately sends a danger signal to the appropriate purchasing group and shuts off the signal only when the track is clear. Responsibility for inventory control is, therefore, centralized in materials control where each purchasing group has its counterparts with commodity lines separated into logical material groupings. The vendor quality control section was set up to insure optimum handling of rejected shipments, "and it must either arrange to use or reject a shipment within 24 hours after receipt."

In some companies the materials and inventory control organization is placed under the **direct supervision of the treasurer** or controller. This is particularly likely to happen when inventories have not been well controlled and drastic measures are necessary in order to conserve working capital. It is usually in the interest of the manufacturing department to build up sizable stocks of material and parts so that danger of running out is minimized. It is usually the function of the financial department to see that the dollar investment in inventories is limited to reasonable amounts. But this check and balance mechanism usually can be effected without centering the direct organizational responsibility for materials control under the financial department.

The organization of the materials control function depends upon the industry, the size of the company, the product line, the capability of management personnel, and other factors. Each company should review its own operations, background, and personnel to decide on a division of responsibility which will most effectively promote lowest cost operation and best control.

ESTABLISHING THE BASES FOR MATERIALS CONTROL. There are several basic decisions which have to be made before a materials control system can be properly set up. The most important of these are as follows:

1. Group material into classes and decide which department or section is responsible for each class of material.
2. Determine inventory status with reference to policy of producing finished products:
   a. To individual customer order only.
   b. To a grouping of customer orders.
   c. To a grouping of customer orders plus stock orders for finished items.
   d. To stock by means of a sales forecast or manufacturing schedule.
3. Modify control methods and stock status according to the value of the items involved.

Once these steps are taken, the materials control system can be set up on a proper basis. The considerations involved in each of these decisions are explained below.

Grouping Materials into Classes. Materials may be grouped or classified according to their general nature, use, or condition. Five such classes cover practically all cases:

1. **Raw materials** comprise items which must be purchased and processed to convert them into component parts or to prepare them to go into (or to be converted into) a finished product.
2. **Component parts** are used in finished assemblies or for repair parts and are of two kinds:
   a. Parts purchased from vendors in completed form.
   b. Parts produced in the plant from raw materials.
3. **Supplies, expense, nonproductive, or "indirect" items** are used in the manufacturing process but do not form a part of the finished product. Such supplies are usually purchased. They include cutting and lubricating oils, cleaning or pickling solutions, waste and wiping rags, janitors' supplies, office supplies, construction materials, repair parts for machines and equipment, other maintenance items, etc.
4. **Work in process** includes all materials, parts, subassemblies, and assemblies which are being processed or assembled into finished products. These items are those actually undergoing productive operations or in temporary storage between processes or operations in manufacturing departments.
5. **Finished products** are units or assemblies carried in stock in completed form ready for delivery to customers. They are usually items which have been manufactured or processed by the company, but they may be items purchased in finished condition for purpose of resale.

The above classes, except for supplies (item 3), are direct materials because they go into or are the product which is delivered to the customer. Supplies do not form a part of the finished product and are therefore indirect materials.

Materials control is generally concerned with the procuring of raw materials and purchased parts and the supplying of these to production. Usually when parts manufactured in the shop are completed, they are returned to stores, where they are under the control of the materials control department until they are issued to the assembly floor.

The materials control section sometimes stores and controls supplies and indirect items, reordering these when necessary. In other cases, supplies are ordered and stored by the maintenance department or by factory supervision.

Work in process is the primary concern of the manufacturing department since this comprises all material being worked on in the shop. Finished units are often shipped directly to customers by the shipping department, or they may be put into a stockroom under the control of the sales or production control department. These two classifications of inventory are usually not a concern of the materials control section.

DETERMINATION OF INVENTORY STATUS. Each producer or manufacturer must decide on what time basis he will ship his products to customers. He usually must tell his customers that he will ship immediately upon receipt of their orders or a specified number of weeks or months after receipt. This decision as to the delivery time to be quoted to customers determines the amount and stage of completion of inventory which must be carried.

Custom-made Lines. If the product is designed specifically for the customer and is not a part of the manufacturer's regular product line, no material or parts can be ordered until the design is finalized and the customer has approved the design.

Standard Lines. If the company has a standard line of product but the customers are willing to wait long enough, the manufacturer does not have to order any material until the customer order is received. At that time, or upon completion of any engineering or planning necessary, each part and each item of raw material can be purchased specifically for the particular customer order.

Batch Production. In other cases, customer orders may be grouped after receipt by similar specifications and produced on a batch basis. This is especially true in steel production where several orders are grouped to make up a "heat" of steel with the exact specifications for that group of orders. Later, each order may be rolled to a different size specification called for by each customer order. In this case, raw material is usually kept on hand in sufficient quantities to produce for any combination of orders.

Production for Stock. In many cases, customers want immediate delivery, and finished products must be produced in advance of receipt of their orders. These finished products are held in stock and shipped when customer orders are received. In this case, the manufacturer usually offers a standard product line which is produced to predetermined specifications. In this type of manufacturing it is necessary to predict what customers will want, since the manufacturing process must be completed before customer orders are received. The usual procedure is for the sales department to prepare a sales forecast which gives the number of units of each type and model which are expected to be sold in each successive time period. (See section on Production Planning and Control for discussion and example of sales forecasts.)

Using Sales Forecasts. The manufacturing department uses the sales forecast as a basis for preparing a **manufacturing schedule** which specifies by time periods the quantity of each finished product to be manufactured. The manufacturing schedule may differ from the sales forecast because of current inventory conditions, build-ups for seasonal sales peaks, and economies of manufacturing in larger lots or in a different sequence from the sales pattern. The only requirement commonly imposed on the manufacturing department is that the finished units be available at the times set forth in the sales forecast. Thus, the sales department can quote delivery to customers based on expected availability as shown by the sales forecast.

In this type of manufacturing the schedule is "exploded" to show the number of each part and the **quantity of each type of raw material** necessary to produce the schedule. This is done by multiplying each part on the bill of material by the quantity of finished units times the number of parts used per unit to determine the total requirement. This explosion process may be done manually or with tabulating equipment. The requirements as determined by the explosion are compared with the quantity of material or parts in stock or already on order. Requisitions are placed to cover any additional material or parts necessary.

Modified Products. In some industries customers want standard products modified in some way so that they will better suit their particular requirements. In many cases, this is also coupled with a requirement for quick delivery.

In highway trailer manufacturing, for example, a standard trailer is often modified in some way to suit customer requirements. Standard raw materials and parts are carried in stock, but special items are ordered specifically from vendors upon receipt of customer orders. Therefore, the delivery time quoted to the customer must include the fabrication time required for the modification, plus the lead time for any special items that are purchased.

Speeding Materials Procurement. Since there is generally a reluctance on the part of the customer to wait any longer than necessary, some companies have developed ways to speed up the ordering of material. The engineering department itself often places the necessary requisitions for the special parts or material as soon as they design the specific part, or they may give an **advance notice** to the production department so that they can order the parts. This often saves one or several weeks normally required to complete the final design and engineering paperwork and to process the order through the industrial engineering and the production control departments.

Optimum Stock Requirements. The most important determinant of which material to stock, therefore, is the lead time between receipt of a customer order and the time when the finished product must be shipped. This sets up a **minimum condition for inventory** which the company must carry by classes of material. The shorter the quoted delivery time, the more stock must be carried, and it must be carried in a more advanced stage of completion, as shown in Fig. 4.

	Items Maintained in Stock			
Delivery Time Quoted to Customers	Finished Products	Standard Sub-assemblies	Standard Purchased and Manufactured Parts	Raw Material
1. As much time as the manufacturer wants.................				
2. Relatively long time......				X
3. Relatively short time.....		X	X	X
4. Immediate shipment upon receipt of customer order..	X	X	X	X

Fig. 4. Relationship of stock policy to delivery time.

There are, however, several other **reasons for stocking standard parts and raw material** even though there would be sufficient lead time to purchase them after receipt of a customer order:

1. **Price advantage** due to purchasing or producing parts in larger quantities than presently needed. This is explained later in this section.
2. **Flexibility advantage** for producing on short notice additional quantities of finished goods over and above those forecast or scheduled. Some companies insist that a certain percentage of reserve raw material and purchased parts be carried on hand at all times to allow for sudden increases in schedules which could not be accommodated by maintaining normal inventories.
3. **Protection against market change.** In some cases, manufacturers carry base stocks of raw material and purchased parts which they can use to produce customer orders if suppliers should take longer than the normal lead time provided or if shortages of these materials should develop. Material is taken from these base stocks and replaced when it is received.

The maintenance of a stock position is also a worth-while idea where an assembly line or process flow is involved. The base stock acts as protection against the line or process being shut down in case material is not received according to schedule.

MATERIALS CONTROL CYCLE. The materials control cycle comprises all of those procedures which are necessary for the provision of materials for the manufacturing process with a minimum of investment and at lowest cost possible. A knowledge of this cycle is fundamental to an understanding of the principles and practices of materials control. This **materials control cycle** is as follows:

1. Determining material needs.
2. Preparing requisitions for purchased items and requests for work orders for parts made in the shop.
3. Receiving purchased materials and finished parts into the plant.
4. Inspecting purchased material and parts, and inspection of finished shop parts. Delivering all material and parts to the storeroom for storage.
5. Entering receipts in store records or perpetual inventory records; apportioning material in the records to current orders; authorizing requisitions of materials from stores for production of shop parts and requisitions of parts from stores for assembly into finished items.
6. Issuing of parts and material to the shop for production and assembly.
7. Recording the issue in store records or perpetual inventory records.
8. Entry of receiving and issuing transactions into cost and accounting records.
9. Determination of necessity for replenishment of stores, which leads to step No. 1 above.

There are three **auxiliary materials control activities** which parallel the materials control cycle. They are as follows:

1. Determining the proper quantity to requisition for each item of material and for each purchased and manufactured part.
2. Physically checking the quantity on hand in the storeroom of each part and each item of raw material in order to verify the balances shown in stock on store records or perpetual inventory cards.
3. Standardizing materials and parts for lowest cost manufacturing.

The materials control cycle is taken up in detail in the following pages and the three auxiliary activities are discussed later in this section.

Records and Procedures for Materials Control

DETERMINING MATERIAL NEEDS. Once the company has decided which items it will offer as its standard product line, the delivery time to be quoted for each of these items, and which parts and raw materials must be carried in stock in order to achieve these delivery times or to effect manufacturing or purchasing economies, the company will have created a list of standard parts, materials, subassemblies, and assemblies which are to be stocked and carried in inventory. This list is usually known as the **stock material and parts list.**

All special items needed for production which are not on this list have to be ordered for each customer or production order. Each of the standard stock items is ordered in advance so that an adequate quantity will be on hand at all times.

Magee (Harvard Business Review, vol. 34) distinguishes two different methods for ordering standard stock items. While the two are basically similar in concept, they have a somewhat different effect on reserve or safety stocks. The objective of each is the same, that is, to determine "scientifically" when to reorder so that production levels may be maintained and inventory held to proper levels.

The first is the **fixed order system,** by which "the same quantity of material is always ordered, but the time at which an order is placed is allowed to vary with fluctuations in usage. The objective is to place an order whenever the amount on hand is just sufficient to meet a reasonable maximum demand over the course of the lead time which must be allowed between placement of the replenishment order and receipt of the material."

The second method, the **periodic reordering system,** is based on reviewing stocks at fixed time intervals and varying the order quantity according to the usage since the last review, or according to predicted usage. This is often used in monthly ordering for assembly schedules, such as in appliance manufacturing.

Magee says that the fixed order system is advantageous:

1. Where some type of continuous monitoring of the inventory is possible, such as with perpetual inventory records or bin-tag methods.
2. Where the inventory consists of items of low unit value purchased infrequently in large quantities compared with usage rate, or where otherwise there is less need for tight control.
3. Where the stock is purchased from an outside supplier and represents a minor part of the supplier's total output, or is otherwise obtained from a source whose schedule is not tightly linked to the particular item or inventory in question, and where irregular orders for the item from the supplier will not cause production difficulties.

He considers the periodic reordering system useful under the following conditions:

1. Where tighter and more frequent control is needed because of the value of the items.
2. Where a large number of items are reordered jointly, as in the case of a warehouse ordering many items from one factory for freight advantage.
3. Where items representing an important portion of the supplying plant's output are regularly reordered.

One of the modifications of this scheme is the **base stock system,** by which inventory stocks are reviewed on a periodic basis but replenishment is made only when the stocks on hand and on order have fallen to or below some specified level. When this happens, an order is placed to bring the amount on hand and on order up to a specified maximum level.

FIXED ORDER SYSTEMS. On the fixed order basis, material is reordered whenever the quantity on hand reaches a certain predetermined point, established by usage and reserve policy. Orders are placed whenever the balance declines to this reorder point figure. At that time a new order is placed for an amount equal to or greater than an **economical order quantity.** In some companies the reorder at this point is called the **"review" point,** since each time it is reached the current and projected usage is reviewed and the point is changed if usage has changed or policy in regard to reserves has been changed. The balance in stock continues to decline while the replacement order is in process, and at the time when it is received, the balance in stock is at a minimum figure. The addition of the quantity received raises the balance in stock to a maximum figure, and the balance again starts to decline as additional quantities are issued.

There are several methods of control, ranging from very simple to fairly complex, which use the basic principles of the fixed order system. The simplest methods merely involve keeping track of quantities on hand and on order, and reordering whenever the balance of available material is "getting low," as judged by the man watching the quantity on hand. Other methods attempt to allocate stock to customer orders or manufacturing schedules, and the most sophisticated methods attempt to determine "scientifically" reorder points, order quantities, and reserve stocks. Due to gradations and adaptations it is not easy to make an exact classification, but four general types, ranging from simple to complex, are discussed below:

1. Bin-tag methods.   3. Allocation methods.
2. Stores record card methods.   4. Demand and supply methods.

Bin-Tag Methods. These methods are based on reordering when the quantity of parts remaining in the bin reaches a low level, as shown on the bin tag. A representative bin tag is shown in Fig. 5. These tags are hung on hooks at the bins or shelves where the items are kept. They are usually posted when the material is withdrawn from the bin and when material is received and placed in the bin or on the shelf. Tags are used front and back. The S.O. numbers in the

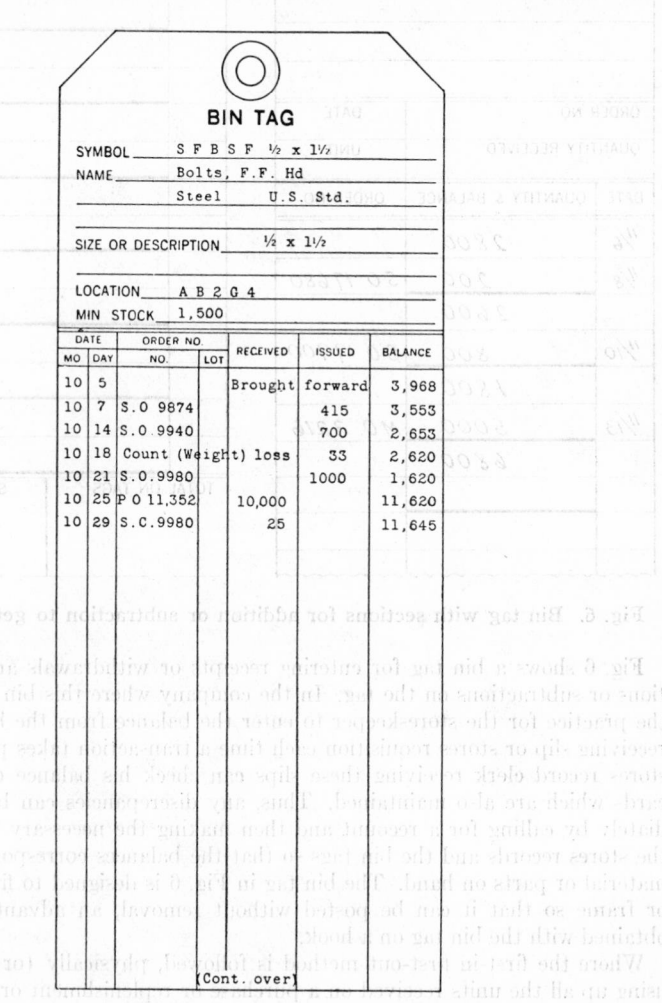

BIN TAG

SYMBOL____ S F B S F ½ x 1½ _____
NAME_____ Bolts, F.F. Hd _____
_____ Steel   U.S. Std. _____

SIZE OR DESCRIPTION____ ½ x 1½ _____

LOCATION____ A B 2 G 4
MIN STOCK____ 1,500

DATE		ORDER NO.		RECEIVED	ISSUED	BALANCE
MO	DAY	NO.	LOT			
10	5			Brought	forward	3,968
10	7	S.O 9874			415	3,553
10	14	S.O.9940			700	2,653
10	18	Count (Weight) loss			33	2,620
10	21	S.O.9980			1000	1,620
10	25	P O 11,352		10,000		11,620
10	29	S.C.9980		25		11,645

(Cont. over)

Fig. 5. Bin tag (recording is done by hand).

illustration represent shop orders on which items are issued from stores or are made in the plant and placed in stores. The P.O. numbers represent purchase orders on which shipments have arrived. The S.C. numbers represent stores credits for materials returned from jobs of the same number.

The lot column on the tag may be used when incoming shipments on a purchase order or stock replenishment order come in by lots, or when a job order is put through in successive lots which it is desirable to distinguish. Otherwise it may be omitted.

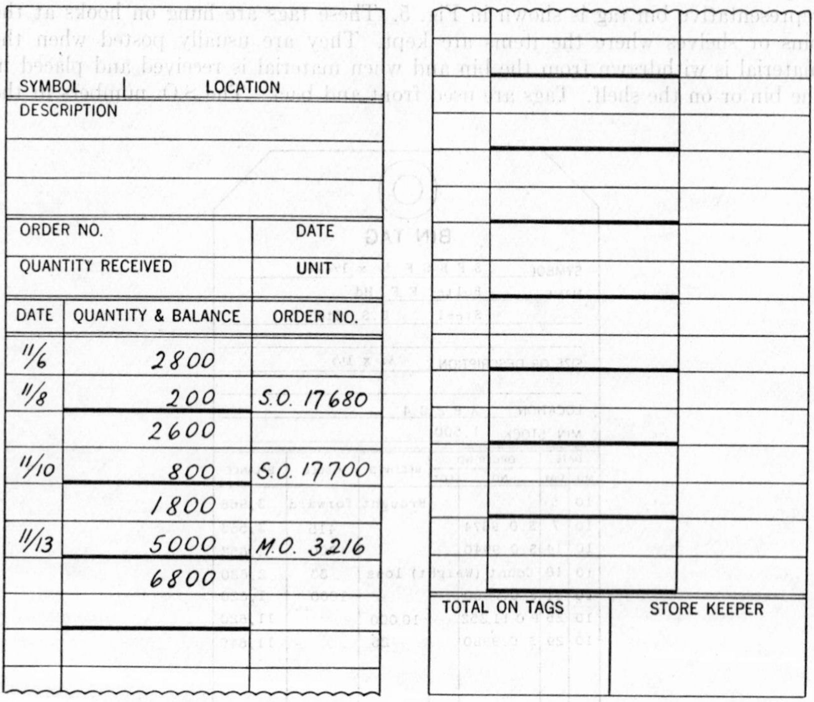

SYMBOL		LOCATION	
DESCRIPTION			
ORDER NO.		DATE	
QUANTITY RECEIVED		UNIT	
DATE	QUANTITY & BALANCE	ORDER NO.	
11/6	2800		
11/8	200	S.O. 17680	
	2600		
11/10	800	S.O. 17700	
	1800		
11/13	5000	M.O. 3216	
	6800		
		TOTAL ON TAGS	STORE KEEPER

Fig. 6. Bin tag with sections for addition or subtraction to get new balance.

Fig. 6 shows a bin tag for entering receipts or withdrawals and making additions or subtractions on the tag. In the company where this bin tag is used it is the practice for the storeskeeper to enter the balance from the bin tag onto the receiving slip or stores requisition each time a transaction takes place so that the stores record clerk receiving these slips can check his balance on stores record cards which are also maintained. Thus, any discrepancies can be caught immediately by calling for a recount and then making the necessary changes in both the stores records and the bin tags so that the balances correspond with existing material or parts on hand. The bin tag in Fig. 6 is designed to fit in a metal slot or frame so that it can be posted without removal, an advantage not always obtained with the bin tag on a hook.

Where the first-in first-out method is followed, physically (or in the records) using up all the units received on a purchase or replenishment order before using any stock from later orders or lots, a separate bin tag may be used for each such lot. When the last units are issued, which sometimes means taking some from a new lot to make up the required quantity, the old bin tag is canceled, the tag for the new lot comes into use, and the same procedures are then followed. In the case of materials subject to deterioration, the actual lots are properly tagged and are issued in order of arrival. If changes in design have made component parts subject to withdrawal from use, the corresponding bin tags will be so marked.

Stores Record Card Methods. The simplest form of a stores record or **perpetual inventory card** merely shows the receipts, issues, and balance on hand (see Fig. 7).

Description				Item No.	
Received		Issued		Balance in Stock	
Date	Quantity	Date	Quantity	Date	Quantity

Fig. 7. **Stores record card.**

Receipts are posted from receiving reports or from finished goods tickets and initialed by the stock room, with any discrepancies noted thereon. Issues are posted from material requisitions which are turned in at the store room for material or parts. The storeskeeper initials these forms and sends them to the stores record section where they are posted to stores records cards. The difference between the quantity received and the quantity issued is the **balance in stock.**

The posting of receipts and issues and the balance in stock may be done manually or by mechanical equipment such as posting machines, punch card machines, and electronic computers.

The stores record clerk is responsible for watching the quantity in stock for each item and for reordering when the balance gets below "a safe level." This is usually a quantity the stores record clerk has in mind at which to place the order so that the stock will not be depleted before new stocks are received. The clerk usually makes some notation of this quantity on the stock record card and increases it if he runs out of stock before the new order is received.

Where requirements are computed for several months ahead or where requirements are likely to be recomputed before outstanding orders are received in the plant, information regarding orders for replacements which have not yet been received are also placed on the card. (See Fig. 8.)

The determination of whether it is necessary to order material based on the balance on hand or the available balance is determined by the **replenishment cycle.** If the replenishment cycle is long compared to the amount which will be ordered, some purchase orders are always outstanding and must be taken into account in placing other orders. For example, if the replenishment cycle is three months but only a one-month quantity is purchased at a time, it is obvious that there will be several orders outstanding at all times.

If, however, the replenishment cycle is fairly short compared to the amount on order and, in general, the replenishment will be received before another order is placed, there will very seldom be any orders outstanding. In this case the available column would substantially be the balance on hand, since there would be no quantities on order.

								STORES SYM.	UNIT	MIN.
								SVMS	Ea	5,000
								LOCATION IN STORES AD-4-F-5		
DATE	ORDER NO.	QUAN. ORD'RD	BAL. ON ORDER	QUAN. RECD.	QUAN. ISSUED	ISSUED TO	BAL. ON HAND	DATE	PRICE	TOTAL COST
5-11	7428	30,000					5,000	6-1	.005	$50.00
6-1	7428		20,000	10,000			15,000			
6-8					5,000	SO-1875	10,000			
								DATE	APPOR'TD	ORDER NO.
								5-11	10,000	SO-1875

Fig. 8. Component parts stores record.

In some plants the stores record-keeping function is decentralized to the store-room location. This is perhaps permissible for certain types of inexpensive and expendable material, but records are normally centralized to permit having a picture of the inventory in one place and promote coordination with other functions.

Allocation Methods. In the first part of this section, emphasis was placed upon the importance of preplanning to fit the materials control program definitely into the schedules of production, which in turn are planned in advance to conform to future sales demands. Under this plan, which is followed by a growing number of manufacturing concerns in many lines of industry—even those not engaged in standardized product manufacture—an allocating or apportioning of materials is carried on when the production programs are originated. When the kinds and quantities of products to be made in the forthcoming period are scheduled, materials are ordered in kinds and amounts to carry on such production and to deliver finished products at the times specified. In other words, the materials flow in at a rate to keep production going and are thus actually allocated when ordered under purchased contracts.

Where conditions such as the nature of the business, inefficiencies in making sales forecasts or controlling production, or lack of a capable staff to administer the procedure do not permit a coordinated master plan to be put into effect, a more detailed and localized control is needed, but the clerical cost of the work is relatively higher. A greater burden is likewise placed on the stores record system itself. Materials should be allocated to production in advance so that material shortages may be eliminated.

The plan followed is to set up the stores records so that, by inclusion of **allocation and available columns,** materials may be allotted to current orders in advance of production. This plan avoids running short, which may happen when the records show only the balance on hand of the needed items and not how much of each will be withdrawn for work still to go into manufacturing.

The **allocation procedure** is to send the materials requisition slips written during the planning of the order for production, or the bill of materials where this form can be more readily applied, to the stores record clerk so that he may enter in the allocated column on the card for each item the quantity to be reserved and the order number to which it will be applied. He then subtracts this same quantity from the balance in the available column to show how much remains for future orders. When asked subsequently to check a bill of materials for a new order coming through to find out the materials status, he can indicate by checks against the items on the list the ones for which there are sufficient materials available, knowing that these materials will not be required for any work previously planned to go into production. Stores are replenished when the available balances reach stated reduced levels and there is thus maintained a cushion stock sufficient for the regular course of production. Any unusual demands can be met by putting through purchase requisitions while such large new orders are being planned in time to get deliveries made before the materials must actually go into production.

Fig. 9 is a typical **allocation record form,** accompanied by an explanation of entries, which may be printed on cards or loose-leaf ledger sheets in any convenient standard size. The headings are representative and may be changed as desired to fit any stores system. The columns are the minimum number needed and may be increased in number if additional data are required, or if it is desired to have order numbers and dates appear immediately adjacent to the respective postings instead of all at the left. One line across the entire sheet is used for each transaction even though this plan leaves spaces blank in several of the columns. The records can be inspected to obtain data much more quickly under this plan.

Fig. 9 is the general type of form, a result of the practice of Taylor, Gantt, Barth, and others of this group. Where considered helpful, the sequence of columns shown in the form can be changed, a good arrangement being: 1—Ordered, 2—Apportioned, 3—Available, 4—On Hand.

The **stores record principle** behind this form is expressed in the following equation:

$$\text{Amount on order (total)} + \text{Amount on hand (balance)}$$
$$= \text{Amount allocated (total)} + \text{Amount available}$$

All postings may be checked against this equation to test the correctness of the record, the last entry in each column being the one used in the equation.

In the form illustrated, the unit cost or price of the item and the total value of the amount (inventory) on hand is included. In the case of received materials the stores record clerk posts such data from information supplied by the purchasing department through copies of the purchase order which indicates prices and amounts ordered. Receiving reports show the quantities actually received. The amount of any cash discount is deducted and the cost of freight added to get the cost delivered. For issues, he uses the unit costs thus determined. In the illustration the **average method of costs** is used as shown in one of the calculations. Other methods—**standard cost, first-in first-out**, etc.—are also used, according to the accounting procedures of individual companies. The stores record clerk performs these calculations and entries so that he can price the materials requisition slips as he posts issues of material, thus saving duplication of certain handlings and operations by the cost accounting department. **Inventory value summaries** also can be made up rapidly for accounting reports and financial statements from the source which has the latest assembled data on this point at

STORES RECORD

Name Bushing, Bronze Symbol SBBB 1 x 1¼ x 2
Description 1" i.d. x 1¼" o.d. x 2" long Part No. W-16842
Specification No. 2,240 Dwg. No. C-14750
Unit Each Location in stores AC3F4
Minimum economic order quantity 6,000 Requisition when available shows 1,500

Date	Order No. (Shop or Purchase Order)	1—Ordered (But not delivered)			Received	2—On Hand (In the storeroom)				3—Allocated (Not yet issued)		4—Available (For new orders)
		Req. No.	Quantity	Total		Issued	Balance	Unit Price	Total Value	Quantity	Total	Quantity
Jan. 3					Inv'y		3,000	$ .09	$270.00			3,000
4	S.O. 115					300	2,700	.09	243.00			2,700
5	S.O. 131									+200	200	2,500
7	S.O. 156									+700	900	1,800
10	S.O. 131					200	2,500	.09	225.00	−200	700	
11	S.O. 210									+400	1,100	1,400
11		Req. 230	6,000	6,000								
14	S.O. 115				(credit)	+50	2,550	.09	229.50			1,450
15	S.O. 156					700	1,850	.09	166.50	−700	400	
18	P.O. 471		+6,000	6,000								7,450
19	S.O. 275									+300	700	7,150
21	S.O. 210					400	1,450	.09	130.50	−400	300	
27	P.O. 471		−6,000	0,000	6,000		6,000	.10	600.00			
							7,450	.0980	730.50			
28	S.O. 131				(Repl)	20	7,430	.0980	731.96			7,130
31	S.O. 275					300	7,130	.0980	702.56	−300	000	

EXPLANATION

Entry Date	Kind of Entry	Procedure in Making Entry
Jan. 3	Inventory	Assume that sheet is started from physical inventory (Equation: 0 + 3,000 = 0 + 3,000).
4	Issue	System just started so this order was not preapportioned.
5	Apportion	Balance on hand (2,700) unchanged but quantity available reduced (= 2,500).
7	Apportion	Add to total apportioned (= 900), subtract from available (= 1,800).
10	Apportion	Subtract from balance (= 2,500) and from apportioned (= 700).
11	Apportion	Add to total apportioned (= 1,100), subtract from available (= 1,400).
11	Requisition	Available (= 1,400) is now below 1,500, the reorder point. Standard purchase amount is requisitioned for ordering by purchasing department (if a purchased item).
14	Credit	Received back from previously issued shop order. Add to balance (= 2,550) and to available (= 1,450).
15	Issue	Subtract from balance (= 1,850) and from apportioned (= 400).
Jan. 18	Purchase	Standard order placed. Ordered (= 6,000) is considered to be bought to arrive before stock falls below cushion or reserve, therefore to be available for planning future manufacturing (= 7,450). Some authorities do not count purchases as available until actually received.
19	Apportion	Add to apportioned (= 700), subtract from available (= 7,150).
21	Issue	Subtract from balance (= 1,450) and from apportioned (= 300).
27	Receipt	Subtract from ordered (= zero), post to received, insert in balance column, put unit price and total value of new order in their respective columns.
28	Calculation	Add old balance and new receipt (= 7,450), add old and new values (= $730.50). Divide: $730.50 ÷ 7,450 = .0980, new unit price under average method.
28	Replacement	Spoilage or shortage on shop order. Subtract from balance (= 7,430), price valuation of balance at new unit rate, subtract from available (= 7,130).
31	Issue	Subtract from balance (= 7,130) and from apportioned (= zero).

The total value is recalculated whenever the balance is increased by receipts or reduced by issues, and at the unit price of that date. The equation, Ordered (total) + On hand (balance) = Apportioned (total) + Available (quantity), can be checked at any point by taking the last entry in each of these columns and inserting it in the equation. If the equation does not balance, an error has been made in posting.

Fig. 9. Stores record for allocation method.

any one time. When a **standard cost system** is in use in the company, the current cost of the item is entered at the top of the sheet or card and the stores record clerk does not have any calculations to perform. When the standard is changed, he is notified to change his records, and accordingly, he makes his entry on the card.

When a company prefers to omit the inventory value data from the stores records, even though the dollar value of the inventory is desired monthly, the quantity balance can be extended to a price balance when the need arises. A good way to secure total inventory value, usually by material classifications, is to carry a separate summary record for each stores ledger or group of stores cards, with each classification as a minimum for a group. Under this method, a **daily dollar value** is secured by (1) costing requisitions as they clear through the stores records, (2) sorting costed requisitions by material classification, (3) totaling them, and (4) posting the totals to the disbursement columns of the summary cards. Receipts are accumulated in a similar manner. While more than one item will usually appear on the posting media (invoices), the fact that most vendors' materials fall into only one classification simplifies the distribution. Transportation costs and discounts, of course, must be prorated.

Ritchie (Production and Inventory Control) states the following regarding allocations:

Allocations are not always concerned with "paper" inventories. Physical allocation may also be used. In the case of physical allocation, materials are actually removed from a general storage bin or area and placed where they may be identified readily with a particular production order. This may mean storage in a separate pan or compartment, movement to another stock room or merely a shift to another area of the same stock room. In any event, the amount required is physically separated from the general mass of that material available. Paper allocations, on the other hand, require no movement of stock. They merely involve clerical operations within the inventory control group.

Paper allocations alone are usually sufficient to check the danger of double assignments. In addition, they involve no movement of material. They are flexible because changes can be accommodated by a few erasures. They record where each portion of the balance on hand has been diverted. On the negative side, paper allocations add one more complication to the routine of inventory control, and shortages can still result from clerical errors.

Shortages stemming from errors are less likely with physical handling and counting than with clerical posting. The material is either there or it is not. Physical allocations are often used in addition to paper allocations where the availability of certain parts is so critical that an additional guarantee is required. They may also be used where "loose assembly" increases assembly efficiency or where change orders can be effected more conveniently when all the parts for a production run are grouped together. When physical allocations are used independently, a simple requisition form will reduce the balance on hand and move the stock to an accumulation stall or allocated stock room. This eliminates all extra clerical routine but it can only occur with safety when there is little chance that the order for which the material is allocated will be canceled or delayed or that the material will have to be diverted to a more pressing order. In either of these situations, considerable difficulty is involved in locating the material and returning it to general stock.

Allocated stocks should not be used unless there is a definite need for them. The additional handling, storage space, or clerical effort which allocation entails all increase the cost of inventory control. Unless exceptional safeguards are required, it is usually less expensive in the case of parts and materials which are common to many products, whose delivery interval is short, and whose unit cost is not too high, to maintain inventories at a level high enough to care for all normal requirements.

The weakness of all of these allocation methods is that, although information is supplied relative to the status of each item controlled, the reorder points are usually not set very scientifically, and hence more stock may be on hand than needed, thus raising operating costs and inventory levels; or too little material may be on hand, thus resulting in costly expediting and permitting possible shutdowns of production lines or work stations.

Demand and Supply Methods. Demand and supply methods of materials control utilize principles of planning the demand for and supply of each item at the lowest cost possible and the lowest possible inventory consistent with operating requirements.

The basic difference between these and less "scientific" types of record-keeping and ordering is that much more time and effort is devoted to developing for each part or item an **order point** based on objective analysis of past and projected usage. **Economic purchasing and manufacturing lot sizes** are also developed to minimize the total cost of procuring, storing, and utilizing each specific item of material and parts. (See section on Purchasing and section on Production and Planning Control.)

This method is usually used to keep track of quantities only, and dollar or financial controls are maintained in the accounting department.

In order to use this method of materials control, certain information must be known or estimated for each part and raw material item controlled:

1. **Average Usage.** The expected usage of the particular part or raw material in the future. Since this is difficult to determine, past usage is usually taken as the best indication of the future and this quantity per time period is usually used. If usage is expected to increase or decrease substantially in the future, the usage figure should reflect this trend.
2. **Lead Time.** The average elapsed time between the initiation of the order paperwork and the receipt of the material from the shop or from vendors.
3. **Reorder Point.** The quantity expected to be consumed during the replenishment lead time plus a reserve. It is computed by multiplying the lead time in periods by the average usage per period and adding the reserve quantity.
4. **Reserve Stock.** An extra amount which is kept on hand to take care of greater than normal usage during the replenishment lead time or an average usage during a greater than normal lead time, or a combination of the two. It is usually expressed as usage during some additional time period, although it may also be a certain fixed quantity determined in some empirical way.
5. **Economical Order Quantity.** The quantity which is most economical to order and to stock, considering all factors bearing on the situation. It is peculiar to each part, as is explained in detail in the section on Purchasing.

The **demand and supply control card,** shown in Fig. 10, provides a detailed and comprehensive history of all transactions and planning related to each particular part. The types of information kept on the card are:

1. Actual balance in stock.
2. Quantity available to cover future usage.
3. Detailed record of open orders.
4. Reorder information.
5. Usage information.

Information on the heading of the card includes part number and name, material to be furnished, approximate cost to make or to buy, economic order quantity, average usage per month, order point, reserve quantity, lead time requirement, inventory account and classification, unit measure and weight, and stockroom location.

DEMAND AND SUPPLY CONTROL CARD

PART NAME

PART NO.

UNIT — MEASURE, WEIGHT

INVENTORY — ACCOUNT, CLASS

APPROXIMATE COST

ORDER POINT 1,500

ECONOMICAL ORDER QUANTITY 6,000

RESERVE 500

AVERAGE USAGE PER MONTH 2,000

LEAD TIME 1/2 mo.

MATERIAL TO BE FURNISHED

APPROVED BY

STOCKROOM LOCATION 2G12

SUMMARY

(1) Supply Reference	Demand Reference	(2) Detail Entry	(3) Cumulative Supply	(4) Cumulative Demand	(5) Demand Coverage	(6) Cumulative Receipts	(7) Cumulative Issues	(8) Actual Balance in Storeroom
1/3 Inventory			3,000		3,000	3,000		3,000
4	S.O. 115	300		300	2,700		300	2,700
5	S.O. 131	200		500	2,500			2,500
7	S.O. 136	700		1,200	1,800			
10	S.O. 131	200		1,400	1,400		500	2,500
11	S.O. 210	400		1,600				
11	P.O. 471	6,000	9,000		7,400	3,050		2,550
14	S.O. 115	50	9,050		7,450		1,200	1,850
15	S.O. 156	700		1,900	7,150			1,450
19	S.O. 275	300					1,600	1,450
21	S.O. 210	400						7,450
27	P.O. 471	6,000				9,050		7,450
28	S.O. 131R	20		1,920			1,620	7,430
31	S.O. 275	300		1,920	7,130		1,920	7,130

(9) OPEN PURCHASE OR SHOP ORDERS

	Balance on Order		
	Date of Entry	Receipts	Balance Open
ORDER NO. P.O. 471	1/11	—	6,000
DATE DUE 1/25	1/27	6,000	0
DATE RELEASED 1/11			
DATE STARTED 1/18			
ORDER NO.			
DATE DUE			
DATE RELEASED			
DATE STARTED			
ORDER NO.			
DATE DUE			
DATE RELEASED			
DATE STARTED			

EXPLANATION

Entry Date	Kind of Entry	Procedure in Making Entry	Entry Date	Kind of Entry	Procedure in Making Entry
Jan. 3	Inventory	Physical Inventory of 3,000 recorded as shown.	Jan. 14	Credit	Received 50 back from previously issued shop order. Add to cumulative receipts (= 3,050), to balance (= 2,550), to cumulative supply and to demand coverage (= 7,450).
Jan. 4	Issue	System just started so this order for 300 was allocated at time of issue.	15	Issue	Issue 700 and subtract from balance (= 1,850).
5	Allocation	Balance in storeroom (2,700) unchanged but demand coverage reduced (= 2,500) by order for 200.	19	Allocation	Add 300 to cumulative demand (= 1,900), subtract from demand coverage (= 7,150).
7	Allocation	Add 700 to cumulative demand (= 1,200), subtract from demand coverage (= 1,800).	21	Issue	Issue 400 and subtract from balance (= 1,450).
10	Issue	200 shown as issue and subtract from balance in storeroom (= 2,500).	27	Receipt	Post 6,000 to cumulative receipts, increase balance in storeroom to 7,450. Record receipt in open purchase order column.
11	Allocation	Add 400 to cumulative demand (= 1,600) subtract from demand coverage (= 1,400).	28	Replacement	Spoilage or shortage on shop order. Add to cumulative demand, subtract from demand coverage (= 7,130); add to issued (= 1,620). Subtract from balance (= 7,430).
11	Requisition	Demand coverage (= 1,400) is now below 1,500, the reorder point. Standard purchase amount 6,000 is requisitioned for ordering by purchasing department (if a purchased item).	31	Issue	Add to cumulative issues (= 1,920) and subtract from balance (= 7,130).

Fig. 10. Demand and supply control card.

The following information is posted to the card as transactions are reported to the materials control man:

1. **Cumulative Demand.** The cumulative requirements for this particular part as "exploded" from bills of material or drawings to cover manufacturing schedules or as posted from customer orders. This is an allocation of all material presently available in stock or soon to become available through replenishment orders.
2. **Cumulative Supply.** The total quantity of the item which has been ordered plus any physical inventory on hand when the card was opened. This is sometimes called the "ordered" column.
3. **Demand Coverage.** The quantity of material which is available to cover future demands for the part. It is the excess of the supply over the demand or a quantity ordered and in stock over the amount apportioned and used. This figure is compared with the order point, and whenever the demand coverage declines to or below the order point a new order is placed for the economical order quantity.
4. **Cumulative Receipts.** A posting of the quantity as received in the storerooms.
5. **Cumulative Issues.** The total quantity of material issued from the storeroom to the shop.
6. **Balance in Stock.** The actual physical balance in the storeroom. It is the difference between receipts and issues.
7. **Open Purchase or Shop Orders.** The details of all open orders which have not been received.

After posting, the following information is available on the card:

1. **Balance on Order.** Equals cumulative supply minus cumulative receipts. (This figure should check with the totals shown in the "balance open" columns of open purchase or shop orders.)
2. **Actual Balance in the Storeroom.** Equals cumulative receipts minus cumulative issues.
3. **Unfilled Demand.** Equals cumulative demand minus cumulative issues. This is the quantity allocated to orders which has not been requisitioned or issued to the shop.
4. **Demand Coverage.** Equals cumulative supply minus cumulative demand. This is the quantity which can be allocated to future orders or manufacturing schedules.

In this example the **calculation of the order point** is as follows:

Order point = Lead Time (in months) × average usage per month plus reserve
= ½ × 2,000 + 500
= 1,500

Rather than automatically reordering whenever the order point is reached, the expected usage should be reviewed in light of current conditions and the order point revised if necessary. Whenever the lead time is changed, the purchasing department and the shop should advise the materials control section, which will revise the affected order point accordingly.

Last Bag Method. Oftentimes the posting of receipts, issues, and balance on stores record can be eliminated completely by the use of the so-called last bag, sealed quantity, or double bin method. A quantity sufficient to last during the lead time necessary to get a replacement order and allow a generous reserve is bundled into a separate bag or carton, kept in a separate bin, or in some way identified clearly as being the reorder stock.

When the stores department uses the first piece of this quantity, they forward the identification and reorder tag attached to the quantity to the purchasing or production control department, which places a replacement order. The reorder stock is large enough to supply production and leave some parts on hand when the new order is received.

The usage of these parts should be reviewed periodically and new reorder quantities set. This can be done by reviewing the quantity ordered by the purchasing or production control departments during the previous year or six months. This gives an average usage per month which can be used in determination of the reorder quantity.

ADJUSTMENT OF REORDER POINT. It is, of course, advisable to keep the reserve quantity as low as possible in case of model or engineering changes. But so doing always involves the risk of running short, since the shop or vendors may be late in supplying the parts ordered or actual usage may exceed predicted usage. A method for allowing for these factors is described in Factory Management and Maintenance (vol. 113), using a chart which takes three factors into account:

1. Excess use over estimated production requirements.
2. Excess use plus a slight delivery delay by vendors or the plant.
3. Maximum delivery delay only.

Excess usage is the difference between maximum usage and normal usage for the maximum delivery time. Slight delivery delay is expressed as normal or excess usage times the amount of the delivery delay. Thus, by selecting the combination of factors which is most likely to happen, the proper quantity of material can be ordered. The steps in using this chart (Fig. 11) are as follows:

1. Determine normal delivery time and maximum delivery time.
2. Determine maximum estimated usage.
3. Decide the degree of protection needed for the particular order.
4. Follow a vertical line down the column (indicated by arrow) for the appropriate delivery time, maximum delivery time, and estimated maximum usage.
5. Follow a horizontal line across the row (indicated by arrow) for the degree of protection required.
6. Read the order point factor at the intersection of the vertical and horizontal lines you are following.

This factor is used to find the quantity to order as shown in Fig. 12. The estimated usage is multiplied by the order point factor to get the order point quantity. From this are deducted any quantities on hand and on order to determine the quantity to order.

PERIODIC REORDER SYSTEM. By the periodic reorder system, manufacturing or production schedules are reviewed on a periodic basis and the quantity to reorder of each part and raw material is determined. The basic feature of this system is that each part and each item of raw material necessary to produce the schedule is ordered each time a schedule is issued.

Parts Required and in Stock. In order to determine the quantity of each part required, the manufacturing schedule is "exploded" by multiplying the total quantity of each finished item by the quantity required per unit of each part and each item of raw material. These requirements are sorted and totaled by part number to get the **total requirement** for each part and for each item of raw material for the coming period or for several periods to come.

Normal delivery time (weeks)	4	4	4	4	4	3	3	3
Maximum delivery time (weeks)	6	6	5	5	5	4	4	4
Estimated maximum usage (normal usage=1.0)	1.2	1.1	1.3	1.2	1.1	1.3	1.2	1.1

Formulas for finding order-point factors beyond chart range

Degree of protection needed								
A. Excess usage only = $\left(\text{Normal delivery time}\right) \times \left(\text{Estimated maximum usage}\right)$	4.8	4.4	5.2	4.8	4.4	3.9	3.6	3.3
B. Excess usage plus slight delivery delay = $\left(\text{Normal delivery time}\right) + \left[\left(\text{Maximum delivery time}\right) \times \left(\text{Estimated maximum usage} - 1.0\right)\right]$	5.2	4.6	5.5	5.0	4.5	4.2	3.8	3.4
C. Excess usage and maximum delivery delay = $\left(\text{Maximum delivery time}\right) \times \left(\text{Estimated maximum usage}\right)$	7.2	6.6	6.5	6.0	5.5	5.2	4.8	4.4
D. Maximum delivery delay = $\left(\text{Maximum delivery time}\right)$	6.0	6.0	5.0	5.0	5.0	4.0	4.0	4.0

Fig. 11. Determination of order point factor.

Item Description	A Est. current usage (weekly)	B Ordering code. (See order-point. factor chart)	C Order-point factor (from order-point factor chart)	D Order-point quantity (A×C)	E Quantity on hand	F Quantity on order	G Total (E+F)	H *Quantity to order (D−G)
0.008 in. × 25.25 in. sheet aluminum coils	5,000 lb.	4-5-1.2-B	5.0	25,000	8,500	10,500	19,000	6,000 lb.
4-in. strap hinge	5	4-5-1.2-C	6.0	30	6	10	16	14
⅝ × 2¼ hex. head screw caps	10 gross	3-4-1.2-A	3.6	36	6	15	21	15 gross
200-watt, 120-v. med. base incandescent lamp bulb	75	3-4-1.2-B	3.8	285	150	75	225	60
0.016 in. × 28.25 in. sheet aluminum coils	5,000 lb.	4-5-1.2-C	6.0	30,000	6,000	28,000	34,000	0

*or economical minimum-ordering quantity, whichever is greater

Fig. 12. Use of order point factors to order material.

Under this system it is desirable to know the **quantity of each item remaining in stock** (if any) so that this quantity may be deducted from the requirements of the schedule and a lesser quantity ordered. This information may be obtained by physically counting the parts or material in stock each time a schedule is issued, or some record may be kept of receipts, issues, and balances in stock (see Fig. 8). Using the information from these cards, the schedule requirements are then compared with the total "In Stock" and "On Order" by placing these quantities on a **periodic reordering work sheet,** Fig. 13. Since this work sheet serves as a record of the requirements, it is usually not necessary to post the requirements to inventory control cards. Thus, either three- or four-column cards (including an "on order" column) can be used, and no allocated and available columns are required.

Part No.	Description	In Stock	On Order	Total Available	Required for Schedule	Place Orders for
1	X	1,000	0	1,000	3,000	2,000
2	XX	500	3,000	3,500	6,000	2,500
3	XXX	1,000	1,000	2,000	3,000	1,000
4	XXXX	0	0	0	3,000	3,000
5	XXXXX	5,000	0	5,000	12,000	7,000
6	XXXXXX	3,000	0	3,000	3,000	0

Fig. 13. Periodic reordering schedule.

If the schedule is projected for several months in advance, it is important to indicate the dates on which specific quantities of material are required. Thus in Fig. 13 it would be necessary to have several extra columns headed "Place Orders For" and to show the quantity required for each schedule and the date when that material was due. It is also advisable to show the date when the "On Order" material is due so as to be able to verify that the material will be in the plant in time to complete the monthly or weekly schedule.

One appliance manufacturer using this method schedules his production of castings, sheet metal stampings, and spot-welded subassemblies 30 days in advance. He schedules the enameling of the stampings and spot-welded assemblies and the production of electrical and other subassemblies three days in advance of his assembly line schedule so that these items will be available on the line when the finished units are assembled.

MODIFYING CONTROL METHODS ACCORDING TO VALUE OF ITEMS.

Richmond explains a relatively new technique for classifying and controlling production and supply items, both purchased and manufactured, in accordance with the value of the item involved (Control of Production Supply Items on a Proportional Value Basis, AMA Special Report No. 5).

The basic principle involved is that the measure of control exercised and the quantity of reserve stock carried varies directly with the **usage value of the item** involved. High value items are more closely controlled than low value items. The advantages of the system are that clerical costs are reduced and the inventory is balanced and maintained at an optimum level.

The A–B–C Control Method. This method is usually called the A–B–C method because each item of material used is given an A, B, or C designation, depending upon the total dollars expended for that particular item during the year. Richmond describes these as follows:

A Items: These are a small number, and therefore small percentage, of the total items which represent a large percentage of the company's expenditures for material during the year. It is not at all unusual to find that 10% of the total parts and raw material used in manufacturing represents 75% of the dollars spent for material. These A items should be ordered, scheduled, and re-scheduled for receipt on a weekly, daily, or even hourly basis in order to keep the investment in inventory as low as possible. Their movement through the shop should have priority and represent the least possible time to flow through the shop. Protective or reserve stock on such items should be kept to an absolute minimum. Both the vendors and manufacturing department supervision should watch the flow carefully to be sure that no interruption is permitted.

B Items: These are of secondary importance because they do not require as detailed and close control as A items, but they need more attention and control than C items. They are the intermediate items which may represent 10 to 20% of the total quantity of items and may make up 15 to 20% of the total expenditures for material.

C Items: These are the numerous, inexpensive items that make up perhaps 5 or 10% of the total expenditures for material. They may represent as much as 70% of the total number of production items used in manufacturing, and production may be held up if any one of them is lacking. The method of control is exactly opposite to that prescribed for A items. The C items should be purchased in large quantities in order to secure purchase discounts and minimize time and effort required on the part of buyers, order clerks, record clerks, stock keepers, engineers, cost accountants, and receiving clerks. The company should carry a large protective supply of each of these items since the investment is small and this decreases the possibility of ever shutting down operations. At the same time the clerical procedures involved can be considerably simplified with consequent savings in cost. Under this concept it is absolutely inexcusable ever to have one of these C items require special expediting or run the risk of shutting down a production line or work station due to lack of parts.

The key difference in the handling of these parts is that large reserve stocks should be established on C items so that there is never a possibility of running short of them. On A items, however, the reserve quantities are held to an absolute minimum in order to decrease the investment in inventories.

The **quantity of reserve stock** should vary with the usage value of the item. In the case of C items, the reserve should be set high enough so that even with maximum delivery time and maximum usage above normal, the plant will not run out of material by the time the replenishment quantity is received. In the case of A items, however, the reserve should be kept as small as practical and extensive expediting used to make certain that parts are received when scheduled. C items should almost always be run by the shop or purchased in economic lot quantities. A items are often procured in smaller quantities so that inventory investment will be as low as possible.

Inventory Analysis. An example of an A–B–C analysis of inventory presented by Barnett (Industrial Management Society Bulletin, 1955) is described below. The "average usage" and "factory or purchase cost" of each item in inventory is extended to get a **"usage times cost" value** as shown in Fig. 14. Separate sheets should be used for raw materials, purchased parts, and shop parts. Items are then recapped and grouped by dollar classifications as shown by Fig. 15. The classifications on the recap sheet are then combined at logical break points. In this example, the final A–B–C classification of inventory is:

Class	No. of Items	Percent of Items	Value	Percent of Value
A	328	9	$630,000	75
B	672	20	142,000	17
C	2,421	71	67,000	8

From the above table it will be noted that 71 percent of the total quantity or number of items in stock comprise only 8 percent of the total dollars expended for material, and 9 percent of the total number of items used during the year comprise 75 percent of the total dollars spent for material.

Part No.	Average Usage	Factory or Purchase Cost	Usage Times Costs
F10	5	$ 2.10	$ 10.50
F11	75	.15	11.25
F14	2	30.10	60.20
F15	2,000	.05	100.00
F16	700	.80	560.00
F17	1	180.00	180.00
F19	250	1.10	275.00
F21	10,000	.005	50.00
F22	400	.30	120.00
F23	650	.25	162.50
F31	10	.08	.80
F32	25	.60	15.00
F35	90	1.10	99.00
F36	200	8.50	1700.00
F38	50	.80	40.00
F40	1,500	.40	600.00
F41	150	.10	15.00
F42	20	.50	10.00

Fig. 14. Work sheet for making an A-B-C analysis of inventory.

Usage Times Cost Value	No. of Items	Cumulative Total	Cumulative Percent	Value of Items	Cumulative Value	Cumulative Percent
$700 and over	242	242	7	$580,000	$580,000	69
500–700	86	328	9	50,000	630,000	75
400–500	55	383	11	25,000	655,000	78
300–400	95	478	14	34,000	689,000	82
200–300	170	648	19	42,000	731,000	87
100–200	352	1,000	29	41,000	772,000	92
Under 100	2,421	3,421	100	67,000	839,000	100

Fig. 15. Recap of items from A-B-C work sheet.

COORDINATION FOR OPTIMUM INVENTORY. Aude (Factory Management and Maintenance, vol. 108) describes the procedure of **controlling materials in a process industry.** In his company the materials coordinator obtains and distributes information regarding material requirements and takes the necessary steps to maintain optimum inventory. Another of his duties is to

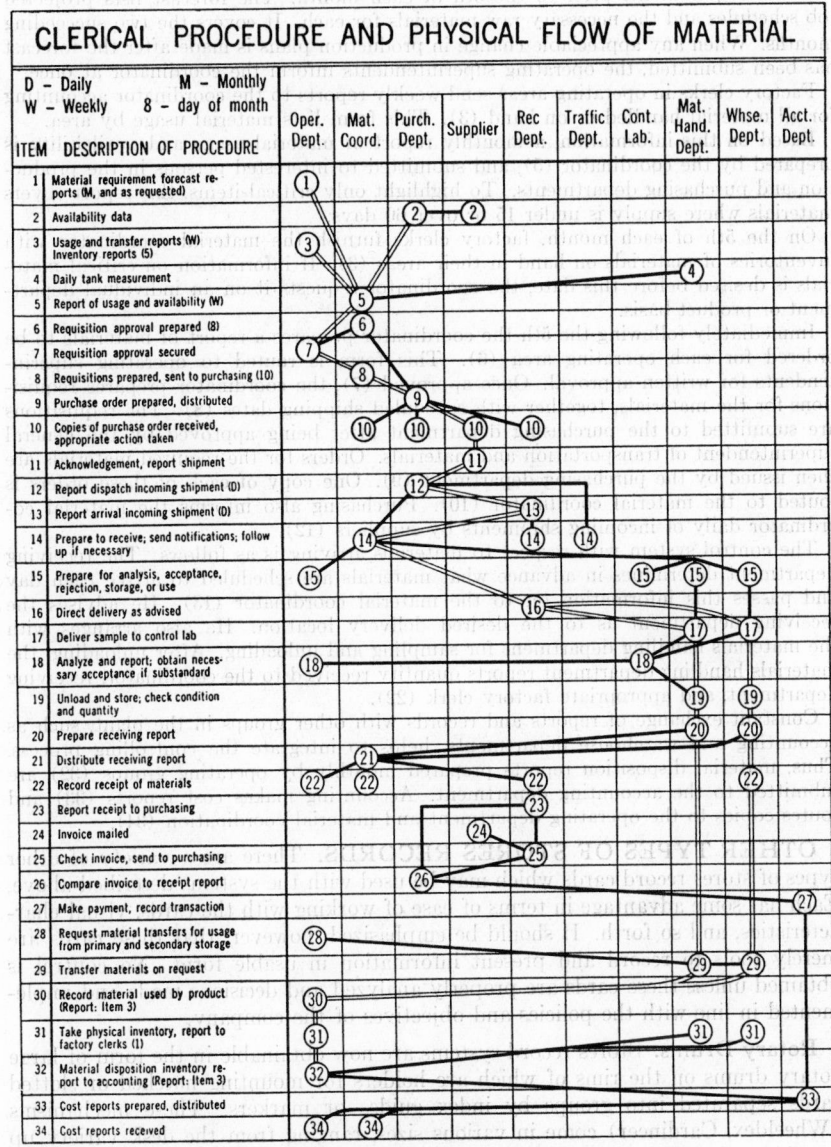

CLERICAL PROCEDURE AND PHYSICAL FLOW OF MATERIAL

ITEM DESCRIPTION OF PROCEDURE	Oper. Dept.	Mat. Coord.	Purch. Dept.	Supplier	Rec Dept.	Traffic Dept.	Cont. Lab.	Mat. Hand. Dept.	Whse. Dept.	Acct. Dept.
1 Material requirement forecast reports (M, and as requested)	①									
2 Availability data			②	②						
3 Usage and transfer reports (W) Inventory reports (5)	③									
4 Daily tank measurement									④	
5 Report of usage and availability (W)		⑤								
6 Requisition approval prepared (8)		⑥								
7 Requisition approval secured	⑦									
8 Requisitions prepared, sent to purchasing (10)		⑧								
9 Purchase order prepared, distributed			⑨							
10 Copies of purchase order received, appropriate action taken	⑩	⑩	⑩	⑩						
11 Acknowledgement, report shipment				⑪						
12 Report dispatch incoming shipment (D)				⑫						
13 Report arrival incoming shipment (D)					⑬					
14 Prepare to receive; send notifications; follow up if necessary		⑭			⑭	⑭				
15 Prepare for analysis, acceptance, rejection, storage, or use	⑮						⑮	⑮	⑮	
16 Direct delivery as advised					⑯					
17 Deliver sample to control lab								⑰	⑰	
18 Analyze and report; obtain necessary acceptance if substandard	⑱						⑱			
19 Unload and store; check condition and quantity								⑲	⑲	
20 Prepare receiving report								⑳	⑳	
21 Distribute receiving report		㉑								
22 Record receipt of materials	㉒	㉒			㉒				㉒	
23 Report receipt to purchasing					㉓					
24 Invoice mailed				㉔						
25 Check invoice, send to purchasing					㉕					
26 Compare invoice to receipt report			㉖							
27 Make payment, record transaction										㉗
28 Request material transfers for usage from primary and secondary storage	㉘									
29 Transfer materials on request								㉙	㉙	
30 Record material used by product (Report: Item 3)	㉚									
31 Take physical inventory, report to factory clerks (1)	㉛							㉛	㉛	
32 Material disposition inventory report to accounting (Report: Item 3)	㉜									
33 Cost reports prepared, distributed										㉝
34 Cost reports received	㉞	㉞								

D – Daily   M – Monthly
W – Weekly   8 – day of month

Double lines represent reports on or actual flow of materials. Single lines represent flow of auxiliary information.

Fig. 16. Flow chart showing control of material.

advise production supervisors as to approaching critical materials situations. He also maintains constant contact with the purchasing department and, through it, with outside suppliers. His system is diagrammed in Fig. 16 and explained as follows:

Our operating superintendents furnish the material coordinator with a forecast of material requirements prior to the 5th of each month. The forecast lists projected job schedules and the necessary raw materials for each. It covers the two succeeding months. When any appreciable change in production plans is made after the forecast has been submitted, the operating superintendents inform the coordinator at once.

Factory clerks in operating areas send weekly reports to the coordinator accounting for all material handled or on hand (3). This form lists material usage by area.

Based on this information, a monthly report of material usage and availability is prepared by the coordinator (5), and submitted to interested persons in the production and purchasing departments. To highlight only critical items, this report covers materials where supply is under 15 or over 60 days.

On the 5th of each month, factory clerks furnish the material coordinator with inventories of materials on hand in their areas (3). If information on critical materials is desired before this date, the coordinator requests it on an individual department or product basis.

Immediately following the 5th the coordinator prepares a report of materials to be ordered for each operating area (6). This form is routed to operating superintendents for written approval. Once approved (7), the coordinator prepares requisitions for the materials, together with scheduled shipping dates (8). The requisitions are submitted to the purchasing department after being approved by the general superintendent of transportation and materials. Orders for the required materials are then issued by the purchasing department (9). One copy of each of these orders is routed to the material coordinator (10). Purchasing also informs the material coordinator daily of incoming shipments by suppliers (12).

The control system with respect to materials arriving is as follows: The receiving department determines in advance what materials are scheduled to arrive each day and passes this information on to the material coordinator (13). He advises the receiving department as to the desired delivery location. He also arranges with the materials handling department for sampling and unloading. After unloading, the materials handling department reports quantity received to the coordinator, receiving department, and appropriate factory clerk (22).

Constant exchange of reports and records with other groups in the plant, such as accounting and warehouse departments, helps to integrate the controlling process. Thus, material disposition reports prepared monthly by operating groups (32) are submitted to the accounting department. Accounting makes cost reports (33) and routes copies to the operating department and material coordination (34).

OTHER TYPES OF STORES RECORDS. There are a variety of other types of stores record cards which may be used with the systems described above. Each has some advantage in terms of ease of working with the cards, visual characteristics, and so forth. It should be emphasized, however, that these cards are merely tools to record and present information in usable form. No control is obtained unless these cards are properly analyzed and decisions made and implemented in line with the policies and objectives of the company.

Rotary Drums. Stores record systems are now obtainable in the form of large rotary drums on the rims of which are holders for mounting notched or slotted cards separated into groups by index guides or markers. These mechanisms (Wheeldex, Cardineer) come in various sizes, ranging from the desk variety up to cabinet sizes holding 5,000 cards. With the simplified units, over 100,000 cards can be brought within the working area of an operator. A card resembling the stores ledger records previously described is shown in Fig. 17.

For quicker distinction between kinds of items and greater ease of operation and control, cards of different colors are used for different general classes of items. One company utilizing the drum variety of equipment has buff cards headed "Raw Material," salmon cards headed "Purchased Part," and green cards headed "Manufactured Part."

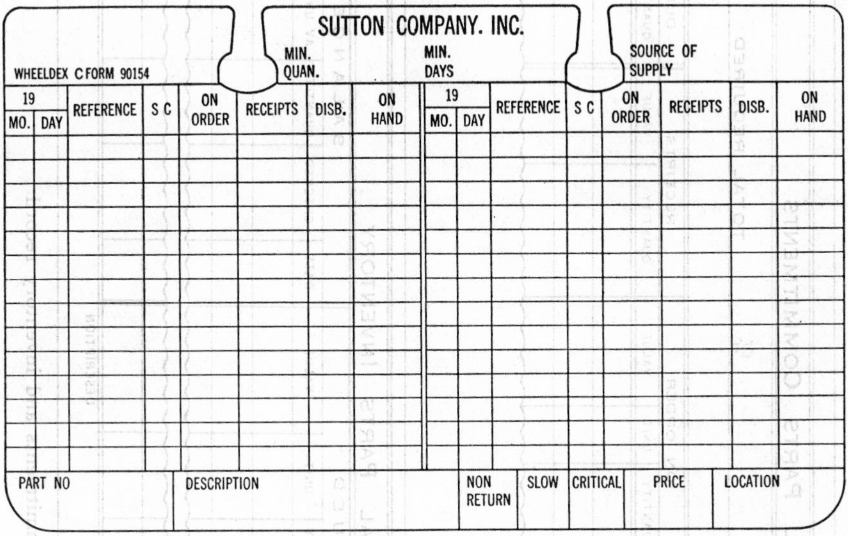

19 MO.	DAY	REFERENCE	S C	ON ORDER	RECEIPTS	DISB.	ON HAND	19 MO.	DAY	REFERENCE	S C	ON ORDER	RECEIPTS	DISB.	ON HAND

SUTTON COMPANY. INC.

WHEELDEX C FORM 90154

MIN. QUAN.   MIN. DAYS   SOURCE OF SUPPLY

PART NO   DESCRIPTION   NON RETURN   SLOW   CRITICAL   PRICE   LOCATION

Fig. 17. Inventory control card for use in a rotary drum.

Visible Index Cards. One company using a Kardex system substituted for a single materials control form a series of **three foldover forms.** A buff-colored form for standard commercial parts has a foldover front showing commitments (upper part of Fig. 18) and the main inventory portion underneath carrying the visible index (lower part of Fig. 18). The raw materials card is the same (commitments on the front, inventory underneath), except for the name heading and the color, which is salmon. The third form, for consigned material, is light blue.

A Tra-Dex visible index card for stores records is shown in Fig. 19. The cards are laid in a wide file with a series of pockets. In each pocket a number of cards are overlapped horizontally so that the part number or balance on order on each card is visible. The notches in the bottom of the card fit over a series of rods which hold the card in position. The cards may have various types of signal devices cut into the exposed margin, which is clearly visible. Twenty-five thousand cards can be filed within an arm's length of one clerk.

The system shown in Fig. 20 is used by an aircraft manufacturer for materials control for production orders or contracts. The visible index (bottom card, left) shows the kind of material covered by the card, and the signal at this location is set over the number corresponding to the plane model for which this material is needed. When new plane orders are received on which this material is needed, the right-hand signal is moved over the "order" space on the bottom margin. The cards thus signaled are then checked by use of the material requirement cards in the pockets, on which in each case are shown the model numbers on which the material is used, the numbers and names of the parts made from it,

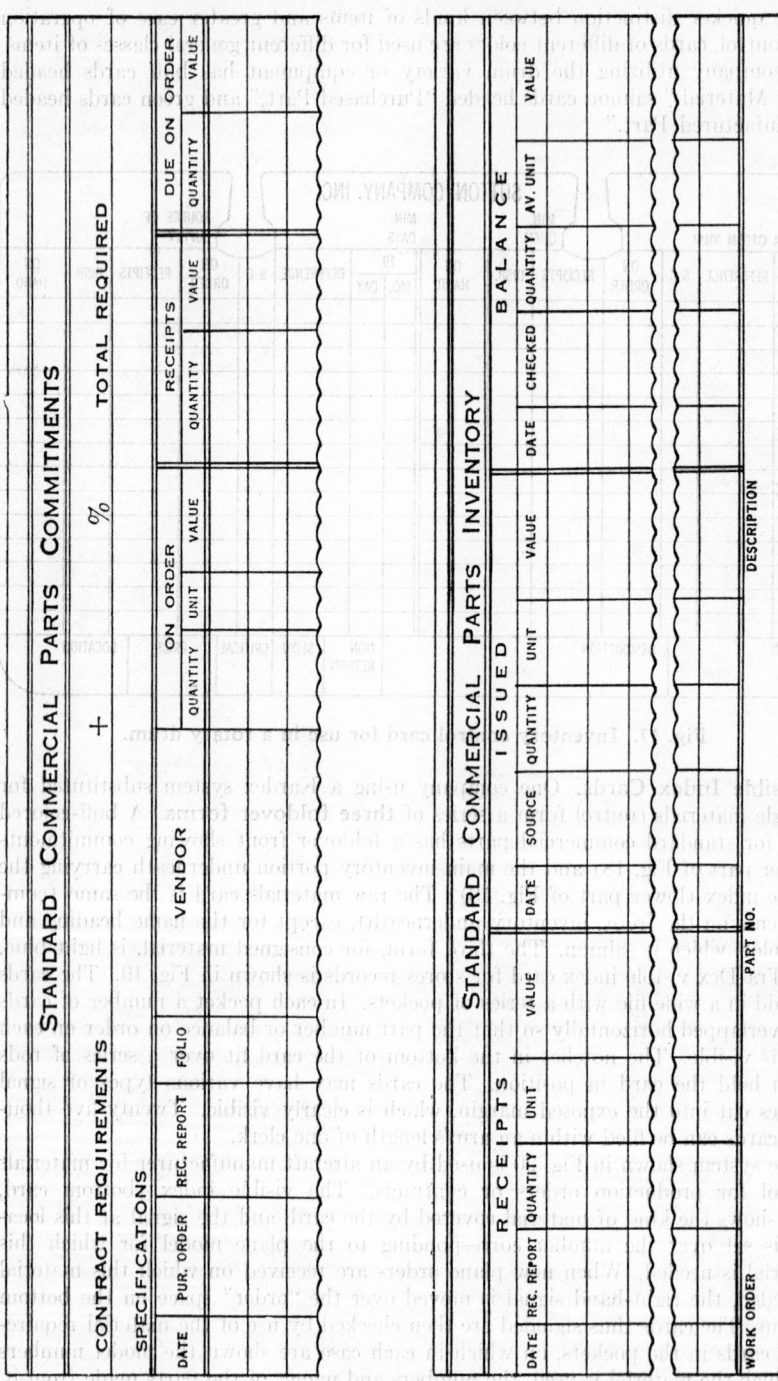

Fig. 18. Commercial parts commitments and inventory record.

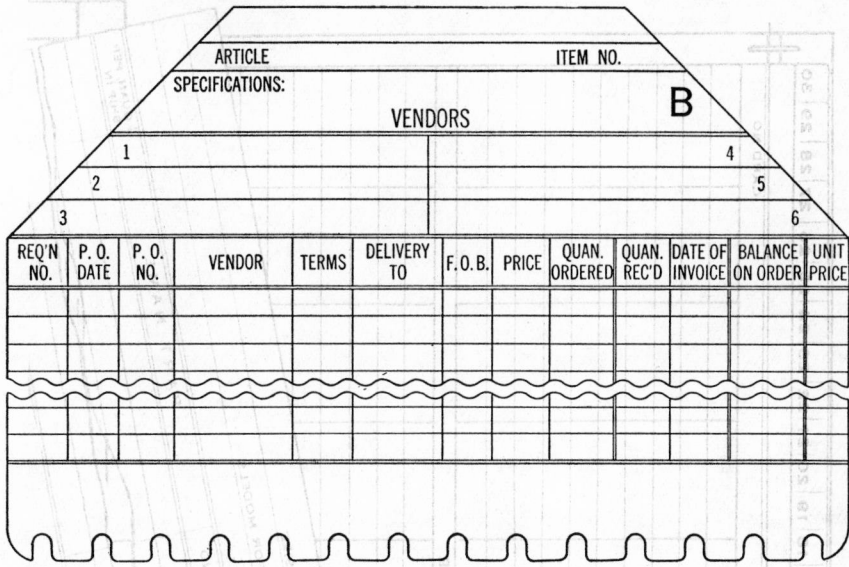

Fig. 19. Stores record card of the visible index type.

the quantity of material required for each part, and the number of parts required for each plane. The requirements for each contract are then calculated and posted on the **delivery schedule chart** in terms of the amounts needed each month. Total monthly requirements and receipts with cumulative totals are entered at the right of this card. The lower card is used for receipts and disbursements and determining the balance in stock. The Kardex Graph-A-Matic signal at the right of the lower card is set at the month in which the material is required and thus facilitates the purchase, follow-up, and delivery of this material.

Control Boards. Another system for handling stores records is that developed by the McCaskey Register Co. Four types of forms are used: a **receiving slip,** which can also be used as a materials credit slip, a **materials requisition and stock record,** a **stock inventory,** and **permanent stock cards.** The two former are carbon-backed and are made out in triplicate (receiving—blue, salmon, pink; requisition—white, pink, salmon). The stock inventory is in duplicate (pink, salmon) and the permanent record (blue) is a folded tab card made out singly.

One set of boards is usually located in the storeroom and another in the stores record department, but a single control is used in some cases. The clips are mounted on boards in rows running horizontally and vertically; the boards constitute panels which are used on both sides, and they are mounted on wall brackets so that a series can be grouped together and swung back to give access to whatever board is wanted. The clips are numbered with the bin or shelf-location number where the material is stored. A visible index system shows the bin number and the corresponding clip-board number of any item in stores.

Receiving slips are made out in the receiving department (or if used for stores credits, in the department from which the material is returned) and sent to the purchasing department and to the storeroom with the material. When the material is checked and stored, the storeskeeper notes from the top (last-posted)

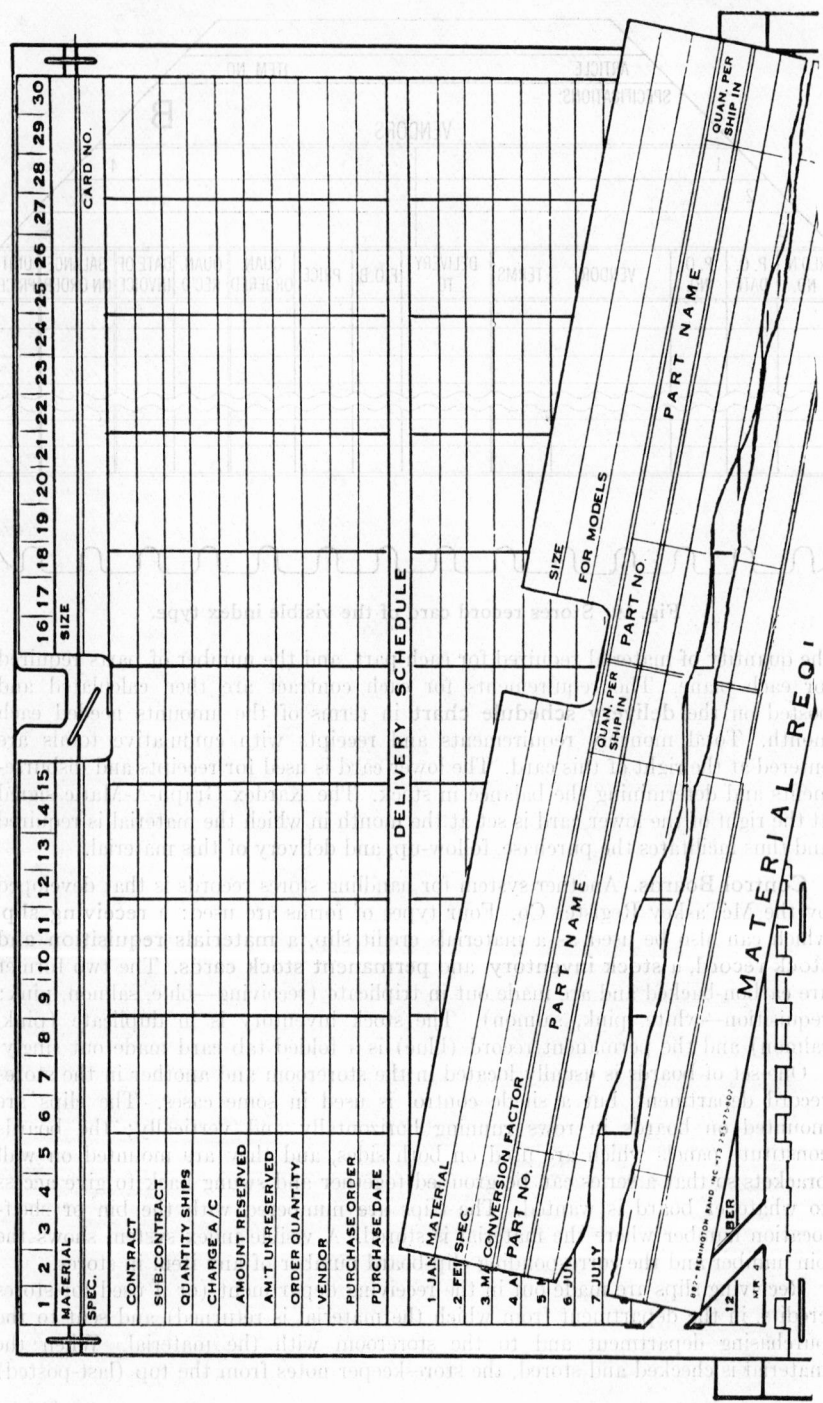

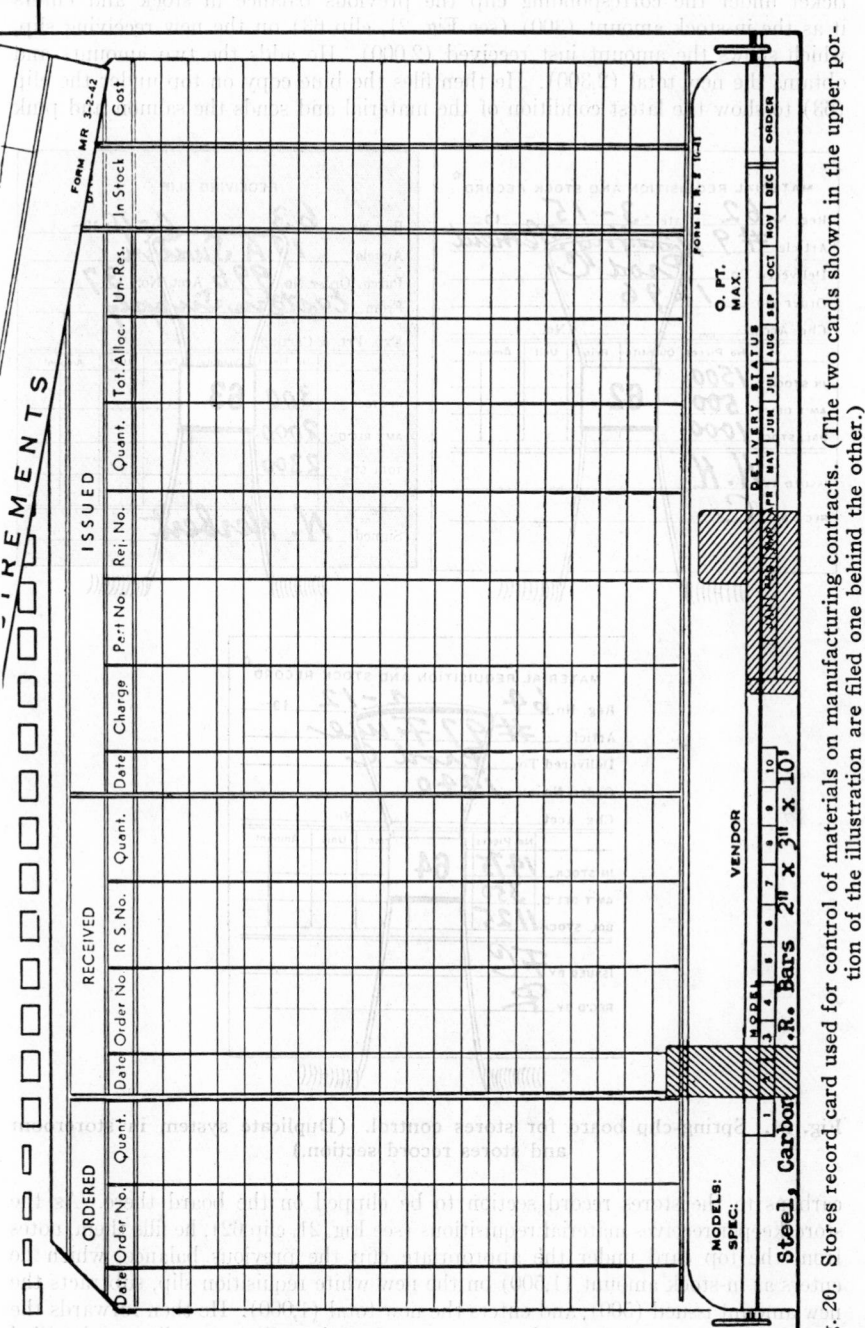

Fig. 20. Stores record card used for control of materials on manufacturing contracts. (The two cards shown in the upper portion of the illustration are filed one behind the other.)

ticket under the corresponding clip the previous balance in stock and enters it as the in-stock amount (300) (see Fig. 21, clip 63) on the new receiving slip, which shows the amount just received (2,000). He adds the two amounts and obtains the new total (2,300). He then files the blue copy on top under the clip (63) to show the latest condition of the material and sends the salmon and pink

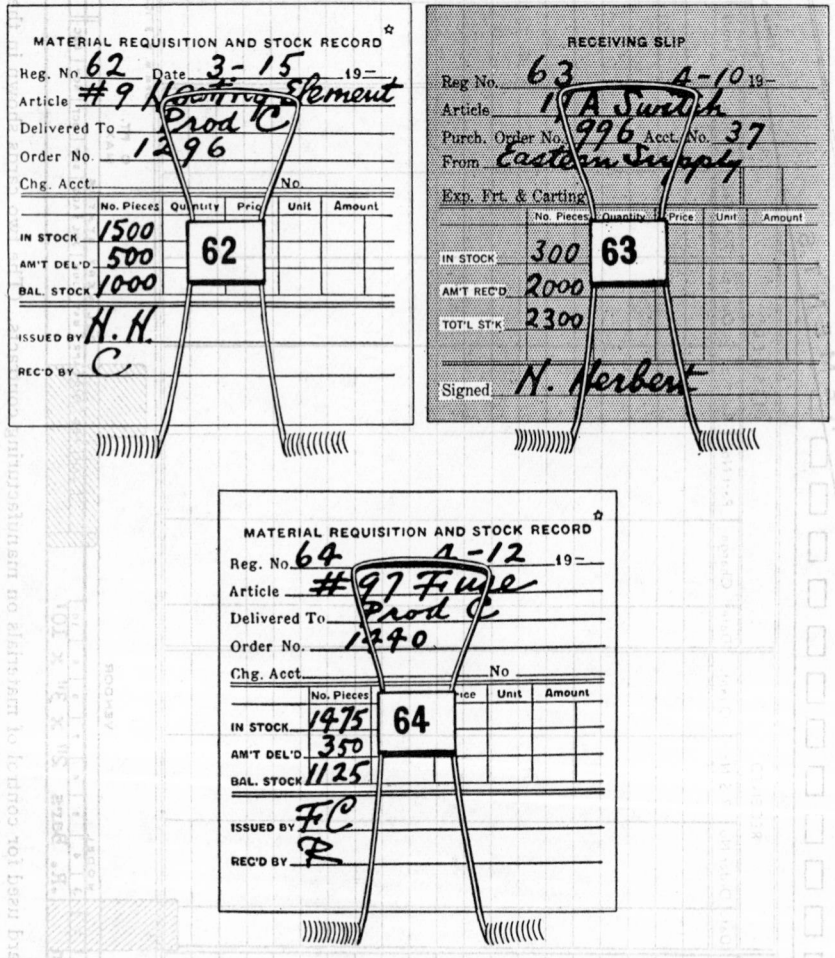

Fig. 21. Spring-clip board for stores control. (Duplicate system in storeroom and stores record section.)

carbons to the stores record section to be clipped on the board there. As the storeskeeper receives material requisitions (see Fig. 21, clip 62), he fills them, notes from the top card under the appropriate clip the previous balance, which he enters as in-stock amount (1,500) on the new white requisition slip, subtracts the new amount issued (500), and enters the new total (1,000). He then forwards the pink and salmon carbons to the stores record section. Stores credits are handled like receiving slips.

The stores record clerk checks each slip as it comes in and verifies it with the previous tickets for the same item. Then he enters the necessary cost data, which are not recorded in the storeroom, posts his copy of the ticket on his board according to bin number, and sends the carbon to the cost department, accounting department, or wherever designated. Additional copies of tickets can be provided in the system if more are needed. The boards in the storeroom and stores record department are identical as to postings. **Stock inventory checks** (and periodic physical inventories, for which special report and summary forms are used) can be made in the same way as under other systems and the tickets handled as above to show the check or make corrections in quantities. The stock inventory tickets call for quantity, price, units, and amount entries. For group issues, apportioning of material, and other purposes, the system is varied slightly to conform to needs.

REG NO 63	MINIMUM 1,000		PRICE 54							
Part No. A 2875										
Description 17 A Switch										
DATE ORDERED	QUANTITY	ORDERED FROM	DATE REC'D	QUANTITY	PRICE	PER	AMOUNT	TERMS	FREIGHT - EXPRESS	
9-15-	3,000	General Mfg	9-26	3,000	05	Ea				
1-7-	4,000	Eastern Supply	1-17	4,000	05	Ea				
3-31-	2,000	" "	4-10	2,000	05	Ea				

Fig. 22. Permanent stores card for spring-clip board system.

The **tabbed permanent stock card** (Fig. 22) is used only in the stores record section. It is folded at the vertical line beside the price tab when filed, and is placed behind all of the tickets under the clip (bin tab 63), with the tabs showing above the tickets. The minimum (reorder) quantity shows on the middle tab so that when the balance falls to this figure a reorder requisition can be placed. A copy of this requisition may go on the board under the clip as a record. The price tab is used for quick reference in entering costs on requisitions. A permanent record of purchase or manufacturing orders to replenish stock is entered with sources, deliveries, prices, etc.

REQUISITIONS FOR NEW ORDERS. Requisitions for the purchase of production material or for making a part in the shop are usually initiated by the materials control section. There are several ways to **initiate requisitions for procuring materials,** depending upon the method of control used:

1. On the periodic order basis, requisitions for purchased raw materials and parts are initiated whenever manufacturing schedules are reviewed and the need to place orders determined, as explained above.
2. On the fixed order basis, purchase orders and shop requisitions are initiated whenever the reorder point is reached for these stock items, as explained above. Special items are purchased or produced as needed.
3. In commodity purchasing, purchase orders may be initiated for planned programs, whenever it is decided to buy material on a speculative basis, or when there is a threatened shortage due to a strike or excessive demand.

Purchase Requisitions. The **sources of requisitions** for specific purchases are mainly (1) the materials control section, for items carried regularly in stores and controlled through stores records; (2) the planning or scheduling section, for production items which are not regularly stored or which are controlled by a production schedule; and (3) individuals authorized to issue purchase requisitions as needs arise. The nonstocked items are usually ordered by the planning section from data on bills of materials or parts lists, with the exception of those requisitioned by the superintendent or other operating authority for materials or parts specially required for experimental jobs or other unusual uses.

JONES MANUFACTURING COMPANY

Purchase Requisition

TO _____   REQ. NO. _____

Please purchase the following items: Date _____

Quantity	Description		

Ship to _____   Date Required _____
Via _____

Signed _____   Approved _____

Fig. 23. Purchase requisition.

With a good system of materials control, the operating departments are not responsible for the kinds or quantities of production items stored and do not do any ordering or requisitioning of materials for production, this work being the function of the planning and stores records section of production control.

Purchase requisitions for stock items are usually issued by the materials control section whenever a reorder point is reached or a new schedule is worked. Sometimes requisitions are originated by the storeskeeper if he keeps the stores record. The purchase requisition is often made out in two copies, with one copy being retained by materials control until they receive a copy of the purchase order. An example of a purchase requisition is shown in Fig. 23. (Also see section on Purchasing.)

Repeating Purchase Requisitions. Some companies have developed a repeating purchase requisition for stock material and parts which are ordered on

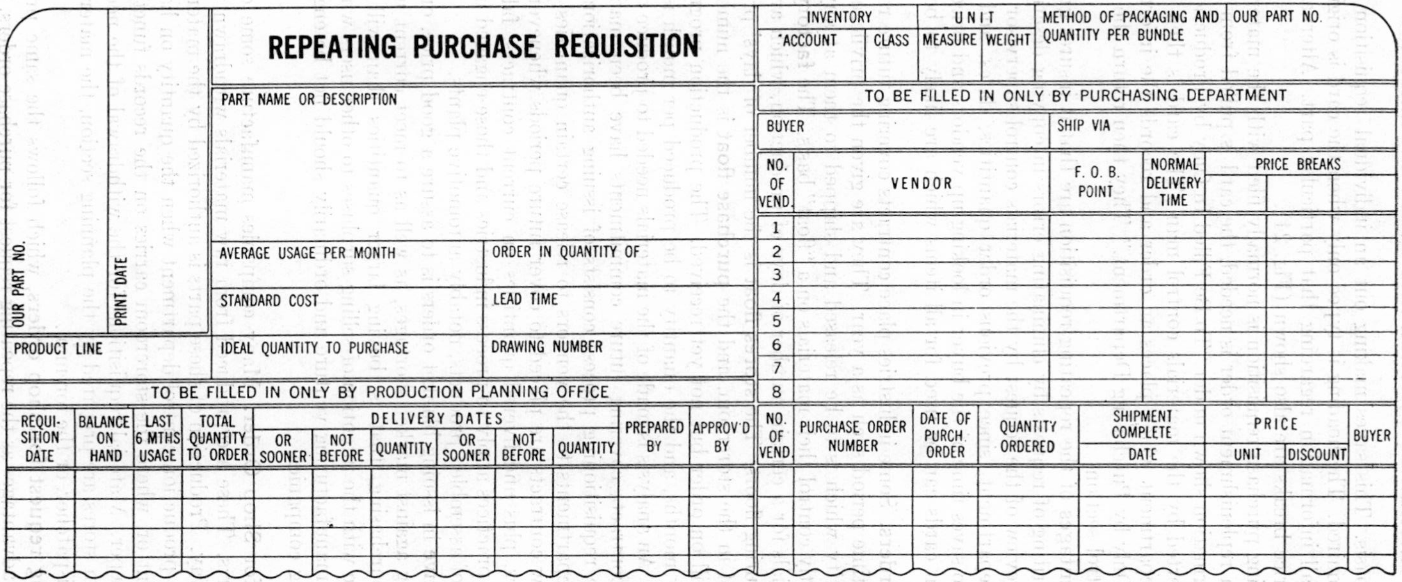

Fig. 24. Repeating purchase requisition.

a repetitive basis. This saves making out an individual requisition every time material is required. The heading is typed only when the card is originally made up and lists all information regarding that particular part. Alternate vendors, prices, and price breaks are also shown (Fig. 24).

The repeating purchase requisition is normally filed with the materials control card. When a replenishment order is needed, the card is pulled from the file and all of the information shown under "To Be Filled In Only by Production Planning Office" is inserted by the materials control man. The card is then sent to the purchasing department which places an order and records the information "To Be Filled In Only by Purchasing Department." They then return the card to the materials control section.

Other **advantages** of the repeating requisition are that it insures greater accuracy in the writing of requests by eliminating errors in copying descriptions, and it facilitates review of the request by the materials control supervisor and by the purchasing department, since previous order quantities, dates, and prices are shown. It also saves time of the buyer in looking up vendors and prices. Repeating requisition cards can be used for all items which are likely to be reordered.

Blanket Orders. Some industries place contracts covering future requirements for a certain time period such as a year. They are given the privilege of specifying the quantity which is to be released and shipped to them at any one date. They frequently control their materials on a "float" basis. The **factory float** consists of materials for a certain number of days of production, which are stored on the manufacturing floors. The **stores float** is the number of days' production of materials kept in the storeroom, and the **purchase float** is the number of days' production still on order but not yet received. The production program usually is built up by months, and the quantity to be produced per month is stated for each product. An analysis is made of the materials needed to produce on schedule. If purchase contracts covering future commitments have been made for such materials, the requisitioning process consists of issuing authorizations from the purchasing departments to the vendors to release certain quantities against the contract. New contracts are placed to cover future periods whenever the quantities in stores, plus undelivered quantities on current contracts, fall to stated levels. These practices apply to process industries and those engaged in repetitive manufacture of assembled products, notably automotive plants.

The **objective** in issuing blanket orders is to assure a good price, or to protect manufacturing against market shortages, as well as to meet current needs. Pure speculative purchasing, that is, buying larger quantities than will be needed for production with the intention of selling surpluses to other users when markets rise, is not a manufacturing venture and ordinarily should not be engaged in by manufacturing companies.

Requests for Shop Order. Many companies manufacture some or many of their own parts. These are produced from raw materials withdrawn from stores in the usual way. Production of these parts is authorized by the materials control section of the production control department when the quantity on hand reaches a reorder point or, where the storeroom carries on the records function, by the chief storeskeeper. Material requisitions for the withdrawal of the necessary raw materials from stores are prepared by the planning section, the materials control section, the dispatcher, or the foreman.

A **repeating request for shop orders**, which follows the same principle and nas the same advantages as the repeating request for purchase orders, is shown as

UNIT SIZE ____ **REPEATING REQUEST FOR SHOP ORDER** PART NO ____

DESCRIPTION

MATERIAL FROM ____ PRODUCT CODE ____

DELIVER TO ____

PAT NO & MAT'L ____ M.O. ____ S.O. ____ AVER. USAGE ____ COST ____

PART NO

DATE	QUAN. REQ'D	DATE REQ'D	M.O. OR S.O. NO	AUTH BY	REMARKS	PREP BY	DATE	QUAN REQ'D	DATE REQ'D	M.O. OR S.O. NO	AUTH BY	REMARKS	PREP BY
						P S							P S
						P S							P S
						P S							P S
						P							P

Fig. 25. Repeating request for shop order.

Fig. 25. All heading information remains constant and the person requesting a shop order has only to date the card, indicate the quantity required, indicate the date required, assign a shop order number, and initial the card. The **shop order preparation section** can then pull the appropriate repeating master and run off the required shop order and material requisition.

A combined purchase or production order requisition and low stock notice used to request the replenishment of either stores or manufactured component parts carried in stock is shown in Fig. 26. It is issued to the purchasing department or to the particular shop in the plant which makes the part in question. Checks beside the notations "Forge, Machine, Assemble" and "Cancel, Manufacture, Purchase" indicate the use of the form for the individual purpose. Old

ORDER REQUISITION
AND
LOW STOCK NOTICE №

ISSUED TO ____ DATE ____ CHARGE SYMBOL ____

NAME OF PART ____

DATE WANTED ____

FORGE	CANCEL	BASIS
MACHINE	MANF'R	
ASSEMBLE	PURCHASE	

OLD MAX.	OLD MIN	AMOUNT ON HAND	LAST ORDER NUMBER	BAL. CLERK	SUPERVISOR	QUANTITY	UNIT
NEW MAX.	NEW MIN						

1	2	3	4	5	6	7	8	9	10	11	12

SYMBOL ____ DRAWING NO ____ SHEET ____ LOCATION IN STORES ____

REMARKS

FORGING ORDER NO. ____ QUANTITY ____

MACHINE ORDER NO. ____ QUANTITY ____ BALANCE CLERK ____ SUPERVISOR ____

Fig. 26. Order requisition and low stock notice.

and new maximums and minimums are given, together with amount on hand, last order number, initials of balance-of-stores clerk and supervisor, quantity required, and unit in which item comes. The numbered spaces can be used to show monthly consumption. Entries are provided for symbol, drawing number, sheet, location in stores, and remarks. At the bottom are spaces for showing the order numbers issued for forging or machining and the quantity received from either operation, together with signatures of supervisor and balance-of-stores clerk upon completion and posting.

RECEIVING AND INSPECTION. In many companies receiving is a function of materials control, although sometimes materials control takes over after the materials are in and accepted. The **basic receiving functions** are unloading and unpacking materials, checking materials against the purchase order and invoice, having any necessary inspection done, making out receiving and inspection

		No. ________
RECEIVING REPORT Jones Manufacturing Company		
Received From	Purchase Order No.	Date
Quantity	Description	
Material Received	Checked	Delivered To
Via	Freight Paid	Signed

Fig. 27. Receiving report.

reports, putting materials into standard containers (often in standard lots), and delivering the materials to the storeroom. One copy of the receiving and inspection report is kept in the receiving department and others go to the purchasing department and the storeroom, the latter copy finally to the stores record section. Fig. 27 is a typical receiving report.

In some cases, copies of purchase orders are used as receiving reports, particularly if the number of copies necessary for the internal procedure is limited. If the purchase order is for one item, only one or two copies of the purchase order are furnished to the receiving department, which files and holds them until the material is received. If there are several items on the purchase order, or if the quantities are large enough to be sent in several shipments, several additional copies of the receiving reports are sent to receiving, and one is used for each receipt. In cases where a ditto master is ordered to prepare the purchase order, the master itself may be sent to the receiving department and copies run off as required. Usually the quantity column is blocked out in the reproduction process so that the receiving people have to count the exact quantity and record their count in the receiving report.

The number of copies of each receiving report to be made up and distributed depends on the organization, procedures, and internal control of the particular companies. Copies may be sent to the following departments:

1. **Purchasing Department.** To indicate receipt so that expediting is informed and to clear the files.
2. **Materials Control Department.** For entry into stores ledgers.
3. **Accounting Department.** To confirm receipt so invoices can be paid.
4. **Receiving Department.** File copy.
5. **Storeroom.** To identify and accompany material.

In some cases one copy may be routed through several departments.

DELIVERY TO STOREROOM. Upon release from receiving and inspection, materials are sent to the storeroom (or user), accompanied by a copy of the receiving report or sometimes by a special identification form. For parts manufactured in the plant and sent to the storeroom, a **finished goods report** is often made out by the dispatcher or foreman. A typical form is shown in Fig. 28.

FINISHED GOODS REPORT		No. 18231			
T O	STOREROOM	SHOW LOCATION IN STOREROOM		SHOP ORDER NO.	
F R O M	AREA	CHECK TO SHOW WHETHER		INVENTORY ACCT. NO.	
		PARTIAL ORDER	COMPLETE ORDER		
QUANTITY	PART NO. OR SIZE	NAME OF PART		UNIT	UNIT COST / TOTAL COST
PREPARED IN SHOP BY		DATE	RECD. IN STOREROOM AND COUNTED BY		DATE
INSTRUCTIONS ON USE OF FORM: WHITE COPY - Mailed to Central Dispatch to close out Shop Order. Matched with Pink, then mailed to Cost Dept. PINK COPY - Travels with pieces. Mailed to Central Dispatch by Storeroom. Matched with white. Posted to D. & S. Card, then filed. YELLOW COPY - Travels with pieces. Used in Storeroom as Identification Tag.					

Fig. 28. Finished goods report.

This is often made out in several copies which may be used as follows:

1. Travels with the pieces to identify them and is used as an identification tag in the storeroom.
2. Travels with the pieces and is then sent to the materials control section for posting receipt of materials after they are checked in and counted by the storekeeper.
3. Sent directly to the production control section to inform them to close out shop orders. Then sent to the cost department for closing out their records.

When items to be stored are received from the receiving department or from the manufacturing departments, the kind, condition, and count should be checked with the accompanying receiving report, finished goods ticket, or materials credit ticket. Discrepancies should be noted and reported at once for adjustment. The storeskeeper is responsible for what he receives and, in fact, must usually sign or initial such forms to acknowledge his acceptance and responsibility. When he has accounted for the delivery and posted his records, he will send the form, so initialed, to the stores record section for entry in the materials control records.

ISSUING FROM STOREROOM. Materials should be issued from stores only upon the presentation of duly authorized requisitions. These **requisitions for production materials** may originate and the materials may be delivered in the following ways:

1. Where no central production control system exists, foremen or department heads make out requisitions as materials are needed for jobs.
2. Under regular production control, the materials requisitions are written in the materials control or planning section, usually sent to the stores record section for apportionment or reservation on the records against the job order, are delivered with other papers to central dispatching, and are sent from there to the manufacturing department where the materials will be needed. Here the local dispatcher, or the foreman, if there is no dispatcher, will send them to the storeroom in advance of setting up the job and will thus have them delivered in time to start the work.
3. For continuous production (chemicals, cement, etc.), a production schedule often is made out and materials are forwarded to the using departments according to daily needs in accordance with this schedule. Changes in amounts forwarded will be authorized by changed production schedules. These schedules may be issued monthly or as authorizations to run as specified until further notice.
4. For continuous production, also, materials may be stored in the production areas and placed under control of the manufacturing departments, which make periodic checks on quantities and originate requests or requisitions for replenishment at predetermined reorder points.
5. For mass production of repetitive lots, as in automobile assembly plants, materials sufficient for each day's run may be sent in from parts plants or outside vendors, under planned control from the central order control division. They are delivered directly to subassembly stations or to the main assembly lines. Some materials, usually smaller items which are not economically handled in small lots, may be stored in the assembly plants in quantities for a month's (or more) regular production and withdrawn to supply the assembly lines as required.
6. For special or irregular use, foremen, department heads, or executives may authorize the issuing of materials or parts which may be needed to replace those damaged in production or found unsuitable, or to compensate for shortages on a previous requisition.

Supplies and materials for any nonproductive purposes in the plant, office, construction, or service departments, and parts and supplies used in maintenance work, are withdrawn with **special materials requisitions** authorized by the heads of any of these units. Often the maintenance department will have its own storeroom and control its own materials because of the recurrent nature of its work and the need for parts and supplies at hours when the regular storerooms are closed.

In all well-run plants, it is a fixed rule that storerooms must be kept locked, outsiders must not be admitted, and no materials must be given out except upon duly authorized requisitions.

Stores Requisitions. The important information on any materials or stores requisition includes the following:

1. Description of item wanted.
2. Quantity wanted, and unit of issue (piece, foot, pound, etc.).
3. Point to which material should be delivered (department, location, etc.).
4. Date wanted.
5. Charge or order number.
6. Signature of person making out or authorizing requisition.
7. Date of signing.
8. Initials or signature of person receiving material.
9. Initials or signature of storeskeeper.

Simpler forms carry the above data, but often additional entries are needed. Fig. 29, for example, has space also for stores location, new balance on the bin tag, amount issued, cost data, initials of stores record clerk who may apportion material in advance of issue, initials of "balance" or stores record clerk who posts the actual issue, and initials of the cost clerk who enters the issue on the cost

MATERIAL ISSUE								CHARGE OR ORDER NO.	
CREDIT OR TRANSFER								CREDIT	
DELIVER TO	SHOP SYMBOL		NAME SHOP		LOCATION			DATE WRITTEN	
DESCRIPTION	(Specify UNIT WANTED as lbs., pieces, coils, barrels, each, etc.)							DATE WANTED	
								UNIT WANTED	
								QUANTITY WANTED	
								APPROVED BY	
NEW BAL. BIN TAG	ISSUED		BOOK SPEC.	PRICE	STORES VALUE	HANDLING	TOTAL COST		EXCESS
	QUANTITY	UNIT							
APPORTIONED	STOREKEEPER		BALANCE CLERK		COST CLERK		MATERIAL REC'D BY		

Fig. 29. Material issue, credit, or transfer slip.

records for the job. It is the usual practice to put the cost data on these slips as they are posted to the stores record (if they are shown on these records), to save unnecessarily repeated work for the cost clerk in looking up materials costs. The space for apportionment provided on the stores issue form eliminates the need for a special reservation slip to assign and hold quantities sufficient for the orders covered.

Forms like these for issuing single kinds of material are used most frequently when the items come under different cost-charge classifications, when the items are in different storerooms, when they are issued at different times, and when job order methods of costing are used.

Group Stores Issues. When a number of items for the same production order are to go to the same manufacturing department at the same time and from the same storeroom, considerable clerical work and stores and transportation labor are saved by the use of a **group requisition or materials issue form** on which all such items are listed, the remainder of the data being the same as with single issues. Stores record and cost record work on these forms are handled in the same way as for single issues.

When the bill of materials required for a complete order can be conveniently arranged to serve as a group stores issue, as in the case of an assembly order, a form similar to Fig. 30 may be employed. This form is prepared as a master from which duplicates can be made, the black squares showing up white on the print. Ink or pencil data can then be inserted to cover any particular order,

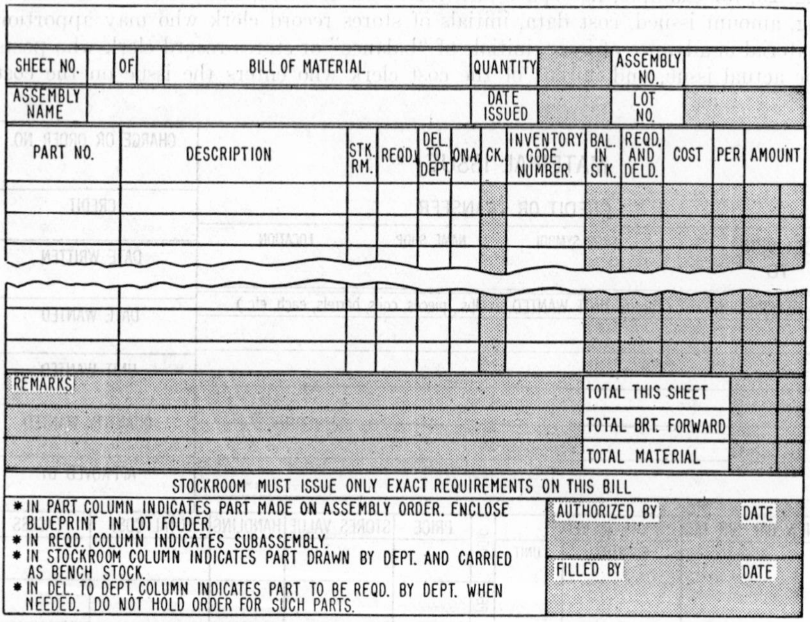

Fig. 30. Assembly bill of materials, "master" for group issue requisitions.

giving quantity, date, lot number, a check column to show delivery, balance in stock of each part, amount required and delivered, cost, unit on which cost is based, and total cost amount for each item. Total cost may be added up and brought forward from sheet to sheet and finally summarized. Special notations may be made under remarks. Authorization and filling, with dates, are indicated by names or initials of the requisitioner and storeskeeper.

Some companies **bundle** parts—tie together a fixed number of parts to utilize space better, to facilitate counting of, and to eliminate the posting of detail requirements and issues for individual releases. **Bundling quantities** are determined from the best available information to represent roughly a month's usage, considering weight, size, or other factors. The bundling quantity should usually be in multiples of 10 or more. Bundling quantities are reported in whole bundles only and the remaining pieces are disregarded in the posting to quantity records. The parts are considered issued from the quantity records at the time that the tag is broken and forwarded to the material control for posting as an issue. Individual issues are still made by the storeroom, based on the quantity shown on the bills of material, parts list, or individual requisitions.

Material Transfer. In cases where materials issued for one order are to be switched to another order, a material transfer (Fig. 29) is used to make the charge to the new order and credit the old. Since a new stores requisition slip will be needed to get other materials for the old order if it is still to be put through, the issuing and cost accounting for the new transactions will proceed automatically under regular procedures. The material transfer serves merely to switch the charges on the material already issued so that the cost accounting records may be correct.

Material Deliveries. The required materials asked for on a requisition will be taken from the bins or shelves for delivery to the requisitioner. There are various ways for **handling stores or materials requisitions** and moving stores to the required point:

1. Workmen in small plants or where no organized production control system exists may go to the storeroom with the requisitions to get materials. This method is also usually used in emergencies, to get a special item or replacement materials for spoiled work.
2. Move men carrying requisitions may be sent for materials by the dispatcher or foreman.
3. The storeroom may have its own move men who deliver materials to the requisitioning department.
4. The plant transportation department may make the deliveries through its shop express system on scheduled or special trips.
5. Conveyors may connect the storeroom and the user departments where a regular route and need for a continuous supply exist.
6. Materials may be stored in using departments, as stated above, when large quantities are regularly required.

In cases 3 and 4 the production control requisitions are sent to the storeroom by the dispatcher or foreman a day or so before deliveries are due. The storekeeper then sorts and groups the requisitions and has his assistants make up the orders in a section of the storeroom. In this way all orders from one department may be grouped and deliveries can be made economically. For convenience, requisitions may be filed in the storeroom by due dates and according to departments, and the items on requisitions to be filled and delivered in any one day may be assembled and held until time for removal. This **requisition date file** usually insures prompt handling on the proper dates.

Stores Credits. If any materials or parts are left over from any job because the order was cut down or quantities supplied were in excess of needs, they should be returned to the storeroom with a **material credit slip** (Fig. 29). When it is not desired to place the items in stores, they may be sent to the salvage planner, who determines their disposition and enters the notation and his signature on the form.

Entry in Cost and Accounting Records. Materials issue and stores credit slips are sorted in the stores record section by classes or groups in the manner in which the accounts are kept, and posted and priced if the price file is maintained in the stores records. The slips are then sent to the cost accounting department for financial control purposes. Receiving reports are similarly classified and charged to the accounts. Discrepancies between stores records and stores counts must likewise be posted as adjustments to obtain agreement.

The stores requisitions are sorted by classes of products or by job numbers and overhead expense accounts, in accordance with the way costs are set up. They are then entered on the cost records, together with direct labor costs from time tickets. With the addition of proper overhead costs, those totals show the **manufacturing costs of products or specific jobs.** They are used for checking actual costs against estimates or previous records and for studying new work so that plans for holding costs within limits, or reducing them, can be applied. Under a standard cost plan, of course, procedures are simplified by the use of the predetermined cost of each item.

Summary of Materials Issuing Procedure. The course of a materials requisition slip, the activities with which it is associated, and the entries that are made from it are better understood from Fig. 31, developed by Bangs, and the following explanation:

1. A materials requisition is written in the planning department from the bill of materials for a production order which authorizes the manufacture of a product and the withdrawal of the necessary parts and materials from stores.

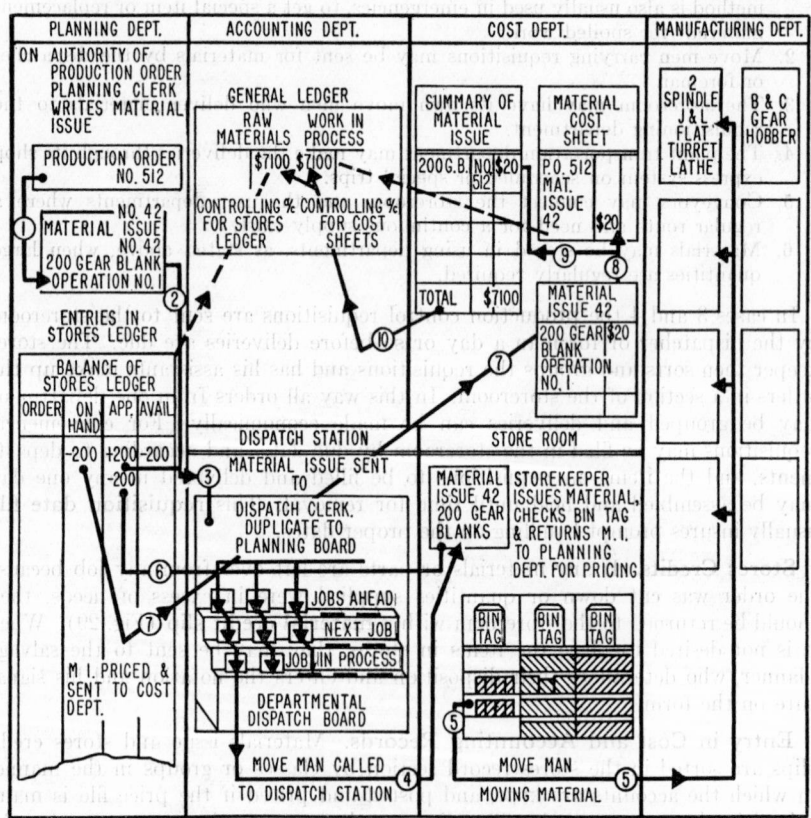

Fig. 31. Fundamental procedures in issuing stores.

2. This materials issue slip is sent to the stores record or balance-of-stores clerk for addition to the apportioned column and consequent subtraction from the available column on the sheet for the parts shown, gear blanks. (Note that balances are not shown in the diagram, only the transactions on this materials issue slip.)

3. After it is apportioned, the materials issue slip goes to the shop dispatcher in the gear manufacturing department, who files it and posts the corresponding work order in the control board pocket or other place for keeping data for the machine on which the work is done.

4. When the job is about to be started, the dispatcher takes out the materials issue slip and sends it with a move man to the storeroom.

5. Here the storeskeeper issues the material which the move man takes to the gear manufacturing department.

6. The storeskeeper, after posting the issue to the bin tag, sends the materials issue slip back to the balance-of-stores clerk, who subtracts it from both the apportioned and on-hand columns of the sheet for the gear blanks. At the same time he enters the unit cost of the gear blanks on the materials issue slip and calculates and enters the total value of the issue ($20, Fig. 31).

7. The materials issue slip is forwarded to the cost department for posting.

8. It is entered in the materials cost sheet for the particular production order.

9. It is also posted to the summary of material issues for the period, which is later totaled ($7,100 for all items issued, Fig. 31).

10. The summary sheet is later sent to the accounting department and posted as a credit to the raw materials account and a debit to the work-in-process account. The debit postings must agree with the total of material issues for jobs in the shop, and the credit postings must agree with the balance-of-stores postings of withdrawals from stores.

Raw materials and parts or subassemblies which are stored are all handled in the manner described. Shipping orders for the withdrawal of finished products from stock for delivery to customers are handled according to a similar plan.

Miscellaneous Stores. Under the designation of miscellaneous stores are the following kinds of items:

1. Parts or materials temporarily stored for current work.

2. Parts ordered for special jobs and not used because they are surplus or are replaced by other items.

3. Materials ordered for special jobs but not used.

4. Repair or replacement parts on old models or obsolete models of the company's products for which orders are only infrequently received.

5. Items or materials no longer used on current products and for which there is no demand.

6. Parts from miscellaneous dismantled products or equipment which may be considered usable for certain purposes around the plant.

7. Maintenance parts and items little used or superseded.

Such items are usually kept in separate bins in the regular storage locations to prevent them from becoming mixed with or issued in place of the items regularly carried, to make room for regular items, and to simplify stores issuing. Because they may be used from time to time, however, they are kept in the storeroom and entered on the stores records so that they are known to exist and will be available if wanted. Since they are not regularly issued and stocks are not replenished, it is necessary only to sort them into groups, put them in a suitable place, and record them on simple records of standard size but specially printed and filed in a separate section of the regular stores record system. Bin tags or identification tickets should be placed with them in the storeroom.

The **miscellaneous stores cards** or sheets used require usually only the following information:

Heading:

1. Material or part name.
2. Symbol.
3. Specification or description.
4. Original source, such as purchase requisition and order number.
5. Date originally entered in records.
6. Use—for what purpose, on what product or equipment, or for what department.
7. Any restrictions on use or issue.
8. Location in storeroom.
9. Unit of issue.

Columns for entries:

1. Date of any transactions.
2. Order number (issue, purchase, manufacture).
3. Quantity
   a. Received
   b. Issued
   c. Balance
4. Unit price.
5. Total value.
6. Reason or circumstance of issue, or department or person requisitioning.

Certain of the above data are historical but will be of service in settling questions of demand, disposal, etc.

Other Forms. Other forms used in some cases are: a **materials shortage slip,** issued when materials are not on hand or are not on hand in sufficient quantity to fill the order completely; a **notice of danger point,** made out by the storeskeeper and sent to the materials control section when materials fall to a very low point because of delays in receipt of materials; an **order to stock material,** sent to stores records when a new material is to be stocked; a **verification slip,** sent by the stores record clerk to the storeskeeper to verify the quantity on the stores records with the bin-tag record; and a **stores count report,** used to enter a physical count made in the storeroom and sent to stores records and to the accounting department to adjust differences between the records and accounts and the actual quantities on hand.

Determining Economic Lot Sizes

UNIT COSTS. There are several auxiliary procedures necessary to implement the materials cycle. One of these is to determine the economic purchasing quantity for each purchased part and item of raw material (see section on Purchasing) and an economic manufacturing quantity for each part produced in the shop (see section on Production Planning and Control).

The **economic lot size** is that quantity which will give lowest unit cost, but it is necessary to be certain that all costs have been included. It is the over-all unit cost of the material as delivered to the production department, rather than the specific price quotation at which material is purchased or produced which is important. Thus the cost of storing, handling, and keeping records of the part must also be considered.

There are a number of **factors influencing the ultimate unit cost of the product.** Those which are usually of most importance are:

1. The price paid for a purchased item or the cost of a manufactured item.
2. The cost of placing the order for replenishment quantities.

3. The cost of carrying the item in inventory.
4. The amount of money tied up in inventory.
5. Physical deterioration or obsolescence of the item while held in storage.

The effects of these factors may be reduced to a fairly definite **schedule of costs** which may be classified as follows:

1. Unit costs which tend to decrease as the size of the order is increased:
   a. Purchase price or cost of manufacturing.
   b. Cost of purchase or shop orders.
2. Unit costs which tend to increase as the size of the order is increased:
   a. Inventory storage costs, which include expenses for rent, heat, light, janitor service, plant protection, etc. If materials are stored in buildings owned by the company, space charges such as depreciation, repairs, maintenance, insurance, and taxes on the building replace the rental charge.
   b. Inventory carrying charges, which include interest on investment in the larger average inventory carried, personal property taxes and insurance on the materials, risk of spoilage, depreciation, and possible obsolescence, excess materials handling, record-keeping costs, etc.

The factors involved in economic purchasing quantities for raw materials and purchased parts and the computation relative to economic lot sizes for purchased items are covered first.

ECONOMIC PURCHASING QUANTITIES. The possibility of securing advantageous terms by buying in larger quantities is the most important single factor in determining an economic purchasing quantity. In many cases, purchase discounts are given for buying in larger quantities.

If larger quantities are purchased on each order, it means that fewer orders will be placed during the year. This may provide savings which should also be taken into account in determining the economic lot size. The **average cost of placing a purchase order** may be computed by adding the costs of requisitioning, purchasing, receiving, and paying for materials during a given period, and dividing this total cost by the number of purchase orders placed during that period. Or purchase orders may be classified as to type and the total cost may be allocated to each group depending upon the estimated time taken to purchase each particular group. From these figures, in turn, average purchase order costs per group are determined. One company was surprised to find its cost of procurement per order was $21.11. A rule-of-thumb figure by other companies is in the neighborhood of $8.00 to $12.00 per purchase order.

Another company found that the cost of initiating and processing a purchase order based on a volume of 1,200 to 1,500 purchase orders per month and a purchasing department expense of approximately $5,500 per month was as follows:

Cost of preparing purchase requisition in production control department...... $0.40
Cost to process order through purchasing and follow-up...................... 5.34
Cost to process and distribute receiving reports........................... 1.11
Cost to process invoice.. 0.87
$7.72

Dickie (Factory Management and Maintenance, vol. 111) says that "the cost to be considered in making this decision is not the cost of placing a purchase order, but rather the difference in cost between obtaining a given amount in one order or in two orders, and includes the cost of ordering, purchasing, inspecting, laboratory certification analysis, receiving, stock handling, recording, invoice payment, difference in transportation cost, etc."

Others have held that any consideration of the savings in procurement costs through placing fewer purchase orders should only include the strictly variable costs or proven savings which can be made if the number of purchase orders is decreased.

INVENTORY CARRYING CHARGES. There are a number of storage and inventory carrying costs which tend to increase as the size of the purchase order is increased. As larger quantities are purchased at one time, the quantity comprising the average inventory also increases. For example, suppose that an item is purchased for stock and the usage is $2,000 per year. One order could be

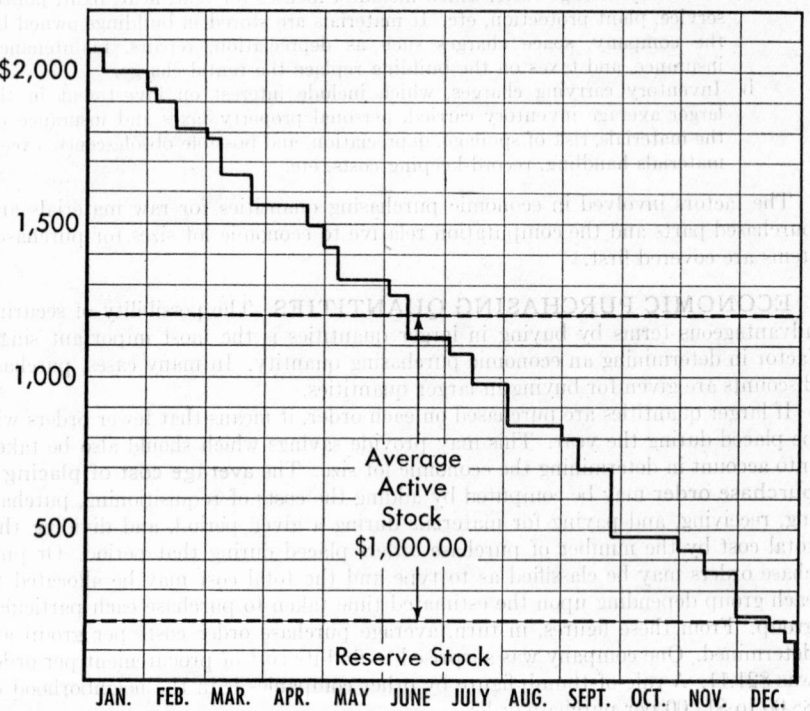

Fig. 32. Average inventory with one order per year.

placed for $2,000, or 12 orders might be placed for $166 each. In the first case, the cost of ordering is only ½₂ of that in the second case. However, the average inventory in the first case is $1,000 plus reserve stock (see Fig. 32), whereas the average inventory in the second case is $83 plus reserve stock (see Fig. 33). Therefore, the carrying costs for interest, taxes, insurance, space charges, etc., will be substantially higher for the first case than for the second.

Computing Storage Costs. Inventory storage costs such as rent, heat, light, janitor service, and plant protection may be computed by allocating all the costs of renting and operating storerooms to the items stored in proportion to the space occupied or on some other reasonable basis. Storage charges may tend to increase rather abruptly at a certain level of inventory if existing storage space is entirely utilized and new space must be constructed. Inventory storage costs are usually converted to a percent of the value of the items carried in inventory.

Carrying Charges. Inventory carrying charges are concerned with such items as taxes and insurance on the material carried in inventory, the investment of capital in inventory, loss from damage or spoilage of the material, and loss in value due to obsolescence. There is a further possibility of loss in value due to a price decline.

Taxes and insurance can usually be allocated on a value basis directly. **Interest on investment** is a function of the dollars invested in each item and can be computed in several ways. In some cases a nominal interest charge of 5 or

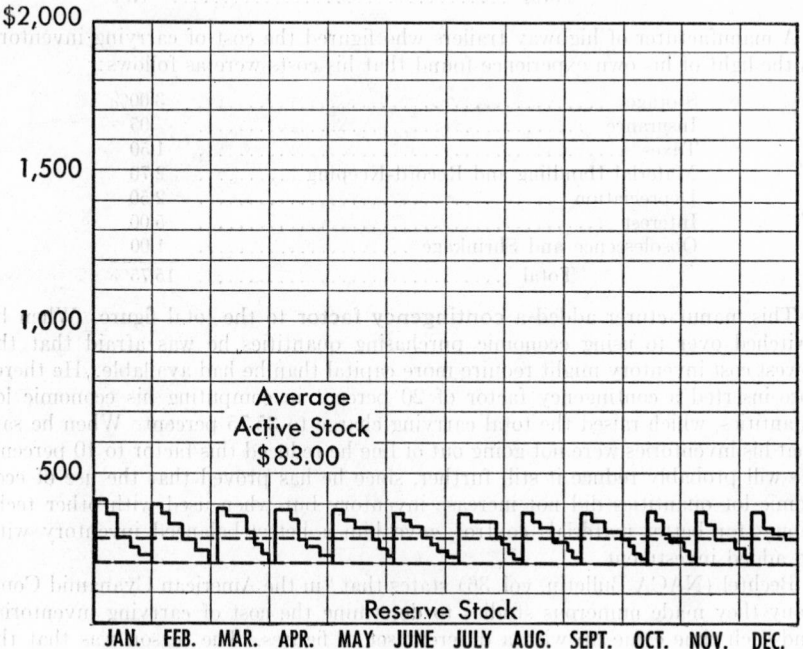

Fig. 33. Average inventory with ten orders per year.

6 percent is used for the capital tied up in inventory. Other companies charge a much higher rate in the belief that inventories should be expected to contribute to profit in the same manner as any other investment or asset. Thus, if the company is achieving a return of 25 percent on its other assets, it would include a charge of 25 percent as the interest cost of the inventory.

Damage, depreciation, and spoilage can sometimes be computed by classes and assigned on a percent of value basis. **Obsolescence** may be computed on an accounting or judgmental basis and may differ for various classes of material. Once the figure is determined, however, it is usually expressed as a percent of value for each class of inventory. The possibility of obsolescence increases with time, and some managements have made it a policy never to order more than a year's supply of any item on the theory that almost any item might be changed after a year and, therefore, the obsolescence factor rises to 100 percent at that time.

Total Cost of Carrying Inventory. The total of these charges usually runs from 10 percent to 20 percent of the value of the inventory per year. One large automotive manufacturer uses 25 percent per year as its figure. One commonly used estimate of the **percentage cost per year of carrying inventory** is as follows:

Storage Facilities	2%
Taxes and Insurance	1
Material Handling and Record-Keeping	4
Interest on Investment	5
Depreciation, Obsolescence, and Shrinkage	5
Total	17%

A manufacturer of highway trailers who figured the cost of carrying inventory in the light of his own experience found that his costs were as follows:

Storage	3.00%
Insurance	.05
Taxes	1.50
Material Handling and Record-Keeping	2.70
Depreciation	2.50
Interest	5.00
Obsolescence and Shrinkage	1.00
Total	15.75%

This manufacturer added a **contingency factor** to the total figure. When he switched over to using economic purchasing quantities he was afraid that the lowest cost inventory might require more capital than he had available. He therefore inserted a contingency factor of 20 percent in computing his economic lot quantities, which raised the total carrying charge to 35.75 percent. When he saw that his inventories were not going out of line he reduced this factor to 10 percent. He will probably reduce it still further, since he has proved that the use of economic lot quantities did not increase inventory but when used with other techniques for better materials control, gave him a better-balanced inventory with no added investment.

Bechtel (NACA Bulletin, vol. 36) states that "in the American Cyanamid Company they made numerous studies to determine the cost of carrying inventories and each time came up with a different set of figures. The reason was that the different sets of inventories involved different sets of costs-to-carry, since different types of items require different types of costs. They found that a range of 12 percent to 20 percent of the annual inventory valuation was an appropriate cost, with the lower percentage applying to standard goods such as bulk acids, alums, fertilizers, etc., which did not deteriorate or go out of date. Other items which fell into the higher percentage included such items as packaged and dated pharmaceuticals, antibiotics, certain types of dye, etc."

Bechtel states that "a recent calculation was made to show the estimated annual average cost of carrying inventories by U.S. industry. Starting with interest on investment at 3 percent and carrying down through obsolescence, handling and records, deterioration, spoilage and repair, insurance and taxes, and storage charges, an annual percentage cost of 20 percent was arrived at. If a 5 percent interest rate were used, it would increase the carrying cost to 22 percent per year." He cites another study of three different types of inventories, using a 6 percent interest rate, where the totals were 17.3 percent, 18.2 percent, and 22 percent, respectively.

Effect of Economic Climate. Inventory carrying charges for warehouse stocks are classified by Hartigan and Grad (Mill and Factory, vol. 54) according to the economic climate. They have established charges for the three basic economic conditions as shown below.

Economic Condition	Carrying Charges Per Year (Percent of Inventory Value)
Deflationary	17.0
Stable	32.3
Inflationary	30.9

They further consider the following items and costs (in percent) as contributing elements to the carrying charge:

Item	Charges for Respective Economic Condition (Percent of Inventory Value)		
	Deflationary	Stable	Inflationary
Possession Costs			
Space	0.0	1.4	1.9
Equipment	0.1	1.0	1.0
Handling	3.7	3.7	3.7
Insurance	0.1	0.1	0.2
Taxes	0.6	0.6	1.6
Cost to take inventory	0.5	0.5	0.5
Value Losses			
Obsolescence	0.8	0.8	0.8
Deterioration	1.2	1.2	1.2
Return on Investment	4.0	20.0	20.0
General Business Influence			
Cost improvement	3.0	3.0	3.0
Value of dollar	3.0	0.0	−3.0

INVENTORY COST COMPUTATION. Mitchell (Purchasing) illustrates by a concrete case the use of **cost standards,** in determining the economical order. He assumes that the following information is available for commodity X:

1. Total annual requirements—5,000 units.
2. Average daily requirement—16 units.
3. Estimated time required for securing delivery after the placement of an order —30 days.
4. Estimated maximum requirements during any 30-day period—680 units.
5. Estimated minimum requirements during any 30-day period—100 units.
6. Estimated cost of handling a purchase order—$5.
7. Estimated storage cost for average inventory—30 cents per unit, per annum.
8. Estimated carrying charges for the average inventory, including interest on the investment, insurance, risk of damage, etc.—10% of the average annual inventory valuation.

In addition, the purchasing department has prepared an estimate of the prob. able unit purchase price, depending upon the size of the order placed. This schedule is shown in columns 1 and 2 of Fig. 34.

(1) Size of Order	(2) Est. Unit Price	(3) Est. Unit Buying Expense	(4) Average Inventory in Units	(5) Est. Value of Average Inventory
100	$2.20	$ .05	250	$ 550.00
200	2.10	.025	300	630.00
500	2.05	.01	450	922.50
800	2.00	.0062	600	1,200.00
1,000	1.95	.005	700	1,365.00
1,500	1.93	.0033	950	1,833.50
2,000	1.92	.0025	1,200	2,304.00

Fig. 34. Data for inventory computation.

From information available, the data appearing in columns 3, 4, and 5 can be computed. The estimated unit buying expense in column 3 is obtained by dividing the cost of handling a single order, that is, $5.00, by the number of units included in an order as shown by column 1. The average inventory, as shown in column 4, is computed by the formula:

$$\text{Average inventory} = \frac{\text{Standard order}}{2} + \text{Minimum}$$

The minimum is computed according to the method previously explained as follows:

Ordering point, which by definition is the maximum requirement during the period required to fill an order, including the "cushion" stores which might have to be drawn upon in case of emergency.......... 680 units
Less: Average requirements during the time required to fill an order:
Average daily requirements............................ 16 units
Time required to fill an order.......................... 30 days   480 units
Minimum or "cushion" stores........................... 200 units

Calculation of Economical Order. The cost of the year's supply of commodity X and the effect of variation in the size of purchase order is then computed by Mitchell. The results are shown in Fig. 35. This chart shows that the economical order is approximately 1,000 units. Therefore, the quantity standards for commodity X are as shown below.

Minimum .... 200 units
Ordering Point .... 680 units
Standard Order .... 1,000 units
Maximum .... 1,580 units

A full treatment of the determination of the most economical quantity to buy will be found in the section on Purchasing.

Trial Ordering Quantity	100	200	500	800	1,000	1,500	2,000
Purchase Cost: Total year's requirements × Corresponding unit price . . . (5,000 × Corresponding price appearing in column 2, table above).	11,000	10,500	10,250	10,000	9,750	9,650	9,600
Buying Expense: Total year's requirements × Corresponding unit buying expense . . . . (5,000 × Corresponding unit appearing in Column 3).	250	125	50	31	25	17	12
Cost of Storage: Average inventory × unit storage cost . . . . (Column 4 × 30 cents, unit storage cost).	75	90	135	180	210	285	360
Inventory Carrying Charges: Average inventory valuation estimated percentage . . . . . . (Column 5 × 10%, estimated rate).	55	63	92	120	136	183	230
Totals	11,380	10,778	10,527	10,331	10,121	10,135	10,202

Fig. 35. Inventory cost computations for orders of varying sizes. (Table references are to Fig. 34.)

INVENTORY TURNOVER. Proper investment in inventory under varying manufacturing and selling conditions is of vital importance. If the company expects to increase its sales activities during the coming year and if the inventory is under good control, it is usually necessary to plan for the required increase in inventory to support the higher level of sales. If, on the other hand, the company intends to decrease its sales, then the inventory should be reduced accordingly on a planned basis even before sales drop off. A part of financial planning is to establish a **materials budget for each class of materials** as a part of the company's financial budget. This step is necessary not only as a plan for guidance of those who are deciding the quantities of material to be maintained in inventory, but also for checking actual conditions. Each class may be subdivided as advisable.

Turnover Ratio Computation. There are several measures of the adequacy of inventory by classes; one of these is the **inventory turnover ratio.** This ratio indicates the number of times that inventory is used on the average within a given period. It is a convenient measure of the efficiency of materials control and the utilization of materials. Different industries have radically different turnovers, but the rate in any given industry is usually somewhat uniform, depending as it does upon its particular operating and distributive processes. If this ratio is not controlled, however, it tends to decrease, since it is in the interests of the operating people to increase the size of the inventory to prevent delays in production and secure economies in manufacture without reference to increases in other costs.

The method of computing the turnover is to divide the cost for the year of goods sold by the average inventory value.

Types of Turnover Ratios. In manufacturing industries, turnover of inventories should be figured for the business as a whole, for the several departments or units, and for the **classes of inventory—raw materials, work-in-process, finished stock, and supplies.** Turnover of raw materials should be based on the average raw materials inventory and the amount that has gone into process.

The turnover of work-in-process inventory is based on the average work-in-process inventories and value of products completed during the period as represented by credits to work-in-process accounts. The turnover of finished goods is based on average inventory of finished goods at cost as related to the cost of sales. The turnover of supply inventories is based on average investment in supply stocks divided into the amount of supply expenses for the period.

Frequent review of quantities carried is highly important and should be done by an **organized analytical procedure.** Quantities carried can sometimes be reduced, especially in the case of slow-moving materials, and obsolete materials can be disposed of.

Inventory turnover ratios for some selected companies as listed by Block (AMA Special Report No. 5, Successful Production Planning and Control) are shown in the accompanying tabulation.

Company	Inventory Turnover Per Year
Automobile Manufacturer A	6.8
Automobile Manufacturer B	5.5
Building Materials Manufacturer A	7.9
Building Materials Manufacturer B	2.6
Chemical Company A	6.0
Chemical Company B	3.7
Electrical Equipment Manufacturer	3.6
Food Processing Company	8.5
Machine Tool Manufacturer	4.5
Meat Packing Company	9.6
Tire Manufacturer	3.6
Steel Company	4.0

Physical Inventories

NEED FOR PHYSICAL COUNT. As explained above, the basic record in a materials control system is the stores record or perpetual inventory record of raw materials and parts. Receipts and disbursements are entered on these records which show the quantity of each part or item of raw material in the storeroom or in the plant ready for use. It is very important that these records show the exact physical quantity of raw materials and parts which are available for use, or production may be delayed with consequent loss of labor efficiency and customer good will.

Occasionally, however, clerical errors, erroneous descriptions, wrong counts or weights, and perhaps omission of materials issues result in inaccurate records. It is therefore necessary to verify the perpetual inventory and accounting records by a physical inventory.

METHODS OF TAKING INVENTORY. There are several methods of taking a physical inventory, which are as follows:

1. A complete or year-end physical inventory.
2. Rotating counts of material.
3. Out-of-stock counts of material.

Complete or Once-a-Year Count. The most common methods of checking inventory records and accounting records is to make a complete or once-a-year count of all materials, parts, and in-process and finished goods in the plant. By this method each item in stock, and usually those on the production floor as well, are counted during the same short period of time. If the inventory is taken in this manner, it should occur at or near the end of the fiscal year for accounting purposes.

Rotating Physical Counts. Regular stores personnel may make physical counts of the items in stock during lulls in storeroom activity or whenever specific requests for a check are forwarded from the stores record section. This is often a planned periodic program in which each item in the storeroom is physically counted at least once a year, and the more important items are often counted semiannually, quarterly, monthly, or sometimes oftener.

This rotating count is sometimes made by counters who are attached to the staff of the controller and who do nothing else except take counts on a planned basis.

Where this method is used, a **stores count report** is sent by the storeskeeper or counter to the stores record section where any corrections necessary are made in the stores record or perpetual inventory cards, after which the reports with the notation of discrepancies are sent to the accounting department for periodic adjustment in the materials accounts.

Where this method is used, the plan of physical count should be related to the A–B–C value classification of inventory so that the more expensive and important items under closer control are counted more often than those of low value.

Out-of-Stock Counts. The quantity is reported under this method whenever the supply of a particular part is exhausted, when only a small quantity remains in the bin, or when the "last bag" is broken in the case of the "sealed minimum" or "last bag" method out-of-stock counts are made and reported. The storeskeeper notifies the stores record or perpetual inventory department of the count, and corrections are made in the records.

The advantages of rotating and out-of-stock count methods are as follows:

1. The plant does not have to be shut down.
2. The count is not made under pressure; hence it may be more accurate.
3. Records are kept more nearly up to date when subject to a continuous check.
4. Errors and irregularities are discovered and adjusted more quickly.

One of the difficulties of this type of physical check is that both the stores record section and the accounting department must have an accurate cut-off date for each transaction in order to coordinate the count with the exact status of receipts of material and issues of material. Thus, the **time of the count** in relation to receipts and issues immediately preceding and following it must be accurately specified.

PROGRAM FOR PHYSICAL INVENTORY. Stans (Corporate Treasurers' and Controllers' Handbook) points out that "a successful physical inventory program requires that certain preliminary arrangements be made well in advance of the time set for taking the inventory." These arrangements include:

1. Selection of the inventory date.
2. Selection and organization of inventory crews.
3. Development of program instruction and forms.
4. Development of accounting procedures.
5. Preparation of stock for counts.
6. Establishment of controls and supervision.

The date of a complete physical inventory should be as close to the end of a month as possible to facilitate comparison with the financial records. It should also be as close to the end of the fiscal year as possible so as to serve for verification of the inventory on the financial statement. Physical inventory should be made when there is the least possible interference with operations, but sufficient time must be taken to complete the inventory accurately or the whole purpose is lost. It is, of course, desirable to take inventory at a time when stocks in the plant are at a low level if this is possible.

Physical inventories in many plants take longer than one day but should be completed as rapidly as possible to shorten the shut-down of the plant and to minimize the movement of materials if some of the count has to be made when the plant is not idle.

Organization and Personnel. Since the year-end physical inventory is primarily a financial check, it is usually under the general supervision of a financial executive, preferably the controller. The actual physical direction of the counting is usually a responsibility of the factory or production manager, and detailed supervision of the counters is usually by the various factory department heads. A good technique to insure responsible coverage of all areas is to make up a map of every area to be inventoried showing the supervisors who are responsible for the inventory in each location. Counters should be familiar with the shop and the material and very accurate in their counts. It is wise to have people available who can identify material and accurately describe it on the inventory tickets.

Programs, Instructions, and Forms. The need of adequate preplanning and preparation for taking the annual physical inventory cannot be overemphasized. The larger the inventory the more important the preparation. Complete written instructions should be prepared in ample time for all individuals to become familiar with the plan. These **inventory instructions** should cover the following points:

1. Date of inventory and duration.
2. The personnel and their individual duties.
3. General procedures to follow in taking inventory.
4. Classes of material and special instructions concerning each class.
5. Forms to be used and special instructions concerning them.
6. Methods of evaluation in tabulations.
7. Method of checking against stores records and adjusting discrepancies.

Some large concerns have complete **inventory manuals** containing very explicit instructions on every phase of inventory-taking. Such manuals are advantageous in that procedures become standardized and are consistent from year to year except for modifications to suit current conditions. Thus, the inventory personnel become more expert in carrying out the procedure, fewer mistakes are made, and the inventory is completed more quickly.

Before the inventory starts, meetings should be held with all of the personnel concerned to go over the instructions in detail and to answer any questions. An **inventory schedule** should be prepared detailing areas to be inventoried and including a time-table for each of the departments to be covered. One of the primary functions of the inventory supervisory force during the actual physical inventory is to check continually to see that this schedule is being maintained. If any department is lagging other crews may be transferred in to help.

Preparation of Stock for Counts. It is very important that a number of preparations be made before the date on which the counting is to begin in order that the counting may be accurate and proceed according to plan. Some of these measures are as follows:

1. Restacking and sorting of material into piles which are easy to count.
2. Returning material to storerooms from machines and production lines.
3. Proper identification of all material.
4. Bringing like items of material and inventory together wherever possible.
5. Disposal of all obsolete and damaged stock.
6. Waste and scrap material moved out of the plant and disposed of.
7. All rejected purchased material returned to vendors before inventory starts.
8. All incoming material cleared out of the receiving department into stores and put away.
9. A general cleanup of the plant so that accurate counts are possible.
10. Verification by purchasing department of all invoices covering material received to inventory date.
11. Listing by purchasing department of all items in transit and all materials which have been received but for which invoices were lacking at delivery date.
12. Listing by the person responsible for subcontracting of all materials at the subcontractors.
13. Preferably during the inventory period no delivery to or receipt of materials from the shop should be permitted.
14. All paperwork cleared and stores and accounting records brought up to date, including latest receipts and issues.
15. Work in process identified as to its stage of completion so that it can be inventoried properly.

Forms To Be Used. The principal forms to be used during the physical inventory should be described in writing and detailed written instructions issued as to how to handle and fill them out. The most important forms used are **inventory tags** and **inventory sheets.**

The tag method is considered the best way of inventorying materials since it provides a visible check of material which has been inventoried and is a convenient way to work to summary sheets and company records. The form shown as Fig. 36 is suitable for all classes of materials. Spaces are provided for name, part number, descriptions, operations performed (if the item is work in process), unit quantity, location, and counter's initials. The tag is divided into two sections by perforations. The reverse side provides space for recording movement of materials after count is made, which, in the case of slow-moving parts, is frequently done several days before actual date of inventory.

One person should be responsible for assigning **blocks of tags** to the supervisors of the physical inventory in the individual areas. He should keep an accurate record on a **summary sheet,** as shown in Fig. 37, of who has received the tags, where they were issued, and how they are being return. When the tags are returned they should be checked in on the summary sheet and any missing tags posted to a sheet such as Fig. 38 so that a search can be made for the missing tags.

Those actually counting should work in teams of two or more, one person to write tags and place them upon the materials, and the others to identify and to count or measure. When a team has completed its work, each departmental supervisor should check each kind or lot of material in his department or storeroom to see that it is covered by an inventory tag completely filled out. Tags for work-in-process materials should clearly indicate the stage of completion or progression of that material.

In inventories of precious metals, or when incomplete stores records are maintained, a tag containing three sections is sometimes used, and a double count is made of all items. The two lower sections of the tags are filled in by separate

Form Shop 21 ⊙	
INVENTORY	4043
Material Symbol_____	
Quantity _____ Unit_____	

4043		Date	Received After Count	Issued After Count
Material Symbol_____				
Description_____				
_____				
Operations Performed_____				
_____				
Quantity_____ Unit_____				
Location_____				
Counted By_____				
Remarks_____				
_____				

Fig. 36. Inventory tag.

Date _____

Supervisor _____

Issued	Group & Location	Issued			Ret'd Used			Ret'd Unused (Red)		
		From (Incl)	By	To (Incl)	From (Incl)	By	To (Incl)	From (Incl)	By	To (Incl)

Fig. 37. Issues and receipts of inventory tags.

Date _____

Supervisor _____

When corrected, cross out and initial in Red and post to Form "A."

Ticket No.	Entry By	Storeroom and Group	Issued To	Remarks (To aid in checking)	Block of Tickets Returned	Checked

Fig. 38. Record of missing tags.

sets of counters and reconciled before the departments are permitted to resume production. Where perpetual inventory records are maintained, such a method is a duplication of effort and is not recommended.

After these checks, which should be made as nearly simultaneously and as near the end of inventory period as practicable, the lower sections of the tags are torn off and returned to the person responsible for their issuance. The top sections of the tags remain with the materials to facilitate check for lost tags and to enable recounts to be made when necessary. Spoiled tags should be returned marked "Void." All unused tags should also be returned. The issuing authority makes a numerical check and all tags must be accounted for before a department is authorized to resume production.

Establishment of Controls. After the tags have all been checked in and missing tags accounted for they are sorted in different ways for various purposes and in general are used as follows:

1. To check stores location records so that locations of all items in the storeroom are known. If two or more locations are shown in the storeroom area the storeskeeper should investigate and try to consolidate these amounts unless the storeroom is run by having the reserve stock segregated from an active location.
2. To check in the stores records or perpetual inventory records the quantities shown as balance in stock. The book records should be adjusted to the actual count in such a way that the nature and date of the adjustments are clearly shown. Stans (Corporate Treasurers' and Controllers' Handbook) suggests that it may be desirable to set up limits to this automatic adjustment of the book records. For example, the inventory instructions might include the following provisions for the adjustment of the control records:
   a. Difference between inventory cards and physical counts involving amounts of $5.00 or less are to be adjusted on the cards without a recount.
   b. Differences between inventory counts and physical counts involving amounts of more than $5.00 and less than $100.00 require a recount before adjustment.
   c. Difference between inventory count cards and physical counts involving amounts of $100.00 or more require a recount initialed by the section head and approved by the inventory officer before adjustment.

Stans also suggests keeping a record to tabulate all adjustment to the perpetual records and to arrive at a total difference or adjustment from the book record to the physical. An example of this is shown in Fig. 39.

Department: **Assembly**   Date: **December 31, 19xx**

| Stock No. | Item | Unit | Quantity-Units | | | Unit Price | Amount | |
			Control Records	Actual Count	Variance		Inc.	Decr.
11641	Manifold	Each	62	42	20*	$3.50		$70.00
11694	Hinges	Pair	210	225	15	1.00	$15.00	
11752	Handles	Pair	18	2	16*	2.00		32.00
11840	Knives	Doz.	61	55	6*	3.00		18.00
11841	Knives	Doz.	48	54	6	2.00	12.00	

*Denotes red figure

Fig. 39. Listing of inventory adjustments.

In cases where unit prices are not kept on the inventory records, the price and extension are filled in by the accounting department.

The materials control section should take immediate action to reorder items whose record balance is substantially different from the inventory.

The inventory tags are then listed on **inventory sheets** which may be compiled according to classes of material so that a group of sheets will correspond with the items included in one accounting control account. These sheets are sent to the accounting department for pricing and extension and for adjustment of material control accounts. Work-in-process tags are reconciled to work-in-process accounts and records.

Simplification and Standardization of Materials

DEFINITION. Spriegel (Industrial Management) states that: "Simplification refers to the elimination of superfluous varieties, sizes, dimensions, etc. It is essentially a reducing process, a cutting down of varieties and types with relatively little regard for the use of any scientific procedures or methods. On the other hand, standardization refers to the setting up of fixed sizes, types, qualities, measures, etc. Standardization implies careful consideration of relationships and values usually involving scientific procedures."

Standardization and simplification are usually not considered direct materials control functions, but they have such a direct effect on the materials control function that in many companies materials control managers have found it to their advantage to take the lead in spurring this type of company effort.

From a manufacturing standpoint, production managers prefer to have only one of each kind of product in the product line. This simplification of product line would mean lower unit cost, a lower investment in inventory, a lower labor cost due to specialization, best utilization of a minimum variety of machinery, highest utilization of manpower, and improved quality of product.

The sales department, on the other hand, prefers to have wide differences in their product line as a way of selling more products. Each company must reach a decision as to how diversified its product line shall be and at what point an economical balance is achieved between a simple product line, resulting in lower production costs, and diversification of product, resulting in greater sales but increased production costs. This is often a top management decision.

Once the **composition of the product line** has been determined, however, it is often possible to simplify the design of the product by eliminating needless or little-used varieties, types, sizes, styles, shapes, and other irregularities in each of the basic items to be produced. Many companies have developed a **standard base model** with minor adaptations which give it the style needed for sales appeal.

If standard models are adopted it is usually possible to reduce the number of items in inventory by standardizing on sizes and specifications of raw material to be used in the product and on parts which are interchangeable among a number of products. This will limit the number of different items carried in inventory, decrease the number of items which have to be planned and accounted for, and reduce planning and clerical costs.

The effect of standardization and simplification, therefore, is to reduce the amount of machinery and equipment required to produce the product, to reduce labor cost, and to reduce the quantity of different parts and raw materials which must be kept in inventory.

RESULTS OF STANDARDIZATION AND SIMPLIFICATION.

Malnitsky (Management of Industrial Inventory) reports that "simplification results in increased turnover of inventory and in countless economies implicit therein." He cites the experience of "a shoe manufacturer who formerly produced three grades of shoes in 2,500 sizes and styles. By limiting his output to one grade with 250 varieties, he cut his production costs by 31 percent, direct overhead by 27 percent, inventories by 27 percent, and increased his turnover an impressive 50 percent." He also cites the economies reported by a manufacturer of steel barrels and drums after adopting simplified practice recommendations. Significant economies were effected in the following areas:

Inventory reduction
Interest saved in capital formerly tied up in stock
Release of storeroom space for productive use
Reduced handling charge
Fewer interruptions for adjustment of machinery
Increased productive capacity of employees and machines
Improved quality of product
Increased turnover
Improved facilities for planning for reinvestment in inventories of raw material
    and finished goods
Reduced selling expenses

Malnitsky also cites an example of Westinghouse Electric Corporation in which prior to simplification, 2,800 parts were required to assemble 3,000 types and ratings of Westinghouse motors. After standardization, 126 parts did the same

STANDARDIZATION OF SHEET
AND STRIP STEEL THICKNESSES

Sizes	Before		After	
	No.	Percent	No.	Percent
Standard	14	43	21	75
Nonstandard.	19	57	7	25
Total	33	100	28	100
Ledger Accounts (including widths)	No.	Percent	No.	Percent
Standard	46	62	46	75
Nonstandard	28	38	15	25
Total	74	100	61	100
Usage	1,000 lb.	Percent	1,000 lb.	Percent
Standard	225	56	228	72
Nonstandard	175	44	112	28

Fig. 40. Inventory status before and after standardization.

job with a consequent reduction in storing, handling, identifying, classifying, recording inventory charges, and the investment in capital.

Barrow (Factory Management and Maintenance, vol. 109) points out the advantages of controlling inventory of raw materials by standardizing common metals used in fabricated products, such as sheet and strip steel. Figure 40 shows the inventory status of sheet and strip steel before and after reclassifying thickness. The figures show a modest reduction in total number of sizes but a more significant one in the number of ledger accounts because duplicate widths were eliminated within each group. Fig. 41 shows the results of this program in terms of a reduction in inventory and an increase in the turnover ratio.

Size of Inventory	Before	After
Stock standard sizes	40,000 lb.	42,000 lb.
Stock nonstandard sizes. . .	44,000 lb.	22,000 lb.
Total	84,000 lb.	64,000 lb.
Reduction in Inventory		−20,000 − 25%
Inventory Turnover Rate		
Turnover rate, standard . . .	5.7	7.0
Turnover rate, nonstandard	4.0	5.0

Fig. 41. Results of standardization program.

ORGANIZATION FOR STANDARDIZATION. Programs of material standardization will not work unless placed under effective organization and administration, with power for action properly allocated and exercised. There is no one logical place in an organization where standardization invariably should be located, because the work involved and its results affect many departments—sales, engineering, purchasing, production control, manufacturing, storing, accounting, and others. Responsibility for control is usually centered in the department where the question is most important or fundamental, or where action can or will be taken. Often the whole plan is better handled by a representative committee from all departments concerned, but this committee must have a chairman preferably connected with production control and must report to some executive. Materials standardization also may be part of the work of a general plant standards committee.

Materials standardization and simplification thus may be centralized in one of the following departments or may report to one of the designated individuals:

DEPARTMENT	INDIVIDUAL
Engineering	Chief product engineer or industrial engineer
Production Control	Production control manager
Purchasing	Purchasing agent
Manufacturing	Works manager
Inspection	Chief inspector
Accounting	Controller or cost accountant

Materials Standards Committee. Where a materials standards committee is set up, it most frequently reports to the works manager, quite frequently to the production control manager or chief engineer, and much less frequently to any of the others.

The committee should include representatives of most, or all, of the departments listed above for purposes of coordination, quick advice, reactions, or proposals, to carry on specific studies on certain phases of the work, to adapt plans to the all-around needs of the plant, and to sell the idea to and get cooperation from the different departments. For best results perhaps three of the key men should act as a sort of executive committee, having the others associated but not burdened with major responsibilities or details. Usually such committees carry on the work as need arises or suggestions are submitted. Where a definite continuous program is carried on, a materials engineer with the necessary staff should be appointed to direct it, but he may receive the aid of members of a materials standards committee.

PROCEDURE IN STANDARDIZING MATERIALS. The procedures found most successful in any program of standardizing materials are stated by Davis and Jucius (Purchasing and Storing) as follows:

1. A complete list of items regularly carried in stores must be obtained. Often the lists obtained by the last annual inventory are a satisfactory beginning. The records of the purchasing department, also, will aid in the preparation of such a list.

2. These items should be classified by kind or use. As far as possible, the existing stores grouping should be used for economy. The basic stores grouping probably will conform to the general accounting classification of accounts. However, it is often found that the one existing has not been worked out to facilitate the operating control of inventories. As a result, some changes usually are necessary.

3. The uses to which each item is put should be determined. It is often found that different materials are used for the same or similar purposes in different departments. Here, obviously is an opportunity for simplification.

4. The materials in the same classification should be compared to determine those having similar characteristics. It may be found that certain materials, used for different purposes, are similar. For instance, two kinds of steel may be similar in tensile strength, ductility, and other characteristics. It may be possible to eliminate one of them, and use the other for all purposes formerly served by both.

5. Possible substitutes for standard materials should be determined. In the above case, the kind of steel that was eliminated may be listed as a possible substitute for the other. Sometimes the purchasing department is unable to procure the standard material without too great delay or too great purchase cost. In such cases it is desirable for production engineers to have reasonable leeway. Substitutions for standard materials, however, should not be permitted without the approval of some higher authority.

6. On the basis of the above considerations, a revision of the standard list of classified stores is made. Such lists are important for control of inventories. Requisitions for items not included in the lists will not be honored, unless approved by higher authority. Usually each department and storeroom is further restricted to a list of items within the classified list.

7. For each item that is retained in the classified list, the qualities that it should possess to meet the purposes for which it is to be used should be determined. These qualities are recorded permanently in the form of specifications for the use of the purchasing, receiving, and other departments that need them.

8. To facilitate the work of ordering, requisitioning, accounting, etc., a material symbol system should be worked out and a distinctive symbol assigned to each item in the classified list.

9. Finally, there should be some organization for controlling and enforcing observance of the standards. This may be a materials committee. Such a committee would pass on the inclusion of new items in the classified list and similar problems.

MATERIALS SPECIFICATIONS. Materials may be designated or specified in a number of ways:

1. Common trade names.
2. Manufacturer or source.
3. Brand names.
4. Manufacturers' specifications.
5. Trade specifications.
6. Engineering society standards, or recognized specifications.
7. Laboratory specifications (consulting or commercial groups.)
8. Government specifications.
9. The user company through its own research.

The common ways in which specifications for materials, parts, or supplies may be given or expressed are by:

1. Nomenclature: use of specific terms or indicators, such as the common symbols, codes, manufacturers' catalog symbols, product symbols, or trade names or designations.
2. Descriptions.
3. Dimensions and proportions.
4. Quality or composition.
5. Ratings or performance.
6. Methods of analysis or test.
7. Specific requirements, as for safety.

Specifications, when set, must define, limit, state, or clearly indicate the characteristics required so that the materials or component parts covered will be:

1. Suitable for the product from the standpoint of dimensions, physical and chemical properties, etc. (engineering), and from the viewpoint of the customer (sales).
2. Conformable to technical requirements (engineering inspection).
3. Obtainable or produced with minimum difficulty (purchasing, manufacturing).
4. Convenient to handle, store, and issue (storing).
5. Workable, if possible, without undue special provisions (production control, manufacturing).
6. Standard to whatever extent feasible (engineering, purchasing, production control, manufacturing, inspection, storing).
7. Replaceable by substitutes if temporarily difficult to obtain (engineering, purchasing, production control, manufacturing).
8. Low in cost (purchasing, production control, manufacturing).

Development of Specifications. In most cases specifications for materials and component parts will be adopted or developed by the engineering department or plant manufacturing research or control laboratory. Sometimes they may be prepared or formulated by a specialist or someone in the plant acquainted with their uses and applications.

Once the **list of standard materials and standard parts** is drawn up, engineers will be instructed to design using only the standard materials and parts. Executive engineering approval is required wherever there are departures from the standard list. The establishment of such a standard material and parts list aids the engineering department in that it reduces costs by eliminating the repeated detailing of small utility parts used in many designs by a particular company. Block (Mechanical Engineering, vol. 78) states that: "Creation of design standards for items such as fastener installations, electric wiring assemblies, conduit assemblies, and sheet metal cutouts, eliminates the constant repetition of extensive drawing notes and dimensioning."

Many engineering departments have a separate section called **process engineering** which takes the design drawings and converts them to production drawings, using standard materials and standard parts whenever possible and specifying parts which can be made on standard equipment available in the plant.

Specifications established in the engineering department are conveyed to other departments by means of drawings, bills of material, reference to standard specifications, or special specification write-ups. Occasionally a materials standards committee will have something to say in regard to specifications, but more often the specifications will be merely referred to such a committee for consideration as to their effect on purchasing, production control, manufacturing, and inspection, and for fitting them into any simplification and standardization program in effect. If some material already in use can be employed instead of a special kind, or if some other single variety can be adopted for both old and new uses, the inventory problem is aided.

Adequate attention to specifications, and standardization of sizes and varieties of items called for or carried, to eliminate the odd and the little-used, are of decided benefit in manufacturing and production control. The plant frequently will be well equipped with machines, fixtures, tools, and equipment to handle certain kinds and sizes of material, and any work within this range is perfectly acceptable. The production control department will have operation lists, route sheets, tooling setups, time studies, instruction cards, wage rates, machine outputs, and stores controls established for such materials. Specifications will be familiar to those using these materials. If new specifications are introduced with reason and with the opportunity to cut costs or bring about further standardization, there is justification for making the substitution. If materials of another specification are introduced without some such definite engineering, operating, or economic advantage that outweighs the time, trouble, cost, and possible temporary upset of making the change, there has been a loss instead of a gain.

Sources of Specifications. The sources of formulated specifications are much the same as those for standards because specifications are developed with the idea of having them become standards. Among the many agencies and sources are:

American Standards Association.
Underwriters' Laboratories.
Bureau of Standards.
American Society for Testing Materials.
American Institute of Electrical Engineers.
Federal Bureau of Specifications.
American Society of Mechanical Engineers.
Society of Automotive Engineers.

Several of the above technical societies and some of the trade associations have created an American Engineering Standards Committee which is to develop standards for industry through mutual action. When a standard is needed, a subcommittee is usually formed from representatives of the group, and if the standard set is approved by the executive committee, it is adopted as the American Standard.

Specifications for materials, parts, or products which have been standardized can be obtained from the agency, laboratory, technical society, trade association, government body, or manufacturer developing them. Most manufacturing companies try to use in their products materials and parts which have been standardized and for which specifications exist, and to develop specifications only for the items for which no market product will do.

Items Covered by Specifications. Specifications developed within a plant must be carefully written and then reviewed by all departments concerned or by an executive or engineer thoroughly familiar with the matter. **Specification information** of the following nature must usually be given:

1. Name of item.
2. Symbol or number.
3. Class or kind (if any).
4. Description, sizes, etc.
5. Uses or applications.
6. Material made from (if a part, product, or compound).
7. Methods of manufacture (if important).
8. Physical and chemical properties (if any).
9. Other standard requirements.
10. Tests or inspections to be applied or met.
11. Finish.
12. Method of packing for shipment.
13. Acceptance inspection by purchaser.

Copies of specifications should be prepared in whatever form is convenient, some duplication process being preferable to the use of carbons. The engineering, production control, purchasing and receiving departments, and materials standards committee would be most concerned. In many cases copies are also needed for bidders and vendors. Whenever changes in parts or materials specifications are to be made, a regular **change order** should be put through and copies should be sent to all of the departments which should know of the changes. If there is a materials committee, it should approve the changes before they are put into effect to prevent a departure from standards and the accumulation of unnecessary varieties of the same item.

NATIONAL AND INTERNATIONAL STANDARDIZATION AND SIMPLIFICATION. Each leading country has its standards association for the purpose of national standardization and the development of the necessary specifications, and there has been cooperation among such agencies. The most active agency in national simplification to reduce varieties, types, sizes, styles, etc., has been the Division of Simplified Practice, Bureau of Standards, U.S. Department of Commerce. This agency carries on its work on a basis of voluntary development of, and agreement upon, simplification programs for industries, through the cooperation and preponderantly major vote (80 percent or more) of the authorized representatives of users, retailers, dealers, manufacturers, technical societies, government agencies, and the public.

PURCHASING

CONTENTS

PAGE

Purchasing Functions

Definition 1
Major importance of purchasing 1
Duties of the purchasing department 2
Functional organization of purchasing 2
    Functional organization chart of a pur-
    chasing department (f. 1) 3

Purchase Organization

Centralization of purchasing 4
Largely localized purchasing 4
Centralized-localized purchasing 5
    Purchasing organization in a company
    with combined central and local buy-
    ing. (Manufacturer of chemicals with
    15 scattered plants. Annual purchases
    over $25,000,000.) (f. 2) 5
Conditions governing centralized-localized
    buying 6
Combination of purchasing with other func-
    tions 6
Relation of purchasing department to other
    departments 7
Stores department 7
Production control and maintenance de-
    partments 9
Engineering department 10
Traffic and other departments 10
Purchasing department organization 10
Purchasing agent 11
Responsibilities of the purchasing agent .. 11
Assistant purchasing agent 12
Buyers 12
    Organization of purchasing in a company
    with more than one plant. (Shoe man-
    ufacturer. Purchasing centralized.
    Purchases less than $5,000,000 per
    year.) (f. 3) 12
Commodity assignment 14
    Grouping of materials for purchase by
    an individual buyer (f. 4) 13
    Grouping of materials for purchase by
    several buyers (f. 5) 14
Follow-up section 14
Clerical force 15
Purchasing office manager 15

Purchase Budgets and Policies

The purchase budget 15
Advantages of the budget 15
Checking budget performance 16

Purchasing policies 16
Costs and savings 16
Two phases to policies 17
Long-term buying policies 17
Use of graphic methods 18

Methods of Purchasing

Classification of purchases 18
Raw materials 18
Supplies 18
Fabricated parts 18
Industrial equipment 19
Purchase methods 19
Purchasing by requirements 19
Purchase for a specified future period 20
Purchasing according to market 20
Speculative purchasing 20
Contract purchasing 21
Grouping items 21
Scheduled purchasing 22
Value analysis 23

Buying Proper Quality

Purchase specifications 23
Requirements for an industrial specifica-
    tion 24
Inspection as a check upon specifications ... 25

Buying Proper Quantities

Factors determining the quantity to buy ... 25
    Graphical analysis of when and how
    much to buy (f. 6) 25
Analytic method for determining lot sizes .. 26
Minimum ordering quantities 27
    Graphical determination of economic lot
    size (f. 7) 28
Purchase lot formulas 27
    Most economic purchase and storage lots 28
    Purchase lot for highest return on work-
    ing capital 29
Examples of economic purchase lots 30
    Units in which different items are
    ordered (f. 8) 31
Limits on quantities or expenditures 32

Buying at the Proper Price

Commodity classification 32
Price established by market movement ... 32
Price data given in catalogues 33

CONTENTS (*Continued*)

PAGE

Items subject to price negotiation 33
Purchasing department request for quotation (*f. 9*) 34
Obtaining competitive quotations 35
Buying at the best price 35
Bargain or cut prices 36

Purchase Contracts

Contract requirements 36
Specifications 36
Price 36
Terms 37
Time clauses 37
Statements of ownership 38
Inspection at vendor's plant 38
Guaranties 38
Penalty clauses 38
Blanket contracts 39
Legal aspects of contracts 40
Standard purchase contract forms 40

Purchasing Procedure

Steps in the procedure 40
Origin of purchase requisition 41
Form of requisition 41
Purchase requisition (*f. 10*)............... 42
Requisition for a number of items, providing for several necessary approvals (*f. 11*) 43
Route of the requisition 45
Purchase order procedure flow chart (*f. 12*) 44
Request for quotation 45
Inquiry for prices (*f. 13*) 46
Request for quotation (*f. 14*) 47
Information on the request 45
To whom to send requests 46
Follow-up on requests 48
Use of the quotation record card 48
Quotation record card or analysis sheet (*f. 15*) 49
Selecting the vendor 48
The purchase order 51
Purchase order (face) (*f. 16*) 50
Conditions upon which order is accepted (reverse of Fig. 16) (*f. 17*) 51
Number 52
Quantity ordered 52
Description 52
Delivery and shipping instructions 53
Billing and terms 53
Prices 54
Miscellaneous clauses 54
Acceptance by the vendor 55
Other data 56
Form and number of copies 57
Standard arrangement of purchase order (*f. 18*) 56
Follow-up of purchase order 57
Follow-up of purchase order (*f. 19*) 58
Self-signaling follow-up folders 59
Receiving 60
Receiving voucher (*f. 20*) 61
Receiving ticket (*f. 21*) 62

PAGE

Handling invoices 63
Routine followed 63
Invoice checking 64
Invoice record sheet (*f. 22*) 65
Invoice form supplied by customer (*f. 23*) 66

Purchasing Department Records

Variety of records 67
Purchase record 67
Purchase record card (*f. 24*) 68
Contract record 69
Blanket order record (front and back) (*f. 25*) 70–71
Vendor record 69
Vendor rating 74
A typical vendor rating chart (*f. 26*)....72–73
Price or quotation record 74
Summary of purchase work 76
Purchasing department summary-of-work sheet (*f. 27*) 75
Miscellaneous records 76

Reorder Control Systems

Systems to fit the company's needs 76
Standard card record forms 76
Standard reorder control forms (*f. 28*) 77
The computing chart 78
Order point on the computing chart (*f. 29*) 78
Folding the computing chart (*f. 30*) 79
Inserting the computing chart (*f. 31*) .. 80
Split-card stock control system 80
Traveling requisition card system 81
Traveling requisition form (*f. 32*) 82

Purchasing Department Manuals

Purpose of manuals 82
Policy manual 82
Procedures manual 83

Reports to Management

Purchasing department reports to management 83
Proved savings on price 84
Proved savings by substitution 84
Purchasing department claim for savings (*f. 33*) 84
Departmental expenses 85
Report of purchasing department expenses (*f. 34*) 85
Loss and error account 85
Summary report of loss and error account (*f. 35*) 85
Failures to receive material on time 85
Summary of delivery or orders (*f. 36*) .. 86
Other reports 86
Purchasing department activities report (*f. 37*) 86
Evaluation of purchasing department efficiency 87
Purchasing department efficiency record (*f. 38*) 87

PURCHASING

Purchasing Functions

DEFINITION. In industry, purchasing is the procuring of materials, supplies, machines, tools, and services required for the equipment, maintenance, and operation of a plant.

The purchasing department is the department intrusted with this procurement duty. The function of the purchasing department is to procure needed materials, supplies, machines, tools, and services at an ultimate cost consistent with economic conditions surrounding the item being purchased; to safeguard the standard of quality, continuity of service, the competitive position, and the company's reputation for fairness and integrity. Modern trends in legislation make it essential that the purchasing department also should watch carefully the enactment of new laws as to taxes, business regulation, etc., and insure the company against their violation.

Procurement of goods through purchase accounts for about half the money spent by the average industrial concern, the range among different industries being from about 20 percent to 90 percent. The financial aspect of purchasing, therefore, is obviously of great importance. Only by close and intelligent cooperation between financial and purchasing functions can proper financial control be effected.

MAJOR IMPORTANCE OF PURCHASING. Purchasing is of major importance because:

1. It is a primary function. Proper sales cannot be made unless materials being used for manufacture or for resale are bought at an ultimate cost commensurate with that available to competitors.
2. Efficient operation of any industry depends upon proper turnover of investment. The purchasing department must arrange its purchases so as to insure receipt of proper materials when wanted and in sufficient quantities to maintain production and on-time shipment; at the same time it must not increase investment beyond that required to meet current needs and maintain a reasonable factor of safety.
3. By its close contacts with many other companies and the general market, the purchasing department is in a position to advise its company on:
   a. New materials which may be used to advantage as substitutes for materials in use.
   b. Possible new lines of products to be added.
   c. Changes in trends, either in prices or other factors, that will affect the sales of the company.
   d. Building up goodwill in the business world with which it deals.
4. Its contacts with vendors, market trends, and the manufacturing and marketing policies of other industries make it possible for this department to contribute invaluable help in framing plans, whether for initiation of new products, scheduling of production, determination of marketing policies, or some other branch of industrial operation.

The relative importance of the purchasing function, compared with the functions of other departments, will vary with the industry and, usually, the ratio between material cost and the value added by manufacture.

DUTIES OF THE PURCHASING DEPARTMENT. The duties of the purchasing department cover all dealings with vendors. No contacts looking to the purchase of any goods or services should be made without cognizance of this department. Only with the consent of, and preferably in the presence of, some member of the purchasing department should other departments receive or confer with vendors' representatives.

Its principal duties, not necessarily listed in order of importance, are:

1. Locating and selecting sources of supply for materials or services required.
2. Interviewing suppliers' representatives, arranging conferences and plant visitations.
3. Requesting quotations and conducting negotiations.
4. Procuring materials and services when required.
5. Verifying quality and quantity received.
6. Approving invoices and handling rejections and adjustments.
7. Maintaining records necessary for proper operation of its function.
8. Keeping informed on business trends, assembling and analyzing pertinent data on markets, supply, demand, price trends, etc.
9. Disposing of scrap and surplus.

FUNCTIONAL ORGANIZATION OF PURCHASING. Fig. 1 shows a functional organization chart covering most of the duties which may be assigned to a purchasing department. A large metalworking plant purchasing organization is illustrated in the chart. Here the assistant purchasing agent heads the buying section. Under him are subsections or units, each headed by a buyer. Recently, the practice of adding one or more subcontracting sections, for implementing outside manufacture of components or assemblies, has been noticed. A cost reduction section maintains surveillance over research in lowering costs and increasing purchasing effectiveness. At the General Electric Company this function is called "value analysis"; in other cases the task falls under "purchasing research." Some companies centralize full accounting for materials in the purchasing department, including invoice procedure, pricing of requisitions, and compiling of reports on materials disbursements. In cases where these related functions fall under the same organizational control as the buying group, the whole is often called "materials management" or "materials control."

The various functional sections, in the case of smaller plants, may be combined in groups under fewer heads, according to each plant's own requirements, or assigned elsewhere in the company organization. But all of these functions must be provided for in some way in any company—even though only in a rudimentary way—as the following comment indicates:

1. **Buying section.** At least one person must do the buying. In a large company the function is subdivided more and more according to specialized lines.
2. **Follow-up section.** Separate in large companies. Buyer does or directs the work in small companies. Supervision by buyer is important for efficient conduct.
3. **Invoice section.** Invoices checked by invoice clerks in large companies, by buyer or purchasing agent in a small company. Sometimes, however, this work is done in the accounting department.
4. **Stenographic section.** Separate in large companies where work can be pooled to cut down number of stenographers. Buyers sometimes prefer to have full time of definite stenographers. One stenographer in a small company will probably do follow-up, invoice checking, stenographic work, and filing.

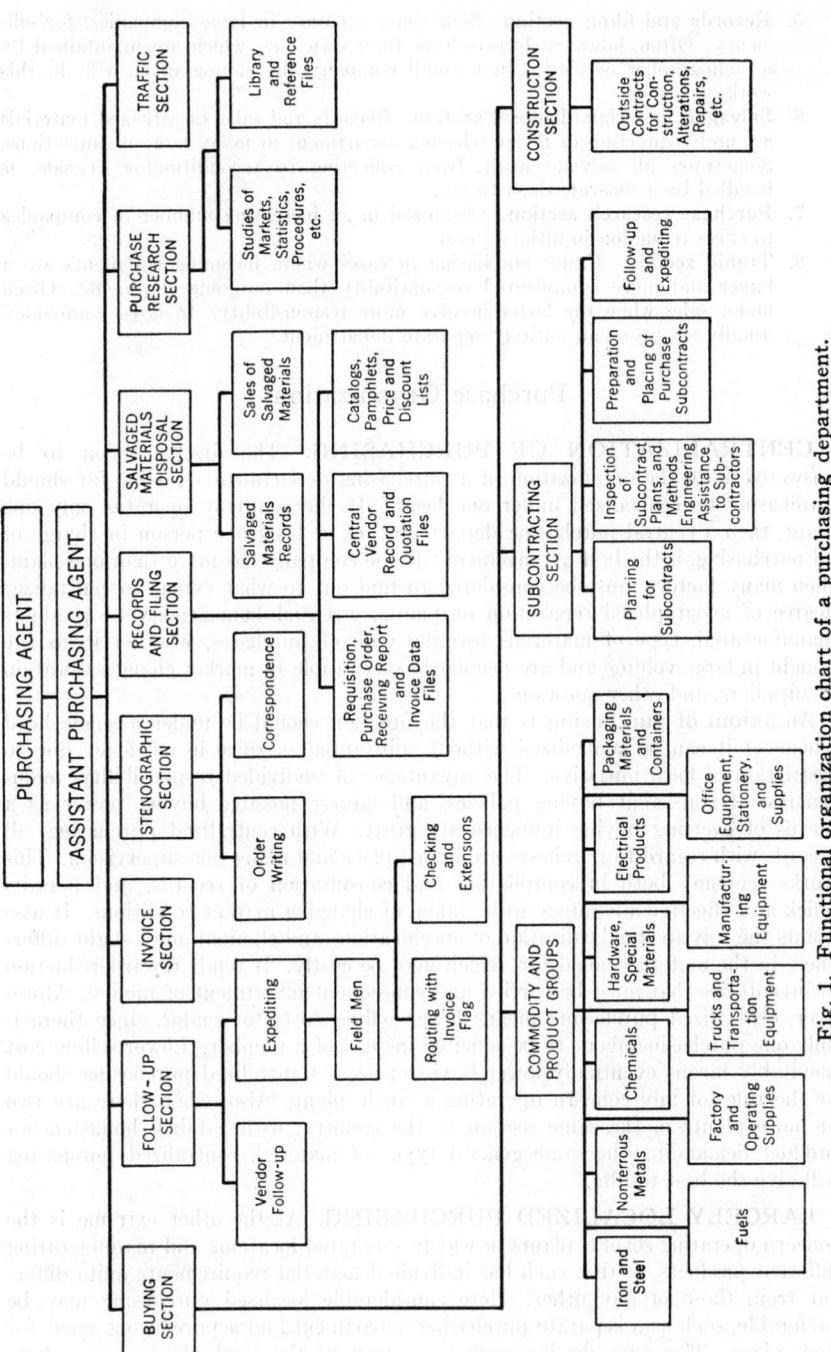

Fig. 1. Functional organization chart of a purchasing department.

5. **Records and filing section.** Sometimes separate in large companies, for efficiency. Often, however, buyers have their own files, which are maintained by a stenographer or clerk. In a small company the stenographer will do this work.
6. **Salvaged materials disposal section.** Records and sales of salvaged materials are under direction of the purchasing department in many large organizations. Sometimes all salvage work, from collecting to reconditioning or sale, is handled by a separate department.
7. **Purchase research section.** Organized in an increasing number of companies to effect reduction in ultimate cost.
8. **Traffic section.** Under purchasing in cases where incoming shipments are a larger and more complicated responsibility than outgoing shipments. Often under sales when the latter involve more responsibility. In large companies, usually set up as an entirely separate department.

Purchase Organization

CENTRALIZATION OF PURCHASING. The first question to be answered as to the organization of a purchasing department is: How far should purchasing be centralized under one head? If the company operates only one plant, then a central purchasing department, or at least one person in charge of all purchasing, is the best arrangement. If the company has more than one plant, then many factors must be considered to find out to what extent to centralize: degree of geographical separation of plants, essential homogeneity of products manufactured, type of materials forming bulk of purchases, whether items are bought in large volume and are peculiarly susceptible to market changes, location of suppliers, and other questions.

An **axiom of purchasing** is that the function should be under a single head whenever it can be centralized without substantial sacrifice in efficiency due to restriction of local initiative. The advantages of undivided responsibility, maintenance of consistent buying policies, and largest possible buying power as a means of exerting buying influence are great. With centralized purchasing, all records with regard to purchases are in one place and under one supervision. This works economy both in compilation and consultation of records, and permits quick and effective advantage to be taken of changing market conditions. It also points the way to standardization of specifications and elimination of slight differences in the material called for, which may be costly. It tends toward reduction of inventories that must be carried and consequent investment of money. Moreover, centralized purchasing means lower selling costs to vendor, since there is only one purchasing agent to be solicited instead of a number. Lower selling cost inevitably means eventually lower buying prices. Centralized purchasing should be the rule for any concern operating a single plant. Also, when there are two or more plants in the same section of the country, with a fairly homogeneous product demanding the same general types of material, centralized purchasing will give the best results.

LARGELY LOCALIZED PURCHASING. At the other extreme is the concern operating several plants in widely separated locations and manufacturing different products, so that each has individual material requirements quite different from those of any other. Here considerable localized purchasing may be preferable, such as a separate purchasing department and a purchasing agent for each plant. These purchasing agents are part of the local plant organization. They serve the needs of their own respective plants but are supervised by a general purchasing agent who establishes and enforces the general purchasing policies and sees that the mechanics of purchasing are enforced at each plant, and that there is proper interchange of ideas and information. The general purchasing agent will execute most of the contracts to be drawn upon by more than one plant and will check or audit the work of the local purchasing agents, who will usually submit periodic reports to him.

CENTRALIZED-LOCALIZED PURCHASING. Between these two extremes are many companies operating several plants whose geographical locations may not be too widely scattered and whose product and material requirements, while to a considerable degree heterogeneous, may nevertheless cover purchases of a large number of similar parts and materials used in common and in large quantities. Under such conditions it is desirable partially to centralize and partially to localize the purchasing function. A general purchasing department should be set up to establish general policies, to do actual buying when advisable, and to supervise and direct the work of local purchasing departments which will be set up at each plant.

Where a large degree of **localized purchasing** is practiced, consideration must be given to items used by all plants, on which preferential discounts for quantity contracts are available, but which can be obtained only by contracting for the requirements of all plants and specifying delivery to individual plants against the contract. Such situations are covered by a form of pooled buying. The individual plant which is the largest user of the material, especially if it is in the locality from where this material comes, buys for all plants on the basis of estimates, although such contracts may actually be written and put through by the central purchasing organization. Goods are shipped to each plant as specified and charged to the plant receiving them. Here again there must be coordination through a central purchasing department, because the plant using the major portion of the requirements may not be in the best position to buy the total amount needed.

A typical setup of a partially centralized, partially localized purchasing department is shown in Fig. 2.

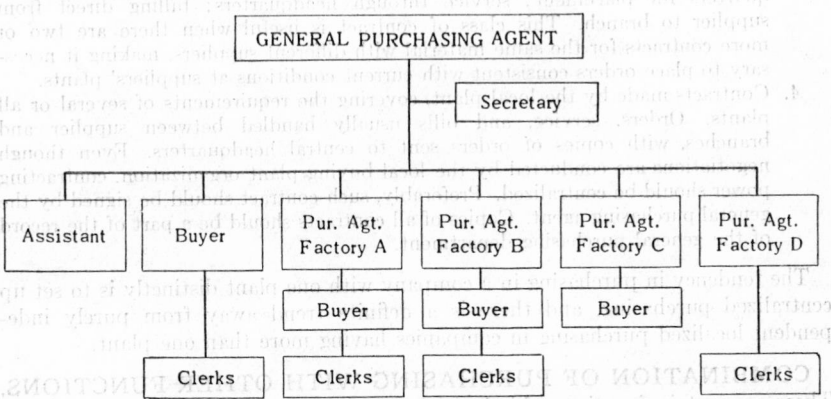

Handbook of Purchasing Policies and Procedures, vol. 1, N.A.P.A.

Fig. 2. Purchasing organization in a company with combined central and local buying. (Manufacturer of chemicals with 15 scattered plants. Annual purchases over $25,000,000.)

Conditions Governing Centralized-Localized Buying. The requirements for the successful operation of a centralized-localized buying plan are:

1. The general purchasing agent will establish policies, procedures, basic forms, record-keeping methods, and other fundamentals necessary for uniformity throughout purchasing and adequate central control and will delimit the authority and the range of buying of each local purchasing agent.
2. All local transactions will be reported at once to the central office, duplicates of contracts, and perhaps periodic summary reports of activities, being sent there.
3. Local commitments must remain within the purchase budgets of the respective plants as to the amounts for each material, and the total monthly expenditures.
4. A limit may be placed upon the amount which the respective local purchasing agents may expend upon any one purchase order.
5. Special purchases, excessive-quantity purchases, and any other deviation from the range of authority given to the local purchasing agents must have the approval of the central office.
6. The local situation as to requirements, stocks, etc., and data on local vendors, markets, prices, etc., for important material and supplies bought locally will be reported by each branch purchasing agent to the central headquarters.
7. Local purchasing agents will draw orders to ship against contracts placed by the central purchasing department covering the needs of two or more plants.
8. The plan should be kept flexible. Different local buying authority or assignments may be given at different times, as markets or conditions shift or change.

Some of the different **types of contracts** negotiated under such a plan of organization are:

1. Contracts made by headquarters, copies sent to branches. Orders placed directly by branches on supplier, duplicates being sent to central headquarters; all service questions handled directly by branch with supplier; bill sent by supplier to branch and paid by branch.
2. Contracts made by headquarters, copies sent to branches. All orders sent to headquarters for placing; all service questions handled through headquarters; bills rendered to and paid for by headquarters, which rebills to branches.
3. Contracts made by headquarters, copies sent to branches. Orders sent to headquarters for placement; service through headquarters; billing direct from supplier to branch. This class of contract is useful when there are two or more contracts for the same material with different suppliers, making it necessary to place orders consistent with current conditions at suppliers' plants.
4. Contracts made by the local plant, covering the requirements of several or all plants. Orders, service, and bills usually handled between supplier and branches, with copies of orders sent to central headquarters. Even though negotiations are conducted by the local buying plant organization, contracting power should be centralized. Preferably, such contract should be signed by the general purchasing agent. Copies of all contracts should be a part of the record of the general purchasing department.

The tendency in purchasing in a company with one plant distinctly is to set up centralized purchasing, and there is a definite trend away from purely independent localized purchasing in companies having more than one plant.

COMBINATION OF PURCHASING WITH OTHER FUNCTIONS.
There are certain functions of industrial organization which are so closely correlated to purchasing as to lead to the consideration of the question of whether or not they should be included under purchasing and made an integral part of the purchasing organization. These are: receiving, materials inspection, storeskeeping, and traffic.

Receiving is part of the job of procurement in many organizations. In some companies the purchasing department is held responsible also for storeskeeping, inventory control, and physical handling. Some industrial engineers support the theory that the purchasing department, which negotiates the buying arrangements, should be checked by a separate department which reports the completion of the transaction. However, one must recognize that the purchasing agent, responsible for the procurement function as previously defined, should not be deprived of control of any phase of the procedure before the transaction is completed.

In cases of centralized purchasing for a number of plants, **individual receiving departments** for each plant under direction of the local purchasing agent, or as part of the manufacturing or the production control department, are desirable. Even in such cases, the receiving department may report to the general purchasing department, which should conduct with vendors all negotiations about shortages, nonreceipt, etc. In very large organizations the receiving department may include sections responsible for traffic, claims handling, and internal transportation. The receiving department in such cases may be directly responsible to the plant manager.

Inspection of incoming materials, while a direct responsibility of the purchasing department only in some of the largest companies, is a function in which the procurement officer must be closely interested. (See section on Inspection.) Usually, the actual organization, personnel, and procedures are under the quality control department, a separate, independent organization. The purchasing agent should have voice in the selection of goods to be inspected, should handle all disputes and negotiations with vendors arising from inspection, should receive reports of all inspection results, and should have a voice in the ultimate disposition of rejected goods. He must also be sufficiently aware of the techniques of **statistical quality control** to be able to discuss this phase of the contract at the time of both negotiation and rejection. (See section on Quality Control.)

Storeskeeping may or may not be part of the purchasing duty. In an organization having a planning department, stores, as well as other control functions, are likely to fall under its jurisdiction (Heinritz, Purchasing). In other cases, where top management dictates fundamental inventory policy, the actual control of stocks falls quite naturally to the purchasing department. As long as decisions of how much and when to buy are delegated to purchasing, the stores-control function, wherein stocks are maintained and replacement orders are initiated, should be a responsibility of the purchasing agent.

Traffic, like storeskeeping, is not always a purchasing function. Incoming traffic deals with purchased materials in large part; outgoing traffic has no such relation. The general practice is toward separation of traffic and purchasing, except in a very small organization where economy makes consolidation essential.

RELATION OF PURCHASING DEPARTMENT TO OTHER DEPARTMENTS. The departments in an industrial organization with which the purchasing department must coordinate most closely are: storeskeeping, production, engineering, traffic, accounting, sales, and financial.

Stores Department. Whether or not the organizational responsibility for stores rests in the purchasing department, the procedural contact between the two is most direct. On all commodities which are carried in stock, the stores department sends requisitions for replenishment to the purchasing department, and the purchasing department buys on the strength of these requisitions. Upon receipt of goods from the receiving department, the stores department is responsible for their safekeeping and disbursement. Beyond these contacts, the two departments have other interests in common in which they must cooperate—inventory control and the determination of order quantities. On the one hand, the stores department must keep the purchasing department informed as to rate of use, etc., of each item in order that the purchasing department may buy efficiently (see section on Storeskeeping). Hence, every **requisition from stores to purchasing** should contain all such information about stock on hand, rate of use, and known future requirements as will enable the purchasing department to place its order with the vendor for the most desirable quantity from all points of view and for delivery at proper time. If the stores department is not a division of the purchasing department, the purchasing department should follow a systematic method of informing the stores department about prospective changes in market conditions or price levels that may make it advisable for stores to anticipate its requirements for a given commodity. The purchasing department has a primary opportunity for initiating information of this kind.

The stores department, on the basis of its record, will often requisition from the purchasing department a quantity of some material which carries a higher purchase price than would apply to a moderately larger quantity. It is obviously the duty of the purchasing department to increase such a requisition to a quantity economical for purchase. This step should not be taken, however, without notification to the stores department, because:

1. The stores department is primarily responsible for control of inventory, and it is unfair to take any steps which will increase inventory without notifying the stores department in such detail as to make the increase satisfactory or to give opportunity to debate its advisability.
2. The stores department is entitled to a knowledge of the quantity it is to receive against its requisition, and will undoubtedly question the receipt of a quantity greater than requisitioned.
3. It is a matter of clerical economy to have the stores department keep records on economical ordering quantities and other data which will enable it to requisition in proper quantities in the future and save further notifications.

A distinction is made between **authorization to purchase,** which is a stores department's agreement to a commitment to take material over some period in the future, and a **purchase requisition,** which specifically requests a definite quantity at a definite date. An authorization to purchase is a prelude to the execution of a purchase contract covering a future period, whereas a purchase requisition results in a direct purchase order or in the placing of an order for a partial shipment against a contract already placed. The term "purchase authorization" is also used in some companies to distinguish more clearly between the purchase requisition and the stores requisition.

There is also a clear distinction between **ordering quantities** and **commitments.** Most companies include as commitments all quantities contracted for, whether or not specific deliveries are scheduled. In many cases specific delivery orders are placed against such contracts. In such cases the purchasing and stores departments can agree, for example, that all orders for a contracted article put up in standard cases will call for multiples of the standard cases and that some material will always be ordered in multiples to make up a minimum or a maximum carload. Where a quotation is given f.o.b. supplier's plant (freight allowed on shipments over a certain total weight), the purchasing and stores departments may arrange to place orders exceeding the minimum necessary to get the allowance for freight.

Another condition requiring agreement of the purchasing and stores departments is the **quantity and period to be covered by future commitments** or contracts. It is the purchasing department's responsibility to determine the probable price trends and to estimate the possible savings by making commitments for the period recommended. It is the stores department's function to balance these estimated savings with the possible cost or losses in storing which may be caused by the commitment. For example, the purchasing department may be able to obtain an exceptionally low price by buying a year's supply, taking immediate delivery, and making cash payment. This apparent saving may be wiped out if the stores department must rent outside storage space, increase its handling expenses, and run the risk of a possible change in design which would make the material obsolete before the stock was exhausted. This case also involves the financial department, as a cash payment at that time may seriously affect the bank balances, and it may be inadvisable or impossible to borrow to meet the payment. Cases occur, generally involving company relationship as well as price and delivery, where future commitments are sufficiently important to be laid before the board of directors. **Records as to future commitments** are ordinarily kept in the purchasing department, and the responsibility for taking out the full amount of commitments and deciding when new commitments are advisable rests with the purchasing department.

Another point on which agreement is necessary is the distinction between items that move regularly in large quantities and are dependent upon a **predetermined production schedule** of the production department, and **regularly stored items** on which the use fluctuates. In an automobile assembly plant, for example, parts for bodies come from one plant and bolts and nuts for assembly usually from the plant of an outside vendor. In the first case little or no stocks are carried, daily deliveries being made according to the rate of consumption. In the case of the bolts a stock is maintained, and orders are placed when predetermined order points are reached.

The importance of unified policy in all of these decisions, as well as the recognition of the basic responsibilities of procurement—to have what is wanted where it is wanted and when it is wanted—has been a major influence in developing the trend toward **materials management** in which the actual buying division is combined with receiving, storeskeeping, and materials inventory control in a single department.

Production Control and Maintenance Departments. Production control department requisitions are based on determined manufacturing schedules. Quantities, therefore, are not open to increase by purchasing department action without provision of a use for the amount above that required for the production schedule. The same reasoning applies to requisitions from the maintenance department or any department that requisitions for use for a particular job or purpose and not for stores. It is good practice to route all requisitions not originated by the stores department through that department, so as to eliminate the possibility of duplication (i.e., ordering the same material for stores and for production or maintenance, with the resulting building of unnecessary stocks and failure to make full use of stores). When such requisitions are not so routed, the purchasing department must assume the responsibility for seeing that purchase orders are not sent to vendors for items which are in stores. There will be exceptional cases, of course, in which production or maintenance may require sufficient material for a given project to justify separate requisitions and orders, reserving the stock in stores for regular and minor uses.

The **joint responsibilities** of the production control and purchase departments in planning to buy and in buying are given below. Assume that the production control department has complete charge of the needs of the plant and determines the materials required and the rate at which they are required. With this assumption the several responsibilities are:

Production Control:

    1. To supply information, by item or class of material, regarding the estimated future demand as far in advance as necessary (this period to be determined by joint conference between purchasing and production control), rate of consumption, and any other special factors that are peculiar to the item.
    2. To furnish definite authorization for commitments.

Purchasing:

    1. When to buy.   3. How to buy—spot purchase, contract, etc.
    2. From whom to buy.   4. Price to pay.

Joint:

    1. Order point.   4. Advance purchases.
    2. Minimum ordering quantities.   5. Stocks to be carried.
    3. Ordering multiples.

Engineering Department. When the engineering department develops the designs of products, or checks and adapts customers' drawings if the design is prepared outside, the purchasing department is interested in having as many as possible of the specifications set up conform to materials, parts, and products on the market. Cost of items bought will thus be held to reasonable figures. Likewise, it is desirable to have the engineering department standardize on certain materials, parts, etc., so that these may be bought in large quantities to get good discounts, cut down the number of purchase orders placed, and reduce the quantity and variety of items carried in the storeroom. In the designs, also, the purchasing department is concerned with simplicity. Drawings of cast parts, for example, may indicate so many possible complications in casting that the purchasing department may have difficulty in securing acceptable quotations from outside vendors.

The engineering department often prepares **bills of materials,** which are highly important to the purchasing department as central sources of information on materials and parts. Because their preparation centralizes and speeds up the issuing of purchase requisitions, rush shipments from vendors are seldom delayed by late purchase orders.

Traffic and Other Departments. The relationships of purchasing with traffic arise principally through the routing and tracing of incoming shipments; with sales through the budgets, for the purchase budget is dependent upon the sales estimates; and with accounting through the paper transactions that originate or pass through the purchasing department and supply original information for certain of the accounting records.

PURCHASING DEPARTMENT ORGANIZATION. The purchasing department organization in a small or medium-sized company will consist of a purchasing agent, buyers or assistants to the purchasing agent, a follow-up section, perhaps an invoice section, and a clerical force. In a large company the buying division of an integrated purchasing department may consist of a purchasing agent (director or manager of purchases, or general purchasing agent), buyers, junior buyers, and a general service section (under the direction of a purchasing office manager). These will be subdivided into a correspondence unit, follow-up unit, price-checking unit, file unit, stenographic unit, and mail room, each headed by a unit head responsible to the purchasing office manager. In such an organization, the purchasing office manager reports directly to the head of the purchasing department, and the service section handles all matters regarding purchase orders occurring subsequent to the placing of the order, but in cooperation with the interested buyer and subject to his direction as far as any action affecting vendor relations or purchasing policies is concerned.

Purchasing Agent. The purchasing agent should be selected with careful regard for his ability, personality, versatility, and breadth of vision. He must be, at one and the same time, an organizer and leader for his department, a worthy representative of the company in its contacts with other concerns, a keen student of business, a man capable of consideration and prompt decision, having balanced judgment and clear foresight. He should be of the executive, not the clerical, accounting, or mechanical type, although insight into these fields is an asset.

The recognition of the necessity for **managerial ability** in the purchasing agent was expressed by Benjamin F. Fairless as president of the United States Steel Company in the following statement:

We consider the job of purchasing to be one of the major functions of management, requiring expert leadership supported by a well-organized and efficiently operated purchasing department with specially trained and experienced personnel. We in U. S. Steel look to our purchasing department to do more than the actual buying of goods and services. Their knowledge of world affairs gained from purchasing materials in many parts of the globe helps to keep us informed on international supply situations. In addition, through their contacts, our operating people depend on our buyers to keep them informed of the development of new commodities and equipment. With these responsibilities, we consider that our financial success is in no small measure dependent on the initiative, judgment, and efficiency of our purchasing department.

Responsibilities of the Purchasing Agent. The principal responsibilities of the purchasing agent, some deputized to assistants, are:

1. Keeping up the company's standard of quality production by his share in the choice of materials used.
2. Organizing and directing the purchasing department and acting as sole head of its personnel.
3. Spending a large portion of the company's money and being responsible for its wise expenditure.
4. Preserving the operation of the company's production schedules without interruption.
5. Representing the company in one branch of its major contacts with other firms.
6. Maintaining the company's reputation for integrity and fair dealing by his method of negotiating with vendors.
7. Acting as an executive of the company and a partner in its councils, particularly in preparing the purchase budget.
8. Keeping the company in step with progress and competition by research and openmindedness on new materials, new tools, etc.
9. Acting as final check, in the interest of economy, on all goods requisitioned, questioning need, quantity, and quality specifications.

These functions are in large part deputized by him to members of his department. In some small plants the purchasing agent retains responsibility for keeping in touch with and signing all contracts. The purchasing agent's actual **personal duties** are as follows:

1. Interviewing salesmen to obtain up-to-date information, securing and comparing quotations, and placing orders for such main commodities as he shall reserve to himself to purchase.
2. Establishing purchasing policies for his department to execute.
3. Preparing, or at least overseeing, all general reports on purchasing presented to management.
4. Conducting all major adjustment negotiations which are sufficiently vital to affect his company's goodwill.
5. Taking part in interdepartment conferences, whether for planning, formulating of company policies, or other purposes.
6. Approving materials specifications on major commodities.
7. Supervising other functions of his department.

Assistant Purchasing Agent. The assistant purchasing agent is, under the purchasing agent's supervision, responsible for aiding in department operation, conduct of staff functions, and buying assigned classes of purchased goods. His duties in buying are to inform himself thoroughly about the market and manufacturing conditions of the class of goods so assigned, to interview salesmen, to secure and compare quotations, and to place orders for all materials intrusted to him. In a smaller company he usually conducts correspondence as to shortages, defects, and adjustments and, in some companies, as to follow-up on orders. When general service or follow-up sections are maintained, the respective correspondence duties may be delegated to these sections.

Buyers. The buying section in a centralized purchasing department includes the purchasing agent, his immediate assistants, and a number of buyers. Items to be purchased are divided between buyers by **types of material** rather than by point of use or any other consideration. For example, a large purchasing department might have a buyer of ferrous metals, of nonferrous metals, of tools, of stationery and supplies, of textile products, and so on. Division of items to be purchased by this method allows specialization on correlated materials, reports on which are generally grouped and analyzed together in trade papers, forecasts, etc.

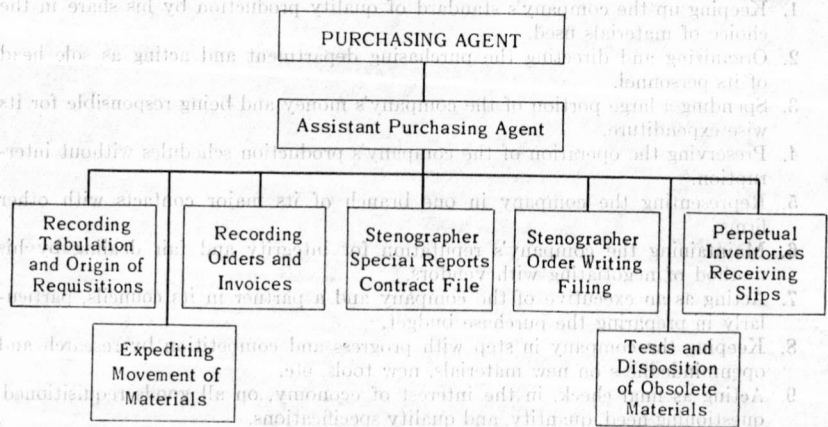

Handbook of Purchasing Policies and Procedures, N.A.P.A.

Fig. 3. Organization of purchasing in a company with more than one plant. (Shoe manufacturer. Purchasing centralized. Purchases less than $5,000,000 per year.)

It also provides for opportunity to acquire acquaintance with the vendors' representatives and the vendors' plants by continued interest in and association with the same type of materials.

In some organizations the purchasing department may be set up on a **divisional or functional** rather than a commodity basis. In that case one buyer would handle all purchasing for a particular division or function of the business. The theory behind this plan is that the buyer thus becomes familiar with the particular needs and specifications of that division and learns to work with the plant organization responsible for that function. This plan also eliminates separation or double handling of requisitions containing several items belonging in different commodity groups. Except under unusual conditions, however, commodities rather than divisions or function should be the basis of buyers' assignments. Otherwise, duplication of effort and loss of total purchasing influence in the commodity field are inevitable.

The **number of buyers** will be controlled by volume of purchases and variety of materials purchased. In a company of moderate size the purchasing agent may

---

Group A

Lumber (including poles, ties, etc.), wooden crates, packages, and packing.

Woodwork (turned and constructed), wooden ware (including bobbins, reels, etc.), wood patterns.

Castings, bolts, nuts, washers, rivets, screws, screw-machine work, drop forgings.

Construction materials, factory supplies (except coal and petroleum products), painters' supplies, chemicals.

Leather (including all kinds of belting), hardware, glass, insulation, polishing and grinding supplies.

Coal, oils (petroleum products including greases).

Small tools.

Stationery, furniture, office supplies, printing paper, rope, twine, janitors' supplies.

Large tools and machinery; steam, gas, and water supplies; transmission machinery and appliances.

Nonferrous metals, including wire; special nonferrous parts (punched, drawn, stamped, die-cast, or assembled).

Sheet steel (all grades), wire (iron and steel), bar steel, steel shapes.

Pig iron, coke, limestone, foundry supplies.

Group B

Abrasives	Gums, waxes, and compounds	Plastics
Asbestos		Precious metals
Building materials	Hospital supplies	Precious stones
Ceramics	Insulating material	Printing
Chemicals and acids	Leather supplies	Rubber
Coal and coke	Machines—parts and machine tools	Supplies—office and janitorial
Electrical supplies		
Factory supplies	Metals—ferrous	Textiles
Furniture and fixtures	Metals—nonferrous	Timber products
Greases	Oils	Tools
	Paints and varnishes	Vehicles and accessories
	Paper and products	Wearing apparel

Fig. 4. **Grouping of materials for purchase by an individual buyer.**

have only one assistant purchasing agent or buyer. Even here it is desirable to follow the plan of division of the buying task by class of materials, the purchasing agent to handle those items which are of major importance either for the value involved or for some other reason, and to delegate the buying of less important items to his assistant or buyer with such safeguards as may be necessary to cover the individual case. It is usual for the purchasing agent in a machine shop, for example, to buy coal, fuel, lubricants, and those raw materials used in large volume, while an assistant buys maintenance, stationery, and miscellaneous supplies which involve the larger number of contacts but smaller financial commitments. Fig. 3 shows the organization of a typical purchasing department in a well-organized company.

Commodity Assignment. In assigning commodities to be purchased among buyers, it is well to have in mind groupings which have market tendencies in common and which are capable of being studied together to the best advantage. The related use of products may also be a factor in combining them for buying purposes. How far such grouping should be carried is affected by volume of

Buyer 1	Buyer 2	Buyer 3
Subcontracts	Resale items	Machine tools
Construction	Hardware	Capital equipment
Fuel	Fasteners	Machine maintenance
Utilities	Abrasives	Lubricants
Automobiles	Electrical	Power transmission
Car rentals	Photographic	Perishable tools
Lumber		
Buyer 4	**Buyer 5**	**Buyer 6**
Metals	Chemicals	Paper
Castings	Cleaning supplies	Advertising
Forgings	Paints and lacquers	Office supplies
Molded parts	Hospital supplies	Office equipment
Plastic materials	Textiles and fibers	Packaging
Fiber	Leather	Dining room and kitchen
Precious metals	Safety equipment	supplies and equipment
Precious stones	Clothing	Containers
	Laundry	

Fig. 5. Grouping of materials for purchase by several buyers.

purchases of various items, total volume of purchases, size of organization, and many other factors and must be worked out to meet conditions in the individual case. Fig. 4 illustrates grouping of items to be purchased by a single buyer, showing two different types, Group A and Group B. Fig. 5 illustrates a method of dividing major procurement classes among several buyers to provide:

1. Ease of sales interview through relationship of items handled.
2. Full utilization of the technical ability of each buyer and easier study of new developments.
3. Close relationship with personnel of using departments.

Follow-up Section. The duties of the follow-up section are to see that all goods ordered are received in time for requirements or in accordance with specified delivery dates and always to have on its record a definite acknowledgment of each order and promise of delivery. Some companies have found definite advantages in making the follow-up function part of each buyer's duties. If such routines are well set up, a buyer can perform more efficiently, exert more mature judgment, and feel greater responsibility.

Clerical Force. The duties of the clerical force are to record purchase orders, invoices, and receipts, to keep all necessary departmental or interdepartmental records, and to do the necessary typing, checking, and filing. Clerical work in the purchasing department should be directed and checked in exactly the same manner as any other clerical routine.

Purchasing Office Manager. The purchasing office manager in a large organization supervises the entire correspondence and clerical function of the department. The necessity of his close cooperation with buyers is obvious. Often he is responsible with the personnel department for the hiring and supervision of all department personnel except buyers.

Purchase Budgets and Policies

THE PURCHASE BUDGET. The purchase budget is the purchasing department's plan or schedule of operations. The purchasing department's function in budget preparation is to combine estimates of use as submitted by the production department and a statement of inventory now carried as submitted by the storeskeeping or materials control departments, with the purchasing department's special knowledge of market conditions, in order to form a workable plan for procurement of materials needed—and no more—in time for production requirements, and at the least possible cost in inventory investment consistent with purchasing under favorable market conditions.

The following **responsibilities** are involved:

1. To advise as to the period in advance that should be covered by the commitment.
2. To determine, with the cooperation of the production control and stores departments, the amount of stocks to—
   a. Protect production schedules.
   b. Keep from paying a high bonus for rush shipments.
   c. Keep inventories down to prevent excess carrying costs.

Items in the purchase budget with regard to a program for a production period are:

1. Estimated use (furnished by the production control department).
2. Quantities on hand (furnished by the stores department).
3. Time required for delivery from vendor (furnished by purchasing records).
4. Probable price variations or market trends (furnished from purchasing department data or charts).

From these four elements the purchasing department can plan its purchases, according to market trends, seasonal variations, etc. It may contract for a reasonable period in advance, specifying deliveries on schedules consistent with use, state of inventory, and necessary time allowance for delivery, with due consideration to margin of safety for emergency demand, spoilage, transportation delays, and the like.

ADVANTAGES OF THE BUDGET. The purchase budget is an important factor in efficient purchasing. It tends to eliminate costly emergency orders, and allows full advantage to be taken of price movements. It also makes possible quantity purchasing—with its consequent advantages—on deferred deliveries. It is a statement of the probable future need for materials and supplies, and the further ahead its estimates are made, the better will be the plans for meeting the demands. The length of time covered by the estimates depends entirely upon the item estimated. In some cases it may be as short as 30 days and in others several years. The important point is that the purchasing department must have knowledge of the needs for the various materials and supplies purchased as far in advance as possible. In contrast with this understanding of the budget as a plan is the definite authorization to purchase, which covers a limited period only.

CHECKING BUDGET PERFORMANCE. The purchasing agent must have the authority to check frequently the record of performance against the purchase budget and to suggest its revision on the basis either of performance or of altered purchasing conditions. Particularly in times of unusual economic stress or change, the continuing advice of the purchasing agent in continuing or revising the budget is essential.

PURCHASING POLICIES. The primary objectives of the purchasing department are threefold:

1. To procure the necessary materials, supplies, etc., of proper quality.
2. To procure them in time for plant requirements and have them delivered to the proper place.
3. To procure them at the lowest possible ultimate cost.

To state these factors as a single **purchasing objective:** The task of the purchasing department is to have on hand necessary goods to insure uninterrupted production of a product of satisfactory quality at the lowest possible expense. More briefly summarized: It is to obtain what is wanted, when it is wanted, where it is wanted, of the right quality and at the right cost.

COSTS AND SAVINGS. Upon analysis the above objective becomes entirely a matter of **ultimate cost.** Interruption of operations and poor quality of materials are undesirable because they add to cost. Cost must not be confused with price, because the price of materials is only one element in the cost of purchasing. Departmental expense, cost of errors and losses, cost of carrying inventory, cost of interruption of production go with the price paid for purchased goods to make up the ultimate procurement or purchasing cost. The **fundamental purchasing plans,** then, must contemplate economy in departmental expenditures; elimination of errors, losses, and interruptions; a low inventory; and a low purchase price as the ideal. The size of the department and its consequent expense and the elimination of losses are matters of departmental efficiency rather than of policy. Inventory and prices paid for materials, however, are items of policy.

The purchasing department must **weigh the savings** to be effected by buying in quantity at low spots in commodity markets against the expense of carrying excess quantities over immediate requirements in inventory until used. Determination of a purchasing policy involves: (1) knowledge of carrying cost of inventory, (2) forecasting of trends in commodity markets. Ordinarily, inventory carrying charges will more than counterbalance possible savings in price on items whose market prices are stable to a degree. On many commodities, market changes cover a wide range, sufficient to make savings from purchases spotted at low points in the swing outweigh the cost of carrying a large inventory.

TWO PHASES TO POLICIES. There are, therefore, two phases to purchasing policies:

1. On items on which price changes are narrow, purchases should be strictly in accordance with estimated use, and no further covering should be done other than to insure a reasonable margin of safety for uninterrupted operation.
2. On items on which market changes are wide and frequent, the policy should be to buy at low points in market movements for periods dependent upon the extent of swing and the forecast of use.

Inventory carrying charges for average warehouse stocks including desirable and active items are set by Parrish at 25 percent per annum. The carrying charges include charges for storage facilities, insurance, taxes, transportation, handling and distribution, depreciation, interest, and obsolescence. (See section on Materials Control and Standardization.) Parrish points out that depreciation, including deterioration, obsolescence, shrinkage, and perverted or uneconomical use, and expense, including extra handling, accounting and miscellaneous costs, in addition to those mentioned, are higher for undesirable than for active items. He, therefore, recommends as conservative for excess or undesirable items a rate of depreciation of 20 percent. It is obvious that the cost of carrying inventory will vary greatly for different classes of material. Each company should make its own estimate based on its own experience of handling and storage charges, and losses from depreciation, obsolescence, etc.

LONG-TERM BUYING POLICIES. Policies for long-term buying can be adopted safely only on the basis of an ample statistical background, which depends upon records gathered from the past experience of the purchasing department, market reports, government data, business forecasts, etc. Market statistics are available in trade papers, special reports, and in some cases in government publications. They include production figures, stocks on hand, current rate of operation, unfilled orders, and other indications of probable price change or stability. Price movements may be followed through charts published in trade papers or through charts maintained in the purchasing department. The latter are preferable, since purchases may then be spotted on the charts to indicate the success of the department in buying at a saving.

Taxes and other governmental action, actual or contemplated, may be factors in buying policy. At times, also, the continuation versus the possible interruption of sources of supply may determine the policy.

Seasonal trends should be noted and allowance made for them in planning policies regarding commodities affected by the seasons. **Cyclical trends,** or variations in the business cycle, are interesting and often suggestive. For forecasts it is advisable to depend on actual data rather than on the continuation of a line in a cyclical graph. **Secular trends,** or long-time tendencies, must be weighed, and in some instances even weather forecasts and style changes are strong indications of the buying policy to follow.

Vendors from whom goods are purchased are necessarily familiar with conditions in their trade. Information from sources of supply is one of the best indications of the wisdom of buying for the future.

It would be gratifying to be able to advise some general principle of purchasing policy, possibly on the theory of cyclical movement, by which the purchasing department could refrain from buying at peaks in general movements, buy only from hand-to-mouth on the down curve, begin to accumulate stock on the bottom arc, and buy heavily on the upswing. It is safer, however, to limit any definite application of such a purchasing policy to the individual commodity to be bought

USE OF GRAPHIC METHODS. It is strongly recommended that graphs be maintained for presentation in a comparative form of various items of information on which a purchasing policy may be based. The techniques and principles of graphical problem solving are explained in the section on Charting and Graphic Methods. Graphic representation permits an over-all perspective of the problem which is usually not possible through tabulation alone. One example of a simple graphic method used to solve purchasing problems is illustrated with the vendor rating chart in Fig. 26.

Methods of Purchasing

CLASSIFICATION OF PURCHASES. Purchases may be classified according to type of goods to be bought, and these classifications affect methods of purchase. There are four general classes: raw materials, supplies, fabricated parts, and machinery and equipment.

Raw Materials. Raw materials are basic, unfabricated materials bought in large quantity. They include such items as pig iron, copper, lead, tin, cotton, rubber, lumber, sand, leather, steel (except in fabricated forms), etc. In the main they are materials from which products are fabricated. Coal, coke, and fuel oil should be included with raw materials. Although they do not enter directly into the product, the methods and conditions of their purchase and their nature classify them as raw materials.

Raw materials as a rule are bought in carload lots, and usually contracts are made covering requirements for a considerable period. Prices are governed by quotations in commodity markets and are subject to rapid and wide change. The use of raw materials in a plant is relatively constant, quantities bought are large, and information indicating price trends is readily available. Such materials, therefore, lend themselves readily to forward buying in anticipation of future needs. They should be bought on specification by chemical analysis or physical characteristics. It is the practice in the automotive industry to buy material to do the job rather than by physical specifications. For example, steel is purchased to make a certain fender, and so on. Raw materials are bulky, so storage space is an item to be considered. Transportation rates and handling charges form a large part of their cost.

Supplies. Supplies are the many items necessary for the operation and maintenance of plant, shipping department, office, etc. In general they are items which do not enter into the product but which are necessary in operation. They include stationery, electrical supplies, pipe and pipe fittings, shipping containers, belting and transmission supplies, bolts, nuts, washers, screws, packings, lubricants, hardware, abrasives, etc.

The purchase of supplies is characterized by the presence of many small items which, generally speaking, are standard items of manufacture, subject to published lists and discounts, though there may be specialties among them. There is little occasion to buy supplies for future requirements. Storage space is not a factor, but the clerical labor of checking, storeskeeping, and accounting is great because of the variety of items in comparison with the value involved. An excellent **supply yardstick** is the relationship between unit price of the item and total purchase cost. One might buy enough paper clips for a year but grinding wheels for only 60 days.

Fabricated Parts. Under the designation of fabricated parts are included parts and small tools or accessories which are bought for resale, either as a part of the product manufactured or in connection with it. This class may include bearings, chucks, abrasive wheels, pumps, wrenches, tools, etc. It also includes special small parts which can be manufactured elsewhere more profitably than in the plant. Purchases of fabricated parts should be made on competitive quotations, which, wherever possible, should be checked against shop estimates for making the same parts in the plant. The chief factor in such purchases is the **margin of resale profit** in the transaction. In the case of standard catalog items so purchased, the purchasing department is entitled to jobbers' prices. Future buying should be closely limited to the needs indicated by known production schedules.

Industrial Equipment. Equipment items include machine tools, furnaces, boilers, automobiles, trucks, blowers, safes, and all such other major items bought for the plant or office. Equipment purchase requisitions should be approved by the management before being handled by the purchasing department. Technical considerations are supreme in buying equipment, and such purchases should be covered by careful specifications, preferably by a description of purpose and result or performance demanded. Contributions made by the purchasing department in the purchase of **capital equipment** are:

1. Obtaining quotations.
2. Offering alternate sources.
3. Negotiating the contract.
4. Verifying the specification to prove conclusively that the machine will perform as required.
5. Maintaining an up-to-date library of catalog information.
6. Being alert to new developments, which might be more efficient than present processes, and seeing that interested persons are informed.

PURCHASE METHODS. Methods of purchase vary according to the nature of demand in the plant and conditions in the market in which goods are to be bought. There are seven principal purchasing methods:

1. Purchase strictly by requirements.
2. Purchase for a specified future period.
3. Market purchasing.
4. Speculative purchasing.
5. Contract purchasing.
6. Group purchase of small items.
7. Scheduled purchasing.

The first four of these methods are classified by the factors entering into the determination of the time to buy, the quantity, and the duration for which the purchase is made. The last three are classified by the form of the purchase itself. Consequently these methods overlap. Contract purchasing may be market purchasing, purchase for a specified future period, speculative purchasing, or even purchase strictly by requirement. The same is true of scheduled purchasing and, to a lesser degree, of group purchasing.

Purchasing by Requirements. Purchasing by requirements means that no purchase is made until a need arises, and then sufficient is bought to cover the existing need and no more. This method applies principally to emergency requirements or to goods used so infrequently that they would not be stocked. It is essentially emergency buying and ordinarily makes the procurement of the goods the sole or at least outstanding requirement. The task of the purchasing department is to have vendor connections that can be depended upon to fill such orders promptly and without taking advantage of the situation.

Purchase for a Specified Future Period. Purchase for a specified future period is standard practice for buying goods regularly used, but not in great quantity, and on which price variations are negligible. Most supplies are bought by this method. The period for which the purchase is made may be fixed by a production schedule or by the stores record of past use or by a combination of both. Savings to be gained by the purchase of a given quantity also affect the determination of the period, as does the cost of carrying the items in inventory. It is important to note that no fixed periods should be set for all purchases but that a separate and flexible period should be set for each item.

Purchasing According to Market. Market purchasing is defined as purchasing according to conditions of the market to take advantage of price fluctuations, rather than in strict accord with a prearranged program or for a specified period.

So long as market purchasing conforms to the production schedule and its possible changes, or to the demands of the plant or business, it cannot be classed as speculative purchasing. It is entirely possible to purchase wholly with reference to demand and yet take reasonable advantage of market fluctuations. This procedure is followed in the case of railroads, public utilities, and some manufacturing corporations, which have definite construction or manufacturing programs mapped out for long periods ahead. By constant study of market statistics and factors that affect prices, an efficient purchasing department will be able to forecast the trend of market prices and buy to best advantage. When its studies indicate that the price range is at a reasonably low point and that the future trend will be toward higher levels, the purchasing department will cover its requirements for a considerable period ahead. If indications are that prices are close to peak and that the trend will be downward, a hand-to-mouth purchasing program is indicated until prices have become stabilized at a lower level. There are cases where it is possible to do market purchasing and not take spot delivery or make immediate payment. This condition applies especially to fabricated or partly fabricated materials where the fabricator can "cover" at an advantageous price for his raw materials but does not want to make a commitment without being sure of an outlet for at least part of his finished goods.

Market purchasing applies to the buying of coal, coke, pig iron, and raw materials generally.

Advantages of this method are:

1. Large savings in purchase prices.
2. Greater margin of profit on the finished product, the price of which does not fluctuate as does that of the raw material.
3. Consolidation of purchases of a given material into one transaction with resulting saving in purchase expenses.

Disadvantages are:

1. Higher inventories with consequent higher carrying charges and tying up of storage space.
2. Liability to obsolescence in case radical changes are made in specifications.
3. Possibility of error in judgment of market tendencies, which may mean large losses.

Speculative Purchasing. Strictly speaking, speculative purchasing consists in buying when the market is low, more than can possibly be used in manufacturing, with the idea of later reselling much of the material at a considerable price advance to users who may come on the market when the price is high. The term, however, is often applied to a more-than-normal purchase risk in acquiring an excess of materials on low markets in the belief that the price will advance very substantially, thus saving the company considerable money. It goes a step further than market purchasing, makes price trends in commodity markets the primary factor, and gives less regard to a fixed program of use as a basis for buying. It does not base decisions on demands of the business itself but on the possibility of market price savings. In some conversion industries the cost of a single raw material alone is more than 50 percent of the total cost of production. In some branches of the textile industry, cost of cotton outweighs all other elements of cost in producing cotton cloth. Here a saving of a few cents a pound on raw cotton offers a greater chance of profit than does any other activity of the business. In such a case successful speculation is often a primary means of earning dividends.

Speculative purchasing is not properly a function of the purchasing department. It should be authorized only by direct action of a financial executive or the directors. The purchasing agent should present the full facts, including hazards as well as possible advantages, together with his conclusions as to the advisability of taking the gamble. For ordinary manufacturing, the method is to be discouraged. Its single advantage is the possibility of huge speculative profits. Its **disadvantages** are many, including:

1. Tying up large amounts of capital.
2. Endangering the manufacturing schedules by waiting for profitable buying points.
3. Using large storage spaces.
4. Running the risk of obsolescence in case of radical change in specifications.

Contract Purchasing. Contract purchasing offers advantages comparable to those of market or speculative purchasing without some of the latter's disadvantages. By a contract calling for deferred delivery over a period, advantage can be taken of low prices in effect on materials at the time of placing the contract, while spreading delivery of the materials over a schedule consistent with estimated future requirements. Thus the price advantage is obtained without adding unduly to inventory. When contracting is possible it should be done in cases of raw materials fluctuating widely in price from time to time, although often contract prices will not be as favorable as prices for spot purchases of the same quantities. Sometimes contracts are made to purchase items at current prices with a fixed top price.

Contract purchasing may be a means of **assuring continuous supply** as well as a method of getting price advantages. It then becomes applicable to the purchases of parts, tools, etc. It is particularly helpful on these items where the production program is known, but the timing of it is not entirely certain. In effect it then becomes **scheduled purchasing**, as described below, but is embodied in contract form for the better protection of both vendor and purchaser.

Grouping Items. Group purchasing of small items is an interesting development in purchasing with the possibility of large savings. Every purchasing agent finds that he must buy hundreds of small items so trivial in value that the cost of placing an order often exceeds the value of the goods purchased. The problem then is to handle such purchases as quickly and as inexpensively as possible. The purchasing department must continually watch the items included in the group, as it often happens that the demand for an item originally in a group may grow so large that it should be removed from the group and bought as an individual item. Arrangements may be made to send orders for all such items to some certain dealer who agrees to handle and bill them at a fixed percentage of profit above dealer's cost, his cost records being open to inspection by the buyer on demand. A considerable saving in clerical and purchasing expense is achieved by this plan, or by annual quotations.

The method is used chiefly in such fields as pipe fittings, general hardware, electrical supplies, and stationery. Often the practice is to secure from a reasonable number of bidders their quotations on a list of these small items with the understanding that the prices will be guaranteed on all requirements in the class of items covered for a period of three months. Then all orders go to the successful bidder without further inquiry or bid. An interesting variation is that some purchasing agents forward merely a copy of the requisitions to the supplier to eliminate the expense of orders and accept a single monthly bill to avoid the checking of multiple invoices. The small order is one of the most costly elements in buying. When the costs of the extra multicopy purchase order forms, the typing, the addressing, and the handling and filing operations are added up, the excessive expense is readily understood.

Scheduled Purchasing. The schedule plan for purchasing materials used regularly in large quantities can be a source of important savings. It was devised to reduce investments in stocks. Essentially it consists in giving suppliers approximate estimates of purchase requirements over a period of time, thus placing them in a position to be able to anticipate orders and be prepared to fill them when received.

Although **minimum inventory is probably the most important objective** in this plan, other objects sought after are good quality, timely deliveries, and low cost. Good quality can be obtained only by giving suppliers enough time to produce. Timely arrival of materials can be better assured by laying down in advance a definite material requirement. Low cost results from giving suppliers advance information on requirements, thus permitting them to produce materials in the most economical manner.

The **danger inherent in this plan** is that requirements or specifications may be changed, and goods made up or allocated but not now required may become a matter of dispute between vendor and purchaser. Scheduled purchases should be restricted, therefore, to items definitely known to be required within a closely limited period and should be established as to specifications. Also, the purchaser should make very clear in his correspondence the responsibility he assumes and the risk the supplier assumes.

Blanket orders are purchase orders placed and accepted for large quantities of materials to be delivered as later specified. By the agreement the vendor agrees to furnish and the purchaser agrees to accept a stated number of units, usually within a given period. Orders based on customers' requirements are characteristic of the automotive industry. The vendor is then in a position to manufacture or procure the full amount in the assurance that the purchaser will authorize shipment in due time. The blanket order saves some of the formality of the contract method and achieves many of the desirable features of scheduled purchasing, but with a greater certainty as to the legal rights involved. Blanket orders often cover semifabricated parts or tools and contain a binding price based on the vendor's best estimate of his costs and the desirability of having a certain outlet for his product.

Value Analysis. "Value analysis" is the term applied to the study of materials, parts, or components, whether purchased or manufactured, by trained personnel in the purchasing department. The specific purposes of this study are, first, to determine the value received for each dollar spent and, second, to start specific action which will improve that value. Value analysis as a purchasing method is gaining rapidly in popularity in both large and small operations. The methods employed may vary but often include efforts to increase value through:

1. Better buying techniques	5. Lower cost maintenance
2. Better suppliers	6. Substitution
3. Design revaluation	7. Standardization
4. Better processing methods	8. Better materials handling

The ten points of analysis, developed by L. D. Miles, of General Electric Company, are typical of the customary approach:

1. Does use of the item contribute value?
2. Is the cost of the item proportionate to its usefulness?
3. Does the item need all of its features?
4. Is there anything better for the intended use?
5. Can a usable part be made by a lower-cost method?
6. Can a standard product be found which will be usable?
7. Considering the quantities used, is the item made on proper tooling?
8. Do materials, reasonable labor, overhead, and profit total its cost?
9. Will another dependable supplier provide the item for less?
10. Is anyone buying it for less?

In the larger organizations value analysis activity is large enough to warrant full-time specialists who correlate their activities with the buyers in the purchasing department. Nevertheless, smaller companies are training their buyers in the technique of value analysis so that they can apply these principles in their day-to-day purchasing program.

Buying Proper Quality

PURCHASE SPECIFICATIONS. Buying proper quality depends on: (1) having proper specifications from which to work, (2) placing the order with reliable vendors, and (3) checking material bought against specifications. A specification is no more than an accurate description of material to be purchased. Definiteness tends to minimize costs.

There are many forms of specifications indicated by:

1. Brand or trade name.
2. Blueprint or dimension sheet.
3. Chemical analysis or physical characteristics.
4. Detail of material and method of manufacture.
5. Description of purpose or use.
6. Identification with standard specification known to the trade generally and to the vendor.
7. Vendor's sample.
8. Buyer's sample.

Specification by **brand or trade name** reduces competition and places the buyer in entire dependence upon the vendor's reputation for quality. It should be used only in cases where the branded product has been found to be superior to all others for the purpose intended, or where it is deemed to be satisfactory but the formula of its composition is secret or unknown, or the desired characteristics of quality can only be tested by destroying the material. It also may be used in cases of standard products used in unimportant processes or in small quantities, when the extent of use does not justify expense of investigation and detailed specifications. The purchasing department should attempt to have at least two, and preferably more, approved brands. There are comparatively few brands that do not now have a competitive or equal grade.

Specification by **blueprint or dimension sheet** is advisable in the purchase of tools and fixtures or of components of an item to be manufactured, to meet special requirements worked out by the engineering department of the purchasing company. Blueprints provide a safe and easy method of checking against specifications when items are received and inspected.

Specifications by **chemical analysis or physical characteristics,** or both, are ideal for raw materials in the metallic class. Such specifications can be checked accurately by laboratory tests.

Specifications by **detail of material and method of manufacture** are usually confined to subcontract purchases. Because this type of specification is often used in conjunction with inspection at the vendor's plant, it is considered too expensive for extensive use.

Specification by **description of purpose or use** is highly effective. If the vendor is dependable and accepts such a specification, the responsibility is entirely his. This form of specification is the least difficult to prepare and is recommended especially in the purchase of machines or tools about which the purchaser has no particular technical knowledge.

Specifications by identification with some **standard specification** already published and accepted is a most satisfactory form of specification, provided such a standard specification can be accepted without undue and unnecessary expense.

Specification by **vendor's sample** is used where particular characteristics of quality are not readily measurable or easily described in words. Natural products, such as basic ores, chemicals, leather, and products involving color, are examples. Buyers should be careful that all characteristics of desired quality present in the sample are known to the seller at the time of purchase.

Specification by **buyer's sample** is recommended only where no other type of specification is possible, as in buying printed forms and containers, where copy is necessary or where color is involved. Samples are too often subject to change, loss, or misinterpretation, and no adequate record of the purchase is available for reference.

Requirements for an Industrial Specification. Some companies, usually large ones, develop their own **standard industrial specifications.** Although difficult to prepare and expensive to develop and maintain, they effectively increase competition and reduce rejections and disputes. An industrial specification should:

1. Be as simple as is consistent with exactness. Unnecessary detail in the specification is expensive.
2. Incorporate nationally recognized commercial standards wherever possible.
3. Contain reasonable tolerances. Unnecessary exactitude is expensive.
4. Be capable of being met by several vendors for sake of competition.
5. Be capable of being checked and contain suitable testing methods as well as characteristics to be checked.
6. Include packaging specifications and units of purchase.

7. Include, wherever possible, the use to which the material or equipment will be put by the buyer.

Where commodities purchased are covered by **commercial standards,** the purchaser's task is greatly lessened, since it is necessary only to specify the desired grade according to the standard, and the seller may guarantee conformance. Frequently provision is made for a **certifying label** as an assurance to open-market buyers. These labels normally state the name of the guarantor, the commodity and grade covered, the name and number of the commercial standard, and a definite, concise guarantee of conformance to all requirements.

Federal specifications can be secured from the Bureau of Standards of the Department of Commerce, Washington, D. C., which publishes a directory of such specifications. Many agencies prepare specifications which are largely accepted by manufacturers, among them, the American Society of Testing Materials, the Underwriters' Laboratories, and the American Society of Mechanical Engineers. The amount of standard specification material available to the purchasing agent is great and always growing. No purchasing department library is complete without references to the various directories of specifications and copies of individual specifications applying to the particular industry.

INSPECTION AS A CHECK UPON SPECIFICATIONS. All products ordered according to specifications must be reasonably checked. Inspection is not usually a function of purchasing, but the purchasing department should demand adequate inspection.

Buying Proper Quantities

FACTORS DETERMINING THE QUANTITY TO BUY. The physical factors in the analysis of when and how much to buy are graphically represented in Fig. 6, adapted from Koepke. The symbols used are defined in the chart itself.

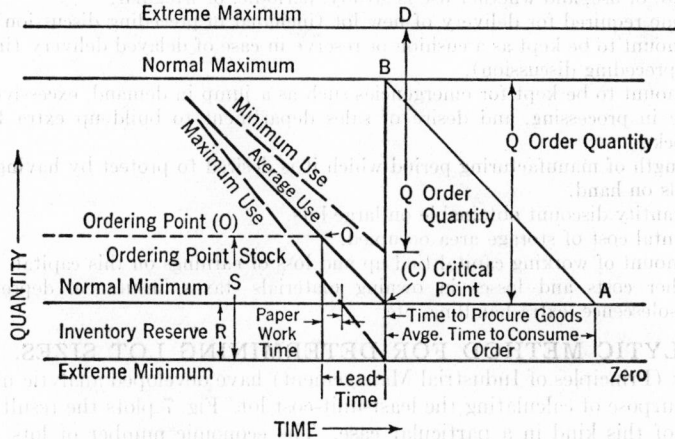

Fig. 6. Graphical analysis of when and how much to buy.

The order quantity should be the order-point quantity or the most economical quantity to manufacture, whichever is higher. Various analytical and mathematical methods for determining the most economical purchase and storage quantity are discussed here. Methods for determining the most economical quantity to manufacture are presented in the section on Production Planning and Control.

If the following conditions apply to a certain material, what is the proper quantity to purchase from a vendor, and how soon should the purchase order be issued?

750 = Amount on hand, in units
3 weeks = Delivery time
4 weeks = Reserve stock supply to allow for unexpected emergencies
300 = Average rate of use per month in units
17 weeks = Maximum supply to be on hand

The amount on hand, 750, divided by 300, rate of use per month, gives 2.5 months' supply, or 2.5×4.33 (average weeks per month) $= 10.825 +$ weeks' supply on hand, say 11 weeks. Four weeks' reserve stock is kept, and 3 weeks' time is required for delivery. So the purchase order should be placed in $11 - 7 = 4$ weeks. The order point, therefore, is reached when the quantity on hand and available falls to $7 \times 300/4.33 = 485$ units. Since the maximum quantity to be carried is 17 weeks' supply, or 1,177, including 4 weeks' reserve stock, the quantity to order is 13 weeks', or 3 months', supply, which is $3 \times 300 = 900$ units. Thus the material will be ordered four times per year. The minimum stock is $4 \times 300/4.33 = 277$ units.

The above figures have not taken into account a calculation of the economic purchase lot, which besides serving production needs and providing proper cushions and order points, also introduces the analysis of discounts or reduced unit prices on quantity purchases versus the costs incurred in the owning and storing of the material. In determining the **economic purchase lot size** for an item there are a number of factors to take into consideration:

1. Quantity on hand and available (not apportioned) in stores.
2. Rate of use, and whether use is steady, periodic, or irregular.
3. Time required for delivery of new lot (included in preceding discussion).
4. Amount to be kept as a cushion or reserve in case of delayed delivery (included in preceding discussion).
5. Amount to be kept for emergencies such as a jump in demand, excessive spoilage in processing, and desire of sales department to build up extra finished stocks.
6. Length of manufacturing period which it is desired to protect by having materials on hand.
7. Quantity discount obtainable on large lots.
8. Rental cost of storage area occupied.
9. Amount of working capital tied up and loss of earnings on this capital.
10. Other costs and losses in owning materials—taxes, insurance, depreciation, obsolescence, extra handling, etc.

ANALYTIC METHOD FOR DETERMINING LOT SIZES. Alford & Beatty (Principles of Industrial Management) have developed analytic methods for the purpose of calculating the least-unit-cost lot. Fig. 7 plots the result of one analysis of this kind in a particular case. The economic number of lots to buy per year is that whole number (6) nearest to the point of intersection of the two lower lines.

The following analysis gives a rough approximation of the quantity to buy under conditions such as those stated and is a rough-and-ready method to employ. Assume that the conditions exist in regard to a certain material or part carried in stores and that the time to reorder and the amount to buy is to be determined:

On hand and available .... 300 units

Needed within next 30 days .... 150 units

Normal constant demand per month .... 100 units

Time required for delivery of a lot .... 1 month

Minimum reserve stock allowance to protect against
failure of delivery, period to cover .... 1 month

Additional allowance for possible increased use, spoilage,
losses, period to cover............................. ½ month

The 300 units on hand and available will take care of the next 30 days' needs of 150, reducing the stores to 150, or 1½ months' normal supply. But it takes 1 month to get a lot in, and just before this lot arrives there should remain in stock 100 (1 month's use) to protect against delivery failure, and 50 (½ months' supply) to protect against increased use, spoilage, etc., or a total of 150 units. Thus, $300 - 150 = 150$ is the amount on hand in excess of the delivery reserve and extra reserve allowance, and this amount is just enough to take care of the next 30 days' needs. So, since a month is required for delivery, an order must be placed at once for the next lot. If the item is not too costly, and prompt delivery is not always assured, the order may be placed for, say, a 6 months' supply, or 600 units. When this lot arrives there will be $600 + 150 = 750$ units in the storeroom.

MINIMUM ORDERING QUANTITIES. A determination of the minimum ordering quantity in a case of the above kind could be made as follows:

Supply for demand during period up to delivery........... +150 units

Supply for demand for period during delivery of next lots.. +100 units

Margin of safety .... + 50 units

Present surplus over demand (or, if there is an excess of
demand over supply, use as a + quantity) .... −150 units

The net result of this calculation is that $150 + 100 + 50 - 150 = 150$ is the minimum quantity which could be ordered and still keep demand supplied.

Minimum quantities would be ordered only when there is no appreciable saving obtainable by quantity orders, when the current price is high or fluctuates widely and a drop is expected, and when delivery is easy to secure from any one of several assured sources. As previously pointed out, excess quantities, while bringing some saving in quantity discounts, also entail carrying and storage costs, which may run up to 25% of the purchase cost, or about 2% for each month in which the inventory is carried. Each company must determine the approximate percentage from its own data and experience on the various factors. A balance between these two conflicting factors is necessary to secure the greatest economy. There is a range of lot sizes within which the lowest total purchase cost is obtained, as already pointed out (see Fig. 7), and any lot within this range may be ordered with approximately the same savings.

PURCHASE LOT FORMULAS. Formulas have been devised by a number of investigators for determining the quantity to buy to obtain the minimum unit cost and the quantity to obtain a desired rate of return on working capital. The application of mathematical processes of analysis to the determination of

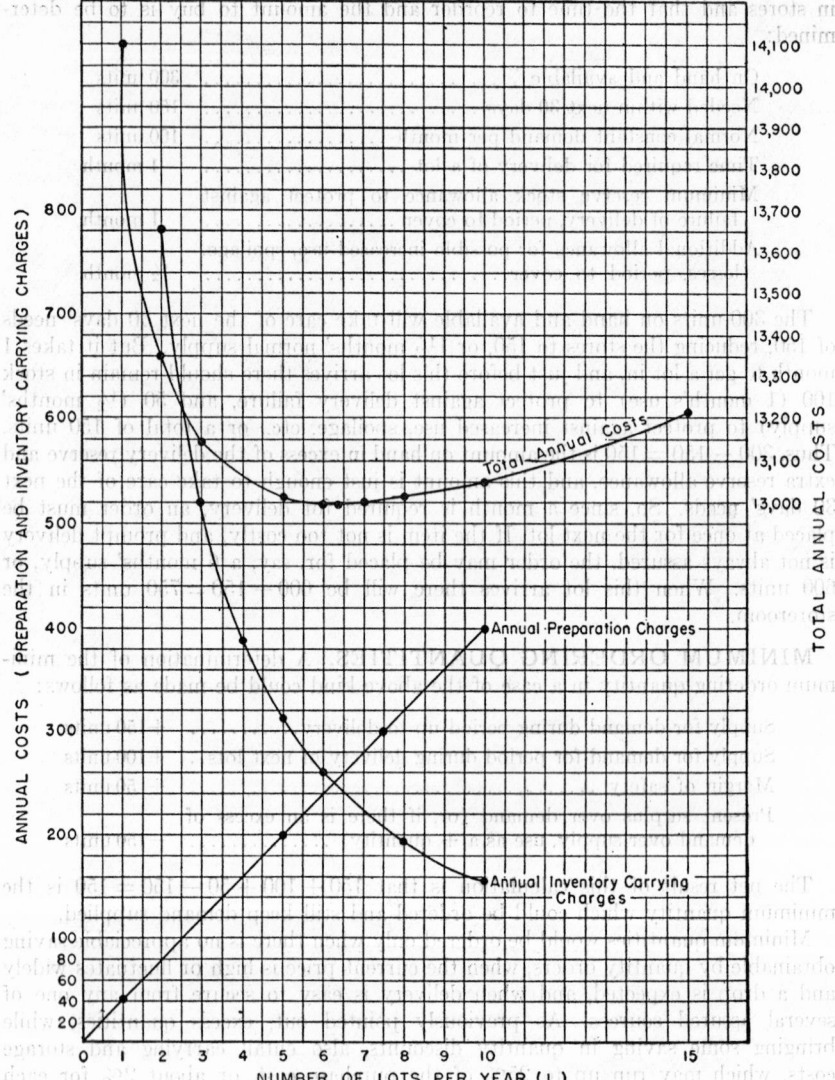

Fig. 7. Graphical determination of economic lot size.

the optimum size of a purchase quantity is discussed in the section on Operations Research. Other formulas have been developed using empirical data. These formulas give only approximate answers, but so, also, do all other methods; and the results in every case must be subject to the exercise of judgment in purchasing. While their effectiveness is limited to certain cases, every purchasing agent should know about them.

Most Economic Purchase and Storage Lots. Under the formula suggested by Killorin (Modern Materials Handling, vol. 10), the mathematical calculation (not given here) of the most economical quantity to buy considering procurement, activity, and carrying charges, results in the following equation:

$$Q = \sqrt{\frac{2\,CA}{K}}$$

The symbols are defined as follows:

$Q =$ order quantity, in dollars
$C =$ ordering cost, in dollars per order
$A =$ annual use, in dollars per year
$K =$ carrying charges, in dollars per \$100 per year

This equation gives the most economical dollar volume to buy at one time to get the lowest over-all unit cost of purchasing the material and carrying it in stores.

One company uses a formula which it developed itself to determine an economic purchasing quantity, which is as follows:

$$(S \times Q) + (P \times N) = (C \times E)\,(I \times U)$$

$S =$ reduction in unit price due to quantity discount
$Q =$ quantity purchased to achieve lower price
$P =$ purchase order cost
$N =$ number of purchase orders saved
$C =$ inventory carrying charge as a percent of inventory
$E =$ fraction of year excess inventory is carried
$I =$ excess average quantity carried in inventory
$U =$ unit price

Basically, the formula compares the savings achieved by buying a larger quantity at the next price break with the costs incurred on carrying the larger quantities in inventory.

Another formula used to determine the economic lot size for purchased items is as follows:

$$Q = \sqrt{\frac{AD}{KB}}$$

$Q =$ economic lot size of purchase
$A =$ fixed cost of every order (including cost of initiation of requisition, placing of order, receipt of material, checking in and inspecting of material and placing it in stores)
$D =$ consumption in units per year
$K =$ annual carrying charges expressed as a fraction of the unit value. This figure may be expressed as:

$$\frac{I + H + D}{2} + S$$

where $I =$ interest charges on entire lot purchase
$H =$ obsolescence charge
$D =$ deterioration charge
$S =$ storage charge. (This is not an average, since space must be available for the entire lot when it arrives.)
$B =$ the base price per unit with freight and discounts considered

Purchase Lot for Highest Return on Working Capital. It is often desirable to base the calculations on the quantity to buy to obtain the highest rate of profit on the working capital tied up in the purchase, rather than the lowest over-all unit cost of buying and carrying the material. The equation used under the highest-rate-on-working-capital plan is:

$$Q = \frac{2S\,(p - T_1\,[F - 1]\,Z)}{Z}$$

where S = rate of consumption of material in units per year

  p = actual net profit desired on cost-ready-to-sell as the unit of material (or item) is later sold to the customer in the finished product, in percent and used as a decimal

  T_1 = time required for delivery of a new lot, in years and expressed as a decimal

  $F = R \div R_1$ = ratio between actual order point and theoretical order point (no cushion stock), both expressed in units of material

  Z = desired annual gross profit on working capital, in percent and used as a decimal

Assuming now that a proposed purchase order is to be placed under the following conditions, what is the lot to buy to obtain the highest return on working capital?

$$S = 8,000$$
$$p = 5 \text{ percent}$$
$$T_1 = 1 \text{ mo.}$$
$$Z = 25 \text{ percent}$$
$$R = 1,400$$
$$R_1 = 700$$
$$F = R \div R_1 = 2$$

From the standpoint of desired rate of profit on working capital turnover, the approximate quantity to order would be:

$$Q = \frac{2 \times 8,000\,(.05 - 1/12\,[2 - 1] \times .25)}{.25} = 1,870, \text{ say } 1,900$$

or a little less than 3 months' supply

EXAMPLES OF ECONOMIC PURCHASE LOTS.

Two examples illustrate the determination of economical ordering quantities:

Example 1. Commodity—Pig iron—2x grade.

Use per week .... 100 tons
Stock on hand .... 300 tons
Time required for delivery .... 2 weeks

Price of pig iron stable with no changes indicated. Carload shipments cost at the time $19 per ton delivered at purchaser's plant.

A bargeload of 1,000 tons can be secured at $18.50 per ton delivered, at the time.

Minimum ordering policy would dictate ordering to provide not over 8 weeks' supply, including a week margin of safety. This would mean an order of 500 tons, which, plus 300 tons in stock, gives an 8-weeks' supply.

Cost of carrying additional 500 tons, or additional 5 weeks' supply, at carrying charge of 25 percent per annum on 500 tons at $18.50 per ton, equals $222.35.

Saving on 1,000 tons at $.50 per ton equals $500.

Advisability of bargeload purchase is clearly indicated.

Example 2. Commodity—General purpose machine oil.

Use per week .... 5 bbl.
Stock on hand .... 15 bbl.
Time required for delivery .... 2 weeks

COMMODITY	UNIT	COMMODITY	UNIT
Abrasive powder	Pound	Hose	Foot
Acids	Pound	Hose clamps	Gross
Alcohol	Gallon	Hose couplings	Dozen
Aluminum—sheets, bars, etc.	Pound	Hosiery	Dozen
Asbestos	Square yard	Iron (all forms)	Pound or cwt.
Asphaltum	Pound	Lacquer	Gallon
Babbitt metal	Pound	Lamp black	Pound
Bands for cotton bales	Pound	Lath (metal)	Square foot
Belt lacing	Each or foot	Lead	Pound
Belting	Foot	Leather	Square foot or pound
Boiler tube	Foot	Lime	Pound
Bolts	Each or 100	Lumber	1,000 board feet
Brass—sheet, plate, tube, bar, etc.	Pound	Mica	Pound
Brick	1,000	Nails	Pound
Brooms	Dozen	Naphtha	Gallon
Brushes	Dozen	Nipples	Each
Calcium chloride	Pound	Nuts	Pound
Casks	Each	Oils	Gallon or barrel
Cement	Bag or barrel	Pails	Dozen
Chain	Foot or pound	Paints	Gallon or pound
Chalk	Pound	Paper	Pound or ream
Chaplets	100	Paper (roofing)	Roll
Charcoal	Bushel	Pig iron	Ton (2,240 lb.)
Cloth	Yard	Pins	Gross
Coal	Pound or ton	Pipe	Foot
	(2,200 lb. whsle.)	Pipe fittings	Each
	(2,000 lb. retail)	Pitch	Pound
Coke	Ton (2,000 lb.)	Plastic (rod and tube)	Foot
Compressed air	Cubic foot	Plastic (sheet)	Pound or square inch
Concrete work	Cubic yard	Printing	Per 1,000
Copper rivets	Pound	Pulleys	Each
Copper—sheet, bar, tube	Pound	Red lead	Pound
Corks	Gross	Rivets	Pound
Dirt removal	Cubic yard	Rope	Pound
Electric batteries	Each	Rosin	Pound
Electric fuses	Each	Sal soda	Pound
Electric lamps	Each	Sand	Ton (2,000 lb.)
Electricity	Kilowatt-hour	Sandpaper	Ream or sheet
Emery cloth or paper	Ream or sheet	Saws	Each
Enamels	Gallon	Screws	Gross
Excelsior	Pound	Shovels	Dozen
Felt	Square foot or pound	Steam	Pound
Fiber	By dimension	Steel	Pound or cwt.
Files	Dozen	Steel rails	Ton
Fillets—leather	1,000 feet	Stone	Ton or cubic yard
Fillets—wood	100 feet	Straw	Ton
Fire brick	1,000	Talc	Pound
Flour	Barrel or bag or pound	Tallow	Pound
Fusible plugs	Each	Tar	Barrel
Gas	1,000 cubic feet	Tin	Pound
Gasoline	Gallon	Twine	Pound
Glass	Light and size	Varnish	Gallon
Glue	Pound	Water	Gallon or cubic foot
Grease	Pound	Wax	Pound
Grinding wheels	Each	Wire	Pound
Hair	Bushel or pound	Wood	Cord, or 1,000 board feet
Hammers	Dozen	Woolen fabrics	Yard
Hangers, shaft	Each	Zinc	Pound

Fig. 8. Units in which different items are ordered.

Delivered price, including transportation on less than carload shipments, $7.15 per bbl., at the time. Carload of 60 bbl. can be secured at delivered price of $6.95 per bbl.

Minimum ordering policy would indicate ordering to provide for 5 weeks' demand, including a one week margin of safety. This would mean an order of 10 bbl., which, plus 15 bbl. in stock, gives 5 weeks' supply, including margin of safety.

Cost of carrying additional 50 bbl., or additional 10 weeks' supply, at 25 percent per annum equals $16.70.

Saving on 60 bbl. at $.20 per bbl. equals $12.

The indication is that buying the carload quantity is not advisable.

A record of economical ordering quantities is desirable. There is no necessity for working out these quantities on every purchase, though they should be open always for consideration as conditions change. Stores records and purchasing records should contain, as an integral part of their information, the economical ordering quantity established on previous lots, and all the facts necessary to revise such figures. Fig. 8 gives units of measurement, weight, or volume, as established by custom, in which some of the more common commodities are bought and sold.

LIMITS ON QUANTITIES OR EXPENDITURES. Some times maximum ordering quantities are set, in effect, by the management. Often authority of the purchasing department to buy is limited by a ruling that not over, say, 9 months' supply of any commodity can be bought ahead without special executive authorization. In other cases the limit to the purchasing agent's authority may be a dollar limit, whereby purchase requisitions amounting to more than, say, $25,000 or $50,000 must be approved by the general manager, president, or even the board of directors. Even when such limitations are not set by a higher authority, it is desirable that the purchasing agent should require his buyers to be limited by two factors: value of the purchase and length of the commitment. For example, the purchasing agent may authorize a buyer to handle without further authorization purchases up to $10,000 but no higher, and future commitments that do not exceed 6 months' consumption.

Buying at the Proper Price

COMMODITY CLASSIFICATION. The variety of items to be purchased, as to type, volume, and purchase conditions, requires that the purchasing department should build up a system of obtaining and recording price information in quickly available form. From the viewpoint of price, commodities may be classified as follows:

1. Commodities on which prices are established by market movements.
2. Commodities on which the price is given in catalogues and on discount sheets.
3. Commodities subject to price negotiation.

Price Established by Market Movement. In the first group are commodities on which prices are established by market movements, information about which may be drawn from market reports, published quotations, etc. These commodities include the majority of raw materials, such as pig iron, steel in commercial grades, nonferrous metals, hides, cotton, and rubber. The purchasing department follows market reports, trade papers, and other sources of published information and maintains charts or graphs on prices and conditions which govern prices, such as production and demand. Daily reports are available in trade papers of metal industries and in general business dailies. In specific instances it is necessary even to have cabled or wired reports from the markets. A purchasing department library of **market information** on such items should be built in accordance with the necessity for prompt and accurate data.

Even though items are covered by catalogues and price list, the buyer, in the case of important orders, should determine the factors that go to make up the price and if conditions warrant, try for a reduction, not waiting for conditions to force a revised price. As an example, in New York City there is a fairly well-established price list on paper bags. The major item of cost is kraft paper. When the market on kraft makes a steady decline the buyer should not wait for a revised price list but should find a vendor who, because of small stocks, can give him a reduction on the price of bags warranted by the drop in the price of kraft paper.

There are many such commodities in which the price of the finished goods is dependent very directly on **raw material prices.** Some typical examples are steel drums (which fluctuate in price with the market on steel sheets), cardboard containers (which follow the market on chipboard or kraft), leather belting (which varies with the market on hides), and many secondary chemical products (which follow very closely the price of their chief constituent primary chemical). Other commodities depend on two or several primary constituents.

Price Data Given in Catalogues. The second group consists of commodities on which prices are governed by issuance of catalogue and periodical discount or net price sheets. This group includes most standard mill supply and hardware items such as regular drills, taps and dies, wrenches, and many commodities of this general type. The purchasing department must have a **catalogue file** and a **file of current prices on catalogue items,** carefully indexed and kept strictly up to date. The clerk or assistant responsible for catalogues and net prices or discounts should check his files with the vendor's at regular periods. All trade papers should be followed for news items about new or revised publications affecting items bought.

Catalogues should be filed in ample storage cabinets or drawers or on shelves and should be indexed by commodities and cross-indexed by suppliers. Arrangement should be under major commodity headings, so that related subjects may readily be investigated. In other cases the preference is for arrangement by size and the type of binding. In this way a much neater, more orderly library can be maintained. A typical division of a catalogue file into classes follows:

Section	Section
1. Metals (except steel)	6. Belting and transmission
2. Steels	7. Machinery and equipment
3. Small tools (taps, dies, drills, reamers, etc.)	8. Foundry supplies
4. Hardware	9. Machine accessories (chain, bearings, etc.)
5. Pipe-shop and plumbing supplies	10. Miscellaneous

Where buying is divided among several buyers, it is often the practice for each buyer to keep his own catalogue and price file. It will be necessary under any arrangement, for buyers to keep certain catalogues and price lists in their personal files, but it is desirable, even at expense of some duplication, to have a general catalogue and price file under care of a clerk designated as price clerk.

ITEMS SUBJECT TO PRICE NEGOTIATION. Even on catalogued items with standard price lists and discount sheets, it is frequently necessary to request vendors to supply quotations on new prices and discounts to keep price

7

CADILLAC MOTOR CAR DIVISION
GENERAL MOTORS CORPORATION
2860 CLARK AVE.
DETROIT 32, MICHIGAN   DATE

THIS IS A

REQUEST FOR QUOTATION

THIS IS **NOT** AN ORDER

YOUR QUOTATION MUST BE RETURNED ON
THIS FORM NOT LATER THAN

John H. Lamb

MANAGER OF PURCHASES

GENERAL MOTORS DATES FOR PAYMENT OF
15TH OR 25TH PROXIMO ARE REQUESTED.

RETURN TO_____ **VOID** _____

BUYER PURCHASING DIVISION

QUANTITY	MATERIAL	PRICE	TOOLS

VOID

TERMS_____ BIDDER _____
F.O.B._____ DATE_____BY_____

If your quotation deviates from specifications in any way, such exceptions must be
noted hereon. If unable to quote please indicate and return to us. We reserve the
right to accept or reject all or any part of this bid.

Fig. 9. Purchasing department request for quotation.

information up to date. For a large group of purchases, price can be determined by no other means. Construction, services, castings, plastic molded parts, and special tools are common examples. One request for quotation (Fig. 9) carries staggered carbons behind the original request so that six vendors can be addressed on the original copy, and the name of each vendor will appear on only the one carbon copy to be sent to him. The original copy is kept by the purchasing department.

Obtaining Competitive Quotations. On special tools, forgings, castings, and many other items there are no market quotations or standard catalogue prices and discounts available. To obtain proper prices, the purchasing department is dependent upon two factors: an understanding of the cost of items going into their manufacture, and competitive bids establishing the lowest price to be obtained. When large quantities of such items are to be bought, a study is justified of material and labor costs going into their manufacture, to an extent sufficient to insure that prices quoted are fair and not excessive. On the large majority of such items the only safe way to buy is by inquiry to a number of sources and comparison of their competitive quotations.

To be effective in getting the best price, quotations should be:

1. Considered on a truly competitive basis. Award should be made to lowest bidder, except under unusual circumstances, such as doubts arising about the lowest bidder's financial ability or ability to complete on time or within specifications, or cases where the money value of bids does not represent a proper comparison in the light of final cost.
2. Considered as final at the first figure submitted. Allowing of continual revision of bids or quotations after submission may bring a better price on that one transaction, but it militates against truly competitive quotations with the best obtainable prices in future transactions.
3. Considered as confidential by buyer. The policy of hinting to competitors of a bidder as to the nature of quotations destroys bona fide competition and in the long run is expensive.

Quotations, after receipt and action, become part of the purchasing department information file in the hands of the price clerk. Losing as well as winning quotations should be recorded to give a proper price perspective on future purchases.

Buying at the Best Price. The best assurance that a purchasing department can have that it is buying at the best price is mutual confidence between purchaser and vendors. Sales representatives are excellent sources of information on price trends, contemplated revisions, and vendors' price policies. While price checks may be made periodically, it is, nevertheless, highly desirable that the purchasing department should choose and stay with vendors who have proved that they intend to give the buyer the best prices. There are many items to be purchased on which there is no available reliable price information and the volume of which is insufficient to justify an exhaustive study of costs. Sometimes competition is impractical, either because of lack of time to secure competitive bids, or because of the fact that only one source of supply is considered capable, or because the transaction is of such a nature that open competition would disturb the market and bring about higher prices. In such cases dependence on sources of supply is the only course open to the purchasing department. A record of previous purchases of an item over a period, together with knowledge of changes in general conditions over the same period, offers a valuable means of price checking. "Price alone is not a sufficient reason for us to change a source of supply" are the words of one purchasing agent.

Bargain or Cut Prices. Many "bargains" and "cut prices" are offered by houses which are not dealt with regularly. It is a safe rule to regard such offers with suspicion and demand of the supplier proof of the quality of goods and his credit standing. There are exceptional cases in which a purchasing agent has the opportunity to buy below the right price through some special concession. But as a rule, all that the purchaser can expect to do is to buy at the right price consistent with the volume of the purchase, the credit standing of the vendor, and market conditions.

Purchase Contracts

CONTRACT REQUIREMENTS. Purchase contracts should always be reduced to writing. Verbal modifications of written contracts should be avoided. The contract should set forth clearly in definite terms what the agreement is as to quantity, specifications, price, terms, time, special conditions, inspection, guaranties, penalties.

Quantity may be expressed as a definite figure in pieces, pounds, or other unit or it may be expressed as "purchaser's requirements, estimated at _____." Quantity may be expressed as a rate of manufacture to be maintained by the vendor or in terms of the stock he binds himself to keep on hand for the purchaser. It is common to have quantity expressed in terms of tolerances, by which the vendor agrees to furnish not more than a certain maximum or less than a stated minimum. A usual expression is "purchaser's requirements not to exceed _____." From the purchasing standpoint the greater the margin allowed on quantity, to allow for possible error or change in estimate, the better the contract.

SPECIFICATIONS. Specifications should follow the same rules laid down for buying specifications, as previously discussed. When specifications are vital and rigid, provision should be made in the contract for a clear and definite agreement on the basis of inspection and rejection, where and how inspection is to be made, and what equipment or labor, if any, the vendor must supply to help make the inspection. Suppliers of creosoted products, for instance, to provide for inspection under certain specifications must furnish a laboratory with certain equipment. High-tension insulators for meeting certain specifications must be tested where certain voltage combinations are available. Such points must be known to the buyer and specifically covered by the contract, as they may be an item of cost overlooked by the supplier. In many cases inspection by an outside agency or company may be called for. In such cases the outside company should be named and clear provision made as to who should bear the expense of the inspection.

PRICE. Price may be fixed at a determined figure by contract. In the case of goods whose price fluctuates beyond the control of the vendor, definite agreement on a fixed price cannot be had. In such instances it is often desirable to make the provision that price shall be based on market price at date of shipment, stating accurately the means of determining what market price is, such as the standard price reports in a reputable trade paper. When possible to do so, **sliding-scale agreements** should be safeguarded by inserting a maximum price, above which a vendor shall not charge, regardless of market changes. A most favorable type of price agreement is that by which a vendor fixes current prices as a maximum price and agrees to give the buyer advantage of all declines in market prices. Price terms in contracts sometimes include so-called **escalator clauses,** which provide for advances in the price under certain conditions which may concern the vendor's cost of material or of labor. It is essential that such escalator clauses be carefully worded, so as to avoid any misunderstanding between the parties.

TERMS. Terms such as **f.o.b. point** and **cash discount** should be plainly stated. The f.o.b. point is preferably on cars at the purchaser's freight station or siding, since this provision leaves title to goods in the vendor's hands and at the vendor's risk during transport. In instances where the contract is for delivery of goods at more than one plant, delivery f.o.b. point of origin is preferable, title to the goods then transferring to the purchaser. In some instances vendors refuse to accept hazards of ownership during transport but are willing to allow the purchaser the transportation charges, and terms being f.o.b. shipping point with freight allowed.

The National Industrial Conference Board (Industry Terms and Conditions of Sale) lists certain common cash discount terms as follows:

1/10/30	1 percent 10 days from date of invoice, net 30 days
2/10/I	2 percent 10 days from date of invoice
Net/30	Net 30 days from date of invoice
Net	Net, no time specified
8/10/Proximo	8 percent 10th of the following month
1/10/S	1 percent 10 days from date of shipment
1/10/D	1 percent 10 days from date of delivery
2/SM	1st–15th payable 25th; 15th–end of month payable on 10th proximo
4 E.O.M.	4 percent by end of month
2/10/E.O.M.	2 percent 10 days from end of month

Although terms are usually comparable between companies within the same industry, customs vary widely between industries. The most common terms among metal working industries are 2/10/30, while textile convertors and apparel manufacturers often extend 6/70/I with 6 percent per annum added for anticipation. In some cases buyers negotiate special terms with suppliers to enable the buyer's company to take discounts and still pay only one or two checks per month. There is a growing tendency among nearly all industries to discontinue the practice of granting cash discount.

TIME CLAUSES. Time clauses are important in purchase contracts. The contractors may agree upon delivery within a certain period, on a certain date, or in accordance with purchaser's instructions. The most favorable kind of contract in this respect is one that calls for delivery "within period from _____ to _____ as called for by purchaser." The statement of the delivery agreement should be clear.

Time should be of the essence in purchase contracts. A clear statement of the right to cancel and refuse deliveries if they are not made on time should be included in the contract. Every contract should contain a definite statement as to its termination, either by lapse of time or by action of the parties. Many contracts are so loose in their conditions covering time of delivery that they have little effect, except that of a price agreement during the period for which the contract runs. Many purchasers favor this kind of contract, since it binds the vendor to responsibility, while placing no responsibility upon the purchaser. It is a mistake, however, to think of such limited price agreements as contracts of purchase.

Special conditions are sometimes necessary in purchase contracts for the protection of the purchaser's or vendor's interest. Such conditions should be stated specifically and not left to mutual understandnig. Examples of such special conditions are given in the following paragraphs.

STATEMENTS OF OWNERSHIP. Statement of ownership of special patterns, tools, fixtures, etc., required for the manufacture of certain products is an extremely important point to cover definitely, whether in a contract or an order form. Custom varies widely as to ownership of such items. In certain instances the purchaser of the goods pays for these facilities, and they are his property, subject to removal by him at any time that he desires to place his orders elsewhere. Often their cost is included in the price of the first order, and subsequent orders are filled at a lower price. A purchaser, in such a case, may regard himself as owner with the right of taking them away whenever he desires. It has been held, however, that special devices are not necessarily the property of the purchaser unless specific arrangements to this effect have been made at the time of the initial order. Where their number and cost are large, ownership by the vendor practically dictates placing all orders with him. Even were the purchaser willing to go to the expense of providing a second set, the time involved in their production might preclude this step.

In some cases special tools and fixtures may not be adapted to the equipment of another manufacturer. In other instances, while patterns, tools, etc., are the purchaser's property, he has no right to remove them from the vendor's possession. Such a contract may be of advantage to the purchaser, however, if it prevents the vendor from using them to make products for other customers.

Purchase contracts should cover, in considerable detail, the following points in regard to special equipment:

1. Ownership.
2. If title rests with the vendor, whether or not the purchaser has a right of purchase of this equipment.
3. Limiting use of special equipment to the purchaser's product and forbidding their use on material manufactured for competitors.
4. The party who should bear expenses of maintenance and repairs of special patterns, tools, and fixtures.

INSPECTION AT VENDOR'S PLANT. Inspection at the vendor's plant should be included in the purchase contract if such inspection is contemplated. The vendor should agree, and the extent of inspection should be stated as specifically as is practical. Such equivocal expressions as "satisfactory quality," "reasonable inspection," etc., should be avoided. Definiteness in stating inspection standards and privileges with a clean-cut agreement as to whose decision shall be final, avoids many difficulties. Perhaps the most satisfactory form of agreement to cover inspection ties the inspection in with a definite printed specification identified beyond question in the contract.

GUARANTIES. Guaranties are contract obligations of the vendor to furnish quality, quantity, or service. A guaranty adds nothing to a purchase contract unless it is a definite guaranty of a specific thing not covered by the general contract. A guaranty of service for a fixed period after delivery, or against defect discovered within a fixed period, is a valuable protection to the purchaser in some cases.

PENALTY CLAUSES. Penalty clauses in contracts obligate the vendor to make good any specified losses suffered because of his failure to meet the time obligations in the contract. The vendor may file a bond to guarantee performance of the contract, or the contract may contain a statement of the amount of payments which shall be accepted as liquidated damages in full settlement for defaulting on the contract. Such a clause is seldom used in buying equipment, materials, or supplies.

BLANKET CONTRACTS. Blanket contracts are useful in the case of companies operating several plants where there is a sufficient degree of localized purchasing authority, so that the purchasing departments of the several plants may order shipments against them. In such cases invoices are against the several plants and are paid by them. Such contracts are valuable in securing a sufficient volume of purchase for a price advantage when the demand of any one plant is too limited to give that advantage.

Typical contract clauses are listed below:

It is agreed that we will issue from time to time a manufacturing schedule or will issue shipping instructions covering the quantity of material hereunder so as to provide a reasonably uniform rate of production.

It is agreed that you will invoice us as of _____ for such material manufactured by you and for which we have not issued shipping instructions. It is understood that such manufacture shall not be in excess of the total quantity of material specified hereunder.

As to such material not manufactured as of _____ we shall have the option, to be exercised within a period of _____ days thereafter, either of canceling this contract as to such unmanufactured portion of said material or of continuing this contract for a period not to exceed three months, in which latter event you agree to manufacture within this period the remaining quantity of the material not so manufactured. In the event that shipping instructions have not been issued for such material within the three months' period, you will at the expiration of such three months invoice us for such material. It is expressly understood that we reserve all of our rights to hold you liable for damages sustained as a result of your failure to perform any of the provisions of this contract, notwithstanding anything to the contrary herein contained.

It is agreed that all material invoiced to us and carried by you as our property will be properly stored by you and shipped as specified by our orders without further charges to us, provided such shipping instructions are given within a period of six months after the expiration date of this contract. It is understood that the storage of this material does not obligate you to pay for any insurance or taxes on the same.

It is agreed that upon request you will plainly mark such stock of material so invoiced as being our property and will execute and deliver a bill of sale in form acceptable to us together with satisfactory evidence that the material is free from all liens, charges, or encumbrances.

Deliver as ordered, bill as shipped, except as otherwise provided.

You agree to follow such routing instructions as may be furnished by our general traffic department.

It is understood that any of our houses or subsidiary or allied companies may place orders with you applying on this contract.

If shipping orders are issued for shipment during any period, in excess of the schedule as shown or such other schedules as we may issue, not to exceed the maximum covered by this contract, manufacture shall be increased, if possible, for such period so as to cover fully such shipping orders. Such increases in excess of the schedules as shown, however, shall not increase the maximum quantity of material hereunder.

It is agreed that we will issue from time to time a manufacturing schedule or will issue shipping instructions covering the minimum quantity of material hereunder, so as to provide a reasonably uniform rate of production, and within thirty days prior to the expiration date hereof, we shall have the option of issuing an additional manufacturing schedule or shipping instructions covering the maximum quantity as above set forth.

By accepting this contract you hereby warrant the merchandise to be furnished hereunder will be in full conformity with the specifications, drawing, or sample and agree that this warranty shall survive acceptance of the merchandise and that you will bear the cost of inspecting merchandise rejected.

By accepting this contract you hereby guarantee and agree that the merchandise to be furnished hereunder will not infringe any valid patent or trade-mark and that you will, at your own expense, defend any and all actions or suits charging infringement and will save us, our customers, and those for whom we may act as agent in the purchase of said merchandise, harmless in case of any such infringement.

LEGAL ASPECTS OF CONTRACTS. Legal aspects of purchase contracts demand close attention. In drawing up contracts which involve liquidated damages or any clauses of a complicated legal nature, legal advice should be sought. Important factors in the writing of contracts follow.

1. Only the matter which appears above the signature is binding.
2. Any additions or revisions in the original text of a contract should be initialed or signed by the parties to avoid any claim of alteration after signature.
3. All necessary provisions should be placed in the contract. It is not safe to depend on formal clauses printed at the bottom of the page or on its back. If they are used, a clause such as the following should be printed above the signature on the contract: "The clauses printed on the back (at the bottom) of this order are hereby made a part of this contract."
4. Printed matter in the body of the contract and above the signature is binding. Such printed matter, no matter how small the type, should be read carefully before signing.
5. The entire agreement between the parties should be expressed in the contract.
6. Every clause of the contract should be made definite to the point of making misunderstanding impossible.

STANDARD PURCHASE CONTRACT FORMS. Standard purchase contract forms are adopted by some large manufacturers for the sake of assurance that their interests will be safeguarded without the necessity of legal advice on each purchase agreement. It is difficult, however, to make up a standard purchase contract which will cover all circumstances and be satisfactory to all vendors. Special clauses or insertions are required, therefore, when some unusual condition is included in a contract.

Purchasing Procedure

STEPS IN THE PROCEDURE. The main steps in the procedure of procuring goods for industrial production, as stated by Davis, are listed below, together with the typical forms used at each step. On important items the actual issuing of the order is but one step in the procedure. The general plan of operation, sources of supply, period to be covered, and other significant factors should all be determined in advance.

1. Initiation of request in the form of a purchase requisition from department needing the goods—the purchase requisition to the purchasing department.
2. Determination of what and how much to buy.
3. Making a study of market conditions to find out if the time is favorable to buy.
4. Determination of source of supply from which goods shall be purchased—catalogues, indexes, quotation and price records, and vendor records in the purchasing department.
5. Obtaining, by inquiry, quotation, or bid, a favorable price and selecting the specific vendor—quotations or bids, bid analysis sheets,

6. Entering into contractual relations with the vendor—the purchase order.
7. Securing performance by the vendor in delivering the goods on time—follow-up service.
8. Actually receiving the goods and delivering them to the storeroom or the department that requires them—receipt and inspection (in many cases not a function of the purchasing department).
9. Checking and completing the transaction—checking receiving report for quantity and quality factors, purchase contract for price, invoice for extensions, and adjustment of any discrepancies in quality, quantity, etc., vendor's invoice, and returns for credit and exchange.

ORIGIN OF PURCHASE REQUISITION. The purchase requisition may be originated by the stores records supervisor, production control department, head of some operating department, the chief storekeeper, plant or maintenance engineer, office manager, or other responsible person authorized to request that items which he needs be obtained from an outside vendor, if within the department's budget allotment. Limitation of power to issue purchase requisitions is necessary, and a general procedure order should be set up by the management, stating definitely which persons in the company are permitted to issue or sign purchase requisitions for the kinds of items they are allowed to obtain. Requisitions from all other persons must be turned back to be countersigned if approved, by the proper authorized person or canceled if not approved. It is likewise standard practice in well-run companies to require that all purchase requisitions be "edited," that is, reviewed to see first whether the items requested are carried in the storeroom, whether the request for some unusual items could not be satisfactorily filled by something carried in the storeroom, or whether something requested of a highly special nature which has to be purchased outside could not be replaced by some more standard item more readily obtainable and costing less than the article requested. The requisition also should be checked against the purchase budget, if such work is assigned to the purchasing department, to see that the item is within the current allotment for that class of materials and within the current period's total budget allotment of the requisitioning department.

Form of Requisition. The purchase requisition (see Fig. 10) will vary somewhat in form according to its point of origin and the accounting system in use. The form should contain the following essential information:

1. Name and accurate description of goods wanted, also stores symbol.
2. Quantity needed and units of issue in which it should arrive to save repacking upon receipt.
3. Date on which goods will be needed.
4. Account to which goods are to be charged.
5. Statement of need that justifies requisition. Executive or departmental approval may relieve the purchasing department of the responsibility for justification of the requisition, provided the executive order definitely releases the purchasing department of that responsibility on condition of proper approval.
6. Amount on hand and past or current rate or record of use.
7. Point of delivery within the plant to which the shipment should go either after passing through receiving and inspection or directly, as in the case of such items as machinery which should be unloaded as close to point of use as possible.
8. Vendor's name, but in certain special cases only, as in repair parts for equipment. Selection of the vendor is ordinarily a purchase duty.
9. Authority for purchase, by either signature to requisition, or whatever approval by the superintendent, the stores department, etc., is required.

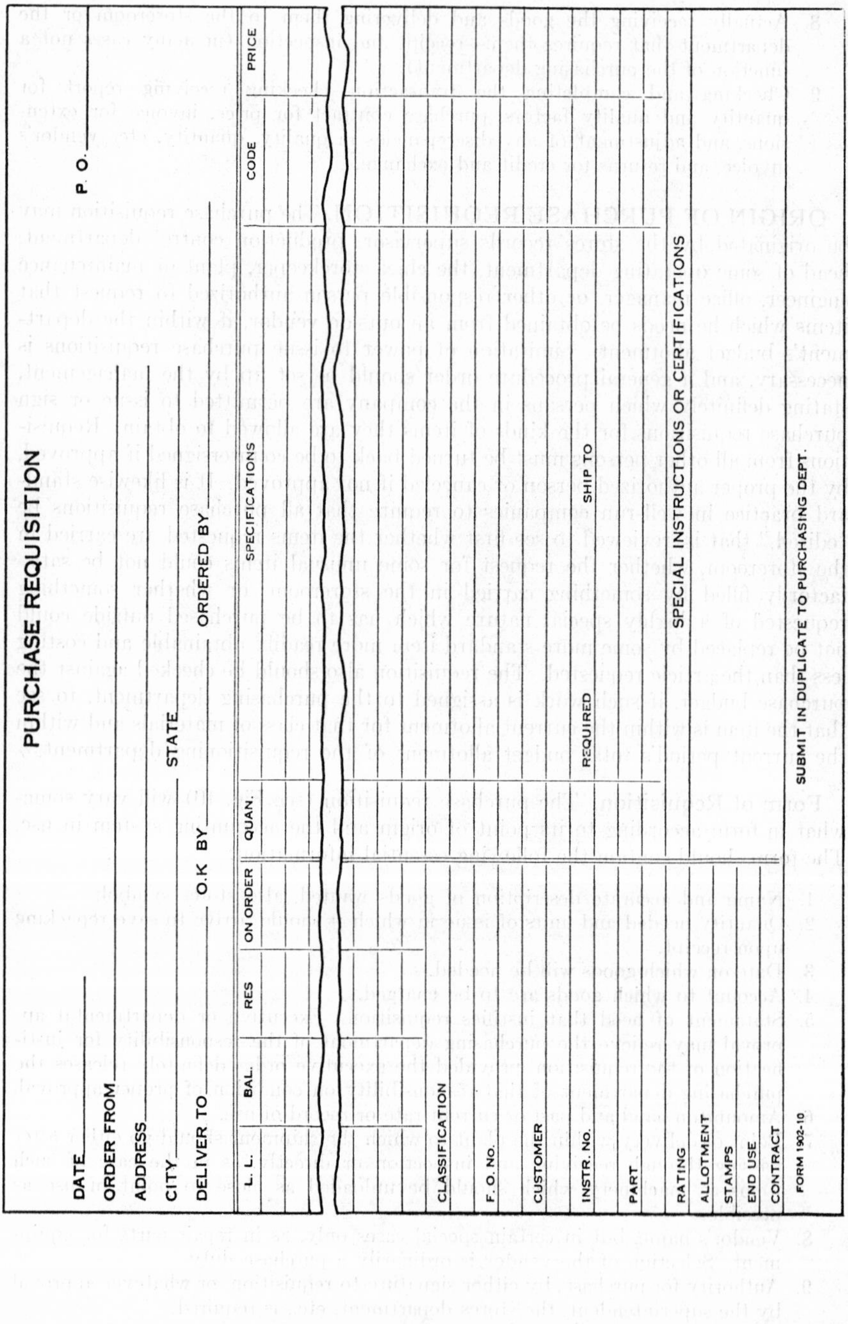
PURCHASE REQUISITION P. O.

DATE

ORDER FROM

ADDRESS

CITY STATE

DELIVER TO O.K BY ORDERED BY

L. L.	BAL.	RES	ON ORDER	QUAN.	SPECIFICATIONS	CODE	PRICE

CLASSIFICATION

F. O. No.

CUSTOMER

INSTR. No. SHIP O REQUIRED

PART

RATING SPECIAL INSTRUCTIONS OR CERTIFICATIONS

ALLOTMENT

STAMPS

END USE

CONTRACT

FORM 1902-10 SUBMIT IN DUPLICATE TO PURCHASING DEPT.

Bausch & Lomb Optical Co.

Fig. 10. Purchase requisition.

REQUISITION
GULF 127

FROM _____ DISTRICT, DIVISION OR REFINERY

TO BE SHIPPED TO _____

DATE _____ 19 ____

REQ. NO. _____

ON HAND	QUANTITY	MATERIAL	ITEM	PRICE	VIA	F.O.B.	TO BE PURCHASED FROM OR TRANSFERRED FROM	ORDER NO.	WHEN NEEDED	TO BE USED FOR
			1							
			2							
			3							
			4							
			14							
			15							
			16							
			17							
			18							
			19							
			20							

APPROVED BY _____

APPROVED BY _____

APPROVED BY _____

SIGNATURE OF PERSON MAKING REQUISITION

Fig. 11. Requisition for a number of items, providing for several necessary approvals.

10. A space or form for use of the purchasing department in adding vendor's name, price, terms, routing, estimated weight, number of purchase order issued, and all other information necessary for typist in making out purchase order. Later, entry of delivery date promised by vendor.

In case of requisitions from the control department, production reference to the order or lot number of a production job is sufficient justification, and this information is sometimes conveyed by the account number to which goods are to

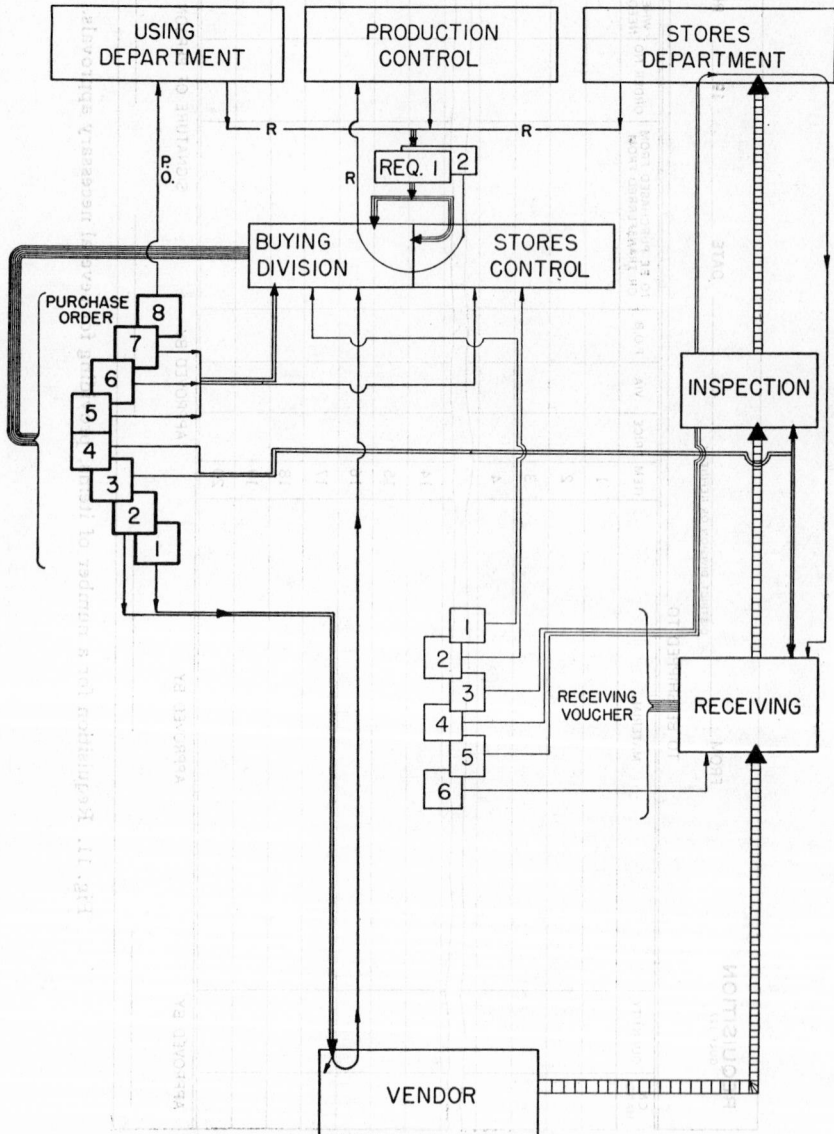

Fig. 12. Purchase order procedure flow chart.

be charged. In requisitions from the plant engineer, office manager, etc., enough information should be included to enable the purchasing department to pass intelligently on questions of need and quantity.

The form of purchase requisition will vary with many factors. Two typical forms are shown in Figs. 10 and 11. Requisition forms should be of a size to fit standard files and preferably should be distinctive in color from other forms in the purchasing system.

Route of the Requisition. The purchase requisition may go first to the purchase or quotation record desk on entering the purchasing department, to be compared with records of previous transactions for the same commodity. If the goods asked for by some department are carried in stores, the requisition can be returned to the requisitioning department with instructions to secure the items from stock. If the quantity wanted is in excess of previous requirements as indicated by the record, the reason for such unusual requirements can be checked. If the quantity varies from a standard package or economical ordering quantity, the quantity can be adjusted. The purchase record or quotation card for the particular item may be attached to the purchase requisition, and both may be submitted for the buyer's consideration, since the purchase record will also show possible sources of supply, past experience with these sources, price variations over a period, terms on previous orders for the goods, and all essential facts to make a complete picture of the transaction contemplated.

An alternative routing of purchase requisitions takes them first to the buyer's desk and then to the record desk only when the buyer feels that comparison with the record of previous transactions is desirable. Fig. 12 is a **flow chart** showing the course of the purchase authorization (requisition) and other forms and procedures in the purchasing department.

REQUEST FOR QUOTATION. The buyer must decide—once a purchase requisition has reached him and received his approval as to quantity, form, and propriety—with what vendor the order shall be placed. His primary interest is to secure, from a list of vendors in whom he has confidence as to quality of product and ability to make proper delivery, one who will give him the best or, at least, the right price. He may have price information available either in the form of catalogues and price lists submitted by some vendor or in the general quotations already received.

If he is not satisfied with his knowledge of the right price to be paid, or if there is any doubt as to which vendor will give the best price, the buyer should issue a request for a quotation on the items covered by the purchase requisition (see Figs. 13 and 14). This request should be specific in describing the material and in identifying it with the vendor's product, by catalogue designation when possible.

Ralph O. Keefer, general purchasing agent of the Aluminum Company of America, points out that every buying organization has its own **preferred terms and conditions of purchase.** He recommends that these be printed on the back of the request for quotation and the clause shown in Fig. 14 printed on the front of the request above the space for seller's signature. Under these conditions the order becomes an acceptance of the offer, where otherwise the order may become a counteroffer. The identical conditions are printed on the back of the purchase order. This procedure saves much delay and misunderstanding.

Information on the Request. The request for quotation should give the following information, essentially in the form in which it will appear later on a purchase order.

1. Quantity to be ordered.
2. Name and full specifications of material, including inspection procedure.
3. Point to which goods are to be delivered.
4. Delivery time which is to be allowed.
5. Date on which quotations will be considered.
6. Purchaser's conditions.

It should ask for the following information:

1. Price.
2. F.o.b. point.
3. Terms of payment.
4. Delivery time.
5. Any special condition or terms the vendor wishes to make. This point is often covered by a clause on the request for a quotation form which reads: "Except as stated specifically in your reply, your quotation will be considered as subject to the following conditions." All conditions of purchase desirable from the buyer's point of view are then tabulated.
6. Approximate shipping weight, provided this information is necessary. Often this question applies to purchases for export.

To Whom To Send Requests. The question of to whom requests for quotation should be sent depends upon the buyer and his records. The purchase or quotation record card should indicate any sources of supply that previous experience has shown to be unsatisfactory and why. It also should reveal **past experience**

INQUIRY FOR PRICES

THIS IS REQUEST FOR QUOTATION ON THE ITEMS ENUMERATED HEREIN

NO.____ DATE____ QUOTATIONS MUST BE IN BY____

THIS INQUIRY IMPLIES NO OBLIGATIONS ON THE PART OF THE BUYER

IF SUBSTITUTES ARE OFFERED MAKE FULL EXPLANATION

FOR SHIPMENT TO____ DATE SHIPMENT CAN BE MADE____

DELIVERY F.O.B.____ TO BE SHIPPED FROM____

TERMS: NET CASH____ DAYS____ %____ DAYS

KEEP ONE COPY FOR YOUR FILES.   RETURN ONE COPY WITH FULL INFORMATION.

ITEM NO.	QUANTITY	ITEM AND SPECIFICATIONS	UNIT	LIST PRICE OF UNIT	DISCOUNT OFFERED	NET UNIT PRICE	ESTIMATED GROSS WT

THIS IS NOT AN ORDER

THE UNDERSIGNED OFFERS THE PRICES, TERMS AND DELIVERY HEREIN SET FORTH

BY____ PURCHASING AGENT   BY____ SELLER'S SIGNATURE

Fig. 13. Inquiry for prices.

REQUEST FOR QUOTATION

PURCHASING DEPARTMENT
1501 Alcoa Building, Pittsburgh 19, Pa.   Date_____

Gentlemen: Please quote itemized prices for materials listed below for shipment
via

TO_____

RALPH O. KEEFER
General Purchasing Agent

Refer to   Requisition No.

SUBSTITUTIONS, IF ANY, MUST BE CLEARLY SHOWN	List	Trade Dis.	Net

Delivery Date Required at Destination_____   Approximate
Quotation must be in our office on or before_____   Shpg. Weight_____

We offer to sell to you the above material at the price and terms specified
hereon and upon the conditions printed on the back hereof.

Terms of payment (including Cash Discount if any)_____
F.O.B._____ Shipping date promised____days after receipt of order.
Offer No._____ Date_____ (Signed)_____

Bidder Check one Space   ➤ | Under 500 | Over 500 |
to indicate number of employees in
his Company (including all his
affiliated Companies.)

Return one copy to 1501 ALCOA BUILDING, PITTSBURGH 19, PA.
Keep duplicate for your files.

THIS IS NOT AN ORDER

Fig. 14. Request for quotation.

with vendors in regard to price, quality, delivery, and service. In the case of
a new item of purchase, dependence must be placed on the buyer's knowledge of
the vendor field or on manufacturers' or dealers' registers, files of advertising
matter, catalogues, etc.

Requests for quotations should be sent usually to not less than three and not
more than five possible sources of supply, the companies selected being those
giving the broadest possible price picture. In a plant situated in a small city
about equidistant from two large cities, it would seem desirable to secure one
quotation from each of the two large cities and one from a local source, especially

in the case of goods purchasable from dealers, where variation of price might be expected in different geographical locations because of local trade conditions. On some goods it is well to send inquiries to both manufacturers and dealers, particularly on items which are being purchased from some dealer. If the buying company sells through dealers or jobbers it would have an interest in purchasing from them. If not, it may find it advantageous to buy from whichever source—dealer or manufacturer—offers the best price in each individual case.

It is common practice to send requests for quotation **in duplicate,** one copy to be filled in and returned as a quotation by the vendor. The advantages of reply forms for quotations are:

1. Uniformity of quotations for tabulation and filing.
2. Assurance that all points will be covered in quotation.
3. Certainty that buyer's terms of purchase will be either accepted or specifically negatived.
4. Economy in quotation contact.

One method of determining when and to what extent quotations should be requested in advance of placing an order is to establish **a dollar amount as the dividing line.** If the order exceeds this amount, quotations must be received and the price shown on the purchase order sent to the vendor. Below this amount no quotations need be secured. Such a procedure allows small orders to go out unpriced.

Follow-up on Requests. How far requests for quotations should be followed up depends on how badly quotation information is needed. Some companies make it imperative that all quotations be submitted on or before a given date and rule out all not received by the time the closing of bids arrives. Often it is desirable to secure all quotations requested before orders are awarded. For this purpose the quotation record card or analysis sheet may be used as the basis of a **follow-up system,** showing at all times what requests for quotations have been sent out and what quotations received. This card may be placed in a tickler file to bring up unanswered requests in time for follow-up, or it may be keyed by a marker as to follow-up date and placed in a visible index or other card record file.

Use of the Quotation Record Card. The quotation record card is another medium for tabulating and comparing quotations and deciding from whom the goods shall be ordered. Quotations should be tabulated with extreme care to note all deviations from specifications or essential items and to show in columnar form the comparison of prices, deliveries, and terms, all reduced to the same basis. Fig. 15 shows a typical quotation record card or analysis sheet. In some cases it is simpler to use the file copy of the inquiry instead of a quotation record card or analysis sheet. The file copy is then used for follow-up purposes where desirable, and provision may be made on the file copy for tabulation of quotations when received. This system has the advantage of placing before the buyer, on one document, an exact copy of his request for quotation, a record of all concerns to whom the request was sent, and a tabulation of the quotations received.

SELECTING THE VENDOR. From the data on questions thus assembled and analyzed on the quotation record card, or a corresponding form of the copy of the request for quotation, the buyer selects the vendor with whom he wishes to place the purchase order. Frequently the purchase requisition form is used as the basis of writing the order. This form, after the buyer adds to it the necessary information on source of supply, price, etc., passes to the typist who makes

QUOTATION ANALYSIS SHEET

REASON FOR SELECTION OF VENDOR (If not Low Bidder)

*SPECIFICATIONS ☐   DELIVERY ☐   ONLY SOURCE ☐

*SPECIFICATIONS APPROVED BY _____

OTHER REASON OR REMARKS

VENDOR AND DATE OF BID	1	2	3	4	5	6	7	8
F.O.B. F.A.S.								
TERMS								
WEIGHT								
BEST DELIV'Y								
ITEM	✓	✓	✓	✓	✓	✓	✓	
1								
2								
3								
4								
5								
6								
7								
8								
9								
10								
11								
12								
TOTAL								

(✓) Check Column Designating Low Bidder Per Item.

BUYER'S SIGNATURE _____

Fig. 15. Quotation record card or analysis sheet.

out the purchase order. All information should be in such clear form that the typist need have no questions or misunderstanding regarding the order. The requisition is given to the buyer with the purchase order for comparison and checking, after which the latter is signed and mailed. The purchase requisition

BAUSCH & LOMB OPTICAL CO.

Established 1853

ROCHESTER, NEW YORK

PURCHASE
ORDER

Date

┌   ┐

THIS ORDER NUMBER MUST
APPEAR ON ALL PACKAGES,
INVOICES, PACKING SLIPS,
AND B/L.

└   ┘

KINDLY ENTER OUR ORDER AS PER SPECIFICATIONS SUBJECT TO ALL TERMS AND
CONDITIONS ON FACE AND BACK HEREOF.

DESCRIPTION

"SHIP PARCEL POST IF CONSIGNMENT DOES NOT
EXCEED GOVT. LIMITATIONS. ABOVE THIS WEIGHT
SHIP TRUCK OR FREIGHT UNLESS OTHERWISE
SPECIFIED."

AUTHORIZED RETURNS FOR REPLACE-
MENT OR CREDIT WILL BE CHARGED
BACK TO OUR SUPPLIERS BY A "DEBIT
MEMO." YOUR INVOICES WILL BE PAID
AND DEBIT MEMOS DEDUCTED FROM
OUR NEXT REMITTANCE. ALL RE-
PLACEMENTS SHOULD BE REBILLED
WHEN SHIPPED.

BAUSCH & LOMB

OPTICAL COMPANY

PURCHASING AGENT

Fig. 16. Purchase order (face).

is then marked with the purchase order number for reference purposes and is filed under department of origin. If in duplicate, the copy is returned to the department which originated it, with purchase order number and other needed information added. Often, however, a copy of the purchase order, perhaps with certain information blanked out, is sent to the requisitioner to indicate that his request is being filled.

THE PURCHASE ORDER. The purchase order is the vendor's authority to ship and charge for the goods specified and is the buyer's commitment to the vendor for the value of the goods ordered. It is an integral part of the sales agreement and establishes a **contractual relationship** immediately upon issuance, when it is an acceptance of a previous quotation or offer. Otherwise it is an

---

CONDITIONS

I. Cash Discount

The purchaser reserves the right to withhold payment of invoices until merchandise has been received and checked and does not waive the right to deduct the cash discount.

II. Patents

The seller agrees to defend, protect and save harmless, the purchaser, his subsidiaries and customers from any loss, damage or expense because of actual or alleged infringement of any patent rights resulting from the purchase, sale or use of the material covered by this order.

III. Federal and State Laws

The seller, in accepting this order, agrees to comply with all Federal and State Laws applicable to the manufacture and sale of the products specified hereon.

IV. Price

No changes may be made in terms, conditions, specifications or prices appearing on this order without the written permission of the buyer.

V. Cancellation

(a) This order may be cancelled by the buyer at any time without cost in the event that the seller shall be in default of any of the terms or conditions hereof.

(b) If this order is placed in connection with a government contract and is cancelled by reason of the cancellation of the prime contract, the rights of the buyer and the seller shall be determined in accordance with applicable government regulations in force at the time of cancellation.

(c) In the event that either the buyer or the seller shall be prevented from fulfilling his obligation under this order by acts of God, including but not limited to, civil strife, strike, fire, windstorm, or explosion, each shall save the other harmless from the liabilities arising from this order.

VI. Waiver of Conditions

Any waiver of, or exceptions to, the above enumerated conditions or of any special terms or provisions relating to this order, to be valid, must be specifically agreed to in writing by an authorized officer of the purchaser.

Fig. 17. Conditions upon which order is accepted (reverse of Fig. 16).

offer to negotiate such a contractual relationship which is completed by its acknowledgment or acceptance by the vendor. It is the most important of purchasing forms, and its provisions should be planned with care and continually considered as to desirable revision. A typical purchase order form is shown in Figs. 16 and 17, and the simplified practice recommendation nationally adopted for zoning purchase orders is shown in Fig. 18.

The purchase order should cover definitely and precisely the essential elements of purchase to be made, in a manner which will render future misunderstandings impossible and minimize the necessity of correspondence. It should be worded as far as possible exactly like the request for quotation, if one was sent out, and should include the following data:

Number. A purchase order number which will identify the transaction in future correspondence will be used by the vendor in shipping and billing the goods and will enable the contract to be recorded and filed for future reference. The vendor should be instructed to put the purchase order number on all packages and on all his invoices, so that they may be identified with the purchase order, for comparison and checking purposes. Since the receiving department will have a copy or a record of the order, including its number, all receipts of goods against it will be identified.

Quantity Ordered. The quantity of goods ordered is expressed in the units proper for the commodity. A clause should appear in the order form, limiting the vendor's right to overship or undership the order. A few illustrations of clauses of this nature follow.

The quantity of material ordered must not be changed without permission of buyer.

Quantity of material must not be exceeded unless buyer's permission in writing has been obtained.

The right is reserved to return excess shipments at shipper's expense.

Quantities received by us in excess of quantities specified herein may be returned, at our option, at shipper's expense.

In expression of units the Aluminum Company of America guards against misunderstandings by the following instructions to its buyers:

1. Never use the abbreviation CWT but write one hundred pounds or the figures 100 lb.
2. Never specify tons without stating kind—net ton, gross ton, or metric ton.
3. Never write dimensions using symbols for feet and inches; write 8 feet 3 inches or 8 feet 0 inches instead of 8'–3" or 8'.

Description. Description of goods ordered should be specific and wherever possible should state the basis and means by which quality is to be checked. Existing standards of quality and standard specifications are the most satisfactory for this purpose. Any unusual test, inspection, etc., to which goods are to be subjected should be stated. Material specifications of quality should be fortified by inserting in the purchase order form a clause stating the **rights of rejection and return** which purchaser reserves. Specimen clauses of this kind are:

All material furnished must be as specified and will be subject to inspection and approval of buyer after delivery. The right is reserved to reject and return at the risk and expense of the supplier such portion of any shipment as may be defective or fail to comply with specifications, without invalidating the remainder of the order. If rejected it will be held for disposition at expense of and risk of the seller.

All material and supplies furnished on this order will be subject to inspection before acceptance. If rejected, they will be held subject to the order of the shippers with accrued charges.

Goods subject to our inspection on arrival, notwithstanding prior payment to obtain cash discount.

Goods rejected on account of inferior quality or workmanship will be returned to you with charges for transportation both ways, plus labor, reloading, trucking, etc., and are not to be replaced except upon the receipt of written instructions from us.

Delivery and Shipping Instructions. Delivery specification may be stated either as a date on which goods are to be shipped or as a date on which goods are to arrive at the buyer's plant. The latter date is preferable because it can be taken directly from the purchase requisition without computation of time allowed for transit and also because it shifts to the vendor the responsibility for transportation delays. A specific date should be stated, and expressions such as "Urgent," "Rush," "Prompt Shipment," "At Once," etc., should be avoided.

Delivery specifications may be buttressed by a clause in the purchase order stating the buyer's rights of **cancellation for default in time of delivery:**

Buyer reserves the right to cancel this order or any portion of same if delivery is not made when specified, time being of the essence of this order, and to charge seller for any loss entailed.

Failure of shipper for any reason to fulfill delivery as promised will be considered sufficient cause to cancel this order.

Delivery must be made within the time specified on order. If material is not delivered within such specified time, buyer reserves the right to purchase elsewhere and charge seller with any loss incurred as a result thereof, or, at buyer's option, to cancel the order or any part thereof.

Shipping instructions include a statement of the point at which goods are to be delivered, routings, instructions concerning packing material, and designation of **method of shipping**—parcel post, express, freight, etc. Many firms state in their orders: "Ship cheapest way unless otherwise specified" and reserve the right to charge back transportation charges in excess of the cheapest rate for shipment. A clause in the purchase order form may protect the buyer from charges which he is unwilling to bear in connection with packing and shipping. Sample clauses of this nature are:

No charge allowed for packing or cartage unless designated on order.

Packing or cartage will not be included in the invoice price unless agreed upon in writing.

No charge allowed for packing or cartage.

All containers, drums, carboys, etc., to be returned, must be shipped on a no-charge or consignment basis. We will pay for only such containers as we do not return in a reasonable time.

Billing and Terms. Billing instructions cover the number of copies of invoice required, information desired on invoices, how invoices should be marked, to what point they should be mailed, etc. A typical provision is: "Invoice in duplicate and mail with shipping papers the day shipment is made." Billing instructions are usually uniform for all orders and may be included in the printed part of the purchase order form.

A definite statement of the f.o.b. point avoids misunderstanding. It is generally stated in connection with the price if the price is placed in the purchase order.

Terms of payment, including cash discount terms, are usually at the option of the vendor. They are stated in connection with quoted prices mentioned in the purchase order, but otherwise omitted. Understanding of cash discounts should be established by correspondence with vendor firms and recorded in a file for checking invoices. Special terms concerning payment by trade acceptance or draft should be stated in the purchase order in accordance with the agreement. Many companies include in their purchase order forms a statement protecting against drafts without specific agreement. Typical clauses of this nature are:

No drafts for purchases made will be honored unless by agreement.
No drafts for purchases made by this company will be honored.

Prices. Prices should be stated in the purchase order if the order is based on a quotation or an agreement as to price, together with a reference to quotation or agreement. Some vendors price all orders as received. This practice has the advantage of certainty of cost prior to billing. It has the disadvantages of added clerical expense for pricing and the tendency of the vendor's billing clerks to follow the price in the order and not give the advantage to declines which might not be known to the buyer.

Stock clauses in the purchase order form are used to afford the buyer **price protection.** Typical examples are:

If price is omitted on order, it is agreed that seller's price will be the lowest prevailing market price.
This order must not be filled at prices higher than those above given or last quoted.
If price is not stated on this order, material must not be billed at a price higher than paid, without notice to buyer and its acceptance thereof.
If price is not shown on the original order sheet, it must be inserted by seller on the attached acknowledgment to be returned to buyer.
It is understood and agreed that seller will not charge, without buyer's consent, a higher price for the goods called for by this order than was last quoted or charged to this office.

Miscellaneous Clauses. Miscellaneous clauses and conditions will vary with trade conditions or customs, nature of goods, and many other factors. **Patent infringement** is often the subject of a clause, such as follows:

Seller shall indemnify and save harmless the buyer and/or its vendees from and against all cost, expenses, and damages arising out of any infringement or claim of infringement of any patent or patents in the use of articles or equipment furnished hereunder.
As a part of the consideration hereof, it is expressly agreed that the seller will indemnify and hold harmless the buyer from any loss, damage, or injury arising out of a claim or suit for alleged infringement of patents relating to the property described herein and will assume the defense of any and all such suits and will pay all costs and expenses incidental thereof.
It is agreed that goods ordered shall comply with all federal laws relative thereto and that seller will defend and save harmless this company from loss, cost, or damage by reason of actual or alleged infringements of letters patent concerning same.

Other typical clauses on various conditions are:

The material on this order must be furnished only by the person or firm to whom the order is addressed unless otherwise authorized by the purchasing agent.
Seller agrees that no part of this order shall be sublet without purchaser's approval.

This order is confidential between the purchaser and the seller, and it is agreed by the seller that none of the details connected therewith shall be published or disclosed to any third party without purchaser's written permission.

When the cost of tools involved in the manufacture of parts covered by this order is included in the price per unit, tools become the property of this company upon the completion of our orders.

Any controversy or claim arising out of or relating to this contract or the breach thereof, shall be settled by arbitration in accordance with the rules then obtaining of the American Arbitration Association, and judgment upon the award rendered may be entered in the highest court of the forum, state or federal, having jurisdiction.

It is agreed that the waiver or acceptance by us of any breach on seller's part of any of the terms of this order shall not operate to relieve seller of responsibility hereunder for any prior or subsequent breach.

It is impracticable to list or illustrate all special conditions which may require mention in a purchase order. Child labor laws, federal food and drug acts and revenue acts, and other statutes may require provisions in particular cases. In addition, there may be clauses covering responsibility for patterns, special causes for cancellation, penalties for default, etc., and other requirements. Clauses which are general and apply to all purchase orders of the company will be made part of the printed purchase order form. Special conditions peculiar only to the order in question must be typed in.

Many clauses have recently been developed as a result of state sales and use taxes, federal social security tax provisions, and federal and state wage and hour laws, etc. Ordinarily it is sufficient to include a general provision that "nothing in the purchase order shall vary the legal responsibilities of either vendor or purchaser under federal or state laws." It is generally true that any attempt to insert clauses which shift such liability is nugatory.

Acceptance by the Vendor. Acceptance or acknowledgment of the order must be made by the vendor to bind the agreement unless the purchase order is itself acceptance of a quotation or offer. It is desirable to insert as a stock clause in the purchase order form, a provision requiring acknowledgment or acceptance by the vendor. Typical provisions are these:

Shipment of any part of this order constitutes acceptance of all its conditions without reservation. (This company used an acknowledgment form attached to the purchase order.)

Acknowledge this order promptly, giving date of shipment. (No means of acknowledgment furnished.)

Acknowledgment of this order must be made on acceptance copy attached and returned to us promptly. No other form will be accepted.

Mail this company's acknowledgment form of this order promptly and fill in complete, as we require this information for our records. We must have definite delivery date . . . "soon as possible" will not do. If delivery date is not satisfactory we reserve the right to cancel.

Acknowledgment of this order must be made in writing by return mail. Seller's failure to acknowledge may be considered an acceptance by the buyer.

In cases where previous quotations have not been obtained because of time conditions or the fact that only one vendor can furnish the material, the acknowledgment may be made the means of establishing a quoted price for the purchase records. A typical clause of this sort is:

In acknowledging this order it is essential that seller furnish complete quotation, including f.o.b. terms, cash discount terms, and approximate shipping weights, as well as its promise as to the time of delivery.

Other Data. Accounting information given on the purchase requisition tells the purchasing department the account or job number to which the purchase is to be charged. This information need not go to the vendor. It should be typed into the purchase order, however, so that it will appear on duplicate, triplicate, etc., copies which are used internally for receiving and charging material.

Date, signature, vendor's name, etc., obviously are essential features. The signature should show the company name and the name and position of the purchasing agent or officer authorizing the purchase. Each order should be signed either by him personally or with his name and "By _____," with the name of the person actually signing.

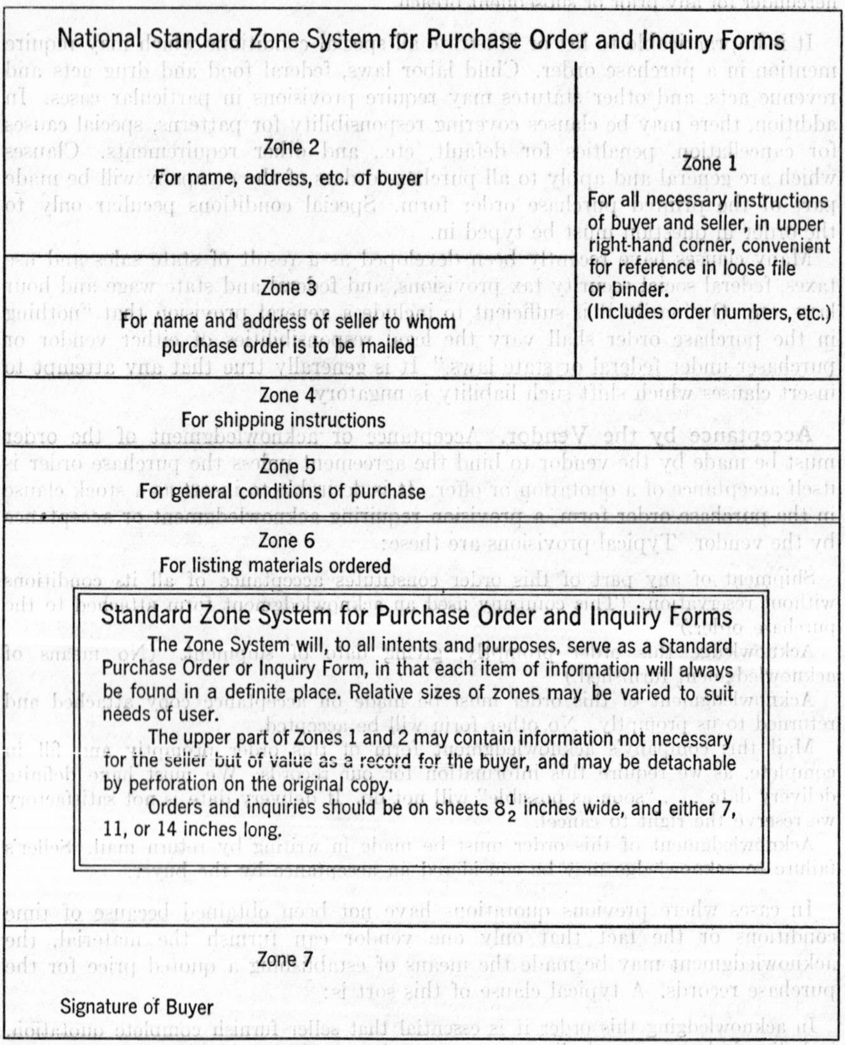

National Standard Zone System for Purchase Order and Inquiry Forms

Zone 2
For name, address, etc. of buyer

Zone 1
For all necessary instructions of buyer and seller, in upper right-hand corner, convenient for reference in loose file or binder.
(Includes order numbers, etc.)

Zone 3
For name and address of seller to whom purchase order is to be mailed

Zone 4
For shipping instructions

Zone 5
For general conditions of purchase

Zone 6
For listing materials ordered

Standard Zone System for Purchase Order and Inquiry Forms

The Zone System will, to all intents and purposes, serve as a Standard Purchase Order or Inquiry Form, in that each item of information will always be found in a definite place. Relative sizes of zones may be varied to suit needs of user.

The upper part of Zones 1 and 2 may contain information not necessary for the seller but of value as a record for the buyer, and may be detachable by perforation on the original copy.

Orders and inquiries should be on sheets $8\frac{1}{2}$ inches wide, and either 7, 11, or 14 inches long.

Zone 7

Signature of Buyer

Fig. 18. Standard arrangement of purchase order.

Form and Number of Copies. A specific form of purchase order is advisable as long as it is readily understood, economically handled by the vendor, and suited to the requirements of the purchaser's accounting system. It is highly advantageous, however, to use the standard purchase order form developed by the National Association of Purchasing Agents and adopted as a simplified practice recommendation by the Division of Simplified Practice, National Bureau of Standards, and in wide use. Advantages of its use are:

1. Fewer misunderstandings and clerical errors.
2. Lower printing costs.
3. Economical use of standard paper stock.
4. Economy in filing due to standard size.
5. Economy in typing and recording.

The form is standard as to zones where data are located (see Fig. 18). Details of entry differ according to the needs of each company. Fig. 16 conforms to this standard. The number of copies of the purchase order to be made will vary with the requirements of the accounting system. A typical setup uses six copies:

1. Vendor's copy, mailed to vendor.
2. File copy, posted to purchase record card and filed under vendor's name.
3. Receiving copy, sent to receiving department.
4. Receiving ticket, sent to receiving department.
5. Follow-up copy, goes to follow-up clerk, is filed in tickler file, and is used to assure delivery of the goods when needed.

See Fig. 12 for distribution and use of copies of the purchase order under this setup. Another typical setup calls for eight copies:

1. Vendor's copy.
2. Acknowledgment forms, to be filled in by vendor and returned.
3. File copy for purchasing department, used for record purposes and for checking of invoice.
4. Follow-up copy.
5. Accounting department copy.
6. Receiving department copy.
7. Inspection department copy.
8. Requisitioner's copy.

There is a growing need for a greater number of purchase order copies to simplify receiving department procedures, satisfy requirements of government contracts, etc. Several easy reproduction systems are now available.

FOLLOW-UP OF PURCHASE ORDER. The importance of follow-up is obvious, since maintenance of uninterrupted production schedules depends primarily on receipt of material on time. Its importance is greatly increased in a seller's market. Every order should bear a delivery date, and the follow-up section should see that that date is kept or learn of unavoidable delays in time to prevent crippling the plant for lack of materials. The follow-up section should:

1. Secure an acknowledgment or acceptance of order.
2. Secure a promise of delivery consistent with requirements.
3. Check with vendor on progress of filling the order—several times if the order is highly important.
4. See finally that the delivery promise is kept.

Some companies send the vendor two copies of the order, one of which is an acknowledgment form for signature and return. Another common practice is to print a perforated acknowledgment slip on the purchase order, to be torn off,

----

IBM INTERNATIONAL BUSINESS MACHINES CORPORATION
LOCATION: ,

┌ ●   ┐   DATE
To   *We are trying to conserve your time*
                                        as well as ours by using this form. It
                                        is sent in duplicate to enable you to
                                        use original for a reply and keep the
                                        other copy for your files. Answer only
└   ┘   *those questions asked.*

Gentlemen:

   We are interested in securing information about our purchase order _____
dated _____ Your No. _____

For (Material):

1. Kindly send us by return mail an acknowledgment of order, so that we may be assured our order has been accepted.	4. Material urgently needed. Advise us when you expect to ship.
2. With regard to Sample Inspection Report _____ which was (Approved) (Rejected), what action may we expect to be taken?	5. In accordance with our Rejected Purchase Report _____ dated _____, when may we expect replacements?
3. Will you ship _____ as (promised), (requested)? If not please furnish definite shipping date.	6. Please advise the present status of our order and when you expect to complete it.

Your penciled reply here will be sufficient.   Very truly yours

                          ▼   INTERNATIONAL BUSINESS MACHINES
                                                      CORPORATION

Date _____   _____
                                                        Signature

_____

_____

_____

_____

_____

┌   ┐   _____
   International Business Machines Corporation   *Signature*
To

   Attention: Department
└   ┘

Fig. 19. Follow-up of purchase order.

5·58

filled in, signed, and returned to the purchaser. In general, the full size 8½ × 11 in. order copy is easier to handle, record, and file. It is good practice to demand acknowledgment by return mail as a condition of the order. If acknowledgment is not received after a reasonable lapse of time for exchange of mail, the follow-up section should write requesting acknowledgment. Form letters may be used for this purpose, or form postcards. However, the personally directed, individually written letter will usually get better attention. Routine action anticipates only clerical attention.

After acknowledgment is secured with a statement of delivery date, the follow-up section, if the order is important or special, will make later checks on the vendor by letter, postcard, or in urgent cases by telephone or telegraph. Reply forms may be included with requests from the follow-up section to get a specific reply. Fig. 19 shows one large company's form, developed to simplify follow-up procedures. The clerk, preparing the form to cover a specific purchase, enters the order number information and specifications and checks the box or boxes covering the specific information requested. The supplier is requested to reply on the same form in the simplest manner possible.

When a broken delivery promise endangers shop schedules, emergency action should be taken through the purchasing agent or a buyer. Follow-up is usually based on a carbon copy of the order, with proper headings for notation of delivery information, etc. Follow-up copies should be filed in a tickler file under dated headings, which will bring each order up for review as to delivery conditions in ample time to allow for action. If the tickler file is to be divided among two or more clerks, it should be divided by local and out-of-town vendors rather than by commodities or alphabetically. Division on the basis suggested allows the employment of clerks adapted to telephone communications for local accounts and those skilled as correspondents for out-of-town connections. In very large buying organizations, where volume of purchase demands several subdivisions of the follow-up task, it is wise to vary the rule laid down above and divide the follow-up file on the basis of commodities, making each follow-up division subordinate to the particular buyer. An alternative practice is to file follow-up copies of orders numerically, or even alphabetically by vendors. In such cases, however, it is essential that there be a routine under which a numerical section of the orders or an alphabetical section shall be covered regularly, or some keying system to accomplish the same purpose, namely, periodic review of all orders for delivery purposes.

Self-signaling Follow-up Folders. Special universal-type follow-up folders— used also in a follow-up system to get in bids—for letter-sized forms now come with transparent plastic guides across the top to hold the title inserts, and movable transparent colored signals or indicators. To the right of the title insert space is a section divided by months, January to December, across which a red signal may be moved to indicate the month of follow-up. To the far right across the remainder of the top are the dates 1 to 31, over which a green signal can be moved to show the day of follow-up. Copies or memos of purchase orders are put in the folders, which are keyed by the signals for month and day of follow-up and may be filed in order of such date. Each day, inspection of the signals locates the folders holding purchase orders to be followed up on that day. The results of the follow-up are then noted on the respective forms, which may be resignaled and refiled for later follow-up if necessary. Such a system avoids the necessity for having a large folder file covering every date in the year. Only sufficient folders are required to cover the period for follow-up of current purchase orders.

Another system, utilizing open tubs for open-order files, is based upon the use of card stock for the open-order file copy of the purchase order. This copy, filed alphabetically by vendor, has space for the month and date signals on the right side. Often colored signals are added to make the visual check quicker.

RECEIVING. Duties of the receiving department include:

1. Checking incoming shipments to see whether items and quantities conform to order.
2. Recording receipt.
3. Taking necessary steps to insure inspection or testing when required.
4. Notifying department or storeroom of receipt of shipment and its amount and condition.
5. Informing purchasing agent or buyer of all facts which require an adjustment with vendor or carrier, whether for overshipment, shortage, or defective material.
6. Delivering material to proper point in plant for storage or use.

The receiving department should receive a copy of the purchase order or purchase requisition with which to check incoming shipments for proper goods, quantity, quality, and all other essentials. Any variation from shipping instructions on the order should be noted. It is good practice to avoid showing the quantity ordered on all copies of orders sent to the receiving department, so that this department must actually count or weigh goods without knowledge of amount ordered. The packing slip may be a good guide but should not be considered proof of contents.

The record made of goods received should be in a form suitable for checking against the vendor's invoice and against bills for transportation charges. It is usually given in the form of a **receiving report.** Such a record should show:

1. Purchase order number.
2. Date of receipt.
3. Vendor's name and address.
4. Kind of goods.
5. Quantity received.
6. Condition when received (whether damaged, etc.).
7. Units in which the goods came in (pieces, quantity per box or package, etc.).
8. Type of container.
9. Any necessary identifying marks on shipment.
10. Medium of transportation.
11. Transportation charges.
12. By whom received.
13. To whom delivered.

Four copies of the receiving report may be made, one copy remaining as a receiving record, one going to the purchasing department for comparison with the order, and one to the department to which the shipment is sent (usually the storeroom), and perhaps one to the accounting department as a voucher for invoices. It is a good practice to send two copies of the receiving report with the goods, having one copy signed by the receiver and returned to the receiving department. Sometimes the record may be made on copies of the purchase order, typed as a measure of economy at the same time as other copies of the order. Such receiving copies of the order are headed and spaced to allow entering of receiving information. When duplicating methods are employed to produce purchase orders, receiving reports can be run from the original master with delivery information added.

The receiving department's copy of the purchase order must show the point where the goods are to be delivered. A receipt should be secured from this department. If receiving tickets have been sent with the copy of the purchase order to the receiving department, this department will then enter the receipt of the goods on its record form and the receiving tickets in one operation, retain the record form, and send the receiving ticket in duplicate with goods to the requisitioning department, which signs both copies and forwards one to the accounting department and returns the other to the purchasing department as a voucher for receipt of the goods. Fig. 20 shows a typical receiving voucher or record form, and Fig. 21 a receiving ticket.

RECEIVING VOUCHER

THE FOLLOWING MATERIAL HAS ARRIVED AT THE RECEIVING DEPT.   Date_____19__

SHIPPED BY   FROM   PUR. ORDER NO.

| Packages | | Quantity | DESCRIPTION | Weight | Chargeable to |
No.	Kind				

Delivered	Carting Co.	Pur. Agent's Bill No.	Received by:
Via	R.R.or Exp.Co.	Date of Invoice	Count and Weight Checked by:
Car No.	Initial	Checker's Report No.	Received for Division Stores by:
Pro. No.	Weight	Condition of Shipment Upon Arrival:	Checked Against Invoice by:
Rate	Frt.or Exp.Ch'g's $		

Fig. 20. Receiving voucher.

Because of the difficulty of keeping goods and tickets together during shop transit, **identification tags** are often used as a form of receiving ticket. These tags are particularly useful when inspection is required between receiving and delivery to the requisitioning department.

If **inspection or test** of the items after receipt is required by the specifications, the receiving department must see that this inspection takes place. Often it is practical to hold goods in the receiving department pending reports on tests or inspection. Often it is more practical to transfer the goods to an inspecting or test room where the necessary apparatus is present.

Inspection prior to receipt concerns the receiving department only in that it should have on file an approval of goods before accepting them. The extent and rigidity of inspection cannot be dictated except in individual cases. Practice varies with requirements and circumstances. Sometimes every unit must be inspected. In other cases, representative samples can be selected, and lot quality determined by statistical methods (sequential analysis or Dodge-Romig tables). In testing carload shipments of bulk raw materials, the general practice is to take samples from the top, bottom, and middle of the car. Reports of inspection results should be available to the purchasing department as guides to placing future orders.

If **goods are rejected** and are to be returned, or if there is a shortage or overshipment on the order, all correspondence looking to adjustment by the vendor should be conducted by the purchasing agent or the buyer. What constitutes an adjustable shortage or overshipment depends on the value of goods and trade customs. In certain trades there is a custom that a variation of 10 percent either way in quantity must be accepted.

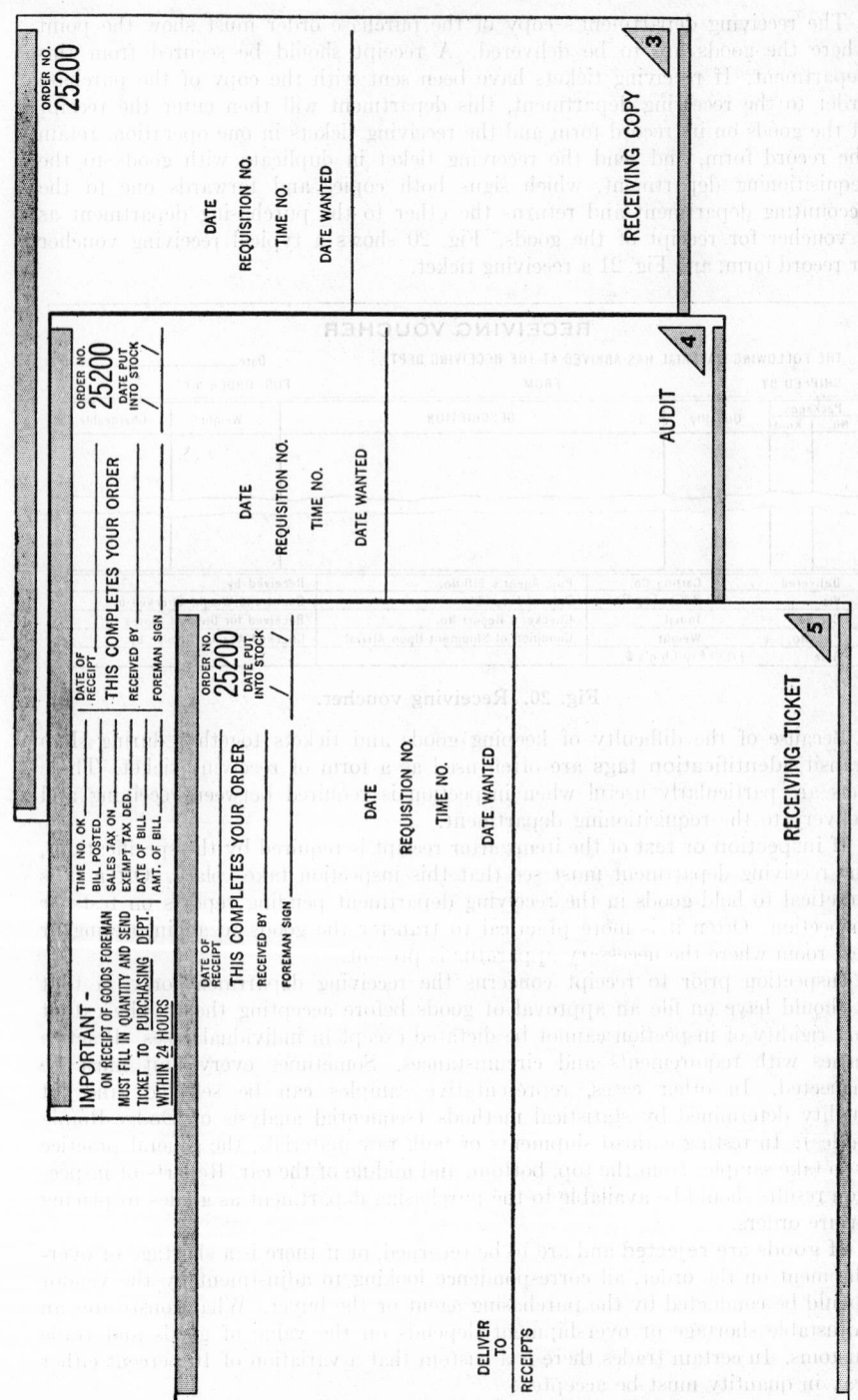

Fig. 21. Receiving ticket.

Brown & Sharpe Mfg. Co.

Defective material to be returned should be accompanied by the inspector's report showing in detail the nature of the defect, and an order for replacement, if desired, should be issued. It is usually good practice to pay for goods shipped, pending inspection, and obtain credit memoranda for any defective goods returned. Some companies obtain authorization and shipping instructions from vendors before shipment and bill back to vendor at the same time. In the case of vendors whose credit rating is doubtful, it is safe to hold invoices until inspection is completed and deduct for defective goods.

Returns for defects and all forms of requests for adjustments should be made only on authorization by the purchasing agent or buyer. In a large purchasing department there may be a claim clerk whose sole duty relates to defects, shortages, etc.

If goods are returned for credit, there should be a **record of the goods returned and the claims made,** this record to be closed only by receipt of a credit memorandum or replacement on a no-charge basis. This claims record preferably should be in the accounting department as a check on the purchasing department's closing of claims. It is also desirable that the purchase record contain a notation of all claims and their disposal as part of the history of the transaction, to guide buyers in the placing of future business.

HANDLING INVOICES. The invoice is the vendor's bill or charge against the buyer, on the basis of which he claims payment for the goods furnished. It is based upon the purchase order and should refer to it and follow it in all details of description, terms, and prices.

When the invoice is received, it is sometimes stamped with the route through which it must pass to obtain the checkings and approvals necessary for payment. Two **typical invoice stamps** used for this purpose are shown on page 5·64.

Routine Followed. The date on which the invoice is received in the purchasing department is stamped on the invoice by a dating device on the stamp used. The invoice is then routed to the purchase record desk for entry and comparison with the copy of the purchase order, and to the follow-up section to which a copy of the receiving report is sent to close out the follow-up procedure. It then is passed to the price clerk for approval for price only. This price may be checked from catalogue lists and discounts, from quotation records, etc. It then passes over the purchasing agent's or buyer's desk for final purchasing department approval. The invoice then leaves the purchasing department for the accounting department, where it is compared with the receiving record if this check has not been made in the purchasing department, and the date and number of the receiving record sheets are noted. The standing order or job number to which the invoice is to be charged is also entered on it, and proper charges are made against this account. A voucher requesting the drawing of a check to pay the invoice is then prepared, and voucher and invoice are forwarded to the treasurer's department for payment.

Variations of this routine are many, depending on the setup of the organization, the kind of system in use for accounting, etc. Often, as indicated above, the invoice is checked against the receiving report in the purchasing department. In many companies entry of the job or standing order number to which goods are to be charged is made from purchasing department records and checked in the accounting department. A variation of this routine is desirable in the case of invoices on which a discount is to be taken, when waiting for a check with receipt of goods would involve loss of discount. In such cases the invoice is checked as to charge only by the purchasing or accounting department, is passed on for payment, and returns after payment to await checking for receipt of goods and comparison of quantities. Another common practice is to prepare an invoice flag, or printed form, containing spaces for the entry of all the above checking data, properly initialed by the checkers, and other data which it might be desirable to record regarding the invoice.

Cash discount terms ....
Entered on purchase record ....
Approved for price ....
Buyer's approval ....
Date received in plant ....
Receiving record No. ....
Date of receipt of goods ....
Accounting department O. K. ....
Charged to ....
Paid by check No. ....

TAXABLE ☐ AMT.		
NON TAXABLE ☐ AMT.		
	Date	**CLASSIFIED**
Date:_____		**OK**
Extension O. K._____		
Receipt O. K._____		**Factory Data**
Price O. K._____		
Recorded P. R._____		
Terms %..........	**Date ....**	

Duplicate bills are demanded by some companies. The duplicate comes to the purchasing department with the original, is stamped conspicuously to avoid confusion with original, and is used to inform the follow-up section as to shipment of orders. It is then filed in the purchasing department under the vendor's name.

Invoice Checking. Important features of invoices which must be checked are:

1. **Quantity.** The quantity check must be made against the order or purchasing department record to guard against overshipment or undershipment of requirements. Quantity must also be checked against the receiving record or receiving ticket as a means of preventing payment for goods not received. This checking may be done in the accounting department, which can refer discrepancies found to the purchasing department for adjustment. The checking may be done, however, in the purchasing department.

2. **Quality.** The invoice should not be paid, or if it has been paid in order to secure a cash discount, a credit memorandum from the vendor should be secured provided the quality is not in accordance with specification. So far as the invoice

is concerned, checking should be done at the same time as checking against the receiving record for quantity. Inspection approval or a record of satisfactory test should be entered on the receiving record or attached to it and should be a prerequisite to passage of the invoice by the accounting department.

3. **Prices.** The purchasing department should be primarily responsible for the price paid for purchased goods. Prices on the invoice should be checked and approved by the purchasing agent or one of his buyers to whom that authority is delegated. The accounting department, however, should operate as a check upon the purchasing department. Extensions can perhaps be more conveniently checked in the accounting department.

4. **Terms.** Terms such as "f.o.b. point" are a part of a price and should be checked as such. Cash discounts are to be secured by the purchasing department, but the terms of such discounts should be on file in the treasurer's or financial department, since that department pays the bills.

5. **Transportation Charges.** Bills for transportation or items for transportation in bills for goods should be checked by the purchasing department for the vendor's authority to ship in the manner indicated and for f.o.b. point. They should be sent to the traffic department for approval of rate.

The **function of the accounting department** in the handling of invoices is double. Its duties are:

1. To see that the correct charges are made against the proper job or standing order numbers.
2. To check the purchasing department against errors and carelessness in records or calculations.

The first of these functions is purely an accounting function and need not be discussed. As to the second, the accounting department should check the purchasing department on two points. These points are paying for goods not received and paying excessive prices for goods received. For the first of these

INVOICE REGISTER

DATE: NUMBER   000

INVOICE		Vendor	Amount	P.O. No.	Date	INVOICE		Vendor	Amount	P.O. No.	Date
No.	Date					No.	Date				
001						051					
002						052					
003						053					
004						054					
005						055					
006						056					
007						057					
042						092					
043						093					
044						094					
045						095					
046						096					
047						097					
048						098					
049						099					
050						100					

Fig. 22. Invoice record sheet.

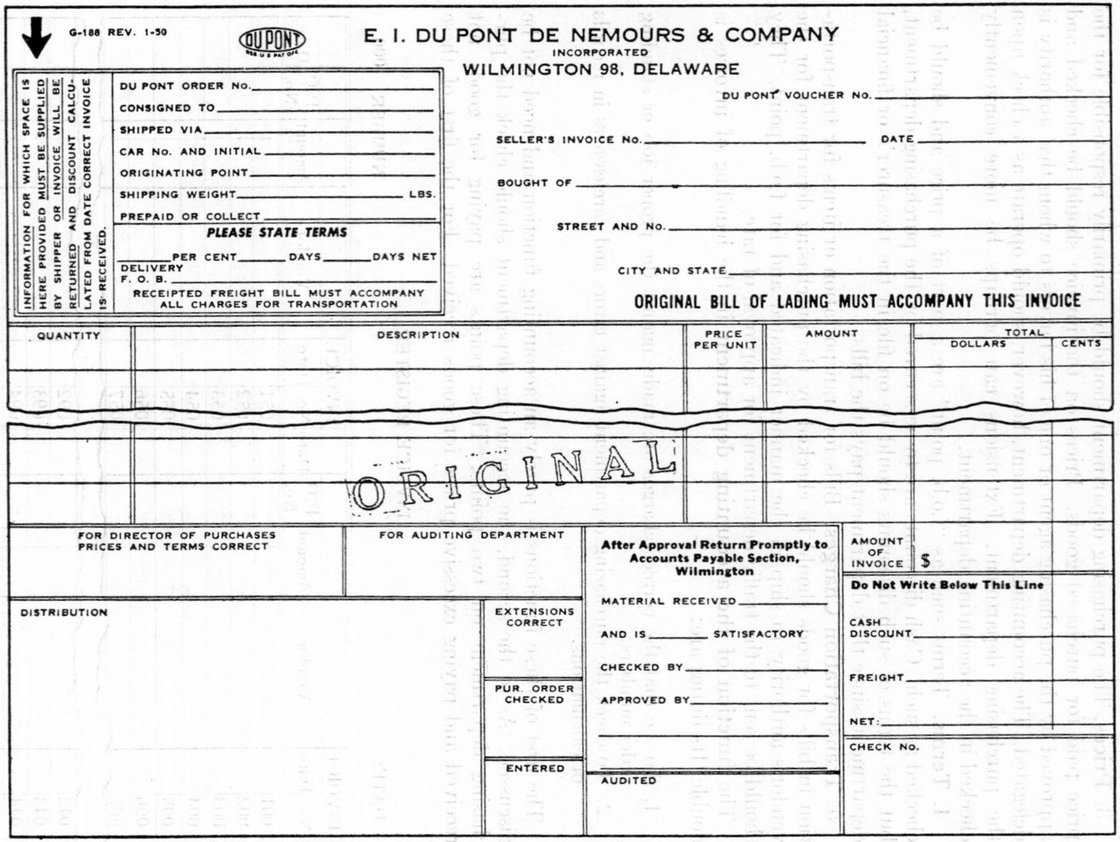

Fig. 23. Invoice form supplied by customer.

Fig. 22. Invoice record sheet.

checks, the receiving reports should go to the accounting department and be compared with the invoices. The matter of excessive prices is not so easily checked. Explanations may be asked for variations in price not accounted for on the surface of the transaction. Stores records should contain a unit price and should be the basis for questioning purchase prices when variations in price level appear.

Another method of checking the purchasing department on prices paid is **spot auditing.** By this method the accounting department or auditor periodically takes certain purchase transactions and audits them, obtaining from the purchasing department all data and making an actual check of market prices, quotations received, receipt, inspection, etc.

Prompt payment of bills is important not only because of credit standing but for efficiency of buying. The purchasing department has a real interest in prompt payment in accordance with terms. It is desirable that a strict check be kept upon movements of invoices after their receipt. They should be entered upon an **invoice record sheet** by the financial department or by the invoice clerk in the purchasing department if checked there first. This invoice record is watched daily, and if as discount dates approach, invoices have not been checked and released, they are followed up to be paid in order to obtain the discounts. Fig. 22 is an invoice record sheet.

The form of the invoice is in the vendor's hands, but a number of companies furnish their own forms for billing and send them to the vendor with the purchase order. Fig. 23 shows a typical invoice form furnished by the buyer.

Standardization of invoice forms has many advantages in economy of clerical effort, reduction of errors, and efficient handling of invoices. The National Association of Purchasing Agents, in cooperation with the National Association of Cost Accountants and others, has developed a **standard invoice form** which has gained wide recognition in industry and has been promulgated as a simplified practice recommendation by the Division of Simplified Practice, National Bureau of Standards.

Purchasing Department Records

VARIETY OF RECORDS. The most important records to be kept by the purchasing department are:

1. Purchase record.
2. Contract record.
3. Vendor record.

4. Price or quotation record.
5. Summary of purchase work.
6. Miscellaneous records.

PURCHASE RECORD. There should be a separate purchase record card for each commodity and usually for each size or variety of each commodity. On the **purchase record card** are entered all orders placed and sometimes all deliveries or shipments against them. Copies of purchase orders are used from which to post whatever information may be desired, such as date, quantity, price, requisition number which authorizes purchase, account number to which goods are to be charged, vendor's name, and all other facts pertinent to a complete record of the orders. From the vendors' invoices may be posted, if desired, quantity shipped, date of invoice, price, unit, discount, and terms. Some companies do not consider it necessary, however, to post each invoice to the record card, on the theory that the buyer is not interested in the invoice unless it differs from the quotation.

The record should be arranged to allow quick and accurate comparison between different purchases of the same commodity. This record is in many

Fig. 24. Purchase record card.

respects the heart of the purchasing routine, as it shows the buyers the facts regarding each order as to choice of vendors, previous experience as to volume of purchases, prices, etc., and allows each invoice to be checked with the corresponding facts in view. For a moderate-size concern, however, the following information is all that is necessary:

1. Purchase order numbers.
2. Full description of materials ordered, including specification or drawing numbers.
3. List of vendors asked to quote on the orders, including date of quotation, price, f.o.b. point, freight to point of consumption, terms of payment, quantity.
4. Vendor or vendors with whom orders were placed and a space for remarks. Under the latter heading can be placed special information as to good or poor service or quality.

Fig. 24 shows a simpler form of purchase record card than the one just described. Information is to be put on the card as follows:

1. When the bids are requested, a notation of the date and the firms from whom quotations are requested.
2. Upon receipt of quotations, prices are to be posted.
3. When the order is placed, prices, terms, and the name of the vendor are to be posted.

A modification of the purchase record can be made in the case of items carried in the storeroom. On the regular **stores record card** there can be considerable data, such as supplier's name, order numbers, shipping instructions, as well as the usual notations of receipts, balance on hand, ordering multiples, etc. By having this card sent to the purchasing department with each new purchase requisition and making use of the information on it, the buyer can limit the information on his card to the list of bidders, quantity, price, terms, delivery cost (including freight), and other data of concern only to the purchasing department.

Another form of purchase record is maintained for internal control of purchasing procedure. Purchase requisitions are all directed to the record clerk, who in each case assigns a purchase order number and returns a copy to the originator so marked. The buyer to whom the requisition is assigned is recorded, and when the order is typed, the supplier's name. Finally, deliveries are recorded to close the record.

CONTRACT RECORD. It is essential to have available at all times a complete record of purchase contract commitments. The contract record should show commodity, vendor, order number, total quantity contracted for, time limits of contract, price and unit, and all other necessary information for filling the contract properly and recontracting upon expiration. There should also be spaces for posting quantities ordered or received against contract, together with a perpetual balance column. This record should be on or near the buyer's desk and should be maintained by the clerical or service section. A tickler file is often used to bring contracts up for action by the buyer prior to expiration. Fig. 25 shows the front and back of a simple blanket contract record card.

VENDOR RECORD. Records of vendors on the purchase record card may be sufficient when supplemented by directories, registers, etc., which are available. Many purchasing agents prefer, however, to keep a separate card file of vendors, arranged and filed by commodity headings. This file constitutes a list of

Fig. 25. Blanket order record (front and back).

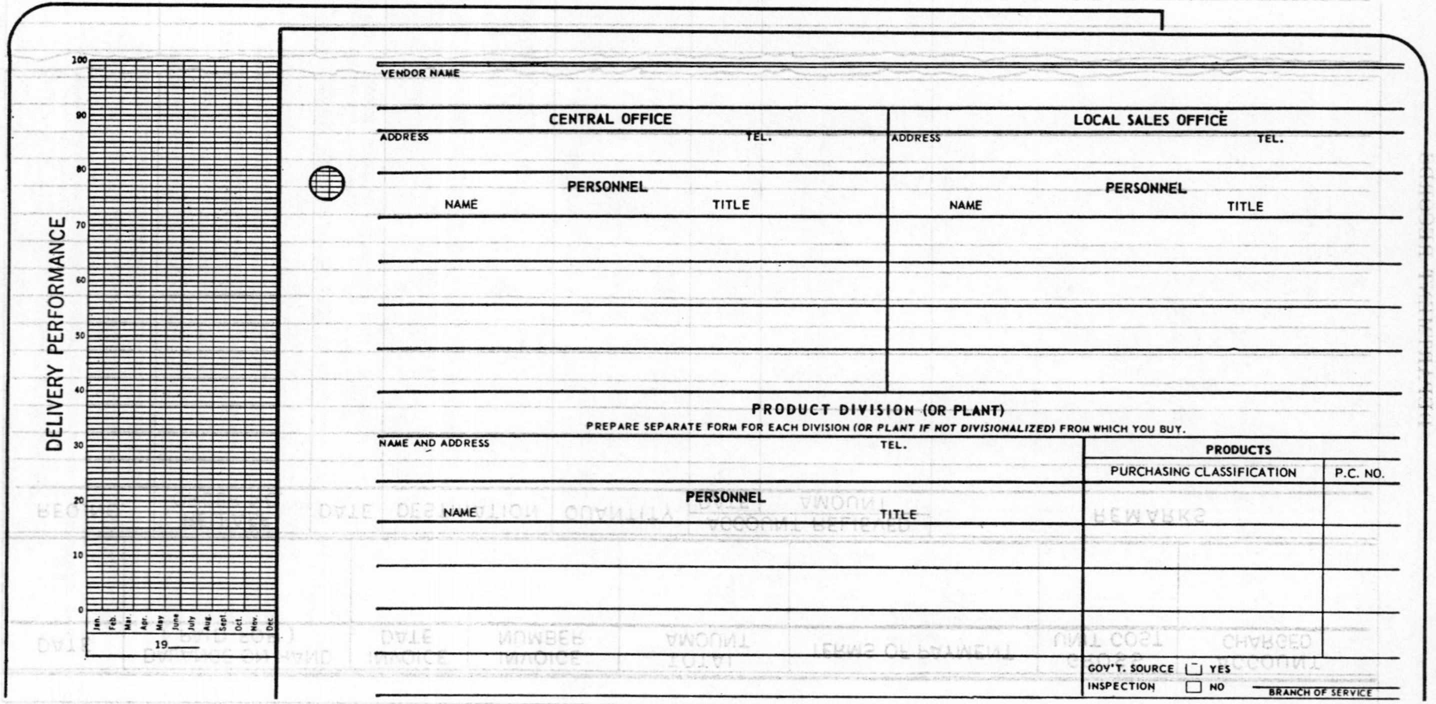

VENDOR PLANT RECORD

VENDOR NAME

CENTRAL OFFICE

ADDRESS   TEL.

PERSONNEL

NAME	TITLE

LOCAL SALES OFFICE

ADDRESS   TEL.

PERSONNEL

NAME	TITLE

PRODUCT DIVISION (OR PLANT)

PREPARE SEPARATE FORM FOR EACH DIVISION (OR PLANT IF NOT DIVISIONALIZED) FROM WHICH YOU BUY.

NAME AND ADDRESS   TEL.

PERSONNEL

NAME	TITLE

PRODUCTS

PURCHASING CLASSIFICATION	P.C. NO.

GOV'T. SOURCE ☐ YES ☐ NO

INSPECTION ☐ YES ☐ NO

BRANCH OF SERVICE

DELIVERY PERFORMANCE

100 90 80 70 60 50 40 30 20 10 0

19___

Jan Feb Mar Apr May June July Aug Sept Oct Nov Dec

Fig. 5-6 Blanket order record (front and back).

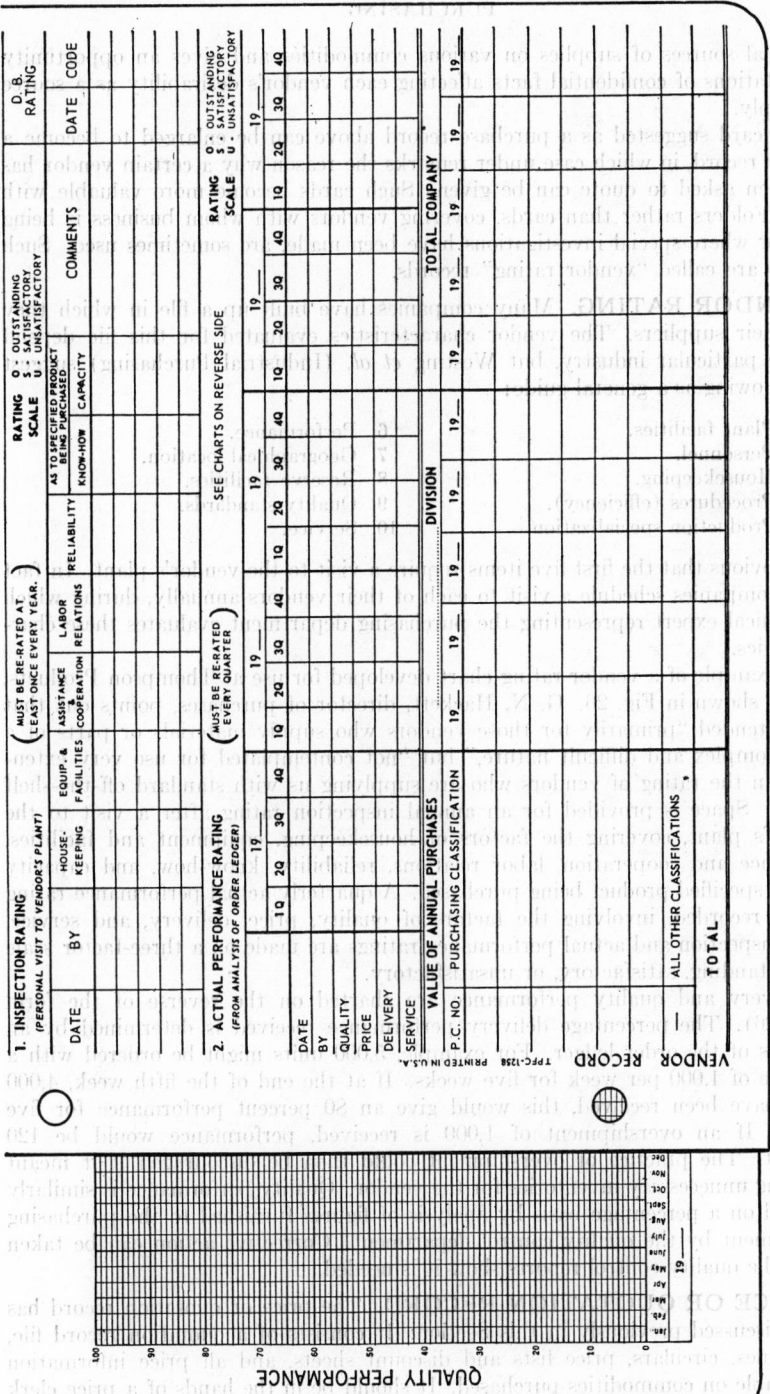

Fig. 26. A typical vendor rating chart.

Thompson Products, Inc.

potential sources of supplies on various commodities and gives an opportunity for notations of confidential facts affecting each vendor's desirability as a source of supply.

The card suggested as a purchase record above can be enlarged to become a vendor record, in which case under remarks the reason why a certain vendor has not been asked to quote can be given. Such cards become more valuable with time. Folders rather than cards, covering vendors with whom business is being done or where special investigations have been made, are sometimes used. Such folders are called "vendor rating" records.

VENDOR RATING. Many companies have built up a file in which they rate their suppliers. The vendor characteristics evaluated for this file depend on the particular industry, but Westing *et al.* (Industrial Purchasing) suggest the following as a general guide:

1. Plant facilities.	6. Performance.
2. Personnel.	7. Geographical location.
3. Housekeeping.	8. Reserve facilities.
4. Procedures (efficiency).	9. Quality standards.
5. Production specialization.	10. Service.

It is obvious that the first five items require a visit to the vendor's plant. In fact some companies schedule a visit to each of their vendors annually, during which a technical expert representing the purchasing department evaluates these characteristics.

An example of a vendor rating chart developed for use at Thompson Products, Inc., is shown in Fig. 26. G. N. Hackett, director of purchases, points out that it is intended "primarily for those vendors who supply materials or parts of a more complex and difficult nature," but "not contemplated for use very extensively in the rating of vendors who are supplying us with standard off-the-shelf items." Space is provided for an annual inspection rating after a visit to the vendor's plant, covering the factors of housekeeping, equipment and facilities, assistance and cooperation, labor relations, reliability, know-how, and capacity for the specified product being purchased. A quarterly actual performance rating is also recorded, involving the factors of quality, price, delivery, and service. Both inspection and actual performance ratings are made on a three-factor scale as outstanding, satisfactory, or unsatisfactory.

Delivery and quality performance are charted on the reverse of the form (Fig. 26). The percentage delivery performance received is determined by an analysis of the order ledger. For example, 5,000 units might be ordered with a promise of 1,000 per week for five weeks. If at the end of the fifth week, 4,000 units have been received, this would give an 80 percent performance for five weeks. If an overshipment of 1,000 is received, performance would be 120 percent. The practice of overshipment could then be discouraged if it meant carrying unnecessary inventories for the vendor. Quality performance is similarly charted on a percentage basis by analysis of figures furnished to the purchasing department by the quality control department. Corrective action can be taken when the quality control reports show it is needed.

PRICE OR QUOTATION RECORD. The price or quotation record has been discussed previously in this Section. It consists of a quotation record file, catalogues, circulars, price lists and discount sheets, and all price information obtainable on commodities purchased. It should be in the hands of a price clerk whose sole duty is keeping the price record up to date and checking invoices.

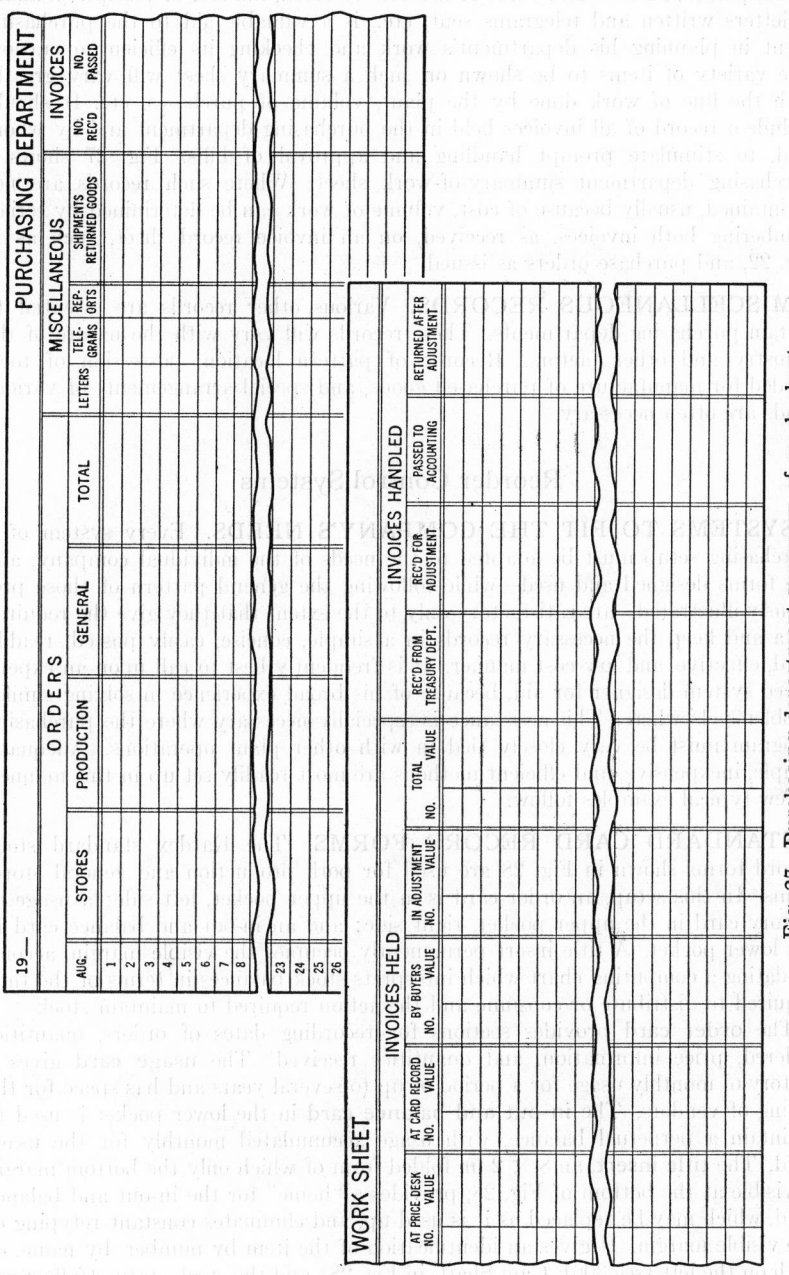

Fig. 27. Purchasing department summary-of-work sheet.

SUMMARY OF PURCHASE WORK. A running record of number of orders placed, number and value of invoices received, number of receipts, number of letters written and telegrams sent, etc., is a valuable aid to the purchasing agent in planning his department's work and checking its efficient operation. The variety of items to be shown on such a summary sheet will vary greatly with the line of work done by the plant, volume of purchases, etc. It should include a record of all invoices held in the purchasing department and by whom held, to stimulate prompt handling and approval of bills. Fig. 27 shows a purchasing department summary-of-work sheet. Where such records are not maintained, usually because of cost, volume of work can be determined by serial-numbering both invoices, as received, on an invoice record sheet, such as in Fig. 22, and purchase orders as issued.

MISCELLANEOUS RECORDS. Various other records are essential to certain purchasing departments. These records will vary with the nature of the industry and other factors. Records of pattern location, possession of tools needed for manufacture of purchased goods, and special arrangements of various kinds are often necessary.

Reorder Control Systems

SYSTEMS TO FIT THE COMPANY'S NEEDS. Every system of a purchasing setup must be adapted to the needs of the individual company, and the forms designed and used—while following the general pattern of those previously illustrated—are satisfactory only to the extent that they give the required data and keep the necessary records in a simple, concise, easily posted, readily used, effective, and low-cost manner. It is frequently best to call upon an experienced system designer for aid, because of his broad experience in solving similar problems elsewhere. This assistance is especially necessary where the purchasing program must be very closely tied in with other plant operations. Adequate, simple, inexpensive, and efficient methods are most readily set up in this manner. A few typical examples follow.

STANDARD CARD RECORD FORMS. The Kardex standard stock record forms shown in Fig. 28 are used for both production and general stores items. In this setup, an order card is in the upper pocket, left side; a usage or history card in the upper pocket, right side; and an in-out and balance card in the lower pocket. A title insert permanently occupies the visible margin, accommodating a computing chart which interprets stock balances in terms of the time required to distribute or consume and the action required to maintain stock.

The **order card** provides sections for recording dates of orders, quantities ordered, price information, and quantities received. The **usage card** gives a history of monthly usage for a period of up to several years and has space for the listing of vendors. The **in-out and balance card** in the lower pocket is used to maintain a perpetual balance, with usage accumulated monthly for the usage card. The **title insert,** an 8 × 2 in. folded form of which only the bottom margin is visible at the bottom of Fig. 28, provides a "home" for the in-out and balance card, which may be replaced as it is used up, and eliminates constant retyping of the visible margin. It gives an identification of the item by number, by name, or both on the left (see 3061, Cam Shaft, in Fig. 28) and the stock status (follow-up, order, normal, or overstock) with the computing chart on the right. It also provides space for noting the reorder quantity and for revisions in it.

3061 Cam Shaft

ARTICLE

	UNIT		ORDERED			RECEIVED	
DATE	VEN	QUAN.	LIST	DISCOUNT	INV COST	DATE	QUAN.
2-1	1	5400	22.00	NET		3-6	5400
5-14	2	5400	21.50	NET			

MAKE DEL'D COST ADD ____ % FOR FREIGHT

CAT. NO. 1-5217

3061 Cam Shaft

ARTICLE

VENDORS
1 ACE MACHINE CO.
2 JOHNSON TOOL & SUPPLY
3
4

MONTHLY SALES

	19	19	19	19	19	19	19
JAN	2125	1300					
FEB	1975	1700					
MAR	1825	1800					
APR	1175						
MAY	1000						
JUNE	1275						
JULY	1450						
AUG	1700						
SEPT	1950						
OCT	2250						
NOV	2325						
DEC	2175						
TOTAL	21225						

MEMO: AUG MO. USAGE 1800

CAT. NO. 1-5218 PRINTED IN U. S. A.

3061   CAM SHAFT   IN-OUT AND BALANCE RECORD

DATE	ORDER NO.	RECEIVED	USED	TOTAL MONTH TO DATE	BALANCE	DATE	ORDER NO.	RECEIVED	USED	TOTAL MONTH TO DATE	BALANCE
3-1	BALANCE				2200	4-22	1314		200	1300	4500
3-1	1025		200	200	2000	4-26	1341		200	1500	4300
3-3	1041		300	500	1700	4-28	1362		200	1700	4100
3-4	1052		100	600	1600						
3-8	1069		200	800	1400	5-2	1365		100	100	4000
3-10	1078		100	900	1300	5-8	1403		200	300	3800
3-10	8742.1	5400			6700	5-13	1409		200	500	3600
3-14	1104		100	1000	6600	5-15	1448		100	600	3500
3-17	1160		200	1200	6400	5-20	1460		200	800	3300
3-20	1180		100	1300	6300						
3-22	1191		100	1400	6200						
3-25	1206		100	1500	6100						
3-28	1217		200	1700	5900						
3-30	1219		100	1800	5800						
4-2	1228		100	100	5700						
4-4	1233		100	200	5600						
4-5	1251		200	400	5400						
4-10	1278		300	700	5100						
4-13	1285		100	800	5000						
4-15	1289		200	1000	4800						
4-18	1293		100	1100	4700						

DATE JAN
RE-ORDER QUANTITY 5400

3061 Cam Shaft
3063 Cam Shaft Front Bearing
3066 Cam Shaft Bearing Ring
3071 Cam Shaft Dowel Pin

Fig. 28. Standard reorder control forms.

Over the January–December scale (1–12) on the left-hand side of the title insert, a quarter-inch signal is set to show the month of last usage of the item (May, or the fifth month, in the case of item 3061). Thus, items which are not moving are quickly spotted and action can be taken.

The Computing Chart. Unit balances, such as those shown on the in-out and balance card, mean little unless interpreted in terms of the time in which they are used. This interpretation usually depends on the arithmetical accuracy and mechanical consistency of clerks doing routine postings. In combination with the title insert and the Graph-A-Matic signal (at the right of the title insert), the computing chart eliminates calculations of how long quantities will last at given rates of use. The computing chart (Figs. 29 and 30) has rows of proportionate

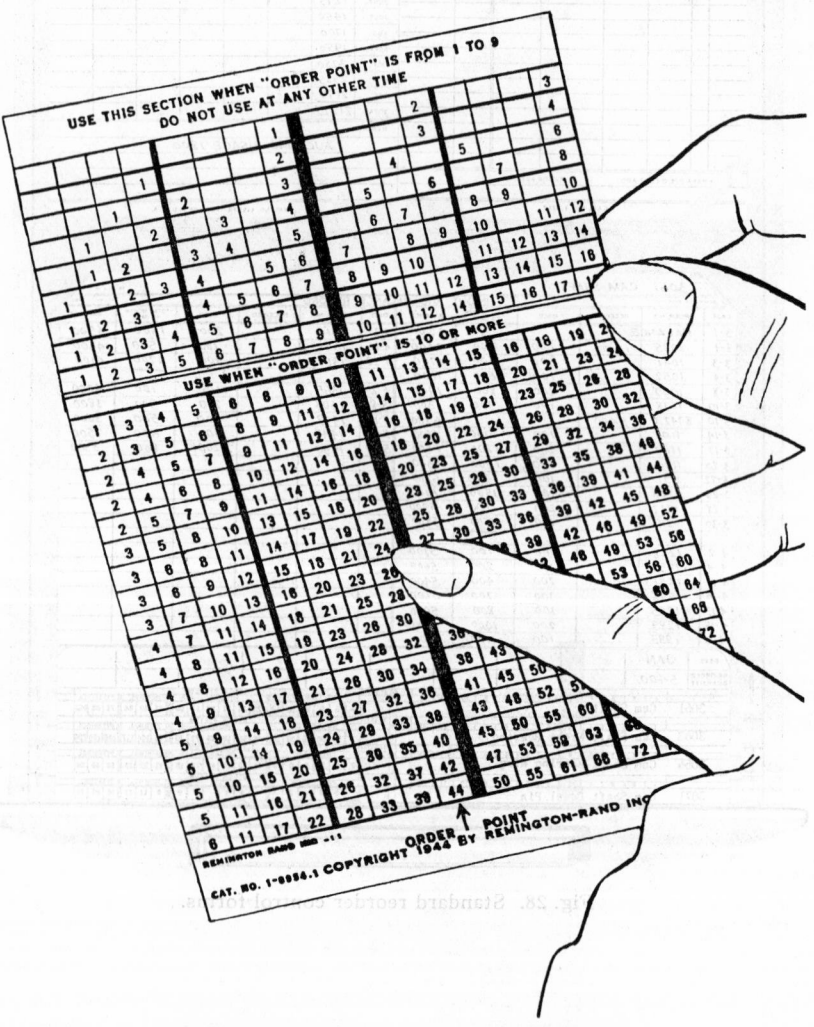

Fig. 29. Order point on the computing chart.

numbers representing number of items, divided by three vertical bars into **stock status** categories of follow-up, order, normal, and overstock. The column of numbers immediately to the left of the heavy center bar (indicated by the finger in Fig. 29) constitutes **order points.** When the order point for an item has been determined, on the basis of its rate of use and time required for its replenishment plus an adequate reserve, the chart is folded at that order point (24 in Figs. 29 and 30) and placed in the title insert, as shown in Fig. 31.

In Fig. 28, the order point for Cam Shaft No. 3061 is 36, standing for 3,600 items. When making the last entry of May 20 on the in-out and balance card of a balance of 3,300, the clerk sets the Graph-A-Matic signal to the immediate left of the number 33 on the computing chart, which automatically shows that the stock of this item has fallen 300 units below the reorder point of 3,600. Similarly, the Graph-A-Matic signal shows a normal supply of 2,700 units of item No. 3066, Cam Shaft Bearing Rings, and immediately alerts the clerk that he has 900 units remaining before the order point is reached. The supply of 800 units of item No. 3071, Cam Shaft Dowel Pins, shows him that these have just reached the order point. (Similar methods are used with the Acme, Post Index, and other visible systems to establish control of inventory items.)

Figures to the left and right of the order point number on the computing chart are proportionate. The standard computing chart carries order point figures of

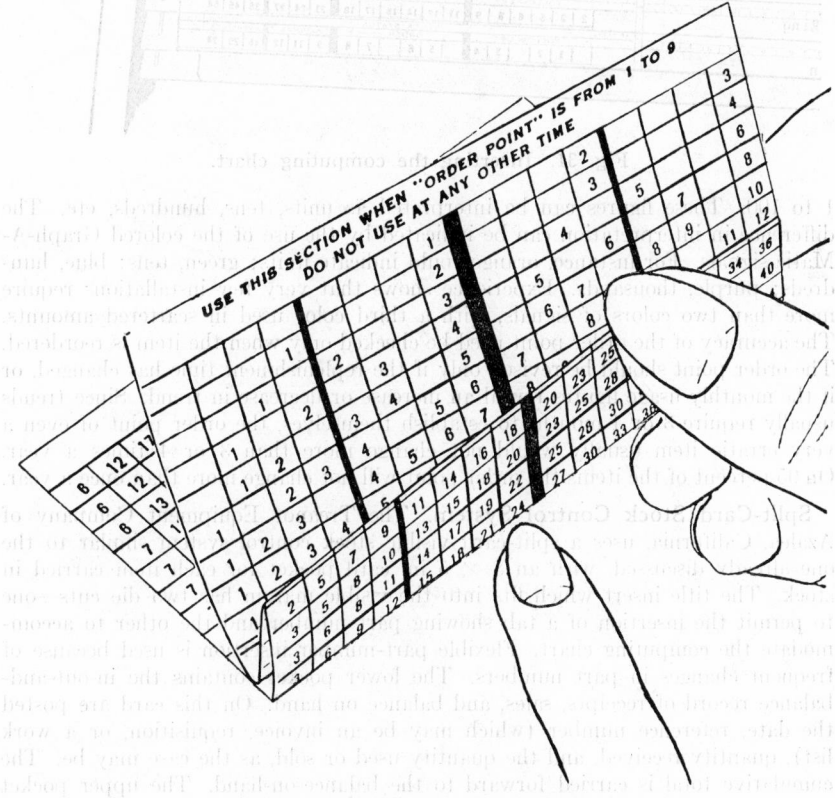

Fig. 30. Folding the computing chart.

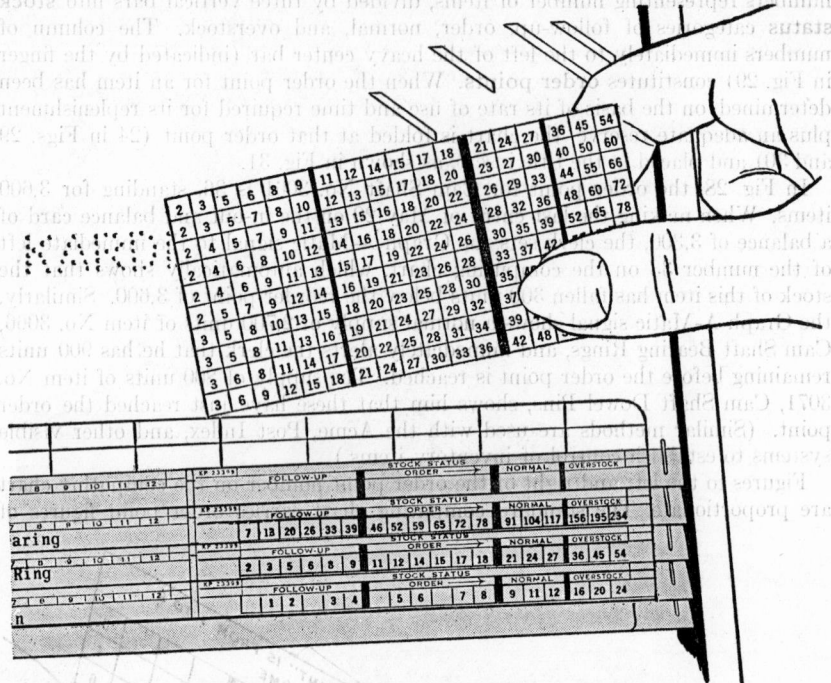

Fig. 31. Inserting the computing chart.

1 to 100. These figures can be interpreted as units, tens, hundreds, etc. The difference in interpretation can be indicated by the use of the colored Graph-A-Matic signals. For instance, orange could indicate units; green, tens; blue, hundreds; purple, thousands. Experience shows that very few installations require more than two colors of signals, with a third color used in scattered amounts. The accuracy of the order point need be checked only when the item is reordered. The order point should be revised only if the replenishment time has changed, or if the monthly usage figures reveal an increase or decrease in trend. Since trends usually require 3 or 4 months to establish themselves, the order point of even a very erratic item usually would not change more than 3 or 4 times a year. On 95 percent of the items the order point will not change more than once a year.

Split-Card Stock Control System. The Treanor Equipment Company of Azalea, California, uses a split-card visible stock control system similar to the one already discussed, with an 8 × 5 in. card pocket for each item carried in stock. The title insert which fits into the visible margin has two die cuts—one to permit the insertion of a tab showing part number and the other to accommodate the computing chart. Flexible part-number insertion is used because of frequent changes in part numbers. The lower pocket contains the in-out-and-balance record of receipts, sales, and balance on hand. On this card are posted the date, reference number (which may be an invoice, requisition, or a work list), quantity received, and the quantity used or sold, as the case may be. The cumulative total is carried forward to the balance-on-hand. The upper pocket contains two 4 × 5 in. cards. At the left is the order record, which shows the item number penciled in on the visible margin and a typed item description. On this card are posted the date of order, the order number, quantity ordered, date received, quantity received, balance due, and the time of delivery. The card to the right carries the item description, the names of the vendors, and the quarterly sales. The Graph-A-Matic signal is set to reflect changes in balance.

In addition to the Graph-A-Matic signals, ¼-in. signals are used as follows: A green signal on the right-hand corner of the description box indicates an ordered item; a black-and-white ¼-in. striped signal immediately to the left of the green indicates an item that is back-ordered; a purple signal indicates an item that has not moved since the last physical inventory, and therefore serves as a warning to dispose of excess stocks. The third signal at the left corner of the description box indicates an item is not returnable for credit.

Traveling Requisition Card System. The Spicer Manufacturing Corporation of Toledo, Ohio, uses another variation of the basic Kardex Visible Inventory record. It adapted its old vertical stock record cards by die-cutting them to fit in the upper part of the pocket of the Kardex slide as a traveling requisition. Monthly consumption over a 6-year period is posted on a small blue ticket which slips into the upper pocket. On this ticket replenishment time and order point are both noted. Split cards are housed in the lower Kardex pocket. The card to the left shows orders and receipts, that to the right indicates disbursements. A title insert carries the part description and identifying number, the monthly usage, the order point, a 1st-to-31st-day-of-month scale, the schedule of weeks' supply on hand, and whether this is an overstock, normal supply, the normal supply in the period of replenishment, or a draft on reserve stock. Reordering is an automatic process because of the permanently approved traveling requisition which is pulled to create the purchase order whenever the signal indicates that the balance has fallen to the follow-up point.

The traveling or permanent requisition has been found to be an economical and practical short cut on many regularly used and readily available items carried in stock. Although there are many types in use, all have certain characteristics in common:

1. The complete and accurate specification for ordering is typed on the form and virtually eliminates the possibility of error from faulty copying by the stores record clerk.
2. The accepted sources are shown, relieving the buyer of the need to refer to other records to select the source.
3. Previous purchase records of delivery, price, and costs are shown in order to aid in source selection.
4. Monthly consumption provides a means of determining consumption trends as an aid in determining proper order quantities.

Whatever system of stores record is adopted, the traveling requisition procedure is the same. The form is stored with the record card and pulled when the order point is reached. The stores clerk enters the balance on hand, brings the consumption record up to date, and forwards the card to the buyer. The buyer determines the vendor and the order quantity, price, and delivery schedule. The requisition is then ready for the order typist. If further approval is required, the traveling requisition again saves time by providing all information necessary to permit qualified decision. After the replenishment order is written, the traveling requisition, with order number and date filled in, is returned to the stock record clerk, who enters receiving data as the order is filled and refiles the requisition for subsequent use.

The traveling requisition in Fig. 32 is a sample designed for use with the Kardex system. It is made to slide in the pocket behind the stock record card. This form carries all the significant information on the front side and on the reverse may have space for supplier quotations, substitutions, and engineering changes or uses. When the Graph-A-Matic signal indicates that a reorder should be placed, the traveling requisition is removed from the pocket, and the ordering procedure begins.

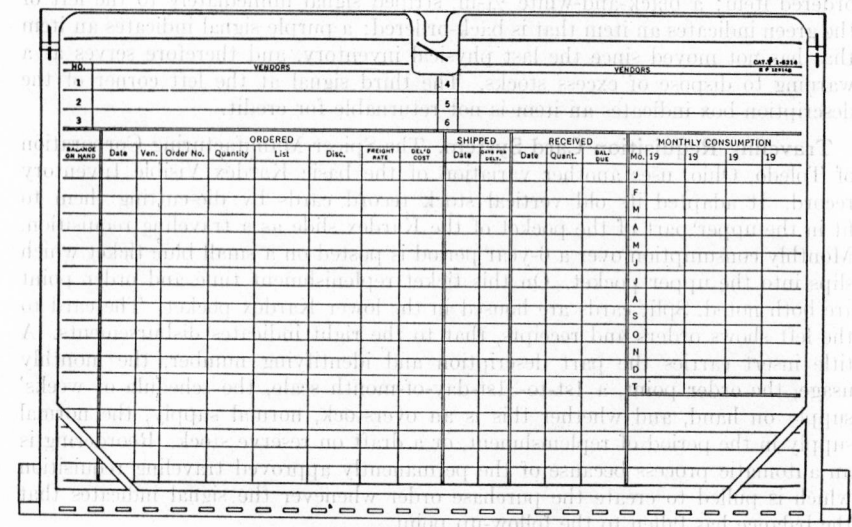

Fig. 32. Traveling requisition form.

Purchasing Department Manuals

PURPOSE OF MANUALS. As long as industrial management and organization remain outside the realm of exact science, as long as the delegation of function and responsibility vary between companies, there will be need for the purchasing department manuals. Manuals are designed to avoid conflicts between departments, clarify responsibility, simplify instructions, and reduce explanations. There are two types of purchasing department manuals in common use: the **policy manual** and the **procedures manual**.

POLICY MANUAL. The policy manual should be compiled with assistance and advice from purchasing department personnel, from other departments, and from suppliers. Moreover, since its principles must be coordinated with general company policy, the advice and support of top management is a primary requisite to its successful adoption and operation.

In general, policy manuals will include **definitions of policy** for:

1. Selection of and relations with sources of supply.
2. Making commitments; placing orders on contracts.
3. Reciprocity.
4. Commercial bribery.
5. Employee purchases.
6. Relations with other departments.
   a. Scope and limits of the responsibility of the purchasing department.
7. Policies with respect to proper quality, quantity, and price.

While the written policy is indeed a valuable tool when used only for reference, some companies extend its use by placing copies in the hands of regular suppliers. In all cases the need for flexibility and ease of amendment make it desirable to use loose-leaf construction and to keep a control over all copies.

PROCEDURES MANUAL. The manual of procedures, although not always a separate document, is confined to intracompany procedural responsibilities. Since only policy manuals can be of value when placed in the hands of suppliers, the custom of separation has merit. The procedural manual must be developed in much the same way as the policy manual, with greatest care being given to analysis, proposal, counterproposal, revision, trial, confirmation, and finally adoption and standardization. Since most of the procedures involve action on the part of other departments, the cooperation of these other departments at the time of development is essential.

Among the **topical headings in a procedural manual** one might find:

1. Inventory control or materials control.
2. Stores control.
3. Requisition (stores) procedure.
4. Requisition (purchase) procedure.
5. Purchase order routine.
6. Contracts and agreements.
7. Follow-up procedures.
8. Invoice procedures.
9. Merchandise returns.
10. Sample and information practices.
11. Purchasing department records.

Although revisions in procedure will of necessity be more frequent than in policy, the task of revision is less complicated, since practically all copies are retained within the company.

Reports to Management

PURCHASING DEPARTMENT REPORTS TO MANAGEMENT. The modern concept of a purchasing department demands that there should be means for measuring its efficiency to the satisfaction of the company management. A plan for measuring this efficiency serves a double purpose:

1. It permits management to keep an actual check upon how well the purchasing department is doing its job.
2. It permits the purchasing agent to analyze and measure his own task and his performance of it, and such a measurement is sure to result in improvement.

Factors in determining purchasing efficiency are:

1. Proved savings. These will include:
   a. Proved savings from purchases under market prices for goods bought.
   b. Proved savings achieved by initiation of improved methods or substitution of better or cheaper materials.
2. Intangible savings.
3. Expense of operating purchasing department.
4. Expense caused by purchasing department failures—which include:
   a. Purchasing loss and error account.
   b. Cost of failure to have material on hand when needed.
5. Inventory expense.

Of these factors items 1 and 2 are credits to the purchasing department's account, while items 3, 4, and 5 are debits.

To establish any yardstick of purchasing efficiency, there must be reports to management indicating the purchasing department's standing as to each of these factors. Some of these reports will originate in the purchasing department, while others must come from department heads capable of evaluating performance.

Proved Savings on Price. Proved savings on price should be established by charts or tabular reports on the principal commodities purchased, showing comparatively the average market prices of the commodities and the actual prices paid over the period covered by the report. It is impractical to keep such charts or reports on all items bought. Since published market prices are a necessary part of such a study, it is usual to maintain them on basic commodities only and assume that all other items are bought at market prices. From these charts or reports on individual commodities is drawn a summary of proved savings on price.

Proved Savings by Substitution. Proved savings by substitution cannot be established merely on the claim of the purchasing department. Other departments may have an equal claim to credit for substitutions made. It is necessary, therefore, to initiate claims for such savings in the purchasing department, then have them substantiated by the proper plant authority, and finally have each claim approved by the management before it is credited to the purchasing department. Fig. 33 shows a claim sheet for savings by substitution of material.

Savings made through substitution or
changes initiated by Purchasing Department

Commodity ....

Explanation ....
....
....
....

Amount claimed as saved.......$4,800.00.................................

Signed ....
                                        Purchasing Agent

Approved ....
                      Vice-President in charge of Production

Date ....

Fig. 33. Purchasing department claim for savings.

Another way of proving savings is to show the differential between the price paid for a fabricated article and the market price of the component materials. For example, for solder, grade 50–50, the metal content is established, and there are published prices on lead and tin. The purchase records will show the price paid over the price of metals. If by developing a new source of supply or by developing a new method of purchasing, the differential is lowered, the purchasing department can claim the credit for the difference between the new and old differential.

It is difficult to apply an accurate yardstick to purchasing work. Gross inefficiency will soon show up, but unfortunately there is no way to prove that a job well done cannot be done still better. Methods of measuring, such as cost per order, cost per dollar spent, all have in them so many variables that are beyond the control of the purchasing department that without full, detailed explanation and adjustment they become misleading. Ten orders for a stock size of strip steel can be handled much more cheaply per order than one order for some fabricated item made according to special specifications, which requires special tools, samples to be submitted, etc.

Departmental Expenses. The departmental expense of the purchasing department includes salaries and wages, stationery and supplies, light, heat, charges for premises occupied, telephone, telegraph, and postage expenses, and all other expenses incurred by the company in operating the department. The account should be as inclusive as possible, and the report showing this expense will originate in the accounting or finance department. Fig. 34 shows a purchasing department operating expense sheet.

	January	February	March	April	etc.	Year
Salaries and Wages	$1,528.60	$1,503.79	$1,463.87	$......	$......	$17,143.10
Traveling Account	5.00	25.47	73.56			315.25
Stationery and Supplies....	256.78	179.54	193.56			1,767.24
Subscriptions and Dues....	75.00	15.00	63.00			285.00
Rent, Heat, Light and Equipment	312.50	312.50	312.50			3,750.00
Telephone and Telegraph..	315.47	259.42	236.15			2,480.00
Excess Transportation Charges	569.73	445.02	379.81			3,144.37
Totals	3,063.08	2,740.24	2,722.45			28,885.15
Orders Issued during Period	3,600	3,155	3,325			29,697
Cost per Order	0.8509	0.8685	0.8188			0.9727

Fig. 34. Report of purchasing department expenses.

Loss and Error Account. The purchasing department loss and error account covers all expenses caused by errors in specifying material, loss in receiving, shortages not adjusted by vendors, defective goods not replaced or adjusted by vendors, etc. The accounting department should keep this record and submit a report which summarizes it. Goods returned for defects should be charged to this account, and credit memoranda received, or replacements should be credited to it. All transportation charges on such transactions as well as handling charges should be debited except so far as borne by the vendor. Fig. 35 shows a summary of the purchasing loss and error account.

Loss and Error Account Summary

January	$ 10.43	July	$ 12.44
February	4.17	August	5.67
March	85.96	September	189.53
April	136.38	October	75.01
May	3.77	November	3.87
June	15.23	December	80.98

Total for year ending Dec. 31, 19—.......... **$623.44**

Fig. 35. Summary report of loss and error account.

Failures To Receive Material on Time. There should be a definite report on failures of the purchasing department to receive material on time. So far as the accounting system provides a means for charging actual expenses caused to the company by such failures, actual expenses should be used. When the actual expense is not ascertainable, as is generally true, some method for making a fixed charge against the purchasing department for delivery failures should be adopted. A fair method is to charge the purchasing department on each order received late with the cost of placing the order. This plan rests on the theory that the purchasing department is paid a certain sum to do a job which includes getting material by a certain date. Not having done the job, since material was not received as specified, the department should be debited with the cost of the job. For the purpose of determining its efficiency in this respect, the purchasing department should maintain a record of orders received on time and orders received late, with the ratio of each to total orders. Fig. 36 shows a purchasing department report on delivery of purchase orders.

	Jan.	Feb.	Mar.	Apr.	May	etc.	Total
Open orders in file 1st of month...........	645	580	613	575	560	.....	.....
Orders issued during month..............	3,600	3,155	3,325	3,267	3,159		29,697
Orders received during month.............	3,665	3,122	3,363	3,282	3,224		29,950
Orders open at end of month.............	580	613	575	560	495		
Orders received on time.................	3,209	2,850	3,113	3,169	2,998		27,134
Orders received 1 day to 1 week late......	318	176	150	76	145		1,977
Orders received 1 week to 2 weeks late....	90	82	69	33	60		599
Orders received later than 2 weeks........	48	14	31	4	21		240
% received on time........................	87.6%	91.3%	92.6%	96.6%	92.9%		90.6%
% received 1 day to 1 week late...........	8.7	5.6	4.5	2.3	4.5		6.6
% received 1 week to 2 weeks late........	2.4	2.6	2.0	1.0	1.9		2.0
% received later than 2 weeks.............	1.3	.5	.9	.1	.7		.8

Fig. 36. Summary of delivery of orders.

Other Reports. Inventory carrying charges are charges against purchasing department efficiency, whether or not the purchasing department controls inventory. This condition is true because the amount of stock carried has a direct bearing on the difficulty of the purchasing task and prices that can be obtained. A report of total inventory carried with carrying charges thereon is part of the management's record of purchasing department efficiency. This report will be initiated by the materials control department.

In addition to the above, the management should have before it a report showing in some detail a record of the activities of purchasing. Such a report

	January	February	March	etc.	Total for Year
No. in Dept.	9	9	9	....	9
Orders issued	3,600	3,158	3,325		29,697
Total purchases	$213.117.00	$175,765.48	$164,859.41		$1,234,567.89
Value per order	$59.20	$55.71	$49.58		$41.57
Invoices rec'd	4,487	3,996	4,416		38,062
Letters written	1,160	912	1,125		9,306
Telegrams sent	143	100	103		843
Carloads rec'd	11	8	15		131
L. C. L. rec'd	114 tons	149 tons	115 tons		1,025 tons
Parcel post	2,340	2,134	2,419		23,813
Express	524	447	429		3,868
Overland	1,160	490	690		6,352
Returns	206	175	227		1,848

Fig. 37. Purchasing department activities report.

should include the number of orders placed, number of invoices, average money value per order, and all other pertinent facts indicating the volume and scope of the purchasing department's activities. This report will be initiated in the purchasing department. Fig. 37 shows a report of purchasing department activities.

EVALUATION OF PURCHASING DEPARTMENT EFFICIENCY. With these seven reports before it, the management may proceed to evaluate the efficiency of the purchasing department. The methods used for this purpose will vary with size of the company, the type of purchases, and other factors. It is important that evaluation should rest upon the sound theory that the measure of efficiency shall be the ultimate cost of spending a dollar compared with the savings achieved. The adaptation of an efficiency record (Purchasing, vol. 37) shown in Fig. 38 indicates a method of summarizing the purchasing department's cost to the company and the job it has done.

I. CHARGES		I. CREDITS	
A. Prices paid above std. for material	$ 15,000	A. Prices paid below std. for material	$ 10,000
B. Department Expense (Salaries, supplies, rent, lighting, phone, etc.)	27,000	B. Savings by substitution	2,000
C. Freight Charges	10,000	C. Salvage Sales	1,000
D. Discrepancies, Losses and Delays.	5,000	Total Credits	$ 13,000

E. Expense of carrying
Inventory ....($2,000,000)
   Int. .... .06
   Obs. .... .08
   Det. .... .01
   Tax & Ins. .... .005
   Rent .... .04
   Clerical .... .01
   Handling .... .02
   Repairs .... .01
   Carry. Chgs. .... .20
      .20 (2,000,000) ¼ = 100,000
                        $157,000

II. Net cost of purchasing = Charges — Credits (per quarter)
   Charges $157,000
   Credits 13,000
   Cost 144,000

III. Amount of material purchased (per quarter) $1,800,000

IV. Deficiency Index = Total purchases divided into the net cost of purchasing (Also equals the amount of cents a company spends to buy a dollar's worth of goods) = $\frac{144,000}{\$1,800,000}$ = .08 or 8%

V. Efficiency Index = 100 — 8
                        = 92%

NOTE: All figures are fictitious and are listed for the purpose of explaining the technique.

Fig. 38. Purchasing department efficiency record.

The final index of purchasing efficiency may be stated as a percentage. The net ultimate cost of the department (including operating expense, cost of its failures, and cost of carrying inventory) with proved savings subtracted, divided by total volume of purchases, gives a percentage figure which is actually an expression of ultimate purchasing cost in ratio to value of goods purchased. Subtraction of this percentage from 100 percent gives an **index figure of purchasing efficiency.** Fig. 38 illustrates the computation of this efficiency index.

STORESKEEPING

CONTENTS

PAGE

Nature and Administration of Storeskeeping

Definition 1
Objectives 1
Storeskeeping functions 1
Administration of storeskeeping 2
Organization of storeskeeping 2
Place of storeskeeping in plant organization (f. 1) 3
Storeroom personnel 2
Responsibilities of storeskeepers 4

Planning for Storeskeeping

Space planning 4
Space forecasts 5
Forecast of storage requirements (f. 2)... 5

Layout for Storeskeeping

Basis for layout 6
Determination of storage space required 6
Location of the storeskeeping department ... 7
Centralized storerooms 7
Reorganization and rebuilding of storage space 8
Allocation of storage space 9
Designation of unit loads 9
Methods of storing 9
Good layout of aisles in a storeroom (f. 3) 10
Moving materials into and out of stock ... 10
Wheel conveyor storage providing first-in first-out control (f. 4) 11
Aisles 10
Auxiliary storeskeeping areas 13
Typical method of storeroom layout and section and row symbols (f. 5) 12

PAGE

Symbols for sections, rows, and bins or tiers 13
Method of designating bin columns and tiers by symbols (f. 6) 13

Storeroom Equipment

Shelves, bins, and racks 13
Storage equipment types 14
Open-type removable bins in counter unit (f. 7) 14
Stack racks with drawer inserts (f. 8a).. 15
Stacking boxes (f. 8b) 15
Rack for lumber, bar stock, or pipe (f. 9) 15
Portable gravity-feed stock-selecting rack (f. 10) 16
Storeskeeping handling equipment 17
Special pallet for handling and piling cylindrical stock (f. 11) 18
Racks designed for stacking and handling short bar stock by fork or lift trucks (f. 12) 19
Shelf truck for storing and handling material (f. 13) 20
Auxiliary storeskeeping equipment 18
Self-supporting movable ladder (f. 14a).. 20
Movable ladder operating on overhead rail guide (f. 14b) 20

Stores Records and Protection

Classification 20
Classification systems 21
Record-keeping 21
Protection of stores 22
Hazardous conditions 22
Weather 22
Deterioration 22
Theft 22

STOREKEEPING

CONTENTS

Page

Nature and Administration of Storekeeping

Definition 1
Objectives 1
Storekeeping functions 1
Administration of storekeeping 2
Organization of storekeeping 2
Place of storekeeping in plant organiza-
tion (1. 1) 3
Storeroom personnel 3
Responsibilities of storekeepers 4

Planning for Storekeeping

Space planning 4
Space forecasts 5
Forecast of storage requirements (1. 2) 5

Layout for Storekeeping

Basis for layout 6
Determination of storage space required 6
Location of the storekeeping department 7
Centralized storeroom 7
Decentralization and rehabiliting of storage
space 8
Allocation of storage space 8
Designation of unit loads 9
Methods of storing 9
Good layout of aisles in a storeroom
(1. 3) 10
Moving materials into and out of stock ... 10
Wheel conveyor storage providing first-in
first-out stock (1. 4) 11
Aisles 11
Auxiliary storekeeping areas 13
Typical method of storeroom layout and
aisle and row symbols (1. 5) 12

Page

Symbols for sections, rows, and bins or tiers.. 12
Method of designating bin columns and
tiers by symbols (1. 6) 13

Storeroom Equipment

Shelves, bins, and racks 13
Storage equipment types 14
Open-type removable bins in counter
unit (1. 7) 14
Stock racks with drawer inserts (1. 8a).. 15
Stacking boxes (1. 8b) 15
Rack for lumber, bar stock, or pipe (1. 9) 15
Portable gravity-feed stock-selecting rack
(1. 10) 16
Storekeeping handling equipment 17
Special pallet for handling and plac-
ing cylindrical stock (1. 11) 18
Racks designed for stacking and handling
short bar stock by fork or lift truck
(1. 12) 19
Shelf truck for storing and handling
material (1. 13) 20
Auxiliary storekeeping equipment 20
Self-supporting movable ladder (1. 14a) ... 20
Movable ladder operating on overhead
rail guide (1. 14b) 20

Stores Records and Protection

Classification 20
Classification by items 21
Record keeping 22
Protection of stores 22
Hazardous conditions 22
Weather 22
Deterioration 22
Theft 22

STORESKEEPING

Nature and Administration of Storeskeeping

DEFINITION. Storeskeeping is primarily a service function in which the storekeeper acts as a custodian of all items carried in the store. Alford and Beatty (Principles of Industrial Management) describe storeskeeping as "that aspect of materials control concerned with the physical storage of goods." Knowles and Thomson (Industrial Management) depict the stores department as "the connecting link between the planning, or production department, and the shops. Parts and materials move through it much as money moves into and out of the commercial department of a bank."

OBJECTIVES. The efficient planning and carrying out of the storeskeeping function should aim at **minimizing the costs** involved, while providing effective storeskeeping **service.** In addition to the costs of over- or understocking of materials as required for production, there are the costs of storage itself. These include the cost of capital invested in materials and supplies; the cost of getting the materials and supplies to the factory; the costs of protecting, handling, and record-keeping, as well as for providing space for materials storage. Other storage costs are the storeroom expenses for heat, light, taxes, insurance, and the losses due to spoilage or obsolescence.

Failure to locate storerooms properly and the inefficient use of available storeroom space can be most costly. These failures may require excess handling of materials, greater handling personnel and facilities, difficulty in locating materials, and overstocking and its attendant costs. Problems in materials control and time involved in supplying materials when needed are frequently the results of improper storeroom location and use.

STORESKEEPING FUNCTIONS. The detailed functions of storeskeeping are:

1. Receipt of materials into storage.
2. Record-keeping of materials in storage.
3. Storage of materials.
4. Maintaining stores.
5. Issuing stores.
6. Coordinating storeskeeping with materials control.

Raw materials, supplies, and purchased parts are usually received at a designated **receiving dock,** unloaded, inspected, and then moved into storeskeeping. The storekeeper identifies the material in accordance with the stores classification, dispatches it to the appropriate storage area and position, and records the receipt of materials into storage.

In general, semiprocessed parts in transit between operations are the responsibility of manufacturing or materials handling. However, semiprocessed materials may be placed in storeskeeping when the parts are very valuable and subject to pilferage, very fragile, or in need of special protection or aging.

The maintenance of **storeskeeping records** in an efficient and orderly manner is of the utmost importance in order to locate incoming and outgoing materials quickly and accurately, to provide the necessary information concerning the exact whereabouts of the materials, and to supply the materials control and cost-keeping departments with correct and timely data.

The proper storage of materials involves holding the materials for safekeeping and protection until they are required elsewhere by **authorized requisitions.** Therefore, it is necessary to have a sufficient area for the materials and suitable storage devices such as boxes, bins, and racks. The storage facilities should be selected so as to provide the maximum of protection and accessibility and to utilize a minimum amount of space.

Materials in storage may require not only protection but maintenance as well. To keep the stores in the desired condition over a period of time may require very simple or very elaborate measures, depending on the nature of the material, the length of time in storage, and the rates of deterioration. Proper **stores maintenance measures** may range from special covering or periodic lubrication to controlled atmospheric conditions.

Another primary function of storeskeeping is issuing of stores. When this function is performed efficiently, the materials will be delivered quickly with a minimum of delay, and records will be correctly adjusted immediately. The physical and clerical facilities for storeskeeping must be carefully preplanned if the issuance of stores is to be prompt, positive, and accurate.

Coordination of storeskeeping with materials control is an essential aspect of a properly functioning storeskeeping department. Coordination must be planned or designed into a good storeskeeping system. Duly authorized storage requisitions must originate at the proper source and records of storage changes must be maintained for use by the materials and cost control centers. The responsibility for such coordination may rest only in part with the storeskeeping center, depending on the type of production in the plant, the size of the company, and the organizational makeup of the company.

ADMINISTRATION OF STORESKEEPING. The way in which the storeskeeping department is organized and administered will depend on a number of factors, such as the size and plan of the over-all company organization, the degree of centralization desired, the types of products manufactured, the relative flexibility of production facilities, and the prospective manufacturing plans.

Organization of Storeskeeping. These factors will determine whether one or more permanent or temporary storerooms are established, the size of the storeskeeping personnel, and the internal organization of the storeskeeping department, as well as the relationship of storeskeeping with other company activities. Fig. 1 is an organization chart showing a typical relationship of the storeskeeper with other individuals or departments in a factory. The **organization chart** will vary for different companies, however (see section on Plant Organization), and may show the storeskeeper reporting to the manufacturing superintendent, the purchasing agent, or even the controller. In some cases, the storeskeeper of finished products may report to the sales manager or merchandise manager.

Storeroom Personnel. The number of persons required to operate a storeskeeping system varies widely, depending on the size of the company and the plan of the over-all company organization. Typical storeroom personnel would consist

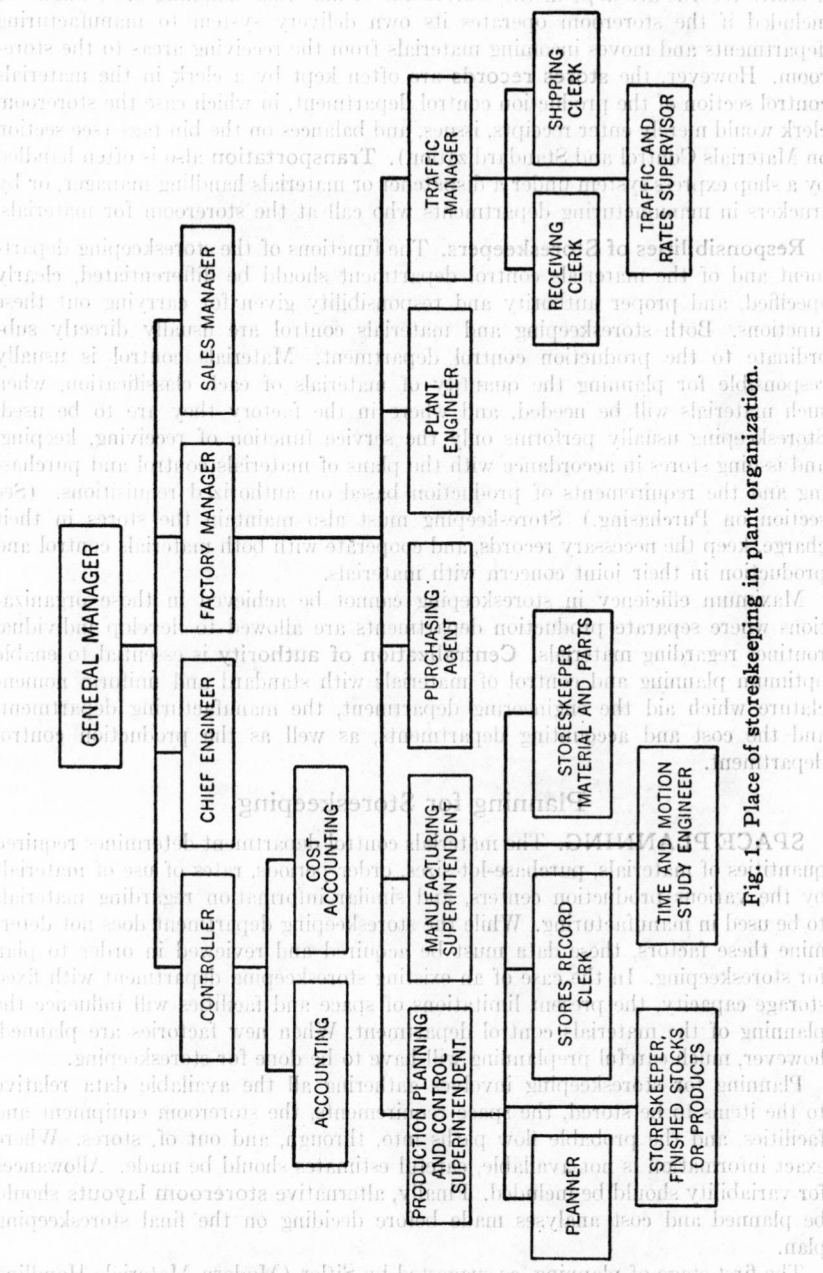

Fig. 1. Place of storeskeeping in plant organization.

of a **chief storeskeeper, assistant storeskeeper,** and one or more **stores clerks** if stores records are kept in the storeroom. A materials handling crew might be included if the storeroom operates its own delivery system to manufacturing departments and moves incoming materials from the receiving areas to the storeroom. However, the **stores records** are often kept by a clerk in the materials control section of the production control department, in which case the storeroom clerk would merely enter receipts, issues, and balances on the bin tags (see section on Materials Control and Standardization). **Transportation** also is often handled by a shop express system under a dispatcher or materials handling manager, or by truckers in manufacturing departments who call at the storeroom for materials.

Responsibilities of Storeskeepers. The functions of the storeskeeping department and of the materials control department should be differentiated, clearly specified, and proper authority and responsibility given for carrying out these functions. Both storeskeeping and materials control are usually directly subordinate to the production control department. Materials control is usually responsible for planning the quantity of materials of each classification, when such materials will be needed, and where in the factory they are to be used. Storeskeeping usually performs only the service function of receiving, keeping, and issuing stores in accordance with the plans of materials control and purchasing and the requirements of production based on authorized requisitions. (See section on Purchasing.) Storeskeeping must also maintain the stores in their charge, keep the necessary records, and cooperate with both materials control and production in their joint concern with materials.

Maximum efficiency in storeskeeping cannot be achieved in those organizations where separate production departments are allowed to develop individual routines regarding materials. **Centralization of authority** is essential to enable optimum planning and control of materials with standard and uniform nomenclature which aid the engineering department, the manufacturing department, and the cost and accounting departments, as well as the production control department.

Planning for Storeskeeping

SPACE PLANNING. The materials control department determines required quantities of materials, purchase-lot sizes, order periods, rates of use of materials by the various production centers, and similar information regarding materials to be used in manufacturing. While the storeskeeping department does not determine these factors, these data must be acquired and reviewed in order to plan for storeskeeping. In the case of an existing storeskeeping department with fixed storage capacity, the present limitations of space and facilities will influence the planning of the materials control department. When new factories are planned, however, much careful preplanning will have to be done for storeskeeping.

Planning for storeskeeping involves gathering all the available data relative to the items to be stored, the space requirements, the storeroom equipment and facilities, and the probable flow paths into, through, and out of, stores. Where exact information is not available, careful estimates should be made. Allowances for variability should be included. Finally, alternative **storeroom layouts** should be planned and cost analyses made before deciding on the final storeskeeping plan.

The first stage of planning, as suggested by Sitler (Modern Materials Handling Manual, No. 1), is to determine the over-all **cubical space requirements** for storeskeeping. These requirements should be estimated on both a short-term and long-term basis in order to anticipate future as well as present requirements. It is necessary to determine the quantities of materials to be stored and the specifications which may affect storage, such as size, weight, fragility, susceptibility to pilferage, and other factors which may require special handling or storage treatment. Then data must be gathered covering the purchasing lead time, and the rates of delivery and rates of use in the factory of the materials to be serviced by storeskeeping. This information must be translated into space requirements. Changes in anticipated quantities of certain materials may or may not affect the total space required since there may be compensating changes in other material requirements. Thus, it is necessary to project the space requirements over a long period of time, such as five to twenty years, depending on the classification of industry for which a given type of factory is being designed.

SPACE FORECASTS. The estimate of trends is not sufficient. In addition, the expected variations in space requirements caused by probable **fluctuations of demand** for the product or products being manufactured and the ratio of items to be manufactured for stock versus those to be delivered directly to the customer have a bearing on the quantities which must be stocked.

Single-source items, or items purchased from industries in which collective bargaining covers the entire industry, must also be stocked in greater quantities at certain times of year to provide for the possibility of strikes. Statistical analysis, explained in fundamental principle in the section on Statistical Methods, should be used as a tool for determining the optimum space required, both for long-term and short-term operation. Accurate historical records must be analyzed in conjunction with data from the latest forecasting techniques to determine the limits within which space must be provided for storeskeeping. Fig. 2 is a typical example of such a forecast. The upper and lower limits may have a **nonuniform variation.** It is obvious that the further into the future such a projection is made, the smaller the chance of complete accuracy.

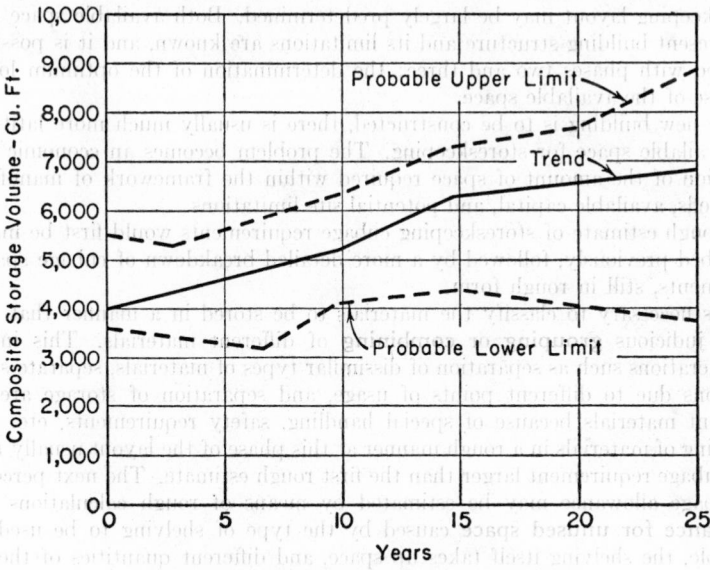

Fig. 2. Forecast of storage requirements.

The costs involved for allowing **excess space** are the building and land costs, the interest on capital invested, and the possible additional handling costs due to extra travel distance. The costs due to **inadequate space** may be the cost of ordering more frequently, lack of large lot discounts, cost of extra warehouse rental, possible temporary shutdown or slowdown on operations, and customer dissatisfaction due to inability to supply product or spare parts as rapidly as desired.

The cubage required will then have to be increased to allow for storing different items independently and to allow for space which cannot be utilized because of shelving, aisle, and handling equipment considerations.

The proper layout for storage results from the determination of the most effective **space utilization.** Consequently, planning for storage and layout of storage space are interdependent activities and should either be done concurrently or separately, but with full understanding of considerations involved in each activity. Materials handling equipment selection (Modern Materials Handling Manual, No. 1) is also directly related to the planning and layout of storage and therefore should be considered simultaneously (see section on Materials Handling).

Layout for Storeskeeping

BASIS FOR LAYOUT. Three important phases of layout for storeskeeping are:

1. Determination of the area of storage space required.
2. Determination of the optimum location for the storeskeeping space.
3. Determination of the optimum allocation of space within the storeskeeping area.

DETERMINATION OF STORAGE SPACE REQUIRED. If an existing building is to be used for the manufacturing enterprise, the first phase of storeskeeping layout may be largely predetermined. Both available space within the present building structure and its limitations are known, and it is possible to proceed with phases two and three: the determination of the optimum location and use of the available space.

If a new building is to be constructed, there is usually much more latitude in the available space for storeskeeping. The problem becomes an economic determination of the amount of space required within the framework of manufacturing needs, available capital, and potential site limitations.

A rough estimate of storeskeeping cubage requirements would first be made as described previously, followed by a more detailed breakdown of cubage space requirements, still in rough form.

It is necessary to classify the materials to be stored in a manner that allows for a judicious **grouping** or **combining** of different materials. This involves considerations such as separation of dissimilar types of materials, separate storage locations due to different points of usage, and separation of storage areas for different materials because of special handling, safety requirements, etc. Thus, grouping of materials in a rough manner at this phase of the layout usually results in a cubage requirement larger than the first rough estimate. The next percentage of cubage allowance may be estimated by means of rough calculations of an **allowance for unused space** caused by the type of shelving to be used. For example, the shelving itself takes up space, and different quantities of the same parts can be stored in one large container as against several shelves occupying the same area. Another allowance should be added for aisles and materials handling equipment. It is emphasized that the allowances must be crude at this phase. The interdependence of these allowances can be seen from the fact that usually a different depth of shelving will result in a different percentage of space required for aisles. In general, the deeper the shelving, within practical limits, the less aisle space will be required.

LOCATION OF THE STORESKEEPING DEPARTMENT. The determination of the final location of the storeskeeping areas will depend on the needs of the plant and will vary greatly from plant to plant. Certain basic **storage location factors**, however, should be taken into account in order to arrive at the best decision:

1. **Materials classification.** It may be desirable to locate materials of the same classification together, regardless of differences in size, weight, and destination. For example, one area may be designated for supplies, raw materials, and purchased parts; another area may be designated for semiprocessed parts, and another for finished inventory.

2. **Similarity of materials.** Articles of similar size, shape, and weight may be stored together even though they may be classified differently or be required at different production locations. All small parts may be kept in one place, bar stock in another, and castings and bulky items in still another place.

3. **Point of use.** It is sometimes desirable to locate all materials to be used at each production center as close as possible to that particular center. This may involve **storeroom decentralization** or merely special grouping of materials within a centralized storeroom.

4. **Materials handling considerations.** Materials which require similar handling equipment may be grouped together. For example, liquids which must be specially measured or moved by special handling equipment may be placed together. Items lending themselves more efficiently to truck handling or conveyorized handling may be placed together. Also, items which are to be handled more often because of the greater frequency of requisition may be placed at more accessible locations than infrequently handled items.

5. **Special requirements.** Certain materials have to be handled or stored in a special manner because of their physical characteristics. They may be fragile, explosive, extremely valuable, or may require special **atmospheric conditions.** Such materials will have to be stored in locations affording the proper facilities even though, in many cases, the facilities may not be ideally located for point of use delivery or for best materials handling utilization.

Centralized Storerooms. Usually, a combination of the preceding storage location factors must be taken into consideration in order to achieve the best internal storeroom location. Also, there may be building limitations which require a storeroom location other than the optimum location because of these factors. This is especially true in the case of adapting an existing building to the needs of a new manufacturing enterprise. Not only is there the problem of deciding the best location of adjacent storage groupings, there is also the necessity of deciding whether all stores should be located in one centralized storeroom or in two or more decentralized areas. There are advantages and disadvantages either way. The **advantages** of centralized storing are:

1. Fewer persons are required in the storeroom.
2. The entire stores personnel becomes familiar with all materials stored. There is less trouble if someone quits or is absent.

3. Better control is afforded over inventory and storeroom records all in one place.
4. Less total inventory is usually carried because of lack of duplication.
5. There is more leveling off of load on personnel.
6. Less total space is occupied.
7. Less obsolete stores are carried and there is quicker discovery of practically duplicate items and of items declining in use.
8. Periodic physical inventory checks against balance-of-stores records are easier to take.
9. Clerical costs are lessened.

The **disadvantages** of centralized storing are:

1. The storeroom may be far away from some departments so that greater transportation is required to and from the storeroom by those departments. More materials handling equipment and greater time and labor are involved for distant departments.
2. Centralized stores clerks are less familiar with the needs and peculiarities of each individual area being served.
3. Greater time is required for delivery to distant departments.
4. Longer waiting lines tend to form with only one storage area as opposed to several areas.

In order to make the best decisions both as to internal grouping of storage areas and as to centralization or decentralization, it is necessary to attempt to total the factors involved and to express the alternative advantages and disadvantages in terms of costs. This can best be done by the use of sound engineering judgment coupled with the use of analytical techniques. According to Richman (Journal of Industrial Engineering, vol. 7), certain systems analysis and operations research techniques may be utilized for solving storage location problems. Klein and Milberg (Modern Materials Handling, vol. 10) state that handling, order picking, and delivery patterns may be analyzed with the aid of a linear programming **transportation model.** As suggested by Morris (Journal of Industrial Engineering, vol. 6), **queueing theory** may be used to analyze the waiting-line problem involved in the centralization-decentralization storage location problem. Well-known industrial engineering layout and handling problem-solving techniques such as **sequence analysis** and **circle charting,** as reported respectively by Buffa and Smith (Journal of Industrial Engineering, vol. 6), help make the best use of the grouping and relative positioning of substorage areas.

REORGANIZATION AND REBUILDING OF STORAGE SPACE. Despite the care exercised in the planning of storeskeeping facilities, changing conditions may require the reorganization and rebuilding of storage space. Even though the manufacturing requirements may have greatly changed, it is often possible to utilize existing storage space and facilities more effectively by merely regrouping materials. Perhaps, changing from location of materials by classification to location by similarity of materials or by point of use (Modern Materials Handling Manual, No. 1) may make the utilization of the storage space and equipment more suitable for the new production requirements. Of course, the greater the flexibility of the original storage setup, the easier will be the reorganization to meet new conditions. Thus, in an industry where frequent change may be anticipated, Bright (Modern Materials Handling Manual, No. 1) suggests that **storage shelving** and **handling equipment** should be chosen for their flexibility as well as for the ability to do the present job.

Often, however, more drastic measures must be taken to meet the new storage requirements. Richman and Vorsteg (Modern Materials Handling, vol. 12) report that making **structural changes** in the building to allow for a different layout or for providing additional strength for handling devices of greater capacity is occasionally required. Because of the high cost of making such changes, it is desirable to keep them to a minimum. An engineering analysis should be made to determine the optimum amount of redesign of storage layout and facilities which should be made, consistent with the new production requirements.

ALLOCATION OF STORAGE SPACE. After deciding on the degree of centralization of storage areas, blocking out subgroupings of materials, and crudely determining the relative locations of each area, there remains the detailed layout of storeroom space. The objectives of good utilization of space are as follows:

1. Intensive utilization of space.
2. Optimum accessibility of materials.
3. Greatest base of control of materials.
4. Maximum flexibility of arrangement.
5. Complete protection of materials.

Designation of Unit Loads. It is highly desirable to arrive at a proper unit load designation for all materials to be stored. Actually, it would be most convenient if it could be arranged so that materials arrive packaged in the best unit load containers, packs, or pallet loads. Thus, they could be taken from receiving through stores and on to the manufacturing department in the same package or unit so as to eliminate unpackaging and repackaging, and where possible this should be done. Unit loads should be specified and arranged in **standard containers** or **pallets** as soon as possible after receipt of materials, where prepackaging in unit loads cannot be done. In this manner, the standard size pallet or container, rather than the small, individual article, becomes the unit in which the item is handled. The article itself may be the standard unit, where the article is large, such as bags of cement or large castings. The exact size of the unit load will depend on the size and shape of the individual item, the handling equipment to be used, and the rate at which the item is required at the production center.

Methods of Storing. Before detailing the dimensions of the storage area, both the unit loads and the methods of storage will have to be worked out. The materials may be piled, stacked, or placed in bins, racks, or shelving.

If the material is to be piled or stacked, it may be placed directly on the floor or on pallets or skids. The practice of piling on the floor either in cubical piling or in pyramid form should be discouraged. There are few cases where some sort of palletization or stacking on skids cannot be substituted with substantial savings. The time and cost of eliminating floor piling will be greatly offset by reduced handling costs, ease of counting, and more efficient utilization of space. **Stacking height** will depend on the floor-load capacity, the crushability of the materials, the floor-to-ceiling height and the speed and lifting capacity of the equipment to be used. Also, the height permitted should not interfere with the effective operation of the sprinkler or lighting systems.

Where large quantities of materials are to be stacked, block stacking is most effective. **Block stacking** is the stacking of pallets or containers in rows such that each row contacts the adjacent row. For small quantities, row stacking is preferable. **Row stacking** is the stacking of materials in rows with sufficient space between rows so that any row of pallet stacks can be withdrawn without interference. Row stacking is more flexible than block stacking but requires **greater** total aisle space. Also, it is important to consider the orientation of the rows or blocks of tiered materials relative to the aisles. If the long dimension of the rows of pallets is perpendicular to the cross aisle, the ratio of occupied area to total area is greater than an arrangement whereby the long dimension is parallel to the aisle as may be seen in Fig. 3.

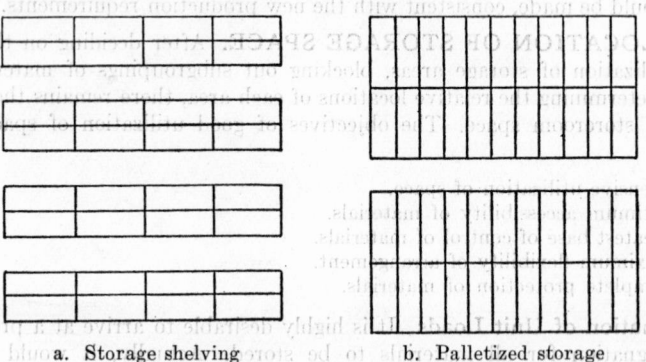

a. Storage shelving   b. Palletized storage

Fig. 3. Good layout of aisles in a storeroom.

A large proportion of the materials serviced by the storeskeeping department are best kept in **bins, shelves,** or **racks.** This is because so many items can be handled in and out of the storage area without the aid of mechanical handling devices, even though these same items will often be transported to the production center, sometimes together with other items, by means of handling equipment. The type of bin, shelf, or rack selected is important in determining the most efficient use of the storeroom. Bins, racks, and shelving vary in size, material, and construction, and it is advisable to standardize them, once the proper specifications have been determined. The dimensions of storage areas can then be proportioned in multiples of unit dimensions. For example, if unit dimensions are 3×5 ft., and another unit which might be stored in the same area is 4×7 ft., a storage area depth of 11 ft. would always have some unused space, but a depth of 12 ft. would provide efficient accommodations for both items.

Adjustable and portable bins and racks provide a most efficient storage medium where they can be used to advantage. Adjustable racks should combine structural rigidity and still lend themselves to rapid assembly and dismantling. The addition of **caster bases** to standard bins or tiering racks is most effective where they can be used for storage at the storerooms and then moved to the production center for direct **point-of-use storage.** Detailed examples of these common types of storage equipment will be given in the treatment of storeroom equipment which follows.

Moving Materials Into and Out of Stock. Consideration in the layout must be given to the system of moving materials into and out of stock. In many instances it is important that a first-in first-out system be used where deterioration may result from keeping materials in stock too long. There are several means of achieving **first-in first-out storage:**

1. **Coupon systems.** Two coupons are made out for each container. One coupon is attached to the container and the other coupon, with the storeroom location on it, is placed in a file. When material is requisitioned, the oldest coupon is referred to first and thus the corresponding material is removed first.

2. **Double-area system.** An area twice that required for the lot is allocated to each item. Incoming units are placed in one section and withdrawals are made from the other area until it is depleted, before removal may begin at the first area. Often the additional space and equipment required for this system are not available.

3. **Moving-division system.** A variation of the double-area system, requiring somewhat less space, is the moving-division system. Goods are removed from one end of a tiered row and added to the other end. In this manner, the pile will shift in position over a period of time. This can be allowed to go on up to a limit line and then the remaining section will have to be shifted.

4. **Gravity-feed systems.** Certain types of materials dispensed in bulk may be stored in gravity-feed storage bins. Materials in drums or circular packages can be moved by gravity first-in and first-out by constructing a sloping rack of the pitch required by the type of goods. Wheel or roller conveyor racks are a most satisfactory method of obtaining first-in first-out storage for a wide variety of materials packed individually or on platforms or pallets, as in Fig. 4. No aisles are required except at the ends of the lines.

Rapids-Standard Co.

Fig. 4. Wheel conveyor storage providing first-in first-out control.

Even where first-in first-out storage is not required, it is important to have a specified manner of adding to and withdrawing materials from rows of stored materials to achieve efficient utilization of space. If materials are removed and added at random to different rows of a section, empty spaces which cannot be utilized will occur in this section. Such **honeycombing** can be minimized by stacking in short rows and withdrawing or adding to only one row at a time.

Aisles. Aisle space is required to provide passageways for store clerks and handling equipment to, from, and within the storage area. Aisle space should be planned to give adequate operating space for handling and stacking supplies and should provide the proper relationship to doors and fire protection equipment. The **turning radius** of fork trucks and other handling gear must be checked on the layout before starting work on the area.

Main aisles should run the entire length of the storeroom. These aisles should be wide enough to permit easy passage of materials handling equipment going in opposite directions. Widths of 6 to 12 ft. should be adequate. Large storerooms often require **subaisles** parallel to the main aisle at distances of about 20 ft.

Cross aisles usually run perpendicular to the main aisles, connecting them and providing access to bins, racks, or tiered pallets. Cross aisles need accommodate one-way traffic only and should allow sufficient space for loading and unloading as shown in Fig. 3. Additional service aisles should be provided to break down areas

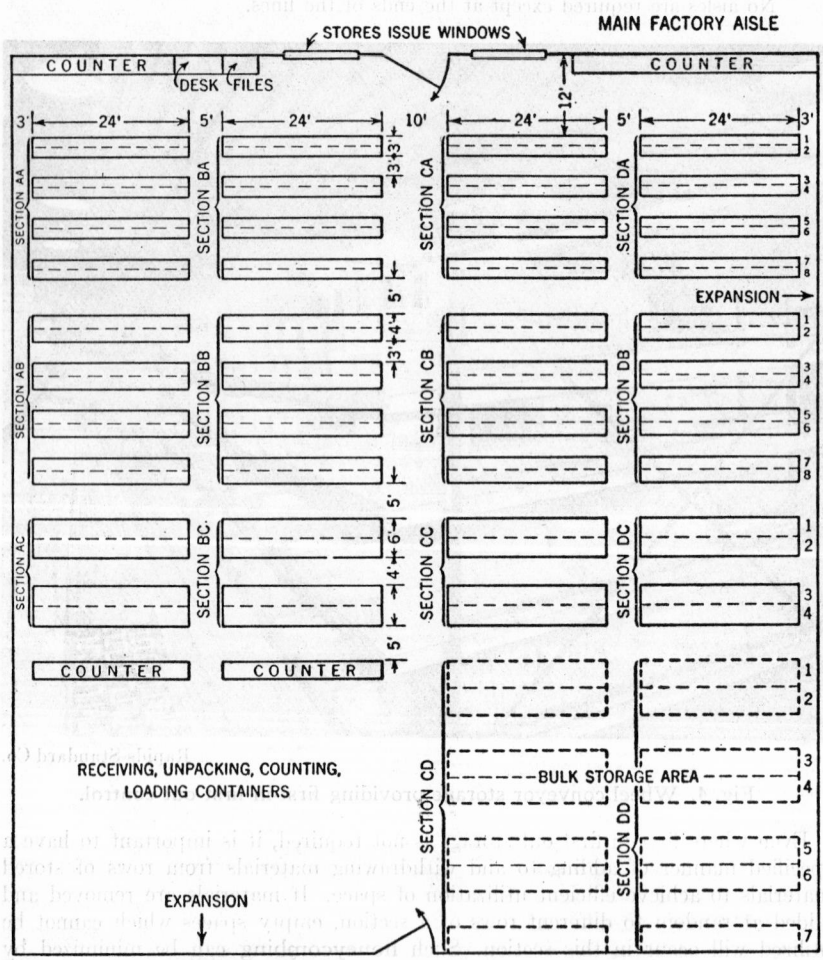

Fig. 5. Typical method of storeroom layout and section and row symbols.

for accessibility of small lots as required. However, in order to conserve aisle space, small lots should be stored in pallet racks or in box pallets at the end of large storage sections at the intersections of main and cross aisles. Aisles should be straight, clear of obstacles, and clearly marked with pressure-sensitive tape or paint stripes.

Auxiliary Storeskeeping Areas. Distributing counters are usually located adjacent to or along the stores issue windows. Additional tables or counters may be located near the issue windows or booths and in the receiving areas. Such counters are convenient for inspection, sorting, weighing, or temporary storage. An area should also be allowed for receiving, unpacking, counting, loading containers, and similar operations. Fig. 5 portrays a typical storeroom layout.

Symbols for Sections, Rows, and Bins or Tiers. The numbering or marking system for the sections, rows, and bins, should start at a permanent corner and increase in the direction toward which there may be storeroom expansion. **Letters** and **numbers** may be used alternately, letters being more convenient for sections and columns or stacks, and numbers for rows and tiers. Correspond-

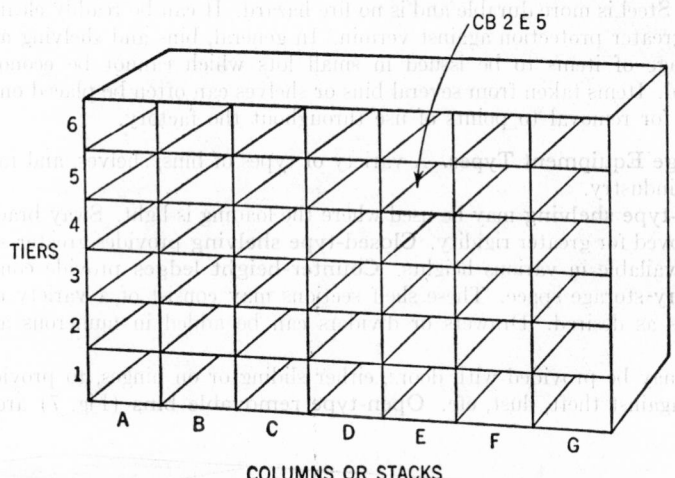

Fig. 6. Method of designating bin columns and tiers by symbols (section CB, row 2, column E, tier 5).

ing stacks or bins should be given corresponding designations. A **standard symbol system** should also be followed for labeling subdivisions of bins or stacks throughout the system. For example, if one bin in a row should be omitted for some reason, its number should be omitted in order to preserve the regularity of notation. Fig. 5 shows a typical storeroom layout with sections and rows marked. Fig. 6 shows a sound method of designating bin columns and tiers.

Storeroom Equipment

SHELVES, BINS, AND RACKS. Effective storeskeeping depends in large measure on the correct selection of storeroom equipment. Such equipment consists of a variety of shelving, bins, and racks; materials handling equipment; and auxiliary storeroom equipment such as scales, ladders, and record-keeping equipment. Shelves and bins are usually constructed from lumber and plywood, or from steel. Each has advantages and disadvantages. Either wood or metal bins and shelving may be fixed or adjustable and may have dividers for maximum flexibility.

Wood shelving has several advantages. It can be made from ordinary lumber obtainable locally and can usually be bought in specified lengths so as to minimize waste. Wood shelves can be readily adapted to unusual layouts where special steel equipment might be required. Wood also has a softer and more resilient surface than steel and thus provides greater protection for delicate equipment. However, combinations of wood and metal shelving may be used to gain the advantages each has to offer.

Steel shelving has come into widespread use because of the use of standard forms and sizes that can be mass produced at low cost and can be shipped in knocked down form for compactness and ease of handling. Standard steel shelves are easy to assemble at the point of use and, because they can be easily taken apart again, provide maximum flexibility, adaptability, and expandability. Steel shelving requires thinner members than wood and thus provides more space for storage. Steel is more durable and is no fire hazard. It can be readily cleaned and affords greater protection against vermin. In general, bins and shelving are used for storage of items to be issued in small lots which cannot be economically palletized. Items taken from several bins or shelves can often be placed on pallets or skids for removal to points of use throughout the factory.

Storage Equipment Types. A variety of types of bins, shelves, and racks are used in industry.

Open-type shelving may be used where the loading is light. Sway braces may be employed for greater rigidity. **Closed-type shelving** provides greater stability and is available in various heights. **Counter-height ledges** provide convenient temporary storage space. These shelf sections may consist of a variety of combinations as desired. Drawers or dividers can be added in numerous arrangements.

Bins may be provided with doors, either sliding or on hinges, to provide protection against theft, dust, etc. **Open-type removable bins** (Fig. 7) are useful

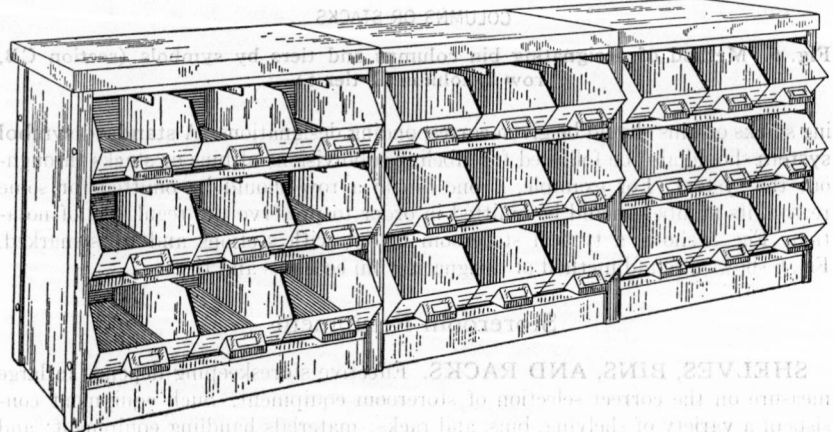

Fig. 7. Open-type removable bins in counter unit.

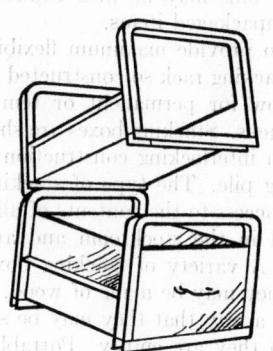

Fig. 8a. Stack racks with drawer inserts.

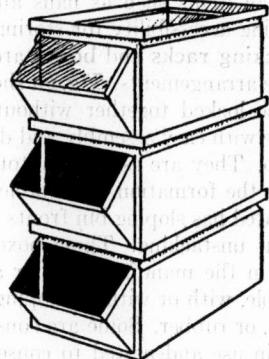

Fig. 8b. Stacking boxes.

Fig. 9. Rack for lumber, bar stock, or pipe.

for small items such as nails and bolts. These bins may be in a counter unit providing accessibility for storing and issuing unpackaged items.

Stacking racks and **boxes** are widely used to provide maximum flexibility of storage arrangements. Fig. 8a shows a typical stacking rack so constructed that it may be locked together without tools and allow for permanent or temporary storage with easy assembly and disassembly of racks. Stacking boxes are shown in Fig. 8b. They are essentially tote boxes with an interlocking construction allowing for the formation of a stable, self-supporting pile. The type of stacking box illustrated has sloping bin fronts allowing ready access to the contents of all boxes without unstacking. These boxes may be used in the stockroom and are also useful in the manufacturing or assembly area. A variety of stacking boxes are available, with or without sloping bin fronts. They may be made of wood, metal, plastic, or rubber. Some are constructed in such a way that they may be stacked when in use and nested to conserve space when they are empty. Portable shelf and bin storage provides a high degree of versatility in the use of storage equipment for small parts.

Storage racks for lumber, bar stock, or pipe are also available in many varieties in both stationary and portable models. Fig. 9 illustrates one consisting

Fig. 10. Portable gravity-feed stock-selecting rack.

of posts with horizontal arms attached. Other racks are made of structural shapes and may be more solidly built. An A-frame structure, with or without a caster base for portability, is another widely used rack form. Fig. 10 shows another type of portable **stock-selecting rack** (M-H Standard Co.) which makes order picking easy for items that will slide or roll. This rack has three shelves that can be raised or lowered to vary the angle of slope or distance between shelves. Dividers on each shelf are adjustable for articles of different widths.

STORESKEEPING HANDLING EQUIPMENT. The selection of suitable materials handling equipment for receiving, storing, and delivery of materials is of utmost importance for storeskeeping. The common types of handling equipment used are various types of trucks for skid and pallet handling, conveyors for storage and handling of stores, overhead crane systems, and tractor-trailer systems.

An economic analysis should precede the selection of materials handling equipment for storeskeeping (see section on Materials Handling). The analysis should take into consideration the characteristics of the items to be handled, the distances to be covered, the volume to be handled, and the relative cost of alternative combinations of handling equipment and labor. Where possible, standardization of handling equipment should be attempted both for storeskeeping and the whole plant.

There are a number of common types of **pallet, skid,** and **fork lift truck** equipment. Such trucks may be manually operated or may be gasoline or electrically power driven. They may be of a counterbalanced design where the load is carried ahead of the front axle or of a straddle arm design where the forks are located between two outriggers or straddle arms which extend alongside the pallet load. (Details concerning these trucks may be found in the Materials Handling section.)

The use of these trucks in conjunction with skids and pallets is often of great value to storeskeeping. It makes possible the receipt, storage, and movement of materials in standard unit load sizes. Materials suitable for such handling should be made up into standard skid or pallet loads upon their arrival at the plant. In some cases, the vendor may be asked to package the items in standard quantities of issue. In other cases the items may be put in standard quantities into boxes or containers or directly on to pallets or skids as the shipment is unpacked and inspected in the receiving department. The practice of having vendors actually ship the goods on skids or pallets in standard loads is increasing. This allows the unloading, checking of materials through receiving, and placing them in stores to be done by fork or lift trucks without manual handling.

The **skid** is a wood or metal platform with wood or metal runners or legs. The use of skids is generally much more limited than that of pallets, primarily because skids usually do not allow tiering.

Pallets are usually made of wood, metal, plastic, fiberboard, or combinations of these materials. The double-faced pallet is most widely used. It consists of stringers attached to an upper and lower platform. Because the bottom platform distributes the weight of the load evenly rather than at concentrated points, stacking or tiering of these pallets to heights of about 16 ft. is common. The actual height, of course, will depend on the density of the material, the desired unit load size, the floor loading allowed, the capacity of the truck, and the floor-to-ceiling space available. These pallets may be constructed for two-way entry of the truck forks, or for four-way entry for greater flexibility. The single-faced pallet, the straddle-truck-type pallet, the disposable pallet, and the box pallet are other types which may prove useful (see section on Materials Handling).

Special pallets and racks may be designed to accommodate articles which cannot be stacked in cubical piles, such as drums, pipe stock, or irregular castings. Examples of these are shown in Figs. 11 and 12.

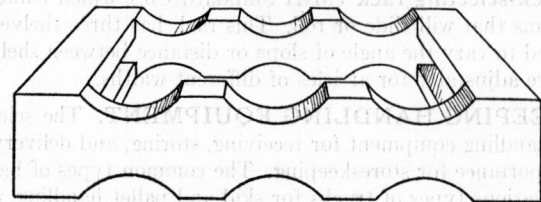

Fig. 11. Special pallet for handling and piling cylindrical stock.

Also in widespread use for storeskeeping order-picking are numerous types of **stock-selecting trucks.** These trucks are often designed to accommodate the types of items to be handled. They may have several shelves, be open or closed, and have many different types of wheel combinations. Fig. 13 shows a typical shelf truck. These trucks may have special coupling pins for use with dragline conveyors, or they may have trailer couplings for movement in tractor-trailer combinations.

Conveyors of various types lend themselves to efficient storeskeeping handling. Gravity conveyors, powered conveyors, and dragline conveyors are most widely used for storeskeeping. There are two basic types of gravity conveyors, roller and skate-wheel, which may be used for storage or for transporting **order-picking boxes.**

Standard power-driven belt conveyors or overhead conveyors may be used for moving stores over longer distances, or for raising or lowering materials. Dragline conveyors may be of the overhead type, or may be imbedded in the floor. This type of conveyor is constantly in motion at slow speeds, so that flat bed trailers, or portable bins or trucks with the necessary coupling pins, may be quickly and easily attached or removed. In this manner, stores may be transported with great flexibility, without using an operator or one or more tractors, as would be required for tractor-train operation.

Tractor-train operation for moving one or more trailers or bins offers a power-driven means of conveyance of materials directly between point of receipt, storage, and use of materials. Operatorless tractor-trains may be employed, guided by an electronic guide wire imbedded below the surface of the floor. The tractor is equipped with a set of hand controls for operator use when desired.

Overhead cranes may be used with hoists for lifting and placing heavy materials or used with a traveling pallet stacker. This combination of crane, pallet stacker, and pallet shelving permits a highly efficient utilization of storage space.

AUXILIARY STORESKEEPING EQUIPMENT. A number of other items such as scales, ladders, package-labeling equipment, and record-keeping equipment, may commonly be found in the storeroom.

Weighing scales are used for measuring bulk materials issued by weight and also for measuring quantities of small items like screws and bolts, where the approximate weight is a sufficient indication of the count. Scale types used range from counter scales to in-the-floor scales for weighing trucks or portable bins of materials.

Movable ladders are required in storerooms to provide access to materials where shelving and bins are over 8 ft. high. These ladders may be the movable

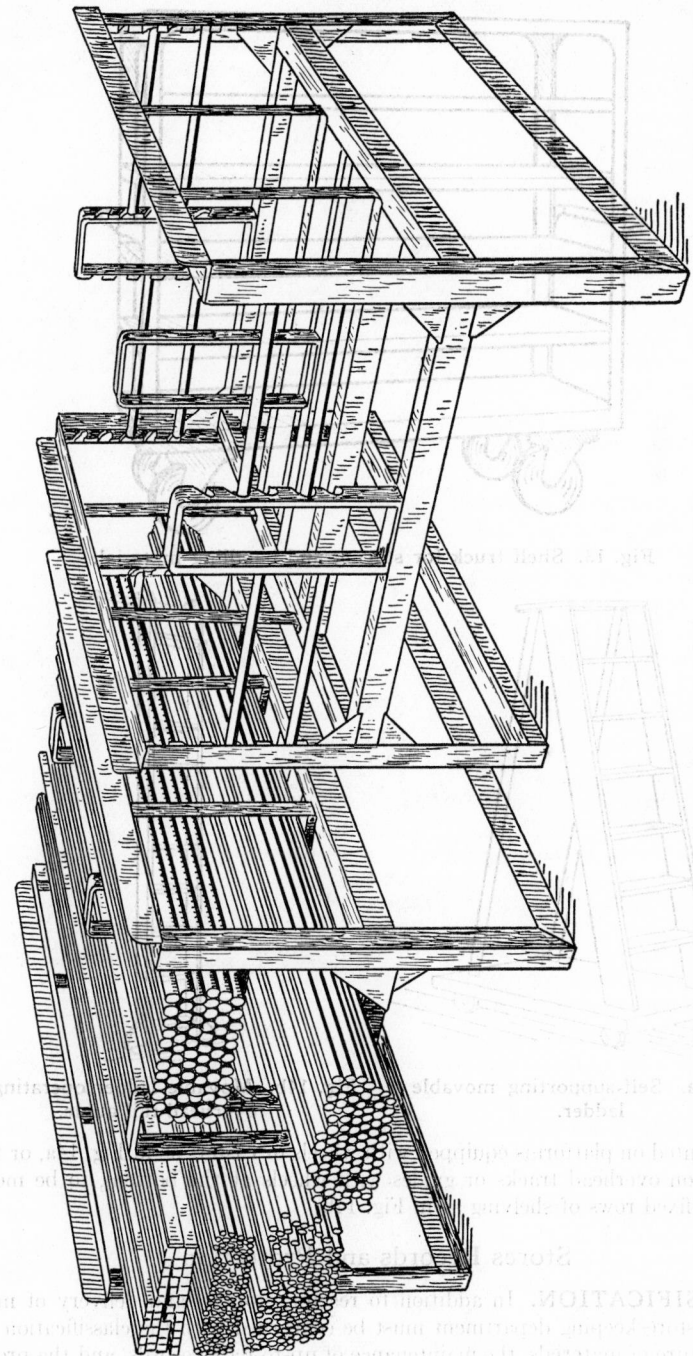

Fig. 12. Racks designed for stacking and handling short bar stock by fork or lift trucks.

Fig. 13. Shelf truck for storing and handling material.

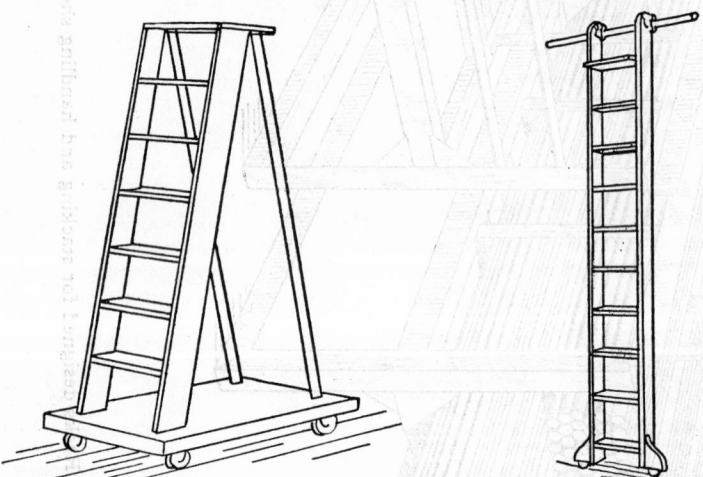

Fig. 14a. Self-supporting movable   Fig. 14b. Movable ladder operating on
          ladder.   overhead rail guide.

type mounted on platforms equipped with wheels or casters as in Fig. 14a, or they
may run on overhead tracks or guides with wheels at the bottom, to be moved
alongside fixed rows of shelving as in Fig. 14b.

Stores Records and Protection

CLASSIFICATION. In addition to receipt, storage, and delivery of materials, the storeskeeping department must be concerned with the classification and
nomenclature of materials, the maintenance of up-to-date records, and the protection and safekeeping of all stores which are entrusted to it.

Attention should be given to the designation of materials by the adoption of names and symbols which will be used throughout the plant to avoid confusion when referring to materials.

A typical method of categorizing materials, which usually ties in with the accounting system, the engineering department, and the manufacturing department, is to classify the materials by type as follows:

1. **Raw materials**—such as castings, forgings, bar stock, sheet stock, and all other materials to be processed in the plant.
2. **Supplies**—such as paper, typewriter ribbons, and ink for the offices, and lubricants and packing materials for the shop.
3. **Purchased parts**—all parts not requiring manufacturing operations, which can be directly assembled or used in conjunction with other parts.
4. **Semiprocessed parts**—purchased parts which have had one or more manufacturing operations performed on them.
5. **Finished inventory**—finished parts or subassemblies, or finished products awaiting shipment.

Classification Systems. It is important to designate materials by choosing symbols that are simple, clear, and free from duplication. The two main classification systems are arbitrary systems and classified symbol systems.

In the **arbitrary systems,** as each item comes up for classification, a different letter symbol or number is given to it, without attempting to give adjacent or similar numbers to similar items. Thus, number 2341 may refer to a casting and number 2342 may refer to a chemical compound. **Letter prefixes** may be used to reduce the size of these numbers by restarting from zero using different letter prefixes. For example, designations may run from 1 to 1,000, then from A1 to A1,000, and so on through the alphabet. Catalogues of parts according to name and function should be carefully cross-referenced with arbitrary nomenclature and kept up to date.

The two general types of **classified symbol systems** are the decimal and the mnemonic systems. In the **decimal** system, a separate number is used to represent each specific characteristic of an item. Often, this system is too detailed and cumbersome.

In the **mnemonic** classification system, combinations of letters and numbers are used. The letters are chosen as abbreviations of the name and characteristics of the item, while the numbers indicate dimensions. In order to differentiate between items, it often becomes necessary to adopt lengthy symbols, which may invalidate the usefulness of the symbol. For example, a screw might bear the symbol SFSMR.250x1.25N (stored item, fastening class, screw, machine type, round head, .250 in. in diameter and 1.25 in. in length, with a nickel finish).

Most frequently, individual plants will combine the features of the different classification systems to meet their own needs. A typical **combined classification system** would first identify the items within major classifications and then assign arbitrary designations to different items within these classifications. Often, it may be desirable to reserve a second or third mnemonic or decimal classification before employing the arbitrary designations, or to reserve certain ranges of members for certain specific groups of items.

RECORD-KEEPING. The responsibility of the storeskeeping department regarding record-keeping is to check incoming materials to see that the kind, count, and conditions are as indicated; to enter their arrival on records; to record withdrawals and enter the balance on hand of each item; and to make periodic and systematic check counts to verify balances and report such counts to the stores record or materials control section of the production control department.

The responsibility for storeroom records should be centralized, usually under the **materials control section,** even where storeroom operation is quite decentralized. Thus, all records and forms relative to the issue and receipt of stores should be standardized. These forms should be as simple as possible, kept to a minimum number, and tied in with the cost and accounting records. Details as to the type and composition of storeskeeping records and forms may be found in the section on Materials Control and Standardization.

PROTECTION OF STORES. An important aspect of storeskeeping is the protection of stores against hazardous conditions, weather, deterioration, dust, and theft. Each kind of material, such as textiles, rubber goods, leather goods, and metals, requires its own kind of care. Briefly, the protection to be afforded each type of situation is outlined in the following paragraphs:

Hazardous Conditions. Extreme care should be taken with hazardous and explosive commodities, and hazardous conditions should be minimized as far as possible. Commodities such as oxidizing agents should be kept apart from combustible materials. Strong acids should be segregated or kept in a **fire resistant enclosure.** Adequate explosion venting and approved fire doors should be provided.

Adequate fire-fighting equipment, such as high pressure water lines, modern sprinkler systems, suitable chemical extinguishers, fire pails, sand, axes, and ladders, should be provided. Fire-consciousness should be encouraged and periodic fire drills established. (See section on Safety and Fire Prevention.)

Storage areas should be kept orderly and clean, with clear aisles and passageways.

Weather. Materials whose bulk and nature require that they be stored out of doors, such as lumber and steel shapes and bars, can be protected by open sheds or by textile or plastic coverings.

Air-conditioned rooms should be supplied for materials which are affected by changes in temperature. Some commodities require heat to prevent possible freezing, some may require freezing to prevent spoilage, and others may require a high relative humidity to prevent drying out.

Deterioration. Some materials deteriorate with age. Such materials should not be overstocked and a first-in first-out storage system should be adopted. Often, aging can be retarded by temperature and moisture control. Some materials which deteriorate due to the absorption of odors can be protected by suitable **segregation measures.** Another form of deterioration is the damage which may result from improper materials handling. The adoption of the most suitable containers, handling equipment, and methods can do much to reduce this source of damage.

Theft. Unfortunately, many concerns have found that pilferage of materials by employees may constitute a sizable loss in money, inventory control, and delay in production. Thus, it is usually advisable to provide **closable storage areas.** Valuable items should be kept in locked cabinets or in a safe. Materials should not be issued without proper requisitions.

INSPECTION

CONTENTS

PAGE

Nature of Inspection

Inspection objectives 1
Definitions 1
Accuracy and precision 2

Organization of Inspection

Place in plant organization 2
Development of inspection organization .. 2
Inspection department functions (f. 1) .. 3
Functional plan for small inspection department (f. 2) 3
Functional plan for a large inspection department (f. 3) 5
Functional inspection organization for a corporation with several divisions (f. 4) 6
Level of authority of inspection 4
Place and organization of inspection in a machine-tool company (f. 5) 7
Inspection department in an arms manufacturing company (f. 6) 8
Cost control as a factor in organization .. 4
Effect of precision on cost in the manufacture of gage blocks (f. 7) 8
Personnel 9
Quality responsibility check sheet (f. 8) 9
Typical inspection positions 9
Women as inspectors 11
Qualifications of inspectors 11
Training inspectors 12
Remuneration for inspection work 12

Location and Inspection Systems

Location 13
Factors in location 13
Patrol and centralized inspection 14
Centralized inspection 14
Advantages and disadvantages of central inspection 14
Advantages and disadvantages of floor inspection 15
Combined system 16
Layout 16

Kinds of Inspection

Methods in use 16
Trial-run inspection 16
First-piece inspection 17
Pilot-piece inspection 17
Working inspection 17
Key-operation inspection 17

PAGE

Sampling inspection 17
Percentage inspection 17
Preassembly inspection 18
Functional inspection 18
Efficiency inspection 18
Endurance inspection 18
Destructive inspection 18
Piecework inspection 18
Product inspection 18
Tests of completed mechanism 18
Inspection tickets 19
Inspection ticket (f. 9) 19

Nature and Extent of Inspections

Conditions indicating extensive inspection .. 19
Unnecessary inspection 20
Information from inspection procedure 20
Trouble reports 20
Salvage or replacement of defective parts .. 21

Precision Measurement Standards

Dimensional standards for production 21
International measurement standards 21

Fundamentals in Inspection

Principles of inspection 22
Methods based on objectives 22
Inspection procedure 23
Design 23
Inspection standards 23
Fits and limits 24
Preferred basic sizes 25
Basic sizes for specifying fits in mating parts (f. 10) 26
Standard fits 25
Running and sliding fits 25
Locational fits 25
Force fits 27

Equipment and Techniques for Dimension Measurement

Equipment for dimension inspection 27
Relationship of the metrology laboratory to other phases of dimensional control (f. 11) 28
Hand measuring tools 27
Nonprecision line-graduated instruments . 29
Precision hand measuring instruments 29
Fixed gages 29

CONTENTS (*Continued*)

PAGE

Gage tolerance table 1 (Army Ordnance
  Standard ORD-M608-12) (*f.* 12) 32-33
Gage tolerance tables 2 and 3 (Army
  Ordnance Standard ORD-M608-12)
  (*f.* 13) 34-35
Special design mechanical gages 30
Gage materials 30
Standard sequence of gage use 30
  Gages supplied in boxes 31
  Mounting gages on boards 31
Gage surveillance and records 31
Measuring or gage laboratory equipment ... 36
  Horizontal external measuring machines.. 36
    Horizontal measuring machine (*f.* 14) .. 36
  Internal measuring machines 36
    Internal measuring machine (*f.* 15) 37
  Surface plates and accessories 37
    Stone surface plate with height gage
      (*f.* 16) 38
  Vertical comparators 37
    Vertical comparator using electronic
      amplifier (*f.* 17) 39
  Profile comparators and optical equipment 38
  Gage blocks 39
Gage amplifying systems 40

PAGE

Electrical and electronic systems 40
  Electrical gaging elements (*f.* 18) 40
  Mechanical amplifying devices 41
    Basic operating principle of dial indica-
      tor (*f.* 19) 41
    A comparator combining optical and
      mechanical principles (*f.* 20) 42
Air gages 43
  Flow type of air gage circuit (*f.* 21) 43
  Typical air gage setups (*f.* 22) 44
Optical gaging and measuring devices 43
Automatic gages 44
  In-process control 45
    In-process control with automatic gages
      (*f.* 23) 45
    Automatic gage for checking output of
      several machine tools (*f.* 24) 46
  Post-process control 46
    Post-process control of machined parts
      (*f.* 25) 46
    Automatic gaging and segregating ma-
      chine (*f.* 26) 47
    Characteristics of ammunition checked
      by an automatic gaging and segregating
      machine (*f.* 27) 47

INSPECTION

Nature of Inspection

INSPECTION OBJECTIVES. The development of new products and the quality improvement of old products stem from constantly increasing precision capabilities in measurement and manufacturing techniques. The vital elements of quality, quantity, and cost are so interrelated in the modern manufacturing complex that they demand that the inspection function apply the most advanced principles of engineering, science, and mathematics. The basic purpose of inspection is to prevent the production of unsatisfactory materials, parts, subassemblies, and assemblies. Inspection plans and operations directed toward a minimizing of the **after-production examination** technique, the detection of unsatisfactory quality trends in **process measurement,** and prevention of defects, along with the **feedback** of quality information for prompt quality improvement, are the fundamental approaches to low cost and high quality in mass production.

DEFINITIONS. A broad definition of inspection which is generally accepted is that of Kimball:

Inspection is the art of comparing materials, product, or performances with established standards.

A somewhat narrower definition is adopted by Alford:

Inspection is the art of applying tests, preferably by the aid of measuring appliances, to observe whether a given item of product is within the specified limits of variability.

The U. S. Department of Defense (Military Standard 109) defines inspection as it pertains to all production for the Army, Navy, and Air Force:

Inspection means the examination (including testing) of supplies and services (including, when appropriate, raw materials, components, and intermediate assemblies) to determine whether the supplies and services conform to contract requirements, which include all applicable drawings, specifications, and purchase descriptions.

Examination is an element of inspection consisting of investigation, without the use of special laboratory appliances or procedures, of supplies and services to determine conformance to those specified requirements which can be determined by such examination. Examination is generally nondestructive and includes (but is not limited to) visual, auditory, olfactory, tactile, gustatory, and other examination; simple physical manipulation; engaging; and measurement.

Testing is an element of inspection and generally denotes the determination by technical means of the physical and chemical properties or elements of materials, supplies, or components thereof, involving not so much the element of personal judgment as the application of established scientific principles and procedures.

In machine-shop practice inspection often connotes a procedure to determine if materials, parts, and assemblies conform to drawings and specifications in every respect.

Modern large-scale manufacture of products like sewing machines, vacuum cleaners, and automobile engines would be impossible were it not for the development of the tolerance system and inspection procedure which keeps performance under control. Combined, they permit employment of less skilled labor to produce a superior product. **Interchangeable manufacture** presupposes accurate production of each component in the place or plan of its origin so that no supplemental machining or labor is required at point of assembly.

This section is concerned with inspection in the somewhat narrow sense. Its emphasis is on inspection of product rather than process, and of the qualities of dimension and finish. This is the type of inspection which is of widest application throughout industry, is a common denominator of the greatest range of manufacturing industries, and is most highly developed in technique. There is, of course, corresponding inspection in the process industries, but it commonly involves setting up standards peculiar to the particular industry, often under laboratory rather than shop control, and much of it is merged into, and difficult to separate from the processes themselves. Therefore, such inspection is not considered here.

ACCURACY AND PRECISION. Accuracy in inspection is considered to be the quality of conformity, and precision to be the quality of refinement. A **tolerance** is a permissible variation in size. An **allowance** is an intentional difference in size between mating parts. **Limits of size** are the maximum and minimum acceptable sizes of a part.

In the inspection of a one-inch shaft having a tolerance of minus 0.001 in., all parts having dimensions within the limits of 0.999 in. to 1.000 in. would be accurate but probably would not be classified as precise in present-day production capabilities. If the part had a tolerance of minus 0.0001 in., all parts inspected and found to be within the limits of 0.9999 in. to 1.0000 in. would probably be considered precise in the light of today's production capabilities. Parts should be designed with the largest tolerances that will give desired function, considering cost and capabilities of process, and measurement techniques. The tools used for inspection must be more precise than required **product tolerances.** For example, tolerances which are only 10 percent of the production figures are desirable. Progressive increases in precision are required in the measurement and standards necessary to assure accuracy in the tools and instruments of inspection.

Organization of Inspection

PLACE IN PLANT ORGANIZATION. As to the best organization for the inspection department, much depends on size and layout of plant, type of product or products, and quality and standards to which work is produced. Basically, however, inspection should be an independent function concerned only with moving the work through inspection.

Development of Inspection Organization. In establishing an organizational position for the inspection department, the first step, as suggested by Thompson (Inspection Organization and Methods) is to examine thoroughly the functions involved in the inspection process. Thompson says:

The obvious function of Inspection is maintenance of established quality standards for a given end item or end items. The execution of this function requires a variety of supporting activities to develop the inspection plan, prepare necessary instructions and procedures, develop liaison and coordination with other departments, provide administrative and analysis services, and maintain necessary clerical functions and records.

Analysis of basic inspection activities readily reveals that the prime functions are (1) examination, (2) administration, and (3) analysis. All inspection activities can be grouped under these three headings, and the functional breakdown in Fig. 1 lists the work normally relating to each.

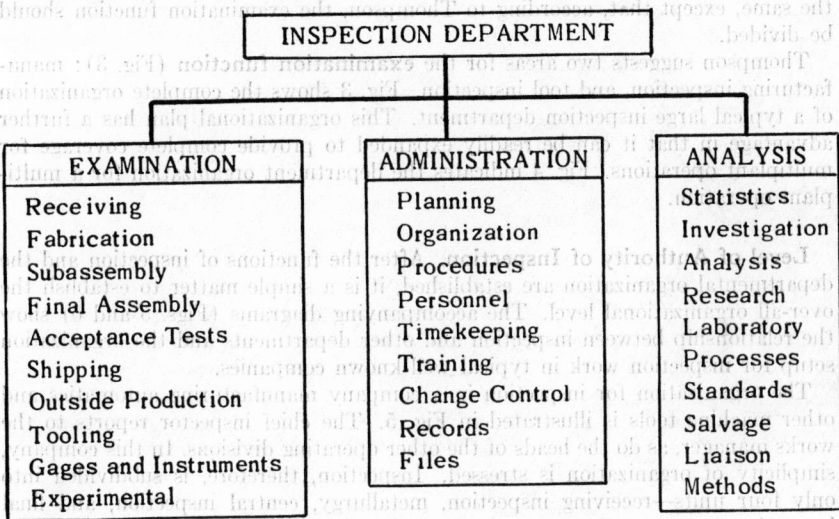

Fig. 1. Inspection department functions.

Thompson then suggests that the functional examination leads readily to an inspection department organization. An examination of Fig. 2 shows that there is

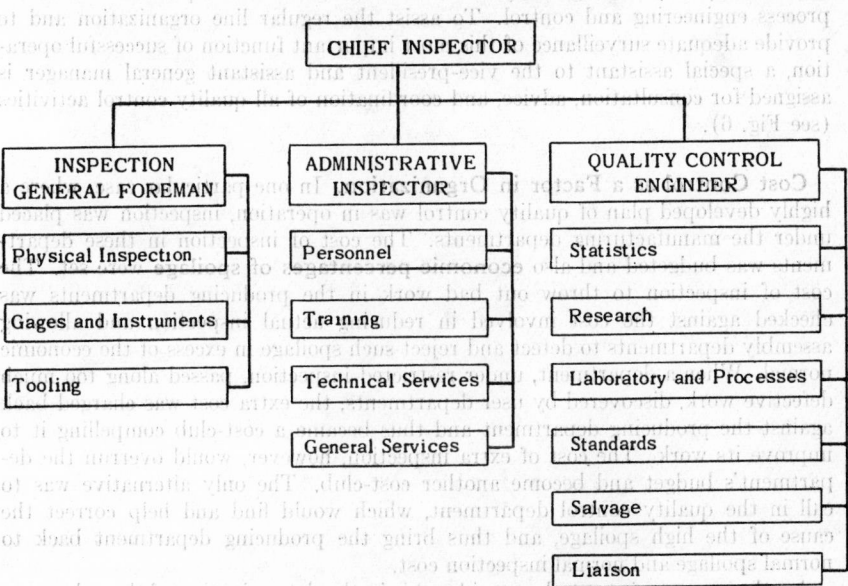

Fig. 2. Functional plan for small inspection department.

a supervisor for each of the basic functions, as originally defined. These supervisors are responsible to the chief inspector, who is responsible to management for the inspection operation. Fig. 2 shows the organization of a small inspection department. As the inspection staff increases, the basic organization will remain the same, except that, according to Thompson, the examination function should be divided.

Thompson suggests two areas for the **examination function** (Fig. 3): manufacturing inspection, and tool inspection. Fig. 3 shows the complete organization of a typical large inspection department. This organizational plan has a further advantage in that it can be readily expanded to provide complete coverage for multiplant operations. Fig. 4 indicates the department organization for a multiplant operation.

Level of Authority of Inspection. After the functions of inspection and the departmental organization are established, it is a simple matter to establish the over-all organizational level. The accompanying diagrams (Figs. 5 and 6) show the relationship between inspection and other departments and the organization setup for inspection work in typical well-known companies.

The organization for inspection in a company manufacturing automatics and other machine tools is illustrated in Fig. 5. The chief inspector reports to the works manager, as do the heads of the other operating divisions. In this company, simplicity of organization is stressed. Inspection, therefore, is subdivided into only four units—receiving inspection, metallurgy, central inspection, and final inspection.

In an arms manufacturing company inspection and quality are under the director of production who delegates responsibility to the works manager. Although the production section is responsible for maintenance of quality standards, control of quality is assigned by the works manager to the superintendent of the process engineering and control. To assist the regular line organization and to provide adequate surveillance of this most important function of successful operation, a special assistant to the vice-president and assistant general manager is assigned for consultation, advice, and coordination of all quality control activities (see Fig. 6).

Cost Control as a Factor in Organization. In one particular case, where a highly developed plan of quality control was in operation, inspection was placed under the manufacturing departments. The cost of inspection in these departments was budgeted and also **economic percentages of spoilage** were set. The cost of inspection to throw out bad work in the producing departments was checked against the cost involved in reducing actual inspection and allowing assembly departments to detect and reject such spoilage in excess of the economic normal. When a department, under restricted inspection, passed along too much defective work, discovered by user departments, the extra cost was charged back against the producing department and thus became a cost-club compelling it to improve its work. The cost of extra inspection, however, would overrun the department's budget and become another cost-club. The only alternative was to call in the quality control department, which would find and help correct the cause of the high spoilage, and thus bring the producing department back to normal spoilage and normal inspection cost.

Another aspect of cost to be considered is in the determination of the value contributed by increasing accuracy. Michelon (Industrial Inspection Methods) sub-

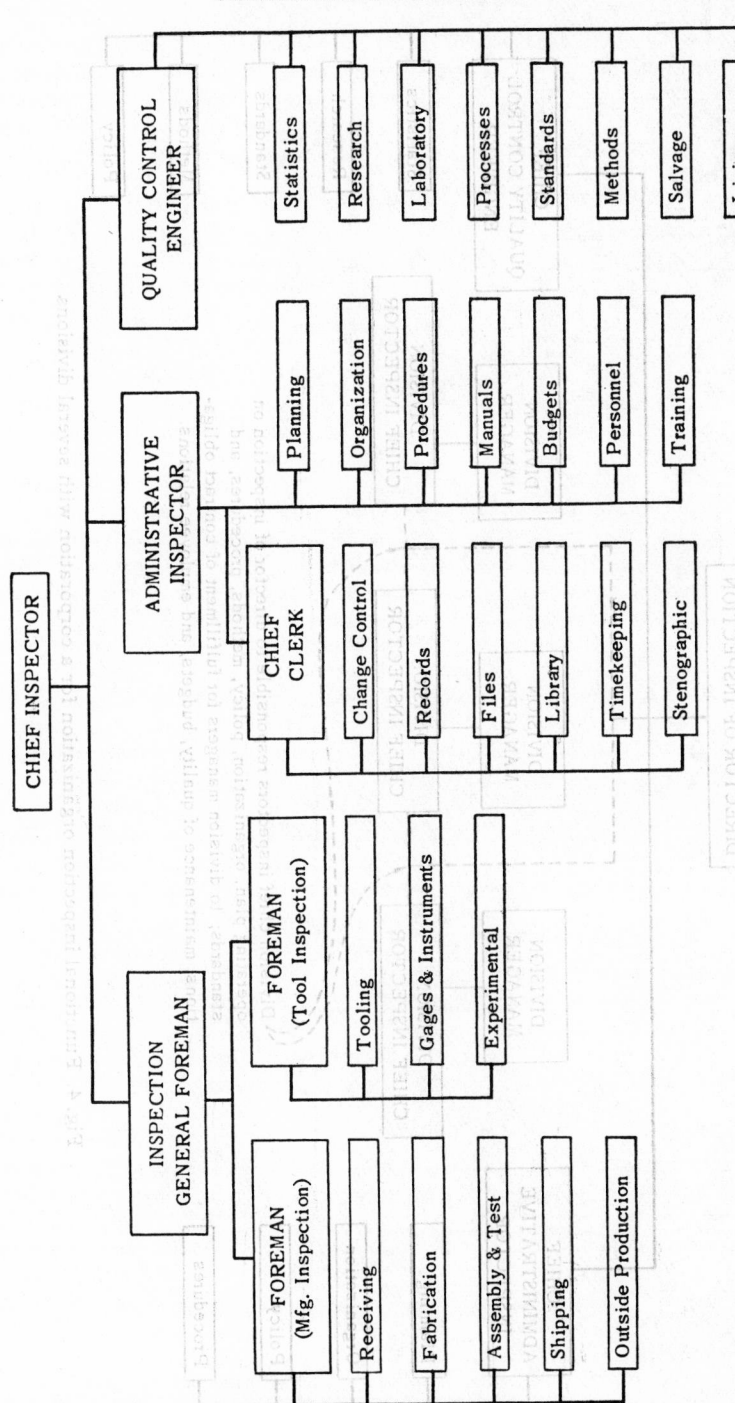

Fig. 3. Functional plan for a large inspection department.

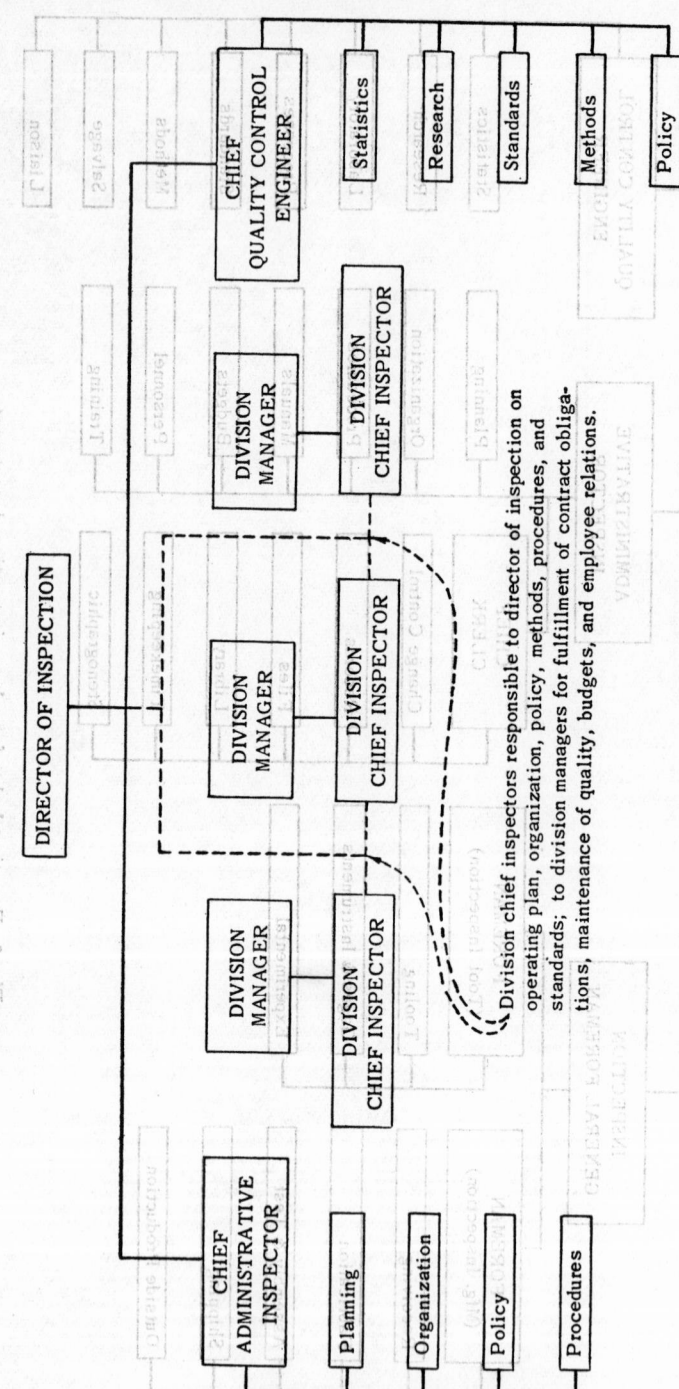

Fig. 4. Functional inspection organization for a corporation with several divisions

Division chief inspectors responsible to director of inspection on operating plan, organization, policy, methods, procedures, and standards; to division managers for fulfillment of contract obligations, maintenance of quality, budgets, and employee relations.

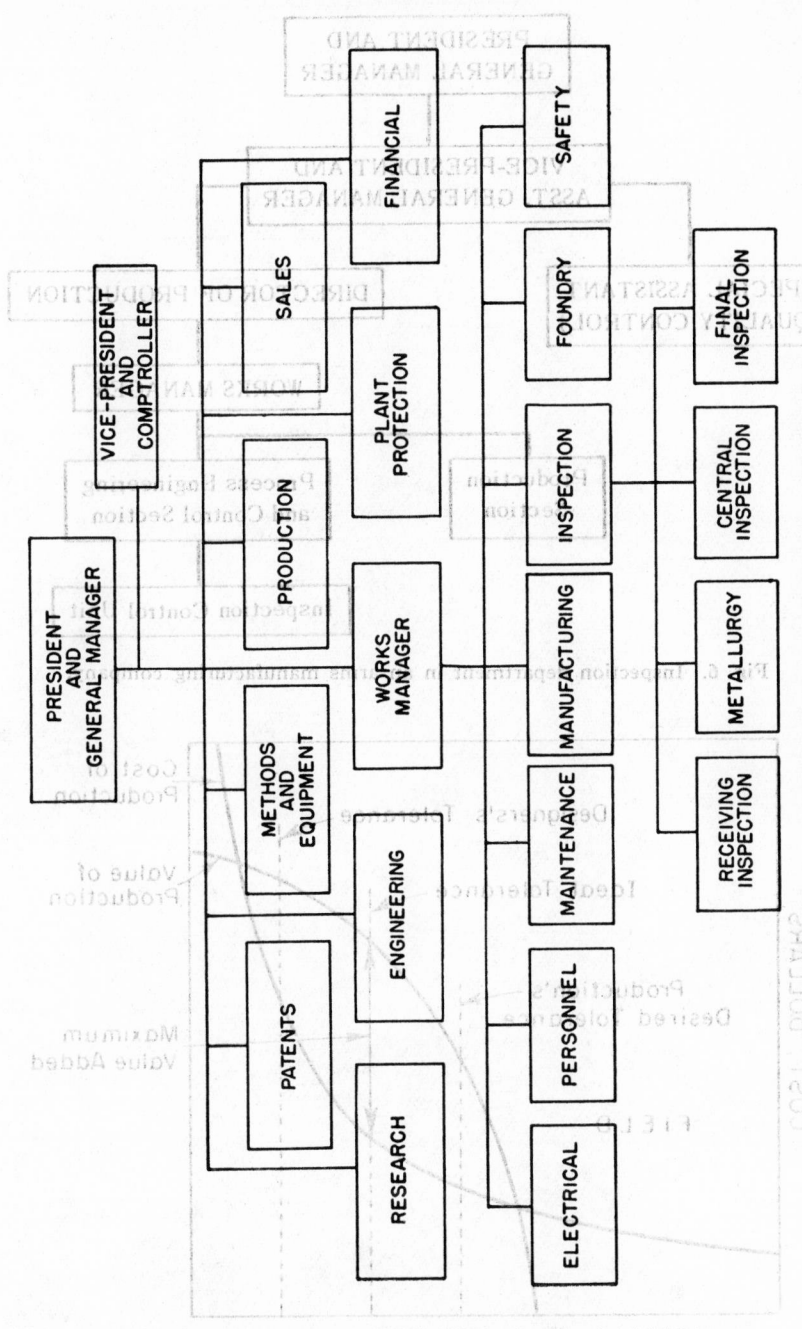

Fig. 5. Place and organization of inspection in a machine-tool company.

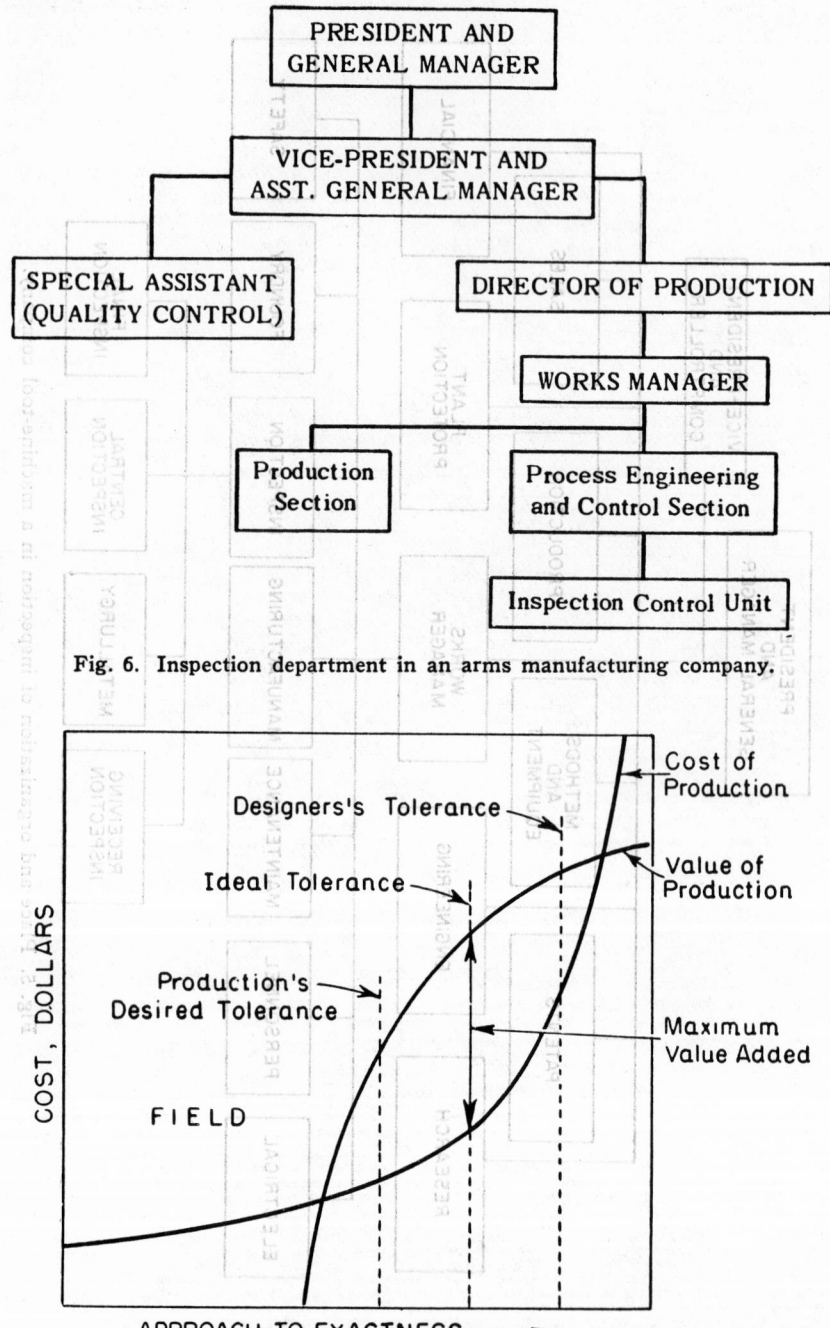

Fig. 6. Inspection department in an arms manufacturing company.

Fig. 7. Effect of precision on cost in the manufacture of gage blocks.

mits a graph (Fig. 7) showing the relationship (hypothetical) between value and precision. His accompanying comment is:

The diagram will help explain final stabilizing of tolerances. It is purely hypothetical because it is virtually impossible to plot actual curves. However, considering the relative prices of Grades B, A, and AA gage blocks and other controlling equipment and devices, the cost of production curve shown appears reasonable in form. Needless to say, absolute accuracy to the maximum metal condition will not increase the usefulness or life of parts greatly over conditions of slightly greater clearance, but the value will decrease to zero when the limit of functioning due to extreme clearance is reached. The value of production curve would appear to represent that the ideal tolerance condition is where the value added by production is maximum.

PERSONNEL. The ratio of inspectors to productive employees in departments in the same plant varies with the class of work to be inspected. Some work demands 100 percent inspection, other work is based on liberal tolerances requiring but a small ratio of inspectors to workmen. Proportional to size of working force, there must be the required number of inspectors, group leaders, subforemen, foremen, a general foreman, a group of experts for special assignments, and a chief inspector and his assistants.

Who is Respon- sible for →	Approving Machine Setups?	Shutting Down a Running Machine?	Accepting Completed Lots of Product?	Sorting Defective Lots of Product?	Defect Prevention		
					Recording Basic Data?	Analyzing of Data?	Acting on Data?
Operator							
Setup man							
Foreman							
Patrol inspector							
Bench inspector							
Quality engineer							

Fig. 8. Quality responsibility check sheet.

Juran (Factory Management and Maintenance, vol. 110) suggests specific responsibility areas for inspection personnel on a functional basis. He suggests using a **quality responsibility check sheet** (Fig. 8) in establishing the responsibility according to the operation. However, inspection personnel responsibilities can be examined from still other viewpoints.

Typical Inspection Positions. The **chief inspector** must be a man of executive ability, able to select and guide a staff of men, and knowing how far to make use of experts when necessary. A wide general experience in industry rather than specialized knowledge of particular work is desirable. Usually, his sphere will include:

1. Selection and training of inspection staff.
2. Organization of men into such groups and in such relation to work as may be best, i.e., planning the inspection framework.
3. General supervision of gages, tools, templates, and other precision devices, both as used in production and for testing purposes.

4. General supervision, in some cases, over salvage work, wherein defective parts are worked over into useful forms for avoidance of loss and waste.

5. In some plants the chief inspector has jurisdiction over testing laboratories, etc., in which raw material is examined and passed on. This is particularly the case where the same laboratory equipment is utilized for testing and controlling process work. In other cases, examination and analysis of raw materials is carried on by a separate organization.

6. Expense budget for his department and operating under this budget.

The **assistant chief inspector,** as an understudy, aids the chief inspector in directing the work of the department and takes the place of the chief inspector in the latter's absence. Sometimes he has special charge of some important part of the routine, wherein close supervision is normally necessary. He is available to take charge of important special operations, changes in methods, advising on tools, gages, etc.

A **staff of experts** on particular tool and inspection problems is sometimes conveniently located in the main inspection department to handle special assignments that would interfere with routine duties of regular line organization inspectors.

In large plants a **complaints division** is also located in the main inspection office. Such a division handles complaints of defective workmanship, or defective material, as received from sales and service departments in the field. In some cases, future shipments are held up until causes of complaint have been located and rectified. The division acts also as a clearing house for all reports on defective workmanship, doubtful points of design, and defective material in work in process. Information on errors and mistakes is analyzed and grouped, so that the conditions responsible are disclosed without undue delay.

A **supervisor of gages** is also an important figure in an inspection organization. Purchase or design and building of all gages and measuring instruments, and training of men in their proper use, are his principal duties. The gage supervisor and his assistants should be located in the main machine-tool and gage department, so that contact is maintained with manufacturing tool supervisors and their problems.

Foremen inspectors are responsible for control of quality in a particular division of manufacturing operations. In some plants a general foreman inspector coordinates these activities, but more often the foremen inspectors report directly to the chief inspector. Each foreman inspector has a staff of inspectors, sorters, and counters, often subdivided into groups under subforemen or group leaders. Each foreman inspector should be located in the center of the manufacturing territory for which he is responsible.

The **main office force** of the inspection department should be kept at a minimum number.

An inspector's job is to inspect, rather than to sit at a desk doing work that should be done by a clerical force. It is therefore desirable to keep inspectors on the "firing line" at all times and to organize routine work with that end in view. Routine work of the main office will usually include:

1. Personnel matters—pay, promotion, training, etc., of employees of the department.

2. Checking up work of inspectors to see that prescribed standards are being adhered to.

3. Maintaining contact with the production engineer to coordinate inspection and production requirements.

4. Statistical work affecting control of quality.

Women as Inspectors. For many inspection jobs women have proved most satisfactory, being generally careful, patient, and better suited than men to repetitive types of inspection. Careful training is necessary, however, and in general this training should be for specific kinds of inspection rather than for all-round inspection. Some women are adept at setting up work on a surface plate, others on comparators, others on special gaging fixtures, but all are not usually equally proficient in all kinds of inspection. Great caution must be observed against discoloration and corrosion of fine instruments or brightly finished surfaces of work due to excess acid condition in workers at certain times. At such times, or when perspiring, the hands should be rubbed with "Pro-tec," a harmless, white salve-like preparation which is easily washed off.

QUALIFICATIONS OF INSPECTORS. Michelon (Industrial Inspection Methods) establishes the qualifications for an inspector as follows:

A good inspector must thoroughly know his job. This demands technical knowledge and skill of a high order, the possession of much factual information and a mastery of the physical art of inspecting. Familiarity with blueprints and inspection tools is presupposed. The inspector must have a working knowledge of general quality standards and a complete command of the quality standards affecting the materials or processes to which he is assigned. A good inspector knows the reasons for the standards through an understanding of the materials or processes themselves. Above all the inspector must possess and exercise good judgment, for industrial inspection is not a "yes-or-no" affair. The material which the inspector passes upon usually is neither perfectly good nor absolutely bad, but falls somewhere between these extremes. As established quality standards are rarely exact, the inspector must often dispose of doubtful cases on judgment alone.

It should be cautioned that the good inspector always realizes his responsibility for obtaining **concurrence** of the design and quality control functions on any decisions of judgment beyond the limits of specifications.

In a certain instance in the inspection of glass blanks for imperfections, **performance standards** for inspection were attained by having the individual inspectors go over work with the foreman inspector until it was felt that the dividing line between good and bad was generally understood. All would go well for a few days and then rejections would pile up, which on revised inspection were found to be unjustified. Investigation showed an unexpected cause of this breakdown. The inspectors looking for scratches or bubbles, day after day, became so skilled in detecting them that presently they were noticing minute defects with the same degree of effort that a novice would require to notice a large one. In other words, the standard was actually a shifting one, approaching high refinement and perfection in product, thus being psychological rather than physical. The remedy was found in a set of samples containing defects just under and just over the borderline with which comparisons could be readily made, combined with a recheck of a random percentage of both good and bad work, after each inspection.

Bench inspectors on repetitive work should be of temperament that develops willingness to follow strict instructions. They will be called upon to conform to rigid rules which require them to divide inspected product into three groups: (1) good, (2) clearly bad, and (3) doubtful. The latter class is reviewed by group leaders or foremen inspectors for acceptance or rejection.

Floor inspectors are required to exercise judgment, which must be backed by considerable technical experience. Among their duties are first-piece inspection, with authority to hold up the machine until it is properly adjusted, if the work is defective, and patrolling inspection which involves the right to stop any machine from which defective work is coming, in each case promptly notifying the shop foreman. Both tact and firmness, therefore, are necessary ingredients in the floor inspector's make-up.

TRAINING INSPECTORS. G. S. Radford has stated that as a management device for inspection economy, instruction of inspectors comes next after sampling to ensure that no more work is done than is necessary. The instruction should not be casual but should be combined with the work of one of the technical men on the chief inspector's staff. Even the most cursory use of motion study reveals large possibilities for saving time in inspection. Unskilled help should receive adequate instruction, not only by teaching but also by providing accessible reference data, such as samples, large-scale drawings with gaging points distinctly marked, and **gage instruction cards.** This educational work should begin as soon as the new inspector is employed.

In establishing a training course for inspectors, Juran (Factory Management and Maintenance, vol. 110) suggests as a minimum the following items for coverage:

1. How to use the measuring instruments, how to read them, how to care for them.
2. How to identify what is good and what is defective for qualities that cannot be measured.
3. The why of the defects—that is, what will happen if the defects get through.
4. How to decide on the sample size, how to select the sample, how many defects to allow in the sample.
5. What records to keep and why. Show him how the records are used. (The temptation to fake inspection data is greatest where subsequent use is not known.)
6. How to identify the product so that it does not get mixed up.
7. How to do the incidentals of the inspection job—materials handling, cleaning, and counting.
8. How to deal with his industrial neighbors on the factory floor: operators, setup men, foremen, engineers.
9. How to earn the respect that is the just reward of the ethical and factual inspector.

REMUNERATION FOR INSPECTION WORK. Inspection is usually regarded as belonging to the "expense" or "overhead" class of costs, and the tendency is to pare this cost as closely as possible, notwithstanding that in some operations high-grade qualifications are requisite in the personnel. To prevent the force from being permeated with chronic discontent, either a definite plan of **promotion at increasing pay,** or some form of **piecework,** may be introduced in some cases. Desirability of obtaining some check on the work of individuals, as to both quantity and quality of inspection done, offers the possibility of payment by results.

Inspection can be done on a piecework basis, but the proper conditions must prevail—the object of inspection being primarily thoroughness, not quantity. Sloppy inspection, in the endeavor to make high earnings, can cause untold delays and increased cost in assembly, in addition to subsequent malfunctioning of the finished product, with ultimate loss of customers and reputation. There have been cases, however, where piecework in inspection—with proper reinspection and checks, adequate rewards for good work, and penalties for poor work—has increased output and maintained high quality of inspection. Where possible, inspectors should be given the same opportunity as production workers to increase their earnings.

The inspector's **hourly average** of pieces inspected is the best indicator of his efficiency. Too sudden a rise in output in the case of novice, where a visual inspection embraces half a dozen or more points, is more unhealthy than a slow increase in output, as it indicates lack of care. The best control over an inspector's work is obtained by rechecking a certain portion of products which he passes and a portion of those he rejects. An experienced examiner can make this check on each inspector once a week. The percentage of errors is recorded against the inspector, and, if low, may be used as the basis for a weekly or monthly grading list, with or without bonus payments, or, if high, for private admonition including training to help him improve his record.

Where a piecework price is arranged for inspection work, which is chiefly practiced where there is a continuous run of small parts, the recheck carries a **penalizing effect,** drastic reductions being made for any defective parts that have been accepted, and less heavy penalties being exacted for rejections that should not have been made. Piecework has been successfully applied in many plants, with large increases in output where the method has been based on a sound plan. Many executives, however, are opposed to piecework in inspection and many consider that penalizing is undesirable (see section on Wage Plans and Controls).

Location and Inspection Systems

LOCATION. Since some inspection is done on the floor in factory departments where work is in process, while other inspection is conducted in one or more central inspection areas, the location of inspection centers depends largely on which plan is followed. In a large plant there would be a **central inspection headquarters** for the chief inspector and a staff of experts, but there would be many **inspection rooms,** each equipped with instruments and facilities for checking the work in its immediate department or area. **Floor inspectors** would work under supervisors in the local inspection areas. In a small plant, the inspection department would have a central headquarters in which gages, instruments, etc., would be kept, and where certain inspection operations might be carried on. Floor inspectors usually would operate from this central point.

Factors in Location. The whole problem is, first, one of accessibility to work areas served; second, whether inspection requires moving of parts into a central location because of the use of instruments or the greater speed that is possible with routine mass inspection; third, distances which work would have to be moved to reach inspection centers; fourth, time consumed and congestion brought about by the moving; and fifth, the possibility of moving inspection out to the work, as in product layout of equipment, to take advantage of straight-line methods of production.

Because it uses precision instruments, sometimes delicate in themselves, and always susceptible to injury from grit, dust, and sudden or great temperature variations, the inspection section should be located where there is no vibration, air is clean, and light is plentiful. Air conditioning and temperature control should be provided when practical, and the inspection area should be partitioned off from rest of shop. Daylight from the north is preferred to obviate strong sunlight and deep shadows. The fluorescent type of artificial lighting is being adopted in many plants because it gives more even distribution of white light with little heat.

PATROL AND CENTRALIZED INSPECTION. Inspection to maintain control over quality of work in process is carried on under two main systems: (1) floor, or patrol, inspection; (2) centralized inspection. Under the floor or patrolling plan, inspection takes place at or near the machines. Under centralized inspection, parts are transported to a special enclosure or room, where, for particular work, careful measurements and tests may be applied free from disturbance, and, for routine mass inspection, special gages and other equipment can be set up to run the work through rapidly and at the same time remove all the rejects.

Floor inspection ranges from general patrolling supervision—keeping a general eye on work at machines—to close inspection and careful measurement of product at its place of production. Floor inspection is sometimes conducted from a cage or enclosed space placed in the line of work, product flowing through this space as though the area were one unit in a chain of machines.

CENTRALIZED INSPECTION. Centralized inspection permits the employment of men and women of a lesser degree of skill and experience than are needed for floor inspection because supervision is always at hand. Division of labor is sometimes possible, leading to economy in inspecting processes. Elimination of disturbance and interference is facilitated. Understandings between workers and inspectors are less possible. It is therefore easier to hold quality to definite standards, and obtain a better flow of work. Highly centralized inspection becomes impracticable when large parts are in question, as in the manufacture of large machines, steam turbines, ships, and products of corresponding size. The latter must be inspected at the machine or in the work area. Where work is performed by highly skilled mechanics, less inspection is necessary. As the type of production tends toward small repetitive manufacturing, the desirability of central inspection makes itself felt.

When parts have to undergo many consecutive operations, it is important to discover faulty work as early as possible. Floor inspection at each stage may then supplement final inspection of processed parts in a central room.

Central inspection does not imply one inspection room only. The basic idea is separation of inspection from manufacturing. Several such rooms or cribs may therefore be employed, each located centrally in respect to the machines which it is to serve. It is usual to place the crib parallel with the flow of work through the shop.

Advantages and Disadvantages of Central Inspection. The **advantages** of centralized inspection, combined with a storeroom for parts in process, are these, summarized from Radford:

1. Work can be stored in self-counting trays. A workman will come to the issuing window and obtain a box of parts, which he will machine and return. Inspection will show some good pieces and some bad, and the man will be credited accordingly. Collection of accurate data on production is thus facilitated, and can be used for checking piece payments. Losses from misplaced, stolen, or destroyed parts will be at a minimum.
2. Only one box of parts, that being worked on, will be at the machine. The result is a clean, clear shop.
3. Systematic arrangement of all parts in flow makes it possible to check on movements of materials, particularly when schedules are in arrears.
4. Control of quality is more certain. Work of inspectors is more easily supervised. Less skilled workers may be employed, reducing labor costs. Decisions on doubtful cases may be made at once by an authority. Custody of work in

process is well centralized. Each such station can be furnished with standard samples, lists of gages to be applied, and all other pertinent data.

5. Fixed and automatic inspection devices make mass inspection possible and lower costs.

6. Accurate inspection with delicate instruments can be done under controlled conditions. Such instruments cannot be taken into the shop.

7. Fewer gages and special fixtures are required because the same tools can be used for inspection of a number of parts from different departments.

There are certain **disadvantages** under centralized inspection, mainly those which constitute the advantages of floor inspection. These disadvantages are:

1. Considerable spoiled work may result from failure to detect machining errors in time.

2. Aid to the shop comes after a job is done, not in time to correct the trouble on the spot.

3. More materials handling is required.

4. Banks of work in process may develop in the inspection department, thus increasing the total amount under manufacturing.

5. Unless the inspection room is in the line of flow, there is often a break in the plan of product layout for straight-line manufacture.

6. Delays and piling up of work sometimes cause the inspection room to be a bottleneck in the production cycle.

7. Routing, scheduling, and dispatching through inspection increase the work of production control.

Advantages and Disadvantages of Floor Inspection. Floor inspection has certain **advantages**, among which the following are important:

1. If inspection is done on a systematic basis, errors often will be caught in time to prevent spoilage of large lots of parts.

2. Difficulties in the doing of work come to the attention of the inspector, who can aid in clearing up trouble when it arises.

3. Materials handling is reduced because work does not have to be moved to and from a central inspection room.

4. Some reduction can be made in the amount of work in process.

5. The plan fits in well with product layout and mass production, keeping work flowing.

6. Bottlenecks and delays, which often occur at inspection rooms, are obviated.

7. Routing, scheduling, and dispatching parts through inspection rooms are eliminated. The floor inspector, however, can route parts through a central inspection department when he finds more thorough inspection is indicated.

The **disadvantages** of floor inspection are to a large extent the antitheses of those favoring central inspection. They arise from the following conditions or causes:

1. It is difficult to get the count of good and bad pieces.

2. More work is piled up at machines. The worker has his completed work awaiting inspection while he is doing his next lot.

3. Presence of large quantities of work on the floor complicates the timing of the actual moving to keep work flowing.

4. It is difficult to control quality of work. Inspectors cannot be readily checked. They may become careless or may play favorites with certain workers. More highly skilled inspectors are required, thus raising labor costs. Delays occur in deciding doubtful cases. Work in process is scattered, from the inspector's standpoint, and he may lose track of some lots and delay their removal. The inspectors must carry their own cases of instruments and samples with them, or else go to their offices when these facilities are needed.

5. Inspection of a high accuracy on delicate instruments cannot be performed. Sometimes such instruments cannot be taken into the shop, and shop conditions (dust, vibration. etc.) would prevent close inspection even if the instruments could be moved.

COMBINED SYSTEM. While either floor inspection or centralized inspection may predominate in a plant because of the nature of work, shop conditions, and other factors, in most cases the two plans will be found combined. There will be large work, which will require floor inspection. Patrolling inspectors are often necessary to keep operations flowing and clear up troubles on the spot. Checks of this kind often stop spoilage of work almost as soon as it begins. Costs and inconveniences of moving work, and the low value of many individual pieces which are merely sampled, may make a floor check the most economical procedure for many operations.

On the other hand, the need for accurate inspection of certain parts or subassemblies may require that they be moved to a central inspection department. The advantages of automatic inspection devices, routine inspection at high speed by experienced inspectors, the lesser skill required, and the low costs which these conditions bring about, encourage doing as much of the work as possible in central rooms or cages. Each inspection operation should be studied in reference to its nature and importance and its relation to other work, and the place of inspection can then be determined to bring about the desired control of quality at the most reasonable cost. The total result will be the best program of inspection for maintaining production standards, and the lowest over-all cost for inspection, which, although vital and indispensable, is not a directly productive operation.

LAYOUT. Provision should be made for storage of incoming work, work in process of inspection, work accepted, work provisionally rejected but subject to correction, and work rejected as scrap or salvageable for other uses. Ample room should be provided so that inspectors have the sense of unhampered movement. **Height** of tables, benches, stools, and chairs should be given careful consideration to avoid strain and fatigue. The height of table for a toolmaker's microscope may not be the best height for a large surface-plate. Metal locker-type cabinets, with locks, should be provided for the storage of all portable instruments not in use, and glass cases or cloth covers should be furnished for heavy instruments permanently located. Every precaution should be taken to keep dust and grit from being tracked in or blown in through ventilators or windows. Floors should be covered with heavy linoleum. Tables and instrument stands, if of metal, should be topped with heavy green or brown linoleum or hard Masonite with well-waxed finish. Green is preferred as most restful to the eyes. **Projection-type** instruments should be screened against interference from lights outside instrument or screen. Provision should be made for degreasing or cleaning incoming work and greasing or otherwise protecting outgoing work.

Kinds of Inspection

METHODS IN USE. There are a number of different kinds of inspection, each carried on because of the necessity for controlling quality of work in the best manner and detecting spoilage as early as possible, so that further loss can be prevented. Most plants inspect in several of the ways described, each method being applied for its own definite purposes.

Trial-Run Inspection. This method calls for the inspection of the tool and testing it preliminary to a production run. Such procedures are common in departments of automatic or semi-automatic machinery. The tool may be checked against its drawing and specifications and may be found to be at variance with requirements. Then a trial run of a single piece will be made and this piece may be found to conform to tolerances.

First-Piece Inspection. Inspection under this plan consists in running a trial piece after a machine has been set up for a job, and checking the dimensions of the work against the drawing or sample. If the piece conforms to specification, the machine is turned over to the operator for the complete run. If not, the setup man makes adjustments or changes the tool, until finally a good piece is obtained. Then the machine is released for production.

Pilot-Piece Inspection. A further step beyond first-piece inspection is the running of a part through its entire sequence of operations on a series of machines set up for its production, especially in the case of product layout of equipment. Each tool and each machine setup are thus tested and all defective tools are replaced and all wrong adjustments are corrected. When a good piece results from the cycle, the production line is released for actual operation.

Working Inspection. Working inspection requires that the inspector shall check pieces, preferably at definite intervals, to make sure that the work is still being produced within tolerances. Tools wear or break and the operator may neglect to grind or replace them (unless the setup man must do this), and machines may be sprung or adjustments may loosen. A systematic means is necessary for detecting and correcting these happenings, and working inspection is this means.

Automatic machinery requires that the same precautions be taken. Periodic inspections during the run are necessary. Many automatic machines are now equipped with automatic signals or stops which act to shut down the machine when tool or machine trouble develops. Punch presses, for example, may shut down when a punch breaks. **Patrolling inspection,** however, is advisable on all long runs to prevent accumulation of excessive spoilage due to tool wear, or the failure of an automatic stop to operate

Key-Operation Inspection. Inspection is made prior to, and immediately after, a critical or expensive operation; first, to avoid doing expensive work on a part already not up to standard and, second, to check the accuracy of critical work before proceeding with succeeding operations.

Sampling Inspection. Often inspection is performed on samples taken at random from lots of small parts. These samples are considered representative of the lot when it is not practical to inspect each piece. If the samples are unsatisfactory, the entire lot may be inspected, or it may be rejected. The number of pieces to sample depends on the work or part and its value and importance. Statistical methods have been developed to determine the sample quantities, but often past experience or careful judgment forms the basis for the decision (see section on Quality Control).

Percentage Inspection. Amount of inspection to be done is sometimes expressed in terms of percentage, 100 percent meaning each and every piece in the entire lot. Inspection may be in excess of 100 percent, meaning that each part is subject to inspection as it passes from one operator to the next. Thus, in assembly of time fuses for projectiles, each individual visually inspects each piece to see that the previous individual actually contributed his or her part before blindly adding the next component. In this way, each assembler in turn becomes an inspector checking the performance of the previous assembler; and a final assembly inspection consists of weighing the completed fuse on a sensitive balance which immediately indicates the omission of even the smallest component.

Preassembly Inspection. This is performed on finished parts as a final inspection prior to going to assembly.

Functional Inspection. It is not sufficient that all components of an assembly pass preassembly inspection. Functional inspection after assembly checks the accuracy of assembly and assures that the assembly will function as intended. Thus, assembled breech blocks are fitted to a dummy cannon breech; if they function on the dummy they will function on any accepted cannon of the same size and type.

Efficiency Inspection. This inspection is synonymous with the trial run of a completed ship, locomotive, turbo-generator, or other equipment, for purposes of securing performance data to check against anticipated results.

Endurance Inspection. This is given to assemblies to determine how much use they can withstand and to locate weaknesses for correction. Telephone receiving sets and army rifles, for example, are given endurance inspections.

Destructive Inspection. This determines the ultimate resistance or effectiveness of the objects tested. It is regularly carried on at proving grounds to test guns, projectiles, and armor. Guns are sometimes tested to destruction to check the factor-of-safety calculations. A few shells are selected at random from a lot and fired to determine fragmentation or ability to penetrate armor. Sample armor plate is used as a target to determine resistance to penetration. This kind of inspection differs from other inspection in that the specimen tested is destroyed.

Piecework Inspection. Work produced on a piecework basis requires much more inspection than work produced on a straight time basis. Operators anxious for maximum earnings become careless, and a poorer quality of work is likely to result. A change-over from a time basis to a piecework basis generally requires an increase in inspection, the added cost of which, of course, must be more than offset by any advantages of the latter over the former system.

Product Inspection. Product inspection is the art of applying tests, by the aid of measuring appliances, to observe whether a given item of product is within the specified limits of variability. The term **quality control** is more comprehensive than product inspection. Included in its concept are problems of design, specification, standardization, manufacturing facilities, and inspection. The end procedure in production control is inspection of the product to determine whether it conforms, or the degree to which it conforms, to established specifications and standards (see section on Quality Control).

Tests of Completed Mechanism. After parts of a mechanism have been assembled, a final operating test or series of tests should be made, simulating maximum demands to be made on the mechanism after it is placed in service. **Strength tests** are in themselves the maximum limit. An armature will spin at twice its rated speed without bursting, or it will not; a derrick will lift the specified overload without permanent set, or it will not; a gun barrel will stand a heavy proof charge without bursting or bulging, or it will not. In such tests there is but one limit.

Final tests must be made under a complete assembly or to some subassembly. These final tests must be made under conditions as near as possible to those which the mechanism will encounter in actual service. If **service conditions** cannot be duplicated, test conditions should always vary from service conditions in a known way and to the same degree, that is, all mechanisms should be tested under like conditions.

INSPECTION TICKETS. In all kinds of inspection it is necessary to make reports on the work, to indicate the quantities of good parts available after each operation. If rejections are high, the causes must be promptly located and corrected, and replacement orders may be required to make up shortages. Moreover, operators are often paid only for the number of good pieces produced from an operation. A simple typical inspection ticket or report form is shown in Fig. 9.

INSPECTION TICKET

Model	Piece No.	Dept. No.	Date

Order No. _____ Emp. Name _____ No. _____
Name of Piece _____

Name of Operation _____
No. of Operation _____
No. Rejected { Stock Defective _____
Labor Defective _____
No. Received _____ No. Accepted _____ No. Returned _____
Remarks _____

Inspector _____

Fig. 9. Inspection ticket.

Nature and Extent of Inspection

CONDITIONS INDICATING EXTENSIVE INSPECTION. Conditions indicating the desirability of an extensive development of the inspection function have been enumerated by Babcock as follows:

1. Product demands frequent and thorough inspection, as when great accuracy is required.
2. Models are changed with frequency, as in a swiftly advancing art.
3. Labor is unskilled or rapidly changing.
4. Quality standards are being raised.
5. Considerable judgment must be used because standards are being shifted or have not been reduced to a definitely measurable basis.

Inspection is specifically necessary where the item to be tested has many parameters and limits, some of which are critical.

Every industry has its peculiar problems, not only in regard to inspection of product at various stages but also in relation to the closely allied work of maintaining satisfactory conditions. Upkeep of tools and gages in machine-shop work can be compared in some degree with the ceaseless scrutiny of temperatures, pressures, end points, and other controlling conditions of processing in non-machine-shop industries. More than any other department of the factory organization, an inspection service must be specially designed and adapted to the precise circumstances in the particular plant.

UNNECESSARY INSPECTION. Another feature which requires attention is elimination of unnecessary inspection. Many operations require no inspection whatever. Sometimes fixtures on succeeding operations can be so designed as to serve as gages to detect a missing or incomplete operation. Inspection, in other cases, may be dropped for the first operations in a series when a check at some later key operation can pass the work of several preceding operations. This plan is one of the economies attending **product layout** whereby all the work on a part is done on machines arranged together in sequence of operations. Similarly, and especially in the case of floor inspection, if the first several parts inspected are found to be right, inspection of the remainder of the lot may be waived. This procedure is safer, however, if a few of the last parts made are inspected in the same way. In other cases parts may be of such minor importance and slight cost as to make it advisable to drop inspection in favor of the more certain test of their **acceptability for use** in the assembling department. This condition is true of most small screws and minor screw-machine products.

INFORMATION FROM INSPECTION PROCEDURE. One of the greatest benefits of inspection service comes from its power to bring promptly to the attention of management information as to the true state of manufacturing operations so that faults and inefficiencies in processing may be corrected. The foreman inspector of each shop is close to what is going on in that shop and is likely to be unbiased because he is an observer rather than a producer. Thus he is excellently situated to locate manufacturing troubles, frequently to isolate their causes, and sometimes to offer suggestions for their cure.

Production difficulties ordinarily appear in the form of too great losses in spoilage, or through slowing down of production at some operation, thus creating a bottleneck or a partial choke-point. It is essential to correct the difficulty as soon as possible, but to do this it is necessary to develop and bring to light the true causes, which usually are due to poor materials, inadequate or poorly maintained machinery and tools, unsuitable inspection devices, careless setup of work, untrained or incapable workers, or ineffective supervision and control.

Trouble Reports. A useful device for the prompt collection of trouble data is provision of a printed form or "trouble report" to be made out and sent by foremen inspectors of shops to the chief inspector, who will transmit such facts as seem worth attention to the department that should correct the trouble—management being furnished with a copy. A detailed list of the usual **sources of trouble** (tools, gages, material, and so on) may be included for convenience, but the essential idea is to make the foreman inspector feel responsible for promptly reporting the full facts and nothing but facts. Hence he is required to state either that he "knows" or that he merely "thinks" trouble is due to the cause stated in his report. For the trouble report to be used successfully, the foreman inspector must have confidence in the judgment, fairness, and courage of his chief—he must feel sure that he will be backed up if he is right. Further, the management should make quite clear that it is looking for facts to cure troubles and not to find someone to blame. There is no surer way to put a premium on the concealment of facts than by trying to fix blame on an individual, nor does blaming someone help to cure the trouble. Presumably, each individual holds his job because he is the best available man for the position. If he is not, the management will know it much sooner if he and his associates are not continually placed in the position of being called upon to make excuses (G. S. Radford).

SALVAGE OR REPLACEMENT OF DEFECTIVE PARTS. When work fails to pass inspection, three courses are open: (1) The item may be worked over again to eliminate the defect, (2) it may be converted to some other purpose, or (3) it may be condemned altogether and sent to the scrap heap. If it is not fully brought up to standard by reworking, it may be sold for a second-grade product. In repetitive work, many plants have salvage departments, wherein defective work is examined and when possible rectified for productive purposes. If it is not possible to refit the item for use, the next lot going through should be made larger to replace the pieces so withdrawn. In nonrepetitive work, spoilage of one piece usually entails its remanufacture, from casting or forging up. A carefully organized procedure is advisable, therefore, to make good the loss, including prompt issue of replacement orders for all materials and operations, and their incorporation in machine-loading and progress schedules and in route sheets. **Spoilage** and **replacements,** being exceptions to a well-ordered routine, require a standard routine of their own if delays and confusion are to be avoided.

Precision Measurement Standards

DIMENSIONAL STANDARDS FOR PRODUCTION. The inch is the customary unit of measurement in the United States. It is derived from the prototype meter bar maintained by the National Bureau of Standards in Washington. The **inch** is defined from the relation:

$$1 \text{ yd.} = \frac{36.00}{39.37} \text{ meters}$$

Legal measurements in the United States are based on the metric equivalent of 1 in. = 25.40005 mm. The Canadian inch is derived from the relation: 1 in. = 25.4 mm. In England, the inch is derived from the imperial yard and is equal to 25.39997 mm. These differences in the value of the inch may be of significance in the calibration of very precise gage blocks and long distance geodetic land measurement.

Gage blocks are widely used dimensional standards in machine shops, tool rooms, gage shops, gage laboratories, and industrial standards laboratories. Quality specifications of gage blocks are established by the federal government. The wave length of red cadmium light under prescribed conditions of excitation, and with corrections for refractive effects of the medium in which it is travelling, is the most precise and adaptable dimensional standard for the **absolute calibration** of gage blocks for size, flatness, and parallelism to an accuracy in the order of one millionth of an inch.

INTERNATIONAL MEASUREMENT STANDARDS. For purposes of comparison and consistency, some standard temperature at which precise measurements should be made, or to which they can be reduced if made at other temperatures, is essential. During the First World War many difficulties arose in producing goods for international trade because, although temperature standards had been independently adopted by various countries, there was no international standard. In Great Britain, the standard was 62° F., in France 32° F., in Germany 58° F., in the United States 68° F., and so on. After that war the **inter-**

national temperature standard accepted was 68° F., or its equivalent of 20° C. This, however, did not solve the international measurement problem because there yet remained no internationally accepted factor for converting English measurement units into metric units and the reverse. Through the efforts of the International Standards Association the standard of 1 in. equals 25.4 mm. was adopted by the United States, France, Germany, Japan, Denmark, Finland, and several other countries, as the **conversion factor.** We now have an international standard for the conversion of measurements and an international standard of temperature at which to make them. Thus, in times of warfare, it is possible for allies to cooperate in the production of munitions, each for the other according to their best abilities. In peacetime, the manufacture of machine tools and machinery for export now offers no greater problem than for home consumption, as far as measurements are concerned. Likewise, standardization of machinery parts, fittings, etc., has been simplified by the adoption of standards, as in screw threads, and in some cases even in design, as in American Gage Design Standards.

Emphasis cannot be too strongly put upon the importance of designers' referring to standards, where standards exist, for the elements of their designs. Lists and copies of many important standards are obtainable through the American Standards Association.

Fundamentals in Inspection

PRINCIPLES OF INSPECTION. Quality of the desired degree must necessarily be worked into the product by control of processes. Inspection cannot perform this task; it does not make goods but only passes on them. Responsibility for production of standard quality rests on those responsible for manufacturing. Inspection checks the achievement; it is measurement plus judgment.

Failure to attain expected standards of quality occurs (1) from faulty engineering or design, or (2) from failure of the manufacturing department to give effect to design. If inspection is subordinate to engineering, design defects will tend to be concealed. If it is subordinate to manufacturing, poor methods of production will fail to show up, and quality will slip, probably all along the line.

METHODS BASED ON OBJECTIVES. Inspection methods, in general, are based upon the objectives sought, such as hardness, surface finish, measurement, dielectric properties, and in each case call for the application of appropriate standards. Colors may be graded in terms of intensity of color or by stipulating the amount of primary colors plus black and white. Textiles, paper, and metals have standards of strength and their physical properties are capable of measurement. Inspection may also require determining constituents of materials and critical points in processing. The proportion of contained elements is determined by chemical analysis. Internal structure, cavities, flaws, and variations in homogeneity are revealed by the X-ray. "End points," or the stage where opposing chemical forces are in equilibrium, are determinable by use of the hydrogen electrode. Other characteristics and properties are discovered through the microscope, as in metallographic studies. **Linear** and **angular measurements** are obtained by use of scales, micrometers and verniers, protractors, comparators, and a host of special measurement instruments. All the foregoing and many others are tools for inspection, the applications of which must be definite and specific, that is, reduced to simple yes-or-no tests. Usually but one property of the material is studied at any one time. The question to be answered and the terms and limits of the answer must be carefully predetermined.

Inspection Procedure. Procedures in the various methods of inspection are quite definitely set forth in fullest detail in handbooks and standards promulgated or sponsored by various technical societies and the American Standards Association, and in many texts. Descriptions of apparatus and instruments are readily available in trade catalogs and special texts, affording the inspector means for predetermining the suitability of a particular instrument or selecting a more suitable instrument.

DESIGN. Between design and execution of a given piece of work, every opportunity exists for difference of opinion regarding permissible variations. The designer will tend naturally to specification of limits as fine as possible. The production man, knowing that precision under ordinary conditions is costly, will tend toward demanding looser limits. The need for compromise under expert guidance is evident. An **ideal standard** prescribes no variations, but the nearer the approach to this dead theoretical accuracy, the greater the difficulties in manufacturing and the higher the cost. In making an objective for a great observatory telescope, a very close approach to absolute accuracy is essential, but such work requires months of the most skillful and patient application, quite outside the range of any commercial production. Beginning with an ideal design, the first step toward realization in the usual case is to determine **practicable variation limits**, having due regard (1) to the purposes to be secured by high accuracy, (2) to its cost, and (3) to the method of manufacture.

INSPECTION STANDARDS. Inspection standards for **raw materials** are first considered. Selection of material is dependent partly on the use to be made of it, and partly on the nature of the processes through which it must go. Much study has been given to this subject. Various societies and public bodies have issued standard specifications for various kinds and grades of material and these are largely used. Permissible variations in the chemical constituents of material (e.g., metals) and limiting conditions for important physical characteristics are given.

Inspection standards for **work in process** may be classified as follows: (1) relating to physical condition or properties of material, (2) relating to degrees of finish, (3) relating to form and dimension, (4) chemical, and (5) functional or performance.

Inspection of **condition of product** after any given process may have reference to either (1) result of the process, or (2) fitness of the product for an ensuing process. For example, after heat treatment auto gears may be subjected to Rockwell, Brinnell, and scleroscope tests to check hardness of finished product. Heat treatment of such gears may be divided into five steps: normalizing for forging strains, annealing for rough machining, carbonizing, heating to refire the core, and finally hardening, quenching, and drawing of the finished product. Absolute control over heat treatment is maintained by taking test pieces from time to time, and making microphotographs after each step, to check grain structure.

Control is maintained by continuous observation and recording of pressures, temperatures, and other processing conditions.

Most machine-shop, engineering, and mechanical industries rely largely on standards of **form and dimension** to maintain control of quality. Interchangeable manufacturing is based on such standards. In any given piece, limits of variation may be more important in one direction than another. Outside surfaces may vary within wide limits, but surfaces that must come together or "fit" must have carefully prescribed limits of variation. Naturally, these limits are not the same for all surfaces even when they are to be fitted together. Limits in watch manufacture are evidently not the same as those used in making agricultural machinery.

Fits and Limits. The following definitions (American Standard Preferred Limits and Fits for Cylindrical Parts, ASME-ASA/B4.1–1955) give the accepted meanings of the terms normally used for fits, limits, sizes, and tolerances in inspection procedure.

Nominal Size. The nominal size is the designation which is used for the purpose of general identification.

Dimension. A dimension is a geometrical characteristic such as diameter, length, angle, or center distance.

Size. Size is a designation of magnitude. When a value is assigned to a dimension it is referred to hereinafter as the size of that dimension. It should be noted that it is recognized that the words "dimension" and "size" are both used at times to convey the meaning of magnitude.

Allowance. An allowance is an intentional difference between the maximum material limits of mating parts. (See definition of "fit.") It is a minimum clearance (positive allowance) or maximum interference (negative allowance) between mating parts.

Tolerance. A tolerance is the total permissible variation of a size. The tolerance is the difference between the limits of size.

Basic Size. The basic size is that size from which the limits of size are derived by the application of allowances and tolerances.

Design Size. The design size is that size from which the limits of size are derived by the application of tolerances. When there is no allowance the design size is the same as the basic size.

Actual Size. An actual size is a measured size.

Limits of Size. The limits of size are the applicable maximum and minimum sizes.

Maximum Material Limit. A maximum material limit is the maximum limit of size of an external dimension or the minimum limit of size of an internal dimension.

Minimum Material Limit. A minimum material limit is the minimum limit of size of an external dimension or the maximum limit of size of an internal dimension.

Tolerance Limit. A tolerance limit is the variation, positive or negative, by which a size is permitted to depart from the design size.

Unilateral Tolerance. A unilateral tolerance is a tolerance in which variation is permitted only in one direction from the design size.

Bilateral Tolerance. A bilateral tolerance is a tolerance in which variation is permitted in both directions from the design size.

Unilateral Tolerance System. A design plan which uses only unilateral tolerances is known as a unilateral tolerance system.

Bilateral Tolerance System. A design plan which uses only bilateral tolerances is known as a bilateral tolerance system.

Fit. Fit is the general term used to signify the range of tightness which may result from the application of a specific combination of allowances and tolerances in the design of mating parts.

Actual Fit. The actual fit between two mating parts is the relation existing between them with respect to the amount of clearance or interference which is present when they are assembled. It should be noted that fits are of three general types: clearance, transition, and interference.

Clearance Fit. A clearance fit is one having limits of size so prescribed that a clearance always results when mating parts are assembled.

Interference Fit. An interference fit is one having limits of size so prescribed that an interference always results when mating parts are assembled.

Transition Fit. A transition fit is one having limits of size so prescribed that either a clearance or an interference may result when mating parts are assembled.

Basic Hole System. A basic hole system is a system of fits in which the design size of the hole is the basic size and the allowance is applied to the shaft.

Basic Shaft System. A basic shaft system is a system of fits in which the design size of the shaft is the basic size and the allowance is applied to the hole.

Preferred Basic Sizes. In specifying fits, the basic size of mating parts shall be chosen from the table given in Fig. 10. All dimensions are given in inches.

Standard Fits. Standard fits are designated by means of the symbols given below (ASME-ASA/B4.1–1955) to facilitate reference to **classes of fit** for educational purposes. These symbols are not intended to be shown on manufacturing drawings; instead, sizes should be specified on drawings.

The letter **fit symbols** used are as follows:

RC Running or sliding fit.
LC Locational clearance fit.
LT Transition fit.
LN Locational interference fit.
FN Force or shrink fit.

Running and Sliding Fits. Running and sliding fits are intended to provide a similar running performance, with suitable lubrication allowance, throughout the range of sizes. The clearances for the first two classes, used chiefly as slide fits, increase more slowly with diameter than the other classes, so that accurate location is maintained even at the expense of free relative motion.

These fits may be described briefly as follows:

RC 1 **Close sliding fits** are intended for the accurate location of parts which must assemble without perceptible play.

RC 2. **Sliding fits** are intended for accurate location, but with greater maximum clearance than class RC 1. Parts made to this fit move and turn easily but are not intended to run freely, and in the larger sizes may seize with small temperature changes.

RC 3. **Precision running fits** are about the closest fits which can be expected to run freely. They are intended for precision work at slow speeds and light journal pressures but are not suitable where appreciable temperature differences are likely to be encountered.

RC 4. **Close running fits** are intended chiefly for running fits on accurate machinery with moderate surface speeds and journal pressures, where accurate location and minimum play are desired.

RC 5 and 6. **Medium running fits** are intended for higher running speeds, or heavy journal pressures, or both.

RC 7. **Free running fits** are intended for use where accuracy is not essential, or where large temperature variations are likely to be encountered, or under both these conditions.

RC 8 and 9. **Loose running fits** are intended for use where materials such as cold-rolled shafting and tubing, made to commercial tolerances, are involved.

Locational Fits. Locational fits are fits intended to determine only the location of the mating parts; they may provide rigid or **accurate location,** as with interference fits, or provide some **freedom of location,** as with clearance fits. Accordingly they are divided into three groups: clearance fits, transition fits, and interference fits.

Dimension (inches)			Dimension (inches)		
...	0.0100	...	2¼	2.2500	2.25
...	0.0125	...	2⅜	2.3750	...
1/64	0.015625	...	2½	2.5000	2.5
...	0.0200	...	2⅝	2.6250	...
...	0.0250	...	2¾	2.7500	2.75
1/32	0.03125	...	2⅞	2.8750	...
...	0.0400	0.04	3	3.0000	3.0
...	0.0500	...	3¼	3.2500	3.25
...	...	0.06	3½	3.5000	3.5
1/16	0.0625	...	3¾	3.7500	3.75
...	0.0800	...	4	4.0000	4.0
3/32	0.09375	...	4¼	4.2500	4.25
...	0.1000	0.10	4½	4.5000	4.5
⅛	0.1250	...	4¾	4.7500	4.75
...	...	0.15	5	5.0000	5.0
5/32	0.15625	...	5¼	5.2500	5.25
3/16	0.1875	...	5½	5.5000	5.5
...	...	0.20	5¾	5.7500	5.75
¼	0.2500	0.25	6	6.0000	6.0
...	...	0.30	6½	6.5000	6.5
5/16	0.3125	...	7	7.0000	7.0
...	...	0.35	7½	7.5000	7.5
⅜	0.3750	...	8	8.0000	8.0
...	...	0.40	8½	8.5000	8.5
7/16	0.4375	...	9	9.0000	9.0
½	0.5000	0.50	9½	9.5000	9.5
9/16	0.5625	...	10	10.0000	10.0
...	...	0.60	10½	10.5000	10.5
⅝	0.6250	...	11	11.0000	11.0
11/16	0.6875	...	11½	11.5000	11.5
...	...	0.70	12	12.0000	12.0
¾	0.7500	0.75	12½	12.5000	12.5
...	...	0.80	13	13.0000	13.0
⅞	0.8750	...	13½	13.5000	13.5
...	...	0.90	14	14.0000	14.0
1	1.0000	1.0	14½	14.5000	14.5
...	...	1.1	15	15.0000	15.0
1⅛	1.1250	...	15½	15.5000	15.5
...	...	...	16	16.0000	16.0
1¼	1.2500	1.25	16½	16.5000	16.5
1⅜	1.3750	...	17	17.0000	17.0
...	...	1.40	17½	17.5000	17.5
1½	1.5000	1.50	18	18.0000	18.0
1⅝	1.6250	...	18½	18.5000	18.5
1¾	1.7500	1.75	19	19.0000	19.0
1⅞	1.8750	...	19½	19.5000	19.5
2	2.0000	2.0	20	20.0000	20.0
2⅛	2.1250	...	20½	20.5000	
			21	21.0000	...

Fig. 10. Basic sizes for specifying fits in mating parts.

These are more fully described as follows:

LC **Locational clearance fits** are intended for parts which are normally stationary, but which can be freely assembled or disassembled. They run from snug fits for parts requiring accuracy of location, through the medium clearance fits for parts such as spigots, to the looser fastener fits where freedom of assembly is of prime importance.

LT **Transition fits** are a compromise between clearance and interference fits, for application where accuracy of location is important but a small amount of either clearance or interference is permissible.

LN **Locational interference fits** are used where accuracy of location is of prime importance, and for parts requiring rigidity and alignment with no special requirements for bore pressure. Such fits are not intended for parts designed to transmit frictional loads from one part to another by virtue of the tightness of fit, as these conditions are covered by force fits.

Force Fits. Force or shrink fits constitute a special type of interference fit, normally characterized by maintenance of **constant bore pressures** throughout the range of sizes. The interference therefore varies almost directly with diameter, and the difference between its minimum and maximum value is small to maintain the resulting pressures within reasonable limits.

These fits may be described briefly as follows:

FN 1. **Light drive fits** are those requiring light assembly pressures, and produce more or less permanent assemblies. They are suitable for thin sections or long fits, or in cast-iron external members.

FN 2. **Medium drive fits** are suitable for ordinary steel parts, or for shrink fits on light sections. They are about the tightest fits that can be used with high-grade cast-iron external members.

FN 3. **Heavy drive fits** are suitable for heavier steel parts or for shrink fits in medium sections.

FN 4 **Force fits** are suitable for parts which can be highly stressed, or for and 5. shrink fits where the heavy pressing forces required are impractical.

Equipment and Techniques for Dimension Measurement

EQUIPMENT FOR DIMENSION INSPECTION. This equipment includes hand measuring tools; fixed gages; special design mechanical gages; measuring instruments and single- or multiple-dimension gages utilizing mechanical, optical, electrical, electronic, or pneumatic amplifying systems; machine control gages; and automatic gaging devices. Their geometric and precision capabilities vary with the geometry and tolerances of the product or parts to be inspected. They may be used for pre-process, in-process, post-process, or acceptance inspection. **Gaging systems** may be applied to single or multiple dimension inspection functions. They may be manual, semi-automatic, or fully automatic in operation. Measuring equipment requirements and environmental control conditions for gage manufacturing shops, gage laboratories, and standards laboratories require precision capabilities consistent with accuracy objectives. Measurements to an accuracy of one-millionth of an inch may be required in these upper echelons of the production precision structure (see Fig. 11). The science of measurement called **metrology** is often referred to in describing high-precision measurement techniques required for support of production operations.

HAND MEASURING TOOLS. The instruments falling in this category can be further classified into two types—nonprecision line-graduated and precision hand measuring instruments.

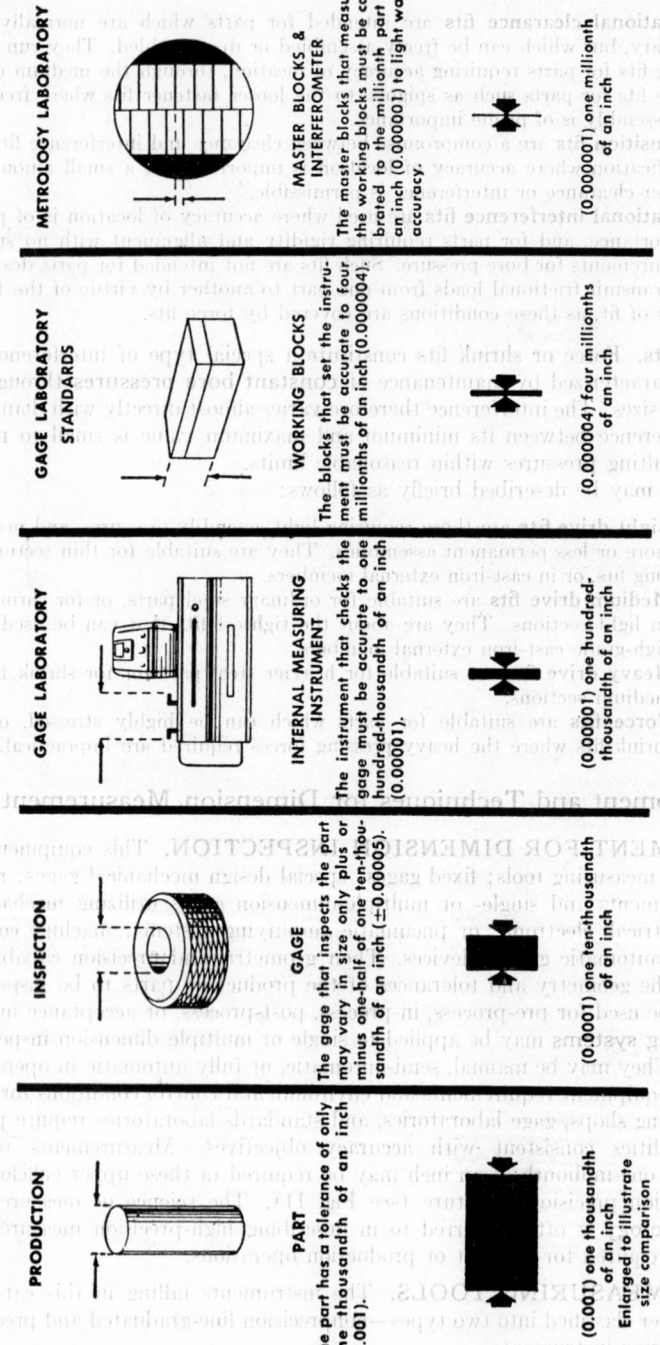

METROLOGY LABORATORY

MASTER BLOCKS & INTERFEROMETER

The master blocks that measure the working blocks must be calibrated to the millionth part of an inch (0.000001) to light wave accuracy.

(0.000001) one millionth of an inch

GAGE LABORATORY STANDARDS

WORKING BLOCKS

The blocks that set the instrument must be accurate to four millionths of an inch (0.000004).

(0.000004) four millionths of an inch

GAGE LABORATORY

INTERNAL MEASURING INSTRUMENT

The instrument that checks the gage must be accurate to one hundred-thousandth of an inch (0.00001).

(0.00001) one hundred-thousandth of an inch

INSPECTION

GAGE

The gage that inspects the part may vary in size only plus or minus one-half of one ten-thousandth of an inch (±0.00005).

(0.0001) one ten-thousandth of an inch

PRODUCTION

PART

The part has a tolerance of only one thousandth of an inch (0.001).

(0.001) one thousandth of an inch

Enlarged to illustrate size comparison

Fig. 11. Relationship of the metrology laboratory to other phases of dimensional control.

Nonprecision Line-graduated Instruments. The nonprecision line-graduated types are used where measurements in the fractional parts, such as 1/64- or 1/32-inch are sufficiently accurate. Such instruments are:

Line-graduated Scale. Basically a scale scribed on a steel strip. The most commonly used are those with ⅟₁₆-, ⅟₃₂-, and ⅟₆₄-inch graduations.

Caliper Rule. A rule with a fixed jaw on one end and a sliding jaw with the ends of the jaws so shaped that it is possible to measure both inside and outside surfaces.

Depth Gage. An instrument especially adapted to measuring the depths of holes and slots.

Combination Square or Set. Consists of a steel rule, a center head, a sliding head or beam which also contains a spirit level, a protractor head, and a scriber. It is used to square a piece with a surface, to find the centerline of cylindrical objects, as a height gage, or to find an angle.

Precision Hand Measuring Instruments. Precision hand measuring instruments such as the micrometer and vernier types are used where measurement accuracy is in the range of 0.001 in. However, a new micrometer of good quality may be accurate within 0.0001 in. in the range of spindle travel.

The **micrometer principle,** basically, is the use of the relation of the circular movement of a screw to its axial movement. In most applications one full turn of the screw advances the spindle contact 0.025 in.

Some of the common types of micrometers are:

Inside and Outside Micrometer Calipers. The most common types, applicable to many different measurements including diameter of holes and shafts. With special anvils they can measure narrow lands and pitch diameters.

Inside Micrometer. A rod-type gage used to check inside dimensions larger than those covered by the inside micrometer caliper.

Micrometer Depth Gage. Used in measuring depths of blind holes and slots.

Telescope and Small Holes Gages. Facilitate hole measurements which cannot be obtained with a standard micrometer.

The **vernier** consists of a short auxiliary scale usually having one more graduation in the same length as the longer main scale. **Vernier instruments** in general —the vernier caliper, vernier height gage, vernier depth gage, and vernier protractor—are similar in use to the micrometer types listed above, the difference being that the measurements are read from a vernier scale rather than a plain scale or micrometer.

FIXED GAGES. These include plug, ring, and snap gages made from blanks. (U. S. Commercial Standard CS 8–51.) Finished gage dimensions are related to the size and tolerance of the workpiece. General practices for determination of **gage size** and **tolerance** include the system used by commercial gage makers:

Size (inches)		Gagemakers' Tolerance Classes			
Above	To and Including	XX	X	Y	Z
0.029	0.825	0.00002	0.00004	0.00007	0.00010
0.825	1.510	0.00003	0.00006	0.00009	0.00012
1.510	2.510	0.00004	0.00008	0.00012	0.00016
2.510	4.510	0.00005	0.00010	0.00015	0.00020
4.510	6.510	0.000065	0.00013	0.00019	0.00025
6.510	9.010	0.00008	0.00016	0.00024	0.00032
9.010	12.010	0.00010	0.00020	0.00030	0.00040

A Class XX gage is a precision lapped gage for the highest degree of accuracy practicable in cylindrical plug and ring gages. Class XX gages should be used only in the inspection of close tolerance parts or as reference gages. Class X cylindrical plug and ring gages, also precision lapped, are usually applied to close tolerance inspection. Proceeding from Class X to Class Z, tolerances become progressively greater and the gages are used for the inspection of parts having progressively greater tolerance limits. A new class of gage quality (halving XX tolerances) known as XXX is being introduced for use as setting masters for comparators and air gages where product tolerances are smaller than 0.0001 in. Gage tolerances used by Army Ordnance are listed in Figs. 12 and 13.

A basic consideration in fixed gage policies is the direction of allocation of wear allowances and gage tolerances with reference to the **product limits.** Under one system (Military Standards 110, 111, 112, and 113 for plain plug and ring gages) all products accepted by correct gages will be within prescribed limits but some parts whose dimensions fall in the narrow borderline between actual gage size and extreme product limits may be rejected. It is customary to avoid borderline acceptability problems by referring to more precise measuring instruments or by changing to a high-sensitivity air gage. A fixed gaging practice that places gage tolerances on **go gages** outside the product limits may endanger product interchangeability. Some fixed gaging systems place the **not-go tolerances** all or in part outside the product limits, which may effect a slight increase in the product tolerance toward more looseness in assembly but has no effect on interchangeability.

SPECIAL DESIGN MECHANICAL GAGES. Special gages such as flush pin, fixture, template, concentricity, taper, depth, and length gages have their own design details (Acceptance Equipment Design Manual for Ordnance Material ORD M608-12).

Thread gages of the plug and ring types for plain and tapered threads are generally used for the dimensional quality control of threaded product. Segment and roll thread snap gages are used for some special inspection operations (ASA B1.2 and Screw Thread Standards for Federal Services, Handbook H28).

Gage Materials. Important quality characteristics of gage materials are economical machinability, wear resistance, and dimensional stability. Hardened tool steels with appropriate artificial seasoning treatments for attaining dimensional stability are widely used in gages. Chrome plating may offer **gage wear life** four times that of a hardened steel gage. Gages made from tungsten carbide may offer wear life ten times that of a steel gage. Flame plating of carbide offers the long gage wear life of solid tungsten carbide without the disadvantage of possible brittle characteristics in the latter. Boron carbide and synthetic jewels are sometimes used in **contact tips** of measuring devices for long-wear life. Stone of suitable composition is widely used to replace scraped cast iron in surface plates and parallels.

STANDARD SEQUENCE OF GAGE USE. Modern **multiple-dimension gages** for manual, semi-automatic, or automatic operation minimize the decision errors and high manpower costs related to the use of fixed, manually operated **single-element gages** such as plug, ring, snap, flush-pin, or dial-indicator gage types. Where process planning indicates the necessity for use of manual single dimension types of gages, arrangements for assembling groups of gages for **standard sequence of use** with a minimum of motion by the inspector may prove helpful in reducing costs and improving quality of inspection.

Gages Supplied in Boxes. Rapidity, convenience, protection of gages, and high accuracy in inspection have become paramount factors in many lines of work. Aids to these objectives are typified by methods adopted in the Nash-Kelvinator Corporation (Aero Digest, vol. 42). **Operators** in the manufacturing departments who must check dimensions of work are provided with specially fitted boxes containing all the necessary gages, arranged in the order of use, and held in suitable receptacles such as holes, slots, and recesses. The boxes are numbered to correspond with the operations checked. The simplified drawings from which the machine operators work list the tools required and the gages used in inspection.

Bench inspectors are also supplied with fitted gage boxes, the work being so planned that the gaging operations of all inspectors will take about the same amount of time. The schedules thus set up determine the number of gages assigned to each inspector. When indicator gages are provided, masters for setting the indicators are built in and dials are marked in red to show limits.

Mounting Gages on Boards. A further improvement in the case of small and easily handled parts was the permanent mounting of gages on heavy plywood boards, according to the sequence of inspection operations. The instruments are so spaced that the parts can be positioned conveniently as they are put through each step in the inspection. Rows of boxes are labeled for the segregation of rejects— the top row for oversize and the bottom row for undersize parts—and the separation in each row is by dimension being tested. The operation producing excessive rejects can thus be quickly determined.

Data entered on **rejection tags,** which are put on the fronts of the boxes, or on separate pieces, reduce the number of inspection records required. The data are part name, part number, date, shift number, inspector's name, inspection point, and disposal—special, repair in department, hold, or scrap. Outline drawings of the parts on the tags allow the location of the errors to be marked.

GAGE SURVEILLANCE AND RECORDS. Gages and measuring equipment for the dimensional control of modern mass production require constant surveillance to insure their continuous accuracy. Just as the surveillance of the accuracy of watches is accomplished by periodic checks against radio time signals or authoritative clocks, so also does each gage or item of measuring equipment require periodic checking against accurately known standards.

A suggested outline for such **accuracy control** (American Machinist, Special Report 387) is:

1. An effective inventory control system for gaging instruments.
2. Periodic inspection and calibration procedures.
3. Standardized calibration methods.
4. Adequate instrument laboratories.
5. Uniform gaging practices.
6. Standards for instrument design and purchase.

Gage record cards are most useful for inventory control and for inspection records. They should be so designed as to show dates of and for inspection of the item, vendor, and cost, along with a gage life history and detailed data referencing the gage to the part and actual dimensions of the gage.

The **surveillance system** or calendar should be one that checks the use and abuse, wear, and damage. It should allow for the tolerances being checked by the various gages and measuring equipment and should provide for planned periodic reinspection as often as the surveillance shows it to be necessary.

TABLE 1

This table shall apply to:

1. Taper plug and ring gages (included angle up to and including 15°), fixed snap gages, flat plug gages (excluding flat cylindrical type). Wear allowance required. Columns 1, 2, and 3 are applicable.
2. Taper plug and ring gages (included angle greater than 15°). Wear allowance not required. Columns 2 and 3 are applicable.
3. Max. and min. gages, e.g., depth, length, and flush pin types. Wear allowance not required. Column 2 applicable for both max. and min. tolerances.

Size Range Above	To & Incl.	Component Tolerance	Col. 1 Wear Allowance	Col. 2 Tolerance GO	Col. 3 Tolerance NOT-GO
0.0	0.825	.0005	.00010	.00004	.00004
0.825	1.510		.00010	.00006	No "NOT-GO" Gage Used
1.510	2.510			.00008	
2.510	4.510			.00010	
4.510	6.510			.00013	
6.510	8.510			.00015	
8.510	10.510			.00017	
10.510	up			.00020	
0.0	0.825	.001	.00010	.00005	.00005
0.825	1.510			.00006	.00006
1.510	2.510			.00008	.00008
2.510	4.510			.00010	.00010
4.510	6.510			.00013	No "NOT-GO" Gage Used
6.510	8.510			.00015	
8.510	10.510			.00017	
10.510	up			.00020	
0.0	4.510	.002		.00010	.00010
4.510	6.510			.00020	.00013
6.510	8.510			.00020	.00016
8.510	up			.00020	.00020

Size Range Above	To & Incl.	Component Tolerance	Col. 1 Wear Allowance	Col. 2 Tolerance GO	Col. 3 Tolerance NOT-GO
0.0	1.510	.008	.00040	.00020	.00010
1.510	2.510		.00040	.00020	.00020
2.510	4.510		.00030	.00030	.00030
4.510	6.510		.00030	.00040	.00030
6.510	8.510		.00030	.00040	.00040
8.510	10.510		.00020	.00050	.00040
10.510	12.510		.00020	.00060	.00050
12.510	14.510		.00020	.00070	.00050
14.510	up			.00080	.00060
0.0	0.825	.009	.00040	.00020	.00010
0.825	1.510		.00040	.00030	.00010
1.510	2.510		.00040	.00030	.00020
2.510	4.510		.00040	.00040	.00030
4.510	6.510		.00040	.00050	.00040
6.510	8.510		.00030	.00060	.00040
8.510	10.510		.00030	.00070	.00050
10.510	12.510		.00030	.00080	.00050
12.510	14.510			.00090	.00060

Gage tolerances for components with tolerances .003 to .007

Over	To	Component tolerance	Gage tol. 1	Gage tol. 2	Gage tol. 3	Gage tol. 4
0.0	0.825	.003	.00010	.00010	.00010	.00010
0.825	4.510		.00010	.00020	.00010	.00010
4.510	8.510		.00010	.00020	.00020	.00010
8.510	10.510			.00030	.00020	
10.510	up			.00030	.00020	
0.0	2.510	.004	.00020	.00020	.00010	.00020
2.510	4.510		.00020	.00020	.00020	.00020
4.510	8.510		.00020	.00030	.00020	.00020
8.510	12.510		.00010	.00040	.00030	.00010
12.510	up		.00010	.00050	.00030	.00010
0.0	2.510	.005	.00030	.00020	.00010	.00020
2.510	4.510		.00020	.00020	.00020	.00020
4.510	8.510		.00020	.00030	.00020	.00030
8.510	10.510		.00020	.00040	.00030	.00040
10.510	up		.00010	.00050	.00030	.00050
0.0	2.510	.006	.00030	.00020	.00010	.00040
2.510	4.510		.00030	.00020	.00020	.00030
4.510	6.510		.00020	.00030	.00020	.00040
6.510	8.510		.00020	.00030	.00030	.00050
8.510	10.510		.00020	.00040	.00030	.00060
10.510	12.510		.00010	.00050	.00040	.00070
12.510	up		.00010	.00060	.00040	.00080
0.0	1.510	.007	.00040	.00020	.00010	.00040
1.510	2.510		.00030	.00020	.00020	.00040
2.510	4.510		.00030	.00030	.00020	.00030
4.510	6.510		.00030	.00040	.00030	.00040
6.510	8.510		.00020	.00050	.00030	.00050
8.510	10.510		.00020	.00060	.00040	.00060
10.510	12.510		.00020	.00070	.00040	.00070
12.510	14.510		.00010	.00080	.00050	.00080
14.510	up					

Gage tolerances for components with tolerances .010 to .025 and up

Over	To	Component tolerance	Gage tol. 1	Gage tol. 2	Gage tol. 3	Gage tol. 4
0.0	0.825	.010	.00040	.00030	.00010	.00010
0.825	1.510		.00040	.00030	.00010	.00020
1.510	4.510		.00040	.00040	.00020	.00030
4.510	6.510		.00040	.00050	.00020	.00040
6.510	8.510		.00040	.00060	.00030	.00040
8.510	10.510		.00040	.00080	.00030	.00050
10.510	12.510		.00030	.00090	.00040	.00050
12.510	14.510		.00030	.00100	.00040	.00060
14.510	up		.00020	.00100	.00050	.00060
0.0	1.510	.012	.00040	.00060	.00020	.00020
1.510	4.510		.00040	.00070	.00020	.00030
4.510	8.510		.00040	.00080	.00030	.00040
8.510	12.510		.00030	.00090	.00040	.00050
12.510	up		.00020	.00100	.00040	.00060
0.0	1.510	.014	.00040	.00060	.00020	.00020
1.510	4.510		.00040	.00080	.00030	.00030
4.510	8.510		.00040	.00100	.00040	.00040
8.510	12.510		.00040	.00120	.00040	.00040
12.510	up		.00040	.00140	.00060	.00060
0.0	1.510	.016	.00040	.00060	.00020	.00020
1.510	4.510		.00040	.00080	.00030	.00030
4.510	8.510		.00040	.00100	.00040	.00040
8.510	12.510		.00040	.00120	.00040	.00050
12.510	up		.00040	.00140	.00060	.00060
0.0	2.510	.020	.00040	.00100	.00040	.00020
2.510	6.510		.00040	.00100	.00040	.00040
6.510	12.510		.00040	.00150	.00040	.00060
12.510	up		.00040	.00200	.00040	.00080
0.0	4.510	.025	.00040	.00100	.00040	.00040
4.510	6.510		.00040	.00100	.00040	.00060
6.510	12.510		.00040	.00150	.00040	.00080
12.510	up		.00040	.00200	.00040	.00100
—	up	up	.00040	.00200	.00040	.00200

For component tolerance and/or size range not shown, use next smaller component tolerance.

Fig. 12. Gage tolerance table 1 (Army Ordnance Standard ORD-M608-12).

TABLE 2
This Table Shall Be Used For All Cylindrical Plug and Ring Gages
— GO GAGES —

Size Range Above	To & Incl.	Component Tolerance	Col. 1 Wear Allowance	Col. 2 Tolerance
0.031	.825	Master		.00002
0.825	1.510			.00003
1.510	2.510			.00004
2.510	4.510			.00005
4.510	6.510			.00006
6.510	9.010			.00008
9.010	12.010			.00010
0.031	0.825*	.0005		.00004
0.825	1.510*			.00006
1.510	2.510*			.00008
2.510	12.010		Use approved coml. measuring device	.00010
2.510	4.510*	001		.00010
4.510	12.010		Use approved coml. measuring device	
0.031	0.825	002	.00010	.00007
0.825	1.510		.00010	.00009
1.510	2.510		.00008	.00012
2.510	4.510		.00006	.00015
4.510	6.510		.00005	.00019
6.510	12.010		Use approved coml. measuring device	
0.031	0.825	004	.00020	.00010
0.825	1.510		.00020	.00012
1.510	2.510		.00020	.00016
2.510	4.510		.00020	.00020
4.510	6.510		.00010	.00025
6.510	9.010		.00010	.00032
9.010	12.010			.00040

TABLE 3
This Table Shall Be Used For All Adjustable Snap and Length Gages
(tolerances are in ten-thousandths of an inch)

Component Tolerance	SIZE RANGE					
	To & Incl 2.500	5.687	12.000	18.750	25.500	30.125
	Above 0.0	2.500	5.687	12.000	18.750	25.500
.020 up	4	5	6	7	8	8
.015	4	5	6	7	7	7
.012	4	5	6	6	6	6
.010	4	5	6	6	6	6
.009	3	4	5	5	5	5

COMPONENT TOLERANCE

008	3	4	5	5	5
007	3	4	5	5	5
006	3	4	5	5	
005	3	4	5	5	
003	2	2	3		
001	1				

For component tolerance and/or size range not shown, use next smaller component tolerance.

NOT-GO GAGES

Size Range		Component Tolerance	Wear Allowance	Col. 3 Tolerance
Above	To & Incl.			
0.125	1.510	008 & up	00040	00030
1.510	2.510		00040	00040
2.510	6.510		00030	00050
6.510	12.010		00020	00060
0.031	0.825	.0005	Snug fit on GO	.00004
0.825	2.510			
2.510	12.010			
0.825	1.510	001	Use coml. meas. device	00006
1.510	2.510			00008
2.510	4.510			00010
4.510	12.010	002	Use coml. meas. device	00013
6.510	12.010	004	Use coml. meas. device	00016
				00020
0.125	0.825	006 & up	Use coml. meas. device	00010
0.825	1.510			00012
1.510	2.510			00016
2.510	4.510			00020
4.510	6.510			00025
6.510	9.010			00032
9.010	12.010			00040

*Use for all gages requiring air grooves

Fig. 13. Gage tolerance tables 2 and 3 (Army Ordnance Standard ORD-M608-12).

MEASURING OR GAGE LABORATORY EQUIPMENT. The principal types of metrology laboratory equipment are described in the following paragraphs.

Horizontal External Measuring Machines. These instruments incorporate the principle of micrometer screw, scale and vernier, controlled pressure, and varied measuring capacity to permit measurements greater than the range of the micrometer head which is ordinarily limited to 1 in. The accuracies afforded range from 0.0001 in. for the **bench micrometers** to 0.000010 in. for the more complex measuring machine. The external measuring of screw threads, plug gages, and thread wires are samples of the type of work done.

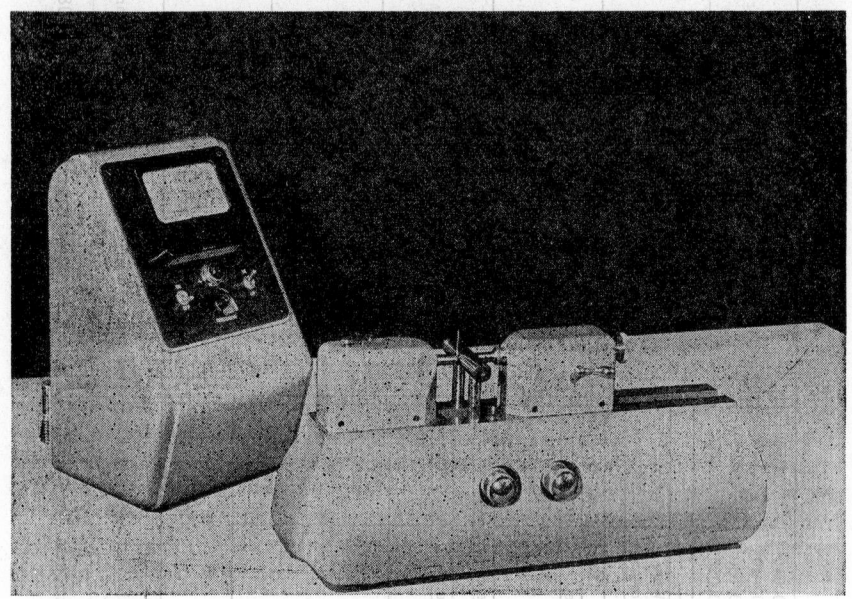

Fig. 14. Horizontal measuring machine.

Fig. 14 shows a horizontal measuring machine, the tailstock of which houses a contact pressure regulating mechanism and a high amplification electrical gaging cartridge. The headstock may include a high-precision micrometer screw or fixed contact as shown. The setup shown is for measurement of thread wire over a ¾-in. hardened roll to an accuracy of ±0.00001 in., as required by the U. S. Screw Thread Standards.

Internal Measuring Machines. These instruments measure the diameter of holes, generally utilizing electrical or pneumatic amplifying systems. Work is positioned on the table and the **measuring fingers** brought into contact with the bore to be measured. The fingers are set to a stack of precision gage blocks and deviations read on the indicating dial.

Fig. 15 shows a ring gage on the work table of an internal measuring machine. The ring gage is supported by rolls for free movement during contact with internal contact fingers. The contact fingers are movable vertically by a crank for exploration of the bore through the length of the hole under measurement. One

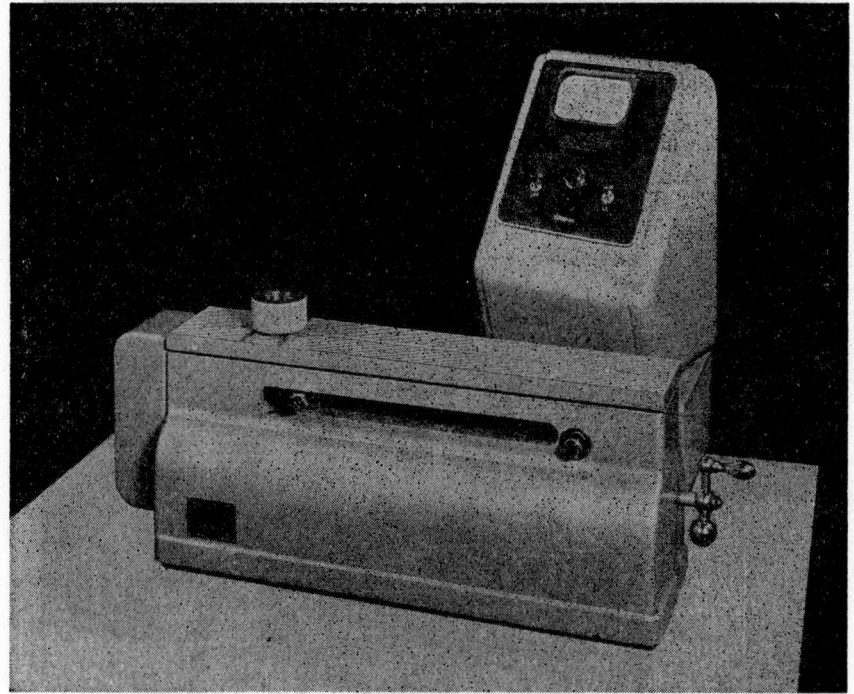

Fig. 15. Internal measuring machine.

contact finger actuates an electrical amplifying transducer with output indicated on the amplifier unit. Amplifier ranges may be as high as 20,000 to 1.

Surface Plates and Accessories. The surface plate is a rigid block or table of cast iron or granite whose flat or finished surface provides a **reference plane** for inspection and layout work. Accessory equipment includes parallels, both rectangular and box style, accurately ground on four sides to be used as spacers between the work and the surface plate, and angle irons for perpendicular reference or work positioning. V-blocks, squares, cylindrical squares, and straightedges are additional aids in the holding or positioning of work on the surface plate. With the use of gage blocks and height gages, many types of measurements may be checked, such as height of lands, concentricity of parts, centerline distances, or location of holes.

Fig. 16 shows a stone surface plate set up with a height gage and an electronic test indicator with the stylus being trammed over a cylindrical feature for measurement of taper. Surface plate setups are widely adaptable to a variety of measurements of **geometric features.** Mechanical and pneumatic test indicators may also be used effectively with surface plates.

Vertical Comparators. These instruments are devices which incorporate a means of holding the part being inspected, a master or setting gage block with which the part is compared, and a means of amplification whereby small variations from basic dimensions can be observed easily. Numerous types are available, the main ones being mechanical comparators with dial indicators, mechanical-

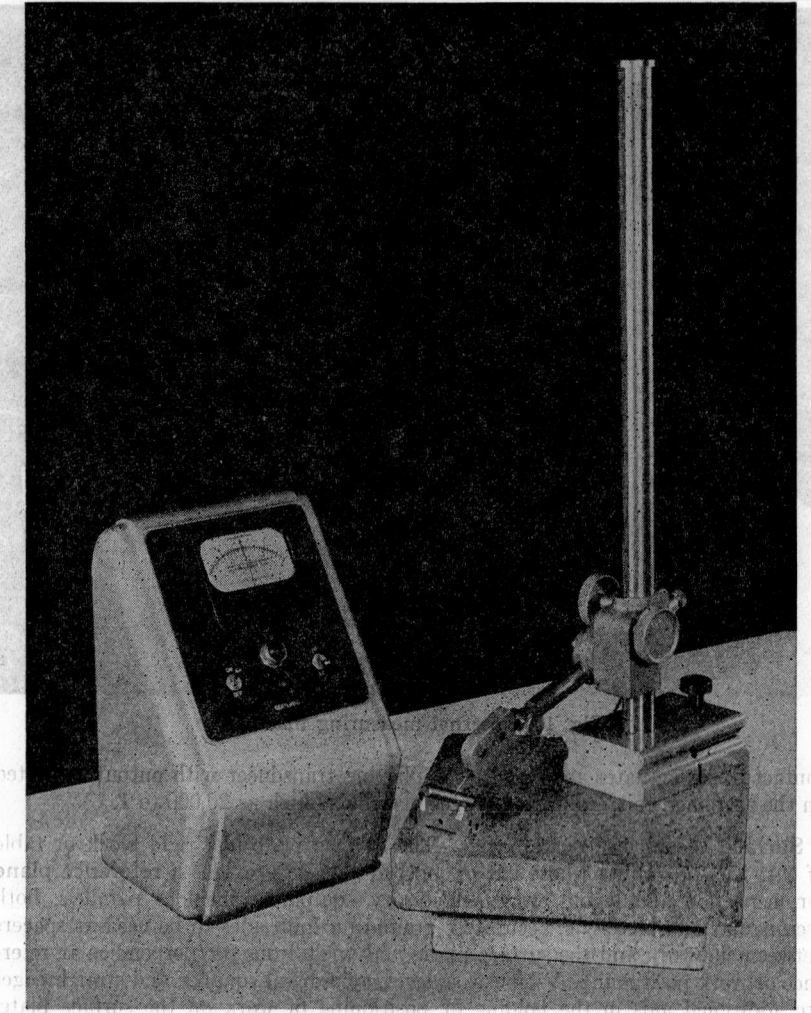

Fig. 16. Stone surface plate with height gage.

optical having a "reed-type" mechanism, electrical and electronic with a variety of electrical circuits, and air comparators which utilize the flow of air to indicate variations of dimensions.

Fig. 17 illustrates a vertical comparator using an electronic amplifier. A gage block is shown in setting position on the work-holding anvil. Contact pressure is controllable by adjustment of the knob on the side of the gage head. The contact stylus may be raised by a wire-type lifter.

Profile Comparators and Optical Equipment. The **optical comparator** is a measuring instrument which projects an enlarged shadow of the part being measured upon a screen, where the shadow is compared with straight or curved lines on a chart; these lines correspond to the limits of the dimensions or the

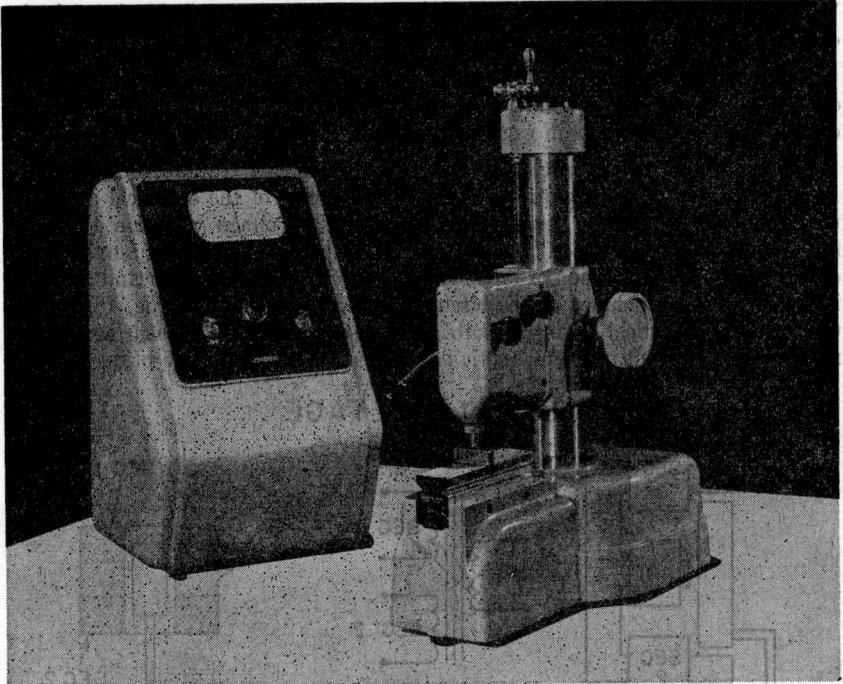

Fig. 17. Vertical comparator using electronic amplifier.

contour of the part being checked. Thread angle form, and radii and location of holes, are samples of work checked.

The **shop microscope**, simple in design and application, is a common instrument found in the laboratory along with the **compound microscope** for use in inspection of quality defects and measuring surface characteristics.

Optical flats are glass or fused quartz discs whose surfaces are so perfectly flat that, when placed in contact with another flat surface, they divide a ray of light into two paths and recombine them in such a way that the phenomenon of **interference fringes** occurs. This affords lines following the contour of the part being inspected at a known distance apart, usually 11.6 millionths of an inch, that are used to determine flatness or planeness of the part to a few millionths of an inch. Further application possible is the determination of parallelism, comparison of size of a ball or a cylinder with gage blocks, and comparison of a gage block against a master gage block.

Gage Blocks. A precision gage block is a piece of hardened alloy steel, chrome-plated steel, or carbide steel of square or rectangular cross section with a measuring surface on each end. These **measuring surfaces** are lapped and polished to be optically flat and parallel. Individual gage blocks vary in size from 0.010 in. to 20 in. They are usually purchased in sets of from 5 to 85 blocks of different lengths and in accuracies of from 2 millionths in. per inch to 8 millionths in. per inch. The application of gage blocks is widespread, as the **master reference** of length in the laboratory, as **setting masters** for instruments, and as direct measuring instruments themselves in setting snap gages and in measuring heights.

With the proper care and understanding of their use, the gage block might be called a "precision laboratory in a box."

GAGE AMPLIFYING SYSTEMS. A variety of electrical components and circuitry, as well as mechanical devices, may be employed for amplification of dimensional displacements in gages and measuring instruments.

Electrical and Electronic Systems. The differential transformer (Fig. 18, *A* and *B*) is used as a pick-up or contact unit in some of the electrical and electronic amplifying system devices. The output is a voltage variation that is a function of displacement of the measuring contact. To further amplify and eliminate effects of variation of input voltage, an electronic oscillator and amplifying tubes may be included in the circuit. **Inductance bridges** (Fig. 18, *C*) are used in some electrical gaging circuits. In these systems the measuring contact moves a steel element in the magnetic field, causing a change in the bridge balance

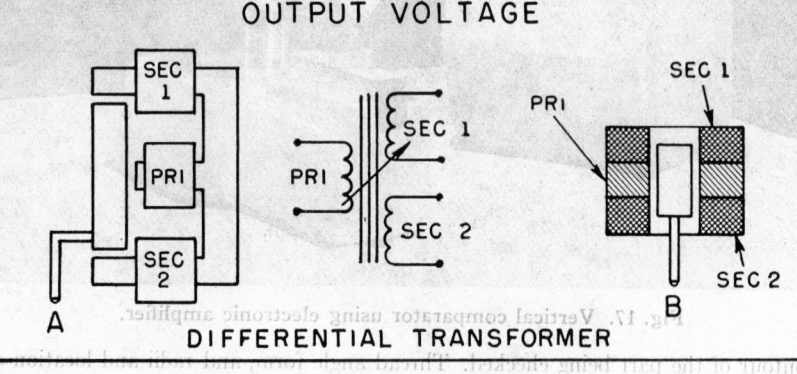

OUTPUT VOLTAGE

DIFFERENTIAL TRANSFORMER

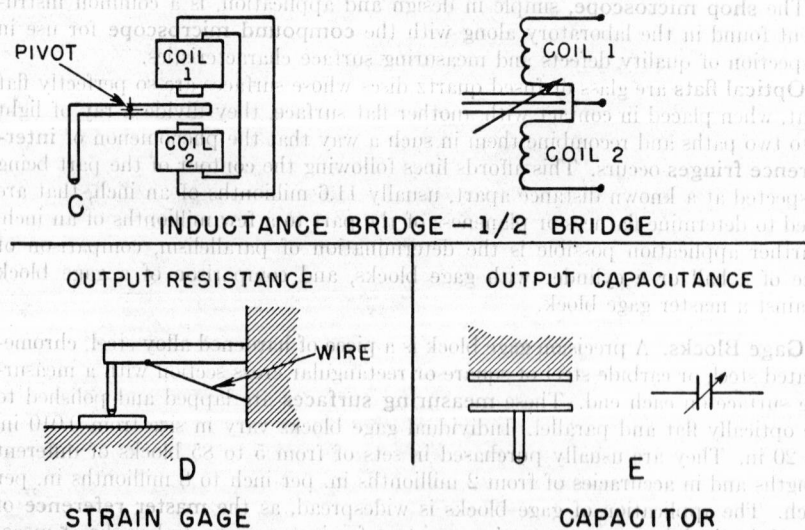

Fig. 18. Electrical gaging elements.

that is electrically indicated as an analog of the dimensional displacement. **Resistance strain** gages (Fig. 18, D) bonded to an element strained by a dimensional displacement provide an amplified output that results from the change in resistance due to the magnetostrictive effect in the stretched wire. **Change in capacity,** (Fig. 18, E) when an electrical condenser plate in an electronic tank circuit is moved by a measuring contact, is another variation of electronic gaging. Some of these systems can provide dimensional amplifications as high as 200,000 to 1 or where a displacement of 0.00010 in. would cause a deflection of 20 in. on the indicating meter if such a scale range were available.

Mechanical Amplifying Devices. Mechanical indicating gages employ various methods to achieve amplification of movement. The purpose of this amplification is to translate a minute displacement of a stylus or gage point, resulting from contact with a specimen, into a value on an indicating scale. It is desirable that this value be read quickly and easily.

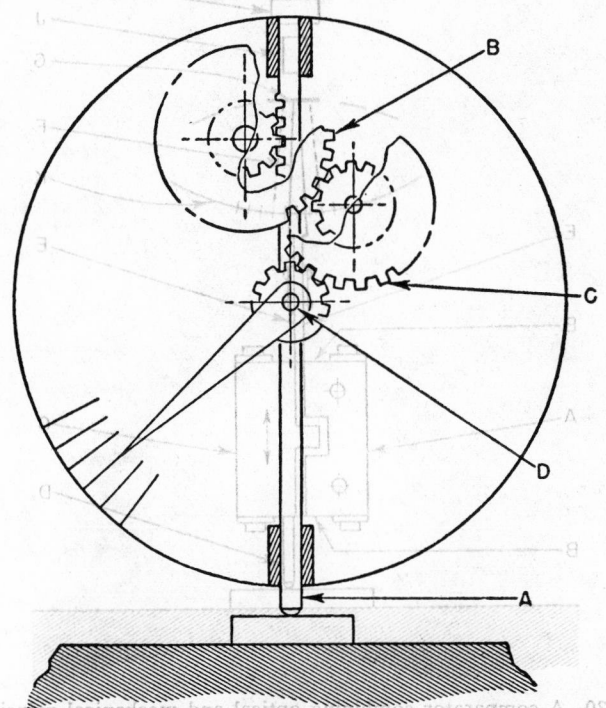

Fig. 19. Basic operating principle of dial indicator.

Amplifying units in such gages utilize many commonplace mechanical devices such as: simple and compounded levers; racks, pinions, and gears; spring-steel reed mechanisms; and optical elements, including lenses, prisms, and mirrors. In some cases various combinations of these relatively simple devices are employed to provide greater accuracy or a higher magnitude of amplification.

Probably one of the most commonly known gages in this category is the **dial indicator,** Fig. 19 (The Sheffield Corp.).

Essentially, this gage consists of a gaging stylus *A*, having involute rack teeth on one end meshing with assembly *B*, compounding through assembly *C* to the pointer shaft *D*. Thus amplification of this gage is obtained solely by the ratio of the various pinions and gears, plus the length of the indicating pointer. The scale is arranged radially around the outer periphery of the scale plate. The dial-indicator gage when rigidly mounted on a gage stand or in fixed position on a gaging fixture will indicate dimensional deviations of the part being gaged with respect to a reference surface.

A widely used indicating **comparator-type gage** embodying combinations of mechanical and optical elements is shown diagrammatically in Fig. 20 (The Sheffield Corp.).

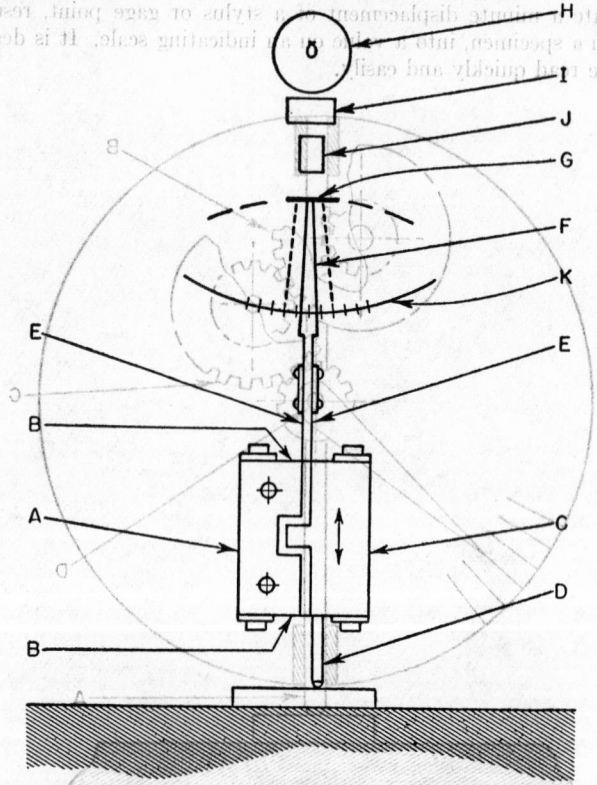

Fig. 20. A comparator combining optical and mechanical principles.

The fixed block *A* supports a vertically floating block *C* by means of two horizontal reeds or flat springs *B*. The floating block carries the gaging stylus *D*. Between the fixed block and the floating block are two vertical reeds *E*, to which the pointer *F* carrying the target *G* is attached. The target intercepts a beam of light initiated by the light source and optical assembly, *H*, *I*, and *J*. The resulting image projected upon the scale *K* indicates, highly amplified, any stylus movement.

This unit is usually of the bench comparator type because of its size. It has extreme accuracy, speed of response, and fixed amplification. Because of its rugged construction and completely frictionless mechanism, it has a very long life with little maintenance. The mechanical amplification is usually less than 100, but is multiplied by the optical light lever so that amplifications range from 500 to 20,000.

AIR GAGES. Pneumatic components and circuitry are widely used in dimensional gages and measuring instruments. The **size-sensing element** may be a spindle with diametrically spaced jets from which the air escape varies with the dimension under measurement. The **flow type** of air gage circuit (Fig. 21) has this type of spindle, together with the maximum and minimum size **setting**

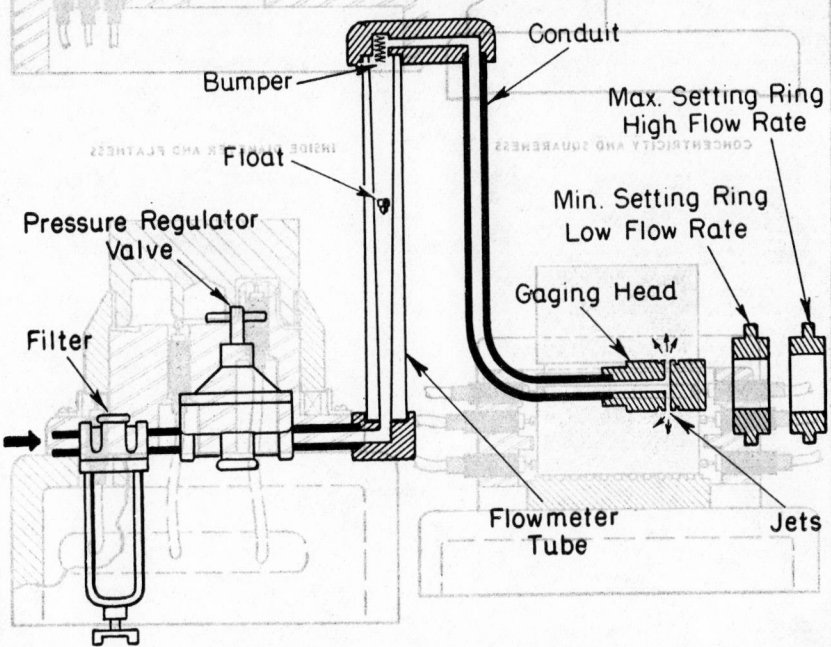

Fig. 21. Flow type of air gage circuit.

masters for the tolerance to be measured. The flow-type indicator using a float in a precision-tapered tube in series with the measuring jet outlets provides the fastest response and most precise indication obtainable from air gages. Air gaging instruments, particularly of the flow types together with **plunger-type** gaging contact cartridges, are adaptable to many complex geometrical features and precise tolerances as illustrated in Fig. 22.

OPTICAL GAGING AND MEASURING DEVICES. This class includes microscopes with measuring reticles for measuring or for viewing line-graduated precision scales. A **toolmaker's microscope** consists of a base carrying a precise coordinate stage with various accessories for variable magnification, special reticles for thread forms, and work-holding elements, such as centers and indexing plates. **Interferometers** using the wave length of special light sources provide for the most precise measurement of size, flatness, and parallelism of precision standards such as gage blocks. The most widely used instruments for optical measurements are projectors or **comparators.** They consist of a base, a work-

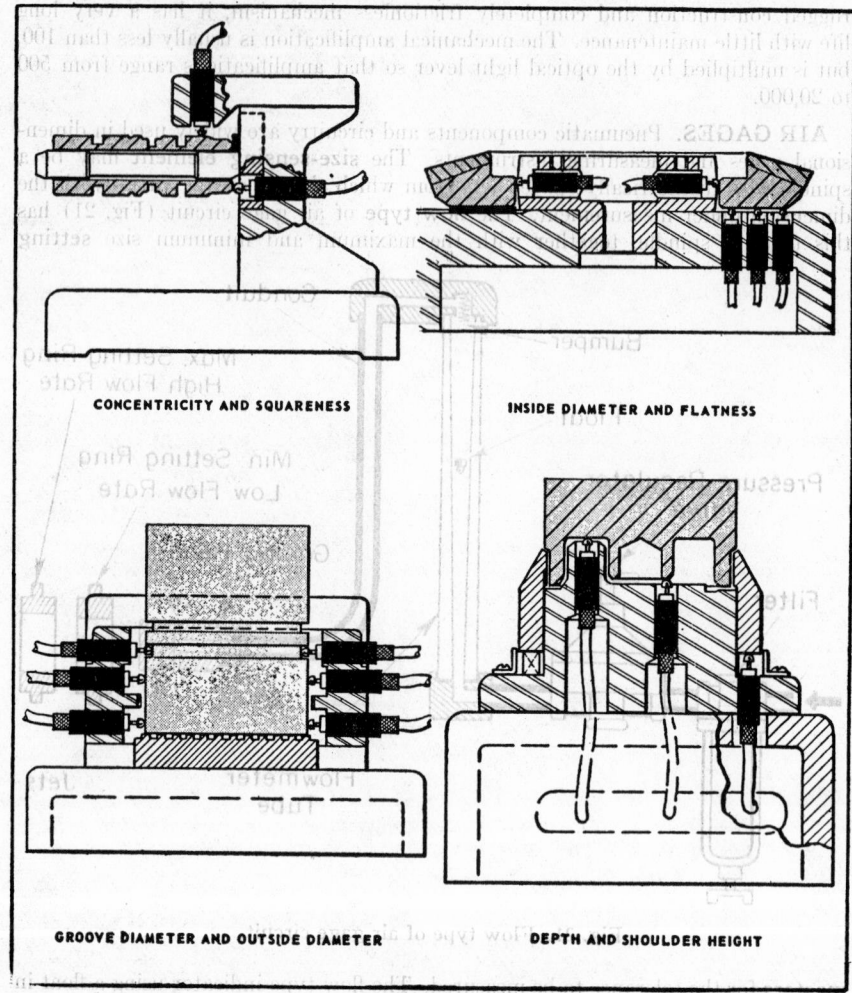

CONCENTRICITY AND SQUARENESS

INSIDE DIAMETER AND FLATNESS

GROOVE DIAMETER AND OUTSIDE DIAMETER

DEPTH AND SHOULDER HEIGHT

Fig. 22. Typical air gage setups.

holding table, light sources, and collimating lenses, objective lens, and enclosed optical path to a translucent screen. The magnified image of the workpiece is viewed on the screen and measurements made by movement of the work-holding table, by comparison with a special screen chart, or by angular movement of a precise indexing element holding the screen. Optical gaging techniques utilize special design work-holding stages and special screen charts having magnified layouts of the geometrical features to be checked. They are widely used for checking position and form type of measurements.

AUTOMATIC GAGES. Automatic gages are a machine type of device incorporating one or more of the electrical or pneumatic instrument gage types of circuits and usually performing a multidimensional check of a given part. They are frequently placed in a production line to conduct in-process, post-process, or final acceptance inspection of a part as it passes along the production or assembly line conveyor. However, this type of gage may be placed anywhere in a manufacturer's plant. Automatic gages are designed as a built-in, automated system of measurement instrument and control for most high-precision, high-production industries and for much short-run precision operation. **Automatic gaging capabilities** include:

1. Adjusting movement of cutting or forming tools.
2. Replacing or signaling for replacement of worn tools or other operations.
3. Stopping machine.
4. Segregating parts at any stage of production.
5. Weighing or checking weight relationships.
6. Correcting or straightening parts such as shafts or connecting rods automatically.
7. Match assembling of high precision parts.
8. Inspecting finished parts.
9. Classifying and properly marking parts.
10. Selectively packing parts.

In-Process Control. In-process control, or gaging during machining (see Fig. 23) provides the machine or cutting tool with signals to:

1. Automatically stop or change the tooling from a roughing to a finishing cut.
2. Automatically retract the cutting tool when the part is to finished size.
3. Automatically indicate and adjust the tool when the size trend is toward either limit of tolerance.
4. Automatically stop the machine after the tools become worn and parts no longer can be machined within limits.

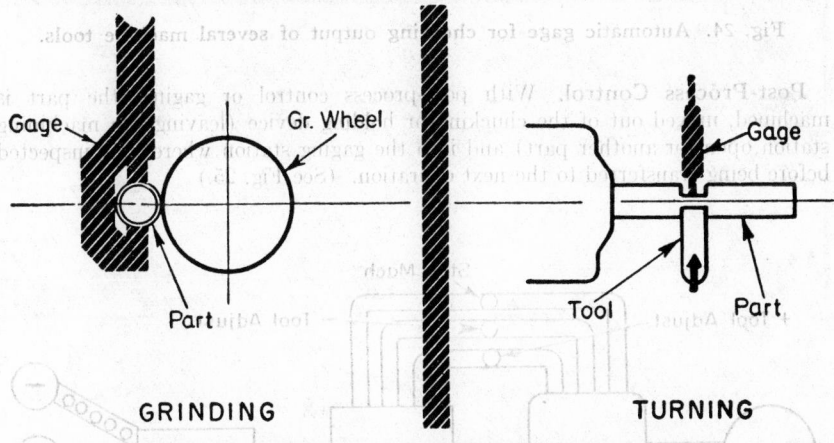

GRINDING   TURNING

Fig. 23. In-process control with automatic gages.

In-process control prevents faulty parts from being made by initiating signals for tool correction or replacement before part size is out of control.

A multiple feedback device used to control multiple machines from a single automatic gage is shown in Fig. 24 (The Sheffield Corp.). It combines an automated precision gaging and machine control system in a single unit. The letter *M* points out the location of the unit's "memory system" which is used to feed gaging information back to individual machines and thus automatically control dimensional quality of parts produced by a series of machines.

Fig. 24. Automatic gage for checking output of several machine tools.

Post-Process Control. With post-process control or gaging, the part is machined, moved out of the chucking or holding device (leaving the machining station open for another part) and into the gaging station where it is inspected before being transferred to the next operation. (See Fig. 25.)

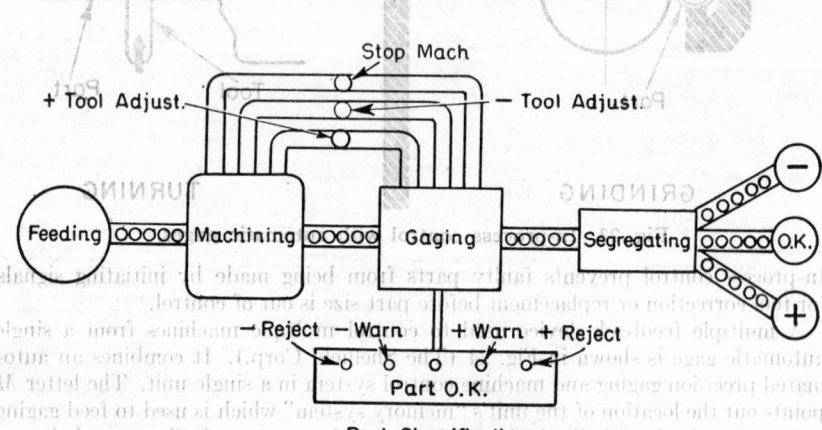

Fig. 25. Post-process control of machined parts.

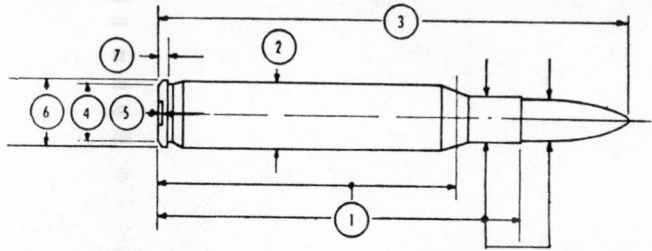

Fig. 26. Automatic gaging and segregating machine.

1. Profile and alignment.
2. Excessive body diameter.
3. Over-all length dimension.
4. Extractor groove dimension.
5. Primer depth dimension.
6. Head diameter.
7. Head thickness dimension.
8. Weight.

Fig. 27. Characteristics of ammunition checked by an automatic gaging and segregating machine.

A major advantage of post-process control over in-process control is that the parts are gaged in a free state—without influence from chuck or machine. In post-process control, signals are initiated to:

1. Automatically warn and/or adjust the tool when part size is approaching the extreme limits of control.
2. Automatically stop the machine in event of tool failure.
3. Automatically stop the machine if a specified number of consecutive parts is beyond tolerance.
4. Automatically actuate segregating mechanism so that faulty parts are rejected before reaching the next operation.

Post-process control means on-the-spot inspection and rejection of faulty parts.

With this type of control, the gaging station is generally located adjacent to the machining operation. Or, it may be remotely located and the parts from several machines channeled to it in sequence, so that the machine that produced the faulty part is indicated and shut down after a specified number of consecutive parts has been rejected.

The self-contained, fully automatic gaging and segregating machine shown in Fig. 26 (The Sheffield Corp.) inspects for final acceptance 3,600 rounds of loaded caliber 30 ammunition per hour for the characteristics shown in Fig. 27. Rounds are automatically segregated into four classes: acceptable, reject on dimensions, reject on overweight, and reject on underweight.

Fig. 26. Automatic gaging and segregating machine.

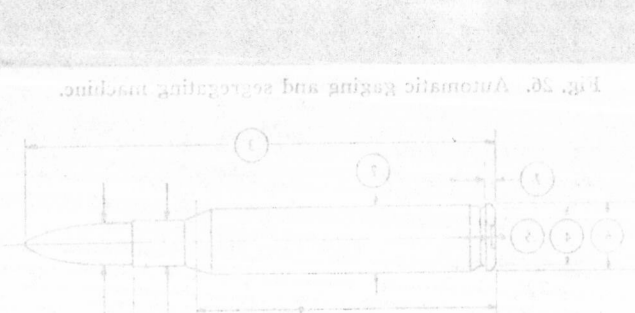

1. Profile and alinement.
2. Excessive body diameter.
3. Over-all length dimension.
4. Extractor groove dimension.
5. Primer depth dimension.
6. Head diameter.
7. Head thickness dimension.
8. Weight.

Fig. 27. Characteristics of ammunition checked by an automatic gaging and segregating machine.

QUALITY CONTROL

CONTENTS

PAGE

The Nature of Quality Control

Meaning of quality 1
Quality of design 1
Quality of conformance 1
Achievement of economical conformance .. 2
Balance of cost and value for most economical degree of conformance (f. 1).. 2
Purpose of quality control 3
Quality control during production 3
Ineffective controls 3
Feedback of information 4
Introduction of quality control as a coordinator (f. 2) 4
Feedback example 5
Benefits of quality control 5

Organization for Quality Control

Quality functions 6
Assignment of the quality activities (f. 3) 7
Size of staff 6
Place of quality in the organization 6
Position of quality on the organization chart (f. 4) 8
Quality control supervision 6
Multiplant organization 8
Position of quality organization in a company with several plants (f. 5) 8
Quality control staff 8
Responsibility 9
Authority 9

The Quality Control Program

Planning for quality 9
Factors involved in a quality control program compared with those involved in a marketing program (f. 6) 10
A quality audit 11
Resistance to change 12
Improvement of product specifications 12
Improving product specifications (f. 7).. 13
Use of statistical methods 12
Results of statistical quality control 14
Starting statistical quality control 14

Inspection Record Analysis

Location of main sources of loss 14
Factory records 15

PAGE

Purchased materials 18
Record of supplier's quality (f. 8) 15
Parts in process 18
An original record of disposition (f. 9) ..16–17
Weekly summary for scrap (f. 10) 19
Check list for defects (f. 11) 20
Action based on quality records 19

Special Process Studies

Diagrams for diagnosis 21
Inspection tally sheet (f. 12) 22
Interpretations of tallies (f. 13) 23
Process capability studies 24
Visual indications of capability 24
Charts of individual measurements in the study of capability (f. 14)......... 25
Numerical ratings of capability 26
Proportionate costs of obtaining various tolerances (f. 15) 26
Statistical determination of capability 27
Distribution of parts according to one dimension, for three different machines (f. 16) 27
Typical form used in conducting a machine capability study (f. 17) 29
Control charts 29
Control chart functions 30
Procedure in applying control charts 30
Choice between $\bar{X}$, R, p, and c charts 31
Use of p and c charts 32
Selection of samples 32
Establishing trial control limits 33
Formulas and factors for constructing control charts (f. 18) 33
Trial limits for $\bar{X}$ and R charts 35
Data sheet for X and R charts (f. 19) .. 34
$\bar{X}$ and R charts for automatic bag-loader (f. 20) 35
Trial limits for p charts 36
Trial limits for c charts 36
c chart for cable defects (f. 21) 37
Chart review and action 37
Recomputation of limits 38
Comparing chart results with specifications 38
Changes to satisfy specifications 38
Control to given standards 39

Examples of Process Studies

Machine capability study 39
Capability study on automatic screw machine (f. 22) 40

PAGE

Molding-machine capability study 41
    Molded part for which a capability
      analysis was applied (*f.* 23) 41
    Molding machine capability analysis be-
      fore correction (*f.* 24) 42
    Molding machine capability analysis
      after correction (*f.* 25) 42
    Corrections in condition 42
Screw machine capability study 42
$\overline{X}$ and R charts applied to springs 43
    Spring on which an $\overline{X}$ and R chart was
      applied (*f.* 26) 43
    Control inspection measurements on
      spring leg lengths (spring shown in
      Fig. 26) (*f.* 27) 44
    Control charts used to highlight assign-
      able causes of variation (*f.* 28) 46
    Conditions discovered by study 45
    Corrections introduced 45
Fraction defective chart approach 49
    Inspection data used in a fraction defec-
      tive chart (*f.* 29) 47
    Fraction defective (*p*) charts prepared
      from the data in Fig. 29 (*f.* 30) 48–49
Special problems with multiple machines ... 50
    Base for electron tube, showing pin in-
      serts and glass button (*f.* 31).......... 50
    Causes of variations 51
    Data sheet for control inspection of ex-
      posed pin lengths (*f.* 32) 51
    Control charts for mean pin lengths ob-
      tained from two heads of dial-feed
      machine (*f.* 33) 52
    Improvements made 51

Sampling Tables for Acceptance and Control

PAGE

Sampling 52
    Advantages of sampling 52
    Limitations of 100 percent inspection 53
Acceptance by attribute inspection 53
Single, double, and multiple sampling 54
Sampling plans and their protection 54
    A typical operating-characteristic curve
      with key points identified (*f.* 34) 55
    Lot tolerance percent defective (p_t) 56
    Acceptable quality level (AQL) 56
    Average outgoing quality limit (AOQL).. 56
Use of published sampling tables 56
Dodge-Romig tables 58
    Lot tolerance plans 58
    A typical Dodge-Romig table for a
      single sampling plan (*f.* 35) 59
    AOQL plans 58
    A typical Dodge-Romig table for a
      double sampling plan (*f.* 36) 60–61
Military-standard tables 58
    Military-standard table for double sam-
      pling (*f.* 37) 62–63
Sampling tables for process control 60
    Plan for use when output can be segregated 61
    A plan for patrol inspection (*f.* 38) 64
    Plans for use in continuous production 64
    Operation of a typical Dodge CSP-1
      plan for continuous sampling (AOQL
      = 1 percent) (*f.* 39) 65
Acceptance by variables inspection 64

QUALITY CONTROL

The Nature of Quality Control

MEANING OF QUALITY. No manufacturer needs to be convinced that reduction of costs is desirable. However, he may doubt that an improvement of quality will reduce costs. If so, he may hold this view because he associates quality chiefly with elaborate design, stylish appearance, extra accessories, and the like. A broader view of quality is shown by the expectations of the buyer, who may complain if a product does not function as intended, does not wear long enough, or does not look attractive. To have these qualities, a product must be sufficient in two respects. The designer must first develop an adequate **pattern**, and the factory must then follow it with adequate **fidelity**. Juran (Quality Control Handbook) terms these concepts "quality of design" and "quality of conformance."

Quality of Design. As applied to floor coverings, for example, an ankle-deep carpet has higher quality than a paper-thin one. The former has been designed to use more and better materials in a more complex weave to give superior satisfaction and life. Increases in quality of design normally increase the costs of design and production. This is profitable only to the extent that the higher grade of product leads to a rise of sales income which exceeds the rise in costs.

Quality of Conformance. Two deep, expensive carpets made to the same specification in the same mill may still differ. One may have a uniform, attractive color while another is off-color or blotchy or has loose tufts. These conditions involve lack of conformance to specification.

In general, conformance can be sought either by sorting the good from the bad after manufacture or by taking preventive measures at any source of trouble. Obviously, **sorting after manufacture** is costly. **Prevention,** on the other hand, not only reduces the need for sorting but also reduces the amount of scrap, seconds, and rework; reduces customer complaints; and in many industries avoids much trouble with fitting of spare parts in the field. Thus an increase in conformance can be profitable even without an increase in price. In addition, increased conformance adds to product reliability, which is itself a marketable characteristic.

The consumer may not distinguish between quality failures due to design weakness and quality failures due to lack of conformance. If tufts fall out of his rug, he is dissatisfied. He is not interested in whether the designer erred in his specification or the mill failed to conform to it. Nevertheless, the distinction is important to the supplier. The one form of quality improvement may add to costs, the other cuts costs if properly carried out. The choice as to quality of design is made only occasionally, generally at the time a new product is being planned and launched. The struggle to maintain conformance continues as long as the product is made.

8·1

Achievement of Economical Conformance. Obviously, the decision to manufacture a heavy rug or a light rug can be made quite separately from the decision on the level of conformance or adherence to tolerances. Regardless of the price commanded by the grade of an article, the question of conformance still needs to be weighed. Savings from this source in the factory may be large even when the selling price is low. The necessity for control of conformance springs from the clash of two facts. George S. Radford (The Control of Quality in Manufacturing) describes them as follows:

It is general experience that economy of production, distribution, and consumption are greatest when the products of industry are of definite and uniform quality, that is, of standardized quality.

It is a physical truth that no two articles are alike; that is, quality varies continually. Raw materials, coming from nature as all do primarily, are of varying quality; no matter what manufacturing processes are applied to them subsequently, the quality of the resulting product varies more or less, depending upon the degree of technical refinement attained. Thus, quality in fact is always tending to slip away from the desired or ideal standard.

The desired uniformity is opposed by the fact that quality is a variable. The situation is met in a practical way by striking a compromise between the two.

Fig. 1 shows how this balance of costs may be struck for a particular product so as to find the most **economical degree of conformance** to specifications.

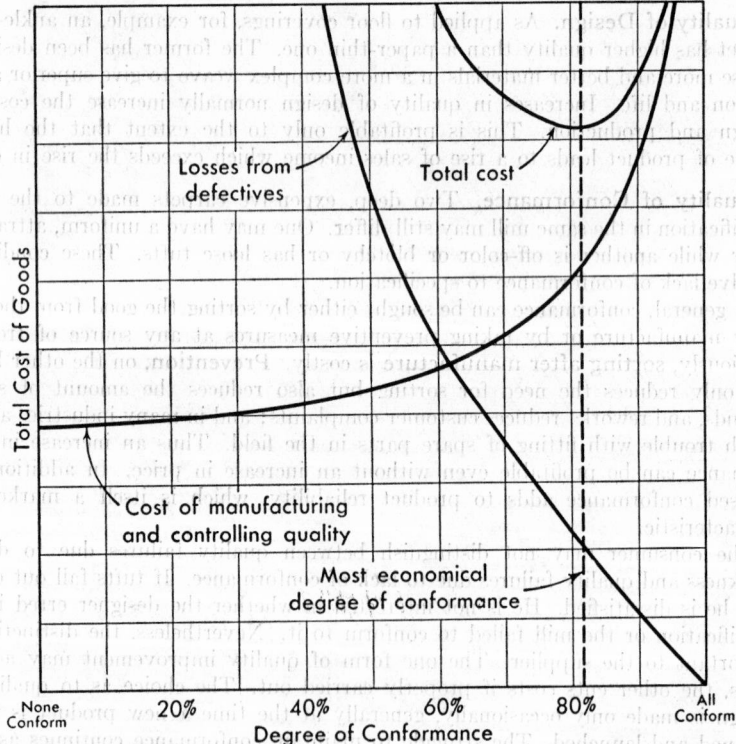

Fig. 1. Balance of cost and value for most economical degree of performance.

A large segment of inspection and quality control effort is profitably devoted to the **conformance problem,** which involves:

1. a. Locating products and operations which are wasteful because of inadequate conformance.
   b. Making necessary studies to improve control and conformance.
2. a. Locating products and operations which are wasteful because of excessive or unnecessary efforts to secure conformance.
   b. Reducing inspection and special checks on these items.

PURPOSE OF QUALITY CONTROL. Early handicraft production was concerned with simple tools, incidentals to skills, and preferences of individual craftsmen. Each unit of product was unique, meeting its maker's current judgment of utility, and was purchased after direct customer inspection and valuation in an environment of "buyer beware."

Modern manufacturing began with an emphasis upon the control of variability in quality characteristics, permitting random assembly and interchangeability. Subsequently, the stresses in a growing economy made essential the use of large-scale enterprises and volume utilization of fixed capital investments. With mounting complexity of enterprise organization, and the problems of cost reduction and price competition, there arose a demand for professional managements with the approach of scientific method.

Quality control, however, has been viewed vaguely as a problem of process design, labor supervision, and screening inspection, approached in high scrap periods with a "do something about it" ultimatum, in periods of average scrap by acceptance of and allowance for the related costs. Modern quality control, through **systematic observation** and **action, can** refine and maintain existing processes for optimum performance. It completes the tools of scientific management for the three basic control problems—production (volume), cost, and quality (value).

QUALITY CONTROL DURING PRODUCTION. The term "quality control" has been used widely but in varied meanings. In some cases it has been used to describe ordinary **patrol inspection or sorting inspection,** perhaps employing records whereby defects could ultimately be classified according to departments, batches, inspectors, etc. In other cases it has been applied to **statistical investigations of the manufacturing process** or to complaint analysis. It is now becoming recognized that these activities are simply components of quality control. In its broader meaning quality control is a system of principles and methods for the **prevention of defects.** It aims at proper regulation of the process rather than at the sorting inspection of the parts that come from it.

Ineffective Controls. Complete and reliable screening inspection of all parts and products is expensive; in cases where inspection is destructive, it is impossible. Assuming complete screening, and shipping only acceptable quality, poor control of the variability must result in high scrap losses along the production line, as well as interruptions, loss of capacity, costly salvage operations, and often selective assembly. The act of screening inspection, even if perfectly performed, can not "inspect" quality into the product; it merely shunts the unacceptable units to one side after manufacture. Planned action must be added to simple inspection. In contrast, quality control steps in before faulty parts are made. It uses facts, analysis, and identification and removal of important causes of defects for progressive refinement of production processes.

Analysis of performance usually requires more advanced methods and a broader viewpoint than is found in the acceptance work of a conventional inspection department. In many organizations the inspection people take the attitude that they are there primarily to protect the customer and "it is up to production to figure out how to make parts right." However, production needs help in this. Production foremen are busy with the assignment and instruction of men, the planning of work, and with meeting minute-to-minute emergencies. In addition, causes of defects are often found outside the shop in which the effect is felt. Foremen have neither the jurisdiction nor the training to study all the complex effects of materials and prior work. Such a study requires trained staff personnel.

Feedback of Information. There is strong need for **feedback of inspection information** to the operators and also to those who issue specifications. In a startling number of factories the relation between designer, production operators, and inspectors is the coldly formal one illustrated in Fig. 2a. In his drawings and

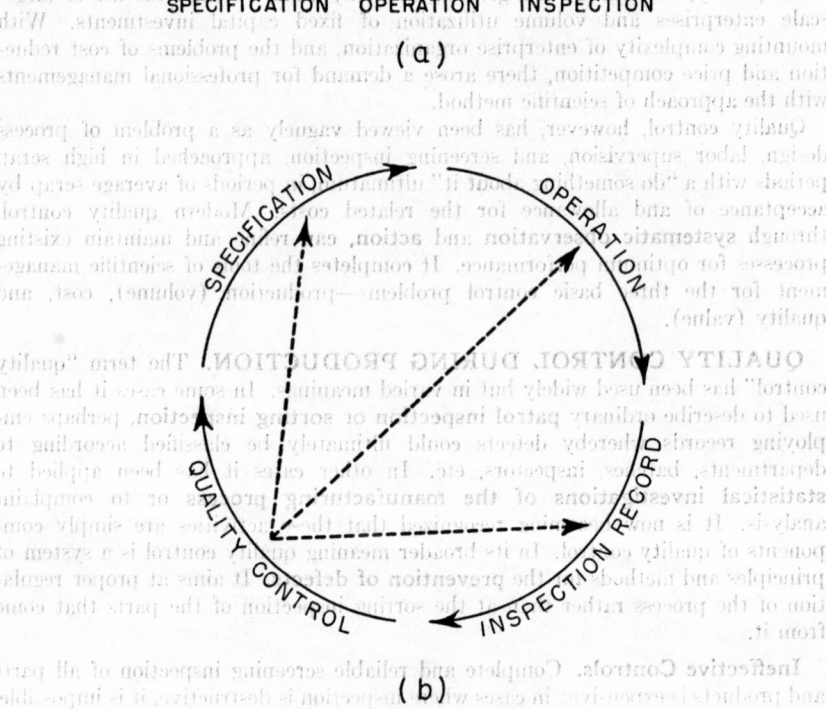

Fig. 2. Introduction of quality control as a coordinator.

specifications the designer sets up the quality legislation. The operators make an effort to live within the law but may not know how to go about it. Even worse, they often lack instruments to tell when they are breaking the law. The inspector, in his judicial capacity, passes sentence but makes no provision for reform of the guilty.

The modern concept of quality control as a **coordinator** is indicated by the completed circuit in Fig. 2b. Inspection records and special studies are used to identify the chief defects and their causes. Four alternatives are open at this point:

1. Study and improve the process.
2. Change to a more capable machine or operator.
3. Revise the specification.
4. Sort the product.

It is **quality control's responsibility** to get the facts, compare the costs, and find the best way out. Sometimes complex experiments are needed to root out the facts. Sometimes a simple procedure is all that is required.

Feedback Example. H. H. Brock reports a 50 percent reduction in the amount of defective cloth woven in a large weave shed, as a result of merely **revising the inspection procedures** to identify a given cut of cloth with the loom which produced it. The former inspection procedure, which had indicated only whether the cloth was of first or second quality, was replaced by a system which also showed what defects were present in the cloth, the extent of these defects (by numerical grading), and—most important—what loom produced the cloth. Inspection reports showing second quality cloth were placed directly on the "offending" looms. The weavers and loom fixers now knew not only that bad cloth was being produced but also what defects were causing the cloth to be classed as second grade. Thus they could take steps to prevent these defects.

The first week found the weave room producing 40 percent seconds. After four weeks under the new system the weave room was down to 20 percent seconds. Further reduction of this figure required other measures, including the use of a **quality incentive program.** The fact that losses could be quickly cut in half by putting simple information in the right hands is important to note.

Benefits of Quality Control. The benefits of systematic control of quality in manufacturing may be summarized as:

1. Reduction of the costs of scrap, rework, and adjustment.
2. Reduction in the costs of the factors of production through random assembly, uninterrupted production, and greater utilization of labor and facilities.
3. Reduction in costs of inspection.
4. Improved attainable quality standards, with either higher market values for a given sales volume, or greater volume for a given price.
5. Lower cost designs of products and processes for a given product quality standard.
6. Improved technical knowledge, more reliable engineering data for product development and manufacturing design, and reliable characterization of the attainable performance of processes.

A guide to areas of first attack and to justifiable levels of expenditure for control is found in a calculation of the costs associated with at least the first category above. In emphasis, each one thousand dollars of annual expenditure for analytical quality control is profitable if there can be maintained a reduction of shrinkage and rework costs of at least a like amount, since the less tangible savings add much to the margin.

One distinguished expert who has made an extensive continuing study of the costs of poor quality concludes that **losses from defectives** in an average company amount to the startling total of $500 to $1,000 per yr. per productive worker. He has found that companies in which the cost of defectives exceeds gross profits before taxes are not uncommon. A successful quality-control program may well cut the cost of defectives in half.

Organization for Quality Control

QUALITY FUNCTIONS. There are many separate activities involved in obtaining quality. It is necessary to recognize the component parts of the quality problem and to assign the responsibility for them. Fig. 3 illustrates a modern division of the duties between an inspection and a quality control group. These groups are commonly headed respectively by a chief inspector and a chief quality-control engineer. The appraisal phase may logically be isolated (just as auditing is separated from day-to-day accounting) in a large firm and headed by a chief of quality assurance. The heads of these groups in turn report to a quality manager.

SIZE OF STAFF. A survey of industrial practice (Ratios of Staff to Line Employees) shows that a ratio of one inspector to each 14 direct-production workers is roughly average. As would be expected, the proportion of inspectors differs widely among industries and even in a single factory is much greater in some departments (for example, electrical assembly) than in others. Though the activities of the quality control group (Fig. 3) are many, they can be carried out successfully by far fewer men. Experience shows good results in many plants, with ratios of the general order of 1 quality control engineer to 350 direct-production employees. Very dramatic dollar savings can be achieved through the assistance of these few quality control men in carrying out a carefully conceived program for quality.

PLACE OF QUALITY IN THE ORGANIZATION. The position of the quality department on the company organization chart varies widely in practice. Probably the best case can be made for having the head of the quality organization report to a manufacturing executive, such as the vice-president in charge of manufacturing, as in Fig. 4. While the quality function is usually assigned to manufacturing, cases are found where it is assigned to engineering (in an aircraft company) or to the chief of maintenance (in a transportation company), etc.

The quality organization should report to an authority high enough to have reasonable freedom from pressure of factory personnel who might urge too strongly that production goals be met at the sacrifice of quality. On the other hand, the quality organization should not be permitted to become so independent an authority as to encourage arbitrary and immoderate insistence on unnecessary perfection. The lower echelons of the production organization naturally feel primary concern for quantity, date, and low cost of production. The lower echelons of the quality organization naturally feel primary concern for quality and value of product.

Quality Control Supervision. The company as a whole is best served by a well-considered balance between the two sets of aims. Juran (Management of Inspection and Quality Control) suggests that this is more likely to be achieved if the first common supervisor of the operator and the inspector is at the lowest level of authority staffed with executives who reflect the company's policy on the balance between cost of quality and value of quality. In practice the rank of the executive who meets this requirement will vary somewhat in different companies according to their size, usual channels of promotion, etc. The factory manager or the vice-president in charge of manufacturing is more likely to meet the test than is a foreman, general foreman, or production superintendent.

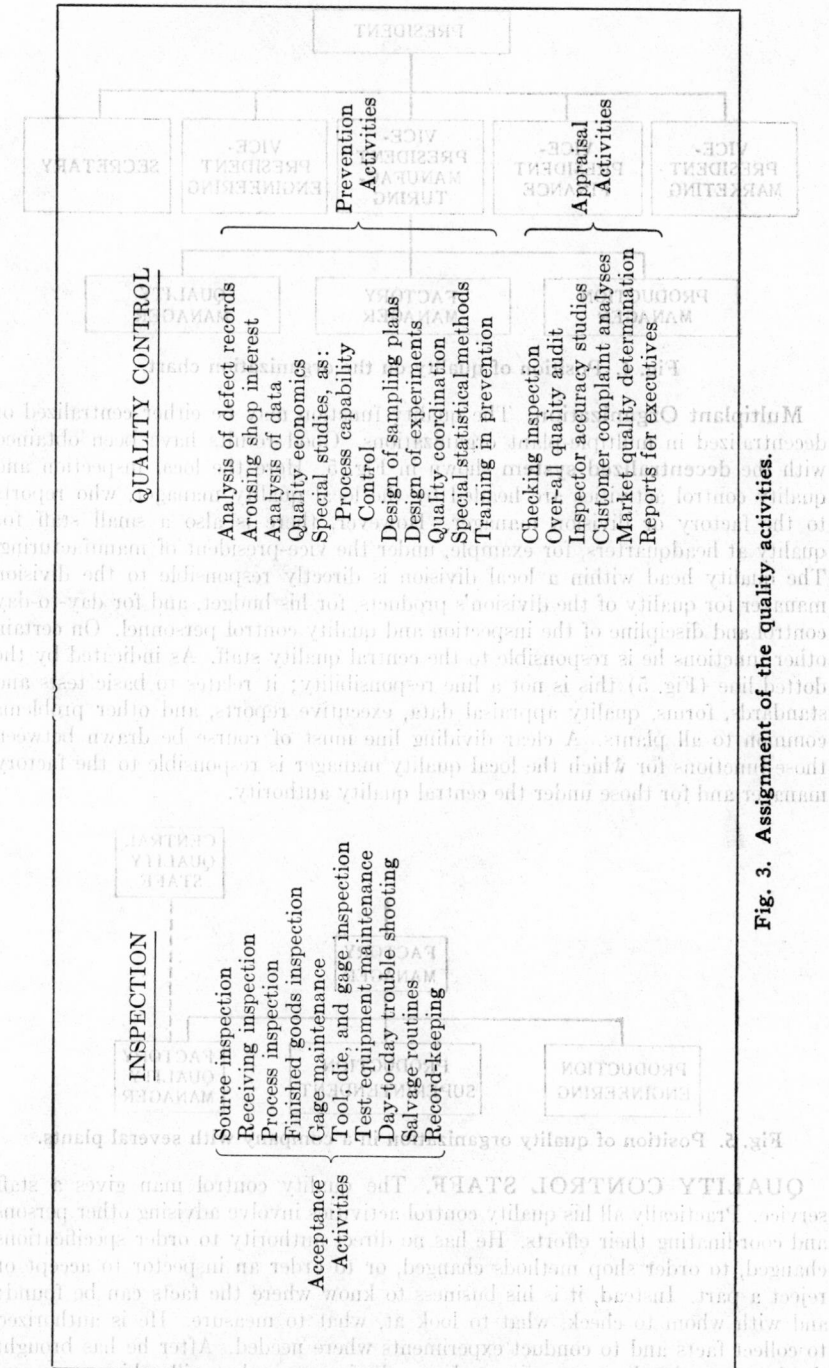

Fig. 3. Assignment of the quality activities.

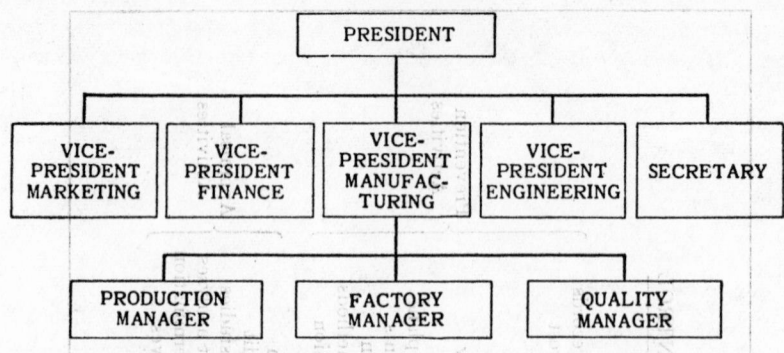

Fig. 4. Position of quality on the organization chart.

Multiplant Organization. The quality function may be either centralized or decentralized in multiple-plant organizations. Good results have been obtained with the **decentralized system** shown in Fig. 5. Here the local inspection and quality control activities are headed by the local quality manager, who reports to the factory or division manager. However, there is also a small staff for quality at headquarters, for example, under the vice-president of manufacturing. The quality head within a local division is directly responsible to the division manager for quality of the division's products, for his budget, and for day-to-day control and discipline of the inspection and quality control personnel. On certain other functions he is responsible to the central quality staff. As indicated by the dotted line (Fig. 5) this is not a line responsibility; it relates to basic tests and standards, forms, quality appraisal data, executive reports, and other problems common to all plants. A clear dividing line must of course be drawn between those functions for which the local quality manager is responsible to the factory manager and for those under the central quality authority.

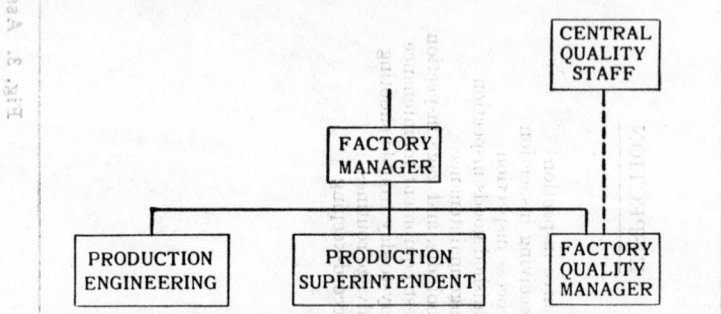

Fig. 5. Position of quality organization in a company with several plants.

QUALITY CONTROL STAFF. The quality control man gives a staff service. Practically all his quality control activities involve advising other persons and coordinating their efforts. He has no direct authority to order specifications changed, to order shop methods changed, or to order an inspector to accept or reject a part. Instead, it is his business to know where the facts can be found: and with whom to check, what to look at, what to measure. He is authorized to collect facts and to conduct experiments where needed. After he has brought the facts together he must present the results in a way that will achieve cooperation. He must assist the production supervisors and others, not direct them. When a project is successful, he cannot afford to alienate line personnel by seizing credit.

Responsibility. The most usual responsibilities of the quality control staff are the following:

1. To prepare a plant-wide quality control program for the management.
2. To advise engineering on the capabilities of machines, uniformity of materials, reproducibility of tests, and other quality aspects of specifications.
3. To advise manufacturing on capabilities of machines, instrumentation, control of processes, and other means of obtaining quality.
4. To assist purchasing in the evaluation of supplier's records and the analysis of defects in incoming material.
5. To advise and assist inspection in the planning and analysis of inspection records, in studying the capabilities of gages, and in selecting or designing sampling plans.
6. To assist sales in making use of quality and guarantees as marketable features of the product.
7. To determine the cost of quality losses.
8. To discover where the most serious losses occur and to find the causes.
9. To conduct special process studies and experiments to learn how to eliminate defects.
10. To assist the management in all ways of campaigning for quality-mindedness.
11. To train quality control personnel in means of defect prevention.
12. Optionally, to analyze customer complaint reports.
13. Optionally, to develop and operate a system for appraising quality of product.

Authority. The authority of the quality control staff should parallel its responsibilities. Since on most matters the staff is formally responsible only for advising and fact-finding, it will have correspondingly little formal authority. It may earn a practical, **informal authority of expertness** which goes far beyond this. To win this informal authority the quality control man needs first-class skill in human relations and the ability to provide facts and findings which command respect. Contributing factors are the rank of the quality manager in the organization and the support given by top management to the quality program. These last are of importance because they suggest to the rank and file that quality is a matter worthy of attention and because they imply the possibility of appeal through higher channels in the event that men down the line ignore reasonable recommendations on matters of quality.

There is a temptation to seek more direct authority over shop or inspectors so that improved methods may be ordered into use without delay. However, the shop is directly responsible for making the product to specifications, and the inspectors are responsible for protecting the customer by determining whether the product conforms to the specifications. It is a basic principle of organization that **authority should match responsibility.** Since we cannot logically relieve the shop or inspectors of these responsibilities, we cannot give the corresponding authority to other persons, such as the quality control staff.

The Quality Control Program

PLANNING FOR QUALITY. If efforts to obtain profits through preventing defects are to be successful, they must be made according to a clearly defined plan. A haphazard, uneven attack on the problem may fail to pay for itself. A detailed **master program** for attaining quality should be drawn up at the outset.

Element	As Applied in Marketing	As Applied in Quality Control
Magnitude	What is total market volume in field we are entering?	What is total extent of existing quality loss in this company?
Goal	What part of market can we capture?	What part of existing losses can we recover?
Location	Where is biggest market situated?	What products and operations show the largest dollar losses due to defects?
Leader	Who will coordinate the sales program?	Who will draw up and coordinate program? Who has the necessary managerial abilities?
Individual Quotas	What quota is to be assigned to each agency or salesman?	What saving in quality losses is to be target in each department?
Schedule	When are sales targets to be reached? What manpower schedule is implied? What production planning is required?	When is each step to be completed, each target to be reached?
Plan	Sales to jobbers? To retail stores? Direct to public? What kind of sales campaign? Who is to be primarily responsible for advertising, etc.?	What detailed methods will be used: To get data on losses? To refine design specifications? To assist purchasing? To identify causes of production trouble? To improve inspection procedures? Who is to be responsible for each?
Publicity	How, when, and where is product to be advertised? How can public interest be aroused?	What means are to be used to enlist interest and aid of shop? Of inspectors? Of supervisors? Of top management?
Records	What sales data are needed for salesmen's pay, for control, etc.?	What means are to be used to record progress? Reductions in dollar losses and in percents defective?
Incentives	What contests, commission systems, etc., can be used to stimulate sales force?	How can slogan contests, suggestion systems, competitions be used to get ideas and participation? Should incentive pay be given for quality?
Training	What special training is necessary in sales techniques? In regard to product design? In sales engineering?	What method is to be used to show operators, inspectors, supervisors, engineers, how to improve quality? How are quality control personnel to be developed?
Budget	What funds will be needed for sales staff, sales promotion, and advertising?	What funds will be needed for staff salaries? For publicity? For equipment? For training?

Fig. 6. Factors involved in a quality control program compared with those involved in a marketing program.

The vital elements of a quality control program can be visualized by comparing the form they take in the more familiar but quite parallel problem, the marketing of a new product. Fig. 6 briefly lists at the left the essential elements for a program. The columns headed Marketing and Quality Control list the questions which the program must be designed to answer.

A QUALITY AUDIT. In order to judge the kind and extent of quality program that is needed, it is appropriate to begin by taking stock of results with the company's present organization and procedures. A ten-point check list of items to be reviewed in such a **quality evaluation** is given below:

1. Review of dollar losses due to defectives for:
   a. Amount.
   b. Evidence they are being recovered systematically.
2. Review of specifications for:
   a. Completeness.
   b. Measurability.
   c. Freedom from ambiguity.
   d. Evidence that they describe the properties the customer wants.
3. Review of customer complaints for:
   a. Extent.
   b. Adequacy of corrective action.
   c. Making sure inspection is checking properties complained about.
4. General review of systems for prevention of:
   a. Vendors' defects.
   b. Own process defects.
5. Review of inspection system on such points as:
   a. Organization.
   b. Physical layout.
   c. Gage maintenance.
   d. Number of inspectors.
   e. Attitudes of inspectors.
   f. Standard inspection instructions and operation sheets.
   g. Inspection of components and early operations.
   h. Extent and purpose of 100 percent inspection.
6. Check of attitudes and quality training of production personnel:
   a. Quality taken seriously?
   b. Know what is wanted?
   c. Have means to measure?
   d. Have means to correct?
   e. Attitude toward inspectors?
   f. Training at time of induction?
   g. How is foreman as example?
   h. Posters or other campaign?
   i. Is department's quality record known?
7. Review of organization for:
   a. Quality of top organization.
   b. Clearness of responsibility at firing line (who is responsible for investigation, analysis, action?).
8. Review of salvage procedures:
   a. Too loose or too tight?
   b. Information fed back to the shop?
9. Review of reports:
   a. Adequate summaries to produce management action where needed?
   b. Adequate presentation and classification to bring persistent defects to attention of shop, of quality control personnel, etc.?
10. Review of training of inspectors and other quality control personnel on how to make inspection data useful to production for prevention of future defects.

Resistance to Change. In designing and "selling" a new program one should take into account the reasons for the apparent reluctance of some companies to utilize quality control principles to their fullest extent. Among these reasons are:

1. The problems quality control has been designed to solve were much less common only a generation ago. Tolerances are now tighter and harder to meet—a tenth or hundredth of their former breadth. Also, factories have grown in size, making communication and uniform interpretation of quality requirements harder,

2. Managements have often regarded quality control as a service which can be used only with mass production. While the selection of control tools will vary, quality control is equally necessary in an industry with a large volume of small orders. Existing quality losses may in fact be greater there.

3. Managements have associated the idea of quality with expense rather than savings. It is necessary to show them from the record how expensive nonconformance is. The size of the prospective saving will tell whether a large or small effort is worthwhile.

4. Executives and employees do not know the language. Top management and shop personnel alike have sometimes been alienated by engineers who have tried to introduce analyses and charts that were too technical. They got the impression that quality control was altogether mathematical. Engineers get bridges built without explaining the equations to the riveters. A similar effort to provide just the simplest, most usable tools is advisable in quality control work.

5. There is hesitation to start any new practice. "We're doing all right now. Why should we change?" A competent cost study will tell in an impersonal way what needs to be done.

6. There is fear and insecurity in the face of the unknown. Some inspectors, in particular, may look on quality control as a threat to their jobs. They feel the jobs might be changed or even abolished. It is a fact that some jobs may be altered to put more emphasis on prevention of defects. The goal, however, is a saving in product, not reduced wages.

7. Specific techniques have in the past sometimes been oversold and have failed to produce the economies claimed.

IMPROVEMENT OF PRODUCT SPECIFICATIONS. Usually inspection and quality control personnel have no direct control over engineering drawings and written specifications for a product. This is as it should be. Still, rejects cannot be successfully prevented unless all major parties to the specifications (a) have the same understanding as to what they mean and (b) regard the requirements as realistic and necessary.

It is in order for the quality control department to explore the possibility that ambiguous requirements of blueprints are among the significant causes of rejection of pieces of product. Sometimes obscure language and devious dimensioning are uncovered by a **systematic review of drafting-room standards.** If the uncertainties as to the designer's meaning are really frequent, it may be wise to start revisions here before launching any new quality maneuvers in the shop.

If the prints are only an occasional source of dispute, the troubles can be pinpointed as the shop program goes on. Specific suggestions can then be made to the designers (or others) who issue and control the drawings and specifications. Some of the common flaws to be noted and corrected are given in Fig. 7.

USE OF STATISTICAL METHODS. Much has been written in recent years on the purely statistical aspects of control. They are basic in any competent understanding of control. But the methods are tools, like trigonometry and chemical analysis, to be adapted to the background of each problem. With a

Cause of Difficulty	Solutions To Consider
Division of engineering work into production design, manufacturing, engineering, metallurgy, etc.	Make designers responsible for issuance of specifications; arrange for others to advise them.
Use of specifications by many people, leading to many interpretations.	Write carefully in standard way using numbers rather than adjectives wherever possible.
Impracticability of expressing all requirements in numbers or unambiguous words. Examples: stains on bulb sockets; colors of rugs; smoothness of finish of paints; scuffs, scratches; fits.	Resort to physical standards. Consider use of "fade-out" or disappearance distance beyond which defect cannot be seen. Specify method of processing so fully as to ensure sufficient uniformity of product, or Specify method of test rather than dimension (etc.) wanted.
Impracticability of specifying against everything undesirable that could possibly occur (e.g. discoloration of molded parts).	Make a reasonable effort; then make a designer arbiter over other requirements when disputes arise; add later restrictions to prints when necessary.
Lack of knowledge of special tolerances needed and of abilities of machines, before going into production.	Pilot runs. Group decisions.
Problem of obtaining perfect conformance and, therefore, the resulting uncertainty as to realism of specifications.	Reject all pieces which do not meet specifications exactly, and Provide a salvage (material review) procedure as a safety valve.

Fig. 7. Improving product specifications.

product of simple design, exacting specifications, and relatively high unit value (illustrated by the ball bearing), the reclamation afforded by more advanced methods may warrant an expenditure of as much as a third of manufacturing labor-hours in purely statistical control methods. With a product of relatively low precision requirements, assembled from semifinished components of relatively low unit value (illustrated by a lamp base), the simpler and more direct approaches of routine patrol and screening inspection may suffice, with perhaps only a small outlay of control effort warranted.

The essential benefits of the modern analytical approach to quality control derive from an emphasis upon economic and systematic ways of thinking about cause and effect, through observation, interpretation, and action. A fully developed system of statistical quality control is capable of brilliant results, but it is not the initial step in quality work. Statistical thinking starts with the idea that variability is to be expected. It recognizes that strength or size of parts produced by a process is not a constant but a **frequency distribution**. Simple principles derived from this fact are useful long before it is advisable to make a full-dress installation of control charts.

The statistical tools used should be in keeping with the prevailing **level of technical development** in the shop. In an industry where little attention has been given to quality control, first emphasis would rightly center on planning for ordinary inspection, the procedure for marking and charging rejects, the system to be used for salvage, etc. Scarcely any statistics would be involved. Where inspection is already an established function, the first step is to build up the prevention function. This step involves a study of the economics of the situation, problems of coordination and jurisdiction, quality-mindedness, record analysis, and some simple statistical tools such as the **bar chart** and the **process capability chart.** When work of this kind has become familiar, further results can be obtained progressively with control charts, correlation studies, analysis of variance, etc. The more complex tools are usually set up and interpreted by the quality control staff rather than by shop personnel, but only at such time as the shop personnel are receptive and ready to make real use of the results.

Results of Statistical Quality Control. Armstrong (Industrial Quality Control, vol. 2) describes an application of statistical quality control to the casting of tank parts at Electric Steels, Ltd. Some 100 control charts were maintained by one senior man and two untrained clerks. Statistical studies were made on the relative importance of variables in the materials, such as metal analysis and sand characteristics. Other studies were made on variables in melting and pouring practice, such as time and temperature. In addition, the methods and accuracy of the different kinds of measurements were analyzed. The quality record was continually posted on wall charts, which included identification of the work crews.

Carefully kept government records attributed a saving of $300,000 in 18 months to an outlay of $15,000 for the quality program. Average rejections from all causes dropped from some 13 percent to 2 percent within 9 months.

Starting Statistical Quality Control. Programs of statistical quality control should be applied gradually, allowing sufficient time for specific methods to show results and sell themselves. One or two promising men may be encouraged to familiarize themselves with process capability charts, control charts, and other elementary statistical techniques. Applications can then be made to a few problems, perhaps at existing inspection points, in a department having a progressive supervisor. As these applications prove themselves, the techniques can be extended to other problems in the department, using the experience of the original inspectors. Reports on progress can be drafted for the department supervisor's approval and signature. A good record will interest other departments.

Results can be described at a supervisors' round-table conference. A further possibility is designation of a **steering committee for new methods,** with representatives of engineering, production, and inspection. Additional applications can be made as requested in various areas of high scrap loss. Nontechnical talks on what is being accomplished can be set up for operators as well as for foremen and leadmen. Clinics on problems and methods can be organized for such groups as inspectors and engineers.

Inspection Record Analysis

LOCATION OF MAIN SOURCES OF LOSS. In launching a program for the prevention of poor quality, one of the very first needs is to discover where defects are occurring. It is obvious that firemen, to extinguish a fire, must first have means of knowing where the fire is. In quality control work corresponding means are not always found ready-made. A **list of defects** should be made if such a list does not already exist. This list should show the severity of trouble in terms of percentage of parts having the defect or, still better, the dollar loss involved.

The **major sources of quality loss** should also be determined. Experience shows that most quality losses occur in a small number of places. For example, in a textile plant it was found that half of the possible kinds of defects caused 97 percent of the rejections. The concentration is likely to be even more pronounced when the severity is measured in dollars. Efforts to avoid losses should be directed to the most fertile fields, not spread thinly over all operations. This principle may not seem to need underscoring, but experience shows that, owing to lack of data, it is often not followed as closely as it deserves to be.

FACTORY RECORDS. Information on rejection percentages comes primarily from inspection department records. Information on dollar loss comes primarily from cost accounting records. Complete data on **cost of quality losses** is usually the more difficult to obtain. Ideally it should include labor and material cost of scrapped parts, extra inspection involved after repairs or in unnecessary sorting, extra operations for repairs, cost of making good on guarantees, and loss of good will. Cost systems seldom identify all these factors. It may be possible to estimate some of the missing ones from those available.

At the outset it is not unusual to find that the labor and materials charged to a job make no distinction between the base amount and the extra amount required to cover replacement of junked parts, repairs, and the like. This lack adds difficulties for production control as well as for quality control. A good method for obtaining this information is to stipulate that no finished or semifinished parts may go into the scrap barrel until a **scrap charge ticket** has been made out. This ticket carries such data as the part number, quantity, operation, reason for junking, and name of operator. Such a system may well put on record large losses not included in inspectors' reports, since in some shops parts junked by an operator may never be seen by an inspector. Where this has been the case, the unavoidable expenses of scrap (metal shavings, punchings, sawdust, short ends, etc.) are hopelessly merged with the preventable loss due to scrap (defective

VENDOR'S RECORD

Part No. *113,562* Part Name *Contact* Vendor xx Co.

Receiving Report Data			Inspection Results				Percent Defective Chart
Date of Receipt	Receiving Rpt. No.	Total Quantity	Quantity Inspected	Quantity Rejected	Percent Defective	Disposal of Lot	1 2 3 4 5 6
12/7	27651	5,000	225	3	1.33	Accept	
12/15	27892	8,300	300	6	2.00	Accept	
12/22	27999	6,700	225	2	0.89	Accept	
12/31	28308	5,000	225	4	1.78	Accept	
1/21	29010	10,140	300	4	1.33	Accept	
2/13	29786	4,650	225	6	2.67	Sort	
3/3	30453	7,490	225	13	5.77	Return	
3/25	31224	9,025	300	5	1.67	Accept	
Totals							

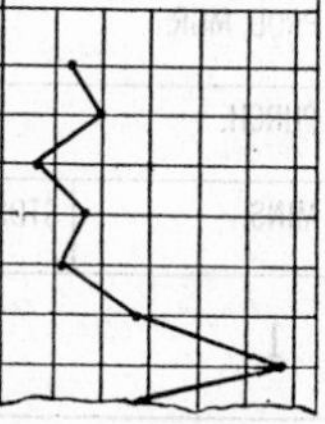

Fig. 8. Record of supplier's quality.

MATERIAL DISPOSITION ORDER				253445

PART NO.		ENG. CH. LET.	PART NAME	
WORK ORDER NO.		VENDOR OR MFG. GROUP		DATE
LAST OPER. NO.	ENG. S. O. NO.	P. O. NO.	R. R. NO.	SHIFT / % OR SAMP.
LOT NO.	SPEC. NO.	SERIAL NO.	R. R. DATE	CAST OR FORGE NO.

DISPOSITION

ACCEPT	QTY.	TYPE	REF.	INSP.
HOLD	QTY.	STAMP	SOURCE	INSP. SUPER.
REWORK	QTY.	STORES		GOVT. INSP.
CASE HARD REQ.	CORE HARD REQ.	CASE HARD OBS.	CORE HARD OBS.	INSP.

	REWORK		HOLD	
QTY.	WORK TO BE DONE OR DESCRIPTION OF DEVIATION			DISP.

DETAILS INCLUDED IN ASSEMBLIES

PART NO.	QTY.	PART NO.	QTY.	PART NO.	QTY.

URG. OR EMERG. REWORK	DATE	MATL. REV.		ACCEPT
DEPT. CHG.	DEPT. CR.	SUPER.		REWORK
RET. TO VENDOR	VENDOR CHG. / WAC. CHG.	ENGRG.		SCRAP
PROD. MGR.		GOVT. INSP.		RET. TO VENDOR
PURCH.		FINAL CHG.	CHG. ACCEPTED	
MINS.	STDS. SIG.	DEV.	SHIP ORD. NO.	DATE

1	**PRINT OR WRITE LEGIBLY** **USE HARD PENCIL**	

(a) Front, original copy.

Fig. 9. An original record of disposition (continued on next page).

THIS SIDE FOR COST ACCOUNTING USE ONLY

PARTS STANDARD COST

| QTY | UNIT STANDARD COST | | | TOTAL STANDARD COST | | |
	PUR. FIN.	MAT'L	LABOR	PUR. FIN.	MAT'L	LABOR

CURRENT SHOP STANDARD LABOR VALUE

DEPT	UNIT STD. MINS	UNIT LABOR VALUE	TOTAL STD. MINS.	TOTAL LABOR VALUE

SUMMARY TOTALS

| CURRENT SHOP LABOR | | STANDARD COST | | |
MINS.	AMT.	PUR. FIN.	MAT'L	LABOR

Wright Aeronautical Corp.

(b) Back, accounting copy.

Fig. 9. (Concluded.)

parts). Where no cost system is in use, an alternate possibility is to set up a system for **weighting defect percentages** by estimated cost or severity of defect.

Purchased Materials. Analysis of findings in receiving inspection shows where advice and coordination with vendors are needed. It also guides in the selection of suppliers for future purchases. It is comparatively simple to set up a system for collection of data on rejections of incoming material. For example, the **receiving report** can show the desired facts on quantity received and disposal of material in each shipment. Alternatively, a **material disposal report** or tabulating card can be filled out.

The method of summarizing these original records for action depends on the complexity and volume of the product and on the number of vendors. In most cases a clerk can enter the facts on ledger cards. In this system there is an individual card for each part number and each vendor (see Fig. 8). If quantity and diversity of incoming materials make hand entries too inconvenient and time-consuming, automatic tabulating machines can easily do the sorting and summarizing. (For an analysis of modern computing equipment, see section on Electronic Computers.)

The object of this system is identification of unreliable vendors and faulty parts or materials, so that action can be taken to drop suppliers whose shipments do not meet company standards. The effort is wasted unless:

1. The quality staff investigates and shows how to correct the trouble.
2. The purchasing department presses the supplier to take corrective action or, failing in this, buys from a reliable supplier.

An early step for the quality men must be a study of the grounds for rejection of any troublesome product. When these grounds have been determined, the first question is the cause of trouble. Some indication of what is taking place at the supplier's factory can be obtained by examining charts of the product measurements (see Figs. 12 and 13). Beyond this it may be necessary to call in the supplier or to send a representative to study the quality picture at the source.

When sizable rejections are being made on all vendors for a particular part or specification, a re-examination of the requirement itself is in order.

Parts in Process. The procedure in searching out points of loss along the production line is similar to that for collecting data on rejections of incoming material, though it usually puts more emphasis on the dollar losses. Disposition of faulty parts or materials is recorded on tabulating cards or on orders similar to the one shown in Fig. 9. The parts listed on these orders are priced by the cost accounting department. Parts scrapped are valued at the material cost plus added direct-labor and overhead costs. If detailed figures are not available, the value can be approximated by multiplying the estimated percentage of completion of the part by the total cost of a finished part. Repairs are valued at the added labor and overhead. These charges are assigned to the department whose work caused the rejection.

The losses thus arrived at can be summarized periodically according to department, operation number, or the like (see Fig. 10). The quality control staff then selects from the summary the operations showing the largest losses. The problem of finding the causes of loss still remains. The next step in this direction is to discover the exact nature of the defects observed. The grounds for rejection are seldom specific enough, if previously classified at all.

Inspection or quality control may therefore have to prepare a listing of the essential **quality characteristics** for the operations under study. In some cases

WEEKLY SCRAP REPORT

DEPT.	WEEK ENDING		PART NUMBER	OPERATION NO.	PARTS SCRAPPED THIS WEEK	VALUE OF SCRAPPED PARTS	
						THIS WEEK	LAST WEEK
1 4 0	3	8	2 4 6 0 1	6 0	7	3 9 2	2 8 0
1 4 0	3	8	2 4 6 0 1	6 6	2 3	4 4 8 5	2 5 3 0
1 4 0	3	8	2 5 2 3 7	6 2	4	1 8 0	5 4 0
1 4 0	3	8	2 9 8 6 2	6 7	2	9 6 0	2 4 0 0
1 4 0	3	8	2 9 8 6 2	8 1	6	3 1 8 0	2 2 2 0
1 4 0	3	8	2 9 8 6 2	9 0	3	1 7 0 1	1 7 0 1
1 4 0	3	8	2 9 9 8 3	6 6	1 8	3 3 3 0	
1 4 0	3	8	3 0 1 7 2	6 5	4	1 2 6 4	2 8 4 4
1 4 0	3	8	3 0 1 7 2	6 6			1 8 3 7
1 4 0	3	8	3 0 1 7 3	6 0	9 0	8 1 9 0	6 7 3 4
1 4 0	3	8	3 0 1 7 3	6 5	2 6	2 8 3 4	2 2 8 9
1 4 0	3	8	3 0 1 7 3	7 0	1	1 2 6	3 7 8
1 4 0	3	8	3 0 1 7 4	8 4	1 2	1 0 2 0	
1 4 0	3	8	3 0 1 7 5	8 9	2 4 8	2 2 3 2	5 4
1 4 0	3	8	3 0 1 7 5	6 0	2 5	3 0 0	3 7 2
1 4 0	3	8	3 0 1 7 6	6 4	8	3 1 6 0	4 7 4 0
1 4 0	3	8	3 0 1 7 6	6 6	9	3 7 1 7	1 2 3 9 0
1 4 0	3	8	3 4 2 2 9	6 1	4 0 3	6 0 4 5	7 2 0
1 4 0	3	8	3 9 3 4 8	6 9	3 4	5 3 0 4	1 5 6 0
1 4 0	3	8	3 9 3 4 8	7 1	3 4	5 6 1 0	3 4 6 5
1 4 0	3	8	3 9 3 4 8	6 6	6 2	1 1 5 9 4	2 6 1 8
1 4 0	3	8	3 9 9 7 6	8 5	1	9 6 3	2 8 8 9
1 4 0	3	8	4 2 0 3 7	6 6			4 4 4 4
						6 6 5 8 7	5 7 0 0 5

Sperry Rand Corp.

Fig. 10. Weekly summary for scrap.

this is a separate record (see Fig. 11). As each lot is inspected, the inspector notes the quantity that conforms to blueprint specifications (B/P) in that column. Any product that does not conform is identified and classified according to whether it can be reworked or is to be submitted for material review (M.R.). The counts for these two situations are recorded in their respective columns. In other cases the inspectors are simply provided with a detailed list of defects and a code number for each. The appropriate code number is entered by the inspector on the regular tabulating card or disposition order to explain each rejection listed. The code number then appears in a subsequent sheet made up as a weekly summary of scrap.

Action Based on Quality Records. The result of the foregoing procedure is a focus of attention on the two or three kinds of defects which cause the most frequent rejections of the part. All forces can then be brought to bear on the

CYLINDER BARRELS

SHIFT _____ DATE _____

INSPECTOR _____ INSP. SUPER. _____

CHARACTERISTIC	B/P	Rework	M.R.	B/P	Rework	M.R.
Oper. 60 Visual						
I.D.						
Oper. 150 Visual						
Oper. 460 Visual						
Toolmark						
Radii, sharp edges						
Chatter marks, finish						
Bore size						
Radius, angles, chamfers						
Neck profile and diam.						
Concentricity						
Pilot Diam.						
Pilot length						
Groove width, diam. and loc.						
O.D. of fins						
Threads: form, P.D. and O.D.						
Thread form comparator						
Undercut and profile at thread end						
Flange thickness and diam.						
O.D. of skirt						
Height of skirt from flange face						
Length from end to flange face						
Location of thread to flange holes						
Oper. 540 Visual						
Cadmium plate						
Pilot diam.						
P.D. of threads						

Wright Aeronautical Corp.

Fig. 11. Check list for defects.

prevention of these defects. After careful consideration, some of the following steps should be taken to **prevent further defects:**

1. Call attention of production supervisors to trouble points by circulating reports on quality losses. (Accounting department or quality control staff.)
2. For any particular defect, determine which employee has the greatest opportunity to control causes of the defect. Make certain that he already knows he has or is now assigned definite responsibility for exercising such control. (Shop supervision.)
3. Show specimens of defective work to operator, explain importance of correction, and check on adequacy of his instructions. (Shop supervision.)
4. Check operator's gages for adequacy to plot his course. (Quality control staff and gage specialists.)
5. Increase frequency of floor inspection for these defects in order to detect slips promptly. (Inspection supervision.)
6. Make a process capability study. (Quality control staff with help of inspection staff.)
7. Make a control chart study. (Quality control staff.)
8. Design and conduct special experiments to trace causes of defects. (Quality control staff.)
9. Improve jigs and fixtures if shown necessary by quality control studies. (Production, tool, or methods engineers.)
10. Overhaul machine if shown necessary by quality control studies. (Plant engineers and plant maintenance staff.)
11. Transfer job to more capable machine or operator if shown necessary by quality control studies. (Production engineers, dispatcher, or shop supervision.)
12. Discuss necessity for close tolerances with product designer. (Quality control staff.)

The above procedure is for evaluation of **parts in process.** Similar procedures can of course be applied in analyzing rejections at **final assembly** or final inspection and for **customer complaints** as well.

Special Process Studies

DIAGRAMS FOR DIAGNOSIS. The analysis discussed up to this point refers to records of the number of good parts or bad parts in a lot. Where size, tensile strength, or other measurements of degree of goodness are made, it is possible to get a better understanding and control of a manufacturing process.

The use of simple charts at selected inspection points often brings out features of the data that would otherwise escape attention. **Bar charts** or **tally sheets** give a picture of the variability of a product and often suggest adjustments in the process that will give better results. They put a magnifying glass on the inspection reports to supply additional detail. These **frequency distribution charts** give much information that is lost in inspection with go-no-go gages. They show the characteristics of the good parts as well as of the bad parts; they emphasize that all parts are not identical; and they remind that important decisions should not be made on the basis of only one piece, as, for example, in so-called first-piece inspection (see section on Inspection).

In some cases the same information can be obtained in other ways, as from a process capability study or a control chart study. The particular advantages of the bar chart or tally sheet are (1) that it can be applied even if the order of production is unknown (as in receiving inspection), (2) that it shows the pattern of quality in the lot of material as a whole, and (3) that it is easily made by an inspector.

A typical tally sheet is shown in Fig. 12. The inspector has only to write down the possible readings of his instrument at the left and to put a mark to the right of the correct number of each measurement as he makes it. Fig. 13 shows the common appearances and causes of ten types of tallies that occur in practice.

	QUALITY REPORT No.	**2798**	

PRODUCT *Compr. Spring*	CUSTOMER *XYZ Co.* QUOT. No. *21621-A*
CHARACTERISTIC *Length @ P-25#*	PART No. *K-6162713* REF. *SR 316.1*
INSP. METHOD *217-PM-27-1*	SPECIFIED LIMITS *24.2-25.8# at 2.000"*
SAMPLE DRAWN *After cad. pl.*	EQUIV. INSP. LIMITS *1.965-2.035", at 25#*

HPS ORDER No.	25160		
CUSTOMER ORDER No.	17432		
INSPECTED BY	R.W.B.		
DATE	1/21		

Length			
1.955 – 1.959			
1.960 – 1.964			**MIN.**
1.965 – 1.969			24.2#
1.970 – 1.974			
1.975 – 1.979	I	1	
1.980 – 1.984	III	3	
1.985 – 1.989	HHT I	6	
1.990 – 1.994	HHT HHT III	13	
1.995 – 1.999	HHT HHT HHT I	16	
2.000 – 2.004	HHT III	8	
2.005 – 2.009	HHT I	6	
2.010 – 2.014	HHT	5	
2.015 – 2.019	II	2	
2.020 – 2.024	I	1	
2.025 – 2.029			
2.030 – 2.034			**MAX.**
2.035 – 2.039			25.8#
2.040 – 2.044			

Hunter Pressed Steel Co.

Fig. 12. Inspection tally sheet.

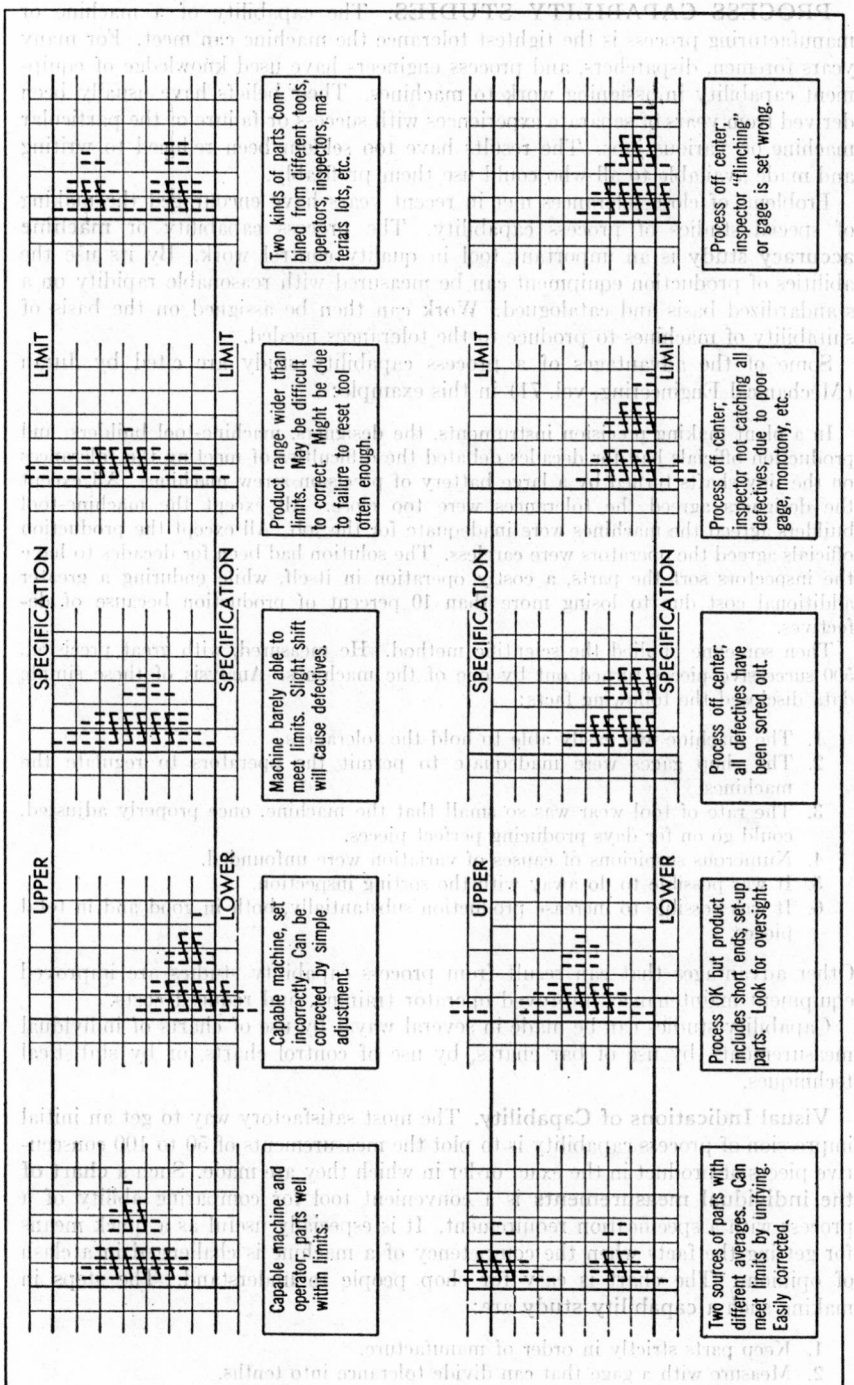

Fig. 13 . Interpretations of tallies.

PROCESS CAPABILITY STUDIES. The capability of a machine or manufacturing process is the tightest tolerance the machine can meet. For many years foremen, dispatchers, and process engineers have used knowledge of equipment capability in assigning work to machines. Their beliefs have usually been derived from years of separate experiences with success or failure of the particular machine on various jobs. The results have too seldom been reduced to writing and made available to all who could use them profitably.

Problems of close tolerances met in recent years have encouraged the making of special studies of process capability. The process capability or **machine accuracy study** is an important tool in quality control work. By its use the abilities of production equipment can be measured with reasonable rapidity on a standardized basis and catalogued. Work can then be assigned on the basis of suitability of machines to produce to the tolerances needed.

Some of the advantages of a process capability study are cited by Juran (Mechanical Engineering, vol. 71) in this example:

In a plant making precision instruments, the designers, machine-tool builders, and production officials had for decades debated the difficulties of meeting the tolerances on the tiny shafts turned by a large battery of precision screw machines. All except the designers agreed the tolerances were too close. All except the machine-tool builders agreed the machines were inadequate for the job. All except the production officials agreed the operators were careless. The solution had been for decades to have the inspectors sort the parts, a costly operation in itself, while enduring a greater additional cost due to losing more than 10 percent of production because of defectives.

Then someone applied the scientific method. He measured, with great precision, 500 successive pieces turned out by one of the machines. Analysis of these simple data disclosed the following facts:

1. The machine was easily able to hold the tolerances.
2. The shop gages were inadequate to permit the operators to regulate the machines.
3. The rate of tool wear was so small that the machine, once properly adjusted, could go on for days producing perfect pieces.
4. Numerous suspicions of causes of variation were unfounded.
5. It was possible to do away with the sorting inspection.
6. It was possible to increase production substantially, both in good and in total pieces.

Other advantages that can result from process capability studies are improved equipment maintenance, improved operator training, and reduced costs.

Capability studies can be made in several ways: by use of charts of individual measurements, by use of bar charts, by use of control charts, or by statistical techniques.

Visual Indications of Capability. The most satisfactory way to get an initial impression of process capability is to plot the measurements of 50 to 100 consecutive pieces of product in the exact order in which they are made. Such a **chart of the individual measurements** is a convenient tool for comparing ability of a process with a specification requirement. It is especially useful as a quick means for getting the facts when the competency of a machine is challenged in a clash of opinions. The chart is easy for shop people to understand. The steps in making such a **capability study** are:

1. Keep parts strictly in order of manufacture.
2. Measure with a gage that can divide tolerance into tenths.

3. Keep a log of changes in tool settings, materials lots, operators, machine speeds, temperatures, etc.
4. Chart the measurements.
5. Look for significant patterns and associations.
6. Compare the chart with the specification requirements.

Fig. 14 shows five patterns typical of those found in these charts of individual measurements. Since the order of production is known, these charts have a clear advantage over tally sheets. They often reveal tool wear, effects of adjustments, and other reasons for variability. It is not unusual to find that a machine which

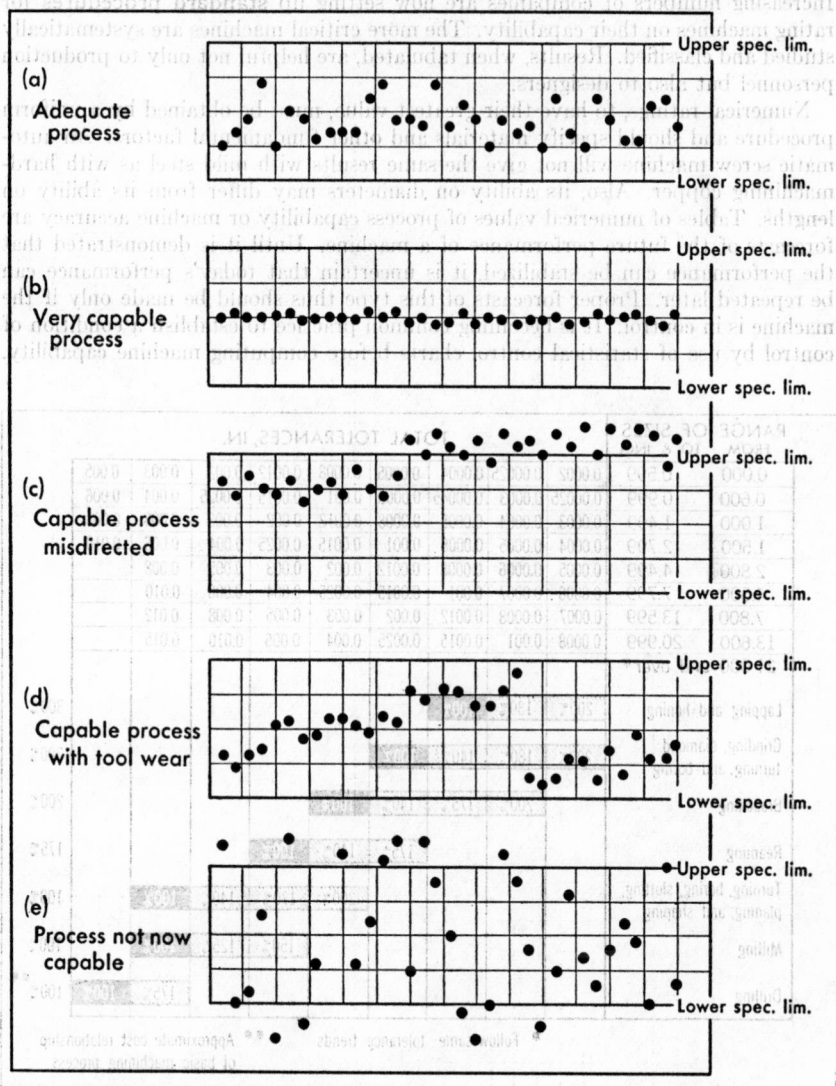

Fig. 14. Charts of individual measurements in the study of capability.

allegedly "can't hold the tolerance" is actually adequate but is not being operated in the best possible way. Common causes are:

1. Improper setting of the tool, that is, not at the center of tolerance.
2. Inadequate provisions for tool wear.
3. An inadequate gage in the hands of the operator.
4. Resetting of a machine on the basis of one measurement.

Numerical Ratings of Capability. Successes of the capability study in trouble shooting showed that it could be even more valuable if applied to prevent trouble. Increasing numbers of companies are now setting up **standard procedures** for rating machines on their capability. The more critical machines are systematically studied and classified. Results, when tabulated, are helpful not only to production personnel but also to designers.

Numerical ratings, to have their greatest value, must be obtained by a uniform procedure and should specify materials and other fundamental factors. An automatic screw machine will not give the same results with mild steel as with hard-machining copper. Also, its ability on diameters may differ from its ability on lengths. Tables of numerical values of process capability or machine accuracy are forecasts of the future performance of a machine. Until it is demonstrated that the performance can be stabilized, it is uncertain that today's performance can be repeated later. Proper forecasts of this type thus should be made only if the machine is in control. It is becoming common practice to establish a condition of control by use of statistical control charts before computing machine capability.

RANGE OF SIZES FROM	TO & INCL.	TOTAL TOLERANCES, IN.								
0.000	0.599	0.0002	0.00025	0.0004	0.0005	0.0008	0.0012	0.002	0.003	0.005
0.600	0.999	0.00025	0.0003	0.00045	0.0006	0.001	0.0015	0.0025	0.004	0.006
1.000	1.499	0.0003	0.0004	0.0005	0.0008	0.0012	0.002	0.003	0.005	0.008
1.500	2.799	0.0004	0.0005	0.0006	0.001	0.0015	0.0025	0.004	0.006	0.010
2.800	4.499	0.0005	0.0006	0.0008	0.0012	0.002	0.003	0.005	0.008	
4.500	7.799	0.0006	0.0007	0.001	0.0015	0.0025	0.004	0.006	0.010	
7.800	13.599	0.0007	0.0008	0.0012	0.002	0.003	0.005	0.008	0.012	
13.600	20.999	0.0008	0.001	0.0015	0.0025	0.004	0.006	0.010	0.015	
21.000 and over*										

Process										Cost
Lapping and honing	200%	180%	100%							300%
Grinding, diamond turning, and boring	200%	180%	140%	100%						300%
Broaching		200%	175%	140%	100%					200%
Reaming			175%	140%	100%					175%
Turning, boring, slotting, planing, and shaping				200%	170%	140%	100%			100%
Milling					150%	125%	100%			100%
Drilling						175%	100%			100%**

* Follow same tolerance trends   ** Approximate cost relationship of basic machining process

Fig. 15. Proportionate costs of obtaining various tolerances.

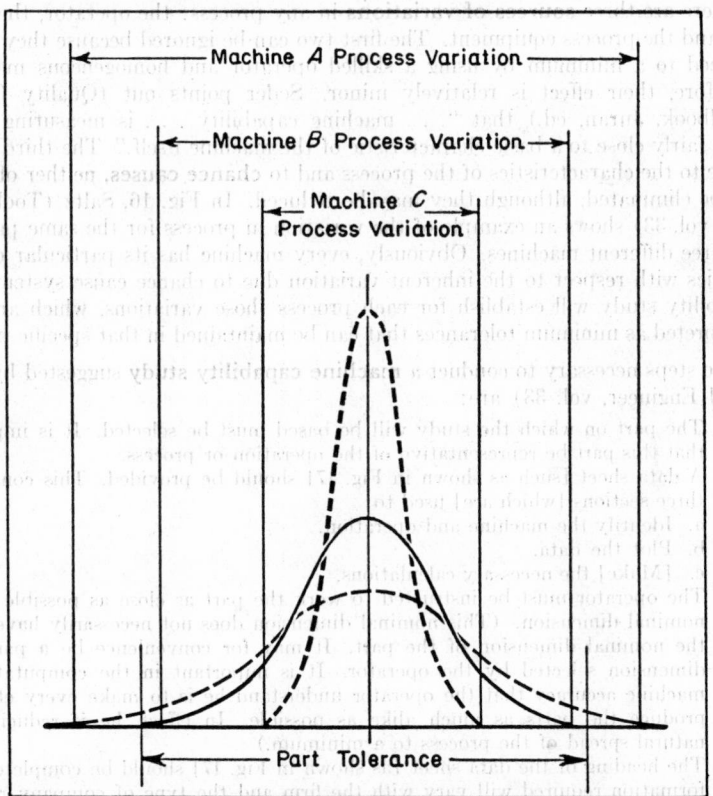

The process variation for machine *A* exceeds the part tolerance; the variation for machine *B* is slightly less than the part tolerance; and the variation for machine *C* is much less than part tolerance.

Fig. 16. Distribution of parts according to one dimension, for three different machines.

A development of this technique is reported by Meckley (American Machinist, vol. 100) and is shown in Fig. 15. The relative capabilities in reaching tolerances and the relative costs of some machining processes are shown in this figure as determined by capability studies at the York Corporation. A single setup, operating under control, should produce all pieces within one-third to one-half of these tolerances. Solid sections of bars suggest the tolerances for economical manufacture; crosshatched sections show obtainable tolerances at increased costs due to tooling errors and machining time. Assigned tolerances must therefore be a compromise between design function and machining process. All percentages shown are rough values of labor and tooling costs (Tool Engineering Handbook).

Statistical Determination of Capability. The **process capability study** is an application of statistical techniques which can be conducted in a short time. The primary purpose of this study is to determine quantitatively the variation inherent in any given process. It can be applied to any process such as machining, heat-treating, weaving, etc., where quantitative values of variation can be obtained.

There are three **sources of variations** in any process: the operator, the material, and the process equipment. The first two can be ignored because they can be reduced to a minimum by using a skilled operator and homogeneous material; therefore, their effect is relatively minor. Seder points out (Quality Control Handbook, Juran, ed.) that ". . . machine capability . . . is measuring something fairly close to a basic characteristic of the machine itself." The third source is due to the characteristics of the process and to **chance causes,** neither of which can be eliminated, although they may be reduced. In Fig. 16, Saltz (Tool Engineer, vol. 33) shows an example of the variation in process for the same part run on three different machines. Obviously, every machine has its particular characteristics with respect to the inherent variation due to chance cause systems. The capability study will establish for each process those variations, which are then interpreted as minimum tolerances that can be maintained in that specific process.

The steps necessary to conduct a **machine capability study** suggested by Saltz (Tool Engineer, vol. 33) are:

1. The part on which the study will be based must be selected. It is important that this part be representative of the operation or process.
2. A data sheet [such as shown in Fig. 17] should be provided. This consists of three sections [which are] used to:
   a. Identify the machine and operation.
   b. Plot the data.
   c. [Make] the necessary calculations.
3. The operator must be instructed to work the part as close as possible to the nominal dimension. (This nominal dimension does not necessarily have to be the nominal dimension of the part. It may for convenience be a particular dimension selected by the operator. It is important in the computation of machine accuracy that the operator understand he is to make every effort to produce the parts as much alike as possible. In effect, he is reducing the natural spread of the process to a minimum.)
4. The heading of the data sheet [as shown in Fig. 17] should be completed. Information required will vary with the firm and the type of company records.
5. Measuring equipment with the capacity to measure beyond the accuracy of the machine being tested should be selected and made available.
6. Data sheets should be scaled to allow room for plotting all variations expected.
7. As each part is produced by the operator, the inspector should inspect the part and record a cross mark in the appropriate position on the data sheet. This step should be repeated for not less than 50 pieces. For more dependable results 100 pieces should be checked.
8. Based on this data the machine accuracy is given by 6σ, where sigma is a measure of the process variation.

The measurements in Fig. 17 are made to ten-thousandths of an inch, and four decimal places are dropped in order to simplify the calculation. These decimal places are of course picked up, as shown, to arrive at the machine capability value. The symbols used in Fig. 17 are defined as follows:

f = frequency of occurrence of each measurement

X = deviation of the dimension from the nominal dimension (in ten-thousandths)

n = total number of measurements

$\bar{X} = \dfrac{\Sigma f X}{n}$

σ = standard deviation

Therefore, this machine cannot be expected to hold to any total tolerance smaller than .0023. As a practical matter, the most desirable situation would be where

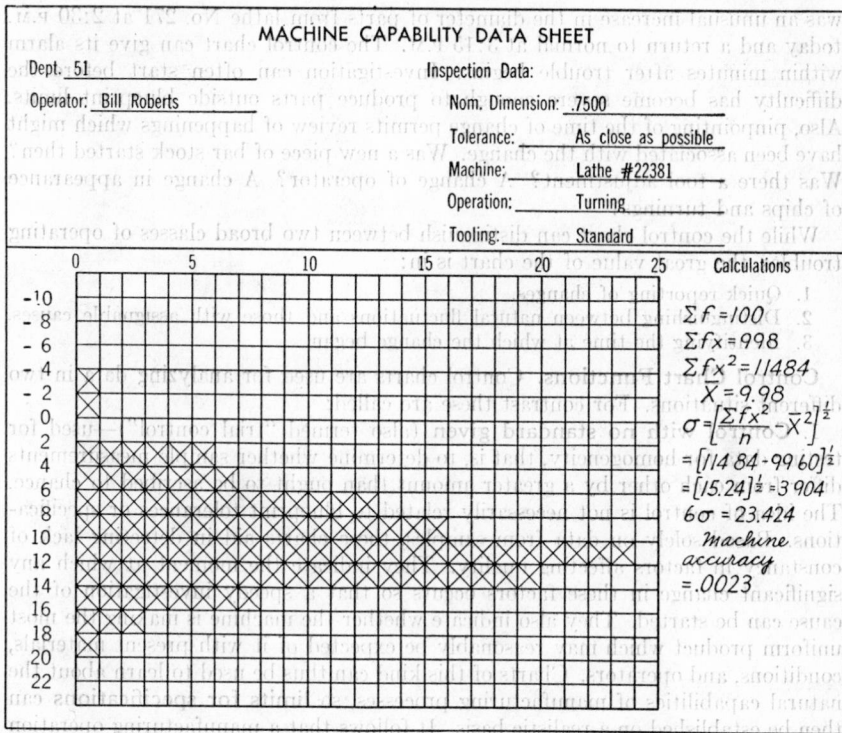

MACHINE CAPABILITY DATA SHEET

Dept. 51

Operator: Bill Roberts

Inspection Data:

Nom. Dimension: .7500

Tolerance: _____ As close as possible

Machine: _____ Lathe #22381

Operation: _____ Turning

Tooling: _____ Standard

Calculations

$\Sigma f = 100$

$\Sigma fx = 998$

$\Sigma fx^2 = 11484$

$\overline{X} = 9.98$

$\sigma = \left[\dfrac{\Sigma fx^2}{n} - \overline{X}^2 \right]^{\frac{1}{2}}$

$= [1484 - 99.60]^{\frac{1}{2}}$

$= [15.24]^{\frac{1}{2}} = 3.904$

$6\sigma = 23.424$

machine
accuracy
$= .0023$

Fig. 17. Typical form used in conducting a machine capability study.

the capability value is less than three-fourths of the total part tolerance. Seder points out that this situation results in production of practically all good work over a long period, as long as the process is in control.

This study evaluates the very best performance that the process equipment is capable of producing. However, under some circumstances it may be advantageous to know what the variation is in the process under production conditions. The study would follow a similar pattern except that the variations are due to all three cause systems: operator, material, and process equipment. Saltz refers to this type of study as a **machine operational accuracy study.** The advantage of this study, of course, is that the tolerances calculated are more directly applicable to the process.

CONTROL CHARTS. In manufacturing, the problem of identifying causes of poor quality occurs again and again. The operator finds that successive parts differ slightly even under good conditions. When is a change substantial enough to justify action such as resetting the machine or looking for faults in the material? Methods which tell the operator exactly when an assignable source of trouble has entered the process are valuable. Not only can they warn of coming difficulty in time to prevent scrap; they also tell when the machine should not be touched because it is already producing to the limit of its inherent accuracy.

Ordinary inspection records usually give only general information; for example, turret lathe No. 271 produced more out-of-limit parts yesterday than the day before. The object of the control chart is to be more specific: to warn that there was an unusual increase in the diameter of parts from lathe No. 271 at 2:30 P.M. today and a return to normal at 3:15 P.M. The control chart can give its alarm within minutes after trouble begins. Investigation can often start before the difficulty has become severe enough to produce parts outside blueprint limits. Also, pinpointing of the time of change permits review of happenings which might have been associated with the change. Was a new piece of bar stock started then? Was there a tool adjustment? A change of operator? A change in appearance of chips and turnings?

While the control chart can distinguish between two broad classes of operating troubles, the great value of the chart is in:

1. Quick reporting of changes.
2. Distinguishing between natural fluctuations and those with assignable causes.
3. Identifying the time at which the change began.

Control Chart Functions. Control charts are used for analyzing data in two different situations. For contrast these are called:

1. **Control with no standard given** (also termed "trial control")—used for testing data for homogeneity, that is, to determine whether sample measurements differ from each other by a greater amount than ought to be ascribed to chance. The idea of control is not necessarily related to blueprint tolerances or specifications. Based solely on data from samples, these charts aid in detecting lack of constancy in factors affecting quality. They indicate the moment at which any significant change in these factors occurs so that a speedy investigation of the cause can be started. They also indicate whether the machine is making the most uniform product which may reasonably be expected of it with present materials, conditions, and operators. Charts of this kind can thus be used to learn about the natural capabilities of manufacturing processes, so **limits for specifications** can then be established on a realistic basis. It follows that a manufacturing operation may be "in control" in the sense that it is as stable as it is able to be; yet it may not be conforming to tight specification limits. Charts of this kind may therefore be said to analyze primarily for **stability.**

2. **Control with respect to a given standard**—used to test inspection results for conformance to specifications, that is, to determine whether measurements on samples differ from desired measurements by a greater amount than ought to be ascribed to chance. The **standard values** may be aimed-at levels, such as dimensions set by specifications or drawings. In other cases they may be standard levels selected from experience as practical and economical to adhere to, such as an accepted "normal" percent of defectives. Control charts based on such desired values are used in inspection work to aid in distinguishing the variations expected in the manufacturing process from those which are significantly larger than the standards permit. Charts of this kind may be said to analyze for **conformance.**

Usual practice is to make initial control studies on the "trial limit" or no-standard-given basis. This shows what uniformity can be obtained from the process. The chart compares present performance of a machine with its past performance. Thus the limits for action are set from past average behavior of the man-machine-material combination. They are not derived from the engineering specifications for the product. When the trial control limits have been set up and examined they will indicate what should be done next.

Procedure in Applying Control Charts. The process of control charting may be divided into the following steps:

1. Selecting the quality characteristics worthy of control.
2. Analyzing the manufacturing process for probable sources of trouble.

3. Choosing the statistical measures.
4. Planning the selection and grouping of data.
5. Collecting the preliminary data.
6. Establishing trial control limits and starting the charts.
7. Reviewing results and drawing conclusions.
8. Maintaining control.

The starting point for choice of the quality characteristics to be controlled is in the quality records already described. The purpose of control is to reduce defects. The processes to be controlled are those where defects appear in numbers which are serious from the point of view of cost. The first step, then, is to review available inspection records for trouble points.

It does not automatically follow that the control chart should be set up at the existing inspection station. This is particularly true where the output of several machines is mixed together in the shop and reaches the inspector as a single stream of product. Best results are usually obtained by working toward the source of this stream. Much of the contamination may occur at one place, and analysis several steps downstream from that point may be ineffective, because the defects will be likely to appear there at random times and in changing patterns which seem inexplicable. For example, in one plant the record showed a high percentage of finish defects on a bearing surface. The parts came from two centerless grinders; the product from both contained the defects. The grinders were supplied with semifinished parts from three lathes. Control studies at the lathes showed that one of the three was much less capable than the others. As a result the replacement of a worn bearing was recommended. After the overhaul the trouble virtually disappeared.

Choice Between $\overline{X}$, R, p, and c Charts. A control chart shows a plot of some characteristic for a series of samples. The characteristic plotted for each sample is most usually one of the following: the average measurement $\overline{X}$ (read as "bar-X"); the range of measurements, R; the percentage of defective parts, p; or the count of defects, c. Each sample, except the c chart, consists of a number of pieces of product—never one alone.

$\overline{X}$, p, and c report on the trend or **prevailing level of quality.** They raise the hue and cry if the average quality gets out of hand. In contrast, R reports on the scatter or nonuniformity of product. R charts warn when a process becomes erratic. Where the greatest ability to diagnose is needed, charts for average, $\overline{X}$, and range, R, are both used. Together they form a very sensitive instrument for detecting and correcting **changes in the process.** Charts for average and range require actual measurements on the product, not just results of go-no-go gaging. If measurements are available or can be provided, $\overline{X}$ and R charts will make the most efficient use of the data.

The $\overline{X}$ chart will warn of **changes tending to affect all pieces.** It can detect results of wear of an abrasive wheel, dilution of a chemical solution, a change in heat treatment at a previous operation, improper calibration of a machine for filling and weighing sugar sacks, a decrease of vacuum at the sealing of radio tubes, and the like. The R chart will warn of a **significant loss (or gain) in uniformity** of the pieces. It can detect results of spotty quality of raw material, unreliability of a worn machine, balky behavior of a weighing scale, inconsistent practices of an operator or inspector, or the like. In general the discovery of erratic quality (from an R chart) requires corrective measures different from the discovery of a shift in trend (from an $\overline{X}$ chart).

Use of p and c Charts. When it is either impossible or uneconomical to collect actual measurements, p or c charts may be used. For example, an inspection might have the object of noting whether a serial number was present or absent, and no measurement is involved. In other instances, measurement may be possible but so costly as to seem unwarranted. If electric cable is passed or failed on the basis of a moderate overload, only a faulty length is destroyed by the test. If measurements on break-down voltage are to be obtained, each sample taken must be tested to destruction.

Charts of p and c are not as sensitive as charts of $\overline{X}$ and R. They are not as specific in indicating what is wrong. They require more observations per point plotted and thus may not report the presence of trouble so quickly. Nevertheless these charts have great value to supervisors in telling when to apply pressure for improvement. They can often be set up without any change in existing inspection methods. They distinguish between those fluctuations in fraction defective p or count of defects c which warrant action and those which are probably the result of ever-present small, unidentifiable causes.

The p chart is used for **control of fraction defective.** It can be applied wherever one can count the possible number of defective articles as well as the actual number of defective articles. The c chart is used for the **control of defect.** (A defect is a flaw of some kind. A single defective article might have several defects.) The c chart is applied chiefly in the special case where the number of defects can be counted but the number of opportunities for defects cannot. Examples are nicks and scratches on silverware, spots on photographic film, punctures in insulating paper, flaws in bearing surfaces. c charts are useful in judging control over complex items, such as radio sets, engines, and watches. The c chart is appropriate only if the total number of possible defects is large (though perhaps not exactly known) and the actual number of defects experienced is relatively small, say less than 10 percent of the possible number.

Selection of Samples. For charts of $\overline{X}$ and R, samples of 5 or 4 are nearly always used. However, for charts of p, much larger samples are needed. The sample should not be so small that the finding of only one defect indicates lack of control. Some authorities advocate a size large enough to lead to an average of at least six defects in a sample. For a p chart this would require the following as an approximate **minimum sample size:**

Average Percent Defective	Sample Size
0.1	60
0.05	120
0.01	600
0.005	1,200

Charts of c may be used for the count of defects found in a stated number of articles or in an arbitrary (but constant) amount of material, such as a selected length of cable or area of carpet. In general it is desirable to have the number of articles or the area of opportunity of a single specimen sufficient to produce an average count of perhaps **six defects per sample.** It is quite possible that the average count of defects may be large enough in samples of one, since a single specimen may have a number of defects of the same kind and since defects of different kinds may be counted together besides.

Samples for $\overline{X}$ and R charts are generally taken often enough to include from 1 percent to 10 percent of all product made. Samples for p and c charts commonly include 20 percent to 50 percent—sometimes 100 percent—of all product made. The upper percentage is used when the process is unstable or the production rate is small. The lower percentage is used when the process is fairly stable or the production rate is large.

Samples for control purposes should be selected in a way which assures that the specimens in any one sample were produced under the same essential conditions, according to Grant (Statistical Quality Control), so that suspected causes of trouble will operate between one sample and the next. This favors **segregation by source,** that is, forming the sample from the product of one man, machine, batch of raw material, or the like. In the case of $\overline{X}$ and R charts this is usually carried out by taking four or five pieces made consecutively.

Where large samples are necessary, as with p charts, it is sometimes impossible to segregate by source as fully as would be desired. The best that can be done may be to take the sample from the work of one shift, or from one large heat of metal, for example.

ESTABLISHING TRIAL CONTROL LIMITS. After data have been collected for a preliminary period, the figures are charted, together with trial control limits. These initial limits are to determine whether there is control in the sense of stability. They do not automatically imply control at a suitable level or in sufficient degree to assure acceptable product. The trial control limits are calculated as shown in Fig. 18, in which values of H are after C. Eisenhart and values of A_2, D_3, and D_4 are from the ASTM (Manual on Quality Control of Materials).

LIMITS FOR CONTROL CHARTS

Type of Chart	Central Line	Lower Limit	Upper Limit
Average, $\overline{X}$	$\overline{\overline{X}}$	$\overline{\overline{X}} - A_2\overline{R}$	$\overline{\overline{X}} + A_2\overline{R}$
Range, R	$H\overline{R}$	$D_3\overline{R}$	$D_4\overline{R}$
Fraction defective, p .	$\overline{p}$	$\overline{p} - 3\sqrt{\dfrac{\overline{p}(1 - \overline{p})}{n}}$	$\overline{p} + 3\sqrt{\dfrac{\overline{p}(1 - \overline{p})}{n}}$
Count of defects, c...	$\overline{c}$	$\overline{c} - 3\sqrt{\overline{c}}$	$\overline{c} + 3\sqrt{\overline{c}}$

n	A_2	H	D_3	D_4	d_2	n
3	1.023	0.938	0	2.574	1.693	3
4	0.729	0.961	0	2.282	2.059	4
5	0.577	0.970	0	2.114	2.326	5
6	0.483	0.975	0	2.004	2.534	6
7	0.419	0.978	0.076	1.924	2.704	7
8	0.373	0.980	0.136	1.864	2.847	8
9	0.337	0.982	0.184	1.816	2.970	9
10	0.308	0.983	0.223	1.777	3.078	10

Fig. 18. Formulas and factors for constructing control charts.

made. The higher percentage is used when the process is unstable or the production rate is small. The lower percentage is used when the process is fairly stable
or the production rate is large.

Product Sodium bicarbonate
Operation Filling 100-lb. bags
Machine #4 Valve packer with preweigh scale; spout #2

Specified Limits:
Maximum __None__
Minimum __100.0 (+0.7 tare)__
Unit of Measure __0.1 lb.__

Date 1/30
Dept. 370
Plant 2

SAMPLE No.	1	2	3	4	5	6	7	8	9	10	11	12	13
	101.1	101.0	101.0	101.3	101.2	101.3	100.9	101.3	101.5	101.5	101.5	102.0	101.6
	101.3	100.9	101.3	101.4	101.6	102.0	101.6	101.6	101.3	101.3	101.3	101.3	101.1
	101.5	101.2	100.8	100.9	100.9	101.1	101.7	102.0	100.9	101.9	100.8	101.5	101.2
	101.5	101.2	101.4	101.0	101.0	101.6	101.0	101.4	100.8	101.6	101.2	101.4	101.0
	100.8	101.3	101.3	101.5	101.3	101.5	101.9	101.5	101.2	100.9	101.8	101.2	100.9
TOTAL	506.2	505.6	505.8	506.1	506.0	507.5	507.1	507.8	505.7	507.2	506.6	507.4	505.8
X̄	101.2	101.1	101.2	101.2	101.2	101.5	101.4	101.6	101.1	101.4	101.3	101.5	101.2
R	0.7	0.4	0.6	0.6	0.7	0.9	1.0	0.7	0.7	1.0	1.0	0.8	0.7

SAMPLE No.	14	15	16	17	18	19	20	21	22	23	24	25	26
	100.9	101.0	101.9	101.4	101.6	101.0	101.0	101.5	101.6	102.0	100.8	101.6	
	101.2	101.2	102.0	101.2	101.6	101.0	101.2	101.7	101.6	101.7	101.1	101.2	
	101.2	101.3	101.5	100.8	101.3	100.3	100.3	101.5	102.0	101.5	101.5	101.1	
	101.3	101.5	101.5	101.2	101.2	100.5	100.5	101.6	102.0	101.8	101.8	101.5	
	101.5	100.9	101.5	101.7	101.0	100.4	100.7	101.9	101.9	101.0	101.7	101.3	
TOTAL	506.5	506.1	508.4	506.3	506.7	503.2	503.6	507.8	509.1	505.9	507.1	506.6	
X̄	101.3	101.2	101.7	101.2	101.3	100.6	100.7	101.6	101.8	101.2	101.4	101.3	
R	0.7	0.8	0.5	0.9	0.6	0.7	0.9	0.7	0.4	0.6	0.8	0.6	

No.	TOTALS	R
1	506.2	0.7
2	505.6	0.4
3	505.8	0.6
4	506.1	0.6
5	506.0	0.7
6	507.5	0.9
7	507.1	1.0
8	507.8	0.7
9	505.7	0.7
10	507.2	1.0
11	506.6	1.0
12	507.4	0.8
13	505.8	0.7
14	506.5	0.7
15	506.1	0.8
16	508.4	0.5
17	506.3	0.9
18	506.7	0.6
19	503.2	0.7
20	503.6	0.9
21	507.8	0.7
22	509.1	0.4
23	505.9	0.6
24	507.1	0.8
25	506.6	0.6
TOTAL	**12,662.1**	**18.0**

$$\bar{\bar{X}} = \frac{12,662.1}{125} \qquad \bar{R} = \frac{18.0}{25}$$
$$\bar{\bar{X}} = 101.30 \qquad \bar{R} = 0.72$$

LIMITS FOR CHART OF AVERAGES:

U.C.L. $= \bar{\bar{X}} + A_2\bar{R} = (101.30) + (0.577)(0.72) = 101.72$

L.C.L. $= \bar{\bar{X}} - A_2\bar{R} = (101.30) - (0.577)(0.72) = 100.88$

LIMITS FOR CHART OF RANGES:

U.C.L. $= D_4\bar{R} = (2.114)(0.72) = 1.52$

L.C.L. $= D_3\bar{R} = (\quad)(0.72) = 0$

REMARKS: ⑱ Following previous practice, operator check-weighed one bag and adjusted automatic scale accordingly. ⑳ Operator rechecked one bag after adjustment, found weight too low, set scale up. ㉒ Operator reweighed one bag, found weight high, set scale down again.

Fig. 19. Data sheet for X̄ and R charts.

Trial Limits for $\overline{X}$ and R Charts. Average and range charts are ordinarily set up after collection of about 100 observations (20 or 25 samples). Fig. 19 gives a typical work sheet, here applied to the study of a machine loading 100-lb. bags of sodium bicarbonate.

The central line of the $\overline{X}$ chart is located at the mean value of all 125 measurements, 101.30 lb. This quantity is termed the grand average, $\overline{\overline{X}}$ (read as "double bar-X"). The central line for the range chart is found from the average range, $\overline{R}$ (read as "bar-R"). $\overline{R}$ is obtained by adding the 25 separate ranges and dividing by 25. Here $\overline{R}$ is 0.72 lb.

Consulting Fig. 18 for the constants needed, it is found that for samples of five, $A_2 = 0.577$, $D_3 = 0$, $D_4 = 2.114$, $H = 0.970$. The lower control limit for averages is placed at:

$$\mathrm{LCL}_{\overline{X}} = \overline{\overline{X}} - A_2\overline{R} = 101.30 - 0.577(0.72) = 100.88 \text{ lb.}$$

and the upper control limit for averages at:

$$\mathrm{UCL}_{\overline{X}} = \overline{\overline{X}} + A_2\overline{R} = 101.30 + 0.577(0.72) = 101.72 \text{ lb.}$$

The 25 averages observed are plotted with these limits in the upper chart of Fig. 20.

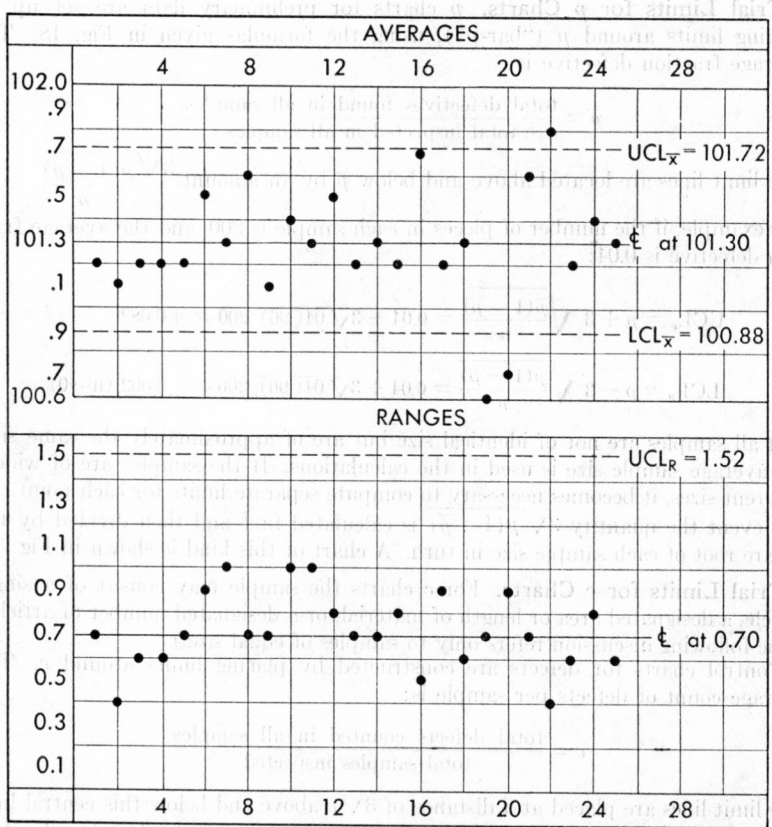

Fig. 20. $\overline{X}$ and R charts for automatic bag-loader.

The central line for the range chart is located at $HR = 0.970(0.72) = 0.70$ lb. The lower and upper limits, respectively, for the range are located at:

$$LCL_R = D_3\bar{R} = 0(0.72) = 0$$
$$UCL_R = D_4\bar{R} = 2.114(0.72) = 1.52 \text{ lb.}$$

The 25 ranges observed are plotted with these limits in the lower chart of Fig. 20.

This process at the time of the study is not in the state of control, as all points do not lie within the control limits. Therefore, the control chart is showing that there is an assignable cause of variation in the process. As soon as the assignable source of variability is discovered and eliminated, new trial limits will be calculated to determine if the process is then in control.

If a point lies outside control limits, there is strong evidence that the out-of-control sample was not produced under the same conditions as the others. If a **sample average** is outside, it indicates that a shift affecting all specimens has occurred. The log kept while collecting the data should be consulted to see if there was some known change of operator, tool setting, material, or the like which could account for the out-of-control point. If a **sample range** lies outside the limits, it indicates that the uniformity of the product has changed.

Trial Limits for p Charts. p charts for preliminary data are set up by placing limits around $\bar{p}$ ("bar-p"), using the formulas given in Fig. 18. The average fraction defective is

$$\bar{p} = \frac{\text{total defectives found in all samples}}{\text{total inspected in all samples}}$$

The limit lines are located above and below $\bar{p}$ by an amount $3\sqrt{\dfrac{\bar{p}(1-\bar{p})}{n}}$

For example, if the number of pieces in each sample is 200, and the average fraction defective is 0.04:

$$UCL_p = \bar{p} + 3\sqrt{\frac{\bar{p}(1-\bar{p})}{n}} = 0.04 + 3\sqrt{.04(.96)/200} = +0.082$$

$$LCL_p = \bar{p} - 3\sqrt{\frac{\bar{p}(1-\bar{p})}{n}} = 0.04 + 3\sqrt{.04(.96)/200} = -0.002 \text{ (use 0)}$$

If all samples are not of identical size but are of approximately the same size, the average sample size is used in the calculations. If the samples are of widely different sizes, it becomes necessary to compute separate limits for each point. In this event the quantity $3\sqrt{\bar{p}(1-\bar{p})}$ is calculated first and then divided by the square root of each sample size in turn. A chart of this kind is shown in Fig. 30.

Trial Limits for c Charts. For c charts the sample may consist of a single article, a designated area or length of material, or a designated number of articles. (The following discussion refers only to samples of equal size.)

Control charts for defects are constructed by placing limits around $\bar{c}$. The average count of defects per sample is:

$$\bar{c} = \frac{\text{total defects counted in all samples}}{\text{total samples inspected}}$$

The limit lines are placed at a distance of $3\sqrt{\bar{c}}$ above and below this central line.

In a plant making ignition cable, a high-voltage test was applied to all cable. A defect chart was kept on the number of insulation failures. The sample was in each case a 5,000-foot reel of cable. In the trial period 20 counts were recorded as follows: 6, 0, 3, 4, 3, 8, 1, 2, 5, 2, 3, 2, 5, 4, 1, 9, 1, 3, 2, 0. The average number of defects per reel was therefore $^{64}/_{20} = 3.2$, and this value was used for the central line. The resulting c chart is pictured in Fig. 21.

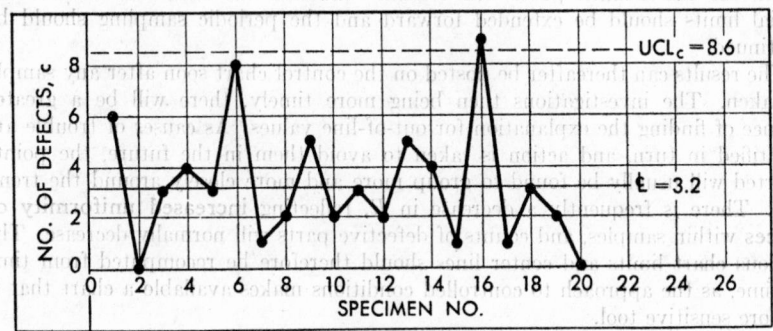

Fig. 21. c chart for cable defects.

CHART REVIEW AND ACTION. After the data for the initial period have been charted, the first step is to observe whether they indicate lack of control. **Lack of control** is associated with any of the following:

1. One or more points above the upper limit.
2. One or more points below the lower limit.
3. Several consecutive points close to one limit.
4. A marked upward or downward trend among successive points.
5. A sustained period in which the number of points above the central line is quite different from the number below.

The **causes of out-of-control samples** should be tracked down immediately. The process is studied. Notes and recollections concerning changes of material, tool setting, gage, operator, etc., are checked in search of explanations. The chance of identifying causes of trouble at this stage is obviously greatest while memories are still fresh.

Out-of-control points in the direction of extra-good quality should be investigated as energetically as the others. When a point is **below the lower limit** on a p chart, for example, one of four factors is usually responsible:

1. Unexpected improvement in process.
2. Faulty inspection.
3. Error in charting.
4. Chance variation.

A new operator may have adopted a better method; a more uniform batch of raw material may have been received. Once the value of any such factor has been seen, it may be possible to change the standard practice to conform. If on the other hand the change was a spurious one, produced by an incorrectly set gage or through inspector carelessness, the chart will have warned in time to avoid customer complaints.

Occasionally investigation will not reveal the cause for an out-of-limits point, and it must simply be put down as one of the three samples in a thousand for which a chance departure from the center line by this much may be expected.

Recomputation of Limits. When causes of trouble have been detected and steps have been taken to assure that they will not recur, the figures corresponding to the relevant point on the chart may be eliminated and the trial-period limits recomputed without them. If there are grounds for suspecting that findable causes for out-of-limits points still remain—and this will often be the case—the initial limits should be extended forward and the periodic sampling should be continued.

The results can thereafter be posted on the control chart soon after any sample is taken. The investigations then being more timely, there will be a greater chance of finding the explanation for out-of-line values. As causes of trouble are identified in turn, and action is taken to avoid them in the future, the points charted will usually be found to group more and more closely around the trend line. There is frequently a decrease in R, reflecting **increased uniformity of pieces** within samples, and counts of defective parts will normally decrease. The various chart limits and center lines should therefore be recomputed from time to time, as the approach to controlled conditions makes available a chart that is a more sensitive tool.

Comparing Chart Results with Specifications. The ultimate object of control charts is to secure adequate conformance of product to the design specifications. The control chart is a means, not the end in itself. Thus the quality control engineer must determine not only whether there is control but whether the control is sufficient and at the best level to meet the specification.

In this regard p and c charts offer the least problem. The question is simply: Is $\bar{p}$ or $\bar{c}$ sufficiently low that the dollar loss through defectives is not excessive? If not, a more detailed study of the process is necessary, possibly including the use of $\bar{X}$ and R charts.

For $\bar{X}$ and R charts the question is: Are the individual articles being made within the **authorized tolerance?** Analysis of the $\bar{X}$ and R data will disclose one of four conditions:

1. The process is in control
   a. and meets the specification requirements or
   b. does not meet the specification requirements.
2. The process is out of control
   a. but meets the specification requirements anyway or
   b. does not meet the specification requirements.

If the process is in control, it is easy to forecast its behavior with regard to the specification. The expected **scatter of sizes** of individual parts is estimated from the control chart data. (A symmetrical pattern such as in Fig. 14a or 14b is assumed.) The limits which will include virtually all parts made are stated as:

$$\overline{\overline{X}} \pm 3\overline{R}/d_2$$

with values of d_2 as given in Fig. 18.

Changes To Satisfy Specifications. For the bag-loading operation discussed in connection with Figs. 19 and 20, for example, $\overline{\overline{X}}$ was 101.25 and $\overline{R}$ was .55 after control was subsequently secured. It could then be forecasted that at prevailing settings individual bag weights would range from $101.25 - 3(0.55)/2.326 = 100.54$ lb. gross weight, to $101.25 + 3(0.55)/2.326 = 101.96$ lb. gross weight.

These limits representing actual performance are then compared with the specification requirements. In the case at hand, allowance for the weight of the empty sack set the lowest permissible gross weight at 100.7 lb. It is evident that some sacks are underweight at the present setting, and an immediate upward readjustment of the scale is needed. Usually such a change of **level** is easily made on a machine.

Sometimes the comparison of actual with intended performance reveals another type of shortcoming not so easy to correct. This is where the range or dispersion of values is too large to satisfy the specification even when the machine is set to give the most favorable average. In the event the **specification cannot be met,** one of the following steps must be taken:

1. Change the job to a more capable machine or operator.
2. Continue as at present but sort the product.
3. Change the specification
   a. to use a material or form more easily made or
   b. to authorize more variation (a wider tolerance).

The control limits for a controlled process capable of its task will usually occupy no more than the middle fourth or third of the available tolerance span. If the control limits are so tight as to occupy much less space than this, the process is an extra-capable one. In this event it may be feasible to reduce the frequency of sampling and, possibly, to eliminate the chart.

Where the trial limits do not show control, it is not possible to make a firm forecast of future conformance. (Without control over the rudder, one cannot be sure that a ship will hold to its present course in the future.) However, it is common practice even in this case to use the method outlined above, if only to get an idea of what might occur. Depending on the results, it is possible to:

1. Change to a more favorable average level.
2. Improve uniformity by continuing to use the chart until control is obtained.

Control to Given Standards. The procedure described in the preceding sections leads ultimately to control to given standards through the following steps:

1. Set up trial limits.
2. Obtain control.
3. Concurrently, compare actual results with results required by blueprint, etc.
4. Improve level of uniformity if necessary.
5. Finally, adopt the most satisfactory trial central lines and limits as standard values for the future.

Alternate procedures are available under which limits can be derived directly from the specification requirements.

Examples of Process Studies

MACHINE CAPABILITY STUDY. In this example 5,000 bushings (see sketch in Fig. 22) were scheduled to be made on an Acme-Gridley 4-spindle automatic. Shortly after the job was started, inspection found that 11 percent of the bushings were outside limits on the 1.000 ± 0.002 diameter. In discussing the problem the tool-setter asserted that this was the best that could be done; if this tolerance was to be met, the parts would have to be sorted. The foreman, on the other hand, pointed out that the machine had been used without trouble on ±0.002 work about three months before. The tool-setter retorted that the machine had been in better condition at the time and that inspection had not been so tight.

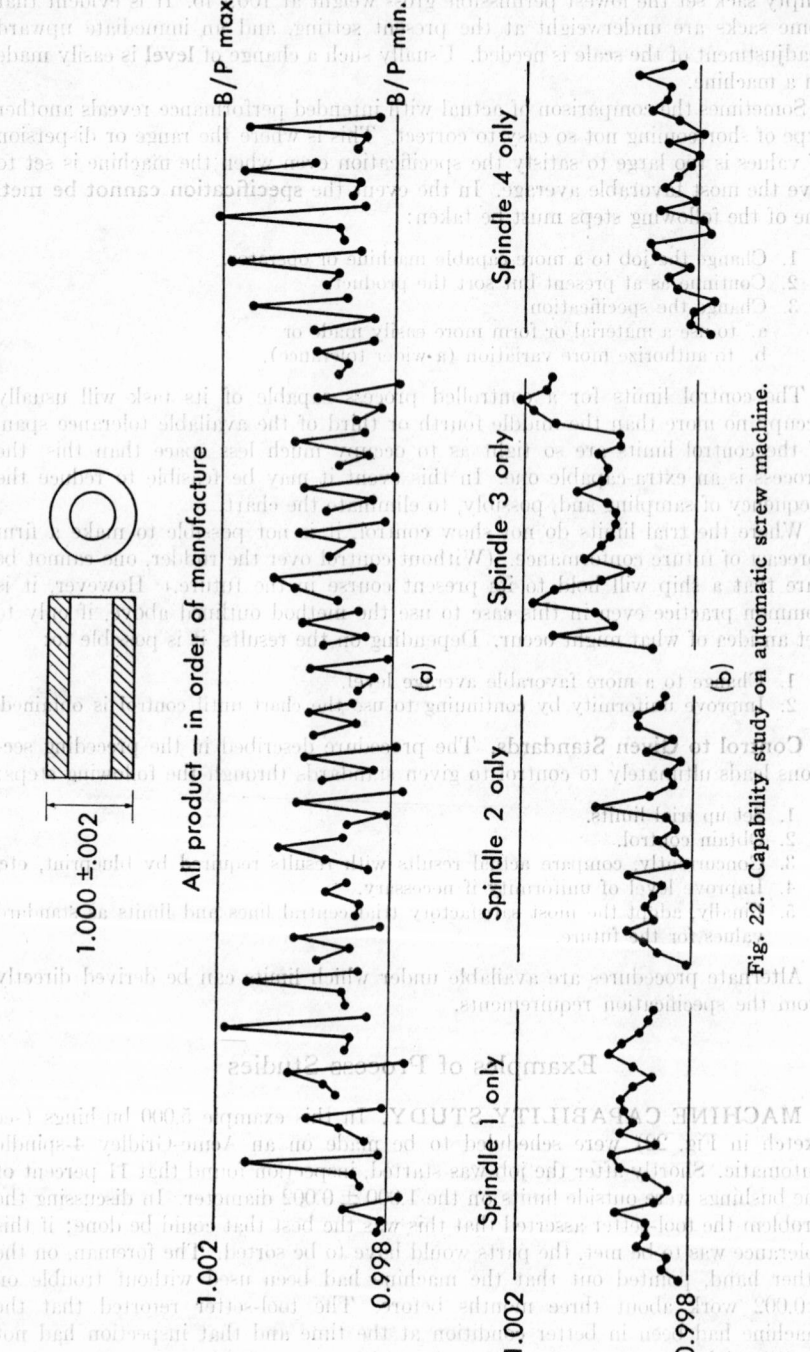

All product — in order of manufacture

B/P max.

B/P min.

1.000 ±.002

1.002

0.998

1.002

0.998

Spindle 1 only

Spindle 2 only

Spindle 3 only

Spindle 4 only

(a)

(b)

Fig. 22. Capability study on automatic screw machine.

It was decided to get the facts by means of a **chart of individual measurements.** An inspector was assigned to take bushings in sequence and measure them. In all he measured 100 pieces. A plot of the hundred measurements is shown in Fig. 22, diagram *a.* At first glance this chart may appear to bear out the tool-setter's contention. However, this is a 4-spindle machine. Bushings 1, 5, 9, 13, etc., are thus made on one spindle; bushings 2, 6, 10, 14, etc., on a second, and so on. Closer examination of the plot shows that pieces coming from spindle No. 3 average about .0015 larger than those from spindles 1 and 2. Pieces from spindle No. 4 are usually the smallest in each group of four. To show this more clearly the points have been regrouped, according to source, in Fig. 22, diagram *b.*

It was immediately evident that an adjustment at spindle No. 3 was necessary to lower the average diameter of bushings made on it. An adjustment at spindle 4 to raise the average diameter of its bushings was also desirable. With the facts before him the tool-setter was able to make the necessary corrections. Rejections practically disappeared.

A by-product of the study was additional knowledge on **tool wear.** The small upward trend in the diagrams indicates a wear rate of roughly 1/1,000 in. per 200 (total) pieces made. In this short study the product from spindle No. 3 not only had a high average but was the most variable and governed the length of run possible between tool resets. If the machine is initially set with all spindles producing diameters near the lowest dimension permitted, the tool will not have to be reset until about 400 bushings have been turned. If continued study of spindle 3 reduces the variability of its product with that from the other spindles, it may be possible to increase runs without resetting to 700 or 800 bushings.

MOLDING-MACHINE CAPABILITY STUDY. The following discussion by Manuele (Tech Engineering News, vol. 25) suggests useful approaches to control problems:

A good application of statistical analysis is the molded part shown [in Fig. 23]. This part is made in a 16-cavity mold, and considerable difficulty was being experienced in maintaining the 0.245 ± 0.003 in. dimension. Therefore, the first step was to determine whether the part could be made.

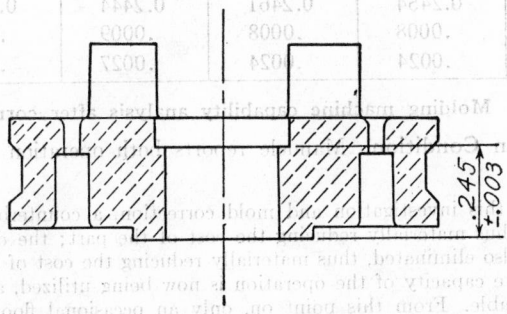

Fig. 23. Molded part for which a capability analysis was applied.

Thirty-three pieces were taken from each cavity and carefully measured. From these measurements the average, $\overline{X}$, of the pieces produced by each cavity was calculated. The standard deviation, σ, was also calculated or it can be estimated from $\sigma = \dfrac{R}{d_2}$. (See section on Statistical Methods.) These two statistics, for 8 cavities, are shown [in Fig. 24].

	No. 1	No. 2	No. 3	No. 4
$\overline{X}$	0.2471	0.2535	0.2579	0.2573
σ	.0009	.0009	.0010	.0006
3σ	.0027	.0027	.0030	.0018
	No. 5	No. 6	No. 7	No. 8
$\overline{X}$	0.2559	0.2599	0.2576	0.2542
σ	.0008	.0007	.0005	.0006
3σ	.0024	.0021	.0015	.0018

Fig. 24. Molding machine capability analysis before correction.

Remembering that according to the normal curve, 99.7 percent of the parts will be produced within the limits $\overline{X} \pm 3\sigma$, we find that the parts are being produced within the proper tolerances (3σ is smaller than 0.003 in. for each of the cavities), but $\overline{X}$ is too far from the drawing nominal dimension (0.245 in.) in every cavity. This means that the part can be made within the tolerances required, but the individual mold cavities must be adjusted to bring the average of each cavity to 0.245 in.; cavity No. 1 will have to be closed 0.0021 in., cavity No. 2 will have to be closed 0.0085 in., and so on.

[Fig. 25] shows the average and standard deviation for 50 pieces produced in each of 8 cavities after the mold was corrected. This shows that the operation should produce parts which are all satisfactory. A detail inspection of 1,000 parts revealed no rejections; an inspection of 10 percent of a subsequent lot of 6,000 parts also failed to reveal any defective units.

	No. 1	No. 2	No. 3	No. 4
$\overline{X}$	0.2444	0.2446	0.2442	0.2460
σ	.0006	.0005	.0009	.0009
3σ	.0018	.0015	.0027	.0027
	No. 5	No. 6	No. 7	No. 8
$\overline{X}$	0.2454	0.2461	0.2444	0.2442
σ	.0008	.0008	.0009	.0007
3σ	.0024	.0024	.0027	.0021

Fig. 25. Molding machine capability analysis after correction.

Corrections in Condition. Manuele reports both operation and inspection improvements:

As a result of this investigation and mold correction, a counterboring operation was eliminated, thus materially reducing the cost of the part; the detail inspection of all parts was also eliminated, thus materially reducing the cost of inspection; also the full productive capacity of the operation is now being utilized, as all parts produced are acceptable. From this point on, only an occasional floor inspection, to guard against mold wear, is required to insure the continued production of satisfactory parts.

SCREW MACHINE CAPABILITY STUDY. Juran reports (Factory Management, vol. 110) that,

The Hamilton Watch Co. cut inspection and sorting, also scrap, of screw machine products. Variations in critical dimensions of parts made it necessary to do a lot of detail gaging and sorting. Naturally, the variations scrapped many parts. A study of the machines proved they could meet the required specifications. But the study also showed that the operators were checking the product with gages that were less precise than the machines. They were adjusting the tooling to conform with inaccurate gaging—thus setting the tools to cut to wrong dimensions. Once the company knew the process capability and what caused the limitation, correction was simple. New, more accurate gages for the operators eliminated the trouble and the excess cost.

$\overline{X}$ **AND** R **CHARTS APPLIED TO SPRINGS.** In another case, a fine wire spring was required, as specified in Fig. 26. Note that this specification is rather incomplete, that the right angle with the axis of dimension a is merely implied, that dimension b of the short leg is referred to the somewhat ideal form of the first loop.

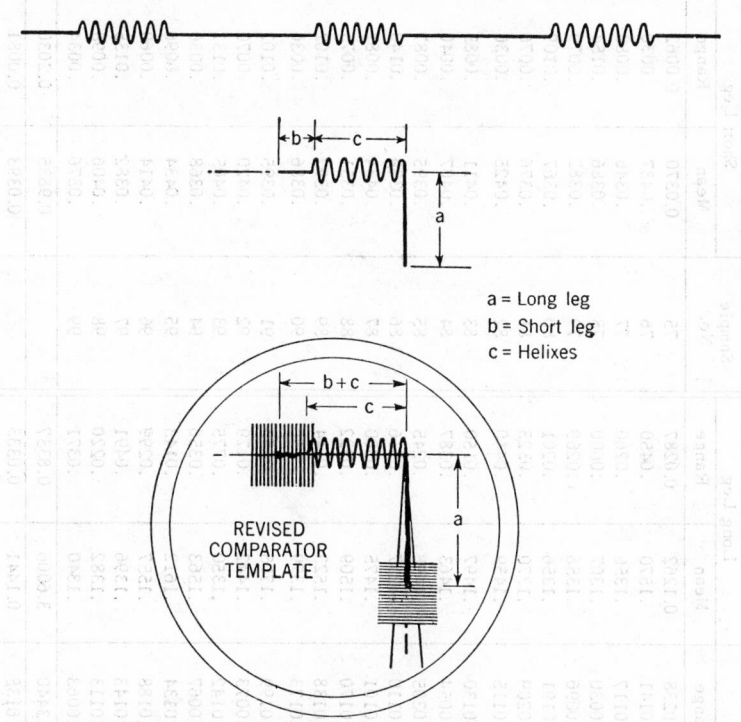

Fig. 26. Spring on which an $\overline{X}$ and R chart was applied.

The helixes were first wound intermittently on a small mandrel, with straight-wire connecting links. The connected helixes were then fed off the mandrel one at a time; the projecting long leg of the end helix was bent down by the operator's index finger; and the short leg was cut by a blade positioned from what appeared to be the end loop of the helix. The dimensions were then checked on the template of an optical projection comparator, using hourly samples of four.

The means and ranges for a single machine and operator are shown in Fig. 27 for short and long legs. As a first step, the historical period was developed in the first 25 samples, plotting points without limits. From this period, average means and ranges were used for computing statistical standards of central lines and control limits.

In the case of short-leg means, the sequence level or grand average was obviously very close to bogey of specification limits, and the specification limit

(Sample Size n = 4. Machine No. 1)

Sample No.	Short Leg Mean	Short Leg Range	Long Leg Mean	Long Leg Range
1	0.0432	0.0238	0.1262	0.0287
2	.0399	.0141	.1570	.0450
3	.0302	.0117	.1356	.0260
4	.0384	.0030	.1307	.0600
5	.0405	.0096	.1358	.0269
6	.0399	.0191	.1356	.0201
7	.0383	.0209	.1370	.0323
8	.0411	.0115	.1459	.0440
9	.0432	.0130	.1497	.0150
10	.0435	.0054	.1463	.0387
11	.0437	.0305	.1498	.0245
12	.0385	.0110	.1277	.0516
13	.0368	.0101	.1475	.0300
14	.0419	.0170	.1509	.0222
15	.0390	.0138	.1523	.0144
16	.0477	.0173	.1379	.0156
17	.0421	.0199	.1705	.0553
18	.0443	.0073	.1442	.0179
19	.0250	.0142	.1350	.0775
20	.0420	.0067	.1563	.0356
21	.0401	.0134	.1612	.0143
22	.0446	.0188	.1557	.0299
23	.0369	.0143	.1396	.0491
24	.0470	.0113	.1382	.0220
25	.0378	.0063	.1340	.0371
Sum	1.0047	0.3440	3.6006	0.8337
Average	0.0402	0.0138	0.1441	0.0333

Fig. 26. Spring on which an X̄ and R chart was applied.

Sample No.	Short Leg Mean	Short Leg Range	Long Leg Mean	Long Leg Range
75	0.0370	0.0062	0.1514	0.0259
76	.0437	.0030	.1559	.0197
77	.0346	.0080	.1653	.0430
78	.0386	.0154	.1529	.0254
79	.0382	.0079	.1554	.0153
80	.0367	.0109	.1413	.0286
81	.0376	.0076	.1600	.0532
82	.0425	.0036	.1731	.0352
83	.0411	.0085	.1639	.0270
84	.0407	.0040	.1604	.0097
85	.0395	.0087	.1485	.0336
86	.0370	.0140	.1554	.0179
87	.0434	.0087	.1718	.0515
88	.0351	.0075	.1540	.0251
89	.0392	.0102	.1547	.0185
90	.0386	.0036	.1538	.0458
91	.0395	.0102	.1542	.0314
92	.0420	.0070	.1655	.0594
93	.0405	.0131	.1426	.0175
94	.0368	.0036	.1616	.0218
95	.0434	.0096	.1486	.0415
96	.0414	.0060	.1578	.0090
97	.0382	.0135	.1673	.0231
98	.0406	.0098	.1575	.0280
99	.0376	.0034	.1639	.0487
Sum	0.9835	0.2030	3.9468	0.7558
Average	0.0393	0.0081	0.1578	0.0302

Fig. 27. Control inspection measurements on spring leg lengths (spring shown in Fig. 26).

mid-point was therefore used for a central line. This is desirable in such cases. Where the level is appreciably different from bogey, it is better to use a grand mean central line so that **control** can be judged, aside from level, and the more actionable points distinguished from the others. Otherwise, all points would call for action where there may be very few if any causes to investigate, except those creating a systematic displacement of **level**.

The statistical standards of central lines and central limits, computed as above stated, were projected into the then future period of another 25 points, in Fig. 28. It is usually held more desirable to have up to 25 points in the historical or qualifying period before projecting a statistical standard. However, in the earlier stages of a problem, a shorter sequence is permissible. As each sample was taken thereafter, the mean and range were easily calculated and plotted on a chart hung near the operator.

Conditions Discovered by Study. When the first statistical standards were computed and also projected back over the past 25 points of the historical period for initial judgment of the process, several conditions were suggested, as follows:

1. The short-leg means were at or near the correct level of specification mid-point but displayed slight trouble in one point outside limits and in a tendency to trend in points 4 to 10, inclusive.
2. The short-leg ranges were in control but at too high a level: $\overline{R} = 0.0136$, which indicated a dispersion of individual values that would have high scrap.
3. Long-leg means are at a level (0.1441) far below the desired one and show lack of control by a point outside limits and considerable trend in points 4 to 11, inclusive.
4. Long-leg ranges are reasonably in control with an average range of only 0.0333. This suggests possibility of a low rate of scrap if control of means were obtained at proper level.

Corrections Introduced. The systematically low level of long-leg means was at first puzzling, since a supplementary control investigation of the initial coil-forming operation demonstrated that the **average** spacing between coils on the mandrel was correct. Upon examination of the projection-comparator inspection it was immediately apparent that the long legs were being bent in an inconsistent manner to angles varying from 45° to 80° instead of 90°. The inspector was measuring only the leg-tip distance perpendicular to the axis of the helix. A tool fixture was designed to remove this effect; i.e., the process was redesigned. Also, both product and inspection specifications were made more objective by requiring angle limits on the long leg, which were in turn placed on the comparator template. Here an assignable cause due to poor specification was removed. Thus, the long-leg systematic difference of means from bogey would be corrected, and with the improvement in the process the degree of variability (level of range) would be reduced. The erratic condition indicated on the chart of means was found to be due partly to spotty wire, which affected the degree of variability in spacing by the coil winder, and partly to inconsistency in operator application. The former factor was worked upon and improved. The latter was due to skill requirements on fine work at the limit of controlled human performance. Use of fixtures and other aids improved the condition.

In the case of the short legs, the cutting operator did not have a well-defined loop from which to reference the cutting blade, and the inspector likewise had difficulty in referencing the measurement. In processing, the end loops were smaller and in some cases not clearly definable. Specification dimensioning was revised, in terms of actual functioning of the part, referencing all dimensions from the apex of the long-leg tolerance angle limits.

After these steps, i.e., correcting for assignable causes in specifications, operations, and inspection, considerable improvement was obtained. The charts for a third period, points 76 to 100 inclusive, are shown in Fig. 28. Control was attained

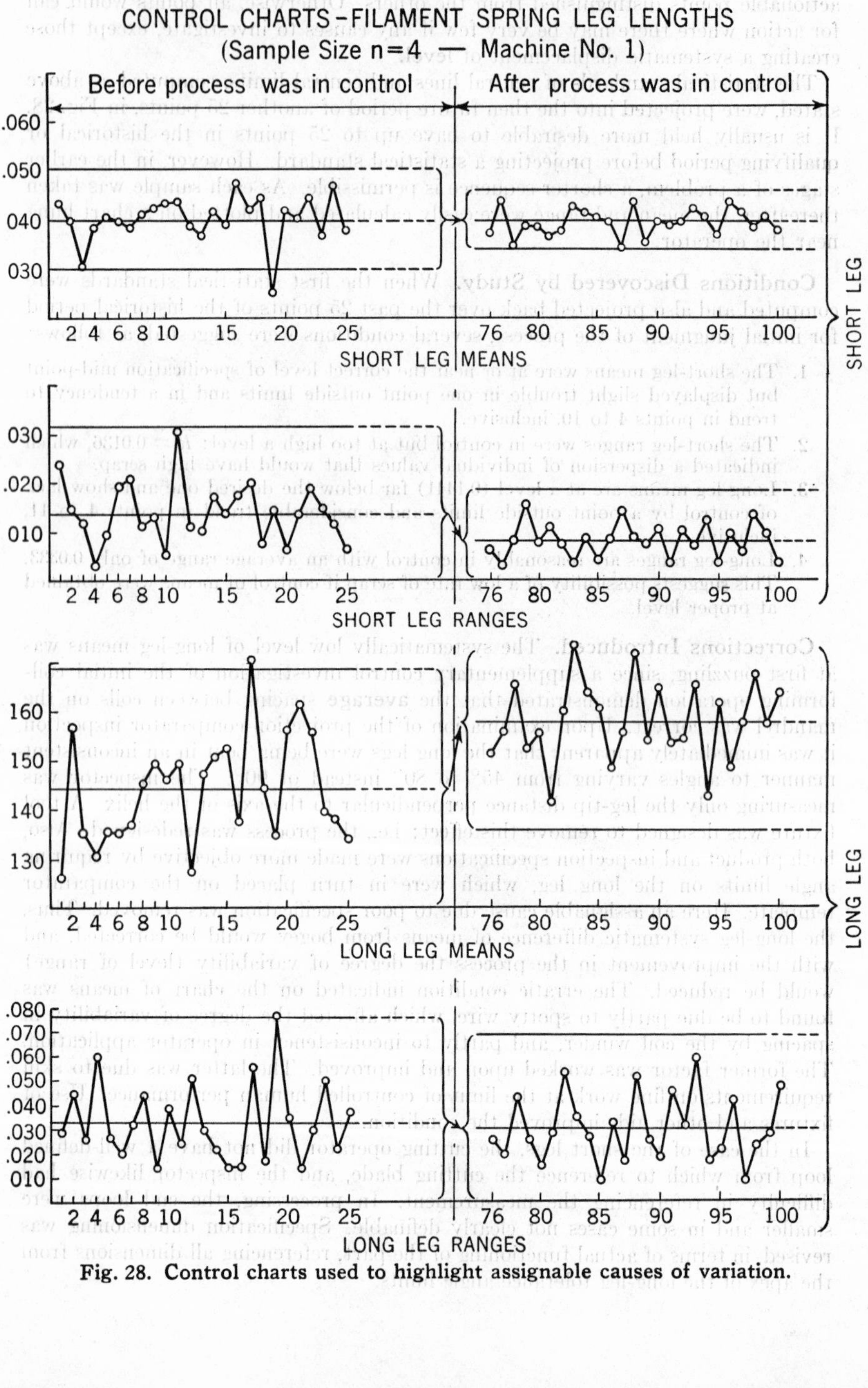

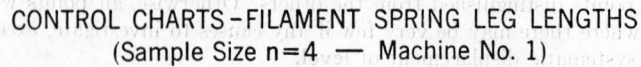

CONTROL CHARTS – FILAMENT SPRING LEG LENGTHS
(Sample Size n=4 — Machine No. 1)

Before process was in control | After process was in control

SHORT LEG MEANS

SHORT LEG RANGES

LONG LEG MEANS

LONG LEG RANGES

SHORT LEG

LONG LEG

Fig. 28. Control charts used to highlight assignable causes of variation.

PRODUCT: Control Device   DRAWING NO.: D11807   DEPARTMENT: 870-6
AMOUNT INSPECTED: 100%   INSPECTION LOG REFERENCES:

Lot No.	Lot Size N	Gross Def. r	Gross Def. Fract.	A (1 Item) r	A (1 Item) Fract.	B (1 Item) r	B (1 Item) Fract.	C (6 Items) r	C (6 Items) Fract.	D (5 Items) r	D (5 Items) Fract.	E (8 Items) r	E (8 Items) Fract.	F (Others) r	F (Others) Fract.
1	2,999	599	.200	103	.0344	131	.0437	73	.0244	67	.0224	49	.0163	176	.0588
2	3,237	537	.166	98	.0303	98	.0219	49	.0151	83	.0256	38	.0117	171	.0512
3	3,156	457	.144	101	.0320	36	.0114	66	.0209	99	.0314	23	.0073	132	.0418
4	3,423	623	.182	156	.0455	62	.0181	68	.0198	142	.0415	45	.0131	150	.0438
5	3,727	727	.195	146	.0391	63	.0169	94	.0252	154	.0413	55	.0147	215	.0577
6	4,263	763	.179	168	.0394	43	.0101	135	.0317	138	.0324	71	.0167	208	.0488
7	3,687	487	.132	80	.0217	38	.0103	41	.0111	79	.0214	24	.0065	225	.0610
8	2,881	676	.234	235	.0815	23	.0080	58	.0201	77	.0267	99	.0344	184	.0638
9	2,262	562	.248	211	.0931	39	.0172	65	.0287	132	.0582	18	.0079	97	.0428
10	2,922	697	.248	234	.0799	94	.0321	96	.0328	90	.0308	31	.0106	152	.0520
11	3,785	875	.231	240	.0634	138	.0364	93	.0246	95	.0251	104	.0274	205	.0542
12	4,814	914	.190	207	.0430	104	.0215	142	.0294	111	.0230	67	.0319	283	.0588
13	2,159	359	.166	84	.0390	44	.0204	55	.0255	50	.0232	20	.0043	106	.0515
14	3,089	484	.157	56	.0189	98	.0317	54	.0175	55	.0178	34	.0110	187	.0605
15	3,156	616	.175	187	.0532	46	.0139	62	.0177	80	.0228	51	.0145	190	.0602
16	2,139	434	.203	110	.0515	36	.0168	45	.0210	56	.0262	12	.0056	175	.0818
17	2,139	503	.194	93	.0359	84	.0324	42	.0162	109	.0421	37	.0143	138	.0533
18	2,510	487	.194	98	.0390	45	.0179	57	.0227	59	.0235	51	.0203	177	.0705
19	4,103	803	.195	197	.0480	121	.0295	92	.0224	150	.0365	39	.0095	204	.0497
20	2,992	547	.183	163	.0545	45	.0150	79	.0264	51	.0170	26	.0087	183	.0612
21	3,545	555	.156	107	.0302	57	.0160	80	.0226	60	.0236	21	.0070	230	.0649
22	1,841	401	.218	65	.0353	40	.0217	27	.0147	132	.0716	18	.0098	119	.0646
23	2,748	418	.156	115	.0419	26	.0095	78	.0284	36	.0131	15	.0054	148	.0539
24	3,924	667	.170	141	.0351	59	.0150	144	.0367	55	.0140	24	.0061	244	.0622
25	2,056	319	.155	82	.0399	29	.0141	21	.0102	20	.0097	16	.0078	151	.0734
26	3,650	474	.130	74	.0203	65	.0178	80	.0219	80	.0219	51	.0140	124	.0340
27	4,001	535	.134	144	.0360	28	.0070	40	.0100	96	.0240	36	.0090	191	.0477
28	2,950	379	.128	88	.0298	38	.0129	74	.0251	50	.0169	24	.0081	105	.0356
29	3,162	550	.173	158	.0499	54	.0171	82	.0259	82	.0259	35	.0110	139	.0439
30	3,827	483	.126	134	.0350	42	.0110	69	.0180	58	.0152	24	.0063	156	.0408

Fig. 29. Inspection data used in a fraction defective chart.

at proper levels. The degree of variability was reduced to a point where very few units of product were outside specification limits. Control inspection was here used for acceptance inspection as well, and because of ultimate **stability** of the control, sampling was stretched out to one set of four in 4 hr. for each operator.

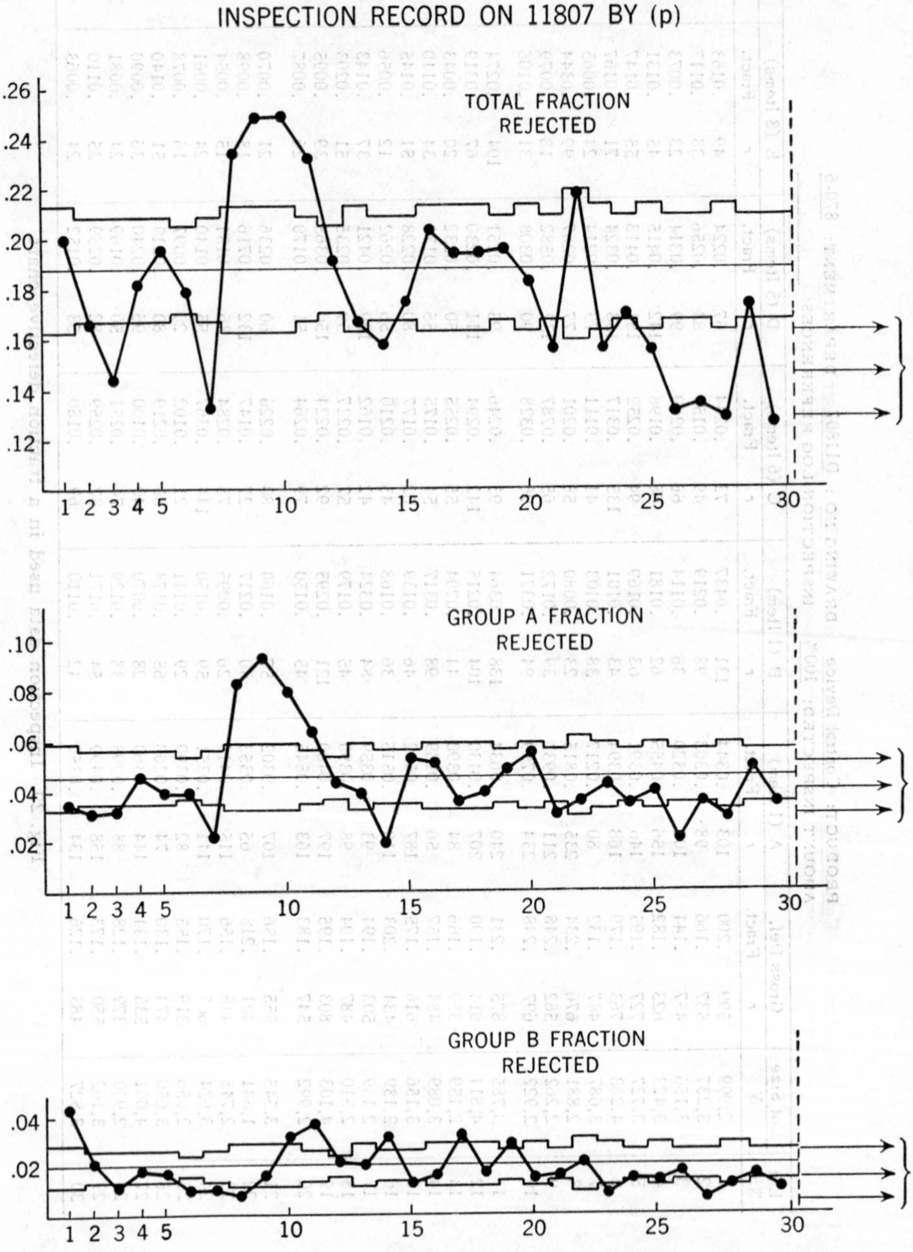

INSPECTION RECORD ON 11807 BY (p)

TOTAL FRACTION
REJECTED

GROUP A FRACTION
REJECTED

GROUP B FRACTION
REJECTED

Fig. 30. Fraction defective (p) charts

FRACTION DEFECTIVE CHART APPROACH. An illustration of control from existing works inspection records demonstrates that it is not always necessary to collect data in order to apply these control techniques. Frequently, usable data are available and only require interpretation.. The data in Fig. 29 have been summarized from the inspection records of a precision control device.

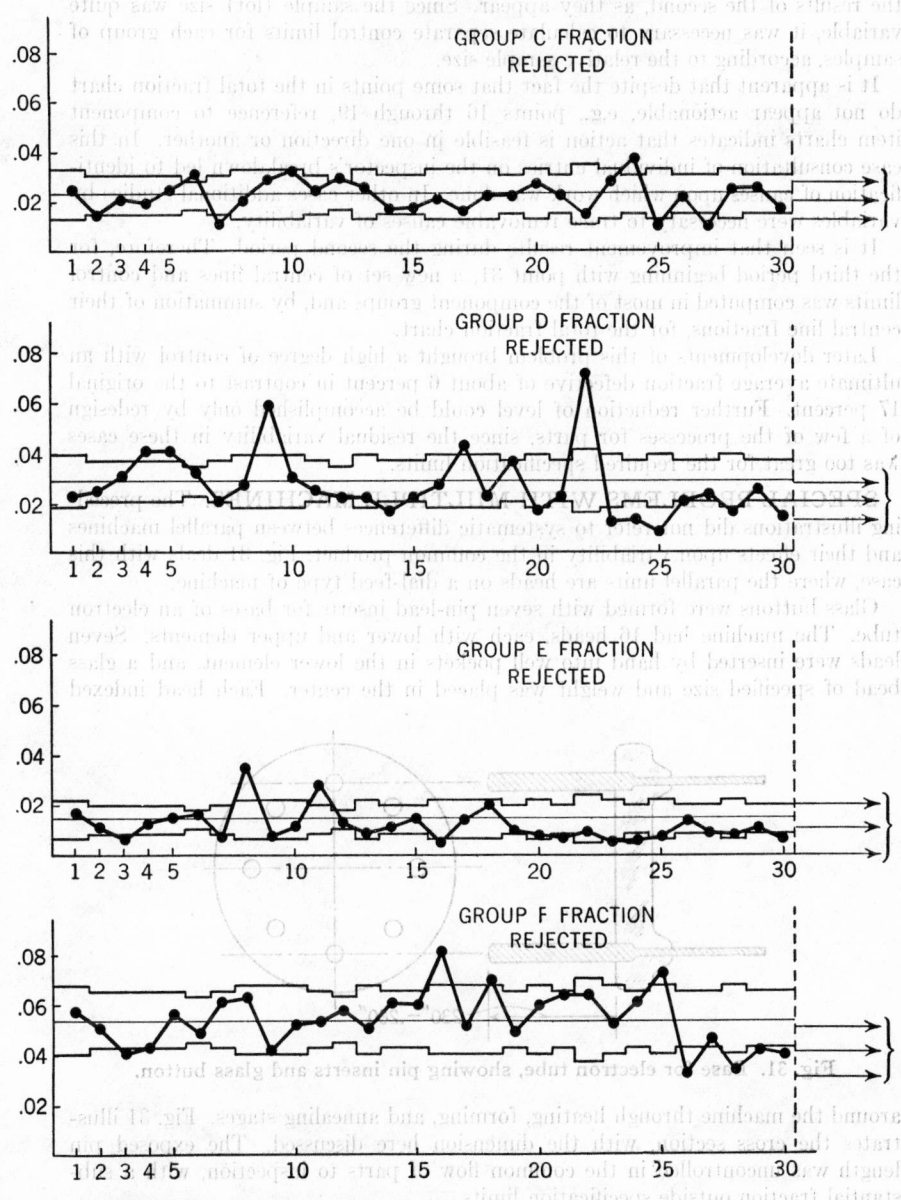

prepared from the data in Fig. 29.

The gross number of devices defective is enumerated for each lot, together with the fraction it represents. Items *A* through *E* are groups of individual characteristics of similar nature for which the group numbers and fractions defective are given. Item *F* represents all remaining characteristics of the breakdown.

Control charts prepared for these items are shown in Fig. 30. The central lines and control limits for the second 15-lot period are based upon the historical record of the first period. These were projected at the end of the first period to judge the results of the second, as they appear. Since the sample (lot) size was quite variable, it was necessary to calculate separate control limits for each group of samples, according to the relative sample size.

It is apparent that despite the fact that some points in the total fraction chart do not appear actionable, e.g., points 16 through 19, reference to component item charts indicates that action is feasible in one direction or another. In this case consultation of individual entries on the inspector's breakdown led to identification of causes upon which work was done. In other cases additional studies by variables were necessary to trace removable causes of variability.

It is seen that improvement results during the second period. Therefore, for the third period beginning with point 31, a new set of central lines and control limits was computed in most of the component groups and, by summation of their central line fractions, for the total fraction chart.

Later developments of this problem brought a high degree of control with an ultimate average fraction defective of about 6 percent in contrast to the original 17 percent. Further reduction of level could be accomplished only by redesign of a few of the processes for parts, since the residual variability in these cases was too great for the required specification limits.

SPECIAL PROBLEMS WITH MULTIPLE MACHINES. The preceding illustrations did not refer to systematic differences between parallel machines and their effects upon variability in the common product. Fig. 31 deals with this case, where the parallel units are heads on a dial-feed type of machine.

Glass buttons were formed with seven pin-lead inserts for bases of an electron tube. The machine had 16 heads, each with lower and upper elements. Seven leads were inserted by hand into well pockets in the lower element, and a glass bead of specified size and weight was placed in the center. Each head indexed

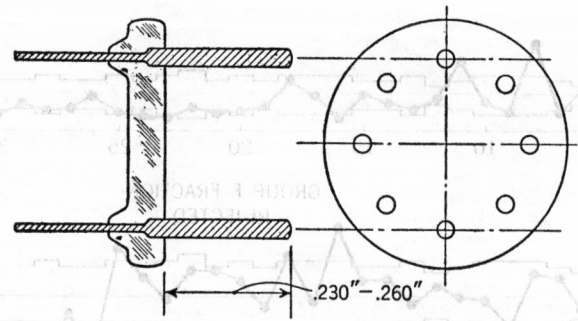

Fig. 31. Base for electron tube, showing pin inserts and glass button.

around the machine through heating, forming, and annealing stages. Fig. 31 illustrates the cross section, with the dimension here discussed. The exposed pin length was uncontrolled in the common flow of parts to inspection, with a substantial fraction outside specification limits.

Causes of Variations. Possible assignable causes were: improper placing of leads in well pockets due to carelessness or to fouling of the pockets, adjustment of well-pocket depths, improper maintenance of cams and rollers operating the head movements, etc. Since assignable differences were suspected to exist between heads and between each head and specification bogey, one button (here considered as a sample of seven leads) was taken each hour from each head.

Control charts were made up for means of seven leads for each head. A data sheet illustrating the tabulation is shown in Fig. 32. The mean range was computed over a representative chronological period for each head. Control charts for means and ranges were posted on the operating floor.

(Values in Thousandths of One Inch)

Head	Pin Numbers							Mean $\bar{X}$	Range R	Remarks
	1	2	3	4	5	6	7			
1	246	252	252	249	252	249	238	248	14	
2	255	263	265	264	265	265	258	262	10	
3	251	253	251	247	248	247	250	249	6	(1)
4	235	222	246	246	238	250	240	239	28	
5	256	265	261	262	264	261	257	261	9	
6	241	239	240	242	246	248	234	241	14	(2)
7	257	260	260	257	258	255	255	257	5	
8	258	263	260	261	259	260	257	259	4	
9	264	260	265	260	254	256	259	259	11	
10	243	250	245	252	250	239	243	246	8	
11	251	253	254	255	255	251	247	252	8	
12	240	244	234	238	244	247	248	242	14	(3)
13	250	253	252	254	255	252	247	252	8	
14	237	236	236	230	236	238	233	235	8	(4)
15	248	251	254	253	253	255	255	253	7	
16	256	256	258	258	258	257	255	254	3	(3)
Total								4,009	157	
Average								250.6	9.8	

(1) Fouling reported by operator.
(2) Head weight recently adjusted.
(3) Recurrent trouble with cam mechanism on this head.
(4) Recently adjusted.

Fig. 32. Data sheet for control inspection of exposed pin lengths.

Fig. 33 illustrates the charts of the means for two of the heads. It was soon apparent to the maintenance men that some heads were averaging high, others low. Successive approximations of adjustment quickly brought the heads to average on bogey. In addition, the charts provided prompt indications of the entrance of occasional assignable causes, such as glass particles and fouling in well pockets. The charts for ranges not only indicated such failure in individual pockets, but through improper levels (average range, $\bar{R}$) showed which heads needed cleaning and equalization of the pocket depths by the toolmakers.

Improvements Made. In a relatively short period the control of exposed pin length was improved to a point where extremely few pins were outside the limits; and it was planned to drop 100 percent acceptance inspection in favor of patrol sampling inspection when the stability of control was established. Control charts were continued for supervision, upon the insistence of the production maintenance department.

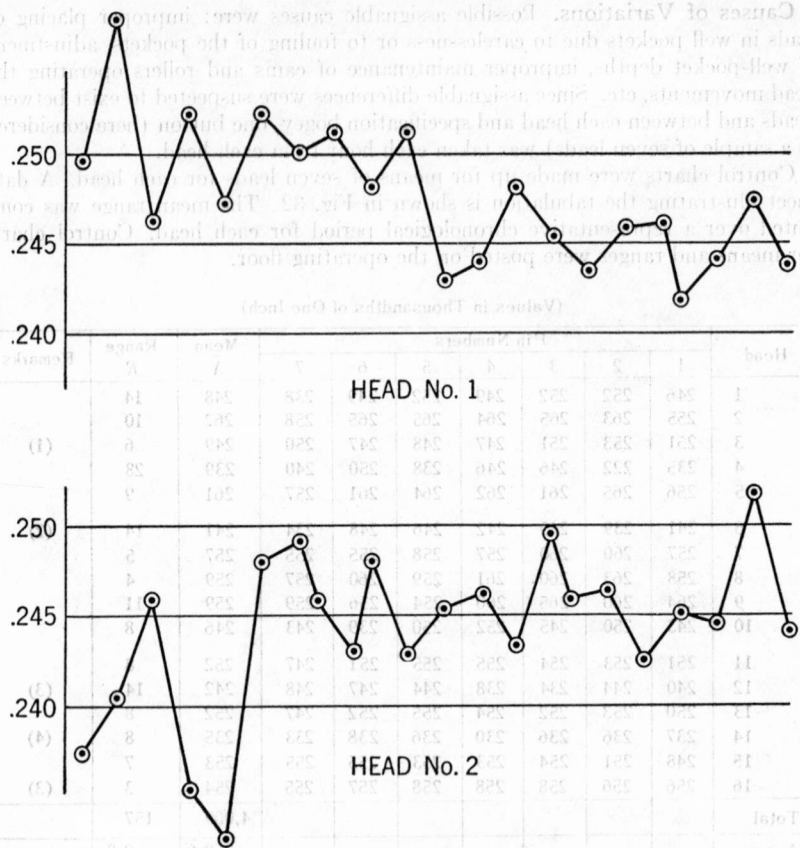

Fig. 33. Control charts for mean pin lengths obtained from two heads of dial-feed machine.

Sampling Tables for Acceptance and Control

SAMPLING. Sampling for purposes of acceptance, rejection, or other action upon specific lots of material has been for some time a tempting alternative to 100 percent inspection. It can be applied to purchased parts and materials, to semifinished items in or passing between different departments or plants of a company, or to final inspection of finished items ready to go to the consumer.

Advantages of Sampling. The benefits of sampling center on the ability to obtain decisions of calculable reliability at least cost. The advantages are:

1. Facts needed for choice of a sampling plan require a conscious consideration of actual quality needs.
2. Less man-hours are allotted to sorting the bad parts from the good so more inspection effort can be applied to prevention of poor quality at its source.
3. More separate quality characteristics can be regularly inspected, as the cost of reaching a decision on any one characteristic is low.
4. A small inspection staff can make decisions on a large volume of material.

5. As the lot size or production rate rises or falls, it is easily possible to adjust the proportion inspected in such a way as to maintain a given assurance of quality.
6. Rejection of an entire lot of material (rather than defectives only) applies strong enough pressure to the supplier to encourage reform.
7. More time can be spent on each unit, since fewer parts are examined.
8. The inspector's care, feeling of importance, and responsibility are increased by the knowledge that his findings from the sample are the basis for an important decision on an entire shipment of material.
9. Sampling inspectors make fewer errors due to monotony, since they usually check fewer parts of the same type before changing to a different measurement or blueprint.
10. Sampling can be used to obtain assurance of quality even where only destructive tests are available.
11. The cost of damage incidental to inspection is reduced because less parts are handled.

Limitations of 100 Percent Inspection. Obviously, 100 percent inspection cannot be applied where tensile strength, life, corrosion resistance, fading, or the like must be measured by destructive tests. Moreover, careful experiments by the Western Electric Company, the Ford Motor Company, and others have shown that inspectors performing 100 percent inspection do not locate all the faulty parts that are present. In general they find only 70 percent to 95 percent of the defects. The greatest difficulty is with large lots containing only small percentages of defective parts. If defective parts are once produced, it is clear that several inspections will have to be made subsequently if defectives are to be reduced to a really low number.

It is true that the most careful inspection of part of a lot still leaves some doubt as to what would be found by inspecting the whole. However, the risk of being misled here can be calculated. With sampling plans an attempt is made to face the difficulties and measure the risks involved. Also, as indicated above, more inspector accuracy is obtained with sampling inspection.

Neither sampling nor screening is able to assure beyond every doubt that material accepted is completely free of defects. The best way known to assure 100 percent conformance is to concentrate on control of the manufacturing process. The use of sampling as a measure of results permits a transfer of effort from sorting to prevention of defects.

ACCEPTANCE BY ATTRIBUTE INSPECTION. Where large numbers of parts are involved, the most general type of inspection used in industry is that known as the **method of attributes.** In this system the inspector merely notes whether the part is accepted or rejected. Usually he determines this with a go-no-go gage. Actual measurements are not taken, or if they are observed they are often not recorded.

Most existing **acceptance sampling plans** are for use in connection with attribute inspection. This situation is a natural outgrowth of the common availability of this type of data. It is also a result of the fact that such plans, once computed, can be tabulated in a way which makes use easy and altogether unmathematical. This is seldom possible with acceptance plans using measurements.

The best-known published sampling plans for use in civilian industry were jointly developed by Dodge and Romig of the Bell Telephone Laboratories. Other plans originally devised to meet special needs in procurement of matériel for the armed forces are also increasing in use, for civilian goods as well as military.

SINGLE, DOUBLE, AND MULTIPLE SAMPLING. Acceptance sampling systems may be classified according to the number of samples taken. In single-sampling plans, only one set of specimens is drawn from the lot. The **single-sampling procedure** may be outlined as:

1. Collect and inspect a random sample of n pieces.
2. If the number of defects found is not more than the acceptance number given by the plan, accept the entire lot.
3. If the number of defects found is more than the acceptance number given by the plan, inspect all remaining pieces in the lot, or return the entire lot to the vendor.
4. Replace or repair any defective pieces found.

In double-sampling plans a smaller initial set of specimens is taken. If the quality is either very good or very poor, a decision is reached on the basis of this sample alone, with a saving in the amount of inspection. A second set of specimens is taken only if the first sample shows a borderline quality. Double sampling usually requires less total inspection than single sampling, by amounts ranging from 10 percent to 50 percent. The **procedure in double sampling** is:

1. Collect and inspect a random first sample of n pieces.
2. If the number of defects found is not more than the acceptance number for the first sample, accept the entire lot.
3. If the number of defects found is equal to or more than the rejection number for the first sample, inspect all remaining pieces in the entire lot.
4. If the number of defects found falls between the acceptance and rejection numbers for the first sample, collect and inspect a random second sample.
5. If the total number of defects found in the first and second samples together is not more than the acceptance number given for the second sample, accept the entire lot.
6. If the total number of defects found in the first and second samples together is equal to or more than the rejection number, inspect all remaining pieces in the entire lot or return the entire lot to the vendor.
7. Replace or repair any defective pieces found.

In **sequential-sampling plans** the same line of reasoning is carried further. Provision is made for taking a number of samples if necessary to reach a decision. For simplicity each of these samples usually has the same size, and this sample size is very small as compared with the corresponding single-sampling plan. The average number of pieces per lot inspected is usually less than required by double sampling by amounts of the order of 30 percent. Balanced against this, however, are the costs of administration and training, the necessity to reopen or rehandle the lot for each additional sample, and the more complex records. The procedure in **multiple-sampling plans** is similar to the one outlined for double-sampling plans. Three additional steps equivalent to 4, 5, and 6 above are added for each further sample taken.

SAMPLING PLANS AND THEIR PROTECTION. A sampling plan is simply a set of instructions for an inspector. The behavior of the sampling plan is established by specifying the lot size N, for which it is to be used; the sample size n, to be inspected; and the number of faulty pieces which will cause acceptance or rejection of the lot. From this information it is possible to predict the results that will be obtained when the plan is used in practice. Specifically, it is possible to measure the risk that a wrong decision will be made.

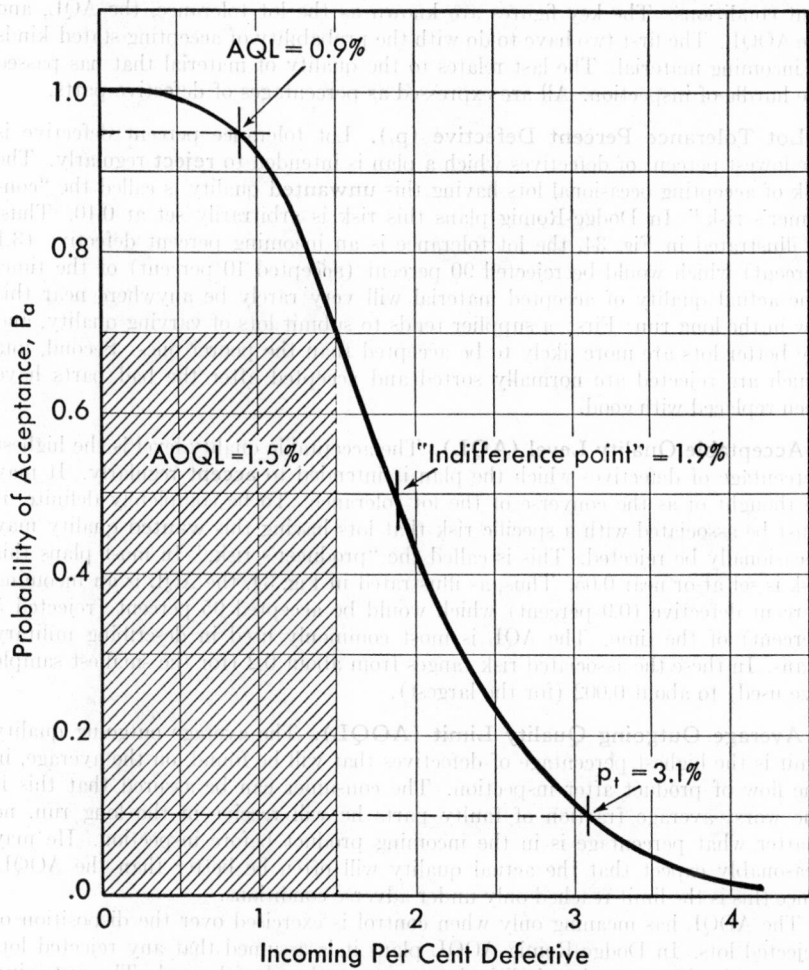

Fig. 34. A typical operating-characteristic curve with key points identified.

Such predictions are made from the **operating-characteristic (OC) curve** of the sampling plan. A typical curve is given in Fig. 34. This particular curve shows the performance that would be obtained if an inspector were instructed to take from a very large lot a sample of 300 pieces and to accept the lot if he found no more than 5 defective pieces. The curve gives the probability that a lot of any stated quality will be accepted if submitted for sampling. For example, if a "good" lot—containing only 1 percent of defective parts—is submitted, the probability is 0.92 that it will be accepted. On the other hand, if a "bad" lot—containing 3 percent of defective parts—is submitted, the probability is only 0.12 that it will be accepted.

In general no two sampling plans have identical curves, although their characteristics may sometimes be very similar. The practical difficulty of printing, comparing, and using hundreds of curves to show the behaviors of available plans has led to tabulation of the plans by their responses to a few particularly important conditions. The key figures are known as the lot tolerance, the AQL, and the AOQL. The first two have to do with the probability of accepting stated kinds of incoming material. The last relates to the quality of material that has passed the hurdle of inspection. All are expressed as percentages of defective parts.

Lot Tolerance Percent Defective (p_t). Lot tolerance percent defective is the lowest percent of defectives which a plan is intended to **reject** regularly. The risk of accepting occasional lots having this **unwanted** quality is called the "consumer's risk." In Dodge-Romig plans this risk is arbitrarily set at 0.10. Thus, as illustrated in Fig. 34, the lot tolerance is an incoming percent defective (3.1 percent) which would be rejected 90 percent (accepted 10 percent) of the time. The actual quality of accepted material will very rarely be anywhere near this low in the long run. First, a supplier tends to submit lots of varying quality, and the better lots are more likely to be accepted than the poorer ones. Second, lots which are rejected are normally sorted and accepted after the bad parts have been replaced with good.

Acceptable Quality Level (AQL). The acceptable quality level is the highest percentage of defectives which the plan is intended to **accept** regularly. It may be thought of as the converse of the lot tolerance. To be completely definite, it must be associated with a specific risk that lots having this **wanted** quality may occasionally be rejected. This is called the "producer's risk." In most plans this risk is set at or near 0.05. Thus, as illustrated in Fig. 34, the AQL is an incoming percent defective (0.9 percent) which would be accepted 95 percent (rejected 5 percent) of the time. The AQL is most commonly used in describing military plans. In these the associated risk ranges from about 0.2 (for the smallest sample size used) to about 0.002 (for the largest).

Average Outgoing Quality Limit (AOQL). The average outgoing quality limit is the highest percentage of defectives that will be found, on the average, in the flow of product after inspection. The consumer can be assured that this is the worst average fraction of faulty parts he will receive in the long run, no matter what percentage is in the incoming product before inspection. He may reasonably expect that the actual quality will often be better than the AOQL, since this is the limit reached only under adverse conditions.

The AOQL has meaning only when control is exercised over the disposition of rejected lots. In Dodge-Romig AOQL plans it is assumed that any rejected lots are completely screened and all bad parts are replaced with good. The **outgoing quality** is viewed as a predictable mixture of these perfect lots with the known small number of defectives in lots which the plan accepts.

Final inspection and material-in-process inspection usually furnish the control needed. The conditions for control may or may not be met in inspection of purchased materials and parts. If rejected lots are returned to the supplier for sorting and correction, results are doubtful, and plans should be selected on the basis of AQL or p_t instead.

USE OF PUBLISHED SAMPLING TABLES. The application of sampling plans to acceptance inspection can be reduced to a routine procedure involving no mathematics. The important steps are common to all types of plans.

First, the quality standards (Step 1) must be set. This is normally done by an inspection or quality control executive who can bring together information on cost and value of quality from sales, accounting, production, etc. In some cases the standards are directly imposed by the customer, especially if the government is the customer. The detailed sampling procedure (Step 2) may be established by the same executive. If routine, it may be established by an inspection supervisor. The actual sampling operation (Step 3) is carried out by a line inspector. The subsequent review of results (Step 4) is normally made by the inspection supervisor.

The following **sampling check list** shows in more detail the questions that must be dealt with in several stages:

1. What degree of conformance is to be set as standard?
    What will constitute an item to be inspected?
      One part?
      A set of parts normally sold or used together?
    What stage of manufacture?
    What defects are to be looked for?
    Are these all of the same severity?
    Can more minor than major defects be tolerated?
    Will different standards of conformance then apply?
    What quality level (AOQL or AQL or p_t) is appropriate for each class of defect?
      Does this defect class involve
        Risk to human life?
        Risk of injury?
        Certain failure of product?
        Damage which cannot be repaired in the field?
        Shortened life of product?
        Damage cheaply repaired?
        A flaw that will be revealed in a later stage of manufacture?
        Mere annoyance with appearance?
    What is the existing record of defects in this factory?
    What is the comparable record for competitors?
    What is the cost of nonconformance?
      How many customer complaints on this defect?
      What is the cost of customer returns?
      What is the cost of repairs or reworks?
      Are extra production operations made necessary?
    What is chance and cost of improvement?
      Has real effort been made yet?
      Is the process in control?
      Are better methods known to be available?
2. What sampling procedure is to be installed?
    How large a lot can be brought together for sampling?
    Will such a lot be homogeneous in quality?
    If not, can it be subdivided into homogeneous sublots based on date of receipt, time of manufacture, source, or operator?
    How is the random sample to be taken?
    Will single, double, or multiple sampling be most desirable?
    What plan for this is given in the tables?
    What data sheets or instructions are needed for the inspector?
3. In operation, which lots are to be accepted?
    How many defective items does the sample contain?
    Is this a passable number for the defect in question?
    Where are the various defects to be listed in the records?
4. What results are being secured?
    What process average does sampling show?
    Is a different plan indicated for future lots?
    Is the process average better than expected?
      Worse than expected?

DODGE-ROMIG TABLES. Dodge and Romig (Sampling Inspection Tables) have developed an extensive and valuable set of ready-made tables. Four separate groups of plans are listed:

1. Single-sampling lot-tolerance tables.
2. Single-sampling AOQL tables.
3. Double-sampling lot-tolerance tables.
4. Double-sampling AOQL tables.

The first and third groups of plans are tabulated according to lot tolerance percent defective (p_t) with a consumer's risk of 0.10. The second and fourth groups of plans are tabulated according to the average outgoing quality limit (AOQL) which they assure. Of the four kinds of plans, those of the AOQL double-sampling type have found the widest acceptance.

Lot Tolerance Plans. A constant low consumer's risk is stressed by lot tolerance plans. They give considerable assurance that individual substandard lots will be rejected. Plans from the lot tolerance tables are particularly applicable in cases where lots retain their identity after inspection, as when a lot is shipped as inspected to a consumer in a specific transaction. **AOQL plans** stress the limit on poor quality in the long run but do not maintain uniform assurance that individual low-quality lots will be rejected. Plans from the AOQL tables are particularly applicable when lots are merged in a common supply whose average performance is of interest, as in subsequent operations within the plant or in cases of continual deliveries on large quantity orders. A typical single-sampling lot-tolerance table is shown in Fig. 35. All of the plans in this table afford the same quality protection as measured by the lot tolerance. Plans appropriate to a wide variety of lot sizes are given.

Under acceptance sampling there are two sources of inspection work. For each lot the sample of n items must be inspected. In addition, whenever a rejection occurs, the remaining $N-n$ items in the lot must also be inspected. If the incoming quality is known, it is possible to forecast the total amount of inspection that will result with a given plan. This leads to the possibility of choosing from among several available plans having the same p_t as the one which will involve the least total amount of inspection.

Dodge and Romig have made the extensive calculations needed for this choice. Thus each of the six columns in Fig. 35 lists plans for a specified average value of incoming quality. For example, if the item to be inspected has averaged 0.5 percent defective in the past and no change is foreseen, the least total amount of inspection can be anticipated if a plan is chosen from the column headed 0.31–0.60.

AOQL Plans. Fig. 36 shows a typical double-sampling AOQL table. Once again a whole series of sampling plans is provided to suit varying needs as to lot size and past process average fraction defective. These plans differ considerably from each other as to lot tolerance but have the same AOQL (10 percent).

MILITARY-STANDARD TABLES. The U. S. Armed Forces have adopted standard tables and procedures for single, double, and multiple sampling. These military-standard plans (MIL-STD-105A, Sampling Procedures and Tables for Inspection by Attributes) are tabulated by acceptable quality levels (AQL) rather than AOQL or lot tolerance.

At the outset no account is taken of the process average; instead, the government specifies the AQL and advises which of three "inspection levels" is to be

Single Sampling (Lot Tolerance Percent Defective = 3%)

Process Average % Lot Size	0–0.03			0.04–0.30			0.31–0.60			0.61–0.90			0.91–1.20			1.21–1.50		
	n	c	AOQL %	n	c	AOQL %	n	c	AOQL %	n	c	AOQL %	n	c	AOQL %	n	c	AOQL %
1–40	All	0	0	All	0	0	All	0	0	All	0	0	All	0	0	All	0	0
41–55	40	0	0.18	40	0	0.18	40	0	0.18	40	0	0.18	40	0	0.18	40	0	0.18
56–100	55	0	.30	55	0	.30	55	0	.30	55	0	.30	55	0	.30	55	0	.30
101–200	65	0	.38	65	0	.38	65	0	.38	65	0	.38	65	0	.38	65	0	.38
201–300	65	0	.40	70	0	.40	70	0	.40	110	1	.48	110	1	.48	110	1	.48
301–400	70	0	.43	70	0	.43	115	1	.52	115	1	.52	115	1	.52	155	2	.54
401–500	70	0	.45	70	0	.45	120	1	.53	120	1	.53	160	2	.58	160	2	.58
501–600	75	0	.43	75	0	.43	120	1	.56	160	2	.63	160	2	.63	200	3	.65
601–800	75	0	.44	125	1	.57	125	1	.57	165	2	.66	205	3	.71	240	4	.74
801–1,000	75	0	.45	125	1	.59	170	2	.67	210	3	.73	250	4	.76	290	5	.78
1,001–2,000	75	0	.47	130	1	.60	175	2	.72	260	4	.85	300	5	.90	380	7	.95
2,001–3,000	75	0	.48	130	1	.62	220	3	.82	300	5	.95	385	7	1.0	460	9	1.1
3,001–4,000	130	1	.63	175	2	.75	220	3	.84	305	5	.96	425	8	1.1	540	11	1.2
4,001–5,000	130	1	.63	175	2	.76	260	4	.91	345	6	1.0	465	9	1.1	620	13	1.2
5,001–7,000	130	1	.63	175	2	.76	265	4	.92	390	7	1.1	505	10	1.2	700	15	1.3
7,001–10,000	130	1	.64	175	2	.77	265	4	.93	390	7	1.1	550	11	1.2	775	17	1.4
10,001–20,000	130	1	.64	175	2	.78	305	5	1.0	430	8	1.2	630	13	1.3	900	20	1.5
20,001–50,000	130	1	.65	225	3	.86	350	6	1.1	520	10	1.2	750	16	1.4	1,090	25	1.6
50,001–100,000	130	1	.65	265	4	.96	390	7	1.1	590	12	1.3	830	18	1.5	1,215	28	1.6

n = size of sample; entry of "All" indicates that each piece in lot is to be inspected.
c = allowable defects for sample (acceptance number).
AOQL = average outgoing quality limit.

Fig. 35. A typical Dodge-Romig table for a single sampling plan.

Process Average %	0–0.20					0.21–2.00					2.01–4.00				
	Trial 1	Trial 2			P_t %	Trial 1	Trial 2			P_t %	Trial 1	Trial 2			P_t %
Lot Size	n_1 c_1	n_1+ n_2	n_2	c_2		n_1 c_1	n_1+ n_2	n_2	c_2		n_1 c_1	n_1+ n_2	n_2	c_2	
1–3	All 0	–	–	–	–	All 0	–	–	–	–	All 0	–	–	–.	–
4–15	3 0	–	–	–	50.0	3 0	–	–	–	50.0	3 0	–	–	–	50.0
16–50	5 0	3	8	1	53.5	5 0	3	8	1	53.5	5 0	3	8	1	53.5
51–100	5 0	3	8	1	55.0	6 0	8	14	2	43.0	6 0	8	14	2	43.0
101–200	5 0	4	9	1	52.0	7 0	7	14	2	42.0	7 0	12	19	3	38.0
201–300	7 0	7	14	2	42.5	7 0	7	14	2	42.5	7 0	13	20	3	37.0
301–400	7 0	7	14	2	42.5	7 0	7	14	2	42.5	8 0	17	25	4	35.0
401–500	7 0	8	15	2	40.0	7 0	8	15	2	40.0	8 0	18	26	4	34.0
501–600	7 0	8	15	2	40.0	8 0	13	21	3	35.0	8 0	18	26	4	34.0
601–800	7 0	8	15	2	40.5	8 0	13	21	3	35.0	8 0	18	26	4	34.5
801–1,000	7 0	8	15	2	40.5	8 0	13	21	3	35.0	9 0	18	27	4	33.0
1,001–2,000	7 0	8	15	2	40.5	8 0	14	22	3	34.0	9 0	23	32	5	31.0
2,001–3,000	7 0	8	15	2	41.0	8 0	14	22	3	34.0	9 0	24	33	5	30.0
3,001–4,000	7 0	8	15	2	41.0	8 0	14	22	3	34.5	9 0	24	33	5	30.5
4,001–5,000	7 0	8	15	2	41.0	8 0	14	22	3	35.0	10 0	29	39	6	29.5
5,001–7,000	7 0	8	15	2	41.0	9 0	18	27	4	32.5	16 1	29	45	7	28.5
7,001–10,000	7 0	8	15	2	41.0	9 0	18	27	4	32.5	17 1	38	55	8	26.0
10,001–20,000	7 0	8	15	2	41.0	9 0	18	27	4	32.5	17 1	38	55	8	26.0
20,001–50,000	7 0	8	15	2	41.0	9 0	18	27	4	32.5	18 1	42	60	9	25.5
50,001–100,000	8 0	14	22	3	33.5	9 0	25	34	5	30.0	18 1	52	70	10	24.5

n_1 = size of first sample.

n_2 = size of second sample. Entry of "All" indicates that each piece in lot is to be inspected. The second column under Trial 2 in each case equals $n_1 + n_2$.

Fig. 36. A typical Dodge-Romig

used. A table is consulted to find the sample-size code letter appropriate to this inspection level and to the lot size involved. This letter and the AQL are then used to extract the actual sampling plan from a master table. The military-standard **master table** for double-sampling plans is shown in Fig. 37. (The standard also includes master tables for single and multiple plans.) The procedures provide for reduced inspection if the supplier's quality performance proves to be good. They also provide for tightened inspection in the event that his performance becomes poor. Thus the process average is taken into account as experience is obtained.

SAMPLING TABLES FOR PROCESS CONTROL. The tables described in the previous two sections stress the element of acceptance. They are particularly valuable for checking the quality of incoming parts and materials. Where acceptance is the main issue, they may also be applied to inspection of materials in process and to final inspection. Where **control of the process** is the main issue, taking smaller samples more frequently is likely to be more effective, as indicated in the discussion of control charts. This gives an operator the chance to make a correction before a seriously large number of defective pieces have

4.01–6.00						6.01–8.00						8.01–10.00					
Trial 1		Trial 2			p_t %	Trial 1		Trial 2			p_t %	Trial 1		Trial 2			p_t %
n_1	c_1	n_2	n_1+n_2	c_2		n_1	c_1	n_2	n_1+n_2	c_2		n_1	c_1	n_2	n_1+n_2	c_2	
All	0	–	–	–	–	All	0	–	–	–	–	All	0	–	–	–	–
3	0	–	–	–	50.0	3	0	–	–	–	50.0	3	0	–	–	–	50.0
6	0	6	12	2	48.0	6	0	6	12	2	48.0	6	0	6	12	2	48.0
7	0	11	18	3	38.5	7	0	11	18	3	38.5	7	0	16	23	4	36.5
8	0	16	24	4	35.5	13	1	20	33	6	33.5	14	1	24	38	7	32.0
8	0	17	25	4	35.0	14	1	26	40	7	31.5	19	2	29	48	9	31.0
8	0	22	30	5	34.0	15	1	30	45	8	31.0	21	2	44	65	12	29.0
15	1	23	38	6	30.5	16	1	39	55	9	28.5	22	2	53	75	13	27.0
16	1	28	44	7	28.5	22	2	38	60	10	27.5	28	3	52	80	14	26.5
16	1	28	44	7	29.0	22	2	43	65	11	27.0	29	3	56	85	15	26.0
16	1	34	50	8	28.0	24	2	56	80	13	25.5	36	4	69	105	18	24.5
17	1	38	55	9	27.5	24	2	61	85	14	25.0	45	5	95	140	23	23.0
17	1	48	65	10	26.0	33	3	72	105	16	23.0	50	6	115	165	27	22.0
24	2	46	70	11	25.0	41	4	99	140	21	21.5	70	8	150	220	34	20.5
26	2	54	80	12	23.5	44	4	111	155	22	20.0	80	9	195	275	41	19.0
27	2	63	90	13	22.5	50	5	120	170	24	19.5	90	10	240	330	47	18.0
27	2	68	95	14	22.0	60	6	145	205	28	18.5	110	12	265	375	53	17.5
28	2	77	105	15	22.0	70	7	165	235	32	18.0	125	14	320	445	62	17.0
28	2	87	115	17	21.5	80	8	205	285	39	17.5	140	16	355	495	69	16.8
36	3	99	135	20	21.0	85	8	245	330	44	17.0	150	17	390	540	77	16.6

c_1 = allowable defects for first sample (acceptance number).
c_2 = allowable defects for first and second samples combined.
p_t = lot tolerance percent defective corresponding to a consumer's risk (pc) = 0.10.

table for a double sampling plan.

been made. There is some loss of good sampling-plan characteristics, but this is at least partly outweighed by the value of up-to-the-minute facts to the operator.

Plan for Use When Output Can Be Segregated. A. V. Feigenbaum (Quality Control) describes a simple plan for **systematic patrol inspection.** This plan is applicable when the production from a short period can be set aside to await a periodical visit from the floor inspector. Approval from the inspector is required before the production run may be started. After this is obtained the operator proceeds with production, making checks with his own inspection tools as necessary. The time between visits of the inspector is set by the plan and depends on the past stability of the process as well as the rate of production The uninspected product is held separate from inspected material until the inspector checks and releases it.

Fig. 38 shows such a sampling table for process control. Schedule A gives the time between checks of the inspector. Schedule B shows the sample size to be used for various approximate AQL values. One object of the plan is to make patrol inspection more certain and systematic. As part of the system a card is placed at each machine so that the inspector's visits and findings are made a matter of record.

Acceptable Quality Levels (normal inspection)

Sample size code letter	Sample	Sample size	Cumulative sample size	0.015 Ac	Re	0.035 Ac	Re	0.065 Ac	Re	0.10 Ac	Re	0.15 Ac	Re	0.25 Ac	Re	0.40 Ac	Re	0.65 Ac	Re	1.0 Ac	Re	1.5 Ac	Re	2.5 Ac	Re	4.0 Ac	Re	6.5 Ac	Re	10.0 Ac	Re
A	*	*	*	No double sampling plans for these sample size code letters. Use single sampling.																											
B																															
C																															
D	First	5	5																			⇒		*			⇐			1	3
D	Second	10	15																											2	3
E	First	7	7																			*		⇒		⇐				0	3	1	5
E	Second	14	21																											2	3	4	5
F	First	10	10																	*		⇒		⇐				0	3	1	4	2	6
F	Second	20	30																							2	3	3	4	5	6
G	First	15	15															*		⇒		⇐			0	3	1	4	1	5	3	7
G	Second	30	45																					2	3	3	4	4	5	6	7
H	First	25	25													*		⇒		⇐		0	3	1	3	2	5	3	7	5	11
H	Second	50	75																		2	3	3	4	4	5	6	7	10	11
I	First	35	35										*		⇒		⇐		0	3	1	4	1	5	2	6	3	12	6	15
I	Second	70	105															2	3	3	4	4	6	6	7	11	12	14	15
J	First	50	50								*		⇒		⇐		0	3	1	4	1	5	3	7	3	10	5	15	8	21
J	Second	100	150													2	3	3	4	4	5	6	7	9	10	14	15	20	21

⇐ = Use first sampling plan above arrow.
⇒ = Use first sampling plan below arrow.
* = Use corresponding single sampling plan (or alternatively use double sampling plan below, where available).
Ac = Acceptance number. Re = Rejection number.

Table for a double sampling plan.

Fig. 37. Military-standard table for double sampling.

*(Double sampling plan — tightened inspection. Arrows: ⇩ = use first sampling plan below arrow; ⇦/⇨ = use first plan to left/right; * = use corresponding single sampling plan. Each cell gives the First and Second (cumulative) Ac Re values.)*

Code	Sample	Sample size	Cumulative sample size	0.035	0.065	0.10	0.15	0.25	0.40	0.65	1.0	1.5	2.5	4.0	6.5	10.0
K	First	75	75	⇩	⇩	*	⇦	⇦	⇨	0 2	0 3	2 8	4 9	5 12	7 20	12 29
	Second	150	225	⇩	⇩	*	⇦	⇦	⇨	0 3	1 2	2 7	4 8	5 11	7 19	12 28
L	First	100	100	⇩	*	⇦	⇨	0 3	1 3	1 6	2 6	3 8	5 12	7 17	10 31	14 49
	Second	200	300	⇩	*	⇦	⇨	0 2	1 2	1 5	2 5	3 7	5 11	7 16	10 30	14 48
M	First	150	150	*	⇦	⇨	0 3	1 3	2 5	2 7	3 8	5 14	7 19	11 29	15 47	21 65
	Second	300	450	*	⇦	⇨	0 2	1 2	2 4	2 6	3 7	5 13	7 18	11 28	15 46	21 64
N	First	200	200	⇩	⇨	0 3	1 3	1 6	2 7	3 8	4 10	6 17	9 25	12 36	18 67	27 89
	Second	400	600	⇩	⇨	0 2	1 2	1 5	2 6	3 7	4 9	6 16	9 24	12 35	18 66	27 88
O	First	300	300	⇨	0 3	1 4	1 6	2 7	3 9	4 11	6 17	8 26	12 36	18 55	26 88	38 123
	Second	600	900	⇨	0 2	1 3	1 5	2 6	3 8	4 10	6 16	8 25	12 35	18 54	26 87	38 122
P	First	500	500	0 3	1 4	1 6	2 9	3 10	5 13	6 22	9 25	12 37	18 65	27 89	43 131	62 191
	Second	1000	1500	0 2	1 3	1 5	2 8	3 9	5 12	6 21	9 24	12 36	18 64	27 88	43 130	62 190
Q	First	1000	1000	1 4	1 6	2 9	4 13	5 17	7 26	11 33	15 47	22 65	34 113	50 160	79 243	119 348
	Second	2000	3000	1 3	1 5	2 8	4 12	5 16	7 25	11 32	15 46	22 64	34 112	50 159	79 242	119 347

Acceptable Quality Levels (tightened inspection)

PROCESS CONTROL SAMPLING PLAN

SCHEDULE A: HOW OFTEN TO SAMPLE–NUMBER OF HOURS BETWEEN CHECKS

Hourly Production	Process Condition		
	Erratic	Stable	Controlled
Under 10	8 hr.	8 hr.	8 hr.
10–19	4 hr.	8 hr.	8 hr.
20–49	2 hr.	4 hr.	8 hr.
50–99	1 hr.	2 hr.	4 hr.
100 and over	½ hr.	1 hr.	2 hr.

Erratic: a process that is intermittently good and bad or that changes from good to bad with little advance notice.

Stable: a process that gives fairly uniform performance but has gradual change or drift in one direction due to tool wear or other factors.

Controlled: a process showing past and present evidence of being under control.

SCHEDULE B: SAMPLE SIZES FOR GO-NO-GO INSPECTION

Determine acceptable quality level (AQL) as a percent defective; sample regularly according to schedule A; use sample sizes below.

Acceptable Quality Level (AQL)	Sample Size
Under 1.0%	20
1.0 – 1.9%	10
2.0 – 4.9%	5
5.0 or more	2

Job is in control when *no* defects are found in sample; when out of control, correct process or start 100% inspection.

Fig. 38. A plan for patrol inspection.

Plans for Use in Continuous Production. H. F. Dodge (Industrial Quality Control, vol. 7) has formulated several plans for use where articles are manufactured continuously, as on a conveyor. Fig. 39 outlines the operation of one of the simpler plans of this type.

ACCEPTANCE BY VARIABLES INSPECTION. The sampling tables so far described are all based on sampling by attributes (presence or absence of a desired characteristic). Great progress has also been made in recent years with acceptance sampling systems based on measurements. In general, such plans extract more information from inspection or test of a given number of pieces of product. This means that the same protection for the buyer can be obtained

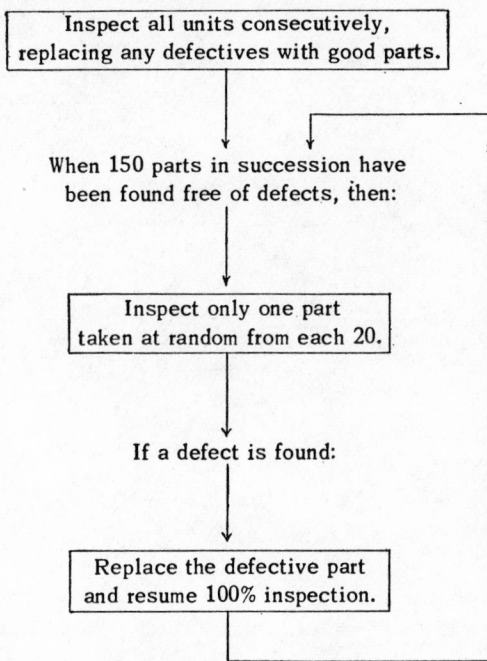

Fig. 39. Operation of a typical Dodge CSP-1 plan for continuous sampling (AOQL = 1 percent).

with smaller samples. This possibility is particularly attractive when the property to be tested is one which requires a costly inspection process. Examples are life tests of electron tubes, chemical or metallurgical analyses, tensile or other tests of physical properties, velocity tests for ammunition, and blowing-time tests for fuses.

The design or application of **variables sampling plans** is preferably undertaken only by a person well versed in statistical methods. Analysis of the data is rather more complicated with variables sampling than with attributes sampling (see section on Statistical Methods).

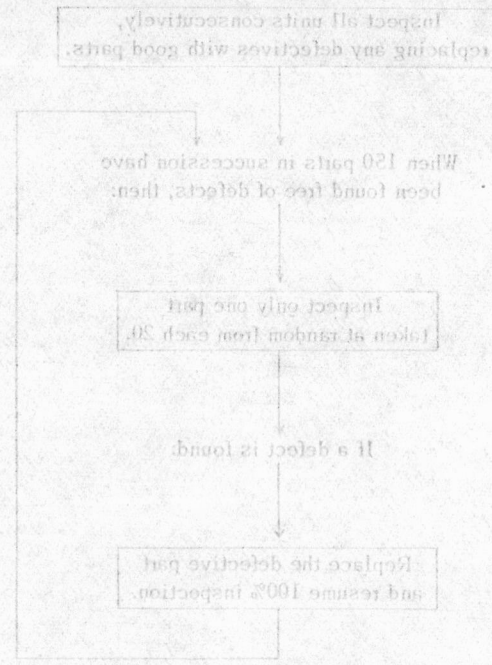

Fig. 39. Operation of a typical Dodge CSP-1 plan for continuous sampling (AOQL = 1 percent).

with smaller samples. This possibility is particularly attractive when the property to be tested is one which requires a costly inspection process. Examples are life tests of electron tubes, chemical or metallurgical analyses, tensile or other tests of physical properties, velocity tests for ammunition, and blowing-time tests for fuses.

The design or application of variables sampling plans is preferably undertaken only by a person well versed in statistical methods. Analysis of the data is rather more complicated with variables sampling than with attributes sampling (see section on Statistical Methods).

STATISTICAL METHODS

CONTENTS

PAGE

Application of Statistics

Statistics in industry 1
Types of industrial data 1
Variation in data 2
Systematic accumulation of data 3

Frequency Distributions

The normal distribution 3
  Normal frequency distribution of incentive earnings (f. 1) 5
  Tests for normality 4
  Cumulative frequency distribution of incentive earnings plotted on normal-probability paper (f. 2) 7
The binomial distribution 6
  Machine down-time computed by use of the binomial distribution (f. 3)........ 8
The Poisson distribution 6
  Frequency distribution of lost-time accidents per month based on the Poisson distribution (f. 4) 9
Measures of central value 8
  The arithmetic mean 9
  Graphical method for computing the mean. 10
  The median 11
  The mode 11
Measures of dispersion 11
  The range 11
  The mean deviation 11
  The standard deviation 12
  Graphical method for determining the standard deviation 14
Other frequency distributions 14
  Special types of frequency distributions (f. 5) 15
  Bimodal 14
  Screened 14
  Rectangular 14
  Skewed 16

Sampling

Need for sampling 16
Drawing a random sample 16
  Ways to avoid sampling bias 17
Estimating central tendency and dispersion by sampling 17
Sampling distributions 18
  Sampling distribution of $\overline{X}$ (f. 6)....... 19
Confidence limits 19
  Tolerance limits for the items in a population 19
  Test for the rejection of extreme values.. 20

PAGE

Confidence limits for the population mean. 22
Determining limits for the mean when the population standard deviation is not known 22
Determining confidence limits for the mean when the population standard deviation is known 22
Determining confidence limits for the mean through use of the range 23
Determining confidence limits for the population standard deviation 23
Determining confidence limits for the population proportion 24
Determining sample size 24
  Nomograph for determining number of observations 26
  Nomograph to estimate the number of observations necessary to result in a satisfactorily precise average value, (f. 7) 25

Tests for Significant Differences

Making sampling accurate 26
Statistical inference 27
  Example of t-test 27
Risks of a wrong conclusion 28
Tests for differences between averages....... 29
  Test for significance of a difference between a sample mean and a population mean 29
  Sample and population means compared... 29
  Effect of new tool tested 30
  Test for difference between a sample mean and a population mean when the population standard deviation is known 31
  Example from battery industry 31
  Test for significance of a difference between a sample mean and a population mean based on the use of the range..... 31
  Test of effect of new tool on output...... 32
  Test for significance of difference between two sample means 32
  Comparison of average times of assembly methods 33
  Comparison of average weights of containers 34
  Test for the significance of difference between two sample means when the standard deviation is known 35
  Example of crew differences in shrinkage.. 35
  Test for difference between two samples based on the use of the range 36
  Test of machine attachment 36

CONTENTS (*Continued*)

PAGE

Tests for differences between proportions.... 37
  Test for differences between two sample
    proportions 37
  Departmental turnover differences tested.. 37
  Test for difference between a sample pro-
    portion and a population proportion.... 38
  Change in clerical procedures checked 38
Test for an extreme mean 39
  Extreme work element time retained 40

Probability

Laws of probability 40
  The multiplication law 41
  Conditional probability 41
  The addition law 41
Direct solution of probability problems..... 42
  Probability of availability of one of two
    processes 42
  Processes and machine probabilities (*f.*
    8) 42
  Assignment of machines by probability ... 43
Use of the binomial formula 44
Use of the Poisson distribution 45
  Poisson distribution table 45
  Lost-time accidents per month (*f.* 9).... 46
Probability solutions for the normal dis-
  tribution 46
  Percentage of operators with piecework
    earnings under $40.00 (*f.* 10).......... 47
Limits for a frequency distribution.......... 47

The Analysis of Variance

Terminology 48
Test for difference in variances 48
  Steps in the *F*-test 49
  Application of the *F*-test 49
Test for difference among means........... 50
  Test procedures 50
Differences between averages—an application 52
  Computations from coded weekly earn-
    ings of crews (*f.* 11) 53
Factorial studies 54
  Factorial design procedure 55

PAGE

The analysis of variance in factorial studies. 56
  Steps in the procedure 56
  A factorial design study with analysis of
    variance 58

Regression and Correlation

Relationships between variables 60
Graphic methods 60
  Line fitted by eye showing the relation-
    ship between hole operations and labor
    hours (*f.* 12) 62
The method of least squares 61
  Regression analysis 61
  Curvilinear relationships 63
  Computation of linear regression.......... 63
  Line of regression computed by the
    method of least squares (*f.* 13)....... 65
Confidence limits 64
  Formulas for determining limits 64
  Computation of a confidence limit........ 66
  Other confidence limit formulas 66
The correlation coefficient 67
The analysis of variance 68
  F-test procedure and formulas 69
Test for dependence 70

Statistical Tables

Purpose 70
Table of *z*—normal distribution areas (*table*
  1a) 71
Table of *z*—normal distribution areas (*table*
  1b) 71
Table of *t* (*table* 2) 72
Table of t_R (*table* 3) 73
Table of t_{ER} (*table* 4) 73
Table of *K*—tolerance factors for normal
  distributions (*table* 5) 74
Table of *F* (probability = .10) (*table* 6a)... 75
Table of *F* (probability = .05) (*table* 6b)... 76
Table of *F* (probability = .01) (*table* 6c) .. 77
Table of *γ*—criteria for testing for extreme
  value or mean (*table* 7)................. 78
Cumulative terms of the Poisson distribution
  (*table* 8) 79–82

STATISTICAL METHODS

Application of Statistics

STATISTICS IN INDUSTRY. The term "statistics" is used as a general name for a large group of mathematical tools based on the laws of probability which are used to collect, analyze, and interpret numerical data. These tools have for many years been indispensable in the various fields of the physical and social sciences. In recent years they have been applied in some areas of engineering and management. In one of these areas—quality control—they have been adapted and applied with outstanding success. In other areas their application is increasing and will continue to increase as their usefulness to the engineer and administrator becomes more generally known.

The statistical method has been simply described as common sense reduced to calculation. However, the techniques are not intended to be substitutes for method, reasoning, judgment, common sense, or experience but rather to serve as supplemental tools. More specifically, the **application of statistical techniques** can help in the following ways:

1. In summarizing a mass of data or observations into a concise and understandable summary which will be most useful for the problem at hand.
2. In determining limits of precision for conclusions reached from the analysis of sample data; in other words, ascertaining the degree of confidence one may have in information obtained by sampling.
3. In determining the number of observations that must be made or the amount of information that must be gathered and summarized to give conclusions of the required degree of accuracy.
4. In extracting the maximum amount of useful information from available data and observations. Generally, the use of statistical methods considerably reduces the amount of data that must be collected and analyzed to reach conclusions with a required degree of confidence.
5. In appraising in specific terms the uncertainties or variability that is inherent in most procedures, processes, materials, activities, and situations.
6. In planning studies, planning for the collection of data, and in reaching conclusions in such a way as to avoid the effects of known sources of bias and to minimize the possible effects of unknown sources of bias.
7. In giving a more complete and meaningful interpretation of experimental results.
8. In computing the probability of some specified event happening. A more precise appraisal of the uncertainty in a situation may be made than that given by hunch or guess.
9. In giving evidence of relationships between factors in a process or system that might be unnoticed if a statistical approach were not used.
10. In placing emphasis on planning for a study and for the collection of data so that only necessary information will be gathered and so that there will be a suitable balance between the different kinds collected.

TYPES OF INDUSTRIAL DATA. Many kinds of data are used in industry. From the standpoint of statistical procedures, however, there are two useful

9·1

ways in which data may be classified. First, they may be classified either as sample data or as population data. When all the individuals or items involved are measured or observed, the observations are **population data.** Such is the case, for example, when production figures for each operator in a plant are compiled every day. When population data are compiled, statistical methods may be of help in summarizing them in a useful way.

In many areas of industrial engineering and management, studies and procedures for control must be based on observations from a sample of items taken from the population. Time standards, for example, must be determined from time studies of a sample of work cycles for the activity. The number or percentage of errors in the clerical work of a mail-order house may have to be estimated from data collected from selected samples of work. When **sample data** are all that are available or that can be justified, statistical procedures may be of much help in drawing conclusions and in making decisions. (See section on Work Measurement and Time Study.)

Data may be classified in another way. They may be classified as **data in variables form** or as **data in attribute form.** When each item is measured by some scale and the measurement itself observed and used, the data are in variables form. Examples of this are time measurements in decimal minutes obtained by a time study, and the weight in ounces of packages leaving a filling machine.

Data are in attribute form when each item has been checked or measured and simply classified as falling in one of two or more possible categories. Checking clerical entries and classifying each as right or wrong, or observing a group of machines and noting whether each machine is or is not running, will give attribute data.

In some cases one may choose between taking data in variables form or taking them in the form of attributes. An item may be measured, for example, and the measurement used only to classify the item as good or bad or as above or below standard. When there is a choice, the most satisfactory form to use will depend on the kind of information desired and on the respective costs of obtaining, compiling, and using the data for each of the two forms. Generally, it is more costly to obtain variables data than attribute data, and more work is required for compilation and summary. On the other hand, variables data give more complete information about the items or activities in most cases than an equivalent amount of attribute data.

VARIATION IN DATA. Data taken from any product, procedure, system, or activity will almost certainly show some variation from observation to observation, even when an attempt is made to hold all significant factors constant. The reason for this is that it is impractical, too costly, or even impossible to hold all factors strictly constant. Many minor causes of variation are inherent in any system or procedure. Variation due to these inherent causes is frequently referred to as **chance variation.** However, the variation is not due to chance but due to a system of causes that by choice have been ignored—ignored because they are relatively unimportant or because their nature cannot easily be ascertained. Also, the method of measurement for obtaining observations may vary somewhat in its preciseness from measurement to measurement. This, too, will add to the variation in data.

For example, time measurements for a work element—say, for getting a part from a tote box and putting it in a jig—will vary from cycle to cycle, even for the same job and the same operator. Among the inherent causes of such variation may be: (1) variations in distance of reach because parts occupy different positions within the tote box; (2) different amounts of fumbling from cycle to cycle prior to the time the hand selects and grasps a part; (3) different amounts of time spent in positioning the part prior to insertion in the jig, the amount depending on the position of the part in the tote box; (4) differing degrees of operator effort from cycle to cycle; and (5) variations in reading the watch hand from cycle to cycle. Many other inherent causes of variation for this simple activity could be mentioned.

In addition to the effect of these inherent causes in the product or activity and in the method of measurement, observed variation may also be due to a **change in level** of some important factor. Generally, the purpose of a study is to determine what effect, if any, may be attributed to such a change. In the case of the time requirement for picking up a part and putting it in a jig, for example, a study may be made to determine the effect of a new jig design or of a change to a piece part of a different size or shape.

If the change in level for a factor has an appreciable effect on the activity or product, this may be readily determined by a **comparison of observations** made before the change with observations made after the change. The same remarks also apply, of course, to cases in which the study is not of changes to a factor but of the effects of different levels that already exist for a factor.

If the inherent causes of variation themselves cause an appreciable variation from observation to observation, the effects of a difference in level for some one factor may be difficult to determine. Any effect that a difference in level would have on the observations may be obscured by the variation in data produced by the inherent causes. The effect will be particularly difficult to evaluate if the number of observations available for one or more of the levels is small or if the effect of the change in levels on the observations is small compared to the effects of the inherent system of variation-producing causes.

One of the principal objectives of statistical procedures is to deal with this **variation from inherent causes**—to evaluate the effect it may have in drawing conclusions from study data and to use this evaluation in determining the risk of error in reaching conclusions.

SYSTEMATIC ACCUMULATION OF DATA. Often little thought is given to the mechanics of accumulating data. This is usually a natural result of the engineer being under pressure to get the necessary figures quickly or of his being concerned only about the use of the data and the end results. It is of some importance, however, to plan for the collection of data and to have a systematic procedure for its accumulation. Among the many benefits may be the following:

1. A saving in time for the person making and recording the observations.
2. A reduction in the probability of error in recording data, in working it up, or in using it.
3. The possibility, if the system of accumulation is good, of making some analysis of the recorded data during the course of the study. This analysis may be helpful in deciding how many more observations will be needed, in determining what other kinds of data may be required, or in other ways.
4. A saving in time in summarizing the data, in posting them to other records, or in using them in other ways.

Frequency Distributions

THE NORMAL DISTRIBUTION. Production management decisions are frequently based on knowing the nature of the variation existing in the products, processes, or events which are to be controlled or managed. This section illustrates methods of describing, measuring, and interpreting patterns of variation. Description of a pattern of variation can generally be accomplished, either graphically or in terms of an equation, by showing what proportion of values were, or are likely to be, of each magnitude. Such a description is called a frequency distribution because it shows the frequency with which values are distributed along their range.

The most frequently encountered frequency distribution is the so-called "normal" distribution. This distribution, when plotted and connected with a line, gives the familiar **bell-shaped curve**. The most frequently occurring measurements are those close to the average; measurements lying at a greater distance from the average occur less frequently. This distribution is usually the result of **item variation** produced by some system of many chance-acting causes. The distribution is found widely in all the fields of physical and social science as well as in fields of industrial engineering and management. Many of the most commonly used statistical methods are for normal distributions and so depend for fully effective use on the distribution for the measurements under study approximating the normal.

The normal distribution is illustrated by the following figures for weekly incentive earnings for a group of piece-workers in a shop, all working at the same piece rate.

Incentive Earnings	No. of Employees
$34–36	1
32–34	4
30–32	5
28–30	8
26–28	21
24–26	32
22–24	34
20–22	38
18–20	35
16–18	26
14–16	18
12–14	7
10–12	5
8–10	2
6–8	1
4–6	1
Total	238

These data have been plotted to scale in Fig. 1. A dashed line has been drawn to show the **theoretical normal curve** that the actual frequency distribution approximates.

Tests for Normality. Most statistical procedures depend on some assumption regarding the form of the frequency distribution for the characteristic under study. A majority of the procedures depend on the distribution being normal or, for practical application, depend on its approximating a normal distribution. When a procedure based on this form of distribution is to be used, it may be necessary in some cases to check for normality.

Generally, the procedure is to rely simply on one's experience with the activity or product or with similar cases to indicate the form the distribution will be likely to take. In many areas of study, common practice is to assume the distribution is normal unless there are known reasons why it should differ or indications that it may have some other form.

If there is some doubt about the form, the most simple and most generally useful test is to summarize the observations or a fairly large sample of the observations (preferably a hundred or more, if available) in the form of a **frequency distribution** as in Fig. 1. It can then be observed whether the frequencies found for each measurement (or range of measurements) correspond approximately to frequencies that would be obtained from a normal distribution.

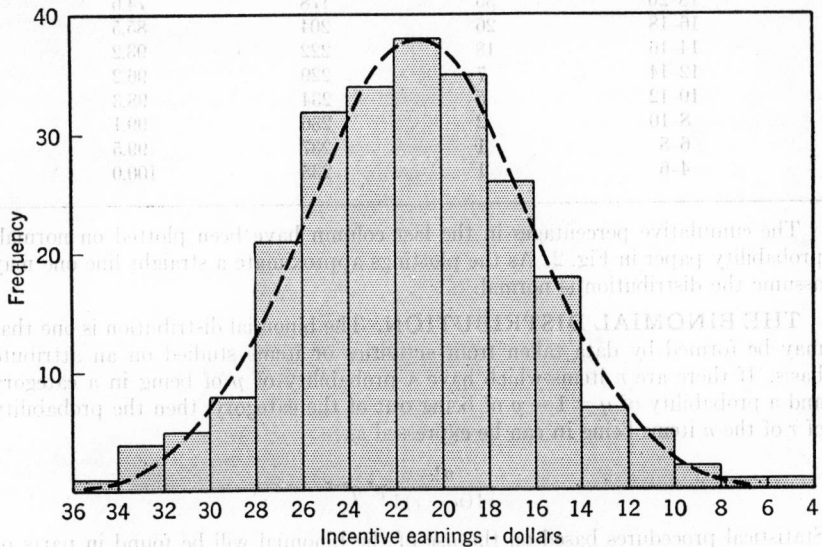

Fig. 1. Normal frequency distribution of incentive earnings.

If there is still some doubt, the frequencies may be **plotted graphically** and connected with a free-hand curve, fitted approximately by eye. The shape of the curve may then be observed to see whether or not it exhibits the typical bell-shaped normal form. In special cases where a more precise test seems necessary, a more involved **statistical procedure** for comparing observed frequencies with frequencies that could be expected if the distribution were normal will be found in any standard textbook on statistics. Also, measures exist for **skewness**—for distributions that are not symmetrical—and for **kurtosis**—for distributions for which the peak is sharper than normal or flatter than normal.

Another method of testing for normality is to plot the cumulative distribution of the sample or population on **normal-probability graph paper.** The vertical scale on this paper is so spaced that if the distribution plotted is normal it will plot as a straight line. The plot may also be used to determine the average, to measure dispersion, and to determine the proportion of cases beyond any specified limit. These uses are discussed in portions of this section that follow. The accompanying data illustrate the computation of the cumulative frequency distribution for the incentive earnings example.

Incentive Earning	Frequency	Cumulative Frequency	Cumulative Percentage
$34–36	1	1	0.4%
32–34	4	5	2.1
30–32	5	10	4.2
28–30	8	18	7.6
26–28	21	39	16.4
24–26	32	71	29.8
22–24	34	105	43.7
20–22	38	143	60.0
18–20	35	178	74.6
16–18	26	204	85.5
14–16	18	222	93.2
12–14	7	229	96.2
10–12	5	234	98.3
8–10	2	236	99.1
6–8	1	237	99.5
4–6	1	238	100.0

The cumulative percentages in the last column have been plotted on normal-probability paper in Fig. 2. As the plottings approximate a straight line one may assume the distribution is normal.

THE BINOMIAL DISTRIBUTION. The binomial distribution is one that may be formed by data taken from activities or items studied on an attribute basis. If there are n items which have a probability of p of being **in** a category and a probability of $q = 1 - p$ of being **out** of the category, then the probability of r of the n items being **in** can be expressed as

$$\frac{n!}{r!(n-r)!} p^r q^{n-r}$$

Statistical procedures based on the use of the binomial will be found in parts of this section that follow and in the section on Operations Research.

In observation of machine down-time for a group of five like machines, for example, it was observed that for about one-third of the time all of the machines would be running, for a little more than one-third of the time one machine would be down, for about one-fifth of the time two machines would be down, and only rarely would more than two be down requiring attention. However, a more precise analysis of machine down-time was required.

Time studies were available which showed that each machine ran without attention on an average of 80 percent of the time and required attention at irregular intervals for 20 percent of the time. By letting $p = .20$, $q = .80$, and $n = 5$, the above formula gives the proportions of times during which $r = 1$, 2, 3, or 4; that is, the probability that 0, 1, 2, etc., machines will be down simultaneously. Fig. 3 shows the computations for the frequency distribution.

THE POISSON DISTRIBUTION. The Poisson distribution is a distribution that applies for situations in which there are a great many opportunities for a specified event or category to occur but in which for only a relatively few of the opportunities does it actually occur. If n represents the number of items in a sample or segment of a population and p represents the probability of an item falling in a certain category, the Poisson distribution then applies when n is

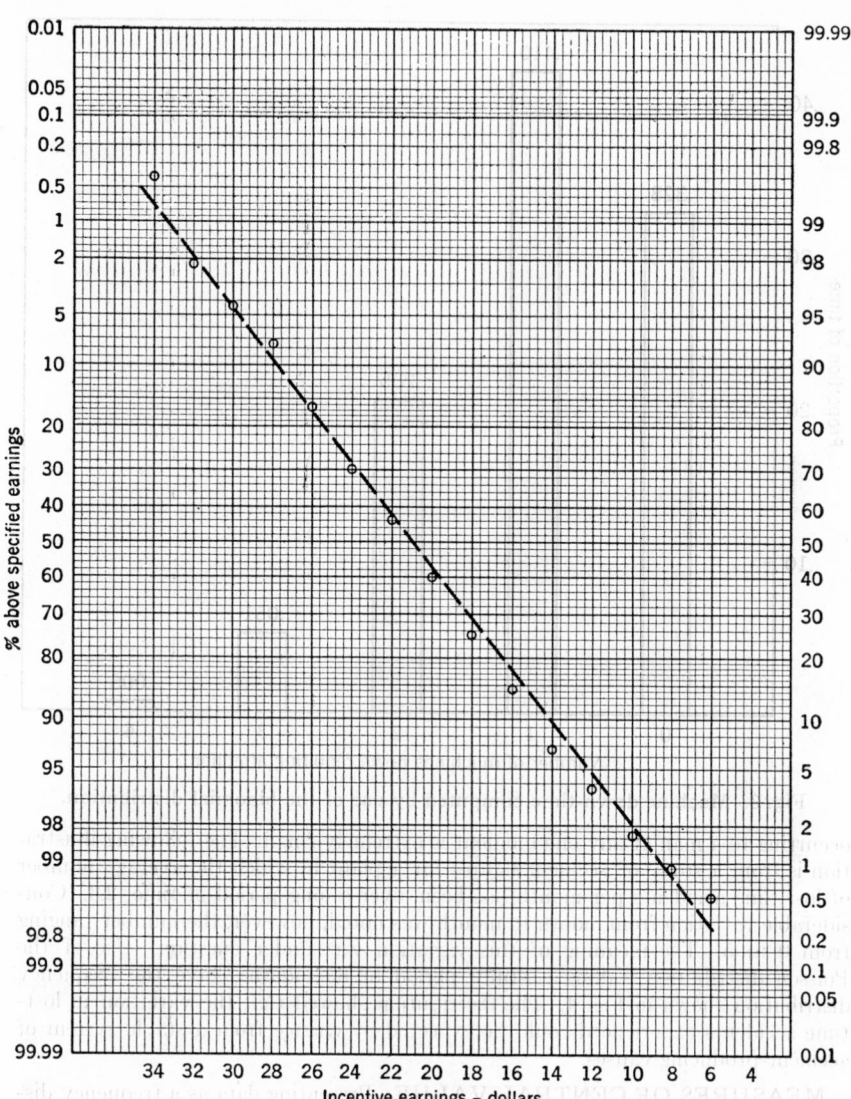

Fig. 2. Cumulative frequency distribution of incentive earnings plotted on normal-probability paper.

very large and p very small. The Poisson is not only a useful distribution in its own right but is useful as an approximation to the binomial distribution. With a table of the probabilities for the Poisson distribution, the computations for problems and probabilities based on the use of attribute data are very simple. The method of solution is discussed later in this section.

The Poisson distribution may be applied to the study of lost-time accidents in industry. For every workman in a plant there are countless moments throughout every day in which a lost-time accident could occur. The probability of one

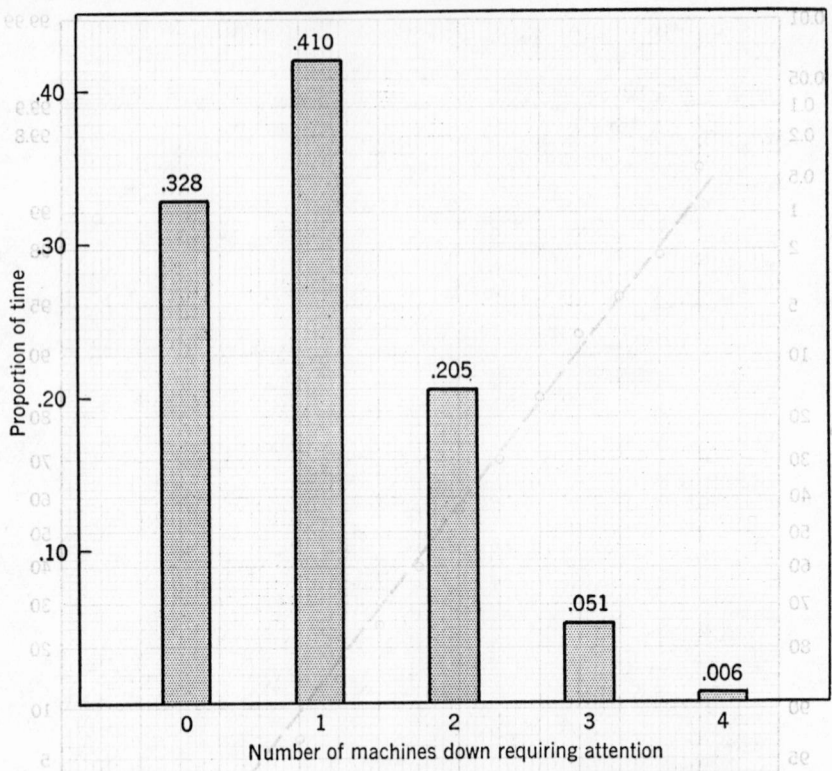

Fig. 3. Machine down-time computed by use of the binomial distribution.

occurring to a man at any one moment is extremely small. The following illustration is from a study of accident figures for a plant in which the average number of lost-time accidents per month has been, over a long period of time, 2.3. Considerable variation from month to month was noted, however, the number ranging from 0 to 5. The meaning of this variation was under question. Use of the Poisson distribution, taking a study period of 60 months, gave the frequency distribution shown in Fig. 4. The distribution showed that the variation in lost-time accidents experienced could be expected by chance from a stable system of accident-producing causes.

MEASURES OF CENTRAL VALUE. Presenting data as a frequency distribution will be most useful in some cases. Generally, however, the data may be more usefully presented or summarized by one or both of two measures: (1) the "average" of the measurements—some measure of central value or central tendency—and (2) some measure of the dispersion of measurements about their average.

The use of an average to indicate central tendency makes it possible to:

1. Use one figure to give a useful, meaningful, and concise summary of a body of data.
2. Readily compare one distribution or population with another.
3. Readily use sample observations to obtain data or make inferences about a population.

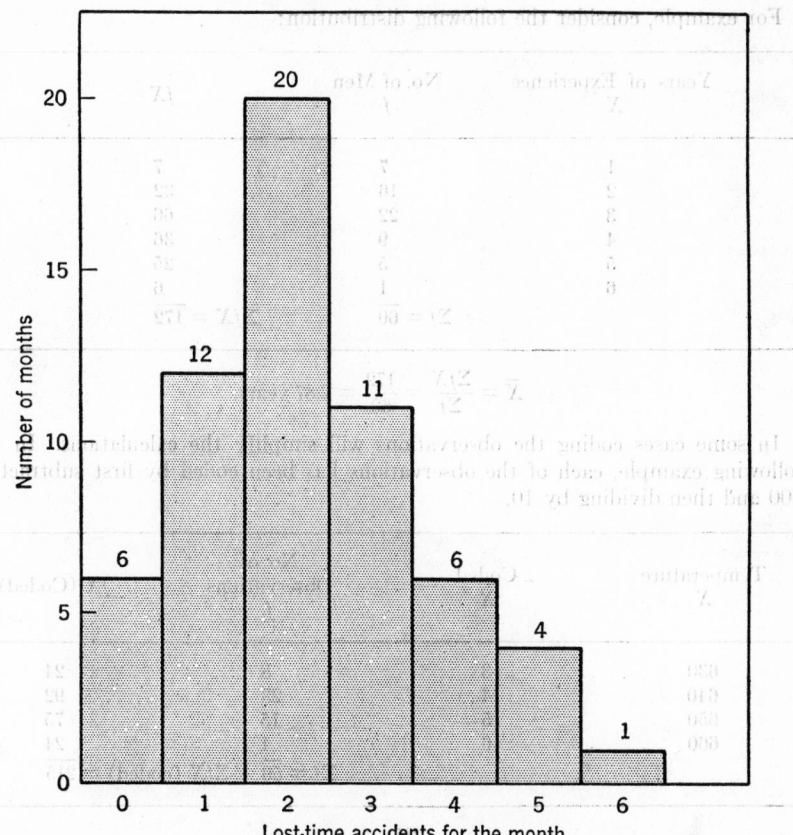

Fig. 4. Frequency distribution of lost-time accidents per month based on the Poisson distribution.

The Arithmetic Mean. The most generally useful measure of central tendency is the arithmetic mean. The arithmetic mean, symbolized by $\overline{X}$, is obtained by taking the sum of the observations and dividing by the number of observations used. In equation form,

$$\overline{X} = \frac{\Sigma X}{n}$$

For example, suppose the arithmetic mean of the following observations of parts per package is required: 15, 19, 16, 15, 18, 14, 15, 18.

$$\overline{X} = \frac{15 + 19 + 16 + 15 + 18 + 14 + 15 + 18}{8} = \frac{130}{8} = 16\frac{1}{4}$$

If the observations have been arranged as a frequency distribution, the computation may be more readily made by the following equation:

$$\overline{X} = \frac{\Sigma f X}{\Sigma f}$$

For example, consider the following distribution:

Years of Experience X	No. of Men f	fX
1	7	7
2	16	32
3	22	66
4	9	36
5	5	25
6	1	6
	$\Sigma f = 60$	$\Sigma fX = 172$

$$\bar{X} = \frac{\Sigma fX}{\Sigma f} = \frac{172}{60} = 2.87 \text{ years.}$$

In some cases coding the observations will simplify the calculations. In the following example, each of the observations has been coded by first subtracting 600 and then dividing by 10.

Temperature X	Coded X	No. of Observations f	fX (Coded)
630	3	8	24
640	4	23	92
650	5	15	75
660	6	4	24
		$\Sigma f = 50$	ΣfX (coded) $= 215$

$$\bar{X} \text{ (coded)} = \frac{215}{50} = 4.3$$

$$\bar{X} \text{ (decoded)} = (4.3 \times 10) + 600 = 643$$

The **advantages** of the arithmetic mean as a measure of central tendency are:
1. It is relatively simple to compute.
2. It is generally the most efficient of all possible measures when using sample data to obtain an estimate of the central tendency of a population.
3. The method of computation is easily understood and seems reasonable.
4. It is the measure most persons assume has been computed when the term "average" is used. Hence when it is used there is relatively little chance of misunderstanding.
5. It is the measure of central tendency required in most statistical tests.

Graphical Method for Computing the Mean. If the data have been compiled as a cumulative frequency distribution and plotted on normal-probability paper, a close estimate of the arithmetic mean may be very simply determined. The method is to simply read the value at the bottom of the graph at which the fitted line crosses the 50 percent point on the scale at the side. This value is an **estimate of the mean.** For the incentive-earnings illustration previously plotted in Fig. 2, the mean is read as $21. This method depends on the distribution being normal.

The Median. The median is the middle value in a group of observations that have been arranged in order of magnitude. If there is an even number of observations, the mean of the two middle values may be taken as the median.

For example, suppose the base wage rate for a certain operation has been ascertained for nine different plants and that they are as follows (in ascending order of magnitude): $1.08, $1.10, $1.20, $1.22, $1.25, $1.25, $1.30, $1.30, and $1.35. The median rate is the fifth observation, $1.25.

When a more precise measure is not necessary, the median may be a useful measure, particularly under the following circumstances:

1. When extreme values must not be given undue weight.
2. When the exact magnitude of extreme items is not known. For such items it is necessary to know only whether they lie above or below the median.
3. When ease of computation is important.
4. When the number of observations is small.

The Mode. The mode for a group of observations is the observation that occurs most frequently. For the observations of parts per package—15, 19, 16, 15, 18, 14, 15, 18—the mode is 15.

The mode is a useful measure of central tendency in many cases, particularly if the number of observations is relatively large. In time study, for example, the modal value for the time observations recorded for a work element serves as a useful measure of the time typically required for performing the element. The general **advantages** of the mode as a measure of central tendency are:

1. It is very easy to determine, particularly if the data have been put in the form of a frequency distribution.
2. Extreme values among the observations do not have undue influence.
3. The exact magnitude of extreme values does not have to be known.
4. It is the most typical value. In many situations this may be the most meaningful measure of central tendency.

MEASURES OF DISPERSION. In many cases the average must be supplemented by some measure of dispersion to summarize or describe a body of data adequately. Also, most statistical tests depend on the use of some measure of sample dispersion. The most commonly used measures are briefly described in the following divisions of this section.

The Range. A useful measure of dispersion when the number of observations is small is the range. The range, symbolized by R, is simply the difference between the largest and the smallest observation in the group. For example, suppose the following measurements have been obtained: 16.4, 14.7, 17.5, 13.2, 14.5, 16.2, 18.3, 15.8, 14.1, 15.4. Then

$$R = 18.3 - 13.2 = 5.1$$

The range is very easy to compute and is easily understood. However, as only the two extreme values of a group are used in its computation, it is an inefficient measure, particularly when the number of observations available is large. For this reason its use, particularly when working from sample data to estimate the dispersion of a population, should be registered to applications where the sample size is small.

The Mean Deviation. Another measure of dispersion that is relatively easy to compute is the mean deviation. The mean deviation is the arithmetic mean of the absolute deviation of each observation in the group from the group mean. In terms of an equation,

$$\text{M. D.} = \frac{\Sigma\,|\,X - \bar{X}\,|}{n}$$

For an example, consider the following performance ratings made by a group of eight time-study men during a rating test:

Man	Rating X	$\bar{X}$	$|\,X - \bar{X}\,|$
A	115	111.5	3.5
B	112	111.5	.5
C	120	111.5	8.5
D	107	111.5	4.5
E	110	111.5	1.5
F	110	111.5	1.5
G	100	111.5	11.5
H	118	111.5	6.5
	$\Sigma X = 892$		$\Sigma\,|\,X - \bar{X}\,| = 38.0$

$$\bar{X} = \frac{892}{8} = 111.5$$

$$\text{M. D.} = \frac{38.0}{8} = 4.75$$

The mean deviation is useful as a simple way of describing the dispersion of a group of observations. However, it is not a generally useful measure for statistical procedures. The standard deviation (or the range, in some cases) must be used.

The Standard Deviation. The most generally useful, and therefore the most commonly used, measure of variability is the standard deviation. The standard deviation of a population is the square root of the average of the squared deviations of each value from their average. The symbol used by the statistician for this measure is the lower case Greek letter sigma. The equation is

$$\sigma = \sqrt{\frac{\Sigma\,(X - \bar{X})^2}{n}}$$

The standard deviation of a sample of observations tends to be slightly less than that for the population from which it is drawn. If the **sample** standard deviation is computed to serve as an estimate of the **population** standard deviation, this bias may be automatically corrected by dividing the sum of the squared deviations by $n - 1$ instead of by n. Since this is almost always the purpose for computing the sample standard deviation and since almost all data are sample data, the following is the equation for general use:

$$s = \sqrt{\frac{\Sigma\,(X - \bar{X})^2}{n - 1}}$$

The letter s is used instead of the Greek letter σ to indicate clearly that the measure is obtained from sample data. Note that the statistician's notation differs from the notation in the field of statistical quality control where σ is the symbol used for the sample standard deviation and σ' the symbol used for the standard deviation of the population.

For the sample of performance ratings used to illustrate the computation of the mean deviation, the computation of the standard deviation, s, is as follows:

X	$X - \overline{X}$	$(X - \overline{X})^2$
115	3.5	12.25
112	.5	.25
120	8.5	72.25
107	− 4.5	20.25
110	− 1.5	2.25
110	− 1.5	2.25
100	−11.5	132.25
118	6.5	42.25
		$\Sigma (X - \overline{X})^2 = 284.00 \quad n - 1 = 8 - 1 = 7$

$$ s = \sqrt{\frac{284}{7}} = \sqrt{40.6} = 6.4 $$

A **short-cut method** for more easily computing the standard deviation, particularly when a computing machine or a table of squares is available, is given by the following equation:

$$ s = \sqrt{\frac{\Sigma X^2 - \dfrac{(\Sigma X)^2}{n}}{n - 1}} $$

The following is an illustrative application using the data of the previous illustration. Observations have been **coded** by subtracting 110 further to simplify the computations. Note that since the standard deviation involves only differences between each observation and the mean, no decoding step is required. Only if coded numbers are obtained by dividing or multiplying by some constant is decoding of the computed value necessary.

X	Coded X	Coded $(X)^2$
115	5	25
112	2	4
120	10	100
107	− 3	9
110	0	0
110	0	0
100	−10	100
118	8	64
	$\Sigma X = 12$	$\Sigma X^2 = 302$

$$ s = \sqrt{\frac{302 - \dfrac{12^2}{8}}{7}} = \sqrt{\frac{284}{7}} = \sqrt{40.6} = 6.4 $$

Graphical Method for Determining the Standard Deviation. If the frequency distribution for the population or sample has been plotted on normal-probability paper and a straight line fitted to the points, a close estimate of the standard deviation may be made quite simply. The method is to determine first the point on the line above which 84 percent of the distribution lies. Next, determine the point on the line below which 16 percent of the distribution lies. The range between these two points, measured on the scale at the bottom of the graph, is an estimate of twice the standard deviation. For the incentive-earnings illustration previously plotted, the 84 percent point is at $16 and the 16 percent point at $26. This gives a value of $\dfrac{\$26 - \$16}{2}$, or $5 for the standard deviation. This method depends on the distribution being normal.

OTHER FREQUENCY DISTRIBUTIONS. Occasionally other forms of frequency distributions will be found in industrial engineering and management data. For these special forms the common statistical techniques developed for the normal, the binomial, and the Poisson distributions will ordinarily not apply. For this reason one should be reasonably sure of the nature of the distribution before any such application is made. Usually past experience in the study of similar activities or a knowledge of the variation-producing causes inherent in the activity will indicate the form of the distribution to expect. If there is any doubt, a frequency distribution may be made of a reasonably large sample of observations (at least one hundred) and studied visually to determine its form.

Among the more commonly encountered variations are the bimodal, the screened, the rectangular, and the skewed (see Fig. 5).

Bimodal. This distribution is usually formed as a result of combining, in effect, two separate distributions with different averages. Such might be the case, for example, for time-study observations for a work element in which a piece part is taken from a container and placed in an assembly jig. Many of the parts may be entangled in the container and when this is the case the grasp and separation may be difficult, giving a longer average time for the element. A distribution of time values obtained when this occurs would give one distribution. A distribution with a lower average value would be formed from time values obtained when parts were not entangled. As one or the other of these situations occur at random during the study, the resulting distribution will be bimodal and appear as shown in Fig. 5a.

Screened. When data are from an activity or product for which all items or events measuring beyond a specified limit (or between a pair of specified limits) have been removed, a screened distribution is formed. **Out-of-limit items** may have previously been removed by sorting all items, or by use of some procedure or device which automatically or as a matter of routine removed them. Such a distribution would be formed, for example, in a study of cash refunds in a retail store if a standard practice was to pay all refunds over $10 by check. The illustrations shown in Figs. 5b and 5c are typical forms for screened distributions.

Rectangular. The term "rectangular" is applied to a long, flat distribution such as the one shown in Fig. 5d. Usually such a distribution results from a steady drift in one direction during the course of the study of the average tendency of the activity being measured. It may also be a result of several separate frequency distributions. Such might be the case when materials from several different sources, each with different means for the measured characteristic, are mixed.

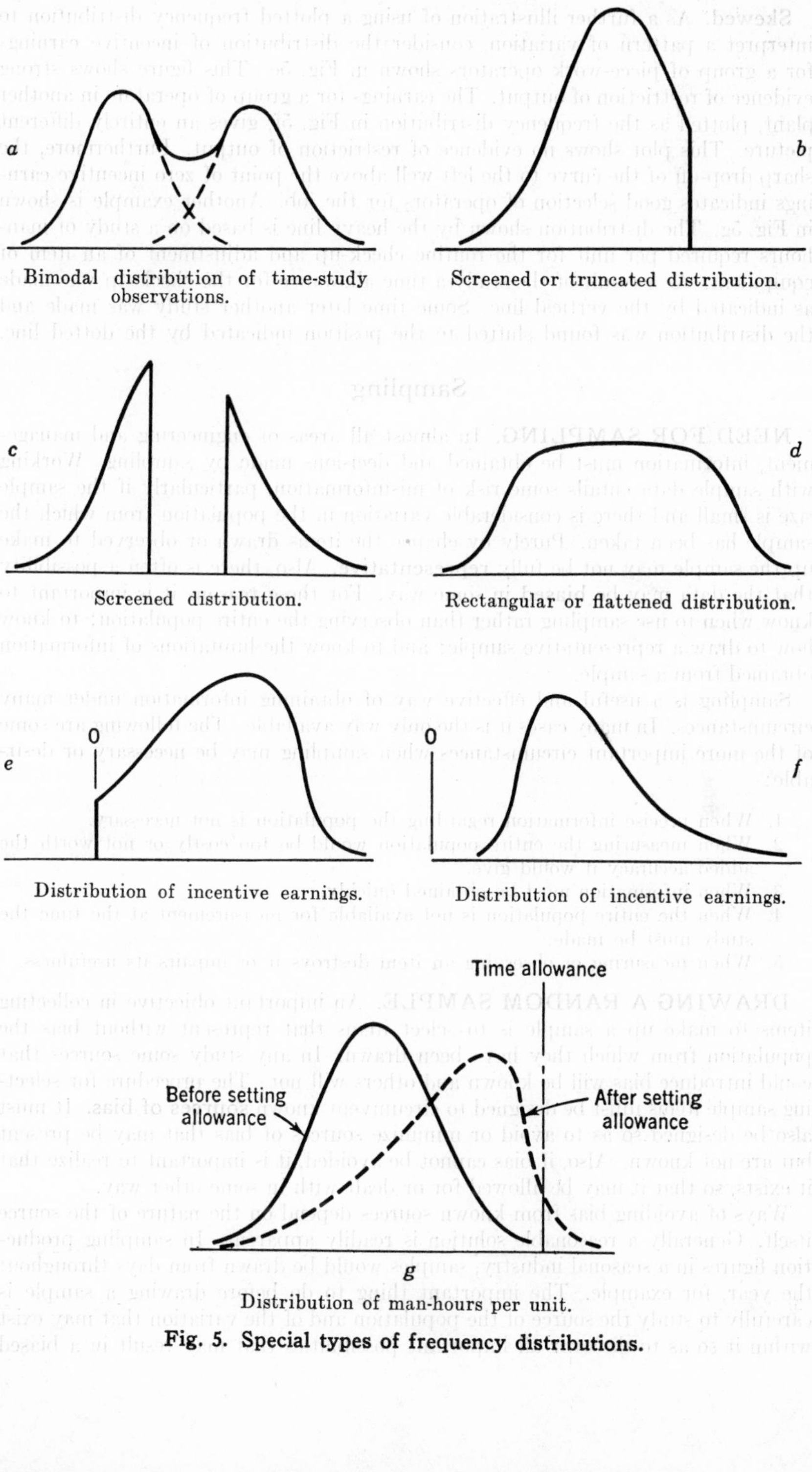

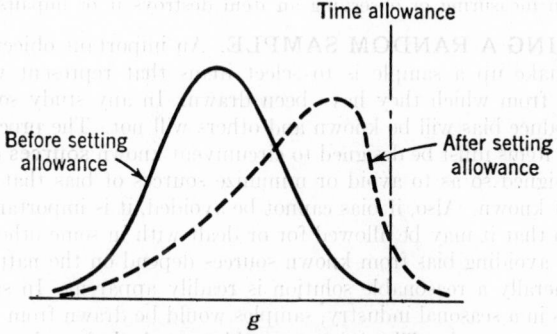

a

b

Bimodal distribution of time-study
observations.

Screened or truncated distribution.

c

d

Screened distribution.

Rectangular or flattened distribution.

0

0

e

f

Distribution of incentive earnings.

Distribution of incentive earnings.

Time allowance

Before setting
allowance

After setting
allowance

g

Distribution of man-hours per unit.

Fig. 5. Special types of frequency distributions.

Skewed. As a further illustration of using a plotted frequency distribution to interpret a pattern of variation, consider the distribution of incentive earnings for a group of piece-work operators shown in Fig. 5e. This figure shows strong evidence of restriction of output. The earnings for a group of operators in another plant, plotted as the frequency distribution in Fig. 5f, gives an entirely different picture. This plot shows no evidence of restriction of output. Furthermore, the sharp drop-off of the curve to the left well above the point of zero incentive earnings indicates good selection of operators for the job. Another example is shown in Fig. 5g. The distribution shown by the heavy line is based on a study of man-hours required per unit for the routine check-up and adjustment of an item of equipment. As a result of the study a time allowance for the check-up was made as indicated by the vertical line. Some time later another study was made and the distribution was found shifted to the position indicated by the dotted line.

Sampling

NEED FOR SAMPLING. In almost all areas of engineering and management, information must be obtained and decisions made by sampling. Working with sample data entails some risk of misinformation, particularly if the sample size is small and there is considerable variation in the population from which the sample has been taken. Purely by chance the items drawn or observed to make up the sample may not be fully **representative.** Also, there is often a possibility that the data may be **biased** in some way. For these reasons it is important to know when to use sampling rather than observing the entire population; to know how to draw a representative sample; and to know the limitations of information obtained from a sample.

Sampling is a useful and effective way of obtaining information under many circumstances. In many cases it is the only way available. The following are some of the more important circumstances when sampling may be necessary or desirable:

1. When precise information regarding the population is not necessary.
2. When measuring the entire population would be too costly or not worth the added accuracy it would give.
3. When information must be obtained quickly.
4. When the entire population is not available for measurement at the time the study must be made.
5. When measuring or observing an item destroys it or impairs its usefulness.

DRAWING A RANDOM SAMPLE. An important objective in collecting items to make up a sample is to select items that represent without bias the population from which they have been drawn. In any study some sources that could introduce bias will be known and others will not. The procedure for selecting sample items must be designed to circumvent known **sources of bias.** It must also be designed so as to avoid or minimize sources of bias that may be present but are not known. Also, if bias cannot be avoided, it is important to realize that it exists, so that it may be allowed for or dealt with in some other way.

Ways of avoiding bias from known sources depend on the nature of the source itself. Generally a reasonable solution is readily apparent. In sampling production figures in a seasonal industry, samples would be drawn from days throughout the year, for example. The important thing to do before drawing a sample is carefully to study the source of the population and of the variation that may exist within it so as to discover all important possibilities that may result in a biased sample. For example, in taking a sample of elapsed times for a work element by a stop watch time study, possible sources of bias are nonstandard working conditions, timing an operator who is not of average ability, unconscious but consistent overreading of the stop watch hand, and the like.

The best practice for avoiding or minimizing the effect of bias sources that are unknown is to draw or select sample items purely at random. This practice will also, of course, be effective in dealing with known sources. To **select an item at random** simply requires that every item in the population have an equal probability of being selected. While this requirement may be simple to state, it may often be difficult to meet it effectively. Some parts of the population may be more difficult to get at than others. Simply glancing at an item may indicate at once the category into which it will fall. The items may differ in appearance; this may have a subconscious effect on the person selecting the sample. The physical arrangement of the items or figures may also have a subconscious effect.

Ways To Avoid Sampling Bias. The following practices may be of help in avoiding some of the more common sources of bias:

1. Assign a number to each item or the position of each item and select items by number through use of a table of random numbers or simply by drawing numbers out of a hat. This is a particularly useful practice when the nature of an item, such as its size, is apparent before a decision can be made on its selection as a sample item.

2. Avoid any arbitrary scheme for selecting items, such as taking every tenth item in succession. Such an arbitrary scheme might result in taking each observation from the same day of the week, from the same operator, from the same shift, or from the same machine, for example.

3. Try to avoid any influence of physical location of items. Do not tend to take most items from the tops of lists, groups, or cartons, for example.

4. When a sample must be taken from some one period of time or on some one date, be sure the time is representative.

5. Be sure that bias is not introduced into the observations by the method or practice of measurement. In a poll, for example, the response may be influenced considerably by the way questions are worded or by the dress or personal characteristics of the person doing the polling.

6. If a sample is made up only of replies voluntarily returned in a questionnaire or poll, be sure the results will not be biased by those who fail to reply because of pride, lack of interest, fear of a wrong response, or some other reason. On a questionnaire to determine by sampling what proportion of the employees in a company would like to have a lunchroom in the plant, for example, a greater proportion of those sampled who wanted the lunchroom might return their questionnaire than of those who did not.

7. If a population is stratified or divided in some arbitrary way, **proportional sampling** may be of help. In this form of sampling, the number of sample items drawn from each segment of the population is in proportion to the number of items or individuals in each segment. In taking a sample of employees or employee records from a plant employing 500 persons on the day shift and 300 persons on the night shift, for example, to make a sample of 40 items, 25 would be selected from the day shift and 15 from the night shift.

ESTIMATING CENTRAL TENDENCY AND DISPERSION BY SAMPLING. When industrial engineering studies must be made with sample data, the measures of central tendency and dispersion for the sample must be used to estimate central tendency and dispersion for the population from which the sample has been drawn. The arithmetic mean of the sample gives the most accurate estimate available for the arithmetic mean for the population. In cases where the sample size is small, say five or less, the mid-range or the median of the sample may give an estimate nearly as reliable as that given by the arithmetic mean.

The standard deviation for the sample (computed by using $n - 1$ in the denominator as explained in the previous division of this section) gives the most accurate estimate for the population. For **small samples,** the sample range may be used to compute a fairly reliable estimate of the population standard deviation. A procedure for doing this will be found in the section on Statistical Quality Control.

Likewise, the percentage or proportion of a specified item or event found in a sample is the best estimate available of the proportion or percentage in the population.

SAMPLING DISTRIBUTIONS. Due to the effects of chance in the selection of sample items, the characteristics of a sample are likely to differ somewhat from the characteristics of the population from which the sample was taken or differ from the characteristics of another sample, if another were to be drawn. Both the arithmetic mean and the standard deviation for a sample of 25 items, for example, will be somewhat more or somewhat less than the average or the standard deviation for the population. Whether one measure is more or less than the other and the exact extent of the difference cannot be known in any single case. However, useful statistical theory and techniques have been developed to use in estimating the probability of any specified **difference between sample and population values.**

The approach is through a study of sampling distributions. To consider a simple illustration, suppose we were to draw many samples of 25 items, each from a normally distributed population with a mean, μ, of 200 and a standard deviation, σ, of 15. Suppose, further, that the mean of each sample is computed. It would be found that these means would form a frequency distribution of their own—a distribution with considerably less dispersion than the population distribution, but one that centered about the same mean value as for the population. Sampling distribution theory would show that the mean for the distribution of sample averages, $\mu_{\bar{x}}$, does coincide with the mean, μ, of the population from which they have been drawn. That is,

$$\mu_{\bar{x}} = \mu$$

Also, the theory would show that the standard deviation of the distribution of sample averages was equal to the standard deviation for the population divided by the square root of n, the sample size. That is,

$$\sigma_{\bar{x}} = \frac{\sigma}{\sqrt{n}}$$

Finally, sampling distribution theory would show that the distribution of sample averages was a normal distribution. These two distributions are shown in Fig. 6 below.

Useful conclusions can be drawn with this theory regarding the **reliability of sample data.** In the above illustration, for example, note that if a sample of 25 items is drawn from a population whose standard deviation is 15, that one may be confident the mean of the sample will be no more than 9 units away from

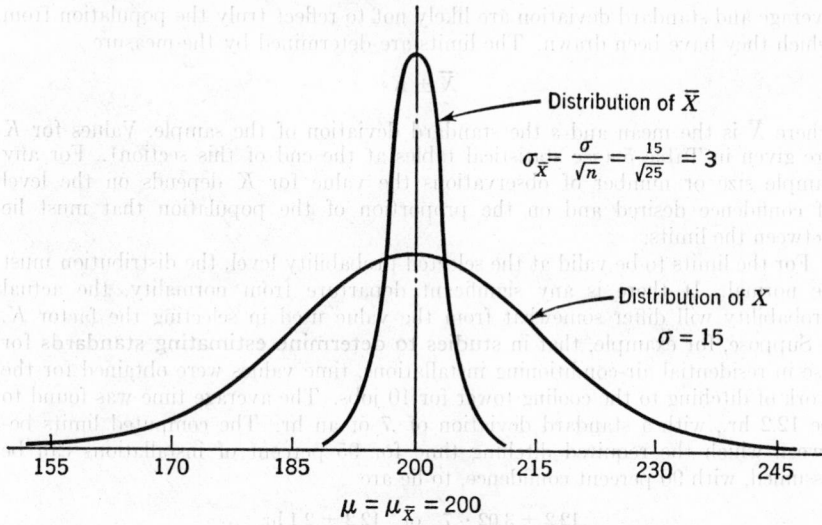

Fig. 6. Sampling distribution of $\bar{X}$.

the mean of the population. More precise techniques based on sampling distribution theory for use in determining confidence limits are described in the division that immediately follows. Theoretical knowledge regarding sampling distributions and the sampling-distribution approach also forms a basis for many other statistical procedures.

CONFIDENCE LIMITS. In many areas of management the nature of a population or universe must be determined from a limited sample of observations. For example, in time study the average time required to perform a work element must be estimated by using a relatively small number of stop-watch observations. Because of the effects of chance, a sample will not represent exactly the population from which it has been drawn. The average of the observed times for an element in a time study, for example, will differ to some extent from the true average. If the sample is quite small, or if the universe is inherently quite variable, information given by a sample may by chance differ considerably from true values.

A number of simple statistical tests are available for indicating the extent to which population values may possibly differ from values obtained from sample observations.

Tolerance Limits for the Items in a Population. Often it is necessary to determine the limits between which will be the measurements for all or some specified proportion of the measurements for individual items in a population. If the average, μ, and the standard deviation, σ, of the population are known, this can be done by use of the table of normal areas by a method that is described in a subsequent division of this section. Usually, however, these values for the population are not known and the limits must be ascertained by the use of sample data. A simple statistical procedure has been developed for determining limits in such cases with any desired **degree of confidence.** These limits will be somewhat wider than those computed by the use of the population average and standard deviation because allowance must be made for the fact that the sample average and standard deviation are likely not to reflect truly the population from which they have been drawn. The limits are determined by the measure

$$\overline{X} \pm Ks$$

where $\overline{X}$ is the mean and s the standard deviation of the sample. Values for K are given in Table 5 (see statistical tables at the end of this section). For any sample size or number of observations the value for K depends on the level of confidence desired and on the proportion of the population that must lie between the limits.

For the limits to be valid at the selected probability level, the distribution must be normal. If there is any significant departure from normality, the actual probability will differ somewhat from the value used in selecting the factor K.

Suppose, for example, that in **studies to determine estimating standards** for use in residential air-conditioning installations, time values were obtained for the work of ditching to the cooling tower for 10 jobs. The average time was found to be 12.2 hr., with a standard deviation of .7 of an hr. The computed limits between which the required ditching time for 95 percent of installations can be assumed, with 90 percent confidence, to lie are

$$12.2 \pm 3.02 \cdot .7 \quad \text{or} \quad 12.2 \pm 2.1 \text{ hr.}$$

This variation in the actual time that might be required for this element of work was considered of no practical significance. It was decided that in making a cost estimate for a new job, a detailed estimate for ditching need not be made but that an average time figure could be used.

Studies of labor time for sheet-metal and insulation work for ducts for the same 10 installations gave an average of 108 hr. and a standard deviation of 14.8 hr. For this element, 90 percent confidence limits within which the time for 95 percent of the installations could be expected to fall were computed as

$$108 \pm 3.02 \cdot 14.8 \quad \text{or} \quad 108 \pm 44.7$$

These limits showed that in making a bid for a new job, it would pay to make a detailed estimate for the duct work rather than to use an average figure.

Another typical application would be to use the factors to determine the **limits for a manufacturing process.** Suppose, for example, that for a sample of 50 items from a machine, the diameter of each has been measured and the average diameter, $\overline{X}$, found to be 2.518 in., with the standard deviation, s, equal to 0.006 in. An estimate is desired of the limits between which virtually all the items produced will measure. The use of a value of 3.13 will give limits between which, with 95 percent confidence, 99 percent of the items will lie. The limits are

$$2.518 \pm (3.13 \times 0.006 \text{ in.})$$

or 2.499 and 2.537

Test for the Rejection of Extreme Values. Occasionally a group of observations will contain some one value considerably larger (or considerably smaller) than the others. This value may be due to an error in measurement or may be due to some abnormal circumstance. In such cases it may be best to discard it. On the other hand, the extreme value may simply represent an extreme item in the population being measured. If this is so, it may be best to retain it to make the group of data more representative.

* All numbered tables referred to in this section appear at the end of the section.

A simple statistical test has been determined to **test for rejection.** The procedure is:

1. Arrange the observations in their order of magnitude.
2. Compute γ.

When the number of values is from 3 to 7,

$$\gamma = \frac{X_2 - X_1}{X_k - X_1}$$

When the number of values is from 8 to 10,

$$\gamma = \frac{X_2 - X_1}{X_{k-1} - X_1}$$

When the number of values is from 11 to 13,

$$\gamma = \frac{X_3 - X_1}{X_{k-1} - X_1}$$

When the number of values is from 14 to 30,

$$\gamma = \frac{X_3 - X_1}{X_{k-2} - X_1}$$

In the equations above, X_1 represents the extreme observation; X_2, the observation nearest to it; X_3, the next in order; and so on to the end of the series, which is represented by X_k.

3. Select a suitable probability level. The probability values in the heading of Table 7 show the probability of a computed γ being numerically greater than the table value if the extreme observation is not abnormal but is actually a part of the normal population from which the rest of the observations were obtained.

4. Using the selected probability level, determine the table value for γ from Table 7.

5. Compare the computed value for γ with the table value. If the computed value is numerically larger than the table value, the extreme observation may be rejected at the selected probability level.

This test is for observations from a normal distribution. In cases that may only approximate the normal, the table probability values will not be exact.

The table of factors used in the above test may also be used as a test for the rejection of extreme means. This use is discussed in a subsequent division of this section. For an example, consider the following sample observations obtained in the course of a study:

52.4, 46.6, 49.7, 52.7, 53.6, 51.8, 51.6, 50.9.

The extreme value, 46.6, may be questionable. Arranging the observations in order of magnitude gives 46.6, 49.7, 50.9, 51.6, 51.8, 52.4, 52.7, and 53.6. For these values

$$\gamma = \frac{X_2 - X_1}{X_{k-1} - X_1} = \frac{49.7 - 46.6}{52.7 - 46.6} = .508$$

Selecting a probability level of .05 gives a table value of .554 for γ. As the computed value is smaller than the table value, the extreme value may not be rejected at the selected probability level.

Confidence Limits for the Population Mean. The best estimate of the population mean, μ, is given by the sample mean, $\overline{X}$. Limits within which the real value for the population mean will lie can be computed for any desired degree of confidence by the following procedures. The procedures are for normal distributions but they will give satisfactory results in cases where a distribution only approximates the normal.

Determining Limits for the Mean When the Population Standard Deviation Is Not Known. The limits between which the population mean, μ, lies are given by:

$$\overline{X} \pm t\frac{s}{\sqrt{n}}$$

where $\overline{X}$ is the mean for the sample, s is the sample standard deviation, and n is the number of items in the sample. The value for t may be obtained from Table 2. This table is entered according to the number of **degrees of freedom** for the data. For the test, the degrees of freedom are $n - 1$ or one less than the number of measurements in the sample. The **probability value** to use in selecting t from the table depends on the desired amount of confidence in the real value being between the computed limits. The values in the table heading show the probability of the real value being outside one or the other of the computed limits. The probability of it being beyond a specified one of the limits is one-half the value in the table heading. Thus if a probability of .10 is used, the probability is .10 or 1 out of 10 that the real mean is outside the limits and .90 or 9 out of 10 that it is inside the limits. The probability that it is, say, greater than the upper limit is one-half the value in the table heading or .05.

An example may be taken from a plant in which certain parts are made from leather. In studies to determine material cost standards it was found that for a sample run of 30 hides the average number of parts per hide was 137 with a standard deviation of 14. To determine the reliability of this average figure, 95 percent confidence limits were computed as follows:

$$137 \pm 2.04\frac{14}{\sqrt{30}} \quad \text{or} \quad 137 \pm 5.2 \text{ parts}$$

Determining Confidence Limits for the Mean When the Population Standard Deviation Is Known. The t-factor in the procedure above allowed for sampling variations in the sample standard deviation. If through past data and computations the standard deviation for the population has been determined, and if it can be assumed this value is good for the current situation, closer confidence limits can be determined. The formula is

$$\overline{X} \pm z\frac{\sigma}{\sqrt{n}}$$

where σ is the population standard deviation. The value for z may be obtained from Table 1a. For any value of z this table shows the probability of the population mean being beyond one of the limits. For example, with $z = -1.645$ the probability is .05 that the population mean will be above the upper of the computed limits and .05 that it will be below the lower. This gives a probability of .90 that it lies between the limits.

If in the previous illustration, for example, the population standard deviation for parts per hide was known to be 11, the limits could be computed as follows:

$$137 \pm 1.96\frac{11}{\sqrt{30}} \quad \text{or} \quad 137 \pm 3.9 \text{ parts}$$

Determining Confidence Limits for the Mean Through Use of the Range.
If the number of observations in the sample is small, a simple alternative procedure using the **sample range**, R, as a measure of dispersion is available. (The range is the difference between the largest observation and the smallest observation in the sample.) The limits are

$$\overline{X} \pm t_R R$$

The value for t_R may be obtained from Table 3. The probabilities in the table heading are for a value beyond one or the other of the limits. As in the previous procedures, use of $P = .10$ gives a probability of .10 of the mean lying beyond one limit or the other or a probability of .90 that it lies between them. The range is not as efficient as the standard deviation as a measure of dispersion. For this reason the limits for any selected level of confidence will be wider than those determined by the procedure using the sample standard deviation.

Suppose, for example, the man-hours required for an activity have been measured for 8 cycles. The shortest time measured was 43.5 hr. and the longest 46.2 hr. with a mean time for the 8 cycles of 44.7 hr. Confidence limits for the population mean, say at 95 percent confidence, are required. The computations are:

$$44.7 \pm .29 \cdot 2.7 \quad \text{or} \quad 44.7 \pm .78$$

The range, 2.7, was obtained by subtracting the smallest measurement from the largest. Table 3 was entered at a probability level of .05 to give 95 percent confidence limits.

Determining Confidence Limits for the Population Standard Deviation.
The best estimate for the population standard deviation, σ, is given by the **sample standard deviation**, s, where s is computed by the equation

$$s = \sqrt{\frac{\Sigma(X - \overline{X})^2}{n-1}} \quad \text{or} \quad s = \sqrt{\frac{\Sigma X^2 - \frac{(\Sigma X)^2}{n}}{n-1}}$$

Limits between which the real value for the population standard deviation will lie can be computed for any desired degree of confidence. The procedure is for normal distributions. Any substantial deviations from normality will result in a confidence level somewhat different from that selected.

$$\text{The upper limit for } \sigma = \sqrt{F s^2}$$

The value for F for the upper limit is obtained directly from Table 6. The probability value to use in selecting F from this table depends on the required degree of confidence that the true value for the standard deviation will lie between the computed limits. The table heading shows the probability of the true value lying above the upper limit. In entering the table for the F-value for this limit, the degrees of freedom for the **greater mean square** are ∞ and for the **smaller mean square** $n - 1$.

$$\text{The lower limit for } \sigma = \sqrt{\frac{s^2}{F}}$$

The value for F for this limit is also obtained from Table 6, but with this difference: the degrees of freedom for the greater mean square are $n - 1$, and the degrees of freedom for the smaller mean square are ∞. The probability value for the table gives the probability of the real value being less than the lower limit. Thus if a probability value of .01 is used for each limit, the probability is .02 that the true value will be outside the computed limits or .98 that it lies between them.

A simple illustration is an application of the study of consistency in an experimental model of a container-filling machine. Twenty-five packages were filled and carefully weighed. The standard deviation, s, of the weights was found to be .17 ounces. The limits between which one could be 90 percent confident that the true standard deviation for the machine would lie were required. The computations for this case were:

$$\text{Upper limit} = \sqrt{F s^2} = \sqrt{1.73 \cdot .17^2} = .22$$

$$\text{Lower limit} = \sqrt{\frac{s^2}{F}} = \sqrt{\frac{.17^2}{1.52}} = .14$$

Thus with 90 percent confidence the true standard deviation could be said to lie between .14 and .22 (with the best estimate being, of course, .17).

Determining Confidence Limits for the Population Proportion. Under many situations the proportion of times a specified event occurs in a population must be estimated by determining the proportion of times the specified event is found in a sample. The proportion found for the sample is the best estimate available for the proportion for the population. However, the information given by the sample is likely to differ somewhat by chance from the true population figure.

The following procedure gives **approximate limits** to indicate the extent to which the population proportion may differ from the sample proportion. The limits are:

$$p_s \pm z \sqrt{\frac{p_s(1 - p_s)}{n}}$$

where p_s is the proportion of the specified event for the sample and n is the number of items in the sample. The value for z may be obtained from Table 1a (ignoring the negative sign). For any value of z the table gives the probability of the population proportion being beyond one of the limits. The probability of the population proportion being outside one or the other of the computed limits is thus twice the table probability.

For example, in a work-sampling study 300 random observations of an activity were made, and for 39 of them the operation was delayed. This gave 39/300 or .13 as the proportion of observations for which a delay was noted. Approximate limits between which one could be 90 percent confident that the population proportion would lie were computed as follows:

$$.13 \pm 1.645 \sqrt{\frac{.13(1 - .13)}{300}} \quad \text{or} \quad .13 \pm .032$$

DETERMINING SAMPLE SIZE. There is no simple procedure for determining precisely the most appropriate size of sample for a study. The **number of observations to obtain** should depend, among other things, on the following:

1. The cost of obtaining a sample observation. If obtaining observations is relatively costly, comparatively few observations may have to suffice.
2. The time and staff available for sampling and for recording data.
3. The value of added confidence in conclusions given by larger sample sizes.

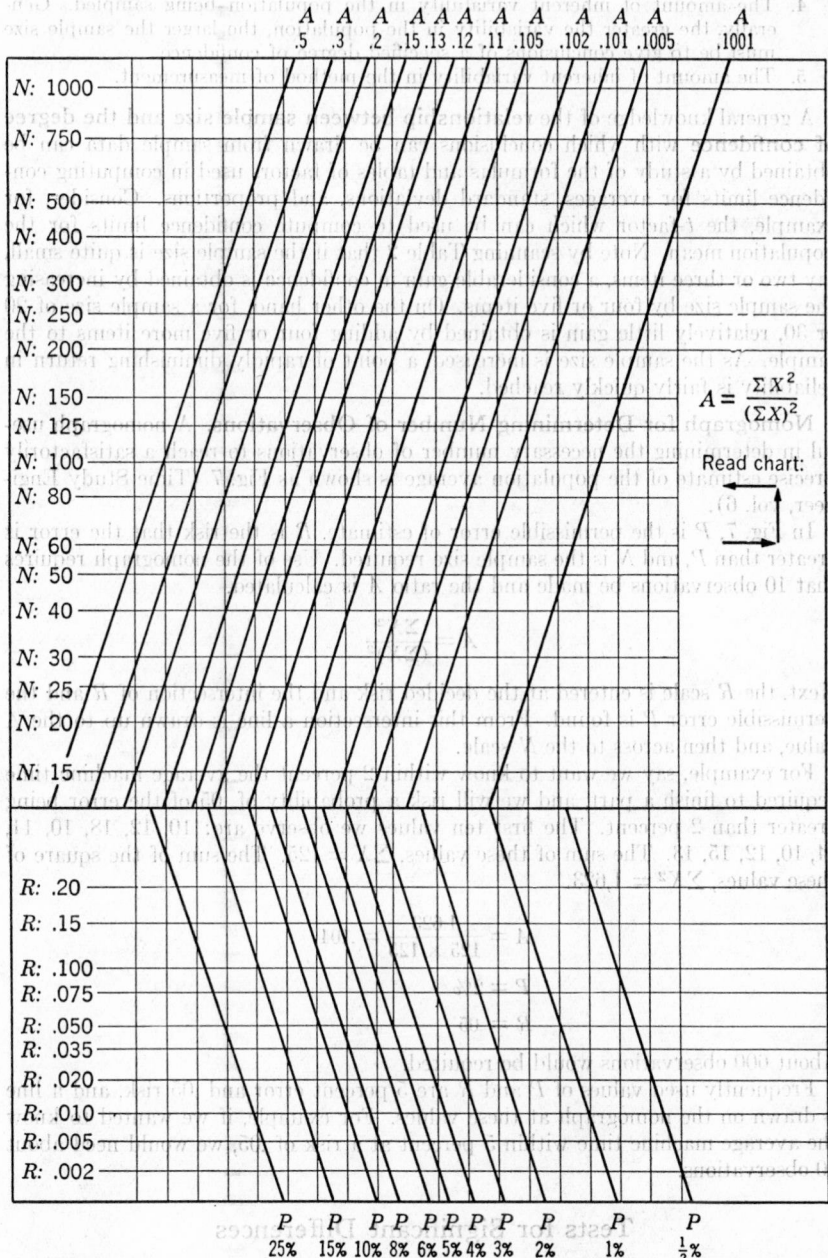

Fig. 7. Nomograph to estimate the number of observations necessary to result in a satisfactorily precise average value.

4. The amount of inherent variability in the population being sampled. Generally, the greater the variability in the population, the larger the sample size must be to give conclusions of a specified degree of confidence.
5. The amount of inherent variability in the method of measurement.

A general knowledge of the **relationship between sample size and the degree of confidence** with which conclusions can be drawn from sample data can be obtained by a study of the formulas and tables of factors used in computing confidence limits for averages, standard deviations, and proportions. Consider, for example, the t-factor which can be used to compute confidence limits for the population mean. Note by scanning Table 2 that if the sample size is quite small, say two or three items, a considerable gain in confidence is obtained by increasing the sample size by four or five items. On the other hand, for a sample size of 20 or 30, relatively little gain is obtained by adding four or five more items to the sample. As the sample size is increased, a point of rapidly diminishing return in reliability is fairly quickly reached.

Nomograph for Determining Number of Observations. A nomograph useful in determining the necessary number of observations to reach a satisfactorily precise estimate of the population average is shown as Fig. 7 (Time Study Engineer, vol. 6).

In Fig. 7, P is the permissible error of estimate, R is the risk that the error is greater than P, and N is the sample size required. Use of the nomograph requires that 10 observations be made and the ratio A is calculated.

$$A = \frac{\Sigma X^2}{(\Sigma X)^2}$$

Next, the R scale is entered at the decided risk and the intersection of R and the permissible error P is found. From this intersection a line is drawn up to the A value, and then across to the N scale.

For example, say we want to know within 2 percent the average machine time required to finish a part, and we will risk a probability of .05 of the error being greater than 2 percent. The first ten values we observe are: 10, 12, 18, 10, 11, 14, 10, 12, 15, 13. The sum of these values, $\Sigma X = 125$. The sum of the square of these values, $\Sigma X^2 = 1,623$.

$$A = \frac{1,623}{125 \times 125} = .104$$

$$P = 2\%$$

$$R = .05$$

About 600 observations would be required.

Frequently used values of P and R are 5 percent error and .05 risk, and a line is drawn on the nomograph at these values. For example, if we wanted to know the average machine time within 5 percent at a risk of .05, we would need about 80 observations.

Tests for Significant Differences

MAKING SAMPLING ACCURATE. Characteristics of products, processes, and events must frequently be estimated by measurements made on a sample of the total group. If two or more samples are measured, there is likely to be a difference in the average measurements. When it is possible that the samples have been taken from different total groups, it is convenient to have a means of determining and expressing the likelihood that the exhibited difference could have resulted from chance variations in sampling the same total group. In other words we should like to be able to say with precision: A difference as large as this is unlikely to have occurred if the samples were drawn from the same population; or, a difference as large as this is likely to have occurred between samples of the same population.

In situations where we are determining whether the characteristic of the total group is above or below or between certain values, we should like to be able to say with precision: It is unlikely that a sample with characteristics such as these could have come from a population such as we have described; or, it is likely that a sample with characteristics such as these could have come from a population such as we have described.

Making the words **likely** and **unlikely** precise is achieved, statistically, by stating the risk that we are wrong in terms of the percentage of cases in which the likelihood of error will occur. If the situation is such that we risk being in error 1 time in 20, we should intend the word "likely" to mean 19 times out of 20. The **risk of being in error** must be determined for each situation. What is done about it will depend on the cost of making more measurements and the cost of being wrong.

Differences of **statistical significance** are not necessarily differences of practical significance. The fact that two samples exhibit a statistically significant difference indicates that they were probably drawn from two different groups. A constant difference will appear more and more statistically significant as larger samples are measured. Whether the difference between the groups is of **practical significance** must be determined by the individual situation. A difference so large as to be of practical significance need not necessarily be statistically significant; that is, it may have appeared just due to chance sampling errors. When this occurs, additional sampling will show either that the difference is stable and real or that the difference will diminish and disappear as more samples are measured. The decision for action should be based on results that are both practically and statistically significant.

STATISTICAL INFERENCE. The logical approach to evaluating the statistical significance of differences is through a form of reasoning known as statistical inference. The general method takes the following steps:

1. Set up a hypothesis that such samples as are measured have been drawn from the same total group; or alternately, from a described total group.
2. Draw a sample from the population (or each of the populations if several are under study).
3. Compute one or more statistics or measures from each of the samples.
4. Using known data regarding sampling distributions for the statistics computed, test to see whether the hypothesis is likely to be true; that is, see if the measured samples are likely to have come from the same total group or from the described total group.

The following division describes the statistical techniques used in step 4.

Example of *t*-Test. For example, suppose that a supplier of small purchased parts guarantees that each carton of parts will contain an average of 500 pieces. For the first shipment the contents of 6 cartons are counted and the average number per carton found to be 491.2 with a sample standard deviation, s, of 5. As there may be considerable variation in the number of parts from carton to carton, the significance of the difference between the average number guaranteed and the average number found for the sample must be questioned. Could the difference be solely due to chance; that is, is it possible that it just happened that the 6 cartons selected for counting tended to be light? Or is the difference in averages too great for this to be likely?

This difference may be tested by first setting up the hypothesis that the average for the shipment is 500 pieces per carton. Next, the extent to which the average for a sample of 6 might deviate from the population average is determined by consulting a table of the sampling distribution for the statistic involved (in this case, a table of t). This table would show, for example, that the probability is .02 or 1 in 50 of a sample average being more than $3.37 \times s/\sqrt{n}$ units lower or higher than the population average purely by chance. (The figure 3.37 is the value for t obtained from the table.) This is $3.37 \times 5/\sqrt{6}$, or 6.9 units. The observed difference is $500 - 491.2$, or 8.8 units. As the observed difference is greater than the difference that could occur by chance at the selected probability level, the hypothesis that the average number per carton for the shipment is 500 is rejected. The difference is considered significant and thus good evidence that the supplier's shipment does not meet his guarantee.

While the general approach is as described in the illustration above, the **working procedure** as used by most statisticians may differ slightly in detail. In the above test, for example, the common method of computation is first to determine a computed t by dividing the difference in means by $s/\sqrt{n}$. For this example

$$t = \frac{500 - 491.2}{5/\sqrt{6}} = 4.30$$

The computed value for t is then compared with the table value. If it is greater, the hypothesis is rejected. Note that the procedure is equivalent to the one described, differing only in the form of comparison made.

RISKS OF A WRONG CONCLUSION. In using information obtained from a sample of observations to test a hypothesis, there is always some risk of reaching incorrect conclusions. The average for a sample, for example, may deviate considerably from the average of the population from which it has been drawn, particularly if the sample size is small and the population is widely dispersed. The extent of the deviation or the direction of the deviation is not known. In fact, in testing a hypothesis by means of a sample, there are two possible forms of error. One is to assume the hypothesis is false when it really is true. The other is to assume the hypothesis is true when it really is false. These two possibilities of error always exist whether statistical tests are used or not. However, the advantage of the statistical approach is that a precise appraisal of these risks, particularly the first, may be made. Knowing the odds of reaching an incorrect conclusion, or being able to choose such odds, is of much help in many situations.

The usual procedure in statistical inference is to select an appropriate probability figure for the first kind of error mentioned—that of assuming the hypothesis is false when it really is true. This **risk** is measured by the probability level used in working with the tables of sampling distributions such as the table of t and the table of F. In the example above, a probability level of .02 was used in getting a value for t to test the hypothesis regarding the population average. The result of using this level was that the risk of assuming the hypothesis was false when it really was true, was .02 or 1 in 50 or less. The choice of a probability level for the test depends largely on how costly are the consequences of making an error of this kind. In the above example, the level would depend on the costs (both those that may be reduced to money terms and those that are irreducible) of assuming the shipment did not meet the supplier's guarantee and consequently returning it, when in reality it did meet his guarantee.

The second kind of risk, that of assuming the hypothesis is true when it really is false is more difficult to evaluate. Also, it cannot be expressed as a single figure, as the risk depends in part on the extent to which the population actually deviates from the hypothetical value. In the above test, for example, the risk of assuming the average number per carton for the shipment was 500 when it really was not would depend on how much the actual average differed from 500. The extent of this second kind of risk depends also on the sample size and on the probability value selected for the first form of risk. Methods for computing this risk usually require much involved computation. For this reason these risks generally have not been determined as a routine step in statistical applications. Risks for specific tests in the form of **operating characteristic curves** have been developed.

TESTS FOR DIFFERENCES BETWEEN AVERAGES. In many situations it is necessary to compare a sample mean with a population mean and to evaluate the difference between them. If this difference is not great, and if there is considerable inherent variation among the items being measured, the observed difference may not represent a real difference in population means. Simply by chance the mean for a sample may be greater (or less) than the mean of the population from which it was drawn.

Test for Significance of a Difference Between a Sample Mean and a Population Mean. The steps in the test are:

1. Select a suitable probability level for testing the difference for significance.
2. Compute t where

$$t = \frac{\bar{X} - \mu}{s/\sqrt{n}}$$

3. Using the selected probability level, determine the table value for t from Table 2.
4. Compare the computed t with the table value for t, ignoring its sign. If the computed t is numerically less than the table value, the observed difference in means is not significant at the probability level selected. If the computed value is numerically greater, the difference may be considered significant.

In using Table 2 for this test, the **degrees of freedom** are $n - 1$, or one less than the number of measurements in the sample. The probability levels in the table heading give the probability of a computed t being by chance numerically greater than the table t, if the mean of the population from which the sample has been drawn is the same as the mean μ. For a test of significance of difference in one direction only, the probability values in the table headings should be divided by 2. That is, if a table value with probability of .05 is used, the probability is .025 of a computed t being by chance greater than the positive table value. There is an equal probability, .025, of its being less than minus the table value.

Sample and Population Means Compared. The following is an illustrative application. For an automobile battery distributor the average number of batteries per order has for the past several years been 27 batteries, although the number on any order may vary considerably from this figure. A new kind of battery has been introduced which can be stored for some time without loss of charge. After its introduction a sample of 100 orders is tallied and the average number found to be 30.6, with a standard deviation for the sample of 3.9. It will be helpful to know how much significance can be attached to this apparent increase in average order size. If the increase observed from the sample represents a real increase, plans will have to be made promptly for revised truck routes and schedules, revision of warehouse space, and the like.

A probability level of .02 is selected to test for significance. The population average, μ, is 27; the sample average, $\overline{X}$, is 31.6; the sample standard deviation, s, is 3.9; the sample size, n, is 100. Thus the computed value for t is

$$t = \frac{X - \mu}{s/\sqrt{n}} = \frac{30.6 - 27}{3.9/\sqrt{100}} = 9.2$$

Using $n - 1$ or 99 degrees of freedom and a probability level of .02, the table value is found from Table 2 to be 2.37. As the computed value exceeds this numerically, the difference is considered significant. The probability is .02 of a computed t being numerically greater than 2.37 by chance if the true average has not changed. The probability of a sample average being greater, that is of getting a positive t greater than 2.37, is one-half the table probability, or .01.

Effect of New Tool Tested. This test may be adapted as needed to fit the problem at hand. For example, consider a case in which a costly tool was being studied for use in large numbers in a factory. The vendor of the tool guaranteed its use would increase the average output from 207 units, the present figure, to 260 units per operator per day. **Economy studies** showed that a changeover to this tool would be economical only if this average increase of 53 units per operator were to be made. One tool was purchased for trial. Twenty days' use gave daily figures ranging from 242 to 275 units per day, the average being 261.4 units per operator-day with the standard deviation for the 20 observations being 4.7 units. The significance of these trial figures was questioned. How confident could one be that the average for the group would increase to 260 units? Was this sufficient evidence to warrant making the purchase of the additional units needed or should further study be made?

Computation of t gave the following figure:

$$t = \frac{261.4 - 260}{4.7/\sqrt{20}} = 1.33$$

The table of t gave a value of 2.45 for t, using a probability level of .02. As the computed t was not numerically larger than the table value, the difference could not be considered significant at the probability level selected. Only if the computed t were greater than 2.45 would this be evidence (at a probability level of $.02 \div 2$, or .01) that the new average was 260 or greater. A sample average (for a sample size of 20) could by chance be 261.4, with the true average being somewhat below 260. To be reasonably certain that the average was 260 or greater, an **additional trial period** was needed. After 160 operator-days were recorded, the average output was 259.2 and the sample standard deviation was 4.0 units. Now,

$$t = \frac{260 - 259.2}{4.0/\sqrt{160}} = 2.53$$

which indicates that if the true average were 260 or greater, it is unlikely that we could get 160 operator-days averaging as low as this.

Test for Difference Between a Sample Mean and a Population Mean When the Population Standard Deviation Is Known. If the standard deviation for the population is known, an alternative test is available. If this alternative test can be used, the observed difference between means does not have to be as great as in the previous test in order to be significant. The **test procedure** is:

1. Select a suitable probability level.
2. Compute z where

$$z = \frac{X - \mu}{\sigma/\sqrt{n}}$$

3. Using the selected probability level, determine the table value for z from Table 1a.
4. Compare the computed value for z with the table value. If the computed value is less than the table value, the observed difference in means is not significant at the probability level selected. If the computed value is greater, the difference may be considered significant.

The probabilities listed in Table 1a give the probability of a computed z being less than the table value. There is an equal probability of its being more than plus the table value. Thus, for a test of difference in either direction, the table value gives one-half the probability of a real difference, either plus or minus, being indicated in the event that no difference really exists.

Example from Battery Industry. For example, suppose that a new ingredient is added in making the plates for automobile storage batteries in an attempt to increase their life. Experience has shown that any change of this kind will have an effect, if any, only on the average life and not on the dispersion from battery to battery. Ten batteries are manufactured and put through the relatively lengthy and costly life tests. The increase over the normal life for a battery of this type averaged 1.6 months per battery. The standard deviation for this type battery has been found through past research and mortality studies to be 1.8 months. Assuming the standard deviation has not been affected by use of the new material, does this test indicate the new material has resulted in real improvement? Can one be 95 percent confident, for example, that the average difference in life shown by the 10 test batteries indicates a real increase in battery life?

Computation of z gives the following:

$$z = \frac{X - \mu}{\sigma/\sqrt{n}} = \frac{1.6}{1.8/\sqrt{10}} = 2.81$$

The table value of z, using a probability level of $1.00 - .95$ or $.05$, is -1.65. As the computed value for z is numerically greater than the table value, the observed difference is significant at the selected probability level. The probability is only 5 out of 100 of getting a computed z beyond 1.65 if there had been no increase in the life average, μ.

Test for Significance of a Difference Between a Sample Mean and a Population Mean Based on the Use of the Range. A simple alternative procedure which uses the sample range as a measure of dispersion is available. (The range is the difference between the largest and the smallest observation in the sample.) This test is a fairly efficient one when the number of observations is small, but it is generally not as precise as the t-test using the standard deviation. A greater observed difference in averages will be required for an equivalent degree of confidence. The **steps in the test** are:

1. Select a suitable probability level.
2. Compute t_R where

$$t_R = \frac{\overline{X} - \mu}{R}$$

In the above formula, R is the range for the measurements in the sample.

3. Using the selected probability level, determine the table value for t_R from Table 3.
4. Compare the computed value for t_R with the table value. If the computed value is numerically less than the table value, the observed difference in means is not significant at the probability level selected.

The probability values in the table heading give the probability of a computed value being numerically greater than the table value by chance, when there is no real difference between the mean of the population sampled and the mean μ. For a test of significance of difference in one direction only, the probability values in the table heading should be divided by 2.

Test of Effect of New Tool on Output. This test can be illustrated by one of the previous examples in which a new type of tool was tested for its effect in improving output. The average for 20 sample observations was 261.4 units with a range of 275 − 242, or 33 units. The question was whether or not the sample average, 261.4, was sufficiently high to be sure the guaranteed average output for the plant, 260 units, had been met. A probability level of .02 was used.

The **computation** of t_R is

$$t_R = \frac{\overline{X} - \mu}{R} = \frac{261.4 - 260}{33} = .042$$

From Table 3 the table value for t_R is found to be .15. As the computed value is not numerically greater, the difference is not significant at the selected level of probability. Note that this is the same conclusion as that reached by the t-test.

Test for Significance of Difference Between Two Sample Means. When two sample averages are compared and the difference between them is found to be small, the significance of the difference may be questionable. This is particularly true if the number of observations is relatively small and if there is considerable variation among the observations within a sample. The difference may be due to chance and not to a real difference in averages between the two populations sampled.

A test for general use is available. (A similar and more precise test for use when the population standard deviation is known is outlined later.) The **steps in the test** for use when the population standard deviations are not known are:

1. Select a suitable probability level for testing the difference for significance.
2. Compute t where

$$t = \frac{\overline{X}_A - \overline{X}_B}{s_p \sqrt{\dfrac{1}{n_A} + \dfrac{1}{n_B}}}$$

In the above formula $\overline{X}_A$ stands for the arithmetic mean for one sample, $\overline{X}_B$ for the mean of the other. Likewise, n_A is the number of observations in sample A, n_B the number of observations in sample B. The term s_p represents the estimate of the population standard deviation obtained by pooling data from both samples. The following equation may be used to compute s_p:

$$s_p = \sqrt{\dfrac{\Sigma X_A{}^2 - \dfrac{(\Sigma X_A)^2}{n_A} + \Sigma X_B{}^2 - \dfrac{(\Sigma X_B)^2}{n_B}}{n_A + n_B - 2}}$$

If the standard deviation has been computed for each group of observations, the following alternative formula may be used instead:

$$s_p = \sqrt{\dfrac{(n_A - 1)s_A{}^2 + (n_B - 1)s_B{}^2}{n_A + n_B - 2}}$$

3. Using the selected probability level, determine the table value for t from Table 2. For this test enter the table with $n_A + n_B - 2$ degrees of freedom.
4. Compare the computed t (ignoring signs) with the table value for t. If the computed t is numerically less than the table value, the observed difference in means is not significant at the probability level selected.

For this test, the probability levels in the t-table heading give the probability of a computed t being numerically larger than the table value if the means of the two populations from which the samples have been drawn do not differ; that is, the probability or the risk of assuming the observed difference in sample means seems significant when it really is not. To test for a change in one direction only, use one-half the probability value given by the table heading.

The above test is exact if the distributions are normal and if the standard deviations of each are equal. For cases that only approximate these requirements, the table probability values will not be exact. However, a test for use when the population standard deviations differ considerably has been developed.

Comparison of Average Times of Assembly Methods. For an example, consider a case in which two different assembly methods for a product were being studied for possible adoption. A time study was made on a trial setup for each of the possibilities with the following results:

	Method A	Method B
Average Time	4.37 min.	4.09 min.
Standard Deviation	0.28 min.	0.21 min.
Number of Observations............................	20	25

There was a question as to whether the difference in averages represents a real difference in the time requirements or whether it might simply be a chance difference due to sampling fluctuations. A probability level of .10 was selected to test the observed difference.

The **computations** were:

$$s_p = \sqrt{\dfrac{(n_A - 1)s_A{}^2 + (n_B - 1)s_B{}^2}{n_A + n_B - 2}} = \sqrt{\dfrac{19 \cdot .28^2 + 24 \cdot .20^2}{20 + 25 - 2}}$$

$$= .24$$

$$t = \dfrac{\overline{X}_A - \overline{X}_B}{s_p \sqrt{\dfrac{1}{n_A} + \dfrac{1}{n_B}}} = \dfrac{4.37 - 4.09}{.24 \sqrt{\dfrac{1}{20} + \dfrac{1}{25}}}$$

$$= 3.89$$

Using $n_A + n_B - 2$ or 43 degrees of freedom and a probability level of .10, the table value for t was found to be 1.68. As the computed value for t was numerically larger, this was accepted as evidence (at the selected probability level) that the true average time requirements for the two methods were not the same. A further conclusion, of course, was that method B was the better of the two.

Comparison of Average Weights of Containers. For another illustration, consider the figures below for the weights of sample containers from two companies.

	Company J	Company K
	124.4 lb.	107.1 lb.
	121.4	107.6
	121.3	108.8
	126.5	115.6
	118.0	108.7
		110.5
		112.4
Average	122.3 lb.	110.1 lb.

The containers from Company J are supposed to weigh at least 10 lb. more, on the average, than those from Company K. A question may be raised as to whether or not these sample observations furnish proof that this is the case.

The observed difference is $122.3 - 110.1$, or 12.2 lb. If this difference is sufficiently larger than 10.0 lb. to be significant—that is, if it is so large that it could not be obtained by chance with the true averages just 10 lb. apart—then the observations may be taken as valid evidence that the population average for Company J is at least 10 lb. greater than that for Company K. Suppose that a probability level of .01 seems appropriate for the test.

The **computations** are shown below. Observations have been coded by subtracting 110 lb. from each one so that the computations will be easier to carry out.

Company J		Company K	
X_J	X_J^2	X_K	X_K^2
14.4	207.36	-2.9	8.41
11.4	129.96	-2.4	5.76
11.3	127.69	-1.2	1.44
16.5	272.25	5.6	31.36
8.0	64.00	-1.3	1.69
		.5	.25
		2.4	5.76
$\Sigma X_J = 61.6$	$\Sigma X_J^2 = 801.26$	$\Sigma X_K = .7$	$\Sigma X_K^2 = 54.67$
$n_J = 5$		$n_K = 7$	
$\overline{X}_J = \dfrac{61.6}{5} = 12.3$		$\overline{X}_K = \dfrac{.7}{7} = .1$	

$$s_p = \sqrt{\frac{\Sigma X_J^2 - \frac{(\Sigma X_J)^2}{n_J} + \Sigma X_K^2 - \frac{(\Sigma X_K)^2}{n_K}}{n_J + n_K - 2}}$$

$$= \sqrt{\frac{801.26 - \frac{61.6^2}{5} + 54.67 - \frac{.7^2}{7}}{5 + 7 - 2}}$$

$$= 3.11$$

$$t = \frac{(\overline{X}_J - \overline{X}_K) - 10}{s_p \sqrt{\frac{1}{n_J} + \frac{1}{n_K}}} = \frac{(12.3 - .1) - 10}{3.11 \sqrt{\frac{1}{5} + \frac{1}{7}}}$$

$$= 6.7$$

To obtain a table value for t the probability values in the table headings are divided in one-half—as this is a test for change in one direction only—for J to be significantly larger than K. Thus with $n_J + n_K - 2$, or 10 degrees of freedom and a selected probability of .01 (which requires the use of the .02 column in the table) the table value for t is found to be 2.76. As the computed t is larger, the difference is significant. The tests may be taken as evidence that the average weight per container for Company J will run 10 lb. heavier than for Company K.

Test for Significance of Difference Between Two Sample Means When the Standard Deviation Is Known. If a good estimate of the population standard deviation, σ, has been found, and if it appears that any changes will affect only the population average, an alternative test is available. The **steps in this test** are:

1. Select a suitable probability level.
2. Compute z where

$$z = \frac{\overline{X}_A - \overline{X}_B}{\sigma \sqrt{\frac{1}{n_A} + \frac{1}{n_B}}}$$

3. Using the selected probability level, determine the table value for z from Table 1a, using one-half the selected probability level to enter the table.
4. Compare the computed value for z with the table value. If the computed value for z is numerically less than the table value, the observed difference in means is not significant at the probability level selected.

As for the t-test, the probability of the computed z being numerically greater by chance when no real difference in population means exists is twice the value in the table heading.

For a test in one direction only—for $\overline{X}_A$ to be significantly greater than $\overline{X}_B$, for example—the table of z should be entered at the selected probability level.

Example of Crew Differences in Shrinkage. For an example, consider the case of a cannery in which it has been found through extensive studies of shrinkage that, while the average may vary throughout the season or from lot to lot of fruit, the standard deviation remains fairly constant at about 8.6 lb. per day per operator. At the start of a new season it seemed desirable to compare the shrinkage of 2 different crews of 8 women each. Shrinkage was measured over 2 days which gave a sample of 16 woman-days for each crew. One crew had an average shrinkage of 132.5 lb. per woman per day and the other 137.6.

The difference between crews was tested for significance by the following computations (a probability level of .01 was used):

$$z = \frac{\bar{X}_A - \bar{X}_B}{\sigma\sqrt{\dfrac{1}{n_A} + \dfrac{1}{n_B}}} = \frac{132.5 - 137.6}{8.6\sqrt{\dfrac{1}{16} + \dfrac{1}{16}}}$$

$$= 1.68$$

From the table of z, Table 1a, a table value of z is found to be -2.58. As the computed value for z was not numerically larger than the table value, the difference was not considered significant. It could have been a chance difference.

Test for Difference Between Two Samples Based on the Use of the Range. A simple alternative procedure using the range instead of the standard deviation as a measure of dispersion is available. It is fairly efficient when the number of observations is small. The number of observations for each sample must be the same. The **test procedure** is:

1. Select a suitable probability level.
2. Compute t_{2R} where

$$t_{2R} = \frac{\bar{X}_A - \bar{X}_B}{1/2(R_A + R_B)}$$

   In the above formula, R_A is the range for the measurements in sample A and R_B the range for sample B.
3. Using the selected probability level, determine the table value for t_{2R} from Table 4.
4. Compare the computed value for t_{2R} with the table value. If the computed t_{2R} is numerically less than the table value, the observed difference in means is not significant at the probability level selected.

Note that for Table 4 the t_{2R} value is determined by using the sample size and not the number of degrees of freedom. The probability values in the table heading give the probability of a computed t_{2R} being numerically larger than the table value if the means of the two populations from which the samples have been drawn do not differ. To test for a change in one direction only, use one-half the probability value shown by the table.

Test of Machine Attachment. For an illustration, suppose that a new attachment is tested at a machine for its effect on increasing productivity. Daily production is measured for five days with the device and for five days without the use of the device with the following results:

Units Produced with the Device	Units Produced without the Device
2,214	1,966
1,858	1,707
2,261	1,760
1,918	1,758
1,830	1,581
Average $= \dfrac{10,081}{5} = 2,016$	Average $= \dfrac{8,772}{5} = 1,754$
Range $= 2,261 - 1,830 = 431$	Range $= 1,966 - 1,581 = 385$

The vendor of the device claimed it would increase average daily output by 200 units. It was desired to know whether this test was valid evidence that his claim would be met over the long run or whether an additional period of testing would be required to be sure. A probability level of .025 seemed best for use in this case.

Computation of t_{2R} gave the following:

$$t_{2R} = \frac{(\overline{X}_A - \overline{X}_B) - 200}{1/2\,(R_A + R_B)} = \frac{(2{,}016 - 1{,}754) - 200}{1/2\,(431 + 385)}$$

$$= .15$$

Entering Table 4, the table of t_{2R}, at a probability level of .05 (as this is a test for a change in a specified direction), gives a table value for t_{2R} of .61. As the computed value is not numerically larger, the sample observations do not offer proof at the selected probability level that the claim of a 200-unit gain has been met.

TESTS FOR DIFFERENCES BETWEEN PROPORTIONS. In many areas of engineering and management, sample proportions of percentages must be compared for significance of difference. A simple but approximate procedure is available to test such differences. It will give satisfactory results in all applications where the sample size or the proportion observed (or both) are sufficiently large to result in the specified event occurring at least four or five times in each sample.

Test for Differences Between Two Sample Proportions. The steps in the test are as follows:

1. Select a suitable probability level for testing the difference for significance.
2. Compute s_p where

$$s_p = \sqrt{\frac{p_A(1 - p_A)}{n_A} + \frac{p_B\,(1 - p_B)}{n_B}}$$

   and where p_A = the proportion in sample A

   p_B = the proportion in sample B

   n_A = the number of items in sample A

   n_B = the number of items in sample B

3. Compute d, where

$$d = zs_p$$

   The value for z may be determined from Table 1a (ignoring the sign for z).
4. Compare the difference in sample proportions with the value found for d. If it is numerically smaller than d, the difference in the direction indicated by the sample values is not significant at the probability level used. On the other hand if the difference in sample proportions is numerically larger, the difference in the direction indicated may be considered significant.

Departmental Turnover Differences Tested. For an example, suppose that in a manufacturing plant the following figures on quits have been obtained: Department A—out of 810 men hired 109 have quit; Department B—out of 456 men hired 34 have quit. Can these figures be taken as evidence of a real difference between departments? An answer is needed in order to know whether or not to look into working conditions, supervisory practices, and the like for an explanation of the higher proportion of voluntary separations in Department A. A probability level of .05 seems suitable in applying a test.

For the above figures

$$p_A = \frac{109}{810} = .135$$

$$p_B = \frac{34}{456} = .075$$

$$s_p = \sqrt{\frac{p_A(1 - p_A)}{n_A} + \frac{p_B(1 - p_B)}{n_B}}$$

$$= \sqrt{\frac{.135\,(1 - .135)}{810} + \frac{.075\,(1 - .075)}{456}}$$

$$= .0173$$

From Table 1a the value for z is found to be 1.645 for a probability of .05. Thus

$$d = zs_p = 1.645 \cdot .0173 = .028$$

The observed difference is $.135 - .075$, or .060. As this is larger than the computed value for d, the proportion of quits for Department A may be considered significantly larger than the proportion for Department B.

Test for Difference Between a Sample Proportion and a Population Proportion. A variation of the preceding test is available to test the difference between a sample proportion and a population proportion. This variation is also an approximate test, but one that is satisfactory under most circumstances.

The **test procedure** is as follows:

1. Select a suitable probability level for testing the difference for significance.
2. Compute σ_p where

$$\sigma_p = \sqrt{\frac{p\,(1 - p)}{n}}$$

and where

p = population proportion

n = the number of items in the sample

3. Compute d, where

$$d = z\sigma_p$$

The value for z may be determined from Table 1a (ignoring the sign for z).
4. Compare the difference between the sample proportion and the population proportion with the value for d. If it is numerically smaller than d, the difference in the direction indicated is not significant at the probability level used and could be due to sampling error. If it is numerically larger, the difference may be considered significant.

Change in Clerical Procedures Checked. Suppose, for example, that in an area of activity in a mail order house extensive studies have shown the errors in making clerical entries have averaged .87 percent of the total entries made. A change in the clerical procedure is made. A sample of 1,000 entries are checked and the weighted proportion defective found to be .72 percent. At a probability level of .02, could this be taken as evidence of a real reduction in errors, or is it possible that for a sample of 1,000 entries a figure of .72 percent could be obtained simply by chance with the population-proportion remaining at .87 percent? Computation of σ_p gives:

$$\sigma_p = \sqrt{\frac{p\,(1-p)}{n}} = \sqrt{\frac{.0087\,(1-.0087)}{1,000}}$$

$$= .000294, \text{ or } .0294\%$$

$$\text{Computed } d = z\sigma_p = 2.055 \cdot .0294\% = .061\%$$

The value for z was obtained from Table 1a, using a probability of .02.

The observed difference is .87 percent −.72 percent, or .15 percent. As the observed difference is greater than the computed value for d, it may be considered significant. A reduction of the observed magnitude for a sample of 1,000 items could not be a chance occurrence at the probability level selected.

TEST FOR AN EXTREME MEAN. A simple test has been determined to test an extreme mean to see whether or not it is significantly larger (or smaller) than the remainder of the means involved. Such a test might be useful, for example, in determining whether or not to discard an extreme mean as not being representative of the population from which the others have been obtained (perhaps because of an incorrectly drawn sample). Or it may be useful, in some cases, to test for an apparent shift in a population average.

The test for significance of the difference between the **extreme mean** and the **other means** is:

1. Arrange the means in the order of their magnitude.
2. Compute γ.

   When the number of means is from 3 to 7,

   $$\gamma = \frac{\overline{X}_2 - \overline{X}_1}{\overline{X}_k - \overline{X}_1}$$

   When the number of means is from 8 to 10,

   $$\gamma = \frac{\overline{X}_2 - \overline{X}_1}{\overline{X}_{k-1} - \overline{X}_1}$$

   When the number of means is from 11 to 13,

   $$\gamma = \frac{\overline{X}_3 - \overline{X}_1}{\overline{X}_{k-1} - \overline{X}_1}$$

   When the number of means is from 14 to 30,

   $$\gamma = \frac{\overline{X}_3 - \overline{X}_1}{\overline{X}_{k-2} - \overline{X}_1}$$

   In the formula above, $\overline{X}_1$ represents the extreme mean, $\overline{X}_2$ the mean nearest to it in magnitude, X_3 the next mean in magnitude, and so on to the end of the series which is represented by $\overline{X}_k$.

3. Select a suitable probability level.
4. Using the selected probability level, determine the table value for γ from Table 7. The probability values in the table heading show the probability of a computed γ being greater than the table value for γ because of the extreme mean being obtained by chance from the same population from which the other means were obtained.

5. Compare the computed value for γ with the table value. If the computed value is smaller than the table value, the extreme mean may not be considered significantly different at the probability level selected. If it is larger than the table value, the difference may be considered significant with the probability of error indicated by the probability level selected.

Extreme Work Element Time Retained. For an example, consider a case in which a number of time studies have been made for a work element. It is an element that is considered constant—that is, one whose time requirements, on the average, should not vary from job to job. A number of stop-watch time studies have been made, the average time for the element computed for each study, and a leveling factor applied. The leveled average (in minutes) for each of the studies is as follows: 13.29, 13.27, 11.79, 13.63, 9.49, 12.87, 10.67 12.33, 11.78, and 10.89. A question of discarding the 9.49-min. study in working up the time for the element has arisen as the value seems to be abnormal. If it is the result of poor leveling, of nonstandard work material, or of some other non-representative condition it should be discarded. On the other hand, if it was at this low figure simply by chance, discarding it before working up the time to allow for the element will not be appropriate.

In order to discover, by testing, whether the value could be obtained by chance from the population from which the other values were obtained, the values are first arranged in their order of magnitude: 9.49, 10.67, 10.89, 11.78, 11.79, 12.33, 12.87, 13.27, 13.29, and 13.63.

$$\gamma = \frac{\overline{X}_2 - \overline{X}_1}{\overline{X}_{k-1} - \overline{X}_1} = \frac{10.67 - 9.49}{13.29 - 9.49} = \frac{1.18}{3.80} = 3.11$$

Assuming that a probability level of .05 will be appropriate, Table 7 gives a table value for γ of .477. As the computed value for γ is smaller than the table value, the extreme mean may not be rejected as significantly different at the probability level selected.

Probability

LAWS OF PROBABILITY. Production management is constantly confronted with the need to make decisions involving risk and uncertainty. The risk of mistakes in clerical work must be compromised with the cost of checking the details. The cost of having extra machine capacity available must be compromised with the risk of being unable to operate if one key machine is down. The probability of paying overtime must be compromised with the risk of investing training costs in an operator who will not be needed.

The concepts, reasoning, and simple techniques dealing with probability which are discussed in this division are useful in calculating risks under varying circumstances.

Probability may be defined in several ways. One definition is that probability is relative frequency in the long run. If many tosses of a coin were made we would expect heads to come up 50 percent of the time and tails 50 percent of the time. If 1,000 clerical extensions were checked for accuracy and 40 of them found to be wrong, we could say that the probability of any one entry being wrong is 40 out of 1,000 or 4 out of 100. Another useful way of defining this concept is that probability is the number of ways a specified event can happen compared to the total number of ways for an event. There are two ways a coin may fall since it has two sides. There is one way it may fall with heads up. Therefore, the probability of heads is one out of two, or 1/2. If one card is drawn from a full deck, there are 52 different cards from which it will be drawn. The probability of drawing an ace is 4/52 as there are 4 possibilities of drawing an ace out of the 52 possible cards.

In working problems in probability it is usually most convenient to express the probability fraction in decimal form. The probability of getting tails is .50; of drawing an ace in a single draw is .077. When an event is certain to happen, the probability is, of course, 1.00; when it is certain not to happen, the probability is 0.

The Multiplication Law. The probability of one specified event happening and then another specified event happening may be solved by a law of probability known as the multiplication law. This law is:

Probability of Event A and then Event B
= (Probability of A) × (Probability of B)

This law depends on the two probabilities being independent of each other; that is, the probability for Event B is the same whether Event A happens or does not happen. By way of example, the probability of getting two heads in two tosses of a coin is .5 × .5, or .25.

In assuring the accuracy of engineering drawings, for example, if the probability of the draftsman making a mistake is .02, and if the probability of the checker overlooking a mistake is .015, the probability of both events happening, resulting in an erroneous drawing, is .02 × .015 = .0003, or 3 in 10,000. This law may be extended to cover more than two specified events. For example, the probability of Event A happening, and then Event B, and then Event C equals the probability of A times the probability of B times the probability of C.

Conditional Probability. If the probabilities for the different specified events are not independent of each other, a slight modification of the multiplication law has to be made. It must read:

Probability of Event A and then Event B
= (Probability of A) × (Probability of B, given A)

For example, suppose two cards are drawn from a deck, the first one not being replaced before the second one is drawn. What is the probability of drawing two aces? The probability of getting an ace on the first draw is 4/52 or .077. If an ace is drawn on the first draw, the probability of an ace on the second draw is now a different figure. It is 3/51, or .059, as there are only 3 aces left out of a total of 51 cards left in the deck. The probability of drawing two aces is .077 × 0.59, or .0045.

The Addition Law. The probability of either one specified event or another specified event happening may be solved by a law of probability known as the addition law. This law is:

Probability of Event A and then Event B
= (Probability of A) × (Probability of B)

For example, in a single draw from a deck of cards the probability of getting an ace is 4/52, or .077. Likewise, the probability of getting a king is 4/52, or .077. In drawing a single card, the probability that it will be either an ace or a king is .077 + .077, or .154.

Note that these two events are **mutually exclusive,** that is, the card drawn cannot be both an ace and a king. In many industrial situations the events are **not** mutually exclusive, and then the probability of any one of several events occurring is the sum of the separate probabilities less the probability of simultaneous occurrence of more than one. The law is:

Probability of either Event A or Event B
    = (Probability of Event A) + (Probability of Event B) − (Probability of both
                    Event A and Event B)

The probability of both Event A and Event B is figured, using the reasoning of the previous division.

For example, if in a clerical step on a form the probability of an error in posting is .006 and the probability of an error in making an extension is .017, the probability of any error occurring (if these are the only possible sources) is:

$$.006 + .017 - .006 \times .017$$

This law may be extended to more than two possible events. The probability of either Event A or Event B or Event C equals the probability of Event A plus the probability of Event B plus the probability of Event C. If the events are not mutually exclusive—that is, if two of the events could happen on the same trial—the probabilities of **simultaneous occurrence** would be subtracted.

DIRECT SOLUTION OF PROBABILITY PROBLEMS. Problems in probability may often be solved by direct application of the probability laws. Typical methods of computation will be illustrated by the examples that follow. In many studies, however, a direct approach by application of the laws would be impractical or require an excessive amount of computation. In such cases, solution may be made through use of the binomial distribution, the Poisson distribution, or the normal distribution as shown in the subdivisions that follow.

Probability of Availability of One of Two Processes. For an example of a **direct solution,** consider the case of a product that may be made by either Process I or Process II, as sketched in Fig. 8. Process I requires the simultaneous use of Machines A and B. Process II requires the simultaneous use of Machine C, Machine D, and Machine E. For each machine, the probability that it will be available and in operating condition at any selected time is shown. What is the probability of being able to use either Process I or Process II at any required time?

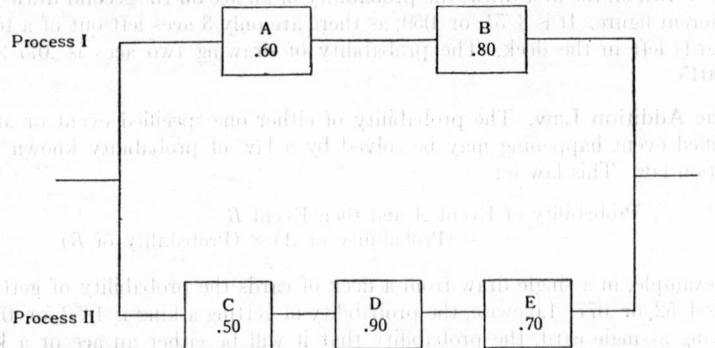

Fig. 8. Processes and machine probabilities.

The probability of Process I being available is the probability of Machine A being available and then B being available. This is the product of the two probabilities or .60 × .80, or .48. The probability of Process II being available is the product of .50 × .90 × .70, or .315.

To determine the probability of at least one of the processes being available, all possible cases must be considered. One possibility is that Process I and Process II will be available simultaneously. The probability of this being true is .48 × .315, or .151. Another possibility is that Process I will be available and that Process II will not. This probability is .48 × (1 − .315), or .329. A third possibility is that Process II will be available and Process I will not. The probability of this is .315 (1 − .48), or .164. The probability of at least one process being available is the sum of these probabilities, .151 + .329 + .164, or .644. This figure may be checked by computing the probability that neither will be available. This is (1 − .48) × (1 − .315), or .356. The probability that one or more will be available is 1 minus the probability that neither will be, or 1 − .356 which equals .644 An answer might also be determined by use of the formula previously given for use when events are not mutually exclusive. The probability of either Process I or Process II equals the probability of Process I being available (.48) plus the probability of Process II (.315) minus the probability of both I and II being available (.48 × .315). This gives .48 + .315 − .151, or .644, as the answer.

Assignment of Machines by Probability. For another example, consider a problem in determining the number of machines to assign to one operator. These machines run 70 percent of the time unattended. For 30 percent of the time they need the attention of the operator. This operator attention is required at irregular intervals. It is proposed that three machines be assigned per operator. For this arrangement (or any other) the machine time that will be lost because two or more machines are down and require operator attention at the same time can be solved directly through use of the laws of probability. The possible combinations of machines running (R) or down (D) at any time and the probabilities for each can be computed as follows:

Machine 1	Machine 2	Machine 3	Probability
$R = .70$	$R = .70$	$R = .70$	$.70 × .70 × .70 = .343$ (a)
		$D = .30$	$.70 × .70 × .30 = .147$ (b)
	$D = .30$	$R = .70$	$.70 × .30 × .70 = .147$ (b)
		$D = .30$	$.70 × .30 × .30 = .063$ (c)
$D = .30$	$R = .70$	$R = .70$	$.30 × .70 × .70 = .147$ (b)
		$D = .30$	$.30 × .70 × .30 = .063$ (c)
	$D = .30$	$R = .70$	$.30 × .30 × .70 = .063$ (c)
		$D = .30$	$.30 × .30 × .30 = .027$ (d)
			Total 1.000

From these probabilities, the proportion of the time that 0, 1, 2, and 3 machines, respectively, will be down can be summarized. With this summary, the machine time that will be lost with this arrangement of 3 machines per operator can be determined. The computations are given below:

Case	No. of Machines Down Together	Percentage of Time	Machine Days Lost per Day
(a)	0	.343	0
(b)	1	$3 \times .147 = .441$	0
(c)	2	$3 \times .063 = .189$	$.189 \times 1 = .189$
(d)	3	.027	$.027 \times 2 = .054$
			Total .243

$$\text{Proportion of machine time lost} = \frac{\text{machine days lost per day}}{\text{machine days available per day}}$$

$$= \frac{.243}{3 \times 1.000} = .081$$

If only two machines were assigned to an operator, the proportion of machine time lost could be computed in the same manner. It would, of course, be somewhat less. If four or more machines were assigned, a greater proportion of machine time would be lost. With figures for the cost per day for operator time and for machine time, it would be possible to determine the most economical number of machines to assign to an operator.

USE OF THE BINOMIAL FORMULA. Direct solution of probability problems like the above becomes cumbersome if the number of items in the sample or population is large. A more convenient method for solution is to use the binomial distribution formula. If we let p represent the probability of an item falling in a specified category, let q represent the probability that it will not, and let n represent the number of items in the sample or population, frequencies for the distribution of possible occurrences could be computed by expanding the binomial $(p + q)^n$. In practice, the actual expansion need not be made. The frequency or probability of exactly r occurrences of the specified event can be computed by the equation

$$\text{Probability} = \frac{n!}{r!(n-r)!} \, q^{n-r} p^r$$

For the machine-assignment problem described above, the computations are as shown below. For this problem $n = 3$, the number of machines. The probability, p, for the specified event is .30. The probability of the specified event not occurring, q, is .70.

No. of Machines Down Together r	Probability	
0	$\dfrac{3!}{0!\,(3-0)!} \times .70^{3-0} \times .30^0 = .70^3$	$= .343$
1	$\dfrac{3!}{1!\,(3-1)!} \times .70^{3-1} \times .30^1 = 3 \times .70^2 \times .30 = .441$	
2	$\dfrac{3!}{2!\,(3-2)!} \times .70^{3-2} \times .30^2 = 3 \times .70 \times .30^2 = .189$	
3	$\dfrac{3!}{3!\,(3-3)!} \times .70^{3-3} \times .30^3 = .30^3$	$= .027$
		Total 1.000

USE OF THE POISSON DISTRIBUTION. For cases in which n is relatively large and p is fairly small, the Poisson distribution closely approximates the binomial distribution and so may be used as a means for solving probability problems. Also, in situations in which there are a great many possibilities of a specified event or category occurring, but in which for only a relatively few of the opportunities does it actually occur, the Poisson may apply not as an approximation to the binomial but as a distribution in its own right. In some cases, too, the values for n and p may not be known separately, but the average number of occurrences per sample is available. In such cases the Poisson may be used because only this average is needed to reach a solution.

If we let p' represent the probability of an item falling in a specified category and let n represent the number of items in the sample or segment of the population, then the probability of exactly r occurrences of the specified event can be determined by the formula

$$\frac{(np')^r}{r!} e^{-np'}$$

where np' is either equal to the average number of events per sample or population segment or equal to the probability of the specified event happening times the number of items in the sample. The meaning taken will depend on the form of the data that are available.

Poisson Distribution Table. In practice, the formula need not be used to obtain a solution; the solution may be obtained more easily by use of a table of the Poisson distribution. Table 8 gives values of the cumulative Poisson distribution for a range of values for np'. The figures shown in this table represent the **cumulative probability** of obtaining r or more of the specified event for any given value for np'. For example, if $np' = 1.40$, the probability of observing four or more of the specified events is given by the table as .054. The probability of obtaining or observing exactly r events can be obtained by subtraction of the table probabilities. The probability of observing exactly three events, for example, can be obtained by subtracting the probability of observing four or more events, which is .054, from the probability of observing three or more events, which is .167. This gives .167 − .054, or .113, as the probability of observing just three of the specified events.

To take a simple example, consider accident figures in a factory which has had a good program of safety engineering for some time and for which over the past months there has been little change in the number of men employed, in processes, methods, or in other factors that might have an appreciable effect on accident experience. While the number of lost-time accidents has varied somewhat from month to month, the numbers have centered around an average figure of 4.50 per month. Figures for the previous two years are charted in Fig. 9. During the previous month, however, there were seven lost-time accidents. The question was raised as to whether this figure was simply a chance occurrence that could be expected from the normal month-to-month variation or whether it might be due to some significant but unknown change in the accident-producing situation. By examination of Table 8 it was found that for an np' of 4.50 (the average number per month) a monthly figure of 7 is possible. The probability of 7 or more accidents per month is .169; of 8 or more, .087. Therefore, the probability of getting just 7 is .169 − .087, or .082. Only if, say, more than 10 occurred could the figure be taken as good evidence of a significant change in the accident-producing situation. It may be useful, when accident figures are charted, to draw a line on the chart showing the limiting figure which might occur purely by chance with the average at some known value. A line has been drawn at 10 accidents per month in Fig. 9. The table of the Poisson distribution shows that with $np' = 4.50$ the probability is only .007 of getting a monthly figure of 11 or more. Only about 1 time out of 100 could a monthly figure higher than the limit line be experienced purely by chance. A plotted point above this line might be taken as good evidence of a significant change in the conditions that result in accidents.

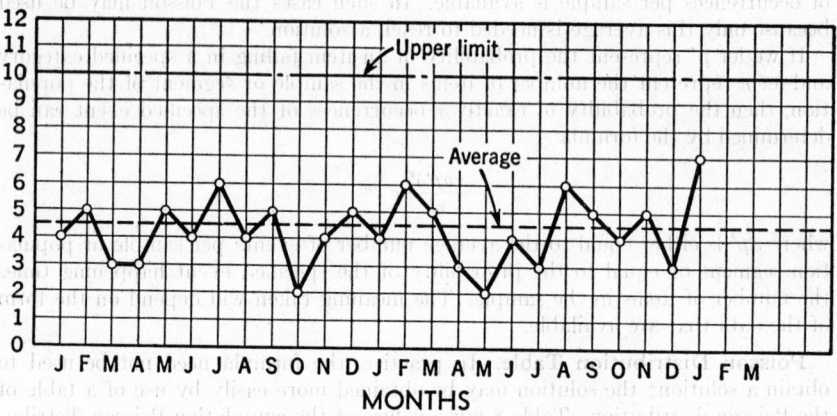

Fig. 9. Lost-time accidents per month.

PROBABILITY SOLUTIONS FOR THE NORMAL DISTRIBUTION.

If the mean, μ, and the standard deviation, σ, are known for a population or can be closely estimated, the probability of getting an observation beyond some specified limit can be computed by use of a table of **areas for the normal distribution curve.** The table of z, Tables 1a and 1b in this section, is such a table. The **procedure** for its use is as follows:

1. Compute z, which is simply the distance in standard deviations from the average to the specified limit. If X_L stands for the specified limit, then

$$z = \frac{X_L - \mu}{\sigma}$$

2. Enter Table 1a or 1b with the computed value for z (enter Table 1a if z is negative, 1b if it is positive). The probability value given by the table is the probability that an item or observation will fall below the specified limit. If the probability of an observation above the limit is desired instead, this may be determined by finding the probability of an item below the limit and subtracting this probability from 1.00. Also, if the proportion of items in a population below a specified limit is to be determined, the probability figure given by the table may be used as the proportion of items below the limit.

Suppose, for example, that following an increase in the guaranteed minimum hourly rate the industrial engineer in a plant has adjusted the piece rates upward in a department. He expects as a result that the new average earnings per operator will be $45.75 for a 40-hr. week, with a standard deviation of $4.80. (These figures are estimates based on a knowledge of the frequency distribution of earnings at the old piece rates and on the amount of increase in the piece rates.)

He is interested in estimating or predicting the proportion of operators whose piecework earnings will fall below $40.00 per week at the new piece rates. For this case,

$$z = \frac{40.00 - 45.75}{4.80} = -1.20$$

From Table 1a the probability figure of .1151 is found for z equal to -1.20. This result may be expressed in another way as a prediction that 11.5 percent of the operators will have weekly piecework earnings below $40.00 per week. Since make-up pay would be required for this relatively high proportion of operators, the company decided on a further increase in piece rates. This problem and its solution is illustrated in Fig. 10.

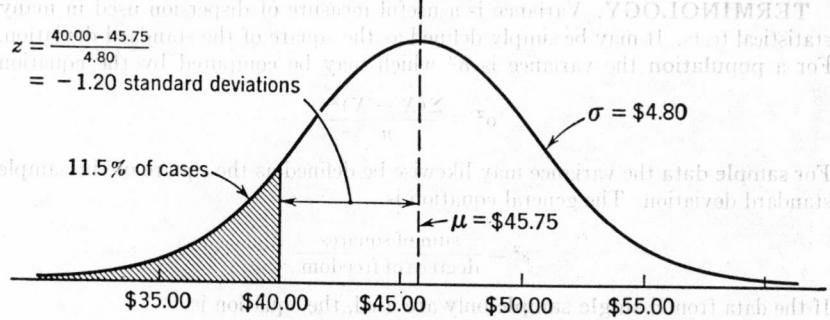

Fig. 10. **Percentage of operators with piecework earnings under $40.00**

If the frequency distribution has been tabulated as a cumulative distribution and plotted on normal-probability paper, the proportion of items beyond some specified limit may be read directly from the graph. Refer to Fig. 2, for an example. Suppose we wish to estimate for this case the proportion of operators that will have incentive earnings of more than $24.00 over base earnings. By entering the graph at the bottom with this amount we can read at the side that approximately 30 percent of the operators will have incentive earnings above the specified figure.

LIMITS FOR A FREQUENCY DISTRIBUTION. For a normal frequency distribution, virtually all the observations fall within the range $\mu \pm 3\sigma$. We may note from Table 1b that with $z = 3$—that is, with a limit 3 standard deviations above the mean—the probability is .9987, which means that 99.87 percent of the distribution lies below $\mu + 3\sigma$. From Table 1a one may note that .13 percent of the distribution will lie below $\mu - 3\sigma$. Thus 99.87 $-$ .13, or 99.74 percent of the observations fall between plus or minus three standard deviations from the mean. Similar analysis will show that 97.72 $-$ 2.28, or 95.44 percent of a normal distribution lies within two standard deviations of the mean.

The above remarks apply only for a normal distribution. Limits so computed will be practical, however, for any distribution that approximates the normal reasonably well. It is possible to compute limits which will be valid for a distribution of any form by means of an inequality known as **Tchebycheff's inequality.** This inequality states that for any distribution, not more than $1/z^2$ of the observations will be more than z standard deviations from the mean. Thus no more than $1/3^2$ or $1/9$ of a distribution will lie outside limits that are plus and minus three standard deviations from the mean. No more than $1/2^2$ or $1/4$ of the observations will lie outside limits at plus and minus two standard deviations.

For non-normal distributions which are known to have only one mode or peak, and whose mode is at or near the value for the mean, an inequality known as the **Camp-Meidell inequality** may be used to compute limits. This inequality states that for any distribution meeting the above two requirements, not more than $1/2.25z^2$ of the observations will be more than z standard deviations from the mean. Thus no more than $1/2.25 \cdot 3^2$ or $1/20$ of a distribution will lie beyond plus or minus three standard deviations; no more than $1/2.25 \cdot 2^2$ or $1/9$ will lie beyond plus or minus two standard deviations.

The Analysis of Variance

TERMINOLOGY. Variance is a useful measure of dispersion used in many statistical tests. It may be simply defined as the square of the standard deviation. For a **population** the variance is σ^2 which may be computed by the equation

$$\sigma^2 = \frac{\Sigma(X - \overline{X})^2}{n}$$

For **sample data** the variance may likewise be defined as the square of the sample standard deviation. The general equation is

$$s^2 = \frac{\text{sum of squares}}{\text{degrees of freedom}}$$

If the data from a **single sample** only are used, the equation is

$$s^2 = \frac{\Sigma(X - \overline{X})^2}{n - 1}$$

As explained in a previous division of this section, the standard deviation for a sample tends to be somewhat smaller than the standard deviation for the population from which it has been drawn. Dividing the sum of squares by $n - 1$ instead of n corrects for this bias and makes s^2 the best possible estimate of σ^2. Computation of s^2 when more than one sample is involved will be discussed in subsequent divisions.

In the analysis of variance, the general procedure is to set up the hypothesis that the samples in question have been drawn from the same population or that they have been drawn from populations with equal variances. This hypothesis is then tested by comparing sample variances. If the sample variances do not differ more than the difference possible due to chance or sampling error, the hypothesis is allowed to stand. If they differ more than can be explained as due to chance, the hypothesis is rejected and the difference in sample variances considered significant.

TEST FOR DIFFERENCE IN VARIANCES. A simple application of the analysis of variance is available to test for the significance of the difference between two sample variances or a sample variance and a population variance. To consider an example, suppose that experimental changes have been made to a manufacturing procedure to reduce the amount of inherent variability and so produce a more uniform product. The variance for a sample of parts run and measured after the change is somewhat smaller than the variance for a sample of parts produced and measured before the change. The question may be raised as to whether the reduction in sample variance is good evidence of a real reduction in variability for the process or whether the difference is simply due to chance. It is possible that no real improvement has been made but that, by chance, the items selected for measuring the variation in the old procedure had measurements more widely scattered than those selected for measurement after the change. If putting the experimental changes into effect on the production floor will require considerable investment of money, assurance that the changes have really helped will be required.

Steps in the F-Test. The F-test for significance of difference in a specified direction between two variances requires the following steps:

1. Select a suitable probability level for testing the difference for significance.
2. Compute the variance separately for each sample. The equation is

$$s^2 = \frac{\Sigma(X - \bar{X})^2}{n-1}$$

An equivalent equation for ease in computation is

$$s^2 = \frac{\Sigma X^2 - \frac{(\Sigma X)^2}{n}}{n-1}$$

3. Compute F by dividing the larger variance by the smaller; that is,

$$F = \frac{s^2_A}{s^2_B}$$

where s^2_A is the larger of the variances and s^2_B the smaller.
4. Using the selected probability level and $n-1$ degrees freedom for each sample, determine the table value of F from Table 6. If one of the variances being compared is the known variance for the population, the degrees of freedom for this mean square are ∞.
5. Compare the computed value for F with the table value. If the computed value is smaller than the table value, the difference in variances could be a chance happening with no real change in population variance. If the computed value is larger than the table value, the difference could not be assumed to be a chance happening at the selected probability level. The difference in sample variances may be considered an indication of a real difference (in the direction indicated) between population variances.

Application of the F-Test. To take a specific application, suppose that the standard deviation for the tensile strength of paper used as an electrical insulator has been stable at about 13 lb. For a new shipment a sample of 10 pieces has been tested and the standard deviation found to be 21 lb. The user wishes to know whether this represents a real increase in variability or whether perhaps by chance the items in the sample were more variable than they typically would be. A probability level of .01 is selected as suitable for the test, as it was desirable to take no action in the case unless there was strong evidence of a real change. For this case

$$F = \frac{s^2}{\sigma^2}$$

with σ^2 representing the known variance for the paper as it has been running in the past. Thus,

$$F = \frac{s^2}{\sigma^2} = \frac{21^2}{13^2} = \frac{441}{169} = 2.61$$

The table value of F obtained from Table 6 (using 9 degrees of freedom for the greater mean square and ∞ degrees of freedom for the smaller mean square) is 2.41.

Since the computed value for F is larger than the table value, the sample standard deviation for the new shipment can be considered significantly larger. If the population standard deviation for the new shipment was at the usual value, 13 lb., chances are only 1 in 100 that the value for F for a sample of 10 would be greater than 2.41 purely because of sampling fluctuations.

TEST FOR DIFFERENCE AMONG MEANS. The analysis of variance may be used not only as a test for significance of apparent differences in dispersion but also to test for significant differences among a number of sample means. For example, suppose that time studies for a work element that has been considered constant show some variation in average time from job to job. There is then the question of whether there is a real difference in required time from job to job or whether the observed differences in time-study averages could be due simply to chance or to sampling error.

The general method for the test is first to set up the hypothesis that there is no difference among the population averages from which the samples have been drawn. This hypothesis is then tested by first estimating the variance of the populations by studying the variation of items within each sample. (In using the test it must be assumed that the variances for each of the populations are approximately equal even though the averages may differ.) The variance of the populations is then estimated again. This estimate is made by analysis of the variation between the sample averages. This second estimate depends on the fact that, for a normal distribution $\sigma^2 = \sigma_X^2 n$. The population variance, σ^2, is estimated by computing $s_{\bar{X}}^2$ directly, using the differences between means, and then multiplying by n, the sample size. The two variances are then compared by computing the ratio between the larger and the smaller, or F. If the averages of the populations are all the same, the variance ratio, F, will tend toward unity. In any event sampling error will not result (for any selected confidence level) in a computed value for F beyond the limiting values given by the table of F, Table 6. On the other hand, if the computed ratio exceeds the limiting value given by the table, the hypothesis of equal population means may be rejected. Then it cannot be assumed that the difference in variances computed by the two methods are due to chance; part of the difference is probably due to a difference in population averages.

Test Procedures. In specific detail, the steps for the test are as follows:

1. Select a suitable probability level for testing for significance of the differences.

2. Estimate the population variance by use of the differences between each observation in a sample and the mean of the sample. A **pooled estimate** of the population variance is obtained by pooling the information from each of the samples by using the following equation:

$$s^2 = \frac{\Sigma(X_1 - \bar{X}_1)^2 + \Sigma(X_2 - \bar{X}_2)^2 + \cdots \Sigma(X_m - \bar{X}_m)^2}{n_1 + n_2 + \cdots n_m - m}$$

where X_1 represents an observation in the first sample; $\bar{X}_1$, the arithmetic mean of that sample; n_1 the number of observations making up the sample, and so on; and where m represents the number of samples involved in the test.

An equivalent formula which greatly simplifies the computation of the sum of the squares which makes up the numerator of the equation just given is

$$\Sigma X^2 - \left[\frac{(\Sigma X_1)^2}{n_1} + \frac{(\Sigma X_2)^2}{n_2} + \cdots \frac{\Sigma(X_m)^2}{n_m}\right]$$

where X represents each of the observations making up all the samples.

3. Estimate the population variance by use of the differences between each group or sample average and the grand average of all the groups. Such an estimate of the population variance is obtained by the following equation:

$$s^2 = \frac{\Sigma n(\overline{X} - \overline{\overline{X}})^2}{m - 1}$$

where $\overline{X}$ represents the average for a sample and $\overline{\overline{X}}$ the grand average of all the sample averages.

An equivalent formula which greatly simplifies the computation of the sum of the squares in the formula just given is

$$\left(\frac{(\Sigma X_1)^2}{n_1} + \frac{(\Sigma X_2)^2}{n_2} + \cdots \frac{\Sigma(X_m)^2}{n_m}\right) - \frac{(\Sigma X)^2}{N}$$

where $N = \Sigma n$ or the total number of observations in all the samples.

4. As a check on the above computations, the total sum of squares can be computed, considering the observations in all the samples as one grand sample. The formula is $\Sigma(X - \overline{\overline{X}})^2$. An equivalent formula which simplifies the computations is

$$\Sigma X^2 - \frac{(\Sigma X)^2}{N}$$

As a routine check on the denominator or degrees of freedom for each of the variance computations, the total number of degrees of freedom can be computed. It is $N - 1$.

If the computations are correct the sum of squares for within-group variation (obtained in step 2) plus the sum of squares for between-means variation (obtained in step 3) should equal the total sum of squares (obtained in step 4). Likewise, the degrees of freedom for within-group variation plus the degrees of freedom for between-means variation should equal the total number of degrees of freedom.

5. Compute F, the variance ratio, by dividing the between-means variance by the within-group variance.

6. Using the selected confidence level and the degrees of freedom computed in steps 2 and 3, determine the table value for F from Table 6.

7. Compare the computed value for F with the table value. If the computed F is greater than the table value, reject the hypothesis that there is no difference among the averages for the populations sampled and consider the difference among sample averages as significant. If the computed F is less than the table value, accept the hypothesis and assume the observed differences between sample averages to be due to chance. Customary practice is to compute and tabulate the sums of squares and the degrees of freedom separately and to show the results in table form. Also, variance is generally referred to as the **mean square** which is obtained by dividing the **sum of the squares** by the **degrees of freedom**. This practice will be illustrated in the example that follows.

As mentioned previously, for this test to be exact, the standard deviation for each of the populations must be equal (even though their averages may not be), and the distributions must be normal. It has been found, however, that these requirements need be only roughly approximated for the test to be generally satisfactory.

DIFFERENCES BETWEEN AVERAGES—AN APPLICATION. For an example, consider the following figures for individual weekly incentive earnings for four different crews of women, each crew being made up of five women. A question may be raised as to whether the differences in average weekly earnings among the crews could simply be chance differences, or whether there is evidence that they represent real differences in crew abilities or in conditions of work.

	Weekly Earnings			
	Crew 1	Crew 2	Crew 3	Crew 4
	$44.00	$32.10	$47.90	$43.20
	38.80	33.90	42.90	41.50
	35.40	38.20	43.60	39.70
	36.00	37.20	44.40	43.20
	39.50	35.80	40.30	41.20
Average	$38.74	$35.44	$43.82	$41.76

The computations from the weekly earnings of the crews appear in Fig. 11. Each value has been coded by subtracting $30.00. In the analysis of variance no correction need be made later for coded values if the coding is made simply by subtracting a constant amount from each observation. A probability level of .01 was selected as most appropriate for this study. Using the results from Fig. 11, the further computations are:

$$\Sigma X = 14.00 + 8.80 + \cdots 11.20 = 198.80$$

$$(\Sigma X)^2 = 198.80^2 = 39,521.44$$

$$\Sigma X^2 = 196.00 + 77.44 + \cdots 125.44 = 2,286.68$$

Sum of squares—within-crew variation

$$= \Sigma X^2 - \left[\frac{(\Sigma X_1)^2}{n_1} + \frac{(\Sigma X_2)^2}{n_2} + \cdots \frac{(\Sigma X_m)^2}{n_m} \right]$$

$$= 2,286.68 - \left(\frac{1,909.69}{5} + \frac{739.84}{5} + \frac{4,774.81}{5} + \frac{3,457.44}{5} \right)$$

$$= 2,286.68 - 2,176.36 = 110.32$$

Degrees of freedom—within-crew variation

$$= n_1 + n_2 + \cdots n_m - m = 5 + 5 + 5 + 5 - 4 = 16$$

Sum of squares—between-crew variation

$$= \left[\frac{(\Sigma X_1)^2}{n_1} + \frac{(\Sigma X_2)^2}{n_2} + \cdots \frac{(\Sigma X_m)^2}{n_m} \right] - \frac{(\Sigma X)^2}{N}$$

$$= \left(\frac{1,909.69}{5} + \frac{739.84}{5} + \frac{4,774.81}{5} + \frac{3,457.44}{5} \right) - \frac{39,521.44}{20}$$

$$= 2,176.36 - 1,976.07 = 200.29$$

Coded Observations and Observations Squared

Crew 1		Crew 2		Crew 3		Crew 4	
X_1	$X_1{}^2$	X_2	$X_2{}^2$	X_3	$X_3{}^2$	X_4	$X_4{}^2$
14.00	196.00	2.10	4.41	17.90	320.41	13.20	174.24
8.80	77.44	3.90	15.21	12.90	166.41	11.50	132.25
5.40	29.16	8.20	67.24	13.60	184.96	9.70	94.09
6.00	36.00	7.20	51.84	14.40	207.36	13.20	174.24
9.50	90.25	5.80	33.64	10.30	106.09	11.20	125.44
$\Sigma X_1 =$ 43.70		$\Sigma X_2 =$ 27.20		$\Sigma X_3 =$ 69.10		$\Sigma X_4 =$ 58.80	
$n_1 = 5$		$n_2 = 5$		$n_3 = 5$		$n_4 = 5$	
		$N = 5 + 5 + 5 + 5 = 20$		$m = 4$			
$(\Sigma X_1)^2 = 1{,}909.69$		$(\Sigma X_2)^2 = 739.84$		$(\Sigma X_3)^2 = 4{,}774.81$		$(\Sigma X_4)^2 = 3{,}457.44$	

Fig. 11. Computations from coded weekly earnings of crews.

Degrees of freedom—between-crew variation

$$m - 1 = 4 - 1 = 3$$

Total sum of squares

$$= \Sigma X^2 - \frac{(\Sigma X)^2}{N} = 2{,}286.68 - \frac{39{,}521.44}{20} = 310.61$$

Total degrees of freedom

$$N - 1 = 20 - 1 = 19$$

Tabulation of the above values in the following way furnishes a helpful summary:

Source of Variation	Sum of Squares	Degrees of Freedom	Mean Square	F-Ratio
Between Crews ...	200.29	3	$\frac{200.29}{3} = 66.8$	$F = \frac{66.8}{6.9} = 9.7$
Within Crews	110.32	16	$\frac{110.32}{16} = 6.9$	
Total	310.61	19		

Using 3 as the degrees of freedom for the greater mean square and 16 as the degrees of freedom for the lesser mean square and a probability level of .01, interpolation in Table 6 gives a table value for F of 5.3. A comparison of the computed value with this figure shows the computed value to be greater. Thus the observed differences between averages may be considered significant. If the observed differences had simply been due to chance, with the real average earning possibilities being the same in each case, the probability of getting a computed F of more than 5.3 would be one in a hundred or less.

FACTORIAL STUDIES. In some industrial engineering or management studies there may be several factors which must be studied for their effect. A common method of approach is to study the effect of each factor separately, taking one factor at a time. Measurements may be made at a range of levels for the factor while holding all the other factors constant at some one level. This has been the traditional experimental method.

In many cases a much more efficient approach may be taken through use of a **factorial design for the study.** In this approach the effects of all the factors are studied simultaneously through use of a planned design for the collection and analysis of data. There are a number of advantages in this approach over the customary method in which only one factor at a time is varied and studied.

1. Much less data and study are required to give conclusions of the required degree of confidence. Each measurement or observation is used in the study of each of the factors instead of in the study of just one, as under the customary approach.
2. The data used in evaluating the effects of one factor are based on the full range of values for each of the other factors. Holding the levels of other factors constant at some arbitrarily selected level, as under the customary approach, may not give, in many cases, a representative picture of the effects of the factor under study.

3. Observations will be in a most suitable form for the analysis of variance. Through the analysis of variance the observed effect of varying the level for a factor may be tested for significance. When there is considerable inherent variation in a process, it may be difficult to tell whether an observed effect of varying a factor represents a real effect, or whether it may be due to chance or experimental error.

4. Observations will be in suitable form for study for possible interactions between one or more of the factors. If there are interactions, the effect of varying one factor will depend on the level of one or more of the other factors. Likewise, the results of varying two factors together will not be the same as the sum of the effects that would be found if they were to be varied separately as under the customary study approach.

Factorial Design Procedure. In a factorial design for a study, each level for each factor is combined with each possible combination of levels for each of the other factors. For each combination of levels one or more observations are obtained. The general plan for collection and arrangement of the data for analysis is indicated by the following illustration. A similar plan may be developed for any number of factors and any number of levels for each. Also, the number of observations obtained for each combination of levels may be any number desired. In this plan three will be obtained. The number will generally depend on the amount of inherent variation in the procedure, the importance of the study, the precision required for the conclusions, and like factors. The assignment of factors to lines and columns may follow any convenient pattern.

Factors:

Operator: Operator A, Operator B, Operator C
Material: Material X, Material Y
Tool: Tool 1, Tool 2

The effect, if any, of each of these factors singly or in combination on output is to be determined.

	Material X		Material Y	
	Tool 1	Tool 2	Tool 1	Tool 2
Operator A	$O_A \ T_1 \ M_X$	$O_A \ T_2 \ M_X$	$O_A \ T_1 \ M_Y$	$O_A \ T_2 \ M_Y$
	$O_A \ T_1 \ M_X$	$O_A \ T_2 \ M_X$	$O_A \ T_1 \ M_Y$	$O_A \ T_2 \ M_Y$
	$O_A \ T_1 \ M_X$	$O_A \ T_2 \ M_X$	$O_A \ T_1 \ M_Y$	$O_A \ T_2 \ M_Y$
Operator B	$O_B \ T_1 \ M_X$	$O_B \ T_2 \ M_X$	$O_B \ T_1 \ M_Y$	$O_B \ T_2 \ M_Y$
	$O_B \ T_1 \ M_X$	$O_B \ T_2 \ M_X$	$O_B \ T_1 \ M_Y$	$O_B \ T_2 \ M_Y$
	$O_B \ T_1 \ M_X$	$O_B \ T_2 \ M_X$	$O_B \ T_1 \ M_Y$	$O_B \ T_2 \ M_Y$
Operator C	$O_C \ T_1 \ M_X$	$O_C \ T_2 \ M_X$	$O_C \ T_1 \ M_Y$	$O_C \ T_2 \ M_Y$
	$O_C \ T_1 \ M_X$	$O_C \ T_2 \ M_X$	$O_C \ T_1 \ M_Y$	$O_C \ T_2 \ M_Y$
	$O_C \ T_1 \ M_X$	$O_C \ T_2 \ M_X$	$O_C \ T_1 \ M_Y$	$O_C \ T_2 \ M_Y$

This design is for 36 observations, 3 each for each combination of levels for the three factors. The observations may be taken in any convenient order. However, if there is any possibility of changes in other factors while data are being collected, observations should be collected in random order. This will minimize the possibility of such a change showing as an effect of changing one of the factors under study.

The effect of changing each factor is determined by simply computing the average for all the readings for each level and then comparing these averages. Any difference among the averages for a factor that might seem to be due simply to chance may be tested for significance by the analysis of variance. This procedure and the procedure for testing for interactions will be described in the subdivision that follows.

THE ANALYSIS OF VARIANCE IN FACTORIAL STUDIES. In some studies there may be some question for one or more of the factors as to whether the observed difference among averages for each of the levels for the factor represent real differences or whether they might be only chance differences arising from the inherent variation in the activity. When such a question does arise, the analysis of variance technique can be used to test the observed differences for significance.

The averages for each level of each factor may also be compared by simple observation to determine what interactions between factors, if any, exist and to determine their importance. In cases where an interaction seems to be present but where there is some question as to whether the variations noted in the observations may simply be chance variations, the analysis of variance may again be used as a test for significance.

Steps in the Procedure. In the analysis of variance for a factorial study, the total sum of squares and the total number of degrees of freedom for all the observations are separated into:

1. The sum of squares and the degrees of freedom for each factor that may be assigned to changes in levels for that factor.

The sum of squares for between-level variations for a factor may be determined by the following equation:

$$\text{Sum of squares} = \left[\frac{(\Sigma X_1)^2}{n_1} + \frac{(\Sigma X_2)^2}{n_2} + \cdots \frac{(\Sigma X_m)^2}{n_m} \right] - \frac{(\Sigma X)^2}{N}$$

where ΣX_1 represents the sum of all the observations at level 1 for the factor being studied and n_1 the number of observations at that level. Likewise, ΣX_2 represents the sum of all observations at level 2, n_2 the number of observations at that level, and so on through all levels. The expression ΣX represents the sum of all the observations for the entire study and N the total number of observations.

The degrees of freedom for between-level variation are $m - 1$ or 1 less than the number of levels for the factor.

2. The sum of squares and the degrees of freedom that may be assigned to each of the possible interactions between factors.

The sum of squares for variation due to **interaction between any two factors** may be determined by first computing the sum of the squares, using the sum of the observations for each of the combinations of levels for the two factors, and then subtracting the sum of squares for between-level variation (previously computed) for each factor. The equation may be written:

$$\text{Sum of squares} = \left[\frac{(\Sigma X_1)^2}{n_1} + \frac{(\Sigma X_2)^2}{n_2} + \cdots \frac{(\Sigma X_m)^2}{n_m} \right] - \frac{(\Sigma X)^2}{N}$$
$$- \text{sum of squares for between-level variation for one factor}$$
$$- \text{sum of squares for between-level variation for the other factor}$$

In the preceding equation, ΣX_1 represents the sum of the observations for one combination of levels for the two factors, ΣX_2 the sum of observations for another combination of levels, and so on until all possible combinations have been included. The value for n_1 is the number of observations for the first combination of levels, and so on.

The sum of squares for variation due to **interaction between three factors** may be determined by first computing the sum of squares, using the sum of the observations for each of the combinations of levels for the three factors, and then subtracting the sum of squares for between-level variation (previously computed) for each factor and in addition subtracting the sum of squares for each of the two-factor interactions as previously computed.

The number of degrees of freedom for any interaction is the product of the degrees of freedom for between-level variation for each of the factors in the interaction.

3. The sum of squares and the number of degrees of freedom that may be assigned to the within-group or inherent variation in the activity under study. This sum of squares and degrees of freedom may be obtained by subtracting all the previously computed sums of squares from the total sum of squares and all the previously computed degrees of freedom from the total degrees of freedom. An alternative procedure is to compute these measures directly, using the following equations:

$$\text{Sum of squares} = \Sigma X^2 - \left(\frac{(\Sigma X_1)^2}{n_1} + \frac{(\Sigma X_2)^2}{n_2} + \cdots \frac{(\Sigma X_m)^2}{n_m} \right)$$

$$\text{Degrees of freedom} = n_1 + n_2 + \cdots n_m - m$$

In the above equations, ΣX_1 represents the sum of the observations for one combination of levels for the factors; n_1 represents the number of observations for that combination; ΣX_2 represents the sum of observations for the next combination of levels, and so on.

4. The total sum of squares and the total number of degrees of freedom may be computed. The equations are:

$$\text{Total sum of squares} = \Sigma(X^2) - \frac{(\Sigma X)^2}{N}$$

$$\text{Total degrees of freedom} = N - 1$$

After this breakdown of the total sum of squares and total number of degrees of freedom has been made, the results may be posted to an **analysis-of-variance table** for easy reference. Next, the mean-square values for each source of variation may be computed by dividing the sum of squares for that source by its degrees of freedom.

The F-ratio for each source of variation may next be determined. The observed value for F may then be compared with the table value at the selected probability level. If the computed value is greater than the table value, the observed difference in means may be considered significant.

The interaction of the three factors should be tested first, using the within-group, or residual, mean square to compute F. If the F-test shows the interaction to be significant, this interaction mean square should be used as the denominator to compute F for each of the two-factor interactions. If this is done, the F-test will test for a two-factor interaction effect over and above the three-factor effect. If the three-factor interaction is found not to be significant, its degrees of freedom and sum of squares may be added to the within-group, or residual, sum of squares and degrees of freedom. The resulting mean square from the pooled data may be used as the denominator to compute F for each of the two-factor interactions. If one of the two-factor interactions is found to have a significant effect, the mean-square value for this interaction should be used as the denominator in computing F for the between-level variation for each of the two factors involved. This will test for an independent effect of changing the level of the factor over and above the interaction effect of the factor. If the F-test for the interaction does not show significance, its sum of squares and degrees of freedom may also be pooled with the residual sum of squares and degrees of freedom to give a revised mean square. This new mean square may be used as the denominator to compute F for between-level variation for each of the separate factors.

A Factorial Design Study with Analysis of Variance. A simple example of a factorial design and of variance analysis is given by the following productivity study. There are two crews doing the work under study, one supervised by Foreman A, the other by Foreman B. Both crews are made up of male and female operators. Productivity figures have been obtained for a ten-day period for the crew under each foreman, and for each foreman, separately for male and for female operators. These figures are shown below. Three questions have been asked. (1) Is the apparent difference in productivity between foremen significant? (2) Is there evidence of a real difference in productivity for this work between male and female operators? (3) Is there an interaction between foreman and sex of operator; that is, does the productivity of a specified sex depend on which of the two foremen is the supervisor?

The following are the computations that were made. Actual productivity figures have been coded by subtracting 100 to simplify the arithmetic.

Foreman A		Foreman B	
Male	Female	Male	Female
4	4	4	4
4	4	3	4
5	2	1	0
5	2	2	2
3	2	2	3
6	3	2	0
4	2	3	2
4	5	3	2
4	1	4	3
6	2	1	3
$\Sigma = 45$	$\Sigma = 27$	$\Sigma = 25$	$\Sigma = 23$

$$\text{Average, Foreman } A = \frac{\Sigma X}{n} = \frac{45 + 27}{10 + 10} = \frac{72}{20} = 3.6 \text{ or } 103.6$$

$$\text{Average, Foreman } B = \frac{\Sigma X}{n} = \frac{25 + 23}{10 + 10} = \frac{48}{20} = 2.4 \text{ or } 102.4$$

$$\text{Average, male operators} = \frac{\Sigma X}{n} = \frac{45 + 25}{10 + 10} = \frac{70}{20} = 3.5 \text{ or } 103.5$$

$$\text{Average, female operators} = \frac{\Sigma X}{n} = \frac{27 + 23}{10 + 10} = \frac{50}{20} = 2.5 \text{ or } 102.5$$

$$N = 10 + 10 + 10 + 10 = 40 \qquad \Sigma X = 45 + 27 + 25 + 23 = 120$$

$$\Sigma X^2 = 4^2 + 4^2 + 5^2 + \cdots 3^2 + 3^2 = 442$$

Between foremen:

$$\text{Sum of squares} = \left(\frac{72^2}{20} + \frac{48^2}{20}\right) - \frac{120^2}{40} = 374.4 - 360.0 = 14.4$$

Degrees of freedom $= 2 - 1 = 1$

Between sexes:

$$\text{Sum of squares} = \left(\frac{70^2}{20} + \frac{50^2}{20}\right) - \frac{120^2}{40} = 370.0 - 360.0 = 10.0$$

Degrees of freedom $= 2 - 1 = 1$

Interaction:

$$\text{Sum of squares} = \left(\frac{45^2}{10} + \frac{27^2}{10} + \frac{25^2}{10} + \frac{23^2}{10}\right) - \frac{120^2}{40} - 14.4 - 10.0 = 6.4$$

Degrees of freedom $= 1 \times 1 = 1$

Within-group, or residual:

$$\text{Sum of squares} = 442 - \left(\frac{45^2}{10} + \frac{27^2}{10} + \frac{25^2}{10} + \frac{23^2}{10}\right) = 442 - 390.8 = 51.2$$

Degrees of freedom $= 10 + 10 + 10 + 10 - 4 = 36$

These values are summarized in the table below. The mean square for each source of variation has been computed as shown. The F-values taken from Table 6b are for a probability level of .05.

Total:

$$\text{Sum of squares} = 442 - \frac{120^2}{40} = 442.0 - 360.0 = 82.0$$

Degrees of freedom $= 40 - 1 = 39$

Source of Variation	Sum of Squares	Degrees of Freedom	Mean Square	F-Ratio	Table F Probability $= .05$
Between Foremen	14.4	1	$\frac{14.4}{1} = 14.4$	$\frac{14.4}{6.4} = 2.25$	161
Between Sexes	10.0	1	$\frac{10.0}{1} = 10.0$	$\frac{10.0}{6.4} = 1.56$	161
Interaction	6.4	1	$\frac{6.4}{1} = 6.4$	$\frac{6.4}{1.42} = 4.50$	4.08
Within Group	51.2	36	$\frac{51.2}{36} = 1.42$		
Total	82.0	39			

The analysis shows the foreman-sex interaction to be significant. Accordingly, the plant was rearranged so that all men could be placed under Foreman A and all women under Foreman B. The analysis of variance indicated no significance for the difference in means between foremen or between sexes independent of the interaction effect. This does not mean that workers under Foreman A may not really be more productive than workers under Foreman B or that male operators are not more productive than female. It does mean that the observations for this study give no evidence (at the selected probability level) of an effect of these factors that is independent of the interaction effect.

Regression and Correlation

RELATIONSHIPS BETWEEN VARIABLES. Regression and correlation techniques are useful in estimating the value of one variable when another variable is known. Knowing the relationship between two or more variables is useful in production management applications when: (1) an important variable is difficult to measure and control and it is related to one that is easier to measure and control; (2) unknown variables of future products or events are related to known variables of these products or events.

For an example of the first case, it would be difficult to make a time study of the exact standard hours' worth of work performed by a longshoreman crew handling thousands of different items, but if it is known that a relationship exists between tonnage handled and standard hours, the crew performance may be evaluated on the basis of tonnage handled. Two things must be known about the relationship: what is the average value (how many standard hours per ton), and how strong is the relationship—how wrong we are likely to be. The strength of the relationship can be thought of as the relative importance, in the example, of tonnage compared to the importance of factors such as bulkiness or shape of the goods moved or chance factors such as weather in determining time required.

For another example, consider the control of packaged net weight of a semi-fluid product such as peanut butter. It would be difficult to empty and weigh the contents of many jars, but if it is known that net weight per jar (for a given volume of fill) is related to the viscosity of the contents of the filling hopper, control can be kept on an easily read viscosity measurement. In this example also, we have to know what the relationship is and how reliably fill weight is related to viscosity—how important viscosity is compared to gasket leaks, pressure variations, and other factors.

An example of the second case is the knowledge of the relationship between hours flown and standard hours of repair required by an aircraft, used in forecasting and scheduling workload requirements in aircraft overhaul and repair stations. Another example is described below wherein standard time for new products can be predicted by knowing the relation between measurable product dimensions and standard time.

Regression and correlation techniques are designed to reveal:

1. The **nature** of the relationship between two variables, that is, what formula can be used to determine one from the other.
2. The **strength** of the relationship, that is, how widely deviant are the real values likely to be from the predicted values.
3. How well we know from the observed sample of values the real nature of the relationship; that is, whether a large enough sample has been observed so that the **real relationship** will not be distorted by one factor varying independently of the other.

GRAPHIC METHODS. The simplest approach, and one that is entirely satisfactory in many cases, is to plot the available data on graph paper. It may then be examined for **evidence of a relationship.** If there is good evidence, a curve or line may be fitted readily by eye. This line can then be used directly as a device to predict the value for one variable, given some value of the other, or the line may be used to derive an equation for use in making such predictions.

If the points fit some line closely, placing the line by eye will usually give satis-factory results. If the points have a **linear trend** so that the relationship may be represented by a straight line, some accuracy may be gained in placing the line by the following procedure: (1) compute the mean for the observations for each of the variables; (2) plot a point on the graph representing these two averages; (3) draw the line (fitting it by eye) so as to pass through this point.

For an example, consider the following data used in a study to determine the relationship between the total labor hours required to assemble an airframe sub-assembly and the total number of "hole operations" in the subassembly. (Drilling a hole, reaming a hole, placing a rivet, etc., constitute hole operations.)

Study	Total No. of Hole Operations X	Total Labor Hours for Assembly Y
A	236	5.1
B	80	1.7
C	127	3.3
D	445	6.0
E	180	2.9
F	343	5.9
G	305	7.0
H	488	9.4
I	170	4.8

Computation of the averages gives the following:

$$\Sigma X = 2{,}374 \qquad\qquad \Sigma Y = 46.1$$

$$\overline{X} = \frac{2{,}374}{9} = 264 \qquad\qquad \overline{Y} = \frac{46.1}{9} = 5.1$$

Points representing the number of hole operations and the labor hours for each study together with a point at $\overline{X}$, $\overline{Y}$, have been plotted in Fig. 12. A straight line has been fitted by eye, drawing it so as to pass through $\overline{X}$, $\overline{Y}$.

The **reliability of prediction** is indicated by observing that almost all the actual values are within one hour of the predicted value.

THE METHOD OF LEAST SQUARES. Fitting a line by eye depends on the judgment of the person doing it. No two persons will place the line in exactly the same place. Also, a line placed by eye may be placed far from the most suit-able position, particularly if there are few points and they are widely scattered. Even though there is a relationship between two variables, it may be obscured by the inherent variation in the process or system measured.

Regression Analysis. A relatively simple procedure is available for using sample data to make the best estimate of where to place the line for its intended use. This statistical procedure is referred to as "regression analysis." Specifically, regression analysis places the line so as to give the best estimate of the value for the dependent variable for any specified value for the independent variable. For example, it is the line that would give the best estimate of labor time (the depend-ent variable) for any specified number of hole operations (the independent vari-able) for the assembly.

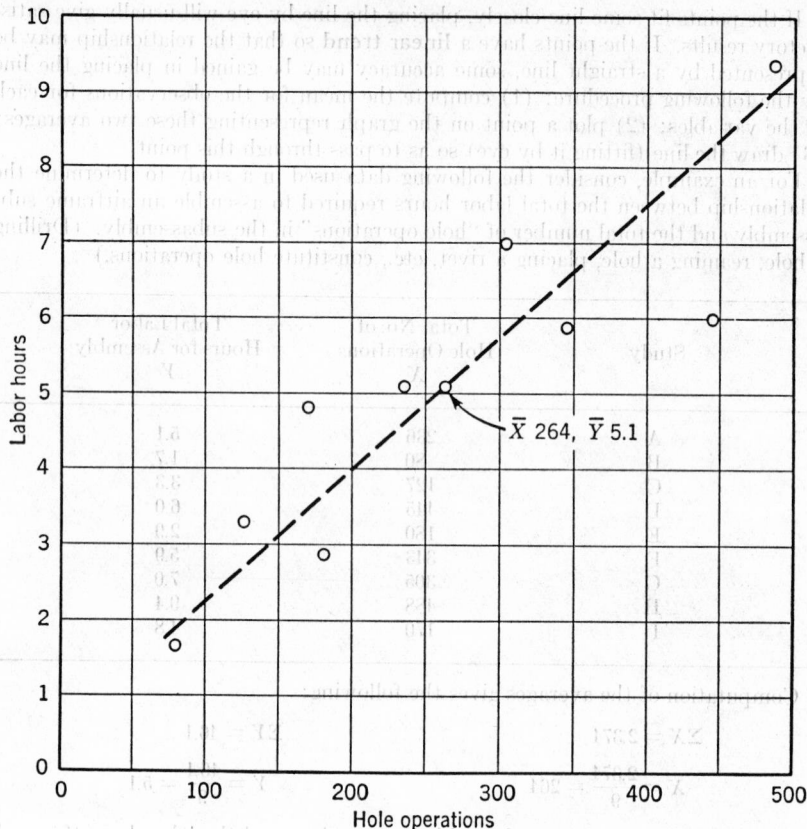

Fig. 12. Line fitted by eye showing the relationship between hole operations and labor hours.

The line is so placed that the sum of the squared deviations of each observed point from the line is a minimum, the deviations being measured parallel to the axis for the dependent variable. A line in this position gives the best estimate (based on the sample of data available) of the average of all the values of the dependent variable that would be obtained in the long run for any specified value for the independent variable. Since the line is placed so as to minimize the sum of the squared deviations, the method is often referred to as the "method of least squares."

In the statistical procedures it is customary to use the Y-axis for the dependent variable and the X-axis for the independent variable. The line is referred to as 'the regression line of Y on X." For **linear** (straight line) **regression**, the equation of the line may be represented by

$$Y_r = a + bX$$

where Y_r is a point on the line for any given value of X. The symbol a is, of course, the value for the Y-intercept for the line, and the symbol b represents the slope of the line. When the values for a and b have been determined, this equation may be used to give the best estimate for Y for any given value for X. An alternative is to use the computed values for a and b to draw the line of regression on the graph and then to use the line for making estimates.

The value for a, the Y-intercept, may be determined by the following equation:

$$a = \frac{\Sigma X^2 \Sigma Y - \Sigma X \Sigma XY}{n\Sigma X^2 - (\Sigma X)^2}$$

where n is the number of pairs of observations.

The value for b, the slope of the line, may be determined by the following equation:

$$b = \frac{n\Sigma XY - \Sigma X \Sigma Y}{n\Sigma X^2 - (\Sigma X)^2}$$

An alternative procedure for finding a and b is available. It is to solve the following simultaneous equations:

$$\Sigma Y = na + b\Sigma X$$

$$\Sigma XY = a\Sigma_x + b\Sigma X^2$$

The point $\overline{X}$, $\overline{Y}$ discussed above lies on the line of regression. These values may be computed and plotted to serve as a check on the values determined by the formulas.

Curvilinear Relationships. The relationship may be more closely approximated by some curved line rather than by a straight line in some studies. When the points fall closely along what seems to be a well-defined line, the line may be placed by eye reasonably well. When this is not the case, a more accurate method may be necessary.

One curvilinear relationship frequently observed is that of a **parabolic regression line.** The formula for this line is:

$$Y_r = a + bX + cX^2$$

The following simultaneous equations may be used to compute the values for the constants a, b, and c:

$$\Sigma Y = na + b\Sigma X + c\Sigma X^2$$

$$\Sigma XY = a\Sigma X + b\Sigma X^2 + c\Sigma X^3$$

$$\Sigma X^2 Y = a\Sigma X^2 + b\Sigma X^3 + c\Sigma X^4$$

Strict application of regression analysis requires that the standard deviation or inherent variation for the Y population be the same for all values of X. Any substantial departure from this requirement will make the line less exact. The distribution of Y for any value of X need not be a normal distribution for the line to be valid. However, for determining confidence limits for the estimates (using the techniques to be described in the next division), the distribution must approximate the normal.

Computation of Linear Regression. For the time studies for the airframe subassembly illustration, the following are the computations to determine the line of regression (the Y^2 values have been computed for later use in determining confidence limits):

Study	Hole Operations X	Labor Hr. Y	X^2	Y^2	XY
A	236	5.1	55,696	26.01	1,203.6
B	80	1.7	6,400	2.89	136.0
C	127	3.3	16,129	10.89	419.1
D	445	6.0	198,025	36.00	2,670.0
E	180	2.9	32,400	8.41	522.0
F	343	5.9	117,649	34.81	2,023.7
G	305	7.0	93,025	49.00	2,135.0
H	488	9.4	238,144	88.36	4,587.2
I	170	4.8	28,900	23.04	816.0
	$\Sigma X = 2,374$	$\Sigma Y = 46.1$	$\Sigma X^2 = 786,368$	$\Sigma Y^2 = 279.41$	$\Sigma XY = 14,512.6$

$$\overline{X} = \frac{\Sigma X}{n} = \frac{2,374}{9} = 264 \qquad\qquad \overline{Y} = \frac{\Sigma Y}{n} = \frac{46.1}{9} = 5.1$$

$$a = \frac{\Sigma X^2 \Sigma Y - \Sigma X \Sigma XY}{n \Sigma X^2 - (\Sigma X)^2} = \frac{786,368 \cdot 46.1 - 2,374 \cdot 14,512.6}{9 \cdot 786,368 - (2,374)^2}$$

$$= 1.245 \text{ hr.}$$

$$b = \frac{n \Sigma XY - \Sigma X \Sigma Y}{n \Sigma X^2 - (\Sigma X)^2} = \frac{9 \cdot 14,512.6 - 2,374 \cdot 46.1}{9 \cdot 786,368 - (2,374)^2}$$

$$= .0147$$

The equation for the **line of regression** thus becomes

$$Y_r = 1.245 + .0147X$$

This line has been plotted in Fig. 13. As a check, $\overline{X}, \overline{Y}$ has been plotted to see that it falls on the computed line.

CONFIDENCE LIMITS. The line of regression gives the best estimate that can be made (based on the available sample data) of the average value for the dependent variable for any specified value of the independent variable. For Fig. 13, the line gives the best estimate that can be made of the average assembly time required for subassemblies with some specified number of hole operations. However, since the time is based on only a sample of observations, it is subject to **sampling fluctuations.** It may differ somewhat from the position of a line representing the true relationship (assuming one actually exists). The probable difference between the line based on a sample and the true relationship depends on the size of the sample and the strength of the true relationship. The smaller the sample, the less likely it is that independent variations will cancel each other. The weaker the relationship, the larger these independent variations will be.

Formulas for Determining Limits. Statistical procedures are available for determining limits between which true values may be expected to lie with any specified **degree of confidence.** Confidence limits for the population average

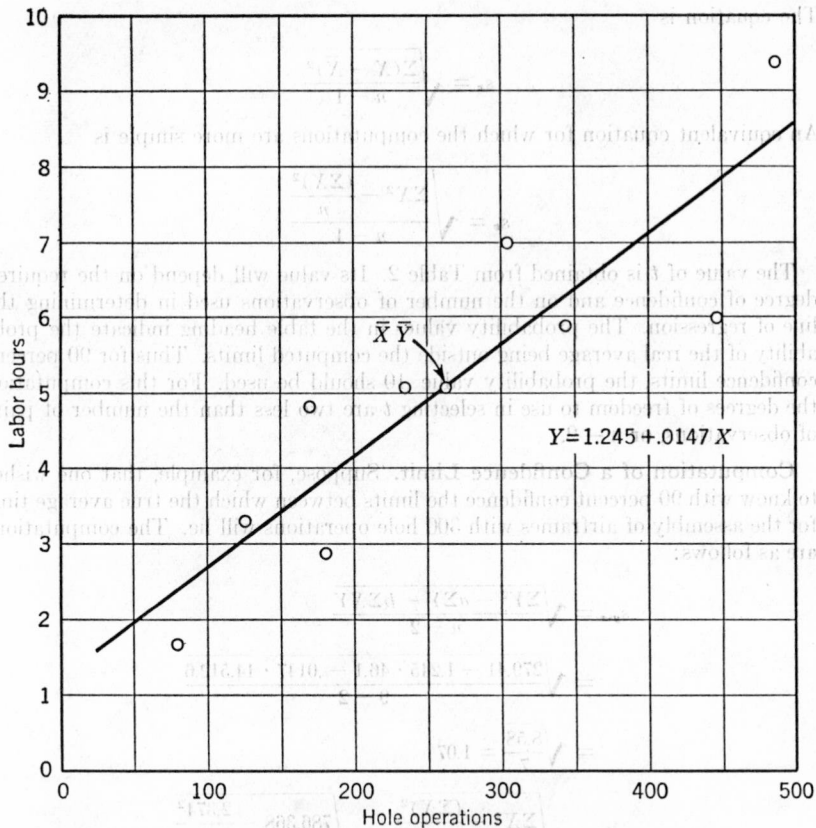

Fig. 13. Line of regression computed by the method of least squares.

($\mu_{y.x}$ for the dependent variable, Y, for any specified value of the independent variable, X) are given by the following equation:

$$Y_{r_x} \pm ts_{y.x} \sqrt{\frac{1}{n} + \frac{(X - \bar{X})^2}{(n-1)s_x^2}}$$

where Y_{r_x} = the value for the average Y given by the least-squares line or equation
$s_{y.x}$ = the standard deviation of the Y-values for the sample observations about the line of regression

The equation is

$$s_{y.x} = \sqrt{\frac{\Sigma(Y - Y_r)^2}{n - 2}}$$

A short-cut equation which does not require determining the amount of the deviation for each point is

$$s_{y.x} = \sqrt{\frac{\Sigma Y^2 - a\Sigma Y - b\Sigma XY}{n - 2}}$$

where s_x = The standard deviation of the X-values for the sample observations about the average of the X-values, $\bar{X}$

The equation is

$$s_x = \sqrt{\frac{\Sigma(X - \bar{X})^2}{n - 1}}$$

An equivalent equation for which the computations are more simple is

$$s_x = \sqrt{\frac{\Sigma X^2 - \dfrac{(\Sigma X)^2}{n}}{n - 1}}$$

The value of t is obtained from Table 2. Its value will depend on the required degree of confidence and on the number of observations used in determining the line of regression. The probability values in the table heading indicate the probability of the real average being outside the computed limits. Thus for 90 percent confidence limits, the probability value .10 should be used. For this computation the degrees of freedom to use in selecting t are two less than the number of pairs of observations, or $n - 2$.

Computation of a Confidence Limit. Suppose, for example, that one wishes to know with 90 percent confidence the limits between which the true average time for the assembly of airframes with 300 hole operations will lie. The computations are as follows:

$$s_{y \cdot x} = \sqrt{\frac{\Sigma Y^2 - a\Sigma Y - b\Sigma XY}{n - 2}}$$

$$= \sqrt{\frac{279.41 - 1.245 \cdot 46.1 - .0147 \cdot 14{,}512.6}{9 - 2}}$$

$$= \sqrt{\frac{8.58}{7}} = 1.07$$

$$s_x = \sqrt{\frac{\Sigma X^2 - \dfrac{(\Sigma X)^2}{n}}{n - 1}} = \sqrt{\frac{786{,}368 - \dfrac{2{,}374^2}{9}}{9 - 1}}$$

$$= \sqrt{\frac{160{,}160}{8}} = 141$$

$$Y_{r_x} = 1.245 + .0147 X$$

$$= 1.245 + .0147 \cdot 300 = 5.66$$

Confidence limits for $\mu_{y \cdot x}$ are

$$Y_{r_x} \pm t s_{y \cdot x} \sqrt{\frac{1}{n} + \frac{(X - \bar{X})^2}{(n - 1)s_x^2}}$$

or

$$5.66 \pm 1.90 \cdot 1.07 \sqrt{\frac{1}{9} + \frac{(300 - 264)^2}{(9 - 1) \, 141^2}}$$

or

$$5.66 \pm .70 \text{ hr.}$$

This means that for units with 300 hole operations one can be 90 percent confident that the average assembly time required will be between $5.66 \pm .70$ hr. or between 4.96 hr. and 6.36 hr.

Other Confidence Limit Formulas. Confidence limits for individual values for the dependent variable can also be determined to indicate how far off one is likely to be in any one individual prediction. In general, the surer we are of the true relationship, the less we will be off on any one value; and the greater the importance of the independent variable in the relationship, the less we will be likely to be off.

The formula for limits for **individual values** is

$$Y_{r_x} \pm t s_{y \cdot x} \sqrt{1 + \frac{1}{n} + \frac{(X - \bar{X})^2}{(n-1)s_x^2}}$$

For the above illustration, 90 percent confidence limits for Y when X is 300 are

$$5.66 \pm 1.90 \cdot 1.07 \sqrt{1 + \frac{1}{9} + \frac{(300 - 264)^2}{(9-1)\,141^2}}$$

or   5.66 ± 2.16 hr.

This means that for any one assembly with 300 hole operations, one can be 90 percent confident that its labor time will be between 5.66 ± 2.16 hr. or between 3.50 and 7.82 hr.

Confidence limits for the **true slope** of the line of regression can also be computed if desired. The formula is

$$b \pm t \frac{s_{y \cdot x}}{s_x \sqrt{n-1}}$$

As in the two tests above, the number of degrees of freedom to use in getting the value of t from Table 2 are $n - 2$.

For the illustration above, 90 percent confidence limits are

$$.0147 \pm 1.90 \cdot \frac{1.07}{141\sqrt{9-1}}$$

or   .0147 ± .0051

This computation shows that one can be 90 percent confident that the real slope of the line of regression lies between .0147 ± .0051 or between .0096 and .0198.

THE CORRELATION COEFFICIENT. In some studies of the relationship between two variables it may be desirable to show by some single figure the extent to which the two variables are correlated. A simple means is to compute a figure known as the "coefficient of correlation." For sample data, the equation for this coefficient is

$$r = \sqrt{1 - \frac{s_{y \cdot x}^2}{s_y^2}}$$

where

$$s_y^2 = \frac{\Sigma Y^2 - \frac{(\Sigma Y)^2}{n}}{n - 1}$$

An alternative equation sometimes used is

$$r = b \frac{s_x}{s_y}$$

This value of r may be used as an estimate of the correlation between the variables.

If there is **perfect correlation**—if the points all fall exactly on the line of regression—the coefficient will have a value of 1. It will be +1 if the slope of the line of regression is positive—if Y increases in value as X increases. Its value will be −1 if the slope of the line is negative. If there is **no correlation** at all, the value of the coefficient will be 0.

If the regression line were not used, the best estimate of Y, given X, would be $\overline{Y}$. However, using a regression line, the efficiency of the estimate has been improved. The correlation coefficient shows the extent of improvement by using the regression line over, using $\overline{Y}$ as the best estimate of Y, given X.

For the illustration above,

$$s_y^2 = \frac{279.41 - \dfrac{46.1^2}{9}}{9 - 1} = 5.41$$

$$r = \sqrt{1 - \frac{1.21}{5.41}} = .88$$

As this value is close to +1.00, this indicates relatively good correlation.

THE ANALYSIS OF VARIANCE. A related procedure for testing the relationship between the two variables for significance is to apply the F-test, a test described in a previous division. In applying this test in regression analysis, the **total variation** in the sample values for the dependent variable is measured by the sum of the squares of the deviations from the average, $\overline{Y}$. This total sum of squares is $\Sigma(Y - \overline{Y})^2$.

Part of this total variation in the Y-values is explained by the computed **line of regression**. For each Y-value the difference between Y_r (the value given by the line of regression) and the average, $\overline{Y}$, or $(Y_r - \overline{Y})$, is the part of the deviation explained by the regression line. That part of the total sum of squares explained by the line of regression may thus be represented by $\Sigma(Y_r - \overline{Y})^2$.

The remainder or **residual of each deviation** is the difference between each value of Y and the corresponding value given by the regression line Y_r, or $(Y - Y_r)$. The sum of squares for the residual is thus $\Sigma(Y - Y_r)^2$.

A summary statement of these sums of squares is shown below. The number of degrees of freedom to use in computing the mean square in each case is also shown.

Source of Variation	Sum of Squares	Degrees of Freedom	Mean Square
Variation explained by the line of regression	$\Sigma(Y_r - \overline{Y})^2$	1	$\dfrac{\Sigma(Y_r - \overline{Y})^2}{1}$
The residual	$\Sigma(Y - Y_r)^2$	$n - 2$	$\dfrac{\Sigma(Y - Y_r)^2}{n - 2}$
Total	$\Sigma(Y - \overline{Y})^2$	$n - 1$	

If there were no actual relationship between the variables, the two mean-square values should be approximately the same. Any difference would be due only to the effect of chance on the sample observations. However, if the **residual mean**

square (which measures the dispersion of the observations about the line of regression) is significantly smaller than the other, one may assume that the line of regression represents a real relationship.

F-Test Procedure and Formulas. The steps in applying the F-test are as follows:

1. Select a suitable probability to test for significance.
2. Compute F, where

$$F = \frac{\text{regression mean square}}{\text{residual mean square}}$$

3. Using the selected probability level, determine the table value for F from Table 6.
4. Compare the computed value of F with the table value. If the computed value for F is larger than the table value, the line of regression may be considered significant.

Equations that may be used for easy computation of the sum of squares are:

$$\Sigma (Y_r - \bar{Y})^2 = b \left(\Sigma XY - \frac{\Sigma X \Sigma Y}{n} \right)$$

$$\Sigma (Y - Y_r)^2 = \Sigma Y^2 - a\Sigma Y - b\Sigma XY$$

$$\Sigma (Y - \bar{Y})^2 = \Sigma Y^2 - \frac{(\Sigma Y)^2}{n}$$

Application of this test to the previous time-study example shows, using a probability level of .05, that the relationship may be considered significant. The computations made in reaching this conclusion are

$$\Sigma (Y_r - \bar{Y})^2 = .0147 \left(14{,}512.6 - \frac{2{,}374 \cdot 46.1}{9} \right)$$

$$= 34.6$$

$$\Sigma (Y - Y_r)^2 = 279.41 - 1.245 \cdot 46.1 - .0147 \cdot 14{,}512.6$$

$$= 8.6$$

$$\Sigma (Y - \bar{Y})^2 = 279.41 - \frac{46.1^2}{9} = 43.2$$

Source of Variation	Sum of Squares	Degrees of Freedom	Mean Square	F-ratio
Variation explained by the line of regression	34.6	1	$\frac{34.6}{1} = 34.6$	$F = \frac{34.6}{1.2} = 29$
The residual	8.6	7	$\frac{8.6}{7} = 1.2$	
Total	43.2	8		

From Table 6b the table value of F for a probability of .05 is found to be 5.59. Only five times out of a hundred could a computed F larger than this value be obtained by chance if there were no relationship between the variables. As the computed F is 29, one may safely assume a real relationship does exist.

TEST FOR DEPENDENCE. The t-test is frequently used to test for the dependence of the dependent variable, Y, on the independent variable, X. The application requires the following steps:

1. Select a suitable probability level.
2. Compute t, where

$$t = \frac{bs_x\sqrt{n-1}}{s_{y \cdot x}}$$

3. Using the selected probability level, determine the table value of t from Table 2. The degrees of freedom are $n - 2$.
4. Compare the computed t with the table value. If the computed t is numerically larger than the table value of t, this may be considered evidence of a real relationship between the two variables.

For the example, the computations are as follows; a .05 probability level is used:

$$t = \frac{.0147 \cdot 141 \sqrt{9-1}}{1.07}$$

$$= 5.5$$

At a probability level of .05 the table value of t is 2.37. The apparent relationship may be considered significant, as the computed value of t is numerically greater than this figure. If a relationship had been indicated purely as an effect of chance in obtaining sample observations, with no real relationship existing, the probability of the computed t being numerically greater than 2.37 would be less than 5 in 100.

Statistical Tables

PURPOSE. The following tables are among those most frequently used in statistical analysis and are necessary for the application of many of the statistical procedures described herein.

Tables are computed from basic data to render easier the work of the statistical analyst. Care must be taken to avoid a "cook book" attitude toward statistical analyis. While the tables are convenient, it is essential that the user understand the fundamental principles involved and the derivation of each factor shown.

Statistics, properly applied, are the ally of the manager and the engineer. But if they become merely "canned" information, irreparable harm can result from misapplication.

Table 1a. Table of z—Normal Distribution Areas

z	Probability	z	Probability	z	Probability
− 3.090	.001	− 2.05	.0202	− 1.00	.1587
− 3.05	.0011	− 2.00	.0228	− .95	.1711
− 3.00	.0014	− 1.960	.025	− .90	.1841
− 2.95	.0016	− 1.95	.0256	− .85	.1977
− 2.90	.0019	− 1.90	.0287	− .842	.200
− 2.85	.0022	− 1.85	.0322	− .80	.2119
− 2.80	.0026	− 1.80	.0359	− .75	.2266
− 2.75	.0030	− 1.75	.0401	− .70	.2420
− 2.70	.0035	− 1.70	.0446	− .674	.250
− 2.65	.0040	− 1.645	.050	− .65	.2578
− 2.60	.0047	− 1.60	.0548	− .60	.2743
− 2.576	.005	− 1.55	.0606	− .55	.2912
− 2.55	.0054	− 1.50	.0668	− .50	.3085
− 2.50	.0062	− 1.45	.0735	− .45	.3264
− 2.45	.0071	− 1.40	.0808	− .40	.3446
− 2.40	.0082	− 1.35	.0885	− .35	.3632
− 2.35	.0094	− 1.30	.0968	− .30	.3821
− 2.326	.010	− 1.282	.100	− .25	.4013
− 2.30	.0107	− 1.25	.1057	− .20	.4207
− 2.25	.0122	− 1.20	.1151	− .15	.4404
− 2.20	.0139	− 1.15	.1251	− .10	.4602
− 2.15	.0158	− 1.10	.1357	− .05	.4801
− 2.10	.0179	− 1.05	.1469	0	.5000
− 2.055	.020	− 1.036	.150		

Table 1b. Table of z—Normal Distribution Areas

z	Probability	z	Probability	z	Probability
0	.5000	+ 1.05	.8531	+ 2.055	.980
+ .05	.5199	+ 1.10	.8643	+ 2.10	.9821
+ .10	.5398	+ 1.15	.8749	+ 2.15	.9842
+ .15	.5596	+ 1.20	.8849	+ 2.20	.9861
+ .20	.5793	+ 1.25	.8944	+ 2.25	.9878
+ .25	.5987	+ 1.282	.900	+ 2.30	.9893
+ .30	.6179	+ 1.30	.9032	+ 2.326	.990
+ .35	.6368	+ 1.35	.9115	+ 2.35	.9906
+ .40	.6554	+ 1.40	.9192	+ 2.40	.9918
+ .45	.6736	+ 1.45	.9265	+ 2.45	.9929
+ .50	.6915	+ 1.50	.9332	+ 2.50	.9938
+ .55	.7088	+ 1.55	.9394	+ 2.55	.9946
+ .60	.7257	+ 1.60	.9452	+ 2.576	.995
+ .65	.7422	+ 1.645	.950	+ 2.60	.9953
+ .674	.750	+ 1.65	.9505	+ 2.65	.9960
+ .70	.7580	+ 1.70	.9554	+ 2.70	.9965
+ .75	.7734	+ 1.75	.9599	+ 2.75	.9970
+ .80	.7881	+ 1.80	.9641	+ 2.80	.9974
+ .842	.800	+ 1.85	.9678	+ 2.85	.9978
+ .85	.8023	+ 1.90	.9713	+ 2.90	.9981
+ .90	.8159	+ 1.95	.9744	+ 2.95	.9984
+ .95	.8289	+ 1.960	.975	+ 3.00	.9987
+ 1.00	.8413	+ 2.00	.9772	+ 3.090	.999
+ 1.036	.850	+ 2.05	.9798		

Table 2. Table of t

Degrees of Freedom	Probability					
	.20	.10	.05	.02	.01	.001
1	3.08	6.31	12.71	31.82	63.66	636.62
2	1.89	2.92	4.30	6.97	9.93	31.60
3	1.64	2.35	3.18	4.54	5.84	12.94
4	1.53	2.13	2.78	3.75	4.60	8.61
5	1.48	2.02	2.57	3.37	4.03	6.86
6	1.44	1.94	2.45	3.14	3.71	5.96
7	1.42	1.90	2.37	3.00	3.50	5.41
8	1.40	1.86	2.31	2.90	3.36	5.04
9	1.38	1.83	2.26	2.82	3.25	4.78
10	1.37	1.81	2.23	2.76	3.17	4.59
11	1.36	1.80	2.20	2.72	3.11	4.44
12	1.36	1.78	2.18	2.68	3.06	4.32
13	1.35	1.77	2.16	2.65	3.01	4.22
14	1.35	1.76	2.15	2.62	2.98	4.14
15	1.34	1.75	2.13	2.60	2.95	4.07
16	1.34	1.75	2.12	2.58	2.92	4.02
17	1.33	1.74	2.11	2.57	2.90	3.97
18	1.33	1.73	2.10	2.55	2.88	3.92
19	1.33	1.73	2.09	2.54	2.86	3.88
20	1.33	1.73	2.09	2.53	2.85	3.85
21	1.32	1.72	2.08	2.52	2.83	3.82
22	1.32	1.72	2.07	2.51	2.82	3.79
23	1.32	1.71	2.07	2.50	2.81	3.77
24	1.32	1.71	2.06	2.49	2.80	3.75
25	1.32	1.71	2.06	2.49	2.79	3.73
26	1.32	1.71	2.06	2.48	2.78	3.71
27	1.31	1.70	2.05	2.47	2.77	3.69
28	1.31	1.70	2.05	2.47	2.76	3.67
29	1.31	1.70	2.05	2.46	2.76	3.66
30	1.31	1.70	2.04	2.46	2.75	3.65
40	1.30	1.68	2.02	2.42	2.70	3.55
60	1.30	1.67	2.00	2.39	2.66	3.46
120	1.29	1.66	1.98	2.36	2.62	3.37
∞	1.28	1.65	1.96	2.33	2.58	3.29

Abridged from Fisher and Yates, Statistical Tables for Biological, Agricultural, and Medical Research.

Table 4. Table of t_{2R}

Sample Size	Probability			
	.01	.02	.05	.10
2	7.92	5.55	3.43	2.32
3	2.09	1.72	1.27	.97
4	1.24	1.05	.81	.64
5	.90	.77	.61	.49
6	.71	.62	.50	.41
7	.60	.53	.43	.35
8	.52	.46	.37	.31
9	.46	.41	.33	.28
10	.42	.37	.30	.25
11	.38	.34	.28	.23
12	.36	.32	.26	.21
13	.33	.29	.24	.20
14	.31	.28	.23	.19
15	.29	.26	.22	.18
16	.28	.25	.21	.17
17	.26	.24	.20	.16
18	.25	.23	.19	.16
19	.24	.22	.18	.15
20	.23	.21	.17	.14

From E. Lord, The Use of Range in Place of Standard Deviation in the t-Test, Biometrika, Vol. 34.

Table 3. Table of t_R

Sample Size	Probability			
	.01	.02	.05	.10
2	31.8	15.9	6.35	3.16
3	3.01	2.11	1.30	.89
4	1.32	1.02	.72	.53
5	.84	.69	.51	.39
6	.63	.52	.40	.31
7	.51	.43	.33	.26
8	.43	.37	.29	.23
9	.37	.32	.26	.21
10	.33	.29	.23	.19
11	.30	.26	.21	.17
12	.28	.24	.19	.16
13	.26	.22	.18	.15
14	.24	.21	.17	.14
15	.22	.20	.16	.13
16	.21	.19	.15	.12
17	.20	.18	.14	.12
18	.19	.17	.14	.11
19	.18	.16	.13	.10
20	.18	.15	.13	.10

From E. Lord, The Use of Range in Place of Standard Deviation in the t-Test, Biometrika, Vol. 34.

Table 5. Table of K—Tolerance Factors for Normal Distributions

No. of Obser- vations	90% Confidence			95% Confidence			99% Confidence		
	90% of Popu- lation	95% of Popu- lation	99% of Popu- lation	90% of Popu- lation	95% of Popu- lation	99% of Popu- lation	90% of Popu- lation	95% of Popu- lation	99% of Popu- lation
2	15.98	18.80	24.17	32.02	37.67	48.43	160.19	188.49	242.30
3	5.85	6.92	8.97	8.38	9.92	12.86	18.93	22.40	29.06
4	4.17	4.94	6.44	5.37	6.37	8.30	9.40	11.15	14.53
5	3.49	4.15	5.42	4.28	5.08	6.63	6.61	7.86	10.26
6	3.13	3.72	4.87	3.71	4.41	5.78	5.34	6.35	8.30
7	2.90	3.45	4.52	3.37	4.01	5.25	4.61	5.49	7.19
8	2.74	3.26	4.28	3.14	3.73	4.89	4.15	4.94	6.47
9	2.63	3.13	4.10	2.97	3.53	4.63	3.82	4.55	5.97
10	2.54	3.02	3.96	2.84	3.38	4.43	3.58	4.27	5.59
11	2.46	2.93	3.85	2.74	3.26	4.28	3.40	4.05	5.31
12	2.40	2.86	3.76	2.66	3.16	4.15	3.25	3.87	5.08
13	2.36	2.81	3.68	2.59	3.08	4.04	3.13	3.73	4.89
14	2.31	2.76	3.62	2.53	3.01	3.96	3.03	3.61	4.74
15	2.28	2.71	3.56	2.48	2.95	3.88	2.95	3.51	4.61
16	2.25	2.68	3.51	2.44	2.90	3.81	2.87	3.42	4.49
17	2.22	2.64	3.47	2.40	2.86	3.75	2.81	3.35	4.39
18	2.19	2.61	3.43	2.37	2.82	3.70	2.75	3.28	4.31
19	2.17	2.59	3.40	2.34	2.78	3.66	2.70	3.22	4.23
20	2.15	2.56	3.37	2.31	2.75	3.62	2.66	3.17	4.16
25	2.08	2.47	3.25	2.21	2.63	3.46	2.49	2.97	3.90
30	2.03	2.41	3.17	2.14	2.55	3.35	2.39	2.84	3.73
35	1.99	2.37	3.11	2.09	2.49	3.27	2.31	2.75	3.61
40	1.96	2.33	3.07	2.05	2.45	3.21	2.25	2.68	3.52
45	1.94	2.31	3.03	2.02	2.41	3.17	2.20	2.62	3.44
50	1.92	2.28	3.00	2.00	2.38	3.13	2.16	2.58	3.39
60	1.89	2.25	2.96	1.96	2.33	3.07	2.10	2.51	3.29
80	1.85	2.20	2.89	1.91	2.27	2.99	2.03	2.41	3.17
100	1.82	2.17	2.85	1.87	2.23	2.93	1.98	2.36	3.10
200	1.76	2.10	2.76	1.80	2.14	2.82	1.87	2.22	2.92
500	1.72	2.05	2.69	1.74	2.07	2.72	1.78	2.12	2.78
1000	1.70	2.02	2.65	1.71	2.04	2.68	1.74	2.07	2.72
∞	1.65	1.96	2.58	1.65	1.96	2.58	1.65	1.96	2.58

Abridged from C. Eisenhart, M. W. Hastey, and W. A. Wallis, eds., Selected Techniques of Statistical Analysis, from a chapter by A. H. Bowker.

Table 6a. Table of F (Probability = .10)

Degrees of Freedom for Smaller Mean Square	Degrees of Freedom for Greater Mean Square																		
	1	2	3	4	5	6	7	8	9	10	12	15	20	24	30	40	60	120	∞
1	39.9	49.5	53.6	55.8	57.2	58.2	58.9	59.4	59.9	60.2	60.7	61.2	61.7	62.0	62.3	62.5	62.8	63.1	63.3
2	8.53	9.00	9.16	9.24	9.29	9.33	9.35	9.37	9.38	9.39	9.41	9.42	9.44	9.45	9.46	9.47	9.47	9.48	9.49
3	5.54	5.46	5.39	5.34	5.31	5.29	5.27	5.25	5.24	5.23	5.22	5.20	5.18	5.18	5.17	5.16	5.15	5.14	5.13
4	4.54	4.32	4.19	4.11	4.05	4.01	3.98	3.95	3.94	3.92	3.90	3.87	3.84	3.83	3.82	3.80	3.79	3.78	3.76
5	4.06	3.78	3.62	3.52	3.45	3.40	3.37	3.34	3.32	3.30	3.27	3.24	3.21	3.19	3.17	3.16	3.14	3.12	3.11
6	3.78	3.46	3.29	3.18	3.11	3.05	3.01	2.98	2.96	2.94	2.90	2.87	2.84	2.82	2.80	2.78	2.76	2.74	2.72
7	3.59	3.26	3.07	2.96	2.88	2.83	2.78	2.75	2.72	2.70	2.67	2.63	2.59	2.58	2.56	2.54	2.51	2.49	2.47
8	3.46	3.11	2.92	2.81	2.73	2.67	2.62	2.59	2.56	2.54	2.50	2.46	2.42	2.40	2.38	2.36	2.34	2.32	2.29
9	3.36	3.01	2.81	2.69	2.61	2.55	2.51	2.47	2.44	2.42	2.38	2.34	2.30	2.28	2.25	2.23	2.21	2.18	2.16
10	3.29	2.92	2.73	2.61	2.52	2.46	2.41	2.38	2.35	2.32	2.28	2.24	2.20	2.18	2.16	2.13	2.11	2.08	2.06
12	3.18	2.81	2.61	2.48	2.39	2.33	2.28	2.24	2.21	2.19	2.15	2.10	2.06	2.04	2.01	1.99	1.96	1.93	1.90
15	3.07	2.70	2.49	2.36	2.27	2.21	2.16	2.12	2.09	2.06	2.02	1.97	1.92	1.90	1.87	1.85	1.82	1.79	1.76
20	2.97	2.59	2.38	2.25	2.16	2.09	2.04	2.00	1.96	1.94	1.89	1.84	1.79	1.77	1.74	1.71	1.68	1.64	1.61
24	2.93	2.54	2.33	2.19	2.10	2.04	1.98	1.94	1.91	1.88	1.83	1.78	1.73	1.70	1.67	1.64	1.61	1.57	1.53
30	2.88	2.49	2.28	2.14	2.05	1.98	1.93	1.88	1.85	1.82	1.77	1.72	1.67	1.64	1.61	1.57	1.54	1.50	1.46
40	2.84	2.44	2.23	2.09	2.00	1.93	1.87	1.83	1.79	1.76	1.71	1.66	1.61	1.57	1.54	1.51	1.47	1.42	1.38
60	2.79	2.39	2.18	2.04	1.95	1.87	1.82	1.77	1.74	1.71	1.66	1.60	1.54	1.51	1.48	1.44	1.40	1.35	1.29
120	2.75	2.35	2.13	1.99	1.90	1.82	1.77	1.72	1.68	1.65	1.60	1.55	1.48	1.45	1.41	1.37	1.32	1.26	1.19
∞	2.71	2.30	2.08	1.94	1.85	1.77	1.72	1.67	1.63	1.60	1.55	1.49	1.42	1.38	1.34	1.30	1.24	1.17	1.00

Abridged from Merrington and Thompson, Tables of Percentage Points of the Inverted Beta (F) Distribution, Biometrika, Vol. 33, and Pearson and Hartley, Biometrika Tables for Statisticians, Vol. I.

Table 6b. Table of *F* (Probability = .05)

Degrees of Freedom for Smaller Mean Square	Degrees of Freedom for Greater Mean Square																		
	1	2	3	4	5	6	7	8	9	10	12	15	20	24	30	40	60	120	∞
1	161	200	216	225	230	234	237	239	241	242	244	246	248	249	250	251	252	253	254
2	18.5	19.0	19.2	19.2	19.3	19.3	19.4	19.4	19.4	19.4	19.4	19.4	19.4	19.5	19.5	19.5	19.5	19.5	19.5
3	10.1	9.55	9.28	9.12	9.01	8.94	8.89	8.85	8.81	8.79	8.74	8.70	8.66	8.64	8.62	8.59	8.57	8.55	8.53
4	7.71	6.94	6.59	6.39	6.26	6.16	6.09	6.04	6.00	5.96	5.91	5.86	5.80	5.77	5.75	5.72	5.69	5.66	5.63
5	6.61	5.79	5.41	5.19	5.05	4.95	4.88	4.82	4.77	4.74	4.68	4.62	4.56	4.53	4.50	4.46	4.43	4.40	4.37
6	5.99	5.14	4.76	4.53	4.39	4.28	4.21	4.15	4.10	4.06	4.00	3.94	3.87	3.84	3.81	3.77	3.74	3.70	3.67
7	5.59	4.74	4.35	4.12	3.97	3.87	3.79	3.73	3.68	3.64	3.57	3.51	3.44	3.41	3.38	3.34	3.30	3.27	3.23
8	5.32	4.46	4.07	3.84	3.69	3.58	3.50	3.44	3.39	3.35	3.28	3.22	3.15	3.12	3.08	3.04	3.01	2.97	2.93
9	5.12	4.26	3.86	3.63	3.48	3.37	3.29	3.23	3.18	3.14	3.07	3.01	2.94	2.90	2.86	2.83	2.79	2.75	2.71
10	4.96	4.10	3.71	3.48	3.33	3.22	3.14	3.07	3.02	2.98	2.91	2.85	2.77	2.74	2.70	2.66	2.62	2.58	2.54
12	4.75	3.89	3.49	3.26	3.11	3.00	2.91	2.85	2.80	2.75	2.69	2.62	2.54	2.51	2.47	2.43	2.38	2.34	2.30
15	4.54	3.68	3.29	3.06	2.90	2.79	2.71	2.64	2.59	2.54	2.48	2.40	2.33	2.29	2.25	2.20	2.16	2.11	2.07
20	4.35	3.49	3.10	2.87	2.71	2.60	2.51	2.45	2.39	2.35	2.28	2.20	2.12	2.08	2.04	1.99	1.95	1.90	1.84
24	4.26	3.40	3.01	2.78	2.62	2.51	2.42	2.36	2.30	2.25	2.18	2.11	2.03	1.98	1.94	1.89	1.84	1.79	1.73
30	4.17	3.32	2.92	2.69	2.53	2.42	2.33	2.27	2.21	2.16	2.09	2.01	1.93	1.89	1.84	1.79	1.74	1.68	1.62
40	4.08	3.23	2.84	2.61	2.45	2.34	2.25	2.18	2.12	2.08	2.00	1.92	1.84	1.79	1.74	1.69	1.64	1.58	1.51
60	4.00	3.15	2.76	2.53	2.37	2.25	2.17	2.10	2.04	1.99	1.92	1.84	1.75	1.70	1.65	1.59	1.53	1.47	1.39
120	3.92	3.07	2.68	2.45	2.29	2.18	2.09	2.02	1.96	1.91	1.83	1.75	1.66	1.61	1.55	1.50	1.43	1.35	1.25
∞	3.84	3.00	2.60	2.37	2.21	2.10	2.01	1.94	1.88	1.83	1.75	1.67	1.57	1.52	1.46	1.39	1.32	1.22	1.00

Abridged from Merrington and Thompson, Tables of Percentage Points of the Inverted Beta (*F*) Distribution, Biometrika, Vol. 33, and Pearson and Hartley, Biometrika Tables for Statisticians, Vol. I.

Table 6c. Table of F (Probability = .01)

Degrees of Freedom for Smaller Mean Square	Degrees of Freedom for Greater Mean Square																		
	1	2	3	4	5	6	7	8	9	10	12	15	20	24	30	40	60	120	∞
1	4052	5000	5403	5625	5764	5859	5928	5982	6023	6056	6106	6157	6209	6235	6261	6287	6313	6339	6366
2	98.5	99.0	99.2	99.2	99.3	99.3	99.4	99.4	99.4	99.4	99.4	99.4	99.4	99.5	99.5	99.5	99.5	99.5	99.5
3	34.1	30.8	29.5	28.7	28.2	27.9	27.7	27.5	27.3	27.2	27.1	26.9	26.7	26.6	26.5	26.4	26.3	26.2	26.1
4	21.2	18.0	16.7	16.0	15.5	15.2	15.0	14.8	14.7	14.5	14.4	14.2	14.0	13.9	13.8	13.7	13.7	13.6	13.5
5	16.3	13.3	12.1	11.4	11.0	10.7	10.5	10.3	10.2	10.1	9.89	9.72	9.55	9.47	9.38	9.29	9.20	9.11	9.02
6	13.7	10.9	9.78	9.15	8.75	8.47	8.26	8.10	7.98	7.87	7.72	7.56	7.40	7.31	7.23	7.14	7.06	6.97	6.88
7	12.2	9.55	8.45	7.85	7.46	7.19	6.99	6.84	6.72	6.62	6.47	6.31	6.16	6.07	5.99	5.91	5.82	5.74	5.65
8	11.3	8.65	7.59	7.01	6.63	6.37	6.18	6.03	5.91	5.81	5.67	5.52	5.36	5.28	5.20	5.12	5.03	4.95	4.86
9	10.6	8.02	6.99	6.42	6.06	5.80	5.61	5.47	5.35	5.26	5.11	4.96	4.81	4.73	4.65	4.57	4.48	4.40	4.31
10	10.0	7.56	6.55	5.99	5.64	5.39	5.20	5.06	4.94	4.85	4.71	4.56	4.41	4.33	4.25	4.17	4.08	4.00	3.91
12	9.33	6.93	5.95	5.41	5.06	4.82	4.64	4.50	4.39	4.30	4.16	4.01	3.86	3.78	3.70	3.62	3.54	3.45	3.36
15	8.68	6.36	5.42	4.89	4.56	4.32	4.14	4.00	3.89	3.80	3.67	3.52	3.37	3.29	3.21	3.13	3.05	2.96	2.87
20	8.10	5.85	4.94	4.43	4.10	3.87	3.70	3.56	3.46	3.37	3.23	3.09	2.94	2.86	2.78	2.69	2.61	2.52	2.42
24	7.82	5.61	4.72	4.22	3.90	3.67	3.50	3.36	3.26	3.17	3.03	2.89	2.74	2.66	2.58	2.49	2.40	2.31	2.21
30	7.56	5.39	4.51	4.02	3.70	3.47	3.30	3.17	3.07	2.98	2.84	2.70	2.55	2.47	2.39	2.30	2.21	2.11	2.01
40	7.31	5.18	4.31	3.83	3.51	3.29	3.12	2.99	2.89	2.80	2.66	2.52	2.37	2.29	2.20	2.11	2.02	1.92	1.80
60	7.08	4.98	4.13	3.65	3.34	3.12	2.95	2.82	2.72	2.63	2.50	2.35	2.20	2.12	2.03	1.94	1.84	1.73	1.60
120	6.85	4.79	3.95	3.48	3.17	2.96	2.79	2.66	2.56	2.47	2.34	2.19	2.03	1.95	1.86	1.76	1.66	1.53	1.38
∞	6.63	4.61	3.78	3.32	3.02	2.80	2.64	2.51	2.41	2.32	2.18	2.04	1.88	1.79	1.70	1.59	1.47	1.32	1.00

Abridged from Merrington and Thompson, Tables of Percentage Points of the Inverted Beta (F) Distribution, Biometrika, Vol. 33, and Pearson and Hartley, Biometrika Tables for Statisticians, Vol. I.

Table 7. Table of γ—Criteria for Testing Extreme Value or Mean

Statistic	Number of means, k	Probability	
		.05	.01
$\gamma = \dfrac{\bar{X}_2 - \bar{X}_1}{\bar{X}_k - \bar{X}_1}$	3	.941	.988
	4	.765	.889
	5	.642	.780
	6	.560	.698
	7	.507	.637
$\gamma = \dfrac{\bar{X}_2 - \bar{X}_1}{\bar{X}_{k-1} - \bar{X}_1}$	8	.554	.683
	9	.512	.635
	10	.477	.597
$\gamma = \dfrac{\bar{X}_3 - \bar{X}_1}{\bar{X}_{k-1} - \bar{X}_1}$	11	.576	.679
	12	.546	.642
	13	.521	.615
$\gamma = \dfrac{\bar{X}_3 - \bar{X}_1}{\bar{X}_{k-2} - \bar{X}_1}$	14	.546	.641
	15	.525	.616
	16	.507	.595
	17	.490	.577
	18	.475	.561
	19	.462	.547
	20	.450	.535
	21	.440	.524
	22	.430	.514
	23	.421	.505
	24	.413	.497
	25	.406	489
	26	.399	.486
	27	.393	.475
	28	.387	.469
	29	.381	.463
	30	.376	.457

From Dixon and Massey, Introduction to Statistical Analysis.

Table 8. Cumulative Terms of the Poisson Distribution. (Continued on next page)

r	np′							
	0.05	0.10	0.15	0.20	0.25	0.30	0.40	0.50
0	1.000	1.000	1.000	1.000	1.000	1.000	1.000	1.000
1	.049	.095	.139	.181	.221	.259	.330	.393
2	.001	.005	.010	.018	.026	.037	.062	.090
3	.000	.000	.001	.001	.002	.004	.008	.014
4			.000	.000	.000	.000	.001	.002
5							.000	.000

r	np′							
	0.60	0.70	0.80	0.90	1.00	1.20	1.40	1.60
0	1.000	1.000	1.000	1.000	1.000	1.000	1.000	1.000
1	.451	.503	.551	.593	.632	.699	.753	.798
2	.122	.156	.191	.228	.264	.337	.408	.475
3	.023	.034	.047	.063	.080	.121	.167	.217
4	.003	.006	.009	.013	.019	.034	.054	.079
5	.000	.001	.001	.002	.004	.008	.014	.024
6		.000	.000	.000	.001	.002	.003	.006
7					.000	.000	.001	.001
8							.000	.000

Abridged from Molina, Poisson's Exponential Binomial Limit.

Table 8 (Continued on next page)

r	1.80	2.00	2.20	2.40	2.60	2.80	3.00	3.20
				np'				
0	1.000	1.000	1.000	1.000	1.000	1.000	1.000	1.000
1	.835	.865	.889	.909	.926	.939	.950	.959
2	.537	.594	.645	.692	.733	.769	.801	.829
3	.269	.323	.377	.430	.482	.531	.577	.620
4	.109	.143	.181	.221	.264	.308	.353	.397
5	.036	.053	.072	.096	.123	.152	.185	.219
6	.010	.017	.025	.036	.049	.065	.084	.105
7	.003	.005	.007	.012	.017	.024	.034	.045
8	.001	.001	.002	.003	.005	.008	.012	.017
9	.000	.000	.000	.001	.001	.002	.004	.006
10				.000	.000	.001	.001	.002
11						.000	.000	.000

r	3.40	3.60	3.80	4.00	4.50	5.00	5.50	6.00
				np'				
0	1.000	1.000	1.000	1.000	1.000	1.000	1.000	1.000
1	.967	.973	.978	.982	.989	.993	.996	.998
2	.853	.874	.893	.908	.939	.960	.973	.983
3	.660	.697	.731	.762	.826	.875	.912	.938
4	.442	.485	.527	.567	.658	.735	.798	.849
5	.256	.294	.332	.371	.468	.560	.642	.715
6	.129	.156	.184	.215	.297	.384	.471	.554
7	.058	.073	.091	.111	.169	.238	.314	.394
8	.023	.031	.040	.051	.087	.133	.191	.256
9	.008	.012	.016	.021	.040	.068	.106	.153
10	.003	.004	.006	.008	.017	.032	.054	.084
11	.001	.001	.002	.003	.007	.014	.025	.043
12	.000	.000	.001	.001	.002	.005	.011	.020
13			.000	.000	.001	.002	.004	.009
14					.000	.001	.002	.004
15						.000	.001	.001
16							.000	.001
17								.000

Table 8 (Continued on next page)

r	np'							
	6.50	7.00	7.50	8.00	9.00	10.00	11.00	12.00
0	1.000	1.000	1.000	1.000	1.000	1.000	1.000	1.000
1	.998	.999	.999	1.000	1.000	1.000	1.000	1.000
2	.989	.993	.995	.997	.999	1.000	1.000	1.000
3	.957	.970	.980	.986	.994	.997	.999	.999
4	.888	.918	.941	.958	.979	.990	.995	.998
5	.776	.827	.868	.900	.945	.971	.985	.992
6	.631	.699	.759	.809	.884	.933	.962	.980
7	.473	.550	.622	.687	.793	.870	.921	.954
8	.327	.401	.475	.547	.676	.780	.857	.910
9	.208	.271	.338	.407	.544	.667	.768	.845
10	.123	.170	.224	.283	.413	.542	.659	.758
11	.067	.099	.138	.184	.294	.417	.540	.653
12	.034	.053	.079	.112	.197	.303	.421	.538
13	.016	.027	.043	.064	.124	.208	.311	.424
14	.007	.013	.022	.034	.074	.136	.219	.318
15	.003	.006	.010	.017	.041	.083	.146	.228
16	.001	.002	.005	.008	.022	.049	.093	.156
17	.000	.001	.002	.004	.011	.027	.056	.101
18		.000	.001	.002	.005	.014	.032	.063
19			.000	.001	.002	.007	.018	.037
20				.000	.001	.003	.009	.021
21					.000	.002	.005	.012
22						.001	.002	.006
23						.000	.001	.003
24							.000	.001
25								.001
26								.000

Table 8 (Concluded)

r	np' 13.00	14.00	15.00	16.00	17.00	18.00	19.00	20.00
0	1.000	1.000	1.000	1.000	1.000	1.000	1.000	1.000
1	1.000	1.000	1.000	1.000	1.000	1.000	1.000	1.000
2	1.000	1.000	1.000	1.000	1.000	1.000	1.000	1.000
3	1.000	1.000	1.000	1.000	1.000	1.000	1.000	1.000
4	.999	1.000	1.000	1.000	1.000	1.000	1.000	1.000
5	.996	.998	.999	1.000	1.000	1.000	1.000	1.000
6	.989	.994	.997	.999	.999	1.000	1.000	1.000
7	.974	.986	.992	.996	.998	.999	.999	1.000
8	.946	.968	.982	.990	.995	.997	.998	.999
9	.900	.938	.963	.978	.987	.993	.996	.998
10	.834	.891	.930	.957	.974	.985	.991	.995
11	.748	.824	.882	.923	.951	.970	.982	.989
12	.647	.740	.815	.873	.915	.945	.965	.979
13	.537	.642	.732	.807	.865	.908	.939	.961
14	.427	.536	.637	.725	.799	.857	.902	.934
15	.325	.430	.534	.632	.719	.792	.850	.895
16	.236	.331	.432	.533	.629	.713	.785	.843
17	.165	.244	.336	.434	.532	.625	.708	.779
18	.110	.173	.251	.341	.436	.531	.622	.703
19	.070	.117	.181	.258	.345	.438	.531	.619
20	.043	.077	.125	.188	.264	.349	.439	.530
21	.025	.048	.083	.132	.195	.269	.353	.441
22	.014	.029	.053	.089	.139	.201	.275	.356
23	.008	.017	.033	.058	.095	.145	.207	.279
24	.004	.009	.019	.037	.063	.101	.151	.213
25	.002	.005	.011	.022	.041	.068	.107	.157
26	.001	.003	.006	.013	.025	.045	.073	.112
27	.000	.001	.003	.007	.015	.028	.049	.078
28		.001	.002	.004	.009	.017	.031	.052
29		.000	.001	.002	.005	.010	.020	.034
30			.000	.001	.003	.006	.012	.022
31				.001	.001	.003	.007	.013
32				.000	.001	.002	.004	.008
33					.000	.001	.002	.005
34						.000	.001	.003
35							.001	.001
36							.000	.001
37								.000

CHARTING AND GRAPHIC METHODS

CONTENTS

PAGE

Nature and Purpose

Function of charts and graphs 1
Preparation 1
Limitations 2

Coordinate Charts

Types 2
Rectangular Cartesian coordinates 2
  Rectangular Cartesian coordinates (f. 1) 3
Types of curves 2
Design features 3
  A line graph on rectangular Cartesian
  coordinates (f. 2) 4
Linear equations 4
  A linear equation on rectangular Cartesian
  coordinates (f. 3) 5
Logarithmic coordinates 5
  A line graph on logarithmic coordinates
  (f. 4) 6
Power equations 6
  A power equation on logarithmic co-
  ordinates (f. 5) 7
Semilogarithmic coordinates 7
  A line graph on semilogarithmic co-
  ordinates (f. 6) 8
Exponential equations 8
  An exponential equation on semilogarith-
  mic coordinates (f. 7) 9
Biaxial coordinates 10
  A line graph on special biaxial coordin-
  ates (f. 8) 10
Network charts 10
  A network chart based on the Hazen-
  Williams formula (f. 9) 11
  A four-variable network chart (f. 10) ... 12
Polar coordinates 13
  A line graph on polar coordinates (f. 11) 12
Triaxial coordinates 13
  A triaxial coordinate chart (f. 12) 13
Three-dimensional coordinates 14
  A three-dimensional coordinate chart (f.
  13) 14

Graphic Scales

Purpose 15
Definition 15
Scale equation 15
  Functional scales (f. 14) 16
Scale modulus 16
Scale layout 16

PAGE

  A uniform scale modulus chart (f. 15) .. 17
  A logarithmic scale modulus chart (f. 16) 18
Conversion scale 16
  A conversion scale (f. 17) 19
Conversion charts 19
  A conversion chart (f. 18) 20
  A multipivot conversion chart (f. 19) 21
Curved scales 21

Nomographic Charts

Definition 22
Advantages of the nomograph 22
Chart layout 23
Three-variable nomographs 23
  Parallel straight scales 23
  Construction of the parallel scale nomo-
  graph (f. 20) 24
  A parallel scale nomograph (f. 21) 25
  Parallel logarithmic straight scales 26
  A logarithmic parallel scale nomograph
  (f. 22) 26
  Parallel and transverse straight scales (Z-
  chart) 27
  Construction of the parallel and trans-
  verse scale nomograph (Z-chart) (f. 23) 27
  A nomographic Z-chart (f. 24) 29
  Concurrent straight scales 29
  Construction of the concurrent scale
  nomograph (f. 25) 30
  A concurrent scale nomograph (f. 26) ... 30
  Straight and curved scales 31
  Construction of the parallel and curved
  scale nomograph (f. 27) 32
  A parallel and curved scale nomograph
  (f. 28) 32
Four-variable nomographs 33
  A four-variable nomograph (f. 29) 34
  A four-variable double-Z nomograph (f.
  30) 35
Nomographic determinants 35
  Derivation of nomographic determinant
  (f. 31) 36

Slide and Disc Charts

Nature and use 37
Slide charts 37
  Sliding scales (f. 32) 38
  Three-variable slide charts (f. 33) 39
  Four-variable slide charts (f. 34) 40
  Alternate scale positions (f. 35) 41
  A logarithmic three-variable slide chart
  (f. 36) 41

CONTENTS (*Continued*)

	Page
Disc charts	40
A three-variable disc chart (*f.* 37)	42
A logarithmic three-variable disc chart (*f.* 38)	42

Pictorial Charts

	Page
Function	43
100 percent bar or column	43
Pie chart	43
A pie chart (*f.* 39)	43
Bar or column chart	44
A column chart (*f.* 40)	44
A compound column chart (*f.* 41)	45
Multiunit bar or column chart	46
Pictographic chart	46
A pictographic chart (*f.* 42)	46

CHARTING AND GRAPHIC METHODS

Nature and Purpose

FUNCTION OF CHARTS AND GRAPHS. As illustrations in reports or articles in books or journal publications, charts and graphs, properly designed and executed, attract the eye and arouse the interest of the reader. They supplement and clarify tabulated data and text, often to such an extent that their use becomes essential to an effective presentation. In large display form or as slide projections, they lend assistance to a speaker in focusing the attention of his audience on the highlights of his commentary. For the analysis and solution of problems, charts are often less time-consuming to use, less susceptible to error, and more readily understood than equivalent algebraic methods. Schmid (Handbook of Graphic Presentation) summarizes the valuable qualities of charts and graphs as follows:

1. In comparison with other types of presentation, well-designed charts are more effective in creating interest and in appealing to the attention of the reader.
2. Visual relationships, as portrayed by charts and graphs, are more clearly grasped and more easily remembered.
3. The use of charts and graphs saves time, since the essential meaning of large masses of statistical data can be visualized at a glance.
4. Charts and graphs can provide a comprehensive picture of a problem that makes possible a more complete and better balanced understanding than could be derived from tabular or textural forms of presentation.
5. Charts and graphs can bring out hidden facts and relationships that can stimulate, as well as aid, analytical thinking and investigation.

Charts differ in the amount of technical training required to read and understand them. Complex types, particularly those involving scales and coordinate systems, have meaning only for persons with special backgrounds. More elementary forms, based on comparison of lineal distances or of areas, may, because of their simplicity, appeal to all readers.

Charts and graphs may be **classified**, according to the purpose for which they are prepared, as those for illustration, those for analysis, and those for computation. Charts may also be classified with respect to form, as pictorial, coordinate, and scale charts. The latter classification forms the basis for the treatment of graphic methods presented here.

PREPARATION. Spear (Charting Statistics) proposes the following steps as "fundamental to the development of graphic presentation that will describe statistical data with clarity and dramatic impact":

1. Determine the significant features of a relationship.
2. Be familiar with all chart forms, and select the type best suited to the presentation.
3. Consider the type of reader to be reached, and meet him on his own level.
4. Give clear and detailed instructions to the draftsman preparing the chart.
5. Make effective use of drafting equipment and materials.

6. Recognize proper form and technique. The smallest detail must be clearly legible and important features emphasized without distortion. Unnecessary lines, lettering, or extraneous matter, tending to confuse or distract the reader, should be eliminated.

A chart for analysis or computation should possess a simple method of manipulation, with the pertinent instructions clearly and concisely set forth. A statement of the conditions, if any, on use of the chart, should be placed thereon.

LIMITATIONS. A knowledge of the limitations as well as the possibilities of the various types of charts is essential to their successful use. If a message is more clearly expressed as a written statement, a chart should not be employed. As Schmid (Handbook of Graphic Presentation) states:

Although graphic techniques are a powerful and effective medium for presenting statistical data, they are not under all circumstances and for all purposes complete substitutes for tabular and other forms of presentation. The well-trained specialist in this field is one who recognizes not only the advantages but also the limitations of graphic techniques. He knows when to use and when not to use graphic methods, and from his repertoire is able to select the most appropriate form for every purpose.

Coordinate Charts

TYPES. There are many two- and three-dimensional coordinate systems. Rectangular and oblique biaxial, polar and triaxial plane coordinates are frequently employed in chart construction. Three-dimensional coordinates are only occasionally used, because of the difficulty of representation.

RECTANGULAR CARTESIAN COORDINATES. The line graph on rectangular Cartesian or rectilinear coordinates is the most extensively used chart form. Two axes, each bearing a uniformly divided scale, are located at right angles to one another through a point of origin. The position of any point in the system is defined by two coordinate values. One, the **abscissa,** is measured along the scale of the horizontal or x-axis. The other, the **ordinate,** is measured along the scale of the vertical or y-axis. The abscissa is positive in sign when measured to the right of the origin, negative when to the left. The ordinate is positive above the origin, negative below. A specific pair of coordinate values locates only one point in the system, and, conversely, a given point may have only one pair of coordinates. The coordinates of point P of Fig. 1 are read: $x = 4$ and $y = 5$, and written: $(4, 5)$.

When two variable quantities are so related that there exists a definite value or set of values of one for each value of the other, then one is said to be a **function** of the other, and the relationship may be expressed as an **algebraic equation.** Such an equation may be represented graphically by a geometric curve or line, all points of which possess coordinate values satisfying the equation. In this manner the curve of Fig. 1 represents the equation $y = 0.25\,(x)^2 + 1$.

Types of Curves. A line graph may exhibit one of several relationships between curve and plotted points. A chart showing plotted experimental data and a "curve" made up of straight-line segments connecting the points often indicates that the correct form of the curve relating the variables is unknown and that intermediate values should not be read from the graph. Test data occasionally result in points scattered to such an extent that a curve is difficult to draw or cannot be drawn at all. This may indicate the absence of a definite relationship or the presence of factors not accounted for in making the test readings. An **empirical curve**, reflecting the author's interpretation of a series of observations, may be located "by eye," to pass through or near to the plotted points, or by first deriving an equation to fit the data. A **theoretical curve**, based on a mathematical formula and located independently of plotted experimental points, may be used to show consistency of observation with theory (see section on Statistical Methods).

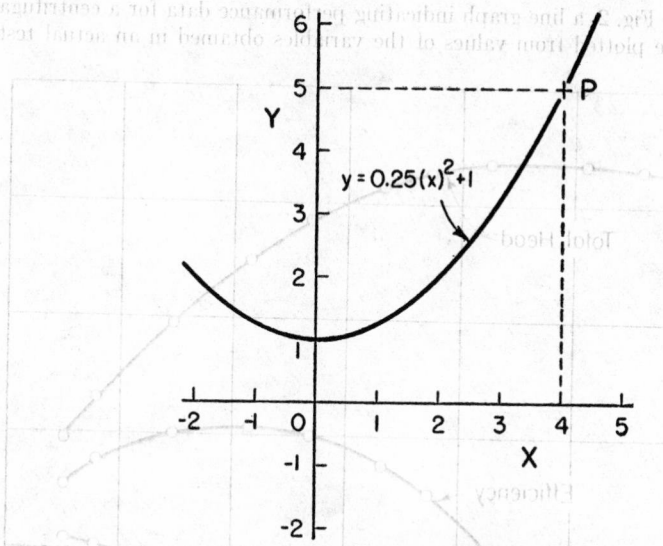

Fig. 1. Rectangular Cartesian coordinates.

Design Features. The American Standards Association (ASA Y-15.1, Illustration Standards for Publications and Projections) gives the following as the desirable features of a well-designed line graph. Many of them apply equally well to other types of charts.

1. A gradation of line weights with the heaviest rulings for the curves and the lightest for the grid.
2. Identification of each one of a group of curves by label or parameter value, reading horizontally, with a leader where needed. One curve may be emphasized among several by an extra-heavy line. Interlaced curves may be differentiated by the use of different line symbols—solid, dashed, dotted, etc.
3. Use of a small symbol, for example, a circle, triangle, or cross, to indicate plotted empirical data.
4. Coordinate scales which provide for effective use of the grid area. The visual impression to be created by the graph must be considered. By expanding or shrinking the vertical scale, changes in ordinate may be made to appear of great or little significance. A steep curve seems to depict a rapidly changing variable, a flat curve the opposite. The zero line is not necessarily included but should be shown if visual comparison of magnitude is intended.
5. Scale values and labels placed outside the grid area, with the scale of abscissas below and the scale of ordinates to the left. The ordinate scale may be repeated on the right side of an unusually wide chart. Scale labels indicate quantity represented and the unit of measurement.

6. Use of a power of ten factor or a clearly worded unit designation to avoid the presence of many digits in scale values.

7. A minimum number of grid lines consistent with desired accuracy in reading coordinate values from the graph.

8. A short main title of a few key words, supplemented by a subtitle and explanatory matter if essential.

9. A simple and legible letter style.

10. Use of standard abbreviations where space is limited.

The curves of Fig. 2, a line graph indicating performance data for a centrifugal water pump, are plotted from values of the variables obtained in an actual test.

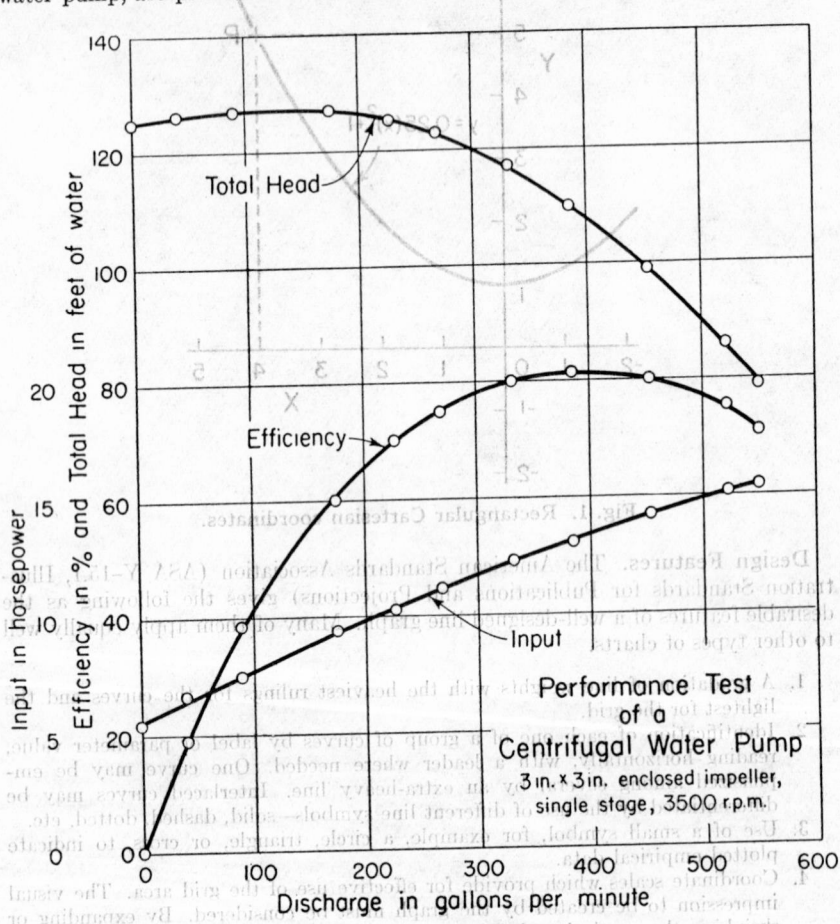

Fig. 2. A line graph on rectangular Cartesian coordinates.

As is customary in the case of observed data, a small symbol is employed to indicate plotted points. The chart illustrates the plotting of more than one curve on a single grid.

Linear Equations. The equation of a straight line on rectangular Cartesian coordinates, $y = a + bx$, where a and b are numerical constants, may be evaluated by reading the coordinates of two selected points, (x_1, y_1) and (x_2, y_2), and substituting in the equation:

$$\frac{y - y_1}{x - x_1} = \frac{y_2 - y_1}{x_2 - x_1}$$

The straight line of Fig. 3 indicates that the electrical resistance of No. 12 AWG standard annealed copper wire varies linearly with temperature. The equation

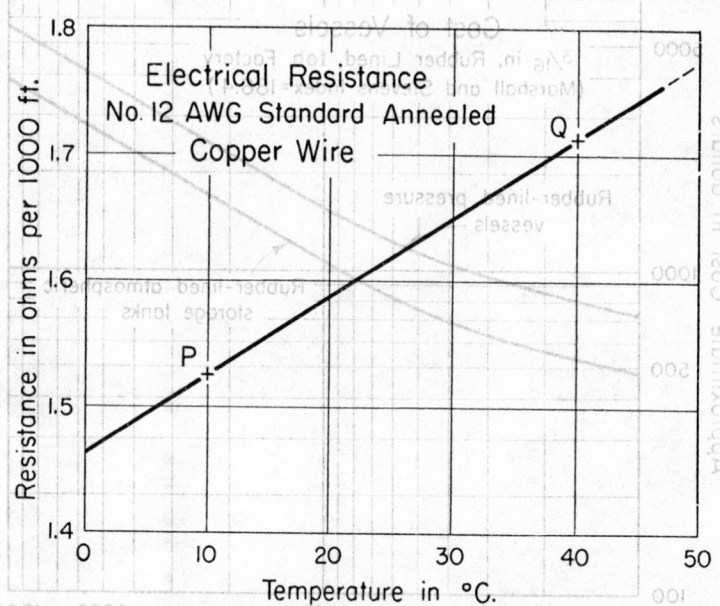

Fig. 3. A linear equation on rectangular Cartesian coordinates.

relating the variables may be obtained by substituting the coordinates of points P and Q, (10, 1.526) and (40, 1.714), respectively, to obtain

$$\frac{R - 1.526}{T - 10} = \frac{1.714 - 1.526}{40 - 10}$$

whence $R = 1.463 + 0.00626\,T$, where $R =$ resistance in ohms per 1000 ft. of wire and $T =$ temperature in degrees centigrade. It is noted that the coefficient 0.00626 is the mathematical slope of the line and that the constant term 1.463 is the ordinate axis intercept.

LOGARITHMIC COORDINATES. The graduations of a **logarithmic scale** are located along the stem by measurements from the origin which are proportional to the logarithms of the scale values. The scale is cyclic, one log cycle representing a change in the scale value by a factor of 10, if based on common logarithms, or e, if based on natural logarithms. It is characteristic of the logarithmic scale that increments of length corresponding to successive multiplications of the scale value by a constant—from 2 to 4, 4 to 8, 8 to 16, etc.—are equal.

Logarithmic coordinates, with logarithmic scales on both axes, provide means for plotting positive numerical values only, since logarithms of negative values do not exist. The point of origin bears the coordinates (1, 1). Fig. 4 shows cost data for rubber-lined vessels of various capacities, adjusted to a Marshall and Stevens Equipment Cost Index of 186.4, presented by Lundeen and Clark (Chemical Engineering, vol. 62) as curves of a line graph on logarithmic coordinates.

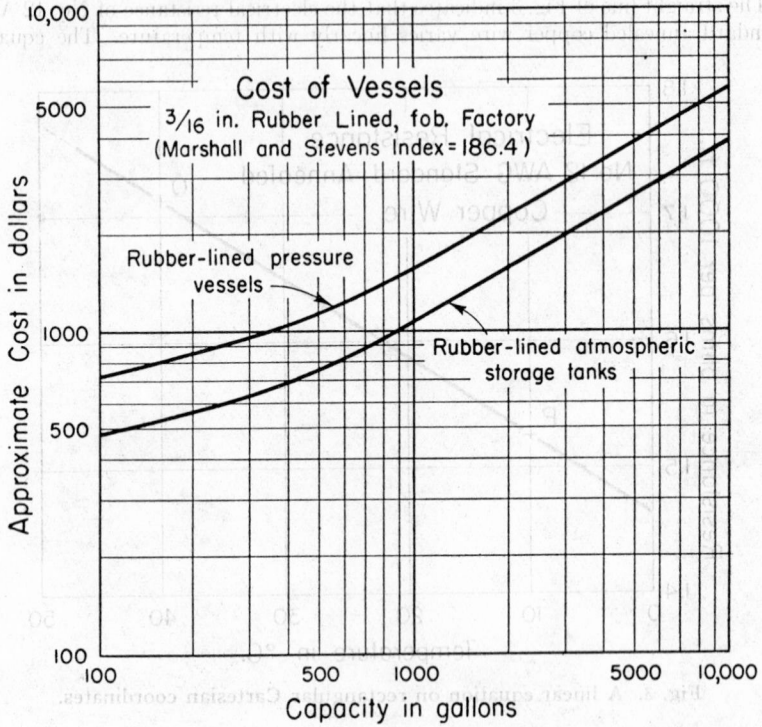

Fig. 4. A line graph on logarithmic coordinates.

Power Equations. The laws of change in nature are of three general types: power, exponential, and periodic. Examples of **power relationships** are found in the formulas for the distance-time relationship of a falling body, the period of a simple pendulum, and the velocity of free discharge of water from an orifice.

The power equation $y = a(x)^b$, in which one quantity varies directly as a constant power of the other, plots on **rectangular Cartesian coordinates** as a family of parabolic and hyperbolic curves, passing through the point $(1, a)$. When the exponent, b, is equal to unity, the curve is a straight line through the origin. For other positive values of b, the curves are parabolic, symmetrical with respect to the y-axis for b greater than one and the x-axis for b less than one. Negative values of b result in hyperbolic curves having the coordinate axes as asymptotes, one variable decreasing as the other increases. The plotting of these power relationships on uniform coordinates requires a considerable number of plotted points. Extension of a curve beyond the range of the plotted data is not considered a safe procedure.

When placed in **logarithmic** form, the power equation becomes

$$\log y = \log a + b \log x$$

in which log y and log x are variable and log a and b are constant terms. Hence, equations of this type rectify, or plot as straight lines, on **logarithmic coordinates**. This procedure is valuable in plotting a relationship for which data are limited, since only two points are needed to locate a straight line. Interpolated and extrapolated values may be more readily obtained from a straight-line plot.

The specific volume of saturated steam exhibits a straight-line relationship with absolute pressure when plotted on the logarithmic coordinates of Fig. 5. The

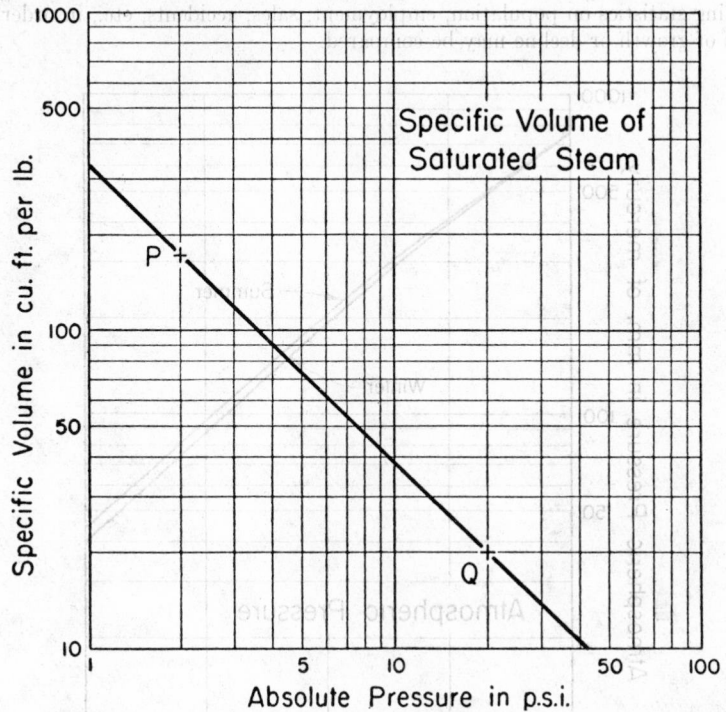

Fig. 5. A power equation on logarithmic coordinates.

equation relating the variables may be obtained by reading the coordinates of points P and Q, $(2, 174)$ and $(20, 20)$, respectively, and substituting in the equation of the straight line

$$\frac{\log V - \log 174}{\log P - \log 2} = \frac{\log 20 - \log 174}{\log 20 - \log 2}$$

whence log $V = 2.523 - 0.939$ log P and $V = 333(P)^{-0.939}$ where $V =$ specific volume in cubic feet per pound and $P =$ absolute pressure in pounds per square inch. It is noted that the coefficient 333 is the ordinate axis intercept at $P = 1$ and that the exponent -0.939 is the mathematical slope of the rectified curve.

SEMILOGARITHMIC COORDINATES. Coordinates based on one axis bearing a logarithmic scale, usually the ordinate axis, and on one bearing a uniform scale are called semilogarithmic coordinates. The point of origin bears the coordinates $(0, 1)$. The curves plotted on the semilogarithmic coordinates of

Fig. 6 indicate summer and winter values of atmospheric pressure at various altitudes.

The semilogarithmic coordinate chart is often called a **rate of change chart** because of its ability to depict relative or percentage change. A straight-line curve indicates a constant rate of change of the logarithmically plotted variable with respect to the uniformly plotted variable. Parallel curves, where several relationships appear on the same grid, indicate equal rates of change. Semilogarithmic coordinates, with time plotted on the uniform scale, are frequently employed in plotting statistics on population, employment, sales, accidents, etc., in order that rates of growth or decline may be compared.

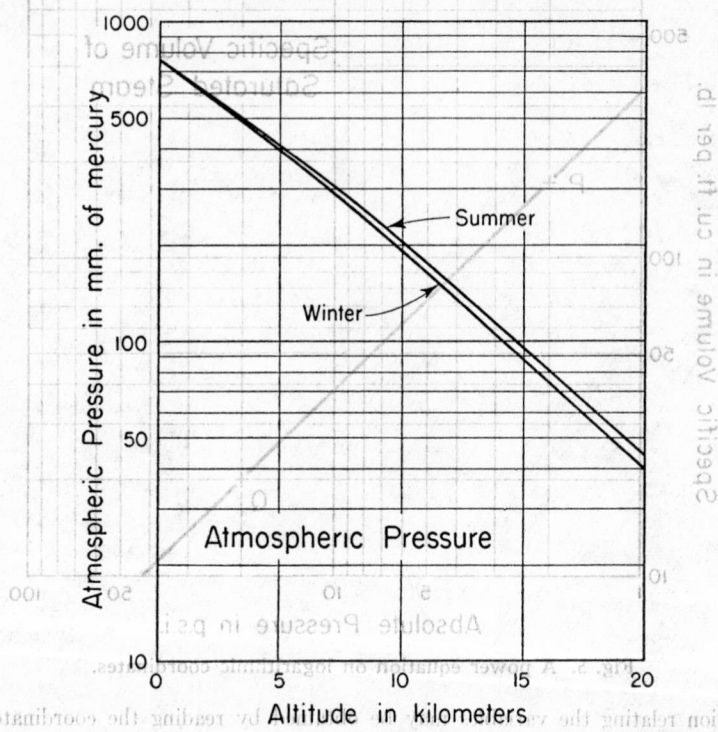

Fig. 6. A line graph on semilogarithmic coordinates.

It should be noted that semilogarithmic coordinates may not replace Cartesian coordinates for all purposes. Semilogarithmic rulings should not be used where comparison of magnitude is intended or where the data to be plotted includes both positive and negative values.

Exponential Equations. Many quantities in nature increase or decrease at a rate which is proportional to the amount present at any given time. As time progresses arithmetically, by a constant difference, the quantity changes geometrically, by a constant factor, that is, at a constant rate. Examples of these **exponential relationships** are found in the formulas for the transient current in an inductive electric circuit, the decrease in intensity of natural radioactivity, and the increase of a sum of money at compound interest. Variables other than time may, of course, be involved. The **Arrhenius equation**, giving the change in rate of chemical reaction with temperature, is exponential.

The exponential equation $y = a(e)^{bx}$, or $y = a(10)^{bx}$, plots on **rectangular Cartesian coordinates** as a family of curves passing through the point $(0, a)$ and having the x-axis as asymptote. When placed in **logarithmic** form, the equation $y = a(e)^{bx}$ becomes

$$\ln y = \ln a + bx \ln e = \ln a + bx$$

in which $\ln y$ and x are variable and $\ln a$ and b are constant terms. Similarly, the equation $y = a(10)^{bx}$ becomes

$$\log y = \log a + bx \log 10 = \log a + bx$$

in which $\log y$ and x are variable and $\log a$ and b are constant terms. Hence, equations of this type rectify on **semilogarithmic coordinates** in which the y-scale is logarithmic and the x-scale is uniform. Where data are limited or where accurate interpolated or extrapolated values are desired, semilogarithmic rulings offer the same advantages for exponential equations that logarithmic coordinates offer in the case of power relationships.

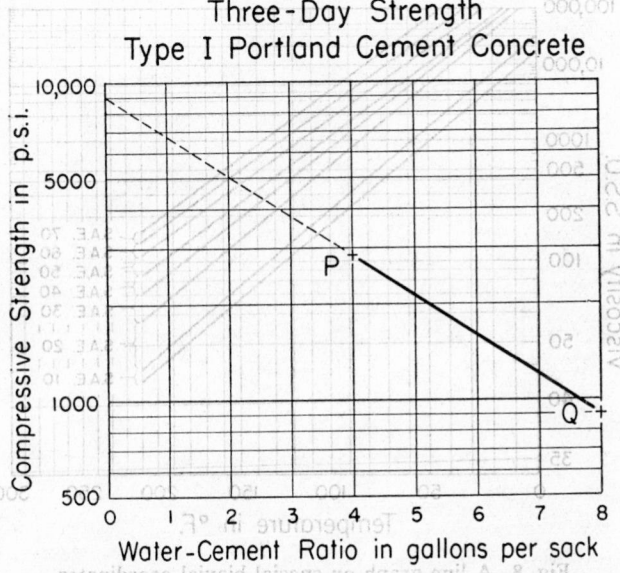

Fig. 7. An exponential equation on semilogarithmic coordinates.

The 3-day compressive strength of a Type I Portland cement concrete having a high early strength exhibits a straight-line relationship with water-cement ratio on the semilogarithmic coordinates of Fig. 7. The equation relating the variables may be obtained by reading the coordinates of points P and Q, $(4, 2850)$ and $(8, 900)$, respectively, and substituting in the equation of the straight line

$$\frac{\log S - \log 2850}{R - 4} = \frac{\log 900 - \log 2850}{8 - 4}$$

whence $\log S = 3.955 - 0.125 \ R$ and $S = 9020(10)^{-0.125 \ R}$ where S = compressive strength in pounds per square inch and R = water-cement ratio in gallons per sack. It is noted that the coefficient, 9020, is the ordinate axis intercept obtained by extending the line to $S = 0$ and that the value, -0.125, is the mathematical slope of the rectified curve.

BIAXIAL COORDINATES. Many coordinate spacings other than uniform and logarithmic find use in the plotting of line graphs. **Reciprocal, power,** and **probability rulings** appear in some applications. Such coordinates may function to bring about rectification of curves in the same manner that logarithmic and semilogarithmic coordinates rectify simple power and exponential curves. They are valuable where data are limited or where interpolation or extrapolation is to be carried out.

It is also occasionally desirable to distort a graph so that the grid lines are no longer parallel. The ASTM standard viscosity-temperature chart for S.A.E. numbered crankcase oils, from which Fig. 8 was taken, illustrates the use of **special scales** and **nonparallel rulings.**

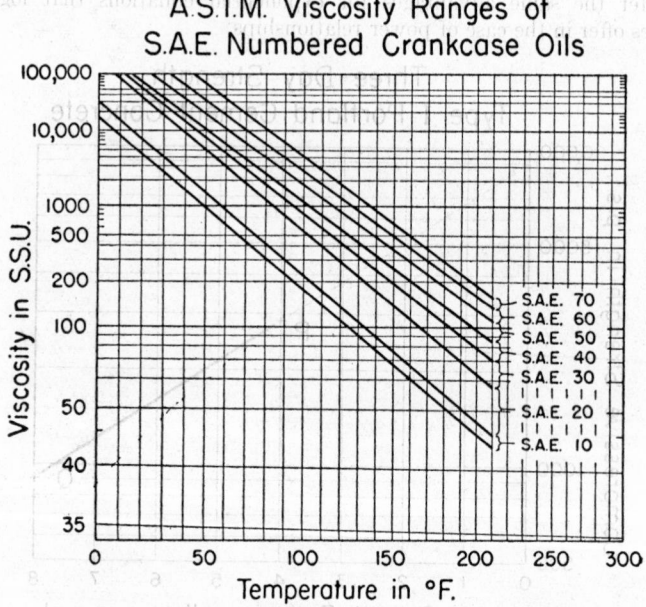

Fig. 8. A line graph on special biaxial coordinates.

NETWORK CHARTS. An equation in **three variables** may be represented on biaxial coordinates as a family of curves. Two of the variables plot along the coordinate axes, and the third functions as a parameter. The network chart shown in Fig. 9, giving friction loss for flow of water in ordinary wrought iron standard weight pipe, is based on the **Hazen-Williams formula:**

$$V = 0.550\,C(D)^{0.63}(S)^{0.54}$$

and on the flow formula:

$$Q = 352\,V(D)^2$$

where $Q =$ flow in gallons of water per minute, $V =$ fluid velocity in feet per second, $D =$ internal pipe diameter in feet, $S =$ friction loss in feet of water per lineal foot of pipe, and C is an empirical constant assigned a value of 100 for ordinary wrought iron pipe. Two straight-line networks are obtained by plotting the equations on a single logarithmic grid.

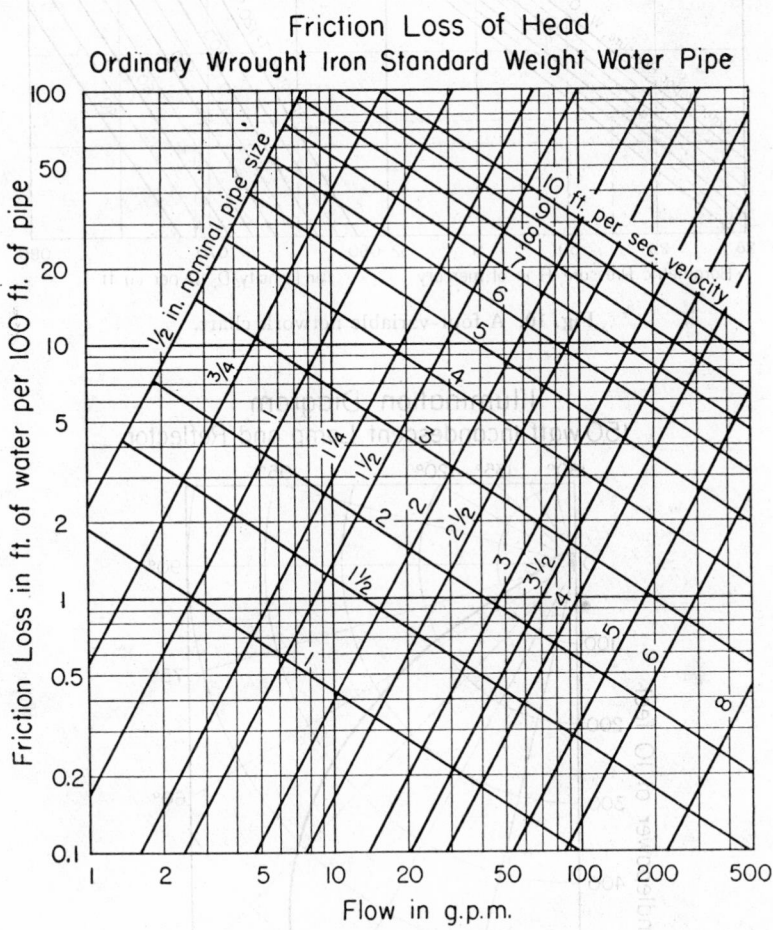

Fig. 9. A network chart based on the Hazen-Williams formula.

An equation in **four variables** may be represented by a combination of two 3-variable networks. The formula for the **density of moist air,**

$$D = 1.326 \left(\frac{B - 0.378\,W}{T + 459.6} \right)$$

where $B =$ barometric pressure and $W =$ water-vapor pressure, both in inches of mercury, $T =$ temperature in degrees Fahrenheit, and $D =$ density in pounds per cubic foot, is thus represented in Fig. 10. The given equation is replaced by two

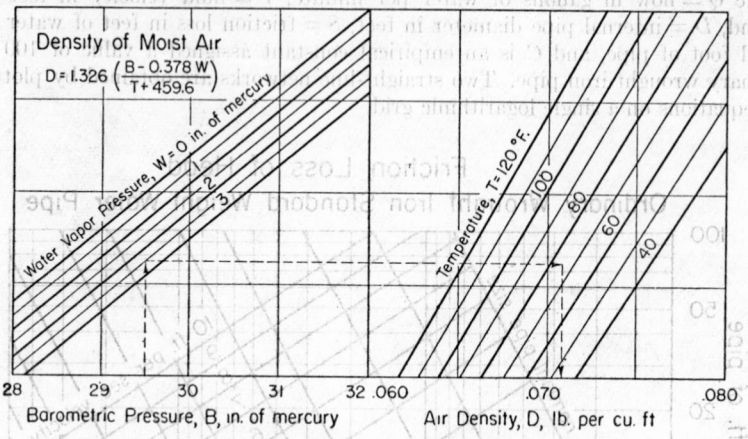

Density of Moist Air

$$D = 1.326 \left(\frac{B - 0.378 W}{T + 459.6} \right)$$

Water Vapor Pressure, W = 0 in. of mercury

Temperature T = 120 F.

Barometric Pressure, B, in. of mercury   Air Density, D, lb. per cu. ft

Fig. 10. A four-variable network chart.

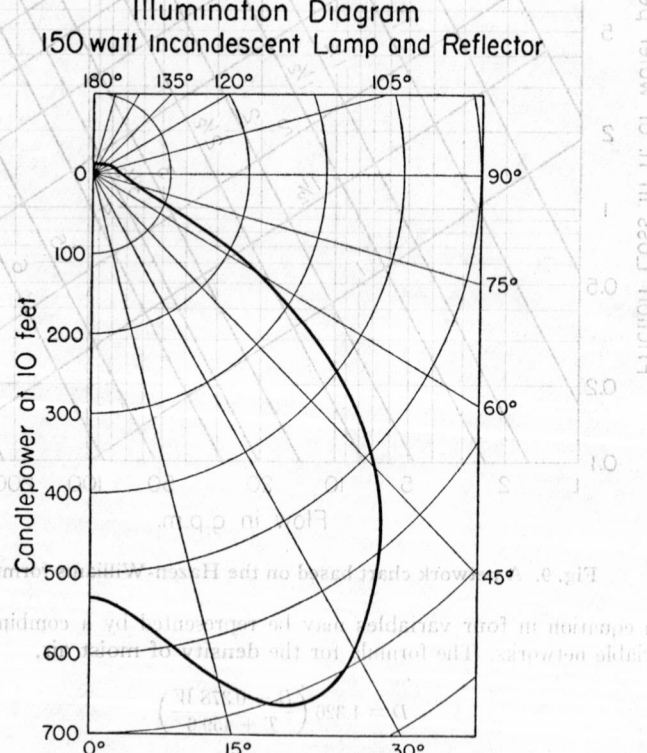

Illumination Diagram
150 watt Incandescent Lamp and Reflector

Candlepower at 10 feet

Fig. 11. A line graph on polar coordinates.

3-variable equations, through the introduction of an additional term, Y, common to both, to give

$$1.326 B - 0.502 W = Y \qquad (1)$$

and

$$Y = D (T + 459.6) \qquad (2)$$

Eq. (1) is represented by a network of straight lines, with B plotted as abscissa, W as parameter, and Y as ordinate. Eq. (2) is represented by a network of straight lines, with Y plotted as ordinate, T as parameter, and D as abscissa. The two charts are plotted with identical ordinate scales and placed side by side. Since values of Y are not desired, the ordinate scale is ungraduated. A typical solution is indicated, giving $D = 0.0708$ when $B = 29.5$, $W = 2.5$, and $T = 75$.

POLAR COORDINATES. Polar coordinates are employed in plotting relationships in which one of the variable quantities is a magnitude and the other a direction. The system is composed of **circular grids**, concentric about the origin, and **radial lines**, one of which serves as a reference for the measurement of direction angles. Two examples of applications in which polar coordinates find

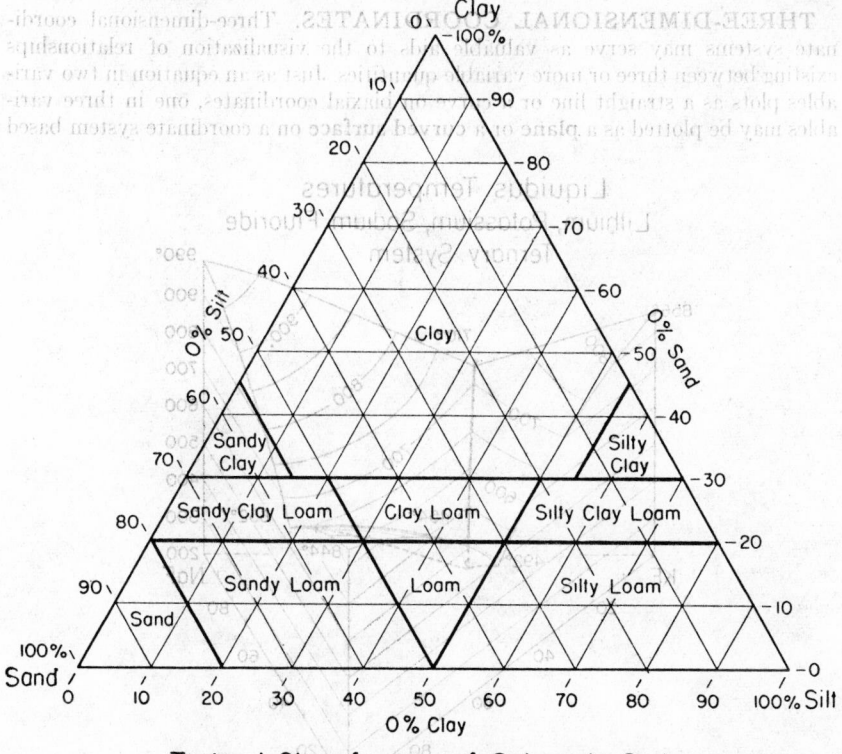

Textural Classification of Subgrade Soils
(U.S. Public Roads Administration)

Fig. 12. A triaxial coordinate chart.

use are the diagrams showing heat or light distribution from a point source and microwave directional antenna patterns.

Fig. 11 is an illumination diagram for a 150-w. incandescent lamp and reflector plotted on polar coordinates. The radial distance from origin to curve indicates intensity of illumination at a given angle with the vertical.

TRIAXIAL COORDINATES. The percentage composition of a mixture of three components may be represented by a point on triaxial coordinates. The chart is in the form of an equilateral triangle, the altitude of which represents 100 percent of each one of the three components. The usefulness of such a diagram depends upon the **geometric principle** that the sum of the perpendiculars to the sides from any point within an equilateral triangle is a constant and is equal to the altitude. Properties of materials may be indicated by locating curves which contain all points representing mixtures of constant density, tensile strength, melting temperature, etc.; or mixtures may be classified by defining areas on the chart.

The textural classification of subgrade soils by the U. S. Public Roads Administration (Principles of Highway Construction as Applied to Airports, Flight Strips, and Other Landing Areas for Aircraft) is shown in Fig. 12 as a triaxial coordinate chart.

THREE-DIMENSIONAL COORDINATES. Three-dimensional coordinate systems may serve as valuable aids to the visualization of relationships existing between three or more variable quantities. Just as an equation in two variables plots as a straight line or a curve on biaxial coordinates, one in three variables may be plotted as a **plane** or a **curved surface** on a coordinate system based

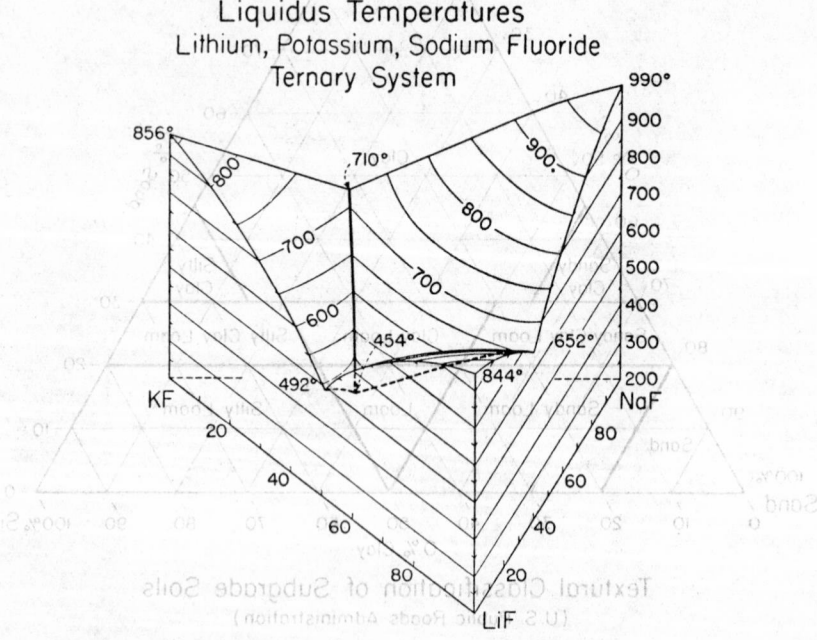

Fig. 13. A three-dimensional coordinate chart.

on three mutually perpendicular axes through a single point of origin. Surfaces may be portrayed on **solid models** constructed of wood, cardboard, or plaster of Paris. Space coordinates may also be represented as a **plane projection** that takes the form of an orthographic, axonometric, or perspective view of the coordinate system.

Metallurgical and mineralogical **phase diagrams** frequently appear as three-dimensional coordinate charts. The phase diagram shown pictorially in Fig. 13 is constructed by plotting temperature at right angles to a horizontal plane containing the triaxial composition diagram for the ternary system—lithium fluoride –potassium fluoride–sodium fluoride. The ordinate of any point on the upper surface of the diagram is a measure of the temperature in degrees centigrade to which the mixture of fluorides must be heated to change it to a completely molten state.

Graphic Scales

PURPOSE. The scale is a useful device of everyday life. The yardstick, thermometer, clock, and automobile speedometer are typical of the manner in which scales provide for the measurement of physical quantities. The scale is a fundamental element of the graphic language. The draftsman or architect uses a scale in laying out a drawing which may be full-, half-, quarter-, or smaller-scale, depending on the relationship between its size and the size of the object represented. Scales are necessary components of charts and graphs where variable quantities are to be represented and coordinate values established. The engineer's slide rule, designed to carry out basic mathematical operations, is an arrangement of scales, as are the many special-purpose slide and disc calculators utilized in the design and selection of industrial machinery and equipment. A conversion scale or nomograph, for the solution of an equation, is composed of scales.

DEFINITION. A scale may be defined as a series of marks or **graduations** located in systematic fashion along a straight or curved line called a **stem**. Certain of the graduations are identified by **numerical calibrations** which increase or decrease along the stem. All scales have an **origin** or beginning from which other points on the stem are located.

Based on the manner in which they are constructed, scales may be classed as **uniform** or **nonuniform**. On a uniform scale, graduations are evenly spaced, and values assigned thereto increase or decrease by equal increments. On a non-uniform scale, graduations corresponding to equal increments of value are unevenly spaced.

SCALE EQUATION. Graduations may be located on a straight scale by means of the equation

$$d = m f(r)$$

where m is the scale factor or modulus; $f(r)$ is any function of the variable, r; and d is the distance in inches from the scale origin to the graduation marking a specific value of r.

Linear, or first-degree, functions result in uniform scales of the type shown at A and B in Fig. 14. Other functions result in nonuniform scales such as those at C, D, E, and F in Fig. 14. Only portions of the scales are shown in the 2.5-in.

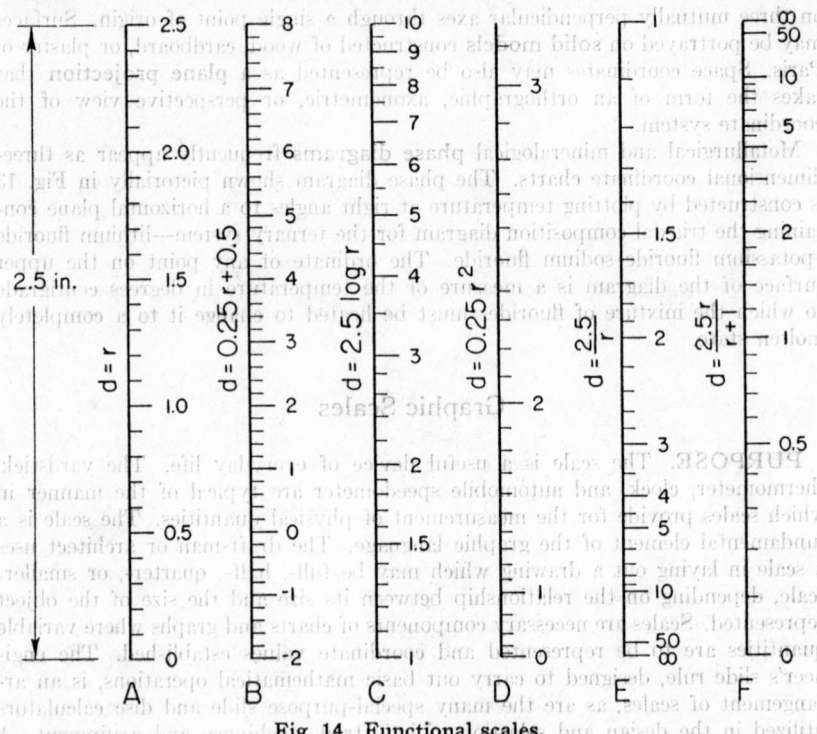

Fig. 14. Functional scales.

length, and they may be extended, in each case, in either the positive or negative direction.

SCALE MODULUS. The scale modulus serves to establish the length of scale corresponding to a given range of the variable. It may be defined as the distance in inches along the stem corresponding to a unit change in the value of the scale function. Scale modulus has no sign; and the distance, d, is positive or negative, according to the sign of the scale function. **Scale length** is the product of modulus and range of function, or

$$\text{Length} = m \; [f_{max}(r) - f_{min}(r)]$$

SCALE LAYOUT. Accuracy and technique are of primary importance in the drafting of scales. Graduations are carefully located with measurements obtained by solution of the scale equation. Points are marked with fine lines at right angles to the stem, the principal divisions having longer marks to distinguish them. Scales may be conveniently subdivided through the use of a **modulus chart,** such as that for uniform scales shown in Fig. 15, and that for logarithmic scales shown in Fig. 16. A properly located vertical line intersects the diagonal rays at points which may be projected or transferred to a stem to form the desired scale.

CONVERSION SCALE. An equation in two variables may be represented by a curve plotted on biaxial coordinates. The relationship may also be indicated by constructing a suitable scale for each variable on opposite sides of a stem

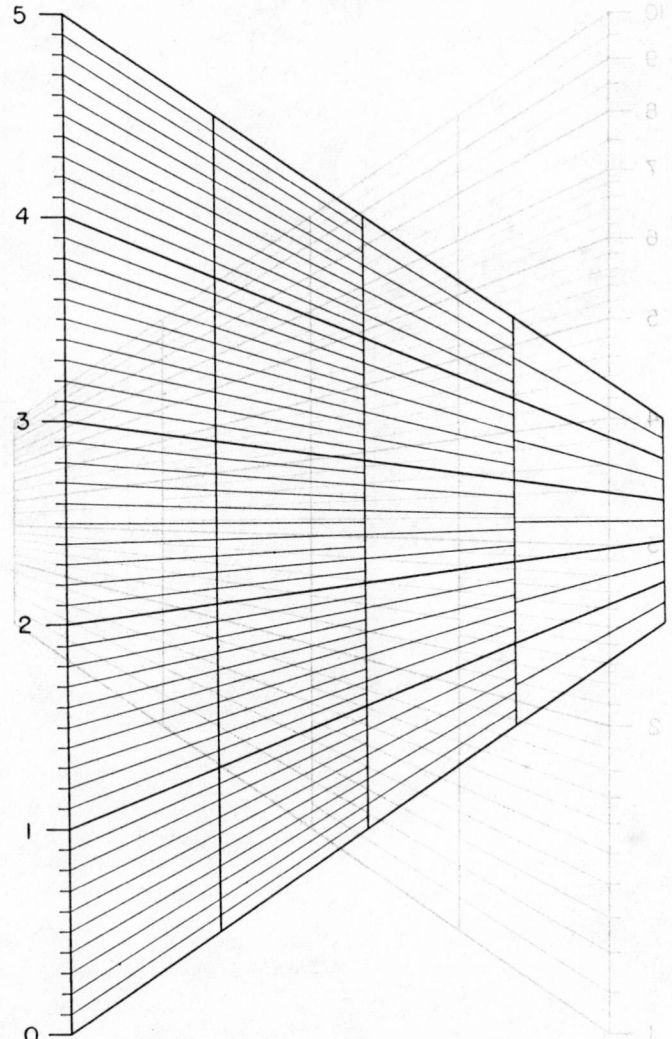

Fig. 15. A uniform scale modulus chart.

using the same origin and modulus. Thus the scales of Fig. 17 provide for the conversion of A.P.I. gravity readings for light petroleum products to specific gravity. The formula for the conversion is

$$\text{Specific Gravity } 60/60°\text{F.} = \frac{141.5}{°\text{A.P.I.} + 131.5}$$

The left side of the equation serves as the function of the uniform specific gravity scale. The scale modulus, 10 in., is obtained by dividing the scale length, 4 in., by the range of function, 0.40. The scale equation is

$$d_{\text{sp. gr.}} = 10 \text{ sp. gr.}$$

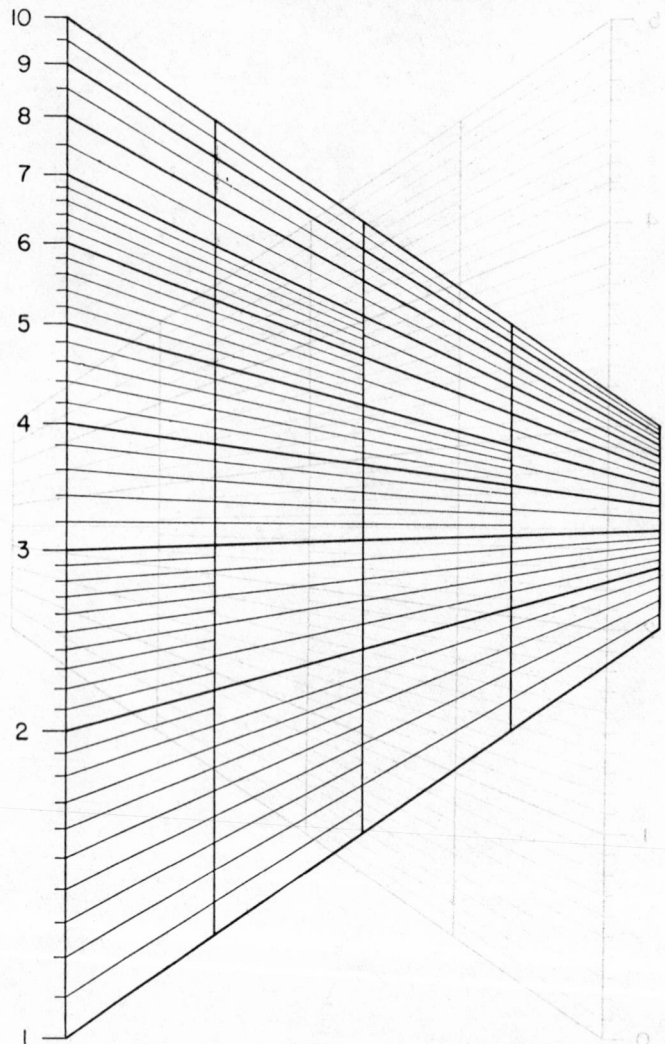

Fig. 16. A logarithmic scale modulus chart.

The scale origin is not included in the range of plotted values but lies 6 in. below the graduation, 0.60.

The expression on the right side of the equation becomes the function of the nonuniform A.P.I. gravity scale. Using the same modulus, the scale equation is

$$d_{\text{A.P.I.}} = 10 \left(\frac{141.5}{°\text{A.P.I.} + 131.5} \right)$$

Substitution of values from 10° to 100° A.P.I. results in measurements for locating the graduations on the A.P.I. gravity scale.

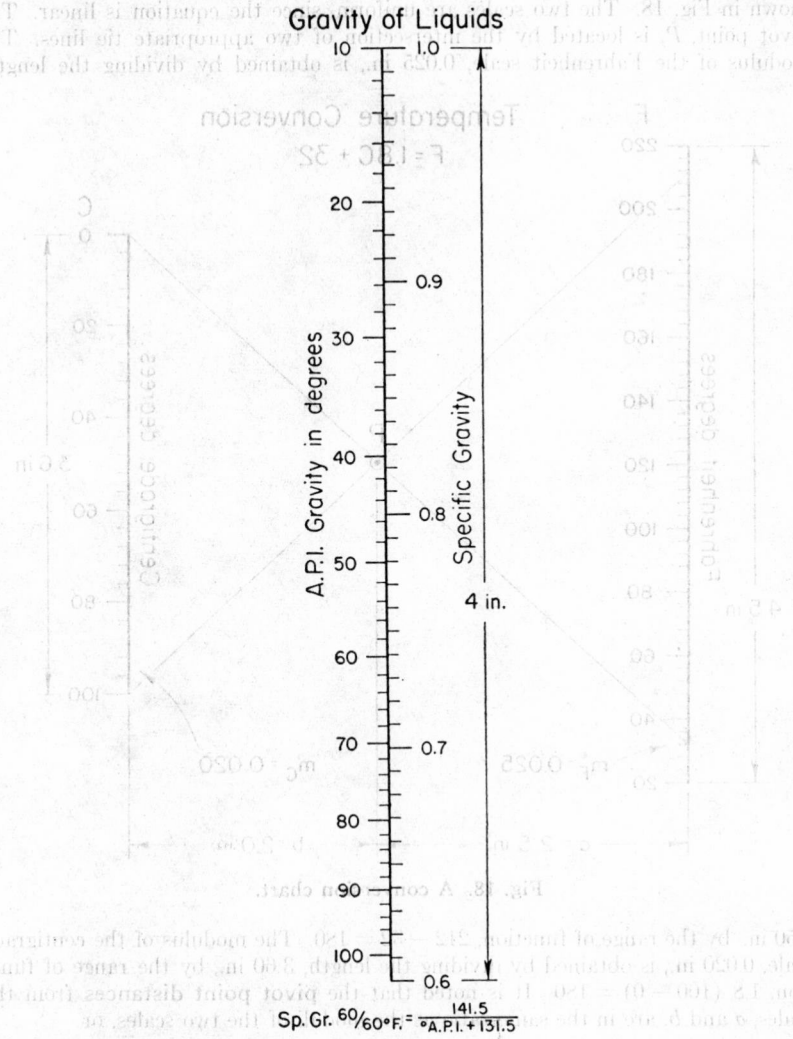

Fig. 17. A conversion scale.

CONVERSION CHARTS. The two scales of a conversion need not be plotted on the same stem but, instead, may be located a convenient distance apart and running in opposite directions. Corresponding values of the two variables are indicated by a straight **tie line,** or join, passing through a **pivot point** and connecting the scales.

Conversion of temperature readings from degrees Fahrenheit to degrees centigrade may be accomplished by the chart for the equation

$$F = 1.8\,C + 32$$

shown in Fig. 18. The two scales are uniform, since the equation is linear. The pivot point, P, is located by the intersection of two appropriate tie lines. The modulus of the Fahrenheit scale, 0.025 in., is obtained by dividing the length,

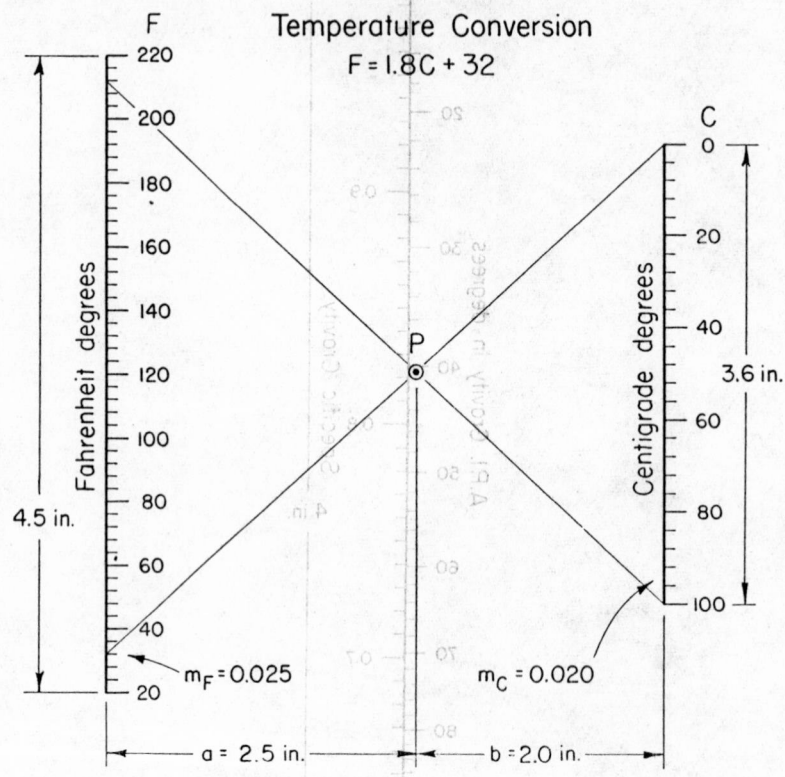

Fig. 18. A conversion chart.

4.50 in. by the range of function, $212 - 32 = 180$. The modulus of the centigrade scale, 0.020 in., is obtained by dividing the length, 3.60 in., by the range of function, $1.8 \ (100 - 0) = 180$. It is noted that the **pivot point distances** from the scales, a and b, are in the same ratio as the moduli of the two scales, or

$$\frac{a}{b} = \frac{m_F}{m_C}$$

A number of similar conversions may be represented on a single chart having two scales and a series of different pivot points. The specific heats of many elements and inorganic compounds in the solid state are given in terms of temperature by equations of the form

$$C = a + b \ (T + 273.1)$$

where C = specific heat in calories per degree centigrade per gram, T = temperature in degrees centigrade, and a and b are empirical constants. The equations for the specific heats of ten metals are the basis for the chart of Fig. 19. A sample tie line indicates a specific heat of 0.074 cal. per °C. per gram for tin at 500° C.

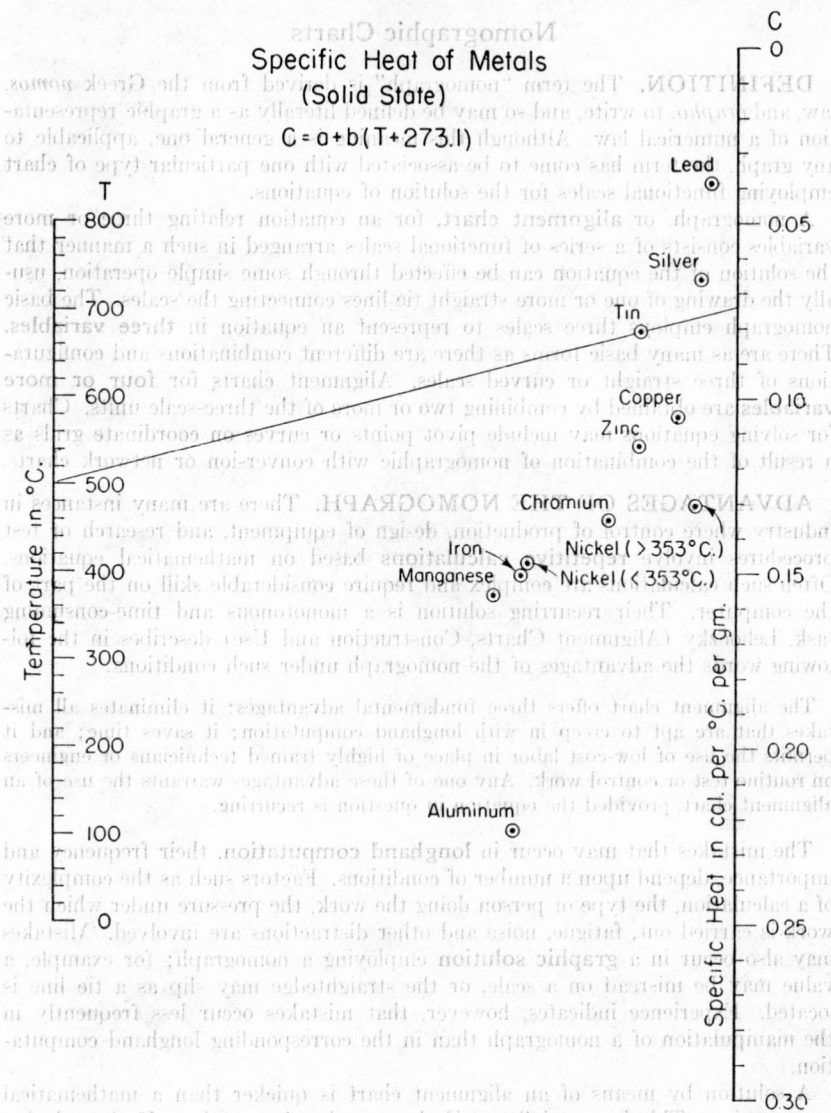

Specific Heat of Metals
(Solid State)

$$C = a + b(T + 273.1)$$

Fig. 19. **A multipivot conversion chart.**

CURVED SCALES. Where a curved scale other then circular appears on a chart, points are located by means of offsets from a pair of reference lines or axes. Two functions of the scale variable may thus be involved, one giving an offset in the y direction and one an offset in the x direction. The stem is drawn through the plotted points in the same manner that a curve is located on the coordinate grid of a line graph. The layout of a curved scale is described in subsequent paragraphs on the construction of nomographic charts.

Nomographic Charts

DEFINITION. The term "nomograph" is derived from the Greek *nomos*, law, and *grapho*, to write, and so may be defined literally as a graphic representation of a numerical law. Although this meaning is a general one, applicable to any graph, the term has come to be associated with one particular type of chart employing functional scales for the solution of equations.

A nomograph, or **alignment chart,** for an equation relating three or more variables consists of a series of functional scales arranged in such a manner that the solution of the equation can be effected through some simple operation, usually the drawing of one or more straight tie lines connecting the scales. The basic nomograph employs three scales to represent an equation in **three variables.** There are as many basic forms as there are different combinations and configurations of three straight or curved scales. Alignment charts for **four or more variables** are obtained by combining two or more of the three-scale units. Charts for solving equations may include pivot points or curves on coordinate grids as a result of the combination of nomographic with conversion or network charts.

ADVANTAGES OF THE NOMOGRAPH. There are many instances in industry where control of production, design of equipment, and research or test procedures involve **repetitive calculations** based on mathematical equations. Often such calculations are complex and require considerable skill on the part of the computer. Their recurring solution is a monotonous and time-consuming task. Lehoczky (Alignment Charts, Construction and Use) describes in the following words the advantages of the nomograph under such conditions:

The alignment chart offers three fundamental advantages: it eliminates all mistakes that are apt to creep in with longhand computation; it saves time; and it permits the use of low-cost labor in place of highly trained technicians or engineers on routine test or control work. Any one of these advantages warrants the use of an alignment chart, provided the equation in question is recurring.

The mistakes that may occur in **longhand computation,** their frequency and importance, depend upon a number of conditions. Factors such as the complexity of a calculation, the type of person doing the work, the pressure under which the work is carried out, fatigue, noise and other distractions are involved. Mistakes may also occur in a **graphic solution** employing a nomograph; for example, a value may be misread on a scale, or the straightedge may slip as a tie line is located. Experience indicates, however, that mistakes occur less frequently in the manipulation of a nomograph than in the corresponding longhand computation.

A solution by means of an alignment chart is quicker than a mathematical computation. This is especially so if the equation is complex. If the solution must be repeated again and again, the **time factor** becomes increasingly important. Indeed, the uninterrupted control of a manufacturing process may present problems that require almost immediate solution and necessitate the use of an alignment chart in place of the slower longhand computation.

A third advantage of alignment charts is their adaptability to the **mathematically untrained worker.** There are many cases in industry where the process of manufacture, test, or research requires the solution of recurring equations. Technically trained personnel command relatively high wages, and their time is ordinarily considered too valuable to be employed on routine computational work.

Any equation, whether simple or complex, can be solved quickly and accurately by less costly labor if an alignment chart is available.

CHART LAYOUT. The construction of a nomographic chart to represent an equation in three variables may follow one of several procedures, depending upon the form of the equation and the degree to which it is desired to become involved with theoretical considerations. Charts representing certain equations for the **simple addition or multiplication** of terms may be constructed by laying out two scales of suitable type and modulus along parallel straight stems. Points on the third scale, which may be straight or curved, are then located by the intersection of appropriate tie lines.

Another procedure is one in which **characteristic chart forms**—parallel scales, concurrent scales, Z-chart, etc.—are associated with particular types of equations. Sufficient geometric analysis is made of each chart form to establish formulas for the layout of the scales. This method is described by practically all texts on nomography.

A third procedure involves the writing of the chart equation as a **zero-valued third-order determinant** of special form. The elements of the first and second columns of the determinant provide functions of each variable which enable the scales to be plotted on Cartesian coordinates. An advantage exists in that all chart forms are embraced by a single theory. Difficulty may be encountered, however, in converting the equation to the proper determinant form. This conversion is often a "trial and error"-type process and may require appreciable time and effort. It may also be the case that after a determinant has been written, the resulting chart does not plot in suitable proportion, and certain adjustments, in the way of introduction of constants or alteration of the form of the elements of the determinant, have to be made to obtain suitable scale configuration.

Care must be exercised in the design and layout of a nomographic chart. Certain **limitations on accuracy** are inherent in all graphic methods. Scales must be accurately located and calibrated if the best possible results are to be achieved in the use of the chart.

THREE-VARIABLE NOMOGRAPHS. The basic nomograph employs three scales to represent an equation in three variables. The most common charts are those composed of three straight scales, and they are the primary concern of this discussion. An example of the nomograph with one curved scale is also presented, to acquaint the reader with the method of plotting such scales.

Parallel Straight Scales. An equation in three variables that can be expressed in the form

$$f_1(p) + f_2(q) = f_3(r)$$

where f_1, f_2, and f_3 are each a function of a single variable, may be represented by a nomographic chart of **three parallel scales**, each calibrated with values of one of the variables, p, q, and r. The scales are so located and graduated that a straight tie line cuts them at values of p, q, and r which satisfy the equation. Thus, if values of two of the variables are known, the unknown value of the third can be determined. The first step in the construction of the chart, shown diagrammatically in Fig. 20, is the location, at a convenient distance apart, of two vertical scales, the p-scale having a modulus m_p, and the q-scale having a modulus m_q. The **scale graduation equations** are

$$d_p = m_p f_1(p) \qquad \text{and} \qquad d_q = m_q f_2(q)$$

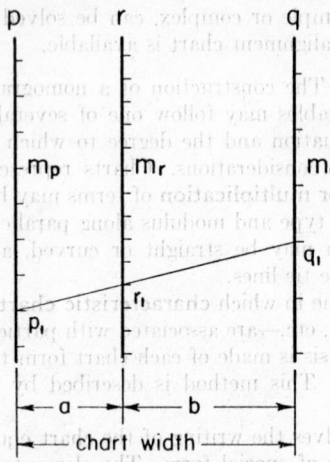

Fig. 20. Construction of the parallel scale nomograph.

A vertical stem is next located intermediate to the p- and q-scales by means of the relationship

$$\frac{a}{b} = \frac{m_p}{m_q}.$$

A straight line is drawn connecting two specific values, p_1 and q_1, and the chart equation solved for the corresponding value, r_1. This base line may be a line connecting the scale origins. The **modulus of the center scale** is evaluated as the product of the moduli of the p- and q-scales divided by their sum, or

$$m_r = \frac{m_p m_q}{m_p + m_q}$$

and the scale is graduated by means of the equation

$$d_r = m_r f_3(r).$$

In positioning the r-scale vertically on the stem, care is taken that the value r_1 falls at the base line.

A parallel scale nomograph for the pressure-velocity relationship of air at standard conditions is shown in Fig. 21. The chart equation is

$$S.P. + \left(\frac{V}{4005}\right)^2 = T.P.$$

where V = velocity in feet per minute, $S.P.$ = static pressure, and $T.P.$ = total pressure, the last two in inches of water gage. Construction of the chart is summarized as follows:

   1. Static pressure scale:
      Modulus: 0.75 in.
      Equation: $d_{S.P.} = 0.75\ S.P.$
      Length: $(0.75)(9) = 6.75$ in.
   2. Velocity scale:
      Modulus: 3 in.
      Equation: $d = 3\left(\frac{V}{4005}\right)^2$

      Length: $(3)\left(\frac{6000}{4005}\right)^2 = 7.73$ in.

3. Total pressure scale:
   Chart width: 5 in.

   Scale spacing: $\dfrac{a}{b} = \dfrac{0.75}{3}$ and $a = 1$ in., $b = 4$ in.

   Modulus: $\dfrac{(0.75)(3)}{0.75 + 3} = 0.60$ in.

   Equation: $d_{T.P.} = 0.60\,T.P.$

   Length: $(0.60)(11) = 6.60$ in.

4. Base line connects $S.P. = 0;\ V = 0,$ and $T.P. = 0.$

A tie line indicates that air moving with a velocity of 4,900 ft. per min. at a static pressure of 7.5 in. of water exerts a total pressure of 9.0 in. of water.

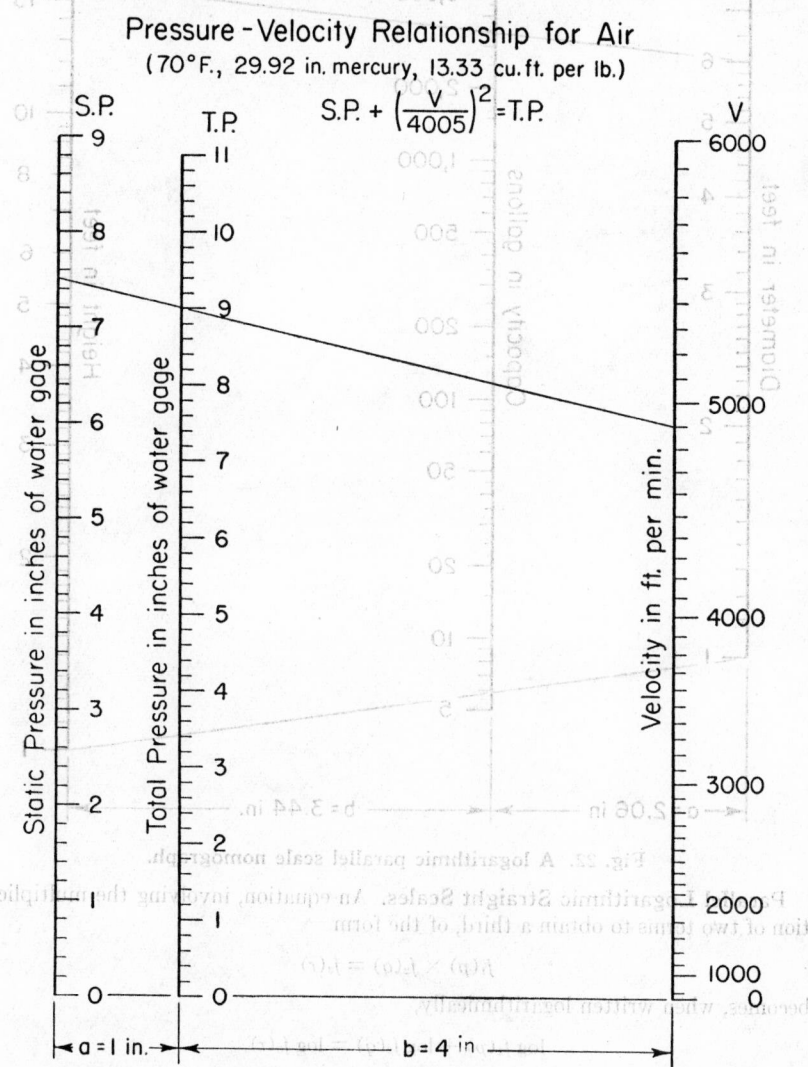

Pressure - Velocity Relationship for Air
(70°F., 29.92 in. mercury, 13.33 cu. ft. per lb.)

$$S.P. + \left(\frac{V}{4005}\right)^2 = T.P.$$

Fig. 21. A parallel scale nomograph.

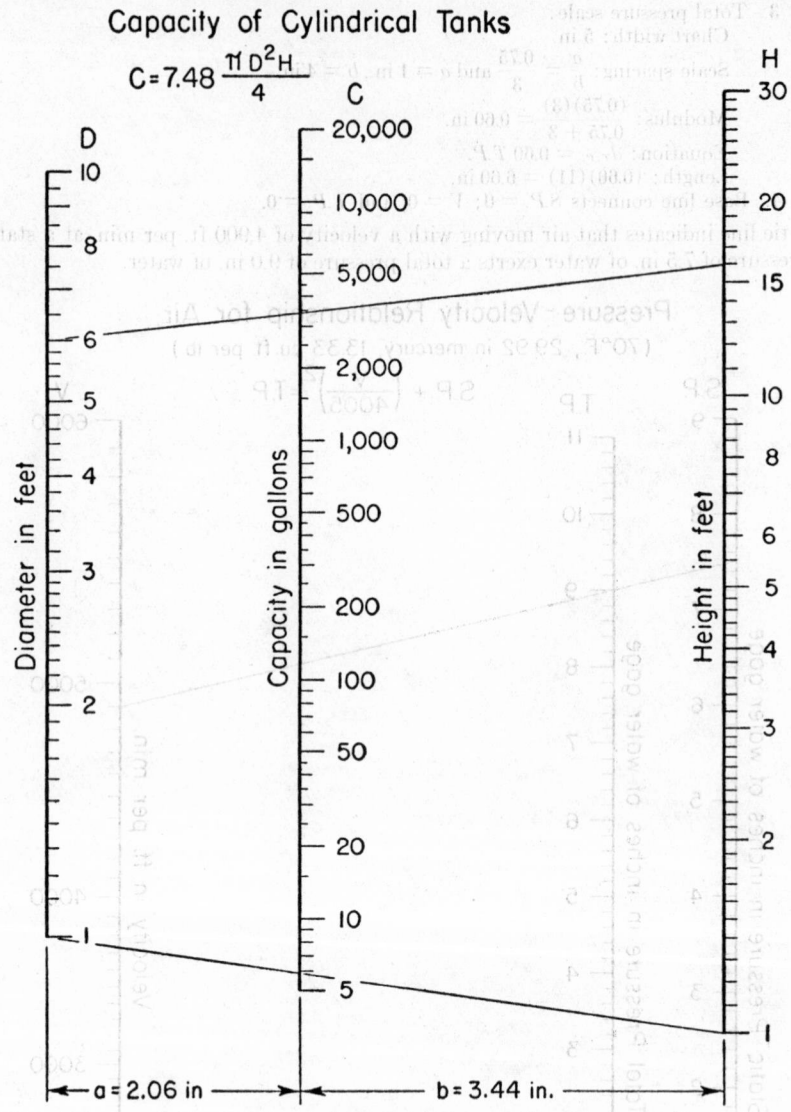

Fig. 22. A logarithmic parallel scale nomograph.

Parallel Logarithmic Straight Scales. An equation, involving the multiplication of two terms to obtain a third, of the form

$$f_1(p) \times f_2(q) = f_3(r)$$

becomes, when written logarithmically,

$$\log f_1(p) + \log f_2(q) = \log f_3(r)$$

and may be represented by a nomograph of three parallel logarithmic scales.

The formula for the capacity of a cylindrical tank,

$$C = 7.48 \left(\frac{\pi D^2 H}{4} \right) = 5.875 \, D^2 H$$

where C = capacity in gallons, D = diameter, and H = height—both in feet—becomes, when placed in logarithmic form,

$$\log C = \log 5.875 + 2 \log D + \log H$$

Construction of the chart in Fig. 22 is summarized as follows:

1. Diameter scale:
   Modulus: 3 in.
   Equation: $d_D = 3(2 \log D) = 6 \log D$.
2. Height scale:
   Modulus: 5 in.
   Equation: $d_H = 5 \log H$.
3. Capacity scale:
   Chart width: 5.5 in.
   Scale spacing: $\dfrac{a}{b} = \dfrac{3}{5}$ and $a = 2.06$ in., $b = 3.44$ in.
   Modulus: $\dfrac{(3)(5)}{3+5} = 1.875$ in.
   Equation: $d_C = 1.875 \log C$.
4. Base line connects $D = 1$; $H = 1$; and $C = 5.875$.

The scales may be graduated by means of a logarithmic modulus chart, as shown in Fig. 16. A tie line indicates a capacity of 3,400 gal. for a cylindrical tank 6 ft. in diameter and 16 ft. high.

Parallel and Transverse Straight Scales (Z-Chart). The equation

$$f_1(p) \times f_2(q) = f_3(r)$$

may also be represented by a nomographic chart of two parallel scales and one transverse scale; hence the Z-chart, shown in Fig. 23. The parallel scales, one

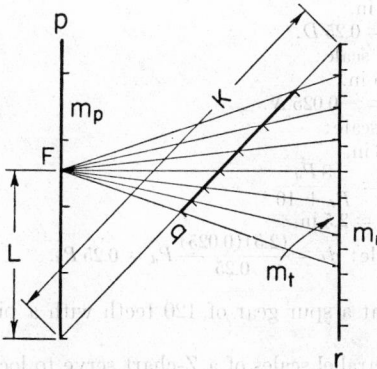

Fig. 23. **Construction of the parallel and transverse scale nomograph (Z-chart).**

of which must represent values of r, run in opposite directions from a base line joining their origins. The transverse scale extends along the base line, its origin coinciding with the origin of the r-scale. The base line may be either horizontal or inclined but is usually inclined to obtain more efficient use of the chart area and sharper intersections between tie lines and scales.

Layout of the chart begins with the location, at a convenient distance apart, of two vertical scales, the p-scale having a modulus m_p and the r-scale having a modulus m_r. The scales are graduated by means of the equations

$$d_p = m_p f_1(p) \qquad \text{and} \qquad d_r = -m_r f_3(r)$$

The length, K, of the base line represents the positive portion of the q-scale covering the range of function from zero to infinity. The scale may be graduated by substituting values of q in the scale equation

$$d_q = \frac{K f_2(q)}{f_2(q) + m_p/m_r}$$

The scale may be more conveniently graduated by projectors from a scale temporarily laid out on the r-scale to a focal point, F, located on the p-scale a distance, L inches, from its origin. The modulus, m_t, of the temporary scale is related to the distance, L, by the equation

$$\frac{m_t}{m_r} = \frac{L}{m_p}$$

and the equation of the temporary scale may be written:

$$d_t = \frac{Lm_r}{m_p} f_2(q)$$

The **temporary scale** and **projectors** are a construction only and are not a part of the finished chart.

A nomograph for determining the diametral pitch of spur gears is shown in Fig. 24. Construction of the chart, representing the equation $D \times P_d = N$ where P_d = diametral pitch, D = pitch diameter in inches, and N = number of teeth, may be summarized as follows:

1. Pitch-diameter scale:
   Modulus: 0.25 in.
   Equation: $d_D = 0.25\,D$.
2. Number-of-teeth scale:
   Modulus: 0.025 in.
   Equation: $d_N = -0.025\,N$.
3. Diametral-pitch scale:
   Length: $K = 8$ in.
   Equation: $d_{Pd} = \dfrac{8\,P_d}{P_d + 10}$.
   Focal point: $L = 2.5$ in.
   Temporary scale: $d_t = \dfrac{(2.5)(0.025)}{0.25} P_d = 0.25\,P_d$.

A tie line indicates that a spur gear of 120 teeth with a pitch diameter of 20 in. is a 6-pitch gear.

The origins of the parallel scales of a Z-chart serve to locate the position of the transverse scale. In those cases where either one or both of the origins are not to be included in the ranges of scale values, the position of the transverse scale is determined by similar triangle relationships. The Z-chart enjoys an **advantage** over the chart of three parallel logarithmic scales in that for many equations its two parallel scales are uniformly graduated and, therefore, more easily con-

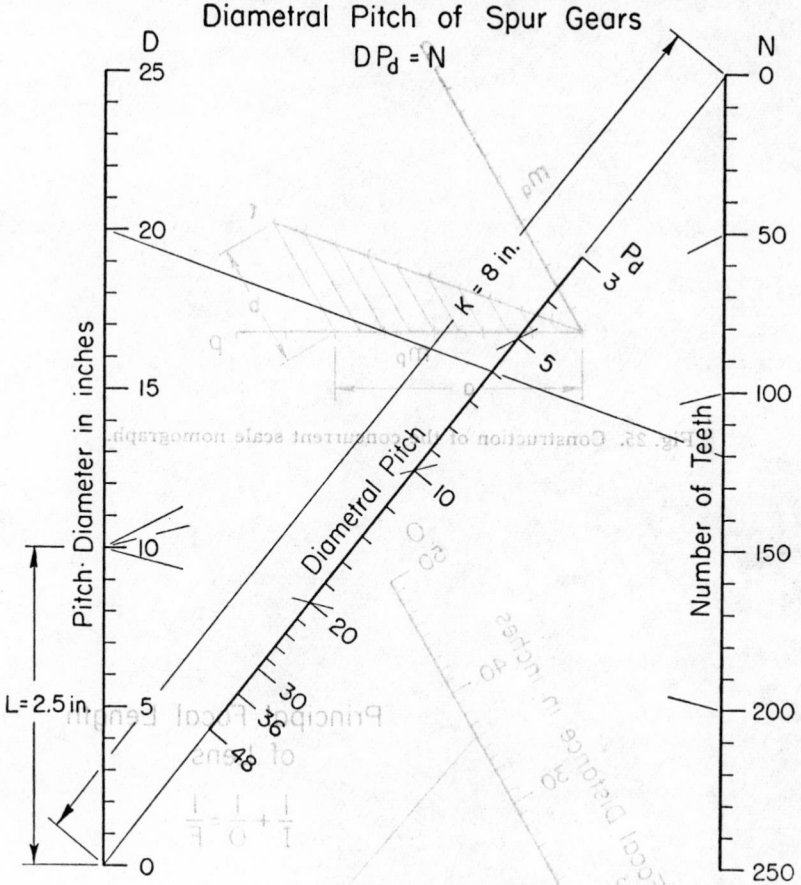

Fig. 24. A nomographic Z-chart.

structed. In the case of equations in four or more variables involving both addition and multiplication of terms, the Z-chart may be combined with parallel uniform scale charts (see Fig. 29). Parallel logarithmic and parallel uniform scale charts may not be so combined.

Concurrent Straight Scales. An equation in three variables that can be expressed in the form

$$\frac{1}{f_1(p)} + \frac{1}{f_2(q)} = \frac{1}{f_3(r)}$$

may be represented by a nomographic chart of three concurrent scales. The **origins** of all three scales are located at the point of intersection. The construction of such a chart, shown in Fig. 25, begins with the location of two scales, a p-scale having a modulus m_p and a q-scale having a modulus m_q, at a convenient angle with one another. The two scales are graduated by means of the equations

$$d_p = m_p f_1(p) \qquad \text{and} \qquad d_q = m_q f_2(q).$$

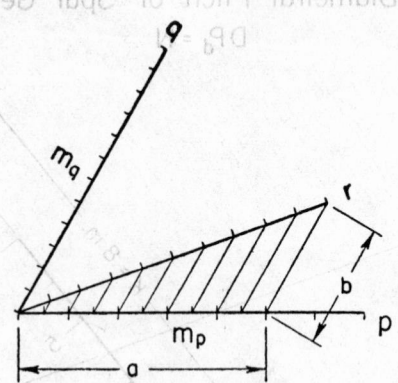

Fig. 25. Construction of the concurrent scale nomograph.

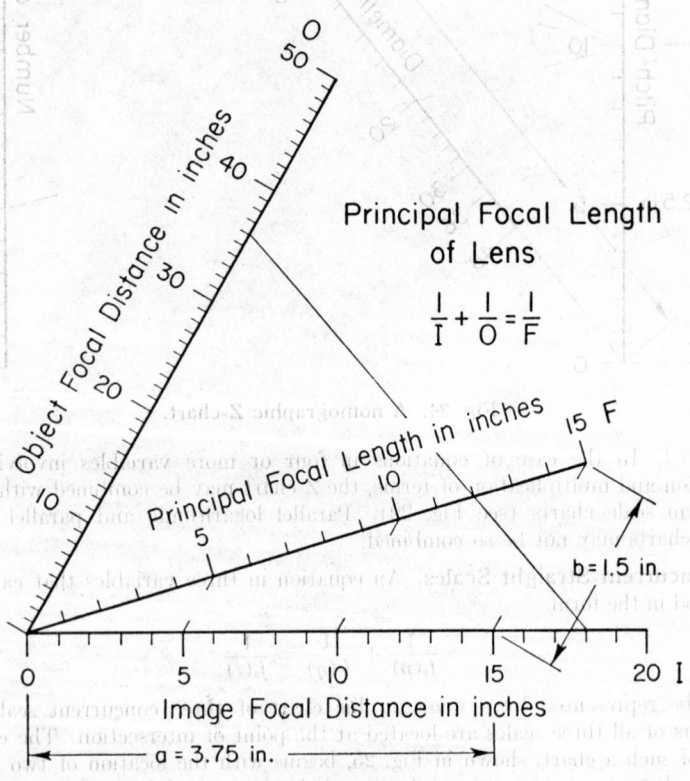

Fig. 26. A concurrent scale nomograph.

A stem for the r-scale is located intermediate to the first two by the relationship

$$\frac{a}{b} = \frac{m_p}{m_q}$$

where a is a measurement of any convenient length along the p-scale and b is an offset parallel to the q-scale. The r-scale is graduated by projectors, parallel to the q-scale, from a temporary scale laid out on and having the same modulus as the p-scale. The equation of the temporary scale is

$$d_t = m_p f_3(r)$$

The **temporary scale** and **projectors** are a construction only and are not shown on the finished chart.

A chart for determining the principal focal length of a lens, shown in Fig. 26, is based on the formula

$$\frac{1}{I} + \frac{1}{O} = \frac{1}{F}$$

where I = image focal distance, O = object focal distance, and F = principal focal length, all in inches. The following outline indicates the manner in which the chart was constructed:

1. Image focal distance scale:
   Modulus: 0.25 in.
   Equation: $d_I = 0.25\,I$.
2. Object focal distance scale:
   Modulus: 0.10 in.
   Equation: $d_O = 0.10\,O$.
3. Principal focal length scale:
   Scale spacing: $\dfrac{a}{b} = \dfrac{0.25}{0.10}$ and $a = 3.75$ in. and $b = 1.50$ in.
   Temporary scale: $d_t = 0.25\,F$.

A tie line indicates a principal focal length of 12 in. for a lens exhibiting an image focal distance of 18 in. and an object focal distance of 36 in.

Straight and Curved Scales. Many three-variable equations of the type in which the same variable appears in more than one term are represented by nomographic charts containing curved scales. A curved scale is located on a chart by coordinates or offsets from a pair of base lines. Although a particular equation may result in as many as three curved scales, charts with more than one such scale are rarely encountered.

An equation in three variables that can be expressed in the form

$$f_1(p) + f_2(q) \times f_3(r) = f_4(r)$$

may be represented by a nomograph of two parallel straight scales and one curved scale. The construction of the chart is shown in Fig. 27. The two parallel scales, a p-scale with a modulus m_p and a q-scale with a modulus m_q are located a convenient distance apart and graduated by means of the equations

$$d_p = m_p f_1(p) \qquad \text{and} \qquad d_q = m_q f_2(q)$$

The curved r-scale is then plotted by means of two offsets, an x coordinate measured away from the p-scale toward the q-scale along the base line joining their origins, and a y-coordinate measured from the base line parallel to the p- and q-

p
r
q
m_p
m_q
y_r
x_r

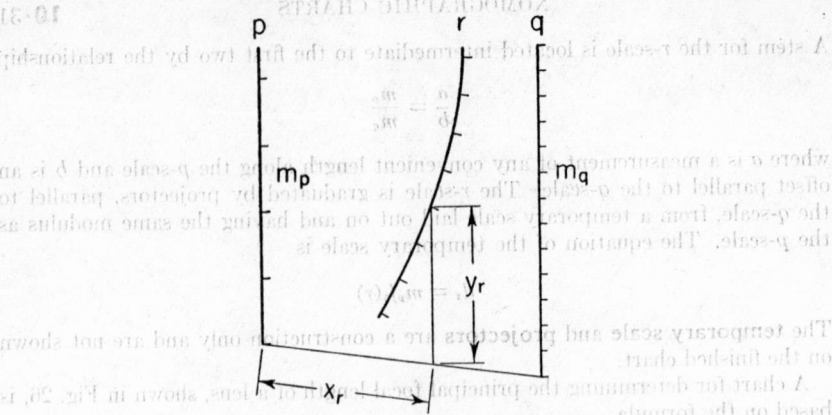

Fig. 27. Construction of the parallel and curved scale nomograph.

Object Projected
Vertically Upward
$H = V_0T - \frac{1}{2}gT^2$
H
1000
800
600
400
200
0
Height in feet
$x_6 = 4.80$ in.
$k = 8$ in.
$y_6 = -1.45$ in.
0.5
1
2
5
10
15
T
Elapsed
Time in seconds
0
50
100
150
200
250
V_0
Initial Velocity in ft. per sec.

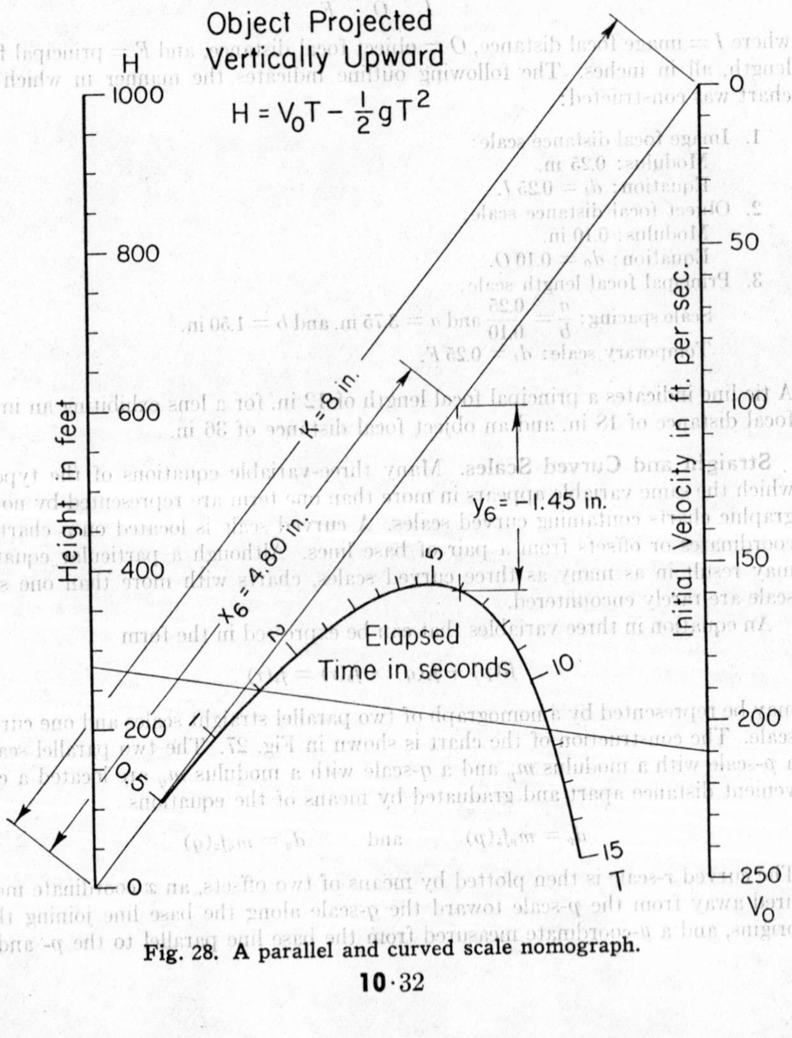

Fig. 28. A parallel and curved scale nomograph.

scales. Values of the offsets are obtained by substituting values of r in the formulas

$$x_r = \frac{K f_3(r)}{f_3(r) + m_q/m_p} \quad \text{and} \quad y_r = \frac{m_q f_4(r)}{f_3(r) + m_q/m_p}$$

where K is the length of the base line.

When an object is projected vertically upward, its height above the ground is given by the formula

$$H = V_0 T - \frac{g\,T^2}{2}$$

where $H =$ height in feet, $V_0 =$ initial velocity in feet per second, $T =$ elapsed time in seconds, and g is the acceleration due to gravity, or 32.2 ft. per sec. per sec. The equation may be rewritten:

$$H - V_0 T = -16.1\,T^2$$

and represented by a nomograph with parallel straight H- and V_0 scales and a curved T-scale. Construction of the chart, shown in Fig. 28, is summarized as follows:

1. Height scale:
   Modulus: 0.00625 in.
   Equation: $d_H = 0.00625\,H$.
2. Velocity scale:
   Modulus: 0.025 in.
   Equation: $dv_0 = -0.025\,V_0$
3. Time scale:
   Base line: $K = 8$ in.
   Coordinates: $x_T = \dfrac{8\,T}{T + 4};$ $\qquad y_T = \dfrac{-0.4025\,T^2}{T + 4}$

A pair of typical coordinates, for locating the graduation $T = 6$ sec., is shown. A tie line indicates that an object with an initial upward velocity of 210 ft. per sec. reaches a height of 280 ft. after 1.5 sec. have elapsed. The tie line crosses the time scale at a second point, 11.5 sec.—indicating that at that time the object again reaches a height of 280 ft. as it falls back to the ground.

FOUR-VARIABLE NOMOGRAPHS. An equation in four variables may be represented by a nomograph composed of two 3-variable charts. The charts are combined by locating them in such fashion that a scale of one coincides with an identically constructed scale of the other. The stem of these **coinciding scales** is usually ungraduated, since it serves only as a pivot or turning scale at which the two tie lines drawn across the charts intersect.

The combination of a parallel scale chart and a Z-chart is illustrated by the nomograph of Fig. 29 for the density of moist air. The equation

$$D = 1.326\,\frac{B - 0.378\,W}{T + 459.6}$$

involves four variables: $B =$ barometric pressure and $W =$ water vapor pressure, both in inches of mercury; $T =$ temperature in degrees Fahrenheit, and $D =$ density in pounds per cubic foot. It may be replaced by two 3-variable equations, through the introduction of an additional term, Y, common to both, to give

$$1.326\,B = 0.502\,W + Y \tag{1}$$

and

$$Y = D\,(T + 459.6) \tag{2}$$

Eq. (1) is represented by the parallel scale chart at "*A*" and Eq. (2) by the Z-chart at "*B*." The two charts are designed with identical *Y*-scales and placed side by side with the *Y*-scale of one coinciding with the *Y*-scale of the other. The *Y*-scale origin, modulus, and range all figure in the construction of both charts and so have to be determined, but since values of *Y* are not desired, the pivot scale is ungraduated. It is noted that the origins of the pivot and density scales

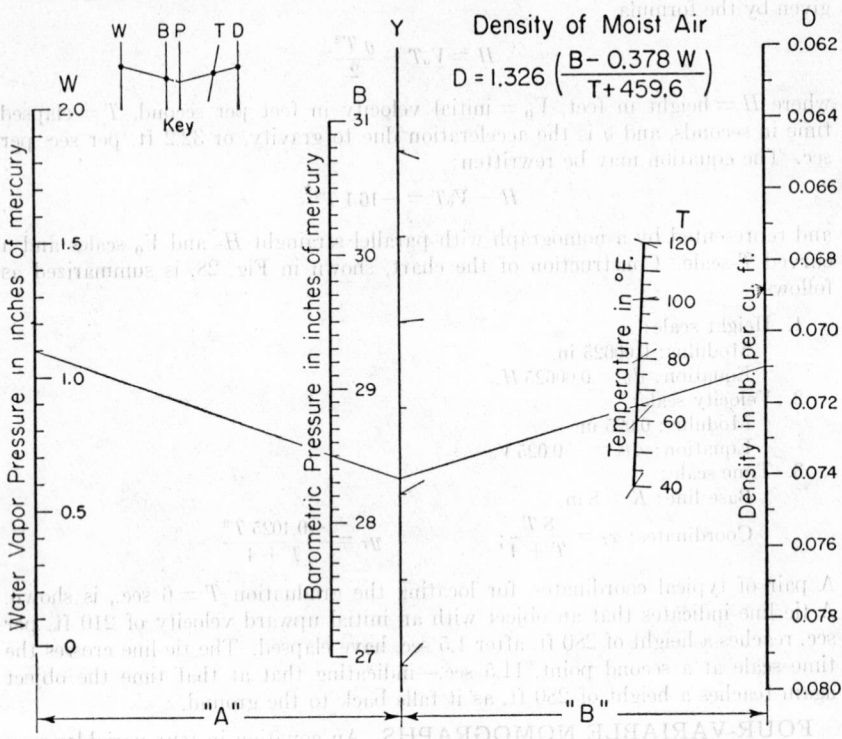

Fig. 29. A four-variable nomograph.

are not included within the ranges of scale values, and so the position of the transverse temperature scale is computed from similar triangle ratios. Two tie lines are used in solving the chart equation, and so a **key** is provided to show how they are drawn. A typical solution indicates that air at 65° F., 28.5 in. of mercury barometric pressure, and 1.1 in. of mercury water-vapor pressure has a density of 0.071 lb. per cu. ft.

Torsional stress in straight coil springs of round wire is given by the formula

$$S = 2.55 \frac{PD}{d^3}$$

where S = torsional stress in pounds per square inch, P = load in pounds, D = mean diameter of coil, and d = wire diameter (the latter two in inches). The formula may be rewritten $S/2.55P = D/d^3$ and represented by the nomograph of Fig. 30, which combines two 3-variable Z-charts about a common transverse pivot scale. The parallel scales of each chart are graduated in terms of the variables. The scale moduli are related by the equation $m_S/m_P = m_D/m_d$. A key is provided to indicate the correct manner of drawing the two tie lines. A typical solution shows a torsional stress of 95,600 lb. per sq. in. for a straight coil spring of 0.20-in. diameter wire and 1.50 in. mean coil diameter supporting a load of 200 lb.

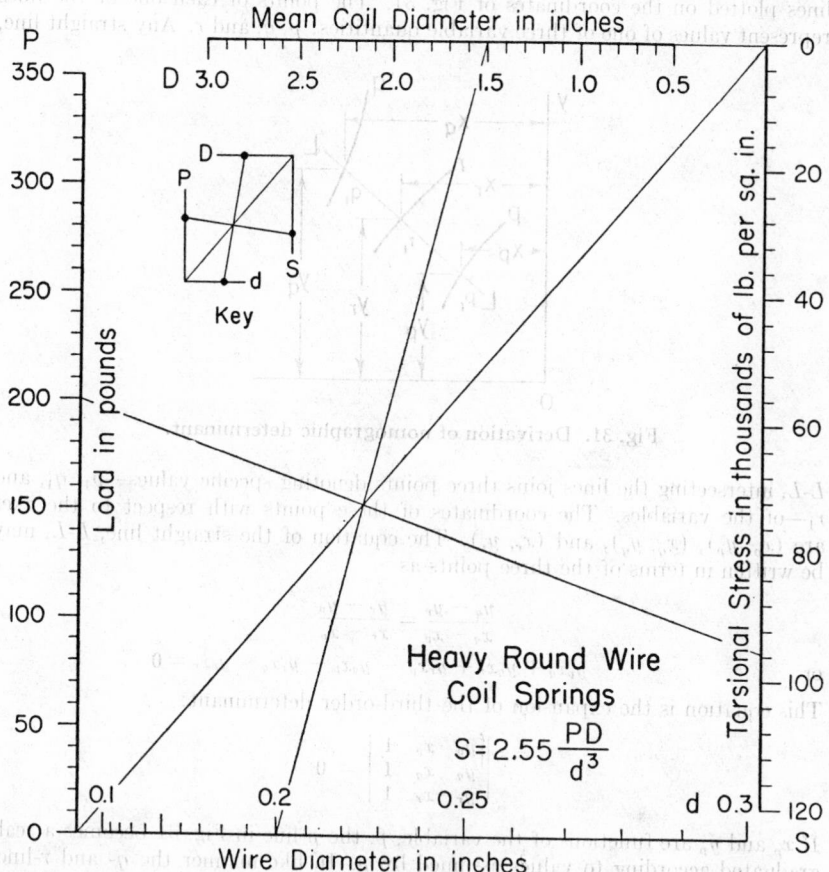

Fig. 30. A four-variable double-Z nomograph.

The process of combining three-scale charts may be extended to the construction of nomographs for equations in five or more variables. Each additional variable requires that one additional graduated scale, pivot scale, and tie line be drawn. Such charts become rather cumbersome, and great care should be exercised in their design and use.

NOMOGRAPHIC DETERMINANTS. An equation expressing a relationship between three variable quantities may be represented by the construction of a nomographic chart according to the following procedure:

1. The chart equation is expressed as a zero-valued third-order determinant of special form.

2. Certain alterations are made in the form of the elements of the basic determinant to obtain suitable scale configuration.
3. The scales representing the variables are plotted on Cartesian coordinates in accordance with the functions provided by the determinant.

The **form** of the nomographic determinant may be derived by considering three lines plotted on the coordinates of Fig. 31. The points of each one of the lines represent values of one of three variable quantities: p, q, and r. Any straight line,

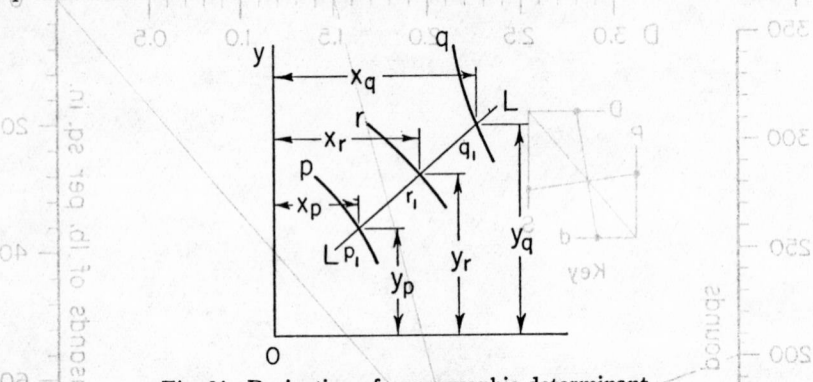

Fig. 31. Derivation of nomographic determinant.

L-L, intersecting the lines joins three points denoting specific values—p_1, q_1, and r_1—of the variables. The coordinates of these points with respect to the axes are (x_p, y_p), (x_q, y_q), and (x_r, y_r). The equation of the straight line, L-L, may be written in terms of the three points as

$$\frac{y_q - y_p}{x_q - x_p} = \frac{y_r - y_p}{x_r - x_p}$$

or

$$y_p x_q + y_q x_r + y_r x_p - y_q x_p - y_r x_q - y_p x_r = 0$$

This equation is the expansion of the third-order determinant:

$$\begin{vmatrix} y_p & x_p & 1 \\ y_q & x_q & 1 \\ y_r & x_r & 1 \end{vmatrix} = 0$$

If x_p and y_p are functions of the variable, p, the p-line in Fig. 31 becomes a scale graduated according to values assumed by p. In like manner the q- and r-lines become scales graduated according to values assumed by these variables. The straight line, L-L, becomes a tie line intersecting the three scales. Any equation in three variables that can be expressed in this determinant form may be represented by a nomographic chart.

The essential **characteristics** of the nomographic determinant are as follows:

1. The value of the determinant is zero.
2. The three elements of the third column are each 1.
3. Functions of only one variable appear in each row. One of these two functions may be zero or a constant, resulting in a scale which coincides with or is parallel to a coordinate axis.

Douglass (Plant Engineering Handbook) presents the basic and constructional determinants for a number of different forms of the three-variable equation. The constructional determinants for the nomographs of Figs. 21, 24, 26, and 28 are given below.

Fig. 21: $f_1(p) + f_2(q) - f_3(r) = S.P. + \left(\dfrac{V}{4005}\right)^2 - T.P. = 0$.

$$
\begin{vmatrix}
m_p f_1(p) & 0 & 1 \\
m_q f_2(q) & K & 1 \\
\dfrac{m_p m_q f_3(r)}{m_p + m_q} & \dfrac{K m_p}{m_p + m_q} & 1
\end{vmatrix}
=
\begin{vmatrix}
0.75\,S.P. & 0 & 1 \\
3\left(\dfrac{V}{4005}\right)^2 & 5 & 1 \\
0.60\,T.P. & 1 & 1
\end{vmatrix}
= 0
$$

The nomograph is plotted on rectangular Cartesian coordinates.

Fig. 24: $f_1(p) \times f_2(q) - f_3(r) = D \times P_d - N = 0$

$$
\begin{vmatrix}
m_p f_1(p) & K & 1 \\
0 & \dfrac{K f_2(q)}{f_2(q) + m_p/m_r} & 1 \\
-m_r f_3(r) & 0 & 1
\end{vmatrix}
=
\begin{vmatrix}
0.25\,D & 8 & 1 \\
0 & \dfrac{8 P_d}{P_d + 10} & 1 \\
-0.025\,N & 0 & 1
\end{vmatrix}
= 0
$$

The nomograph is plotted on oblique Cartesian coordinates.

Fig. 26: $\dfrac{1}{f_1(p)} + \dfrac{1}{f_2(q)} - \dfrac{1}{f_3(r)} = \dfrac{1}{I} + \dfrac{1}{O} - \dfrac{1}{F} = 0$.

$$
\begin{vmatrix}
0 & m_p f_1(p) & 1 \\
m_q f_2(q) & 0 & 1 \\
m_q f_3(r) & m_p f_3(r) & 1
\end{vmatrix}
=
\begin{vmatrix}
0 & 0.25\,I & 1 \\
0.10\,O & 0 & 1 \\
0.10\,F & 0.25\,F & 1
\end{vmatrix}
= 0
$$

The nomograph is plotted on oblique Cartesian coordinates.

Fig. 28: $f_1(p) + f_2(q) \times f_3(r) - f_4(r) = H - V_o T + \dfrac{gT^2}{2} = 0$.

$$
\begin{vmatrix}
m_p f_1(p) & 0 & 1 \\
m_q f_2(q) & K & 1 \\
\dfrac{m_q f_4(r)}{f_3(r) + m_q/m_p} & \dfrac{K f_3(r)}{f_3(r) + m_q/m_p} & 1
\end{vmatrix}
=
\begin{vmatrix}
0.00625\,H & 0 & 1 \\
-0.025\,V_o & 8 & 1 \\
\dfrac{-0.4025\,T^2}{T+4} & \dfrac{8\,T}{T+4} & 1
\end{vmatrix}
= 0
$$

The nomograph is plotted on oblique Cartesian coordinates.

Slide and Disc Charts

NATURE AND USE. In industry the process of manufacture, test, or research frequently involves recurring computations that are time-consuming and monotonous. Specially designed slide and disc charts, employing functional scales to solve equations, offer the same **advantages** over longhand computation that nomographs do. Answers are obtained more rapidly, errors occur less frequently, and the charts are adaptable to use by personnel who do not possess extensive mathematical backgrounds.

Slide and disc charts resemble the standard straight and circular slide rules in the manner in which they employ scales to solve problems but differ in that they are designed to solve specific equations. The special calculator often furnishes a quicker solution than the slide rule and may in some cases provide better accuracy, since scales can be designed to cover only desired ranges of value.

SLIDE CHARTS. Sliding scales serve as graphic devices for adding, subtracting, or equating scale distances. Two parallel straight scales, arranged so that one may slide along the other, provide for the addition of two scale dis-

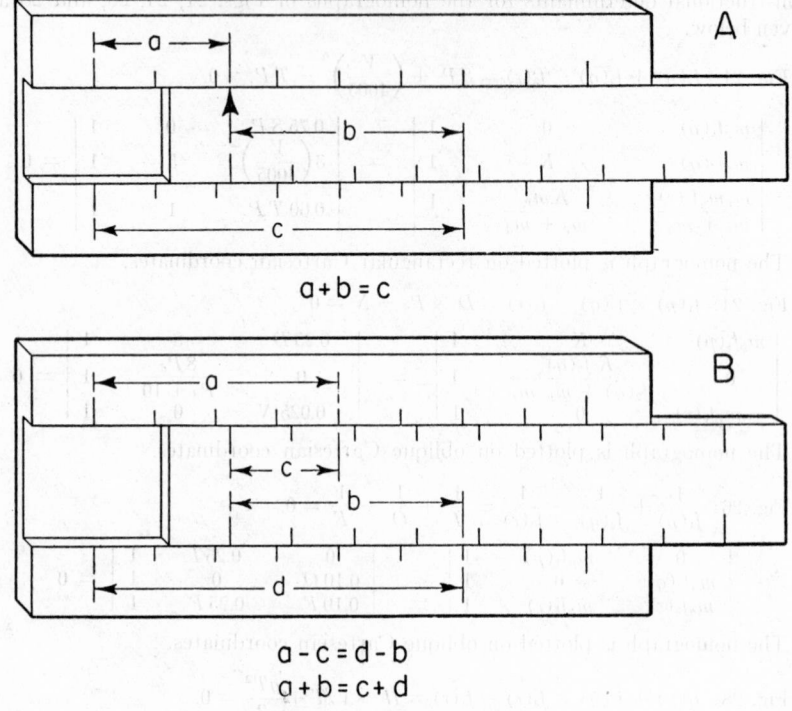

$$a + b = c$$

$$a - c = d - b$$
$$a + b = c + d$$

Fig. 32. Sliding scales.

tances. The total may be recorded on a third scale. Thus, a **stock** with two fixed scales and a **slide** with one scale and an index arrow make possible, at A in Fig. 32, the addition of scale distances, a and b, to obtain scale distance, c. If, as at B, the arrow is replaced by a fourth scale, the sum of the distances a and b may be equated to the sum of the distances c and d. A second slide, with one or two additional scales, makes the manipulation of five or six scale distances possible. A **runner** or **indicator** is occasionally employed to read corresponding values on separated scales or to mark an intermediate value while the slide is re-adjusted.

An equation of the form $f(p) + f(q) = f(r)$, each term of which is a function of a single variable, may be solved with a slide chart of the type illustrated in Fig. 33. **Uniformly graduated scales** represent the linear equation, $2p + q = r - 5$, at A. The equation $p^2q = 0.5\, r$ becomes $2 \log p + \log q = \log 0.5\, r$ when placed in logarithmic form and is represented by **logarithmic scales** at B. Numerical values satisfying the equation are obtained in each case by adjusting the slide to set the arrow at a p-value and reading an r-value opposite a value of q. The scales of each chart are constructed with the same modulus, and scale origins and arrow are aligned on the stock and on the slide.

An equation of the form $f(p) + f(q) = f(r) + f(s)$, each term of which is a function of a single variable, may be solved with a slide chart of the type shown in Fig. 34. Uniform scales make up the chart at A and logarithmic scales the chart at B. Numerical values satisfying the equation are obtained in each case by setting an s value opposite a value of p and reading an r value opposite a value of q. The scales of each chart have the same modulus, and scale origins are

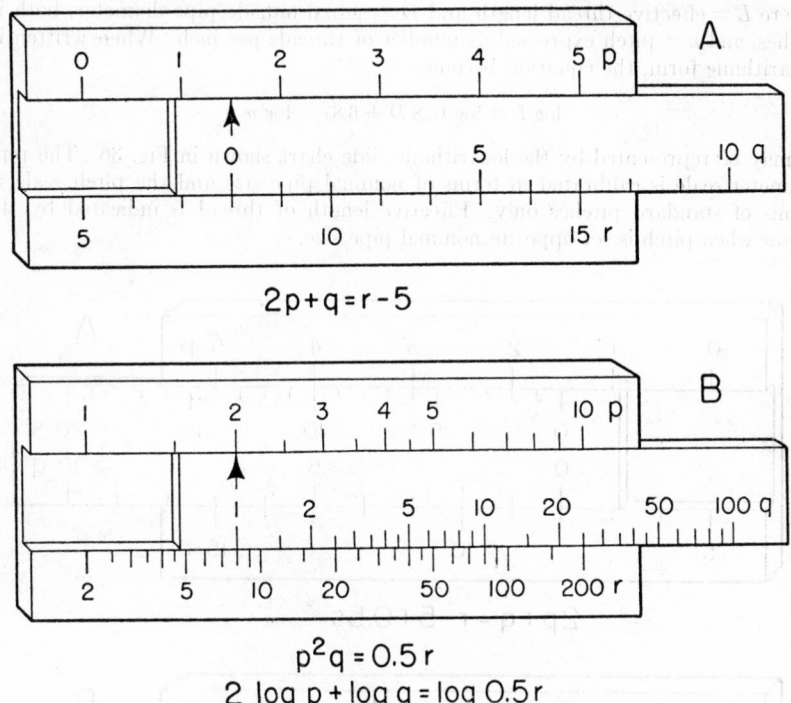

$$2p + q = r - 5$$

$$p^2 q = 0.5\,r$$
$$2 \log p + \log q = \log 0.5\,r$$

Fig. 33. Three-variable slide charts.

aligned on the stock and slide. Comparison of the charts and equations of Figs. 33 and 34 shows that the arrow in Fig. 33 may be considered a scale having but a single graduation.

The **order of scales** on the slide chart is not necessarily that shown in Fig. 33 or Fig. 34. The scale sequence may be altered without affecting the validity of the calculator. Adjacent scales may be inverted, that is, interchanged and reversed. This includes inversion of the slide. Alternate scales may be interchanged without reversal. Thus, the slide chart for the equation $2p + q = r - 5$, shown at A in Fig. 35, may be considered to have been obtained from that at A in Fig. 33 by first interchanging the r scale and arrow and then inverting the slide. Numerical values satisfying the equation are now obtained by setting p and q values opposite one another and reading a value of r opposite the arrow.

Alignment of scale origins and arrow is not necessary on a slide chart, since a shift in the horizontal position of one scale may be compensated for by a similar shift in the position of another scale or the arrow. In the construction of the chart at B in Fig. 35, the three scales are located horizontally in convenient manner and the position of the arrow determined by a trial solution. All scales have the same modulus, the r scale having been lengthened relative to the other two in order to furnish a complete range of values.

The effective length of American Standard taper pipe thread is given by the formula

$$L = \frac{0.8\,D + 6.8}{n}$$

where L = effective thread length and D = actual outside pipe diameter, both in inches, and n = pitch expressed as number of threads per inch. When written in logarithmic form, the equation becomes

$$\log L = \log (0.8\,D + 6.8) - \log n$$

It may be represented by the logarithmic slide chart shown in Fig. 36. The pipe diameter scale is calibrated in terms of nominal pipe size and the pitch scale in terms of standard pitches only. Effective length of thread is indicated by the arrow when pitch is set opposite nominal pipe size.

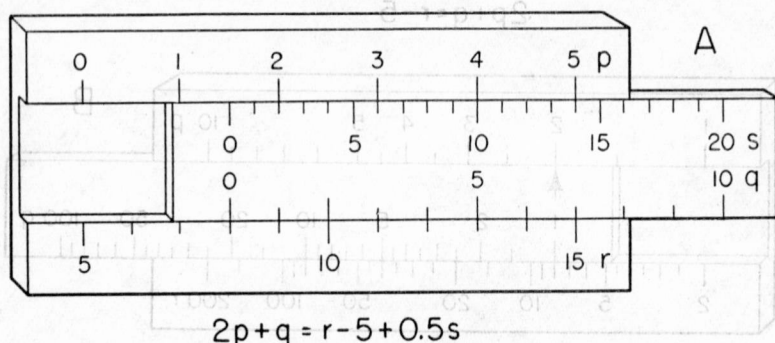

$$2p+q = r-5+0.5s$$

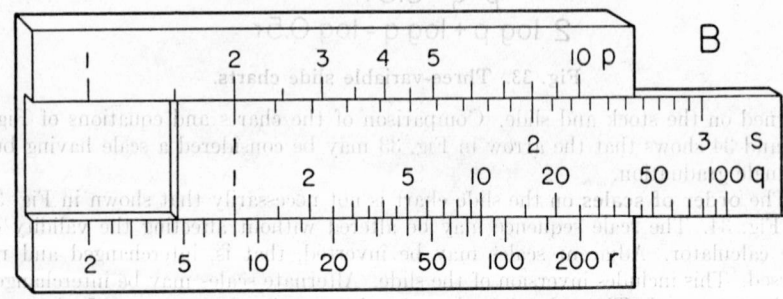

$$p^2q = 0.5\,r\,s^4$$
$$2 \log p + \log q = \log 0.5\,r + 4 \log s$$

Fig. 34. Four-variable slide charts.

DISC CHARTS. Disc charts differ from slide charts in physical form, but their design principles are similar. A disc functions to add distances on circular scales in the same manner that a slide provides for the addition of lineal scale distances. Comparison of the disc chart of Fig. 37 with the slide chart at B in Fig. 35 bears out this fact. The equation $2p + q = r - 5$ is solved in Fig. 37 by rotating the disc to set p and q values opposite one another at the top and reading a value of r indicated by the arrow at the bottom.

The weight of round steel bar stock is given by the formula

$$W = 2.67\,D^2 L$$

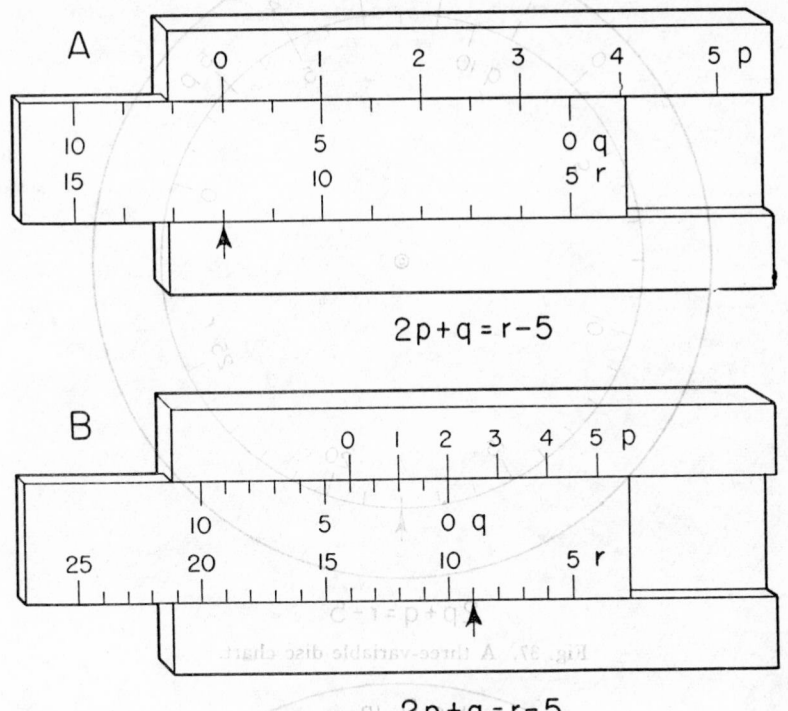

$$2p + q = r - 5$$

Fig. 35. Alternate scale positions.

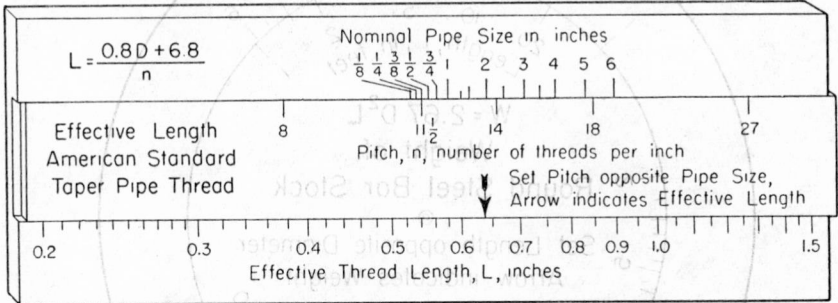

Fig. 36. A logarithmic three-variable slide chart.

where W = weight in pounds, D = diameter in inches, and L = length in feet. When written in logarithmic form, the equation becomes

$$\log \frac{W}{2.67} = 2 \log D + \log L$$

It may be represented by the logarithmic disc chart shown in Fig. 38. The weight of stock is indicated by the arrow when the length is set opposite the diameter.

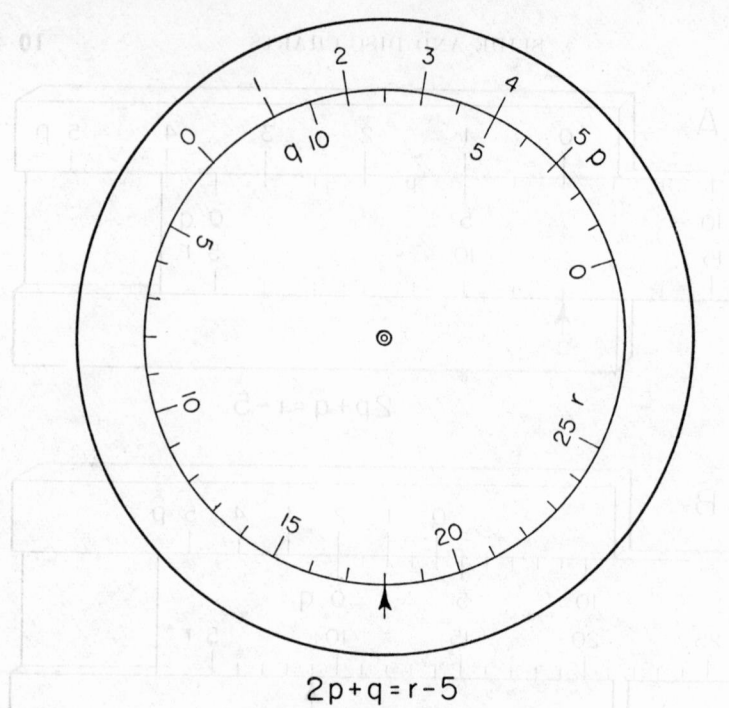

$$2p + q = r - 5$$

Fig. 37. A three-variable disc chart.

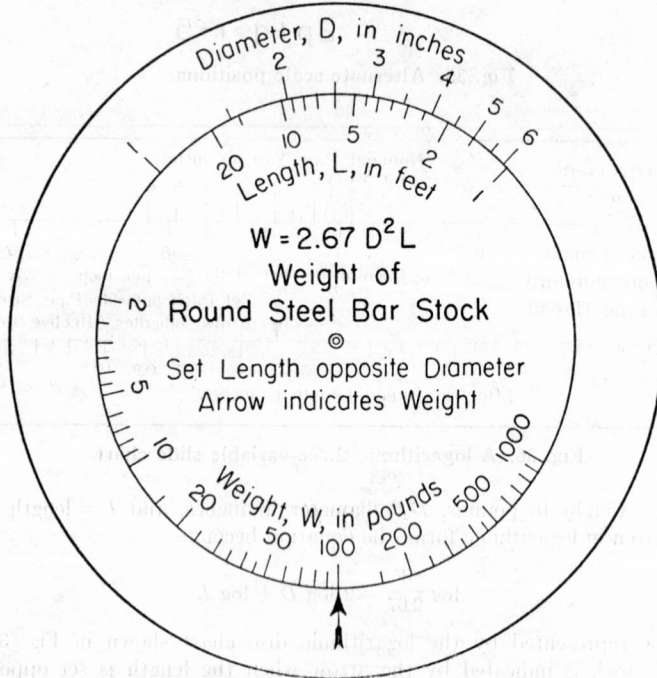

Fig. 38. A logarithmic three-variable disc chart.

Pictorial Charts

FUNCTION. Charts of a pictorial nature are readily understood and so enjoy widespread use in the charting of statistics. The charts are based upon the use of **graphic symbols** to represent numerical magnitudes. Quantities are evaluated or compared by means of the lengths, heights, or areas of the symbols. Pictorial charts are seldom studied critically but rather read at a glance, and care must be taken in their preparation that the impression produced will be quick and accurate. In describing pictorial charts, Schmid (Handbook of Graphic Presentation) states:

Because of their simplicity, as well as their dramatic and interest-creating qualities, pictorial charts are far superior to conventional graphic forms as a medium of popular communication. In addition, there seems to be some evidence that facts portrayed in pictorial charts are remembered longer than facts presented in tables or in nonpictorial graphs.

100 PERCENT BAR OR COLUMN. A single horizontal bar or vertical column may provide a visual comparison of the relative size of the portions of a whole quantity. Length of bar or height of column, representing 100 percent, is subdivided according to the sizes of the component parts. Segments are shaded or crosshatched to provide contrast, percentages are noted, and each segment is identified by label.

PIE CHART. The pie chart may be considered a 100 percent bar in circular form, as it functions in like manner. The circumference of the circle, representing

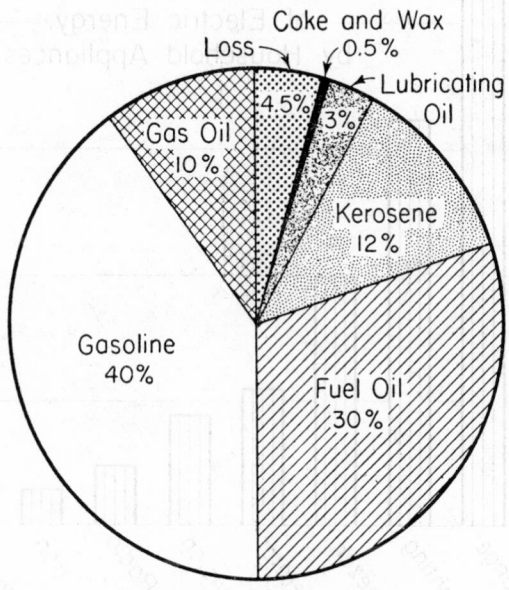

Distillation Products
from a
Typical Mid-Continent Crude Oil

Fig. 39. A pie chart.

100 percent, is subdivided according to the sizes of the component parts. Sectors formed by radial lines are shaded and labeled in the same manner as the segments of the 100 percent bar. A comparison of the amounts of refined products obtained in the distillation of a typical mid-continent crude oil is provided by the pie chart of Fig. 39.

Although the pie chart rates high in popular appeal, it is considered by many experts to be inferior to the segmented bar or column. It is felt that the reader experiences greater difficulty in comparing the relative sizes of circle sectors than he does in comparing rectangular bar segments, because of the shapes involved.

BAR OR COLUMN CHART. A limited number of values of some quantity may be compared graphically by means of a bar chart. Each magnitude is represented by the **length** of a bar. Values are tabulated on the chart or are obtained by measuring bar length against a scale of values running parallel thereto. The scale should include the zero value so that a true comparison is obtained. A limited number of **grid lines** are employed. Bars are crosshatched or shaded to provide a **contrast** with the background rulings and each bar is identified by **label.** Width of bars should be one-half to two-thirds of the center-to-center spacing. Bars should be arranged in some systematic fashion, i.e., according to date or in order

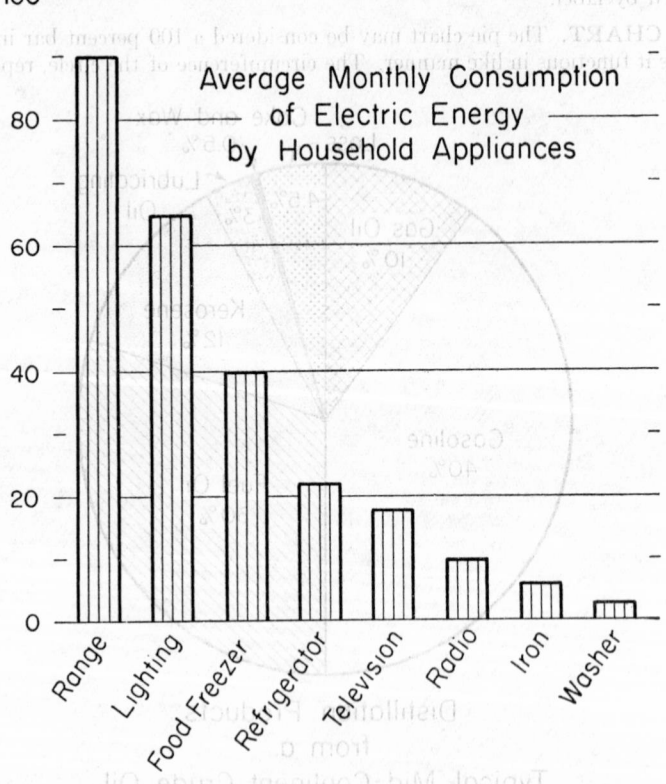

Fig. 40. A column chart.

of increasing or decreasing magnitude. The number of bars affects the impression created by the chart, since, when many are included, the eye tends to note the trend of values rather than the significance of individual ones.

The column chart is identical to the bar chart except that columns run vertically rather than horizontally. The column chart of Fig. 40 indicates the average monthly consumption of electric energy and therefore the relative cost of operation of a number of household appliances.

Grouped bar or column charts result when more than one set of bars or columns appear on a single grid. A group of bars is thus provided at each point of comparison. Each series of bars is shaded in characteristic manner and identified by label or key. A multiple grouping of segmented bars or columns furnishes a comparison of the compositions of a number of similar materials. The **compound column chart** of Fig. 41, on which the proximate analyses of a number of classes of coal are illustrated, exemplifies such an application.

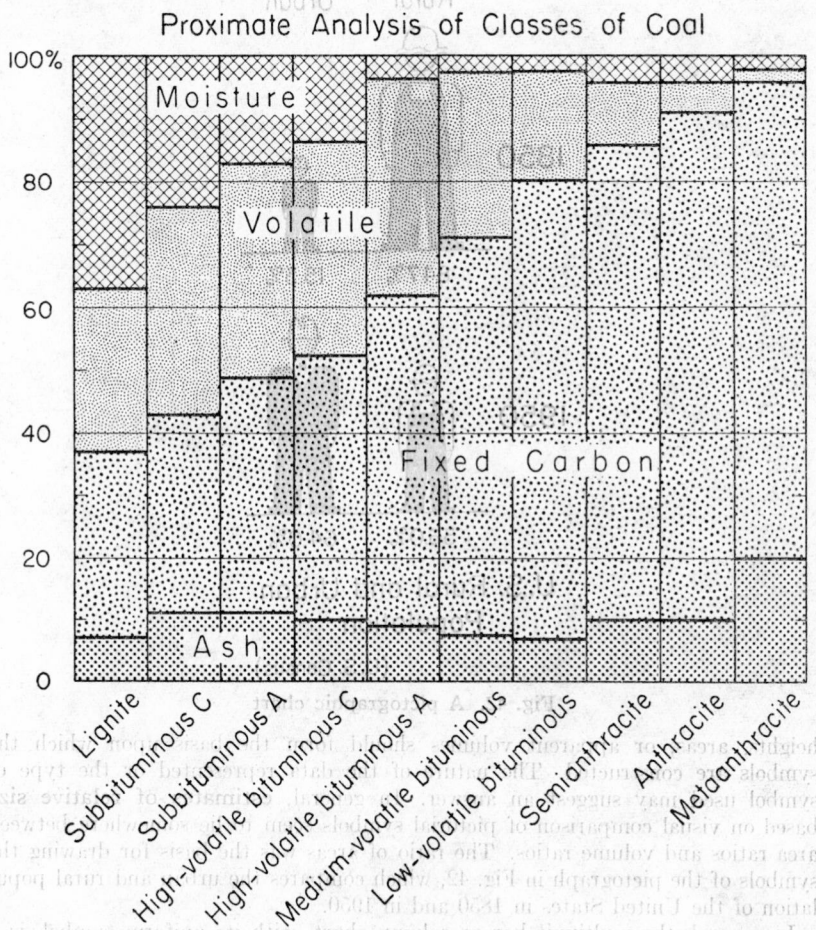

Fig. 41. A compound column chart.

MULTIUNIT BAR OR COLUMN CHART. The multiunit bar or column chart is one on which the bars are made up of rows or columns of small units or symbols, each with a given value. Whether the bars run vertically or horizontally depends upon the symbol employed; that is, coins, boxes, or barrels may be stacked vertically, while men, automobiles, or houses are placed side by side horizontally. The grid is often omitted and the amount of each bar indicated by numerical value. The **pictorial symbol** adds appeal to the chart without detracting from its illustrative ability.

PICTOGRAPHIC CHART. The least satisfactory, but unfortunately a commonly used type of pictorial chart, is the pictograph employing the relative size of pictorial symbols as a basis for comparison of value. It would seem that such a chart would possess the advantages of simplicity, graphic appeal and ease of comparison, but this is not the case. It is difficult to make accurate comparisons based on the sizes of complex symbols. The question arises as to whether

U.S. Rural and Urban
Population

(U.S. Census)

Fig. 42. A pictographic chart

heights, areas, or apparent volumes should form the basis upon which the symbols are constructed. The nature of the data represented or the type of symbol used may suggest an answer. In general, **estimates of relative size** based on visual comparison of pictorial symbols seem to lie somewhere between area ratios and volume ratios. The ratio of areas was the basis for drawing the symbols of the pictograph in Fig. 42, which compares the urban and rural population of the United States in 1850 and in 1950.

In general, the multiunit bar or column chart, with its uniform symbol, is a more suitable form of presentation than the pictographic chart.

PROCESS CHARTS

CONTENTS

PAGE

Nature of Process Charts

Definition 1
Types of process charts 1
Repetitiveness of work 1
Factors involved in the selection of process chart technique (f. 1) 2
Selecting the chart or analysis technique .. 3
Purpose 3
Process chart symbols 3
Types of symbols and definitions for process charts (f. 2) 4

Basic Process Charts

Operation process charts 5
Use of charts 5
Typical operation process chart (f. 3) .. 6
Construction procedures 7
Principles of operation process chart construction (f. 4) 8
Disassembly and alternate process conventions 9
Method summaries 9
Operation process chart showing conventions for indicating unit on which operations and inspections are performed, alternate routes, and combinations (f. 5) 10
Analysis of operation process charts 11
Flow process charts 11
Flow process chart of the material type (f. 6) 12
Construction procedures 13
Prepared forms and symbols 13
Material flow process chart with preprinted symbols (f. 7) 14
Principles of flow process charting 15
A preprinted flow process chart used for comparing methods (f. 8) 16–17
Simple, converging, and diverging charts .. 18
Types of flow process charts (f. 9) 19
Defining the workplace 19

Converging flow process chart (f. 10) 20
Workplace variations (f. 11) 21
Analyzing flow process charts 21
Flow process charts for different definitions of workplace (f. 12) 22
The flow diagram 22
Flow diagram of procedure before improvement (f. 13a) 23
Flow diagram of procedure after improvement (f. 13b) 24
Procedure flow charts 24
Construction procedures 25
Procedure flow chart symbols (f. 14) 25
Procedure flow chart for order form (f. 15) 26
Flow diagram of an office procedure (f. 16) 27

Complex Process Charts

Right- and left-hand charts 28
Construction procedures 28
Types of symbols and definitions used for right- and left-hand charts (f. 17) 29
Right- and left-hand chart with time columns (f. 18) 30
Work area definition 30
Definitions of work area (f. 19) 31
Right- and left-hand charts for different definitions of work area (f. 20) 32
Analysis of the charts 32
Multiple activity charts 33
Types of multiple activity charts 34
Construction procedures 34
Man-machine charts 34
Man-machine symbol chart for operation (f. 21) 35
Man-machine time chart for operation shown in Fig. 21 (f. 22) 36
Multi-man charts 37
Multi-man operation time chart (f. 23) .. 37
Therblig and simo charts 38

PROCESS CHARTS

CONTENTS

Page

Nature of Process Charts

Definition ....
Types of process charts ....
Usefulness of work ....
Factors involved in the selection of
  process-chart technique (I. 1) ....
Selecting the kind of analysis technique ...
Purpose ....
Process-chart symbols ....
Types of symbols and definitions for
  process charts (I. 2) ....

Basic Process Charts

Operation process charts ....
Uses of charts ....
Typical operation process chart (I. 3) ...
Construction procedure ....
Principle of operation process chart con-
  struction (I. 4) ....
Desirability and alternate constructional
  forms ....
Method summaries ....
Operation process chart showing conven-
  tions for indicating units on which
  operations and inspections are per-
  formed, alternate routes, and con-
  struction (I. 5) ....
Analysis of operation process charts ....
Flow process charts ....
Flow process chart of the material type
  (I. 6) ....
Construction procedure ....
Required forms and symbols ....
Material flow process chart with pro-
  vided symbols (I. 7) ....
Principles of flow process charting ....
A material flow process chart used for
  economic methods (I. 8) ....
Route, conveyance, and travelling charts ...
Types of flow process charts (I. 9) ....
Defining the work flow ....

Complex Process Charts

Right- and left-hand charts ....
Construction procedure ....
Types of symbols and definitions for
  right- and left-hand charts (I. 10) ....
Right- and left-hand chart with (one
  column) (I. 11) ....
Work-area definition ....
Definition of work area (I. 12) ....
Right- and left-hand charts (on different
  definition of work area) (I. 13) ....
Analysis of the charts ....
Multiple activity charts ....
Types of multiple activity charts ....
Construction procedure ....
Man-machine charts ....
Man-machine symbol chart for operation
  (I. 14) ....
Man-machine time chart for operation
  shown in Fig. (I. 14, 15) ....
Multi-man chart ....
Multi-man operation time chart (I. 16) ...
Travelling and gang charts ....

Complex Process Charts (continued)

Conveyor flow process chart (I. 17) ......
Workplace variations (I. 18) ....
Assembly flow process charts ....
Flow process charts for different defini-
  tions of workmanship (I. 19) ....
The flow diagram (I. 20) ....
Flow diagram of procedure (table, in-
  coming) (I. 21) ....
Flow diagram of procedure after im-
  provement (I. 22) ....
Procedure flow charts ....
Construction procedure ....
Procedure flow chart symbols (I. 23) .....
Procedure flow chart for order form
  (I. 24) ....
Flow diagram of an order procedure
  (I. 25) ....

PROCESS CHARTS

Nature of Process Charts

DEFINITION. A process chart is defined (Operation and Flow Process Charts, ASME, Standard 101) as a "graphic representation of events and information pertaining thereto occurring during a series of actions or operations." Such charts display in a compact form a great deal of information regarding such activities or operations as those involved in manufacturing a part in a plant or in processing forms in an office. F. B. and L. M. Gilbreth, who developed the process chart technique, state (ASME Transactions, vol. 43),

The process chart lends itself equally well to the routines of production, selling, accounting, and finance. It presents both simple and complicated problems easily and successfully; it provides records that are comparable; it assists in solving problems of notification and interdepartmental discrepancies, and it makes possible the more efficient utilization of similarities in different kinds of work and in the transfer of skill.

As for the types of people in the organization who can use process charting, Barnes (Motion and Time Study) states that, "The process chart may be made profitably by almost any one in an organization. The foreman, supervisor, process and layout engineer, as well as the industrial engineer should be familiar with the process chart and should be able to use it."

TYPES OF PROCESS CHARTS. The major types of process charts discussed in this section are **operation and flow process charts;** the two kinds of flow process charts covered are the man and the product or material charts. A number of subsidiary types such as flow diagrams, procedure flow charts, right- and left-hand charts, and multiple activity charts also will be described. Therblig and simo charts are discussed in the section on Motion and Methods Study. While the major process charts presented here have often been subdivided into many specialized types, Shaw (The Purpose and Practice of Motion Study) recommends that the detailed type of chart should not be followed rigidly, since,

. . . they are all fundamentally process charts and the same theory and method of analysis applies to all. If each chart is made with the definite object of "visualizing a process as a means of improving it," it will be built up so that the controlling factors of the work are brought into prominence by the form of the chart. The result may resemble other charts and fall roughly into one of these categories or it may be something quite new and original though appropriate to the presentation of the facts it records. It is unwise to set out to make a chart conforming to a particular type. A suitable shape and form should emerge in each case if a careful attempt is made to set out the material logically and vividly.

Repetitiveness of Work. Any work performance may be classified in one of three ways:

1. Work (or an operation) which is **repetitive,** that is, repeated over and over on identical parts, forms, or other units.

11·1

2. Work which **varies slightly** from cycle to cycle, such as the work of stock handlers, inspectors, lead men, or clerical workers.
3. Work which is **nonrepetitive**. Supervisory personnel and those doing creative and imaginative work are performing nonrepetitive activities. Other types of such activities include maintenance and the work of production control personnel, foremen, or engineers.

Process Chart Technique	When Used (Characteristics)	Repetitiveness*	Procedure for Gathering Data†
	Analysis of Sequence		
Operation process chart	When information about only process operations or inspections is desired.	1, 2	1, 2
Material or product flow process chart	When information about the process used to manufacture or work with a material or product is desired.	1, 2	1, 2
Procedure flow chart	When information about the work with, and handling of, forms or other paper work is desired.	1, sometimes 2	2, sometimes 1
	Analysis of Method		
Man flow process chart	Man goes from one workplace to another to accomplish his operation.	1, 2	1, 2, sometimes 3
Right- and left-hand or operation chart	Work done at one workplace without time-controlling equipment.	1, 2, sometimes 3	1, 2, 3
Man–machine chart	Work with one or more time-controlling pieces of equipment.	1, 2, sometimes 3	1, 3, sometimes 2
Multi-man chart	Two or more men working coordinately, with or without time-controlling equipment.	1, sometimes 2	3 best, sometimes 1, 2
Therblig chart	Work done at one workplace. Less time and money available for analysis than needed for simo chart.	1, 2	1, 2
Simo chart	Work done at one workplace. Usually long-run, skilled, or finger operations.	1	3

* 1. Repetitive. 2. Slightly varied cycles. 3. Nonrepetitive.
† 1. Observation. 2. Discussion. 3. Motion pictures.

Fig. 1. Factors involved in the selection of process chart technique.

Selecting the Chart or Analysis Technique. The process chart or technique to be used depends on four factors:

1. Whether an analysis of sequence or of methods is desired.
2. Characteristics of the process or work situation.
3. The repetitiveness of the work.
4. The procedure for collecting the information.

These factors are shown with their interrelationships in Fig. 1. Many of the chart techniques are overlapping. Some of them vary on the basis of how much detail is obtained. In some situations, the selection of the chart depends upon the detail required and the time allotted to the project. All the techniques in Fig. 1 are not used for every problem. They are like the tools in a carpenter's kit. The carpenter knows how to use each of his tools, but it is his judgment which determines the tool to be used for a particular problem. An analyst, who is familiar with each chart and knows where and how it can be used best, should select the charts to be used for a problem according to his judgment of the situation.

PURPOSE. Process charts can present a picture of a given process so clearly that an understanding of its every step may be gained by those who study the chart. The Gilbreths (ASME Transactions, vol. 43) state the purpose of the process chart as,

. . . a device for visualizing a process as a means of improving it. Every detail of a process is more or less affected by every other detail; therefore, the entire process must be presented in such a form that it can be visualized all at once before any changes are made in any of its subdivisions. In any subdivision of the process under examination, any changes made without due consideration of all the decisions and all the motions that precede and follow that subdivision will be found unsuited to the ultimate plan of operation. . . . It is not only the first step in visualizing the "one best way to do work" but is useful in every stage of deriving it.

Many writers caution, however, that while process charts are most effective for visualizing a process in order to improve it, process charts are still only one tool among the many available for the study of present and planned plant and office processes and the detailed analysis and comparison of the two. Barnes (Motion and Time Study) concludes that "Therefore, it should be clearly understood that the process chart, flow diagram, activity chart, man and machine chart, operation chart, and the simo chart are merely tools to be used as needed." Shaw (The Purpose and Practice of Motion Study) asserts that a process chart "should be more than a mere list of operations in sequence. Those who in recent times have been content to use only process charting in their motion study investigations, considering the other techniques as laboratory exercises or teaching media, often fail to appreciate this. They have too narrow a conception of the meaning of motion study."

Like statistical methods or charting and graphing procedures, process charts may be effective in analysis and may help in detecting inefficiencies. Their special merit is that they encourage an over-all, yet analytical, **view of processes.** They do not provide any final answers in themselves, however. These are to be found in such **fundamental investigatory methods** as are described for the use of the individual analyst in the section on Motion and Methods Study and for the use of groups analyzing and improving methods in the section on Work Simplification.

PROCESS CHART SYMBOLS. Many types of symbols and variations on them have been used as process charts have developed through study of different

| Process Chart Symbols | | Names of Activities | Activities Represented on Process Charts |
ASME Symbols	Other Symbols		Definitions of Activities
○		Operation	An **operation** occurs when an object is intentionally changed in any of its physical or chemical characteristics, is assembled or disassembled from another object, or is arranged or prepared for another operation, transportation, inspection, or storage. An operation also occurs when information is given or received or when planning or calculating takes place.
	Ⓛ Ⓜ	Labor operation Modification operation	Expenditure of labor or cost on product at one workplace which does not add value to the product. Modification (changing shape or size, machining, permanent assembly or disassembly, etc.) of product at one workplace. (Modification may be accomplished by machines and/or labor expenditure.)
⇧		Transportation	A **transportation** occurs when an object is moved from one place to another, except when such movements are a part of the operation or are caused by the operator at the work station during an operation or an inspection.
	○	Move	Change in location of product from one workplace to another workplace.
□		Inspection	An **inspection** occurs when an object is examined for identification or is verified for quality or quantity in any of its characteristics.
	◇	Verification	Comparison of product with a standard of quantity or quality at one workplace (a specialized labor operation). A control point established by management action.
⌐		Delay	A **delay** occurs to an object when conditions except those which intentionally change the physical or chemical characteristics of the object, do not permit or require immediate performance of the next planned step.
	▷	*Temporary storage	Delay, waiting, or banking of product when no special order or requisition is required to perform next activity.
▽		Storage	A **storage** occurs when an object is kept and protected against unauthorized removal, shown by inverted triangle.
	▷▷	*Controlled storage	Delay, waiting, or banking of product when a special order or requisition is required to perform the next activity.
◻○		Combined activity	When it is desired to show activities performed concurrently or by the same operator at the same work station, the symbols for those activities are *combined*, as shown by the circle placed within the square to represent a combined operation and inspection.

*In much motion and time study literature, the temporary storage symbol is a double triangle, and the controlled, or permanent, storage symbol is a single triangle. Because the temporary storage symbol is used overwhelmingly more than the controlled storage symbol, the principles of methods design (see section on Motion and Methods Study) indicate that it is better to use the symbols as indicated here, i.e., single triangle for temporary storage, double triangle for controlled storage.

Fig. 2. Types of symbols and definitions for process charts.

factory and office processes and through application to different industries. Some standardization has been provided by the grouping of the actions which occur during a given process into five **activity classifications** (Operation and Flow Process Charts, ASME, Standard 101). These are known as operations, transportations, inspections, delays, and storages. Symbols for these actions have been established as standard by an ASME committee. Fig. 2 shows these standard ASME symbols for, and the definitions of, the basic activity classifications which will be found applicable under the majority of conditions encountered in process charting work. Certain other commonly used symbols and their definitions are also shown in Fig. 2, as given by Nadler (Motion and Time Study).

When unusual situations outside the range of these definitions are encountered, the intent of the definitions summarized in the following tabulation will enable the analyst to make the proper classifications.

Classification	Predominant Result
Operation	Produces or accomplishes
Transportation	Moves
Inspection	Verifies
Delay	Interferes
Storage	Keeps

As shown in Fig. 2 and as was originally used by Gilbreth, a small circle is quite commonly used to represent the transportation activity. Sometimes the storage symbol, an inverted triangle, is used to cover both delay and storage; it may also be used to represent **temporary storage,** and one triangle inside another may represent **controlled storage** (or vice versa), when it is desirable to distinguish these two types of storage. It is not so important that everyone use the same symbols as it is that the symbols should be used uniformly and the actions defined accurately and consistently in making a given process chart or developing a related series of charts. A number of other symbols for specialized types of process charts are shown in this section and in the section on Motion and Methods Study, and anyone who uses a given kind of process chart frequently, or becomes involved in a very thorough analysis of an operation, may find it convenient or necessary to develop special symbols for his own purposes.

Basic Process Charts

OPERATION PROCESS CHARTS. The basic process chart, called an operation process chart, is defined (Operation and Flow Process Charts, ASME, Standard 101) as "a graphic representation of the points at which materials are introduced into the process, and of the sequence of inspections and all operations except those involved in materials handling. It includes information considered desirable for analysis such as time required and location." A typical operation process chart is shown in Fig. 3 (ASME, Standard 101).

Use of Charts. As step-by-step accounts of exactly what is done to materials, operation process charts can be made properly only by actually observing what transpires and listing the details in the order in which they occur. They graphically portray every raw material which is purchased and each operation and inspection performed in a productive process. Such charts visualize the entire procession of a single product from beginning to end. They may be used by accounting and purchasing to check on raw material costs and to schedule pur-

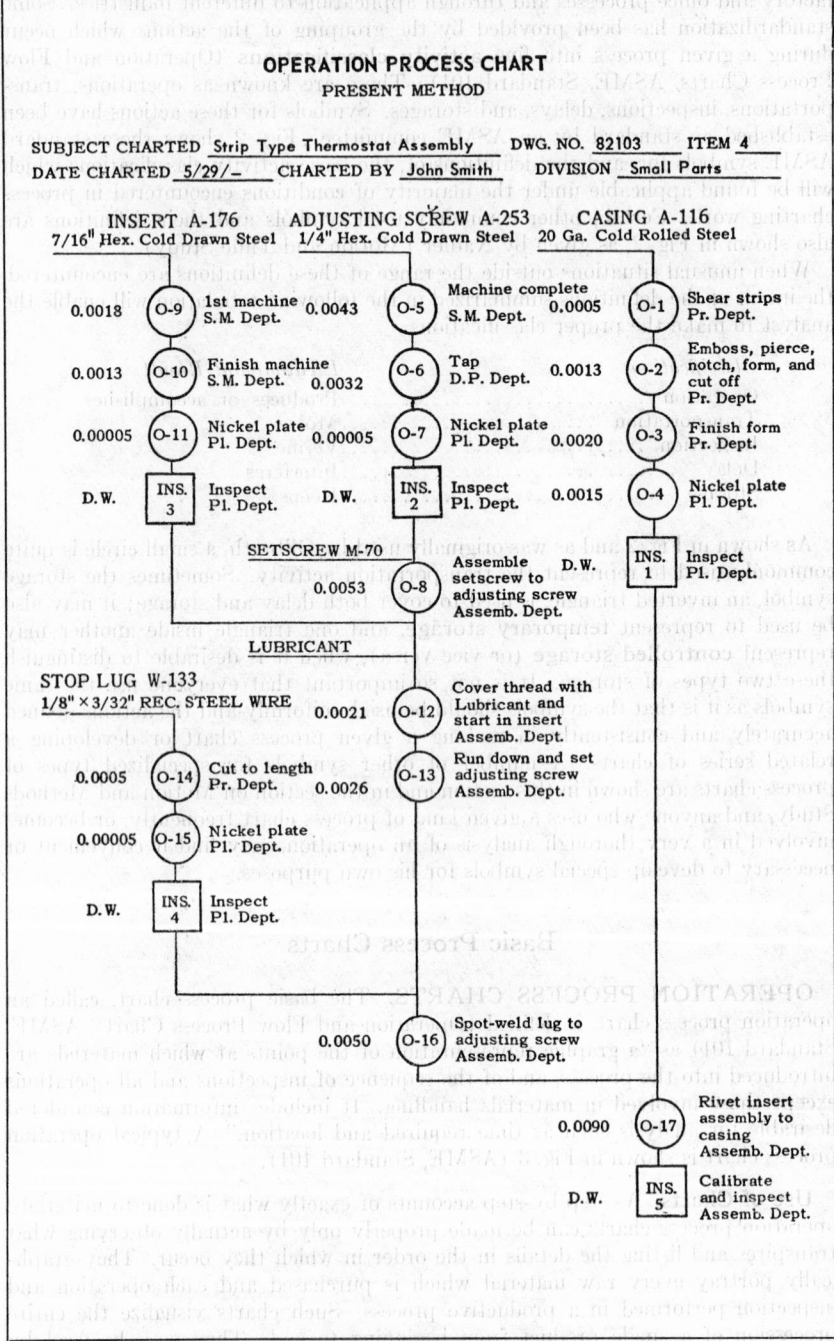

OPERATION PROCESS CHART

PRESENT METHOD

SUBJECT CHARTED Strip Type Thermostat Assembly   DWG. NO. 82103   ITEM 4

DATE CHARTED 5/29/–   CHARTED BY John Smith   DIVISION Small Parts

INSERT A-176   ADJUSTING SCREW A-253   CASING A-116
7/16" Hex. Cold Drawn Steel   1/4" Hex. Cold Drawn Steel   20 Ga. Cold Rolled Steel

0.0018 O-9 1st machine S.M. Dept.	0.0043 O-5 Machine complete S.M. Dept. 0.0005	O-1 Shear strips Pr. Dept.
0.0013 O-10 Finish machine S.M. Dept. 0.0032	O-6 Tap D.P. Dept. 0.0013	O-2 Emboss, pierce, notch, form, and cut off Pr. Dept.
0.00005 O-11 Nickel plate Pl. Dept. 0.00005	O-7 Nickel plate Pl. Dept. 0.0020	O-3 Finish form Pr. Dept.
D.W. INS. 3 Inspect Pl. Dept. D.W.	INS. 2 Inspect Pl. Dept. 0.0015	O-4 Nickel plate Pl. Dept.

SETSCREW M-70

0.0053 O-8 Assemble   D.W. setscrew to adjusting screw Assemb. Dept.

INS. 1 Inspect Pl. Dept.

LUBRICANT

STOP LUG W-133
1/8" × 3/32" REC. STEEL WIRE

0.0021 O-12 Cover thread with Lubricant and start in insert Assemb. Dept.

0.0005 O-14 Cut to length Pr. Dept. 0.0026

O-13 Run down and set adjusting screw Assemb. Dept.

0.00005 O-15 Nickel plate Pl. Dept.

D.W. INS. 4 Inspect Pl. Dept.

0.0050 O-16 Spot-weld lug to adjusting screw Assemb. Dept.

0.0090 O-17 Rivet insert assembly to casing Assemb. Dept.

D.W. INS. 5 Calibrate and inspect Assemb. Dept.

Fig. 3. Typical operation process chart.

chases. They can serve as **labor cost estimate sheets** or as check lists for **facilities needed,** such as workspaces and machines. (See the description of the use of these charts in the sections on Production Planning and Control and Plant Layout.) They are helpful in planning a **new product** and coordinating the efforts of those involved in putting it into production. These charts are often made available on drop curtains in conference rooms where **project teams** may work on improving small portions of the whole. They may be varied readily to suit specific needs. Busy executives keep tabs on what operations are being discussed by reference to these over-all charts.

Construction Procedures. A graphic representation of the principle of operation process chart construction is given in Fig. 4 (ASME, Standard 101).

The **sequence** in which the events depicted on the chart must be performed is represented by the arrangement of the process chart symbols on vertical flow lines. **Material,** either purchased or upon which work is performed during the process, is shown by horizontal material lines feeding into the vertical flow lines (see Fig. 4). One of the parts making up the completed product is selected for charting first, usually the component on which the greatest number of operations is performed or, if the chart is to be used for laying out a progressive assembly line, the part having the greatest bulk to which the smaller parts are assembled.

When the component to be charted first has been chosen, a **horizontal material line** is drawn in the upper right-hand portion of the chart, and a description of the material is recorded directly above this line (see Figs. 3 and 4). A **vertical flow line** is then drawn down from the right-hand end of the horizontal material line, and, approximately $\frac{1}{4}$ in. from the intersection of the horizontal material line and the vertical flow line, the symbol is drawn for the first operation or inspection which is performed. To the right of the symbol, a brief description of the event is recorded, while the time allowed for performing the required work is recorded to the left of the symbol. Other pertinent information which it is considered will add to the value of the chart, such as department in which the work is performed, male or female operator, cost center, machine number, or labor classification, is recorded to the right of the symbol below the description of the event. Thus, the different departments are entered in Fig. 3.

This charting procedure is continued until an **additional component** joins the first. Then a material line is drawn to show the point at which the second component enters the process. If it is purchased material, a brief identification of the material is placed directly above the material line. If work has previously been done on the component in the plant, a vertical flow line is erected from the left-hand end of the material line. The material from which it was made and the operations and inspections performed on it are then charted as indicated above. As each component joins the one shown on a vertical flow line to its right, the charting of the events which occur to the **combined components** is continued along the vertical flow line to the right. The final event which occurs to the completed apparatus will thus appear in the lower right-hand portion of the chart.

Operations are numbered serially for identification and reference purposes in the order in which they are charted; the first operation is numbered 0–1, the second 0–2, and so on. When another component on which work has previously been done joins the process, the operations performed upon it are numbered successively in the same series. **Inspections** are numbered in the same manner in a series of their own. They are identified as INS–1, INS–2, and so on (see Fig. 3).

According to the ASME standard, the **identifying information** which is usually necessary on such charts consists of the subject charted, whether the chart

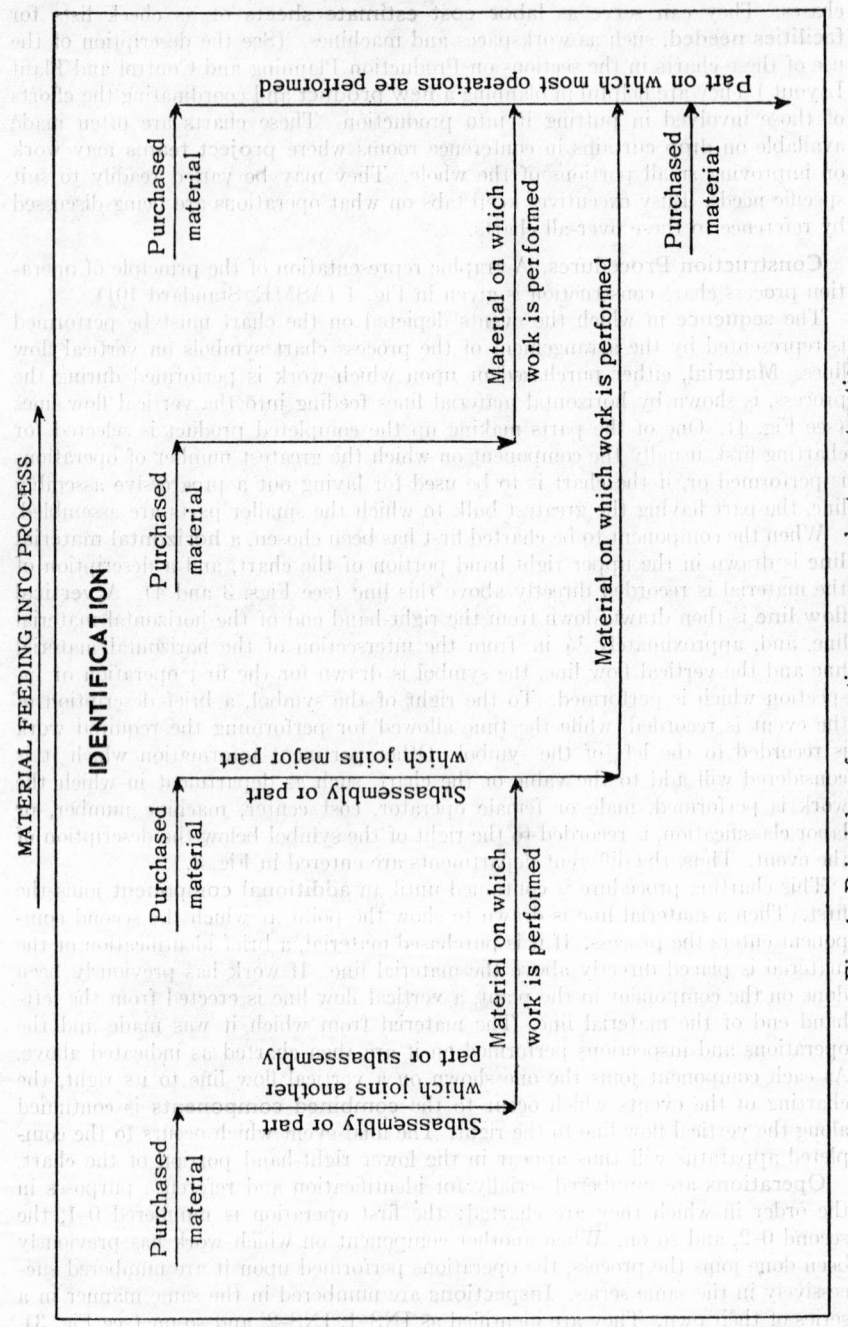

Fig. 4. Principles of operation process chart construction.

represents the present method or a proposed method, any identifying items such as drawing or part number, the date charted, and the name of the chart maker. Additional information which may be valuable is the **location** represented in the chart (plant, building, or department), the chart number, approvals, and the **chart span** from the point in the process at which the chart begins to the point at which it ends.

Disassembly and Alternate Process Conventions. To represent disassembly operations, material is represented as flowing from the process by a horizontal material line, drawn to the right from the vertical flow line approximately ¼ in. below the symbol for the disassembly operations. The name for the **disassembled component** is shown directly above the horizontal material line. The subsequent operations which are performed on the disassembled component, if any, are shown on a vertical flow line extending down from the right-hand end of the horizontal material line. If the disassembled component is later **reassembled** to the part or assembly from which it was disassembled, that part or assembly is shown as feeding into the flow line of the component. This practice moves the major vertical flow line always to the right. In numbering the operations, the operations performed on the disassembled component, after disassembly, are numbered before numbering the operations on the part from which it was disassembled. Then if the part later rejoins the disassembled component, the conventional numbering practices may be followed. This practice also applies to inspections.

Fig. 5 (Operation and Flow Process Charts, ASME, Standard 101) shows several other conventions used in constructing operation process charts. When two or more **alternate courses** may be followed during part of the process, a horizontal line is drawn below the vertical flow line, the central point of the line being at the intersection of the vertical flow line and the horizontal line. Vertical flow lines are then dropped from the horizontal line for each alternative which it is desired to show. If no operations or inspections are performed during one alternative, a vertical flow line only is shown. In all cases, operation and inspection symbols are added in the conventional manner. They are numbered serially, beginning with the first unused number in the operation or inspection series, with the symbols on the flow line furthest to the left numbered first. When all of the alternative paths have been charted, a horizontal line is drawn connecting the lower ends of all the alternate flow lines. From the mid-point of this line, a vertical flow line is dropped and the balance of the process is charted in the conventional manner.

In some cases, the unit shown by the chart changes as the process progresses. The lines "piece 52 in. long," "piece 12 in. long," etc., in Fig. 5 indicate the convention for showing such a **change in the unit.** Fig. 5 also illustrates the convention for **combined operations** and **inspections.**

Method Summaries. When a proposed method is to be presented by an operation process chart, it is often desirable to show the advantages it offers over the present method. This may be done by including with the information shown on the chart a summary of the important differences between the two methods. The summary may show the number of operations and inspections, the time of these for both the present and the proposed methods, and the difference between them; in addition, it may compare the unit cost for direct labor, the total yearly saving for direct labor, the installation cost of the proposed method, and the estimated saving the first year. It should be placed in a prominent location on the chart. On an 8½ in. × 11 in. chart, it will usually be placed in the lower left-hand corner.

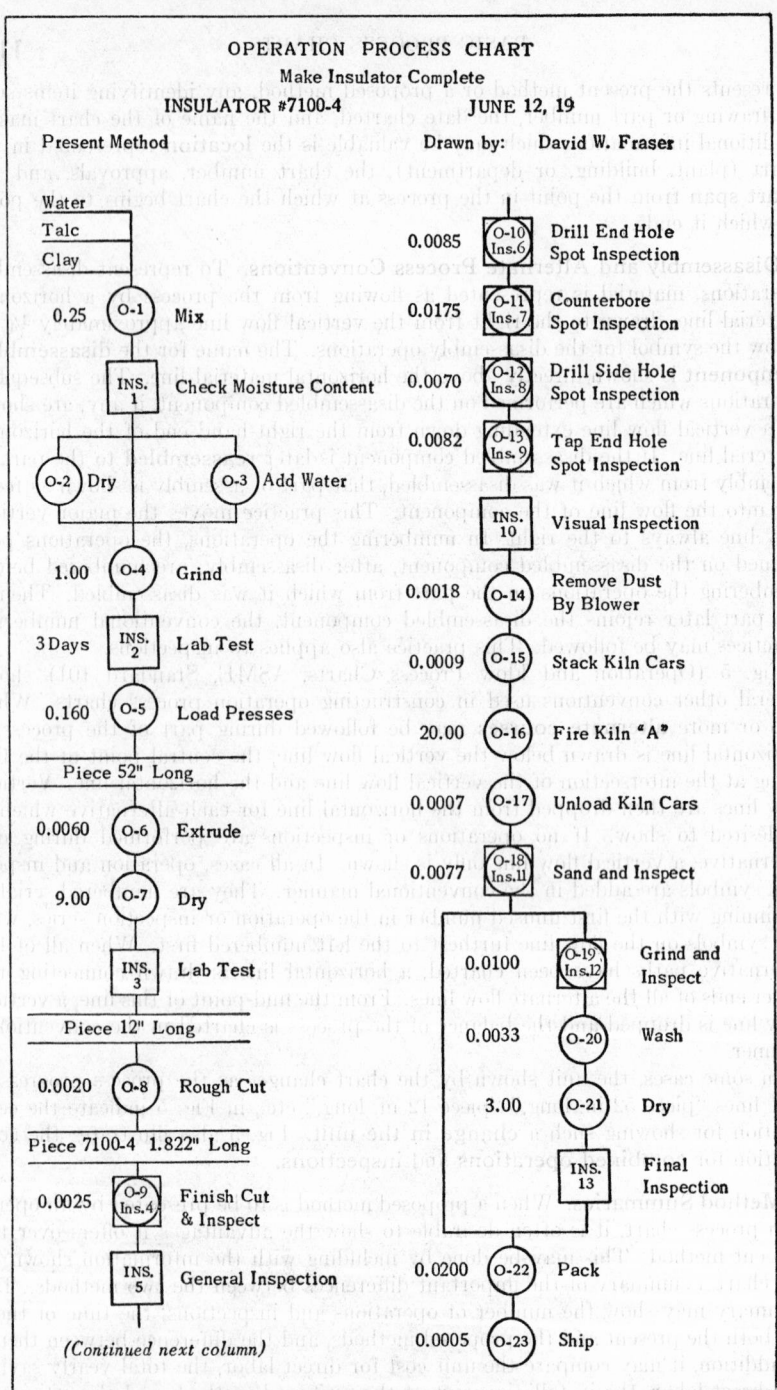

OPERATION PROCESS CHART
Make Insulator Complete
INSULATOR #7100-4   JUNE 12, 19

Present Method   Drawn by: David W. Fraser

Water
Talc
Clay

0.0085   O-10 Ins.6   Drill End Hole
                        Spot Inspection

0.25   O-1 Mix

0.0175   O-11 Ins.7   Counterbore
                        Spot Inspection

INS. 1 Check Moisture Content

0.0070   O-12 Ins.8   Drill Side Hole
                        Spot Inspection

0.0082   O-13 Ins.9   Tap End Hole
                        Spot Inspection

O-2 Dry   O-3 Add Water

INS. 10   Visual Inspection

1.00   O-4 Grind

0.0018   O-14   Remove Dust
                  By Blower

3 Days   INS. 2 Lab Test

0.0009   O-15   Stack Kiln Cars

0.160   O-5 Load Presses

20.00   O-16   Fire Kiln "A"

Piece 52" Long

0.0007   O-17   Unload Kiln Cars

0.0060   O-6 Extrude

0.0077   O-18 Ins.11   Sand and Inspect

9.00   O-7 Dry

INS. 3 Lab Test

0.0100   O-19 Ins.12   Grind and
                         Inspect

Piece 12" Long

0.0033   O-20   Wash

0.0020   O-8 Rough Cut

3.00   O-21   Dry

Piece 7100-4 1.822" Long

INS. 13   Final
          Inspection

0.0025   O-9 Ins.4   Finish Cut
                      & Inspect

INS. 5 General Inspection

0.0200   O-22   Pack

(Continued next column)

0.0005   O-23   Ship

Fig. 5. Operation process chart showing conventions for indicating unit on which
operations and inspections are performed, alternate routes, and combinations.

11·10

Analysis of Operation Process Charts. While operations are being observed so that they can be charted accurately and exhaustively, and particularly after the charts of the present methods have been completed, every element in them should be carefully scrutinized to see if there are any ways in which they may be either discarded or improved. Shaw (The Purpose and Practice of Motion Study) emphasizes that,

In analyzing the main chart or any of its subsidiary charts, it is essential to keep an open mind and not to accept anything in the existing method as inevitable until it has been thoroughly investigated. Every recorded movement of an operator or of material should be questioned. The analysis is made by subjecting first the whole chart, then each section of it, and finally each symbol to a critical examination.

Morrow (Motion Economy and Work Measurement) indicates that during the construction and study of operation process charts the following questions should be kept constantly in mind:

1. Can any of the operations or inspections shown on the charts be **eliminated?** Sometimes operations are performed which are not necessary at all. For example, the backs of metal-plated trays were being buffed at one factory, while at another factory of the same company, the backs of the trays were not buffed. The buffing operation was eliminated at the first factory as unnecessary, thereby saving time and materials.
2. Can one operation be **combined** with another operation? A common example of this is the manufacture of a part involving press operations of perforate, form, and blank. Formerly the part was sold in small quantities, the volume so small that the three operations were done separately. When production volume increased, it was worthwhile to make a progressive die and combine the three operations in one.
3. Can a better **sequence** of operations or inspections be followed? For example, inspections might be made to better advantage at other points in the manufacture of a part. In the manufacture of an amplifier where many connections were soldered, it was found advisable to have an inspection on the assembly line rather than to wait until the amplifier was completely wired.
4. Can operations be **simplified?** Most operations can be simplified by the correct application of the principles of work analysis. In the case of operations in a job shop, the work analysis may be only a visual analysis of the operation. An engineer trained and experienced in motion economy cannot only see all the motions but can recognize those which may be eliminated to simplify the operation. If the operation is highly repetitive and the volume of work is large, it may be worthwhile to go to full micromotion study, using slow motion pictures and simo-motion charts. (See section on Motion and Methods Study.)

Such questions may also be useful in analyzing any other types of process charts.

FLOW PROCESS CHARTS. David B. Porter (Operation and Flow Process Charts, ASME, Standard 101) defines a more highly developed, but still basic, type of process chart—the flow process chart—as

a graphic representation of the sequence of all operations, transportations, inspections, delays, and storages occurring during a process or procedure, and includes information considered desirable for analysis such as time required and distance moved.

(a) The **material type** presents the process in terms of the events which occur to the material.
(b) The **man type** presents the process in terms of the activities of the man.

PROCESS CHART

NAME OF PART OR PRODUCT   Requisition for Supplies — Rush Job

Chart Begins at Machine Shop Foreman's Desk, Ends on Typist's Desk in Pur. Dept.	CHART NO.

ORDER NO.	LOT SIZE	DEPT.	SHEET 1

CHARTED BY C.H.H. DATE CHARTED 7/28/– BLDG. M. E. Lab.	OF 1 SHEETS

Travel in ft.	Time in min.	Symbol	Operations	Remarks
		1	Written longhand by foreman.	
		1	On foreman's desk (awaiting messenger).	
1,000		1	By messenger to secretary of head of department.	
		2	On secretary's desk (awaiting typing).	
		2	Typed.	
15		2	By messenger to head of department.	
		3	On head of department's desk (awaiting approval).	
		O-3 INS-1	Examined, approved, and coded (signed and code stamped).	
		4	On head of department's desk (awaiting messenger).	
2,000		3	To purchasing department.	
		5	On purchasing agent's desk (awaiting approval).	
		2	Examined and approved.	
		6	On purchasing agent's desk (awaiting messenger).	
25		4	To typist's desk.	
		7	On typist's desk (awaiting typing of purchase order).	

SUMMARY

Number of operations 3

Number of delays 7

Number of inspections 2

Number of transportations . . . 4

Total travel in feet . . . 3,040

Fig. 6. Flow process chart of the material type.

The material flow process charts are sometimes known as **product process charts,** while the man type of flow process charts may be called **man process charts.** Both these types will be discussed here. The material or product process chart is the symbolic and systematic presentation of the procedure used to modify and/or work on a product. It assists in gathering and presenting information gathered about the sequence of work on, and handling of, the product, and in planning future production sequences and layouts. The man process chart is the symbolic and systematic presentation of the method of work performed by a man when his work requires him to move from workplace to workplace. The chart depicting work at one workplace is known as a right- and left-hand chart, or an operation or operator chart, and shows the method of work performed by the hands (and other body members, if used) when the work is at one workplace, without the use of cycle-time controlling equipment. Right- and left-hand charts will be discussed later in this section.

It will be noted that flow process charts are distinguished from operation process charts in that the flow process charts show all the basic actions, including transportation, delays, and storages. The latter are not shown on the operation process charts, which are limited to operations and inspections. Flow process charts analyze activities more completely than do operation process charts and may be applied to any processes or operations, whether in plants or offices. Fig. 6 (ASME, Standard 101) is a flow process chart of the material type with preprinted headings and captions, showing the stages followed by a requisition for supplies.

Construction Procedures. The same kind of identifying information is placed on a flow process chart as on an operation process chart, with the addition that the **chart type,** whether material or man, is usually identified. With charts drawn on plain paper where more than one item is to be charted, the same arrangement and conventions which are used for the operation process chart are likewise used for the flow process chart. However, in the man type of flow process chart, there are no horizontal lines representing the entrance of material into a process, and the storage symbol is not used. Flow process charts are usually drawn on plain paper of sufficient size to accommodate them, when they portray the events occurring to more than one item of material, the activities of more than one person, or the alternate routes or procedures followed by material or men.

When a flow process chart is made about a single item of material or a single person, however, usually only one column of symbols is needed, and no horizontal line is used to introduce material (see Fig. 6). The symbols are usually drawn with the aid of a **symbol template** for efficiency and uniformity. There is enough similarity among flow process charts of single items to permit the use of **prepared forms** which are both convenient and time-saving. The simplest of these forms, as shown in Fig. 6, provides headings and identification spaces, but no vertical or horizontal rulings.

Prepared Forms and Symbols. In Fig. 7, Goodwin (Lake Placid Work Simplification Conferences) shows a flow process chart of the material type, depicting what happens to a special order form, and set up on a preprinted sheet using ASME symbols. In constructing the chart, the symbol for an activity is connected with the symbol for the next activity occurring on the next line, and so on. This form features the summary in the upper left-hand corner; it carries the descriptive details of the present or proposed method being analyzed, the columns for the five preprinted symbols for activities, columns for distance, quantity, and time, and columns to check and comment on possibilities for improving

FLOW PROCESS CHART

NO. __1__
PAGE _1_ OF _1_

ANALYSIS WHY? — WHAT? WHERE? WHEN? WHO? HOW? — QUESTION EACH DETAIL

SUMMARY

	PRESENT		PROPOSED		DIFFERENCE	
	NO.	TIME	NO.	TIME	NO.	TIME
O OPERATIONS	12					
⇨ TRANSPORTATIONS	4					
□ INSPECTIONS	3					
D DELAYS	5					
▽ STORAGES	—					
DISTANCE TRAVELED	140 FT.		FT.		FT.	

JOB __Special Will Call & Mail Orders__ while in general office
☐ MAN OR ☑ MATERIAL __The Order Form__
CHART BEGINS __At receptionist's desk__
CHART ENDS __In mail chute__
CHARTED BY __H.F.G.__ DATE _____

DETAILS OF { PRESENT / ~~PROPOSED~~ } METHOD

POSSIBILITIES — CHANGE

#	Details	Dist. (ft)	Possibilities	NOTES
1	Waited in box at reception			
2	Picked up by confid. clerk		Improve ✓	Use wire basket
3	Taken to desk at A	30'	Sequence ✓ / Improve ✓	To files instead—shorter distance
4	Examined (for information)		Place ✓	At files
5	Waited (procure info.)		Eliminate ✓	Not necessary if taken to files
6	Prices written on order ●		Place ✓	At files
7	Taken to post. clerk at B	40'	Improve ✓	Shorter distance
8	Placed in desk tray			
9	Waited for clerk			
10	Picked up			
11	Examined (for information)			
12	Prices added (machine)			
13	Total written on order ●			
14	Waited (clerk gets ledger)			
15	Tot. transferred to ledger			
16	Placed in special out box		Eliminate ✓	Taken directly to mail chute
17	Waited for routing clerk		Eliminate ✓	Not necessary
18	Picked up		Eliminate ✓	Not necessary
19	Taken to desk (C)	40'	Eliminate ✓	Not necessary
20	Examined (determine route)		Combine ✓ / Sequence ✓	By B
21	Placed in envelope		Eliminate ✓	Not necessary—save cost of envel.
22	Addressed to proper dept. ●		Eliminate ✓	Have B route & drop in mail chute
23	Taken to recept. desk	30'	Place ✓ / Person ✓	By B—shorter distance
24	Placed in mail chute			

Fig. 7. Material flow process chart with preprinted symbols.

the methods. Such preprinted forms and symbols are sometimes recommended on the basis that they do not require drawing freehand or with a template. Furthermore, untrained personnel can use them effectively, since they are self-explanatory in arrangement and simple in use.

There has been much controversy over the use of such preprinted charts, with some authorities such as Nadler (Motion and Time Study) and Shaw (The Purpose and Practice of Motion Study) contending that a much better representation is secured with a chart custom-made to suit the situation being charted. The pros and cons of this question are too detailed for complete inclusion here; there is truth on both sides of the argument.

One must examine, however, the purpose of charting: to reveal weaknesses or inefficiencies in a process or system which otherwise might be missed. Whether this revelation is secured through a printed chart or one made to order would seem academic. The important thing is to achieve such a revelation so that action can be taken thereon. The blind use in a routine fashion of a preprinted chart may discourage creativity. Contrariwise, charting is a detailed process and should be a means to an end only, and not the end in itself. The ultimate objective is always the improvement which must follow the analysis.

An example of a more complete development of a **prepared chart form** of the flow process type (Operation and Flow Process Charts, ASME, Standard 101) consists of a 17 in. × 22 in. sheet which is folded twice into an 8½ in. × 11 in. size for filing. Features of this form are: the provision for showing both present and proposed methods; prepared symbols; a summary showing cost data and savings; and more complete information under the identification heading. The reverse side is arranged to provide a **cross section background** for a sketch of a layout or flow diagram. The two center pages are for a detailed explanation of **proposed changes,** and the back cover provides for recording action taken on the proposed method. Fig. 8 (ASME, Standard 101) shows a man-type flow process chart on this form, presenting both the present and the proposed methods and comparing them in the summary in the upper right-hand corner.

Principles of Flow Process Charting. Certain principles and precautions can be helpful in the study of a work process or operation and the construction of a flow process chart representing it.

1. Determine the **subject** which will be followed. Either a person (man chart) or an object (material or product chart) may be chosen as the subject of a flow process chart. The determination is made on the basis of which will portray the flow of activity most effectively. An object (material) is usually charted when several people successively handle the same object during the sequence of events (see Figs. 6 and 7). Otherwise, it would require different charts of the activity of each person to tell the whole story. If one person performs all the work, then that person logically becomes the subject of the chart. Everything he does is then recorded (see Fig. 8). Once the chart has been started in following either an object or a person, it should continue to follow that object or person throughout the activity.

2. Determine the **starting** and **ending points.** If the chart is to be as specific and complete as intended, the starting and ending points of the activity should be selected and recorded. Since most projects involve a portion of an over-all procedure, this indication is helpful in defining the limits of the intended study.

3. Record the appropriate **symbol** and a brief **description** of each detail. Every step or activity which occurs should be listed with an accurate description, no matter how small or insignificant it may seem to be. Every time something

IDENTIFICATION		FLOW PRO

SUBJECT CHARTED _STAMP AND PACK WELDING ROD_	CHART NO. _15-43_
DRAWING NO. ___ PART _3/16" DIA. WELD. ROD_	TYPE OF CHART _MAN_
POINT AT WHICH CHART BEGINS _GET SHIPPING BOX_	SHEET NO. _1_ OF _1_ SHEETS
___ LOCATION _EDGE OF WORKPLACE_	CHARTED BY _WALKER B. WEAVER_
POINT AT WHICH CHART ENDS _COMPLETE PACKING WITH BOX OUT OF_	DATE _MAY 5, 19—_
THE WAY LOCATION _TRUCK OR CONVEYOR_	APPROVED BY _H. W. CHAPMAN_
	DATE _MAY 9, 19—_
QUANTITY INFORMATION	
	YEARLY PRODUCTION _21,000_
	COST UNIT _100-POUND BOX_

PRESENT METHOD

QUANTITY UNIT CHARTED	SYMBOLS	DESCRIPTION OF EVENT	DIST MOVED IN FEET	UNIT OPER. TIME IN MIN.	UNIT TRANSP. TIME IN MIN.	UNIT INSPECT TIME IN MIN	DELAY TIME IN	STORAGE TIME IN
1 BOX	① ⇨ □ D ▽	PICK UP WOODEN WELDING ROD BOX		.103				
1 BOX	O ⇨ □ D ▽	MOVE BOX TO STAMPING TABLE	6		.117			
1 BOX	② ⇨ □ D ▽	POSITION BOX TO STENCIL		.030				
1 BOX	③ ⇨ □ D ▽	STENCIL BOX		.200				
1 BOX	O ⇨ □ D ▽	MOVE BOX AND LID TO SCALE	5		.093			
1 BOX	④ ⇨ □ D ▽	WEIGH BOX AND LID AND MARK		.079				
1 BOX	⑤ ⇨ □ D ▽	REMOVE LID FROM BOX		.051				
1 BOX	O ⇨ □ D ▽	MOVE BOX TO TRUCK	3		.070			
1 BOX	⑥ ⇨ □ D ▽	POSITION BOX ON TRUCK		.059				
1 BOX	⑦ ⇨ □ D ▽	PUT PATENT SLIP IN BOX		.047				
100 LB.	O ⇨ □ D ▽	GO TO STOCK BIN	12		.131			
100 LB.	⑧ ⇨ □ D ▽	REMOVE WELDING ROD FROM STOCK		.755				
100 LB.	O ⇨ □ D ▽	MOVE WELDING ROD TO STAMPING MACH.	12		.154			
100 LB.	⑨ ⇨ □ D ▽	SIT DOWN AT STAMPING MACHINE		.039				
100 LB.	⑩ ⇨ □ D ▽	STAMP ONE PLACE ON WELDING ROD		7.420				
100 LB.	O ⇨ □ D ▽	INSPECT STAMP ON ROD				.039		
100 LB.	O ⇨ □ D ▽	WALK TO SCALE	7		.132			
100 LB.	⑪ ⇨ □ D ▽	WEIGH AND PLACE 100 POUNDS IN BOX		.868				
1 BOX	⑫ ⇨ □ D ▽	PLACE LID ON BOX		.127				
1 BOX	⑬ ⇨ □ D ▽	POSITION BOX TO STRAP		.095				
1 BOX	⑭ ⇨ □ D ▽	PICK UP STRAP AND STRAPPER		.073				
1 BOX	⑮ ⇨ □ D ▽	STRAP BOX IN 3 PLACES		1.055				
1 BOX	⑯ ⇨ □ D ▽	PUT DOWN STRAPPER		.051				
1 BOX	O ⇨ □ D ▽	GET BOX OF NAILS, TACKS + HAMMER	10		.047			
1 BOX	⑰ ⇨ □ D ▽	NAIL LID ON BOX		1.317				
1 BOX	⑱ ⇨ □ D ▽	LAY 2 LABLES ON BOX		.094				
1 BOX	⑲ ⇨ □ D ▽	START 10 TACKS WITH THUMB		.563				
1 BOX	⑳ ⇨ □ D ▽	DRIVE 10 TACKS WITH HAMMER (LABELS)		.172				
1 BOX	O ⇨ □ D ▽	PUT AWAY NAILS, TACKS AND HAMMER	10		.046			
1 BOX	O ⇨ □ D ▽	MOVE BOX TO TRUCK	8		.123			
	O ⇨ □ D ▽							
	O ⇨ □ D ▽							

Fig. 8. A preprinted flow process

CESS CHART

SUMMARY

TOTAL YEARLY SAVING—DIRECT LABOR		PRESENT METHOD	PROPOSED METHOD	DIFFERENCE		
$619.50	(*LABOR RATE = $.70/HOUR*)					
	UNIT COST DIRECT LABOR & INSP	$.1641	$.1341	$.03		
	DISTANCE TRAVELED IN FEET	73	52	21		
INSTALLATION COST OF PROPOSED METHOD		NO.	TIME IN *MIN*	NO.	TIME IN *MIN*	NO.	TIME IN *MIN*

		NO.	TIME IN *MIN*	NO.	TIME IN *MIN*	NO.	TIME IN *MIN*
INSTALLATION COST OF PROPOSED METHOD *$156.00*	◯ OPERATIONS	20	13.198	21	10.758		2.440
	⇨ TRANSPORTATIONS	9	.913	9	.760		.153
ESTIMATED NET SAVING—FIRST YEAR *$463.00*	☐ INSPECTIONS	1	.039	1	.039		0
	D DELAYS						
	▽ STORAGES						

PROPOSED METHOD

QUANTITY UNIT CHARTED	SYMBOLS	DESCRIPTION OF EVENT	DIST MOVED IN FEET	UNIT OPER. TIME IN *MIN.*	UNIT TRANSP. TIME IN *MIN.*	UNIT INSPECT TIME IN *MIN.*	DELAY TIME IN ___	STORAGE TIME IN ___
1 Box	① ⇨ ☐ D▽	PICK UP WOODEN WELDING ROD BOX		.103				
1 Box	◯ ⇨1 ☐ D▽	MOVE BOX TO STAMPING TABLE	6		.117			
1 Box	② ⇨ ☐ D▽	POSITION BOX TO STENCIL		.030				
1 Box	③ ⇨ ☐ D▽	STENCIL BOX		.200				
1 Box	◯ ⇨2 ☐ D▽	MOVE BOX AND LID TO SCALE	5		.093			
1 Box	④ ⇨ ☐ D▽	WEIGH BOX AND LID AND MARK		.079				
1 Box	◯ ⇨3 ☐ D▽	MOVE BOX AND LID TO RACK	4		.076			
1 Box	⑤ ⇨ ☐ D▽	PLACE BOX AND LID ON RACK		.033				
100 LB.	◯ ⇨4 ☐ D▽	GO TO STOCK BIN	12		.131			
100 LB.	⑥ ⇨ ☐ D▽	REMOVE W.R. FROM STOCK TO SCALE		.755				
100 LB.	◯ ⇨5 ☐ D▽	GO FROM STOCK TO STAMPING MACH.	12		.154			
100 LB.	⑦ ⇨ ☐ D▽	SIT DOWN AT STAMPING MACH.		.039				
1 Box	⑧ ⇨ ☐ D▽	REMOVE LID FROM BOX		.051				
1 Box	⑨ ⇨ ☐ D▽	PICK UP BOX		.031				
1 Box	◯ ⇨6 ☐ D▽	MOVE BOX TO CHUTE	3		.053			
1 Box	⑩ ⇨ ☐ D▽	POSITION BOX AT CHUTE		.068				
1 Box	⑪ ⇨ ☐ D▽	DROP CHUTE ON BOX		.039				
1 Box	⑫ ⇨ ☐ D▽	PUT PATENT SLIP ON BOX		.047				
100 LB.	⑬ ⇨ ☐ D▽	STAMP ONE PLACE ON WELDING ROD		7.470				
100 LB.	◯ ⇨1 ☐1 D▽	INSPECT STAMP ON ROD				.039		
1 Box	⑭ ⇨ ☐ D▽	RAISE CHUTE		.053				
1 Box	◯ ⇨7 ☐ D▽	SLIDE BOX FROM UNDER CHUTE	2		.043			
1 Box	⑮ ⇨ ☐ D▽	PUT LID IN BOX (INSERT)		.056				
1 Box	◯ ⇨8 ☐ D▽	SLIDE BOX AWAY ON ROLLERS	4		.046			
1 Box	⑯ ⇨ ☐ D▽	POSITION BOX TO STRAP		.095				
1 Box	⑰ ⇨ ☐ D▽	PICK UP STRAP AND STRAPPER		.073				
1 Box	⑱ ⇨ ☐ D▽	STRAP BOX IN 3 PLACES		1.055				
1 Box	⑲ ⇨ ☐ D▽	PUT DOWN STRAPPER		.051				
1 Box	⑳ ⇨ ☐ D▽	LAY 2 LABELS ON BOX		.094				
1 Box	㉑ ⇨ ☐ D▽	GLUE 2 LABELS ON BOX		.386				
1 Box	◯ ⇨9 ☐ D▽	SLIDE BOX AWAY ON ROLLERS	4		.047			
	◯ ⇨ ☐ D▽							

chart used for comparing methods.

happens, such as a move, delay, or inspection, it should be recorded exactly the way it is observed.

4. Shade in the **do symbols.** Since most **make-ready** and **put-away** details depend on the do activities, it is important to segregate these key details graphically so that they may be challenged first (see Fig. 7). If there is any doubt about whether the detail actually is a do according to definition, the customary procedure is to shade it in anyway, since it is the use of the chart which counts rather than its exactness.

5. Note **transportation distance.** Transportation and handling between operations is expensive, nonproductive work. A significant amount of this type of activity is a challenge to the ingenuity to reduce or eliminate it entirely. Estimates by **pacing** are considered adequate if more accurate measurements are not obtainable easily.

6. Record the **quantities handled.** Often the subject of a flow process chart is handled in varying quantities during the complete sequence charted. Material may start off in a roll, be cut into bundles, and wind up as individual pieces. Such information is pertinent to the formation of a clear picture of exactly what is happening.

7. Indicate **time consumed** or **production rates,** if possible. An idea of the performance attained at each step becomes useful when comparisons are being made between different methods and summaries of savings are being worked up. It is also significant in determining which details are the most costly, and, therefore, should receive the most attention. A convenient way of expressing the time is by noting the production record in units per hour or day.

8. Prepare **summaries.** Total each type of detail, the distance traveled, and the time consumed. The summary is the chart feature in which higher authorities will be most interested. It may be used to make comparisons with the proposed method chart and indicate the extent of improvement attained.

Simple, Converging, and Diverging Charts. Three types of material flow process charts can be made. The first is the simple or **straight line chart,** shown in Fig. 9a (Nadler, Motion and Time Study), using the types of symbols illustrated and defined in Fig. 2. This charts one material or product alone, regardless of what might be added to or taken away from it, and it is usually a part of one of the more complex chart types. The second type is the converging chart (Fig. 9b), made for most **manufacturing** and **assembly work.** The activity charted utilizes different materials which come together to form a final product. The third type is the diverging chart (Fig. 9c), which would be made in industries where a single material is divided into **several final products,** as in the food processing, metal-working, and meat industries. The converging and diverging types of flow process charts are a series of simple charts placed together in proper relationships.

In Fig. 10, Nadler (Motion and Time Study) illustrates a complete material flow process chart of the converging type, using the common symbols defined in Fig. 2, with minimum detail for a repetitive switch box assembly. The assembly of the boxes is the basic activity, so the principal straight line on the left analyzes this. The covers and the cartons converge onto the box assembly at the proper time from the right-hand lines. Fig. 10 is a planning chart, analyzing future work. Before starting production, the industrial engineer, the foreman of the department involved, and the production manager met to discuss the process to be used for assembly of the switch boxes. They knew the floor space available for the assembly, developed a flow diagram for the process, and decided to make up the chart shown in Fig. 10 for the procedure that seemed likely to be the most effective.

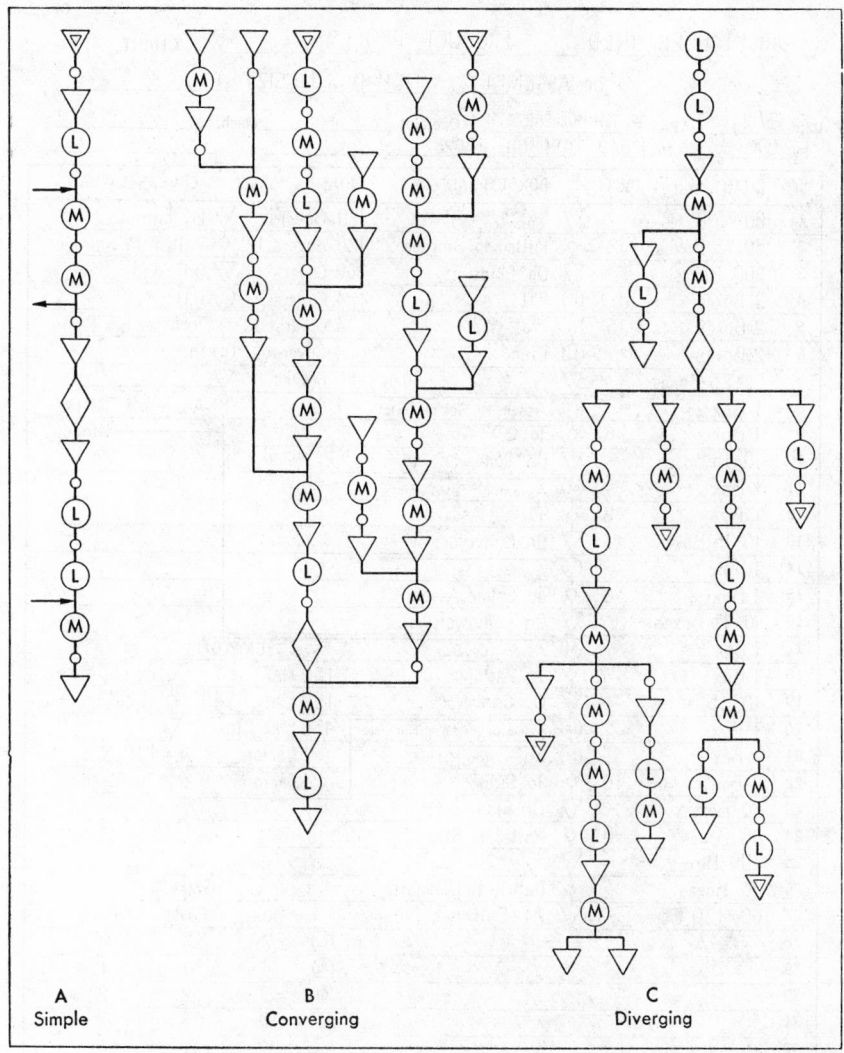

Fig. 9. Types of flow process charts.

Defining the Workplace. Every chart, including the flow process chart, has to be conceived in a flexible manner. There is no one "correct" chart. The key to a good flow process chart is the definition of the workplace for the process.

In Fig. 11a (Nadler, Motion and Time Study), a lathe, a supply table, and a finish table are shown. The operator takes a part and prepares it on the supply table. After machining the part, the operator unloads it onto the finish table. Notice that work is being performed at the supply table, the lathe, and at the finish table. Depending upon the definition of a workplace, the analyst can make different types of charts. In Fig. 11a, the analyst assumed that all the **work stations** were within one **workplace,** contained within the dotted lines. In this

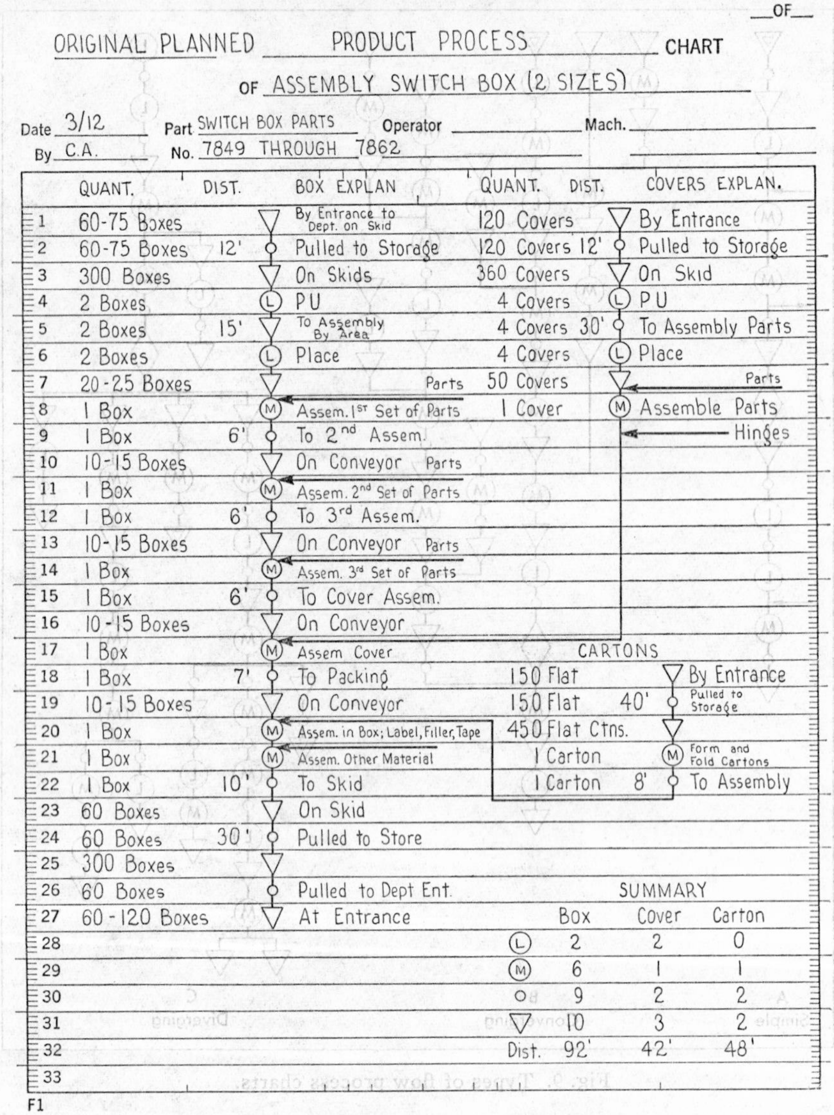

ORIGINAL PLANNED   PRODUCT PROCESS   CHART   __OF__

OF ASSEMBLY SWITCH BOX (2 SIZES)

Date 3/12   Part SWITCH BOX PARTS   Operator _____   Mach. _____

By C.A.   No. 7849 THROUGH 7862

#	QUANT.	DIST.	BOX EXPLAN	QUANT.	DIST.	COVERS EXPLAN.
1	60-75 Boxes		▽ By Entrance to Dept. on Skid	120 Covers		▽ By Entrance
2	60-75 Boxes	12'	Pulled to Storage	120 Covers	12'	Pulled to Storage
3	300 Boxes		On Skids	360 Covers		On Skid
4	2 Boxes		(L) P U	4 Covers		(L) P U
5	2 Boxes	15'	To Assembly By Area	4 Covers	30'	To Assembly Parts
6	2 Boxes		(L) Place	4 Covers		(L) Place
7	20-25 Boxes		Parts	50 Covers		Parts
8	1 Box		(M) Assem. 1st Set of Parts	1 Cover		(M) Assemble Parts
9	1 Box	6'	To 2nd Assem.			Hinges
10	10-15 Boxes		On Conveyor Parts			
11	1 Box		(M) Assem. 2nd Set of Parts			
12	1 Box	6'	To 3rd Assem.			
13	10-15 Boxes		On Conveyor Parts			
14	1 Box		(M) Assem. 3rd Set of Parts			
15	1 Box	6'	To Cover Assem.			
16	10-15 Boxes		On Conveyor			
17	1 Box		(M) Assem Cover			CARTONS
18	1 Box	7'	To Packing	150 Flat		▽ By Entrance
19	10-15 Boxes		On Conveyor	150 Flat	40'	Pulled to Storage
20	1 Box		(M) Assem. in Box; Label, Filler, Tape	450 Flat Ctns.		
21	1 Box		(M) Assem. Other Material	1 Carton		(M) Form and Fold Cartons
22	1 Box	10'	To Skid	1 Carton	8'	To Assembly
23	60 Boxes		On Skid			
24	60 Boxes	30'	Pulled to Store			
25	300 Boxes					
26	60 Boxes		Pulled to Dept Ent.			
27	60-120 Boxes		At Entrance			SUMMARY
28				(L)	2 2 0	Box Cover Carton
29				(M)	6 1 1	
30				o	9 2 2	
31				▽	10 3 2	
32				Dist.	92' 42' 48'	
33						

SUMMARY

	Box	Cover	Carton
(L)	2	2	0
(M)	6	1	1
o	9	2	2
▽	10	3	2
Dist.	92'	42'	48'

F1

Fig. 10. Converging flow process chart.

case, the minimum detailed material flow process chart for the activity at this workplace would be like Fig. 12a. To obtain greater detail with this definition of workplace, the analyst could make a chart like that shown in Fig. 12b.

Fig. 11b represents another way of defining workplaces. Here three different workplaces are shown, divided by the dotted lines. The minimum chart for this workplace concept would be that shown in Fig. 12c. For greater detail, the chart shown in Fig. 12d could be made. There are, then, various ways of charting the same activity, depending upon the determination of the workplace and the detail

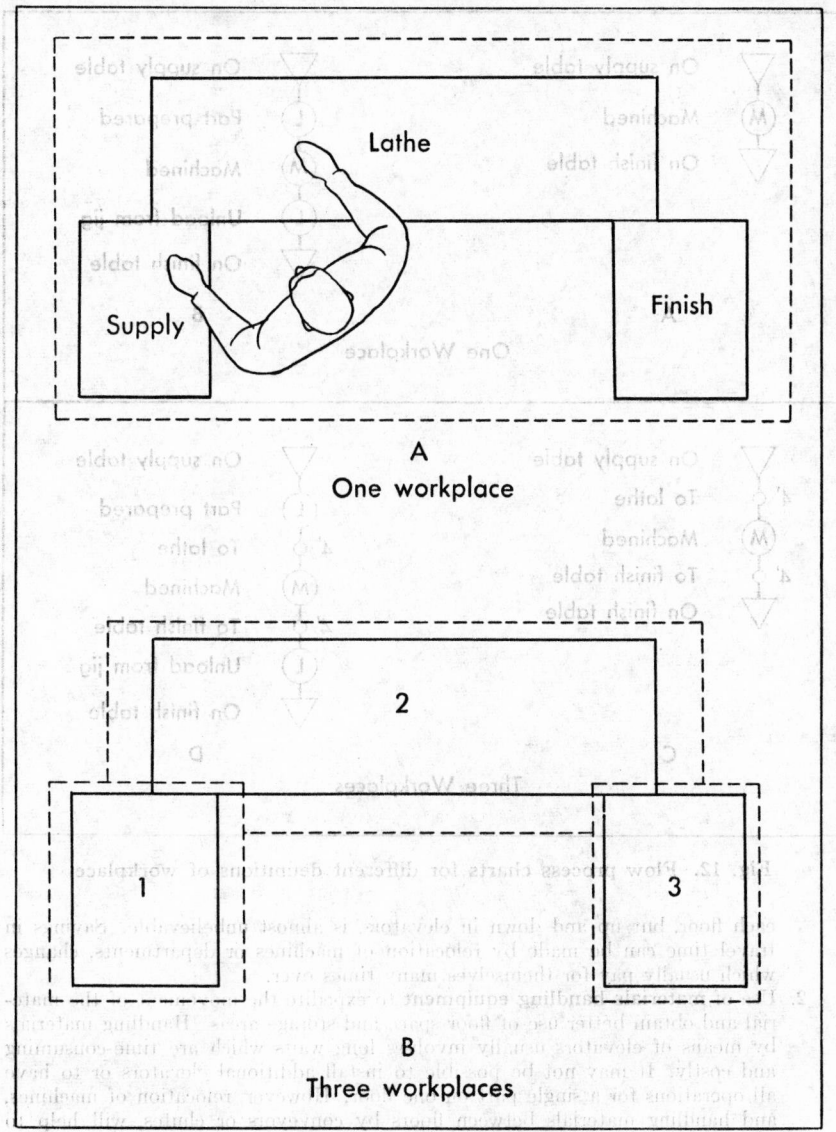

A
One workplace

B
Three workplaces

Fig. 11. Workplace variations.

desired. A consistent pattern of workplace definition should be followed on any given chart.

Analyzing Flow Process Charts. Morrow (Motion Economy and Work Measurement) summarizes the improvements which may result from the development and use of flow process charts and flow diagrams as follows:

1. **Reduction in distances** that the work travels. The distance a part may travel through a factory in the course of manufacture, not only back and forth on

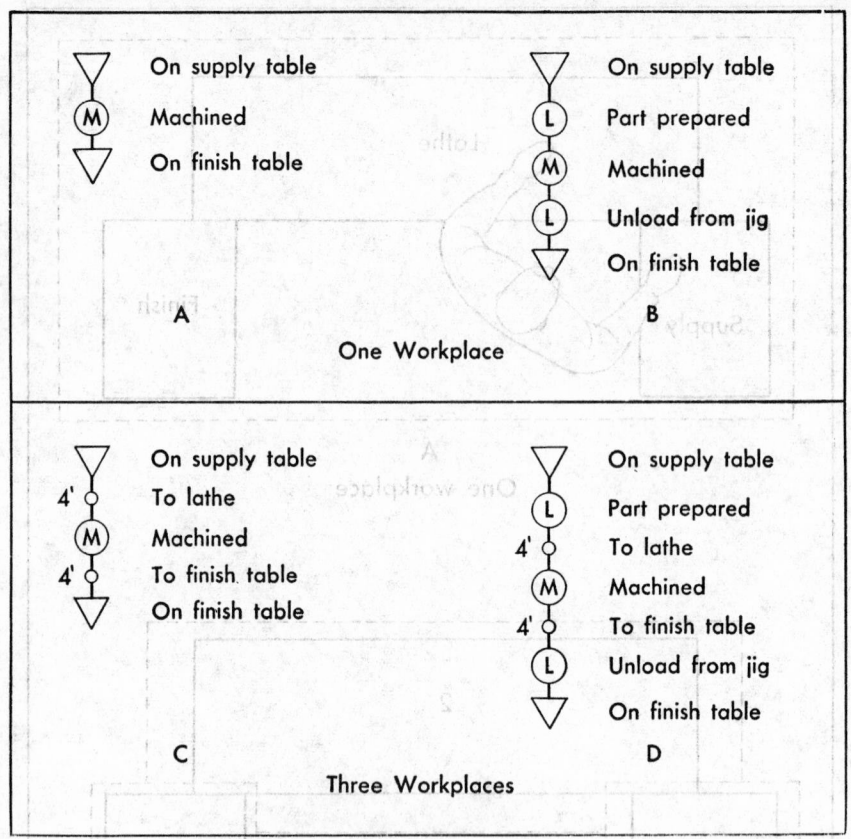

Fig. 12. Flow process charts for different definitions of workplace.

each floor, but up and down in elevators, is almost unbelievable. Savings in travel time can be made by relocation of machines or departments, changes which usually pay for themselves many times over.

2. Use of **materials handling equipment** to expedite the movement of the material and obtain better use of floor space and storage areas. Handling materials by means of elevators usually involves long waits which are time-consuming and costly. It may not be possible to install additional elevators or to have all operations for a single part on one floor. However, relocation of machines, and handling materials between floors by conveyors or chutes, will help to solve this problem.

3. Reduction of number of **periods of temporary storage** of materials between operations or elimination of such storage entirely. This cuts the work in process and saves floor space.

4. Reduction of the number of **inspections** needed, or relocation of inspection points.

THE FLOW DIAGRAM. The flow diagram in its simplest form shows a rough view of the space in which the activity being studied occurs and the location and extent of the work areas, machines, or desks, with a connecting series of

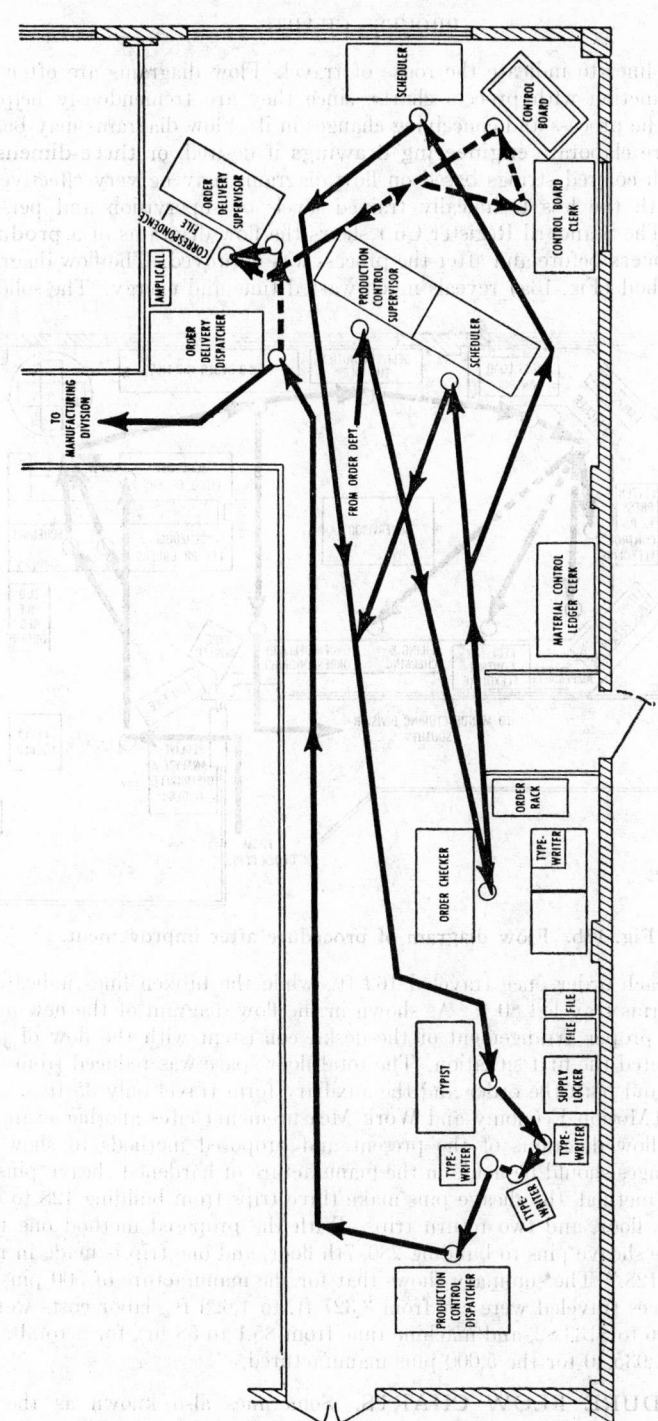

Fig. 13a. Flow diagram of procedure before improvement.

arrows and lines to indicate the route of travel. Flow diagrams are often made up in conjunction with process charts, since they are tremendously helpful in visualizing the process and conceiving changes in it. Flow diagrams may be made up into more elaborate **engineering drawings** if desired, or **three-dimensional models** with colored strings based on flow diagrams may be very effective, particularly with the less technically trained levels of supervision and personnel.

Fig. 13 (The Standard Register Co.) shows the flow diagrams of a **production control process** before and after the process was improved. The flow diagram of the old method (Fig. 13a) reveals much wasted time and energy. The solid lines

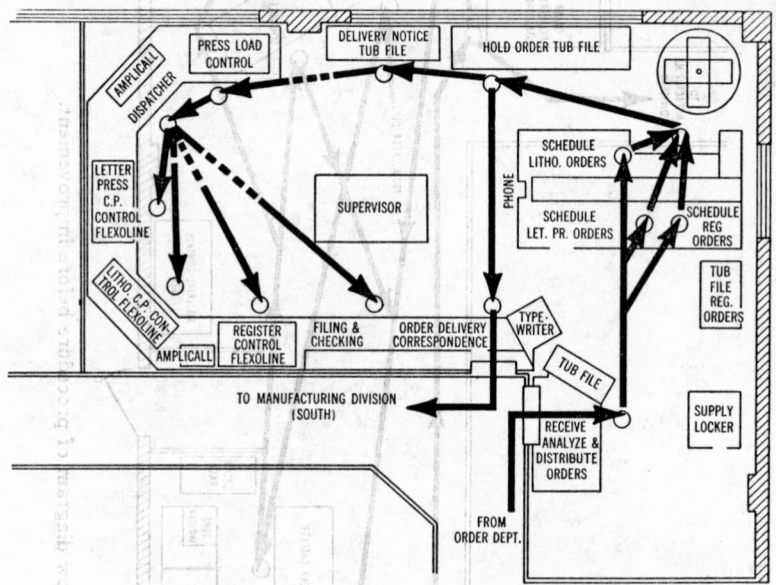

Fig. 13b. Flow diagram of procedure after improvement.

show how each order once traveled 162 ft., while the broken lines indicate how auxiliary forms traveled 80 ft. As shown in the flow diagram of the new method (Fig. 13b), proper arrangement of the desks, consistent with the flow of paper-work, corrected the first situation. The total floor space was reduced from 960 to 460 sq. ft., and both the order and the auxiliary form travel only 35 ft.

Morrow (Motion Economy and Work Measurement) cites another example of the use of flow diagrams of the present and proposed methods to show what process changes should be made in the manufacture of hardened sheave pins: "In the present method, the sheave pins make three trips from building 128 to building 280, 7th floor, and two return trips. With the proposed method one trip is made by the sheave pins to building 280, 7th floor, and one trip is made in return to building 128." The summary shows that for the manufacture of 500 pins only, total distances traveled were cut from 3,327 ft. to 1,623 ft., labor costs were cut from $191.96 to $133.82, and machine time from 85.1 to 58 hr., for a total annual saving of $1,935.40 for the 5,000 pins manufactured.

PROCEDURE FLOW CHARTS. Sometimes also known as the form process chart, the procedure flow chart is a symbolic and systematic presentation of the procedure used to modify, work on, and handle a form or forms. It may be thought of as a specialized type of a flow process chart of the product or material kind. The usual activity charted on a procedure flow chart is a **system** or **procedure**. This refers to the flow of paperwork, since the form process chart is usually made for a complete procedure, like purchasing or employment. However, the procedure flow chart can be made for just one form. Many factory procedures can be analyzed with these charts, such as production control, time records, inventory control, or incentive earnings processing. Paperwork has become so complicated with multipartite forms and new data-gathering needs that those specializing in it have designed this type of chart which they feel more nearly meets their needs. Procedure flow charts are sometimes done on a **horizontal charting** basis, which, of course, can readily be done with any flow process chart.

Construction Procedures. The symbols commonly used in procedure flow charts are shown in Fig. 14. These are similar to those used in the regular flow process chart, it will be noted, although additional symbols are used to take care of information on forms, which is the main product, and the symbols are named

Geometric Symbol	Name	Activity Represented
②	Origination	Form being made out at one workplace. (Number in center represents number of copies made.)
○	Operation	Modification of, or addition to, form at one workplace.
○	Move	Change in location of form from one workplace to another.
▽	Temporary storage	Delay or waiting of form where no special order is required to perform next activity (e.g., in desk basket).
▽	Controlled storage	Delay or waiting of form where a special order is required to perform next activity (e.g., in file cabinet).
◇	Verification	Comparison of form with other information to ascertain correctness of form.
⊣	Information transmission	Reading or removal of information on form for use by someone or some machine.
⊠	Disposal	Form destroyed.

Fig. 14. Procedure flow chart symbols.

and defined somewhat differently. Using the symbols shown in Fig. 14, Nadler (Motion and Time Study) shows in Fig. 15 a procedure flow chart made in a company which was having an extensive cost reduction program which included a review of systems and procedures. The specific goal for the order form was to reduce the time and money spent in working on it.

The columns on the procedure flow chart represent the departments or other units of the organization through which the forms move. Within these columns, the symbols are indicated, with an explanation of them, and with the distances covered by the movement of the forms. **Equipment** used can also be listed when it is an important factor in the procedures being analyzed. The procedure flow chart is started by noting the symbol for the activity first observed at the point where the analysis is to begin. The next activity is charted on the next line, and so on.

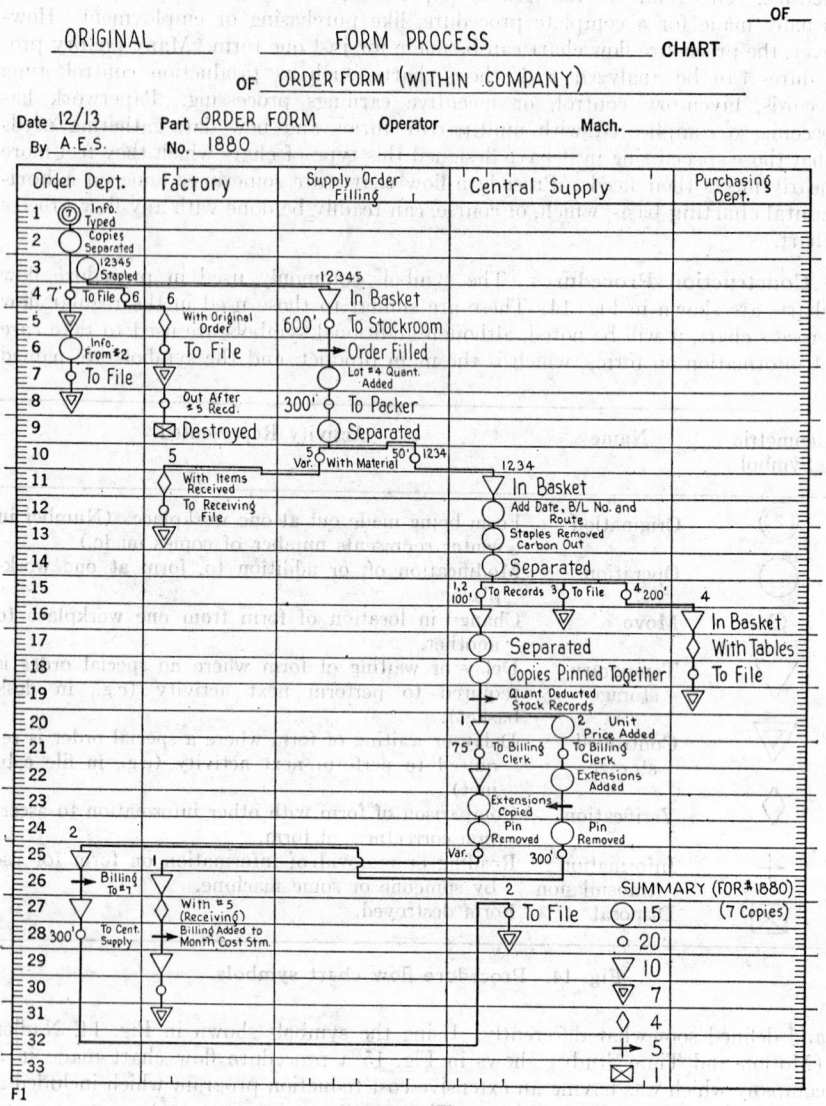

ORIGINAL _____ FORM PROCESS _____ CHART __OF__

OF ORDER FORM (WITHIN COMPANY)

Date 12/13   Part ORDER FORM   Operator _____ Mach. _____

By A.E.S.   No. 1880

Fig. 15. Procedure flow chart for order form.

As is the case with the other types of charts, **specialized symbols** have been developed also for procedure flow charts, particularly when applied to office work. Some of these are illustrated in Fig. 16 (The Standard Register Co.), which shows a flow diagram of an office procedure.

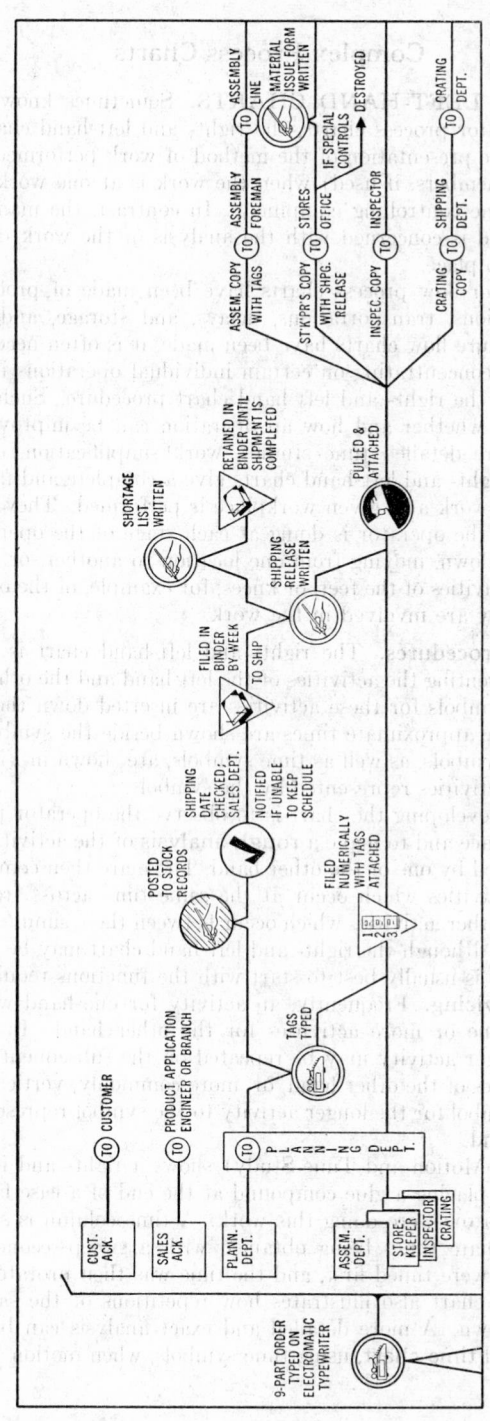

Fig. 16. Flow diagram of an office procedure.

Complex Process Charts

RIGHT- AND LEFT-HAND CHARTS. Sometimes known as operator, operation, or operator process charts, the right- and left-hand chart is the symbolic and systematic presentation of the method of work performed by the hands (and other body members, if used) when the work is at one workplace, without the use of cycle-time controlling equipment. In contrast, the man process chart previously described is concerned with the analysis of the work done by a man going from place to place.

After operation or flow process charts have been made of processes, showing operations, inspections, transportations, delays, and storage, and possibly flow diagrams or procedure flow charts have been made, it is often necessary to make a further analysis, concentrating on certain individual operations involved in the work, by means of the right- and left-hand chart procedure. Such a chart often shows very clearly whether and how an operation can be improved, and sometimes leads to more detailed time studies, work simplification, or motion and method studies. Right- and left-hand charts give a complete and fairly analytical picture of how the work at a given workplace is performed. They show in detail what each hand of the operator is doing at each stage of the operation, whether picking up, laying down, moving from one location to another, or holding a part or tool. Similar activities of the feet, or knees, for example, of the operator can be analyzed, when they are involved in the work.

Construction Procedures. The right- and left-hand chart is set up in two columns, one representing the activities of the left hand and the other those of the right hand. The symbols for these activities are inserted down the center of the chart, and often the approximate times are shown beside the symbols. The basic ASME and other symbols, as well as time symbols, are shown in Fig. 17, with the definitions of the activities represented by the symbols.

The method of developing the chart is to observe the operator performing the work at the workplace and to make a **rough analysis** of the activities of the most active hand, followed by one of the other hand. These are then combined into one chart, with the activities which occur at the same time across from each other on the chart. The other activities which occur between these simultaneous motions are then fitted in. Although the right- and left-hand chart may be started at any part of the cycle, it is usually best to start with the functions required for a **new part** or a **new servicing.** Frequently, an activity for one hand will take longer to perform than one or more activities for the other hand. In this case, the symbol for the longer activity may be repeated on the subsequent lines opposite the varying activities of the other hand, or, more commonly, vertical lines may be drawn from the symbol for the longer activity to the symbol representing the next activity of that hand.

Fig. 18 (Nadler, Motion and Time Study) shows a right- and left-hand chart of the operation of placing a glue compound at the end of a case filled with hard powder. Two operators were doing this work. A time column is shown for each hand, the approximate times being obtained with a sweep-second wrist watch. A group of actions were timed first, and the time was then prorated as indicated on the chart. The chart also illustrates how repetitions of the same work in a given cycle are shown. A more detailed and exact analysis can be made in the right- and left-hand **time chart,** using time symbols, when motion pictures of the work are available.

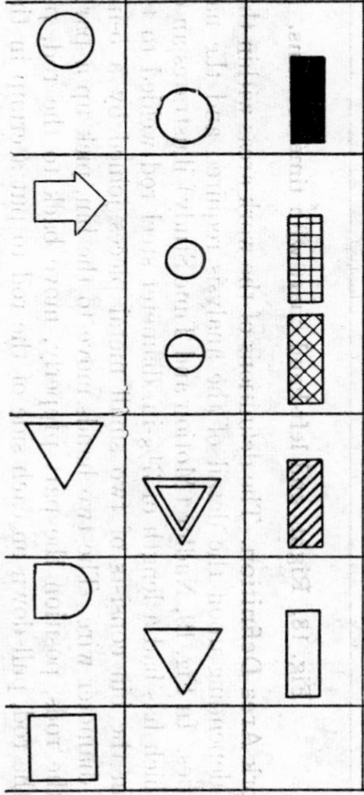

Right- and Left-Hand Chart Symbols			Names of Activities	Hand Activities Represented on Right- and Left-Hand Charts — Definitions of Activities
ASME Symbols	Other Symbols	Time Symbols		
			Operation	An **operation** occurs whenever the hand picks up something, drops, or lays down something, positions, uses, assembles something — each activity a separate detail.
		▰	Sub-operation (1, 2, 3)*	A sub-operation occurs in performing something at one work area in a workplace.
			Transportation	A **transportation** occurs whenever the hand moves from one location in the workplace to another, in order to perform such actions as moving from center to supply of work, or bringing tool from holder to fixture.
		▦	Movement without load (2)*	Changing location without load from one work area to another work area in a workplace.
		▨	Movement with load	Changing location with load from one work area to another work area in a workplace.
			Hold	A **hold** occurs whenever the hand holds a part or a tool so that the other hand may do something to that part or tool.
		▨	Hold	Maintaining an object in a fixed orientation to allow work on or with object
			Delay	A **delay** occurs when the hand is motionless or is not in the performance of an operation or transportation detail.
			Delay (1, 2, 3)*	Waiting or idle.
			Inspection	**Inspection** is occasionally used, but rarely found on pre-printed forms since it occurs so infrequently as a hand motion.

*Used also for (1) Feet (2) Eyes, and (3) Knees.

Fig. 17. Types of symbols and definitions used for right- and left-hand charts.

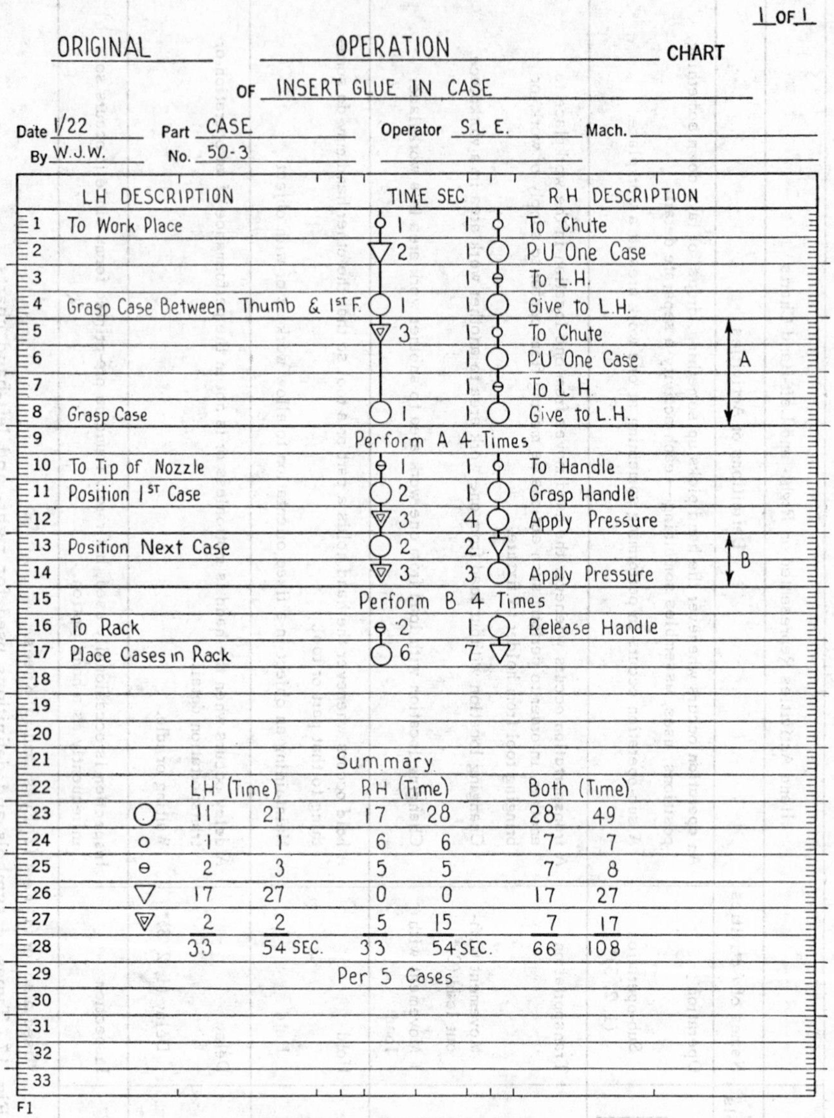

ORIGINAL _____ OPERATION _____ CHART

OF INSERT GLUE IN CASE

Date 1/22   Part CASE   Operator S.L.E.   Mach. _____

By W.J.W.   No. 50-3

	LH DESCRIPTION	TIME SEC			RH DESCRIPTION	
1	To Work Place	○ 1	1	○	To Chute	
2		▽ 2	1	○	P U One Case	
3			1	⊖	To L.H.	
4	Grasp Case Between Thumb & 1ST F.	○ 1	1	○	Give to L.H.	
5		▽ 3	1	○	To Chute	
6			1	○	PU One Case	A
7			1	⊖	To L H	
8	Grasp Case	○ 1	1	○	Give to L.H.	
9		Perform A 4 Times				
10	To Tip of Nozzle	○ 1	1	○	To Handle	
11	Position 1ST Case	○ 2	1	○	Grasp Handle	
12		▽ 3	4	○	Apply Pressure	
13	Position Next Case	○ 2	2	▽		B
14		▽ 3	3	○	Apply Pressure	
15		Perform B 4 Times				
16	To Rack	⊖ 2	1	○	Release Handle	
17	Place Cases in Rack	○ 6	7	▽		
18						
19						
20						
21		Summary				

		LH (Time)		RH (Time)		Both (Time)	
22		LH (Time)		RH (Time)		Both (Time)	
23	○	11	21	17	28	28	49
24	○	1	1	6	6	7	7
25	⊖	2	3	5	5	7	8
26	▽	17	27	0	0	17	27
27	▽	2	2	5	15	7	17
28		33	54 SEC.	33	54 SEC.	66	108
29		Per 5 Cases					
30							
31							
32							
33							

F1

Fig. 18. Right- and left-hand chart with time columns.

Work Area Definition. The definitions of the work areas within the workplace vary, depending upon the detail of the analysis required and the nature of the activities. In Fig. 19, Nadler (Motion and Time Study) illustrates an ordinary lip bin which has had a length of 3⅛-in. diameter steel rod welded to the lip. The part in the bin consists of two small metal pieces joined by a 5-in., 3-strand, ⅛-in. diameter wire. The two hands move to the bin, pick up a part, move out past the rods, position the part properly, move back to the rod, put the wire over the rod, pull down on each side of the rod to put a crimp in the wire, and

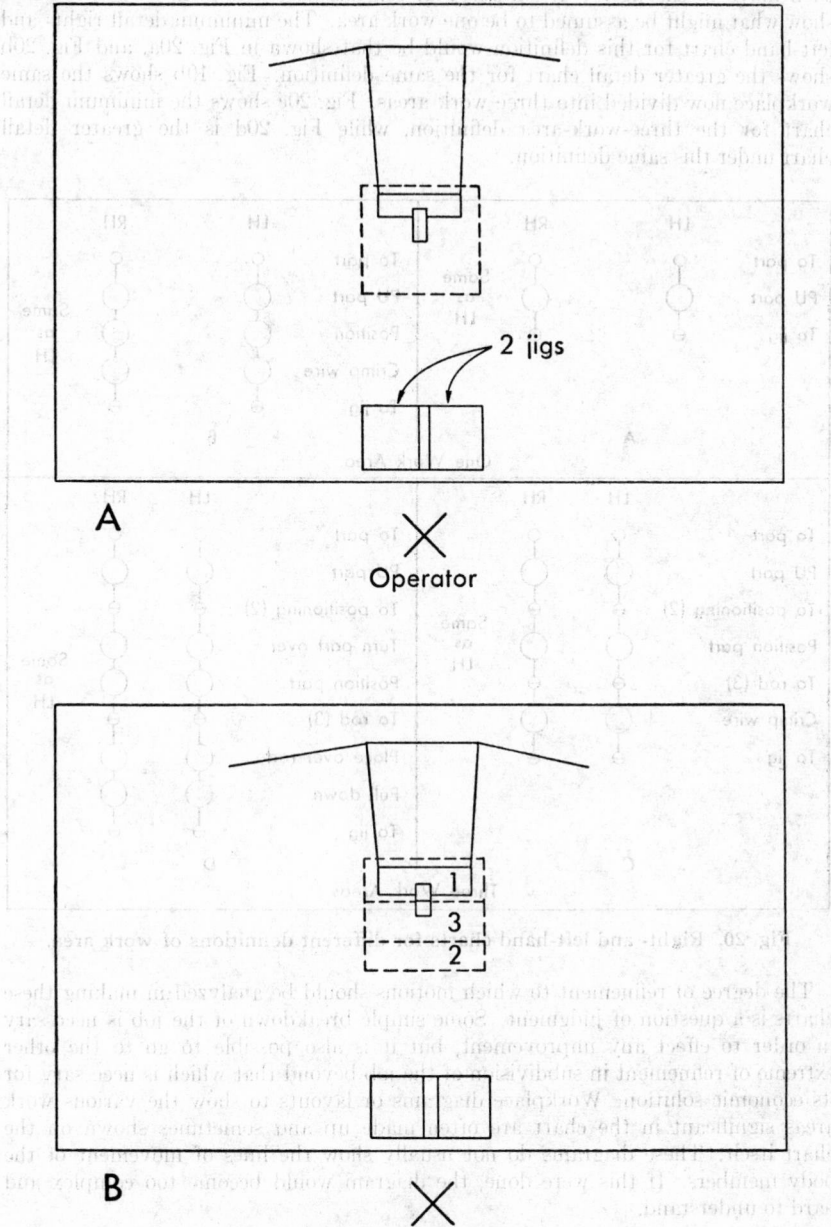

Fig. 19. Definitions of work area.

then move to the jig for assembly. Fig. 19a has dotted lines around the bin to show what might be assumed to be one work area. The minimum detail right- and left-hand chart for this definition would be that shown in Fig. 20a, and Fig. 20b shows the greater detail chart for the same definition. Fig. 19b shows the same workplace now divided into three work areas. Fig. 20c shows the minimum detail chart for the three-work-area definition, while Fig. 20d is the greater detail chart under this same definition.

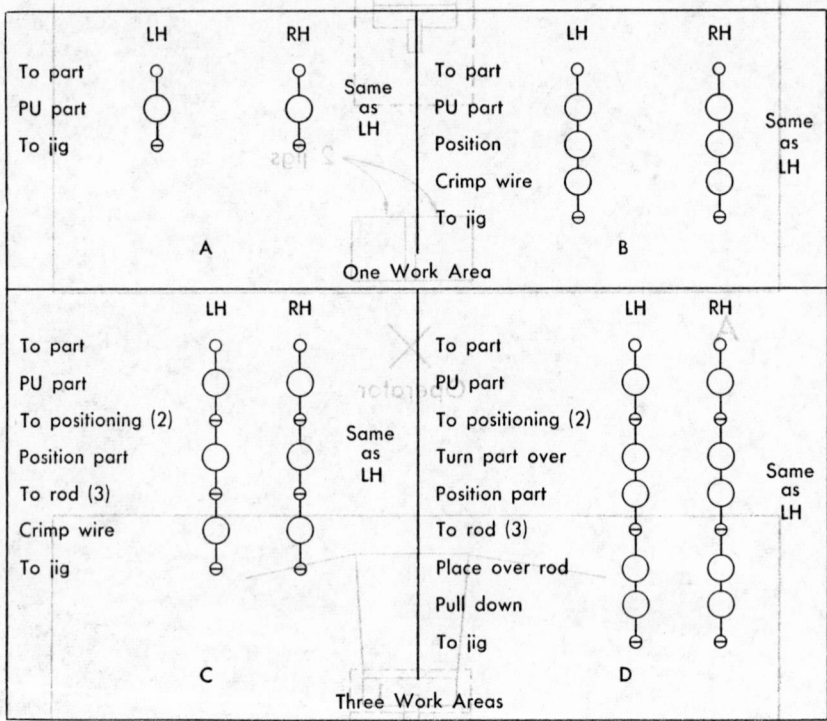

Fig. 20. Right- and left-hand charts for different definitions of work area.

The degree of refinement to which motions should be analyzed in making these charts is a question of judgment. Some simple breakdown of the job is necessary in order to effect any improvement, but it is also possible to go to the other extreme of refinement in subdivision of the job beyond that which is necessary for its economic solution. Workplace diagrams or layouts to show the various work areas significant in the chart are often made up and sometimes shown on the chart itself. These diagrams do not usually show the lines of movement of the body members. If this were done, the diagram would become too complex and hard to understand.

Analysis of the Charts. The act of making the chart helps the observer to acquire an intimate knowledge of the details of the job, and the chart serves as the means whereby he may study each element in the operation by itself and its relation to the other elements. From such a study the **ideas for improvements** are generated. These ideas should be written down in chart form as soon as they are conceived. A normal study may lead to several ideas embracing different ways of improving the job. All these proposals should be charted and then compared. The solution to the problem is usually found in that method which contains the **fewest motions.** As an aid in formulating ideas for improving the work, the questions about the elimination, combination, sequence, and simplification of operations detailed under the analysis of operation charts can be raised about any of the other types of charts, including right- and left-hand charts. A check list to assist in the analysis of operation or right- and left-hand charts is given in the section on Work Simplification.

Johnson (Factory Management and Maintenance, vol. 92) gives a series of points to be considered in making a thorough study of an operation, which are particularly applicable to the analysis of right- and left-hand charts:

1. Is the operation necessary? Could it be entirely or partially eliminated?
2. If more than one operator is working on the same job, are they all using the same method? Why not analyze all the different methods and make a "one best method" from the data?
3. Is the operator comfortable? Sitting down as much as possible? Does the stool or chair being used have a comfortable back? Is the lighting good but not glaring? Is the temperature of the work station all right? No drafts? Are there arm rests for the operator?
4. Can a fixture be used? Are the position and height of the fixture correct? Is the fixture the best one available? Would a fixture holding more than one piece be better than one holding a single piece? Can the same fixture be used for more than one operation? Always keep in mind that the human hand makes a very poor clamp vise, or fixture.
5. Are any semi-automatic tools applicable? For example, a power-driven wrench or screwdriver, or a Yankee socket wrench or screwdriver?
6. Is the operator using both hands all the time? If so, are the operations symmetrical? Wherever possible, both hands should be in motion and moving simultaneously in opposite directions. Could two pieces be handled at one time to better advantage than one? Could a foot device be arranged so that an operation now performed by hand could be done by foot?
7. Are the raw materials placed to the best advantage? Are there racks for pans of material and containers for smaller parts? Can the parts be removed from the containers with ease? Are the most frequently used parts placed in the most convenient location? Remember, the shorter the distance moved, the less the time will be.
8. Are the handling equipment and methods sufficient? Would a roller or belt conveyor improve conditions? Could the parts be placed aside by means of a chute? Drop delivery is desirable where possible.
9. Is the design of the apparatus the best from the viewpoint of the workman? Could the design be changed to facilitate machining or assembly without affecting the mechanical or electrical qualities of the apparatus?
10. Is the job on the proper machine? Are the correct feeds and speeds being used? Are the specified tolerances all right for the use to which the part is to be put? Is the material being used the best for the job? Could one operator run two or more machines?

MULTIPLE ACTIVITY CHARTS. The multiple activity chart is the symbolic and systematic presentation of the method of work performed by a man when his work is coordinated with one or more **cycle-time controlling devices,** such as another man, a machine, a process, or several machines. Because of the large number of activities where two or more men work coordinately, or where machines control part of or all the cycle time, these charts are often used. They help to gather information about such operations and present it properly, as well as help devise procedures for the proper utilization of manpower and equipment. A check list to assist in the analysis of multiple activity charts is given in the section on Work Simplification.

Types of Multiple Activity Charts. Any of the following types of multiple activity charts may be made:

1. Man and machine chart.
2. Man and multi-machine chart. One man is working with two or more time-controlling mechanisms.
3. Multi-man chart. Two or more men are working coordinately on the same work. It is not sufficient to have two or more men working in an area, a department, or side by side. The men must be involved in a given work activity, like moving 20-ft. lengths of steel pipe or carrying a prefabricated house section, and must be dependent on each other in performing each method.
4. Multi-man and machine chart.
5. Multi-man and multi-machine chart.

The analyst has to determine the characteristics of the work in relation to the number of men and machines, and then work up the appropriate chart.

Construction Procedures. The multiple activity charts are made up either with the flow process chart symbols or with the right- and left-hand chart symbols, which are illustrated in Figs. 2 and 17, respectively. The methods used in constructing the flow process and right- and left-hand charts are used also in making multiple activity charts. The man flow process chart breakdown is used when the individual or crew members move from one workplace to another, or when the goal is to rearrange the number or sequence of men or machines for lower product costs or increased production, without changing the actual method for each of the individual activities. The right- and left-hand chart breakdown is used when **methods improvement** is the goal, or when the man or men in the crew stay essentially at one workplace. In general, man and machine charts and man and multi-machine charts tend to be made with the right- and left-hand chart breakdown. All the multi-man charts tend to be made with the man flow process chart methods.

Motion pictures have been used more and more for gathering information about multiple activity operations. (See section on Motion and Methods Study.) This is especially true of work which has seldom been analyzed before, like jobs with large crews numbering 12 to 15 men. It would be virtually impossible to have an analyst watch all these men and make a meaningful chart. However, a motion picture of the same activities permits the analyst to review the same cycle over and over until he has obtained information about each person involved. This provides a well-interrelated chart. The motion picture **speeds** most frequently used for such purposes are 1 FPS or 100 FPM (memo-motion study).

Every multiple activity chart should be accompanied by a workplace diagram or a flow diagram, depending upon the work situation and activity being analyzed. A flow diagram will normally be more useful for a multiple activity flow process chart, and a workplace diagram for a multiple activity right- and left-hand chart.

Man–Machine Charts. Only two symbols are used for a machine in any type of multiple activity chart. These are the operation and the delay symbols. The **operation symbol** is used when the machine, equipment, or apparatus controls the time. It is not necessary for the machine to modify the product, but merely to be controlling the time. The **delay symbol** is used for the machine when it is not controlling the time. In some cases, the machine being used does not always control the time when it is doing work, but it may restrict the operator in some way. A drill press is a good illustration. The operator controls the speed at which the drill goes through the material, but the machine controls as well, and a combination of an operation and a delay symbol may be used for the machine. For the time chart, the column for the machine time would be divided in half vertically; one-half would be blacked in and the other half left blank.

In Fig. 21, Nadler (Motion and Time Study) illustrates a man-machine chart for the process of making a tensile test. The first page of the **time chart** version

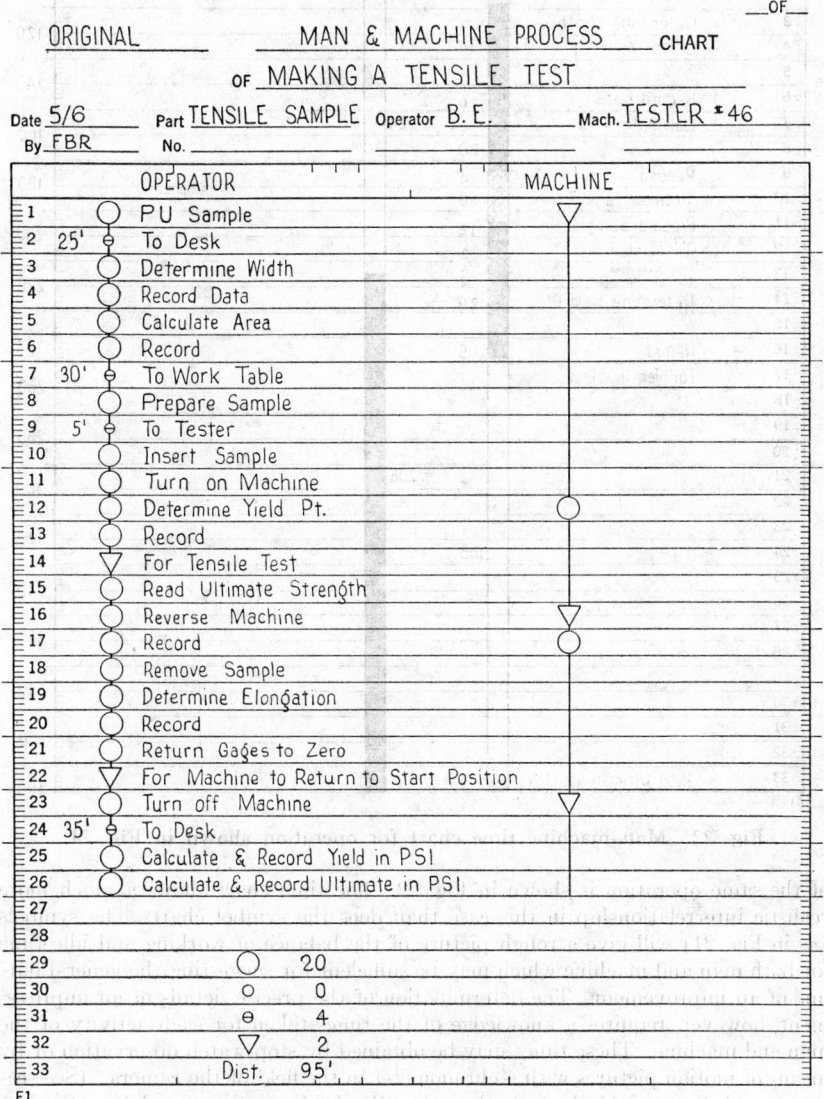

Fig. 21. Man–machine symbol chart for operation.

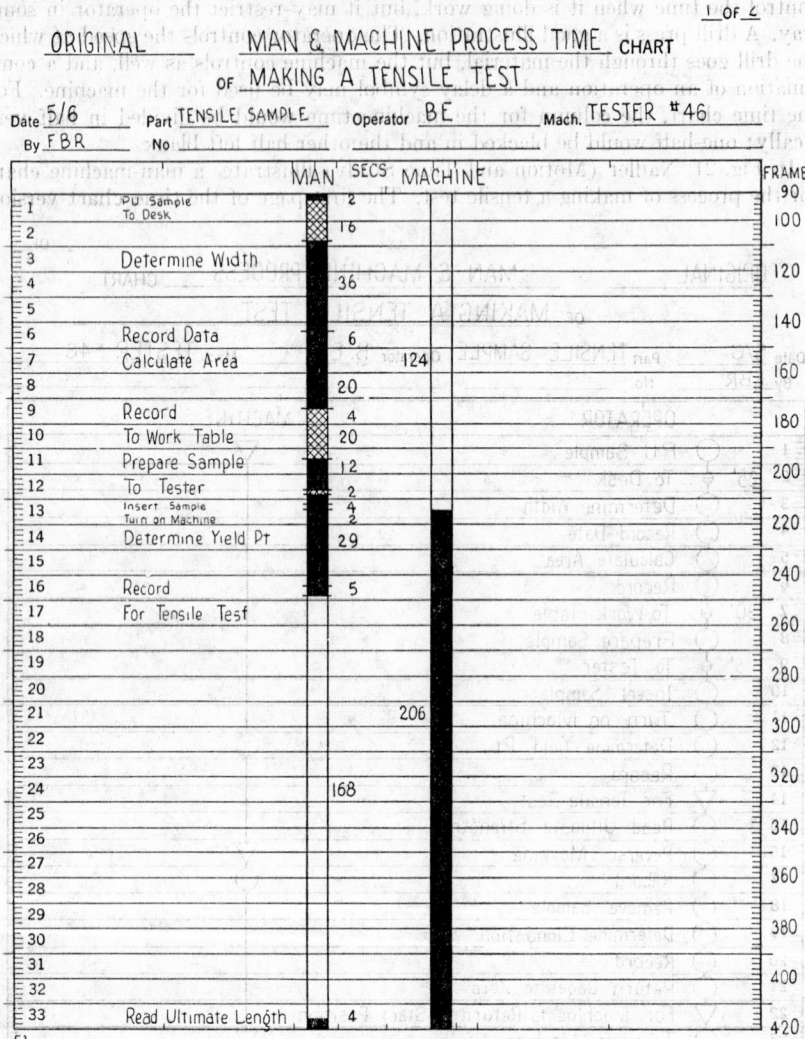

Fig. 22. Man–machine time chart for operation shown in Fig. 21.

of the same operation is shown in Fig. 22. The time chart shows a much more realistic interrelationship in this case than does the symbol chart. The symbols (as in Fig. 21) will give a rough picture of the balance of working and idle time for both man and machine which may be sufficient for suggesting the general outline of an improvement. The determination of the precise details of an improvement, however, requires a knowledge of the times taken for each activity of the man and machine. These times may be obtained by stop-watch observation or by means of motion pictures with a chronometer in the field of the camera. (See sections on Motion and Methods Study and on Work Measurement and Time Study.) The times for each activity of man and machine are charted on a **vertical time** scale (as in Fig. 22). By this means the beginning, ending, and duration of each activity are clearly set forth in the proper time relation with every other activity. By a study of these activities with their corresponding time intervals, it is possible to determine whether a more effective utilization of the operator's time or machine time can be achieved by a rearrangement of the work cycle.

Multi-Man Charts. This type of chart can be used most effectively in showing the work of a group of people with or without machines, when the work of each individual must be coordinated with that of the others with respect to time.

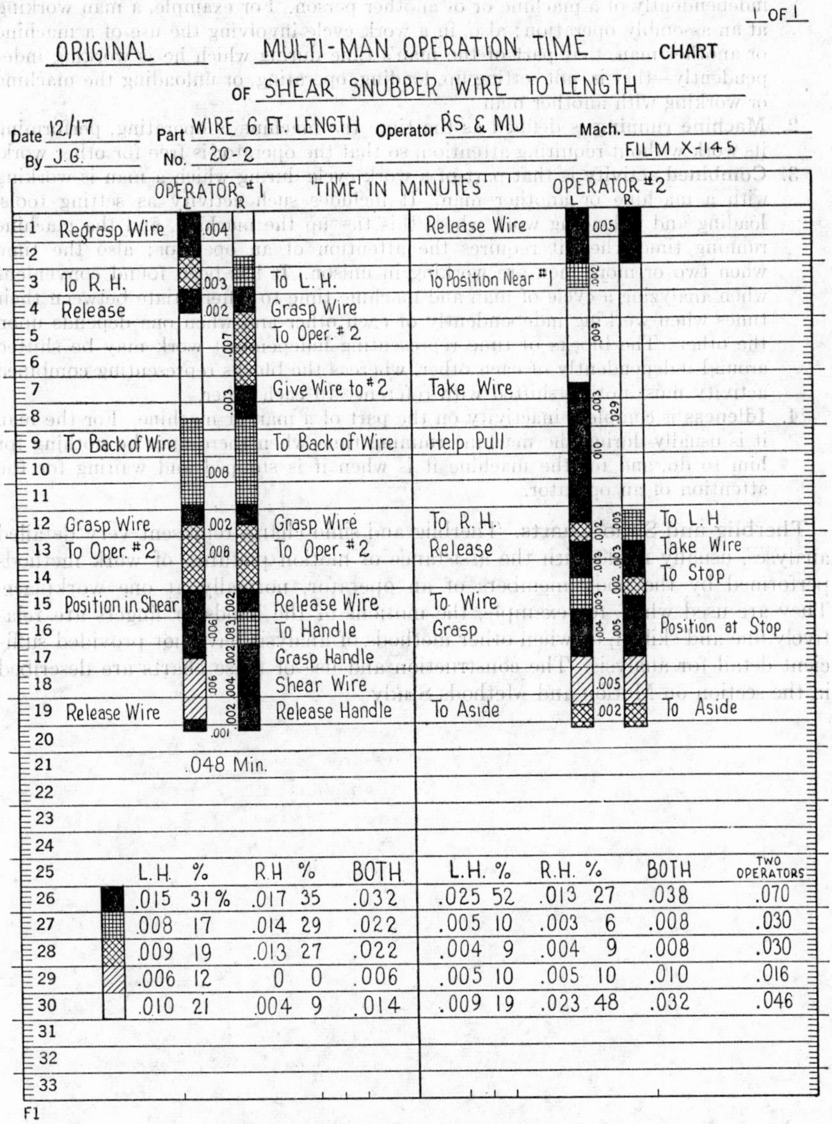

1 OF 1

ORIGINAL   MULTI-MAN OPERATION TIME   CHART

OF SHEAR SNUBBER WIRE TO LENGTH

Date 12/17   Part WIRE 6 FT. LENGTH   Operator RS & MU   Mach.

By J.G.   No. 20-2   FILM X-145

	OPERATOR #1 (L / R)		TIME IN MINUTES	OPERATOR #2 (L / R)
1	Regrasp Wire	.004	Release Wire	.005
3	To R.H.	.003	To L.H.	To Position Near #1 .002
4	Release	.002	Grasp Wire	
5		.007	To Oper. #2	.009
7		.003	Give Wire to #2	Take Wire .003 .029
9	To Back of Wire		To Back of Wire	Help Pull .010
10		.008		
12	Grasp Wire	.002	Grasp Wire	To R.H. — To L.H .002 .003
13	To Oper. #2	.008	To Oper. #2	Release — Take Wire .003 .030
14				To Stop .002
15	Position in Shear	.006 .003 .002	Release Wire	To Wire .001 .002
16		.008	To Handle	Grasp — Position at Stop .004 .004
17			Grasp Handle	
18		.006 .004	Shear Wire	.005
19	Release Wire	.002	Release Handle	To Aside — To Aside .002
20		.001		
21	.048 Min.			

	L.H.	%	R.H.	%	BOTH	L.H.	%	R.H.	%	BOTH	TWO OPERATORS
26	.015	31%	.017	35	.032	.025	52	.013	27	.038	.070
27	.008	17	.014	29	.022	.005	10	.003	6	.008	.030
28	.009	19	.013	27	.022	.004	9	.004	9	.008	.030
29	.006	12	0	0	.006	.005	10	.005	10	.010	.016
30	.010	21	.004	9	.014	.009	19	.023	48	.032	.046

F1

Fig. 23. Multi-man operation time chart.

It serves as a means of making a graphical record of an intricate set of relationships so that they can be more easily visualized and studied for improvement. Fig. 23 (Nadler, Motion and Time Study) is a multi-man time chart of the process of shearing snubber wire to length, using the time symbols given in Fig. 17.

The following definitions of the activities involved when a group of people are working with machines help to select the important and **distinguishable activities** so that they can be used in formulating such charts:

1. **Man working** is a person performing an operation or any part of an operation independently of a machine or of another person. For example, a man working at an assembly operation; also, in a work cycle involving the use of a machine or another man, that part of the man's time during which he is working independently—that is, not setting up, loading, operating, or unloading the machine or working with another man.

2. **Machine running** is defined as the time the machine is operating, performing its work without requiring attention, so that the operator is free for other work.

3. **Combined activity** is that part of a work cycle during which a man is working with a machine or another man. It includes such activity as setting tools, loading and unloading work where this ties up the machine, and the machine running time when it requires the attention of an operator; also the time when two or more men are working in unison. It has been found convenient when analyzing a cycle of man and machine time to differentiate between their times when working independently of each other and when one depends upon the other. The blocks of time representing independent work may be shifted around independently of each other, whereas the blocks representing combined activity must not be shifted with reference to each other.

4. **Idleness** is complete inactivity on the part of a man or machine. For the man it is usually during the machine running time when there may be nothing for him to do, and for the machine it is when it is stopped and waiting for the attention of an operator.

Therblig and Simo Charts. Therblig and simo charts represent very detailed analyses, usually made with the assistance of motion pictures, of work methods performed by the body members of an operator, normally at one workplace. They are used when, for example, the motions of the hands or fingers are relatively fine and skilled, or when other methods of analysis have not provided sufficient detail for analysis. The construction and use of these charts are described in the section on Motion and Methods Study.

WORK MEASUREMENT AND TIME STUDY

CONTENTS

PAGE

Bases of Operations Analysis

Operation analysis, over-all procedure 1
Detailed versus shorter methods 1
Definitions 2
Operation analysis 2
Work measurement 2
Time study 2
Work sampling 2
Standard time 2
Job standardization 3
Elements of an operation 3
Functions of work measurement 3
Analytical technique 3
Determination of a standard or task time 4
Determination of standard time data 4
Indispensable tool of management 4
Operation analysis and time study 4
Distinction between motion study and time study 5
Time study procedure 5
Derivation of standard time 5
Statistics in work measurement 6
Nature of variation and change 6
Population sampling 7
Applicability of a standard time 8
Accuracy 8
Human biases 8
Classification of elements 9
Length of study 9
Randomness 9
General statistical work measurement models 9
Relative frequency of activities 11
Value of statistical analysis of time data.. 12

Time Recording Equipment

Simple stop watch 12
Plain decimal stop watch (f. 1) 12
Split-hand stop watch 12
Split-hand stop watch (f. 2) 12
Decimal-hour stop watch 13
Calibration of watches 13
Marsto-Chron 13
Timing with motion pictures 13
Memomotion camera 13
Microchronometer 13
Wink counter 14
Stop watch, wink counter, and Marsto-Chron compared 18
Mechanical time recorder 18
Time study board 18
Time study board (f. 3) 14

PAGE

Time observation sheets 18
Time study observation sheet for repetitive operations (f. 4) 15
Time study observation sheet for non-repetitive operations (f. 5) 16-17

Stop Watch Time Study Procedure

Preliminary investigation 19
Standardization of methods and conditions.. 19
Standardization by motion pattern 19
Standardization by control chart 20
Selection of operator for study 20
Attitude of analyst 21
Preparation for study 21
Determination of time study elements 21
Recording times 22
Over-all timing 23
Snap-back timing 23
Method of recording snap-back time study (f. 6) 24
Continuous timing 23
Method of recording continuous time study (f. 7) 25
Connected two-watch timing 26
Length of study 26
Number of observations 26
Recommended number of cycles to be observed on the basis of cycle time (f. 8) 27
Recommended minimum number of cycles to be observed on the basis of cycle time (f. 9) 27
Company policy 27
Statistical determination 28
Control chart for cycle times 29
Tabulated data for use on a control chart (f. 10) 29
Control chart for sample means of net cycle times (f. 11) 30
Lack of statistical control 31
Sub-sample size and frequency of sampling 31
Use of the control chart 31
Control chart of variation 32
Formulation of standard time 32
Selected cycle time 32
Base cycle time 33
Standard time 33
Standard write-up of study 33
Specimen task report (f. 12) 34
Instruction card 35

Methods of Rating or Leveling

Need for rating 35
The rating problem 36

CONTENTS (*Continued*)

	PAGE
Concept of normal	36
Accuracy	36
Rating films	36
Localized rating	36
Consistency	37
Simplicity	37
Performance rating	38
Percentage basis	38
Point basis	38
Leveling plan	39
Synthetic leveling	39
Objective rating	40

Allowances

Types of allowances	40
Interruptions	40
Personal and delay allowances	41
Fatigue allowance	41
Other allowances	41
Determination of allowances	42
Interruption studies	42
Data obtained	42
Observation and analysis sheet for an interruption study (f. 13)	43
Summary sheet of an interruption study (f. 14)	44
Computation of allowances from interruption study	44

Work Sampling

Definition of method	45
Results of work sampling observations of three machines (f. 15)	45
Uses of work sampling	46
Procedure in work sampling	46
Defining the parent population	46
Activity classification	47
Length of study	47
Random observations	47
Use of random numbers	47
A table of random numbers (f. 16)	48
Use of random numbers for the selection of observation times (f. 17)	49
Observation procedures	50
Observation sheet for work sampling study (f. 18)	50
Independent studies	51
Number of observations	51
Table for determining the number of observations for a given degree of precision and value of p (f. 19)	52-53
Work sampling study	54
Work sampling study data on four kinds of jobs (f. 20)	54
Comparison of work sampling study data from Fig. 20 with production study data on the same jobs (f. 21)	54
Results of a work sampling study made on three machines (f. 22)	55
Control chart analysis	54
Control chart for percent machine idle time (f. 23)	55
Stratified sampling	56
Standard time from work sampling	56
Application of work sampling	57

Standard Time Data

Standard data method	58
Advantages of the method	59
Accuracy of standard data	59
Deriving standard data	60

	PAGE
Grouping like operations	60
Preliminary studies	60
Time study file	60
Comparison sheet	60
Time study comparison sheet used for compiling standard data (f. 24)	61
Presentation of data	62
Interpolation and extrapolation of base times	62
Curve for interpolating times on sheet copper work (f. 25)	62
Curve showing sudden break due to change in conditions (f. 26)	63
Setup standards	63
Comparative costs	63
Standard time data: parts handling	65
Allowed time for parts handling (f. 27)	64-65
Time allowance curves for handling parts where only finger, wrist, and arm movements are involved (f. 28)	66
Curves giving allowances for handling parts where finger, wrist, arm, and body are used (f. 29)	66
Time allowance curves for turning a part over in a vise and tightening and releasing vise (f. 30)	67

Standard Motion-Time Data

The method	68
Uses and advantages of motion-time standard data	69
Validity of motion-time standard data	69
Application errors	70
Motion-time analysis	70
Predetermined time values	71
Basic time chart using predetermined time value system (f. 31)	72
Standard data sheet for an operation (f. 32)	73
Work-factor plan	73
Work factors	74
Motions identified	74
Typical motions classified according to work-factor analysis (f. 33)	74
Production level	75
Methods-time measurement	75
Uses of methods-time measurement	75
Methods-time data tables and application	75
MTM data for reach, move, and turn and apply pressure (f. 34)	76
MTM conventions for recording motion classifications (f. 35)	77
Model MTM study showing computations and summary completed (f. 36)	78
Basic motion-time study	77
Analysis of basic motions	77
Motion-time determination	79
Tables of BMT data	80
Basic motion-time values (f. 37)	81

Complex Time Studies

Automatic machine operation	81
Man-machine chart for automatic machine cycle (f. 38)	82
Simplest automatic machine cycle	83
Operator waiting for machine	83
Man-machine chart with operator waiting for automatics to finish operations (f. 39)	84
Interference formulas	85
Interference in percentage of attention time, operator running six or fewer machines (f. 40)	86

CONTENTS (*Continued*)

PAGE

Diagram for determining the number of machines to assign to an operator (*f.* 41) 87

Work Assignment

Automatic presses 88
    Delay analysis (*f.* 42) 88
Binomial expansion used 88
Study procedure 89
    Machine assignment when restocking varies greatly (*f.* 43) 91
Automatic screw machines 91
    Factors *K* and *l'* for automatic screw-machine calculations (*f.* 44) 91
    Tool allowances, automatic screw machines (*f.* 45) 92
    Rod (bar stock) and tool adjustment allowances for automatic screw-machine work (*f.* 46) 93
    Procedure for setting a standard 92
Team or group work 94

Measurement of Indirect Labor Operations

Difficulties and reasons for measurement 94
Indirect labor measurement 95
    Janitorial work 95
    Graph of floor area versus time to mop floor (*f.* 47) 96
    Division of office area into subareas for two cases (*f.* 48) 96
    Maintenance operations 97
    Standard per one-way trip (travel chart) (*f.* 49) 98
    Standards for basic maintenance operations (*f.* 50) 99
    Credit for various working conditions (*f.* 51) 100

PAGE

Messenger jobs 101
    Calculation of zone standards on frequency-time chart (*f.* 52) 102

Fatigue in Factory Operations

Nature of fatigue 103
Muscular fatigue 104
    Laboratory experiments in muscular fatigue 104
    Industrial experiments in muscular fatigue 105
    Muscular fatigue and workplace design ... 105
    Results of experiments in muscular fatigue (*f.* 53) 106
Fatigue in sedentary work 107
    Output decrement in sedentary work 107
    Industrial experiments in sedentary work 107
Environmental conditions and fatigue 108
    Noise of work environment 108
    Sound intensity of various operations (*f.* 54) 109
    Reduction of noise 109
    Design changes 110
    Damping 110
    Screening 110
    Absorption 110
    Filtration 110
    Isolation by suspension 110
    Illumination of workplace 110
    Influence of level of illumination (*f.* 55) 111
    Job accidents hazards 111
    Air conditions of work environment 112
Rest periods 112
    Effect of rest periods on production 113
Monotony and boredom of the job 113
    Boredom and repetitive work 113
    Variations in average times in handkerchief folding under continuous and rest-pause conditions (*f.* 56) 114
Emotional factors in fatigue 115
Social factors in worker morale 115

CONTENTS (Continued)

Sleep, need for 191
Calculation of zone standard on the
piece-time chart ($\frac{1}{2}$) 199

Fatigue in Factory Operations

Analysis of fatigue 200
Muscular fatigue 210
Laboratory experiments in muscular fatigue 201
Industrial experiments in muscular fatigue 202
Mental fatigue and work-place design 202
Results of experiments in muscular
fatigue ($\frac{1}{2}$) 203
Factors in monotony work 206
Fatigue movement studies .... soft 207
Industrial application in monotony work 207
Experimental and physiological fatigue 208
Value of rest periods 214
Industrial application of fatigue operations 218

Nutrition in fatigue 210
Sleep, need for 213
Boredom 210
Sickness 216
Absenteeism 217
Vacations 217

Reduction by rest periods 218
Experiments in monotony 219
Influence of rest on monotony work ($\frac{1}{2}$) 211
Job, mental fatigue 221
Classification of work in monotony ($\frac{1}{2}$) 212
Rest periods, value of 222
Effect of rest periods on production 223
Monotony at home job, influence of fatigue 224
Workplace and application, rest 224
Variation in average time in monotony ....
Rest, fatigue, and machine jobs and
measurement studies ($\frac{1}{2}$) 211
Functional fatigue, life, fatigue 211
Rest and fatigue in factory operations 212

Bases for determining the number of
machine to operate in a sample
($\frac{1}{2}$) 69

Work Assignment

Allocation phase ($\frac{1}{2}$) 85
Time studies ($\frac{1}{2}$) 86
Material required, work 88
Machine assignment when machine
vary, family ($\frac{1}{2}$) 91
Machine, time variations ....
Factors R and P for monotonic opera-
machine calculations (A-11) 91
Tool allowance allocation given the
machine (A-12) ....
Raw materials and tool allotment ($\frac{1}{2}$) ....
Factors for allocation given machine ....
Family, loss of life standard ....
Table of study, width ....

Measurement of Indirect Labor Operations

Principles and reason for measurement 93
Indirect labor measurement ($\frac{1}{2}$) 93
Indirect work 890
Group action as average time, job and
time, or other measurement operations
per day (A-15) ....
Standard freeing part on study chart ....
(A-16) ....
Standard for labor measurement operation,
formula ($\frac{1}{2}$) ....
Credit for fatigue and rest operations ....
(A-17) ....

WORK MEASUREMENT AND TIME STUDY

Bases of Operations Analysis

OPERATION ANALYSIS, OVER-ALL PROCEDURE. Orthodox work measurement, and more specifically stop-watch time study, has often been considered as an integral part of the broader concept of operation analysis. The over-all procedure of operation analysis, including the design or improvement of an operation, work measurement, and job standardization, is divided into the following steps:

1. **Preliminary analysis.** Analysis and recording of existing conditions or proposed specifications as to the process, equipment, materials, materials handling, workplace layout, methods, volume of required output, and costs, as well as of limitations in the availability of resources such as capital, space, and labor.
2. **Description of operation.** Breaking the operation down into arbitrarily defined functional or motion elements and a systematic charting of these elements to describe the existing or proposed method.
3. **Detailed analysis.** Critical study of the elements of the operation to determine which ones may be eliminated or improved. This step includes the analysis of methods, tools, equipment, materials, and workplace layout, as well as of the motion pattern used by the operator.
4. **Work measurement.** Analysis of the time consumed by productive and nonproductive elements of the existing or proposed operation.
5. **Synthesis.** Integration of improved elements into alternative operation designs.
6. **Evaluation.** Selection of the best alternative in terms of such specific criteria as unit time, cost, and space required.
7. **Job standardization.** Standardization of methods, job conditions, and unit production times by reducing them to some form of written standard practice. Preparation of detailed instructions covering tools necessary, and explanation of the elements of the method in detail and in proper sequence, with the time allowed for each element.
8. **Installation.** Planning and executing the introduction and installation of new methods, including the training of the operator to perform the task in the manner and time specified.
9. **Control.** Maintenance of standardized working conditions, equipment, methods, material quality and supply, and standard times during the life of the operation prior to a formal redesign of the method. Included in control are the means of detecting deviations between standard and actual performance.

DETAILED VERSUS SHORTER METHODS. This section presents the underlying theory and statistical aspects of work measurement. In established industrial engineering departments, however, numerous short cuts and special techniques are developed when the degree of precision and accuracy required warrant the use of shorter or **approximate methods**. It must be remembered, however, that such methods depend on the established experience and data of particular companies and should be used only by time study men who fully understand the qualifications and limitations.

DEFINITIONS. The basic procedures and concepts are defined and described briefly in the following paragraphs.

Operation Analysis. This term encompasses all those procedures concerned with the original design or improvement of production or service operations and may be described as **methods study, time and motion study, work simplification,** or **job study.** Studies of an entire process may be made to determine whether operations or elements of them can be **eliminated, combined, changed in sequence,** or **improved.** An analysis is made of the method, motion pattern, materials, and tools and equipment used in an individual operation to determine the "one best way." Work measurement is an integral part of operation analysis as a method of quantitative analysis.

Work Measurement. The procedure involved in measuring or forecasting the rate of output of an existing or newly designed operation, as well as in determining how much time is consumed for various productive and nonproductive activities of a process, operation, or job, is known as work measurement. Also involved is the determination of **standard times** which represent the allowable time for the performance of work. The term work measurement is used generically and pertains to all techniques of time measurement of work systems.

Time Study. A procedure used to determine a standard time for an operation by direct time measurement and a technique employing the **stop watch** as the measuring device, the concept of time study is often expanded to include the improvement of an operation resulting from the time measurement.

Work Sampling. The taking of random qualitative observations of a specific work system to determine the percentage of a protracted time period consumed by various activities of the system is known as work sampling.

Standard Time. The results of the application of a formal time study or work sampling may be a standard time which represents "that gross time required by a normal operator, working under normal conditions, and with normal skill and pace to complete a unit of work of satisfactory quality." This subjective criterion of normal or standard performance leaves considerable range for interpretation.

Other terms used to express the idea of standard are "a fair task," or "a fair day's work." Work measurement is more than measurement of time. This has been true since its inception by Taylor, who said (Trans. ASME, vol. 34): "Mere statistics as to time which a man takes to do a given piece of work do not constitute a time study. Time study involves careful study of the time in which work ought to be done."

The determination of what a worker "ought" to produce in a day is a problem potentially fraught with difficulties. Both **operator method** and **pace** are involved. As a formal procedure, time study may contribute to the development of a "best" method, and this may be done with a certain amount of engineering objectivity. But standard pace, or how fast a worker should produce, is a matter of judgment, at least with present knowledge of human capacities. An objective procedure for determining an **optimal worker pace** in terms of physiological and psychological criteria may be developed as our knowledge through research improves.

Proper time study usually locates the task at a level which is not detrimental to the worker's health. Rates of production or tasks resulting from inadequate time studies are sometimes so high as to meet, at first, with incredulity and opposition from operators. It is desirable to all concerned that tasks be measured according to standards which are fair. Management must be prepared to train the operator in the best method, to guarantee his wages during a reasonable period of training, and to guarantee standard conditions of work upon which the study was based.

Job Standardization. Recording the exact method on an **instruction card** together with the **normal time** for each element of the operation constitutes job standardization. Standard job conditions, material specifications, tools, and work-place layout should be carefully recorded.

Once established. time standards should not be changed so long as the method or conditions remain unchanged. When new tools, fixtures, or machines are designed for a standardized job and the standard conditions controlling the job have been changed, the original standard time can no longer apply. A new time standard must then be established.

Elements of an Operation. An operation may be described by functional elements or motion elements. **Functional elements** are arbitrary descriptive subdivisions of a work cycle readily identified and defined. In a given sequence these elements designate what is done to alter material properties or to provide a service by means of a combination of manual movements and mechanical actions. Examples are: pick up part, place part in jig, close jig, drill ⅜-in. hole to ½-in. depth, and open jig. These elements are also referred to as **time study elements** because they are capable of being timed with a stop watch. A time study element which is manually controlled will consist of groups of motion elements.

Motion elements are subdivisions of a motion pattern employed by the operator to complete a unit of output. The 17 fundamental hand motions described by Gilbreth and called **therbligs** are qualitative descriptive elements of human motion (see section on Motion and Methods Study). Because of their short duration, the motion elements in a particular operation can be timed only through the use of motion pictures or special timing devices. There are a number of **predetermined motion-time systems** used today in which normal times are developed for various basic motions. In such systems the variables affecting each motion-time are taken into consideration. Some of these systems are described later.

FUNCTIONS OF WORK MEASUREMENT. Work measurement. an important technique for management to use, includes the major functions described in the following paragraphs.

Analytical Technique. One function of work measurement is to determine where and how time is employed in a present work method or proposed operation. Through the use of the stop watch or other measuring and estimating devices, the time for various elements of the productive cycle of an operation may be measured. Analysis of the results can indicate sources of delays as well as areas where time may be reduced.

Micromotion study constitutes the analysis and improvement of an operation by employing a motion film and special timing devices. Refined qualitative and quantitative information concerning the motion pattern is provided.

Work sampling techniques applied over a protracted period of time for an existing work system will indicate how time is apportioned between productive and nonproductive activities. **Nonproductive activities** include materials handling, setup or tear-down, waiting for material, filling out paper forms, and various other avoidable and unavoidable job interruptions and delays. Analysis will indicate areas of inefficiency in the entire process or operation.

Besides the actual time measurement, the formal time study or work measurement procedure, requiring the breakdown of the operation into elements and the detailed analysis thereof, may be a predominant factor in the development of improved methods.

Determination of a Standard or Task Time. When an operation has been improved and standardized as to method, the primary function of work measurement may be to establish a standard time. This standard reflects the time required for a unit of output. Depending on the level to which it is set, the standard time can become the basis for:

1. Individual or group wage incentives.
2. Evaluating the effectiveness of the actual performance of an individual or group.
3. Scheduling work to an operation or process.
4. Determining the number of operators required for a specific volume of output.
5. Programming work to production or service processes and operations.
6. Estimating cost of jobs performed at the operation.
7. Compiling standard labor and overhead costs and budgets.

It should be noted that the interpretation of standard time will vary according to the ultimate use of the standard. A standard time for incentive purposes might not be the time used for scheduling work or making a cost estimate. That is, the time that management considers representative of **standard performance** may not represent the **expected time in actual practice.** For instance, the "standard time" for incentive plans may have such a relationship with expected performance that the average operator will be expected to earn a bonus (see section on Wage Plans and Controls).

Determination of Standard Time Data. The third major function of direct work measurement is to provide initial data which may be expanded into a system of standard time data. Such standard data constitute an inventory of elemental times which may be synthesized to provide a standard for a job, making direct timing methods unnecessary. Standard data may be expressed in terms of functional or motion elements. During the stages of designing a process or operation, standard data are usually the only practical basis for evaluating **alternative designs** in terms of time, as well as for estimating a standard time for the selected design prior to installation.

Indispensable Tool of Management. Regardless of the method, work measurement is an indispensable technique of management. Methods of work measurement may vary from a crude estimate by an experienced foreman to micromotion and time analysis by an industrial engineer. The decision regarding the technique to be used is primarily an economic one, in which the costs of the measurement procedure must be weighed against the ultimate advantages accruing from the time study. But some sort of time measurement is required in the various facets of the design, planning, improvement, and control of production.

OPERATION ANALYSIS AND TIME STUDY. The contemporary practice of operation analysis (methods study, work simplification, or motion and time study) is the result of the integration of concepts and practices developed by two pioneers in scientific management, namely, Taylor and Gilbreth. Taylor stressed the procedure of time study, and Gilbreth developed motion study as the core of his work. Both time study and motion study were concerned with the systematic analysis and improvement of manually controlled work situations. Both men employed the stop watch and motion analysis as components of their studies.

Distinction Between Motion Study and Time Study. Although in practice the techniques of motion study and time study may be carried on as an integrated activity, they are distinct in concept. Motion and micromotion study are techniques of **methods analysis,** and time study is a technique of **work measurement.** Motion study is usually a qualitative analysis of a work situation leading to the design or improvement of an operation. Work measurement is concerned with those techniques and procedures involved in time measurement, regardless of the ultimate use of the data. Work measurement may specifically contribute to the quantitative improvement of methods, but it is not a substitute for motion or methods study.

In practice, the dichotomy of motion and time study may be difficult to observe. A by-product of formal time study may be the evaluation and improvement of the operation. Similarly, through the use of motion films and motion-time standards, work measurement may be an important by-product of a formal and intensive motion study.

Time Study Procedure. The major steps included in a formal time study are as follows:

1. The objective of the study is clearly defined. This includes a definition of the use of the results, the precision required, and the desired confidence in the estimation of the time parameters.
2. The purpose of the study and necessary preparations are reviewed with the supervisor of the operating department.
3. A preliminary analysis is made of the operation to determine whether standard methods and conditions prevail and whether the operator is properly trained. If necessary a request may be made for a formal methods study and further operator training.
4. Where there is more than one operator, the operator to be studied is chosen.
5. The selected operator is oriented as to the purposes and, if necessary, the method of the study.
6. A detailed record is made of the standard method and conditions, either in writing or by motion picture.
7. The operation is divided into time study elements.
8. A number of time study observations are taken. This provides the basis for estimating certain statistical parameters which are used to determine the total number of observations to be taken. Also, the length of the study period may be specified.
9. The actual measurement is made with the requisite number of observations over the specified time period.
10. The operator is rated during the study by comparison to the performance level of the normal operator.
11. Allowances for various job interruptions and delays are determined by policy or by independent measurement.
12. The standard time is derived from the observed times, the rating factor, and allowances.

Derivation of Standard Time. The procedure involved in formulating a standard time from the study data is as follows:

1. If the **continuous timing method** is used, consecutive observed elemental times are subtracted in order to obtain the actual elemental elapsed time values.

2. Abnormal elemental time values are circled and discarded from the study if the conditions contributing to the values are avoidable by the operator or correctible by management.
3. The average elemental times are calculated.
4. The average elemental times are added and the average or **mean net cycle time** obtained.
5. The rating factor is applied to adjust the observed or selected cycle time to a normal or **base cycle time.** The rating factor may be applied to individual average element times to obtain a **base element time.**
6. Allowances for nonproductive delays and job interruptions are added to the base cycle time to obtain a standard time. In certain cases allowances may be added to individual base element times.
7. The basic standard time formula is derived from five factors. These are expressed as:

$$\bar{X}_j = \text{average or mean net cycle time}$$
$$R = \text{rating factor in percent of normal}$$
$$A = \text{allowances expressed as a fraction of } B, \text{ base time}$$
$$B = \text{base cycle time} = R\bar{X}_j$$
$$S = \text{standard time} = B(1 + A)$$

STATISTICS IN WORK MEASUREMENT. Work measurement is concerned with measuring certain time properties of a dynamic system. The system, such as an operation and its environment, is **dynamic,** in that variation and change occur in one or more of the operational factors over a period of time. This variation or change presents a measurement problem as well as a problem of operation control. The observer must not only reckon with variation at the time of measurement but must consider it in setting standard times which are used to make forecasts of future performance. If the analysis of variation and change and their causes is inadequate, there may be a critical discrepancy between the estimated or **predicted performance** and the subsequent actual results. This discrepancy should not be confused with an expected difference between **standard performance** and **actual performance.** The latter difference may be predicted by the level to which the standard is set.

Nature of Variation and Change. The dynamic nature of the operation is reflected in **variation** in the time taken for successive units of output of a repetitive operation or in the relative time consumed in successive irregular productive or nonproductive job activities. It is also reflected in **changes** in certain average time parameters over a protracted time period. These parameters might be, for example, the **average cycle time** for a repetitive operation, the **average percent time** consumed in handling materials on a job, or the **average amount of variation** in the time for successively produced units.

Gomberg (A Trade Union Analysis of Time Study) devotes considerable attention of the dynamic properties of the phenomena which time study attempts to measure. He poses the question of whether time study deals in an area of complete random variation, an area of statistical laws, or an area of exact physical laws. That is, are industrial time studies taken within a **variable chance cause system,** a **constant chance cause system,** or a **constant cause system?** (See section on Statistical Methods.) Since variation or change in an operation may be attributed to a complex of mechanical, physiological, psychological, and sociological factors, it is suggested that work measurement deals primarily in the areas of variable and constant chance cause systems.

Population Sampling. Work measurement is essentially a sampling procedure. A relatively small number of observations are taken, at random or otherwise, from a **parent population** or **universe** whose time parameters are to be inferred. Sampling may be avoided by observing the entire population, but this is usually uneconomical and unnecessary.

The parent population consists of all possible time units from which sample observations or measurements may be selected. The sample is **randomly selected** if all possible time units in the population have an equal likelihood of being selected for inclusion in the sample. For a repetitive operation the parent population may be defined as the cycle times for all units produced in a given day, for example. From this population a sample of N observations or cycle time measurements may be taken.

The only valid inference that can be made from the sample is to the parent population. It is customary, however, to assume that future performance will have the same characteristics as the parent population. Thus, the inference is in practice extended to future performance as well.

The population time parameters of usual interest are a measure of **central tendency,** such as arithmetic mean or average, and a measure of **dispersion** or variation, such as range or standard deviation. Both parameters refer to whatever time dimension is being measured, such as net cycle time for a unit of output, time required for a given motion, or percent time consumed in setting up a machine.

If the population is a constant chance cause system, the time dimensions for successive units of output or activity will have a constant pattern of dispersion as well as a stable average. Also, the successive unit times will be randomly dispersed around the central tendency. The population is then **statistically stable** or homogeneous. If the population is a variable chance cause system, there will be a lack of stability in the pattern of dispersion or in the average or both. Thus, a statistically stable operation is one in which the known causes for time variation are controlled so that the variation which does exist is due essentially to constant chance causes. **Change** is reflected in shifts in the value of the population parameters, either in the measure of central tendency or in the measure of dispersion.

The fundamental **values of statistical analysis** in work measurement are:

1. It can indicate with a stated degree of confidence whether or not the operation is **statistically stable** and under control with respect to the dimension being measured.
2. If reasonable statistical control exists, the **reliability** of the estimates of population parameters, made from the sample, may be stated to a specified degree of confidence.

Work measurement involves three basic **sampling procedure problems:**

1. The sample estimates of particular time parameters may be used to predict future performance. The **applicability** of the sample estimate to future situations depends on the similarity between the parent population from which the sample was extracted and the extended population over the protracted period of time for which the forecast is made.
2. The estimate should be **accurate** in that it is an unbiased representation of the true value of the parent population. **Accuracy** is a measure of the degree by which the estimated average value of a set of measurements differs from the true value of the quantity being measured. An inaccurate estimate results from sources of bias built into the measuring or sampling procedure.

3. The estimate should conform to a required **precision. Precision** is a measure of the reproducibility of the measured value of the quantity in question. A precise estimate would be reflected in a high degree of similarity between the estimates derived from successive samples. Thus, a sample estimate may be precise but lacking in accuracy.

Applicability of a Standard Time. The predictive value of a time measurement depends on the similarity between the parent population and the extended population for which the prediction is made. The causes for variation must remain essentially constant over the protracted time period. This is basically a problem of standardization and control of job factors both during the study and in the subsequent performance of the job.

When it is apparent, during the life of the operation, that unusual causes for variation have arisen, they must be corrected to bring the operation back into control, or a new time study must be made to account for them in the standard time.

Accuracy. One of the sources of inaccuracy is bias in the time study procedure. A result may be inaccurate due to such biases as:

1. Error in reading the stop watch.
2. Error in interpreting the elements being measured.
3. Influences injected in the method and pace by the operator.
4. Variations from standard in materials, methods, and conditions during the study.
5. Failure to include nonrepetitive or cyclical sources of variation by limiting the length of the study.

Like applicability, accuracy depends on the degree of standardization and control exerted during the study. Taylor recognized this in his early studies and therefore stressed the necessity of standardizing and controlling **job variables** during the actual time study. Much of the early unpopularity of time study, from labor's point of view, can be traced to the failure of practitioners to give sufficient attention to this matter.

The fundamental task of methods and job standardization is to remove and stabilize the causes of variation to the extent that the remaining variability is due to constant chance causes. That is, the **accepted variability** in the time data is essentially random within some specified and predictable limits.

During the formal time study the observer is required to use his judgment as to when standard methods, motions, and conditions prevail, even though the standards may be specified carefully in writing. This is manifested in his refusal to time a job if the specifications are not followed or in his deleting from the study individual readings which represent nonstandard situations.

Human Biases. Work measurement deals with the measurement of a phenomenon which in itself is sensitive to the measuring procedure. In manually controlled operations variation and change can be intentionally initiated and controlled by the operator. The observer can also introduce bias, particularly in the rating procedure.

Hoxie (Scientific Management and Labor) early pointed out the number of factors which could be altered by human will and therefore **contribute bias** in the results of the study:

Such analysis shows that among the factors that may . . . vary, subject to human will are: (1) The general attitude, ideals, and purposes of the management and the consequent general instructions given to the time study man; (2) the character, intelligence, training and ideals of the time study man; (3) the degree to which the job to be timed and all its appurtenances have been studied and standardized looking to uniform conditions in its performance for all the workers; (4) the amount of change thus made from old methods and conditions of performance, e.g., the order of performance, the motions eliminated, and the degree of habituation of the workers to the old and the new situation when the task is set; (5) the mode of selection of the workers to be timed and their speed and skill relative to the other members of the group; (6) the relative number of workers timed and the number of readings considered sufficient to secure the result desired; (7) the atmospheric conditions, time of day, time of year, the mental and physical condition of the workers when timed and the judgment exercised in reducing these matters to the "normal"; (8) the character and amount of special instruction and special training given the selected workers before timing them; (9) the instructions given to them by the time study man as to care and speed, etc., to be maintained during the timing process; (10) the attitude of the time study man toward the workers being timed and the secret motives and aims of the workers themselves; (11) the judgment of the time study man as to the pace maintained under timing relative to the "proper," "normal," or maximum speed which should be demanded; (12) the checks on the actual results used by the time study man in this connection; (13) the method and mechanism used for observing and recording times and the degree of accuracy with which actual results are caught and put down; (14) the judgment exercised by the time study man in respect to the retention or elimination of possibly inaccurate or "abnormally" high or low readings; (15) the method used in summing up the elementary readings to get the "necessary" elementary time; (16) the method employed in determining how much should be added to the "necessary time" as a human allowance; and (17) the method of determining the "machine allowance."

Classification of Elements. If the job is to be timed by elements, the observer must select elements which are clearly defined both as to their content and end points. Otherwise bias may result in improper classification of movements as well as in timing their content.

Length of Study. The results may be biased by excluding from the study times which reflect irregular elements or cyclical influences. Whereas some factors contributing to variability in the data may operate repetitively with each unit of output, others may operate irregularly with a certain number of units produced, or cyclically over a time period such as an hour or day or perhaps longer. The length of the study must be long enough to include these **nonrepetitive factors.**

Randomness. Observations making up a sample should be taken randomly over the predetermined length of the study. This is to avoid a systematic exclusion or inclusion of irregular or cyclical influences. That is, it is conceivable that if observations were taken at the same time of day for several days, they would be consistently in phase or out of phase with cyclical influences. Traditionally, the usual procedure of sampling has been to take a **group of observations** made up of readings of a successively produced number of units from the operation. The period of the study is thereby small. A better procedure is to take small groups or **sub-samples** of readings on successive units of output **randomly** over a longer period of time. The total number of observations would then be equal to the sum of readings taken in all sub-samples.

General Statistical Work Measurement Models. In the determination of standard time for a **repetitive operation** the first problem of actual measurement is the estimation of the **average net cycle time.** This time represents the productive time necessary to complete one cycle of output. The terms **selected or observed cycle time** are often used.

A simple statistical model employed to estimate the parameters of net cycle time is as follows:

Let the time study elements be numbered $1, 2, \ldots, i, \ldots M$. Example: pick up piece and place in jig, close jig, etc.

C_j = the jth observed cycle of output of a successive number of units produced. $j = 1, 2, \ldots N$

x_{ij} = the observed time of the ith element in the jth cycle of output

$\bar{x}_i$ = estimate of average time for the ith element

$$\bar{x}_i = \frac{\sum_{j=1}^{N} x_{ij}}{N}$$

X_j = the jth cycle time

$$X_j = \sum_{i=1}^{M} x_{ij}$$

$\bar{X}_j$ = estimate of average net cycle time for the operation

Where N is a number of units the time study takes the form of a cycle as shown below.

E L E M E N T	i	j	1	2	.	.	.	N	
	1		x_{11}	x_{12}				x_{1N}	$\bar{x}_1$
	2		x_{21}	x_{22}				x_{2N}	$\bar{x}_2$
	.		.	.				.	.
	.		.	.				.	.
	M		x_{M1}	x_{M2}	.			x_{MN}	$\bar{x}_M$
			X_1	X_2	X_j	.		X_N	$\bar{X}_j$

The **standard deviation** of the population of net cycle times is estimated as follows, using the cycle times:

σ_{x_j} = estimate of the standard deviation of the population of net cycle times

$$= \sqrt{\frac{\sum_{j=1}^{N} (X_j - \bar{X}_j)^2}{N-1}}$$

It should be pointed out again that the parameters $\bar{X}_j$ and σ_{x_j} refer to the **measured** or **observed cycle times** and not to base or standard times.

In the above model each cycle time (X_j) represents an observation from units of output. There are disadvantages in confining the length of the observation period to that which is included by N consecutive readings. The observation period will probably be too short unless N is extremely large, and the estimation of the population standard deviation may have little meaning because of a lack of independence between successive observations.

For those who customarily deal in sub-samples, it is possible to take **random sub-samples** of observations over a longer period of time, such as a day or two.

Each sub-sample will consist of a small number of consecutive observations. In this case the following notations apply:

Let

C_{jk} = the jth observed cycle of output in the kth sub-sample.

$$j = 1, 2, \ldots n; \; k = 1, 2, \ldots K$$

$$N = \sum_{k=1}^{K} n$$

$$K = N/n$$

$\overline{X}_{jk}$ = the average cycle time for the kth sub-sample.

The average sub-sample cycle time may be determined from elemental readings of n successive units of output:

$\overline{\overline{X}}_j$ = estimate of average net cycle time for the operation

$$= \frac{\sum_{k=1}^{K} \overline{X}_{jk}}{K}$$

$$\sigma_{xj} = \sqrt{\frac{\sum_{j=1}^{N} (X_j - \overline{\overline{X}}_j)^2}{N-1}}$$

Relative Frequency of Activities. In contrast to the sampling of a **continuous variable**, such as net cycle time measurements, the purpose of the study may be to determine percentage of operator time spent on various job activities. In this case, the **work sampling procedure** is used, dealing with a sampling statistic which is discrete.

The simple statistical model employed in work sampling is as follows:

Let the job activities carried out by the operator in time period t be numbered 1, 2, ..., i, ... M. Example: produce at the machine, handle material, get instructions, etc.

N = the total number of random observations.

r_i = number of observations recorded of the operator found in the state of the ith activity

p_i = actual percentage of time period t consumed in the ith activity

$\bar{p}_i$ = sample estimate of $p_i = r_i/N$

The error in the estimator $\bar{p}$ is a **sampling error.** If the population is large and observations are taken randomly, the probability distribution of $\bar{p}_i$ from a sample of size N is represented by the binomial distribution:

$$\text{Probability } (r_i/N) = \frac{N!}{r_i!(N-r_i)!} (p_i)^{r_i}(1 - p_i)^{N-r_i}$$

$$\sum_{r=0}^{N} \text{Prob}(r_i/N) = 1$$

The standard deviation of the binomial is:

$$\sigma_{p_i} = \sqrt{\frac{p_i(1 - p_i)}{N}}$$

Where the sample size is large the distribution of the sample proportion r_i/N may be assumed to be normal.

Both of the above models, forming the basis for statistical discussion of work measurement, will be applied in specific situations in subsequent pages.

Value of Statistical Analysis of Time Data. The principal uses of statistics in work measurement are as follows:

1. A basis is provided for a quantitative criterion of standardized methods and conditions in terms of **statistical stability** or **control.**
2. The necessity of attaining a state of statistical control may result in the discovery and remedy of causes for significant and undesirable variation in the operation.
3. If a given degree of precision is specified in the study with a given desired level of confidence, the number of observations required in the sample to meet these specifications may be determined.
4. Control charts for sample parameters may be designed as aids in controlling the operation over a given time period. That is, changes in the level of population parameters may be detected by **control charts** and assignable causes for change removed if necessary.

Time Recording Equipment

SIMPLE STOP WATCH. The plain stop watch (Fig. 1) is started by moving A toward the stem, and stopped by moving A away from the stem. Pressure on B brings the hand to zero. The watch has a single large hand making one revolution per minute, and a small one making one revolution in 30 min. The watch will continue for runs of longer than 30 min., but the number of 30-min. periods must be noted or checked from an ordinary watch. This type of stop watch is used more than any other for time study work. It is adapted to both **continuous** and **snap-back** methods of recording.

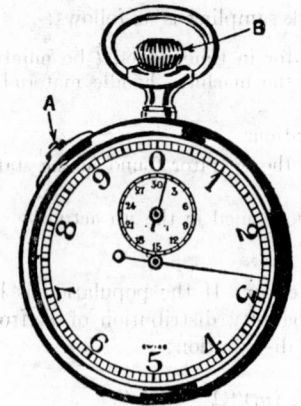
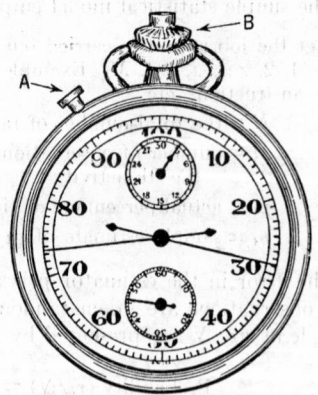

Fig. 1. Plain decimal stop watch.   Fig. 2. Split-hand stop watch.

SPLIT-HAND STOP WATCH. The split-hand watch (Fig. 2) has two large hands. By successive presses of stop B, both hands will start together, stop, and return to zero. By pressing stop A, the lower hand is held wherever it is while the upper hand continues its progress. This is done when a delay occurs so that its time may be read without interrupting the over-all timing. At a second pressure of stop *A*, the lower hand instantly catches up with the upper hand and continues with it. This watch is not adapted for snap-back recording.

Another variation is a series of numbers about a dial which indicate the number of times any elapsed time is repeated per hour. This feature is more confusing than helpful.

DECIMAL-HOUR STOP WATCH. A watch frequently used in time study work is the decimal-hour stop watch. The large dial has 100 divisions. The large hand makes one revolution in 36 sec., or 1/100 of an hour, and the small hand revolves once for each 30 revolutions of the large hand.

CALIBRATION OF WATCHES. Stop watches should be calibrated from time to time by operating them 15 min. and comparing their readings with a regular watch or chronometer of known reliability.

MARSTO-CHRON. When it is necessary to record time intervals which are too short to be measured with a stop watch, a Marsto-Chron may be used. With this device times of 0.01 min. or less can be recorded. The Marsto-Chron consists of a small box through which a **scaled paper tape** is drawn at a uniform speed by means of electric motor. The beginning or end of each element is recorded by pressing one or two control keys mounted on the case. Pressure on a key depresses a type bar which makes a mark on the tape. Elements are identified by use of the keys in different arrangements, such as pressing both keys or double pressing one or the other. The tape moves at a rate of 10 to 20 in. per min., depending upon the motor drive used. When the tape travels at 10 in. per min., 1 in. of tape represents 0.1 min. and 1/10-in. equals 0.01 min.

The principal advantage of the Marsto-Chron is that the observer need not take his eyes off the operator or write anything. The major disadvantage is that there is no means of making notes during the study or of handling many foreign elements or interruptions.

TIMING WITH MOTION PICTURES. The motion picture is an accurate record of both the method employed and time taken during a particular study. (See section on Motion and Methods Study.) If the camera is driven by a synchronous motor, the times for individual motions, elements, or cycles may be taken by converting frame counts to time in terms of the speed of the camera. The usual camera speed is 1,000 frames per min., resulting in time units of 0.001 min.

A special timing device such as a **microchronometer** or **wink counter** may be placed in the subject field, thus giving direct time readings in the film itself. This is particularly valuable if the camera is spring wound or the projector lacks a frame counter.

The disadvantages of using a film as a timing device is the cost of obtaining an adequate sample size. The number of complete cycles observed may be small relative to the number needed to give a required degree of precision.

Memomotion Camera. Mundel (Motion and Time Study) defines memomotion as the taking of motion pictures of operations at slow speeds, such as 1 frame per sec. or 100 frames per min. It is particularly adapted to recording and timing indirect labor operations, crew activities, long cycle operations, and day-long studies. Its obvious advantage is the economical use of film.

MICROCHRONOMETER. A specially designed clock driven by a synchronous motor, the michrochronometer is calibrated in 0.001 min. The clock

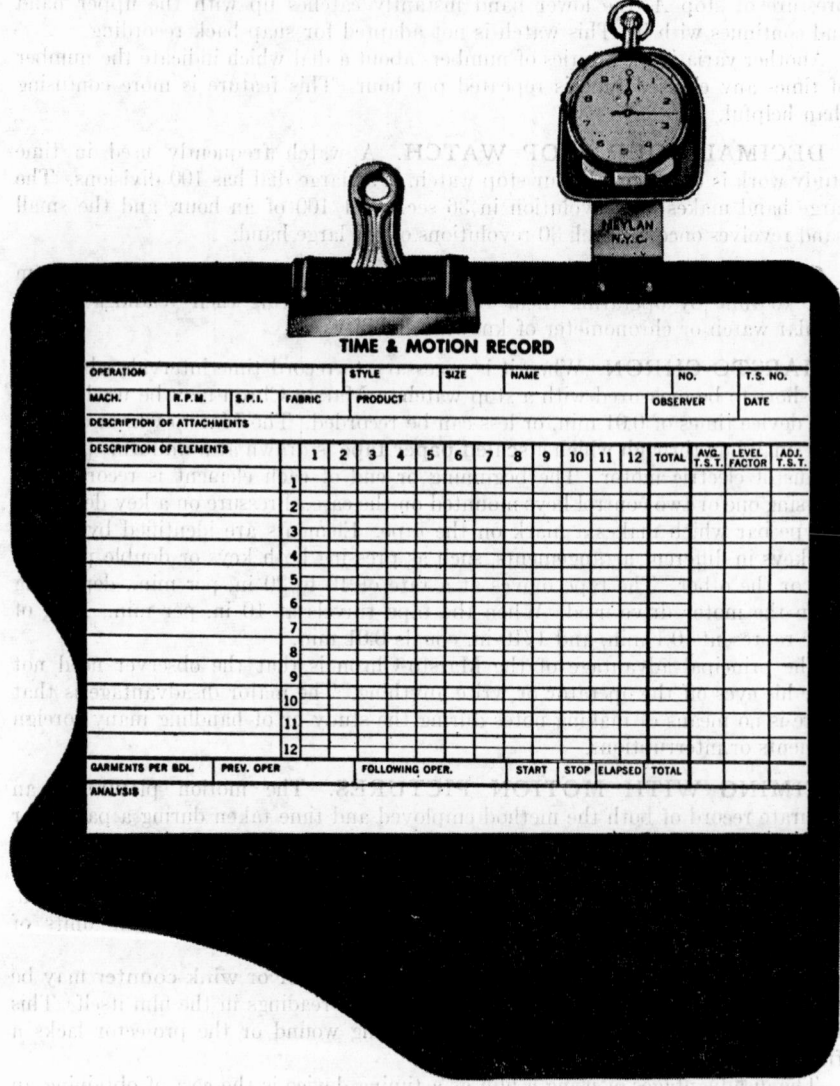

Fig. 3. Time study board.

has two hands, one making 10 revolutions per min. and a small one making 1 revolution per minute. It is adapted for use in motion pictures and provides an excellent means of analyzing motion times.

WINK COUNTER. The wink counter, originated by Porter, is used for both motion and time studies. In appearance it resembles a speedometer. The wink counter has three revolving numbered discs from which the time can be read accurately to 0.005 min. for time studies, and for motion studies a helix on the machine may be used for closer timing. The device is positioned at the workplace.

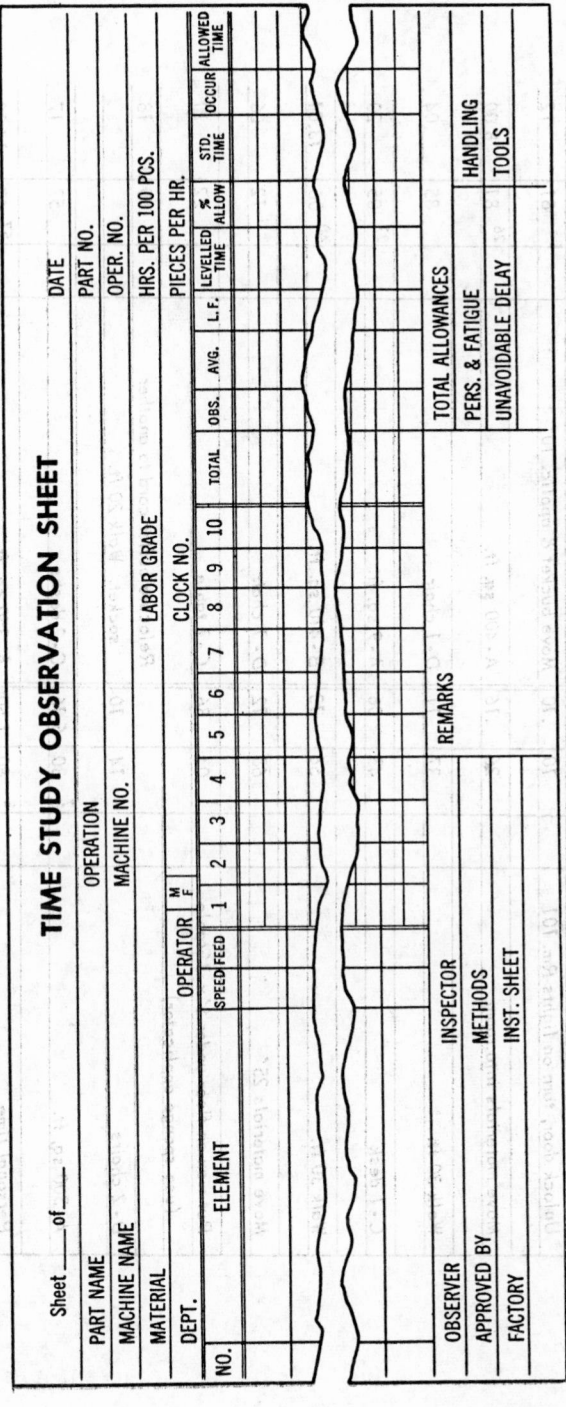

Fig. 4. Time study observation sheet for repetitive operations.

TIME STUDY OBSERVATION SHEET   No 1331

OBSERVER J. O. Moore   DATE 3/4/   SHEET NO. 2 OF 8 SHEETS

ELEMENT	RTG.	READ'G	EXTN.	ELEMENT	RTG.	READ'G	EXTN.
Unlock door, turn on lights Rm. 101		10	.10	Move bucket & applic. 10'		81	12
Move materials into room		26	.16	A - 400 sq. ft.		26 81	8.00
Walk 30 ft.		37	11	D - 1 chair		85	.04
C - 1 desk		43	06	A - 9 sq. ft.		27 05	20
Walk 30 ft.		56	13	B - 410 sq. ft.		40 06	13.01
Move materials 25'		68	12	D - 1 chair		12	06
Put wax on floor under 6' x 3' table (use sponge applicator)		1 04	.36	C - 1 table		22	10
				Relocate buffer cord to another socket. Walk 20 ft.		40	18
D - 2 chairs		14	10				
A - 300 sq. ft.		7 30	6.16	C - 2 desks		57	17
Personal time		8 80	1.50	A - 350 sq. ft.		57 67	17.10
Move bucket and applicator 10'		89	09	B - 100 sq. ft.		61 70	4.03

Plug in buffer cord	9	02	13	Stop buffer - open cover plate -	62	25	55
				adjust belt - place cover plate			
				back on			
Buff under 6' x 3' table		47	45	B - 250 sq. ft.	74	75	12.50
B - 300 sq. ft.	18	52	9.05	D - 2 chairs		87	12
Move 2 waste baskets		58	06				
C - 2 desks		69	11				
				Element Code			
				A - Wax clear area			
				B - Buff clear area			
				C - Move desk or table			
				D - Move chair			

OPERATION AND PRODUCT

Wax and buff office floors – Building 101

SKILL: POOR ☐ FAIR ☐ AVER. ☐ GOOD ☑ EXCEL. ☐ SUPER EXCES. ☐
EFFORT: FAIR ☑

START 5:30 STOP 9:30 ELAPSED TIME 4

PRODUCTION STD. HRS. EARNED OVERALL EFF.

OPERATOR'S NAME L. Brown
M OR F REG. NO. 7268

OVER-	R & D	TOT.
ALL %	%	95 RTG.

Fig. 5. Time study observation sheet for nonrepetitive operations.

and the observer reads the counter at practically the same instant he observes the motion of the operator. Greater accuracy is obtained than with the stop watch and shorter elements can be recorded.

STOP WATCH, WINK COUNTER, AND MARSTO-CHRON COMPARED. Studies of the decimal-minute stop watch, the wink counter, and the Marsto-Chron were made by Porter and by Leng. From these experiments, considering the improved Marsto-Chron, it may be said that for equal confidence in results, 2 to 5 times as many observations are necessary with the stop watch as with the wink counter, and from 10 to 30 times as many with the stop watch as with the Marsto-Chron.

With the Marsto-Chron an element of 0.01 min. can be read as readily as 0.10 min. with the stop watch. For the wink counter, the smallest element recommended is 0.025 min., which is getting below the range of the stop watch method.

MECHANICAL TIME RECORDER. Mechanical time recorders may be used to record productive time lost. (See section on Production Control Systems and Procedures.) One recording device consists of a graduated chart, revolving once in 8 or 10 hr., upon which a jagged line is made by vibration when the machine being timed is running, and a single line is recorded when the machine stops. Delay causes are noted by the operator or other person. This device is known as a Servis Recorder.

TIME STUDY BOARD. The data or observation sheets, and usually the watch, should be held by a specially designed hand. A stop watch has a more delicate movement than an ordinary watch, and it should be handled carefully. If the analyst holds it in his hand, he is sure to lay it down occasionally, often on vibrating machines or benches where it is liable to accident. Moreover, it should be in a fixed position relative to the observation sheet. Therefore, the watch should be mounted on the board, or, for a simpler arrangement, in a homemade, three-fingered brass holder screwed to the upper edge of an ordinary clamp filing board.

The time study board shown in Fig. 3 (Meylan Stopwatch Co.) combines the features needed for general time study work. It provides a convenient writing surface for holding the observation sheet and holds the stop watch in position to be operated by the left hand while the left arm supports the board, leaving the right hand free to record observations. The watch is held in a **locked holder** which gives protection against breakage, permits functioning at an angle to avoid glare on its face, and offers the maximum of visibility in use. The **board material** is a highly polished, smooth, black, rigid plastic material, extremely light and warp-resistant. Its dimensions are 13 by 13 in., and it is $\frac{1}{8}$-in. thick. Boards for left-handed persons are available. A special 3-watch board is sometimes used. A **quick-click lever** at the upper right-hand side of the board is used to actuate all three clocks.

TIME OBSERVATION SHEETS. There is considerable variation in time observation sheets, depending upon the technique used by the analyst in taking observations. The essential feature of a well-designed observation sheet is that it provide space for all necessary data. Both sides should be used, one side for time study observations and the other for all additional data of identification, analysis tools, etc.

The sheet shown in Fig. 4 is designed for studying a **repetitive operation.** The elements of the operation are recorded in sequence on the column to the left. Space is provided in the middle of the sheet for elemental times for ten cycles

The reverse side of the sheet can be used for sketches of workplace layout and information on jigs, fixtures, tools, etc.

If the operation is less repetitive, the sheet shown in Fig. 5 may be used. Two columns are used for writing down each element, or its code letter, as it occurs. This sheet is more adaptable to **indirect labor operations** where the sequence of elements is not fixed. Typical data for such an operation are recorded in Fig. 5. Columns for rating each element, for clock reading, and for element time are included.

Stop Watch Time Study Procedure

PRELIMINARY INVESTIGATION. Prior to the actual measurement of net cycle times the **objective** or purpose of the study should be clearly understood. The objective determines the ultimate use of the standard time. With a clarified objective, a rational determination of allowable error and number of observations to take can be made. For instance, if the standard is to be used as a basis for **wage incentive,** the error that will be tolerated in the measurement may be less than if the standard is to be employed, along with others, in approximating an aggregate **production program** or a **labor budget.** In the latter cases accuracy and precision may be sacrificed if operation and study controls are relaxed and the number of observations are limited.

A preliminary investigation should disclose the extent to which methods analysis has been previously employed and whether further effort in methods improvement and job standardization is desirable. Thus, the time measurements may be deferred until a **methods study** is concluded. The lack of original operation design, standardization, and control may be incompatible with the objectives of the time study, including the accuracy and precision desired. It should be the company policy to permit the time study engineer to recommend a formal methods study when it is apparent that the time study requirements demand it. In certain cases, for expediency, a methods study may be excluded in favor of the immediate setting of a standard time. The standard may then be designated as a **temporary standard** subject to revision after a proper methods study has been made.

Careful **liaison** must be established between the industrial engineer or the time study man and the supervisor of the operating department. Further, this liaison must be extended to the foreman and the operator himself. Reasons for the study and the necessary preparation to insure a valid study must be handled with subtlety and care by the engineer in charge. Without rapport between supervisor, operator, and analyst, the entire study may be either inadvertently or wilfully sabotaged.

STANDARDIZATION OF METHODS AND CONDITIONS. The method and job conditions should be standardized in writing, because the standard time is relevant only to a specific method and set of conditions. After a standard time has been set, considerable difficulties may arise if various interpretations of standard methods and conditions are possible. This is particularly true if the standard time is to be used as a basis for wage payment and an unexpected discrepancy between standard and actual performance may be the result primarily of a methods change. Such a discrepancy in a highly repetitive long-run operation may lead to a loss of confidence in both methods and time study techniques.

Standardization by Motion Pattern. In highly repetitive operations where there is more than one operator a motion pattern may be difficult to standardize as "best." Each operator may employ variations in motion which are peculiar to his own aptitudes. The engineer may have to employ careful judgment in standardizing a given motion pattern which he thinks should be representative for a number of operators.

Changes in the standard method, and particularly of the motion pattern, may be initiated by the operator after the standard has been set, with a resulting gain in performance level. These changes, where minor, may not be readily differentiated from skillful performance or good pace and it may be inadvisable to attempt to change the standard by retiming the job. But where the variation in method is enough to cause a significant change in performance, the job can be retimed. A **significant performance change** is one which permits the operator to have earnings well above the average, or one which can contribute to a specified shift in net cycle times as indicated on a control chart.

A basic problem here is what criteria may be employed to differentiate standard from nonstandard situations. An **operation description** in all of its details may suffice. This refers to sketches of workplace layout and a complete description of such items as the types and relative locations of equipment, motion pattern, machine feeds and speeds, and specifications of material quality. The engineer should allow for a detailed record of these factors to accompany the observation data sheets and should take the actual time readings only under these standard conditions. Where the operation is highly repetitive with short elements, a motion picture can be used to provide an accurate record of the standard method or motion pattern in detail.

Standardization by Control Chart. A more objective criterion of standardized methods and conditions is a control chart of the means of small samples of net cycle times. If the measurements are consistent or in statistical control, that is, taken from a constant chance cause system, the means (averages) of successive and randomly selected small samples would lie within statistically determined **limits.** The distribution of these means and their limits may be depicted on a control chart. These charts can be constructed for each element of the study or for over-all cycle times. Fig. 11 shows an example of such a chart, based on the data given in Fig. 10. (See section on Quality Control also.)

SELECTION OF OPERATOR FOR STUDY. The selection of the worker for the study depends somewhat upon the procedure used but is a very important factor in the success of the study. Micromotion and time study techniques should make use of the best workers. For timing purposes, it is advantageous to select the operator whose motions are performed with ostensible automaticity or without conscious effort. This condition is partially evident when **ballistic movements** are used, as opposed to restricted or controlled movements, and where **rhythm** is present in the repetitive portions of the work.

The foreman and the existing production records can assist the analyst in selecting the worker to study. In general, intelligence and ability to learn are as important as dexterity and ability to maintain high production. The worker should be one who has the respect and confidence of the workers in the same job classification, for he or she interprets the work of the engineer to them and can do much to help or hinder the general acceptance of the standard time.

The engineer should make selection of the worker part of the preliminary investigation. During the preliminary investigation he can learn who are the best operators and which ones are most likely to cooperate and lead. Sometimes the choice may be limited to a few or there may be only a single operator.

In certain cases the labor union contract may assign to the union steward the prerogative of choosing an operator. A typical **contract clause** of this nature reads (Collective Bargaining Provisions, Bulletin No. 908-3, U. S. Dept. of Labor): "Piecework prices shall be set on the work of one or more employees selected by the foreman and the shop committee, which men shall be skilled in their line of work."

ATTITUDE OF ANALYST. The analyst should work in the fullest co-operation with foreman, union steward, and worker. The foreman should intro-duce the analyst to the operator, and the latter should be guaranteed no loss of earnings during the study. The analyst should treat the worker as one sharing in the investigation and should endeavor to win his interest and cooperation. Generally there is little difficulty with intelligent workers who want to avoid delays caused by poor material, irregular serving, bad work on preceding operations, or improper care of equipment, for these delays limit their earnings and cause irritation. The stop watch should be shown to the operator, its use explained, and the idea of measuring explained as against the idea of driving. The operator should be put at ease and instructed to work at his **normal rate.** The time study man should avoid standing in front of or directly behind the operator and should select a position from 4 to 6 ft. away at one side. It is reas-suring to the operator if he can look around at the analyst occasionally, and furthermore the analyst may need to ask questions now and then.

PREPARATION FOR STUDY. The analyst should so arrange and simplify his own routine that he can give his whole attention to the job being studied. He can make himself comfortable but should not lounge or relax his attention. He must keep off outside interference and try to put himself into the worker's situation. He must be on the alert to catch all the **variables** con-sisting of those having to do with the worker, with the surroundings, and with motion. Motions may be classified as frequent and infrequent. The latter are the ones most likely to be overlooked—for instance, starting new stock, oiling ma-chines, or changing tools. In many industries there is **seasonal variability,** changes from light to heavy materials, etc. No variable likely to affect motion and time should be ignored.

Time observation sheets should be prepared and all **general data covering con-ditions** recorded, such as date, time of starting and stopping, operation, work in process, operator, machine or workplace, temperature, humidity, light, and sound. Figs. 6 and 7 show complete blanks for an extensive study of machine operations where considerable supporting data must be recorded. In a particular plant the form can be simplified to contain only the information essential to the products and conditions therein.

DETERMINATION OF TIME STUDY ELEMENTS. The operation is broken down into time study elements and timed accordingly. There are a number of criteria employed to divide the operation into a **pattern of elements.**

1. **Manually performed or hand elements** should be separated from **machine-controlled elements.** For the latter type the **machining time** may be calculated on the basis of the proper tool or table speeds, feeds, depth of cuts, types of mate-rial, etc. This may be done whether the machine feed is automatic or hand fed. Machine elements are not rated against a normal.

2. **Constant elements** should be differentiated from **variable elements** for manually controlled portions of the job. In this case variable does not refer to the inherent variability of individual observed times. It refers rather to the fact that

certain elements common to many jobs are relatively constant in different jobs performed at the operation, while other element times vary with the job, according to some factor such as part size or shape, tolerances required, or location of materials. For instance, the time to close and open a jig, lower drill to work, or rotate jig may be relatively constant over a range of jobs, whereas the time to pick up part, place part in jig, etc., may vary with different parts or jig characteristics. With this sort of breakdown, standard data may be formulated from a small number of studies to apply to a range of similar but not identical parts of jobs performed at the operation in question. Thus the normal time for a job may be determined from the standard data by knowing the elements necessary to complete a cycle of work, the characteristics of the part, and any other factors influencing the selection of the element time.

3. The choice of elements may be influenced by the ease with which the **break points,** points separating successive elements, can be observed or discerned. Thus, sound or some other factor affecting the observer's senses can be employed to designate the end of one element and the start of another with accuracy. This is important where the elements are short.

4. Elements should be made **short** within the limits of accuracy of the timing device. This is more important where methods or motion study is involved than in obtaining a standard time for a well-controlled operation. It also facilitates a detailed description of the standard method. With the stop watch, elements less than 0.04 min. are difficult to time, especially if they are not separated by longer elements.

It is said that breaking the job down into small elements tends to increase "accuracy" due to the canceling out of errors in the elements. This does not have much foundation, in that it assumes that the sources of error lack consistency or randomly affect the elemental readings. It is more likely that biases may be consistent. For instance, if the snap-back method of timing is used, the **consistent error** in this method would be magnified by small elements.

5. Elements should consist of **homogeneous groups of therbligs.** The elements should consist of a "natural" subdivision of work, such as a series of motions with a single part, inspections, or use of a tool.

6. **Irregular elements** should be noted. These are elements which do not occur regularly with each cycle of output but are nevertheless productive elements and must be included in the observed data and prorated over the regular times.

RECORDING TIMES. When time study elements are in a fixed order, it is better to write them down on each blank before beginning the study of time. If the order cannot be fixed, the elements may be listed at the bottom of the sheet and given **element symbols,** *a, b, c,* etc. These symbols can then be used in any sequence which may develop. There is some danger of miscopying, but it is not always possible to fix the sequence completely. Clearness as to just what constitutes an element is important. In such divisions as "adjust tool in post, tighten tool, position," there is danger of being indefinite as to exactly where one ends and the next begins. **Break points** should be definitely given as:

1. From reaching for tool to end of tool adjustment in post. The method should be described on the back of the sheet or on simple motion study.
2. From end of adjustment in post to end of tightening. The motions of tightening should be described as above.
3. From end of tightening to starting machine. The method should be described as above.

These break points must be fixed in mind, and it is safer to write them in advance of timing the job. In establishing these various points, use of judgment to cut out unnecessary detail will avoid too much writing. Minutes need not be repeated with every decimal reading, but they should be put down frequently enough to prevent doubt.

Over-all Timing. This is **timing of cycles** only, without reference to elements. This will not permit any detailed analysis of the operation nor will it indicate minor delays. Where there is some assurance that the operation is normally under control, over-all timing may be used to collect sample data for use in control charts.

Snap-back Timing. At the beginning of each element the watch hand starts from zero. At the end of each element the watch is read, the hands are snapped back to zero, and observed time is recorded (see Fig. 6). No computations are necessary to obtain element times, as these are recorded. Thus the clerical work in computing the study is less than in the continuous method.

A major **disadvantage** of the snap-back method is the bias caused by time taken by the observer to manipulate the watch at the end of each elemental reading. Also, the observer may anticipate individual readings after a number of readings have been taken. An extensive controlled study by Lazarus (Advanced Management, vol. 15) gave the following results: The standard deviation of errors in both snap-back and continuous types of readings was 0.081 min. The average error in the continuous method was +.000097 min. and for the snap-back method −.0008 min. Lazarus concluded also that the absolute magnitude of the error is independent of the size of the element.

Except for highly repetitive, short-cycle operations, the error in the watch reading may be minor in view of the distribution of time study cycle times resulting from the variation in the subject being studied.

Continuous Timing. This procedure gives the most satisfactory results in general on most operations. Elements are recorded in sequence without stopping the watch. The observer keeps the watch going continuously during the period of study, making a mental note of the time as shown on the watch at the instant each elementary operation is completed and recording that time on the sheet opposite its name or appropriate symbol. He should do all this with sufficient speed and concentration to be free to note and write the time of completion of the next elementary operation. As reading of the watch is practically instantaneous, there is no necessity for stopping the hand.

Lichtner (Time Study and Job Analysis) indicates that the advantages of the continuous method are that it gives not only the time for each element as a distinct entity, but also the times of all elements in the order of their performance; furthermore, it charges every minute of time for the duration of the study either to some necessary element, called a **productive** element, or to an unnecessary one, called a **nonproductive** element; it also eliminates any danger of omitting delays. The split-hand watch greatly facilitates the use of this procedure.

Cumulative readings only are recorded during the run. Elapsed times are derived by subtraction later and entered beside the corresponding cumulative readings (Fig. 7). As a check, **the sum of individual times** should equal the final cumulative reading. The individual times should not be entered too far from the original readings. A simple way is to enter the cumulative reading with hard pencil on one-half of each square and the extensions with softer or colored pencil

TIME OBSERVATION SHEET

DATE 5-21-

			PART NO. 62867
FACT. NO.	18		SCHEDULE NO. I4920
DEPT. NO.	22		CANCELS SCH. NO. I-1151
PART NAME	Bearing Cap		GROUP NO. 3
OPERATION NO.	20A	OPERATION Drill 2 (13/32) Holes	PAGE 2 OF 3
MACH. NO.	681	MACHINE 24" Conn. Dr. Press	

IDLE TIME/CYCLE	.60
IDLE TIME/PIECE	✓
DELAY/PIECE	.60
MACH. CAP'TY/HR.	57
OPER. CAP'TY/HR.	57
PIECES/CYCLE	1
REQ'D. PROD./HR.	50
NO. PCS. STUDIED	10
NO. OF OPERATORS	✓
NO. OF HELPERS	✓
FORMER BASE RATE	65¢
NEW BASE RATE	65¢
FORMER STD. TIME	0.160
NEW STD. TIME	0.135
FORMER PROD./HR.	62.5
NEW PROD./HR.	57
% INCREASE PROD.	✓
% DECREASE PROD.	10
% INCREASE TIME	9.4
% DECREASE TIME	✓
FORMER COST / PC.	.0104
NEW COST / PC.	.0114

NO.	DETAILS OF WORK CYCLE	ELAPSED TIME IN DECIMAL MINUTES										ADJ. TIME
	SKETCH (OVER) ✓											
1	Clear part in fixture (27")	03	04	04	05	03	03	07	03	04	05	.04
2	Clamp part (socket wrench & nut)	08	07	09	08	10	09	10	08	07	07	.06
3	Lower drill head (3")	03	03	02	02	03	04	04	03	02	03	.02
4	Drill 2 holes (13/32 x 2)	68	66	65	69	67	66.8	68	67	65	65	.65
5	Raise feed trip, raise head	02	04	03	02	02	03	04	02	03	02	.02
6	Release part (socket wrench & nut)	05	05	06	07	08	05	06	07	06	08	.05
7	Remove part (16")	03	03	04	05	04	03	05	04	05		.03
8	Blow out fixture (hose)	05	05	06	06	06	05	05	04	06	04	.05
9												
10	MATERIAL Mall. Iron											
11												
12												
13												
	DELAYS											
A	(12).08 Examine fixture — 4A go to next spindle to spotface	see oper. #20B										
B	Change drill .74 — 4B spotface 2 holes											
C	— 4C bottom to position											
D												

ITEM #	4
CUTTING DIA.	.693
CUTTER DIA.	"
NO. OF TEETH	2
CUTTER MATL.	HSS
R.P.M.	360
F.P.M.	56
TYPE OF CUT	2r.
FEED/REV.	.010
FEED/MIN.	3.6
FEED/TOOTH	.005
LENGTH OF CUT	2¼
WIDTH OF CUT	✓
DEPTH OF CUT	2"
LIMITS	
REASON FOR CHANGE	Holes were 13/32 dia

		WORK CYCLE TIME PER PIECE		
MULTIPLE PCS./WORK CYCLE ✓	%	PCS.: PRORATE/PC.		.920
MACH.:		MACH.:		✓
OPERS./		OPER.: /OPER.		✓
HANDLE SUPPLIES	MIN. FOR	/PCS.		✓
SCRAP				
STOCK TO WORK AREA	.30	"	15	.020
FROM	.36	"	15	.024
MACH. SET UP TIME ALLOWANCE ✓	% :	MIN./SET UP:		
TOOL CHANGE TIME ALLOWANCE	"	MIN./CHANGE: 200 "		.005
REST OR DELAY ALLOWANCE	✓ "	MIN./DAY.		
MACHINE ALLOWANCE	✓ "	14 "		
SPECIAL ALLOWANCE	"			
PERSONAL ALLOWANCE	✓ "	21 "		
TOTAL ALLOWANCE	9 "	40 "		.063
		TOTAL TIME ALLOWED PER PIECE		1.052

DEMONSTRATION	
GOOD ☑ / FAIR ☐ / POOR ☐	
APPROVED BY:	
ANALYST	✓
CHECKER	✓
FOREMAN	✓
GEN FOREMAN	✓
EFFICIENCY ENG.	✓
SUPERINTENDENT	

Fig. 6. Method of recording snap-back time study.

TIME OBSERVATION SHEET

PART NO. 62867
SCHEDULE NO. T4920
CANCELS SCH. NO. 71151
GROUP NO. none
PAGE 3 OF 3

FACT. NO. 18
DEPT. NO. 22
PART NAME Bearing Cap
OPERATION NO. 2013   OPERATION Spotface (2) 1 3/16 Holes
MACH. NO. 682   MACHINE 24 Cinn. Dr. Press
DATE 5-2-

	NO.	DETAILS OF WORK CYCLE	ELAPSED TIME IN DECIMAL MINUTES								
			CONT	INDV	CONT	INDV	CONT	INDV	CONT	INDV	CONT
SKETCH (OVER)	1										
REMARKS (OVER)	2										
	3	Place part under spotfaces (18")	.02	.02	.60	.03	.94	.02	1.57	.02	1.94	.04
	4	Lower spindle (4")	.04	.02	.63	.03	.96	.02	1.59	.02	1.96	.02
	5	Spotface (1 3/16 x 3/16)	.20	.16	.74	.11	1.06	.10	1.72	.13	2.07	.11
	6	Raise spl. turn part end for end & lower spl.	.23	.03	.77	.03	1.10	.04	1.75	.03	2.10	.03
	7											
	8		.42	.19	.87	.10	1.50B	.11	1.85	.10	2.22	.12
	9	Lower spindle	.44	.02	.90	.03	1.52	.02	1.87	.02	2.24	.02
	10	Remove part (22")	.57A	.03	.92	.02	1.55	.03	1.90	.03	2.26	.04

	NO.						
SAFETY	1	O.K.					
LUBRICANT	3	Soluble oil					
DRIVE	4	direct					
LOT SIZE	5						
LOTS/YEAR	6						
CONT'US PROD.	7	Yes					
CONE STEP US'D	8						
FEED LEVER	9						
SPEED LEVER	10						
MATERIAL	11	Mall. Iron					
DELAYS	12						
	13						
	14						
A Drops to pick up (.13)	15						
	16						
B Move stock .40	17						
	18						
C	19						
	20						
D	21						
	22						

	ALLOWED TIME	
IDLE TIME/CYCLE	none	
IDLE TIME/PIECE	none	
DELAY/PIECE	.02	
MACH. CAP'TY/HR.	162	
OPER. CAP'TY/HR.	162	
PIECES/CYCLE	1	
REC'D. PROD./HR.	50	
NO. PCS. STUDIED	5	
NO. OF OPERATORS	1	.11
NO. OF HELPERS		-.02
NO. OF MACHINES	1	.03
FORMER BASE RATE	65¢	
NEW BASE RATE	65¢	
FORMER STD. TIME	0059	
NEW STD. TIME	0062	
FORMER PROD./HR.	175	
NEW PROD./HR.	162	
% INCREASE PROD.		
% DECREASE PROD.	8	
% INCREASE TIME	5	
% DECREASE TIME		
FORMER COST/PC.	0037	
NEW COST/PC.	0040	.34

WORK CYCLE TIME PER PIECE

		PCS. PRORATE/PC.
MULTIPLE PCS./WORK CYCLE:		MACH.: /MACH.
MACH./		OPER.: /OPER.
OPERS./		
HANDLE SUPPLIES	MIN. FOR /PCS.	
SCRAP	/ : / :	
STOCK TO WORK AREA	/ : / :	
FROM	/ : / :	
MACH. SET-UP TIME ALLOWANCE ✓ %	✓ : MIN./SET-UP:	.007
TOOL CHANGE TIME ALLOWANCE	✓ : 3 MIN./CHANGE: 400	
REST OR DELAY ALLOWANCE	✓ : MIN./DAY:	
MACHINE ALLOWANCE	✓ : .10 / :	
SPECIAL ALLOWANCE	✓ : / :	
PERSONAL ALLOWANCE	✓ : .21 / :	.024
TOTAL ALLOWANCE	7 : .31 / :	
TOTAL TIME ALLOWED PER PIECE		.371

ITEM	5-8
CUTTING DIA.	1 3/16
CUTTER DIA.	4
NO. OF TEETH	4
CUTTER MATL.	H.S.S.
R.P.M.	220
F.P.M.	69
TYPE OF CUT	S.F.
FEED/REV. TOOTH	HD
FEED/MIN. TOOTH	
LENGTH OF CUT	
WIDTH OF CUT	1/16
DEPTH OF CUT	1/16
LIMITS	1/64
REASON FOR CHANGE:	Was 1" dia.

DEMONSTRATION
GOOD ☑ FAIR ☐ POOR ☐

APPROVED BY:
ANALYST
CHECKER
FOREMAN
GEN. FOREMAN
EFFICIENCY ENG.
SUPERINTENDENT

Fig. 7. Method of recording continuous time study.

on the other half. This method keeps the two sets of figures together and yet allows either set to be scanned without confusion.

Connected Two-Watch Timing. The connected two-watch procedure allows for direct reading of elapsed time of elements. Two watches are arranged side by side on the study board. A mechanism of **connecting links** is so arranged that when the first watch is started, the second is automatically stopped. When the second is again started, the first one is stopped. (To use this device, the stop-start arrangement on one of the watches must be reversed, which can be done by any watch repair man by reversing the hairspring which controls the mechanism in the watch.) The analyst reads the watches alternately and gets **direct elapsed time readings.** This method saves the necessity of subtracting successive readings to get elapsed times, thereby avoiding much clerical work.

LENGTH OF STUDY. The length of the study determines the size of the parent population or universe from which samples are taken. The study length affects accuracy where bias may result if the period of study is too short to include all significant sources of variation.

There may be **irregular work elements** that appear at given intervals of production within or between hours. These include such tasks as replenishing supply bins, filling out a production ticket, and inspecting every twentieth unit produced. If such tasks are to be included as productive elements rather than delays, they must be recognized, timed, and **prorated** over units produced in the interval between their appearances.

One factor to consider in the study length is the influence of **fatigue** on the net cycle time. When fatigue results in a between-hour variation of cycle times, the study should be extended over the working day to include such variation. However, it is conceivable that in most light industrial operations fatigue may have little influence on net cycle times. Any fatigue that is not remedied by rest periods may show up primarily in an increase in the number and length of minor delays rather than in a change in pace. These factors are then considered in the **measurement of delay allowances** rather than of net cycle times.

Traditional time study practice usually limits the study to observing net cycle times over a relatively short time period to include essentially between-cycle variation. Consideration is usually given to between-hour and between-day variation by taking the observations during, say, the middle of the morning work period and during the second or third day of the work week, when it is assumed that **production rate** is average as far as these sources of variation are concerned. The actual length of the study is the time necessary to take observations of a consecutive number of units of output equal to the required sample size.

A second method is to extend the study over the period of a day or longer. Observations are then taken randomly, in small sub-sample sizes, over the specified extended time period. This is the recommended procedure where there is reason to believe that net cycle time variation is affected by factors operating irregularly and cyclically over this period.

An intelligent selection of **optimal study length** may be difficult. The economics of the situation, in which costs of a long study are weighed against costs of having some results of inferior accuracy, may favor a short study period. Also, past experience may be reflected in standards of study length set as a matter of policy.

NUMBER OF OBSERVATIONS. When the criterion of statistical control is employed to determine standardized conditions, initial observations may be necessary merely to discover any need for further methods study, training, or control before setting the actual standard. It is possible to **pool** some of the initial observations with those taken in the formal study, provided the initial times represent standard conditions.

Company Policy. Experience and judgment may be the sole basis for deciding the number of readings to take. Fig. 8 shows a table from the Time Study

Cycle Time (Minutes)	Recommended Number of Cycles to Study
0.10	200
0.25	100
0.50	60
0.75	40
1.00	30
2.00	20
4.00– 5.00	15
5.00–10.00	10
10.00–20.00	8
20.00–40.00	5
40.00–above	3

General Electric Co.

Fig. 8. Recommended number of cycles to be observed on the basis of cycle time.

Time for Piece or Cycle (Hours)	Minimum Number of Cycles to Study		
	Activity: Over 10,000 per Yr.	Activity: 1,000 to 10,000 per Yr.	Activity: Under 1,000 per Yr.
8.000	2	1	1
3.000	3	2	1
2.000	4	2	1
1.000	5	3	2
.800	6	3	2
.500	8	4	3
.300	10	5	4
.200	12	6	5
.120	15	8	6
.080	20	10	8
.050	25	12	10
.035	30	15	12
.020	40	20	15
.012	50	25	20
.008	60	30	25
.005	80	40	30
.003	100	50	40
.002	120	60	50
Under .002	140	80	60

Westinghouse Electric Corp.

Fig. 9. Recommended minimum number of cycles to be observed on the basis of cycle time.

Manual of the Erie plant of General Electric, used as a guide for their time study engineers. Fig. 9 shows data compiled by the Westinghouse Electric Corporation relative to the number of cycles to be studied.

Statistical Determination. The sample size necessary to give a certain precision may be determined statistically.

Assume that the engineer desires to have an **assurance** of 95 in 100 that the population average cycle time lies within ±2.5 percent of the estimated observed value $\overline{X}_j$ from a sample of size N. (The symbols used here are explained in the discussion of statistics in work measurement.) In other words he is willing to select a sample size N such that there is a risk of 5/100 that the population value will lie outside the range ±2.5 percent $\overline{X}_j$. The problem might be to determine N for an individual elemental time, but the approach is the same as that employed to determine N for cycle times.

The **validity** of the approach is based on three fundamental statistical laws. First, the mean of the distribution of sample means is the mean of the population of individual values from which the sample is taken. Second, the standard deviation of the distribution of sample means equals $1/\sqrt{N}$ times the standard deviation of the population of individual values. Third, the form of the distribution of sample means approaches the form of a normal probability distribution as the size of the sample is increased.

Now let:

$$\sigma_{\overline{x}_j} = \text{standard deviation of the distribution of sample means}$$

Then

$$2 * \sigma_{\overline{x}_j} = 0.025\overline{X}_j$$

(* For precise determination of the coefficient for σ, see a table of normal distribution.)

In this case $\overline{X}_j$ is the average of the cycle times from a sample of size N. $\overline{\overline{X}}_j$ may be substituted for $\overline{X}_j$ if the average is taken from K sub-samples of size n.

Since

$$\sigma_{\overline{x}_j} = \frac{\sigma'_{x_j}}{\sqrt{N}} \text{ where } \sigma'_{x_j} \text{ is the population standard deviation}$$

then

$$\frac{\sigma'_{x_j}}{\sqrt{N}} = \frac{.025\overline{X}_j}{2}$$

$$N = \left(\frac{2\sigma'_{x_j}}{.025\overline{X}_j}\right)^2$$

Since $\overline{X}_j$ and σ'_{x_j} are usually unknown at the start of the study, an initial number of observations N' must be taken in order to estimate these parameters.

Now assume that the engineer takes an **initial sample** of cycle times, $N' = 16$. The values observed (X_j), in minutes, are:

1.00	.95	.81	.97
.95	.89	.92	.96
.80	1.01	.87	1.11
1.10	1.04	1.01	1.03

The population standard deviation may be quickly estimated from the following computational formula:

$$\sigma_{x_j} = \sqrt{\frac{\Sigma X_j{}^2}{N'} - \left(\frac{\Sigma X_j}{N'}\right)^2}$$

$$N = \left(\frac{2\sigma'_{x_j}}{.025\overline{X}_j}\right)^2 = \left(\frac{2\sqrt{\dfrac{\Sigma X_j{}^2}{N'} - \left(\dfrac{\Sigma X_j}{N'}\right)^2}}{.025\overline{X}_j}\right)^2$$

$$= \left(\frac{\dfrac{2\cdot 40}{N'}\sqrt{N'\Sigma X_j{}^2 - (\Sigma X_j)^2}}{\dfrac{\Sigma X_j}{N'}}\right)^2$$

$$= \frac{80^2[N'\Sigma X_j{}^2 - (\Sigma X_j)^2]}{(\Sigma X_j)^2}$$

Substituting in the values for the initial observations, $N = 52$. Therefore, an additional 52 readings are necessary.

CONTROL CHART FOR CYCLE TIMES. In order to test whether or not the observed time data are consistent, that is, whether the operation is in **statistical control,** a control chart for sample means of cycle times can be constructed. In this case the entire number of observations (N) is broken down into successive sub-samples of size (n) and the means of these sub-samples plotted on the control chart.

For example, assume that, at random times over a two-day interval, samples of four observations each are taken of cycle times of an operation. The cycle times may represent the **sum of elemental times** or they may be **over-all times** without reference to an elemental breakdown. The results of the observations in either event are given in Fig. 10.

Sample No.	Time of Day Randomly Selected	Successive Observed Cycle Time Values X_j				Sample Average (Mean) $\overline{X}_j$
1	8:25	1.00,	0.95,	0.98,	1.01	0.985
2	9:15	1.15,	0.98,	1.00,	1.17	1.075
3	10:00	0.95,	1.30,	1.02,	0.92	1.047
4	11:00	0.80,	0.75,	0.85,	1.08	0.870
5	1:20	0.94,	1.11,	1.25,	1.01	1.077
6	2:30	1.20,	1.17,	1.45,	1.30	1.280
7	3:10	1.12,	0.86,	0.79,	0.82	0.897
8	3:45	0.82,	0.98,	0.97,	1.13	0.975
9	8:30	0.72,	0.63,	0.87,	0.90	0.780
10	9:10	1.10,	1.28,	0.90,	1.13	1.102
11	10:05	0.99,	0.82,	0.86,	0.95	0.905
12	11:30	0.98,	1.17,	1.29,	0.69	1.032
13	1:30	1.05,	1.12,	0.66,	0.93	0.940
14	2:15	0.91,	0.80,	1.18,	1.18	1.017
15	3:25	0.76,	0.91,	1.06,	0.82	0.888
16	4:00	0.75,	1.11,	0.69,	1.17	0.930

n = Sub-sample size = 4
N = Total number of observations = 64

Fig. 10. Tabulated data for use on a control chart.

Assuming the sub-samples of 4 were taken at random, the validity of the control chart is based on the three basic laws previously mentioned.

Thus

$$\bar{\bar{X}}_j = \text{estimate of population average cycle time}$$

$$= \frac{\sum_{k=1}^{K} X_{jK}}{K}$$

and

$\sigma_{x_j} =$ estimate of the standard deviation of the universe of individual cycle times

$\sigma'\bar{x}_j =$ standard deviation of the distribution of sample means

$$= \frac{\sigma' x_j}{\sqrt{n}}$$

If the operation is in a state of statistical control, with respect to mean cycle times, the probability of an individual sample mean $\bar{X}_j$ falling outside the limits $\pm 3\sigma\bar{x}_j$ is approximately 3 in 1,000.

Using the above results, the following parameters are calculated:

$$\bar{X}_j = \frac{1}{16} \sum_{}^{16} X_j = 0.988$$

$$\sigma_{x_j} = \sqrt{\frac{\sum_{N=1}^{64} (X_j - \bar{\bar{X}}_j)^2}{N - 1}} = 0.179$$

$$\sigma\bar{x}_j = \frac{.179}{\sqrt{4}} = 0.0895$$

Upper control limit $= 1.256$
Lower control limit $= 0.720$

The control chart with individual sample means plotted in succession is shown in Fig. 11. It may be seen that the mean of sample No. 6 lies outside the upper control limit, suggesting an absence of statistical control.

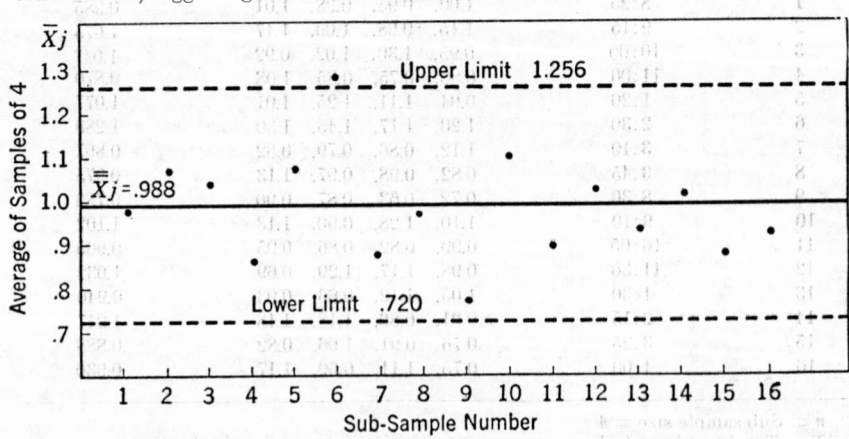

Fig. 11. Control chart for sample means of net cycle times.

Lack of Statistical Control. A number of conclusions may be drawn from the above example concerning the **out-of-control point.**

1. The sample in question (No. 6, Fig. 10) reflects **nonstandard performance** by the operator in unusual pace or method. This presents the fundamental problem of variation which is controllable by the operator. Theoretically, if the cycle times are in a state of statistical control, the manual elements are performed habitually and without conscious effort on the operator's part. Where there is a **conscious effort** on the operator's part to change pace or method, a state of statistical control would probably not exist, as indicated by sample means falling out of control on the chart or by a lack of randomness in the variability of the sample means even if they are within limits.

2. The sample may reflect **nonstandard conditions,** uncontrollable by the operator, such as a change in material quality, tool dimensions, or part locations. Such conditions should be checked and causes removed before making a new study.

3. It is possible that the sample (No. 6) reflects a **cyclical productive activity** which is nevertheless a part of the standard method. That is, the sample may represent the handling of the last few parts in a tote pan, or the initial cycles after a rest period. In these situations it may be desirable to include the out-of-control points as a part of the estimate. Factors which operate cyclically during the work day will be weighted in the normal random observation period so that no points fall out of control. But this phenomenon will show up on control charts by a lack of randomness of sample means about the grand average, by groupings of successive sample points above or below the average line, or by runs of successive readings.

4. Out-of-control points may reflect an irregular or **intermittent element,** which may or may not be an allowable part of the method. The advantage of elemental timing is that such minor delays or interruptions may be noted and causes for their being out of control assigned to them. In some cases, these irregular elements may be studied independently of the repetitive elements and their times prorated over the average number of parts completed between their appearances.

Sub-Sample Size and Frequency of Sampling. In general, small sub-samples are **advantageous** because of the economics of sampling and making the calculations. Where the sub-sample size is small and the samples are taken frequently over a day, shifts in the population mean may be detected more readily than with larger samples taken less frequently. That is, changes in the population average may be masked in the larger sample size. The objective then is to make each sub-sample as homogeneous as possible (to represent a single population), to maximize between sample variation, and to minimize within sample variation.

In the previous example the sample size of four was selected to meet these objectives. The **disadvantage** of small sub-samples is that their means are not normally distributed, particularly if the population distribution is non-normal, which may be typical of net cycle times. Also, a larger sub-sample will be more sensitive to variation because of the narrower limits for a specified degree of confidence.

Use of the Control Chart. The control chart of sample means of net cycle times may be employed in the initial stages of measurement as a **criterion of standardization.** After the standard is formally set, a control chart may be kept over an extended period of time as a **control device.** The results of random samples taken over the extended period of operation will give a current indication of actual performance levels. Such information may be useful in scheduling work, appraising changes in methods, indicating when causes for variation should be checked, etc. The continued use of the control chart will provide a pool of data for revising the control chart limits, if necessary.

CONTROL CHART OF VARIATION. The control chart of means indicates the variability in central tendency. This may be supplemented with a control chart of **sample variability**—in terms either of sample ranges or of sample standard deviations. The control chart of sample variation indicates the consistency of individual time values. Allderige (Journal of Industrial Engineering, vol. 7) believes that a control chart on sample variation is of insignificant value in time study:

A range (R) chart is designed to tell whether or not individual pieces are being produced consistently—sort of a tactical consistency versus the longer range strategic consistency that the $\bar{X}$ (means) chart tests. In work measurement the individual cycle time is of little interest in itself; attention is focused on central tendency ($\bar{X}$). This is all from a measurement point of view, of course; from a methods point of view, inconsistency in variation might be a clue to some better methods. An R chart however, may not automatically be the right consistency test since the distribution may be skewed. More complex statistics would be involved. In work measurement, then, a range control chart is unnecessary since we are not interested in the behavior of individual cycle times.

FORMULATION OF STANDARD TIME. The major steps in arriving at standard time from stop-watch time study data may be diagrammed as follows:

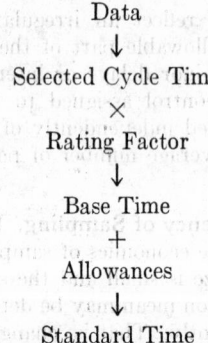

$$\text{Data}$$
$$\downarrow$$
$$\text{Selected Cycle Time}$$
$$\times$$
$$\text{Rating Factor}$$
$$\downarrow$$
$$\text{Base Time}$$
$$+$$
$$\text{Allowances}$$
$$\downarrow$$
$$\text{Standard Time}$$

Selected Cycle Time. The selected cycle time is the sum of the averages of selected elemental times. This includes those elements which appear regularly in every cycle and those which are irregular, whose average times are prorated over the number of cycles intervening between their occurrences. An example of an **irregular element** is, "Inspect every 20th part." The cycle time for this element is equal to the average time for the inspection operation divided by 20.

Prior to determining each elemental average time, certain individual **abnormal elemental times** may be removed from the study by circling the values on the observation sheet. This removal is based on the judgment of the observer, who must decide whether the abnormally high or low value is nonrepresentative of standard or good performance.

The removal of abnormal times should be substantiated with evidence that the times are not indicative of the normal method or conditions. For instance, in an assembly operation the operator may have difficulty in positioning two components during a cycle because of a burr on one of the parts. This may be a periodic occurrence and considered as representative of normal. If it is nonstandard, the time may be removed from the study; however, the causes for the burring should be discovered and remedied, if possible.

Certain abnormal elements of work which appear during the study may be separated from the normal sequence and designated as **foreign elements.** These elements are listed on the side of the observation sheet as they occur, along with the time for their performance. They should be carefully scrutinized to determine that they are not a normal part of the work. If their causes are unavoidable by the operator, they may be considered as part of the productive activity of the job or they may be designated as interruptions to be considered under allowances.

Base Cycle Time. The selected cycle time is an estimate of the actual performance level of the operator observed. This performance may differ from that which would be expected of a **normal operator.** If this is the case, the selected time is adjusted by a **rating factor** to obtain the **base time.** Other terms used to denote the base time are **normal, rated, or leveled time.** The method employed, first to determine a concept of normal, and second to adjust the observed data to normal, is called **rating** or **leveling.**

The operator's performance is rated, in relation to normal, at the time the observations are taken. Only those portions of the job over which the operator has **manual control** are rated. A rating factor may be applied to each manually controlled elemental reading, to the average of such elemental times, or to the selected cycle time if the job is entirely manually controlled. It is conceivable that a separate rating factor can be applied to different elemental average times if the operator does not show the same skill in all elements.

Standard Time. The base time represents "pure" production time per unit of output for a normal operator. It is exclusive of time consumed in **nonproductive activities, interruptions, and delays,** including such activities as setup, personal time, instruction, and filling out production forms, which appear periodically over a protracted period of time. If the activities are considered essential components of the job, they are referred to as **unavoidable delays,** and an allowance must be made for them in the standard time. Delays which are not a part of the normal job performance, whether or not they are controllable or avoidable by the operator, should not be included in the standard.

Allowances for normal unavoidable delays or interruptions to production, figured as a **percent of the base time,** are added to the base time to give the standard time.

The selected net cycle time represents expected performance for the operator observed. When allowances for interruptions and delays are added directly to this time, without reference to rating, the resultant time may be used for forecasting future actual performance. This can be the basis for estimating, scheduling, and budgeting, where **predicted actual** rather than **hypothetical standard performance** is pertinent. However, if an incentive plan is to be installed based on the time study, the actual future performance may deviate significantly from the observed performance due to the influence of the incentive.

Standard Write-up of Study. The write-up of every job studied should be a formal and precise report including a permanent record of all conditions under which the study was made and a detailed description as to the one best way developed. Porter gives Fig. 12 as an example of a formal standard report. At the top, identifying and filing data are entered and the results obtained are stated, as these

MILL SPUN SILK	DEPT. FINISHING	Reeling on 44" Drum	OPERATION Skeins Tied on 2 Sides Previously Controlled	Sizes 20—24 or 1050—1260	DEPT. PDF	OPER.

Mr. H. Blank, Supt.   Date 3-30

We Recommend the Following Task on the Above Work

SIGNED

RATE SYMBOL	HOURS PER —REV. —LB.	Doff Per Reel .33	PERCENT BONUS 20	MAX. RATE WORKMAN	MACHINE SYMBOL	Reels Atwood Auto-Stop

ANALYSIS: Studies have been made to determine the number of doffs an operator should take off one reel for sizes 1050 through 1260 which have been controlled first and which take 2 lebands per skein. The task is based on an average drum speed of 215 RPM, and an average of 2,750 yards of silk per skein with a maximum weight of 2.62 oz. For a description of the operation see the "Discussion of Tasks for Reeling from Large Gasser Spools on Atwood Auto-Stop Reels." Dec. 29, 19—.

DETAIL OPERATION: Time Necessary

A Cut end and tie around skein with other end................. .06 min.
B Put end waste and scissors into pocket, turn reel ¼ turn.... .05
C Lease or band one side of one skein...................... .05
D Turn reel through a ½ turn............................... .02
E Knock down reel drum and strip off the 15 skeins.......... .19
F Walk to pile, place doff on pile, and return to reel........ .06
G Connect 15 ends to the drum............................. .24
H Set automatic knock-off gear and start reel............... .08
J Straighten out two skeins on drum. Does not occur in this
      task ....
K Tie up one broken end (average)......................... .37
L Replace one empty spool with one full spool (average)..... .34
M Walk to the reel (average) .... .07
N Machine running time at 2.50 turns of the knock-off gear.... 10.47 min.

SYNTHESIS: In reeling one doff there are the following hand operations: Cut and tie the ends for 15 skeins; put end waste and scissors into pocket and turn reel through a ¼ turn; band 15 skeins on one side; turn reel through a ½ turn; band the opposite side of the 15 skeins; knock down drum and strip off the 15 skeins; walk to pile and return to reel; connect 15 ends to the drum; set knock-off gear and start reel. The supplementary hand operations are as follows: The average number of broken ends to tie up is 1.35; the average number of empty spools to replace is 3.7, based on 4.06 doffs per set of 15 spools; and the number of times it is necessary to walk to the reel to perform the above hand operations is 2. Therefore there is the following hand time per doff:

(15A + B + 30C + D + E + F + G + H + 1.35K + 3.7L + 2.0M)
(.90 + .05 + 1.50 + .02 + .19 + .06 + .24 + .08 + .50 + 1.258 + .14) 4.94 min.
Add 20% of (15A + B + 30C + D + E + F + G + H) for rest and
   delay .... .61
                                                          _____
            Total Hand Time per Doff..................... 5.55
The necessary machine time to run one doff................. 10.47
Add 5% for variation in speed of the drum................. .52
                                                          _____
            Total Machine Time per Doff.................. 10.99
The total hand time plus the machine time will be 5.55 + 10.99..... =16.54
Add 2¾% for personal time............................... .46
                                                          _____
                                                          17.00
Add 15% for interference................................ 2.55
                                                          _____
            Total Time Allowed per Doff................. 19.55 min.

The rate or time allowed per doff per reel = $\frac{19.55}{60}$ = .326 or .33 hr.

A bonus of 20% is recommended.

CHECKED H. E. F.
APPROVED

Fig. 12. Specimen task report.

are the items most frequently referred to. The report is divided into two main parts, analysis and synthesis.

Analysis includes a detailed description of the method of performing the operation and all details necessary to enable the job to be set up in standard fashion at any time. As part of the analysis, elementary operations are listed in the sequence in which they are performed by all subjects involved in the study. Each detail may be given a symbol at the left, and at the right is shown selected time as determined by the study. The description of detail operations should be so full and complete that no doubt could arise as to the exact series of motions used.

Synthesis consists of putting together the detail operations to form one complete cycle. Explanation of the method of putting the details together is given under this head. If any mathematical formula is used, it is stated by means of symbols in algebraic form. Time for unavoidable delays may be included and allowances for rest and delay made here also.

Calculations of standard and perhaps piece price follow. Space is provided at the bottom of the sheet for the signature of the checker of the study and for approval of the executive who makes the study effective. A special blank form for write-up is not necessary, but it is a convenience and saves time when many studies are to be made. When a prepared form is not used, the write-up is made in the same manner on blank paper and follows a sequential plan.

Instruction Card. The instruction card is an important part of the write-up. Its function is to convey to the worker complete information required for doing the standardized task, covering:

1. Equipment, tools, fixtures, and gages to use, and drawings required, if any. If the same set of tools is used on several different jobs, the list may be made out on a separate card so that it can be used with the instruction card for any job.
2. Feeds and speeds to be used, if they are under the worker's control.
3. What to do and how to do it, including elementary operations listed in their final sequence and in detail, sketches of setup if necessary for clearness, and standardized time allowed for each elementary operation and for the whole operation so that the worker may know in advance all that is expected.
4. Pay, and incentive, if any, allowed for performance of task.

In general, information on the instruction card will follow closely that on the observation sheet covering the final or perfected stage of study, with such additional data on equipment and method as the production worker may require. It forms a complete and permanent record of the task as standardized. With the tools called for and the best motions described, a properly qualified worker, with a reasonable amount of training and practice, should be able to perform the task in the time set.

Methods of Rating or Leveling

NEED FOR RATING. An individual operator's rate of production or speed of performance will show variation from cycle to cycle, hour to hour, and, perhaps, from day to day. Such variation is indicated in the precision of the study and the number of observations to take. The variability in performance among operators is considered in the **rating function** in which each operator is related to a **hypothetical normal operator**.

In order to obtain a standard time, rating is essential unless normal performance is defined as the statistical average of the rate of output of a sample of different operators performing the same operation. However, this may be an inadequate standard of good performance, and in many cases the number of operators on the same job is small. If the number is large, it may be uneconomical to sample more than a single operator.

THE RATING PROBLEM. There are two basic factors to be considered in the rating function. The first is the definition and determination of a concept of **normal performance** for a given type of work. The second is the adjustment of the observed time data to "normal" by some **numerical index.** These problems are not independent and the method of determining "normal" may be related to the method of arithmetically adjusting the observed data.

Concept of Normal. All rating demands some sort of judgment on the observer's part, and therefore the rating procedure has been subjected to considerable controversy throughout the history of time study. Much of the controversy has resulted from the claims of some that rating is a "scientific procedure." As pointed out by Abruzzi (Work, Workers, and Work Measurement), "Since the rating component of time study performs an evaluation function, it cannot possibly be a scientific process. The claims of scientific validity, however, have been so well advertised that almost everyone in this area has examined rating as though it were a scientific activity."

Accuracy. In rating, accuracy has a questionable objective meaning. There is no true objective standard, independent of human judgment, by which to evaluate a given operator's performance. Since judgment is the essential feature, accuracy has meaning only in the sense of a statistical average of the numerical rating indices made by a number of independent observers of a given operator's performance. **Precision** in rating, then, would be related to the variability of the indices around this average. Generally, it is uneconomical to take a large number of independent ratings of a given operation. However, a statistical norm may be determined for **sample basic operations** which are deemed indicative of the types of operations encountered in a given plant. That is, in a given plant films may be taken of basic operations including a sample of different operator paces. These can be rated independently by time study engineers and an agreement made as to what constitutes normal performance for these operations. These standards become the basis for training time study engineers in the concept of normal.

Rating Films. The Society for the Advancement of Management has conducted extensive studies, based on existing practices in industry, to establish a concept of **a fair day's work** and to develop films as a medium for **training in rating** (Rating of Time Studies). Films were made of 24 simple industrial, clerical, and laboratory operations. These were rated by 1,800 men from 200 companies. Norms for the operations were subsequently established and widely circulated for training purposes.

An analysis of the SAM procedure is made by William Gomberg (A Trade Union Analysis of Time Study) in which he states a number of weaknesses in the study. Two fundamental points brought out are: (1) Since the ratings made by each rater were from single estimates of single workers on a specific operation at each pace rated, both within-day and between-day rater variation for a given pace were eliminated. (2) There was a lack of proper statistical treatment of the rating data obtained from the study.

Localized Rating. Opposed to the notion of a universal standard of performance is the idea that effective norms can be established only at the local level of the individual plant and that, within the plant, each operation presents an **individual rating problem.** Coupled with this is the belief that experience on the rater's part in assessing the particular situation is all-important.

Walter A. Mattheiss (The Journal of Industrial Engineering, vol. 6) states that:

Each operation requires an individual search for factors that control its performance. In the process of learning the motions of each operation, the engineer determines the effective speed required to perform the operation. The result is based upon visible factors. In effect, this means that there is no universal norm for all operations, but that each operation has its own effective speed, and therefore its own norm based upon factors that control the operation. It is in the analysis and evaluation of these controlling factors that the operational norm is derived. This basis provides more factual information than any analysis of bare figures.

It is conceivable that the second problem of rating, that of making the numerical adjustment, may be avoided by having the operator work only at **normal pace** and **skill.** It must be noted that the observer still exercises judgment as to what normal performance is and instructs the operator accordingly. This method is basically unsound, due to the problem of attempting to make an operator perform at some pace or skill level which is unnatural to him.

The performance rating procedure may be avoided at the time of a particular time study by employing **standard time data** which are already leveled or rated. However, worker reactions to fairness of standard may not be eliminated, since the standard data were rated at the time of formulation. Also, when the observer applies motion-time standards, he must use his judgment in determining the best method and in interpreting this method in terms of the motion-time system employed.

Consistency. The predominant requirement of good rating practice seems to be consistency. There may be a significant range within which the absolute rating index is acceptable to everyone concerned. But where the rating is inconsistent, as indicated by significant **standard time variation** between like operations performed in the plant, considerable objection will result from the operators concerned.

Simplicity. Another necessary characteristic of a good rating procedure is simplicity. The operator is more likely to accept a standard time if the rating procedure is not too complex for him to understand.

Machine elements are not generally rated. If the machine elements are automatically controlled by the machine, the elemental base times can be determined from engineering data or from a number of stop-watch readings. If the pace of the machine element can be controlled by the operator, an **allowed element time** can be calculated from empirical data. For instance, the time to drill a ¾-in. hole to a depth of 1 in. in 1020 steel can be determined from tables of drill speeds and feeds for the particular material and drill size. The time to lower and raise the drill spindle to and from the material are manually controlled elements which are timed with the watch.

There are a number of rating procedures which have been successfully used by trained time study engineers within the framework of good time study practice. Their success may be due to the manner in which they are employed, rather than to their scientific validity. Some of the more popular ones are discussed in the following paragraphs.

PERFORMANCE RATING. In performance rating the speed of the operator's motions or his general pace is rated against a concept of normal.

Percentage Basis. One widely used method of speed rating is to rate performance on a percentage basis. The **normal** operator is rated at 100 percent. A slower operator would be rated at a percentage less than 100, and for a faster operator the rating would be over 100 percent. For example, data from a time study would be rated as follows:

		Average Time per Piece
a.	Pick up piece, insert in fixture..............................	0.056 min.
b.	DRILL	0.107 min.
c.	Remove piece from fixture to tote box.......................	0.038 min.

		Base Time
a.	0.056 rating at 90%, or 0.056 × 0.90............................	0.050
b.	0.107 rating at 100%, or 0.107 × 1.00..........................	0.107
c.	0.038 rating at 90%, or 0.038 × 0.90...........................	0.034

Point Basis. Rating an operator's time for speed alone on a point basis has the advantage of simplicity, but it also is dependent on judgment. Usually each element is individually rated. Shumard (Primer of Time Study) suggests the use of the following rating table:

Symbol	Speed	Symbol	Speed
100	Superfast	65	Good −
95	Fast +	60	Normal
90	Fast	55	Fair +
85	Fast −	50	Fair
80	Excellent	45	Fair −
75	Good +	40	Poor
70	Good		

Data from a time study on an operator working "good +" for elements *a* and *c*, and "normal" for element *b*, is:

		Average Time per Piece
a.	Pick up piece, place on bench.............................	0.050 min.
b.	BURR piece with file.....................................	0.270 min.
c.	Place piece in tray......................................	0.030 min.

		Rated Time
a.	0.050 time with 75 rating, or 0.050 × 75/60..................	0.063
b.	0.270 time with 60 rating, or 0.270 × 60/60..................	0.270
c.	0.030 time with 75 rating, or 0.030 × 75/60..................	0.038

Elements *a* and *c* were judged to be performed 75/60 or 25 percent faster than normal. The operator performing at 60 on element *b* is producing at normal speed equivalent to **unstimulated day work effort,** and the time does not have to be adjusted.

Shumard says, "From compiled industrial data covering many plants that have attractive wage payment incentive plans which result in excellent quality of product at low unit costs, it was learned that group average speed of the operators in each plant was 33⅓ percent faster than normal. . . . Consequently we may safely set up 80 as the ideal effort-goal in manufacturing . . .," the 80 being 133⅓ percent of 60, normal. This condition, however, will not hold true in all cases.

LEVELING PLAN. Leveling is a method of rating in which the causes producing differences in performance are analyzed according to **factors** of skill, effort, conditions, and consistency (Lowry, Maynard, and Stegemerten, Time and Motion Study). Each of these factors is graded with a numerical index associated with each grade.

Skill is defined as the ability to follow a given method. **Effort** is "the will to work." **Conditions** are those factors which affect the operator rather than the operation, such as lighting, temperature, and minor variations from normal conditions. **Consistency** takes into consideration minor variations not detected as skill, effort, or conditions.

With reference to both skill and effort, characteristics of the six grades are given qualitative description. For example, **good effort** is described as follows:

1. Little or no lost time.
2. Takes an interest in the work.
3. Takes no notice of the time study man.
4. Works at best pace suited for endurance.
5. Follows a set sequence.
6. Conscientious about his work.
7. Has faith in time study man.
8. Encourages advice and suggestions and makes suggestions.
9. Well prepared for job and has workplace in good order.
10. Steady and reliable.

The observer judges the skill, effort, and consistency of the operator and the conditions, checking off each item on the leveling chart. For instance, if skill is at level B_2 (0.08), effort B_2 (0.08), conditions C (0.02), and consistency C (0.01), the sum of these, 0.19, would be the **leveling factor** applied to the average times for each element. All elements are not necessarily given the same grading, for the observer may decide to grade certain elements differently from the general grading applied to the study. In using leveling, it should be borne in mind that the accuracy of the final standard is no greater than the accuracy of the observer's judgment. One aid to the observer's judgment of skill is the record of the operator's length of experience on the class of work or the particular job. The operator's diligent application to work at hand with no unnecessary delays or interruptions is an indication of good effort, the value of which must be judged by the observer. Variations from conditions previously standardized for the job are allowed for in the leveling. Consistency of the operator may be determined while the study is in progress or later from the observations. It should be remembered that use of high or low figures on the **leveling scale** introduces greater chance of error, and in those cases it is better to restudy the job on another operator.

SYNTHETIC LEVELING. Another method of leveling is to compare the actual time obtained for certain elements with predetermined standard elemental times. According to Morrow (Motion Economy and Work Measurement), the method of applying synthetic leveling is to take the time study as usual, break it down into elements, and then compare as many of these elements as possible with the **predetermined standard times.** The percentage of variation of the actual times from the standards is arrived at, and the same percentage applied to parts of the study for which predetermined standard times are not available.

OBJECTIVE RATING. Mundel (Motion and Time Study) reduces the rating procedure to two functions—rating of **observed pace** and of **job difficulty.** As he says, "The actual pace of performance observed must be understood to be a function of the skill, aptitude, and exertion of the operator, but these variables are neither separately identifiable nor is a separate appraisal pertinent." His conclusion is that all three of these factors are reflected in either **pace** or **job difficulty** or both.

The importance of his concept is stated as follows:

In the typical time study procedure, the time study observer first judges job difficulty, in order to form a concept of the appearance of adequate performance for the job (as required by the definition of standard time he is using), and then judges observed pace, against this imagined concept. . . . What makes a more reliable time study rating procedure possible is, first of all, the realization that the difficulty of the job and its effect on maximum possible pace does not need to be judged but may be reduced to tabular form as a function of the strength required, amount of body used, degree of dexterity, and the like.

The procedure of objective rating involves the rating of observed pace against some concept of normal which is gained through studying typical operations, films, or averages of engineer's ratings. The second part of objective rating consists of a percentage adjustment after the application of the numerical rating in the first step. This percentage increment is taken from **experimental data,** in the form of tables, of the effect of various **observable** factors that control the exertion required.

Allowances

TYPES OF ALLOWANCES. The **base time** represents the net production time per unit of output for the normal operator. The **standard time** is a gross unit time at normal performance. This gross time will be greater than the net production time due to interruptions or delays reducing production time, and to certain factors such as fatigue, adverse or extreme job conditions, and rework whose influences on production time were not considered in the measurement or rating stages of the study. The base time is therefore adjusted by percent allowances to account for these factors.

Interruptions. As pointed out in the time study procedure, certain interruptions to the productive cycle, if minor, may be classed as irregular elements of the time study and included in the base time as **prorated items.** Interruptions of a large magnitude and periodic nature may be classed as **separate jobs** or operations and given an independent standard time. Allowances, then, are added to account for those interruptions and delays which are residual and not included in base time or separately standardized. **Allowances** include time necessary for:

1. Personal needs and rest periods.
2. Unavoidable delays, such as:
   a. Setup, tear-down, and cleanup.
   b. Tool and equipment maintenance.
   c. Getting supplies and raw material.
   d. Receiving instructions from the supervisor.
   e. Filling out production or other forms.

f. Periodic inspection of material or parts.
g. Reading blueprints or instruction cards.

Personal and Delay Allowances. Personal allowances cover the time that must be allowed every worker for his personal necessities. They may range from 3 to 5 percent, varying with jobs but tending to be higher when the work is heavy or unpleasant.

Delay allowances may be avoidable or unavoidable. **Avoidable delays** are not included in the standard time. While avoidable delays usually refer to those avoidable by the operator, certain delays classified in this manner may be avoided by better shop management or supervision. Although incidental interruptions and minor delays from tool breakage, machine stoppages, variations in material, and supervisory contacts should be kept to a minimum, they do take place. These are **unavoidable delays** which are covered by an allowance determined by careful observation and study.

The interruptive tasks, which are considered to be normal constituents of the job and are referred to as unavoidable, are susceptible to proper design or improvement as a part of operation analysis. Prior to determining their time for allowance purposes, effort should be made to analyze and standardize these elements of the job just as with productive operations.

Fatigue Allowance. Fatigue in varying degrees is a normal part of every manually controlled operation. Fatigue is manifested during the course of the day in the gradual reduction in rate of output. This is reflected in an increase both in mean cycle time and in the number and intensity of delays. Fatigue is difficult to define objectively and to measure on the job. By extending the length of the time study or work sampling study over the period of at least a day, the influence of fatigue may be reflected in the net cycle time and in delay allowances. Lengthening of the study in conjunction with a sufficient number of observations may make very little direct allowance necessary for a light operation.

Certain companies include an allowance for fatigue as a matter of policy for various classes of jobs. Fatigue may also be taken into consideration in the designation of definite **rest periods.**

Other Allowances. Certain allowances besides those for delays may be added to base time to adjust for circumstances peculiar to the operation in question, such as:

1. **Small production lot sizes.** Sometimes the actual production period is too short to allow the operator to reach a pace in line with his usual performance. Where a large number of small-lot jobs are worked on during the day with various setups included, an allowance as high as 15 percent may be required to allow the normal operator to make normal earnings.
2. **Training.** During a training period an allowance may be added to give the trainee an opportunity to gain reasonable earnings. This may be a "sliding" allowance which is progressively decreased during the training period until it reaches zero at a predetermined time. If the company has sufficient data to show the effect of learning on production rates this training allowance may be correlated with the learning curve. (See section on Wage Plans and Controls.)
3. **Extreme job conditions.** Such conditions as unfavorable weather on outside jobs, and extreme heat, noise, or fumes on inside operations may be allowed for.
4. **Spoilage and rework.** On certain operations experience may indicate that a certain percentage of parts are spoiled due to factors beyond the operator's control. The time required to rework these parts may be included as an allowance.

DETERMINATION OF ALLOWANCES. The direct measurement of many of the factors which are to be included as allowances is difficult. In many cases an allowance may be the result of company policy, judgment based on long experience, precedence, or tradition. In certain instances, allowances for specific types of jobs may appear in the union contract. In still other cases, the individual time study engineer may resort to his own judgment in setting the amount

For allowances such as those for abnormal job conditions and small production lot sizes, the analysis of company data may lead to more objective results. Special studies employing statistical methods may be made to determine the need for and the amount of allowances for the various conditions in question.

For a particular operation, the normal time consumed in a work day in various **nonproductive activities** can be estimated by special studies employing the interruption study or work sampling. These methods are described in the following paragraphs.

INTERRUPTION STUDIES. Interruption studies are sometimes referred to as **production** or **all-day studies.** The general purpose of the interruption study is to determine the various activities carried out by an operator on a job during the normal work day and the time consumed in each activity. The stop watch is usually used as the measuring device. The results of the study may be employed to:

1. Determine allowances for fatigue, and for personal and unavoidable delays.
2. Check the results of a time study.
3. Indicate areas of inefficiency in the operation or job.

Whatever the use of the study, the method of taking the observations is the same. Although the study is very simple to take, it is rather tedious, and a new time study man may be assigned to the job. The method requires a critical observation of the operation or job and a careful record of the activities. The observer starts at the beginning of the work day and keeps a record of the time for each and every delay that occurs, at the same time recording the productive time separately.

Data Obtained. In Fig. 13, Morrow (Motion Economy and Work Measurement) shows a hypothetical example of an interruption study on a drilling operation. The interruption study is shown from 7 A.M. to 8:30 A.M., and it is continued throughout the day in a similar manner. The stop watch is allowed to run continuously and, in addition, every half-hour the time is recorded from an ordinary watch. Observed readings are noted, as shown in the column headed "Ob." It will be noted that symbols have been used for parts of the operation which are frequently repeated:

D—Drilling time.

D-p—Part of drilling time.

H—Handling time, from the end of drilling time to start of drilling again.

H-p—Part of handling time.

In the case illustrated, the **productive time** has been divided into machine and handling time. Ordinarily this separation would not be necessary and the productive time would be kept as one item. The number of pieces produced should be recorded. Symbols can be used for delays if their nature is known beforehand. In this case delays are described, viz., talk, belt broke, adjust oil pump, etc. Production time is recorded as shown. After the study has been completed, the

INTERRUPTION STUDY

Operation: Drill   Department: Drilling
Article: G18M Slide
Time: Start: 7 A.M.   Stop: 4 P.M.   Elapsed: 8 hours (1 hour out)   Units Produced: 135
Operator: #260

Ob — Observations   Df — Differences

	Ob	Df		Ob	Df		Ob	Df		Ob	Df
Start	0.00	— 7 A.M.		4.79	0.38	Adjust oil pump.	1.76	3.18	H-p	19.06	1.32
Get work ticket	4.01	4.01	H	6.51	1.72	D	2.13	.37	D	19.42	.36
Talk	5.26	1.25	D	6.88	.37	H-p	2.43	.30	H	21.00	1.58
Grind tools and adjust	20.10	14.84	H	8.29	1.41	Talk	4.58	2.15	D	21.39	.39
Arrange work bench	22.00	1.90	D	8.60	.39	H-p	5.84	1.26	H-p	21.95	.56
Talk	24.50	2.50	H	10.18	1.50	D	6.19	.35	Talk	22.80	.85
Place tote box	24.63	.13	D	10.56	.38	H	7.77	1.58	H-p	24.05	1.25
H	25.98	1.35	H	12.08	1.52	D	8.15	.38	D	24.42	.37
D	26.34	.36	D	12.45	.37	H	10.01	1.86	H	25.91	1.49
H	28.32	1.98	H	14.33	1.88	D-p	10.38	.37	D-p	26.17	.26
D-p	28.70	.38	D-p	14.53	.20	H	11.99	1.61	Belt off	27.23	1.06
H	30.45	1.75 7:30 A.M.	Belt broke.	24.78	10.25	D	12.38	.39	Adjust oil pump	29.90	2.67
D	30.82	.37	D-p	25.06	.28	H-p	13.94	1.56	D-p	.20	.30 8:30 A.M
H	2.44	1.62	H	26.69	1.63	D	14.31	.37	H	1.87	1.67
D	2.83	.39	D	27.05	.36	H-p	14.59	.28	D	2.25	.38
H	4.41	1.58	H	28.58	1.53 8 A.M.	Adjust Machine	17.74	3.15	Personal	5.00	2.75
									Rest of day not shown. Refer to summary.		

Fig. 13. Observation and analysis sheet for an interruption study.

differences between the recorded times are calculated to obtain the time for each element in the study. Fig. 14 shows the **interruption study summary sheet.** The observation sheet shown in Fig. 5 may be effectively used for the study itself. The study may extend over one or more shifts and possibly for more than a day if it is advisable.

INTERRUPTION STUDY—SUMMARY				
Operation	Productive Time (min.)	Preparation Time (min.)	Delay Time (min.)	
			Unavoidable (and personal)	Avoidable
Drilling time, 135 pieces.	52.30			
Handling time.........	240.50			
Grind and adjust tools..		25.60		
Change work ticket.....		8.00		8.61
Place tote box, arrange work bench..........		2.95		
Talk.................				20.62
Belt broke, slipped off, etc.................			5.00	25.68
Waiting for work.......				35.81
Pump adjustment, packing, etc.............				31.34
Adjust machine........			9.71	
Personal.............			13.88	
Total time 480.00. ...	292.80	36.55	28.59	122.06

Total time, excluding avoidable delays = (sum of 292.80, 36.55, and 28.59) = 357.94 min. *Time per piece,* 2.64 min. excluding avoidable delays.

Fig. 14. Summary sheet of an interruption study.

Computation of Allowances from Interruption Study. Considering the above example, assume that during a previous time study on the same operation the **selected net cycle time** was determined to be 2.04 min. per unit.

Productive time from interruption study .... 292.80 min.
Productive time using independent time study results
   (135 units × 2.04 min./unit) .... 275.40 min.

     Difference .... 17.40 min.

The difference may be assumed to be caused by fatigue. This is based on the assumption that the independent time study was taken at a time of day before the results of fatigue were noticeable. However, the difference could partially be due to sources of bias in the time study, including particularly a change in operator performance level.

Percentage allowance for fatigue ....$\frac{17.40}{275.40} = 6.3\%$

Personal time .... 13.88 min

Percentage allowance for personal time .... $\dfrac{13.88}{275.40} = 5.1\%$

Unavoidable delays .... 14.71 min.

Percentage allowance for unavoidable delays .... $\dfrac{14.71}{275.40} = 5.3\%$

Total Allowances 16.7%

In order to determine standard time, the 16.7 percent of base time is added to the base time per unit. The method of computing delay and personal time allowances shown above is biased toward giving a high value. This is in comparison with use of 292.80 min. as the base rather than 275.40 min. It should also be noted that **avoidable delays** are removed from the study before calculating allowances. It is assumed that these avoidable delays will largely be absent in actual practice due to closer controls. Also, it is assumed that the time consumed in avoidable delays, 122.06 min., will be utilized in production time, personal time, and delays in about the same proportion as observed in the interruption study. The allowances determined from the interruption study may be biased toward the high side if the amount of avoidable delay time in the study is high. That is, the more the time devoted to avoidable delays the smaller becomes the production time which is used as a base for calculating the percent allowances.

If the period needed to study an operation must be long, the interruption study is a relatively uneconomical method of observation. This is particularly true if the purpose of the study is merely to measure **delay times**. A more economical method in this case may be to use work sampling. If the purpose of the all-day study is to gather data for **methods improvement** or for more efficient programming of the operation, there may be no substitute for continuous observation (see the section on Motion and Methods Study).

Work Sampling

DEFINITION OF METHOD. The work sampling procedure involves the taking of qualitative observations of a work system randomly over a protracted time period. The state of the work system is classified by **type of activities** such as production, setup, and idle for repairs. At a given instant for a given machine

Time of Observation (Randomly Selected)	Number of Observations per Trip	Number of Occurrences of Idle Machine
8:20 A.M.	3	3
8:32 A.M.	3	1
9:00 A.M.	3	2
. . .	. . .	. . .
. . .	. . .	. . .
4:50 P.M.	3	2

Totals: 80 Trips   240 Observations   72 Idle Machine Observations

Estimate of percent idle time = 72/240 = 0.30
Estimate of idle machines = 0.30 × 3 = 0.90

Fig. 15. Results of work sampling observations of three machines.

or operator, these activities are mutually exclusive. An instantaneous **sample observation** is taken to determine the state of the operation in terms of the class of activity. A ratio of the number of observations recorded for a particular activity to the total number of observations made in the sample gives an estimate of the **percent time spent in that activity.** If the study is made of a group of similar objects the results may be expressed as a percent of the group in a given activity.

For example, assume that the problem is to determine the **percent idle time** for a group of three machines employed in a certain department. A work sampling study is made with the results shown in Fig. 15.

The procedure of random observations was first put to practical use by Tippett to determine causes for loom stoppages in the English textile industry. It was subsequently employed in the United States, at first for determining operation delay allowances for time studies. The technique is often referred to as **ratio delay** study, although its expansion for uses other than setting delay allowances has resulted in the general term "work sampling."

USES OF WORK SAMPLING. The basic purpose of work sampling is to estimate the percentage of a protracted time period consumed by various activity states of a resource, such as equipment, machines, or operators. The technique has broad application in both **manufacturing** and **service** endeavors. It may be used to:

1. Determine allowances for inclusion in standard times.
2. Indicate the nature of the distribution of work activities within a gang operation.
3. Estimate the percent utilization of groups of similar machines or equipment.
4. Indicate how materials handling equipment is being used.
5. Provide the basis for indirect labor time standards.
6. Indicate areas where methods study may profitably be used.
7. Determine the productive and nonproductive utilization of clerical operations.
8. Determine a standard time for a repetitive operation (as an alternative to the stop watch method).

PROCEDURE IN WORK SAMPLING. Just as in time study, the accuracy of an estimate obtained from work sampling is dependent on the control and execution of the **study procedure,** whereas precision is controlled by the **number of observations** taken.

Defining the Parent Population. The objective of the study must be clearly defined. This is tantamount to defining carefully the parent population to be sampled. This population should be **homogeneous** in the sense of containing items with similar operating or other characteristics. For instance, assume that the purpose of the study in a printing plant is to determine percent down-time on the presses. If there are a number of different types of presses with different operating characteristics, then a number of independent work sampling studies should be taken, each with a population of like presses. On the other hand, if the purpose of the study is to determine time spent for personal reasons by the press operators, the population may cut across dissimilar presses and include all press operators.

Where unlike objects are grouped to constitute a **heterogeneous population,** the sample estimates have only an aggregate meaning, and no real conclusions may be drawn about the characteristics of the unlike individuals in the population.

Activity Classification. The classes of activities for a given population must **exhaust all possibilities** and be **mutually exclusive.** Each type of activity or each state of the entity being measured must be so clearly defined as to its content that a proper **discrimination between classes** can be made at the moment of observation. There should be little opportunity for indecision regarding the activity to which a particular sample observation is assigned. In the example of the three machines, assume that the classification includes, among others, the categories "down-time for adjustment" and "down-time for maintenance." On a given observation the analyst may find a machine undergoing a repair while it is also being adjusted. This leaves a question regarding the state the machine is in.

Length of Study. The period over which observations are taken determines the **size of the parent population.** Just as with time study, the work sampling study should be of such length that all activities which are a normal part of the operation have a chance of being observed and that cyclical influences can also be covered.

If the study is made short for economic reasons, the extended population should be tested at certain intervals for homogeneity. This may be done with the use of the control chart (see Fig. 23). If there are reasons to believe that there are present in the extended population significant causes for variation that were not present in the parent population, then subsequent data may be **pooled** with the original data to provide a new estimate.

Random Observations. A single observation consists of an **instantaneous or snapshot** look at the operation in order to determine the state of activity. Such an observation should be taken at a randomly selected point in time.

A **random selection** of observation times is made in the following manner. The study period, or parent population, is divided into specific time units. For instance, the length of the study may be designated as 10 days (4,800 min.). This period is broken down into units of, for example, 1/10 hr. (6 min.). The parent population contains 800 units, from which a sample of N readings may be selected. The number of observations, N, should be less than 800, unless there is more than one observable entity in the population and a number of observations can be made in a single trip. The randomization can be done with the use of a table of random numbers. If the length of the study is short and the number of required observations large, the trips may be so frequent as to warrant the use of an interruption or all-day time study instead of work sampling.

Nonrandom **systematic sampling** may be employed under certain conditions. By this method sample observations are taken at regular intervals during the course of the study. This has the advantage of greater ease in planning the observer's work. Also, it facilitates the programming of several different studies to be conducted over the same period. That is, several jobs may be observed during a trip.

The use of systematic sampling is recommended only when there is no regular pattern or **cylical behavior** in the elements or activities of the job being studied. If these cyclical conditions exist, then systematic sampling may introduce a significant bias into the estimate, and the models employed to determine precision or sample size will be meaningless.

Use of Random Numbers. In work sampling, the times of observation for any given sample must be selected without **bias.** That is, these observations must be completely random with respect to time. Therefore, the problem is one of determining the times at which observations should be made. The number of observations (sample size) has been determined for a given confidence level, and the specific observation times must be distributed randomly through the study period.

This can be accomplished in several ways. The most effective way, especially where there are multiple studies involved, is through the use of a table of **random numbers**. Fig. 16, adapted from Fisher and Yates (Statistical Tables), shows such a table of random numbers. The study period should be subdivided into equal length increments of time, and each increment is identified in numerical order. Then the table of random numbers will determine the identity of the specific observation times for the sample.

┌Step 3 ┌Step 1   ┌Step 2

87	02	22	57	51	61	09	43	95	06	58	24	82	03	47
39	77	32	77	09	85	52	05	30	62	47	83	51	62	74
28	06	24	25	93	16	71	13	59	78	23	05	47	47	25
97	67	63	99	61	46	38	03	93	22	69	81	21	99	21
69	30	16	09	(05)	88	(69)	58	28	99	35	07	44	75	47
87	03	04	79	88	08	(13)	13	85	51	55	34	57	72	69
52	06	79	79	45	82	63	18	27	44	69	66	92	19	09
52	70	05	48	34	56	65	05	61	86	90	92	10	70	80
15	33	59	05	28	22	87	26	07	47	86	96	98	29	06
85	13	99	24	44	49	13	09	79	49	74	16	32	23	02
41	10	76	47	91	44	04	95	49	66	39	60	04	59	81
82	21	15	65	20	33	29	94	71	11	15	91	29	12	03
98	56	10	56	79	77	21	30	27	12	90	49	22	23	62
99	74	20	52	36	87	09	41	15	09	98	60	16	03	03
23	47	37	17	31	54	08	01	88	63	39	41	88	92	10
77	34	55	45	70	08	18	27	38	90	16	95	86	70	75
42	38	06	45	18	64	84	73	31	65	52	53	37	97	15
60	75	86	90	68	24	64	19	35	51	56	61	87	39	12
22	00	27	69	85	29	81	94	78	70	21	94	47	90	12
91	51	67	62	44	40	98	05	93	78	23	32	65	41	18
68	47	22	00	20	35	55	31	51	51	00	83	63	22	55
36	63	32	08	58	37	40	13	68	97	87	64	81	07	83
22	07	90	47	03	28	14	11	30	79	20	69	22	40	98
92	06	88	07	77	56	11	50	81	69	40	23	72	51	39
34	68	35	48	77	33	42	40	90	60	73	96	53	97	86

Fig. 16. A table of random numbers.

For instance, assume that 15 observations are required for a given study over a one-day study period. The day, which contains 480 min., could be divided into 96 five-minute increments. The first five-minute increment would be identified as observation period No. 1, the second increment as No. 2, etc., so that there would be 96 observation increments. Turning to the table of random numbers (Fig. 16), point a pencil at any one of the numbers, such as that in column 7, row 5 (step 1) and read down, starting with the number 69 as shown in Column (A), Fig. 17. (Obviously, if a number larger than a two-digit number is required, adjacent columns could be combined as needed.) In reading, omit any numbers that numerically exceed the total number of increments (96 in this example).

Therefore, in the sequence read, 98 would be omitted because it is excessive. Furthermore, the second 18 would be omitted because it is a repeat. This is shown in column (A) of Fig. 17. Then the first 15 usable numbers selected, when arranged in numerical order, will identify the specific time periods that will make up the sample as shown in columns (B) and (C). Therefore, the first observation would be 5 increments (20 min.) after the starting time (8:00 A.M.). The observation times are tabulated as shown in column (D). Note that observation 55 would have occurred during the one-hour lunch period; therefore the actual observation time is one clock-hour later. Likewise, each after-lunch reading is one clock-hour later.

(A) Random Numbers As Read	(B) Usable Random Numbers	(C) Arranged in Numerical Order	(D) Corresponding Observation Time
69	69	04	8:20 A.M.
13	13	08	8:40
63	63	09	8:45
65	65	13	9:05
87	87	18	9:30
18	18	21	9:45
04	04	29	10:25
29	29	55	(12:35) 1:35 P.M.
21	21	63	2:15
09	09	64	2:20
08	08	65	2:25
18	84	69	2:45
84	64	81	3:45
64	81	84	4:00
81	55	87	4:15
98			
55			

Fig. 17. Use of random numbers for the selection of observation times.

A word of caution is necessary in the use of a table of random numbers. Repeated use of the same series of numbers should be avoided by reading the series in different directions, i.e., diagonally, bottom to top, etc. Moreover, if these tables are going to be used frequently, the natural tendency to select a position in the middle of the page should be avoided by using the initial number to identify the starting line and the number to the left, the starting column. If there are fewer rows or columns than the number to be selected, the first number below or to the left, respectively, that meets the conditions can be used to locate the starting position. In this example, the first number pointed to was 69, which is used to identify the row. However, since there are not 69 rows of figures, the next figure below would be used to identify the row. Step No. 2 of Fig. 16 shows then, that the 13th row contains the starting position. To find the starting column, the first number to the left of step No. 1 which is less than the number of columns (15 in this table) is picked. This is shown as step No. 3 in Fig. 16, and column 5 of row 13 is therefore the starting position for the series of random numbers. This series, starting with 79, would be used as demonstrated in Fig. 17.

This specific pattern need not be followed, but there should be some specific pattern agreed upon in order for the end result to be a truly random selection.

OBSERVATION PROCEDURES. The observer passes the operation, takes an instantaneous look, and places a check on the observation sheet next to the class of activity observed. Fig. 18 shows a sample observation sheet used for the study of clerical operations, with frequency based on the table of random numbers.

WORK SAMPLING OBSERVATION SHEET

Date _7/5 — 7/7_ Observer _L. R. Jones_ Sheet _1_ of _1_

Dept. _Accounting Dep't_

Subject: Eight Clerical Operations

Activities	Observations	Total
Typing		133
Writing and hand entries		104
Telephoning		63
Machine operation		80
Talking with supervisor		67
Talking with others		56
Walking		31
Handling papers		88
Filing		28
Absent from office		108
Other activities		95
Total observations		853

Fig. 18. Observation sheet for work sampling study.

Since the observation is instantaneous the activities should be clearly defined as to context and demarcation points to avoid indecision in classification. The classification may be difficult to make instantaneously in some cases, and the observer may have to delay the observation momentarily to check the activity. For instance, if the operator is observed bending down to the floor, he may be doing so to change a gear in the machine or to pick up a part from the floor. It is possible that the operator can inject bias into the study by being aware of the observer's presence and anticipating the time of observation. The observer may also rate the operator's performance if the system under observation is manually controlled.

Independent Studies. Different operations may be observed during a single trip by the observer. In this case the observer's time is concentrated on making observations for an extended time. Analysis of the data and formulation of standards can be performed subsequently, without interruptions for making observations. Where more than one study is conducted, the time for starting the trip and the operation to be observed at the start of the trip are randomized. The direction of the trip may also be altered.

When the number of observations and amount of data required are large, the clerical procedure may be reduced by using a **mark-sensitive** tabulating card sys'em. A common method of making the observations is to use a card for each observation. Other information required for the analysis, such as department or file reference code and the date, can either be written on the card or prepunched. It may be desirable to leave two columns for a **reference code** denoting the number of the round of observations, thereby signifying the time of day. The cards are processed to give the required information.

Number of Observations. The number of observations to be taken depends on the **required precision** and the desired **level of confidence** in the estimate. The precision error in the estimate is due to sampling, provided that the observations are randomly taken and are independent.

The general statistical model used to express this **standard error** has been pointed out as the binomial model (see description of statistical work measurement models). It may be used to determine the error in an estimate of a given sample size or to determine the sample size from a given acceptable error and confidence level.

For instance, assume that for the group of three machines the percent idle time is estimated to be 0.30. Usually this is unknown at the start of the study and must be estimated from **preliminary observations**. What number of observations, N, is necessary to give an assurance of 95 to 100 that the true value lies within ± 5 percent? In other words, with the precision interval set at $p = 0.30 \pm 0.05$:

$$\bar{p} = .30$$

$$2\sigma_{\bar{p}} = .05$$

$$= 2\sqrt{\frac{\bar{p}(1 - \bar{p})}{N}}$$

$$.05 = 2\sqrt{\frac{.30 \times .70}{N}}$$

$$N = 336 \text{ observations necessary}$$

The **precision interval** may be expressed either as an absolute error, $\pm x\%$, or as a percentage of the estimated p, that is as $\pm x\% p$. For a given error

Percent of Total Time Occupied by Activity or Delay (p)	Standard Error (Relative)									
	±1	±2	±3	±4	±5	±6	±7	±8	±9	±10
1	3,960,000	990,000	440,000	247,500	158,400	110,000	80,800	61,900	48,900	39,600
2	1,960,000	490,000	217,800	122,500	78,400	54,400	40,000	30,600	24,200	19,600
3	1,293,300	323,300	143,700	80,800	51,700	35,900	26,400	20,200	16,000	12,900
4	960,000	240,000	106,700	60,000	38,400	26,700	19,600	15,000	11,900	9,600
5	760,000	190,000	84,400	47,500	30,400	21,100	15,500	11,900	9,390	7,600
6	626,700	156,700	69,600	39,200	25,100	17,400	12,800	9,790	7,740	6,270
7	531,400	132,900	59,000	33,200	21,300	14,800	10,800	8,300	6,560	5,310
8	460,000	115,000	51,100	28,800	18,400	12,800	9,380	7,190	5,680	4,600
9	404,400	101,100	44,900	25,300	16,200	11,200	8,250	6,320	5,000	4,040
10	360,000	90,000	40,000	22,500	14,400	10,000	7,340	5,630	4,450	3,600
11	323,600	80,900	36,000	20,200	12,900	8,990	6,600	5,060	4,000	3,240
12	293,300	73,300	32,600	18,300	11,700	8,150	5,980	4,580	3,620	2,930
13	267,500	66,900	29,700	16,700	10,700	7,440	5,460	4,180	3,310	2,680
14	245,700	61,400	27,300	15,400	9,830	6,830	5,010	3,840	3,040	2,460
15	226,700	56,700	25,200	14,200	9,070	6,300	4,620	3,540	2,800	2,270
16	210,000	52,500	23,300	13,100	8,400	5,830	4,280	3,280	2,590	2,100
17	195,300	48,800	21,700	12,200	7,810	5,420	3,980	3,050	2,410	1,950
18	182,200	45,600	20,200	11,400	7,290	5,060	3,720	2,850	2,250	1,820
19	170,500	42,600	18,900	10,700	6,820	4,740	3,480	2,660	2,110	1,710
20	160,000	40,000	17,800	10,000	6,400	4,440	3,260	2,500	1,980	1,600
21	150,500	37,600	16,700	9,400	6,020	4,180	3,070	2,350	1,860	1,510
22	141,800	35,500	15,800	8,860	5,670	3,940	2,890	2,220	1,750	1,420
23	133,900	33,500	14,900	8,370	5,360	3,720	2,730	2,090	1,650	1,340
24	126,700	31,700	14,100	7,920	5,070	3,520	2,580	1,980	1,560	1,270

25	120,000	30,000	13,300	7,500	4,800	3,330	2,450	1,880	1,480	1,200
26	113,800	28,500	12,600	7,120	4,550	3,160	2,320	1,780	1,410	1,140
27	108,100	27,000	12,000	6,760	4,330	3,000	2,210	1,690	1,340	1,080
28	102,900	25,700	11,400	6,430	4,110	2,860	2,100	1,610	1,270	1,030
29	97,900	24,500	10,900	6,120	3,920	2,720	2,000	1,530	1,210	980
30	93,300	23,300	10,400	5,830	3,730	2,590	1,900	1,460	1,150	935
31	89,000	22,300	9,890	5,570	3,560	2,470	1,820	1,390	1,100	890
32	85,000	21,300	9,440	5,310	3,400	2,360	1,730	1,330	1,050	850
33	81,200	20,300	9,000	5,080	3,250	2,260	1,660	1,270	1,000	810
34	77,600	19,400	8,630	4,850	3,110	2,160	1,580	1,210	960	775
35	74,300	18,600	8,250	4,640	2,970	2,060	1,520	1,160	915	745
36	71,100	17,800	7,900	4,440	2,840	1,980	1,450	1,110	880	710
37	68,100	17,000	7,570	4,260	2,720	1,890	1,400	1,060	840	680
38	65,300	16,300	7,250	4,080	2,610	1,810	1,330	1,020	805	655
39	62,600	15,600	6,950	3,910	2,500	1,740	1,280	980	775	625
40	60,000	15,000	6,670	3,750	2,400	1,670	1,220	940	740	600
41	57,600	14,400	6,400	3,600	2,300	1,600	1,170	900	710	575
42	55,200	13,800	6,140	3,450	2,210	1,530	1,130	865	680	550
43	53,000	13,300	5,890	3,310	2,120	1,470	1,080	830	655	530
44	50,900	12,700	5,660	3,180	2,040	1,410	1,040	795	630	510
45	48,900	12,200	5,430	3,060	1,960	1,360	1,000	765	605	490
46	47,000	11,700	5,220	2,940	1,880	1,300	960	735	580	470
47	45,100	11,300	5,010	2,820	1,800	1,250	920	705	555	450
48	43,300	10,800	4,810	2,710	1,730	1,200	885	675	535	435
49	41,600	10,400	4,630	2,600	1,670	1,160	850	650	515	415
50	40,000	10,000	4,440	2,500	1,600	1,110	815	625	495	400

Example: If ±5% precision is desired and it is estimated that p will be 40%, then 2,400 observations will be required. Or, if a study has been completed and the results show p to be 50% with a total of 2,500 observations having been made, then the degree of precision is ±4%.

Fig. 19. Table for determining the number of observations for a given degree of precision and value of p (95 percent confidence limits).

$x\%$, the number of observations required using a **relative** measure is greater than those required for an **absolute** measure, assuming that the confidence level is constant. That is, the relative precision interval $\pm 0.05p$ is less than the absolute interval $p \pm 0.05$.

The number of observations necessary for a given precision interval and degree of confidence can be conveniently determined for any value of p, from charts, nomographs, or curves. Barnes (Work Sampling) gives one such table, shown in Fig. 19, where the degree of precision is expressed relatively as a percent of p. (See section on Statistical Methods.)

WORK SAMPLING STUDY. At the J. E. Ogden Co. four jobs were selected for work sampling study, as follows:

A: Attaching two U-shaped wires to a small metal cup on a machine consisting of pliers operated by foot treadles. Usually there were three operators, but the number varied.

B: A packaging job. Either four or five operators were on this job during the observation period.

C: A foot-press shear and packaging job. Either two or three operators were at work during the observation period.

D: A punch-press job, using medium Bliss inclinable presses. An average of four presses were on the work during the observation period.

The method of collecting data was to make observations at random intervals during each day for 18 working days. For purposes of comparison, on each of jobs A, B, and C, a full day's production study was made to determine **delay allowances**. On job D, a **down-time recorder** was used to record each stop and its duration. This latter record was made for 15 days on one of the blanking presses. Fig. 20 shows the totals of the various readings in number and per-

Item	Job A		Job B		Job C		Job D	
	No. of Readings	%	No. of Readings	%	No. of Readings	%	No. of Readings	%
Total readings	372	100.0	649	100.0	387	100.0	608	100.0
Allowable delays	29	7.8	93	14.3	78	20.1	61	10.0
Unnecessary delays	26	7.0	70	10.8	105	27.1	24	4.0
Productive or operating readings	317	85.2	486	74.9	204	52.8	523	86.0

Fig. 20. **Work sampling study data on four kinds of jobs.**

centage distribution. Fig. 21 compares the percentages of allowable delays, unnecessary delays, and productive operation readings in the **ratio-delay** study with those set by **production** studies, and shows the close agreement between results under the two methods.

Item	Allowable Delay				Unnecessary Delay				Running Time			
Job	A	B	C	D	A	B	C	D	A	B	C	D
Work Sampling	7.8%	14.3%	20.1%	10.0%	7.0%	10.8%	27.1%	4.0%	85.2%	74.9%	52.8%	86.0%
Prod. Study..	10.0	16.0	20.0	11.3	8.0	13.6	22.9	0.5	82.0	70.4	57.1	88.2
Difference ..	—2.2	—1.7	+0.1	—1.3	—1.0	—2.8	+4.2	+3.5	+3.2	+4.5	—4.3	—2.2

Above delay percentages are based on percentage of total time rather than percentage of productive time and are useful only in the above comparison.

Fig. 21. **Comparison of work sampling study data from Fig. 20 with production study data on the same jobs.**

CONTROL CHART ANALYSIS. A control chart of p taken from subsamples of size n can be constructed to indicate **consistency** in the study data as well as to detect shifts in the extended population parameters. For instance, assume the results shown in Fig. 22 of a work sampling study made on the three machines.

Date	Number of Observations	Number of Occurrences of Machine Idle	Estimate of $\bar{p}$ from Sub-sample
6/9 A.M.	33	11	.33
P.M.	39	7	.18
6/10 A.M.	36	14	.39
P.M.	30	6	.20
6/11 A.M.	39	10	.26
P.M.	30	7	.23
6/12 A.M.	30	8	.27
6/14 A.M.	33	17	.52
P.M.	39	16	.41
6/15 A.M.	36	7	.19
P.M.	36	11	.31
TOTALS	381	114	.30

Fig. 22. Results of a work sampling study made on three machines.

The limits for the control chart are calculated at $\bar{\bar{p}} \pm 3\sigma_p$. The sub-sample size, n, is set at 35, the average of the number of observations taken at each period.

$$3\sigma_p = 3 \sqrt{\frac{\bar{\bar{p}}\,(1 - \bar{\bar{p}})}{n}}$$

$$= 3 \sqrt{\frac{.30 \times .70}{35}}$$

$$= 0.24$$

The results are shown in Fig. 23.

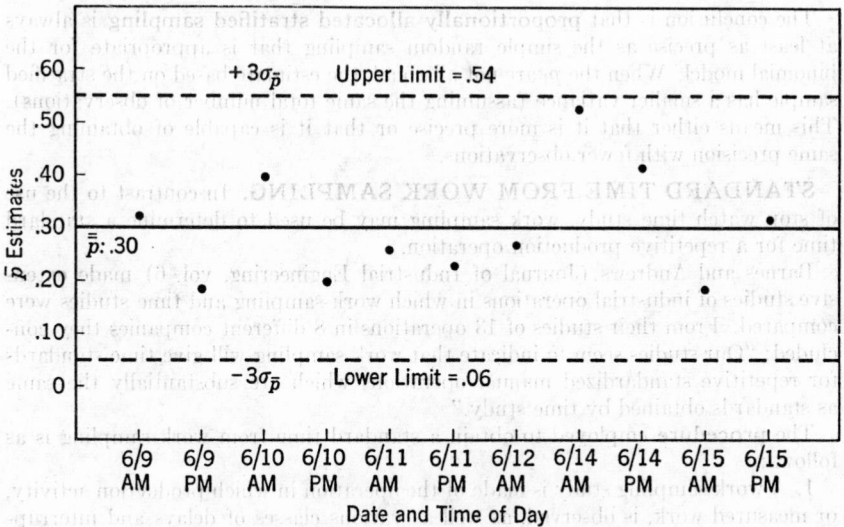

Fig. 23. Control chart for percent machine idle time.

STRATIFIED SAMPLING. The use of the simple binomial model implies that the probability of finding the operation in question in a particular activity state is the same throughout the period of study. This is not the true state of affairs in many applications where a given activity may predominate at the beginning, middle, or end of the day. For instance, more delays may be encountered at the beginning or end of the day or, in an operation such as welding, setup time may predominate during the first part of the day.

In these situations the population may be stratified or divided into periods. Conway (Journal of Industrial Engineering, vol. 8) suggests that such a **stratification study** take the following form:

   f_i is the fraction of the total length of study represented by the ith period or stratum.

   p_i is the probability of finding an observation in the ith stratum in the particular activity state under consideration.

   n_i is the number of observations taken in the ith stratum.

   r_i is the number of observations in the ith stratum for which the activity was in the particular state under consideration.

The over-all proportion of time represented by the particular state of activity in question is given by a weighted average of the **strata probabilities.**

$$\bar{p} = \sum_i f_i p_i$$

An unbiased estimate of this over-all proportion is:

$$\bar{p} = \sum_i f_i \frac{r_i}{n_i}$$

The variance of this estimator is given by:

$$\sigma_p{}^2 = \sum_i \frac{f_i{}^2 p_i (1 - p_i)}{n_i}$$

The conclusion is that **proportionally allocated stratified sampling** is always at least as precise as the simple random sampling that is appropriate for the binomial model. When the p_i are not all equal, the estimate based on the stratified sample has a smaller variance (assuming the same total number of observations). This means either that it is more precise or that it is capable of obtaining the same precision with fewer observations.

STANDARD TIME FROM WORK SAMPLING. In contrast to the use of stop watch time study, work sampling may be used to determine a standard time for a repetitive production operation.

Barnes and Andrews (Journal of Industrial Engineering, vol. 6) made extensive studies of industrial operations in which work sampling and time studies were compared. From their studies of 13 operations in 8 different companies they concluded: "Our studies seem to indicate that work sampling will give time standards for repetitive standardized manual operations which are substantially the same as standards obtained by time study."

The **procedure** employed to obtain a standard time from work sampling is as follows:

1. A work sampling study is made of the operation in which production activity, or measured work, is observed, as well as various classes of delays and interruptions. The production activity is differentiated into **manually controlled** and

machine-controlled categories. During the study the operator's performance is rated at each observation of manually controlled production activity.

2. At the end of the study the individual rating indices are averaged to obtain an **over-all rating index.**

3. A **physical count of parts** produced over the study period is taken.

4. The actual time per unit of output is calculated by dividing the total clock-hours consumed in production or measured work by the number of parts produced. This is equivalent to the **net cycle time** obtained from a stop-watch time study. This unit time is broken down into manually and machine-controlled elements in proportion to the observations made in these two categories.

5. The **base time** is obtained by multiplying the manually controlled portion of observed unit time by the rating index and adding the machine-controlled element, which may be independently calculated from empirical standard data.

6. The **standard time** is obtained by adding allowances obtained from the study or from other sources. It should be noted here that percent delay time obtained from work sampling is normally related to total time. The percent allowances added to base time are **percentages of base time.** Therefore, the total percent allowances for inclusion in the standard time should be obtained by taking a ratio of the total percent delay obtained from the work sampling to 1 minus this percent.

For example, assume that a five-day work sampling study is taken of a repetitive operation with the following results:

Total number of observations		1,000
Observations of production activity		900
Manually controlled elements	650	
Machine-controlled elements	250	
Percent production time, 900/1,000		90%
Total clock time over the study,		
5 days × 8 hr./day × 60 min./hr.		2,400 min.
Total production time, 2,400 × 0.90		2,160 min.
Total units produced		3,860
Actual time per unit, 2,160/3,860		0.56 min.
Manually controlled elements, 0.50 × 650/900	0.404 min.	
Machine-controlled elements, 0.560 − 0.404	0.156 min.	
Rating index, average of individual ratings		112%
Base time per unit, (1.12 × 0.404) + 0.156		0.610 min.
Observations of unavoidable delays		80
Percent unavoidable delay time, 80/1,000		8%
Allowance percent for unavoidable delays, 0.08/0.92		8.7%
Standard time, 0.610 + (0.087 × 0.610)		0.663 min.

APPLICATION OF WORK SAMPLING. The following points should be kept in mind in considering the use of work sampling:

1. Only homogeneous groups should be combined—such as delays on similar operations performed on similar kinds of machines, or delays of operators on work of a similar nature.

2. A large number of observations are recommended. Studies are best adapted to large groups of machines or operators.

3. Results from a few hundred observations may be useful if p is not too small. The use of the normal approximation to the binomial distribution is adequate if $pN \geqq 5$.

4. The accuracy of the results depends on the amount of bias introduced in the study by the sampling procedure.

5. As percentage of delay time increases, more observations are necessary for a given absolute degree of precision.

6. Observations must be taken at random intervals and distributed over a long period of time.

7. Work sampling data provides a basis for evaluating various departmental operations or processes.

8. Two or more studies may be conducted simultaneously during the observation period.

9. Work sampling may produce fewer complaints from operators being studied than continuous or all-day stop-watch studies.

10. The technique is applicable to a wide variety of situations in manufacturing, distribution, or service industries.

11. The cost of work sampling studies is considered to be about a third that of production or interruption studies.

Standard Time Data

STANDARD DATA METHOD. Standard time data consists of an inventory or file of elemental times accumulated from time studies made in the plant or from special studies. These times are expressed in terms of **job variables.** When it is desired to set a standard on a new job, elemental times are extracted from tables, charts, or graphs, and then synthesized in logical sequence to provide the base time for the job. In such cases the elements and variables of the job are similar to or identical with those from which the original data were formulated.

The elements referred to here are **time study** or **functional elements** and are usually peculiar to the experience of a given plant. Standard data based on motion elements, which are more or less universally applicable, are discussed later. The two forms of standard data are often referred to as **macroscopic** (time study standard data) and **microscopic** (motion-time standard data).

The element times comprising standard data are usually **base times** because the standard data may be used on jobs with varying allowance requirements. Allowances must be added at the time the data are used to obtain a standard time.

A particular elemental time used in the standard data may be the average of a large number of independent time studies made on operations which include the element in question. Or the element time can be a single value removed from a data curve. This curve may be the result of interpolation or extrapolation of two or more original times.

The standard data method can be traced back to studies of Taylor and Merrick. It was planned to compile a "dictionary" of fundamental elements necessary to perform work, with times that skilled operators should take for these elements. Taylor stated (Shop Management) his view of this feature of time study as:

No system of time study can be looked upon as a success unless it enables the time observer, after a reasonable amount of study, to predict with accuracy how long it should take a good man to do almost any job in the particular trade, or branch of a trade, to which the time student has been devoting himself.

It is true that hardly any two jobs in a given trade are exactly the same, and if a time study student were to follow the old method of studying and recording the whole time to do the various jobs which come under his observation without dividing them into their elements, he would make comparatively small progress in a lifetime, and at best would become a skillful guesser. It is, however, equally true that all of the work done in a given trade can be divided into a comparatively small number of elements or units, and with proper implements and methods it is comparatively easy for a skilled observer to determine the time required by a good man to do any one of these elementary units.

This plan was carried out by Merrick, inasmuch as he took many studies of machine shop operations and compiled tables of minimum selected times, readily converted into standard times.

ADVANTAGES OF THE METHOD. There are a number of advantages in compiling and using standard time data as opposed to taking direct time studies on every new operation.

1. The **cost** of setting standard times using standard data is less than taking a direct study if the potential requirement for standards in the plant is large. The volume of standard times required must be large enough to justify the time in taking the initial time studies, analyzing the data, and classifying the results.
2. Standard data contributes to a **consistency** in time standards for operations employing the same elements. However, the advantages of consistency can be negated if the elements of the operation for which the standard time is being set are dissimilar to those with which the data are associated.
3. Standard times can be **calculated** before the operation or job is activated. This is an obvious advantage in planning a production process and in estimating labor requirements and costs.
4. Certain **indirect labor** operations, such as materials handling, cleaning and janitorial work, and maintenance, can be timed economically only through the use of standard data.
5. Standard data can be employed to evaluate **methods designs** and to balance production or assembly lines in the design stages.

ACCURACY OF STANDARD DATA. Accuracy is claimed as an advantage of standard data by Morrow (Motion Economy and Work Measurement).

An outstanding advantage is that the standards set are more accurate than under other methods. Leveling or grading errors are reduced or eliminated. Most inconsistencies, or errors, are evident when the comparison sheet is made up, particularly any errors in leveling. As the standard is based on data collected from many studies, it does not reflect too much the unusual variations that may occur in a particular study.

On the other hand there are basic features of the standard data method which make claims of greater accuracy questionable. The first factor is that standard data are collected from time studies and therefore are susceptible to some of the sources of **bias** present in the original timing. This is important where the standard data may represent essentially single studies on different jobs which contribute points on a curve. Also, standard data are based on **rated times** and therefore are subject to criticisms of accuracy applied to the rating procedure. This is less important where times are averages of a large number of independent ratings.

A second factor concerns the **additivity** of element times. Are elements so independent that their times may be extracted from an original job context and resynthesized perhaps in some different order in another context involving a different machine or operator? Research in this area seems to indicate that independence of this sort is not present. In practice the problem can be avoided only by transplanting groups of elements from one job context to another, where possible. This is admittedly difficult in most situations, especially where operations are predominantly manually controlled and subject to variation in method and motions of operators.

A third factor, related to these, is that the elements constituting the standard data may not be similar or comparable to the elements employed in the operation for which a standard time is set. Again, this refers to variation in methods. The only way of reducing this source of error is to ensure that the **similarity of elements** is great enough to justify the use of the data.

A final factor is that there may be sources of error built into the data due to failure to reduce the data in terms of the correct variables or to correctly determine the nature of the variation.

DERIVING STANDARD DATA. Standard data may be derived by the use of a number of procedures and aids.

Grouping Like Operations. Standard data is relevant to similar operations or jobs. Like operations should be grouped for **spot studies.** In some cases the standard data may pertain to like or similar products on a given type of, or identical, machines.

Preliminary Studies. Time studies are taken of a representative number of parts on a given **machine grouping,** including a distribution of spot studies made on a range of product weights, shapes, or other significant variables of the work. Care should be taken to obtain studies on high and low **limits** of the variable in question. For example, where the weight of the part is an important factor, both the heaviest and the lightest parts should be studied. The data will be good for further use between these limits. The results of each individual time study should be summarized on an instruction sheet showing the base time for the various elements.

During the time study, particular care must be taken to segregate the variable elements from the constant and manually controlled from machine elements. Also, elements involved in manipulating tools, jigs, or fixtures should be segregated.

Time Study File. The accumulation of time studies taken over an extended period of time for the purpose of setting time standards is commonly referred to as the time study file. The advantage in using this file of time studies for deriving standard data is that there is no cost involved. The disadvantage is that, because the data has been collected over a long period, it is quite vulnerable to changes in methods, equipment, quality, and conditions, as well as in elemental definitions. Also, there are numerous instances where failure to record certain information when the time studies were taken makes the file an unusable or inferior source of time data.

Comparison Sheet. The results of the initial time studies are compiled on a comparison sheet. The **basic elements** are listed in the left column. **Elemental times** from the various studies are entered in succeeding columns and then compared. At the top of each column representing a given study, **job** or **product variables** are noted.

Morrow (Motion Economy and Work Measurement) gives a comparison sheet illustrating data from drill press operations (Fig. 24). On this sheet the elemental base times are recorded for each study. It is to be noted that the elements in the master list in the left-hand column are not necessarily in the order in which they are performed. For the element "piece up on table," the first four final base times indicated are .24, .09, .27, and .09. Comparing these with the weight of the piece for the first four studies—35 lb., 10 lb., 42 lb., and 14 lb., respectively—it is quite

COMPARISON SHEET — HANDLING UPRIGHT DRILL PRESS

	Standard	R1830	C1790	C1820	R1842	R1843	C1860	R1858	B1863	B1870	R1907	R1902	C1793	C1794	R1906
Study number		R1830	C1790	C1820	R1842	R1843	C1860	R1858	B1863	B1870	R1907	R1902	C1793	C1794	R1906
Part number		12132	14011	11121	17473	10110	12186	10407	15003	14115	15165	10123	12501	16657	10132
Machine name		Barnes	Barnes	Edlund	Sipp	Sipp	Barnes	Buffalo	Barnes	Barnes	Buffalo	Sipp	Edlund	Buffalo	Sipp
Shop number		166	115	92	403	114	121	118	166	115	123	114	92	123	114
Operator		Walsh	Short	Jones	Smith	Walsh	Black	Smith	Jones	Nott	Short	Walsh	Brown	Brown	Walsh
Material		CI	Brz 2	CI	CI	1020 Steel	Brz 1	CI	CI	CI	CI	Brz 2	1020 Steel	CI	CI
Weight piece		35	10	42	14	3	6	26	12	21	7½	26	21	52	26
Jig number		714	731		512	598	285	786			377				
Weight jig		18	4		3	2	3	5		2					
Rate	Standard	70	70	75	65	75	75	60	65	25	80	65	55	60	65
Piece up on table	Curve 1	.24	.09	.27	.09	.05	.06	.16	.11	.17	.07	.17	.14	.38	.15
Piece off and aside	Curve 1	.15	.04	.20	.05	.03	.04	.09	.05	.09	.04	.10	.09	.28	.11
Piece in jig Class 1	Curve 2	.05							.03		.02				
Piece out jig Class 1	Curve 2	.04				.01					.02				
Piece in jig Class 2	Curve 2	.02	.02		.03		.02								
Piece out jig Class 2	Curve 2	.02	.02		.02		.03								
Locate under spindle	Curve 4	.07	.04	.06	.04	.04	.05	.05	.05	.07	.04	.05	.05		.06
Move hole to hole	Curve 4	.04	.03	.04	.02	.02	.02	.03	.03	.04	.02	.04	.04		.03
Move spindle to spindle	Curve 4			.05							.03				
Tighten one screw	Chart 6				.05	.04	.06						.06		
Loosen one screw	Chart 6				.03	.03	.04								
Tighten one strap	.15	.16	.14						.15		.16				
Loosen one strap	.11	.10	.11						.10		.09				
Tighten vise	.04			.08								.04	.06	.08	
Loosen vise	.03			.05								.04	.04	.03	
Tighten chuck	.06							.07							.05
Loosen chuck	.05							.05							.05

Fig. 24. Time study comparison sheet used for compiling standard data.

evident that the lighter the piece the shorter the time. The same relationship applies for the element "piece off and aside." From these data **standard curves** can now be constructed and the standard (base) times determined for the elements for any piece of which the weight is known.

The times for the element "tighten one strap" are .16, .14, .15, .16. Evidently a slight variation in time is due to causes other than the weight of the piece, but the time is considered to be a constant of .15 min.

The comparison sheet can be expanded in complexity to include other factors that will contribute to variability. Its essential purpose is to determine the nature of variability between jobs.

Presentation of Data. If the variation in a part's characteristics is continuous, the usual manner of presenting the data is in the form of a curve showing the elemental base time plotted against a governing characteristic of the part, such as weight. **Alignment charts** can also be employed where a number of variables are involved. Where variation in the data is in discrete units the data can be more advantageously presented in tabular or **chart form.**

INTERPOLATION AND EXTRAPOLATION OF BASE TIMES. In timing similar operations on a range of sizes of the same product, it is usually possible to determine some of the times by interpolation. A few sizes are selected at suitable intervals and their base times plotted. If there is no variation in conditions, an even curve can be drawn through the points, and base times for intervening sizes may be safely interpolated. This principle can be used to determine by extrapolation the time for sizes smaller or larger than those studied, though with much less confidence. The danger in both cases is that with certain sizes sudden changes of condition may be made, which change the operation, for instance, the introduction of crane service. Such factors alter time abruptly. When this change of condition is known, sizes just above and below should be studied and discontinuity determined. (See Figs. 25 and 26.)

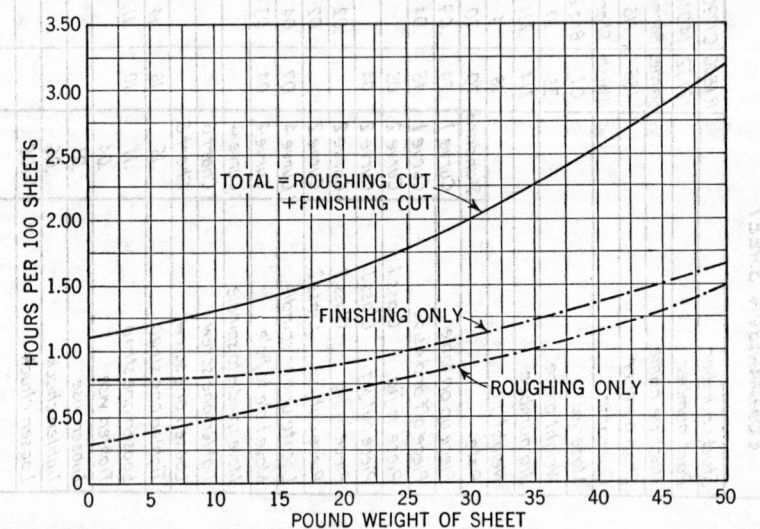

Fig. 25. Curve for interpolating times on sheet copper work.

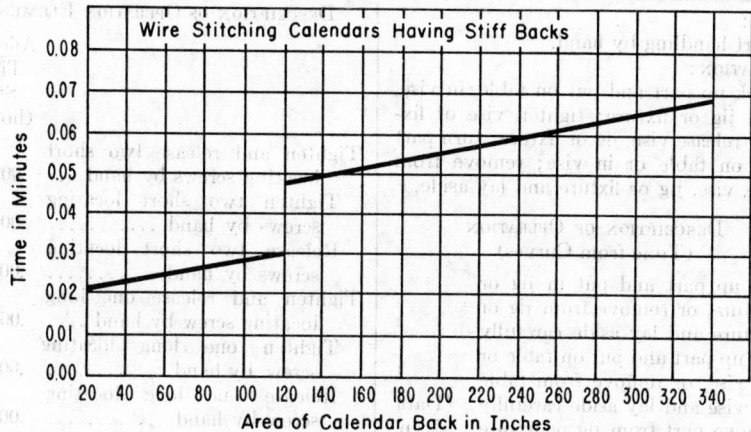

Fig. 26. Curve showing sudden break due to change in conditions.

SETUP STANDARDS. The method of determining setup standards is similar to that described for production operation standards. Usually it is better to have the two types of standards separate, although in some cases setup time may be prorated over the number of pieces in the lot, and the operation standard will then include setup time. The latter method is more convenient for shop records, but it will not be accurate unless the size of lots is uniform or setup time is very short in proportion to operation time.

COMPARATIVE COSTS. Although the indirect or standard data method is slower at the beginning, because no standards are set until many time studies have been taken and computations are made, the cost of time study work by this method is far less than by the direct method. Carroll (SAM Journal, vol. 4) takes a hypothetical case requiring 2,500 standards and shows comparative time and cost for each method.

Direct Method:

Total number of standards required	2,500
Average number of standards set per week per man	25
Number of time study men	3
Approximate weeks required to set 2,500 standards	33
Weekly salary of time study man	$120
Total approximate cost to set standards (3 × 120 × 33)	$11,900
Cost of each standard	$4.70

Indirect Method:

Total number of standards required	2,500
Weeks necessary to assemble data	4
Average number of standards per week per man after data are assembled	125
Number of time study men	3
Approximate weeks required to set 2,500 standards after data are assembled	7
Total number of weeks to assemble and set standards	11
Total cost to assemble and set standards (3 × 120 × 11)	$3,960
Cost of each standard	$ 1.58

Thus **cost per standard** by the standard data or indirect method is only about one-third the cost by the direct method. Frequently, **coverage of work by**

PART:
Part handling by hand.

OPERATION:
Pick up part and put on table, in vise, or in jig or fixture; tighten vise or fixture; release vise, jig or fixture; turn part over on table or in vise; remove from table, vise, jig or fixture and lay aside.

DESCRIPTION OF OPERATION
(Time from Curves)

Pick up part and put in jig or fixture, or remove from jig or fixture and lay aside carefully
Pick up part and put on table or in vise, or remove from table or vise and lay aside carefully   (Data
Remove part from jig or fixture   given
and toss aside ....   on
Remove part from table or vise   curves)
and toss aside ....
Release vise ....
Turn part over on table ....
Tighten vise ....
Turn part over in vise ....

DESCRIPTION OF OPERATION ELEMENT

	Allowed Time Std. (hours)
Open and close cover of jig or fixture when hinged	.0008
Close cover of jig or fixture when hinged	.0003
Open cover of jig or fixture when hinged	.0005
Put on and remove cover of jig or fixture when not hinged.	.0029
Put on cover of jig or fixture when not hinged	.0020
Remove cover of jig or fixture when not hinged	.0009
Tighten and release wing nut...	.0012
Tighten and release thumb screw by hand	.0013
Tighten thumb screw by hand	.0008
Release thumb screw by hand	.0005
Tighten and release one short locating screw by hand	.0018
Tighten one short locating screw by hand	.0010
Release one short locating screw by hand	.0008

DESCRIPTION OF OPERATION ELEMENT

	Allowed Time Std. (hours)
Tighten and release two short locating screws by hand ...	.0023
Tighten two short locating screws by hand	.0013
Release two short locating screws by hand	.0010
Tighten and release one long locating screw by hand	.0037
Tighten one long locating screw by hand	.0021
Release one long locating screw by hand	.0016
Tighten and release two long locating screws by hand ...	.0047
Tighten two long locating screws by hand	.0027
Release two long locating screws by hand	.0020
Tighten and release locating screws with a wrench	.0053
Tighten locating screw with a wrench	.0035
Release locating screw with a wrench	.0018
Tighten and release hexagon or square nut with an open-end wrench	.0034
Tighten hexagon or square nut with an open-end wrench ..	.0018
Release hexagon or square nut with an open-end wrench ..	.0016
Insert and remove bushing from jig or fixture	.0010
Insert or remove bushing from jig or fixture	.0005
Insert and remove locating pin from jig or fixture	.0046
Insert locating pin in jig or fixture	.0018
Remove locating pin from jig or fixture	.0028
Blow cuttings from small or medium jig or fixture with an air hose	.0014
Blow cuttings from large jig or fixture with an air hose	.0020
Clean small jig or fixture with brush	.0020
Clean medium jig or fixture with brush	.0028

Fig. 27. Allowed time for parts handling (continued on next page).

Description of Operation Element	Allowed Time Std. (hours)
Clean large jig or fixture with brush	.0035
Clean very large jig or fixture with brush	.0049
Clean small jig or fixture by turning over	.0014
Clean medium jig or fixture by turning over	.0022
Clean large jig or fixture by turning over	.0029
Clean very large jig or fixture by turning over	.0043
Tighten and release a machine vise, hit part with a rawhide mallet	.0043
Tighten vise on machine with rawhide mallet and hit part	.0031
Release vise on machine with rawhide mallet	.0012
Clean vise	.0020
Set and tighten, release and move clamp already in place	.0059
Set and tighten clamp already in place	.0035
Release and move aside clamp in place	.0024
Place, set and tighten, release and remove clamp not in place	.0116
Place. set and tighten clamp complete	.0076

Description of Operation Element	Allowed Time Std. (hours)
Release and move aside com plete clamp	.0040
Set jack screw	.0021
Make jib crane lift from machine to turn part and return	.0250
Make jib crane lift from floor to lathe and return	.0500
Make jib crane lift from floor to machine table and return	.0622
Make jib crane lift from floor to jig or fixture and return	.0779

Note: The term "allowed time" represents the time required by any worker to perform a given unit of work, using average skill, showing average effort, under average conditions, with average consistency, allowing for fatigue, personal needs, and unavoidable delays. *It is the time within which the worker is expected to perform that work.* All times are given in decimal hours. Accurate conversions to minutes and seconds can be made by means of the following formulas: decimal hours × 60 = decimal minutes; decimal hours × 3.600 = decimal seconds. The data given represent standards developed for use at East Pittsburgh Works of Westinghouse Electric Corp. for conditions of work existing in that plant. Each allowance should be checked in the light of local conditions before being applied in any given plant.

Fig. 27. (Concluded.)

standards is 40 percent under the direct method, as compared with 95 percent under the standard data method.

STANDARD TIME DATA: PARTS HANDLING. Specimen standard data times for a part handled by hand are given in the accompanying tabulation and diagrams, Figs. 27, 28, 29, and 30 (Am. Mach., vol. 82).

The data in the figures have been compiled with the object of standardizing part handling times in all departments of a factory, thus making the information of general value. They were compiled from studies on actual production jobs in several shop sections, some studies being taken with ideal setups to show how various factors affect the time (Westinghouse Electric Corp.). Constants were selected from a wide range of formulas and time studies.

The time values obtained from these data are to be used in formulas or standard data developed for a wide range of shop operations, as too much time would be involved in establishing "each piece" values directly from this information.

Parts always should be placed so that they can be handled to the greatest advantage, without interfering with the movements of the operator. In some cases skids, skid boxes, trucks and other materials handling units may facilitate the handling operations. They always should be introduced where advantageous.

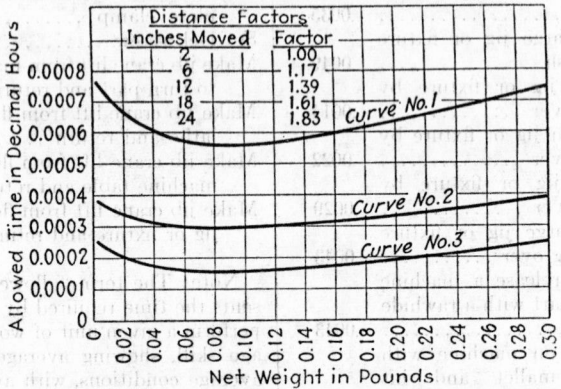

Curve 1 shows allowance for time to pick up a part and place it in a jig or fixture. Curve 2 is read both for time allowed to pick up a part and place it on a table or in a vise, and for time allowed to remove the part from the jig or fixture and lay it aside. Time allowed for laying a part aside is read from curve 3. Distance factor is to be applied in all cases.

Fig. 28. Time allowance curves for handling parts where only finger, wrist, and arm movements are involved.

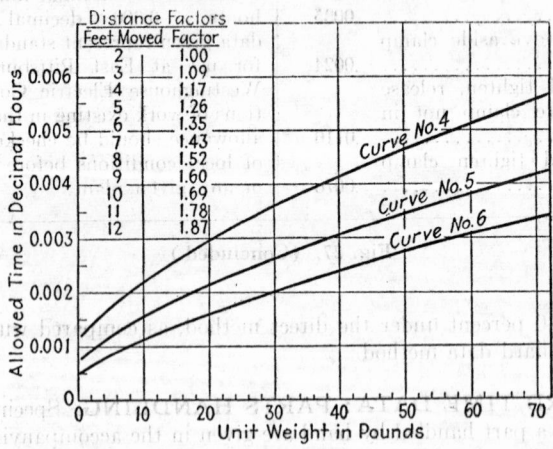

Time allowed to pick up a part and place it in a jig or fixture is read from curve 4. Curve 5 shows both time allowed to pick up a part and place it on a table or in a vise, and time allowed to remove a part from a jig or a fixture and lay it aside. Curve 6 is read for time allowed to lay a part aside. Each reading must be multiplied by the proper distance factor.

Fig. 29. Curves giving allowances for handling parts where finger, wrist, arm, and body are used.

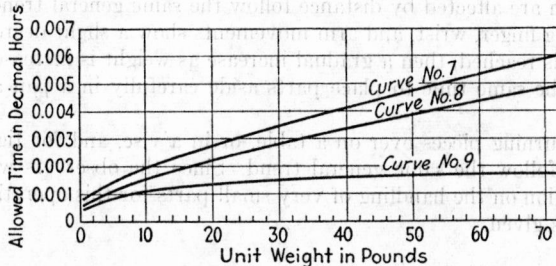

Curve 7 is read for time allowed to turn a part over in a vise. Both time allowed for turning a part over on a table and time allowed for tightening a vise are shown by curve 8. Time allowed to release a vise is read from curve 9. These operations are affected only by the weight of the piece.

Fig. 30. Time allowance curves for turning a part over in a vise and tightening and releasing vise.

No binding rule was made to govern the weight that a man shall lift. While 75 lb. has been chosen arbitrarily as the maximum, this load should be handled only when the operator has been instructed in the correct method of lifting, is physically fit, and the operation is not of frequent recurrence. When lifting is done near acids, hot metals, hot liquids, oily floors, or running machinery, the maximum load should be decreased.

Values were established for electric jib-crane lifts. Air hoists are used only where there is a fire hazard. Speed at which electric hoists operate under load has been found to vary from 36 ft. per min. for a ¼-ton hoist to 15 ft. per min. for a 1-ton hoist. A straight-up lift of 5 ft. in most cases will constitute a maximum distance of lift, and this is the basis for the jib-crane lift time values shown in the tabulation.

Factors for distance moved, curves 1 to 6 in Figs. 28 and 29, were found by moving parts of approximately similar shape, and increasing weights and volumes, through various distances. Parts of approximately the same weight, but of varying volumes and areas were moved definite distances, showing that time was not materially affected when distance moved was constant. This procedure was applied to castings, forged parts, and short bars, but not to bar stock where length is great in proportion to cross-sectional area. Handling times for jigs or fixtures are the same as for any other parts of like weight.

Values have been established for long and short locating screws, a short locating screw being considered as one which has to be tightened or loosened ¼ in. or less.

In some cases more than one part can be handled at a time, but no allowance has been made for this situation in the handling data. Such allowance is made by the individual applying the data.

Curves for such handling time allowances are given in Figs. 28 and 29.

The operations are divided into two classes: first, those which are affected by the distance moved and second, those which are not. Curves 1, 2, and 3 are for small parts up to .30 lb. where finger, wrist, and arm movements only are involved, while curves 4, 5, and 6 are for parts where finger, wrist, arm, and body movements are involved. These curves are based on minimum distances in both cases and the values obtained from the curves must be multiplied by the distance factor given with each set of curves. Curves 7, 8, and 9 are those operations which are not affected by the distance moved (Fig. 30).

Curves which are affected by distance follow the same general trend. Handling curves involving finger, wrist, and arm movements show a slight decrease until an ideal size part is reached, then a gradual increase as weight is increased.

It requires the same time to place parts aside carefully in a pan as it does to pick them up.

Curves for turning pieces over on a table, or in a vise, and for tightening and releasing vise, follow the same general trend. Since the observers were not able to get information on the handling of very small parts for this operation, only one set of curves is given.

Standard Motion-Time Data

THE METHOD. A motion-time standard data system consists of **predetermined times** associated with basic or **fundamental motions,** as the elements of the system. The basic motions employed are similar to therbligs in concept and magnitude. There are numbers of such systems in use today, some of which have been developed and are used by only one company, and others which have been publicized for universal application.

These systems are developed on the basis of two assumptions. The first is that all manual work can be divided into basic units or elements which are universally descriptive and applicable. The second is that an average time in terms of job variables can be associated with each qualitative element. These times also have some degree of universal applicability. Included in the time system is the recognition of **work variables** which influence the time taken to perform certain elements or motions. Thus, the predominant factor of utility in these systems, as compared to time study standard data, is the universality of their application to a wide variety of manual operations within a given plant or within a group of plants in general.

In these plans a time standard for a particular job is synthesized from the motion-time values found in **predetermined time tables.** The data in these tables are the results of studies made in the laboratory or in factories. Such studies include, in principle:

1. The derivation of a system of basic motions including a qualitative definition of the motions.
2. The study of a representative number of operations in the laboratory or factory. This usually involves the recording of the operation method on film.
3. The analysis of individual motions employed in the various operations to determine variables which influence each motion time.
4. A description of the motion system in terms of the critical variables, for instance, the influence of part weight or distance moved on the motion employed to reach with the hand or move a part by hand.
5. The determination of base times for the motions at different values of the critical variables.
6. The presentation of the final data on charts, tables, or curves.

Motion-time standard data should be applied only by **analysts** who have had experience and training in motion and time study and in the particular plan they are going to use. When an inexperienced, untrained person attempts to use these systems, the danger is that he will overlook motions which are quite evident to the experienced observer and that he will classify the motions incorrectly. Both factors will result in incorrect standards.

USES AND ADVANTAGES OF MOTION-TIME STANDARD DATA.
A number of uses and advantages of the motion-time data method are proposed:

1. **Operation design.** One of the major uses of such data is in determining elemental or standard times for operations in the design stages prior to installation or production. This is advantageous for two reasons. The first is that alternative method designs may be evaluated in terms of time without having to set up mock-up operations for actual testing of the methods. Also, the tables indicate the factors which influence time for given motions. During the design of a method these factors can be taken into consideration. The second reason is that a standard time can be set for the chosen method for use in estimating costs, planning labor requirements, etc.

2. **Methods improvement.** The data can be used to detect gradual changes in the methods used in existing operations. If the original method is defined in terms of motion standard times, changes can be detected and their effects evaluated. In the setting of a new standard by using standard data, the method and motion pattern must be analyzed and specified in detail.

3. **Product design.** The influence of alternative product designs on production or assembly times may be determined through the study of motion times. If the standard data indicate the influence of product variables such as weight and shape on the time to perform a motion, then **critical product design variables** can be directly assessed during the design stage. Similarly, the influence of product design changes on an existing job standard time can be determined.

4. **Tool and equipment design.** Tools and equipment should be designed to maximize the manual efficiency of their operation. Alternative tool and equipment designs can be assessed in terms of motion times in order to minimize operating or handling time.

5. **Establishing a standard time.** A standard time can be calculated for an existing job without resorting to a stop watch study. The standard can be used for wage payment purposes or for any use to which time standards are put.

6. **Developing time formulas.** Time formulas are developed to aid the engineer in establishing standards for specific types of work. Motion-time data can be resynthesized for inclusion in such formulas to apply to specific jobs within a given plant. For a given formula, motion times can supplement time study standard data accumulated by the plant in question.

VALIDITY OF MOTION-TIME STANDARD DATA.
The validity and accuracy of any system of motion-time standards must be considered by the analyst before he uses it. In general it can be concluded that most companies using a universal system must make periodic adjustments in the data to fit their own conditions. It is advisable that a firm continually **audit standards** which have been set from motion-time standard data, particularly to determine the influence of job variables which have been ignored in the original data system.

1. The **universality** of the data depends on the similarity between the population from which the data were derived and the population to which the data are applied. The times recorded in tables represent sample averages of data taken from laboratory studies or from studies of actual industrial operations. The population on which studies were originally conducted must of economic necessity be limited.

2. The data presented in tables are usually rated or leveled times. The concept of normal or standard performance may vary between different systems and between a given system and the plant in which the data are applied.

3. The nature of the job or method variables which affect motion times and the interaction between individual motions must be considered. A valid system should allow for the effect of variables influencing motion times. It is essential that the important variables be considered. Although those that have little effect may be ignored, it should be the policy of the investigator to include all variables which may possibly influence the validity of the data.

4. The question as to **additivity** relates to motion-time as well as to time study standard data. The argument of nonadditivity is based on certain evidence that the time for a given motion depends on the preceding and succeeding motions.

The validity of motion-time data in general and a given system specifically is difficult to assess, and considerable research is needed before many of the basic questions can be answered. Buffa (Journal of Industrial Engineering, vol. 7) concludes that "if universal standard data is ever to gain a place of respect in the engineering professions, certain basic requirements must be established for it." In his view these are:

a. Basic additivity of elements or an acceptable error by ignoring nonadditivity.
b. A classification or grouping of motion types such that errors generated could be considered negligible.
c. Data based on carefully planned experimental designs with full disclosure of methods and results.
d. Data expressed as expected (average) values and variances. This imposes the requirement of obtaining population values for the standard data elements similar to anthropometric data on body size, weight, etc.

APPLICATION ERRORS. Besides possible errors in the data themselves, the manner in which the data are applied may cause an inaccurate standard time to be set for a particular job.

For a new operation the analyst must decide which **motion pattern** represents the best method. In the case of an existing operation the analyst must decide which motion pattern is representative of the best method or of expected performance, depending on what use will be made of the standard. Any difference between the motion sequence considered best by the analyst and the sequence which is optimal from the operator's point of view introduces an error into the standard time.

The analyst must interpret the selected method in terms of the motion system employed. This points out the necessity of having clearly **defined motion elements,** including description of situations where each motion applies or does not apply. Failure to select the proper motion element or to omit motions will introduce error.

The analyst must correctly recognize and measure the variables affecting given motion times. This includes those variables which are a part of the system used, as well as those variables peculiar to the operation in question and perhaps ignored in the system.

MOTION-TIME ANALYSIS. One of the original systems of motion-time data was proposed by Segur and called motion-time analysis. Over a period of 25 years Segur has accumulated data on times required for motions of experts when putting forth their best efforts. An **expert** is defined as:

a person in good health whose physical, sensory, and mental characteristics adapt themselves to any method involved, and who is able to perform that method automatically, at a pace which can be maintained at operating efficiency.

The times are synthesized by means of formulas which take into account the conditions and methods involved. Here times are calculated to the fifth decimal of a minute.

Segur does not claim that any worker will maintain these **ideal times** continually. On a short cycle he is likely to attain such times once out of three or four performances. A percentage allowance is therefore made for fatigue, fumbles and errors, and other minor delays. This percentage varies with the number of body members, senses, and mental actions which may be operating simultaneously in performing an operation. The percentage is lowest on such operations as foundry work, where heavy loads are handled and the amount of attention is at a minimum, and highest on such operations as intricate assembly of machine parts, especially where sensory and mental attention is required by the operator. An analysis is made of any job under consideration to determine what motions are used and how they are combined. Times are then calculated as selected from the formulas and their sums checked with a stop watch to make sure that actual work habits have been fully recorded.

These actual motions are then compared with ideal motions and improvements made according to the rules of the **correct human motion.** As permitted by operation and production limitations, one or more synthetic improved methods are set up. The times for these synthetic methods are calculated from predetermined formulas and entered on the analysis. The best practical method is selected and used as a basis for instruction of operators. The selected method is described in sufficient detail to permit accurate and specific instruction to operators, and the allowances are added to the time so that the job is rated before any instruction begins.

The data secured on the original analyses form the basis for further improvement of work or rate-setting on similar allied operations. Since the time values and the analysis are based primarily on conditions rather than on performance, a much closer check can be kept on methods and operating conditions than is possible on time study of operation performance alone. The usual pains are taken in teaching new methods, breaking down old work habits and building new ones until automaticity is achieved.

PREDETERMINED TIME VALUES. An approach to the use of "predetermined time values" was first developed by Engstrom and his associates at the General Electric Company. This system confines itself to certain types of jobs, chiefly those that can be done in the normal individual work area, either sitting or standing. Time values are assigned according to the size of the part, that is, whether it can be handled by one hand, two hands, two fingers, or three fingers, and the values are classified according to the size of the part and also the conditions of getting and placing the part. The **get values** include the motions of transport empty and grasp; the **place values** are for the motions of transport loaded, pre-position, position, and release load. By using the Gilbreth right- and left-hand analysis and breaking the motions into the get-and-place groups, values are assigned according to the size of the part and the condition for getting and placing specific parts. A time chart of an analysis by this system is shown in Fig. 31.

The most effective use of this system is for developing standard data sheets for each type of work (See Fig. 32). The circled items in Fig. 32 represent those which apply to the particular activities with a Hardinge hand-screw machine being analyzed. The times for the machining operations are derived from a chart. This system has its limitations in that it does not attempt to cover the entire

OPERATION CONDITIONS	SIZE OF OBJECT	M.L. (3F)(H)	S. (2F)	V.L. (2H)	CLASS
		TIME IN MINUTES			
GET CONDITIONS NO.1	Very best grasp facility possible, due to design or prepositioning of object for grasp; no interference or hindrance with grasp by other objects. Size of object need not be considered.	.007	.007	.007	C No.1
GET CONDITIONS NO.2	Grasp is easily made but parts may be in quantities requiring some selection of a single part or some prepositioning in grasp.	.007	.013	.013	C No.2 / C No.3
GET CONDITIONS NO.3	The design or finish of parts prevents ready grasping, parts may tangle, nest together or be packed in separators.	.013	.021	.026	C No.4 / C No.1
PLACE CONDITIONS NO.1	Place objects where positioning is normally little more than releasing the object or moving it slightly on the work place.	.007	.007	.013	C No.2
PLACE CONDITIONS NO.2	Place objects where positioning consists of some definite location, simple open nests or fixtures. Loose tolerances.	.007	.013	.021	C No.3
PLACE CONDITIONS NO.3	Place objects where positioning is in difficult or complicated location, assemblies or fixtures requiring positioning of parts with respect to two points or locations in two directions.	.013	.021	.036	C No.4 / C No.5
PLACE CONDITIONS NO.4	Same as Conditions No.3 but close tolerances, more points of location, greater care in handling or application of force.	.021	.026	.048	C No.6

Fig. 31. Basic time chart using predetermined time value system.

gamut of man's work, such as from heavy foundry operations up to light bench assemblies. It is limited, as previously described, to particular sized types in normal work areas. Its advantages are that it is simple to use, it has had some 15 years of usage, and has proven itself to be reasonably correct.

HARDINGE HAND SCREW MACHINE

Std. 113 Hr.	Date 4/16/	Dwg. No. A-25595
Dec. Hr. .00883	Material 17 St. Alum.	Oper. No. 35
Part Name Pilot Light Socket	Max. Dim. .297 Length ½" Dia.	Set By C. D. D.
Operation	Form (.375) dia. and tap (5/16-32)	

							No.	Time
Load Bar Stock	.01 per in. of part length							
Move Stock Forward						04		
Aside After Cut-off						.025		
	Less Than	**Maximum Dim.**						
Pick up — Load – Unload – Aside	1/4"	1/2" to 4"					1	.095
To Round Collet	.120	(095)						
To Square, Hex, odd shaped	.150	.120						
Reverse Piece								
Set Stock						04	1	.040
Turn Power on and off						04	1	.040
Change spindle speed or direction						04	1	.010
Cross slide tool to and form work						04	1	.040
Turret Tool From Work Index Head			**No. of Tools**					
(Move head to position) — Tool to work	1	(2)	3	4	5	6	1	.110
	.04	(.11)	.15	.18	.21	.24		
Break Edges	1	2	3	4	5	6		
File	.080	.115	.150	.185	.220	.255		
Emery	.095	.145	.195	.245	.295	.345		
Scraper	.085	.125	.165	.205	.245	.285		
Gauging Requirements	1	2	5	10	25	50		
Scale	.08	.04	.02	.01	.01	.01		
Mike or depth gauge	.12	.06	.03	(.01)	.01	.01	1	.010
Flush pin or go and no go	.15	.08	.03	.02	.01	.01		
Thread gauge	.25	.13	.05	.03	.01	.03		
Blow out Collet						.065		
Polish								

		Machining Operations							
Tool	**Diameter**	**Depth**	**Point**	**Finish**	**Feed**	**R.P.M.**	**Standard**		
CS1 Form	½"	.375		From	Chart		+.000	.090	1	.090
CS2							−.003			
T1 Stop										
T2 Tap	5/16-32			From	Chart			.060	1	.060
T3										
T4										
T5										
T6										

Compiled by C. D. D.	Total Minutes	.495
	Use Minutes/Piece	.50

Fig. 32. Standard data sheet for an operation.

WORK-FACTOR PLAN. This is a method of analyzing the **factors involved in work** (The Work Factor Co.). It is simply a system of time values for every conceivable individual finger, hand, arm, leg, or body motion which a human being can make. These time values have been set into **moving time tables** and rules have been written for their use.

Work-factor time data were accumulated over a number of years. During this period, more than 20,000 motions were measured by the use of special watches, motion picture cameras, photoelectric relays, and stroboscopic lighting units. All measurements were made at actual workplaces. There was no laboratory time values in the work-factor time table. After the table was compiled, many hundreds of rates were set with it but not used—they were for test purposes only. During succeeding years, the work-factor method has been modified and improved according to problems encountered in actual rate setting in the factory and office.

Work Factors. Although there are dozens of variable factors involved in motions, for practical purposes, the following major ones must be recognized in measuring them for rate-setting purposes.

1. The body member used (arm, leg, finger, etc.).
2. The length of the motion (5 in., 10 in., etc.).
3. Basic motion, which is the simplest and fastest.
4. The kind of motion involving work-factor.
   a. Does it carry weight or overcome friction? (W)
   b. Does it require control to steer it? (S)
   c. Does it require care or precaution? (P)
   d. Does the motion change direction? (U)
   e. Must it end at a definite stop point? (D)

If each of these factors is known about a given motion, that motion can be identified according to the amount of time required to make it. One of the fastest and simplest motions which an operator can make is tossing an object. It is evident that the factors noted above, such as weight or resistance, steering to exact location, moving with care or precaution, making a change in direction, or making a definite stop (controlled by the operator), tend to slow down a motion.

Motions Identified. Fig. 33 shows some examples of motions classified according to work-factor analysis and their time values.

No.	Description of Motion	Work Factor Classification	Work Factor Motion Time (Min.)
1	Move finger 1 in.	F* 1	0.0016
2	Move hand 10 in. (arm)	A 10	0.0042
3	Move hand 20 in.	A 20	0.0058
4	Move hand 20 in. to wrench	A 20 D**	0.0080
5	Move hand 20 in. carrying wrench (3 lb.) to place aside	A 20 WD	0.0102
6	Move hand 20 in. carrying wrench (3 lb.) to place on nut	A 20 WSD	0.0124
7	Move hand 20 in. carrying wrench (3 lb.) around and behind fixture to place on nut	A 20 WSUD	0.0144
8	Move foot to depress machine pedal (leg) (10 in.)	L 10 D	0.0070

* The symbol before the number designates the body member.
** Each symbol used after the number represents a work factor.

Fig. 33. Typical motions classified according to work-factor analysis.

It is apparent from the foregoing examples that if the motion can be described in words, it can be put into its proper work-factor classification. Using the work-factor classification makes it possible to determine the time for the motion from the work-factor **table of motion times.** The time varies as the body member, the distance, or the type of motion varies. Classified time values set up in tables can be converted into shop rates for any combination of manual motions involved in a given operation.

Production Level. All values shown on the work-factor table of motion times are known as "select" times. When allowances for personal time, fatigue, and delays are added to "select" time, the result is the time which the normal skilled operator working at an incentive pace should consistently maintain. This is assumed to be equivalent to 25 percent above a base rate level of output. The following allowances are recommended for use in conjunction with work-factor. For an incentive operation:

Assume select time from tables is................................	1.00 min.
Personal, fatigue, and delay allowances	18%
Incentive allowance	25%
Standard time is..	1.47 min.

On this basis, the normal incentive worker should earn 25 percent above his base rate (or "day" rate when the base and day rate are the same).

METHODS-TIME MEASUREMENT. Maynard *et al.* (Methods-Time Measurement) describe the development of MTM. A methods engineering research project was carried on over a period of many months to arrive at a "methods formula" which would enable determination of effective methods before these methods were introduced into the shop. The investigation was limited at first to sensitive drill-press operations. However, it was found that the data which had been compiled for drill-press work applied equally well and with a very satisfactory degree of accuracy to all classes of work involving manual motions. Hence, instead of a methods formula applying merely to sensitive drill-press work, it was recognized that truly basic methods-time data had been developed. While the present data must be regarded as incomplete, they do apply to the majority of industrial operations.

Uses of Methods-Time Measurement. MTM has been applied for a number of years for:

1. Developing effective methods in advance of beginning production.
2. Improving existing methods.
3. Establishing time formulas or standard data.
4. Estimating.
5. Guiding product design.
6. Developing effective tool designs.
7. Establishing time standards.
8. Selecting effective equipment.
9. Training supervisors to become highly methods conscious.
10. Settling grievances.
11. Research, particularly in connection with methods, learning time, and performance rating.

Methods-Time Data Tables and Application. Tables of time data have been developed for the following motions:

1. Reach.
2. Move.
3. Turn and apply pressure.
4. Grasp.
5. Position.
6. Release.
7. Disengage.

Seven tables cover most types of manual motions. Fig. 34 (MTM/Association for Standards and Research) shows data for three of these: reach, move, and

TABLE I—REACH—R

Distance Moved Inches	Leveled Time TMU				Hand in Motion		CASE AND DESCRIPTION
	A	B	C or D	E	A	B	
1	1.8	2.1	3.6	1.7	1.3	1.5	**A** Reach to object in fixed location, or to object in other hand or on which other hand rests.
2	3.7	4.3	5.9	3.8	2.8	2.7	
3	5.0	5.9	7.3	5.3	3.8	3.6	
4	6.1	7.1	8.4	6.8	4.9	4.3	**B** Reach to single object in location which may vary slightly from cycle to cycle.
5	6.5	7.8	9.4	7.4	5.3	5.0	
6	7.0	8.6	10.1	8.0	5.7	5.7	
7	7.4	9.3	10.8	8.7	6.1	6.5	
8	7.9	10.1	11.5	9.3	6.5	7.2	**C** Reach to object jumbled with other objects in a group so that search and select occur.
9	8.3	10.8	12.2	9.9	6.9	7.9	
10	8.7	11.5	12.9	10.5	7.3	8.6	
12	9.6	12.9	14.2	11.8	8.1	10.1	
14	10.5	14.4	15.6	13.0	8.9	11.5	**D** Reach to a very small object or where accurate grasp is required.
16	11.4	15.8	17.0	14.2	9.7	12.9	
18	12.3	17.2	18.4	15.5	10.5	14.4	
20	13.1	18.6	19.8	16.7	11.3	15.8	
22	14.0	20.1	21.2	18.0	12.1	17.3	**E** Reach to indefinite location to get hand in position for body balance or next motion or out of way.
24	14.9	21.5	22.5	19.2	12.9	18.8	
26	15.8	22.9	23.9	20.4	13.7	20.2	
28	16.7	24.4	25.3	21.7	14.5	21.7	
30	17.5	25.8	26.7	22.9	15.3	23.2	

TABLE II—MOVE—M

Distance Moved Inches	Leveled Time TMU				Multiplying Factor		CASE AND DESCRIPTION
	A	B	C	Hand In Motion B	Wt.	Factor	
1	1.7	1.7	1.7	1.5	Up to 5#	1.00	
2	3.6	4.2	4.2	2.7			
3	4.9	5.7	5.7	3.6			
4	6.1	6.9	7.3	4.3	10#	1.03	**A** Move object to other hand or against stop.
5	7.3	8.0	8.7	5.0			
6	8.1	8.9	9.7	5.7	15#	1.05	
7	8.9	9.7	10.8	6.5			
8	9.7	10.6	11.8	7.2	20#	1.08	
9	10.5	11.5	12.7	7.9			
10	11.3	12.2	13.5	8.6	25#	1.11	**B** Move object to approximate or indefinite location.
12	12.9	13.4	15.2	10.0			
14	14.4	14.6	16.9	11.4	30#	1.14	
16	16.0	15.8	18.7	12.8			
18	17.6	17.0	20.4	14.2	35#	1.16	
20	19.2	18.2	22.1	15.6			
22	20.8	19.4	23.8	17.0	40#	1.19	**C** Move object to exact location.
24	22.4	20.6	25.5	18.4			
26	24.0	21.8	27.3	19.8	45#	1.22	
28	25.5	23.1	29.0	21.2			
30	27.1	24.3	30.7	22.7	50#	1.25	

TABLE III—TURN AND APPLY PRESSURE—T AND AP

Weight	Leveled Time TMU for Degrees Turned											
	30°	45°	60°	75°	90°	105°	120°	135°	150°	165°	180°	
Small— 0 to 2 Pounds	2.8	3.5	4.1	4.8	5.4	6.1	6.8	7.4	8.1	8.7	9.4	
Medium—2.1 to 10 Pounds	4.4	5.5	6.5	7.5	8.5	9.6	10.6	11.6	12.7	13.7	14.8	
Large— 10.1 to 35 Pounds	8.4	10.5	12.3	14.4	16.2	18.3	20.4	22.2	24.3	26.1	28.2	

APPLY PRESSURE CASE 1—16.2 TMU.   APPLY PRESSURE CASE 2—10.6 TMU.

Fig. 34. MTM data for reach, move, and turn and apply pressure.

turn and apply pressure. When the tables are applied with an understanding of the characteristics of the motions covered, it will be found that they make it possible to establish with a certain degree of accuracy the time required to perform the vast majority of industrial manual operations.

In these tables the unit of measurement is a TMU (Time Measurement Unit). 1 TMU = 0.00001 hr. = 0.0006 min. = 0.036 sec. Thus, if the time required to perform a given series of motions is found from the tables to be 325 TMU, the time in decimal hours is 325 × 0.00001 or 0.00325 hr.

The tables are set up in terms of **leveled TMU.** They show the time required by the operator of normal skill, working with a normal effort to make the motion under normal conditions. Conventions for recording motion classification are shown in Fig. 35. Morrow (Motion Economy and Work Measurement) illustrates the application of the MTM tables to a drilling operation with the computations and the summary completed (see Fig. 36).

Table	Example	Significance
I	$R8C$	Reach, 8 inches, case C
	$R12Am$	Reach, 12 inches, case A, hand in motion
	$R14ACD$	Reach, 14 inches, case A with change direction
ll	$M6A$	Move, 6 inches, case A, object weighs less than 5 pounds
	$M16B15\#$	Move, 16 inches, case B, object weighs 15 pounds
III	$T30°S$	Turn 30°, small part
	$T90°L$	Turn 90°, large part
	AP	Apply pressure
IV	$G1a$	Grasp, case 1a
V	$P1NSD$	Position class 1 fit, non-symmetrical part, difficult to handle
VI	$D2E$	Disengage, class 2 fit, easy to handle
VII	$RL1$	Release, case 1

Fig. 35. **MTM conventions for recording motion classifications.**

BASIC MOTION-TIME STUDY. The BMT system for studying motion times was developed by the staff of J. D. Woods & Gordon, Ltd., of Toronto. The system and times were derived from laboratory experiments and were carefully checked against a variety of factory operations before being accepted for general use. The laboratory experiments were set up in such a manner that the variable factors which influence motion times could be introduced either one at a time or in combination and in carefully controlled degrees.

BMT data are based on **basic motions.** A basic motion is considered to be a single complete movement of a body member. A basic motion occurs every time a body member which is at rest moves and again comes to rest. The action of knocking on a door, for example, requires two basic motions for every knock—one to draw the hand back and another to move the hand forward and knock. It can be noted that this system avoids describing a motion in terms of its purpose or in terms of a description of the object being handled. For instance, a grasp is specified by listing the **component motions** as such, and not by describing the shape, size, condition, or location of the object being grasped.

Analysis of Basic Motions. Basic motions are classified as: finger, hand, and arm motions; foot and leg motions; and miscellaneous body motions.

turn and apply pressure. When the tables are applied with an understanding of the characteristics of the motions covered, it will be found that they make it possible to establish with a certain degree of accuracy the time required to perform the vast majority of industrial manual operations.

Methods Engineering Council Form No. 205

Date 2-15 —
Study No. 3
Sheet No. 1
of 1 Sheets

W. A. Foggerty, Observer
DWG 207504 — Item 3
Part — Bracket

Operation – Drill 2 1/4" holes
Skill C-1
Effort C-2
Remarks – Operator has had six months experience on this class of work

Element	LH	T	RH
Get part with LH from tote pan, transfer to RH and place in jig	R10C	12.9	
	Mi5B	15.2	
	R8B	10.1	(M6C)
	G1A	1.7	5.6 G3
	RL1	26.6	P2NSD
	RL1	1.7	RLI
Tighten two locators simultaneously close jig cover with LH and tighten thumb screw with RH	R6B	8.6	R6B
	G1A	1.7	G1A
	T90	5.4	T90
	RL1	1.7	RL1
	G1A	1.7	G1A
	T90	5.4	T90
	AP	16.2	AP
	RL1	1.7	RL1
	R6B	8.6	7.1 R4B
	G1A	1.7	1.7 G1A
	MIOA	11.3	5.4 T90
		1.7	RL1
Reach to spindle lever RH, lower spindle and position jig under drill	P2SD	21.8	11.0 OR15A
		1.7	G1A
		13.4	Mi2B
		8.1	M6A
		5.6	G2
Drill 1/4 hole 1/8" deep			
Raise spindle RH, move to second hole LH, lower spindle and position jig under drill	MIC	1.7	13.4 Mi2B
	P2SD	21.8	8.1 M6A
		5.6	G3
Raise spindle RH, loosen 2 locators simultaneously loosen thumb nut RH and open cover LH	(M8B)	20.8	M22A
	RL1	1.7	RLI
	(R6B)	15.1	RI5B
	G1A	16.2	G1A
	AP		AP
	T90	5.4	T90
	RL1	1.7	RL1
	T90	5.4	T90
	G1A	1.7	G1A
	T90	5.4	T90
		7.1	R4B
		1.7	G1A
		5.4	T90
		1.7	RL1
	MIOA	11.3	6.8 R4E
Remove part from jig RH and toss aside in tote pan on right		7.1	R4B
		8.7	G1C2
		11.8	D2D
		8.6	M10Gm
		1.7	R1

Drilling time computation:

Speed = 70 F.P.M = 1070 R.P.M.
Feed = .0025" per revolution
Lead of drill .025"
Thickness of material = .125"

$$\text{Drilling time} = \frac{(.075 + .125)(.0167)}{.0025 \times 1070} = .00125 \text{ hrs}$$

Summary:

	Get part	Tighten two locators	Reach to spindle	Drill hole	Raise/move 2nd hole	Raise/loosen	Remove part
Element Time TMU'S	81.1	85.3	61.6		50.6	110.8	37.9
Conversion Factor	.00001						
Leveled Time Hours	.000811	.000853	.000616	.00125	.000506	.001108	.000379
% Allowance	15%						
Element Time Allowed	.00093	.00098	.00071	.00144	.00058	.00127	.00044
Occurrence per Cycle	1	1	1	2	1	1	1
Total Time Allowed	.00093	.00098	.00071	.00288	.00058	.00127	.00044

Time Allowed Per Piece .00779 hrs.

Fig. 36. Model MTM study showing computations and summary completed.

be noted that this system avoids describing a motion in terms of its purpose or in terms of a description of the object being handled. For instance, a grasp is specified by listing the component motions as such, and not by describing the shape, size, condition, or position of the object being grasped.

Analysis of Basic Motions. Basic motions are classified as finger, hand, and arm motions; foot and leg motions; and miscellaneous body motions.

The first factor considered in **finger, hand, and arm motions** is the role of muscular control in stopping the motions.

1. A motion can be stopped by impact with a solid object, as in the downstroke of a hammer or in pushing a flat sheet of metal against a stop in metal shearing. These are identified as **Class A motions.**
2. A motion can be stopped in mid-air by muscular control without coming in contact with any object. Motions like this are used for the upstroke in hammering and for tossing objects aside. These are **Class B motions.**
3. A motion can be stopped by grasping or placing an object. Muscular effort is used here to slow down the motion before the object is grasped or placed in position. This is illustrated by a motion used to reach and grasp a desk pad or to carry and place the desk pad on top of the desk. **These are Class C motions.**

In summary, Class A motions are stopped without muscular control by impact with an object; Class B motions are stopped entirely by the use of muscular control; and Class C motions are stopped by the use of muscular control both to slow down the motion and to end it in grasping or placing action.

There are no separate times for **grasping** or **releasing.** Any grasp that is accomplished as part of the initial contact with the object being grasped is really part of the motion to the object. The motion and grasp terminate at the same instant—at the instant of contact with the object. The grasping action may be more complex, such as getting a single object from a large number or picking up a part from a flat surface. Here **extra finger motions** are needed which must be measured separately. Releasing is treated similarly. The releasing action is part of the motion away from the object being released.

Motion-Time Determination. Other factors influencing motion times are:

1. **Distance moved.** The data are classified in terms of distance moved in inches.

2. **Visual attention.** If the eyes move to the ending point of a motion as it is taking place, the motion time is greater than if there were no eye movement. Class B and Class C motions, which use muscular control in the stopping action, may or may not be accomplished by a movement of the eyes to the ending point. When an eye movement is needed to complete these motions, they are said to be visually directed. They are then identified as **Class B visually directed** (*BV*) or **Class C visually directed** (*CV*) motions. *BV* and *CV* class motions occur only when the eyes move with the hand. If the eyes can be fixed on the ending point of the motion before it starts, the basic arm motion is not delayed and no allowance is necessary for visual direction.

3. **Precision requirements.** Precision is the term applied to the **extra muscular control** required where a motion ends in grasping a small object or in placing an object in an exact location. The degree of precision needed in any motion situation can be stated in quite definite terms. In the case of motions that end with a grasp, this is done by determining the limits within which the fingertips must be located in order to make a satisfactory grasp.

4. **Weight.** Whenever a heavy object must be handled or when friction must be overcome, added muscular effort is required. BMT defines the use of this extra effort as **force.** In a motion that involves handling a heavy object, force may be introduced in three phases:

a. To apply pressure in grasping the object in order to gain control of the weight. That is, the fingers are pressed firmly against the object so that it will not slip through the fingers during the move.

b. When the weight is brought under control by this squeezing action, to apply force to start the weight in motion.

c. As the weight is brought near its destination, to apply force in the opposite direction to slow up and stop the weight.

BMT deals with the effect of weight on an individual motion time by first recognizing the separate presence of these different phases of the force factor. Then appropriate allowances are added to the basic motion time. The allowance requirements are determined by both the weight of the object and the length of the motion.

5. **Simultaneous arm motions.** If either of the two motions that are occurring simultaneously can be completed without the use of the eyes to direct it, neither motion will take longer to complete than it would as a single motion. However, when both motions must be visually directed, the eyes are directed first to one ending point and then to the other. This delays completion of the second motion and an allowance must be added. The amount of the allowance depends on both the distance between the end points of the two motions and the precision needed to end the motions.

Tables of BMT Data. Fig. 37 shows a table of BMT data expressed in ten-thousandths of a minute. The "Reach or Move" table supplies the data for the five classes of motion. To assist in describing the activity, the letters R and M are used to indicate when the motion is for the purpose of reaching (R) to an object or of moving (M) an object to a new location. A 10-in. Class C reach would be coded $R10C$.

Arm movements that consist of rotating the forearm, as in using a screwdriver, are called **turns** and are set out in a separate table. Turn motions are described under the same five classes as used in dealing with reaches and moves. A Class C turn that rotates the hand through 90 deg. is coded $T90C$.

Separate tables headed "Precision," "Simultaneous Motions," "Turn," and "Force" set out the **time allowances** that must be added to the basic motion times when a motion involves these conditions. It will be noted that the allowance for precision varies with two factors: the **tolerance limits** at the ending point, and the **distance** covered by the motion. When a 10-in. Class C reach must be terminated in a grasp performed within ¼-in. limits, the coded motion description is set out as follows:

$$R10C$$
$$P\frac{1}{4}$$

The allowance for simultaneous motions that require visual direction also varies with two factors. They are the tolerance limits at the end points of the motions and the distance separating the two end points. **Simultaneous motions** that end with grasps performed within ¼-in. limits when the end points are 12 in. apart are coded as follows:

$$12'' \text{ Simo } \frac{1}{4}''$$

Note that the simultaneous motion allowances increase as the distance between the end points of the motions increase.

When a motion is performed to carry an object weighing 10 lb., the code $3F$ (for apply pressure, start, stop) 10 lb. is shown immediately under the code for the basic motion.

REACH OR MOVE

Inches	½	1	2	3	4	5	6	7	8	9	10	12	14	16	18	20	22	24	26	28	30
A	27	30	36	39	42	45	47	50	52	54	56	60	64	68	72	76	80	84	88	92	96
B	32	36	42	46	49	52	55	58	60	62	64	68	72	76	80	84	88	92	96	100	104
BV	36	42	48	53	57	60	63	66	68	70	73	77	81	85	89	93	97	101	105	109	113
C	41	48	55	60	64	68	71	74	77	79	81	86	90	94	98	102	107	111	115	119	123
CV	45	54	62	67	72	76	79	82	85	87	90	95	99	104	108	112	116	120	124	128	132

PRECISION

Inches	1	2	3	4	5	6	7	8	9	10	12	14	16	18	20	22	24	26	28	30
1/2″ tol.	3	4	6	7	8	9	10	11	12	13	14	16	17	18	19	20	21	22	23	24
1/4″ tol.	13	16	18	21	23	25	27	29	31	32	36	39	42	45	48	51	53	55	57	59
1/8″ tol.	33	37	41	45	48	52	55	58	60	62	67	72	76	80	83	87	91	94	98	101
1/16″ tol.	60	65	69	73	76	80	83	87	90	93	98	103	107	112	115	119	123	127	131	135
1/32″ tol.	90	97	102	106	110	114	117	120	123	126	131	135	139	143	147	150	153	157	161	165

SIMULTANEOUS MOTIONS

Separation Distance	0	2	4	6	8	10	12	14	16	18	20	22	24
1/4″ tol. and over....	0	10	18	27	34	41	47	54	59	65	69	74	78
1/8″ tol. and over....	0	12	21	30	37	44	51	57	63	68	73	78	82
1/16″ tol. and over ..	0	15	27	37	45	53	61	68	75	80	86	91	96
1/32″ tol and over ..	0	19	34	47	58	68	77	84	90	97	103	107	111

TURN

Degrees	30	45	60	75	90	120	150	180
A	26	29	32	34	37	43	49	54
B	33	36	40	43	47	54	60	67
BV	40	44	48	52	56	65	72	80
C	56	60	64	68	72	81	88	96
CV	73	77	81	85	89	98	105	113

BODY MOTIONS

LM (1″–6″)	50	Leg Motion
Add per inch..	2	
FM	55	Foot Motion
W	100	Walk one pace
SS_1 (1″–6″)	60	Side Step
Add per inch..	2	
SS_2 (1″–6″)	120	Side Step
Add per inch..	4	
TB_1	110	Turn Body
TB_2	220	Turn Body
B	180	Bend
S	180	Stoop
K_1	180	Kneel on one knee
AB etc.	200	Arise
K_2	440	Kneel on knees
AK_2	480	Arise from knees
SIT	220	Sit
$STAND$	270	Stand

FORCE

Apply Pressure, Start or Stop

Inches	6	12	24
2 pounds	2	3	3
4	6	6	7
6	8	9	10
8	10	11	13
10	13	14	16
15	18	20	22
20	23	26	28
30	31	35	38
40	38	43	47
50	45	50	55

EYE TIME

80

Fig. 37. Basic motion-time values (expressed in ten-thousandths of a minute).

Complex Time Studies

AUTOMATIC MACHINE OPERATION. When power-feed automatic machines are used and the operator handles two or more machines, computation of standard times becomes somewhat complicated. The operator may place a part or piece in the machine, clamp it in place, start the automatic feed and have nothing further to do on that machine until the cut or machine run is finished and the piece is ready to be removed. An example is the power-feed milling machine, for which a typical operation cycle is: place piece in machine fixture, tap piece, clamp in place, move table, throw lever to start automatic feed, and —when machine "kicks off" at end of the cut—loosen and remove piece from the machine.

However, on automatic screw machine operations, incidental work such as inspection and minor tool adjustments may have to be done during the cutting time. This fact should be taken into account in making machine assignments.

Although cutting or machine time for operations on machines of the types mentioned is taken from a time study, this time should be checked with calculations based on **approved cutting feeds and speeds.** Usually a 5 percent allowance is added to computed machine time for variations. The percent allowance will depend upon kind and condition of machine and upon accuracy of its adjustment.

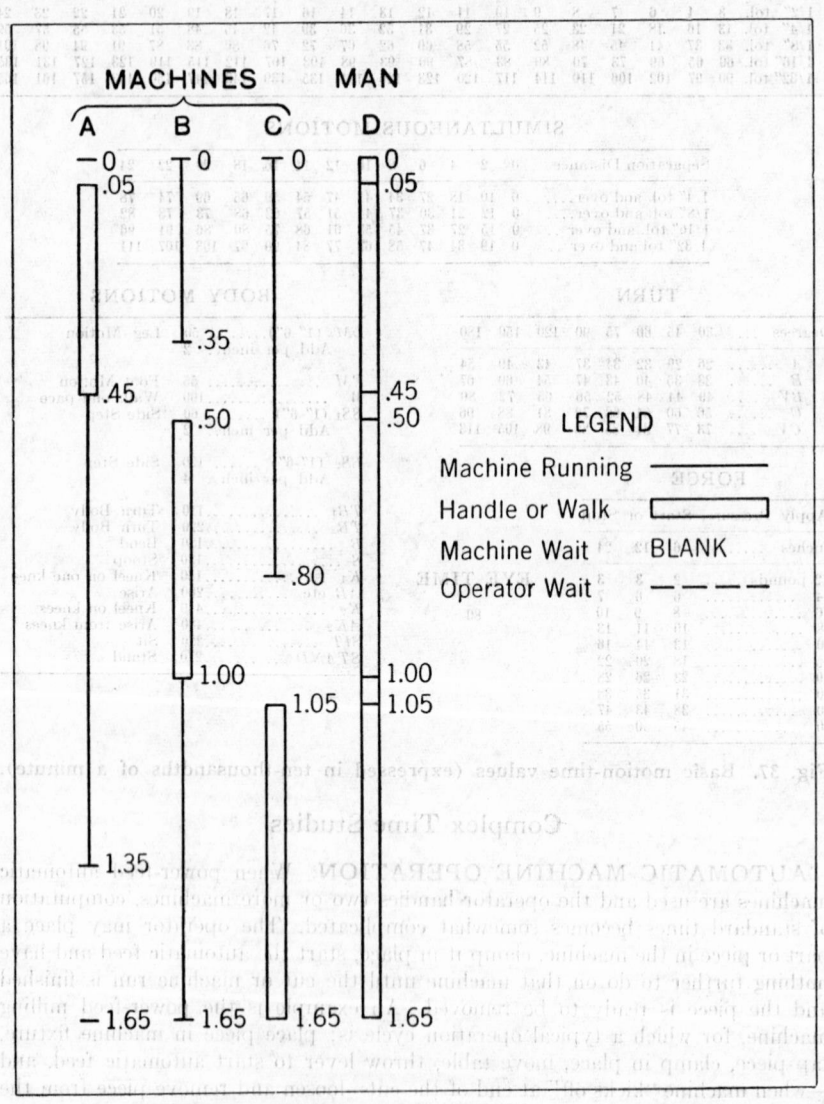

Fig. 38. Man-machine chart for automatic machine cycle.

SIMPLEST AUTOMATIC MACHINE CYCLE. Charts such as that shown in Fig. 38, with time indicated on the vertical scales, are used to show machine running, operator handling, walking, interference, and man-waiting times. A, B, and C are the charts for three machines, and D is a man chart. The figures are the **indicated times.** Charts may be constructed commencing with machines at any desired stage of operation. The chart illustrated indicates the man as walking to A, having just started C, which is now running, while B is partly through its run. While the man is handling machine A, machine B stops at .35 min. and must wait until the operator finishes handing A and has walked to B. At this point, **interference time** is from 0.35 to 0.45, or 0.10 min. If the operator is assigned too many machines, interference time becomes excessive and cost increase becomes uneconomic. Man chart D shows the operator working or walking 100 percent of the time, and computation of standard times can be based on the walking and handling times alone. Allowances for personal time, fatigue, and delays are made as usual.

EXAMPLE OF MAN-MACHINE ANALYSIS

(Time in minutes)

Factor	Machine A	Machine B	Machine C
Machine time	0.900	1.000	0.800
Handling time	0.400	0.500	0.600
Walking time	0.050	0.050	0.050
Handling and walking	0.450	0.550	0.650
Personal, fatigue, delay allowance of 15%....	0.068	0.083	0.098
Working cycle	0.518	0.633	0.748

Preparation, or time for getting tote box of work and removing finished pieces, takes 2.00 min. per 100 pieces, to which an allowance of 20 percent is added. Preparation on each machine is $(2.00 + 20\%) \div 100 = 0.024$ min. per piece.

EXAMPLE OF PREPARATION ALLOWANCES IN MAN-MACHINE ANALYSIS

(Time in minutes)

Factor	Machine A	Machine B	Machine C
Working cycle	0.518	0.633	0.748
Preparation	0.024	0.024	0.024
Standard time per piece in minutes..........	0.542	0.657	0.772

The allowance on handling time for personal needs, fatigue, and delays will vary for different jobs and should be determined from studies.

OPERATOR WAITING FOR MACHINE. The machine time may be so long that the machine will not have completed its run by the time the operator returns to the machine after handling the other machine or machines. This occurrence is shown in Fig. 39, a chart of **two-machine operation.** After the man has

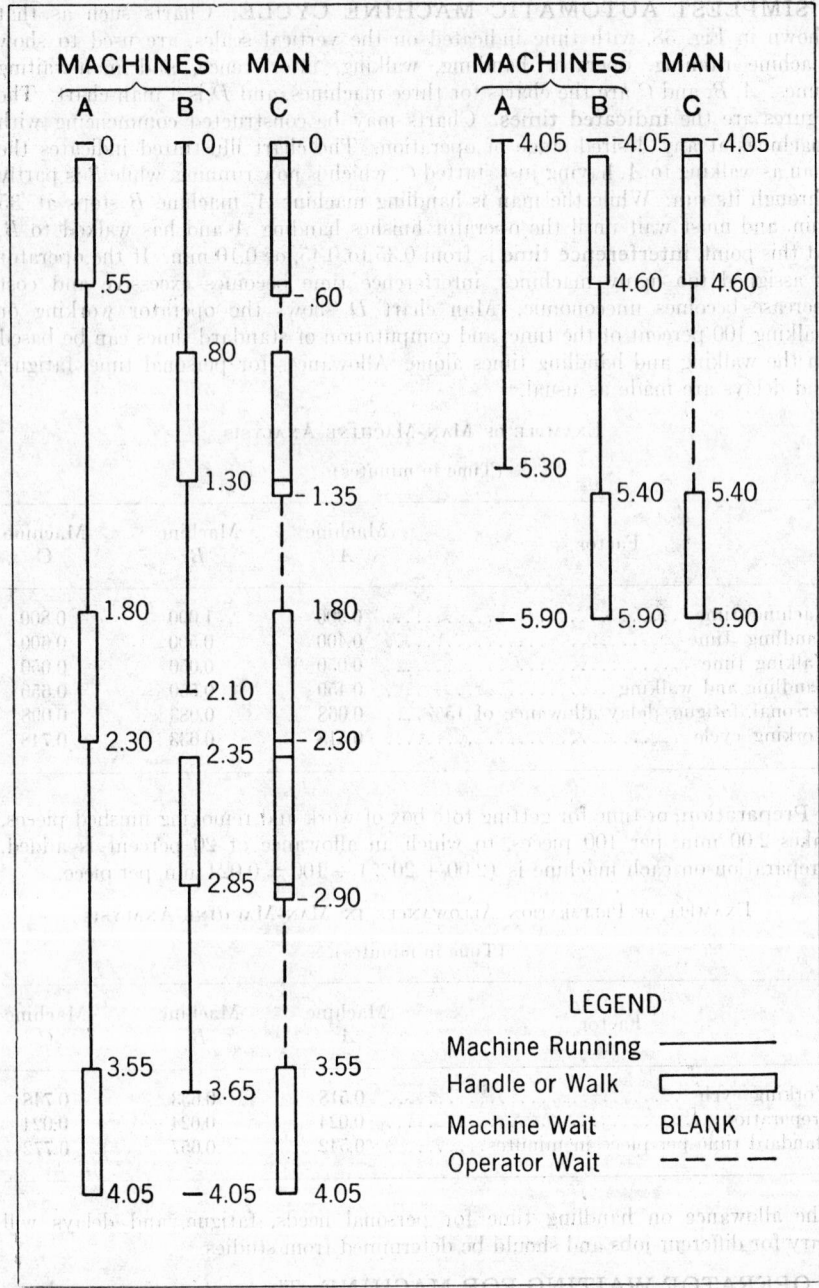

Fig. 39. Man-machine chart with operator waiting for automatics to finish operations.

finished handling machine A, he may walk to B, arriving there at 0.60 min., where he may wait until it is time to handle B. This wait is also shown on man chart C by the dotted line. Other man-waits occur throughout the cycle.

The charts are extended for handling and running machine A three times, and for handling and running machine B four times. How far to carry out the chart is determined by cut-and-try methods.

The **standard time** for this cycle may be computed from the man-machine chart as follows:

Total handling and walking times $0.60 + 0.55 + 1.10 + 0.50 + 0.55 + 0.50$ (shown by double lines, chart C)..	3.800 min.
Personal, fatigue, and delay allowance, 15%............................	0.570 min.
Man-wait $0.20 + 0.45 + 0.65 + 0.80$ (no added allowance) (shown by dotted lines on chart C)...	2.100 min.
Total time	6.470 min.

Operator's handling or walking time:	
Machine A, $1.65/3.80$...	43.5%
Machine B, $2.15/3.80$...	56.5%
Machine A produces 3 pieces:	
Standard time per piece, $(43.5\% \times 6.470)/3$........................	0.938 min.
Machine B produces 4 pieces:	
Standard time per piece, $(56.5\% \times 6.470)/4$........................	0.914 min.

In doing his work, the operator may have to bring tote boxes of work to his machine and remove finished parts. If this moving is merely a lift from floor to bench, taking 0.10 min., it may be done during any waiting time the operator has available and no allowance need be made in the computations. If the work must be obtained from a distance, taking a longer time (2.00 min., for instance), allowance must be made, because both machines will have stopped running during the 2.00 min.

Machine waiting time or delay due to interference decreases productive machine time, eventually a point being reached where it is uneconomic to assign the operator more machines. It is important, therefore, to know the interference time. Graphic charts may be used in cases similar to the foregoing. **Interruption sheets** are sometimes used to record the observations of interruptions.

Another method, with an experienced operator willing to give a good study on the machines, is to take a production or ratio delay study, recording machine running, "down" due to handling or "down" due to interference, together with other usual data. Interference is then obtained as a percentage of the handling time, or as a percentage of handling plus running times.

Interference may be determined from formulas developed to cover particular machines and operating conditions. Such formulas are recommended when their application and limitations are clearly defined.

Interference Formulas. Fry developed a formula for determining interference in congested telephone lines, when calls come through requiring use of the same trunk line. Wright (Mech. Eng., vol. 58) gives a formula which he has adapted from Fry's formula by converting it into terms of machine interference.

$$I = 50 \left[\sqrt{(1 + X - N)^2 + 2N} - (1 + X - N) \right]$$

where I = interference in percentage of attention time
X = ratio of machine running time to attention time
N = number of machine units assigned to one operator

The formula was checked with the analysis of more than 1,100 hr. of actual shop observations during which interference had been measured and recorded. These studies covered the operation of eight entirely different kinds of machines and were therefore considered entirely general. It was found that the formula checked accurately with these actual shop studies for assignments of six or more machine units per operator, but did not agree when the assignment was less than six.

Wright recommends using a set of **empiric curves** (Fig. 40) when the number of machines is six or fewer than six. The curves for two to five machines give interference values which are less than values obtained by solving the formula. For six machines, the chart and the formula give the same results, except at the upper and lower ends of the curve.

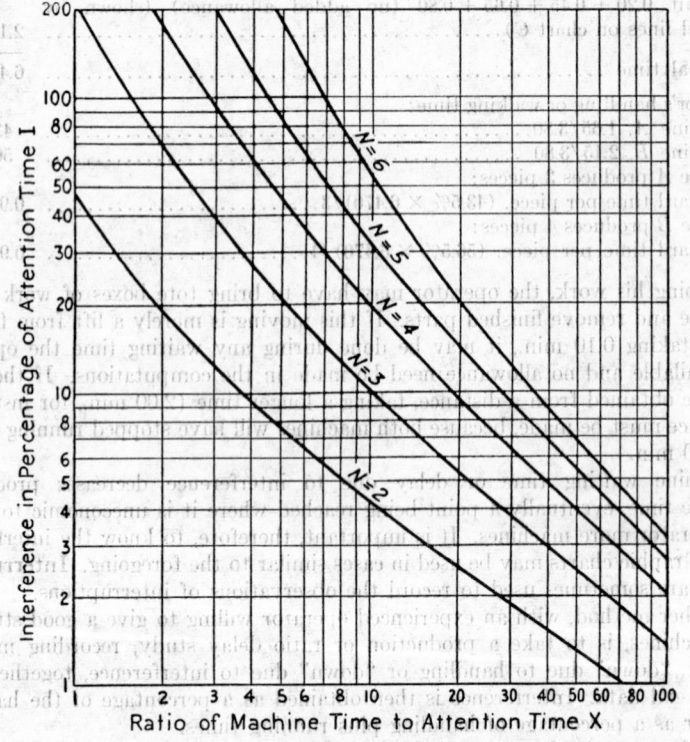

Fig. 40. Interference in percentage of attention time, operator running six or fewer machines.

A further application of this interference study was to develop a formula for obtaining the economic number of machine units that should be assigned to one operator. As the number of units assigned to an operator is increased, the labor cost is decreased and the machine cost is increased. **Economic assignment** is reached when the cost is least, giving due consideration to both man and machine.

Fig. 41 is Wright's chart for determining this economic assignment. Application of chart and formula in a case where

Machine running time = 25 min. per lb.
Attention time = 1 min. per lb.
Cost chargeable to machine = $.50 per unit per hr. ($M$)
Direct labor cost = $2.00 per operator per hr. (L)

In the chart (Fig. 41) line $X = \frac{25}{1} = 25$ and line $M/L = \frac{.50}{2.00} = .25$ intersect at $N = 20$, the economic number of machine units to assign to the operator.
To arrive at the standard time, it is necessary to compute the interference:

$$I = 50[\sqrt{(1 + 25 - 20)^2 + 2(20)} - (1 + 25 - 20)]$$
$$= 136\% \text{ of the attention time, or 1.36 min. per lb.}$$

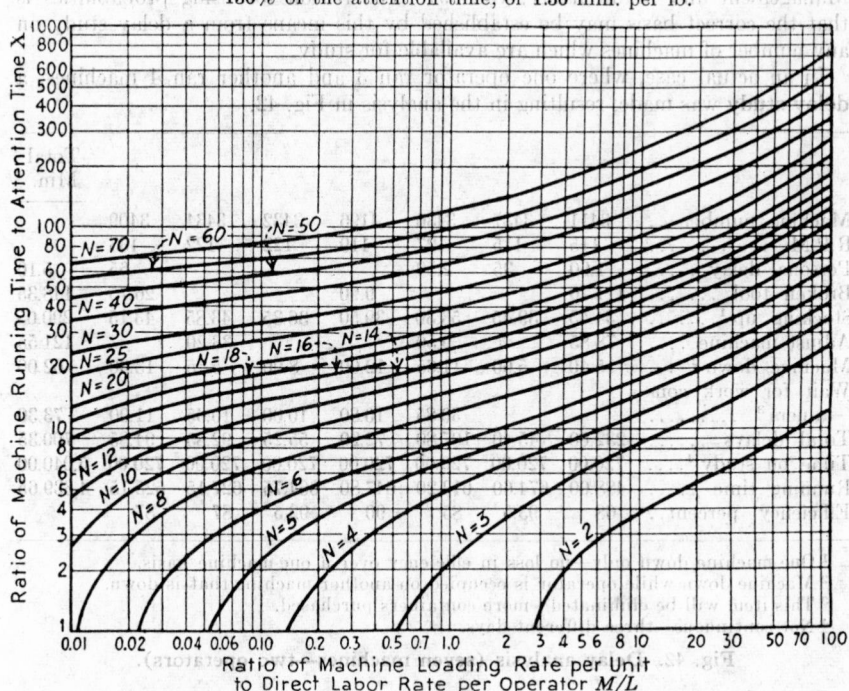

Fig. 41. Diagram for determining the number of machines to assign to an operator.

Machine running time.	25.00 min.
Attention time, including allowances	1.00 min.
Interference	1.36 min.
Total running, attention, interference time	27.36 min.
Personal allowance 3%	.82 min.
Standard time for 20 lb.	28.18 min.

As one pound is produced on each of the 20 machines handled, then:

Standard time per 100 lb.	2.34 hr.
Earning rate	$2.00 per hr.
Piecework price per 100 lb.	$4.68

Wright's adaptation of Fry's formula was checked and compared with synthetic production studies by Hanser and Sandberg (New York University), as were other formulas, including the binomial application by Bernstein, Duval's formula, and several empirical formulas. Of these, Wright's adapted formula checked more closely with production studies than any of the others. A simple formula to apply, it is recommended as one of the best yet evolved. A more recent treatment is Feller's (Probability Theory and Its Applications).

Work Assignment

AUTOMATIC PRESSES. Machine assignments and standard times, or piecework prices, for groups of automatic machines are computed at the Winchester Repeating Arms Company by the law of probabilities (Bernstein, Factory Management and Maintenance, vol. 99). The reason for using probabilities is that the correct basis may be established by this means from a delay study on any number of machines which are available for study.

In an actual case, where one operator ran 3 and another ran 4 machines, a **delay study** was made, resulting in the analysis in Fig. 42.

								Total Min.
Machine number ..	3411	3437	3436	4196	3432	3434	3409	
R.P.M.	115	115	127	119	122	122	135	
Personal delay	1.60	.35	2.50				.65	5.10
Broken tool	111.70			9.90			26.75	148.35
Stocking up [1]......	34.45	39.45	53.30	39.50	36.35	43.85	43.15	290.05
Adjust machine	78.85		9.50			33.20		121.55
Machine down [2] ...	5.40	5.60	11.65	12.00	8.90	5.15	13.30	62.00
Wait for work containers [3]			30.85	10.80	10.00	10.65	11.00	73.30
Total delays	232.00	45.40	107.80	72.20	55.25	92.85	94.85	700.35
Time on study [4]....	720.00	720.00	720.00	720.00	720.00	720.00	720.00	5,040.00
Running time	488.00	674.60	612.20	647.80	664.75	627.15	625.15	4,339.65
Efficiency percent..	68	93.5	85	90	92.5	87	87	

[1] One machine down only—no loss in efficiency over a one-machine basis.
[2] Machine down while operator is occupied on another machine that is down.
[3] This item will be eliminated—more containers purchased.
[4] Not continuous—three different days.

Fig. 42. Delay analysis (seven machines—two operators).

Bernstein states:

For purposes of multiple-machine basis, only the stocking-up item need be considered in relation to the running time, because on other items the adjuster and not the operator does the work; i.e., on tool or machine breaks. The stocking-up time was 290.05 min. and the running time 4,339.65 min. Therefore, considering only these two items, the stocking-up time, or the time when the operator is occupied, is 6.2% of the total, and the running time is 93.8%. Machine and tool delays amount to 269.90 min., and personal delays are arbitrarily set at 30 man-min. per working day. Machine and tool delays amount to 5.8% of total time.

When one machine is down, there is no loss in efficiency on a multiple basis over a unit basis. When two machines are down, interference occurs—one machine must wait while the operator attends the other. When three machines are down, two machines wait while the first is being attended, and one machine waits while the second is attended, a total of 3 **machine waits.**

Binomial Expansion Used. On an eight-machine basis, average interference per machine is determined by using the binomial expansion for 6.2 percent stocking up time and 93.8 percent running time. Interference is determined by multiplying probability times the average machines down. For instance, for four machines down the average is 6 machine waits divided by $4 = 1.5$.

Binomial Expansion	Machines Down At One Time	Interference
$(.938)^8 = 0.5992$	0	0
$8(.938)^7(.062) = 0.3170$	1	0
$28(.938)^6(.062)^2 = 0.0733$	2	$0.0733 \times 0.5 = 0.0366$
$56(.938)^5(.062)^3 = 0.0097$	3	$0.0097 \times 1.0 = 0.0097$
$70(.938)^4(.062)^4 = 0.0008$	4	$0.0008 \times 1.5 = 0.0012$
$56(.938)^3(.062)^5 = 0.0000$	5	0
	Total	0.0475

On an eight-machine basis, the **efficiency per machine** would be:

Efficiency on one-machine basis $= 0.9380$
Interference or machine waits $\quad = 0.0475$
Efficiency on eight-machine basis $= 0.8905$

The above efficiency is running efficiency. However, the operator is allowed 30 man-min. out of 480 for personal delays, so that the actual min.-hr. is 56.2 and not 60. The over-all efficiency is therefore $0.8905 \times 56.2/60.0 = 0.835$. Feller (Probability Theory and Its Applications) cites a different approach.

Study Procedure. The time study man first makes a delay study on one machine of the group, with the operator attending the number of machines which is historically normal. He writes down delays which occur on this one selected machine, differentiating between machine waits for the operator when more than one machine is down at a time, and delays where the operator is attending to that machine. The first named delays, machine waits, are not used in computing the efficiency because that is taken care of in the binomial expansion. Also, at the end of the study, the actual production should be checked against the theoretical in order to see if any loss through nonfeeding or any other shrinkage has occurred. This **shrinkage** should be added to delays in attending the machine in order to compute the one-machine running efficiency to be used in the binomial expansion.

In addition, the operator is attending to gaging work, filling the hopper, etc., while the machines are running. The minutes consumed this way should be added to the delay time to see that the operator is not theoretically occupied more than 100 percent of his available time. If the operator is occupied 6 percent of his time on each machine while it is running, then 48 percent of his available time is used up in this manner. Added to this 48 percent are his attendance times on machines when they are down. For an eight-machine basis, these times are as follows:

Machines Down	Attendance Time, Etc.
1	$.3170 \times 1 = 0.3170$
2	$.0733 \times 2 = 0.1466$
3	$.0097 \times 3 = 0.0291$
4	$.0008 \times 4 = 0.0032$
5	.0000
over 5	.0000
Total	0.4959

Thus, 50 percent plus 48 percent adds up to 98 percent of operator's available time.

Finally, the labor costs for various bases must be determined, to see that the law of diminishing returns has not set in. At certain times, when machine tools are scarce or when production is more important than labor costs, the basis may have to be lowered so that full use can be made of machine time available.

When the operator does his own adjusting, the number of machines handled should be fewer. In the first example, the restocking, adjusting, and attention time will be 11.4 percent and machine running time will be 88.6 percent, computed from Fig. 46.

Hence, for four machines the man is occupied slightly under 50 percent of his time, which is a fair basis, as $11.4 \times 4 = 45.6$ percent.

Binomial Expansion	Machines Down At One Time	Interference
$(.886)^4$ $= 0.6162$	0	0
$(.886)^3 \times (.114) \times 4 = 0.3171$	1	0
$(.886)^2$ $(.114)^2 \times 6 = 0.0612$	2	$.0612 \times \frac{1}{2} = 0.0306$
$(.886)^1$ $(.114)^3 \times 4 = 0.0053$	3	$.0053 \times 1 = 0.0053$
$(.114)^4$ $= 0.0002$	4	$.0002 \times 1.5 = 0.0003$
		$\overline{0.0362}$

Analysis	Percent
One machine down (normal)...................	11.40
Machines down while operator is occupied..........	3.62
Personal delays	5.00
	$\overline{20.02}$
Efficiency	79.98

Considering only labor cost, would it be better to have an operator-adjuster handle four machines or have an operator on eight machines? The task is computed by the formula $RPM \times RE \times MH \times 8$, where RE equals running efficiency and MH equals minute-hour.

Task for 8 machines $= 120 \times 0.8905 \times 56.2 \times 8 = 48044$

Task for 4 machines $= 120 \times 0.7998 \times 56.2 \times 4 = 21575$

Comparative labor costs would be:

No. of Machines	Output at Task for 8 Hr.	Labor Cost for 8 Hr.	Labor Cost per Hundred
8	48044	$14.40	$0.0303
4	21575	10.40	0.0482

The eight-machine basis gives 37 percent lower labor cost and only 10 percent lower production per machine.

For a group of machines on which different components are being run and restocking varies greatly, it is a good practice to rate each machine individually, and let the operator run as many machines as he can look after. Suppose earnings per hour for the correct number of machines is set at $1.00. In a group of ten machines, assume five were being run as shown in Fig. 43.

Machine Number	Percent Restocking	Correct Machine Basis	Task Earnings per Machine
29323	8.8	5	$0.200
29331	6.7	6	0.166
30022	4.7	10	0.100
30021	16.2	3	0.333
29334	5.4	9	0.111
Operator's task earnings			$0.910

Fig. 43. Machine assignment when restocking varies greatly.

To bring his task earnings up to $1.00, he should run an additional machine like No. 30022 or No. 29334.

This method works satisfactorily when the efficiency of operation is approximately the same in the new combination of machines as in the combinations for which the rates were originally set. Otherwise, corrections should be made for the changed efficiencies.

AUTOMATIC SCREW MACHINES. A method for computing hourly production and standard times for Brown and Sharpe automatic screw machines is given by Varga (Neptune Meter Co.):

$$\text{Standard minutes per piece} = \left[\frac{T}{60} + \frac{.50}{\frac{(L \times 12) - K}{l + l'}} \right] \left[1 + \begin{array}{l} \text{Percentage for} \\ \text{tool,} \\ \text{oil, and} \\ \text{general} \\ \text{allowances} \end{array} \right]$$

where T = cam time in seconds per piece, from blueprint
L = length of bar stock, in feet
K = scrap, in inches
l = length of one unit produced, in inches

The tabulations in Figs. 44 and 45 give basic data for the factors K and l' and tool allowances.

Diam. of Material (inches)	Mach. No.	Values for l' (inches)		K Length of Scrap (inches)
		Metallic Material Without Hole	Metallic Material With Hole	
0.062 to 0.312	00	0.055	0.055	1¾
0.343 to 0.500	0	0.072	0.072	2⅜
0.531 to 0.875	2	0.080	0.100	2¹⁵⁄₁₆
0.875 to 1.000	2	0.100	0.100	2¹⁵⁄₁₆
1.032 to 2.000	—	0.125	0.125	2¹⁵⁄₁₆

Note: When facing tool is used, add .01 to values of l'. Rod lengths: Brass = 12 ft.; All others = 10 ft.

Fig. 44. Factors K and l' for automatic screw-machine calculations.

Tool	Metal Being Machined		
	Brass	Steel	Monel
Cutoff	.490	1.850	2.600
Form	1.400	2.070	2.740
Position	0.035	0.035	0.035
Spot face	0.029	0.043	0.049
Drill	0.390	0.660	0.930
Reamer	0.160	0.205	0.250
Box	1.040	1.540	1.750
Die	0.240	0.243	0.246
Tap	0.080	0.119	0.135
Swing	2.500	3.700	4.200
Slotter	0.033	0.048	0.055
General	8.000	8.000	8.000
Oil	2.000		
Inspect	0.950		

Fig. 45. Tool allowances, automatic screw machines.

Procedure for Setting a Standard. In setting a standard on a job of this kind, the following procedure is used:

1. From operation sheets obtain cam time to produce piece and the class of machine job is run on.
2. Apply formula. Refer to tables for values of l' and K. Compute time to produce piece, including the 0.50 min. for loading the rod. Compute the rod time, which equals the product of the time per piece times the number of pieces in the rod.
3. List tools required to machine part. Refer to table of tool allowances and list corresponding percentage tool allowances for given material. List general allowances. Refer to the chart in Fig. 46, and obtain percent allowance for rod running out and also over-all allowance on tool adjustments. Total these allowances.
4. Increase time to produce piece by these allowances.
5. Convert standard time into production per hour.

$$\frac{60}{\text{Standard time}} = \text{Pieces per hour}$$

Illustration: Part: Steel hand shaft. 9/16 in. diameter, steel. Run on No. 2 B. & S. screw machine. Given: $T = 35$ sec., $l = 2\frac{1}{4}$ in., $L = 10$ ft.

$$\frac{T}{60} + \frac{.50}{\dfrac{(L \times 12) - K}{l + l'}}$$

$$= \frac{35}{60} + \frac{.50}{\dfrac{120 - 2^{15}/_{16}}{2.25 + .080}}$$

$$= .583 + \frac{.50}{50}$$

$$= .583 + .01 = .593 \text{ min.}$$

Rod time $= 50 \times .593 = 29.65$ min.

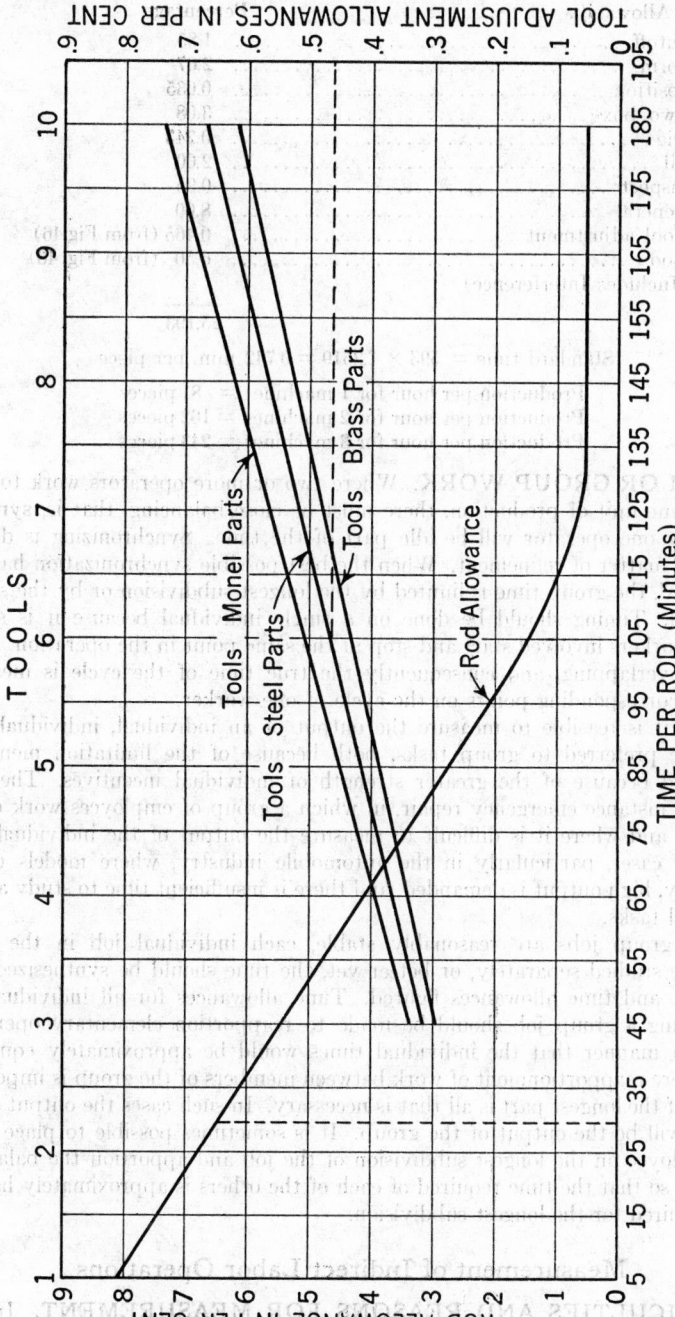

Fig. 46. Rod (bar stock) and tool adjustment allowances for automatic screw-machine work.

Allowances	Percentage
Cutoff	1.85
Form	2.07
Position	0.035
Two box	3.08
Die	0.243
Oil	2.00
Inspect	0.95
General	8.00
Tool adjustment	0.465 (from Fig. 46)
Rod	6.50 (from Fig. 46)
(Includes Interference)	
	25.193

Standard time = .593 × 1.2519 = 0.742 min. per piece

Production per hour for 1 machine = 81 pieces
Production per hour for 2 machines = 162 pieces
Production per hour for 3 machines = 243 pieces

TEAM OR GROUP WORK. Where two or more operators work together on the same unit of production, there must be close balancing, that is, **synchronizing,** or one operator will be idle part of the time. Synchronizing is difficult but not a matter of refinement. When the best possible synchronization has been established, the group time is limited by the longest subdivision or by the slowest individual. Timing should be done on a single individual because it is seldom that all workers involved start and stop at the same point in the operation. There is some overlapping, and consequently the true time of the cycle is measured between corresponding points on the cycle of one worker.

Where it is feasible to measure the output of an individual, individual tasks are to be preferred to group tasks, both because of the limitation mentioned above and because of the greater strength of individual incentives. There are cases, for instance emergency repair, in which a group of employees work on the same job and where it is difficult to measure the output of the individual; and there are cases, particularly in the automobile industry, where models change frequently, high output is demanded, and there is insufficient time to study and set individual tasks.

When group jobs are reasonably stable, each individual job in the group should be studied separately, or better yet, the time should be synthesized from unit data and time allowances figured. Time allowances for all individual jobs constituting a group job should be made to reapportion elementary operations in such a manner that the individual times would be approximately equal. In cases where reapportionment of work between members of the group is impossible, a study of the longest part is all that is necessary. In such cases the output of this portion will be the output of the group. It is sometimes possible to place a second employee on the longest subdivision of the job and apportion the balance of the work so that the time required of each of the others is approximately half the time required for the longest subdivision.

Measurement of Indirect Labor Operations

DIFFICULTIES AND REASONS FOR MEASUREMENT. Indirect labor operations include, among others, materials handling, cleaning or janitorial tasks, maintenance, and clerical jobs. These operation types present an **obstacle**

to **measurement** and standardization for a number of reasons. Some of these reasons are as follows:

1. There is usually an ostensible lack of repetitive pattern to the operational method.
2. The operations may involve a group activity.
3. The unit of output may be difficult to define.
4. The job may be made up of numerous suboperations.
5. A cycle of output is long.
6. The operation may be constantly changing in geographic location.

Besides measurement difficulties, certain **economic factors** must be considered. The period of measurement is usually long, being a matter of weeks or even months. In addition to actual measurement time, considerable engineering hours must be consumed in analysis of data and in compilation and classification of standard data for use in setting standard times for individual jobs. Also, the failure of an indirect labor incentive plan due to improper or hasty measurement and planning can be costly to correct.

The measurement, standardization, and control of these types of jobs should not be neglected. There are a number of **reasons for measurement**, among which are the following:

1. The proportion of indirect labor cost to total labor cost is high, being as much as 75 percent in some plants. Hopton (NACA Bulletin, vol. 29) reports that a survey of 10 Pennsylvania plants disclosed a ratio of indirect to total labor costs of from 13 to 76 percent with the average being 33 percent. The companies selected included some representing the textile, watch, radio tube, boiler, machinery, and chemical process industries.
2. As automation becomes more of a reality, the proportion of indirect costs to total costs will increase.
3. The use of incentive plans on direct labor has resulted in a need to place incentives on indirect labor in order to have some equity in wage-earning opportunities.
4. During critical labor shortages the efficient use of existing labor will be mandatory.

INDIRECT LABOR MEASUREMENT. Both time study and work sampling techniques are applicable to measuring indirect labor jobs. The following applications suggest approaches to the derivation of **standard data** for indirect operations using the stop watch. They show how, in specific instances, standard data have been developed for janitorial, maintenance, and messenger activities. Materials handling is another type of indirect labor for which standard data have been derived.

Janitorial Work. The following steps for measuring the operation of dry-mopping office floors and cleaning desk tops include those necessary to compile basic standard data for the job.

1. Set up procedures covering equipment and methods employed in carrying out the job. Sufficient attention should be given to methods design or improvement. Put these in written standard practice form.
2. Determine the important elemental activities of the operation. In this case these activities might include:
   a. Unlock and open office door and turn on lights.
   b. Get cleaning material out of hand truck.
   c. Mop clear floor area.
   d. Move objects in the room.

    e. Clean desk and table tops.

    f. Mop under objects.

    g. Remove dust from mops and cloths.

3. Time study the full range of operations, with the janitors following the standard methods. Snap-back timing is an economical method where the purpose may be to build up suboperation times. Times can be recorded directly on a floor plan blueprint.

4. Analyze the data, considering the variables and problem of applying the data to obtain standards. The important variables in this case will be:

    a. Area to be cleaned in terms of square feet.

    b. Indirect time necessary to get ready for cleaning.

    c. Shape of the area to be cleaned.

    d. Congestion of the space.

    e. Movable objects.

    f. Walking time.

5. Establish elemental standard data.

    a. **Time to mop floor.** Plot cleaning time versus floor area. Assume that the data plots as shown in Fig. 47. This graph establishes a rate of cleaning in minutes per square foot and a fixed time, *b*, necessary for **initial preparations** prior to actual cleaning. **Congestion** is reflected in additional preparation time during the course of cleaning the room. This can be considered by dividing the total office area into subareas. For instance, in Fig. 48 Case *X* subdivides into two areas, *I* and *II*, and Case *Y* into four or

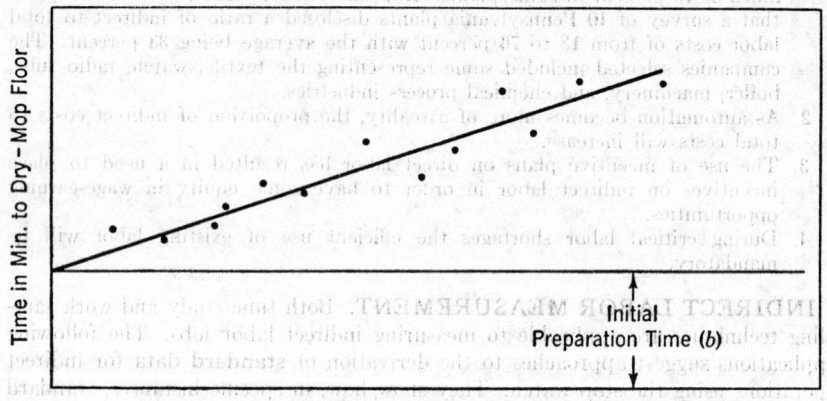

Fig. 47. Graph of floor area versus time to mop floor.

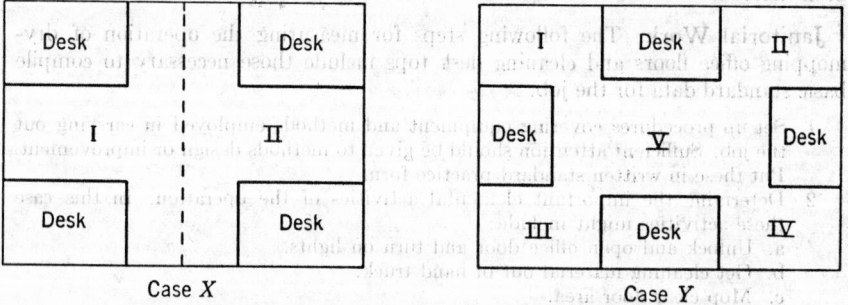

Fig. 48. Division of office area into subareas for two cases.

perhaps five areas. This type of breakdown is more important in operations such as waxing floors, in which a power waxer must be moved between areas and electric lines shifted to different outlets.

b. **Time to clean desk and table tops.** This also is a function of area and number of objects to clean.

c. **Time to move objects and walk.** Time to move objects can be assumed to be a constant per object moved. Walking time can be taken from predetermined times such as MTM.

Now let:

A = total clear floor area in square feet.

a = time to mop 1 sq. ft. of floor as determined from curve.

b = initial preparation time per room, determined from curve or from separate time studies.

b' = preparation time necessary for each subarea. This may be specified as some fraction of b.

N = number of subareas.

d = time to clean 1 sq. ft. of table or desk top.

A' = table- or desk-top area.

C = number of tables or desks.

e = unit time to move an object in the room.

M = number of movable objects.

MTM = MTM standard walking time per foot.

D = number of feet walked.

T = total standard time required to dry-mop an office floor and clean table and desk tops.

$$T = aA + b + b'(N - 1) + dA'C + eM + MTM(D)$$

The standard data in this form provide the basis for planning a program or schedule of janitorial work necessary for a given building or group of offices. If the standard data and a **standard schedule** are to be used as the basis for incentive wages the incentive earnings must be built into the base rate of pay. This assumes that the schedule, representing good performance, will be adhered to. Provisions must be made to insure quality and to evaluate complaints concerning nonstandard job conditions.

Maintenance Operations. An attempt to measure and standardize various maintenance crafts or operations will prove uneconomical if the number of maintenance operators in the plant is small. If the maintenance labor force is large, particularly for a given craft, measurement can be profitable. Heritage (Factory Management and Maintenance, vol. 113) points out what work measurement on maintenance operations did for E. I. du Pont de Nemours & Co.:

1. It sharpens scheduling of maintenance work and preventive maintenance, thus reducing time delay between jobs.
2. Leads to closer project estimates, hence better decisions as to their acceptibility.
3. Makes possible better control of crew sizes by more accurate knowledge of work backlog.
4. Leads to more efficient manning of jobs.
5. Reveals the need for more training of a worker or a group of workers that fail to meet normal effectiveness levels.
6. Leads to more effective use of high-priced tools and equipment by minimizing stand-by time.
7. Minimizes delays on jobs caused by inadequate supply or late arrival of materials.
8. Helps justify new purchases of maintenance equipment for cutting labor costs by clearly proving the tangible savings in manpower.

9. Shows how responsibilities can be improved by revealing supervisory or staff deficiencies in phases of work execution or unproductive areas of operation.
10. Improves material specifications by disclosing operations that consume excessive time in application of materials or in repair of facility.
11. Promotes better supervision by relieving foremen of estimating duties, allowing more time for direct supervision.
12. Spots excessive costs because each job is individually measured.
13. Affords a good check on contractors' bids.
14. Acts as a brake against unavoidable overtime work by virtue of an established fair standard for the job.
15. Provides a common unit of measurement, understood by management and labor, for talking about costs, performance, and goals.

Sadoff (Factory Management and Maintenance, vol. 102) shows how Swift & Co. has applied work measurement to maintenance with certain success. Operations covered include, among others, carpenters, millwrights, pipefitters, boilermakers, tinsmiths, electricians, and painters. A total of 750 mechanics in 20 crafts were measured over a three-year period.

The approach to measuring this type of job is essentially the same as that involved in obtaining standard data. The elements of the operation are determined, the variables affecting time are analyzed, a stop-watch time study is made, and standard data are derived. Swift & Company found that the standards in each of the crafts should be classified into eight major divisions:

1. **Initial trips.** This standard covers the time consumed in going to the job at the start of the day, travel time from job to job, and time for returning to the shop at the end of the day. Standards for travel time are presented in the form of a **travel chart** showing all possible building-to-building combinations (Fig. 49). Other elements include time for picking up tools, ascending or descending stairs, waiting for elevator, etc.

Building number	1001	1002	1003	1004	1005	1006	1007	1008	1009	1019
1001	1.95*									
1002	2.40	1.95*								
1003	2.40	3.30	2.22*							
1004	2.40	1.95	3.30	1.95*						
1005	2.94	2.94	6.36	2.94	2.40*					
1006	2.40	3.30	2.22	3.30	6.36	2.22*				
1007	4.02	3.66	4.02	3.36	5.28	4.02	1.95*			
1008	3.48	3.12	4.74	3.12	4.20	4.74	2.76	2.67*		
1009	4.56	3.84	4.92	3.84	3.12	4.92	7.26	5.37	2.40*	
1019	6.00	6.36	4.92	6.36	6.27	4.92	6.72	8.16	2.40	2.67*

* Within the same building.

Fig. 49. Standard per one-way trip (travel chart).

2. **Material trips.** This covers the time required to transfer repair materials from their storage points in the plant to the job. The elements of this activity are: obtain order, get truck, load material in truck, brace load, etc.
3. **Basic operations.** These are the basic job elements of a given craft, for example: Lay 3×6 in. D&M or shiplap flooring (50–60 d. nails used). Elements of job are: place piece for measuring and mark with square, saw one or both ends of piece, carry piece to location, drive tight into tongue of adjoining

piece, ... fit shims under pieces, open keg of nails, etc. Fig. 50 shows standard times for basic operations.

4. **Miscellaneous jobs.** Example: Miscellaneous steamfitters. Standard includes: receive instructions from foreman, study and plan work, instruct helpers on job, get ladders or equipment to erect temporary scaffold, ... get out tools from tool drawers, obtain extension lights, etc.

5. **Small job standard.** A small job is defined as the operations necessary to start and complete all the work performed on an individual written or verbal order where the total labor required to perform this work does not exceed 120 basic work units. All jobs of more than 90-min. duration are checked to determine whether or not the job falls into this classification.

FLOORING STANDARD PER SQUARE FOOT OF AREA

Spacing of Joists (inches)	Average Length of Piece (feet)							
	2	4	6	8	10	12	14	16
12	3 95	2.73	2.33	2.18	2.04	1.97	1.90	1.85
18	3.58	2.40	2.00	1.80	1.65	1.60	1.52	1.48
24	3.32	2.13	1.73	1.53	1.38	1.33	1.28	1.22
30		2.02	1.60	1.39	1.27	1.20	1.15	1.09
36		1.97	1.55	1.36	1.24	1.16	1.09	1.05

STANDARD FOR STUDYING PIPEFITTING JOB

Number of Pieces of Pipe, Fittings, Hangers Installed, Plus Number of Bends Made in Pipe per Job	New Work	Repair Work
2	8.0	1.0
10	16.0	3.5
30	36.0	9.8
60	65.0	19.0
100	105.0	31.5

STANDARD PER PIECE OF PIPE INSTALLED

Size of Pipe Inside Diam. (inches)	Average Length of Pipe per Piece (feet)							
	Standard Weight Pipe				Extra Heavy Pipe			
	2	8	14	20	2	8	14	20
⅛	1.66	1.75	1.84	1.93	2.08	2.19	2.30	2.41
½	2.03	2.29	2.55	2.80	2.54	2.86	3.18	3.50
1	3.20	3.47	3.74	4.00	4.00	4.33	4.66	5.00
2	6.20	7.07	7.94	8.80	7.75	8.83	9.91	11.00
4	19.00	20.80	22.60	24.40	23.70	25.97	28.23	30.50
6	49.60	52.73	55.86	59.00	62.00	65.90	69.80	73.70

Fig. 50. Standards for basic maintenance operations.

6. **Process.** This includes credit for work where no accomplishment is achieved, such as trouble involved in unscrewing rusty pipe. It also includes credit for minor delays for lack of equipment, waiting for other crafts to perform part of the total job, waiting due to delays caused by operating department personnel, etc.

TEMPERATURE

Degrees of Temperature at Job	Percent of Job Affected									
	10	20	30	40	50	60	70	80	90	100
−20 +130	.020	.040	.060	.080	.100	.120	.140	.160	.180	.200
−10 +120	.015	.030	.045	.060	.075	.090	.105	.120	.135	.150
0 +110	.010	.020	.030	.040	.050	.060	.070	.080	.090	.100
+10 +100	.007	.014	.021	.028	.035	.042	.049	.056	.063	.070
+20 +95	.003	.006	.009	.012	.015	.018	.021	.024	.027	.030

PHYSICAL CONDITION OF LOCATION

	Percent of Job Affected									
	10	20	30	40	50	60	70	80	90	100
Slippery floors, etc.	.010	.020	.030	.040	.050	.060	.070	.080	.090	.100
Interference close objects	.015	.030	.045	.060	.075	.090	.105	.120	.135	.150
Interference other work	.012	.024	.036	.048	.060	.072	.084	.096	.108	.120

PHYSICAL CONDITION AND NATURE OF MATERIAL HANDLED

	Percent of Job Affected									
	10	20	30	40	50	60	70	80	90	100
Unwieldy pieces	.010	.020	.030	.040	.050	.060	.070	.080	.090	.100
Slippery pieces	.015	.030	.045	.060	.075	.090	.105	.120	.135	.150

EXTREME CARE DUE TO HAZARDS

	Percent of Job Affected									
	10	20	30	40	50	60	70	80	90	100
Working near dangerous objects	.020	.040	.060	.080	.100	.120	.140	.160	.180	.200
Handling dangerous material	.015	.030	.045	.060	.075	.090	.105	.120	.135	.150

Fig. 51. Credit for various working conditions.

7. **Variable standard.** The standard for each operation is at the same time a **conversion factor** for converting the production to a common unit of production which is the basis of the variable scale for the group. The checker will multiply each conversion factor by the production of that item, total these equivalents, and divide by man-hours spent producing the work of the group. Equivalent units per man-hour thus found will permit picking the proper standard per equivalent unit of production from the table.

8. **Working conditions.** Fig. 51 shows additional credit for various conditions and contingencies occurring infrequently. These are of such a variable nature as to be impossible to anticipate and allow for when setting up standards for any operation.

The standard time for a particular job is set by a checker. It has been this company's experience that, on the average, one standards checker can obtain the necessary production and other data required for determining the incentive pay of 18 mechanics.

Messenger Jobs. Gavett (NACA Bulletin, vol. 33) describes the application of standards to a special messenger service in a large process plant:

The manufacturing organization consisted of some sixty buildings located over an area of several square miles. The **messenger service staff** consisted of seven boys stationed in a centrally located building. The messengers, under the direction of a dispatcher-foreman, delivered and picked up special mail and small packages among these sixty buildings. Some buildings and offices used the service more than others.

The messengers were already on a group incentive plan prior to the study. This plan seemed inadequate for various reasons. The standard of performance in use was the time to make a delivery trip to or among the buildings. (There was no control over the volume of work, so this could not provide a good unit of measure.) A **single standard time** applied to a trip anywhere within the confines of the firm plus an allowance for each additional call during the trip. Upon making a trip the dispatcher would record the buildings served on the time card and time-punch the boy in and out of the messenger office.

The study of this indirect labor process consisted of the following major steps:

1. The analyst first followed the messengers for several days merely to ascertain the general nature of the operation.

2. . . . existing time cards showed the trips and calls made by each messenger throughout the day. These cards were studied over a two-week period to find out which buildings used the service most and what routes were used between buildings. The routes were easily determined from the sequence of messages delivered and from the use of a plant map, coupled with familiarity with the job.

3. Time studies were made of the time spent by the messengers within the buildings, while picking up or delivering an item. These time studies were made by the same general methods as are used on direct labor jobs. The job was broken down into elements showing the time spent in corridor travel, elevators, and offices. Conditions of the job were recorded, such as floors traveled, doors used, and stair flights ascended or descended. Each operator was rated for performance with respect to effort. The number of studies taken in each building depended on the frequency with which each utilized the messenger service, as indicated by the time card analysis. Those buildings using the service most were studied until some statistical consistency showed up in the time values.

4. Walking times between buildings were derived from standard walking times, using a scaled map to get distances.

The data obtained from the above steps were an excellent aid to establishing standard performance for supervisory and cost control. The study could have terminated at that point, but this company wished to go one step further and work the standard times into a form serviceable for an incentive system. For this purpose, the process or **operational pattern** had to be established in order to describe or define the job in the smallest quantitative elements possible, that is, something similar to the repetitive nature of the direct labor operation had to be determined.

Messenger Service Standard Trip Times Between Buildings

TRIP TO THIS BUILDING + TIME IN BUILDING ◄—

Zone 4	Zone 4	Zone 2	Zone 3	Zone 1	Zone 1	Building Number
11	9	4	3	2	1	
9 9.00 + (5.10) 14.10	40 3.00 + (.80) 3.80	6 .89 + (4.00) 4.89	121 1.65 + (1.00) 2.65	60 .85 + (.90) 1.75	——	Zone 1 1
17 10.00 + (5.10) 15.10	31 2.10 + (.80) 2.90 *	67 .60 + (4.00) 4.60	0 6.00 + (1.00) 7.00	——	70 .85 + (1.10) 1.95	Zone 1 2
22 5.00 + (5.10) 10.10	3 7.10 + (.80) 7.90	19 2.00 + (4.00) 6.00	——	10 6.00 + (.90) 6.90	3 1.65 + (1.10) 2.75	Zone 3 3
3 7.00 + (5.10) 12.10	0 3.10 + (.80) 3.90	——	7 2.00 + (1.00) 3.00	171 .60 + (.90) 1.50	9 .89 + (1.10) 1.99	Zone 2 4
etc.	——	etc.	etc.	15 2.10 + (.90) 3.00	2 3.00 + (1.10) 4.10	Zone 4 9
——	etc.	etc.	etc.	etc.	13 9.00 + (1.10) 10.10	Zone 4 11

Time: Minutes

* Example: It takes 2.10 min. to go from building 2 to building 9.
It takes .80 min. to deliver message in building 9.
There were 31 such trips in the two-week time card study.

Standard for Trip from Zone 1 to Zone 4 = weighted average of all trips from buildings in Zone 1 to buildings in Zone 4.

Std. $= \dfrac{40 \times 3.80 + 9 \times 14.10 + 31 \times 2.90 + 17 \times 15.10 \text{ etc. etc.}}{40 + 9 + 31 + 17 \text{ etc. etc.}}$

(TRIP FROM THIS BUILDING — shown in right margin)

Fig. 52. Calculation of zone standards on frequency-time chart.

In this particular instance, there were three major factors which gave a pattern to the job. First, the foreman was dispatching the messengers according to an informal zoning system. Inasmuch as most messages were carried from centrally located buildings to buildings roughly on the perimeter of the total plant area and then back again to the central zone, the foreman had zoned the perimeter into three zones. It was also a fact that the flow of messages was always from the central zone to any one of the outside zones but never from one outside zone to another. Secondly, as mentioned before, there was a consistency of routes used and buildings served. Thirdly, there was a somewhat repetitive nature to the elements of the job of delivering or picking up a message within a building.

With a pattern thus determined, the data had to be classified in some manner to establish a **zone standard time.** A standard time was needed for a trip from the central zone to any of the perimeter zones and a standard for making a call within each zone. For this purpose, use was made of an especially prepared **frequency-time chart.** This chart was constructed like the mileage chart on the back of a road map. A portion of the chart is illustrated in Fig. 52. The building numbers were listed both across the top and down the side. Walking times between buildings were entered in the appropriate squares. To this time was added the standard time spent in the building *to* which the trip was being made. For instance, it took a messenger 2.10 min. to go from Building 2 to Building 9, and .80 min., on the average, would be spent in Building 9 delivering or picking up the message.

The chart, when complete, showed a standard trip time for every building to every other building. As further study information, the number in the upper left-hand corner of each square represented the number of times a trip was made in the two weeks covered. However, although the chart contained a standard time to deliver a message from any building to any other building, the implied next steps of setting an incentive on a building to building basis was considerd too elaborate a process. The system was easily simplified by obtaining a standard for zones and calls. This was done by taking a weighted average of all route times concerned with each zone

Fatigue in Factory Operations

NATURE OF FATIGUE. The term "fatigue" is used rather indiscriminately to apply to various phenomena present in both **muscular** and **sedentary** or mental tasks. These phenomena may be described and studied from both physiological and psychological points of view.

Ryan (Work and Effort) points out the difficulty of definition and research in the area of fatigue. "One of the primary difficulties is that the term 'fatigue' is not clearly enough defined to aid us in a search for a measure. Not only is the term vague as it appears in common usage, but it has been difficult for scientists to agree upon a common meaning of the term which would put their research upon a straightforward basis."

Bartlett (Psychological Criteria of Fatigue, in Symposium on Fatigue, Floyd and Welford, eds.) defines fatigue in the following terms:

Fatigue is a term used to cover all those determinable changes in the expression of an activity which can be traced to the continuing exercise of that activity under its normal operational conditions, and which can be shown to lead, either immediately or after delay, to deterioration in the expression of that activity, or, more simply, to results within the activity that are not wanted.

More specifically, from the industrial point of view, fatigue is defined as

that effect of work upon an individual's mind and body which tends to lower his rate or grade of quality in production, or both, from his optimum performance.

Fatigue is manifested in a number of ways, some lending themselves to objec·tive measurement and others more subjective. The manifestations of fatigue include:

1. A decrement in performance. A reduction in the rate and quality of output over a specified time period.
2. Reduction in the capacity to do work, such as impairment of a muscle or inability of the nervous system to give stimulus.
3. Subjective reports from workers concerning feelings of tiredness, physical discomfort, or localized pain. This refers to **perceived fatigue.**
4. Changes in other activities and capacities. These include changes in physiological functions or changes in ability to perform psychological activities other than the job itself.

Modern manufacturing methods are eliminating heavy muscular activity from industrial jobs. While these types of jobs are being eliminated, sedentary tasks introduce their own particular problems of fatigue. **Localized** and **static muscular fatigue** are associated with this type of job. Also involved are the kindred problems of boredom, monotony, and nervous or emotional strain. Therefore, fatigue is still an important consideration and should be understood both as to its causes and methods of reduction.

MUSCULAR FATIGUE. Ryan (Work and Effort) considers muscular work in the restricted sense to mean "those kinds of activity in which the primary aim is the development of mechanical force." **Muscular work** would include tasks which make heavy demands upon the whole muscular system, such as running, walking, carrying large loads, shoveling, and scrubbing. It would also include those tasks which involve the development of force by a restricted muscle group. He describes some of the types of muscular activity as:

1. Rapid expenditure of a large amount of energy ("dromal" tasks), e.g., running a competitive race.
2. Steady grind, e.g., a long day, walking under a load, and stoking.
3. Repetitive local task with high local energy expenditure, e.g., lifting a weight with one finger.
4. Postural restrictions ("static work"), e.g., maintaining an awkward position; holding a weight in outstretched hand.

Certain types of work that include muscular activity as incidental to the main objectives of control, timing, skill, and direction activity are referred to as **sedentary tasks,** which will be discussed later.

Laboratory Experiments in Muscular Fatigue. Physiological and psychological studies have been made on muscular activity. Classic experiments upon localized muscular activity have been conducted using the **ergograph.** This instrument graphically records the nature of contraction of specific or local muscles in an intact organism. In a typical ergograph study a weight is attached by a cord to the finger and the subject is asked to raise and lower the weight at specific times until fatigue makes contraction impossible. These studies are useful in attempting to determine such things as: the parts of the organic system—muscle, peripheral nerves, or central nervous system—responsible for loss in capacity for further performance; the nature of the spread of fatigue from a locally stimulated muscle to those surrounding; and the optimal load for a fixed number of lifts of a weight.

Typical studies of **metabolic** factors include the measurement of oxygen inhaled and carbon dioxide exhaled by a man riding a bicycle fixed to known loads. Vernon (Industrial Fatigue and Efficiency) summarizes such tests as follows:

They have shown that fatigue is frequently bound up with the production of various chemical products, some of which, such as sarco-lactic acid, are well-defined chemical substances, whilst others, the so-called fatigue toxins, are very indefinite and uncertain. Experiment has likewise shown that as a rule the chief seat of fatigue is not in the muscles themselves, as subjective sensations would lead us to infer, or even in the nerves supplying the muscles, but in the central nervous system. Here again fatigue is localized, not so much in the nerve cells, as in the junctions between nerve processes and cells, the so-called synapses.

Industrial Experiments in Muscular Fatigue. Studies by Christensen (Symposium on Fatigue, Floyd and Welford, eds.) were made to determine a physiological valuation of work in the Nykroppa Iron Works in Sweden. Measurements were made of oxygen consumption, pulse rate, maximum body temperature, and maximum fluid discharge for various types of work in the plant.

The **oxygen consumption** is an expression of the intensity of consumption in the body which the work entails; the heavier the work, the greater the amount of oxygen consumed. On the basis of oxygen consumption the production of **calories** can be calculated. A small proportion of these calories, estimated at 10 percent, is converted into mechanical work; the larger part degenerates into heat and must be conveyed away from the body.

The **pulse frequency** per minute is determined in order to check that the intensity of work at the time of determination of oxygen consumption was representative.

The **body temperature** can give valuable information about the heaviness of the work. The body temperature normally adjusts itself at a constant level after about one hour's work to a value which depends on the work load. The greater the load, that is, the greater the rate of development of energy, the higher the temperature.

The **loss of fluid** during the shift can also give information about the combined effect of work and heat. A certain amount of perspiration is normal, but it is increased very much if the temperature of the air or the intensity of heat radiation is high. The time of exposure is also a factor determining the amount of fluid lost.

Fig. 53 (adapted from Christensen, Symposium on Fatigue, Floyd and Welford, eds.) shows the results of the tests in terms of a ranking of each job on each factor measured, as well as an over-all grading figure.

Studies such as this are important in determining a number of things, such as the determination of **optimum work loads** for various jobs and under various working conditions. The suitability of a person to handle long continuous heavy work can be determined, for instance, by the capacity for **absorption of oxygen.** Also, according as the absorption of oxygen is great or small, certain conclusions can be drawn with regard to the degree of **strain** in a given stage of work for certain constant conditions.

Muscular Fatigue and Workplace Design. Various factors in work design are considered in relation to endurance of muscular exertion by Darcus (Symposium on Fatigue, Floyd and Welford, eds.):

First, optimum use must be made of the muscle power available. The position of the control to be used should be such that it can be operated with the **maximum**

Work Task	O_2 Litres Per Min. Mean Value	Pulse Rate Per Min. Mean Value Under O_2 Uptake	Pulse Rate Per Min. Mean Value by Shifts	Maximum Pulse Values	Maximum Body Temperature	Litres, Fluid Discharge Exclusive of Urine, Mean Value	Grading
Open hearth:							
Slag removal	1	4	—	8	—	7	5
Dolomite shovelling.	2	3	—	4	—	—	3
Tipping the moulds.	9	10	9	11	7	—	12
Cogging mill:							
Tending the heating furnace	3	6	2	3	2	2	2
Tending the soaking pit	10	—	5	9	3	9	11
Hand rolling	5	1	7	9	6	6	7
Tending the saw pits	8	5	3	3	5	8	6
Wire rod mill:							
Roughing	6	8	4	2	1	4	4
Finishing	10	—	13	13	6	5	13
Wire bundling	3	2	1	1	2	6	1
14-inch merchant mill:							
Merchant mill rolling	4	9	8	6	4	3	8
Large hammer:							
Forging	7	7	$\left\{ \begin{array}{l} 6 \\ 10 \end{array} \right.$	7	8	(1)	$\left. \begin{array}{r} 9 \\ 10 \end{array} \right\}$
Chipping:							
Chipping	10	11	11	10	9	10	14
Overhead crane:							
Operator	11	—	12	12	4	—	15

Fig. 53. Results of experiments in muscular fatigue.

force and that the load on the control should be the smallest proportion of that which can be exerted upon it. . . .

The part of the body used will depend on the nature of the work; for instance, the force required, the speed, the amplitude and the direction of movement. . . .

Much can be done when forces are required by providing suitable counter-pressure for the body. Certain devices which fix the body more rigidly, such as backrests, relieve the fixator muscles and increase the efficiency of the prime mover as well as reducing unnecessary displacements of the body.

A reduction should be made in total static muscular activity. A considerable degree of useless static work can be imposed by the design and positioning of controls. . . .

A further improvement could be made by ensuring that any control that has to be manipulated is placed so that the body can assume a posture which can be maintained with the minimum muscular effort. If the body is at all "off-balance," muscular activity has to be increased in order to preserve equilibrium.

If possible the load should be shared around the body—a division of labour instituted. . . . Improvements might also be effected by allowing the same movement to be produced by different muscle groups; . . . If the task is particularly heavy the operator should have the opportunity of moving from one process to another in which different groups of muscles are used.

Unnecessary body movement can also be reduced by designing the control so that it can be moved with the minimum shift of body position when it is moved through its required range.

FATIGUE IN SEDENTARY WORK. The term "sedentary work" is preferred to "mental work" for the tasks considered since they are truly body activities rather than activities that take place in the mind. Ryan (Work and Effort) describes various types of sedentary work:

1. **Problem solving** (with minimum muscular and sensory involvement). Examples are calculation, solution of mathematical problems, composing, planning, directing the work of others, supervising, and socialized tasks such as selling.
2. **Continued sensory adjustment** (primary visual tasks). Examples are proofreading, visual inspecting, radio code reception, piano tuning, and reading under difficult conditions or when long continued.
3. **Motor skill** (with patterning and accuracy of movement as the central core, and force only an accessory feature). Examples are typing, drawing, various machine operations, assembling machines, woodworking, sewing, acting, and speech-making.
4. **Sedentary muscular** (light muscular tasks with little skill or control involved). Examples are the work of a watchman, crossing guard, or machine feeder, or any task where the main requirement is that the proper movements be made at the proper time. The movements themselves involve few elements of skill or of force.

In many industries these task types predominate over heavier muscular types of jobs. The types of fatigue associated with these jobs must be discerned and reduced where possible. However, the fatigue present in sedentary operations is characteristically difficult to measure and evaluate. It is manifested in **deterioration of performance** or in subjective reports from the worker concerning his feelings of fatigue.

Subjective reports from workers are poor indicators of fatigue if remedial action is to follow. They are usually delayed reactions to the onset of fatigue and come too late for immediate remedies.

Output Decrement in Sedentary Work. An hourly production curve is often presented as typical of output of factory operations. Such curves tend to show a composite of a number of factors which obscure the real influence or presence of fatigue. Some of these factors, such as a daily task or production goal set by the worker, the tendency of rhythmic operations to be more constant in rate of output, or the length of the day, may have an influence on when production will fall off.

Ryan (Work and Effort) points out that it is often difficult to find clear-cut changes in performance which accompany the progress of fatigue. There are few results among the studies of mental work which are clear enough to be of value in understanding the problem.

Industrial Experiments in Sedentary Work. A now classical study in fatigue was conducted at the Hawthorne Plant of the Western Electric Company (The Western Electric Researches, Fatigue of Workers). One part of the study is referred to as the Relay Assembly Test Room. Six girl workers were selected and placed in a separate room where experiments were made with different kinds of working conditions. The operators chosen were assemblers of telephone relays, neither inexperienced nor expert. The experiment was to provide the answers to questions concerning fatigue.

In 13 different test periods spread out over a number of years, various factors were altered, including length of work period, introduction of food during rest periods, number and duration of rest periods, and methods of payment. In general the daily rate of output of the group continued to increase during the overall experimental period. A statistical analysis of the results showed no simple correlation between output changes and changes in the various working conditions. Nor was there any correlation between output and other physical factors of the job for which records were kept, such as temperature, humidity, hours of rest, and changes of relay type.

The significant result of the experiment was the increased output over the entire length of the study. This was considered to be due to psychological and sociological factors. Statements of the subjects indicated the important reasons for increased productivity. In conclusion a company report pointed out that: "Upon analysis, only one thing seemed to show a continuous relationship with this improved output. This was the mental attitude of the operators. From their conversations with each other and their comments to the test observers, it was not only clear that their attitudes were improving but it was evident that this area of employee reactions and feelings was a fruitful field for industrial research."

ENVIRONMENTAL CONDITIONS AND FATIGUE. Besides the physical and movement requirements of a job, certain other factors, both inherent in the nature of the job and environmental to it, introduce fatigue. Some of these factors are noise, illumination, accident hazards, duration and time of work periods, and air condition of work environment.

Noise of Work Environment. Noise has been increasing in factory work as in all modern life. Fortunately, public opinion is bringing some cessation. The first step in abatement of noise nuisance is one of measurement. A unit of measurement called the decibel has been standardized and an instrument made to register sounds in that unit. The **decibel,** abbreviation DB, is defined as the smallest change which the ear can detect in the level of sound. The decibel scale is a logarithmic scale, on which a difference of intensity level of 1 decibel corresponds to a ratio of intensities whose logarithm is 0.1.

Compared with the scale running from the threshold of human hearing (0 decibels) to the threshold of painful sound (130 decibels), Anderson's **measurements of noise** on certain factory machines and operations (Fig. 54) are instructive.

The relative intensity of sound alone does not account for **pitch or quality,** and does not show **regularity or irregularity,** all of which make a difference in the tiring effect. Anderson found that most factory work came between 85 and 40 decibels. Some idea of this upper range may be had from the fact that very loud radio music in a house measures 80 DB and a very noisy restaurant measures 70 DB. Kennedy says:

The effects of noise have been described by research workers as emotional. However, long before the emotions are actively disturbed there are disturbances by reason of the stress vibrations in heightened pulse rate, heightened blood pressure, some irregularities in heart rhythm, and, most important of all, in the increase of pressure on the brain itself, as our experiments have indicated. Emotion is only the end product of the process . . .

Sound Intensity in Decibels	Description of Operation	Sound Intensity in Decibels	Description of Operation
85	Wire Drawing No. 2 Machines	60	Molding Brass Foundry
75	Milling (One Special Job)		Cleaning Castings Gray Iron Foundry
	Heading and Slotting (Heavy Machines)		Bench Work on Loading Coils
	Heavy Punch Press Operations		Spool Assembly (Bench Work)
	Textile Insulating of Wire		Straightening Frames (Bench Work)
	Wire Drawing No. 1 Machines		Hand Screw Machine Operations (Overhead Belt Drive Machines)
70	Multiple Drill Press Operations (Heavy Machines)		
	Automatic Screw Machine Operations		Hand Screw Machine Operations
	Perforate and Blank on Punch Presses		Punch Press Operations (Light Work)
	Heavy Punch Press Operations		Straightening Frames (Bench Work)
	Die Casting Operations		
	Paper Insulating of Wire		Miscellaneous Machine Work
65	Straightening Iron Stock		Cable Stranding
	Loading Coil Winding (Near Machines)		Rubber Molding
	Drilling (Light Machines)	55	Molding in Gray Iron Foundry
	Milling (Regular Work)		Bench Assembly Operations
	Miscellaneous Punch Press Operations		Bench Work on Loading Coils
			Tapping Machines
	Hand Screw Machine Operations (Individual Motor-Driven Machines)		Hot Tin Dipping
			Extruding Lead Cable and Lagging Cable Reels
	Twisting Light Gage Wire	50	Assembling Relays
	Tinsel Manufacture		Wiring Multiple Banks
	Wire Inspection		Jack and Ringer Assembly (Bench Work)
	Hand Screw Machine Operations (Heavy Type Machines)	45	Desk Work (Typing, Filing, etc.)
			Kick Press Operations
	Heading and Slotting (Light Machines)	40	Wire Balancing
	Miscellaneous Punch Press Operations		Desk Work (Typing, Filing, etc.)
	Heavy Punch Press Operations		
	Polishing and Buffing (Heavy Work)		
	Magnet Wire Insulating		
	Cotton Binding		
	Rubber Buffing		

Fig. 54. Sound intensity of various operations.

Reduction of Noise. Kimball (Kent's Mechanical Engineer's Handbook) says that "A noise that cannot be prevented or greatly reduced at the source, by design or by damping, will radiate into the air either directly from the surface of the vibrating body, or from the parts of the structure to which it is attached."

CLASSIFICATION OF NOISE				METHOD OF PREVENTION
Preventable at source				{ Design changes { Damping
Not readily preventable at source	Direct Noise	{ Screening { Absorption { Filtration	}	Higher frequency range, 300 cycles up
	Indirect Noise	{ Isolation by suspension	}	Lower frequency range under 300 cycles

Design Changes. Design changes to reduce noise are brought about by manufacturers' studies. Examples are: car wheels—steel rims insulated from the rest of the wheel by rubber; electric motors—special designs producing lower alternating current electric hum; blowers—whistles from blowers in ventilating ducts, usually blade frequency noises, eliminated by design changes; gear whistles—high-speed gearing improved by accurate design to avoid impacts, and using helical instead of spur gears.

Damping. By covering with a suitable material which reduces vibrations, some noise may be eliminated. Putty lagging—a layer of nondrying putty 1 in. or more thick, covered with varnished material or similar material to prevent drying—is good to reduce ringing noises and high frequency whistles. Felt-like materials sometimes are good as noise reducers, although they are less effective than putty.

Screening. By constructing screens or walls highly resistant to sound transmission, much noise can be confined.

Absorption. Directly radiated noise, such as from office or factory, cannot be screened. Reduction in noise can be made by sound-absorbing materials. Felt-like materials have a high sound-absorbing power as have certain porous materials, for example, Celotex.

Filtration. When direct noise containing definite notes is transmitted along ducts or through openings, it is possible completely to eliminate objectionable harmonics by an acoustic filter. Example of a high-pass filter is an automobile muffler or Maxim silencer. Space is the usual limitation to such applications.

Isolation by Suspension. Forced vibrations may be cured by isolation, through the use of elastic suspension. Spring suspensions, steel, rubber, cork, and gelatin compounds are used.

Illumination of Workplace. Weston (Symposium on Fatigue, Floyd and Welford, eds.) states that "Conditions of lighting which are sub-optimal for particular visual tasks accelerate the onset of fatigue occasioned by seeing, chiefly because they necessitate undue muscular exertion in getting the required visual information, but also because they necessitate undue mental 'exertion' for the processes of interpretation and discrimination."

Ryan (Symposium on Fatigue, Floyd and Welford, eds.) measured electrical potentials in muscles of subjects performing a visual task. The instrument employed measured **muscular potentials** at various points in the body. The subjects worked at a task of comparing two groups of letters or digits to determine differences or similarities. In three experiments in which intensity of illumination was varied the conclusions were "that level of illumination has very little effect upon the individual once it reaches the level required for discriminating the details of the task. If there are effects upon the visual mechanism or other parts of the bodily system, they must be demonstrated by some method still to be discovered."

A study by Luckiesh (Light, Vision, and Seeing) was made to determine the effect of illumination upon a number of factors (Fig. 55). **Acuity** increases rapidly as light passes through the lower levels of intensity and more and more slowly as higher levels of intensity are attained. The increases are proportional to the ratio of increase of light rather than to absolute increase. The gain from added intensity is relatively small beyond 10–20 foot-candles.

Type of Test	Intensity of Illumination (foot-candles)		
	1	10	100
Visual acuity	100%	130%	170%
Contrast sensitivity	100%	280%	450%
Muscular tension (key pressure) while reading	63 grams	54 grams	43 grams
Change in frequency of blinking after reading one hour	100%	77%	65%
Decrease in heart rate while reading one hour	10%		2%
Decrease in convergence reserve of ocular muscles after reading one hour	23%		7%

Fig. 55. Influence of level of illumination.

According to Ryan (Work and Effort):

Glare is probably a more important factor in ocular efficiency than intensity of light. Bright spots in the field of vision make the seeing of details more difficult. Lighting fixtures should not be visible when the subject is working. Fixtures should be removed from the field of vision altogether. "Indirect" systems of lighting are not always satisfactory for this purpose, because the ceiling or walls which reflect the light may themselves become bright spots if sufficient intensity is supplied at the working place.

While there should be no bright areas there should also be no very dark areas in the field around the work. For these reasons it is usually recommended that the room be supplied with a moderate level of even illumination, with extra light falling upon the work from fixtures which are above and behind the worker.

Job Accident Hazards. There are more industrial accidents during January, February, and March than during other months of the year. If such increases were solely due to the lack of daylight, the period ought to begin with November and December. Anderson points out that a better correlation may be found with the trend of health, that is, that periods of high accidents and prevalence of respiratory diseases are identical. There is no evidence that fatigue from work could cause this seasonal increase. Neither is there evidence that fatigue due to summer heat is a general cause of accidents. In fact, Anderson found that the **accident frequency rate** parallels **production rate**. For instance, during any one day the hour between 11 A.M. and 12 M. showed fewer accidents than any other hour in the morning, and the hour between 4 and 5 P.M. showed fewer accidents than any other hour in the day. No matter how much fatigue may contribute to a let-down in production, it evidently does not contribute to accident frequency. Studies of Anderson may not be typical in this respect, but they cannot be wholly exceptional. In the matter of work experiences his findings are consistent with what might be expected. "Inexperience is obviously a big factor in accident causation as evidenced by a rapid decrease in the accident rate for new employees. An analysis by age of employees reveals a decided downward trend as the age limits increase. Accidents at night are relatively more frequent than in day time, probably in part due to poorer lighting."

Air Conditions of Work Environment. Much factory work is done in bad air. Ignoring that which is due to location and to the season of the year, Anderson found that the **loss of production due to excessive summer temperature** was generally around 2 percent, rarely over 5 percent, and that that was partly due to disturbed sleep and to wrong eating, or unavoidable requirement of the manufacturing process.

Measurement and control of humidity have been undertaken where the product required conditioned air but rarely otherwise except in offices. Fortunately, much can be done without expensive air-conditioning equipment (Ventilation, New York State Commission Report):

It must be emphasized that the avoidance of overheating is the primary essential in all systems of ventilation. Air change, direction of flow, and all other factors are secondary. The most important item of ventilating equipment is the thermometer; and however simple or however complex an apparatus may be installed for air conditioning, a constant and intelligent vigilance in regard to operating and over-heating is the price of health and comfort.

REST PERIODS. Because of the cumulative nature of fatigue, it is natural for workers to seek relief in pauses of various kinds. If there is incidental work to be done, that is, work that is legitimate but not directly productive, they will do this intermittently and sometimes prolong it.

The basic question is whether or not **formally authorized** rest periods are better than indiscriminate and unauthorized rest, and if so, what sort of rest program is best. Ryan (Work and Effort) states: "There are enough data to warrant the conclusion that nothing is lost by the use of regular rest periods, and considerable gain in output and 'morale' may result."

The critical question concerns the length and frequency of rest pauses and their distribution in the working day. Friedmann (Industrial Society) states that:

1. Repeated starts must be avoided, for they require a new effort each time and may reduce the interest in the work.
2. The length of rest pauses should be limited, in order not to lose the advantage of drive acquired during the course of production and the warming up of the human motor.
3. Pauses are most useful when placed at the moment in the day when output begins to diminish. The work curves, after the rise corresponding to warming up, become stabilized and then register a decline when the first fatigue sets in.
4. When work is monotonous, the usefulness of pauses is especially clear: increases of from 5 to 13 percent have been obtained as a result of the introduction of ten-minute pauses in the middle of the morning. The checking of small mass-produced articles, the telephone operator's work, are not directly subject to the rhythm of a machine, but require constant attention and a series of voluntary acts. In tasks of this sort, rest pauses have caused an appreciable increase of production.

Effect of Rest Periods on Production. Observations were made of eight girls engaged in folding handkerchiefs (Great Britain, Indus. Fatigue Res. Board Report 32). They were all experienced. Observations were limited to the afternoon, as the manager wished to try the effect of a rest period then. A rest period was already in effect in the morning.

Rate of work was increased on an average of 5.0 percent; the maximum increase for any one operator was 6.5 percent (Worker E) and the minimum increase 2.7 percent (Worker F) (see Fig. 56). Net average increase in hourly output was approximately 1 percent.

MONOTONY AND BOREDOM OF THE JOB. Ryan (Work and Effort) distinguishes fatigue and boredom as follows: "Fatigue reduces the capacity for performance, while boredom reduces the effort level . . . it is a reduced level of motivation of the worker, involving a distaste for the work, a desire to cease work." He states: "The general problem is therefore twofold—to discover the job factors which tend to reduce the general level of interest of the workers in that occupation, and to determine the factors which make an individual especially susceptible to boredom in a given type of work."

Certain characteristics of modern industrial tasks may contribute to boredom, for example, the **repetitive performance** of simple standardized tasks providing little opportunity for varied and capacity performance of skills and development of aptitudes. However, these job characteristics have a different influence on the performance of different individuals. That is, the **susceptibility** to boredom is an individual characteristic.

Boredom is a personal experience and its existence must be verified from reports by the worker. However, the results of boredom may be seen in decreased productivity, increased variability of output, as well as overt manifestations of worker dissatisfaction, such as absenteeism and requests for job changes. These are not reliable indicators of boredom, however, because of the many factors involved in a particular situation.

Boredom and Repetitive Work. Wyatt and Langdon conducted a study for the British Industrial Health Research Board to determine the nature of boredom (Fatigue and Boredom in Repetitive Work). The workers included in the study were employed in four factories situated in widely different parts of the country. Results were obtained from 355 workers engaged in fairly simple forms of repetitive work. **Boredom assessments,** based on the replies to a number of carefully prepared questions, were obtained for each worker. The more important results are summarized as follows:

1. Boredom was a fairly common experience among the operatives included in the study. There were marked individual differences in susceptibility to boredom. Some workers were seldom free from boredom while others showed a definite preference for monotonous work.
2. The amount of boredom experienced seems to be related to (a) intelligence, (b) inability to mechanize simple manual processes, (c) temperamental tendencies satisfied in active contact with external world (extrovert) rather than in phantasy (introvert), and (d) a desire for creative rather than repetitive work.
3. Boredom and discontent are related to the type of work. Slight differences between one job and another may have widely different effects on the worker. Efficiency and contentment may be increased by giving the beginner a short trial on different types of work resulting in assignment to the job which is liked best.

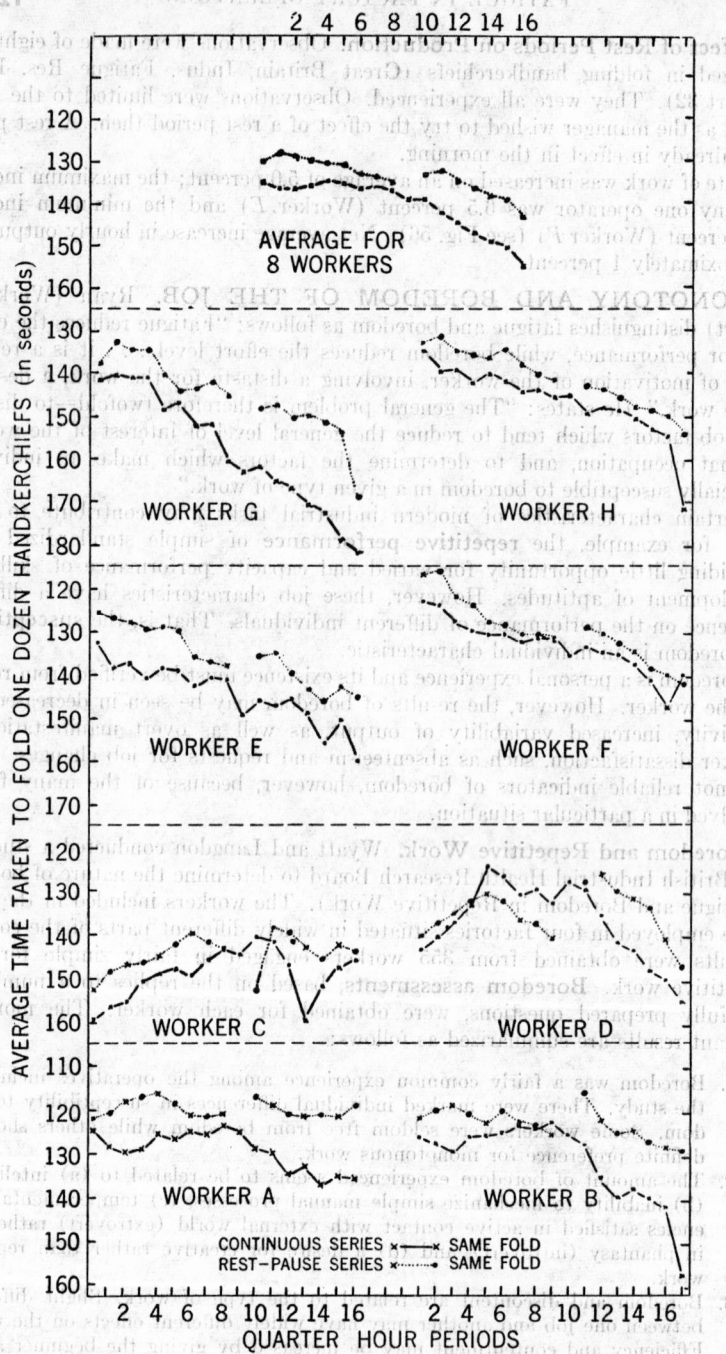

Fig. 56. Variations in average times in handkerchief folding under continuous and rest-pause conditions.

4. The most frequent causes of discontent (as revealed by the number of objections recorded to particular items on a given list) were waiting for work, faulty material, atmospheric conditions, fatigue, monotony, and noise. It seems that boredom increases sensitivity to objectionable features associated with conditions of work.

5. The proportion of workers who complained of fatigue was high (49 percent) but it is significant that only 3 percent referred the fatigue to the parts of the body actually used in the performance of work. The fatigue experienced was mainly static, or concerned with the maintenance of posture, rather than dynamic, or due to bodily movement.

EMOTIONAL FACTORS IN FATIGUE. Emotional strain may have a deleterious effect on the performance of an operator regardless of the type of work. Emotional stress may be traced to poor human relations within the plant or to situations without the plant, such as in the home. As pointed out by the Committee on Work in Industry of the National Research Council, "Social contacts in industry, often close and constant, often unavoidable and formed without choice, are accompanied by emotional strain which may not only interfere with effective collaboration but lead to a marked decline in individual efficiency, and even to incapacity for work." Regardless of the causes of emotional illness, whether they be traceable to relationships within or without the plant, management should make a concerted effort to alleviate them if possible. As the Committee notes, "Neither the direct observation of the worker on the job nor the interview directed to reveal working conditions is likely to be carried out by the doctor unless someone in daily contact with the worker suggests where the trouble may originate."

SOCIAL FACTORS IN WORKER MORALE. Perhaps more subtle in the determination of worker morale and emotional stress are the effects of constraints on effective social organization of work groups.

Zaleznik (Worker Satisfaction and Development) says: "Broadly speaking, constraining forces which prevent a work group from developing its social organization at a minimum level of effectiveness are those which tend to prevent or hinder interaction and communication. These constraining forces fall roughly into three categories, . . . stemming from (1) technological organization of work, (2) the behaviour of the formal leader, and (3) the behaviour of individual(s) inadequately prepared for group membership."

On the basis of a study of mass production workers in an automobile assembly plant, Walker and Guest (The Man on the Assembly Line) stress the importance of technology as it affects social organization of work groups. A sample of 180 workers holding various jobs in the plant were interviewed to determine the sources of job satisfaction and dissatisfaction. As reported by Zaleznik, one of the conclusions of this study was:

The ultimate value and importance of the more satisfying kinds of social relationships were demonstrated by the qualitative comments. In discussing the amount of talking they did, the isolates were the most vehemently negative. The largest group, those working side by side but independently, were most likely to refer to their social relations in the negative terms of how they would feel were they not able to talk and of the effects of interaction in counteracting other job tensions. In marked contrast, those who were members of true teams spoke of their group interaction in positive and cheerful terms.

MOTION AND METHODS STUDY

CONTENTS

PAGE

Nature and Functions

Definitions 1
Objectives 2
Applications 2
Obstacles 2
Basic procedures 3

Determination of Goal

Initial study stages 4
  Project chart for control of study (f. 1) 5
  General goal 4
  Specific problem 4
  Specific goal 4
  General approach 6
Establishing over-all project control 6

Analysis of Work

Basic questions 6
Factors affecting work 6
How to gather information................. 7
  Observation 7
  Discussion 8
  Records 8
  Motion pictures 8
  Uses and advantages of motion pictures (f. 2) 8
  Micromotion study 9
  Memomotion study 9
  Motion and methods study with motion pictures 9
  Motion picture limitations 10
  Motion picture equipment 10
  Timing equipment 10
  Auxiliary equipment 11
  Making the motion pictures 11
  Form for recording filming of operations (f. 3) 12
Presenting the information 13
Therblig charts 13
  Uses 13
  Symbols 13
  Symbols for therblig and simo charts (f. 4) 14-20
  Predetermined time values 21
  Making a therblig chart 21
  Typical therblig chart with summary (f. 5) 22
Simo charts 21
  Types of simo charts.................... 21

Making a simo chart 23
  Film analysis of assembling and packing sprocket (f. 6) 24
  Simo chart of film analysis in Fig. 6 (f. 7) 25
  Simo chart with therblig form symbols (f. 8) 26
Nonrepetitive work analysis 23
  Observer with worker 23
  Memomotion study 23
  Work sampling or occurrence study........ 27
  Operator records his own work........... 27
  Advantages of analyzing nonrepetitive work 27
Miscellaneous analysis techniques........... 27
  Chronocyclegraph 27
  Cyclegraph 28
  Motion paths from motion pictures....... 28
  Other photographic techniques........... 28
  Time study 28
  Combination charts 28
  Operating performance analysis 28
  Unopar 29
  Kymograph 29
  Marsto-chron 29
  Wire models 29

Application of Principles of Methods Design

Basic principles 29
Check lists of principles 30
  Check lists for the five basic methods design principles (f. 9) 30-33
Principles of motion economy.............. 34
  Principles of motion economy (f. 10)..... 34
  Normal work area 35
  Normal working areas for arms and hands (f. 11) 35
  Simultaneous symmetrical hand pattern.. 35
  Number of therbligs in a cycle........... 36
  Foot pedals, cranks, levers 36
  Individual therblig performance.......... 36
  How to apply the principles............. 36
Suggestion lists 36
  Suggestion list for operation improvement (f. 12) 37
  Suggestion guide 37

Selection of Feasible Solution

Factors in selection 38
Evaluation worksheet 28

CONTENTS (*Continued*)

PAGE

Evaluation worksheet of alternative
    solutions (*f.* 13) 40–41
Economic factor 38
How much cost? 38
How much savings? 39
Hazard factor 39
Control factor 42
Psychological factor 42
Basis of reports to management............. 42

Formulation of Methods Design

Purpose 42
Formulation of proposed method 43
    Therblig chart of proposed method
    (*f.* 14) 44

Review and Testing of Methods Design

Purpose of review 45
Review procedures 45
    Good design principles 45
    Details for proper functioning............. 45
    Planning the approach 45

PAGE

Test of methods design 45
Testing procedures 46
    Model or pilot plant 46
    Work place mock-up..................... 46
    Actual jig or workplace set-up........... 46
    Simple methods changes 46
    New machinery 46

Installation of Method

Installation activities 47
    Make the mechanical changes 47
    Train those involved 47
    Use written standard procedure (WSP) .. 47
    Written standard procedure (WSP) for
        assembly operation (*f.* 15) 48
    Follow-up 47

Standards Setting and Training

Definition of standards setting 48
Methods for setting standards.............. 49
Training in motion and methods study...... 49
    Scope of training 49

SECTION 13

SECTION 13

MOTION AND METHODS STUDY

Nature and Functions

DEFINITIONS. The area of motion and methods study has many names, such as methods analysis, methods engineering, methods research, work study, and work analysis. This section covers the general material usually referred to by any one of these terms. Motion and methods study is usually the first part of motion and time study.

F. B. and L. M. Gilbreth (Primer of Scientific Management) define **motion study** as "the science of eliminating wastefulness resulting from using unnecessary, ill-directed, and inefficient motions. The aim of motion study is to find and perpetuate the scheme of least-waste methods of labor." Another definition by the same authors (Applied Motion Study) indicates a procedure: "Motion study consists of dividing work into the most fundamental elements possible; studying these elements separately and in relation to one another; and from these studied elements when timed, building methods of least waste."

As practiced by the Gilbreths, **motion study** included an analysis of the flow and processing of material and paperwork and the movements of men as well as the study of the fundamental elements of each worker's job. However, their development of **micromotion** study and **therbligs** have in many cases indicated to others that motion study concerned only the study of activities within an operation. For the purposes of this section, motion study will be generally confined to the analysis of such individual operations. The concept of studying the whole is contained in the definition of methods study.

Methods study will be considered to be synonymous with such terms as work study, methods engineering, and methods analysis. **Methods study** is defined as a systematic procedure for the analysis of work to:

1. Eliminate unnecessary work.
2. Arrange the remaining work in the best order possible.
3. Standardize the usage of proper work methods.

Because this definition includes the study of all facets of work and all factors affecting the work, motion study is considered a part of methods study. Henceforth, there will be no differentiation between these two terms, because motion study techniques will be integrated into the procedures for methods study. Work simplification, on the other hand, refers to the educational and group procedures which have been developed for studying the whole job or work situation and for improving its efficiency. Time and motion study techniques are often applied after work simplification has indicated that the work is necessary and can be improved.

Therefore, since the four areas—work measurement and time study, motion and methods study, work simplification, and process charts—are not entirely independent, an examination of the four sections dealing with these subjects should be carried on simultaneously, in order to attain the proper perspective. These four areas cover rather completely that phase of industrial engineering concerned with efficient production, and therefore their application contributes the bulk of the gain to the productivity and income of both employee and employer.

OBJECTIVES. Even though the use of motion and methods study has grown rapidly, the total range of applications is not fully appreciated. **Work** is defined as any physical or mental activity. Under this definition, such activities as playing golf and doing work around the house as a hobby are "work," and these activities can be studied with the techniques of motion and methods study. Motion and methods study first tries to eliminate unnecessary work, which is accomplished in many cases by reducing the skills required for the work.

As automation becomes more prevalent, the requirements for technical personnel increase. Here, the second objective of arranging work in the best order possible comes into prominence, namely, to utilize fully the skills of everyone, especially technical personnel. In effect, motion and methods study has led to some of the developments in automation and will play an important role in its development.

APPLICATIONS. Motion and methods study is a pervasive art and science. It can be applied to all industrial enterprises, past, present, or future. Jobs which have been done in the past and may recur can be studied in retrospect, and improvements can be made in procedures before the task reaches the plant again. Motion and methods study has been applied in department stores, on the farm, in the home, in process industries, and in assembly plants. It is very useful in correcting office procedure.

One of the important contributions of motion and methods study is to produce **methods consciousness** in the minds of all operators, supervisors, and managers in an industrial plant or a commercial enterprise. Such methods consciousness permits all personnel to analyze their work habits as they proceed with their daily assignments. While not all people are analytical enough by nature to make self-improvements, many will, and others may be able to make suggestions which will improve the work of those who are not thus analytically minded. Motion and methods study will pay for itself in the creation of motion-mindedness alone.

The classical use for motion study is to determine the "one best way" for performing a given task. This was Gilbreth's original principle, and it has been followed by all of those who have studied and used his methods. The term "one best way" indicates that there is probably no better way of performing a given job under given conditions. It does not presuppose, however, that this is the best way for all time, since one of the implications of modern motion and methods study is continual re-evaluation of what may now be the "one best way" of doing a task.

OBSTACLES. Because motion and methods study is applied to human beings in most cases, care must be exercised. Obstacles to the successful application of motion and methods study come from three groups of people:

1. **The people who are performing the jobs.** A worker might have one or a combination of three reactions when told the method for his work is to be changed. He might resist the change or feel that the analyst is criticizing him. He might be afraid his job will be eliminated or that he may not earn sufficient money in relation to his present earnings and the earnings of others. He might be in a group which does not look with favor upon cooperation with motion and methods study analysts. If any or all of these reactions are present, it might be difficult to apply the techniques and principles.

2. **Managers of the people performing the jobs.** Managers have many of the reactions employees have. They may fear that the analyst is actually criticizing them for some of the things they have established, or they may be resistant to change. Also, some members of management may be pressured not to accept the philosophy of motion and methods study.

3. **The individual applying motion and methods study.** An analyst can be his own worst enemy. He must recognize that in dealing with people he has to practice principles of good human relations and make a concentrated effort to get along with people. If he is overbearing and egocentric, this can spell failure for his applications.

Education is by far the best way to overcome such obstacles, training top management, as well as employees and middle- and first-line supervision, to know what motion and methods study is and how it can be applied.

To overcome some of the other problems of the worker, his job must be guaranteed against elimination through motion and methods study. The company should have good policies for the distribution of savings or profits from changes resulting from motion and methods study.

BASIC PROCEDURES. Nadler (Motion and Time Study) indicates the steps to be followed in trying to solve motion and methods study problems.

1. **Determination of goal.** This step specifies the limits within the over-all objectives of the organization and the problems to which work simplification is to be initially applied. Small units of the work problem, to be studied one at a time, are established, and the scope of the solution is stated. The tentative means by which the analyst will attempt to arrive at the goal are also considered.

2. **Analysis of work.** The attempt is made to get as much information as possible about the work problem. Information is gathered through breakdown of the work into common units and by obtaining data concerning other areas as it relates to the problem.

3. **Application of design principles.** Certain concepts and principles are used in motion and methods study as guides for the proper design of the work. These guides are employed with ingenuity and imagination to arrive at the ultimate methods design.

4. **Selection of feasible solution.** The selection of the one idea or group of ideas which best fits the situation in which the work is performed.

5. **Formulation of methods design.** Formulation of a complete design of the method and other factors needed to put the proposal into operation.

6. **Review of methods design.** Assuming that all details and problems may not have been taken care of, it is advisable to "stop-for-a-moment" to re-examine all designs.

7. **Test of the methods design.** Step 6 represents the mental approach to the same objective that step 7 approaches mechanically or physically. If it is possible to try out the proposal, this is where it is done.

8. **Installation of method.** If all the other steps have been successful, the method is installed. This step also involves the training of those concerned with the activity, and follow-up by the analyst or some other person to make certain the correct procedures are being used.

9. **Setting of standards.** Two basic questions are considered here: Was the goal for the problem met? What should be expected in the future? Many ways are used to establish the standards necessary to answering these questions.

The procedure for solving every motion and methods study problem may vary slightly from one problem to another. If the review, test, or even formulation shows that a design will not work, the analyst must return to the selection or even to the application step. The remainder of this section will present the various techniques used in motion and methods study for accomplishing the various steps.

Determination of Goal

INITIAL STUDY STAGES. In many cases the goal determination can be accomplished mentally. In other cases it is best for the analyst to take time to think through each part and make written notes concerning them. Nadler (Motion and Time Study) presents a form which sometimes assists this written presentation (Fig. 1). In all cases this step should be accomplished by, at least, the person who is directing the activity. The information should be used to clarify the project to those who will carry it out, to those workers affected by it, and to those supervisors directing the area in which the project is to take place. The four stages in goal determination are:

1. General goal.
2. Specific problem.
3. Specific goal.
4. General approach.

General Goal. The management objectives for the plant, area, or department in which motion and methods activities are to take place should be explicitly recognized. In most cases the analyst will be given the general goal for the particular department or area, although sometimes he must, himself, determine the goal, and he will find that it varies from area to area. If there is no other general goal, the analyst can, at least, use the standard goals of **cost reduction** and **increased productivity.**

Other general goals might be: to reduce the cost for a specific product or department; to design the best layout to produce a product for an anticipated volume; to reduce the scrap; to make the work easier; to reduce indirect labor costs; to increase productivity; to change the design of product for lower cost; or to reduce the cost of materials handling. The general goal will remain the same for the area or department until such time as it has been met satisfactorily.

Specific Problem. The most difficult part of goal determination is the selection of the first work activity to study. It is usually essential to limit the initial problem to be worked on to as small a unit of the **work sequence** as possible. Generally, the specific problem will be one operation. In some cases, it may not be possible to limit the study to one operation. Then the specific problem should be the smallest possible **group of operations.** The smaller the problem unit, the more readily the savings may be computed and the faster a solution may be found.

Although the over-all problem is broken down into small units in this step, the procedure of gathering information in the analysis of the work will help relate the small problem to the whole situation. In this way, the whole work activity will remain in perspective while one problem is worked on. After the initial problem is solved, it is necessary to return to this part and select another problem. In this way, all the problems (operations) in the area or department can be solved (proper methods design) to meet the general goal.

Specific Goal. Types of specific goal statements are:

Eliminate time spent in obtaining materials and tools.
Eliminate the bottleneck holding up an operation.
Revise an operation method where an operator looks uncomfortable at his work.

```
                        PROJECT CHART

   Dept.   PBA          Product  Fore Section       File  4M-7943-8
   No.     4M           Part   Bracket              Checked    CA
   Operation  Assembly  No.      7943               Start   17 Feb 19-
   Foreman    EMG       Drawing  437-7943-62        Finished
   Operator   JRD       Analyst    MNO              Results
```

Fill in before starting Analysis

General goal ___ Reduce Cost of Manufacturing this Product

Specific operation ___ Assemble Bracket – 8 Parts, Rivet, Drill (Hand Electric)
All Parts Drawings in 437-7943 Folder (60-67)

Specific goal ___ Reduce Irregular Occurrence Time (Approx. 55% of Time)

```
General approach –          Total cost  $3200/YR.   Time to complete   6 Weeks
  Tentative Chart–PPC  A     FPC
  √ = Make chart            MPC_____  Time
  A = Chart is available    OPCH_____√_____  Time_____
                            M&M_____A_____  Time___A___← On Replenishing
                            MM_____  Time_____  Supplies
                            MM&M_____  Time_____
                            MM&MM_____  Time_____
                            SIMO_____  ----Film taken
              THERBLIG_____   Returned _____
              CHART_____   Analyzed _____
              OCC S_____√_____
              CHRONO_____
            TIME STUDY_____√_____
  Suggestion list:  Written _____√_____   Mental_____
  Suggestion guide: Written _____   Mental_____None √
```

Fill in during progress of project (dates where possible)

Selection of feasible solution: Detailed_____ Moderate_____ Mental_____
Formulation of methods design: Detailed_____ Moderate_____ Mental_____
Review of methods design: All details____ New sug. list: Written_____
        Other persons or groups involved: –   Mental_____

Test of methods design: Yes_____No_____Things to accomplish

Installation of methods design:

Mechanical changes	Training	Follow-up
Who	Who	Who is responsible
How	How	How
When	When	When
Where	Where	

Standards: Yes_____ No_____ Std. Data_____
    Methods description _____ Timing _____
    Pace comparison _____ Difficulty comp. _____
    Allowances _____
Final Standard Installed _____
Standard Data: File _____ Section _____ Checked _____

Fig. 1. Project chart for control of study.

Rearrange a disorganized workplace.
Provide proper equipment for an operation.
Eliminate some make-ready time.
Eliminate some put-away time.
Reduce the effort required.

The specific goal will frequently include **limiting statements** concerning other conditions in the area. Thus, volume has an important effect and floor space limitations are important.

General Approach. Some additional preparations must be made for reaching the specific goal for the specific problem. In some cases, a **preliminary survey** is required to decide whether or not the operation is necessary. This question is one of the most important in all parts of the motion and methods study procedure. If the operation is not necessary and that fact can be determined at this point, much analysis time and effort will be saved.

If the operation is necessary, the preliminary survey determines the approach to the problem and the **economic limits** within which the analyst must work. Typical questions to be answered are:

What authority should be established before the project is worked on?
How should the workers be approached?
How should the supervisory or management staff be approached?
How much time is available to solve this problem?
What are the possible savings?
What amount of money can be spent to meet the goal?
What effect will quality requirements for the operation have on the problem?

With the answers to these questions, the analyst can plan the type of analysis to use and the amount of detail for all the following steps of the motion and methods study procedure. The extent of the analysis to be made must be determined, usually on economic grounds.

ESTABLISHING OVER-ALL PROJECT CONTROL. The project chart (Fig. 1) helps to summarize and clarify the information gathered in the goal determination step. It can also be used to record the progress of the project. This form is only a sample of different possible types. Whoever uses it will wish to substitute the type of chart which he frequently employs. Fig. 1 shows a project chart complete through the general approach part of the goal determination step. It is possible to simplify the analysis and detail by the proper planning.

Analysis of Work

BASIC QUESTIONS. This step concerns getting all the information about the specific problem selected in the first step—goal determination. The analyst must have a **questioning attitude** about everything. He should not assume anything at all. This attitude is associated with the following questions:

What? Why? How? Who? Where? When?

To make a complete analysis, the analyst must ask these questions about each item affecting the work, as described below.

FACTORS AFFECTING WORK. The work selected as the specific problem does not exist all by itself. The work is affected by a number of factors, both within the operation and external to it. Earlier literature refers to "operation analysis" which concerns itself with several factors about which information had to be gathered. Thus, Maynard and Stegemerten (Operation Analysis) list the following:

1. Operations performed.
2. Job performed.
3. Inspection requirements.
4. Material specifications.
5. Materials and work-in-process handling.
6. Machine auxiliary equipment.
7. Tools, jigs, and fixtures.
8. Preparation and setup.
9. Working conditions.
10. Workplace and plant layout.

However, these ten items overlap, are not clear, and are not inclusive. Mundel (Motion and Time Study) specifies five **work factors** which include all those usually associated with operation analysis and are even more inclusive:

1. **Material.**
2. **Design** of product, such as specification and quality requirements.
3. **Sequence** of work on the material to change it to the desired design.
4. **Equipment,** such as tools, workplace, and conditions used at the specific operation.
5. **Method** utilizing the equipment, tools, and workplace to accomplish the specific work being studied.

Therefore, in the analysis of work, information should be gathered about these five factors as they affect the specific work problem. All types of work are affected by them. In some cases, like credit clerk work in a department store, the material and product design may be somewhat difficult to specify, but this can be done in terms of information and design of forms. In other cases, the information about these five factors is easy to gather, such as information about the materials, design of the product, and the equipment, tools, and workplace of the work situation.

The other two factors affecting **work sequence** and **method** are items about which little usually is known in complete detail. This does not mean that the company personnel are not familiar with the work of their organization. Rather, the complexity of production and services does not allow familiarity with all the details concerning the work needed for the process. Most supervisors generally know what is being done while an operation is performed, but it is unusual when complete details of the hand and body motions are known. In general, the techniques presented under **analysis** deal with gathering information about sequence and method to aid an analyst.

HOW TO GATHER INFORMATION. To make an analysis, data must be available. Techniques presented later will show how the data can be organized to obtain the most useful information. However, first it is necessary to determine the means whereby the information can be collected. Each procedure for obtaining information is not exclusive of the others. Frequently, **combinations** of all the techniques may be used for any particular problem.

Observation. This is the most common procedure used for gathering information. In most cases it is necessary for the investigator to trace and verify every step in the process when analyzing present work. This cannot usually be done by sitting at a desk and consulting route sheets in an office. The analyst must make actual observations where the work is occurring and frequently combine this procedure with discussion.

A good analyst must have the ability to notice motions and activities which are usually unobserved by the layman. This is part of the **methods consciousness** required. The symbols of the process charting techniques help methods consciousness.

Discussion. Discussion with those who do or supervise the work can frequently solve the problem of the inability to get all information by observation. The discussion procedure is used most widely where special or **irregular work** is performed. Likewise, discussion is valuable when trying to analyze **past work** in order to improve efficiency in performing future work.

Discussion is a good way to help the analyst get along with people. Discussion is frequently used even where observation by itself may accomplish the purpose of gathering data. This helps to develop a good human relations foundation.

Records. Even if the work being studied was never done before, much valuable information can be obtained from records of all sorts. These include production, costs, time, inventory, and invoice records. Sampling or analysis of records of this type can save much time in predicting or emphasizing future activities.

Motion Pictures. Taking motion pictures represents the most detailed and accurate procedure for gathering information. It is an excellent technique for

Camera Speeds		Situations	Special advantages
Standard	Decimal		
1 FPS	100 FPM	1. Three or more in a coordinate crew. 2. Nonrepetitive work in one area. 3. Long-cycle repetitive work. 4. Gross body motion operations. 5. Need for times in work load determination (for operations with characteristics of 1 through 4 above).	1. Lower film cost. 2. Greater time coverage.
8 FPS 10 FPS	500 FPM	1. Medium (0.75 to 2 min.) cycles. 2. Short-cycle nonrepetitive work. 3. Need for times in work load determination.	1. Slightly lower film cost. 2. More cycles. 3. Relatively continuous motions.
16 FPS	1,000 FPM	1. Short-cycle work. 2. Need for measurement in work load determination. 3. Skilled operation. 4. Transfer operation to another plant. 5. Comparison of methods. 6. Finger or hand operations. 7. Evaluation of equipment.	1. Normal projection speed. 2. Training film.
24, 32, 64 FPS	1,500, 2,000, 4,000 FPM	1. Motion and time study research. 2. Especially skilled or complex operation. 3. Evaluation of complex equipment usage.	1. Fine detail. 2. "Stop" skill, frame at a time. 3. Training in skills.

Fig. 2. **Uses and advantages of motion pictures.**

communication to all levels of an organization. Motion pictures can focus attention at any point or motion in an operation. They help "sell" improved methods. For some work, motion pictures are the only way of getting a good analysis. Work which requires **large crews** is almost impossible to analyze in any other way. Work which requires **care** and **dexterity** is analyzed much better with motion pictures. There are many advantages of motion pictures in addition to the basic purpose of gathering information.

The general **advantages** of motion pictures in motion and methods study are:

1. Greater detail.
2. Permits review of details in quiet surroundings.
3. Greater convenience for study.
4. Enlists cooperation of all concerned.
5. More accuracy of times.
6. Better training aids.
7. Positive record.
8. Evaluate methods changes before the change.
9. Accurate portrayal of simultaneity.

Fig. 2, adapted from Nadler (Motion and Time Study), summarizes the uses and advantages of motion pictures in this kind of work. They can be taken at various speeds. They can be run forward and backward to obtain the exact relationships among work activities. Proper amount of detail is determined by the speed. The **speeds** of motion pictures are measured in frames per second (FPS) or frames per minute (FPM). Normal speeds are 16 FPS or 1,000 FPM, and 24 FPS or 1,500 FPM. Speeds below or above these have special uses. Studies at speeds slower than the usual 16 FPS are frequently called memomotion studies (usually taken at 1 FPS or 100 FPM), and studies at normal and frequently higher speeds are sometimes called micromotion studies.

Micromotion Study. Micromotion study was developed by the Gilbreths. At the same time, they formulated special symbols which divide work into fine detail. These symbols, or therbligs, are described later as used in a technique for analysis of work. Micromotion study employs motion pictures with a timing device to obtain times for each motion or therblig. Generally, micromotion studies are made with 16 FPS or 1,000 FPM motion pictures. However, it is possible to use higher speed if required. In most cases, higher speeds, like 64 FPS, are used for research in motion study and not so much for industrial activities. Because motion pictures with a timing device can be used to make many different types of analysis, the general usage of this term is now applied to gathering information with motion pictures at 16 FPS or more.

Memomotion Study. This study (Mundel, Motion and Time Study) requires motion pictures at usually 1 FPS or 100 FPM, but if slightly more detail is needed the pictures could be taken at 8 FPS or 500 FPM. The detail is less than in micromotion study. Memomotion study is generally for analyzing **longer cycles of work,** and for analyzing work which requires three, four, or more people **working coordinately.** Uses of memomotion study will be discussed later under the appropriate technique.

MOTION AND METHODS STUDY WITH MOTION PICTURES.
Since motion pictures are such an important method for gathering information for motion and methods study, the analyst should be familiar with all phases of their use.

Motion Picture Limitations. The analyst must use his judgment concerning the **adaptability** of motion pictures to a specific situation. Motion pictures take time to be developed, and if information is needed rapidly, this may cause difficulties. Frequently, the **time lag** between the exposure and development of film can be reduced by using more rapid means of transportation to processors. Films require added costs of analysis. There is also the additional time for the photographer and the attendant cost, regardless of the speed at which the film is taken. Although 1 FPS motion pictures (memomotion study) are a **film-cost saver,** it is still necessary to take the pictures and then analyze them, both of which add cost to the analysis. A more detailed analysis of film will be more costly than a less detailed analysis. Motion pictures are not a "cure-all" for motion or method study problems. Fig. 2 should be used as a guide for determining when motion pictures should be taken, in conjunction with a full consideration of the situation (human relations, technical difficulties, etc.) and the disadvantages and economics of motion pictures.

Motion Picture Equipment. The information given here about motion pictures refers to 16 mm. film and equipment. Home movies are frequently 8 mm. Commercial motion picture theaters usually have 35 mm. film. The latter is too expensive in industry or business, and 16 mm. film is usually used instead of 8 mm. because it gives a larger picture. Most industrial rental film is 16 mm.; sound pictures come at the 16 mm. or above speed, and most motion picture accessories and equipment are 16 mm.

The **camera** is the most important piece of equipment needed. An expensive one is not required. The regular home 16 mm. camera can be used satisfactorily. Most 16 mm. cameras are equipped to take pictures at various speeds from 8 FPS to 32 or 64 FPS. In selecting a camera, special consideration should be given to film capacity, drive, lens, and view finder. The camera should take a 100-ft. roll of film. It would be desirable to take motion pictures continuously without stopping, but this is not possible with most spring driven cameras. A **motor drive** can be obtained to take pictures continuously and also to permit variations in speed of film.

The lens is the most important factor in determining picture quality. The camera should be capable of taking **interchangeable lenses** with focusing mounts. There should be at least a wide angle lens of 15 mm. focal length for taking pictures in cramped quarters and a 1-in. lens for normal conditions. The 2-in. or larger telephoto lens is convenient for getting close-up views. If a camera is to be used without auxiliary floodlighting, the lens should be "fast," that is, with maximum **diaphragm openings** of $f.1.9$ or $f.1.5$. On the other hand, if adequate auxiliary illumination can be provided, a less expensive, slower lens (small openings), $f.3.5$, can be used. Also, when pictures are taken with smaller diaphragm openings, the **depth of focus** is increased, which means that the range over which objects will be in sharp focus is increased. This factor is especially important considering the relatively short range of speeds and lighting within which most motion pictures are taken. The **view finder** should show the exact field of the lens being used. If a usual eye-level finder is on the camera, this finder should be adjustable for all focus distances, to compensate for the parallax between the optical axes of the lens and that of the view finder.

Timing Equipment. Some sort of **timing device** should be used with motion pictures to obtain a more complete analysis. In most cases the camera is sufficiently accurate to be used as a timing device. For other situations a timing device should be included, or a synchronous motor drive should be attached to the camera. A micrometer or a wink counter is frequently used when a timing device in the picture itself is desired. (See section on Work Measurement and Time Study for discussion of time-recording equipment.) When taking pictures at 1 FPS or 100 FPM, a special **drive mechanism,** sometimes included on motor drives, is needed. A timing device in the picture is not needed for the usual memomotion study situation. This is fortunate, since many 1 FPS pictures are taken at a distance far from the crew or subject, where a clock would not be visible.

Auxiliary Equipment. For motion study purposes sharp pictures are necessary, and for this purpose the available sensitive or "fast" **films** are needed, sometimes aided by **auxiliary lighting.** Color pictures are desirable for "selling," but the cost is sometimes too much for general purposes. Color films are also not so sensitive as black and white. If auxiliary lighting is needed, **light stands** may be necessary. Reflectors are placed on top of the stand to floodlight the area. Light stands and reflectors are relatively low in cost.

A **tripod** is necessary for taking motion pictures because the hand is relatively unsteady for holding a camera. An **exposure meter** of the photo-electric type should be used to determine the correct setting with a camera lens. An exposure meter determines how much light is available to suit the film and can help determine if more light is needed.

For many purposes, like training, "selling," etc., any normal 16 mm. projector can be used. For analysis purposes, a **projector** to show the pictures one frame at a time is necessary. For the analysis, a special type of projector is required. Porter's **analysis projector** permits operation by one hand, controlling the projector for frame-by-frame movement, both forward and reverse, and for speed of continuous movement from slightly above zero to full speed. There are also hand-crank projectors usable mainly for one frame-at-a-time projection.

Making the Motion Pictures. Taking motion pictures is a simple procedure. Some common errors to be avoided are insufficient lighting, background color too similar to the subject, making panoramic moves too fast, poor camera angle, improper distance, and wrong focus. The procedure to follow in taking motion pictures for motion and methods study is:

1. **Obtain the permission** of the foreman or supervisor and union steward, if any, and the cooperation of the operator(s). Because the people involved are informed of what is going on, they will have the opportunity to ask questions. This helps to get cooperation.

2. **Prepare all the equipment for use.** Load the camera, make certain the photofloods work, the tripod is ready, etc.

3. **Locate all the equipment in the proper places.** The camera should be placed to obtain desired detail. Usually the camera is placed in front of and somewhat above the subject to be photographed. Sometimes a shot over the shoulder of the operator is desirable. Lights should be placed to illuminate the **work area** properly. They should not be pointed into the camera lens and must not be too far away from the workplace. The microchronometer should be placed on the workplace so that it does not cover any action desired in the picture.

4. **Decide on the speed of the camera.** See Fig. 2 for a summary of motion picture uses related to speed of camera.

5. **Make all necessary camera adjustments.** Speed, opening of the aperture of the lens, and distance of camera from the workplace must be set. The **aperture**

MOTION PICTURE RECORD

Operation_____
        Part
        No._____
Drawing
   Dept.
   No._____
Operator
   No._____

Film No._____
Date_____
By_____

Film and Light

Equipment

Camera_____
Lens Type: ƒ_____Focal Length_____
Motor Drive Yes_____No_____
        Type:_____
Exposure Meter_____
Microchronometer_____
Wink Counter_____

Type_____
Length: 50ft.____100 ft.____200 ft.
Color: B & W____Color____
Photofloods: Yes____Number____No____
        Exposure_____On_____
Lens Opening_____
Distance_____
Camera Speed_____

Show Relationship of Camera, Lights, Timing Device, and Work Area

Symbol
Camera   ■■■■→   Film sent_____
Light   (____→   By_____
Clock   C   Returned_____

Fig. 3. Form for recording filming of operations.

opening is determined by the amount of light on the work area and the emulsion speed or exposure index of the film. The exposure meter is used to determine the amount of light on the subject. The camera should be placed to obtain maximum detail of the work itself, avoiding general background views. The camera view finder helps to do this.

6. **Keep records of what is done.** Nadler (Motion and Time Study) presents a motion picture record form, Fig. 3, used to record what is done during the "shooting." This information should enable a photographer to take better pictures in the future.

7. **Make film analysis.** To collect the information, the analyst should record the data on a **film analysis sheet** (see Fig. 6). This sheet requires notations of symbols representing activity (associated with a given chart presented in this section). The sheet has columns for the symbol, clock reading (or frame count from a projector for film from a motor driven camera), subtracted time, and description of the activities of each hand.

PRESENTING THE INFORMATION. After the data have been collected, they must be presented for proper analysis and study. A graphical presentation or chart is the best way to do this. It helps to make for better study and for "selling."

Part of the presentation involves breaking down work into standard characteristics. Work in many different areas is similar. This has led to the development of certain **standard units of accomplishment.** Accomplishment, in this case, refers to universal characteristics of activity, whether good (efficient) or bad (inefficient). A unit of accomplishment is represented by some type of symbol. These units of accomplishment can be used in any work situation. Of course, new units of accomplishment can be developed for special situations. The different units of accomplishment, as well as the chart groupings of the symbols, form the basis for the different techniques presented in the section on Process Charts. The therblig and simo charts, which represent a specialized application of motion and methods study analysis, are discussed below.

THERBLIG CHARTS. The therblig chart may be defined as a detailed symbolic and systematic analysis of the method of work performed by the body members of a man, usually when his work is at one workplace. This chart provides the greatest amount of qualitative detail available. Although mainly devised for **two-hand analysis,** it is usable for the analysis of any type of activity.

Uses. Because the therblig breakdown merely provides a fine detail analysis of activity it is usually used when there is a large volume of work. The hand and fingers perform relatively skilled motions, making it difficult to analyze the work completely with other analysis techniques which have not given sufficient detail.

The therblig chart is very useful in planning work for future operations. With the detailed symbols, it is easier to analyze different methods before the work is done.

Symbols. Nadler (Motion and Time Study) shows the symbols, or therbligs, as given in Fig. 4. The Gilbreths divided work into 18 classifications. Twenty-two classifications are presented here and 5 of these are additions. One of the original Gilbreth's therbligs ("find") is eliminated because it is really the end point of another therblig. The therblig letter symbols are used when typing charts, for example, while the form symbols are used in recording data directly by hand.

Therblig symbols		Therblig name	Activity represented	Color symbol	Approximate time (in 0.0001 min.)
Letter	Graphic				

I. Work classification: "do," or terminal therbligs at one work area

Letter	Graphic	Therblig name	Activity represented	Color symbol	Approximate time (in 0.0001 min.)
1. G		Grasp	B. First contact with object. F. Placing object under control of hand (or other body member). E. Control of object is established. (Control depends on what is to be done with object. Control of bolt to be picked up is different from control of paper to be held on table for writing after control is gained.)	Dark red EP*745 DP†383	20 40
G1 G2	∩	Contact grasp Pinch grasp	When merely touching object comprises control. Thumb opposes finger tip(s) to gain control, or control is gained by any two fingers of one hand opposing each other.		
G3 G4		Wrap grasp Regrasp	Hand wraps around object for control. Shift of object to gain control at another point of the object or, in a few cases, taking the object from the other hand.		60 50
2. RL	ϵ	Release load	B. Initial relaxation of control of object. F. Losing control or letting go of object. E. Control of object has ceased. Losing control by merely raising or lifting body member.	Light red	5
RL1 RL2		Contact release load Other release loads	Loss of control by opening fingers or hand.		20
3. P	9	Position	B. First manipulation of object to align, orient, or line up. F. Manipulation of object to achieve a specific alignment, orientation, or line-up. E. Object has been oriented for proper purpose.	Dark blue EP 741 DP 376	‡
P1		Cylindrical position	Line-up when mating parts are cylindrical.		30
P2		Noncylindrical position	Line-up of noncylindrical and symmetrical or nonsymmetrical mating parts.		60

Code	Name	Description	Color	Time value
P3	Horizontal position	Line-up involving orientation of the hand (with the part) in horizontal plane.		25
P4	Vertical position	Line-up involving orientation of the hand (with the part) in vertical plane.		25
xP5	Turn position	Line-up involving turning of hand and object with center line of arm and hand as axis.		0.75/degree

Note: In place of x substitute number of degrees. P1 or P2 can occur in combination with P3, P4, and/or P5. P1 and P2 do not occur as a combination (combination noted as P13, P245, etc.).

Code	Name	Symbol	Description	Color	Time value
4.PP	Pre-position	(oval symbol)	Same as position except that line-up or orientation of object is used at a later time and/or another place. (This therblig is not used often. However, it could be used more frequently if it referred to line-up or orientation occurring only in conjunction with TL, or one orientation preceding another orientation.)	Light blue	Same as P
5. A	Assemble	(# symbol)	B. First contact of mating parts or objects to be made integral. F. Placing together of objects. E. Objects have been placed together.	Dark violet EP742 DP 377	
xA1	Loose-fit assemble		1/8 in. or above total tolerance.		15/in. or 0.25/degree
xA2	Free-fit assemble		1/32 to 1/8 in. total tolerance.		25/in. or 0.50/degree
xA3	Medium-fit assemble		1/100 to 1/32 in. total tolerance.		40/in. or 0.75/degree
xA4	Snug-fit assemble		Less than 1/100 in. total tolerance.		60/in. or 1/degree

Note: In place of x substitute number of inches (or degrees) required.

B indicates the point at which the **hand** (or other applicable body member, like foot, eye, etc.) **begins** the therblig.
F indicates the basic **function** of the therblig.
E indicates the point at which the **hand** (or other applicable body member) **ends** the therblig.

* Eagle pencils.
† Dixon pencils.
‡ If two classifications of the same therblig occur at the same time, average the time values.

Fig. 4. **Symbols for therblig and simo charts (continued on next page).**

Therblig symbols		Therblig name	Activity represented	Color symbol	Approximate time (in 0.0001 min.)
Letter	Graphic				
6. DA		Disassemble	B. Initial separation of one object from mating or integral object. F. Separation of objects. E. Objects are separated.	Light violet	
xDA1		Loose-fit disassemble	⅛ in. or above total tolerance.		10/in. or 0.20/degree
xDA2		Free-fit disassemble	$\frac{1}{32}$ to ⅛ in. total tolerance.		20/in. or 0.45/degree
xDA3		Medium-fit disassemble	$\frac{1}{100}$ to $\frac{1}{32}$ in. total tolerance.		35/in. or 0.70/degree
xDA4		Snug-fit disassemble	Less than $\frac{1}{100}$ in. total tolerance.		50/in. or 0.90/degree

Note: In place of x substitute number of inches (or degrees) required.

7. U		Use	B. First manipulation, activation, or pressing of control or tool. F. Manipulation, activation, or pressing of control or tool for its designed purpose. E. Completion of employment of control or tool.	Purple	
xUT		Tool use	When object applied, pressed, or manipulated is free to move in all directions.		Estimate
xUC		Control use	When object applied, pressed, or manipulated is restricted in one or more directions.		Estimate

Note: In place of x substitute number of inches, degrees, and/or pounds required. Investigate possibility of another therblig (like P, TL) in combination with Use.

II. Work classification: grasp preparatory therbligs

8. SH		Search	B. Initial groping and/or hunting for object in a group of dissimilar objects. F. Trying to locate an object in a group of dissimilar objects.	Black EP 747 DP 379	

		E. Sought-for object is found.		
SH1	Large object search	Object at least twice as large as other objects in group.		10
SH2	Medium object search	Object from one to two times as large as other objects in group.		20
SH3	Small object search	Object smaller than other objects in group.		30
9. ST ⟶ Select		B. Initial contact with several objects in a group of similar objects.	Gray	
		F. Picking out one object from group of similar objects.		
		E. Object has been located.		
ST1	Large object select	Objects over 1 sq. in.		5
ST2	Medium object select	Objects from ⅝ sq. in. to 1 sq. in.		10
ST3	Small object select	Objects smaller than ⅝ sq. in.		15

III. Work classification: movement therbligs

10. TL	Transport loaded	B. Start of motion with object or load.	Dark green EP 738 DP 416	
		F. Change location of object from one work area to another.		
		E. Arrival at destination or cessation of movement.		
xTL1	Transport loaded to indefinite location	When disposal point of object is not fixed or the object is going to be tossed.		25 plus 5/in.
xTL2	Transport loaded to definite location	When disposal point is fixed or the object is going to be released carefully.		35 plus 5/in.

Note: In place of x substitute number of linear inches moved.

Fig. 4.—(Continued on next page.)

Therblig symbols Letter	Graphic	Therblig name	Activity represented	Color symbol	Approximate time (in 0.0001 min.)
11. TE	)	Transport empty	B. Start of motion of empty hand. F. Reach for object or change in location of hand. E. Cessation of free movement.	Light green	‡
xTE1		From indefinite location transport empty	When origination point varies so hand is already in motion.		15 plus 5/in.
xTE2		From definite location transport empty	When origination point is fixed.		20 plus 5/in.
xTE3		To definite location transport empty	When object moved to is at a definite point.		20 plus 5/in.
xTE4		To indefinite location transport empty	When object moved to varies in its location or when eyes must direct hand to its next activity.		15 plus 5/in.

Note: In place of x substitute number of linear inches moved. TE1 or TE t2 can occur in combination with TE3 or TE4 (xTE4).

IV. Work classification: delay therbligs

12. UD	o	Unavoidable delay	B. Start of idleness. F. Waiting, which is part of method being used, while another body member or machine is doing something. E. Waiting ceases.	Yellow ochre EP 736 DP 412	
UDB		Balancing delay	Waiting for other body member or machine.		Balance with opposite hand
UDC		Change direction delay	When no G or RL occurs between movements in opposite directions.		10

13. AD	Avoidable delay	⌣	B. First motion which is not part of method being used. F. Any activity not needed in method. E. Activity or idleness not part of method ceases.	Lemon yellow EP 735 DP 374	No time
14. H	Hold	∩	B. Start of maintaining an object, controlled by a body member, in fixed orientation. F. Maintaining an object with a fixed orientation. E. When fixed orientation is no longer required or before start of any other therblig.	Gold ochre EP 736½ DP 388	Balance with opposite hand
15. R	Rest	⚲	B. Idleness. F. Overcoming fatigue as part of every cycle. E. Resume the work of the cycle.	Orange EP 737 DP 372	No time

V. Work classification: mental activity therbligs

16. PN	Plan	⫐	B. Idleness or motions which are not productive work. F. Worker deciding on the next work or activity. E. When next activity is determined.	Brown EP 746 DP 378	No time
17. I	Inspect	○	B. Start of examination or testing of object. F. Feeling, viewing, or examining an object to determine quality. E. Quality has been determined.	Burnt ochre EP 745½ DP 398	60 per inspected point

VI. Work classification: gross body movements (not included in original therbligs). Colors are not assigned to these gross therbligs since they are used mainly for the therblig chart which uses no colors.

18. W	Walk	Movement of the body from one workplace to another.	
xWW	Walk without load		40/ft.
xWL	Walk with load		50/ft.

Note: In place of x substitute number of linear feet walked.

‡ If two classifications of the same therblig occur at the same time, average the time values.

Fig. 4. (Continued on next page.)

Therblig symbols		Therblig name	Activity represented	Color symbol	Approximate time (in 0.0001 min.)
Letter	Graphic				
19. B		Bending	Trunk movement with hips as hinge.		150
BD		Bend down			175
BU		Bend up			175
BT		Bend and/or body turn			
20. SI		Sit			200
21. SD		Stand up			250
22. K		Kneel	Movement of the body with the knees as hinge.		150
KD		Kneel down			200
KU		Arise kneel			150
K1		One-knee kneel			
K2		Two-knee kneel			300

Note: KD or KU can occur in combination with K1 or K2, for instance, KD2.

Fig. 4. (Concluded.)

‡ If two classifications of the same therblig occur at the same time, average the time values.

Fig. 4 shows the symbols in two ways: as the basic therbligs developed by the Gilbreths, and as finer detail or conditions for each of the therbligs. The definition of the **basic therblig** provides the beginning and end points and the function of the therblig. The **finer detail therbligs** are special situations of the function. For example, grasp has the function of gaining control. However, the control can be gained by contact grasp (G1), by pinch grasp (G2), by wrap grasp (G3), or by regrasp (G4), as shown by the finer detail therbligs.

A **therblig chart** is usually made with finer detail therbligs. This provides the essential accuracy needed. Basic therbligs can be used in many ways, one of which is to develop over-all methods consciousness.

Fig. 4 also has colors listed for each basic therblig. These colors are used for making the **therblig time chart** (or simo chart). Colors are used in place of black and white and shaded symbols.

Predetermined Time Values. Fig. 4 has time values (listed as "approximate time") for each fine detail therblig. These values are predetermined from studies of many operations. They can be used to make a therblig time chart without using motion pictures or a watch. However, these time values are not accurate, but give good relationships among therbligs. It is theoretically possible to obtain accurate figures for therblig times, but, in practice, the synthesis of such figures into usable increments is too time-consuming.

The numbering of the therbligs (like G1, G2, etc.) proceeds in the order from the least to greater amounts of time to perform. Usually, G1 should take less time than G2. The word "usually" is used, because, as mentioned above, time values are not necessarily accurate. Therefore, G2 in an operation may take more time than G3. However, the predetermined time represents useful information for both analyzing an operation and selecting a feasible solution.

Making a Therblig Chart. The therblig chart is started with the activities of one hand, usually the one doing the most work. The work of the other hand is then charted in relation to the first hand to maintain the **simultaneous activity** concept. Fig. 5 (Nadler, Motion and Time Study) shows a therblig chart made for the operation of filling a transparent paper bag with a ring and expander. This operation was one of six in assembling a set of replacement piston rings. The analyst directly observed the work to get the data for this chart.

SIMO CHARTS. The simo chart (short for the simultaneous motion cycle chart, developed by the Gilbreths) is really a therblig time chart. The simo chart is the detailed symbolic, systematic, and time presentation of the method of work, as recorded by motion pictures, performed by the body members of a man usually when the worker is at one workplace. The simo chart is not made often, and the volume of work must be rather large before it is worthwhile. However, it is an excellent **training device** because it forces the person to record each detail of the motions and accompanying times for both hands. The simo chart was the graphical presentation developed by the Gilbreths when they originated the therbligs. Therbligs and simo charts are generally considered a part of **micromotion study.**

Types of Simo Charts. A simo chart may be made with either the basic therblig breakdown or the finer detail therblig breakdown. In addition, the simo chart may be made for hand and/or body members, or for fingers. The **finger simo chart** gives much more detail than the hand simo chart. Ordinarily, the **hand simo chart** is made with fine detail therbligs, and the finger simo chart with basic therbligs.

_____ OF____

| ORIGINAL | | THERBLIG | CHART |

OF __PACKAGE RING AND EXPANDER___

Date _5/31/_ Part _BAG-RINGS_ Operator _MBY_ Mach._____

By _OHC_ No. _EXPANDERS L207-STD_____

#	L H DESCRIPTION			R H DESCRIPTION
1	Edge of Filled Bag	G2	9TE23	To Rings
2	To Bag Rack (Loaded)	15TL2	G2	Top Ring
3	For Rack	P 24	9TL2	To Bag
4	In Rack	1A1	UDB	For Air tc Open Bag
5	In Rack	RL2	P24	For Bag
6	To Expanders	9TE24	3A1	In Bag
7			RL2	In Bag
8	PU Expander	ST1 &	ITE23	To Edge of Bag
9		G2	G2	Edge of Bag
10			H	Open for L H
11	To Bag	6TL2		
12	For Bag	P24		
13	In Bag	3A2		
14	In Bag	RL2		
15	To Edge of Bag	ITE23	RL2	Edge of Bag
16				
17				
18			LH	RH
19		TE	2	2
20		TL	2	1
21		ST & G	3	0
22		G	2	2
23		P	2	1
24		A	2	1
25		RL	2	2
26		H	0	5
27		UD	0	1
28			15	15
29				
30				
31				
32				
33				

F1

Fig. 5. Typical therblig chart with summary.

Making a Simo Chart. The simo chart could be made directly from the film without making a record of the analysis of the activity. However, this is more difficult than following the usual procedure. The time values and the type of therblig are usually determined in an intermediate step on the form shown in Fig. 6. On this **film analysis sheet** the analyst records, in sequence for one hand, the therbligs and the clock time of the frame in which the therblig first appears (or projector counter if no clock is in the picture). After one hand has been charted, the other hand's activity would be charted. Subtraction is used to obtain the time for a given therblig. Making the simo chart from the film analysis becomes a simple step for a clerk. For almost all cases a **workplace diagram** should be made with a simo chart. A **summary** is sometimes difficult to make. If a clear presentation of the number of symbols can be made, a summary is helpful.

Part of a regular fine detail therblig chart is shown in Fig. 7, based on the film analysis shown in Fig. 6 (Nadler, Motion and Time Study). Fig. 8 shows part of a simo chart with the therblig form symbols.

Although therbligs provide fine detail, an analyst soon learns even therbligs are inadequate. This provides a difficult situation, because trying to make finer divisions makes therbligs less useful. And unless fineness is further developed, it is frequently not possible to obtain sufficient detail. Research is continuing to try to find solutions to this problem.

NONREPETITIVE WORK ANALYSIS. All the techniques presented to this point are used mainly for analyzing repetitive or slightly varied **cycle work.** However, much work in industry is of the nonrepetitive type. Motion and methods study personnel must, through new techniques, take into consideration an analysis of nonrepetitive work if a complete job is to be done. Four techniques are in general use for analyzing nonrepetitive work.

Observer with Worker. In this procedure, an analyst is assigned to a given operator or group, and he follows the worker(s) through all activities. The analyst records the time and activity for every **work situation** in the day. The record shows what was done and how much time was spent doing it.

This procedure is used mainly when people go over many routes and cover great distances in performing their work. The advantages of this technique are that it gives information not otherwise obtainable. However, there are several disadvantages. Ordinarily, the analyst cannot spend too many days following the worker. This becomes too expensive. Therefore, the information gathered is not usually **representative** of all the individual worker might do. This procedure does not result in completely accurate data, because the analyst may be an outside influence on the worker. Only one worker or one small group is followed by this technique, whereas many people or groups may be performing the same activity. A question arises about the similarity between the one person or group and the others doing the same work.

Because the procedure is simple, it has been and will be used frequently in analyzing nonrepetitive work. However, it must be judged in relation to the other techniques to determine its usefulness.

Memomotion Study. This procedure is closely related to the one above. However, the motion picture camera is virtually substituted for the analyst. The film provides the same type of information as gathered above. Motion pictures provide an excellent record of what has gone on and good information about time. If the photographer is the analyst, then analyzing the film will be easier; 1 FPS (100 FPM) pictures can be shown again and again to review what happened. A

	ORIGINAL		FILM	ANALYSIS			OF

OF___ SPROCKET ASSEMBLY_____

Date __1/28/__   Part __SPROCKET__   Operator __F M__   Film No. __35 16FPS__
By __R W S__   No.___849-923-4-5___

	Clo.	T	Sym	Left hand description	Clo.	T	Sym	Right hand description
1	250	13	9TE23	To A	250	15	18TE23	To B
2	263	12	ST3&G2	A	265	27	ST3&G2	B
3	275	15	11TL2	To Jig	292	19	6TL2	To Jig
4	290	3	P13	For Jig	311	5	P13	On Jig
5	293	2	1A2	On Jig	316	8	1A2	On Jig
6	295	1	RL2	On Table	324	1	RL2	B
7	296	22	24TE23	To C	325	12	9TE23	To W
8	318	6	ST3&G2	Pu C	337	9	ST3&G2	W
9	324	23	24TL2	To Jig	346	16	9TL2	To Jig
10	347	4	P13	On Jig	352	6	P13	On Jig
11	351	3	1A2	" "	368	3	1A2	" "
12	354	1	RL2	C	371	2	RL2	W
13	355	22	18TE23	To SP	373	16	15TE23	To HS
14	377	14	UDB		389	12	ST3&G2	PU HS
15	391	13	ST2&G2	Pu SP	401	23	15TL1	To Jig Area
16	404	21	18TL1	To Jig Area	424	9	P23	HS to SP
17	425	5	P3	For Assembly	433	6	½A3	HS on SP
18	430	23	H	" "	439	4	RL2	HS
19	453	2	RL2	SP	443	4	1TE23	To End SP
20	455	10	5TE14	To Sleeve	447	5	G4	SP
21	465	7	UDB		452	6	4TL2	To Jig
22	472	4	G3	Sleeve	458	5	P14	On Jig
23	476	10	2DA2	From Jig	463	4	1½A2	" "
24	486	12	9TL1		467	2	RL2	SP
25	498	4	P4	On Table	469	15	15TE23	To Hammer
26	502	24	H		484	8	G3	PU
27	526	10	9TL2	To Jig	492	20	20TL1	To LH
28	536	4	P14	" "	512	4	UDC	
29	540	6	2A2	On Jig	516	6	U	On Sleeve
30	546	1	RL2	Part	522	22	20TL1	To Table Aside
31	547	4	1TE23	To Assem.	544	4	RL2	On Table
32	551	2	G2	Assembly	548	31	UDB	
33	553	4	2DA2	From Jig Sleeve	579		18TE23	
34	555	18	18TL2	To Tray				
35	571	4	P23	On Tray	250			
36	575	2	1A1	On Tray	329	329		
37	577	2	RL2	Release				
38	579		9TE23					
39								
40	250							
41	329	329						
42								
43								
44								

F3

Fig. 6. Film analysis of assembling and packing sprocket.

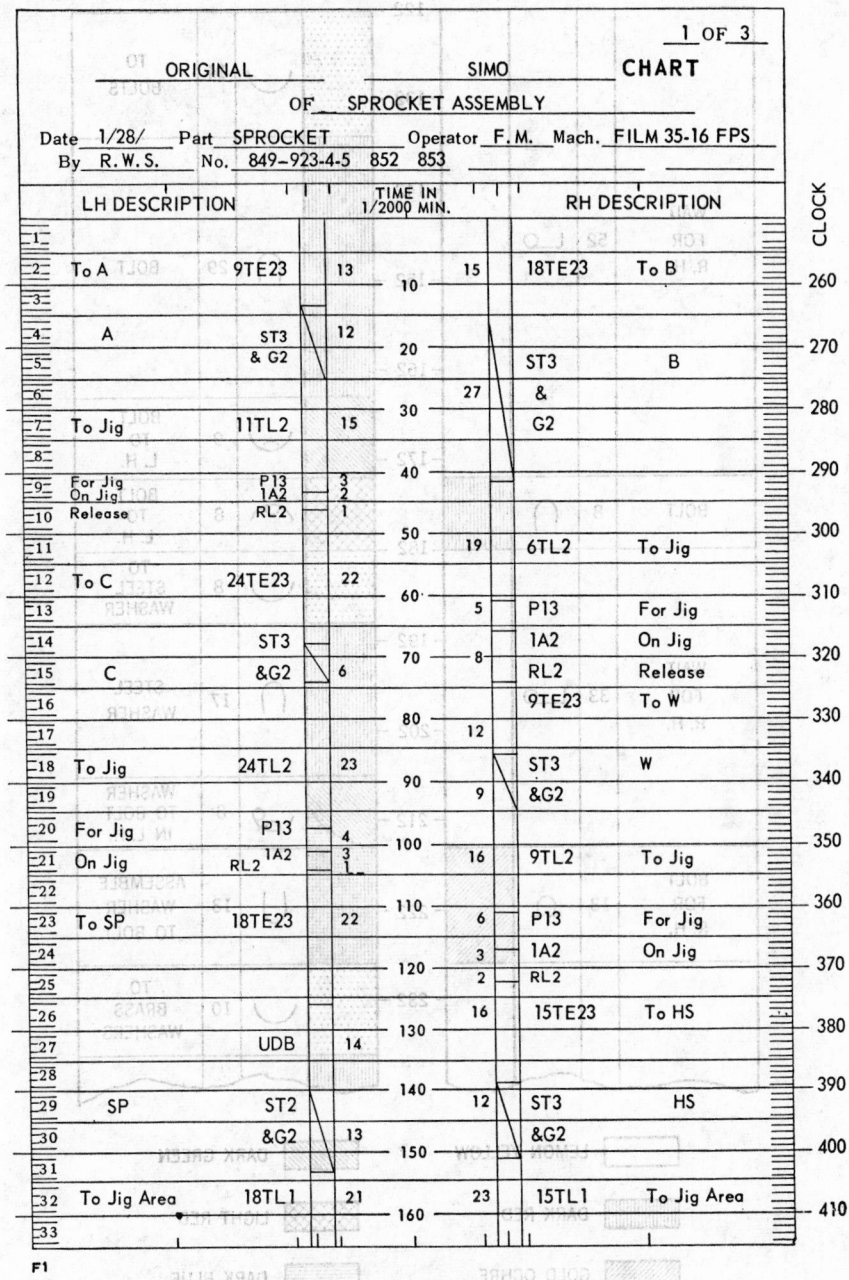

Fig. 7. Simo chart of film analysis in Fig. 6.

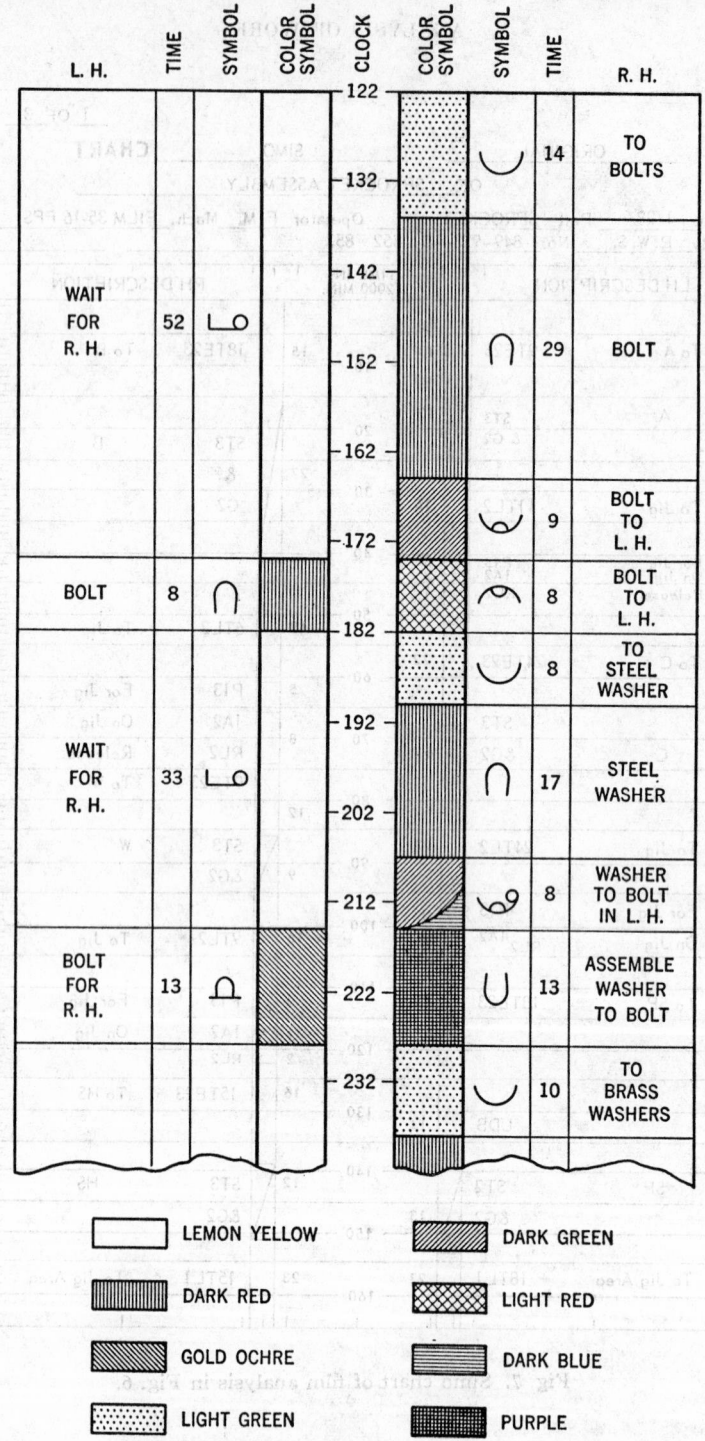

L. H.	TIME	SYMBOL	COLOR SYMBOL	CLOCK	COLOR SYMBOL	SYMBOL	TIME	R. H.
				122			14	TO BOLTS
				132				
WAIT FOR R. H.	52			142			29	BOLT
				152				
				162				
				172			9	BOLT TO L. H.
BOLT	8			182			8	BOLT TO L. H.
							8	TO STEEL WASHER
WAIT FOR R. H.	33			192			17	STEEL WASHER
				202				
				212			8	WASHER TO BOLT IN L. H.
BOLT FOR R. H.	13			222			13	ASSEMBLE WASHER TO BOLT
				232			10	TO BRASS WASHERS

LEMON YELLOW   DARK GREEN

DARK RED   LIGHT RED

GOLD OCHRE   DARK BLUE

LIGHT GREEN   PURPLE

Fig. 8. Simo chart with therblig form symbols.

photographer must stay with the camera, however, and there is the additional cost of analyzing the film later. This technique is not usable unless the work is restricted to a general area which can be covered by a motion picture camera. If the person moves from place to place, it would be difficult to use. Although there is a restriction on the period of time covered by motion pictures, it is not so severe as the first technique above. It is possible to use the camera as a sampling device to obtain information from different periods of time.

Work Sampling or Occurrence Study. The occurrence or work sampling study determines the percentage of time spent by an individual or a group of individuals in various activities by means of random observations. In effect, the analyst samples the activity of the individual to obtain the information for the occurrence study.

The work sampling study has many **advantages** that the other techniques do not have. It can be made for a short period of time or for as long as desired. It is simple and can be made by almost anyone. It also results in fairly accurate information. Work sampling also permits the analyst to do other work while he is making the study. And work sampling can be made on a large group of people doing similar nonrepetitive work as well as on one person or crew. (The procedure for making work sampling studies is described in detail in the section on Work Measurement and Time Study.)

Operator Records His Own Work. Frequently, work is performed by people who move not only throughout the whole plant but from plant to plant, area to area, and even city to city. The easiest way to handle this problem is to provide an **analysis form** with a list of activities down the left and the times or periods during the day across the top so the man can check off his activities throughout the day at, say, 15-minute intervals. It is unlikely that great accuracy will be obtained this way, but at least some valuable information will be available about the type and frequency of activities the man performs.

Advantages of Analyzing Nonrepetitive Work. There are a number of techniques which can be used in the analysis of nonrepetitive work, then, and many variations upon them to suit the tasks at hand. Some of the advantages which will be found in performing such analyses are:

1. Activities to which other techniques of work simplification can be applied are pinpointed.
2. It provides supervisors and management with information for action.
3. It provides facts to form the basis for discussion with the people who perform the work. Frequently, opinion has been the major basis.
4. Areas for training are pinpointed.
5. Skill utilization percentage values are obtained as a base point for future evaluations after programs of improvement or training have been installed.

MISCELLANEOUS ANALYSIS TECHNIQUES. Motion and methods study has developed numerous techniques that help in special problems. Some are generally regarded as seldom used techniques but handy when needed. Some of these techniques are described below.

Chronocyclegraph. This technique was developed by the Gilbreths. A light is attached to the middle finger of each hand. A still camera is used. A relay in the circuit of the lights flashes them on and off, with a variable amount of electricity while the light is on. This forms a **pear-shaped dot** on the exposed film. In this way, a record of the motion and its general speed is obtained. A simplified mechanism can be used to obtain the pear-shaped dot. It involves an alternate black and transparent wedge on a plastic disc which rotates in front of the camera.

Cyclegraph. This is almost the same as the chronocyclegraph except that no flashing lights are recorded on the film. Only continuous white lights (or lines) are recorded.

Motion Paths from Motion Pictures. If motion pictures are projected one frame at a time, and a dot (at a knuckle, or finger tip) is placed on a piece of paper on which the film is projected, the foundation of a **motion path chart** is made. Connecting the dots by a line gives the path followed by the operator's hand. Distance between dots gives some indication of speed and time. The results are somewhat similar to those given by a chronocyclegraph and perhaps more easily obtained.

Other Photographic Techniques. There are other photographic techniques which can be used. Motion pictures alone are a good analysis technique as mentioned previously. There is a special camera for photographing movements of the eyes (Factory Management and Maintenance, vol. 111). A **stroboscopic camera** shows the position or location of the man during various parts of the operation. **Stereo-chronocyclegraphs** and stereo-cyclegraphs can be made to provide three-dimensional information. **Cross-section paper** can be exposed onto motion picture film before the actual operation pictures are taken. This permits the analyst to measure more accurately the activities of the operator.

Time Study. Time study helps to point out actual occurrences during a study and the time it takes to perform them. Such activities as unavoidable delays and irregular occurrences provide the key to many areas where other techniques of motion and methods study or work simplification can be applied. This is especially true when a time study is made on the operation before it is improved. Almost all jobs yield to improvement through proper motion and methods analysis. It is, therefore, foolish to embark upon a time study until at least a cursory analysis of the job has been made and improvements thus uncovered have been implemented.

Combination Charts. An important requirement of a methods and motion study analyst is that he never be restricted by techniques. If he feels he would learn something by combining several of the types of charts he should do this without hesitation. Ordinarily, the combination of charts is made within the **sequence** or **methods** grouping. For example, techniques used to analyze method might be combined. But it might be necessary under some circumstances to combine techniques for analysis of sequence and method. Also, **special symbols** may be developed in the course of a study for ease and accuracy in making an analysis. There are many industries where special symbols can be substituted for general purpose symbols.

Operating Performance Analysis. Frequently information will have to be gathered in ways that cannot be classed as techniques. In most cases this information is vital in developing a better way to do the work.

In a fruit processing plant, it became necessary to measure the amount of good product thrown out with the waste. The method for cleaning the area determined how much good product was wasted. An actual study of all the waste enabled the analyst to develop an economical improvement for saving more of the good product.

Other procedures in the operating performance area include studies of warehouse space utilization, statistical analysis of data (like designing a sampling plan for invoices to determine the general types sent out), and so forth.

String diagrams are something like flow diagrams except that pins are used for the workplaces and string is used to follow the product from one place to another. Where the strings are thickest is where the heaviest traffic flows.

Unopar. The Universal Operator Performance Analyzer and Recorder, developed by Nadler, is an electronic device which obtains the velocity, acceleration, deceleration, position, distance, and time for every motion involved in an operation, even though it is performed in three planes. The device provides the same measurements for each of the three planes as well as the resultant combination of the measurements. Thus, it is possible to decide whether motions are efficient or can be improved.

Although a research tool at the present time, it has great potential industrial use. The device operates with an **ultrasonic speaker** attached to the operator's wrist or hand, and it uses the **Doppler effect** with three microphones oriented in three planes to determine the actual velocity in the planes. The velocity information is processed with electronic devices.

Kymograph. The kymograph consists of a rapidly moving tape on which lines are drawn by pens which are electrically actuated in a direction perpendicular to the travel of the tape to produce jogs in the lines. The circuits which control the pen may be opened and closed by photo-electric and mechanical means. The accuracy of a kymograph is about 1/1000 of a second. Primarily, this is a research instrument, but there are several high volume, repetitive operations in industry where it can be applied.

Marsto-Chron. Originally considered a time study timing device, the marsto-chron is used for some motion study research and industrial purposes. A slow-moving tape is marked for time by manually depressing a key. Another key can be depressed to provide code information about the element or activity being timed.

Wire Models. After motion pictures or still pictures have been taken of a job, it is occasionally desirable to make a three-dimensional model of the activities. This is done by bending wires into the shape of the **motion paths.** The three dimensional presentation is quite helpful.

Other devices are in existence for special purposes, and still others will be developed. An analyst should always be alert for new and better techniques.

Application of Principles of Methods Design

BASIC PRINCIPLES. Through the years, every field tends to build up a set of principles and concepts which can be used as guides for designing or improving activities in the area and this is true of motion and methods study. Principles have been developed through applications, research, and discussions. Of course, every principle is not applicable to every problem. Because the principles are guides, they help design the work properly.

The analysis-of-work step gathered information about the five items affecting the work. In attempting to design the work activity to meet the goal, it seems logical to start in a general way by questioning the conditions in each of these five areas. In this way, five general principles of methods design can be stated. Although these general principles are inadequate for specific designs, they do help provide an initial approach to eliminating some of the more obvious methods errors. The five basic **methods design principles** are:

1. Change the **material** being used or contemplated to help meet the goal for the operation being studied.
2. Change the present or contemplated **design** to help meet the goal for the operation being studied.
3. Change the present or contemplated **sequence** of modification work on the material or product to help meet the goal for the operation being studied.
4. Change the **equipment** used or contemplated for the operation to help meet the goal for the operation being studied.
5. Change the **method** or hand pattern used or contemplated for the operation to help meet the goal for the operation being studied.

This is the stage at which each detail of the work is challenged, whether it has to do with material, design, sequence, equipment, or method. Is it necessary? Who does it? Where is it done? When is it done? How is it done? are questions which should be kept constantly in mind in attempting to find ways to improve the work situation and activities to meet the goal.

CHECK LISTS OF PRINCIPLES. Each of the five basic principles can be divided into many specific suggestions, or principles, for use by the analyst in finding better methods. These have been stated by Nadler (Motion and Time Study) in the form of questions to be asked in relation to each of the five basic principles and are shown on the check lists given in Fig. 9. Each section of the check list is devoted to one of the basic principles.

To assist in applying the principles, they have been grouped into the **basic activity areas** to which they are generally applicable. For example, group *A* questions refer to activity performed at one workplace or work area. This means that an analyst trying to design improvements for work at one workplace or

CHECK LIST FOR BASIC PRINCIPLE No. 1

Can some of the **material** received be **eliminated, combined, simplified,** or **rearranged?** Check such possibilities as:

A. Activities at One Workplace:
Using new material instead of scrap
Using scrap
Substituting another material
Changing packaging
Eliminating frills
Reducing and standardizing parts
Purchasing part
Manufacturing part
Changing size of part
Including positioning devices
Making parts smaller
Stronger material
Lighter-gauge material (heavier)
Supplier performing additional work
Specifying incoming quality strictly
Changing auxiliary materials (oils, etc.)
Changing size received (length, width, etc.)
Changing shape
Changing finish specifications (colors, etc.)
Changing product design to eliminate a material
Better packing material
Using non-tangling parts
Reducing weight of parts

B. Moves Between Workplaces:
Substituting another material
Reducing weight of material
Reducing number of parts
Using new material

C. Storages:
Changing quantities shipped
Ordering palletized loads
Changing quantities packaged

D. Holding Activities:
Enlarging parts

E. Delays:
Changing finishes
Reducing weight
Packing differently

F. Inspection:
Prepacking to specifications
Acceptance sampling

Fig. 9. Check lists for the five basic methods design principles (continued on next page).

CHECK LIST FOR BASIC PRINCIPLE No. 2

Can parts of the **design** of product sent out or sold be **eliminated, combined, simplified,** or **rearranged?** Check such possibilities as:

A. Activities at One Workplace:
Specifying minimum material
Loosening tolerances
Automatic production techniques
Reducing weight
Putting on positioning devices
Larger grasping surface
Chamfering mating parts
Changing physical processing technique
Eliminating frills
Sale of scrap
Better covering of parts to reduce finishing
Reducing weight of parts
Reducing visual requirements
Removing burrs
Reducing lengths of parts assembled
Designing non-tangling parts
Greater interchangeability
Making cylindrical or symmetrical mating
Changing parts to permit simultaneous symmetrical hand pattern
Redesigning for standardization
Reducing weights and resistances
Heat-treating
Change to reduce scrap
New packaging design
Reducing size of parts

B. Moves Between Workplaces:
Reducing weight of product
Reducing number of parts

C. Storages:
Including self-stacking features

D. Holding Activities:
Including location points for jigs
Better container design

E. Delays:
Designing part symmetrically
Shipping differently
New container

F. Inspection:
Changing requirements for finished product
Sampling inspection of finished product
Designing for go-no-go inspection
Establishment of definite requirements

CHECK LIST FOR BASIC PRINCIPLE No. 3

Can parts of the **sequence** of modification on the product be **eliminated, combined, simplified,** or **rearranged?** Check such possibilities as:

A. Activities at One Workplace:
Changing order of performance
Combination jigs
Changing physical processing technique
Dividing one operation into two
Rebalance of work
Changing scrap-handling procedure
Punch-card system
Change in lot size
Performing operation in another department
Performing during machine time on another job
Dispatching material from central point
Reducing number of steps
New equipment
Changing location of performance
Better training of operator
Multispindle setups
Performing two operations at one place
Material changes (see no. 1)
Combination machinery or equipment
Reprocessing scrap
Putting operation(s) on other machine(s)
Correcting performance or method on previous jobs
Changing requirements for succeeding jobs
Doing work while parts are in transit
Reversing order
Arranging steps in best order

B. Moves Between Workplaces:
Moving larger quantities
Relocation and rearrangement of operations
Reducing number of steps
Omitting operations

C. Storages:
Continuous flow-processing
Reducing number of steps
Reducing handlings
Relocation and rearrangement of operations
Reducing in-process inventory
Shipping direct, not from storage
Changing location of storages

D. Holding Activities:
Performing two or more operations
Reducing number of steps

E. Delays:
Reducing or combining number of steps

F. Inspection:
Including with an operation
Electronic devices
Doing more than one at a time
Changing requirements for preceding and succeeding jobs
Performing after more operations than at present
Selecting proper point for verification
Minimizing number of controls

Fig. 9. (Continued on next page.)

CHECK LIST FOR BASIC PRINCIPLE No. 4

Can parts of the **equipment, tools, machinery,** or **workplace** be **eliminated, combined, simplified,** or **rearranged?** Check such possibilities as:

A. Activities at One Workplace:
Changing physical processing technique
Jigs and fixtures for simultaneous symmetrical hand pattern
Table height less than elbow height above floor
Simple machines
Semiautomatic equipment
Continuous or automatic processing equipment
Use of foot pedals
Hoppers with positioned delivery
Lip bins
Air or gravity ejection
Automatic jigs and fixtures (eliminating operation)
Color coding tools and equipment
Increasing lighting
Combination tools
Mechanical ejectors
Locating pins or stops
Vibrator hopper feed
Mechanical guides
Power tools
Using more than one machine per operator
Making easier work (by jig, etc.)
Automatic feeds on machines
Tongs or tweezers
Reducing number of clamps
Multipurpose jigs
Bullet nose guides
Enough space for handling
Use positioning devices
Jig for more than one assembly or work
Quick-acting clamps or cams of any type
Tools with large hand area contact
Any gravity feed
Proper chairs
Relocating service and physical facilities
Special accounting equipment
Legible dials (size, shape, scale)
Standardized controls
Noise and/or sound control
Proper arrangement of dials and controls
Shape coding controls
Reducing weight and resistances
Magnetic or vacuum tools
Funnels
Magazine feed
Suspending tools
Indexing fixtures
Safer equipment
Better mechanical or lever advantages
Reducing visual requirements
Tool holders
Making tool work automatic
Special eyeglasses
Self-centering devices
110° knee angle for foot pedals
Proper color background

B. Moves Between Workplaces:
Picking up more than one at a time
Shortening distances
Fork lift truck
Welding extensions to levers
Moving switches and controls closer
Conveyors or chutes
Air ejection
Hoists
Moving equipment together
Extensions on controls
Counterbalanced tools
Foot-controlled movements
Better bins and trays
Tools to move parts and material
Combination tools

C. Storages:
Tote pans
Pallets
Hoppers
Skids
Dolly
Truck
Conveyor roller belt gravity
Better "housekeeping"

D. Holding Activities:
Jigs and fixtures
Foot pedals
Adhesive or magnetic devices
Vise
Positioning devices
Definite stops
Magnetic or vacuum devices

E. Delays:
Adjustable stool
Increasing lighting
Rubber pads on floor
Tub files
Arm rests
Placing tools, equipment, and cranks at proper height
New equipment
Better tool materials

F. Inspection:
Scales for "weigh" count
Automatic inspection in a jig
Electronic devices
Proper depth relationships
Go-no-go gauges
Easier reading devices
Increased lighting (direct, indirect, etc.)

Fig. 9. (Continued on next page.)

Can parts of the **method,** motion pattern, and body pattern be **eliminated, combined, simplified,** or **rearranged?** Check such possibilities as:

A. Activities at One Workplace:
Performance in normal work area
Giving work to lowest-pay worker
Using lowest body member possible
Part time help for peaks
Pre-positioning parts
Throwing or dropping instead of placing parts
   aside
Using lowest category of therbligs
Performing in a rhythmic sequence
Reducing number of therbligs in cycle
Keeping all parts separate
Removing regrasp
Putting manual work in machine time
Proper location of tools and parts
Using smooth, not zigzag, motions
Reducing eye-hand coordination and fixations
Keeping body and posture straight
Manuals of instructions
Proper size, spacing of identifications
Changing procedure for work assignment
Reducing bending, turning, walking
Changing operators to obtain certain physical
   traits
Quality control charts
Angle of plane of work (30° to 45°)
Reducing number of times grasping same part
Performance in normal work sphere
Assigning proper number of machines
Another higher-skill person
Simultaneous symmetrical hand pattern, alter-
   nate hand pattern
Not going to the same place more than once in
   a cycle
Placing picked-up parts on proper side of table
Eliminating pickups and releases
Label or tag parts
Grasping for proper positioning
Grasp, work, release areas for hands close
   together
Using momentum or ballistic motions
Pre-positioning tools
Changing operators to obtain certain physical
   traits
Standardizing multiplant work
Better training
Easier arithmetical technique
Using more than one operator per machine
Changing procedure for obtaining tools and
   material
Making easier
Increasing machine utilization (reduce machine
   delays)
Handles with large hand contact area
Reducing machine time
Proper depth relationships

B. Moves Between Workplaces:
Shortening distances
Picking up more than one part at a time
Reducing abrupt changes in direction
Simultaneous movements
Gravity
Reducing eye fixations
Moving more parts at a time
Reducing number of parts moved
Using lowest body classification
Sliding part
Using proper body member
Release and grasp areas close together
Smooth motions

C. Storages:
Better "housekeeping"
Improving vertical space utilization

D. Holding Activities:
Inclining workplace to make definite stop
Pressure or friction against table
Balancing work between hands
Reducing number of eye fixations

E. Delays:
Reducing number of eye fixations
Simultaneous symmetrical hand pattern
Balancing work between hands
Relocating tools, parts, and equipment
Rotating operators
Proper training
Proper adjustment of equipment
Balancing work among crew members
Increasing operator utilization
Introducing quotas or incentives
Proper operator selection

F. Inspection:
Keeping part stationary for inspection
Definite eye fixation pattern
Better light
Labeled parts
"Weigh" counting
Sampling inspection

Fig. 9. (Concluded.)

work area should review the questions for group *A*. Group *B* questions refer to moves or movements between workplaces or work areas; group *C*, to storages; group *D*, to holding activities; group *E*, to all types of delays; and group *F*, to verification or inspection activities.

PRINCIPLES OF MOTION ECONOMY. The principles of motion economy, developed by the Gilbreths, and as stated by Nadler (Motion and Time Study), are listed in Fig. 10.

---

1. The hands should begin and end their activity in a cycle at the same time and should work simultaneously with duplicate parts in opposite and symmetrical directions.
2. The hands should not have idle or hold time, but if necessary, the hands should not have idle or hold time occurring at the same time.
3. The operation method should have the fewest number of therbligs possible.
4. The hands should not do work which can be assigned to other body members through the use of jigs, vises, etc., as long as the hands have other work to perform.
5. The tools and parts should be pre-positioned in a definite location and so located that the hands travel the least distance and perform the fewest activities.
6. The workplace should be arranged to permit smooth, continuous motions with a natural rhythm.
7. The classification of body members (muscle groupings) used should be kept to the lowest feasible for the work. (Fingers are the lowest, progressing through wrist, elbow, full arm, and body.)
8. The motions of the hands should be arranged to take advantage of body-member momentum created through either previous motions or ballistic activity.
9. The number of eye fixations required in an operation method should be reduced to a minimum. (No eye fixations is the proper goal.)
10. The work pattern should be performed within the workplace areas which are considered normal (i.e., do not require the operator to use the trunk of his body).
11. The workplace height should be arranged to permit the elbows of the operator to be above the table and allow the operator either to stand or sit while performing the work.
12. Handles, foot pedals, tools, etc., should be designed to permit the fewest number of muscle groupings to be used for activating the object.
13. Gravity should be used wherever possible to deliver parts to the operator and to remove or place aside parts.
14. When eye-hand coordination is required for grasping, positioning, assembling, etc., parts in a simultaneous, symmetrical hand pattern, the points at which the simultaneous activity takes place should be as close together as possible.
15. Reduce the total skills and amount of work involved, so that the operation may be made into an automatic or machine operation, if at all possible.

Fig. 10. Principles of motion economy.

A review of the principles shows that some seem to be conflicting. For example, it may be found that using the lowest category of therblig will not permit a reduction of the number of therbligs in a cycle. But all principles are not used in any given operation. The analyst should review each principle to see which one sparks an idea for possible improvement or design of the work being studied. Some of the more important principles are discussed in subsequent paragraphs.

Normal Work Area. Mogensen shows the normal work areas for arms and hands in Fig. 11. **Normal spheres** can be generated by moving the hands upward and all around with the respective center points of the elbow and the shoulder. Normal spheres should be used for design of workplaces, as long as the total distance traveled is a minimum. The normal work area for the lower arm is

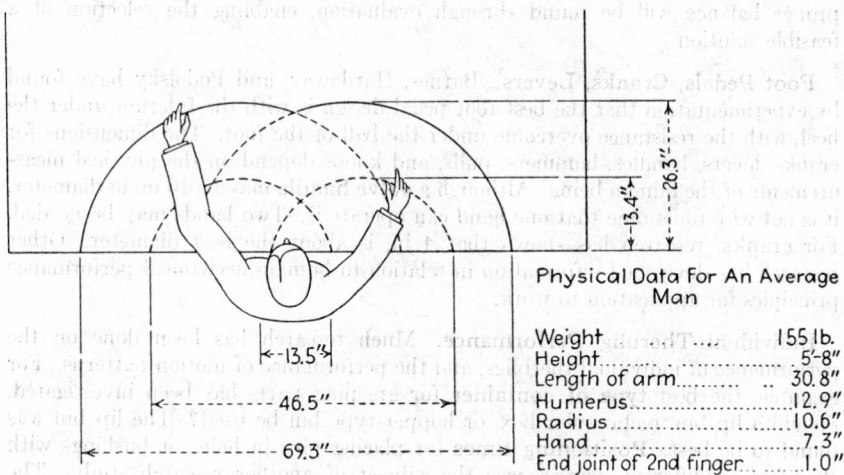

Physical Data For An Average Man	
Weight	155 lb.
Height	5'-8"
Length of arm	30.8"
Humerus	12.9"
Radius	10.6"
Hand	7.3"
End joint of 2nd finger	1.0"

Fig. 11. Normal working areas for arms and hands.

described by an arc generated when the hand moves with the upper arm stationary by the body. The outer limit is generated by the hand when the arm moves with the shoulder as the center point. Placing equipment and activities in these areas means that the body will not move in performing the work. This is desirable. Work should be performed within the **inner circles,** and preferably within the area common to both of the **smaller arcs.**

Simultaneous Symmetrical Hand Pattern. Using two hands to do the same type of work simultaneously is one of the best ways of increasing productivity, at a nominal expenditure of effort. Research has shown that a 30 percent increase in time for work with two hands can be expected as compared to the time for work with one hand. However, twice as many units are produced. In some cases, it is not possible to use a simultaneous symmetrical hand pattern. Some machines or parts do not lend themselves to this activity. In such cases an alternate hand pattern can be considered. Evaluation will show when such alternate hand patterns are worthwhile. The **alternate hand pattern** has one hand doing an activity at one point in the work area while the other hand is doing another activity at another point, and then the two hands alternate.

The simultaneous symmetrical hand pattern may not be desirable where the cost of duplicate jigs and fixtures would not make it feasible. This factor can be evaluated also.

Simultaneous symmetrical hand patterns can be used even where **visual requirements** are high. The two points at which parts will be worked with or grasped visually should be placed as close together as possible, as noted in the principles of motion economy (Fig. 10).

Number of Therbligs in a Cycle. One principle states it is wasteful and expensive to pick up and put down parts many times. Another says the number of therbligs in an operation should be kept to a minimum. However, these conflict. Reducing the number of therbligs might leave nothing but pick-up and put-down activity. There is no way of determining a "proper" number of therbligs in a work activity. There has to be a **balance** between these two activities. The proper balance will be found through evaluation, enabling the selection of a feasible solution.

Foot Pedals, Cranks, Levers. Barnes, Hardaway, and Podolsky have found by experimentation that the best foot pedal design is with the fulcrum under the heel, with the resistance overcome under the ball of the foot. The dimensions for cranks, levers, handles, hammers, pulls, and knobs depend on the physical measurements of the human being. Although a **valve handle** may be 10 in. in diameter, it is not wise to assume that one hand can operate it. Two hands may be needed. For **cranks,** research has shown that 4 in. is about the best diameter. Other research has developed information in relation to human-mechanical performance principles for application to work.

Individual Therblig Performance. Much research has been done on the performance of individual therbligs, and the performance of motion patterns. For example, the best **type of container** for grasping parts has been investigated. Should a lip bin, rectangular box, or hopper-type bin be used? The lip bin was found to be best. **Positioning times** for placing pins in holes or bushings with chamfers at different degrees was the subject of another research study. The bushing with the widest chamfering, about 45°, was the best; it took less time to assemble a pin. Another project involved determination of the change in the time for performing an individual motion when additional motions were added to the cycle. A significant time increase was found as the number of therbligs increased.

An analyst should not assume that the check lists given here are complete. New applications in industry and research are adding to these principles. Every person in the field should continually add to his check list, especially for use within a specific industry.

How To Apply the Principles. The principles of methods design are used as a stimulus to the imagination to find as many ideas as possible concerning probable good methods design for the work. Even though procedures will be given for helping this process, the analyst should always work with other people in the organization. Foremen, operators, supervisors, and persons in other departments of the organization, like purchasing and engineering, are good sounding boards for the application of the principles. It is wise to ask these persons many of the principal questions. Frequently, they come up with good ideas.

Time is required in using the check lists and principles of motion economy, and frequently the analyst does not have enough time to use them all. In these cases, a **mental application** is feasible as long as the basic principles or concepts are applied. The more experience an analyst has, the more likely it is that he can apply the principles mentally.

Generally, the principles for analyzing material, design, and sequence should be used first, and then the principles for improving the equipment and method should be analyzed.

SUGGESTION LISTS. A suggestion list is the written presentation of all the ideas obtained for meeting the goal of the work or operation under study.

Nadler (Motion and Time Study) gives a **suggestion chart form** (Fig. 12) which may be used.

An analyst may get many ideas as he works with the principles. It is important that, regardless of the step in the procedure, all ideas should be recorded. The ideas may come to mind even though the application step has not been reached or has been passed. Ideas should be recorded regardless of how silly or ridiculous they may sound. They may even seem too costly. But, by recording all ideas, it is possible for the analyst to review them later, perhaps to get other, more feasible ideas sparked by the costly or silly suggestion.

			_____ OF ____
		SUGGESTION LIST	CHART
	OF	INSERT GLUE IN CASE	
Date 1/15/	Part	Operator_____ Mach.	
By W.J.W.	No.	SPECIFIC GOAL – INCREASE PRODUCTIVITY	

SUG. NO.	PRINCIPLE NO.	SUGGESTION
1	1	4	Attach foot pedal to handle.
2	2	5	P U two at a time.
3	3	4	Make multi-nozzle.
4	4	5	Place cases in each hand for filling.
5	5	5	Simultaneous - symmetrical hand pattern
6			when foot pedal used.
7	6	1	Use tigbt-fit seal instead of glue.
8	7	4	Move the end of the chute next to nozzle.
9	8	4	Make racks in which case can be placed.
10	9	3	Have preceding operation place cases in
11			rack to make glue placing easier.
12			
13			

Fig. 12. Suggestion list for operation improvement.

Generally, the suggestion list is made with three columns (see Fig. 12). The first column orders the suggestions numerically. The second column gives the number for the most complex principle involved: (1) material is the most complex; (2) design, second most complex, etc. This provides an indication of the area covered and the authority needed to get the change made (more authority is needed to make more complex changes). The third column lists the specific idea. Each idea should be specifically spelled out. For example, an idea for a specific job would not be "use a simultaneous symmetrical hand pattern." It is better to indicate "two jigs for holding parts at assembly area, and two chutes for disposing the assembly."

Suggestion Guide. If time is available, a suggestion guide may be made to give details about each suggestion on the suggestion list. For example, a suggestion may involve a material change, principle No. 1. The suggestion guide has 5 columns on it, one each for material, design, sequence, equipment, and method.

The idea for the change in material would detail what would be changed in each of the 5 areas if the change in material went into effect. This permits the analyst to get some insight into what the suggestion entails and its feasibility. It also permits some of the ideas to be combined to make still better suggestions.

Selection of Feasible Solution

FACTORS IN SELECTION. With all the ideas collected, the analyst next determines which one or group of ideas is best for the circumstances. In determining which is the "best" the analyst must review certain factors which are common to the solution of all problems.

If the same job is performed in different plants or companies, there is nothing to indicate that the same method should be used in each case, because circumstances vary. However, certain **standard factors** have been found to affect the selection of feasible solutions, regardless of where the work situation may occur. There are four of these which usually need to be evaluated when selecting a feasible solution, namely, the economic, hazard, control, and psychological factors —the economic factor being the most important in most situations.

EVALUATION WORKSHEET. To make certain all information about each suggestion in each of these four factors is recorded properly, Nadler (Motion and Time Study) recommends the use of the evaluation worksheet, illustrated in Fig. 13. Most of the space on this worksheet is required for the economic factor. There is space for noting information about the other three factors. Each factor is explained below. The evaluation worksheet permits space for the evaluation of more than one suggestion, and every suggestion that seems feasible should be evaluated. Fig. 13 shows the evaluation of some of the suggestions given in Fig. 12.

Economic Factor. Generally, two economic questions must be asked about the suggestion under consideration: "How much does it cost?" and "How much does it save?"

How Much Cost? There are many factors determining the total cost for a particular suggestion. The major factors are listed at the top of the evaluation worksheet shown in Fig. 13.

New machines refers to the cost (purchasing and often installing) of a major piece of equipment purchased from an outside vendor. **New tools** refers to jigs and fixtures which may be required to put the suggestion into effect. If the tools are purchased from an outside source, then the total charge is listed. If the new device is built within the company, material and labor would be entered separately. Companies have their own policies regarding overhead charges, and these policies should be followed when charging for new tools.

In some companies, charges for **engineering service** are made when new designs are made. Since engineering time will be required to make some of the designs of machines or equipment, or even of product and materials, this charge may be necessary.

Installation charges refers to the labor and small material items needed to install the suggested method. Some companies may include the cost of installing new machines, mentioned above. **Overhead** may or may not be added as a "cost" of a suggestion. In some cases, a company will want to charge overhead for the service functions of the organization to a particular project. In other cases, the overhead here may include interest on money borrowed. **Scrap materials** refers to those losses that occur due to a change in materials or methods. They represent out-of-the-pocket costs to make a change and, therefore, the new method must support any losses of this nature. However, any items of undepreciated capital equipment that would be made obsolete by a proposed methods change cannot properly be charged against the new method. Bullinger (Engineering Economic Analysis) points out that "somebody made a poor guess about the life of the equipment . . ." and, therefore, since the surplus is undistributed profit and arises, in part, from understated depreciation, any book value which remains should be charged to surplus. (See section on Machinery and Equipment Economics.)

Any other charges are included in the miscellaneous category. In some cases, the amount of **lost production** might be charged to a particular suggestion.

This gives the gross cost for a suggestion, from which any salvage value must be subtracted to give the net total cost. Frequently, equipment can be sold to used machinery dealers to obtain some rebates on undepreciated equipment.

Each factor will not be used in every case and other factors may have to be added on occasion, depending on the company and the circumstances.

How Much Savings? Many factors are involved in calculating monetary savings. It is possible to calculate savings on an effort or a reduced skill basis, but even then it is essential to calculate monetary savings.

Monetary savings are based on the present operating cost as compared to the proposed operating cost for the suggestion. Operating costs are made up of direct labor, material, overhead, and machine rate. In some cases machine rate and overhead are in the same category. Usually, **material savings** are relatively simple to calculate. At least, this information is available from many sources. In a similar fashion, it is proper to use the **overhead calculations** of the company, whatever they may be. There are many problems in establishing overhead figures, but the analyst should use the present procedures of his company.

Labor costs are dependent upon the amount of time it takes to perform an operation. The biggest aid to estimating the time for the proposed method is to make a **synthetic chart** for the activity with the suggestion included. If the chart has enough detail, it is possible to compare directly the number of symbols and other activities to obtain an estimate of savings. It should be emphasized that this is only an estimate, and this procedure cannot always be utilized with every type of chart. If a time or simo chart was made of the original method, it is easier to estimate the proposed time because some relationships of time and method are available. The **predetermined time values** presented with the therbligs in Fig. 4 are one of the best ways of estimating time for proposed methods. Although these time values are not precise, their consistent application will result in a reliable estimate. Other ways of obtaining estimated times are to make a **mock-up,** have the analyst go through the hand pattern without the actual setup, use previous time study data, or make an out-and-out guess as a last resort. The time information obtained should be converted to dollars and cents for use on the evaluation worksheet.

Hazard Factor. Industry should always try to make work safer for people. The purpose of evaluating this factor is to make certain the suggestion does not include any factors which make the work less safe. Every industry tends to have a general **safety level,** but hazards should be decreased regardless of the safety level of the plant. Most important, hazards should not fall below this level for an individual activity.

SELECTION OF FEASIBLE SOLUTION
Evaluation Worksheet

Operation: INSERT GLUE IN CASE
Spec. Goal: INCREASE PRODUCTIVITY
Dept: SEALING

Analyst: W. J. W.
Date: 1/26/

How much cost	Suggestion No. 1, 2, 4, 5 METHOD A	Suggestion No. 1, 2, 4, 5 METHOD B	Suggestion No. 3 WITH B	Suggestion No. 6
1. New machines			$150.00	$300.00
2. New tools				
a. Material	$15.00		FOOT PEDAL $25.00	$25.00
b. Labor	5.00			
3. New designs				ENG. EST. $100.00
4. Installation	5.00		$10.00	$50.00
5. Overhead				$50.00
6. Scrap of machinery, tools & materials				SPEC. PARTS $25.00
7. Miscellaneous (loss of production, wages, etc.)				
8. New cost				$550.00
9. Less salvage				$ 10.00
10. Total cost	$25.00	$25.00	$185.00	$540.00

How much savings				
11. Present method				
a. Labor				
b. Material				
c. Machine rate				
d. Overhead & misc.				
12. Total	$\frac{11}{60} \times \frac{150}{60} = 46$¢/CASE	46¢/CASE	46¢/CASE	46¢/CASE 27¢
13. Proposed method			USING B BASICALLY	
a. Labor	$\frac{6.5 \times 150}{3,600} = 27$¢/CASE	$\frac{5.5 \times 150}{3,600} = 23$¢	$\frac{4.5 \times 150}{3,600} = 19$¢	19¢/CASE
b. Material		100% INCREASE IN PRODUCTION		
c. Machine rate	$\frac{11-6.5}{6.5} \times 100 = 69\%$ INCREASE	$\frac{11-5.5}{11} \times 100 = 50\%$ DECREASE IN TIME		
d. Overhead & misc.				
14. Total	19¢/CASE	23¢/CASE	27¢/CASE	19¢/CASE
15. Expected volume 1,200,000 per yr.				
16. Savings per yr.	$2,280.00	$2,760.00	$3,240.00	$2,280.00
10. Less cost	$ 25.00	$ 25.00	$ 185.00	$ 540.00
17. Savings 1st yr.	$2,255.00	$2,735.00	$3,055.00	$1,740.00
18. Hazard factor	NO CHANGE	NO CHANGE	VERY DIFFICULT TO OBTAIN EXACT QUALITY FOR BOTH CASES	SEAL DIFFICULT TO CONTROL WHEN VARIATION IN CASE DEPTH OCCURS
19. Control factor	NO CHANGE	FOREMAN SKEPTICAL - CAN BE CONVINCED FEASIBLE	FOREMAN AND SUPERINTENDENT DO NOT THINK IT CAN WORK	ENGINEERING DEPT. SKEPTICAL
20. Psychological factor	FOREMAN SOMEWHAT SKEPTICAL - CAN BE CONVINCED			SUG. 7 - NO GOOD. CHUTE AS CLOSE AS POSSIBLE

Fig. 13. Evaluation worksheet of alternative solutions.

On the evaluation worksheet, comments are made concerning the analyst's thoughts and knowledge about the safety of the activity with the suggestion included. He should frankly note if he thinks the suggestion increases hazard to the operator so this can be taken into consideration when making the final selection.

Control Factor. Almost every activity has certain characteristics of **quality** or **quantity control.** Making a suggestion for an activity can change these characteristics. Basically, this factor determines how the suggested change affects the specifications of quantity or quality control, and whether the suggestion makes for better product quantity or quality control.

This does not mean it is necessary to increase or decrease quality or quantity control levels. The analyst should evaluate this type of change so a proper decision about feasible solution can be made.

Psychological Factor. Depending upon the circumstances, this factor can be one of the most important of all. It involves both the feelings and attitudes of supervisors of work as well as those performing the work. In most cases, it may be better to use an employee suggestion or a supervisor's suggestion, though technically not the "best," because a well-motivated employee or supervisor using his own fairly good method can frequently outproduce a poorly motivated employee or supervisor using the "best" method.

There is space on the evaluation worksheet (Fig. 13) to permit the analyst to record some of these factors as they may affect the various solutions. The analyst should be perfectly honest with himself in describing the problems which may arise through people. This should help select the "best" and easiest method for the operation.

Evaluating suggestions for nonrepetitive work is much more difficult. Judgment plays a more important role in the final decisions, because frequently the volume or number of times the activity will be performed is not known. The "guesses" can be more reliable if more people are concerned with the decision.

BASIS OF REPORTS TO MANAGEMENT. Usually, additional authority must be obtained before a suggestion is put into effect. The evaluation worksheet permits the supervisor to check all suggestions and to review the care with which the final solution was selected. When this is submitted in conjunction with the project and analysis charts (and frequently with the proposed chart developed in the fifth step, formulation of methods design), the person who must provide the authority has all the information, and it is more likely that the solution will be accepted.

Such reports also permit evaluation of the complete motion and methods study function. Summaries can be made from these sheets to show total benefits. They may even give the person with authority ideas about where future studies might be made.

Formulation of Methods Design

PURPOSE. This might be called the actual design step. Although a synthetic chart may have been made in the fourth step, it is more important now to design all the details regarding the proposed method. In many cases, this involves charting the proposal and making the designs of equipment and workplace. There are cases where only a mental formulation may be possible, for example, where a time study must be made, and there is no other opportunity to make wholesale changes; or where the volume may be low, and not much time can be spent in developing a better method. In all cases, however, some degree of design or formulation of the details is necessary for the proposal. The basic purpose is to prepare the information and details to assure proper performance of the proposed method. Without such information, many proposed methods will not be properly performed. All possible errors should be eliminated. Also, the formulation is a guide to those who will be performing and supervising the work.

FORMULATION OF PROPOSED METHOD. Three processes are usually necessary, although there can be different combinations or additions. Because of the mental process involved, there are no fine lines between the three.

1. **Visualization.** Although visualization was employed in the selection of the feasible solution, it is even more important here to visualize the method so that proper details can be designed.

2. **Design of tools and other material items.** The proposal may involve new equipment or material specifications. This step involves the design of all factors changed in the material, design, equipment, and sometimes, sequence areas. The exact changes must be specified to permit the proposed method to be installed. The analyst does not have to be an accomplished draftsman, but he should be able to sketch his ideas for a tool designer who may make the drawings or even the tool. **Flow diagrams** should also be made as an aid for proper layout, if changes are made, and **workplace diagrams** should be made to describe completely the activity to the supervisors. The material entering the plant and the design of the product leaving the plant must be considered. The analyst may not make drawings for the changes in these areas, but he should be capable of sketching and drawing these changes for submission to the proper authorities.

3. **Design of the actual methods.** Visualization usually includes two concepts, one concerning the design of mechanical aspects, and the other concerning the hand or motion pattern to be used. The general way of recording hand or motion patterns is to make a proposed chart of the same type made in the analysis-of-work step.

   Fig. 14 (Motion and Time Study, Nadler) show a therblig chart of a proposed method designed with a complete recapitulation of time values and symbols, in comparison with the original method shown in Fig. 5. The change involves some simple pieces of metal on the workplace to reposition the parts and permit a simultaneous symmetrical hand pattern. The savings are apparent from the summaries. The work was not put into a simultaneous symmetrical hand pattern until the work components were simplified. This is shown by the information that the original method took .0650 min. per cycle as compared to .0509 min. per cycle for the improved method, and that the improved method produced two parts per cycle instead of one.

   Frequently a new type of chart may be made. For example, an operation analyzed with a right- and left-hand chart, may now need a machine, and therefore the proposed chart will be a man and machine chart. Comparisons between original and proposed charts can be made easily this way.

After the proposed method has been designed, these designs frequently must be submitted for approval. When this is done, it is wise to have a **proposal sheet** to point out the actual changes to be made, the advantages of the change, the savings anticipated, a recapitulation and comparison of the charts made for the original and proposed methods, and the references attached. Some companies have standard forms for summarizing a methods proposal, but the above items are the basic ingredients.

	PROPOSED		THERBLIG			CHART ___OF___
		OF	PACKAGE RING AND EXPANDER			

Date __6/7/__   Part __BAG RINGS__   Operator _____ Mach _____
By __O.H.C.__   No. _____ EXPANDERS _____

#	LH DESCRIPTION		TIME IN .0001 MIN.		RH DESCRIPTION
1	To Expanders	6TE23	50	S	
2	Expander	ST1	5	A	
3	Expander (T & 1st F)	G2	40	M	
4	To Top of Ring Rack	8TL2	75	E	
5	Expander in Ring	P1	30		
6	Grasp Ring (H Expander)	G2	40	A	
7	Pull Ring Off	¼DA3	9	S	
8	To Open Bag	6TL3	65		
9	Ring & Expander to Bag	P23	85		LEFT
10	Ring & Expander in Bag	3A1	45		
11	Pull Bag Toward Self	2TL2	45		HAND
12	Ring and Expander	RL2	20		
13			509		

#	Time Values for Original Method					Original		Proposed		Savings	
14											
15	Left Hand		Right Hand			LH	RH	LH	RH	LH	RH
16	G2	40	65	9TE23	TE	90	90	50	50	40	40
17	15TL2	110	40	G2	TL	175	80	185	185	–10	–105
18	P24	85	80	9TL2	ST&G	45	0	45	45	0	–45
19	1A1	15	30	UDB	G	40	80	40	40	0	40
20	RL2	20	85	P24	P	170	85	115	115	55	–30
21	9TE24	65	45	3A1	A	90	45	45	45	45	0
22			20	RL2	RL	40	40	20	20	20	20
23	ST1&	45	25	1TE23	H	0	200	0	0	0	200
24	G2		40	G2	UD	0	30	0	0	0	30
25			200	H	DA	0	0	9	9	–9	–9
26	6TL2	65				650	650	509	509	141	141
27	P24	85				×2	×2			650	650
28	3A2	75				1300	1300			791	791
29	RL2	20									
30	1TE23	25	20	RL2	% Decrease in Time = $\frac{791}{1300} \times 100 = 61\%$						
31		650	650		% Increase in Production = $\frac{791}{509} \times 100 = 155\%$						
32											
33											

F1

Fig. 14. Therblig chart of proposed method.

Review and Testing of Methods Design

PURPOSE OF REVIEW. Because human beings design methods and equipment, there are possible errors included in the formulation step. There are other problems that may have been overlooked which should be solved. These problems are the reason for the **review step**. It is a "stop, look, and listen" step to make certain all details are taken care of.

REVIEW PROCEDURES. There are three parts of the review step:

Good Design Principles. There are two aspects to the question whether all possible good design principles have been included in the methods design. One concerns the **total possible savings,** and the other concerns the **reaction of the people** involved with the change or new design. Those involved with the work may feel peculiar if changes are made frequently on the same work. They often ask the question, "Why weren't all the changes made at one time?" This aspect can cause difficulty for the analyst in his future work.

Economically, it is wise to install as many changes as possible at one time. If new equipment or **workplace jigs** and **fixtures** are required, then as many changes as possible should be made at the time this equipment is built. Frequently, it is possible that a contemplated change after the jig is built cannot be incorporated because of economic and mechanical problems. In some cases, a small additional change might result in large savings if it could be incorporated at the time the jig or fixture is built.

Details for Proper Functioning. The analyst must check the design of all new **equipment parts** and **products** to make certain they will work as desired. This is economically and psychologically important. The analyst cannot be embarrassed more than when a designed part, product, or jig goes into production and will not work because some design detail has been overlooked. Other people are important in reviewing the designs and checking all details, since they may spot better methods.

The enthusiasm of the analyst can be an important factor in not designing a method properly. He may overlook small parts of the product or jig design which can make the design inoperative. In addition, if he takes more time in looking over the design, he may be able to make the jig or fixture applicable to more than just the one operation he studied. The supervisors of the activity can help outline potential uses of a general design.

Planning the Approach. Supposedly the analyst has been working carefully with the people involved. He has obtained their ideas about the work, and what might be done about it. He has explained to them the purpose and value of the analysis techniques, and the approach he is using. But even with such good preparation, the analyst should take time to plan still further the approach to be used in introducing a new method to the people.

People are an important ingredient of the review step. Even if the analyst decided not to use other people in any way in the preceding steps, the review should force him to do so.

TEST OF METHODS DESIGN. Testing is another way of catching errors before it is too late. It is a way to determine whether any proposed method will actually work. It demonstrates whether the operator can do what is required by the proposed method, whether the mechanical devices will perform as specified, and whether the parts will perform as expected.

TESTING PROCEDURES. Not every new method proposal must be tested. This step is designed as a **check point** for those problems which cannot be solved in the formulation and review steps. If the test step finds a method unworkable, the analyst returns to the fourth step—selection—to start with another proposal.

Testing can be done more often if the organization has a **methods laboratory.** Many companies have such laboratories where tests can be performed prior to installation. Even where a laboratory is not available, some area where the methods analyst can review and test some of the more complicated proposals is desirable. Various ways for making a test of proposed methods changes are discussed below.

Model or Pilot Plant. Frequently a plant layout or materials handling problem, or a large portion of the production sequence, form the basis for a problem being studied. For such gross activities, the only testing procedure is frequently a pilot setup, or a scale model of the involved area. A **model** is the reduced-scale version of the actual situation, and a **pilot plant** is a full-scale version of the layout or area but with a somewhat smaller scope than would be the case in the actual situation.

Workplace Mock-Up. One of the most common tests involves making an actual workplace out of inexpensive materials. This permits the analyst to perform some of the components of the work method at a low cost. This test is about the closest possible approach to getting actual information. Ordinarily, a mock-up is made out of wood and other available scrap material to save the expense of using expensive tool steels and other pieces of equipment. Of course, its use is restricted to activities where there is a great savings potential.

Actual Jig or Workplace Setup. If the volume is sufficiently large, it may even be desirable to make an actual workplace or jig setup just as if the method were going to be used. Another condition where this test would be performed is where there are several operators doing exactly the same thing and where making one of the actual workplaces would be a small part of the total cost of installing.

In some cases, a new proposal requires **commercial equipment.** It may be advisable to purchase this commercial equipment and test the method when it is known that the commercial equipment can be used in other areas in the plant if it fails to work at the suggested point. This type of test is the best for this situation because it will be performed in exactly the way the proposal suggests.

Simple Methods Changes. This procedure is likewise a good way of testing. Frequently, a proposal consists of making some simple changes in present layout or methods. For example, it might require moving a table several feet, or moving a bin several inches or feet. This type of change can be made, tested, and reviewed to see if the desired results are obtained. If the expected results are not forthcoming, it is easy to return the equipment to its previous location.

New Machinery. If the proposed method requires new machinery, it may be possible to test, depending on the type of machinery involved. If the machinery can be borrowed, so much the better. If not, the machinery to be purchased should be "tested" by obtaining as much knowledge as possible about its **operating characteristics.** This information can be obtained from manufacturers or by visiting other plants where similar machinery is used. These are not real tests, but they do provide for some information that would not otherwise be available.

In many cases there is no way of making a test. Enough time may not be available. Frequently the proposal does not lend itself to testing. **Forms systems** and **procedures** fall into this category. The magnitude of the problem may not permit testing. The scope of the change may be too large for even pilot plant or model testing.

Installation of Method

INSTALLATION ACTIVITIES. In some companies, the analyst may be completely responsible for all the activities needed in installation, and in others he may not have any relationship with these activities at all. There are many possibilities between these two extremes. However, the analyst should be interested enough in his proposal to follow up some of these activities.

Make the Mechanical Changes. If a new material specification is required, this must be put into effect now. If a new product design specification is needed, this must be made up. If a new layout or sequence of work is to be used, the changes must be ordered. If new equipment is required, the orders must be placed or the equipment built. This is the step where the activities needed to transform the methods design into the method being used take place.

Train Those Involved. The best changes that can be installed are those which eliminate the work completely. But even under such circumstances, there will be people to be trained for the new responsibilities. If the new method involves operators, the problem is even more critical.

Those concerned with using the new method must be given the opportunity to learn that method. The general way for providing this learning opportunity is through a training program, which can range from just a few words to the operator to extensive training programs in the plant. The people doing the training range all the way from the analyst himself to a company **training instructor.** The amount of time necessary for training ranges from a few minutes to many hours, depending on the skills required in the work.

Use Written Standard Procedure (WSP). This represents a convenient means of training operators. Even if other training techniques are used, it is a good written source for the operator and supervisor to check.

In general, three **classes of information** are required on the written standard procedures. The first is the written statement of the general conditions, equipment, and tools needed for the work. The second is the description of the desired method. The third class is the workplace or flow diagram for the operation.

Fig. 15 shows the written standard procedure for a rather short-run operation, which occurred off and on in a plant. The workplace diagram is not shown. Other WSP's have been made with minute details of work, showing what each hand and finger performs. Some of these include drawings of where the fingers should be placed.

In some plants, the WSP is enclosed in a plastic cover and posted conspicuously at the workplace so that the operator can check his method at any time.

Follow-Up. Even though all the mechanical changes have been made, and the training has been given, there is no assurance that the method will be used the way it was designed. This requires the analyst to follow up the new method. The follow-up is probably most important when operations are not continually running. When the analyst checks on his proposed method, it is somewhat like insurance on his investment of time and effort.

BUS DUCT ASSEMBLY (¼ in. x 3 in.)

(With or Without End Protectors, Two-Man Method)

1st Man	2d Man
1. Go to covers, grasp cover at one end, and pick up with help of 2d man. Help carry cover to squeezer jig and place in position.	Go to covers, grasp cover at one end, and pick up with help of 1st man. Help carry cover to squeezer jig and place in position.
2. Pick up rabbet and two screws. Place and align rabbet and start 1st and 2d screws.	Pick up four insulators and place one in each of the four insulator brackets.
3. Go to copper bars. Grasp one bar at end and slide it toward near end of truck. Regrasp bar at center and pick up. Carry bar to cover and push through all four insulators.†	Go to guide, pick it up, and place in position over insulators.
	Go to truckload of housings, grasp one at its center, and lift it over onto horses.
4. Same as step 3.	Pick up one coupling and four screws. Place and align coupling at end of housing and start each screw in its position.
5. Same as step 4.	
6. Go to center of cover, pick up guide and set it aside.	Go to labels, pick up, and place in water can to soak. Remove labels from water, bring them to housing, and put in place.*
7. Pick up four supports. Go to 1st and 2d positions and place 1st and 2d supports. Close the nearest two squeezers.	Go to end of cover and pick up rabbet and two screws. Place and align rabbet and start 1st and 2d screws.†
8. Go to 3d and 4th positions and place 3d and 4th supports. Close the remaining two squeezers.†	
9. Go to end of cover and pick up length of rope. Double the rope and thread it through holes in ends of bar. Tie the two ends of the rope together.	Same as the 1st man.
10. Go to horses and grasp one end of housing. Pick up the housing with help of 2d man. Help carry housing to cover and place it on the cover so that the holes are aligned.	Same as the 1st man.
11. Pick up four screws and get power screwdriver from overhead hook. Run down the screws at the end of the duct. Place and run up one screw at each of the four screw positions. Replace screwdriver on hook.	Same as the 1st man.
12. Open all four squeezers.	
13. Go to one end of the assembled duct. Grasp and pick up with help of 2d man. Help carry duct to truck and place on truck.	Same as the 1st man.

*If wooden end protectors are used, place them on at this point in the cycle in the following manner:

   1st man: Pick up end protector and four screws. Hold the end protector in position and start the screws.

   2d man: Pick up end protector and four screws. Hold end protector in position and insert one screw, lock washer, and nut in each position. Tighten nut by hand until it is caught by the washer.

†If four copper bars are used, the 2d man puts on two supports and tightens two squeezers at this point.

Fig. 15. Written standard procedure (WSP) for assembly operation.

Standards Setting and Training

DEFINITION OF STANDARDS SETTING. There are two questions to be answered after the installation of new methods: How well has the goal been met? What is to be expected of the new method in the future? Both questions require that some **performance standards** be established if the new method is to be adequately compared to the old method. Standards setting determines the time an operation or element of an operation should take, when performed with a given method under given job conditions by an operator with the necessary skill and training to perform the operation properly, working at the pace, maintainable throughout the day, week, etc., specified as equivalent to the work necessary to earn base pay; and when all the operator's required activity and needs are provided for. It is apparent that the establishment of a standard time can range in accuracy between wide limits. What most people usually refer to as standards setting is the more formal, or accurate, methods of establishing standards. The concept presented here expands the usual references by including wider limits on the accuracy levels; estimates may be considered part of standards setting.

Most of the formal procedures for establishing standards can be applied to work which has not been improved, but an improved method is more likely to be standardized (that is, the operator generally uses the same method over and over again) than a method that has not been improved. It is easier to apply the **formal systems** of establishing standards to improved work, and therefore most standards are set after the work has been improved.

METHODS FOR SETTING STANDARDS. "Work measurement" is the term usually applied to all techniques used in formal standards setting. It consists of two basic methods, the time study and standard data methods, which are described in detail in the section on Work Measurement and Time Study. Either method can be used to establish standards for jobs for which new methods have been designed, when the economic results warrant such study. Also, when an operation has been analyzed into therbligs, approximate standards can be set by means of the times established for the motions, although this is not a very accurate approach.

TRAINING IN MOTION AND METHODS STUDY. The techniques of motion and methods study have steadily improved. Originally, it was thought to be the province of specialists. The specialist is a necessary man in motion and methods study, but the scope of work is so great, that the specialist could never hope to accomplish all that is required. In addition, work deals with people (doing or supervising the work), and they should help to apply the principles of methods design and motion economy.

Scope of Training. Many problems are avoided by teaching all those who are responsible for work methods, and in some cases even those who are doing the work, the principles of methods design and motion economy. This undertaking implies a major **training program** which may reach everyone in the organization. The program should start at the top with the chairman of the board, president and vice-presidents, and continue through the various levels of the organization to the workers. It should include those in staff functions, like engineering design, tool design, and maintenance. In this way, everyone will be familiar with the new techniques of work analysis, and there will be less resistance to change. The people tend to suggest their own changes. The section on Work Simplification shows how such a broad training program can be carried out. The motion and methods study staff specialist still plays a role; when the supervisor or person making suggestions finds that an idea needs more thorough evaluation or analysis, the specialist can assist.

WORK SIMPLIFICATION

CONTENTS

PAGE

Philosophy of Work Simplification

Definition 1
Peg board experiment 1
  Results from experiment 1
  Conclusions from experimental experience.. 2
Motivation 3
  Positive motives 3
  Negative motives 3
Change 3
  Reducing resistance to change 4
Criticism 4
  Symbolic aids to discussion 4
Security 5
  Solving the fear problem 5
  Discussions of the effects of change (f. 1) 5-6
  Improvement and turnover 6
Automation 7

Tools and Techniques

Improvement approach 7
Procedures 7
  Work simplification pattern (f. 2) 8
  Select a job to improve 7
  Get the facts—make a process chart 9
  Challenge every detail—list the possibilities 9
  Develop improved methods 10
  Install improvements 11
  Retraining 11
Process charts 11
  Standard flow process chart symbols (f. 3) 12
Plant layout 12
  A flow process chart illustrating a summary and analysis (f. 4) 13
Workspace layout and motion economy 15
  Normal and maximum working areas for hand motions (f. 5) 16
Multiple activity check list 17
A typical multiple activity chart (f. 6) 18

PAGE

Right- and left-hand check list 18
A right- and left-hand chart using pre-printed symbols and showing workplace diagram and parts sketch (f. 7) 19
Motion pictures 20
Conference leadership and problem solving .. 21
  A problem-solving procedure 21
Work simplification and design 21
Work simplification and standardization 21
  Form to implement problem solving (f. 8) 22
More effective training 23
Work simplification and incentive systems .. 23
Work simplification and suggestion systems.. 23
  Cardinal questions and answers (f. 9) ... 24

A Program of Improvement

Criteria 24
Phases in development 25
  Appreciation 25
  Education 25
  Application 25
Effective coordination of the program 25
  Phases of a complete work simplification program (f. 10) 26
  Yes or no man 27
  The top executive group 27
  Complete management organization 27
  Entire work force 28
  Pilot group 29
  Application by the pilot group 30
  Additional management groups 30
  Application by later groups in organized project teams 31
  Steering committee 32
  Feedback 32
  The ideal project team 34
  Worker groups 34
  The work simplification coordinator 34

WORK SIMPLIFICATION

CONTENTS

Philosophy of Work Simplification

Definition
Personal experiment
Results from experiment
Conclusions from experimental experience
Motivation
Positive motives
Negative motives
Chance
Defined resistance to change
Critique
Individuals need to change up
Security
Solving the real problem
Diagnosis of the effects of change (T. D.)
Improvement and innovation
Automation

Tools and Techniques

Improvement approach
Procedure
Work simplification (Fig. A 2)
Decide to improve
Get the facts—make a process chart
Challenge every detail—ask the foundations
In all improvements
Develop
Process chart
Simplified flow process chart symbols (F. 2)
Blank layout
A flow process chart illustrating at once
Tools and molecules (F. 3)
Workplace layout and motion economy S.
Normal and maximum working areas for
fixed position (F. A)
Multiple activity study for
A typical multiple activity chart (F. 4)

A Program of Improvement

Climate
Phases in development
Appreciation
Education
Application
Efficient coordination of the program
Phases of a standard work simplification
program (A. 10)
Verbal barriers
The top executive group
Complete management cooperation
Line to staff drive
Pilot group
Application by the pilot group
Application by each group in sequence
Steering committee
Feedback
The ideal project team
Written reports
The work simplification coordinator

Right- and left-hand check list
A right- and left-hand chart using pre-
printed symbols and showing workplace
layout and data sketch (F. 7)
Micromotion
Cyclegraphs and problem solving
A problem solving procedure
Mass simplification and design
Work simplification and automation
Learn to innovate! problem solving (T. 8)
Work simplification and creative thinking
Work simplification and suggestion systems
Card and questions and answers (T. 9)

WORK SIMPLIFICATION

Philosophy of Work Simplification

DEFINITION. The term "work simplification" was coined by Professor Erwin H. Schell of Massachusetts Institute of Technology to portray the approach to methods improvement developed by Allan H. Mogensen. Using the principles of motion study established by Frank B. and Lillian M. Gilbreth, Mogensen structured a program in which every member of an organization might participate. He defined this procedure as **"The organized use of common sense to find easier and better ways of doing work."**

As work simplification has become more widely used during the past two decades, it has evolved a broader and deeper meaning. The emphasis has shifted to the human relations involved in the improvement process. A **basic philosophy** of **friendliness, understanding,** and **teamwork** pervades the program. The importance of building the individual as an integral part of the whole is appearing increasingly evident. The tools and techniques of finding improvements are becoming group-oriented. Much more attention is being given to effective application and use of work simplification by organizing a continuous and self-perpetuating program of activity within the enterprise. Year by year, new avenues of communication are being opened for reporting progress, recognizing participants, and introducing new material. The **objective** of work simplification is an increased rate of improvement as a result of the coordinated efforts of everyone in the organization to achieve that goal and the accelerated personal development of the men and women who participate in the program.

PEG BOARD EXPERIMENT. The philosophy of the work simplification approach can be exemplified in any group meeting by a simple experiment known as "peg board demonstration." The peg board, originated by Professor Ralph Barnes of the University of California as a motion study illustration, was first used to develop the work simplification philosophy by Harold Dunlap of H. P. Hood & Sons, Inc. It has since become almost the universal method of introducing the basic concept of work simplification to those unfamiliar with it. In this experiment, one member of the group is requested to assemble some pegs to a board and remove them just as if he were performing an industrial or office operation. Another participant records how long it takes to do it. Spontaneous discussion and numerous trials of different methods of doing the operation follow, in which the leader is often forgotten. Between 10 and 20 people in a group is the most desirable number of participants, although the experiment has been carried on with several hundred by utilizing subgroups, each with one or more boards. Normally, final cycles take less than half the time of initial attempts. The effort expended is quite apparently less. The job is easier and less fatiguing. Conversely, "productivity," for the same amount of time and effort, is increased.

Results from Experiment. The **group's discussion** and **actions** can readily be summarized in the four simple statements which follow.

1. **People like to participate in group activity.** What is done and said, the enthusiasm and laughter which are so apparent, indicate that the group is enjoying the experience. An analysis of why this happens leads to reflections on the importance of teamwork. Most people like to work in groups. Several heads are better than one. When people work together in an atmosphere of friendliness and cooperation, there is usually a much greater feeling of accomplishment, satisfaction, and pleasure as a result of the effort. The most important factor in the group approach is that the people involved come up with the ideas themselves. The common-sense procedure is developed by the group. Ideas are not pressed upon them by someone else.

2. **People like to try to improve** when given the opportunity—unless inhibited. If the leader has taken care not to mention the words "method," "way," "improvement," "better," etc., then the group has demonstrated the spontaneous urge to improve which is inbred in all free people. Our educational system, sports competition, and constant attempts to better our social and financial standing are mentioned by most groups as illustrations on this idea.

It is usually agreed that fear is the universal inhibitor. Loss of security and loss of acceptance by one's friends or fellow workers rank high on the list. Most people hold back if they feel afraid. Work simplification seeks to replace these fears with understanding, mutual confidence, and teamwork. People's natural desires to improve become available for effective use when the people begin to realize that improvement is in their own best interest. They begin to have confidence in their leadership.

3. **It's not what people do, but the way they do it.** It's the method that counts. The time for assembling the pegs to the board is usually cut about in half. Observations by the group include such fundamental concepts as, "No one worked harder or faster, yet productivity was increased." "The group worked smarter, not harder, by finding an easier and better method." It is the method that determines productivity. Likewise, the method of approach is what determines acceptance. Good methods of managing, of leading, of considering the feelings and points of view of other people, are all demonstrated effectively in this experiment. The group is organized in such a way as to utilize the potential of all the people. They respond as a cooperative team. It takes a little longer, but the results are more satisfactory and, therefore, more acceptable to all involved.

4. **It's not what people say, but the way they say it.** Work simplification opens up new avenues of communication. It also sets up standards of courtesy and consideration which establish the approach as one of friendliness and understanding. This point too can be demonstrated in the peg board experiment. The man who first performed the operation readily agrees that he would have resented being "told" he was using a poor method. The rest admit that they would have been inclined to take his side if any remarks had been made in that direction. The sear of sarcasm would have made the resentment still deeper.

Conclusions from Experimental Experience. Nelson states that there are three ways of getting results through others. You can: "tell them, sell them, or consult them." The **telling** approach is resented unless complete confidence exists. The **selling** approach is more desirable but often insincere. The **consultative** approach is generally the most acceptable, since it recognizes the ability of the people involved. It is basically more friendly. If there is a proper balance among the three, with the trend toward the last whenever possible, then, when it becomes necessary in an emergency to "tell," people will usually respond more willingly. **Confidence in leadership** is a quality established through considerate, patient action in an atmosphere of understanding and friendliness.

MOTIVATION. The success of any human activity depends upon the effectiveness of the motives which stimulate it. These can be positive, whereby there is something to be gained, or they can be negative, in which case there is a defense against loss.

Positive Motives. The work simplification philosophy emphasizes the positive motives for improvement. "What's in it for me?" "What is my own objective?" "Is there a common goal toward which we all can work as a team which will help to fulfill the hopes of each as an individual?" A clearer understanding of the **interdependency** of everyone in a free economy is the foundation of progress. Labor, management, owner, and consumer all look to the improvement process in order to achieve a higher standard of living. Henry Ford has said that this objective could be attained by "making the best possible product at the lowest possible cost while paying the highest wages possible."

The **improvement motive** is broad, positive in nature, and easily developed in open discussion with practically any group of people. It can be reduced to specifics in the case of most individuals by reflecting on the following statements from the experiences of Roethlisberger, Williams, Rucker, and others (they are no less applicable to management than to labor):

> We want to belong.
> We want to work for and with people who are understanding, human, and appreciate us as individuals.
> We want to believe our own feeling of importance in the scheme of things.
> We want confirmation by others of our right to enjoy our self-respect in the form of recognition, esteem, and honor.
> We want to associate with people more important than ourselves.
> We want any feeling of increased importance to manifest itself in increased earnings.
> We want to share in the tangible results of our efforts.
> We want an opportunity to enhance our own personal status.

The work simplification philosophy is built on an understanding of these human hankerings. It seeks to provide an opportunity for a higher degree of fulfillment.

Negative Motives. The negative motives which may retard or completely stifle improvements of any nature are almost entirely associated with the fear of loss of a job and the related potential changes in social status or the fear of losing one's feeling of importance and self-esteem. The responsibility of recognizing these defensive stimuli rests in the upper levels of management. A **consistent policy of remedial action** in this regard is basic to the success of work simplification (see discussion of Security). Open discussion of this problem among groups within any specific organization will usually resolve the situations which need treatment.

CHANGE. People appear to resist change. History repeats itself over and over in accounts of the unwillingness of people to accept something new. Iron ships, steamboats, automobiles, airplanes, telephones, and radios are just a few examples of improvements which most people claimed were impractical, would never work, and could not possibly be economically useful. Even today we are prone to scoff at the thought of such things as interplanetary travel and atomic power plants for every vehicle.

Reducing Resistance to Change. The work simplification philosophy recognizes this phenomenon in human behavior as one of the greatest **obstacles to the improvement process.** It attempts to stimulate a desire for a better understanding of why this resistance exists. Participants are urged to test their powers of analysis with respect to the behavior of others by first analyzing themselves. Why do they appear to resist change? What is the frame of reference that dominates their own thinking? What biases and fixed ideas do they have themselves? How do others feel on the same issues? Why?

When the notions which arise as answers to such questions are pursued, it becomes clear, as a common-sense concept, that people do not resist changes toward which their attitude is favorable. The problem then becomes one of **influencing attitudes.** There is no one best method of doing this; rather, it is a combination of several approaches that usually brings success. The atmosphere of the work simplification approach is of itself one of participation, understanding, and friendliness. People are recognized for their knowledge of the job and are given the opportunity to contribute toward its improvement (see treatment below of A Program of Improvement). **Communication channels** are opened and utilized to keep everyone informed of activity which affects them. Information is freely available, and **open discussion** of the facts leads to understanding and confidence rather than mistrust and suspicion. The net result is a new outlook and attitude toward change as a result of teamwork and cooperative effort.

CRITICISM. The implication of any proposed improvement is criticism of the existing procedure. It is next to impossible to criticize a method without criticizing the person doing the job, the one responsible for it, or the person who prescribed that method in the first place. People usually resent criticism. It is necessary to recognize this situation and deal with it effectively if we expect improvements to be acceptable.

Here again, an open discussion of this phenomenon by groups within the organization exemplifies the work simplification philosophy. A sincere effort to realize why people resent criticism reveals a surprising insight by most and leads to better understanding of the problem and a new outlook. People admit that they resent criticism because they would rather be told they are right. We like to have our own good opinion of ourselves verified. Anyone worthwhile has a high degree of pride in his work and naturally resents being told that it is not as good as it could be. A realization that people are trying to help, not to criticize, is a good first step. The **team approach** also does much to alleviate ill effects. If each man knows that his turn is likely to be next, he may be a little more considerate of the others. The very fact that it is a mutual effort and each understands the feelings of the rest is a major part of the answer.

Symbolic Aids to Discussion. Numerous symbolic devices have become almost universally used as aids in dramatizing these points. The **traffic light** is one such symbol. If the green light is on, the mind is open to new ideas and cognizant of the fact that in order for improvement to take place, obsolete ideas must be discarded. The red light symbolizes resistance, resentment, and the closed mind. A desk ornament composed of a ball which is half red and half green serves the same purpose. Its presence is a license to start a discussion over again, if it appears to one of those present that he has run into resistance or resentment. It works well, particularly in cases where there are two levels of the organization involved. The symbol makes the effort impartial. The **parachute** is another such symbol: "The mind is like the parachute. It functions only when open, and you can't go back and get another if it doesn't work."

SECURITY. Fear is without doubt the greatest barrier to improvement and progress. Much of the resistance to change is fear manifested in a manner acceptable to the ego of the individual in question. It is only natural for a man to find reasons why something won't work or can't be done if the doing of it poses a threat to his importance, his job, or his future. The work simplification philosophy recognizes that the opinions and feelings of the people involved are as real as the facts of a situation and must be treated with just as much respect. A worthy objective is to try to get opinion and fact to coincide.

No amount of telling, selling, or convincing will accomplish this end if action belies the words. Moreover, the conduct of a competitor or just a neighbor within any industrial or business community may have as profound an effect on personnel as if it were occurring in their own company. Be sure you are aware of the influences beyond your control—not the least of which is everyday news interpretation by news columnists, radio commentators, and politicians.

Solving the Fear Problem. The area of solution to the problem of fear lies first of all in the **sincerity** of the management leadership. If management fails to accept a responsibility in this regard, there is no reason to expect employees to be anything but wary. What happens to people whose jobs have been removed by improvement or progress is of vital concern to the people involved and likewise to the success of any improvement program. An open discussion of the implications of a hypothetical change which makes it possible for one person to complete the same number of units in a given time as were formerly completed by three people invariably produces the same answers whether the group be executives, supervisors, or hourly employees. The change is progress. It raises the standard of living. It creates employment in the long run. It is a desirable thing, if it doesn't happen too fast, and if management makes provision for **retraining** and **relocating** those displaced.

Fig. 1 lists **implications** of a **hypothetical change** elicited from the three different groups indicated. It is interesting to note that all three started on a note of fear that someone would lose his job and in each case concluded with the assurance that no one had to lose his job.

IMPLICATIONS OF CHANGE

(A high-level group from a hospital)

Someone out of a job
Insecurity
Lower morale
Increased efficiency
Mistrust
Personnel policy problems
Lower cost
Space gained
Transfer problem (other departments may not want)
Capacity increased
Re-education problems
Transition time (time for retraining)
Possible higher capital requirements (initial costs)
Possible higher maintenance costs
May need more people
May have to pay more for higher skills

Fig. 1. Discussions of the effects of change (continued on next page).

IMPLICATIONS OF CHANGE

(A supervisory group in a plastic molding plant)

Two out of a job
Lower cost
Save space
Increase capital
What to do with other two?
Operator more skilled
Shorter delivery
More profit
Improved method
Better product
Better working conditions
More breakdown hazard
New maintenance problems
Could cost be higher?
Less handling
Less setup
How would worker feel?
What happens to pay and thoughts of pay?
Is this the right time to change?
Two people transferred to other jobs
Retraining
Must be able to keep earnings up
New markets
New products

IMPLICATIONS OF CHANGE

(A worker group from an appliance plant)

Two people not necessarily out of work
Save space
Save dollars
Training job must be done
Start with less output
Sell for less
Produce product at lesser cost
Sell more
More help needed to sell it
More people needed to produce product
Cost money to change
More work for builders of equipment
More work for everybody
Easier to do the work

Fig. 1. (Concluded.)

A few companies have gone so far as to guarantee that no one will lose his employment as a result of a work simplification improvement. This may be dangerous as a written policy because of misinterpretations and activity beyond management control. Usually, it is reasonably easy to carry out such a policy.

Improvement and Turnover. The **labor turnover rate** is usually several times the **improvement rate.** It is rare indeed when the rate of displacement of people as a result of improvement is faster than the natural attrition through resignation and retirement. Many firms publicize their turnover rate, since it shows that no turnover has been caused by technological improvements. It is unfortunate that some managers who have been condoning certain methods as satisfactory for 20 years insist on a change overnight once they find out about its possibilities, no matter what the cost in human feelings. A policy of concern expressed in a sincere effort to "do something about it" gains the most respect. The alternative to an **effective reputation for appropriate action** is mistrust, featherbedding, and a slower improvement rate. Conversely, understanding, confidence, and enthusiasm can add new acceleration to the improvement rate anywhere.

AUTOMATION. An open discussion of the implications of automation with groups of executives, supervisors, or workers alike produces thoughts like the following:

This is just another type of improvement. It causes more employment before it even goes into production. It requires people with greater brainpower at higher pay rates. It will make certain products on a high-volume basis which will thus become available to more people at reasonable prices. It will produce certain special products which man has been unable to fashion economically. It will be a fine thing for humanity, if pressure groups don't try to exploit it without regard for the people involved.

The **effective initiation and use of automation** in industry will depend largely on the methods used in installing it. The work simplification philosophy outlined here will be no less helpful in this area than in any improvement procedure. Costly and difficult-to-change errors may be avoided if the people involved have an opportunity to participate. The contribution that can be made by people not skilled in the engineering specialties required for most automation may appear nebulous, yet it is none the less important in obtaining enthusiastic cooperation.

Tools and Techniques

IMPROVEMENT APPROACH. Work simplification is the organized use of common sense to find easier and better ways of doing work. It is the **organization** of thinking in terms of a specific pattern which makes this procedure effective in accelerating the rate of improvement within any enterprise. The tendency to make so-called "flash decisions" or "snap judgments" is overcome by a scientific step-by-step procedure.

PROCEDURES. Frank B. Gilbreth was responsible for the initial thinking which began as an organized search for the "one best way." His wife, Dr. Lillian M. Gilbreth, has admirably carried on his work. Taylor, Porter, Barnes, Mogensen, and a host of others have made substantial contributions to its growth. Thus, the development of the work simplification pattern has been a team effort. As with the peg board demonstration, those who work with it attempt to improve it. Today we have a logical, orderly pattern which exemplifies simplicity. It is complete, thorough, and capable of being effectively utilized by all levels. Fig. 2 shows a typical work simplification agenda. The **step-by-step procedure** is described below.

Step 1. Select a Job to Improve. Too much emphasis cannot be placed on the importance of a good beginning. In selecting a situation which needs improving (Step 1), it should be borne in mind that the end result is a real improvement enthusiastically utilized by the people involved. This, then, is the time to utilize the concepts of the work simplification philosophy previously outlined. The situation is a dynamic one depending on the current attitude toward improvement in any given organization. If an improvement program were well established, the procedure might be quite different from that which would obtain if one were just being launched.

At the outset, the analyst should be urged to select a job, or some part of a job, that he performs himself. In this way, initial resistance to change or any implied "criticism" may be avoided or minimized; moreover, the job a man does himself will be the job he knows best. Jobs that he supervises or is directly concerned with which have high costs are bottlenecks, or are giving trouble, are appropriate situations for selection. Any activity that entails much walking for

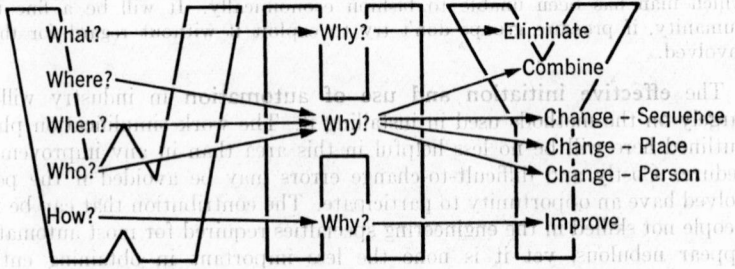

1. Select a job to improve (one you know).
2. Get the facts (make a process chart).
3. Challenge every detail (list possibilities).

What? — Why? — Eliminate
Combine
Where?
When? — Why? — Change – Sequence
Who? — Change – Place
Change – Person
How? — Why? — Improve

4. Develop improved methods (try possibilities).
5. Install improvements (get participation of all concerned).

Fig. 2. **Work simplification pattern.**

materials, tools, or supplies, any place where waste of time, energy, or materials is suspected, is a good possibility. Sometimes we may be "so close to the forest we can't see the trees," and activities which need improving must be hunted out. Groups with common interests but **different frames of reference** from within an organization can generate long lists of such activities if they are requested to do so in a "green light" atmosphere (see the discussion of creativity and brainstorming under Step 3). These lists may then be **segregated** by departmental or individual responsibilities, and priority ratings given to those that seem most important.

Effective selection of projects exemplifies the teamwork and human relations of the work simplification philosophy. Practically any activity is a potential project for improvement, but the objective should be to have everyone select activities that are commensurate with his level of responsibility, as well as those which are more important. Several projects can be under consideration at all times, so that unavoidable delays in the progress of one will allow continual activity on others. While first experimenting with work simplification, the smaller, more easily completed projects are desirable because of the need for experiencing accomplishment during the learning stages. Later, larger projects may be selected for investigation from perpetually kept lists of areas for improvement which may be added to by virtually any level of the work group without implied resentment and resistance.

Step 2. Get the Facts—Make a Process Chart. In order to improve any activity, procedure, or operation which has been selected (Step 1), the facts involved must be assembled in detail (Step 2) in such a way as to render them available for analysis in an orderly and scientific manner. The usual technique for doing this is to make a process chart.

The process or flow process chart is a universal tool of work simplification. It is the most-used means of applying the work simplification pattern just discussed. Once the job to be improved has been selected, a process chart becomes a record of the facts in Step 2 and the work sheet for applying Steps 3 and 4, as well as a summary sheet for Step 5. Depending on the type of process chart made, the important features are graphically portrayed in such a way that they can be easily recognized and readily challenged in Step 3. Techniques for constructing and using the simple forms of process charts most commonly used in work simplification are given later in this section (see Figs. 4, 6, and 7). All forms of process charts, including the more complex and special forms, are fully described in the section on Process Charts.

The tendency in work simplification is to de-emphasize technical perfection in the charting process, which is only Step 2 of the pattern. If necessary, in order to encourage participation at all levels of the organization, technicians are often assigned to make the charts for a project team.

Step 3. Challenge Every Detail—List the Possibilities. This is the creative stage (Step 3) of the work simplification pattern. The green light must be on, the minds must be open, resistance to change and resentment of criticism must be forgotten. The attitude of the people involved must reflect understanding, the basic work simplification philosophy, if this step is to be effective. This is **organized creative thinking** and **brainstorming** with "possibilities for improvement" the objective, catalyzed by a simple but thorough questioning procedure. Judicial thinking and evaluation of the possibilities should be postponed until ideas have been developed. Creative thinking begins with the simple mental procedure of wondering. Why? Why? Why? The ability to ask questions leads to possible answers. If we ask certain specific questions, we are guided in the direction of improvement possibilities.

What? What is being done? Why? What is the purpose of doing it? Why should it be done at all? Can it be eliminated? What are possible alternate methods of accomplishing the same result? The elimination of a detail is the ultimate in simplification. If we can eliminate certain details, other dependent ones may automatically be eliminated. Hence, the "do" details are challenged first, since "make-ready" and "put-away" details depend on them. A chain reaction is often set up. A **"do" detail** is one that actually accomplishes work, brings about a change of condition, or adds value to the product. **"Make-ready" details** such as setup, pickup and load-machine, prepare for the "do." Cleanup, toss-aside, or replace-supplies are **"put-away" details.**

Where? Where is the detail done? Why is it done there? Where else could it be done better, easier, or with less time and energy? Could it be relocated nearer to the next operation? Could it be combined with another detail at a different location?

When? When is the detail done? Why is it done then? Could it be done at another time? Could it be combined with another detail? Could it be done in a different sequence, thus improving some of the make-ready and put-away details?

Who? Who does it? Why does that person do it? Who else could do it? Can someone less skilled do the detail? Can it be combined with another detail done by someone else? Who else is qualified?

How? How is it performed? Why is it performed that way? What other ways are there to do it? Are there easier or safer ways? Can it be economically mechanized?

Answers to these questions on all of the "do" details are noted on the **process chart** along with all possibilities for improvement. The questions are then repeated for the make-ready and put-away details, which are next questioned in the light of the other possibilities as well. It will be noticed that the order of asking questions is organized to follow a descending order of importance in terms of the "steamshovel" improvements first and the "teaspoon" improvements later. **Elimination** is the biggest improvement that can be made. Smaller increments are made by improving minute "make-ready" and "put-away" details, but they are important none the less. This procedure can be carried out by groups of average people with unusually good results. They catalyze each other as a result of diverse experience and different points of view. One idea sets up a chain reaction of several ideas. Group activity and participation really develop into fun in this step. It sets the stage for the steps that follow. The trend in work simplification is more and more toward the task-force or **project-team approach.**

Step 4. Develop Improved Methods. The task now becomes one of organizing the possibilities into the best conceivable procedure under expected conditions and circumstances (Step 4). This is the **judicial step.** Good decision-making is the mark of a skilled leader. A wise person gets all the help he can. The group can be organized at this point to check all people concerned who might not yet have become involved. Their participation now may be the key to their eventual acceptance of the improvement. Engineering, safety, sales—all may have an interest, yet not have been represented on the project team.

Alternate possibilities must be evaluated, and many will have to be discarded simply because they conflict with each other. Wherever practical, trials of proposed or alternate methods are desirable. A laboratory mock-up model is useful in many instances. Comparative cost estimates should be prepared by the appropriate staff people with the help of the project team. The best available information with regard to expected results should be gathered for the final decision-making process.

The following three-part **improvement classification** may be useful:

1. **Conservative:** Those improvements which can be installed with the tools, materials, equipment, and authority available at the level where the study was made.
2. **Radical:** Those improvements which require major changes involving much higher authority and large sums of money.
3. **Intermediate:** Those improvements which lie somewhere between the two extremes.

It is apparent that these classifications are variable, depending on what level of authority is involved in the project. A conservative possibility for the general manager might be a radical one for a setup man or an assistant foreman.

It is desirable at this point to impress upon those making the decision that in many cases, two or more improved methods should be developed. A conservative improvement may often be installed right away and pay for itself many times over before intermediate or radical improvements can be prepared for installation. Frequently, a more radical change cannot be justified on the basis of savings to be realized when compared to a good conservative one. This alone is usually reason enough for making most first improvements conservative. Some advertisements and salesmen urge that you compare costs with the operation as it is, rather than the way it might be with the tools, materials, and authority already available. Such comparisons can be misleading.

A new way of doing something is not easier and better unless the man who is going to use the new method thinks it is better and willingly accepts it. Participation on his part during these steps in the pattern assures more effective application in the next step. A process chart should be made of each proposed method so that those involved in the installation will have a basis for instructing others in the new procedure. **Proposed method charts** often serve to catalyze still further improvements, as well as becoming a convenient method of reporting the details of the change.

Step 5. Install Improvements. If the preceding four steps have been conducted within the framework of the work simplification philosophy, actual application of the improvements developed (Step 5) is a routine matter. Approval must be obtained from those in appropriate positions of responsibility and authority. Their previous participation to a certain extent in some of or all the steps has set the stage. Trial or **pilot runs** are a usual procedure for most changes. These afford opportunity for still further refinement as they proceed. Assumptions may be checked during these experimental runs, and estimates of results compared and validated. The training of those who are going to perform the new method is part of the installation procedure. The process charts that were made up as part of the previous step may thus become instruction sheets.

A major part of the installation procedure is the final **report** on results. This information completes the circuit initiated when alternate methods were discussed in Step 4 and estimates of savings were used to decide on the acceptable improvement. Comparison of the actual with the estimated costs in the report of the final results is a good way of developing confidence. The executive can notice accuracy and conservatism in such estimates and therefore be more inclined to accept future estimates. He is also in possession of information on which he may comment favorably as a form of recognition to those involved in the project.

Retraining. The retraining of people who have previously done the job in a different way needs the concentrated attention of supervisor and worker alike. If both are familiar with the new method through participation in its development, this attention is practically automatic. Productivity and output may even be less during the early stages of the retraining period, since new habit patterns and thought processes must be used. Frustration or discouragement may often retard or even prevent learning of the new method if this point is not understood and anticipated by all concerned. The simple experiment which shows how much longer it takes to write one's name while leaving out every other letter is a fine demonstration of this point. It takes considerably more time, yet it is only about half the work in terms of the number of letters written.

PROCESS CHARTS. The three most common and **basic process charts** are the flow or product process chart, the multiple activity chart, and the operation or right- and left-hand chart.

Of these, the flow process chart has the most general application. It is universally taught as the fundamental fact-gathering tool in the educational phase of a work simplification program. In its simplest form it is easily understood by all levels within the organization and is readily used with the work simplification pattern previous discussed. Fig. 4 (Lake Placid Work Simplification Conference) shows a simple flow process chart made on a preprinted form which was designed to simplify the teaching of the symbols (Fig. 3) and the use of the chart in the work simplification pattern. Once the job to be improved has been selected in Step 1, the flow process chart becomes a record of the facts in Step 2, the work sheet for applying Steps 3 and 4, and the summary sheet for Step 5.

Symbol	Activity	Definition
◯	Operation	When something is done to or by the subject being followed at a given work area. Something is being changed, added to, or created.
⇨	Transportation	When something is moving or being moved from one work-space or location to another.
▢	Inspection	When something is checked or verified for quality or examined for information, or the act of doing so.
D	Delay	When something or someone waits or is delayed or when flow is interrupted.
▽	Storage	When something is kept and protected against unauthorized removal.

Fig. 3. Standard flow process chart symbols.

The making of the flow process chart is a simple procedure of recording information. The steps listed below for making the chart refer to the typical chart shown in Fig. 4.

1. Indicate the job or activity under study.
2. Identify the subject (man or material) to be followed.
3. Indicate the starting and ending points of the chart.
4. Record a brief description of each detail.
5. Assign the proper symbol.

Additional instructions to note in making a process chart are:

1. Shade in the "do" symbols.
2. Record distances of transportation.
3. Record quantities handled.
4. Indicate time consumed, or production rate.
5. Prepare a summary.

All the above steps are explained in detail in the section on Process Charts. **Special-purpose charts** include the simultaneous motion chart and the procedure flow or form process chart. There are a host of other process charts too numerous to mention here, all variations of the three basic ones. They are usually more complicated and less conducive to participative use at all levels than the basic three.

All process charts have the common objective of portraying facts in a complete, orderly, and graphic fashion. Each is handled the same way in the work simplification pattern. The special features of those mentioned above are discussed in appropriate detail in the section on process charts. The ways in which they can be used in work simplification groups are presented below.

Plant Layout. Use of **process charts** with accompanying **flow diagrams** (see section on Process Charts) and the work simplification pattern inevitably leads

FLOW PROCESS CHART

NO. 1
PAGE 1 OF 1

ANALYSIS — WHY? WHAT? WHERE? WHEN? WHO? HOW? — QUESTION EACH DETAIL

SUMMARY

	PRESENT		PROPOSED		DIFFERENCE	
	NO.	TIME	NO.	TIME	NO.	TIME
○ OPERATIONS	14					
⇨ TRANSPORTATIONS	3					
☐ INSPECTIONS	1					
D DELAYS	3	3 Hr.				
▽ STORAGES	1					
DISTANCE TRAVELED	160 FT.		FT.		FT.	

JOB __Fill Out and Approve Repair Order__

☐ MAN OR ☑ MATERIAL __The Order Form__
CHART BEGINS __In Supply Cabinet__
CHART ENDS __On Way to Maintenance__
CHARTED BY __H. F. G.__ DATE _____

POSSIBILITIES

	DETAILS OF {PRESENT / PROPOSED} METHOD	OPERATION / TRANSPORT / INSPECTION / DELAY / STORAGE	DISTANCE IN FEET	QUANTITY	TIME	ELIMINATE	COMBINE	SEQUENCE	CHANGE: PLACE / PERSON / IMPROVE	NOTES
1	In supply cabinet	○⇨☐D▽							✓	Keep forms in desk
2	One set removed	○⇨☐D▽								
3	Taken to desk by A	○⇨☐D▽	20			✓				Not necessary
4	Filled out	●⇨☐D▽							✓	Redesign form
5	Placed in envelope	○⇨☐D▽			✓					Print routing on form
6	Addressed to B	○⇨☐D▽			✓					Not necessary
7	Placed in outbox	○⇨☐D▽								
8	Waited for mail boy	○⇨☐D▽		1hr						
9	Picked up	○⇨☐D▽								
10	Carried to B	○⇨☐D▽	40		✓					Not necessary
11	Placed in B's inbox	○⇨☐D▽			✓					" "
12	Waited for B	○⇨☐D▽		1hr	✓					" "
13	Picked up by B	○⇨☐D▽			✓					" "
14	Removed from envelope	○⇨☐D▽			✓					" "
15	Examined	○⇨☐D▽			✓					" "
16	Signed	●⇨☐D▽				✓	✓	✓		Have A OK minor repairs himself
17	Replaced in envelope	○⇨☐D▽			✓					Not necessary
18	Addressed to maintenance	○⇨☐D▽			✓					" "
19	Placed in outbox	○⇨☐D▽			✓					" "
20	Waited for mail boy	○⇨☐D▽		1hr	✓					" "
21	Picked up	○⇨☐D▽			✓					" "
22	Carried to maintenance	○⇨☐D▽	100		✓					" "
23		○⇨☐D▽								
24		○⇨☐D▽								

Fig. 4. A flow process chart illustrating a summary and analysis.

project groups to propose minor changes in layout or even a complete **rearrangement of facilities.** The work simplification approach brings about closer teamwork between the line organization and the plant layout engineer. Preliminary to a major project involving plant layout, a group discussion by those involved of the fundamentals of different **layout theories** sets the stage. The advantages and disadvantages of each are listed on a general basis, along with the broad factors which influence the eventual decision. After discussion of them, the specific case in point may be reviewed in detail and the actual policy of procedure established. The salient features reviewed in such a session on plant layout are as follows:

THEORETICAL EXTREMES OF PLANT LAYOUTS

Product-Controlled Layout	Process-Controlled Layout
Layout by product	Layout by process
Departmentalized grouping by required activities to complete entire product	Departmentalized grouping by like machines or activity
Continuous flow	Intermittent flow
Balanced operations	Batch method
Team effort (production line)	Lots
	Individual operations

The following typical list of possible advantages to look for under each type of layout was developed by one such project group:

ADVANTAGES OF PRODUCT AND PROCESS LAYOUTS

Product Layout	Process Layout
Less paper work	More flexible
Less handling	Less initial investment
Less dollars in process	Potential greater machine use
Easier production control	Less loss from any breakdown
Quality problems concentrated	Less difficulty from absenteeism
Less floor space	Less technical and management knowledge required
Easier scheduling	
Shorter over-all time cycle	Less of a balancing problem
Concentration of responsibility	Specialization by operation

The objectives of the discussion are, first, to understand the fundamentals behind the decision, and second, to make the decision which will give the most desirable combination of the advantages of both types of layout with the fewest disadvantages. Understanding by all concerned of the factors that underlie the decision leads to more effective application, once the layout is installed. This is particularly true of new products being put into production for the first time. Considerations which should play a major role in making plant layout decisions are:

1. Volume (how many for how long).
2. Control of design (flexibility requirements).
3. Nature of specific product (size, weight, etc.).

4. Laws and regulations.
5. Certainty of supplies.
6. Adaptability of existing equipment and facilities.
7. Adaptability of existing personnel (labor turnover, management know-how).
8. Comparative costs.

Workspace Layout and Motion Economy. One of the most important factors in the development of skill is the continued execution of an unhurried, repetitive sequence of motion which tends to form a smooth, effortless **habit path.** Those who produce at the highest levels of productivity appear to do so with little or no effort. This is the real difference between **speed-up** and **high-speed** work. The former is a hurrying of all motions, both the essential and the nonessential. The latter is attained by eliminating or reducing to a minimum all nonproductive motions and actually making more time available for a better quality performance of the "do." This is working "smarter" and not "harder." It is, in fact, easier.

Individuals left to their own resources rarely use the easiest method without special training or specific instruction. Their own efforts to increase output, particularly under the influence of a financial incentive, will usually result in "speed-up." It is easy to see how this results in increased fatigue and, therefore, lower morale and resentment. Work simplification proceeds on the basis that most people are working at a reasonable level now and that any increase in productivity from their effort must mean a more effective utilization of that effort. Their participation in the development of the improvements, their understanding of the basic principles involved, and their gratitude for being given the opportunity to participate in improvements should combine to raise morale, productivity, and cooperation.

The workspace and the motions of the individual at work within it constitute the area of activity in which the worker is most likely to be capable of making a contribution. This is his area of experience. He should be in a position to know more about it than anyone else. The fundamental principles of the workspace are based on the fact that there are only five different classifications of motion:

1. Finger motions.
2. Motions involving fingers and wrists.
3. Motions involving fingers, wrists, and forearm.
4. Motions involving fingers, wrists, forearm, and upper arm.
5. Motions which include all of these with the addition of a body motion or a change of posture.

A glance at the normal and maximum working areas diagrammed in Fig. 5 shows that the easiest motions are arcs or circles, which vary within the limits established by the dimension of the human body. A full analysis is given in the section on Motion and Methods Study.

Some basic **principles for effective motions** can be stated as follows:

1. Motions should be as **productive** as possible. The elimination of nonproductive motions is the first step.

2. Required motions should be performed within the **lowest classification** possible. Reaching can be reduced to a minimum by locating supplies and tools as near as possible to the normal working area. Any motion beyond the maximum or fourth class should be avoided if at all possible. The shorter the motion, the less time and effort it will take to perform it.

3. Motions should be **smooth and rhythmical.** Simultaneous motions of both hands in equal and opposite directions are natural, smooth, and easy. Different

kinds of motions performed at the same time will require more concentration, with resulting increase in fatigue, and reduce the time for the most rapid to that of the slowest. Abrupt changes in direction should be avoided by smoothing them to circular motions if possible. This point is easily demonstrated by having people

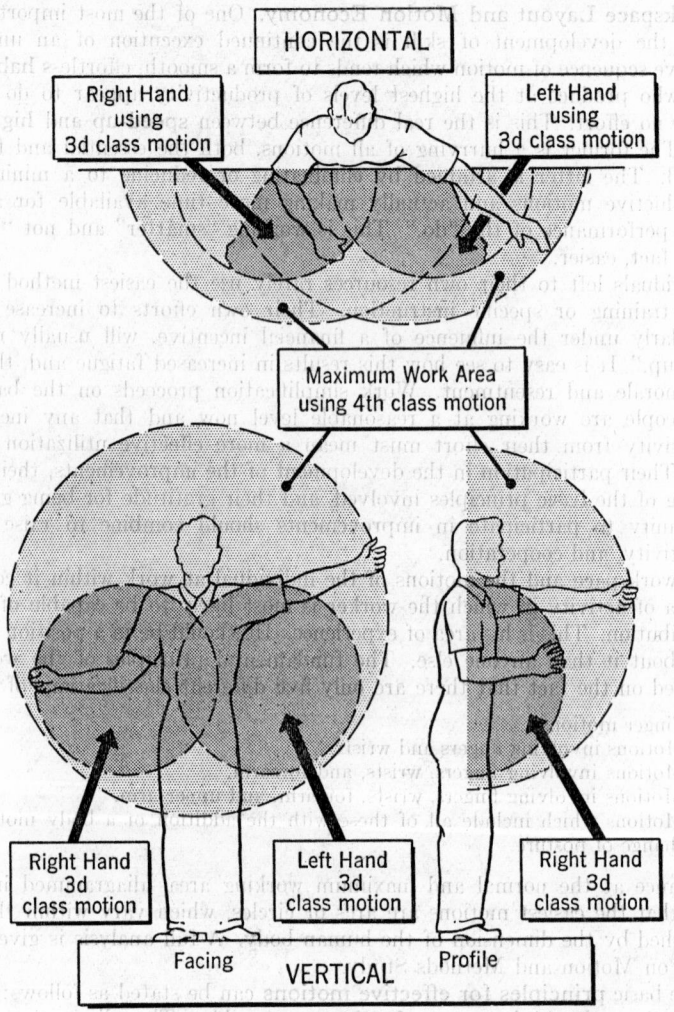

A. H. Mogensen—Work Simplification Programs

Fig. 5. Normal and maximum working areas for hand motions.

try to draw circles, then squares, then triangles. The circle, of course, is easiest. Attempts to draw a circle and a square simultaneously demonstrate the previous point.

4. Tools and materials should be pre-positioned whenever possible: Pre-positioning of tools and materials not only aids in consistently reducing the length of the motion, but minimizes the mental energy necessary. Habit makes the thought process virtually automatic.

Additional principles may be developed by discussion groups as they study their own workspace and motions. They should be encouraged to develop their own check list. Different wordings arise from specific cases. A typical **workspace and motion check list** follows:

1. Supply stations at proper levels.
2. Leverage at the best mechanical advantage.
3. Holding fixtures wherever possible.
4. Sliding grasps instead of pickups.
5. Pre-position for the next operation.
6. Foot pedals may often be useful.
7. Operator should be comfortable.
8. Workspace should be well lighted.

See the Right- and Left-Hand Check List for detailed questions.

Multiple Activity Check List. The multiple activity chart (Fig. 6) is a graphic representation of the coordinated activity of men, or machines, or both, in any combination. It may be used to represent the detailed activity of one man and one machine, one man and several machines, or just several men working as a team (see section on Process Charts). The information presented in the multiple activity chart is subjected to the same searching group attack as that in the flow or product process chart, through the work simplification pattern. Check lists made by each group to fit general conditions in their own organization arouse enthusiasm and catalyze specific ideas. One such follows:

1. Check list for **"do" details.** (Details themselves cannot be generalized because they are specific for each machine.)

a. Is this the right machine for the job?
b. Are we using the most up-to-date attachments and tools for the job?
c. Are machine speeds and feeds at a maximum?
d. Are the tolerances too tight or too loose?

2. Check list for **make-ready details.** (Generalized list; could apply to most machines; aimed at greater machine utilization.)

a. Can we have tools, materials, or blueprints brought out to the machine beforehand?
b. Can we have instructions accompany blueprints or specifications and see that they are faultlessly clear?
c. Where possible, can we have duplicate tools prepared or sharpened by someone else?
d. Can better planning reduce setups by making longer runs possible?
e. Can oiling be done on "off" shift or during lunch periods?
f. Can someone else lay out workspace during setup time?
g. Can machine be left running with safety?
h. Can someone else prepare materials?
i. Can a hopper feed be used to load machine?
j. Are we taking full advantage of guides and stops?

3. Check list for **put-away details.** (Generalized list; could apply to most machines; aimed at greater machine utilization.)

a. Can machine be left running safely?
b. Is a limit switch practical?
c. Can we use a drop delivery?

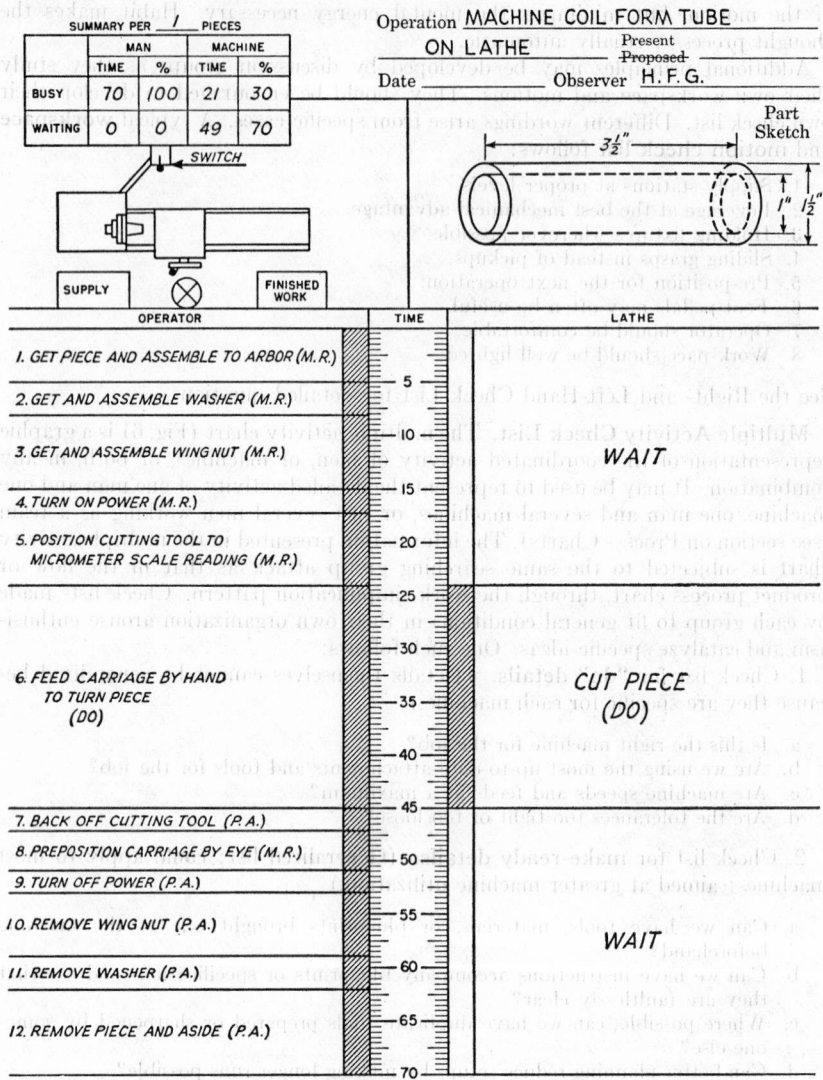

(M.R.: Make-Ready. P.A.: Put-Away.)

Fig. 6. A typical multiple activity chart.

    d. Can someone else inspect work?
    e. Will a chute do the transporting of parts to the next job?
    f. Can cleanup of scrap be done automatically during the "do"?
    g. Why is so much paper work necessary?
    h. Will longer runs result in fewer change-overs?
    i. Can someone else return tools and excess materials?

Right- and Left-Hand Check List. The right- and left-hand or operator chart is an analytic description of the motions of the two hands of an individual operator, as shown in Fig. 7 (Lake Placid Work Simplification Conferences). Like the multiple activity chart, it provides a space for the parts sketch and the workspace layout. In effect, it is a multiple activity chart of the two hands of an operator, although in its simplest form no time scale is included. Rather, the activity of the two hands is coordinated by simply recording what each hand is doing at any instant. Whenever a detail performed by one hand is recorded, that which is being done by the other hand at the same time is noted in the other column (see section on Process Charts).

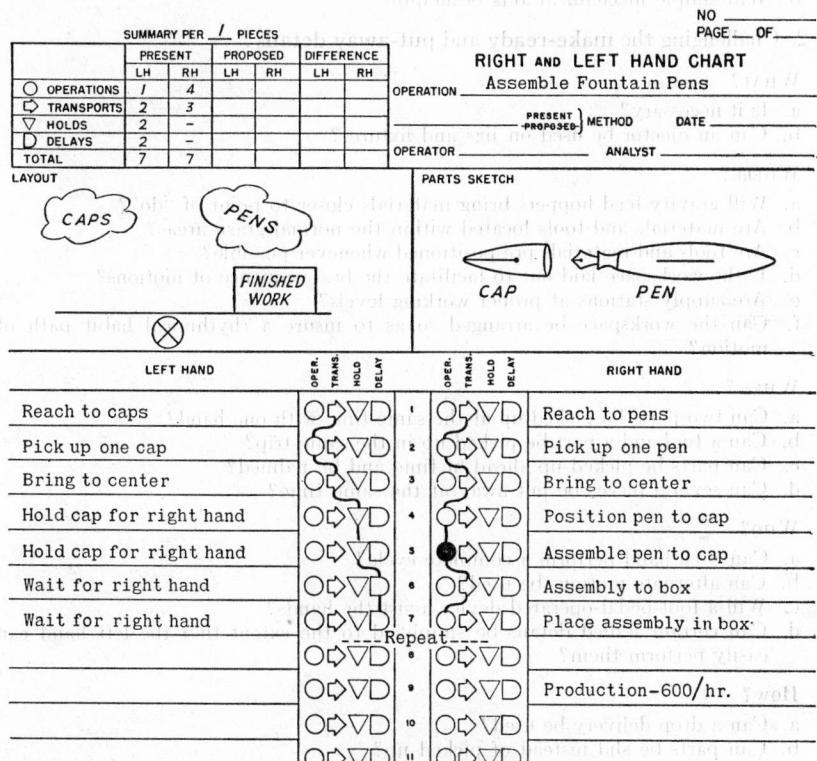

Fig. 7. A right- and left-hand chart using pre-printed symbols and showing workplace diagram and parts sketch.

The same Steps 3, 4, and 5 of the work simplification pattern are again applied just as with the other charts. Check lists developed by each group to fit conditions in their own plant are also helpful. A typical one follows:

1. Challenging the **"do" details:**
   WHAT?
   a. Is it necessary?
   b. Is there some other way of getting the same results?
   WHERE?
   a. Can the "do" be performed in a fixture or holding device?
   b. Is the "do" performed in the most convenient location?

WHEN?

a. Can the "do" be performed on several units at once?
b. Can the "do" be reversed?

WHO?

Are both hands performing "do" details?

How?

a. Are parts designed for easy performance of "do" details?
b. Will simple mechanical aids be helpful?

2. Challenging the **make-ready** and **put-away details**:

WHAT?

a. Is it necessary?
b. Can an ejector be used on jigs and fixtures?

WHERE?

a. Will gravity-feed hoppers bring materials closer to point of "do"?
b. Are materials and tools located within the normal grasp areas?
c. Are tools and materials pre-positioned whenever possible?
d. Is the workspace laid out to facilitate the best sequence of motions?
e. Are supply stations at proper working levels?
f. Can the workspace be arranged so as to insure a rhythmical habit path of motion?

WHEN?

a. Can two parts be picked up at the same time with one hand?
b. Can a tool and a part be picked up in the same trip?
c. Can parts be picked up ahead of time and be palmed?
d. Can several pieces be put away at the same time?

WHO?

a. Can each hand perform a complete cycle?
b. Can alternate motions be used?
c. Will a foot-pedal-operated device assist the hands?
d. Can certain skilled details be simplified to the extent that the left hand can easily perform them?

How?

a. Can a drop delivery be used?
b. Can parts be slid instead of picked up?
c. Is the lowest possible classification of motion being used?
d. Can a foot pedal simplify the detail?
e. Can a change in leverage be made to advantage?

MOTION PICTURES. The motion picture is an integral part of work simplification activity. Films become teaching media and vehicles of recognition and reporting, as well as records of progress. They greatly stimulate the interest of those who are in them, and concentrate thinking in one area in a way that no other technique seems to do. Groups of people can walk by an operation day after day in the office or on the production floor and not see possibilities for improvement. When the group is shown a two-minute movie of the same job, ideas explode like magic. **Magnetic sound stripping** as a sound recording technique adds other opportunities for the people on the job to participate. They not only see themselves, but hear themselves tell of the virtues of working more easily and economically.

Early films customarily showed the old method followed by the new. Today the trend is toward the **documentary** type of film which tells the story of the improvement. The emphasis is on the people involved and the things they tried and did. The failures along the way are no less important than the successes as part of the story. The mock-ups, the trial runs, and the transferred people are all put into the picture. The result is a human story of progress rather than a technical illustration of methods.

CONFERENCE LEADERSHIP AND PROBLEM SOLVING. Since work simplification is rapidly becoming group-oriented and emphasizes the organized team approach, effective leadership of the project group is a necessary adjunct to education in work simplification. Supervisors, as well as some hourly-rated employees, are being regularly included among those who receive instruction in this area while participating in the project's activities. For the upper levels of management, skill in project leadership is an absolute requirement.

Nelson states the step-by-step pattern for **practicing conference leadership,** which is extensively used in improvement projects where process charts are not practical, as follows:

1. The situation: What is unsatisfactory? Why be concerned?
2. The problem(s): define it specifically.
3. Possible solutions: to be arrived at by creativity and brainstorming.
4. Best solution: consolidation of best combination.
5. Summary, program of action: Who does what? When?

The similarity of these steps to the work simplification pattern is quite apparent, and they could be considered as merely a different wording. The important point is that they have the same thread of organization and participation running through them. They have been adopted as part of work simplification now for several years.

A Problem-Solving Procedure. Dunlap has designed a unique form for implementing the problem-solving procedure (Fig. 8). This is the result of many years of development by the participants in their own work simplification program. Many companies find that similar forms designed by their own personnel to fit their special needs are most effective.

WORK SIMPLIFICATION AND DESIGN. Project teams operating within the work simplification framework make improvements in the **design of new products,** as well as in already existing ones, by systematic review of each part in terms of its possibilities. Many companies schedule regular reviews of every product by specially organized task forces under the leadership of the engineering personnel responsible for the design. Such task forces include all levels of production people. Even those whose jobs are completely foreign to the problems of design make contributions. The questioning attitude in a "green light" atmosphere reveals numerous possibilities for such changes as elimination of parts, redesign for easier assembly, better end use of product or equipment, reduction in the cost of materials, and improved styling.

WORK SIMPLIFICATION AND STANDARDIZATION. Standardization of tools and equipment, component parts, and procedures can effectively be promoted by the work simplification approach. This is, perhaps, one of the most important vehicles for involving the engineer and technician in the work simplification program at their own levels. Standards, when established and energetically enforced, provide a variety of economies. Project teams at all levels respond in this area when given the opportunity.

LICK THE PROBLEM	DATE	DIVISION Vehicle	LOCATION	DEPT. Garage	BY	
OBJECTIVE	To cut down on pickup trips for parts					
WHAT IS THE TROUBLE?	CAUSES	CORRECTIVE ACTION	RESPONSIBILITY FOR ACTION ASSIGNED TO	DUE DATE	DATE COMPLETED	
Excessive trips into town to pick up material.	Shop men don't list all parts needed.	Foreman or assistant check list to see that it is complete	Foreman	1/15		
Three or four trips made on some days.	Outside locations not anticipating needs.	Schedule time for sending requisitions weekly.	Branch Foreman	1/15		
Should be one trip only.	Unnecessary "emergency" calls for parts.	Try to get parts locally first, then call in as early as possible.	Branch Foreman	1/15		
	Stockroom inventory incomplete.	Improve inventory.	Foreman	3/15		
	Incorrect part from supplier.	Closer check by pickup man.	Foreman	1/15		
	Wholesaler out of part.	Change source of supply.	Foreman	1/15		

USE REVERSE SIDE FOR COMMENTS, DIAGRAMS, ETC.

Fig. 8. Form to implement problem solving.

H. P. Hood & Sons

MORE EFFECTIVE TRAINING. Improvement means change, which requires retraining in the proposed methods. The process charts of proposed methods become effective **instruction sheets** useful to both supervisor and operator. Perhaps the greatest reduction in the tremendous nonproductive cost of retraining results from attitude changes on the part of those involved. Time invested in reviewing the work simplification philosophy and developing a cooperative atmosphere reduces the learning time considerably. The operator chart in a simplified form, without symbols and with several details grouped into word descriptions, becomes the best instruction sheet available for individual operations. Here is a simple example of five details of a left- and right-hand chart simplified for an instruction sheet.

Normal Detail	Condensed Statement
→ To nut ○ Pick up nut → Nut to fixture ○ Place on bolt ○ Tighten loosely with fingers	Get nut; assemble to bolt; tighten loosely with fingers.

Industrial engineers or time study personnel can cooperate with the work simplification program by using this simplified format in their time study work. Then charts are already made if project teams desire to review them for improvement or if the supervisor wants to instruct his people. The very act of making the breakdown for instruction or time study purposes in the form of a left- and right-hand chart may catalyze an improvement project.

WORK SIMPLIFICATION AND INCENTIVE SYSTEMS. It is difficult for a work simplification program to operate at all levels in a plant where incentives exist unless supervisors and workers alike have confidence in the management and the related systems. This is usually a problem of education. Time invested in developing understanding in this area will pay off not only in a better improvement program but in a better incentive system as well. The power of financial incentives is considered in many circles to be waning, but companies which have them now are not likely to eliminate them in the foreseeable future.

The simple realization necessary is that people live by the clock. All of us are time study men and women as we go about our daily lives. The plant could not run unless it was known how long it should take to do each task. Schedules, machine loads, delivery promises, labor requirements, purchasing rates, and capital requirements are just a few of the things which depend on time and expected performance. A simple graphic representation such as that shown in Fig. 9 is often helpful. The answers to each question, in Fig. 9, involve separate techniques, but they are related to the extent that each must build on the previous group, in descending order. In plants where an incentive program exists, the work simplification activity may be enhanced if people at all levels understand the difference between all of these techniques and the way they depend on each other.

WORK SIMPLIFICATION AND SUGGESTION SYSTEMS. In the early days of work simplification, a suggestion plan was encouraged as part of a program. Because work simplification is becoming group-oriented and suggestion programs are still for the most part directed at the individual, fewer new suggestion plans are being installed. Here, again, is a financial incentive which is beginning to wane in the face of the incentives of recognition, belonging and participation, and personal satisfaction which develop through work simplificaton. Where both programs now exist, they complement each other quite well. Increases in the improvement rate through work simplification stimulate individual initiative. The rate of suggestions submitted usually increases. Rarely do people hold back an idea in a group meeting so they can slip it in the suggestion box later. It usually becomes quite apparent that someone else will think of it anyway. Few companies pay for suggestions made by members of work simplification project teams who leave the job for the specific assignment of working on a project. Most people are so pleased with the opportunity to participate that the subject does not even arise.

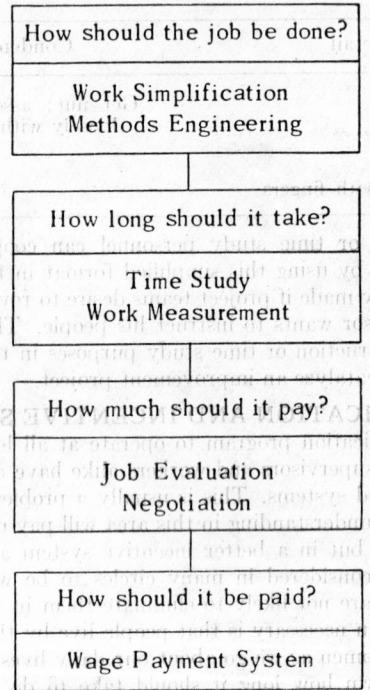

Fig. 9. Cardinal questions and answers.

The philosophy that everyone is responsible for improvement on the job he manages leaves little doubt that, in the long run, each must benefit in proportion to the progress of the company. More group-oriented incentive plans based on profits or productivity on a plant-wide basis are coming into existence. See section on Wage Plans and Controls.

A Program of Improvement

CRITERIA. Goodwin (Advanced Management, vol. 22) states that work simplification becomes an effective "program of improvement" within any organization when:

   1. Costs are lower and the quality of product or service is higher as a result of the coordinated efforts of everyone in the organization to achieve these results.

2. The men and women who make up the organization begin to develop personally at an accelerated rate as a result of the improvement process in which they are participating.

The errors which originally prevented the almost universal acceptance of motion study appear to be the same that plague scientific and technical progress today. So many of us assume that people will accept something new and useful on its merits alone, or that a simple "order" will put the results of new technical knowledge into profitable practice. In actual fact, it becomes increasingly evident that the development of methods for motivating people to understand and use new techniques and to develop a positive attitude toward the application of the results, and the organization of the entire work force to participate to the extent of their ability are by far the most important and the most difficult parts of our task.

A work simplification program is fun. It provides the satisfaction of being part of a team. It furnishes an opportunity for each person to participate to the extent of his ability. It satisfies man's natural desire to improve. It develops an organization which understands and believes that in the method of doing anything lies the secret of progress, and which applies this axiom not only to technical methods and the physical motions of doing a job, but also to the methods of management, leadership, and participation which bring about the enthusiastic use of any improvement. All results are achieved through a medium of communication which is acceptable to and utilized by the entire organization. This is a program of improvement within a framework of executive, supervisory, and worker development, based on a simple philosophy of understanding and teamwork.

PHASES IN DEVELOPMENT. Goodwin identifies three distinct phases through which such a program develops:

Appreciation. In the appreciation phase, the entire organization becomes aware of what work simplification is and understands its implications as it may involve them as individuals and eventual participants in the program. This becomes the key phase in the continuation of the program, by completing the circuit of communications and by constantly adding new grist to the mill.

Education. In the educational phase, the philosophy, the tools and techniques, and the procedures for application are developed internally by small groups using the conference method. The research point of view and the desire to experiment with methodology is the order of the day. Such an approach orients the thinking at the levels of the ability and responsibility of the people in any group. (This phase has been erroneously considered by many as the only phase and thus in many instances has been used as training alone. So employed, its effect is usually meager and short-lived compared to the constantly growing benefits from a complete program.)

Application. In the application phase, organized and continuous use of common-sense tools and techniques is made in order to develop and apply improvements at every level of the organization and in all activities. This is done through appropriate project teams within a policy framework created from within to fit the particular organization and circumstances.

EFFECTIVE COORDINATION OF THE PROGRAM. Goodwin presents these three phases graphically in the accompanying chart (Fig. 10). Here, perhaps, is an ideal composite of the latest thinking. Few organizations have done

The Three Phases of a Work Simplification Program

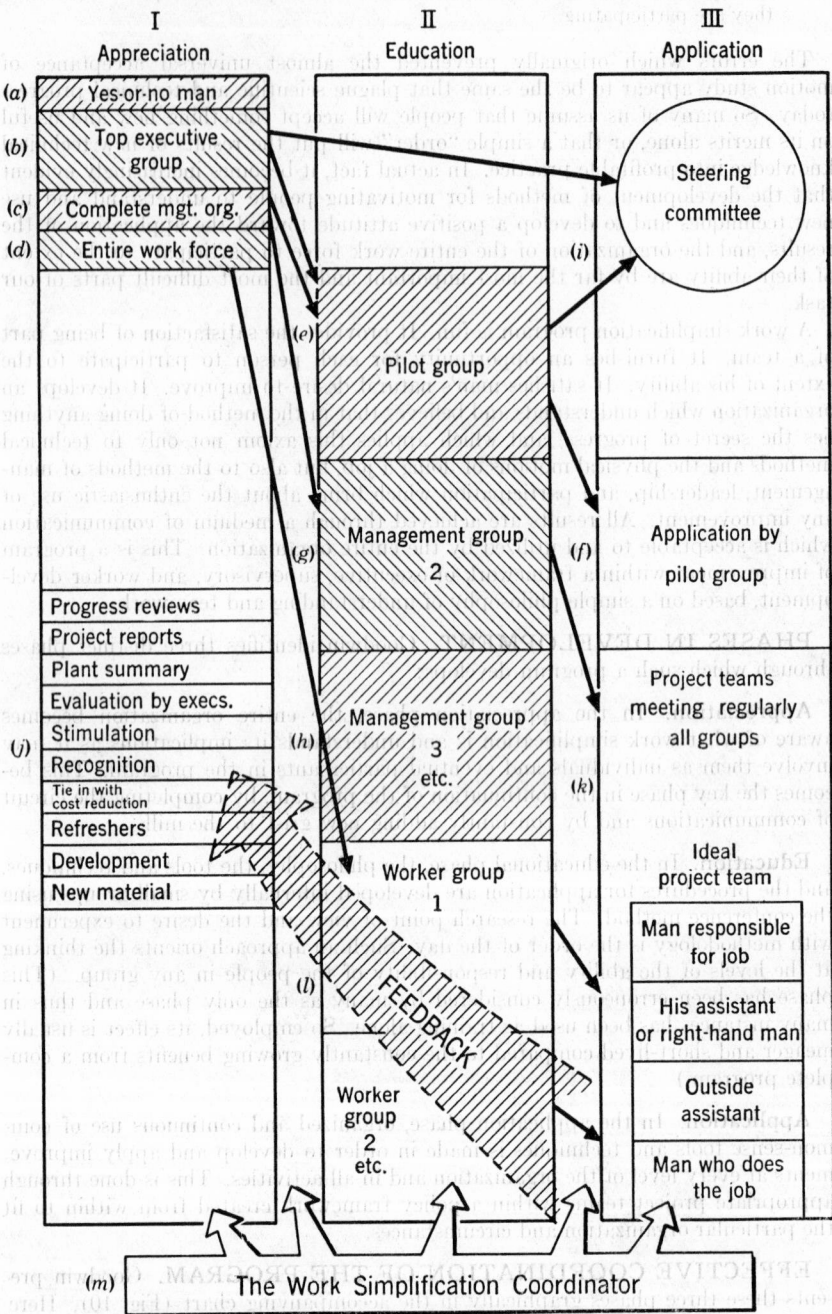

Fig. 10. Phases of a complete work simplification program.

all of it in one program but many are well on the way. Others intentionally are interested only in parts of the program, or take an entirely different approach. The chart is fully explained in the discussion below.

Yes or No Man. Every organization has one man who can say "yes" or "no" and mean it (Fig. 10, a). This may be the president, the treasurer, the chairman of the board, or a little old lady who owns 51 percent of the stock but never puts in an appearance at the place of business. In large corporations with many divisions, the **division head** may be the man who can say "yes" or "no," provided his operation stays appropriately in the black. He may be able to work quite independently of other divisions or of any central policy. Some companies are so organized that a **small group** is expected to make final yes or no decisions. Even so, one individual is often likely to dominate the group.

Whatever the specific situation, the so-called "yes or no man" must somehow find out about work simplification. He must become interested at least to the extent that he wants to learn more about its potential and how to go about setting up a program. This may occur in a host of ways. He may hear of it through someone in his own organization or read of it in a book or periodical. He may learn of it through a friend at a social gathering. He may listen to a convincing address on the subject or sit in on a management seminar where it is discussed. He may become acutely aware of work simplification through its successful use by one of his competitors. Appreciation must eventually permeate the entire organization, but it must begin at the top. This happens when the "yes and no man" wants more information and takes action to get it.

The Top Executive Group. The executive leadership of the organization as represented by the heads of each major activity usually make up the close advisors of the "yes or no man" (Fig. 10, b). They should have an opportunity to influence him in his decision with respect to the advisability of proceeding with work simplification and should participate in any preliminary review and evaluation of it.

This top management team should take whatever steps it can to be as well informed as possible. A three-day session away from the usual place of business is perhaps ideal. One day is a typical compromise. Anything less reduces the possibility of real appreciation accordingly. This meeting is often led by a specialist in the field or a man from within the company who has made a thorough **survey** of work simplification programs in general. Perhaps, in the latter case, he may have taken a special course of study for that purpose.

The subject matter usually consists of a development of the basic philosophy of improvement as utilized in work simplification, a brief review of the tools and techniques employed, and a summary of the three phases of the program as set forth here. The final moments are reserved for a **problem-solving conference** on the advisability of proceeding and, if it seems advisable, how best to do it. The usual result is agreement of those present to experiment with a "pilot group" through the education and application phases in order to evaluate the program more effectively in the light of the specific needs of the particular organization. Appreciation sessions for the organization as a whole (Fig. 10, c and d) are also discussed at this juncture and are scheduled if they appear desirable.

Complete Management Organization. Initial **appreciation sessions** for the entire management organization (Fig. 10, c) are usually limited to a two-hour informative presentation and are often scheduled as an evening dinner meeting. Large organizations often find it easier to arrange the presentation during working hours by planning for two or more sessions. One portion of the management group attends, while the other covers the supervisory needs of the operations; then, vice versa. An evening dinner meeting, however, usually arouses more interest and attaches greater importance to the new activity. Executive preference usually decides this point.

The importance of the initial meeting lies in the fact that it exemplifies the work simplification approach. It is preferably opened by a few words from the "yes or no man." All hear about the proposed program at the same time. "Grapevine" interpretations of unknown activities are therefore minimized—a most important point. Interest and enthusiasm are aroused as much as possible. If a group is small enough, most of the basic work simplification philosophy can be developed during this meeting. Everyone hears that the top executives have participated in an appreciation session and were impressed to the extent that they have approved **experimentation with a pilot group** (Fig. 10, *e* and *f*). This group will begin regular discussions soon and will be followed by other groups if its discussions prove to be successful.

The group hears that progress of the pilot group and the program as a whole will be publicized to the greatest extent possible. A motion picture may be shown as an illustration, and the fact that films will be used may be announced at this time. This group should be notified of the appreciation session for the entire work force if one has been scheduled. Union officers and stewards are often invited to this session as a preview of the work-force session or in lieu of such a session.

Entire Work Force. Appreciation by the entire work force (Fig. 10. *d*) takes on a different degree of importance. The confidence that this group needs in the management in order to supply understanding and cooperation may well depend on the willingness of the "yes or no man" to schedule this meeting or arrange appropriate publicity. People invariably mistrust what they do not understand, and rumor can sometimes twist the facts so that they are unrecognizable. This is particularly true if a few people have unaired grievances.

A meeting of the entire work force at one time or by departments or shifts for about a half-hour appears to be the most effective means of informing workers of the program and soliciting their interest, participation, and cooperation. Such a meeting would review a little of the work simplification philosophy, what it is, and equally important, what it isn't. All get the same first-hand story. They hear of the previous executive and management appreciation sessions and of the decision to experiment with the pilot group. They learn that work simplification is being tried as a long-range improvement and development program that must benefit everyone if it is to be successful. They become familiar with the opportunities they will eventually have to participate in the program. They are assured that they will hear of the progress of the program as it develops. Motion pictures, bulletin boards, and house organs will all become useful **supplements to direct communication.** Actual educational sessions may be scheduled later on (Fig. 10, *l*). Movies may be taken of workers and they may be asked to sit in on some of the early experimental project discussions if they are involved in the activity.

This meeting is the step in the early stages of a work simplification program which is most often omitted. It is quite difficult to implement in the larger plants because of the numbers of people involved and, sometimes, inadequacies of facilities and geography. The cost is often considered too high this early in the program, since there has been no major return from work simplification thus far. When work simplification becomes established, meetings are occasionally scheduled to report on progress.

Alternatives to such a meeting are available in the form of **reports** in the house newspaper or monthly. Sometimes a special issue is prepared to announce the new program. Since work simplification has been set up thus far only as an experimental program and is being tried out only by the pilot group, some executives feel that they should hold back any publicity other than that fact alone. Inadequate early publicity will usually place a heavy responsibility on the supervisory staff. The success of the program may well hinge on the effectiveness of their explanations.

Pilot Group. The "pilot group," usually limited to from 12 to 16 men, is preferably composed of department heads or the **operating leadership** of each area of activity (Fig. 10, *e*). It should include at least one or two of the top executives in order to maintain a continuity between the original appreciation sessions and the pilot experiments.

This group reviews in detail all of the **educational material** which may be used in subsequent sessions by other groups. It participates in the development of the work simplification philosophy, experiments with the use of the tools and techniques, and reviews typical programs of application as developed by other companies. Its schedule typically consists of 15 to 20 meetings of approximately 2 hours duration spaced about a week apart. Some companies are experimenting with fewer but longer sessions spaced farther apart.

The principal responsibility of the pilot group is to analyze critically the material presented with a view toward redesigning it to fit their own organization. So that each participant may have an opportunity to "try out" work simplification as a part of this procedure, each is requested to select five or more operations or activities which seem to need improving or appear to him suitable for experimentation. Subsequently, each member of the group is expected to practice on one of these, thus actually becoming involved in the improvement process at the same time that he is learning about it.

During this exercise, each individual collects all of the pertinent facts about his own project and presents them to the rest of the group. In so doing, he uses the work simplification approach and those tools of analysis which the group has thus far discussed. These usually include the work simplification and problem-solving patterns, the flow process chart and flow diagram, films, and existing reports of any kind which are already available in the particular organization involved. After the data thus collected have been reviewed by the group as a whole, it selects three or four of the projects for further study. **Three- or four-man teams** then concentrate on these projects during the remaining sessions. Actual situations thus become the vehicle for discussing each new tool or technique, and involve the group in the human relations problems incident to the use of these procedures as well. The projects not selected become a backlog for future study.

The teams of three or four also meet apart from the main group between each scheduled session, and a portion of each scheduled session is devoted to progress reports, review of any difficulties encountered, and creative suggestions by the entire group. Films of these small group meetings along with those of the actual activity are effective in adding interest and enthusiasm, and in addition provide catalysts for creative thinking and a means for documenting the progress. Sound supplied extemporaneously by the people appearing in the pictures adds a most effective measure of participation and recognition.

How to proceed most effectively becomes the main subject of discussions as the participants begin to orient their thinking toward the problems involved in useful application of the results of their efforts. This leads to their final session, which naturally becomes a problem-solving conference directed at organizing themselves into the application phase, establishing **committees** to reorient material to be presented to succeeding groups, and scheduling **progress review meetings,** at which time the pilot group will reconvene to check on its own effectiveness.

Experiences of other companies are often brought into the discussion as guides or possible alternate approaches. The group is normally quite willing to accept one of these as an experimental procedure. Members usually feel that they will be in a much better position at a later date to establish their own specific policy. This is a very desirable situation, since it produces a condition of flexibility requiring constant review. This effectively leads the way to subsequent organization of the **steering committee** (Fig. 10, i).

Application by the Pilot Group. Application by the pilot group usually involves experimentation with a few more projects from the list of those previously charted but not studied during the educational phase (Fig. 10, f). Project team groupings become a matter of personal preference rather than the "ideal project team" (Fig. 10, k), since often those in the pilot group may not be directly responsible for the activities they select to study. This very fact usually emphasizes the need of educating the entire organization, meanwhile informally involving everyone concerned with any particular project.

These new project teams meet on their own at times they schedule themselves. It is desirable to set up a procedure for **circulating minutes** of such meetings to all members of the pilot group and to require the scheduling of the next meeting before adjourning. This policy provides excellent control over duplication, establishing good liaison between all members of the group and reducing the likelihood of a few being "just too busy to get at it."

Approximately once a month, the group may reassemble as a whole to hear the progress of each team, review any new films they have taken of the activities under study, and have a round of creative discussion on all aspects of each project. Such meetings lead the way to regular review sessions, with reports of progress becoming the agenda of the meeting (Fig. 10, j). The implications of the review session take on added importance as the second management group (see Additional Management Groups, below) nears the completion of its education phase and prepares to join the pilot group in application. Need for new plans for organizing the application activity becomes apparent as this situation develops.

Additional Management Groups. The second management group is usually made up of the right-hand men of those participating in the pilot group (Fig. 10, g). Often, they are selected by the pilot group as it finishes its own educational sessions. They participate in a similar series of **educational discussions,** which incorporate whatever revisions have been proposed by their predecessors.

There is rarely any major change in the subject-matter of the discussions. Rather, the recommendations usually call for more or less weight on certain topics or sections as they appear to affect the particular situation. Increased emphasis is quite regularly requested in the area of human relations, particularly among the upper levels of management. The way is generally left open for the groups that follow to continue to edit the material. This is highly worthwhile on the basis that it gives every group an opportunity to participate in the development of the program. Since there is new material appearing all the time, it becomes a very convenient arrangement from the point of view of adding new grist to the mill and setting up the need for later refresher sessions (Fig. 10, j).

All members of the second group, and of ensuing ones, are requested to select five or more jobs or activities which appear to them to need improving. These they use in the same manner as the pilot group did. Each member chooses one from his own list as a **practice subject** about which to accumulate all the facts. A few of these subjects are then selected by the experimental project teams. The remainder become a backlog as the group joins the previous one in the application phase. These experimental project teams have the advantage of **counsel** from members of prior groups. They are encouraged to seek assistance in this area, since it initiates the eventual liaison necessary for transition to the application phase.

In essence, each group receives the same treatment as those preceding, except that their final discussions can now be developed out of what has been previously established. The subject of the final session is always the identical theme, "How can this group best merge with the previous ones in an organized program of application?" Once again, there is actual participation on the part of the people who are close to the job. Since the programming procedure remains flexible, each group has a chance to influence the direction in which it will move. Policies set up by previous groups and approved by the steering committee (Fig. 10, i) become a base line. Major changes are rarely recommended, but it would be still more unusual for any group to fail to produce some useful innovation in the procedure.

It may be desirable to bring the pilot group or the steering committee into session to review these recommendations if they are at all radical in nature, or if it appears appropriate in order to give some recognition to those who are responsible for them. This can add a generous measure of team spirit for all who have participated in the development of the program thus far.

This same format is used with each succeeding management group until everyone in the organization has participated in the basic educational phase. Their backlog of "activities which need improvement" becomes a regular source of new project material as they join previous groups in the application phase.

Application by Later Groups in Organized Project Teams. As each new group moves from the educational phase to the application phase, a new opportunity to reorganize for the most effective procedure becomes available. New project teams can be immediately set up to include the new men. Since these are often assistants to previous group members, the ideal project teams (Fig. 10, k) can begin to take shape in some instances. With teams set up on a **vertical basis** within the organization, it becomes easier for upper levels of management to delegate the more detailed work to those who now join them.

Since it is expected that innovation will continue even within the improvement procedure, the atmosphere of research and experimentation is maintained constantly. The questioning attitude and the creative approach are exemplified. New lines of communication are more readily established and old ones are freed for more effective use. As the number of people involved increases, the need for progress reporting and liaison between teams becomes obvious. Published **lists of projects** being studied and the participants on each team keep everyone abreast of activity. It affords executives an opportunity to pass along a word of advice with respect to the importance of one project over another or to add suggestions of their own. They are often in possession of information which may well affect the activity under study, and which they might not normally communicate to lower levels unless they knew of the work through publication of these activity lists. It also allows executives to participate more regularly by giving them the opportunity to add an item or two to the list if they choose to do so.

As **organized application** begins in earnest, it rapidly becomes apparent that the people actually doing the job have an important role. They can most effectively be drawn into the program early in the application phase on an informal basis. Films taken of the activities under study afford a convenient opportunity to do this. Portions of the project teams' discussions may be held right on the job so as to include the workmen involved, or the workmen might be brought into the meetings occasionally. Some means of including them must be found, since a more formal introduction to work simplification must naturally wait until all of the supervisory personnel have participated and the regular worker program (Fig. 10, *l*) can be set up in turn.

Steering Committee. The steering committee is a natural outgrowth of the pilot group's activities (Fig. 10, *i*). It fills the need for establishing broad policies of procedure and for keeping the top executives informed early in the program. This committee is appropriately composed of two or three of the top executive group, preferably including the "yes or no man," in addition to two or three members of the pilot group. The most likely candidates are those who have shown the most enthusiasm and by their actions have indicated a desire to see the program effectively utilized.

This committee now becomes a small, effective team of executives whose responsibility it is to see that the company gets the greatest benefit possible. They should meet regularly to **review** the over-all progress of the work simplification program, **evaluate** its effectiveness, and **clarify** policies with respect to long-range aspects. In the early stages of the program they may wish to meet quite often. Later, once or twice a year is a typical meeting schedule; or they may meet only when requested to by the staff member (Fig. 10, *m*) who has the full responsibility of leading work simplification within the company. Since members of the steering committee are high-level policy-makers, they back the program with prestige and authority and render needed executive recognition. It is through this group that the feedback procedure (Fig. 10, *j*) is initially set up. They also supply needed top-level counsel if any difficulties should arise that involve interdepartmental relations.

Feedback. The feedback portion of the work simplification program (Fig. 10, *j*) completes the **circuit of communication** which began with the "yes or no man" when he first indicated his interest. At regular intervals, reports of progress, statements of dollar or man-hour savings, or summaries of accomplishments are necessary if interest is to be continued. Of equal importance is the need for top-level recognition of the results obtained.

One company holds a monthly progress-review dinner which is attended regularly by each department head. If he cannot be present, he sends a representative in his place. (This group is essentially the original pilot group, or those in the same positions.) All of the top executive group are invited and at least two put in an appearance at each meeting. All persons, including workers, who have participated in projects which have been completed during the last month are also invited. Appearance at the dinner becomes a form of recognition. The after-dinner schedule includes an introduction of each individual who is present for the first time, as well as a word or two from the top executives. This is followed by a review of completed projects with those participating in each telling the story. Any films which may have been taken are shown as part of the presentation. An open discussion usually follows the review of each project, which invariably leads to more projects' being added to the list. A **progress summary** for the year to date is passed out to all those present and circulated to all regular members and the top executive group. This report lists the projects by department, the number undertaken, those completed or discarded, and the man-hour or dollar savings.

There are many other approaches used by various companies. The plant newspaper or magazine is used in some instances. One big department store has a "President's Luncheon" similar to the dinner meeting described above. The president himself always attends. Some feel that less fanfare is more effective, and written reports are simply circulated to interested parties. All successful programs have one thing in common—a realization at the top that the circuit must have complete continuity, that the lines of communication must be open, and that new activity must be stimulated by top management recognition.

Annual **refresher sessions** are scheduled in numerous instances, even though they are not always necessary if everyone is continually participating in the program on an active basis. One company has every person who has ever participated in the educational phase return to the conference room for one full day each year. These persons bring their reference material up to date, discuss the latest developments in the field, and lay plans for their activity in the coming year. This is a constant appreciation procedure.

As programs develop, many of them are integrated into the routine procedures of the plant operation. If a cost-reduction program and/or a suggestion plan exist, most companies tie work simplification in with them. Sometimes companies even initiate such programs to stimulate activity.

The Ideal Project Team. The ideal situation is one where everyone is constantly participating in the improvement process, each to the extent of his ability. The initiative should be in the hands of the man in charge of the activity, and he should be using the most powerful forces for improvement available to him, that are economically appropriate for the particular project. The line organization is emphasized on the basis that staff service functions are desirable and should be requested by the line to the fullest extent available. The ideal project team (Fig. 10. *k*) would then consist of the man responsible for the activity, his right-hand man or assistant, outside assistance, and the man who does the job.

For example, a supervisor wants to improve the production flow through several operations in his department. His logical team might include, besides himself, his assistant foreman, one of the industrial engineers, and the men who are actually performing the operations. The work simplification philosophy brings the foreman to realize that, in addition to the contributions of his own right-hand man, the **different frame of reference** of someone else like the industrial engineer plus that of the men on the job should provide better results and more enthusiastic acceptance. If a new piece of equipment is being considered, the outside point of view might be supplied by a sales engineer of the equipment manufacturer or a technical expert from the mechanical engineering department.

The bigger and more important the project, the higher the level of brains within the organization that should be brought to bear on it. An open mind and experience with creativity among all people lead the man in charge to seek out ideas from everyone who could help. He should make sure that he gives all an opportunity to participate who should be interested in doing so, and he should take the responsibility on himself to create that interest.

It is not always possible to have the best possible team work on any specific project. Often a team is not necessary at all, as in the case of a mechanic arranging his own workspace. An understanding of the need for priority and a constant review of project lists develops into a policy of **delegating** more and more activity down the line as the organization improves its ability and warrants more confidence from above. The project teams change their character as the capacity of each individual becomes more fully utilized. The trend is one of getting closer to the actual doing of the job.

Worker Groups. Some companies balk at the idea of the hourly work force participating in the educational phase on a formal basis (Fig. 10, *l*). There is no doubt that an effective job can be done informally by enlightened and enthusiastic first-line supervision. But we rarely find this type of supervision where executives refuse to allow experimentation at least with a small portion of the work force.

Formal worker participation in the educational phase, while not normally as productive in tangible dollars saved as participation at higher levels of influence, none the less has almost always produced some gratifying results. The very fact that management has considered workers important enough to include in the program has had a marked effect on attitudes and feelings toward the company. Improvement in this area comes with understanding, which is the basis of the work simplification philosophy.

Worker series vary greatly in their content from plant to plant. In some companies, it would appear quite natural that because of their narrower sphere of influence the hourly-paid employees would be given a much narrower version of the basic work simplification material. In others, top management insists they receive exactly the same treatment as management people.

People who read the same papers, listen to the same radio programs, vote for the same representatives in government, can and do understand the simple philosophy of work simplification. If enthusiastically led to apply it on their own jobs, they will do so, if not inhibited by fears of insecurity or criticism from their fellow workers. This is neither allowing people on the job to run the business, nor asking permission of employees before making changes and improvements. It is part of an organized procedure of utilizing all of the brains available.

Workers who have participated in a formal educational series in work simplification for the most part find new interest in their jobs. They look forward to participating in improvement activity which involves them. The successful application of whatever improvement is made depends greatly upon their willingness to make it work.

The Work Simplification Coordinator. The work simplification coordinator (Fig. 10, *m*) is the man who has the detailed operation of the program as his full-time responsibility. He is preferably selected from within the organization. **Qualifying prerequisites** are his interests, his previous training, his knowledge of the plant and its people, and his desire to do the job. He may need **special training** to prepare him for all phases of the activity, but this can often be gained by attending any of a number of courses offered by many colleges and universities or by specialists in the field.

The need for this man becomes acutely apparent early in the appreciation phase, when the "yes or no man" is just getting interested or the top management group is discussing how to proceed with the pilot group. Often a delay is necessary at this stage until the man selected has time to prepare himself to lead such a group. In some cases, professional assistance is used during the early stages and the coordinator is trained along with the pilot and second management groups, and then assumes control.

The coordinator's **responsibilities** include such things as leadership of the educational conferences, scheduling project group meetings, taking motion pictures, compiling or editing progress reports, maintaining projects lists, and compiling plant-wide summaries for evaluation by the executive group. He is a member of the steering committee and keeps that group informed of the state of the program. He **reports** in many instances to personnel, industrial engineering, the comptroller, the vice-president, or the president. The important point is not where he reports in the organization but the implication of that fact in terms of how broad a field he is allowed to cover effectively. If he works out of the industrial engineering department or manufacturing office and this does not limit him to the factory alone, it can work quite well. On the other hand, if any major functional line in the organization avoids representation in the pilot group or succeeding groups, it may be necessary to transfer the coordinator's official reporting to the president's office or to the comptroller in order to give him the needed initial prestige.

In large plants employing several thousands, there may be several men on the work simplification staff, since many groups may be working simultaneously. This activity has been used by numerous companies as an **executive development area**, since it exemplifies improvement-mindedness in an atmosphere of teamwork. In smaller plants, the work simplification coordinator may even take on other duties as the program moves into the application phase and essentially all of the personnel have participated in the educational phase.

Work simplification is an effective program of improvement because it functions in an environment of friendliness. It develops a philosophy of improvement through teamwork and understanding together with the personal development of the individual. It gives each man an opportunity to participate to the extent of his ability. What may be the proper procedure in one organization may not be so in another. Each organization must find out by actually studying its own situation.

WAGE PLANS AND CONTROLS

CONTENTS

PAGE

Purpose of Wage Incentive Plans

Labor productivity and wage incentives 1
Types of wages 1
Incentives and their effects 2
 Nonfinancial incentives 2
 Financial incentives 2
 Cost of a work measurement program 3
 Savings in direct labor costs 3
 Savings in factory burden 3

Basic Elements of Wage Incentives

Standards defined 4
Task and pace 5
 Incentive and normal pace 5
 Deviations from pace 7
Agreement on standards 7
Size of the bonus 7
Efficiency 8
Principles of wage incentives 9
 Setting proper standards 9
 Activity plateau 10

Wage Incentive Administration

Administrative concepts 11
 Motivation 11
 Measurable work content 11
 Measurable output 11
 Effort and output 11
 Bonus determinant 11
 Quality control 11
 Quantity multipliers for exaggerated ratio
  defective (f. 1) 12
 Incentive formulas 12
 Typical bonus 13
 Bonus restriction 13
Correction of standards 13
Allowances 14
Nonincentive assignments 14
 Incentives for experimental work 14
 Separation of daywork and incentive work 14
Bonus periods 15
New standards 15
Supervisory participation 15
Incentive accounting 16
Time study functions 16
Minimum records 16
 Source of reports 16

General Classification of Work

Appropriate wage plan for type of work 16

PAGE

Standard repetitive operations (Class 1) 16
Variable working conditions (Class 2) 17
Limited rates of production (Class 3) 18
Output not economically measurable (Class
 4) 19

Analysis of Wage Plans

Key to symbols 19
Daywork (time rate) plan 21
 Application of daywork plan 21
 Daywork plan formulas 22
 Straight daywork and standard hour
  plans for normal task standards (f. 2) 24
 Straight time or daywork data for Fig.
  2 (f. 3) 25
 Characteristics of unmeasured daywork .. 25
Measured daywork 26
 Characteristics of measured daywork 26
 Measured daywork formulas 27
Differential time (or multiple daywork) plan
 with bonus step or steps 27
 The minimum guarantee 27
 Standard levels 28
 Applications of differential time plan 28
 Differential time plan formulas 28
 Differential time plans with single-step,
  gradual bonus, and the Gantt task and
  bonus plan using high task standards
  (f. 4) 30
 Data for differential time plans and
  Gantt task and bonus plan for Fig. 4
  (f. 5) 31
Differential time plan with gradual bonus .. 32
 Modified differential time plan formulas .. 32
Differential time plan with loss of bonus ... 32
Gantt task and bonus plan 33
 Applications of Gantt plan 33
 Gantt plan formulas 34
 Characteristics of the Gantt plan 34
Monetary piecework plan 34
 Characteristics of piecework plan 35
 Minimum rates 37
 Piecework plan formulas 37
 Piecework and standard hour plans,
  normal task standards (f. 6) 38
 Data for piecework and standard hour
  plans for Fig. 6 (f. 7) 39
Standard hour plan 38
 Standard hour plan formulas 39
 Characteristics of the standard hour plan 41
Halsey constant partial sharing plan (Halsey
 premium plan) 41

CONTENTS (*Continued*)

PAGE

Halsey plan formulas 42
Halsey 50 percent constant sharing plan, low task standards (*f.* 8) 45
Data for Halsey 50 percent constant sharing plan for Fig. 8 (*f.* 9) 46
Characteristics of the Halsey plan 44
Constant sharing plan (40-60) 47
Constant sharing plan (40-60) formulas ... 47
Sharing plan (40-60) for beginners, liberal beginners' task standards (*f.* 10) 48
Data for sharing plan (40-60) for beginners, for Fig. 10 (*f.* 11) 49
Characteristics of the (40-60) constant sharing plan 49
Bedaux point plan 50
Bedaux ratings 50
Bedaux 75 percent sharing plan formulas . 50
Bedaux 75 percent sharing plan, using 60-B standards (*f.* 12) 51
Data for Bedaux 75 percent sharing plan for Fig. 12 (*f.* 13) 52
Bedaux 100 percent plan 52
Machine applications 52
Adaptation to large machines 54
Variable conditions allowance 54
Bedaux 100 percent plan formulas (including VCA) 54
Bedaux full sharing with variable conditions allowance, normal task standards (*f.* 14) 56
Data for Bedaux full sharing with variable conditions allowance for Fig. 14 (*f.* 15) 57
Rowan variable sharing plan 57
Basic Rowan plan formulas 58
Basic Rowan variable sharing plan, average of Rowan mixed task standards (*f.* 16) 60
Data for basic Rowan variable sharing plan for Fig. 16 (*f.* 17) 61
Modified Rowan plan 61
Modified Rowan plan formulas 61
Modified Rowan variable sharing plan, normal task standards (*f.* 18) 62
Data for modified Rowan variable sharing plan for Fig. 18 (*f.* 19) 63
Characteristics of basic and modified Rowan plans 63
Summary of basic wage plan application.... 65
Other wage incentive plans 65
Emerson efficiency-bonus plan 66
Barth variable sharing plan 67
High piece-rate plan 68
Taylor differential piece-rate plan 69
Merrick differential piece-rate plan 70
Effect of guaranteed minimum wages 71
Relative performance levels 72
Relative efficiencies for wage ratio of 1.25 at high task (*f.* 20) 73
Different bonus for incentive performance 73
Relative efficiencies for wage ratio of 1.20 at high task (*f.* 21) 73
Choice of plan according to the standards 74

Group Incentives

Application of group incentives 75
Group leadership 75
Group size 75
Ratio of increased earnings for remaining members of group who maintain full output when 1 member is absent (*f.* 22) 76

PAGE

Group administration 77
Comparison of principal characteristics of individual and group incentive systems (*f.* 23) 78-79

Learners' Allowances

Progress in learning 80
Apprentice record showing theoretical and actual efficiencies (*f.* 24) 81
Learners' allowances in groups 80
Example of learners' allowances in groups 82
Other incentives for apprentices 83

Payroll Calculations

Time records 83
Entrance-clock card 83
Daily time sheet 83
Order and route sheet 84
Group summary sheet 84
Extra standard time allowance 84
Individual pay summary sheet 84

Supplementary Incentives

Incentives for quality of product 84
Quality bonus for office work 85
Quality bonus for production inspectors .. 86
Incentives for reducing material waste 86
Waste bonus applications 86
Defective quality and waste 87

Incentive Plans for Indirect Production

Characteristics of indirect labor 88
Choice of incentive method 89
Application to stores and stock room 89
Application to materials handling 90
Application to maintenance and repairs 91
Details of maintenance incentive plans in eight companies (*f.* 25) 92
Incentives for inspection 93
Monetary budgets as group standards 94

Incentive Plans for Supervisors and Executives

Cost-saving and profit-sharing plans 95
Cost-saving plan for supervisors 95
Profit-sharing plan for executives 96

Plantwide Cost-Saving Plans

Nunn-Bush plan 96
Scanlon plan 96
Rucker share-of-production plan 97

Guaranteed Wages or Employment

Methods for providing security 97
Effect of guaranteed wages or employment.. 98
Advantages and disadvantages of guaranteed wages or employment 98
Supplementary unemployment benefits 99
Example of guaranteed annual wage 99

Installation and Termination of Incentive Plans

Installing a new plan 100
Discarding incentive plans 100
Failure of incentive plans 100

WAGE PLANS AND CONTROLS

Purpose of Wage Incentive Plans

LABOR PRODUCTIVITY AND WAGE INCENTIVES. Statistics have shown a rather well-fixed economic balance in the distribution of the sales dollar among the major functions of an enterprise. Labor's share of the sales dollar or **value added in manufacture** remains practically constant, seldom varying by more than 2 or 3 percent of the sales dollar within an industry. On this basis, certain companies have successfully administered **fixed-ratio wage plans** for many years.

With this normal economic balance, **increase in productivity** or output per operator-hour is the only way to provide more sales dollars for distribution to all factors of production, including labor. Employers can contribute to greater output by providing increased capital investments in equipment and facilities and improved management. The individual employee's contribution must be in more efficient use of available facilities if he is to improve his economic status. However, there is little inducement for an employee to produce much more than the minimum output required to retain steady employment when he is working strictly on a time basis for a fixed wage rate. But, if a reasonable standard or **price for each unit of output** is paid, most employees will respond to the opportunity for greater earnings, exert greater effort, work more effectively, and produce more units. Under a **direct financial incentive plan,** the employee, in effect, goes into business for himself, while the employer provides the necessary capital facilities and becomes a ready customer of the employee's services or products.

TYPES OF WAGES. Total wages may be considered to consist of three segments: a guaranteed minimum or base wage, a production bonus, and additional indirect or fringe benefits.

The **base wage** is the market or going wage which must be paid for the skill and ability which the employee must possess to perform an acceptable amount and quality of work. Although affected temporarily by many local and immediate factors, in the long run the base wage is established by the supply of, and demand for, available labor. In modern industries, however, base wages usually are determined or justified through labor-market surveys correlated with job-evaluation procedures.

The **production bonus** is an extra reward which is paid for extra performance beyond the acceptable minimum for which the base wage is paid. Usually it is closely related to measured output and is administered most conveniently through some form of a direct financial incentive plan customarily affecting individuals or small groups.

The **indirect or fringe benefits** may include such items as company-paid employee life and accident insurance, hospitalization, unemployment insurance, sickness benefits, entertainment or social facilities, annuities and pension plans, and current or deferred profit-sharing payments. Although many of these functions can be treated as items of **expense** when conducted as formal programs, they are actually means of distributing company profits.

Company profits are made possible through efficient production, good management, technological improvements, and a combination of fortunate physical or economic circumstances which contribute to the over-all earnings of the enterprise. All the profits cannot be distributed as wages. To maintain a competitive market position and thereby provide continuous employment, it may be necessary to create additional sales through reduced selling prices. Some of the earnings must be distributed to stockholders as a reward for the use and the risk of their investments. The company must usually retain some of the earnings for expansion or working capital.

Since company profits are the result of the combined efforts of the entire employee group, any excess earnings (after meeting the above obligations) may well be distributed to all employees as a reward for their efforts. But **profit-sharing bonuses** in the form of annual lump-sum payments are so far removed from, and so indirectly related to, the extra efforts which the employees remember expending that they are relatively ineffective as direct inducements toward increased efforts. Accordingly, it has become increasingly feasible for companies to use such funds for improving the general economic status of their entire employee groups through fringe benefits such as insurance programs, stock purchase plans, and other forms of deferred payments. Such programs tend to improve employee morale, loyalty, and stability. They too, however, are so far removed from day-to-day activities as to have little immediate effect upon individual employee productivity. They are therefore classified as indirect benefits, outside the scope of this discussion of direct financial incentives.

INCENTIVES AND THEIR EFFECTS. An **incentive** is that which incites, or tends to incite, to action, and may be any type of stimulus which induces a person to put forth increased effort. There are many types of stimuli or rewards, some of which are quite tangible, such as increased monetary earnings, but many are intangible satisfactions which are extremely difficult to evaluate.

Nonfinancial Incentives. Nonfinancial incentives include many of these **intangible satisfactions**, such as: patriotism; a feeling of duty or responsibility; loyalty in return for favors; self-respect; satisfaction in accomplishment or in meeting a prescribed goal; desire for leadership and potential promotions; desire for additional training or experience; pride, or shame, resulting from the publication of performance records; spirit of competition; desire for recognition and prestige; praise from superiors, or flattery from equals or subordinates; gratitude for superior working conditions; natural response to good leadership and supervision; and fear of losing the security of employment or social position. Under certain conditions, these are strong incentives, although not directly associated with any financial reward. But they are emotional in nature and therefore tend to be temporary and variable in effectiveness. Certain combinations of these intangible incentives are ever present and cannot be replaced successfully by purely financial inducements, but they do not possess the same continuous inducement as direct financial rewards correlated closely with measured productivity. Generally, therefore, highest productivities will be obtained under intelligent administration of appropriate direct wage incentive plans.

Financial Incentives. Direct wage incentive plans usually reduce costs. They can be used wherever a reasonably standard labor content can be established for an operation and where the amount of acceptable output can be measured, but the wisdom of using such plans depends on potential economies. As indicated under the definitions of low task and of normal pace (see Basic Elements of Wage Incentives below), average productivity under typical daywork conditions tends to be only about 83.3 percent of normal productivity. The mere establishment and use of proper **normal standards** provides reasonable goals which even daywork operators will strive to meet under the influence of good supervision and other nonfinancial inducements. Therefore, particularly on manual activities over which operators have more or less direct control, **productivity increases** up to about 20 percent above typical daywork conditions can be reasonably expected. In other words, in a company of 100 direct labor employees, the same total output as obtained under old daywork conditions could be expected with only 83 employees working under standardized and measured conditions, and a payroll savings equivalent to the wages of 17 workers would be effected.

Cost of a Work Measurement Program. Several items must be included in the costs of a work measurement program. Let the annual wages of one average operator represent 1 unit of direct labor payroll; thus 100 employees represent 100 **units of payroll.** One capable methods-and-standards engineer should be able to establish and maintain good standards for 100 incentive workers, even in a jobbing shop with a considerable variety of operations. It should be possible to obtain such a person at a salary about equivalent to three times the wages of an average operator, or for 3 units of cost.

To keep time and production records, a shop time clerk or junior standards engineer may be required at a salary equivalent to 2 units. Secretarial assistance will involve about 1 unit. Because the type of inspection that is tolerated under daywork conditions may not be adequate for a good work measurement program, increased inspection costs may account for 2 units. If actual wage incentives are used, additional payroll clerical costs probably will be equivalent to at least 1 or perhaps 2 units.

Savings in Direct Labor Costs. Administrative costs therefore will be about 10 units, or 10 percent of the direct labor payroll. This should be adequate for most jobbing shops with a wide variety of operations and frequent changes of products. The costs will be considerably lower for well-standardized processes or mass-production plants. With gross direct labor savings of 17 units, but with an additional administrative expense of 10 units, a good **work measurement program** should effect a net saving of 7 units or 7 percent of the previous daywork direct labor payroll; and, because work measurement encourages closer attention to methods improvements, much greater savings are probable.

From this analysis it is seen that reductions in direct labor costs alone are likely to be nearly double the extra administrative costs. These savings are the result, not of requiring operators to work harder, but rather of reducing or eliminating excessive avoidable delays and thereby raising productivity from a low task to a normal level where "a fair day's work actually is obtained for a fair day's (base wage) pay."

Savings in Factory Burden. The savings in factory burden resulting from the introduction of a work measurement program may be even more significant. A large portion of a company's factory burden (overhead costs) tends to be fixed, and practically all the burden costs remain relatively constant at least for short periods. If it is assumed that a work measurement program would increase productivity by 20 percent (from low task to normal), then each dollar of burden costs is distributed over 120 units where formerly it was distributed over only 100 units. Thus the burden cost per unit of output is reduced to 100/120 or 0.833 (83.3 percent) of the former rate, effecting a saving of 0.167 (16.7 percent) in unit burden costs. Thus, if a company's **burden ratio** is as low as 1.00 (100 percent) of the direct labor cost, the reduction in burden cost is equivalent to 16.7 percent of the direct labor payroll. But much higher burden ratios of 2.00 to 3.00 (200 to 300 percent) are more typical, and in such cases, a 20 percent increase in productivity would effect a burden savings equivalent to 33.3 to 50 percent of the low task, direct labor costs.

The introduction of a wage incentive plan results in additional burden savings. Under the inducement of a potential reward for extra performance, typical operators will exert greater effort. Experience indicates that the increase from a **normal** pace to a reasonable **incentive** pace tends to effect an increase of about 25 percent in output, and this should be rewarded by a corresponding 25 percent increase in wages. Assuming a monetary piecework incentive plan for simplicity, the operator's earnings are increased, but the labor cost per unit of output remains constant, the same as at **normal productivity.** Thus, after the savings from a work measurement program are effected by raising productivity from low task to normal levels, further reductions in unit **direct labor costs** are not likely to result merely from a piecework incentive program.

However, this additional 25 percent increase in productivity from wage incentives effects an additional 20 percent reduction in unit burden costs which is equivalent to 20 percent of the daywork level payroll for each 100 percent of the burden-labor ratio.

These various potential savings from work measurement and wage incentive programs may be summarized as follows:

Factory burden (overhead) in percent of low task, direct labor costs	100%	150%	200%	300%
1. Probable savings in direct labor costs from work measurement but without wage incentives	17%	17%	17%	17%
2. Possible cost of maintaining a work measurement and wage incentive program.........	10%	10%	10%	10%
3. Net direct labor savings from work measurement without incentives (1–2)	7%	7%	7%	7%
4. Savings in burden from work measurement without incentives	16.7%	25%	33%	50%
5. Savings in burden from additional influence of wage incentives	20%	30%	40%	60%
6. Total savings, as a percent of the original low task, direct labor payroll (3 + 4 + 5)...	43.7%	62%	80%	117%

These are conservative estimates of results obtainable from modern industrial engineering practices and intelligent administration of work measurement and wage incentive programs. From this analysis it would appear economical to use wage incentives in all situations where work content can be determined and where accomplishments can be objectively measured.

Basic Elements of Wage Incentives

STANDARDS DEFINED. A standard is a unit of measurement indicating a specified level of operator performance. It may be expressed as the specified amount of output within a given amount of time, such as **units per hour;** when thus expressed, the term **task** frequently is used. For payroll calculations, however, it is usually more convenient to express the standard as the amount of time allowed (or budgeted) for each unit of output, thus giving rise to the term **standard allowed time** or such other expressions as **hours per piece** (or per hundred) or **minutes per piece.**

Ideally, standards should be set uniformly so that all will reflect a level of operator performance that can be recognized and accepted as a universal basis for comparison, but in practice this is not always feasible. In some situations rough estimates may be quite acceptable as standards. Some operations may be so well standardized and controlled that standards can be calculated quite scientifically and with great accuracy. In other operations the work content or the material is so variable, or the output is so inaccurately measured, that tight or precise standards are unworkable.

TASK AND PACE. High task refers to a rate of output which reasonably should be expected, day after day, without physical or mental impairment, from a typical operator who is physically able, mentally capable, properly trained and experienced in the general kind of work or trade, familiar with and accustomed to following a prescribed routine on a standardized operation, and well motivated by the opportunity of receiving a suitable reward, usually financial. This level of performance frequently is referred to as the **incentive pace.**

A few operators regularly may exceed this level of performance, but rarely by more than about 50 percent. Some less capable operators may have difficulty in maintaining this pace. But the majority of operators, who are suited to the work and well motivated, should have no difficulty in maintaining the level of performance reflected by high task standards. When an operator meets high task requirements by working at an incentive pace, he should be rewarded by a suitable bonus in addition to his base wages. Opinions of what constitutes a suitable bonus vary from 20 to 35 percent of base wages.

High task standards typically will result where, or if: operations have been subjected to careful motion analysis; all useless activities have been eliminated and the necessary elements have been standardized in the most economical sequence; equipment, tools, and materials are standardized, uniform, and maintained in good condition; surrounding working conditions are favorable; the operators are properly trained and experienced in the prescribed methods and are working under well-motivated conditions (generally under an effective incentive plan); careful time study procedures are followed; and typical operators, working under the above conditions, are given **performance rating indexes** close to unity.

Incentive and Normal Pace. Incentive pace is the most reliable concept of effective operator effort to which other concepts can be related. Ideally, therefore, it should be given a **numerical index** of 1.00 (100 percent). This is done in many installations where high task standards are used. But, if a 25 percent bonus were paid for incentive performance, the total wages would be 1.25 (125 percent) of the base wages. Accordingly it is much more common practice (but not universal) to assign a numerical index of 1.25 (rather than 1.00) to indicate incentive performance. The rare performance of the **exceptional operator,** which experience indicates may be about 150 percent of the incentive pace, then would be indicated by a performance rating index of 1.25×1.50 or 1.875 (187.5 percent).

Normal pace, or normal performance, stems from the concept of the most popular form of output wages in which the operator receives a full 100 percent share of all time saved when output exceeds standard. It is the level of performance which normally should be expected, in return for which properly evaluated base rate wages are paid. It assumes the same general operator qualifications as described under high task, except that the operator is assumed not to be similarly motivated by the opportunity for extra reward for extra performance.

For convenience, normal pace is generally assigned a numerical index of 1.00 (or 100 percent) and indicates an expected performance level of 1.00/1.25 or 0.80 (80 percent) of a true incentive pace.

The average normal work pace probably is closely equivalent to the momentary, nonmotivated, work pace of the daywork operator. But, under the inducement of established goals and measured output, unnecessary delays are avoided, and the operator who maintains the normal pace throughout a majority of the work day may be expected to produce approximately 1.00/0.833 or about 1.20 times as much output as a typical daywork operator.

Normal task refers to a standard indicating a rate of output obtained from a typical operator working at a normal pace. For a given operation, the standard **number of pieces per hour** typically would be 1.00/1.25 or 0.80 (80 percent) of the number for a corresponding high task standard, while the standard allowed **time per unit** would be 1.25 (125 percent) of the high task standard. Thus it is assumed that motivated operators readily will exceed **normal task standards** by about 25 percent and thereby will earn a 25 percent bonus.

Low task refers to a standard indicating a rate of output usually obtained under typical daywork conditions where: supervision is not particularly close and the operators are left chiefly to their own devices; no definite output goals are established for specific operations; accurate records of operator output are not kept; and frequent unnecessary delays or interruptions are tolerated. Frequently such standards are obtained by averaging past performance records obtained under such nonincentive conditions.

Such levels of production are subject to wide variations, but for this discussion the typical low task level of output will be assumed to be at 0.833 (83.3 percent) of normal output, which becomes 0.833/1.25 or 0.667 (66.7 percent) of incentive output. Correspondingly, low task standard times will be 1.20 (120 percent) of normal task times and will be 1.20 × 1.25 or 1.50 (150 percent) of high task standard times.

Lytle (Job Evaluation Methods, 2nd ed.) has developed a table for converting from one task level to another, relating the low task scale to the intermediate (or normal) and the high task scales. Another calculation of the relationships between task levels, more consistent with the relative pace concepts developed in this section, is shown in Fig. 20.

Occasionally a partial sharing incentive plan is found where **past performance records** were used as the standards for the original installation, yet modern time study procedures were introduced later. In such cases, the time studies yield normal or high task standard times; but, for use in the existing wage plan, these normal or high task times are multiplied, respectively, either by 1.20 or by 1.50, thereby loosening the standards to the equivalent of low task performance requirements.

Daywork pace may be defined as the average work pace maintained under typical daywork conditions which would be required just to meet low task standards. Daywork operators are permitted, or involuntarily are subjected to, many and often extended delays which contribute greatly to a low average level of output. During his periods of actual work, the typical daywork operator momentarily will work at a natural pace which probably is close to normal, but, because of his many avoidable delays, his average work pace over the entire work-day will be lower, or perhaps about 83 percent of normal.

Perfect or ultimate performance, attainable only by a very superior or expert operator, is a concept which can be defined and occasionally illustrated, and on which experienced observers will closely agree. The nearer an actual performance approaches this ultimate level, the closer will be the agreement among observers as to the level of the observed performance. Conversely, the lower the perform-ance. or the greater its deviation from the ultimate, the greater will be the disagreement among observers as to the actual level demonstrated.

Deviations from Pace. The difficulty of finding the actual level of perform-ance deviating considerably from the ultimate is well recognized by most experi-enced engineers. Cyrol has indicated repeatedly the relative ease with which agreement is obtained from union representatives on the incentive pace and the difficulty in securing agreement on the extent to which any slower pace deviates from the incentive pace. Segur (Motion Time Analysis) states that the time for a given motion, when performed by an expert, is a constant. Sylvester (Hand-book of Advanced Time-Motion Study) says, ". . . there is no limit to the exces-sive delays that can actually occur. In other words, the maximum performance rates . . . are quite inelastic, but the minimums are very elastic."

Other authors suggest the need for similar precautions but relate the deviations to the normal rather than to the high task pace. Niebel (Motion and Time Study) states, "The speed rating scale usually covers a range from 0.50 to 1.50. Operators performing outside this productivity range . . . may be studied, but it is not recommended. The closer the performance is to normal, the better will be the chance of achieving the true normal time." Morrow (Time Study and Motion Economy) says, "Tests have proven that when the operator's performance level is very low, his rating becomes difficult to determine. The same applies to the operator working at a high production level—it is just as difficult to adjust his time to normal." Shumard (A Primer of Time Study) says, "A Time Study Man generally finds it easier to study and rate operators working at 60 or more [a rating of $60 = 100$ percent normal] because he does not have to reconcile so many erratic movements, delays, and other factors that occur in large numbers in demonstrations by workmen who receive less than 60 ratings . . . he will find it more difficult to rate below 50." (A 50 rating is equivalent to 83 percent of normal.) It appears, however, that these three authors neglect to recognize the incentive pace as a possible basis for setting standards and accordingly direct their attention to the normal pace as the basis for all standards.

AGREEMENT ON STANDARDS. Since the establishment of standards depends to some degree on judgment and arbitrary decisions, it is important to reach a reasonably close agreement among the persons concerned as to the level of performance which the standards supposedly represent. Thus, if one level of performance can be agreed upon, other levels can be related to it by definition. Although the incentive pace is considerably below the possible ultimate, it is probably the **highest level of performance** which reasonably and realistically can be expected day after day from typical trained and well-motivated operators, and on which experienced observers will agree most closely.

SIZE OF THE BONUS. Some authorities are convinced that a 20 percent bonus is adequate to induce an incentive pace, particularly if coupled with proper supervision. Furthermore, an intelligent graphical comparison of the several wage plans can be made only by assuming some fixed bonus percentage as a reward for incentive performance. Accordingly, several earlier published comparisons such as that by Lytle (Wage Incentive Methods) are based on the 20 percent concept. Cyrol supports this concept; and Emerson, in his empiric efficiency-bonus plan, used a 20 percent bonus at (high) task.

The bonus must be large enough to induce true incentive performance, yet not so large that typical operators will be satisfied with bonuses received for lower levels of performance. The original Knoeppel, the Bigelow, and the Bedaux 75 percent sharing plans all used 25 percent. The Bigelow-Knoeppel curve used 30 percent. The trade unions of England stipulated that "a workman of average ability shall be able to earn 33.3 percent above the time rate of his grade." Presgrave (The Dynamics of Time Study) says, "In the Province of Ontario, in which the writer's personal experience mainly lies, there is a minimum wage law for women. It has been found that as soon as earnings potentials under ordinary piece-work fall below a level of 25 percent above the legal minimum, there is a tendency for operators to be satisfied with the minimum. . . ." He continues, "Also, we have seen that the incentive will diminish in effectiveness if the average earnings are not 30 percent greater than the guaranteed earnings." Carroll (Time Study for Cost Control) states, "I would use the one-for-one plan that pays 100 percent premium for good work in excess of standard with an expectancy of 25 percent incentive." A bonus of 25 percent of base wages currently seems to be the general consensus of a proper reward for incentive performance; therefore the 25 percent concept will be the basis for most of the illustrations presented here.

EFFICIENCY. As used in this discussion, efficiency is simply a calculated numerical ratio indicating the relative extent to which an operator's measured output exceeds or falls short of the specified output indicated by whatever standard is used. It may be calculated as the ratio of:

$$\frac{\text{Actual output (actual units per hour)}}{\text{Standard output (indicated units per hour)}}$$

or, as shown later under Key to Symbols, it is more often calculated as the ratio of standard time produced to actual time taken.

A calculated efficiency ratio is not an absolute measure of performance. Standards may be set tight, as with **high task standards** which require an incentive level of performance to meet them; or they may be set to reflect normal performance; or they may be set loose, as with **low task standards.** A given level of actual performance therefore may yield a relatively low calculated efficiency from tight standards, or a relatively high calculated efficiency from loose standards.

Owing to wide variations in industrial situations, it may not be possible, feasible, or economical always to set standards of equal tightness. Some types of work readily lend themselves to high degrees of standardization and control where accurate measures of work content and of output are readily attained. High task standards are possible and quite typical in such cases. Company policy or precedent may dictate the use of normal or low task standards. Some types of work are of such a nature or are so variable in work content and potential rates of output that low task standards are either unavoidable or advisable.

Since all production standards cannot be set with equal accuracy or tightness, it obviously has been necessary to devise different types of wage incentive plans that would be suitable for use with different standards and in different work situations.

PRINCIPLES OF WAGE INCENTIVES. As compared with salaries, daywork wages, or other forms of straight **time payment plans,** wage incentive plans often are classified as **output wage plans.** Unfortunately this term implies that all incentive wages must be in direct proportion to the quantity of output, or that all bonus wages must be in direct proportion to the quantity of output which is in excess of a stipulated quantity or standard. Actually this is a fallacious concept which leads to great misunderstanding and many abuses and failures in wage incentive administration.

Probably the most important and **fundamental principle** of wage incentives is that wage incentive bonuses are additional rewards for extra performance above a standard which requires a "normal" level of effective operator effort and for which a properly evaluated hourly "base rate" is a suitable and typical remuneration.

Recognition of this principle raises at least three problems:

1. A sound structure of **base rates** must be established which will be accepted as proper remuneration for the qualifications that operators must possess in order satisfactorily to perform the assigned tasks of their occupations.
2. Reasonable and proper **standards of performance** must be established, preferably reflecting a "normal" level of effective operator effort, for which the base wage rates are to be paid.
3. An appropriate **formula** for calculating bonuses must be selected or designed, and specifications of administrative procedures and regulations must be established, whereby operators will be rewarded with extra earnings as nearly as possible in direct proportion to their extra effective effort or actual contribution to production, although not necessarily in direct proportion to measured output.

Setting Proper Standards. The wage incentive plan must be suitable for the standards and working conditions with which it is used. Emphasis is on **effective operator effort** rather than on the measured amount of output. Operators tend to balance their total earnings against the amount of effort they are willing to expend to obtain those earnings.

An operator may produce a specific item on one machine at the rate of 100 units per hr. With the same level of skill and effort, another operator may produce an identical item on a different machine at the rate of 200 units per hr. The higher rate of output from the second machine may be due to a different process, management decision or ingenuity, and a higher capital investment to which the second operator made no personal contribution. It is entirely possible that the **attention time** on the second machine has been reduced sufficiently to just balance the extra manual effort involved in handling the additional 100 units, so that the actual effort is identical on both machines. In such a situation the benefits of the higher rate of output must accrue to the company function which made them possible. Certainly it is not feasible that the second operator should enjoy twice the earnings of the first. In fact, if the levels of skill, responsibility, and effort on both machines are identical, the earnings similarly should be identical if inequities are to be avoided. Care must be taken, however, to insure that **manual time** and **effort** actually are the same in both situations.

In too many cases, standards are set carelessly for machine operations which permit the operator to be idle during a significant portion of the cycle. At a later time, improvements in control or method permit higher machine speeds which shorten the cycle. The operator is then required to handle more parts in a given period. If the available **idle time** is more than adequate for this additional handling, there is a temptation to expect the operator to perform the extra work with no increase in the **standard time** allowed. Presumably this process legitimately could be continued until all idle time is eliminated. But, with a precedent established for paying bonus on the idle time, the increased handling requirement appears as unwarranted "speed-up" and has been the source of many employee grievances.

In one such case of increased machine speed the standard time was properly increased to correspond with the increased manual effort, but the union demanded that the standard be increased in direct proportion to the increase in output. The arbitrator ruled that the standard had been correctly adjusted and accordingly denied the union's demand. This illustrates the need for setting all original standards on **man-machine cycles** for the amount of manual work required, and for providing a bonus opportunity on the manual time but not on the idle time. Then, if manual elements are increased, the standard can be adjusted to correspond. Since this provides a bonus opportunity on a greater portion of the operator's elapsed time, there tends to be much less resistance to the change. See analysis of the Bedaux plan for further discussion of this point.

In some man-machine operations, such as punch-press stamping, the operator must perform a definite sequence of motions on every item. Some activities, such as loading and unloading the machine, may be performed externally. Other activities may be performed internally while the machine is in actual operation. If the machine time exceeds the internal time, some **idle operator time** remains. The cycle may be shortened in at least two ways. The machine may be run faster, or the motion sequence may be rearranged by transferring external elements to internal elements. Both methods increase the ratio of the manual time to the cycle time, and, if all idle operator time is eliminated, the ratio becomes 100 percent. Obviously this would be the ideal situation.

Activity Plateau. An interesting phenomenon became evident in the Selby Shoe Co. As stamping cycle times became shorter and shorter, there appeared to develop a practical maximum number of parts which the operators were willing to handle. In other words, there seemed to be a **plateau in parts handling** beyond which the operators would not go although the task otherwise would not be arduous. One explanation is that the operators had reached the degree of expertness where, as Segur states, the motion times were constant. Another view is that a point of balance had been reached where any additional reward available was not sufficient inducement for the additional effort required, and a different type of incentive would be necessary.

Practical administration of wage incentives requires the use of some objective measure of operator productivity. Ordinarily the number of units of output of acceptable quality provides a reasonably satisfactory, and the most objective, measure. But quantity alone, even at a uniform level of quality, is not always an accurate measure of the operator's effective effort or contribution to production.

Not all standards accurately or uniformly reflect the desired normal level of operator effort above which bonuses should be paid. Thus it becomes the responsibility of the industrial engineer and management to select or design that type of wage incentive formula which, under the existing conditions of available standards and output measurements, most nearly will reward the operator in direct proportion to his effective effort or actual productivity.

Wage Incentive Administration

ADMINISTRATIVE CONCEPTS. An almost endless list could be prepared of principles or concepts that could be considered significant in the effective administration of wage incentives. The following paragraphs include some of the more important principles.

Motivation. No wage incentive plan will be effective unless the persons affected are **positively motivated** by the desire for extra earnings. In some cases nonfinancial or intangible rewards (or penalties) may be more effective in promoting (or limiting) production. It appears that this fact has contributed to a lack of popularity of wage incentives in some highly unionized trades.

Measurable Work Content. To place an operation or activity on incentive, it must be possible to determine, to standardize to some extent, and to measure the work content of the activity in terms of time per unit of output, cost, budget, or other **unit of measure** that can be used as a standard with which actual accomplishment can be compared.

Measurable Output. The output or **accomplishment** must be objectively measurable in terms of some acceptable, although perhaps arbitrary, unit. This unit should be the same as, or conveniently converted to, that for which the standard is established.

Effort and Output. There must be some **determinable relationship** between the operator's effort and the measured quantity of output, although this often is not a directly proportional relationship. Occasionally this relationship may not be consistent during short periods, although it must average out to a consistent relationship over long periods. This is particularly true in certain mechanized operations or where uniform working conditions cannot be maintained.

Bonus Determinant. The **increase in the reward** (bonus) should be approximately proportional to the increase in the operator's effective effort, regardless of the amount of increase in actual measurable output.

Quality Control. Quality standards and measurements must be established and enforced. This is such a simple and common assumption that its importance often is overlooked. Occasionally, high quality is erroneously assumed to be inherent in nonincentive work and, conversely, low quality often is blamed on wage incentives. It is quite true that any inducement to increase quantity tends to exaggerate or emphasize the need for suitable quality control that had existed under nonincentive conditions. However, experience has shown that **quality control programs,** properly integrated with wage incentives, have brought about significant improvements in average quality levels. (See examples cited under Incentives for Quality of Product.)

Quality is integrated automatically with production incentives if the quantity credited to the operator includes only that amount of output which meets the quality specifications. Where products are 100 percent inspected and sorted, the proper quantity to be credited is easily obtained.

If products are inspected by **sampling techniques,** one of the available statistics usually will be the ratio defective, which is the ratio of the number of defective units to the total number of units produced. The number of acceptable units to be credited to the operator would be the actual output multiplied by "1.00

minus the ratio defective." (For more information on sampling techniques and ratio defective, see section on Quality Control.)

Frequently some **average ratio defective** is established as standard, and the total quantity produced is credited to the operator if the actual ratio defective does not exceed the standard; or an additional bonus may be given for superior quality by crediting the operator with a quantity that is greater than actual production. For example, if 3 percent defective is standard and the operator produced a "lot" with only 1 percent defective, the quantity credited may be 2 percent greater than actually produced. Conversely, if the actual ratio defective were 10 percent, the quantity credited would be 7 percent less than the quantity produced.

If high quality is particularly important, the crediting factor may be some **exaggerated ratio defective.** The deviation of the actual ratio from the standard may be multiplied by some constant such as 2, 5, or 10, according to the circumstances. Frequently the crediting factor is exaggerated by some power, for example, the square of the deviation of the actual ratio defective from the standard. Fig. 1 gives **quantity multipliers** for a system using the square of the deviation of the ratio defective from a 3 percent standard.

Actual % Defective	Deviation from 3% Standard	(Dev.)^2	Quantity Multiplier
1	2	4	1.04
2	1	1	1.01
3	0	0	1.00 (Standard)
4	1	1	0.99
5	2	4	0.96
6	3	9	0.91
7	4	16	0.84
8	5	25	0.75
9	6	36	0.64
10	7	49	0.51

Fig. 1. Quantity multipliers for exaggerated ratio defective.

Employees and unions tend to oppose severe penalty systems because a positive incentive is more palatable than, and often just as effective as, a punitive one. The ratio defective to be used as a standard of acceptability should be established after careful consideration of both cost and psychological factors. A penalty system for low quality should be installed only after thorough explanation to the employees affected.

INCENTIVE FORMULAS. The type of wage incentive formula should match the conditions. It should be selected, adjusted, or designed with due regard for the type of work involved, the relative tightness or looseness of the standards, and the relationship between the output as measured and the operator's effective effort. No one formula is suitable for all types of work or conditions, nor are all wage incentive formulas suitable for a single set of conditions. Relatively few companies have such a limited range of working conditions that a single wage plan would be suitable for all operations. The wise selection of appropriate wage plans often is sacrificed on the false assumption that the use of more than one plan unnecessarily would complicate payroll calculations. Through the use of simple tables of **efficiency and bonus ratios,** bonus calculations can be made simple and identical for all incentive plans.

Typical Bonus. All incentive plans should pay a typical bonus for true incentive performance. The typical bonus may vary from 20 to 33 percent, but a figure of 25 percent has been adopted for use in this discussion. High task is the one level of performance that is most typical for incentive workers and on which close agreement can generally be reached. Since different wage plans use different formulas, mathematically they can coincide at only one point. The incentive performance with a 25 percent bonus is the most logical anchor point through which all curves theoretically should pass.

Any wage plan with a minimum flat guarantee, or any partial sharing plan, will yield variable unit labor costs for varying efficiencies. If a standard unit labor cost is desired, some one point of efficiency must be selected. The **point of most typical response** would seem to be the most logical point. With a step bonus plan such as the Taylor, the Gantt, or the differential time plan, all of which use high task standards, the strong incentive to meet task standards tends to set the most typical response at high task performance. The same level of response is reflected in the Emerson plan with its very steep slope of empiric bonuses at (or just below) high task. This is therefore the point on which **standard direct labor costs** should be based and from which deviations should be calculated for determining **labor efficiency variances.**

Specthrie (Industrial Accounting) says, "In determining the standard unit cost of an item, consideration is given to engineering studies as to:

1. The kind and grade of materials that should be used.
2. The product layout that minimizes scrap material.
3. How each involved labor operation ought to be performed.
4. How much time each labor operation should take.
5. The job lot which most effectively uses the set-up time and machine capacity."

The emphasis in items 3, 4 and 5 on how the operation ought to be performed, how much time it should take, and the most effective use of machine capacity suggests the point of high task performance, and the bonus granted at high task, as the basis for standard labor costs.

Bonus Restriction. Direct financial bonuses should be paid only for **extra operator effort.** Incentive bonuses should not be paid for increased output obtained from **technological improvements** introduced or approved by the company's management. If this were permitted, the wages of a few fortunate individuals would be inequitable in relation to the wages of other individuals in the same labor grade who may be exerting the same effort but whose jobs were not affected by such improvements. Such a situation inevitably leads to intolerable labor difficulties.

CORRECTION OF STANDARDS. Each production standard is applicable to only one **specific method of operation.** If the method is changed to any degree, however small, the standard immediately should be corrected to correspond, so that the same operator effort under the new method will yield the same total wages. This establishes the precedent of keeping standards always in line with current methods. This policy is especially important if rapid deterioration of the whole incentive installation is to be prevented. In contrast, if several minor uncorrected changes are allowed to accumulate over a relatively long period until a significant correction (of, say, 10 or 15 percent) becomes imperative, the operators will have become accustomed to the looser standards and the correction then appears to them as unwarranted **rate cutting.**

Standards should be corrected for unofficial method changes. The policy of correcting standards to correspond with method changes should be followed even when such changes are introduced unofficially by the operator. Here, again, the basic principle of wage incentives should be recognized, that is, rewarding the operator for his direct contribution. Common practice is to reward the contributing operator for his "invention," either by an appropriate **lump-sum payment** or by a suitable **percentage of savings** effected by the improvement for the first year. If the standard is not corrected, other operators who made no contribution to the improvement eventually will reap inequitable bonuses.

ALLOWANCES. In line with the philosophy of rewarding operators for their direct contribution to production, the **standard time allowed** usually should include time for only the manual work required with appropriate allowances for rest and miscellaneous unavoidable minor delays. (See section on Work Measurement and Time Study.) Wage calculations should include arrangements whereby only base wages are paid for time during which operators are not likely to exert more than normal effort. This is particularly important on certain machine operations and is explained more fully in the analysis of the Bedaux system.

NONINCENTIVE ASSIGNMENTS. Payment of average incentive earnings must be avoided if an incentive plan is to remain effective. After an employee has become accustomed to bonus earnings, it is easy for him to feel that he is being penalized whenever he is assigned to nonincentive work with no bonus opportunity; that is, he should not be deprived of a bonus merely because the company may not have established a standard time for the task. Thus, some companies have acquiesced to demands for average incentive earnings on temporary nonincentive assignments. But high (incentive) productivity will be obtained only when it is a requirement for bonus earnings. For any fixed hourly rate, almost regardless of how high it may be, the effective work pace inevitably tends to be no higher than normal, and often much lower. Thus the payment of average incentive earnings merely guarantees an unearned bonus for daywork performance, with corresponding excessive costs. The situation is greatly exaggerated when average earnings are paid for **down times,** for this merely guarantees a bonus for no productivity whatever. Obviously such a practice is highly inequitable when only base wages would be paid to regular day workers who have not had an equivalent privilege of enjoying bonus wages.

Incentives for Experimental Work. A special evaluated rate is recommended for experimental work. There may be a few exceptions to the rule of base wages for nonincentive work. A superior incentive operator may be asked to perform special experimental or developmental work. If a definite accomplishment can be anticipated, a liberal standard may be estimated to provide a bonus opportunity and make the job attractive. If this is impractical, the particular operator probably is selected because he possesses certain abilities not essential for his usual incentive work but desired for the special assignment. Usually this will justify an **evaluated base rate** sufficiently higher than the operator's regular base rate to make the special assignment attractive. Such a procedure is simple and practical, yet it does not sabotage the incentive installation.

Separation of Daywork and Incentive Work. Daywork (nonincentive) jobs should not be mixed with incentive work for the same operator. This often seems difficult to avoid, but such a mixture encourages the dishonest manipulation of reported elapsed times and greatly reduces the effectiveness of the whole incentive installation. When a special nonstandardized job cannot be avoided, usually it is better to assign a **temporary estimated standard.** With the opportunity to earn a bonus, the operator is encouraged to maintain his customary level of effort. Even if the estimated standard may be relatively loose, the cost of the job is predetermined and under control, and often will be less than if unlimited time is permitted at the base wage rate.

BONUS PERIODS. Payroll periods for which bonus wages are calculated should be long enough to represent an over-all average level of output, yet short enough for the worker to recognize the relation between the bonus received and the effort he remembers expending. Some industrial engineers recommend that the **bonus calculation period** should be one day or one job, whichever is shorter. But such short periods greatly increase the amount of clerical work required; furthermore they not only invite but also encourage dishonest manipulation of the actual times reported on the various jobs to indicate alternate fall-downs and excessive make-outs. Since it is common practice to pay employees at 1-week intervals, the week is the most typical period for which efficiencies are averaged and bonuses calculated.

In some companies, base wages are paid each week for the time actually worked, but production records are accumulated and **average efficiencies** are calculated for a period of either 4 calendar weeks, or 1 calendar month. Bonuses are calculated according to these average efficiencies, and the bonus is paid separately soon after the close of the period. This procedure has several advantages. **Payroll clerical costs** are less than with shorter periods. Minor (unavoidable) inconsistencies in individual operation standards are averaged out. The period is long enough to reflect fairly the operator's averaged sustained level of productivity. The total amount of bonus for the period is sufficiently large to be important to the worker, and, since it is isolated from the straight time wages, it is not so easily misconstrued as regular wages but is more readily recognized as an extra reward for extra performance. Periods longer than 1 month usually are unsatisfactory because of the long delay between the performance of the work and receipt of the bonus.

NEW STANDARDS. The production standard should be **available to the operator** before work is started on an operation, so that he immediately knows his goal and is not encouraged to work indefinitely at a reduced pace in the hope of obtaining a loose standard. For operations which are often repeated, standards can be obtained from time studies on previous orders. In jobbing shops, however, this policy almost necessitates the use of some form of **standard time data** from which standards can be predetermined synthetically for each different lot. (See section on Work Measurement and Time Study.)

SUPERVISORY PARTICIPATION. When first-line supervisors have direct control over the worker's output and consequent earnings, the incentive plan will be more effective if the supervisors participate in the plan. A working group leader often can be made a part of a regular production group so that his wages appropriately become a portion of the direct labor costs and depend entirely upon the quantity and quality of the group's output. Care must be exercised to provide suitable **checks and balances** so that a group leader may not be in a position to cheat the system through collusion with other workers.

INCENTIVE ACCOUNTING. The wage incentive system and bonus calculations should be tied in directly with the regular payroll, cost, and general accounting systems, so that standard costs and variances can be reflected in the normal accounting reports for management control. This is a feature on which Bedaux engineers properly insist, and it should be a part of every incentive installation.

TIME STUDY FUNCTIONS. Normally, the time study function should be responsible only for operating methods and production standards and should not be responsible for the determination of base rates or for routine time-keeping or payroll calculations.

MINIMUM RECORDS. Usually it is not desirable to increase **clerical routines** to collect information with which to administer the incentive plan. Records of measured accomplishment often can be obtained from already established procedures. For example, in a jobbing shop foundry the most accurate measure of output would be to count the number of castings of all different types on which each operator works, but this may require adding several additional inspectors to the payroll. However, nearly every foundry keeps records of the total number of units and the total tons shipped. Where types and sizes of castings vary considerably, this **shipping record** is not so accurate a measure of operator or group performance as could be obtained with the additional inspectors; but in the long run it may be more economical, and sufficiently satisfactory, to adapt the plan to these less accurate production records.

Source of Reports. The **final reporting or approval** of the amount and quality of production should be the responsibility of persons whose earnings are not affected by the production counts or who otherwise could benefit from false reports of output. Occasionally incentive wages are calculated from the operators' own reports, but operators naturally are inclined not to report defective items, and occasionally they indicate quantities somewhat larger than actually produced. This leads to excessive costs and eventual inventory shortages. It may be quite practical, however, to use **production reports** from the operators if these reports are subject to overinspection by random sampling of both quantity and quality.

General Classifications of Work

APPROPRIATE WAGE PLAN FOR TYPE OF WORK. In order better to understand appropriate applications of various incentive plans, it is important to recognize that all work is not alike. In general, any productive activity can be considered under one of the following classifications, for each of which a particular type of wage payment will be most suitable. Admittedly, borderline situations may occur, but a suitable compromise plan usually can be devised by combining various features.

STANDARD REPETITIVE OPERATIONS (CLASS 1). A large portion of productive work falls within this classification, for which the following conditions usually prevail: The activities are repetitive and chiefly manual. Methods are well established. Materials, tools, and working conditions are standardized and uniform. A steady flow of work is available. The output can be, and usually is, measured with considerable accuracy. The work being manual in nature, the rate of output is under the **personal control** of the operator and varies directly with his effective effort or performance pace. On such work, good time study techniques usually yield reasonably accurate standards.

If the time studies are **leveled** to reflect a normal performance pace, the operator should receive all (or 100 percent share) of the time saved when actual output exceeds standard. A suitable wage incentive plan would be any constant (straight-line) full sharing plan such as monetary piecework, the 100 percent standard time premium, or the standard hour plan. However, if the time studies are leveled to reflect high task standards which require an incentive pace just to meet them, the operator should receive more (preferably 20 to 30 percent more) than 100 percent of the time saved. In this discussion the correct amount arbitrarily will be assumed to be 25 percent. For high task standards, a suitable wage incentive plan would be a constant straight-line, high sharing plan such as a high-piece-rate or a 125 percent sharing standard time plan. If it is particularly important to maintain actual production at or above the high task level, a high-piece-rate plan with a step bonus, or the Gantt task and bonus plan may be used. If it is desired to encourage extremely high rates of production, considerably above typical high task performance, an accelerated premium plan might be used; but such plans are uncommon and of doubtful value because of the difficulty in maintaining standards uniformly accurate and tight, and because the plan tends to encourage operators to work at excessive paces, even to the point of self-injury.

VARIABLE WORKING CONDITIONS (CLASS 2). A surprisingly large amount of productive work falls within this classification in which several or all of the following conditions prevail. The units of output, as measured, do not contain a uniform amount of work content. For example, a ton of large castings may involve much less manual work than a ton of small castings. Thus the measured output may not be an accurate representation of the work performed. Uncontrolled variations in such factors as tools, materials, previous operations, temperature, humidity, dust, noise, and lighting may influence the work so that the rate of output is not completely within the operator's control. Thus, **variant output** may exist even with a constant level of effective operator effort; that is, output is not directly proportional to operator effort or work pace.

In many **daywork plants** such variations in working conditions often are allowed to exist even on operations which, if subjected to methods study, could well be considered Class 1 work. But some operations will continue to be subject to variations beyond the requirements for Class 1 conditions.

Such variations in conditions are difficult to measure, and no standard will represent accurately the true work content of the task except for one specific and momentary set of conditions. This situation naturally leads to **loose standards**. If the standards are set from time studies or standard time data, there is a strong and very proper tendency, usually intentional but sometimes unwitting, to set the standards loose enough for conditions that are somewhat worse than the long-run average. In fact, there is good reason to set the standard loose enough for the worst conditions that are likely to occur. This protects the operator against fall-downs when temporarily unfortunate conditions are encountered. For average conditions such standards would be about equivalent to low task. These loose standards can be satisfied with much less than normal operator effort when current conditions happen to be equal to, or better than, the long-run average, and incentive effort would produce unreasonably high calculated efficiencies. Thus, when loose standards are used to protect the operator against temporarily poor conditions, the company must be similarly protected against excessive labor costs when temporary conditions happen to be favorable. Hence some type of partial sharing plan is imperative.

When working conditions and work content are highly variable, standards will not be consistently loose, but there will be an apparent mixture of loose and tight standards; that is, a given standard may appear tight when conditions are poor and loose when they are good. With **tight standards** good operator effort yields only moderate calculated efficiencies and the operator should be rewarded with a high share of the time saved. With loose standards the same effort yields high calculated efficiencies and the operator deserves a much smaller share of the time saved, so his wages will be the same in both cases. The Rowan variable sharing plan automatically includes high sharing at low and moderate efficiencies but relatively lower sharing at high efficiencies. Because of this double protective feature, the Rowan plan, perhaps with slight modification, usually will be the best choice for long-run success where management insists upon using only one plan for all types of work within the company.

In some situations the work is manual, repetitive, and subject to accurate measurement as in Class 1, but standards may be established from past performance records which would reflect low task performance. Time studies, deliberately adjusted to reflect low task performance, may be used. Such standards will be **consistently loose,** rather than a mixture. In this case, a constant partial sharing plan, such as the Halsey 50 percent plan or some modification of it, is most appropriate.

LIMITED RATES OF PRODUCTION (CLASS 3). In many operations the maximum rate of output is relatively fixed, being limited by the capacity of the machine, the design or specifications of the process, or perhaps by company policy. Examples might include constant-speed automatic machines, mechanically paced conveyor assembly lines, chemical processes, or activities where excessive speeds may damage expensive material or endanger the operator, yet where it is imperative to utilize the facilities at nearly full capacity.

The **maximum rate of output** on machine- or process-controlled operations usually can be calculated very accurately from the specifications, and standards therefore tend to be relatively tight. Usually the machine or process can be suitably manned, so that the operators must work at approximately the incentive pace in order to keep the process running at the specified rate; thus the standards naturally tend to reflect high task performance.

When the rate of output is limited by the machine or process, there is little the operator can do to exceed the specified capacity except at the risk of defective products, damaged equipment, or potential injury; but lack of proper operator attention can lower the actual rate of output far below the desired level.

The wage incentive plan should encourage the operator to maintain optimum conditions in order to utilize the available capacity of the process; yet it should discourage **short cuts** or **speed-ups.** In other words, the plan should encourage the operator to meet and consistently maintain, but not significantly exceed, high task performance.

To meet these conditions, high task standards should be used. The base wage should be paid for all levels of output below standard. Incentive earnings should be available for incentive performance; therefore a step bonus of, say, 25 percent should be paid when the standard rate of output is maintained. (Standards should be set so that actual output safely could exceed the specified standards by a small amount, say 5 percent, to provide a cushion against occasional minor difficulties beyond the operator's control.) But no additional bonus should be paid for exceeding the standards. A **two-level flat-rate plan,** sometimes called a **differential time or multiple daywork plan,** contains these features. The step bonus provides a strong inducement to maintain the process at standard capacity, yet the lack of further bonus opportunity discourages undesirable speed-ups. The plan is highly effective, yet is almost as simple to administer as a straight time wage plan.

OUTPUT NOT ECONOMICALLY MEASURABLE (CLASS 4). On some types of work there is no conveniently definable unit of output for which a reasonably specific amount of work content can be determined. There may be no accurate, convenient, or economical methods of measuring a person's output, and, at least for short periods, there is no close correlation between a person's effort and actual accomplishment. Typical examples include research, inventing, learning, and general planning activities. Without some means of objectively measuring output, there is little choice except to pay employees on a **straight time basis** such as by hourly wages, or weekly or monthly salaries.

Most **shop activities,** involving both direct and indirect labor, are somewhat repetitive or contain repetitive elements which can be measured with sufficient accuracy to justify the use of some form of direct financial incentives. For example, in addition to typical direct productive operations, wage incentives have been applied successfully to such activities as: trucking and other types of materials handling; crane operators; storeroom operation; packing and shipping; janitor services; machine repairs; millwright work; building repairs and maintenance; tool making and repairs. Incentives also have been applied successfully to many **clerical activities** such as: typing; bookkeeping; mechanical drafting or tracing work. In most companies these are relatively unexplored fields for incentive application where potential savings are great and are limited only by the foresight of management and the ingenuity of the industrial engineer. Straight time wages are necessary only where it is impossible to establish a reasonable standard of work content and where output is not predictable or measurable with sufficient objectivity to compare with a standard.

Analysis of Wage Plans

KEY TO SYMBOLS. The analyis and comparison of various wage payment plans is greatly simplified by the use of symbols and equations. The symbols used in this discussion are defined as follows:

W = **wages,** in dollars, determined according to the wage plan for a payroll calculation period. Included are **straight time wages,** which usually are guaranteed, plus any **bonus wages** paid for exceeding specified standards of output. Unless otherwise clearly indicated, overtime, shift, or other **premium earnings** are not included.

R = **base rate,** in dollars per hour, which has been established from reliable job evaluation, and/or fairly reflects the **going rate** in the community which must be paid to obtain employees with the necessary abilities to perform the assigned work under nonincentive conditions.

S = **standard,** in hours allowed per unit of output, regardless of how determined, or how loose or tight it may be. Subscripts are used to indicate the specific levels of performance required.

S_n = **normal task standard,** in hours per unit, requiring the normal level of effective operator effort usually obtained from standardized working conditions and measured output, but without the inducement of a bonus opportunity.

S_L = **low task standard**, in hours per unit, reflecting the relatively low average performance usually obtained under typical daywork conditions where conditions and methods are not standardized and output is not measured. Low task standard times are considered to be about 20 percent looser than normal standards, so that $S_L = 1.20S_n$, and therefore require an average of only $1.00/1.20 = 0.833$ (83.3 percent) as much output.

S_H = **high task standard**, in hours per unit, reflecting the level of effective operator performance typically obtained with well-standardized conditions, accurately measured output, and with the inducement of a suitable bonus opportunity. High task performance generally is considered to be 1.25 (125 percent) of normal, so that the time allowed per unit for $S_H = S_n/1.25 = 0.80S_n$.

N = **number of units** of acceptable quality produced during a given payroll calculation period while working under the wage plan currently in effect.

SN = **total standard hours produced** during a given period, i.e., standard hours per unit multiplied by the number of acceptable units produced.

TN = **total actual hours** spent in producing SN standard hours, as determined from job time tickets or, in some cases, directly from entrance clock cards.

T = **actual hours per unit**, or the total actual hours TN divided by the number N of units produced. The term T, by itself, is not significant in payroll calculations, but in this discussion it is useful for comparison with S.

$SN - TN$ = **total hours saved** during a given period when output exceeds the specified standard.

$S - T$ = **hours saved per unit**, when output exceeds standard.

E = **efficiency ratio**, expressed as a decimal fraction (100 percent = 1.00). It is a common and convenient numerical **index of relative performance** and is calculated as the ratio of standard time produced to actual time taken. $E = SN/TN = S/T$.

E_n = **normal efficiency ratio**, calculated from normal task standards.

E_L = **low task efficiency ratio**, calculated from low task standards; therefore $E_L = 1.20E_n$.

E_H = **high task efficiency ratio**, calculated from high-task standards; therefore $E_H = 0.80E_n$.

M = **monetary standard** or **piece rate**, in dollars for each acceptable unit of output. Historically it often has been determined by dividing expected wages by the expected output; but generally it is established by multiplying the standard hours per unit by the base rate, or $M = SR$.

Wr = **wage ratio**, expressed as a decimal fraction. It is the ratio of total incentive wages to the straight time base wages.

B = **bonus wages**, in dollars, or the amount by which total wages exceed straight time base wages.

Br = **bonus ratio,** expressed as a decimal fraction. It is the ratio of bonus wages to straight time base wages.

p = **portion of hours saved,** which is credited to the operator (on certain partial sharing plans) when output exceeds standard.

C = **direct labor cost,** in dollars, per unit of output.

C_s = **standard direct labor cost,** in dollars actually paid per unit of output when the operator is producing at a true incentive pace. In this discussion it is considered that $C_s = S_n \times R$.

Cr = **direct labor cost ratio,** expressed as a decimal fraction. It is the ratio of actual to standard unit cost, or $Cr = C/C_s = Wr \times 100/E_n$.

EVr = **labor efficiency variance ratio,** expressed as a decimal fraction. It is the ratio of the difference between standard and actual unit cost to standard unit cost. $EVr = \dfrac{C_s - C}{C_s} = 1.00 - Cr$.

DAYWORK (TIME RATE) PLAN. This method of wage payment is based upon time alone, without formal regard for the amount of output. The unit of time usually is an hour, and wages are determined by multiplying the number of hours worked by the operator's rate per hour. This is not a wage incentive plan because wages are not directly related to output, but it is an inherent part of most incentive plans since it provides the base above which extra wages for increased output may be recognized as bonus wages.

When an employee is hired on a **time rate basis,** the contract is definite only in the rate of pay per period of time. The employee guesses at the amount of production below which he may be discharged, and the amount for which he may be given a raise. Frequently the former is the more certain and the employee therefore tends to standardize his performance as close to the lower limit as seems safe. The occasional employee who tries to give **superior performance** is likely to receive delayed or inadequate recognition. Individual hourly rate variations can be used to reward versatility, cooperation, loyalty, seniority, etc.; but this occasionally has the appearance of unequal pay for equal work and may appear discriminatory. Without specified tasks (or standards), daywork is the only practical means of wage payment, but it is difficult to determine and to deal justly with **individual performance differences.**

It is difficult to induce daywork operators to render more than **minimum performance.** To induce high performance without financial incentives requires a superior quality of supervision not usually present. If daywork employees do not respond to positive appeals, reasonable performance levels occasionally can be induced by negative (punitive) incentives. The response to time rates varies widely but generally is recognized as being about 80 to 85 percent of normal, or about 60 to 70 percent of high task performance.

Application of Daywork Plan. Time rates are used where work standards and output measurements either cannot be, or have not been, applied. The shorter the duration of a task assignment and the more varied or uncertain its content, the more difficult it is to establish a valid standard. For instance, repair jobs, or small-lot jobs in a "job order" plant are of short duration and, if they recur at all, are likely to recur in varied form. Miscellaneous office duties, drafting and indirect production jobs may be of longer duration but quite irregular and therefore rather unpredictable as to time needed. Extremely **skilled work,**

such as tool making, automatic tool setting, die cutting, pattern making, pipe fitting, and electrical installation, and extremely **unskilled work,** such as sweeping and cleaning, often are alike in the characteristic of uncertainty. In exceptional cases work measurement and incentives have been applied to every one of these jobs. However, such work is characteristic of small companies or small departments where each employee is known by name and reputation and there exists a "public opinion" which prevents him from taking undue advantage of time rates. This is one reason why time payment has been satisfactory in certain trades as well as in small companies where all employees are known personally by the owners or top executives.

In the administration of daywork wages, approved and common practice is to evaluate the basic requirements of jobs regardless of who holds them. Through labor-market surveys a base rate, adequate to attract persons who can meet the basic requirements, is established for each job. Several jobs with a narrow range of basic requirements may be classified into a **labor grade** for which a **rate range** is established. The highest rate for a labor grade frequently is 20 to 30 percent above the base (or lowest) rate. As an individual's performance exceeds the basic requirements for his job, his performance is evaluated by merit-rating procedures and he is given a **personal rate** within the limits of the available range but higher than the job's base rate by an amount indicated by the merit-rating score.

Merit rating is an indirect form of financial incentive in that it tends to reward employees for over-all performance in excess of basic job requirements. However, merit-rating **scores** are obtained through subjective opinions by supervisors rather than from accurate measures of employee productivity, although the latter may be considered. Merit rating is less effective than direct wage incentives for inducing high productivity, but it serves as a reasonably acceptable substitute on unmeasured work. It should be emphasized that merit rating is a substitute for wage incentives and should not be applied to persons who are rewarded otherwise for extra performance by regular wage incentive bonuses. Such a double reward would create inequities between the earnings of incentive and nonincentive employees and inevitably lead to labor strife and excessive costs. Thus the personal rate for any incentive operator should be the same as the base rate for the labor grade in which his job is classified.

Daywork Plan Formulas. Total base wages W are determined by multiplying the total actual time worked TN by the operator's personal rate R_p. See Key to Symbols for definitions of terms. For purposes of convenient comparison with incentive plans, it will be assumed that an incentive operator's personal rate will be the job base rate R.

$$W = TN \times R = TNR \qquad (1)$$

Bonus wages are the excess of total incentive wages over the base wages, and the base wages in all cases (for this discussion) are TNR. Therefore, bonus wages for daywork obviously are:

$$B = TNR - TNR = 0.00 \qquad (2)$$

In order to make an intelligent comparison of all wage plans, it is most convenient to reduce all wages and bonuses to ratios, and the most convenient base for such ratios is the base wage TNR. Thus, for daywork:

$$Wr = \frac{W}{TNR} = \frac{TNR}{TNR} = 1.00 \qquad (3)$$

$$Br = \frac{B}{TNR} = \frac{0}{TNR} = 0.00$$

or

$$Br = Wr - 1.00 = 1.00 - 1.00 = 0.00 \tag{4}$$

For any wage plan, the direct labor cost per unit C will be the total wages W divided by the number of units produced. Thus, for daywork:

$$C = \frac{TNR}{N} = TR \tag{5}$$

which is the actual hours spent on each unit T, multiplied by the base rate per hour. For general application it is desirable to convert the dollar cost C to a cost ratio Cr; this can be done by finding the ratio of actual unit cost C to some reasonable standard unit cost C_s. But a standard cost requires the use of a standard time S. While daywork does not contemplate the use of standard times, it is assumed that normal productivity theoretically should be obtained for base wages. Furthermore it is assumed that S_n represents the hours per unit that would be required at normal productivity. The **standard unit cost** then becomes:

$$C_s = S_n R \tag{6}$$

and the straight time labor-cost ratio, based on normal standards, becomes:

$$Cr_n = \frac{C}{C_s} = \frac{TR}{S_n R} = \frac{T}{S_n} \tag{7}$$

By definition, the efficiency ratio

$$E_n = \frac{S_n}{T}$$

Inverting,

$$\frac{T}{S_n} = \frac{1.00}{E_n}$$

therefore

$$Cr_n = \frac{1.00}{E_n} \tag{8}$$

The **actual unit cost** for any level of efficiency can be determined by multiplying the standard cost by the corresponding cost ratio.

Since typical response under daywork tends to be near low task performance or about 0.83 (83.3 percent) of normal productivity, 0.833 can be substituted for E_n in equation (8) to give a cost ratio for low task output of:

$$Cr_L = \frac{1}{0.833} = 1.20 \tag{9}$$

This indicates that, under daywork conditions of unmeasured work, average low task output will yield unit labor costs about 20 percent higher than if standards were used and approximately normal productivity were obtained.

Actual productivity seldom exactly equals standard productivity, and any deviation from standard (on some wage plans) creates a difference between actual and standard unit labor costs. This difference frequently is identified as an **efficiency variance** (EV). If actual costs exceed standard costs, the variance is negative or unfavorable. Conversely, if actual costs are less than standard costs, the variance is positive, or favorable. The amount of this variance is found by subtracting the actual cost C from the standard cost C_s, or:

$$EV \text{ (in dollars)} = C_s - C$$

A labor efficiency variance ratio (EVr) may be calculated as the ratio of the dollar variance per unit to the standard cost per unit, or:

$$EVr = \frac{EV}{C_s} = \frac{C_s - C}{C_s} = 1.00 - \frac{C}{C_s}$$

and since

$$\frac{C}{C_s} = Cr$$

$$EVr = 1.00 - Cr \qquad (10)$$

But, for daywork,

$$Cr = \frac{1}{E_n}$$

therefore

$$EVr = 1.00 - \frac{1.00}{E_n} \qquad (11)$$

Using normal task standards, the efficiency ratio E_n will be unity (1.00) at normal productivity. For less than normal output, calculated efficiencies will be

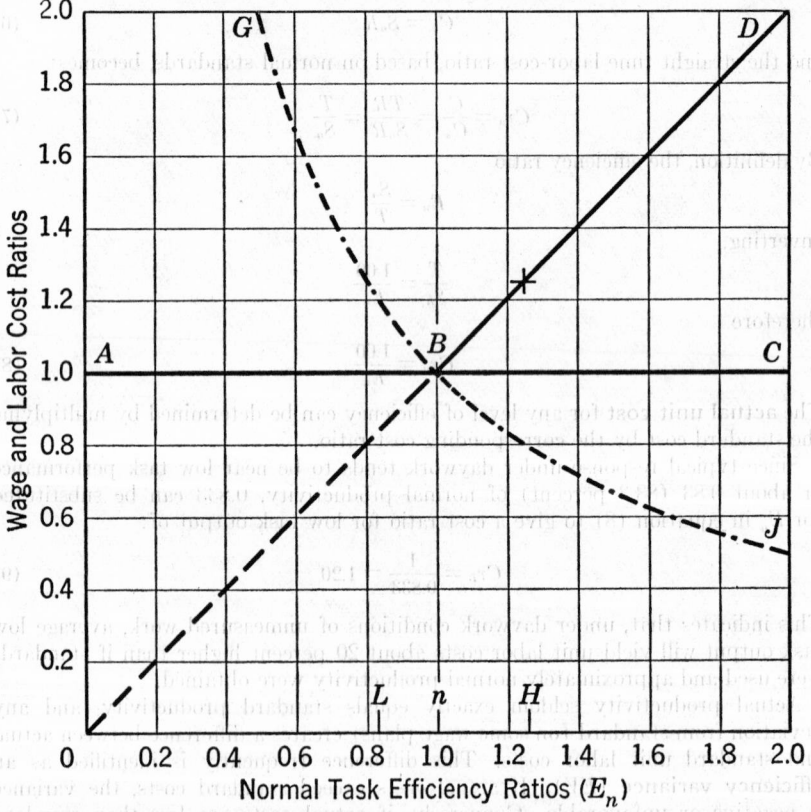

Straight daywork: Wage ratio $(Wr) = ABC$; direct labor cost ratio $(Cr) = GBJ$. Standard Hour: $Wr = ABD$; $Cr = GBC$. Task levels: low $(L) = 0.833E_n$; normal $(n) = 1.000E_n$; high $(H) = 1.250E_n$.

Fig. 2. **Straight daywork and standard hour plans for normal task standards.**

less than 1.00, actual labor costs will be higher than normal, the standard cost ratios will be greater than 1.00, and labor efficiency variances will be negative. Conversely, for higher than normal output, cost ratios will be less than 1.00, and labor efficiency variances will be positive or favorable.

Fig. 2 shows the wage and cost curves for straight daywork and standard hour plans for normal task standards. The corresponding straight time or daywork data appear in Fig. 3.

E_n	Wr (Eq. 3)	$Cr_n = \dfrac{1.00}{E_n}$ (Eq. 8)	$EVr = 1.00 - \dfrac{1.00}{E_n}$ (Eq. 11)
0.50	1.00	2.000	−1.000
0.60	1.00	1.667	−0.667
0.70	1.00	1.429	−0.429
0.80	1.00	1.250	−0.250
0.833	1.00	1.200	−0.200
0.90	1.00	1.111	−0.111
1.00	1.00	1.000	0.000
1.10	1.00	0.9091	+ .0909
1.20	1.00	0.8333	+ .1667
1.25	1.00	0.8000	+ .2000
1.30	1.00	0.7692	+ .2308
1.40	1.00	0.7143	+ .2857
1.50	1.00	0.6667	+ .3333
1.60	1.00	0.6250	+ .3750
1.70	1.00	0.5882	+ .4118
1.80	1.00	0.5556	+ .4444
1.90	1.00	0.5263	+ .4737
2.00	1.00	0.5000	+ .5000

Fig. 3. Straight time or daywork data for Fig. 2.

Characteristics of Unmeasured Daywork. The nature of unmeasured daywork wages may be stated as follows:

1. **Straight time** is the simplest and most common form of wage payment. Payroll calculations are simple, and the employee knows precisely what his earnings will be for every hour worked. For unmeasured work there is generally no other choice.
2. With a fixed hourly wage guaranteed, any **gains or losses** resulting from variations in the rate of output accrue to the employer; however, significant gains are very unlikely because the average level of productivity tends to be low.
3. Effective production tends to require more careful and more detailed **supervision** of unmeasured daywork than is required under incentive plans, all of which have an element of self-policing. However, some managements have been known to prefer time wages as a means of covering up loose production planning and control and other basic weaknesses in supervision.
4. Without standards it is difficult to predict **rates of output**; therefore production scheduling tends to be ineffective.
5. Actual rates of output are highly variable from day to day; thus **production schedules** are unreliable, and broken promises on delivery dates tend to be the rule rather than the exception.
6. Owing to fluctuating rates of output, **unit labor costs** are quite unpredictable; thus an accounting system based on "standard costs" is rather impractical.

7. Cost estimates for new products are little more than pure guesses and are subject to large errors, a distinct disadvantage to many companies facing keen competition.
8. Since employee earnings are not affected, straight time workers are less likely to oppose **methods changes** or **technological improvements.** On the other hand, without the inducements of specified goals and potential bonuses, there is little reason to expect active employee cooperation in putting the improvements into effect.

MEASURED DAYWORK. Attempts have been made to put a measure of incentive into straight time wages through a mixture of job evaluation, production standards, and merit rating. Each man-job is, in effect, assigned an hourly rate composed of two parts. The first part is the **base job rate,** appropriately determined for the basic job requirements, as for any other wage plan, by regular job-evaluation procedures. The second part is based on **employee-controlled factors** such as quantity and quality of output, versatility, and dependability. These merit factors are rated at stated intervals to determine the additional **man-rate,** which may range up to about one-third (say 30 percent) of the base rate. The job rate and the man-rate are combined to give the **measured day rate.**

These are not true measurements, since both job ratings and man-ratings are based largely on interpretations and opinions. However, an element of measurement is introduced, in that production standards are established and outputs are measured and compared with these standards. This measure of **operator efficiency** then becomes one of the factors considered in the merit rating.

An incentive is introduced by periodic reviews of the employee-controlled factors and by appropriate adjustment of the man-job rate, either upward or downward.

The usual **period for rate revision** is 1 month for beginners and 3 months for seasoned employees. At the end of each period the employee's performance is reviewed and merit-rated by one or more superiors. On the basis of this merit-rating score, the employee is given a corresponding portion of the additional 30 percent man-rate range which becomes and remains effective for the following 3-month period. A high merit score would give a large portion of the available man-rate range. A subsequent low score would give a smaller portion and result in a reduction in the operator's hourly rate for the succeeding period.

A simpler concept of this type of plan is first to recognize that a minimum base rate is established by job evaluation for a labor grade containing classified jobs requiring similar basic qualifications. For each labor grade a **rate range** of about 30 percent of the base rate is provided as possible raises for individuals whose performances exceed the basic requirements, and a merit-rating program determines the extent of the raise to be granted.

Characteristics of Measured Daywork. Advantages of measured daywork include the fact that use of standards and output measurements lets the operators know what they are expected to accomplish and how nearly they achieve the goals. It acts as a nonfinancial incentive and tends to increase **productivities** from a low task level to more nearly a normal level. Actual production levels will remain more uniform, thus contributing toward better production scheduling and control and greater feasibility of standard costs.

Several **disadvantages** should be recognized. The use of formal work measurement procedures introduces the complexities of a formal wage incentive program without getting the automatic response that comes from a true financial incentive. Evaluations of such illusive factors as versatility and dependability necessarily are subjective and of highly doubtful validity as indicators of employee performance. The frequent (3-month interval) merit ratings soon become an unwelcome chore for supervisors, particularly in large departments, and accordingly do not receive the attention and care necessary for equitable administration. On the other hand, a 3-month period is too long for typical operators to recognize the relationship between their productive effort and their earnings. The reward (raise, effective for the succeeding period) comes after the fact, rather than because of it, and does not reflect current productivity. For example, a high rate which was obtained as the result of merit rating for a previous period may be enjoyed throughout a current 3-month period regardless of low output.

The periodic merit ratings and the possibility of rate revision introduce an undesirable element of fear. From an incentive point of view, the concept of **raising and lowering the rates** seems entirely logical, but in actual practice it is quite unrealistic. After an employee has enjoyed a high hourly rate for a period as long as 3 months, and therefore has become accustomed to it, any future reduction, resulting from a subsequent low merit-rating score, would create a serious disturbance and is unlikely to be effected. Thus, measured daywork plans, in practice, tend to raise all employee rates very quickly to the tops of the available rate ranges, with seldom any downward adjustments. Once the maximum rate has been reached, there is no further financial inducement to maintain high levels of output, and the average productivity tends to fall to the lowest level that can be tolerated. Complaints arise against imagined tight standards which then are loosened, with a gradual deterioration of the system toward typical daywork conditions. Measured daywork lacks two virtues of genuine incentive plans: automaticity and impersonality; while simplicity, the main excuse for using time wages, is partially sacrificed.

Measured Daywork Formulas. Measured daywork still is daywork and the same formulas apply for wages and costs; but, with the use of standards, actual output tends to be closer to normal task performance, and costs are more easily determined and controlled.

DIFFERENTIAL TIME (OR MULTIPLE DAYWORK) PLAN WITH BONUS STEP OR STEPS.

Originally this was called the **standard time plan**, but recently that term has become associated with the 100 percent plan, which is similar to piecework but uses time standards.

The simplest way of converting a straight time plan to an extra-financial incentive plan is: (1) to establish a standard or task; (2) to pay a low (base) time rate for productivities below task; and (3) to pay a high (say 25 percent higher than base) time rate for productivities at or above the high task level. The change from a low rate to a high rate at some specified level of output creates a **step bonus** incorporating a strong inducement for the employee to produce at the specified task.

The Minimum Guarantee. As in all plans using the **time guarantee**, the hourly rate that is guaranteed below task may be lower than base if desired. Lytle (Wage Incentive Methods) states:

In the case of employees who have heretofore been on the day rate basis, these rates have often been retained as guarantees when an extra-financial incentive plan is installed. This practice is not always necessary however, and if unnecessary it should not be done. If the guaranteed rate is lower than the base rate level, it will act automatically to keep the employee out of its reach, but there are other difficulties in the way of such rates. If the guarantee is at base level, as is customary, then precautions must be taken to prevent less ambitious employees from remaining on it indefinitely. All remuneration along a high guarantee line is costly to the company and should be looked upon as a penalty to deficient management.

It might be added that, regardless of whether the guarantee is high or low, if there are many employees whose productivities continually are lower than a reasonable normal level, the fault may lie with selection, training, and supervision rather than with the design of the incentive plan.

Although Lytle recommends, for excellent reasons, that the minimum guarantee should be less than base, he recognizes that "the guarantee . . . at base level . . . is customary." A few instances have been observed where the hourly rate used for calculating incentive earnings was lower than base; but in nearly all cases the lower rate was used as a protection against loose standards. Theoretically, the lower rate was paid in the event of failure to meet the standards, but the intended purpose of the lower guarantee was counteracted by the use of such liberal standards that, practically, such failures never occurred. Furthermore, the higher **evaluated base rate** was paid for daywork assignments where there was no inducement for any performance above the minimum.

In contrast, instances have been observed where base rates were used for regular daywork operators but a somewhat higher rate, often **average incentive earnings,** was guaranteed to incentive employees whenever they were given daywork assignments.

Standard Levels. If the base rate is an appropriate guarantee for regular daywork where average productivities tend to be low, there seems little justification for using a lower guarantee when standards are introduced and average productivities consequently tend to be normal or higher.

If standards are set to reflect normal performance, there is little justification for a step bonus at standard, as it merely would give an extra reward for no extra performance. Therefore **high task standards** must be used to make a step bonus plan effective. Normal task standards could be used if the bonus step were located at the point of 125 percent efficiency, but psychologically this is undesirable.

If standards are set to require high task performance, a bonus step of less than 20 percent may not be sufficient incentive to induce the necessary incentive level of effort. For this discussion, a 25 percent step will be considered appropriate and has proved effective in holding typical response at, or slightly above, the specified standard. But, with no opportunity for further increases in earnings, additional response (much above standard) cannot be expected.

Applications of Differential Time Plan. The plan is ideally suited to Class 3 type of work, as previously described, where a sustained but fixed rate of output is desired. The single-step plan provides a strong incentive, yet it is simple to comprehend and administer. It tends automatically to do what any good supervisor would like to do with ordinary time wages, that is, raise and lower an individual's wages whenever the individual raises or lowers his productivity. Thus it accomplishes promptly what measured daywork is intended to accomplish but often does so with too much delay.

The plan is well suited to group or closely related individual jobs where close cooperation and high fixed levels of output are more important than individual excellence.

Differential Time Plan Formulas. Under a single-step plan, standards always should be set to require high task performance. But base rate wages are guaranteed for all lower levels of output, and therefore wage equations will be the same as for straight daywork.

Up to high task productivity, where $E_H = 1.00$:

$$W = TNR \qquad (1)$$

$$W_r = 1.00 \qquad (3)$$

$$B_r = 0.00 \qquad (4)$$

With efficiencies calculated from high task standards, cost ratios will appear 25 percent higher than when calculated from normal standards.

Standard unit labor costs should be calculated for the level of output usually expected and most likely to be maintained. With a strong inducement (step bonus) to meet high task standards, actual output is most likely to be at the high task level which is 1.25 (125 percent) of normal. The allowed standard time per unit is:

$$S_H = \frac{1.00}{1.25} \times S_n = 0.80\, S_n \qquad (12)$$

and efficiency ratios calculated from high task standards are:

$$E_H = 0.80\, E_n \qquad (13)$$

In wage plans using normal task standards, the incentive opportunity already is included in the standards. In the single-step differential time rate plan using high task standards the equivalent bonus opportunity is provided in the payroll calculations by using a high hourly rate which, for this discussion, is 1.25 (125 percent) of the base rate, or $1.25R$. At incentive output, therefore, wages and costs will be the same in both cases.

The **standard unit labor cost,** using high task standards and the high hourly rate, will be the same as if normal standards and the base rate were used.

$$C_{s_H} = S_H \times 1.25R = 0.80 S_n \times 1.25R = S_n R = C_{s_n} \qquad (14)$$

When only the base rate is guaranteed, the actual unit labor cost is:

$$C = TR \qquad (5)$$

and the cost ratio Cr, calculated for high task standards, becomes:

$$Cr_H = \frac{C}{C_{s_H}} = \frac{TR}{S_H \times 1.25R} = \frac{T}{1.25 S_H} = \frac{0.80}{E_H} \qquad (15)$$

But since

$$E_H = 0.80 E_n \qquad (13)$$

then

$$Cr_H = \frac{0.80}{0.80 E_n} = \frac{1.00}{E_n} = Cr_n \qquad (16)$$

From equation (12), normal productivity (where $E_n = 1.00$) is represented by a calculated high task efficiency E_H of 0.80. From equation (15), if $E_H = 0.80$, the cost ratio is 1.00, and at high task productivity, where $E_H = 100$, the cost ratio is 0.80. Between these two levels of output, cost ratios are negative, giving positive (favorable) **efficiency variance ratios** ranging from 0.00 at normal output to 0.20 at high task output. But, with the payment of the 25 percent bonus, the cost ratio immediately rises again to unity (1.00), then again gradually decreases for higher efficiencies.

When the operator meets, or possibly exceeds, the high task standards, the 25 percent bonus is calculated by use, in the payroll calculations, of a high hourly rate which, for this discussion, is $1.25R$. Therefore, at and above high task productivity:

$$W = TNR \times 1.25 \tag{17}$$
$$W_r = 1.25 \tag{18}$$
$$B_r = 0.25 \tag{19}$$

and the cost ratio becomes:

$$Cr_H = 1.25Cr_n = \frac{1.25}{E_n} = \frac{1.25}{1.25E_H} = \frac{1.00}{E_H} \tag{20}$$

Equation (20), very simply, gives results that are 1.25 times the results from equation (15).

Fig. 4 shows wage and cost curves for differential time plans with single-step and gradual bonus, and also the Gantt task and bonus plan. The corresponding data are given in Fig. 5.

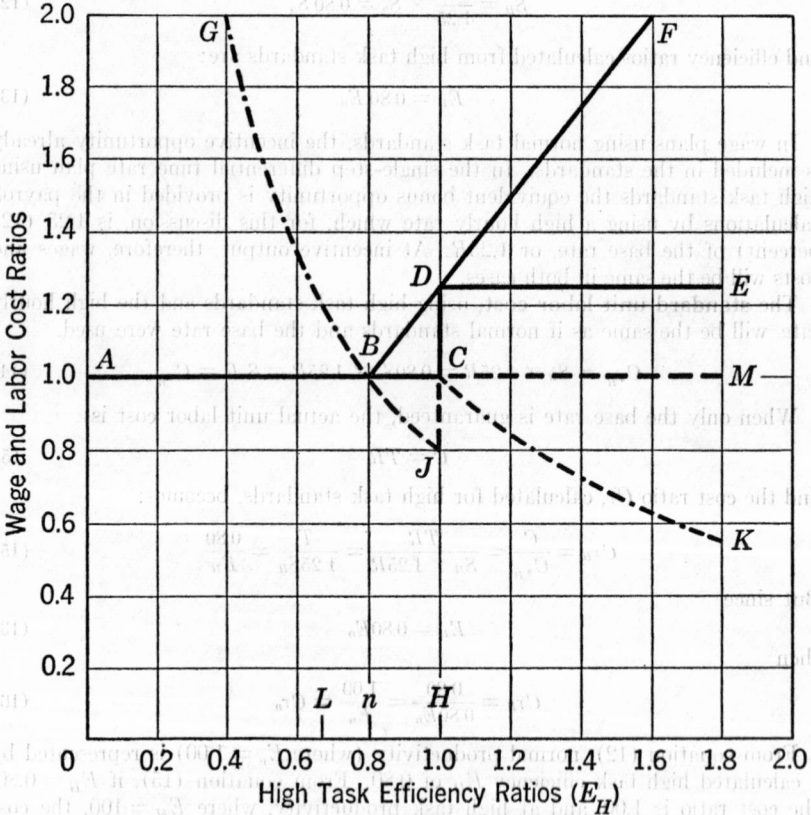

Single-step bonus: $Wr = ABCDE$; $Cr = GBJCK$. Gradual bonus: $Wr = ABDE$; $Cr = GBCK$. Gantt task and bonus plan: $Wr = ACDF$; $Cr = GBJCM$. Task levels: low $(L) = 0.667E_H$; normal $(n) = 0.80E_H$; high $(H) = 1.00E_H$.

Fig. 4. Differential time plans with single-step gradual bonus, and the Gantt task and bonus plan using high task standards.

E_H (1)	Single-Step Differential Plan			Differential Plan with Gradual Bonus			Gantt Task and Bonus Plan		
	W_r (2)	B_r (3)	C_r (4)	W_r (5)	B_r (6)	C_r (7)	W_r (8)	B_r (9)	C_r (10)
	(Eqs. 3, 18)	(Eqs. 4, 19)	(Eqs. 15, 20)	(Eqs. 3, 22, 18)	(Eqs. 4, 23, 19)	(Eqs. 15, 24, 20)	(Eqs. 3, 22)	(Eqs. 4, 23)	(Eqs. 15, 24)
		Col. (2) minus 1.00	Col. (2) × 0.80 ÷ Col. (1)		Col. (5) minus 1.00	Col. (5) × 0.80 ÷ Col. (1)		Col. (8) minus 1.00	Col. (8) × 0.80 ÷ Col. (1)
0.40	1.00	0.00	2.000	1.000	0.000	2.000	1.000	0.000	2.000
0.50	1.00	0.00	1.600	1.000	0.000	1.600	1.000	0.000	1.600
0.60	1.00	0.00	1.333	1.000	0.000	1.333	1.000	0.000	1.333
0.70	1.00	0.00	1.143	1.000	0.000	1.143	1.000	0.000	1.143
0.80	1.00	0.00	1.000	1.000	0.000	1.000	1.000	0.000	1.000
0.90	1.00	0.00	0.8888	1.125	0.125	1.000	1.000	0.000	0.8888
0.99	1.00	0.00	0.8081	1.238	0.238	1.000	1.000	0.000	0.8081
1.00	1.25	0.25	1.0000	1.250	0.250	1.000	1.250	0.250	1.000
1.10	1.25	0.25	0.9091	1.250	0.250	0.9091	1.375	0.375	1.000
1.20	1.25	0.25	0.8333	1.250	0.250	0.8333	1.500	0.500	1.000
1.30	1.25	0.25	0.7692	1.250	0.250	0.7692	1.625	0.625	1.000
1.40	1.25	0.25	0.7143	1.250	0.250	0.7143	1.750	0.750	1.000
1.50	1.25	0.25	0.6667	1.250	0.250	0.6667	1.875	0.875	1.000
1.60	1.25	0.25	0.6250	1.250	0.250	0.6250	2.000	1.000	1.000
1.70	1.25	0.25	0.5882	1.250	0.250	0.5882	2.125	1.125	1.000
1.80	1.25	0.25	0.5556	1.250	0.250	0.5556	2.250	1.250	1.000

Fig. 5. Data for differential time plans and Gantt task and bonus plan for Fig. 4.

DIFFERENTIAL TIME PLAN WITH GRADUAL BONUS. Some persons criticize the single-step bonus on the ground that, if the operator nearly, but not quite, meets the high task standard, he thereby deserves nearly the full bonus and should not be penalized by being paid only base wages. This apparent severity can be softened by adding smaller steps for ranges of output between normal and high task. Increasingly smaller steps eventually result in a smooth straight line, starting from the base wage line for normal performance, and increasing at a full sharing rate up to the 25 percent bonus for high task performance. The **gradual bonus** feature weakens the inducement to achieve a specified high task output, but it is somewhat more palatable, particularly to operators of variable-speed machines.

Modified Differential Time Plan Formulas. For this first modification of the differential time rate plan, base rates are guaranteed up to normal productivity. Thus, up to $E_H = 0.80$, wage ratios are the same as for straight daywork.

Between $E_H = 0.80$ and $E_H = 1.00$, wages are determined from the high rate $(1.25R)$ and the high task standard time produced.

$$W = S_H \times N \times 1.25R \tag{21}$$

$$= \frac{S_H}{T} \times 1.25 \times TNR$$

$$Wr = 1.25 \times E_H \times \frac{TNR}{TNR} = 1.25E_H \tag{22}$$

$$Br = Wr - 1.00 = 1.25E_H - 1.00 \tag{23}$$

The unit labor cost will be the total wages W divided by the number N of units produced:

$$C = \frac{W}{N} = S_H \times \frac{N}{N} \times 1.25R = 1.25 \times S_H R = 1.25 \times 0.80 S_n R = S_n R$$

From equation (14), the standard unit labor cost is $S_n R$. Thus the cost ratio becomes:

$$Cr = \frac{S_n R}{S_n R} = 1.00 \tag{24}$$

and remains constant throughout this range of efficiencies.

At high task output, where $E_H = 1.00$, or above, a flat hourly rate, $1.25 \times R$, is paid for actual time worked regardless of output; therefore the same wage and cost ratios as those developed for similar efficiencies in the single-step plan will apply here. Fig. 4 shows the wage and cost curves for the gradual bonus plan and the corresponding data are given in Fig. 5.

DIFFERENTIAL TIME PLAN WITH LOSS OF BONUS. Another modification of the differential time feature has been applied successfully at Timken Roller Bearing Co. to work involving the grinding of bearing raceways (Factory, Vol. 113). The **operation cycle** is divided into manual elements and machine elements. **Full sharing bonuses** are paid for time saved on the manual elements, with no limits prescribed. The incentive payment for this phase of the work is therefore equivalent to the 100 percent standard hour plan with a base rate guarantee.

For the machine elements, base wages are guaranteed up to the minimum desirable cutting speeds, assumed to represent normal productivity. Hence, up to $E_H = 0.80$, the same formulas apply as in the single-step differential plan. Maximum safe grinding speeds have been established by careful research and are considered to deserve a 35 percent bonus. Between normal machine productivity and the prescribed maximum, bonuses increase along a smooth line at a full sharing rate up to the 35 percent limit. Thus, between efficiencies of $E_H = 0.80$ and $E_H = 1.00$, wages and costs correspond to the previous modified differential time plan with the gradual bonus, and the same wage and cost equations apply.

High efficiencies above $E_H = 1.00$ are obtainable only by the use of excess cutting speeds that are likely to cause irreparable damage to expensive materials. Some action is considered necessary to discourage any desire on the part of the operator to use excessive speeds. High efficiencies are penalized by cancellation of the bonus and payment of base rate only for actual time worked. Thus, again, daywork wage formulas apply. This plan provides effective **protection** against damage to the grinding product.

GANTT TASK AND BONUS PLAN. This plan combines the security of guaranteed base wages, the strong incentive of a single-step bonus to meet definite high levels of output, and high rewards equivalent to high piece rates for exceeding standards.

The plan could be administered with normal task standards if the step bonus were located at the 1.25 (125 percent) efficiency level. However, if an operator exceeds any specified standards, regardless of how loose they may be, he naturally expects some immediate bonus. Psychologically it is more palatable to give the step bonus for just meeting tight standards; therefore the Gantt plan should be used only with high task standards and with the step bonus occurring at a corresponding efficiency ratio of $E_H = 1.00$.

While the time rate guarantee below task is more charitable than straight or differential **piecework** with no guaranteed minimum, Gantt did not intend charity toward habitually low producers. He emphasized both training and good supervision by providing special **foreman's bonuses** related to the proportion of operators making task. Because the guaranteed minimum wages often were below base, the inducement of the step bonus was enhanced, but this also made the hiring of workers more difficult. The size of the step bonus was not always uniform. Gantt found that 10 to 15 percent above base was sufficient for some types of machine tending, but he used steps of 30 to 40 percent on some operations involving high degrees of attention and eye strain. For this discussion, a step bonus of 25 percent is assumed appropriate.

Applications of Gantt Plan. Because of the step bonus and additional high rewards for exceeding standards, the plan is most suitable for skilled operators on Class 1 work where output is proportional to operator effort, but where very accurate and tight standards are established and consistently maintained by good methods and time study procedures. The step bonus encourages operators to meet definite and high production schedules, a distinct advantage in effective production control and in meeting delivery-date promises; and the high rewards above task properly recognize high levels of operator effort. For many years Westinghouse Electric Corp. used this plan extensively with bonus steps of 10 or 15 percent and a base rate guarantee, but called it the **standard time** plan.

As with the differential time plan, the step bonus makes the Gantt plan suitable for application to expensive machines or processes, such as Class 3 work, where high burden ratios make it important to maintain definite high levels of output. However the Gantt plan, with its additional high rewards for extra output, preferably should not be used on such work unless the machine or process speeds can be varied under the operator's control and unless it is safe and desirable to encourage sufficiently high speeds to achieve outputs significantly above the high task level.

Gantt Plan Formulas. For outputs up to, and including, high task, the Gantt plan is identical to the single-step differential time plan; hence the same wage and cost formulas will apply. For performance above high task, wages are calculated from the high task standard time produced and a high hourly rate that is, say, $1.25 \times R$. The same effect is accomplished by the concept of using the base rate R but applying a 25 percent **incentive factor** in the wage calculations when $E_H = 1.00$ or more. With either concept:

$$W = S_H \times N \times 1.25R \tag{21}$$
$$Wr = 1.25E_H \tag{22}$$
$$Br = 1.25E_H - 1.00 \tag{23}$$
$$Cr = 1.00 \tag{24}$$

These equations were developed under the differential time plan with gradual bonus and were applicable between normal and high task output. In the Gantt plan, however, they are applicable at and above high task performance.

Fig. 4 gives the wage and cost curves for the Gantt plan and the corresponding data are given in Fig. 5.

Characteristics of the Gantt Plan. The Gantt task and bonus plan has the following characteristics:

1. Successful administration of this plan requires the use of consistently tight standards that accurately reflect true work content, and requires that the step bonus become effective for performance at true **high task pace.**

2. The plan is most suitable for **skilled operators** on Class 1 type of work, where methods and materials are well standardized and output is accurately measured and directly proportional to operator effort.

3. The plan is very suitable for machine operations where definite high levels of output are needed as in Class 3 work, yet where it is safe and desirable to encourage still higher levels of output by increasing machine or process speeds. It is readily applicable to **mechanically paced assembly lines.**

4. It is equally suitable for both **individual and group incentive** administration, since time, rather than monetary, standards are used.

5. The plan would be difficult to sell to traditional daywork operators, since the output to which the operators are accustomed would have to be increased from low task (83 percent of normal) to high task (125 percent of normal) or by about 50 percent before any bonuses would be realized. This would appear as a formidable hurdle. A considerable length of time and much persuasion probably would be required to overcome **employee resistance.** The plan is relatively easy to install in shops already accustomed to normal or high task standards.

6. The plan is nearly as simple to administer as the standard hour plan. A single base rate, for each person or labor grade, may be used along with tables of calculated efficiencies and corresponding bonus ratios. Or, below task, the base rate may be used with actual hours worked, while at, or above, task a high rate may be applied to the standard hours produced. The former method is slightly simpler and subject to fewer calculation errors.

7. With its step bonus, and continued high sharing of any additional time saved, the Gantt is one of the strongest incentive plans yet devised.

MONETARY PIECEWORK PLAN. The term piecework is commonly applied very loosely. Occasionally it is used broadly to imply any plan of payment for measured output rather than for time spent. In a somewhat more restricted sense, it may imply any one of a limited group of so-called full sharing or 100 percent plans which pays a definite amount of money, or time, for each unit of output, as contrasted with partial or variable sharing plans.

Historically, industrial homework, which characterized the transition from the guild to the factory system, was difficult to supervise and payment by the piece was logical. Time study had not been developed, and money, or its equivalent in bartered goods, was a natural means of payment. Thus arose the concept of paying a definite amount of money for each unit of output.

Early "piece rates" often were **bargained** or **estimated.** Even today some piece rates are established by determining what the expected earnings should be for a given period of continuous work and dividing by an estimated quantity of output considered reasonable for such a period. Piece rates for similar but slightly different products then may be established by comparison or by estimating the value of the differences. This is still common practice in many small shops and in certain industries where it has become a time-honored practice.

In this discussion the term piecework will be used only for reference to wage plans based on the payment of certain amounts of **money** per unit of product. The concept of time is generally absent.

Characteristics of Piecework Plan. Among the characteristics of a piecework plan are the following:

1. Except when productivity falls below guaranteed minimum wages, the wages of the operator are **directly proportional** to the measured output, although they may not always be proportional to the true productivity or effective effort expended. Graphically, wages are represented by a straight line passing through the origin of zero wages for zero output.

2. All gains, or losses, from variations in the rate of output accrue directly to the worker, as contrasted with straight time payment plans where any gains or losses accrue to the employer.

3. Since wages are directly proportional to measured output, such plans are best suited to situations where output and operator effort are directly proportional, as described under Class 1 work.

4. For equitable wages, piece rates should be established so that earnings equivalent to properly evaluated base rate wages would be obtained with the normal level of operator effort; that is, piece rates should correspond with normal task standards. With modern time study procedures, piece rates usually are determined by establishing a **normal time standard** and multiplying this standard by the base rate for the labor grade in which the job is classified. Similar piece rates would be obtained from high task time standards multiplied by 1.25 (125 percent) of the base rate.

5. With piecework, as with all full sharing or high sharing plans, it is important that outputs be measured accurately, and that standards be highly consistent, if gross inequities and employee dissatisfaction are to be avoided.

6. Piecework is simple, both for the employer to administer and for employees to understand. Since standards are in terms of money rather than time, it appeals particularly to operators with a relatively low level of intelligence.

7. Unit direct labor costs are constant for all levels of output unless a minimum wage is guaranteed or different monetary rates are used for different ranges of productivity, as in some differential piecework plans.

8. As long as the piece rate remains constant, the actual unit labor cost is the same as the standard labor cost, and labor efficiency variances will not occur. Cost accounting therefore is simplified.

9. For production scheduling, monetary piece rates must be **converted** to unit times by dividing the piece rates by the appropriate base rates. Not only is this inconvenient, but also in some piecework situations correct base rates may not be known.

10. With piece rates alone, two persons producing the same output on a given task will earn precisely the same wages, and it is impossible to reward individual differences in versatility, dependability, or seniority. Of course, such factors could be recognized by **supplementary hourly rates,** but only at some sacrifice of the simplicity of piecework.

11. Because piece rates historically have been set from estimates and past production records, without regard to methods improvement and standardization, and because they have been applied to unsuitable types of work (such as Class 2 or Class 3), individual earnings frequently have become excessive. In attempts to re-establish some reasonable consistency in earnings, employers have resorted to arbitrary **rate cutting.** This can, and occasionally does, occur with other types of incentive plans; but, since the element of time (or rate of output) is not particularly evident, the stigma of rate cutting is associated more closely with piecework than with other plans.

12. If economic conditions prescribe a general lowering of wage rates (as during depression periods), piece rates must be lowered and this obviously appears as rate cutting. If general wage levels rise, piece rates must be increased. In both cases the piece rates must be changed, and a tremendous amount of clerical work is involved. But wage level adjustments often vary in degree for different grades of labor, according to current economic, and sometimes local, situations. Thus all piece rates seldom can be adjusted simply by a **uniform percentage.** Many individual and arbitrary decisions must be made which may exaggerate existing inconsistencies, or create new ones. Whenever there is a negotiated change in the base rate structure, the tremendous clerical cost of revising piece price sheets is avoided in some companies by applying an appropriate **adjustment factor** to existing **piece price sheets.** This factor represents the amount of adjustment that would have been made if the sheet had been revised and is used in the payroll calculations. In some cases, however, this procedure has reduced the strength of the incentive system because the worker still regards his piece price as the amount stated on the sheet and fails to give the company credit for the amount by which the price is increased when the factor is used in computing his pay.

13. With monetary piece rates alone it is difficult to determine an appropriate adjustment for a change in method, even when it is agreed that such a revision is justified. In contrast, if standards are recorded in terms of time, modern time study techniques provide a ready and accurate means of determining the correction. For this reason many authorities agree that the administration of production standards should be isolated from earnings. This permits the use of trained specialists for determining and maintaining output standards, and properly leaves the establishment of wage levels in the realm of negotiation between the employees and the employer.

14. Piecework is most suitable for individuals. It has been applied to groups, but equitable administration is difficult. **Group piecework** implies that a definite amount of money is paid to the group as a whole for each unit of output. This amount might be distributed equally among the members, but usually not all members of a group are equally productive, and often a group contains more than one grade of labor. Accordingly, it is customary to set up a **personal hourly rate** for each member to reflect both his labor grade and his relative productivity. The group's earnings then are distributed according to these personal rates and the proportion of time that each member serves the group. This in itself is a complicated payroll routine. But, if the employer decides to increase the earnings of one member and raises an individual personal rate, that member will receive a higher portion of the group's earnings at the expense of the other members, and with no additional cost to the employer. If time standards were used, the employer would absorb the cost of the one member's raise, and wages of the other members would not be affected. For this and several other reasons listed above, most larger companies are abandoning piece rates in favor of time standards.

Minimum Rates. Straight piecework assumes that a fixed amount of money will be paid for each unit of output at all levels of output. Theoretically the equivalent of base rate wages would be earned for a normal level of productivity, 25 percent higher wages for incentive productivity, and no earnings whatever for zero output. The same principle is involved in many situations outside of factories. For example, a door-to-door salesman may receive a straight commission on his sales. The owner of a retail business derives his income from a definite markup on the cost of his merchandise, that is, a definite portion of the sales price. A building contractor receives a specified amount of money for each unit of construction. Many other illustrations could be cited, all of which fundamentally are examples of straight piecework where earnings are directly proportional to the delivered output. In fact, the principle applies broadly to large manufacturing enterprises where income depends upon production and sales.

It is only logical that the same principle be applied to factory employees. But many employees have neither the desire nor the ability to assume such risks of individual responsibility. Furthermore, such factors as confinement to the employer's premises, the mutual advantages of specialization in a limited type of work, and the fact that output is not readily measurable on certain types of work, all raised problems of employee security and the necessity of guaranteeing some minimum wage for time spent on the job.

As a result of social pressures, Federal legislation was enacted (Fair Labor Standards Act, 1938) which imposed a **legal minimum hourly rate** of 40 cents per hr. This was raised by stages until in 1956 the minimum was $1.00 per hr. In effect, the use of straight piecework for factory employees is eliminated by this legislation.

Except in some local situations, the legal minimum is lower than the going base rate which must be paid to obtain an adequate supply of even the lowest grade of labor. In actual practice, therefore, the guaranteed minimum hourly rates correspond closely with base rates determined by job-evaluation and labor-market surveys. Thus straight piecework is primarily of academic interest only, and, generally, industrial piecework plans now are piecework with the base rate as a guaranteed minimum.

Piecework Plan Formulas. Piecework wages are simply the product of the monetary piece rate M multiplied by the number N of pieces produced.

$$W = MN \qquad (25)$$

Without a standard in terms of time, there is no convenient method of determining an efficiency ratio. It would be possible to calculate such a ratio if actual piecework earnings were divided by the product of the base rate (if known) and the number of pieces produced. Such an efficiency would be:

$$E = \frac{MN}{RN} \qquad (26)$$

but this calculation is uncommon in regular piecework installations.

With a **minimum guarantee,** the minimum hourly rate, perhaps the base rate, is paid for actual hours worked up to the point where the piecework earnings from equation (25) equal the base wages or the minimum wages required. If piecework earnings exceed the minimum or base wages, straight piecework wages obviously are paid.

But, where modern time study procedures are used, the dollar value M is determined by multiplying a standard time S by the base rate R; therefore,

$$M = SR \qquad (27)$$

Thus, if standards are expressed in hours S, rather than in money M, the plan would become a standard hour or a 100 percent time premium plan. From this point on, therefore, formula development will be in terms of standard time plans and considered equally applicable to piecework.

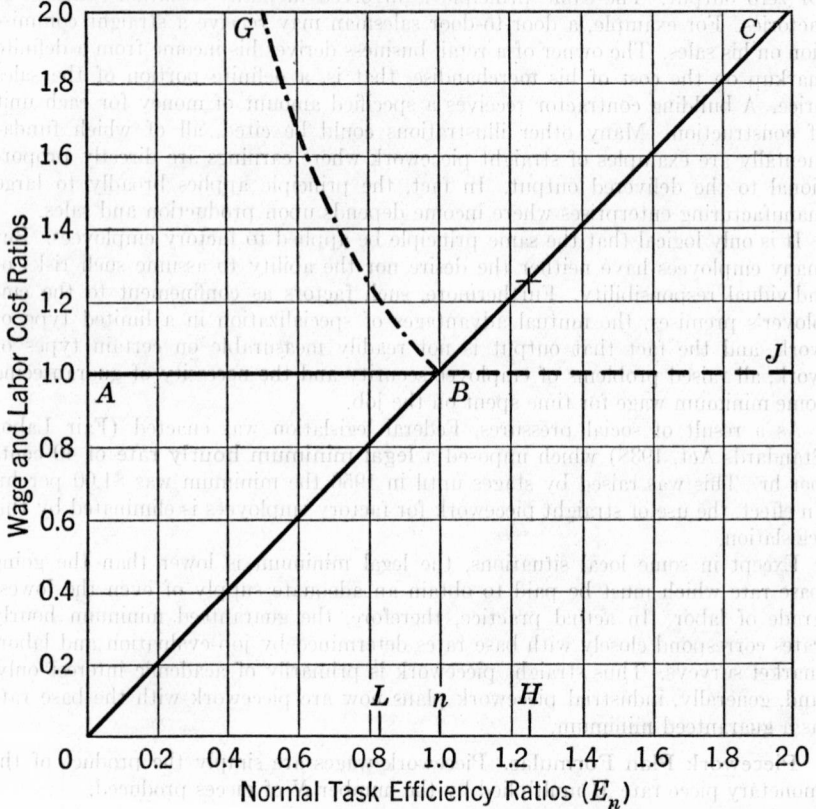

Straight piecework with no guarantee: $Wr = OBC$; $Cr = ABJ$. Standard hour with guaranteed base: $Wr = ABC$; $Cr = GBJ$. Task levels: low $(L) = 0.833E_n$; normal $(n) = 1.00E_n$; high $(H) = 1.25E_n$.

Fig. 6. Piecework and standard hour plans, normal task standards.

Fig. 6 gives the piecework and standard hour plan wage and cost curves. The corresponding data appear in Fig. 7.

STANDARD HOUR PLAN. The standard hour plan is essentially the same as straight piecework, with corresponding limitations of a base rate minimum guarantee. The employee is allowed a **standard time per unit of output.** If he fails to meet standard, he is paid the minimum guaranteed rate for the time actually spent. Usually (but not always) the minimum guaranteed rate is the base rate, and it will be assumed to be in this discussion.

If the employee completes the task in less than the allowed time (or exceeds the standard), he is paid for the allowed (standard) time at his base rate. Thus, if his base rate is $1.00 per hr. and he completes a 10-hr. task in 8 hr., he is paid

$10 \times \$1.00$ or $\$10.00$. His base wages would have been $8 \times \$1.00$ or $\$8.00$, and thus he receives a bonus of $\$10.00 - \$8.00$, or $\$2.00$, for the period. The same bonus would be obtained by first subtracting the actual time (8 hr.) from the standard time (10 hr.) and multiplying the difference (2 hr.) by the base rate to get $2 \times \$1.00$, or $\$2.00$, bonus.

(1) E_n	(2) Wr (Eqs. 3, 32)	(3) Br (Eqs. 4, 33)	(4) Cr (Eqs. 8, 36)
0.50	1.00	0.00	2.000
0.60	1.00	0.00	1.667
0.70	1.00	0.00	1.429
0.80	1.00	0.00	1.250
0.90	1.00	0.00	1.111
1.00	1.00	0.00	1.000
1.10	1.10	0.10	1.000
1.20	1.20	0.20	1.000
1.25	1.25	0.25	1.000
1.30	1.30	0.30	1.000
1.40	1.40	0.40	1.000
1.50	1.50	0.50	1.000
1.60	1.60	0.60	1.000
1.70	1.70	0.70	1.000
1.80	1.80	0.80	1.000
		Col. (2) minus 1.00	Col. (2) ÷ Col. (1)

Fig. 7. Data for piecework and standard hour plans for Fig. 6.

For general administration it is more convenient to calculate **efficiency ratios**. In this case the efficiency ratio E is the ratio of standard time S to actual time T, or $10/8 = 1.25$ (125 percent). The bonus ratio obviously is 0.25 (or $1.25 - 1.00$), and the base wages ($\$8.00$) are multiplied by the bonus ratio (0.25) to get $\$8.00 \times 0.25 = \$2.00$ bonus.

This introduces the concept of **time saved**; and bonus ratios, generally, can be determined as mathematical functions of time saved. Since the ratio of time allowed to time taken is the efficiency ratio (by definition), the ratio of time saved to time taken is $(E - 1.00)$; thus, for comparison of various plans, it is convenient to determine bonus ratios as functions of efficiency.

Standard Hour Plan Formulas. Typically under this plan base rate wages are guaranteed for all levels of output below the standard which should be, and usually is, based on the concept of normal task. Thus the same formulas apply here as developed under straight daywork.

For efficiencies up to $E_n = 1.00$:

$$Wr = 1.00 \tag{3}$$

$$Br = 0.00 \tag{4}$$

$$Cr_n = \frac{1.00}{E_n} \tag{8}$$

At $E_n = 1.00$, and higher efficiencies, total wages often are calculated as the product of the normal standard allowed time per unit S_n, the number of units produced N, and an hourly rate which properly is the base rate R. For effective administration, the base rate always is recommended except in special **group applications** where it is desired to reward some individuals for intangible factors such as versatility, seniority, etc.

$$W = SNR \tag{28}$$

In all cases it is desirable to make the operator aware of the portion of the total wages which represents bonus for extra effort. In the majority of cases the base wages and the bonus wages are shown separately on the stub of the pay check, but often it is more desirable to pay the bonus wages with a **separate check.** Thus the bonus is separated by subtracting the base wages TNR from the total wages SNR.

$$B = SNR - TNR = (S - T)NR \tag{29}$$

Here it is seen that the bonus is the product of: the time saved per unit $(S - T)$, the number of units, and the base rate. Without changing its true value, the concept of efficiency can be introduced by multiplying equation (29) by T/T.

$$B = \frac{(S - T)}{T} TNR$$

and, since

$$\frac{S}{T} = E,$$

$$B = (E - 1.00)TNR \tag{30}$$

Total wages then become:

$$W = \text{base wages} + \text{bonus wages}$$
$$W = TNR + (E - 1.00)TNR \tag{31}$$

The wage ratio is:

$$Wr = \frac{W}{TNR} = 1.00 + (E - 1.00) \tag{32}$$

and the bonus ratio is:

$$Br = (E - 1.00) \tag{33}$$

Thus bonus wages are found by multiplying the bonus ratio $(E - 1.00)$ by the base wages for the actual time spent on incentive work.

The coefficient of the quantity $(E - 1.00)$ may be assumed to be 1.00 (or 100 percent), or

$$Br = (E - 1.00) \times 1.00 \tag{34}$$

This indicates that the operator receives a full (100 percent) share of any time saved through extra productivity.

The actual unit labor cost is found by dividing the total wages SNR by the number of units N:

$$C = \frac{SNR}{N} = SR \tag{35}$$

The standard unit cost C_s is the product of the normal standard S and the base rate R:

$$C_s = S_n R \tag{6^}$$

The cost ratio becomes:

$$Cr = \frac{C}{C_s} = \frac{SR}{S_nR} = 1.00 \qquad (36)$$

Thus the cost ratio remains constant at unity for all levels of productivity above standard, and there will be no labor efficiency variance.

Fig. 6 shows the wage and cost curves for the standard hour plan, and the corresponding data are given in Fig. 7.

Characteristics of the Standard Hour Plan. The standard hour plan possesses the following characteristics:

1. It is applicable to any shop or office situation wherever piecework is suitable, but should be limited to the types of work indicated in Class 1.
2. It will yield the same **unit labor costs** as piecework if the employees' personal hourly rates are the same as the base rates which would be appropriate for determining piece rates.
3. Being a 100 percent or full sharing plan, standard labor costs are easily determined and, like piecework, no **labor efficiency variances** will occur except when output is below standard.
4. With standards expressed in units of time, **personal rates** deviating from the labor grade base rates can be used to reward individuals for intangible factors such as versatility, dependability, and seniority. However, this is not recommended, since it tends to give a double reward for over-all increased performance.
5. If varying personal rates are used within a labor grade, **labor rate variances,** determined from the difference between the weighted average of the actual personal rates and the base rate of the labor grade, are created. This introduces some complexities in the use of standard cost systems, but it provides a means of setting up a control account for keeping actual wage rates in line with specified averages.
6. The use of time standards makes the standard hour plan more convenient than piecework for **group incentives** because personal rates can be altered if desired without affecting wages of other operators in the group.
7. More intelligent and objective discussions of productivities are possible with time standards, since the emotional concept of earnings is not so directly involved.
8. Conversion of relative outputs to calculated efficiencies provides a common denominator for **comparing productivities** of individuals, departments, or whole plants, even for a large variety of operations.
9. With time standards, intelligent **production scheduling** becomes possible and effective.
10. A 100 percent sharing plan provides only a **moderate incentive.** It lacks the strength of a step bonus to induce operators to sustain output at a prescribed level; yet it is stronger than most sharing plans because of its relatively high and seemingly just reward for exceeding normal performance.

HALSEY CONSTANT PARTIAL SHARING PLAN (HALSEY PREMIUM PLAN).

In companies where all work traditionally has been unmeasured and paid with straight time wages, some average level of output is obtained for the daywork wages paid and a precedent thus has been established that this average output is a reasonable and acceptable level. It could be argued that any extra output above this previously acceptable level should be rewarded with some increased earnings, and that these average past performances therefore could be accepted as the standards.

But these past performance averages usually reflect outputs from beginners as well as seasoned employees and include much time lost as a result of many avoidable interruptions. Experience has shown that such daywork outputs can be increased greatly with very little extra operator effort; that is, the extra effort is not directly proportional to the extra output. Furthermore, some increased costs would be involved in reviewing past records to determine the standards, measuring and reporting outputs, and making additional payroll calculations.

A logical proposal, then, would be to share the savings between the employee and the company. For want of any objective reasons to the contrary, these shares may be made equal, giving the operator a 50 percent share of the time saved from output above the past performance averages.

Halsey Plan Formulas. Base wages are guaranteed for outputs below standards. **Up to low task standard,** wage and bonus formulas similar to those for straight daywork apply, but, in relation to low task efficiencies, daywork cost ratios would appear lower than for corresponding normal efficiencies and must be adjusted by $1.20/E_L$.

At and above standard, in general, total incentive wages for any constant sharing plan are equal to the base rate multiplied by the actual time worked, plus the base rate multiplied by a portion of the time saved. The portion of the time saved that is credited to the operator may be represented by the general term p.

$$W = TNR + p(S - T)NR \qquad (37)$$

In the more common applications, the operator receives one-half of the apparent savings, so that $p = 0.50$. With this relatively low share for the operator, standards should be more liberal than normal task standards; usually they are low task standards represented by S_L. More specifically, then, total wages may be represented by the equation

$$W = TNR + 0.5(S_L - T)NR \qquad (38)$$

Multiplying the second term by T/T gives

$$W = TNR + 0.5 \frac{(S_L - T)}{T} TNR$$

$$W = TNR + 0.5(E_L - 1.00)TNR \qquad (39)$$

The wage ratio

$$Wr = 1.00 + 0.5(E_L - 1.00) \qquad (40)$$

and the bonus ratio

$$Br = Wr - 1.00 = 0.5(E_L - 1.00) \qquad (41)$$

For algebraic manipulation, equation (40) can be simplified to

$$Wr = 1.00 + 0.50E_L - 0.50 = 0.50 + 0.50E_L \qquad (42)$$

From equation (42) it is seen that, if base wages were not guaranteed, the wage ratio would be 0.50 for zero output. However, all wage payment plans, by law, must guarantee at least the minimum legal wage in the United States.

The above equations, (37) through (42), recognize that efficiency ratios E are calculated, in actual practice, from whatever standards are available, without regard to whether those standards reflect low task, normal, or high task performance requirements.

Early in this discussion, the concept was developed that the wage ratio should be 1.25 for true incentive performance. Substituting 1.25 for Wr in equation (42) gives:

$$1.25 = 0.50 + 0.50E_L$$

$$0.50E_L = 1.25 - 0.50 = 0.75$$

$$E_L = 1.50$$

Thus a calculated efficiency of 1.50 must be attained under this plan to yield the desired 25 percent bonus. Such high calculated efficiencies usually cannot be attained unless standards are loose enough to require only low task performance; therefore efficiencies calculated from low task standards are designated E_L.

A 100 percent premium (standard hour) wage ratio curve, drawn through standard low task efficiency ($E_L = 1.00$), necessarily would pass through the origin of the chart where both $Wr = 0.00$ and $E_L = 0.00$. Such a curve would indicate $Wr = 1.50$, where $E_L = 1.50$ represents incentive performance. But, in terms of normal standards, incentive performance is represented by $E_n = 1.25$, and the curve would rise at a rate of 1.50/1.25 or 1.20. The equation of such a line would be

$$Wr = 1.20E_n \qquad (43)$$

Low task performance is indicated at the point where this curve crosses the base wage line, or where $Wr = 1.00$. At this point, normal efficiency would be:

$$E_n = \frac{1.00}{1.20} = 0.833$$

indicating that low task standards require only about 0.8333 (83.3 percent) as much productivity as do normal standards; or 0.833/1.25 or 0.667 (66.7 percent) of high task productivity. Correspondingly, low task standards will allow 20 percent more time than normal standards.

$$S_L = 1.20S_n \qquad (44)$$
$$E_L = 1.20E_n \qquad (45)$$

Experience has shown that typical daywork output, as revealed by past performance records, tends to be about 83 percent of normal output, or about two-thirds (66.7 percent) of high task output. Also, low task standards tend to result from foreman's estimates or from rough over-all time studies. In some cases, jobs may be carefully studied, but accomplishment may be uncertain owing to uncontrolled variables, and standards therefore are set deliberately for low task performance.

An **alternative analysis** may be helpful in understanding this relationship. As indicated in the development of equation (43), a wage ratio of 1.50 would be expected from incentive performance if a full sharing plan were used with low task standards. This is excessive in relation to the operator effort required for incentive performance. On the other hand, if the 50 percent sharing plan were used with normal standards, incentive performance would yield a calculated efficiency E_n of only 1.25. Substituting this value into equation (41) gives a bonus ratio of only

$$Br = 0.50(1.25 - 1.00) = 0.125$$

which is too low a reward for incentive performance. But, for incentive performance, where $E_n = 1.25$, efficiency calculated from low task standards will yield:

$$E_L = 1.20 \times 1.25 = 1.50$$

which, substituted into equation (41), gives a desired bonus ratio of:

$$Br = 0.5(1.50 - 1.00) = 0.25$$

The **cost ratio** may be developed in the following manner. Starting with equation (39):

$$W = TNR + 0.5(E_L - 1.00)TNR \qquad (39)$$

Combining terms:

$$W = (0.5 + 0.5E_L)TNR$$

The unit labor cost then becomes

$$C = (0.5 + 0.5E_L)TR \tag{46}$$

Standard unit labor cost is calculated from the point of expected incentive earnings, i.e.. where actual wages are 1.25 (125 percent) of base wages and output is 1.25 (125 percent) of normal.

$$C_s = \frac{1.25}{1.25} S_n R = S_n R$$

The cost ratio then becomes

$$Cr = (0.5 + 0.5E_L) \frac{TR}{S_n R} = (0.5 + 0.5E_L) \frac{1.00}{E_n}$$

But, since, from equation (45),

$$E_n = \frac{E_L}{1.20}$$

then

$$Cr = (0.5 + 0.5E_L) \frac{1.20}{E_L}$$

$$Cr = \frac{0.6}{E_L} + 0.6 \tag{47}$$

Because this is a 50 percent sharing plan, variations in rate of output will create labor efficiency variance ratios EVr. As indicated in equation (10), this variance ratio is 1.00 minus the cost ratio.

$$EVr = 1.00 - \left(\frac{0.6}{E_L} + 0.6 \right) = 0.4 - \frac{0.6}{E_L} \tag{48}$$

From equation (47), if low task efficiency $E_L = 1.00$, the cost ratio Cr becomes 1.20, which is higher than the standard cost because productivity is below normal. At normal productivity, $E_L = 1.20$ and Cr becomes 1.10. At incentive productivity, $E_L = 1.50$ and Cr becomes 1.00 or equivalent to standard. This indicates the liberality of the plan giving higher wages than a 100 percent plan between low task and high task performances, with corresponding negative or unfavorable efficiency variances.

But, for example, if a very high calculated efficiency were attained, say $E_L = 2.00$, the Cr becomes 0.90, indicating a positive or favorable variance. However, since operators receive only a 50 percent share of the time saved, the plan offers no strong inducement for such high efficiencies and they are somewhat unlikely.

Fig. 8 gives the wage and cost curves for the Halsey 50 percent constant sharing plan with low task standards, and the corresponding data appear in Fig. 9.

Characteristics of the Halsey Plan. Some characteristics of the Halsey 50 percent plan are included in the following list:

1. The plan is suitable for Class 2 type of work previously described, where conditions are uncertain, **output measurements** may be inaccurate, and standards unavoidably, or deliberately, are consistently looser than normal and generally reflect low task performance.
2. The incentive is weak. There is **no strong inducement** for operators to attain incentive performance, since some operators will be content with bonuses that are less than 25 percent of base wages. Accordingly it is unlikely that true incentive performance generally would be exceeded.

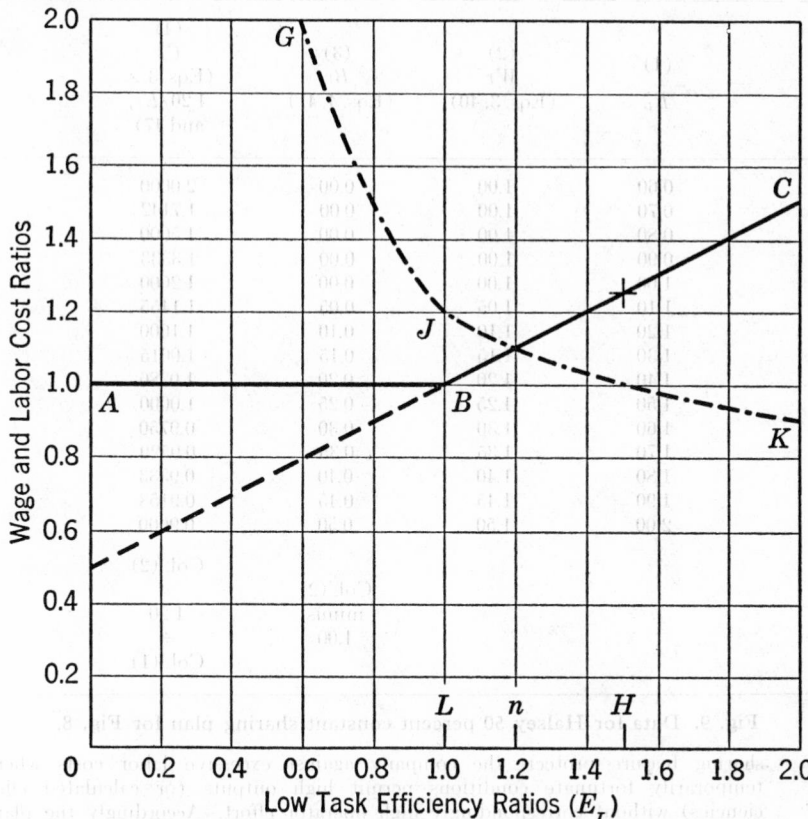

$Wr = ABC$; $Cr = GJK$. Task levels: low $(L) = 1.00E_L$; normal $(n) = 1.20E_L$; high $(H) = 1.50E_L$.

Fig. 8. Halsey 50 percent constant sharing plan, low task standards.

3. Since there is no strong inducement to meet any specified level of output, actual **rates of output** will vary considerably and accurate production scheduling becomes difficult.

4. From a company's viewpoint, the plan is not particularly effective when overhead ratios are high and it is desired to operate machines or processes at or near full capacity. However, the plan frequently is used on machine operations where output is affected greatly by variations in temperature, humidity, and other factors considered beyond the operator's control. In such cases, standards may be set for normal or even incentive performance, but wages equivalent to low task standards are paid. This is accomplished by adding so-called automatic **variable conditions allowances** which frequently are isolated in a separate account for cost-control purposes.

5. Because low task standards are equivalent to daywork performance, this plan may be introduced into daywork shops without requiring a change in the operators' concept of **acceptable performance**. Beginning early, with low task output, bonuses are considerably more generous, up to incentive output, than in a standard hour plan using normal standards. Low task standards thus protect the operator against temporarily unfortunate conditions, yet the 50 percent

(1) E_L	(2) W_r (Eqs. 3, 40)	(3) B_r (Eqs. 4, 41)	(4) C_r (Eqs. 3 × 1.20/E_L, and 47)
0.60	1.00	0.00	2.0000
0.70	1.00	0.00	1.7142
0.80	1.00	0.00	1.5000
0.90	1.00	0.00	1.3333
1.00	1.00	0.00	1.2000
1.10	1.05	0.05	1.1455
1.20	1.10	0.10	1.1000
1.30	1.15	0.15	1.0615
1.40	1.20	0.20	1.0286
1.50	1.25	0.25	1.0000
1.60	1.30	0.30	0.9750
1.70	1.35	0.35	0.9529
1.80	1.40	0.40	0.9333
1.90	1.45	0.45	0.9158
2.00	1.50	0.50	0.9000
		Col. (2) minus 1.00	Col. (2) × 1.20 ÷ Col. (1)

Fig. 9. Data for Halsey 50 percent constant sharing plan for Fig. 8.

sharing feature protects the company against excessive labor costs when temporarily fortunate conditions permit high outputs (or calculated efficiencies) without correspondingly high operator effort. Accordingly the plan has been used during a period of transition from straight daywork to stronger incentive plans. However, the eventual change from low task to normal or high task standards, which are necessary with stronger plans, may appear as rate cutting, because higher outputs are necessary before any bonuses can be realized. This is likely to meet considerable operator resistance. It is recommended, therefore, that the Halsey sharing plan be introduced only where it is suitable for rather **permanent use,** and that other plans be introduced directly where they are appropriate.

6. The 50 percent sharing arrangement carries an aspect of **fair play** and is appropriate where standards, on the average, tend to require about 83.3 percent of normal performance; but other sharing ratios are equally fair in certain situations. Westinghouse Electric Corp. has used numerous proportions down to 10 percent, this share proving fair for stockroom clerks who, on a long-run average, could double their output by a 10 percent increase in effort. A liberal standard was set for an average size of delivered order, but several small orders often could be delivered within the time allowed for one, yielding perhaps from 300 to 500 percent short-run calculated efficiencies. However, the average take-home bonuses corresponded closely with those from other plans on other types of operations. Shares higher than 50 percent also are common. In fact, when the share is increased to 1.00 (100 percent), the plan becomes a standard hour plan.

7. It is important that very **loose standards** be accompanied by low shares, and **tighter standards** (approaching normal performance requirements) be accom-

panied by correspondingly higher shares for the operator. In designing the plan, the goal always is to achieve a combination such that a 25 percent bonus automatically will be paid for true incentive performance.

8. Labor representatives often argue that anything less than a full (100 percent) share is basically unfair to workers. This argument is based on the erroneous assumption that accurate normal task standards can be established for all types of work. If that were possible, there would be no justification for a partial sharing plan. Of course, some companies have been known to abuse the low sharing feature by attempting to use normal task standards. Occasionally, uninformed operators misunderstand a low task standard as reflecting normal performance; then they are disappointed because their earnings are not directly proportional to output in relation to that standard. But, under suitable conditions and with proper standards, a partial sharing plan is sound and appropriate, although its **installation** must be accompanied by thorough explanations and a sincere policy of fair play.

CONSTANT SHARING PLAN (40-60). This plan differs from the Halsey 50-50 plan in two respects; the 50 percent share is replaced by 0.40 (40 percent), and the plan has been used as a substitute for time guarantee for beginners with productivities between zero and **task.** Lytle (Wage Incentive Methods) covers this fully under the Bigelow-Knoeppel plan.

Constant Sharing Plan (40-60) Formulas. By definition, the operator would receive 0.40 (40 percent) of any time saved, giving:

$$W = TNR + 0.4(S_b - T)NR \tag{49}$$

where $S_b =$ the standard hours per unit as set for beginners. Since the plan is not used in the range of productivity where standard task would be exceeded, the formula can be restated:

$$W = TNR + 0.4S_bNR - 0.4TNR$$
$$W = 0.6TNR + 0.4S_bNR$$
$$W = (0.6 + 0.4E_b)TNR \tag{50}$$
$$Wr = 0.6 + 0.4E_b \tag{51}$$

where $E_b =$ efficiency ratio calculated from S_b, beginners' standards.

If the curve were extended to the point of 25 percent bonus (where $Wr = 1.25$), the efficiency E_b would be:

$$1.25 = 0.6 + 0.4E_b$$
$$E_b = \frac{0.65}{0.4} = 1.625$$

which is the incentive pace equivalent to a normal efficiency $E_n = 1.25$. A straight line from the origin to an assumed wage ratio of 1.625 where $E_n = 1.25$ would have a slope of 1.625/1.25 or 1.30 in relation to normal standards. This line would cross the base wage line at task where

$$E_n = \frac{1.00}{1.30} = 0.7692 \text{ or about 77 percent} \tag{52}$$

indicating that the standards used with a 40 percent sharing plan theoretically should require only 77 percent of normal productivity, and standard hours would be:

$$S_b = 1.30S_n \tag{53}$$

These standards theoretically would be slightly looser than low task standards where $S_L = 1.20 \, S_n$, although typical low task standards are suitable.

From equation (51) it is seen that starting hourly rates for beginners would be 0.60 (60 percent) of base rate R; however, such starting rates cannot be less than the **legal minimum**. In addition to the starting rates for actual hours worked, operators are paid 40 percent of all standard time produced, S_bN, multiplied by the base rate R. At specified rate of output these total earnings just equal base wages. Above this point the same plan could be extended, but other plans may be more appropriate.

The cost ratio in relation to normal performance would become:

$$Cr = (0.6 + 0.4E_b) \times \frac{1.30}{E_b}$$

$$Cr = \frac{0.78}{E_b} + 0.52 \tag{54}$$

and the labor efficiency variance ratio is:

$$EVr = 1.00 - \left(\frac{0.78}{E_b} + 0.52\right) = 0.48 - \frac{0.78}{E_b} \tag{55}$$

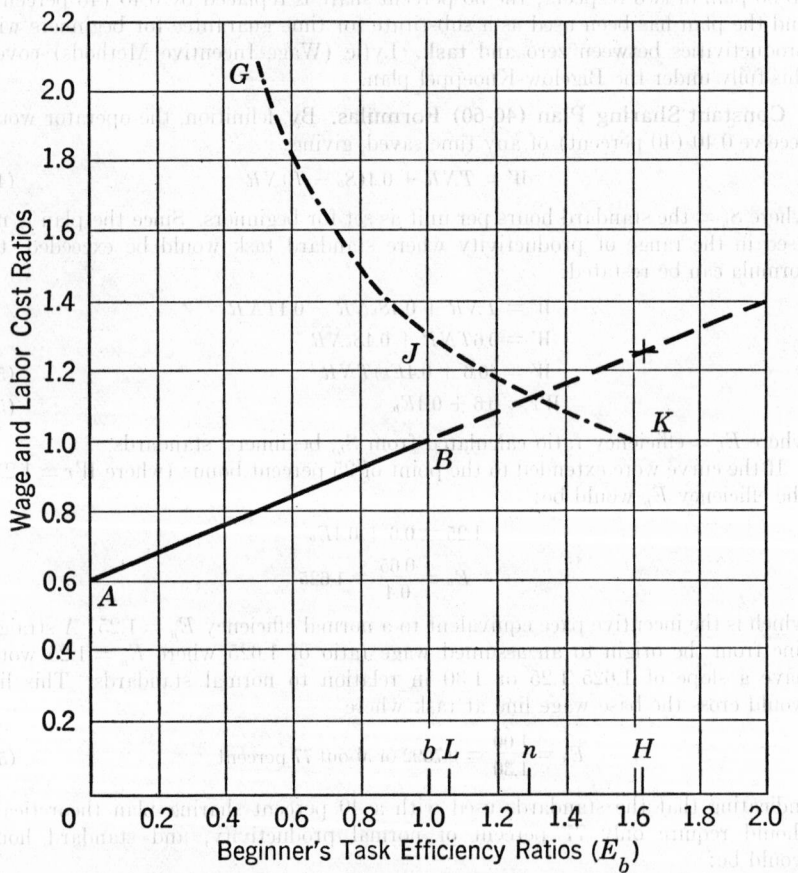

$Wr = AB$; $Cr = GJK$. Task levels: beginners' $(b) = 1.000E_b$; low $(L) = 1.083E_b$; normal $(n) = 1.300E_b$; high $(H) = 1.625E_b$.

Fig. 10. Sharing plan (40-60) for beginners, liberal beginners' task standards.

Fig. 10 shows the wage and cost curves for the 40-60 sharing plan for beginners with liberal beginners' task standards, and the corresponding data are presented in Fig. 11.

(1) E_b	(2) Wr (Eq. 51)	(3) Cr (Eq. 54)
0.00	0.60	——
0.10	0.64	8.3200
0.20	0.68	4.4200
0.30	0.72	3.1200
0.40	0.76	2.4700
0.50	0.80	2.0800
0.60	0.84	1.8200
0.70	0.88	1.6341
0.80	0.92	1.4950
0.90	0.96	1.3867
1.00	1.00	1.3000
1.10	1.04	1.2291
1.20	1.08	1.1700
1.30	1.12	1.1200
1.40	1.16	1.0771
1.50	1.20	1.0400
1.60	1.24	1.0075
1.625	1.25	1.0000
		Col. (2) × 1.30 ÷ Col. (1)

Fig. 11. Data for constant sharing plan (40-60) for beginners, for Fig. 10.

Characteristics of the (40-60) Constant Sharing Plan. Some recommendations for use of the (40-60) plan are:

1. In general, it is suggested that this plan be **limited to low efficiencies,** ranging from zero to about 77 percent of normal performance. Within this range the plan is a compromise between the charity of time wages and the severity of straight piece wages.
2. Bigelow (Lytle, Wage Incentive Methods) found that this plan provided wages closely approximating the time-efficiency progress of **learners.** The plan is suitable for almost any beginner on skilled work requiring at least 1 month to learn. Being less charitable than time wages, it encourages beginners more quickly to achieve at least daywork (low task) performance; and it may be used for older employees who would be satisfied with base wages guaranteed for very low output. The plan was considered successful in at least one textile plant employing a large number of young female operators.
3. If used alone and extended above the base wage level, this plan is closely equivalent to, and as simple to administer as, the Halsey 50 percent plan. In fact, from equation (42), the 50 percent plan could be extended downward to zero efficiency and would provide similar features for beginners with insignificant differences in results. Certainly, if the 50 percent plan were used for bonus payments, it would be better to extend the same plan downward for the beginners than to use two different wage plans for different ranges of output on the same type of work.

4. If the 40 percent plan were used for low outputs, and an entirely different plan, perhaps the standard hour plan using **normal** standards, were used for higher outputs, the over-all structure probably would be too complex for practical administration. To give equitable wages, two different standards, S_b and S_n, would be required for each operation; and different cost and efficiency variance ratios would exist in the different ranges of efficiency. Such differences would be difficult to reconcile in the payroll and accounting procedures. The over-all advantages of such a multiplicity of plans would be doubtful except in very special situations.

BEDAUX POINT PLAN. The original Bedaux plan was basically a Halsey constant sharing plan, but it gave a 75 percent share of time saved to the operators, the remaining 25 percent share going to foremen, service men, and other indirect shop personnel who thereby would have some inducement to contribute actively toward high productivity of the direct labor operators.

The characteristic feature of all Bedaux plans is the use of a standard unit of time called a B, which is a **man-minute of allowed time** for a person working at a normal pace and is defined as a fraction of a minute of effort plus a fraction of a minute of compensating relaxation, always aggregating unity but varying in proportion to the nature of the strain. Every time standard established from good time study is set by determining the amount of uninterrupted time required to perform a task when the operator is demonstrating some defined level of skill and effort, usually based on normal performance. To this base time is added some amount of time, usually by means of a percentage or **allowance factor,** to cover the unavoidable delays inherent in the task. This factor is often called P, F, and D to denote the extra time required for **personal** needs, **fatigue** or relaxation, and miscellaneous **delays.** The total time becomes a standard time S. Each minute of **standard allowed time** is equivalent to one B. The working portion of a B varies. For light work, $9/10$ may be assigned to actual effort, with $1/10$ of the time for rest. For heavy labor, $6/10$ of the time may be the working portion, with $4/10$ allowed for rest and personal needs.

Bedaux Ratings. Under the Bedaux system, the index of normal performance is 60 (rather than 100 percent), on the assumption that 60 units of standard time (60 B's) can be produced with normal effort in 1 hr. (60 min.) of actual time. Incentive performance is assigned a rating of 80. Thus an operator demonstrating incentive effort is said to be working at an 80 B-hour rate, which obviously would be $80/60 = 1.333$ (133.3 percent) of normal. If incentive performance is accepted as a productivity of 125 percent, then normal productivity (100 percent) implies a B index of 64, and a 60-B rate reflects only $125 \times 60/80$ or 93.75 percent of the normal performance previously assumed for the standard hour plan. This indicates that Bedaux standards for a 75 percent sharing plan should theoretically be slightly looser than normal standards.

Bedaux 75 Percent Sharing Plan Formulas. Up to Bedaux task (60 B), daywork (base rate) wages are guaranteed, and the daywork wage formulas apply. Using theoretically correct standards for a 75 percent sharing plan, the daywork cost ratios will appear lower than with normal standards and must be adjusted by the factor, $1/0.9375E_B$. At and above Bedaux task standard:

$$W = TNR + 0.75(S_B - T)NR \tag{56}$$

$$Wr = 1.00 + 0.75(E_B - 1.00) \tag{57}$$

or

$$Wr = 0.25 + 0.75E_B \tag{58}$$

$$Br = 0.75(E_B - 1.00) \tag{59}$$

In relation to normal performance, the cost ratio

$$Cr = (0.25 + 0.75E_B)\frac{1}{E_n} = (0.25 + 0.75E_B)\frac{1}{0.9375E_B}$$

$$Cr = \frac{0.2667}{E_B} + 0.80 \tag{60}$$

and the labor efficiency variance ratio becomes:

$$EVr = 1.00 - \left(\frac{0.2667}{E_B} + 0.80\right) = 0.20 - \frac{0.2667}{E_B} \tag{61}$$

Fig. 12 presents the wage and cost curves for the Bedaux 75 percent sharing plan, and the corresponding data appear in Fig. 13.

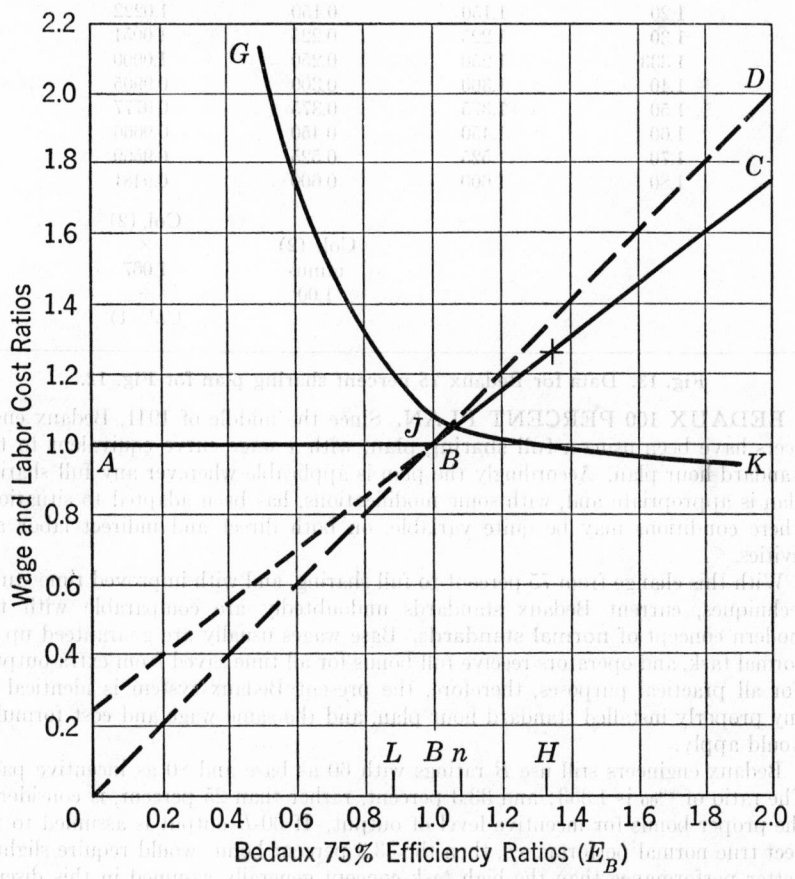

$Wr = ABC;\ Cr = GJK.$ For comparison, 100 percent sharing: $Wr = OBD.$ Task levels: low $(L) = (53.3\ B) = 0.888E_B;$ Bedaux $(B) = (60\ B) = 1.000E_B;$ normal $(n) = (64\ B) = 1.067E_B;$ high $(H) = (80\ B) = 1.333E_B.$

Fig. 12. Bedaux 75 percent sharing plan, using 60-B standards.

(1) E_B	(2) W_r (Eqs. 3, 57)	(3) B_r (Eqs. 4, 59)	(4) C_r (Eqs. 3 × 1.067/E_B; and 60)
0.50	1.000	0.000	2.1333
0.60	1.000	0.000	1.7781
0.70	1.000	0.000	1.5243
0.80	1.000	0.000	1.3333
0.90	1.000	0.000	1.1851
1.00	1.000	0.000	1.0667
1.067	1.050	0.050	1.0500
1.10	1.075	0.075	1.0424
1.20	1.150	0.150	1.0222
1.30	1.225	0.225	1.0051
1.333	1.250	0.250	1.0000
1.40	1.300	0.300	0.9905
1.50	1.375	0.375	0.9777
1.60	1.450	0.450	0.9666
1.70	1.525	0.525	0.9569
1.80	1.600	0.600	0.9481
		Col. (2) minus 1.00	Col. (2) × 1.067 ÷ Col. (1)

Fig. 13. Data for Bedaux 75 percent sharing plan for Fig. 12.

BEDAUX 100 PERCENT PLAN. Since the middle of 1941, Bedaux engineers have been using a **full sharing plan,** with a wage curve equivalent to the standard hour plan. Accordingly the plan is applicable wherever any full sharing plan is appropriate and, with some modifications, has been adapted to situations where conditions may be quite variable, on both direct and indirect labor activities.

With this change from 75 percent to full sharing, and with improved time study techniques, current Bedaux standards undoubtedly are comparable with the modern concept of **normal standards.** Base wages usually are guaranteed up to normal task, and operators receive full bonus for all time saved from extra output. For all practical purposes, therefore, the present Bedaux system is identical to any properly installed standard hour plan, and the same wage and cost formulas would apply.

Bedaux engineers still use B ratings with 60 as base and 80 as incentive pace. The ratio of $^{80}\!/_{60}$ is 1.333; and 33.3 percent, rather than 25 percent, is considered the proper bonus for incentive level of output. If 60-B output is assumed to reflect true normal performance, then the 33.3 percent bonus would require slightly better performance than the high task concept generally assumed in this discussion. Actual **average bonuses,** however, are likely to be closer to 25 percent.

Machine Applications. In some carelessly planned installations for machine operations, the standard allowed time represents the time required to produce one unit, i.e., the time for one **complete machine cycle,** without regard to the portion of the cycle that requires active operator effort. This introduces several difficulties.

For example, in a cycle of 5 min., 1 min. at normal pace may be allowed for manual activities, and 4 min. may be required for power-controlled machine time during which the operator is completely idle. If the operator works at an incentive pace on the manual activities, he should earn a 25 percent bonus; but manual activities constitute only 20 percent of this cycle, so his over-all bonus effectively is limited to 20 percent of 25 percent, or a maximum of about 5 percent of his base wages. This appears inequitable to the machine operator when he knows that other incentive workers, on completely manual work, are enjoying bonuses of 25 percent or more. To relieve this apparent inequity, the company might allow 25 percent more time than the machine actually requires for the **power-feed element,** thereby making the cycle 6 min. Of course, the operator then will receive the desired 25 percent bonus. In effect, he is guaranteed a 25 percent bonus for 80 percent of his time during which he does no work whatever. Obviously this is inequitable for the manual workers, who must work at an incentive pace for the entire day to obtain a similar 25 percent bonus. Furthermore, direct labor costs are increased 20 percent with no additional output. Since the machine operator enjoys a 25 percent bonus for idle time, he will resist any attempts to have him run more than one machine or do other manual work.

The Bedaux system carefully (and properly) avoids these problems by defining the B (standard allowed minute) as a minute (including proper allowances) of actual manual activities or operator effort at normal pace. On manual activities, the operator can earn a bonus through extra effort. But only base wages are paid for any voluntary or enforced idleness, or where increased output from extra effort is improbable.

If a machine operation involves manual activity throughout the cycle, such as on a manually fed sensitive drill press, the operator has full control over his output and the cycle is considered completely manual. But, if the operation involves any form of power feed, particularly if an **automatic stop** is provided, part of the cycle will be machine paced and not subject to change by increased operator effort.

In nearly every machine cycle, some manual elements, such as loading and unloading, must be performed while the machine is not producing. These elements are **external work.** During the power feed or **running** portion of the cycle, other manual elements often can be performed, such as filing burrs, inspecting and disposing of finished items, sharpening replacement tools, and getting new material. These elements are **internal work.** But the required internal work may not occupy the full running time; thus the difference between running and internal work is **idle operator time.**

The **cycle time** is external work plus running time, from which hourly output is determined. The operator is allowed time in the standard for only the external plus internal work on which he has an opportunity to earn bonus. The idle operator time is paid for at only straight time base wages.

This feature of providing bonus opportunity on only the actual working portion of a machine cycle adheres to the fundamental principle of wage incentives, i.e., extra pay only for extra effort. Since the **operator's bonus opportunity** thus is proportional to the time spent on only manual activities, he has an inducement to ask for enough work to keep him busy, either running additional machines or performing other manual operations which can be done at his work station during otherwise idle periods.

Furthermore in the Bedaux system, idle operator time, for which base wages are paid, is charged to a special **foreman's account.** Since it is the foreman's responsibility to keep such charges as near zero as possible, he will attempt to schedule adequate work to his operators. This practice not only is basically sound, but also it provides a doubly strong inducement to keep operators actively busy on productive work.

Adaptation to Large Machines. With some very large machines it is impractical for one operator (or crew) to run more than one machine; or the nature of the machine or process requires the **operator to be constantly available,** even if partially idle. In such a case the cycle time for incentive performance is calculated in much the same manner as previously described but on the assumption that material and other working conditions are excellent, or about as good as they ever are likely to be.

If only **one operator** is needed and no other manual work is possible, the standard time allowed (adjusted to normal) would be equivalent to 1.333 times the cycle time. Thus, with good conditions, the expected output would yield a 33.3 percent bonus. If **several operators** are required on a single machine, the size of the crew should be adjusted so that all external and internal work will require continuous activity at incentive pace (with proper rest allowances) in order to achieve the expected output. Then the standard time allowed (adjusted to normal) would be equivalent to 1.333 times the cycle time, times the number of persons in the crew. But, if other manual work were possible, the standard allowed time would include only external and internal work, adjusted to normal pace.

Variable Conditions Allowance. Variations in temperature, humidity, materials, etc., may require reduced machine speeds or cause interruptions which reduce actual output, even when the operators are doing their best to maintain expected output. To meet such emergencies, Bedaux engineers have provided a variable conditions allowance which automatically makes some compensation for such losses. This extra arbitrary allowance is one-half the difference between the expected earnings of 133.3 percent and the earnings that would have been realized from the reduced output. The **VCA ratio** becomes:

$$VCA = 0.5(1.333 - \text{calculated efficiency}) \tag{62}$$

or

$$VCA = 0.5(1.333 - E)$$

The use of the VCA from equation (62) has a psychological appeal to the operators since it automatically gives them extra time when they fail to achieve the expected output. Presumably such failure would be caused by poor conditions beyond the operators' control, and it would be assumed that this occurred even with incentive operator effort. With good supervision and consequent high morale, this is a reasonable assumption. But the VCA automatically is related to actual output which very well might be low because of low operator effort, even with excellent conditions. Thus the VCA tends to insure high wages, and consequent high costs, for relatively low outputs, regardless of the cause. Accordingly the incentive is weak with respect to inducing operators to maintain any definite level of output. For accounting purposes, however, the VCA provides a means for isolating the extra cost due to less-than-expected output.

Bedaux 100 Percent Plan Formulas (Including VCA). For a straight standard hour (100 percent premium) plan with no minimum guarantee, total wages can be calculated directly from the standard time allowed and the base rate, so that:

$$W = SNR \qquad (28)$$

from which

$$Wr = \frac{SNR}{TNR} = E_n \qquad (63)$$

Adding the VCA from equation (62) gives a combined wage ratio of:

$$Wr = E_n + 0.5(1.333 - E_n) = E_n + 0.667 - 0.5E_n$$

or

$$Wr = 0.6667 + 0.5E_n \qquad (64)$$

From equation (64), base wages would result if $Wr = 1.00$, and would be earned at an efficiency ratio of:

$$E_n = \frac{1.00 - 0.667}{0.5} = \frac{0.333}{0.5} = 0.6667 \qquad (65)$$

Assuming that standards had been set to reflect normal performance, this indicates that output required to yield base wages is only 0.6667 (two-thirds) of normal output.

From equation (64) zero output would yield 66.7 percent of base wages, and from equation (65) 66.7 percent of normal output would yield 100 percent of base wages.

If, instead of using an expected bonus of 33.3 percent, a bonus of 25 percent had been used (as assumed in previous developments), equation (64) would have been:

$$Wr = 0.625 + 0.50E_n \qquad (66)$$

and base wages would occur at 75 percent of normal output. It is interesting to note how closely this compares with the (40-60) beginners' plan, where equation (51) is:

$$Wr = 0.6 + 0.4E_b$$

giving 60 percent of base wages for zero output and base wages at 77 percent of normal output. See characteristic number 3 under the (40-60) plan analysis.

Equation (64) can be converted to a more typical form of base wages plus a bonus by adding and subtracting 0.5.

$$Wr = 0.667 + 0.5E_n + 0.5 - 0.5$$
$$Wr = 1.167 + 0.5(E_n - 1.0) \qquad (67)$$

or

$$Wr = 1.00 + [0.5(E_n - 1.0) + 0.167] \qquad (68)$$
$$Br = 0.5(E_n - 1.0) + 0.167 \qquad (69)$$

For an expected bonus of 25 percent rather than 33.3 percent, equation (67) would have been:

$$Wr = 1.125 + 0.5(E_n - 1.0)$$

and equation (69) would have been

$$Br = 0.5(E_n - 1.0) + 0.125$$

Equation (67) is similar to equation (40) and therefore illustrates that using the variable conditions allowance ratio merely converts a 100 percent (or standard hour) plan into a 50 percent sharing plan. However, with standards now expressed in terms of normal performance, rather than at very low task requiring only 66.7 percent of normal, the wage curve has been retained at the 50 percent slope but has been raised by an amount equivalent to 0.167 (16.7 percent) of base wages. This is necessary to force such a low sharing curve through the point where $Wr = 1.333$ for an efficiency of $E = 1.333$ as calculated from normal standards.

The cost ratio which would apply up to $E_n = 1.333$ can be developed from equation (64); it becomes:

$$Cr = (0.6667 + 0.5E_n) \frac{1.00}{E_n}$$

$$Cr = \frac{0.6667}{E_n} + 0.5 \tag{70}$$

In this illustration, **expected efficiency** from normal standards is the 80-B hour rate or 1.333, rather than 1.25 as used in most of the other illustrations. Ac-

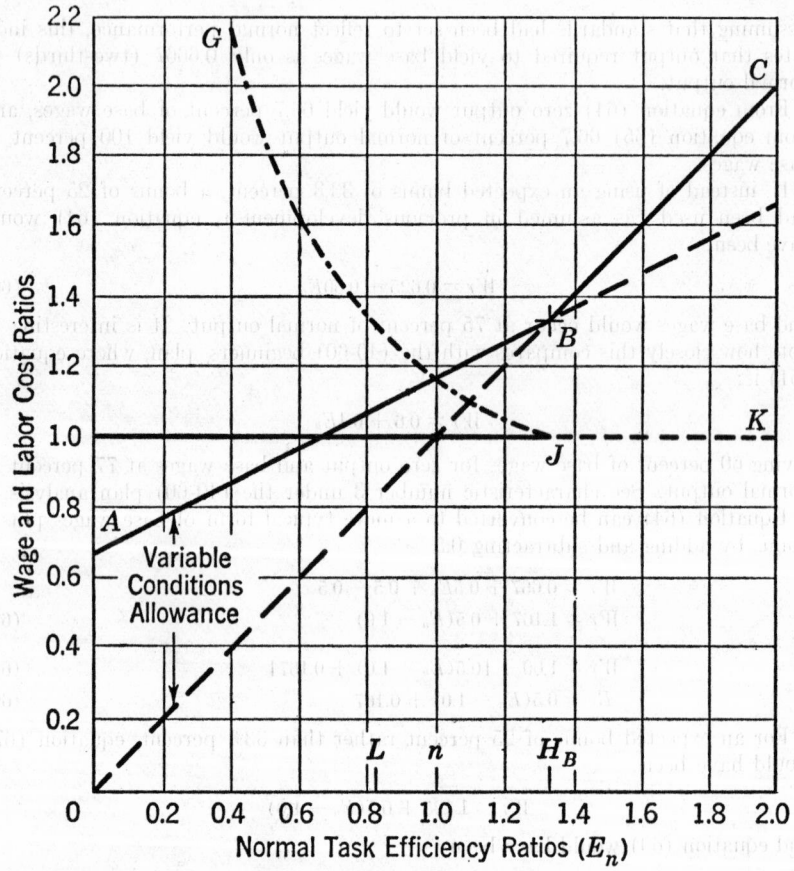

$Wr = ABC$; $Cr = GJK$. Task levels: low $(L) = (50\,B) = 0.833E_n$; normal $(n) = (60\,B) = 1.000E_n$; Bedaux high $(H_B) = (80\,B) = 1.333E_n$.

Fig. 14. Bedaux full sharing with variable conditions allowance, normal task standards.

cordingly the cost ratio becomes unity where $E = 1.333$. For higher efficiencies, wages follow the full sharing formula and the cost ratio remains at unity.

The corresponding labor efficiency variance ratio becomes $1.00 - Cr$, or:

$$EVr = 0.5 - \frac{0.6667}{E_n} \tag{71}$$

Fig. 14 presents the wage and cost curves for the Bedaux full sharing plan with variable conditions allowance, using normal task standards, and the corresponding data are given in Fig. 15.

(1) E_n	(2) Wr (Eqs. 64, 32)	(3) $Br = Wr - 1.0$	(4) Cr (Eqs. 70, 36)
0.000	0.6667		
0.100	0.7167		7.1667
0.200	0.7667		3.8333
0.300	0.8167		2.7222
0.400	0.8667		2.1667
0.500	0.9167		1.8333
0.600	0.9667		1.6111
0.667	1.0000	0.0000	1.5000
0.700	1.0167	0.0167	1.4524
0.800	1.0667	0.0667	1.3333
0.900	1.1167	0.1167	1.2407
1.000	1.1667	0.1667	1.1667
1.100	1.2167	0.2167	1.1061
1.200	1.2667	0.2667	1.0555
1.300	1.3167	0.3167	1.0128
1.333	1.3333	0.3333	1.0000
1.400	1.4000	0.4000	1.0000
1.500	1.5000	0.5000	1.0000
1.600	1.6000	0.6000	1.0000
1.700	1.7000	0.7000	1.0000
1.800	1.8000	0.8000	1.0000
			Col. (2) ÷ Col. (1)

Fig. 15. Data for Bedaux full sharing with variable conditions allowance for Fig. 14.

ROWAN VARIABLE SHARING PLAN.

Because of its seeming complexity, the advantages of this plan have not been recognized or utilized to the extent that they possibly deserve. In general, base wages are guaranteed up to task. Above task, bonuses are paid according to a variable share of the time saved. This share is high for low efficiencies, and it automatically becomes lower as calculated efficiencies increase.

When working conditions and work content are highly variable, a given standard will appear tight under poor conditions and will appear loose under good conditions. With a constant level of effective operator effort, corresponding calculated efficiencies will vary respectively from low to high values. This situation is typical with the Class 2 type of work and causes an apparent mixture of loose and tight standards.

If efficiencies are relatively low (near $E_n = 1.00$), the Rowan plan gives the operator nearly a full share of the time saved and therefore provides about the same incentive strength and reward as the standard hour plan. On the other hand, if efficiencies are very high, say in the neighborhood of 2.00 (200 percent), the share automatically is reduced to about 50 percent of the time saved, giving nearly the same protection as the Halsey 50 percent constant sharing plan. Accordingly, this plan is most suitable for the Class 2 type of work previously described.

However, if management insists upon using only one wage incentive plan for all types of work within the company, the **automatic variable sharing** feature provides a convenient compromise and makes the Rowan plan more suitable than any other single wage incentive plan.

Basic Rowan Plan Formulas. In any constant sharing plan, even if the share is 100 percent or higher, the employee's share of the time saved is a function of T, **the actual time worked.** In the Rowan plan, however, the employee's share of the time saved is a function of S, **the standard time allowed.**

For most plans, wages can be represented generally by the equation:

$$W = TNR + p(S - T)NR \tag{37}$$

where p represents the employee's share of the time saved. Multiplying the second term by T/T gives:

$$W = TNR + \frac{p}{T}(S - T)TNR \tag{72}$$

In a 100 percent sharing plan, $p = 1.00$ and equation (72) becomes:

$$W = TNR + \frac{1.00}{T}(S - T)TNR \tag{73}$$

which includes the straight time wages TNR, plus a second term indicating that bonus wages may be calculated by multiplying the base wages TNR by the function $(S - T) \times 1.00/T$, which previously has been simplified to:

$$Br = E - 1.00 \tag{33}$$

For the basic Rowan formulas the fraction $1.00/T$ is replaced by $1.00/S$, so that bonus wages are calculated by multiplying base wages TNR by the function:

$$Br = \frac{1.00}{S_R}(S_R - T) = 1.00 - \frac{1.00}{E_R} \tag{74}$$

Since the Rowan plan is most suitable where there is an apparent mixture of loose and tight standards, the term S_R is used here to represent the **average level** of such a mixture which theoretically should be used with the basic Rowan plan. Similarly, the term E_R represents corresponding efficiencies calculated from such standards.

Thus, from equation (72), total wages can be represented by:

$$W = TNR + \frac{1.00}{S_R}(S_R - T)TNR$$

which reduces to:

$$W = TNR + \left(1.00 - \frac{1.00}{E_R}\right)TNR \tag{75}$$

and dividing by TNR gives the wage ratio:

$$Wr = 1.00 + \left(1.00 - \frac{1.00}{E_R}\right) = 2.00 - \frac{1.00}{E_R} \tag{76}$$

from which the bonus ratio becomes:

$$Br = 1.00 - \frac{1.00}{E_R} \tag{77}$$

The variable sharing feature can be seen from an analysis of equation (77). When the operator just meets standards, $E = 1.00$ and $Br = 0.00$. If $E = 1.10$, Br becomes $(1.00 - 0.909) = 0.091$, indicating a 9.1 percent bonus or very nearly the 10 percent bonus of a full sharing plan. If standards are sufficiently loose that $E = 2.00$, Br becomes $(1.00 - 0.50) = 0.50$, indicating a 50 percent share of the time saved, the same as with a Halsey 50 percent plan. If standards were so ridiculously loose that E approached infinity, then Br would approach 1.00, indicating that this plan automatically protects the company against loose standards by limiting bonus possibilities to 100 percent of base wages; that is, total possible earnings cannot be more than double the base wages.

As previously illustrated under several wage plans, for example see development of equation (47), the cost ratio for a specific plan is the product of the wage ratio for that plan and $1.00/E_n$; therefore, from equation (76):

$$Cr = Wr \times \frac{1.00}{E_n} = \left(2.00 - \frac{1.00}{E_R}\right)\frac{1.00}{E_n} \tag{78}$$

and the labor efficiency variance ratio becomes:

$$EVr = 1.00 - Cr = 1.00 - \left(2.00 - \frac{1.00}{E_R}\right)\frac{1.00}{E_n} \tag{79}$$

Any wage plan should provide a typical bonus of, say, 25 percent for true incentive performance. To determine the efficiency that would be necessary to yield a 25 percent bonus with the basic Rowan plan, a value of 1.25 may be substituted for Wr in equation (76), giving:

$$1.25 = 2.00 - \frac{1.00}{E_R}$$

Thus incentive performance would be indicated by

$$E_R = \frac{1.00}{(2.00 - 1.25)} = \frac{1.00}{0.75} = 1.333$$

Using normal task standards, incentive performance would be represented by $E_n = 1.25$. The ratio of E_n/E_R is:

$$\frac{E_n}{E_R} = \frac{1.25}{1.333}$$

or

$$E_n = 0.9375 \times E_R$$

indicating that efficiencies calculated from normal task standard would be somewhat lower than efficiencies calculated from standards best suited to the basic Rowan plan.

Correspondingly, the ratio of E_R/E_n is:

$$\frac{E_R}{E_n} = \frac{1.333}{1.25}$$

or

$$E_R = 1.0667 \times E_n$$

indicating that basic Rowan standards theoretically should be somewhat looser than normal task standards.

These values correspond precisely with those for the Bedaux 75 percent sharing plan. Thus the basic Rowan plan is suitable for use with **mixed standards** ranging from normal task to low task and which average about midway between these two levels.

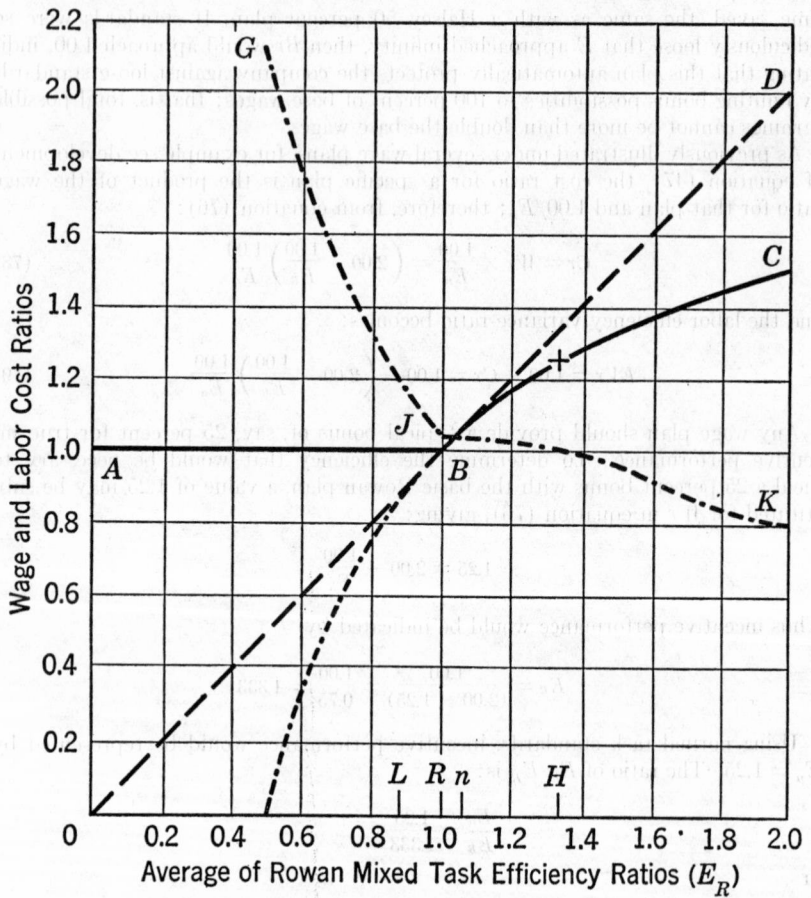

$Wr = ABC$; $Cr = GJK$. For comparison, 100 percent sharing: $Wr = OBD$. Task levels: low $(L) = 0.888E_R$; Rowan $(R) = 1.000E_R$; normal $(n) = 1.067E_R$; high $(H) = 1.333E_R$.

Fig. 16. Basic Rowan variable sharing plan, average of Rowan mixed task standards.

Substituting $0.9375\,E_R$ for E_n in equation (78) gives:

$$Cr = \left(2.00 - \frac{1.00}{E_R}\right)\frac{1.0667}{E_R} = \left(2.1333 - \frac{1.0667}{E_R}\right)\frac{1}{E_R} \qquad (80)$$

and the labor efficiency variance ratio, from equation (80), becomes:

$$EVr = 1.00 - Cr = 1.00 - \left(2.1333 - \frac{1.0667}{E_R}\right)\frac{1}{E_R} \qquad (81)$$

Fig. 16 shows the wage and cost curves for the basic Rowan variable sharing plan, and the corresponding data are given in Fig. 17.

(1) E_R	(2) Wr (from Eq. 76)	(3) Wr, as used (from Eqs. 3, 76)	(4) Br	(5) Cr
0.50	0.000	1.000	0.000	2.1333
0.60	0.333	1.000	0.000	1.7778
0.70	0.571	1.000	0.000	1.5239
0.80	0.750	1.000	0.000	1.3333
0.90	0.889	1.000	0.000	1.1852
1.00	1.000	1.000	0.000	1.0667
1.10	1.091	1.091	0.091	1.0579
1.20	1.167	1.167	0.167	1.0372
1.25	1.200	1.200	0.200	1.0240
1.30	1.231	1.231	0.231	1.0157
1.33	1.250	1.250	0.250	1.0000
1.40	1.286	1.286	0.286	0.9798
1.50	1.333	1.333	0.333	0.9479
1.60	1.375	1.375	0.375	0.9167
1.70	1.412	1.412	0.412	0.8860
1.80	1.444	1.444	0.444	0.8557
1.90	1.474	1.474	0.474	0.8275
2.00	1.500	1.500	0.500	0.8000
			Col. (3) minus 1.00	Col. (3) × 1.0667 ÷ Col. (1)

Fig. 17. Data for basic Rowan variable sharing plan for Fig. 16.

MODIFIED ROWAN PLAN. Because of the variable sharing feature, it has been shown that standards most appropriate for the basic Rowan plan theoretically should average about 6.7 percent looser than normal task standards. This slight difference is too small to be recognized or maintained in actual practice, owing to inherent errors or variations in performance rating. Accordingly it is most convenient to attempt to set standards to reflect normal task performance requirements. If this is done, true incentive performance should be indicated by a calculated efficiency of $E_n = 1.25$ (1.25 percent), and for this efficiency the plan should yield a $Wr = 1.25$ in order to pay the desired 25 percent bonus.

Modified Rowan Plan Formulas. For normal task standards, equation (76) would be written:

$$Wr = 2.00 - \frac{1.00}{E_n}$$

but, if $E_n = 1.25$, this equation gives a wage ratio of only 1.20. Thus the constant (2.00) is too small to yield the desired wage ratio.

Momentarily let X replace the constant 2.00, and substitute 1.25 for both Wr and E_n. Solving for X:

$$1.25 = X - \frac{1.00}{1.25}$$

$$X = 1.25 + 0.80 = 2.05$$

Therefore the modified wage ratio mWr becomes:

$$mWr = 2.05 - \frac{1.00}{E_n} \quad \text{or} \quad 1.00 + \left(1.05 - \frac{1.00}{E_n}\right) \tag{82}$$

and, since $Br = Wr - 1.00$, the modified bonus ratio mBr becomes:

$$mBr = 1.05 - \frac{1.00}{E_n} \tag{83}$$

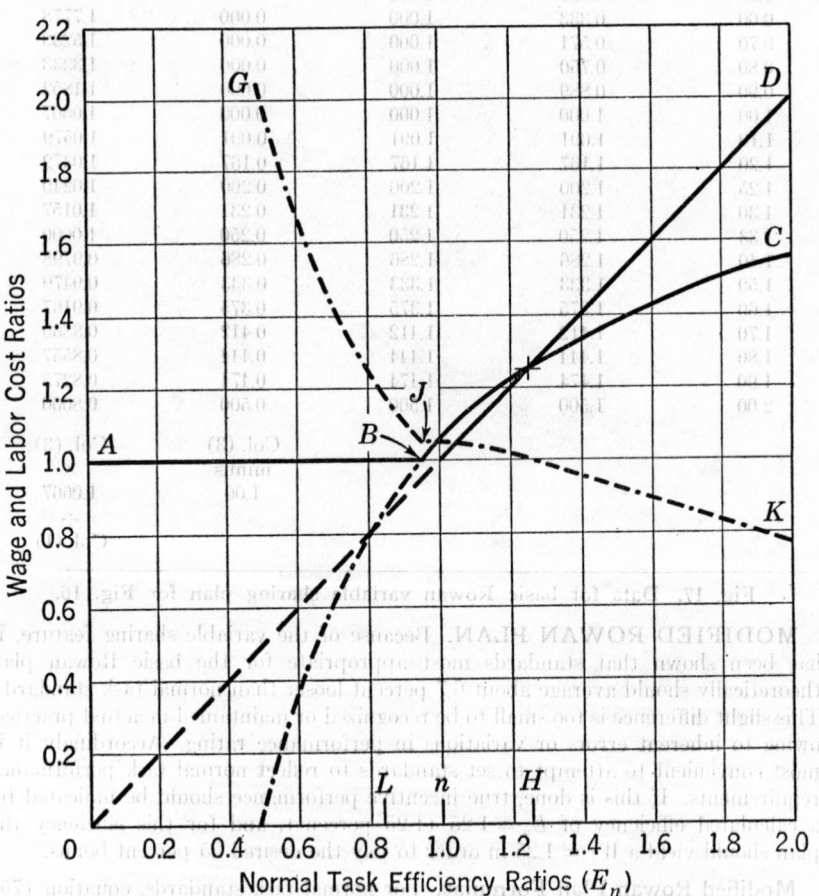

$Wr = ABC; Cr = GJK$. For comparison, 100 percent sharing: $Wr = OD$. Task levels: low $(L) = 0.833E_n$; normal $(n) = 1.000E_n$; high $(H) = 1.250E_n$.

Fig. 18. Modified Rowan variable sharing plan, normal task standards.

From equation (78), the modified cost ratio mCr becomes:

$$mCr = \left(2.05 - \frac{1.00}{E_n}\right)\frac{1.00}{E_n} \qquad (84)$$

Since the modified equations have been developed to yield a 25 percent bonus when $E_n = 1.25$, the efficiency which will just yield base wages can be determined by substituting a value of zero for mBr in equation (83).

$$0.00 = 1.05 - \frac{1.00}{E_n}$$

$$\frac{1.00}{E_n} = 1.05$$

$$E_n = \frac{1.00}{1.05} = 0.9524$$

Thus daywork wage and cost equations will apply for performances up to $E_n = 0.9524$. For higher efficiencies, equations (82), (83), and (84) will apply.

Fig. 18 shows the wage and cost curves for the modified Rowan variable sharing plan; normal task standards and the corresponding data appear in Fig. 19.

(1) E_n	(2) mWr (from Eq. 82)	(3) mWr, as used (from Eqs. 3, 82)	(4) Br	(5) Cr
0.488	0.000	1.000	0.000	2.0500
0.50	0.050	1.000	0.000	2.000
0.60	0.383	1.000	0.000	1.667
0.70	0.621	1.000	0.000	1.429
0.80	0.800	1.000	0.000	1.250
0.90	0.939	1.000	0.000	1.111
0.953	1.000	1.000	0.000	1.050
1.000	1.050	1.050	0.050	1.000
1.10	1.141	1.141	0.141	1.0373
1.20	1.217	1.217	0.217	1.0141
1.25	1.250	1.250	0.250	1.0000
1.30	1.281	1.281	0.281	0.9853
1.40	1.336	1.336	0.336	0.9543
1.50	1.383	1.383	0.383	0.9220
1.60	1.425	1.425	0.425	0.8906
1.70	1.462	1.462	0.462	0.8599
1.80	1.494	1.494	0.494	0.8300
1.90	1.524	1.524	0.524	0.8021
2.00	1.550	1.550	0.550	0.7750
		Col. (3) minus 1.00		Col. (3) ÷ Col. (1)

Fig. 19. Data for modified Rowan variable sharing plan for Fig. 18.

Characteristics of the Basic and Modified Rowan Plans. The basic and modified Rowan plans possess the following characteristics:

1. The Rowan plan, in general, undoubtedly provides one of the best compromises of wage incentive features where unavoidable variations in materials and working conditions, as described for Class 2 work, result in apparent mixtures of relatively loose and tight standards.

2. The basic Rowan plan provides a slightly better margin of protection than the modified plan if standards on the average are suspected of being sufficiently liberal to reflect approximately **low task performance requirements.** This basic plan therefore is most suitable where the mixture of standards tends to average about midway between low task and normal task requirements.

3. The modified plan would be preferable, generally, because most companies attempt to set standards to reflect normal task performance. This modified version of the Rowan plan, developed by H. B. Rogers, can provide a smooth transition, at the point of 25 percent bonus, from a standard hour plan to variable sharing as a protection against accidentally loose standards. For example, this combination has proved highly successful for a group of typists in a large department store.

4. Experienced industrial engineers recognize that time study performance ratings are merely estimates and inherently are subject to **judgment errors** which may be as much as plus or minus 5 to 10 percent, and occasionally greater. Thus, even on Class 1 work where a full sharing plan theoretically is most appropriate, there inevitably is some inconsistency in the standards. In such cases, the cautious manager might consider the modified Rowan plan. Particularly for smaller companies, where high-grade time study procedures may not be available and where several types of work are to be covered by a single wage incentive plan, this modified plan is likely to be a wise choice.

5. The base wage guarantee provides the usual security of daywork wages.

6. The variable sharing feature automatically combines the incentive strength of a 100 percent plan on reasonably tight standards, with the protection of a 50 percent sharing plan on very loose standards. However, like all plans with smooth wage curves, the Rowan plan lacks the strong inducement of a step bonus as used in the single-step differential plan and in the Gantt task and bonus plan. Therefore, it would not be particularly effective on machines where definite high levels of output are desired.

7. When used with appropriate standards, partial sharing plans generally give higher bonuses than 100 percent plans for outputs ranging up to high task. The modified Rowan plan similarly gives higher bonuses in this range, by as much as 5 percent, although it is less liberal than the Halsey 50 percent plan using low task standards or the Bedaux variable conditions allowances.

8. With bonuses starting at about 95 percent of normal output, the modified plan provides nearly the same liberality and encouragement to **learners** or **slower operators** as does the Bedaux 75 percent sharing plan where bonuses start at slightly less than 94 percent of normal.

9. Like any partial sharing plan, the Rowan plan may be slightly difficult to sell to the employees unless accompanied by careful explanations of its mutual advantages to both the employees and the company.

10. The plan is equally applicable to both individual and group incentives, since standards are expressed in time rather than money.

11. Like other partial sharing plans, this plan is not adaptable to monetary standards.

12. Since wages are not directly proportional to output, Rowan plan wages cannot be calculated by simple multiplications of standard time produced and hourly rates, as with a full sharing plan. But **efficiency ratios** provide a convenient method of comparing relative productivities of individuals or departments for purposes of control, and therefore are commonly used. From the equations developed above, master tables can be prepared to show possible calculated efficiencies in 1 percent intervals, with corresponding wage, bonus, and cost ratios. Fig. 19 gives a tabulation in 10 percent intervals. With such **master tables,** payroll and cost calculation routines become simple, rapid, and uniform for all plans. Thus the administration of a Rowan plan can be almost as simple as that of a standard hour plan.

13. The Rowan plan can be modified for use with high task standards by adjusting the wage ratio, equation (76), to:

$$Wr = 2.25 - \frac{1.00}{E_H}$$

With this equation, base wages would be earned at normal productivity where $E_H = 0.80$, and bonuses would accrue for all higher efficiencies. The equation properly yields a wage ratio of 1.25 at high task productivity where $E_H = 1.00$. At $E_H = 0.90$, a full sharing plan would yield a wage ratio of 1.125, while this modification of the Rowan plan would yield 1.139 or a difference of only 0.014 (1.4 percent). This difference is so small that any possible advantages of the Rowan variable sharing feature become insignificant if high task standards are used. Thus normal task standards are recommended.

SUMMARY OF BASIC WAGE PLAN APPLICATION. Most of the plans described above are well known and have proved successful through many years of use. They include the basically sound features which will adequately meet nearly every problem and condition in the practical application of wage incentives. Since no one plan can combine all these features, some of which are conflicting, each plan is intended to include the combination most suitable for a specific situation.

For example, there is little choice beyond **straight time payment** if the work content of a task cannot be prescribed, or if the accomplishment cannot be measured, or both; but, unless wage payment is related to output, little more than marginal average performance usually will be obtained. For well-standardized manual activities, where output is proportional to effort, **piecework** provides a suitably proportional reward. Because time standards provide greater flexibility and better administrative control, piecework, although still popular, gradually is being replaced by the full sharing **standard hour** plan based on normal task standards. Where high task standards can be used, similar rewards are provided with a **high sharing standard time** plan, such as the upper portion of the Gantt wage curve. There are several advantages, more psychological than technical, in using high task standards, although they are somewhat more difficult to maintain.

The step bonus and high sharing features make the **Gantt plan** effective where it is desired to maintain or exceed definite and high production schedules either on manual work or on machines where the rate of output can be chiefly under the operator's control. However, the **single-step differential time** plan is more appropriate in encouraging efficient utilization of limited capacity machines or processes, with less risk of personal injury or defective products.

For loosely controlled standards, **partial sharing** plans provide both liberality to the operator and protection to the company. If standards are consistently loose, a **constant sharing** plan, such as the Halsey plan with the slope of the wage curve adjusted according to the degree of looseness of the standards, is indicated. Bedaux successfully used variations of the constant sharing feature in a wide range of applications. If variable conditions unavoidably create apparent mixtures of loose and tight standards, a **variable sharing** plan, such as the Rowan, automatically provides both high and relatively low sharing features. In fact, the inconsistency of standards actually existing in most companies would indicate that the modified Rowan plan is a simple plan and the most equitable single compromise plan for general application.

OTHER WAGE INCENTIVE PLANS. After Taylor's development of systematic time study procedures and the "Taylor System," many attempts were made to develop **all-purpose** incentive plans, often with principal emphasis on the shape of the wage curve. It was only natural that each engineer should try to develop a curve which reflected his personal philosophy and produce satisfactory results under the conditions with which he was most familiar.

Not all these men were in situations with identical conditions, and several different types of curves were inevitable. Automatic machinery had not been developed to so high a degree as reflected in recent trends, and most of the earlier wage curves therefore were intended principally for use on manual activities. With the exception of Taylor, who emphasized task location by a large step bonus, most of these engineers apparently attempted to avoid abrupt changes in earnings by developing smooth curves which provided **gradual transitions** through all possible levels of productivity.

The following plans are included in this discussion, not so much for their practical applicability, but primarily for their historical background or for their academic interest as illustrations of attempts toward producing single all-purpose plans.

Emerson Efficiency-Bonus Plan. This plan is not widely used, but it is of interest since it illustrates how special features can be designed into a plan to suit the philosophy of an individual engineer. Emerson conceded the logic of emphasizing task, as with the step bonus of the Gantt plan, but considered it too severe and preferred to place less stress on task location. Accordingly he established an **empiric scale of bonus ratios** between low task and high task, starting with zero bonus at $E_H = 0.66$, increasing first by small increments, then by successively larger increments to culminate in a 20 percent bonus at $E_H = 1.00$.

The Emerson plan guarantees base wages up to low task ($E_H = 0.66$), and daywork wage formulas apply. Analysis of the empiric bonus ratios for efficiencies between low and high task reveals a **parabolic** relationship that can be expressed by the formula:

$$Br = 1.73(E_H - 0.66)^2 \qquad (85)$$

and the wage ratio becomes:

$$Wr = 1.00 + 1.73(E_H - 0.66)^2 \qquad (86)$$

The cost ratio equals:

$$Wr \times \frac{1.00}{E_n}$$

or

$$Cr = [1.00 + 1.73(E_H - 0.66)^2]\frac{1.00}{E_n}$$

But, with the 20 percent bonus concept, $E_n = 1.20E_H$ or $0.833E_n = E_H$ and $1.00/E_n = 0.833/E_H$. Therefore,

$$Cr = [0.8333 + 1.4417(E_H - 0.66)^2]\frac{1.00}{E_H} \qquad (87)$$

At and above high task ($E_H = 1.00$), wages for the Emerson plan are calculated as base wages, plus hours saved at base rate, plus 20 percent of base wages, or:

$$W = TNR + [(S_H - T)NR + 0.20TNR] \qquad (88)$$

or

$$W = TNR + [(E_H - 1.00)TNR + 0.20TNR]$$

Dividing by TNR gives the wage ratio:

$$Wr = 1.00 + (E_H - 1.00 + 0.20)$$

or

$$Wr = 0.20 + E_H \qquad (89)$$

and subtracting 1.00 gives the bonus ratio:

$$Br = E_H - 0.80 \qquad (90)$$

Multiplying equation (89) by $1.00/E_n$ or by $0.8333/E_H$ gives the cost ratio:

$$Cr = (0.20 + E_H)\frac{0.8333}{E_H}$$

or

$$Cr = (0.1667 + 0.8333E_H)\frac{1.00}{E_H} \qquad (91)$$

From equation (89), $Wr = 0.20 + 1.00E_H$, and the slope of the wage curve is 1.00 if high task standards are used. If normal task standards were used, E_H would be replaced by $0.833E_n$, giving $Wr = 0.20 + 0.8333E_n$. Thus it is seen that the plan actually becomes an 83.3 percent constant sharing plan and, like all sharing plans, gives wages that are truly proportional to output at only one point, namely at $E_H = 1.00$.

The Emerson plan as a whole is not especially effective on any particular class of work, although it would be most suitable for Class 1. As with most other plans, the **base wage guarantee** is a little more charitable for beginners than the (40-60) plan for outputs below low task. Between low task and normal, the bonuses are so small that operators have very little encouragement toward achieving normal production, yet any bonus at all in this range increases unit labor costs. Between normal and high task performance, the bonuses are closely equivalent to those of the differential time plan with the gradual bonus (which would be simpler to apply), and therefore lack the strength of a single-step bonus for use on fixed-speed machines or processes. Above high task performance, the 83.3 percent sharing feature lacks the strength of incentive for well-standardized manual work and also the automatic protection of the Rowan plan for variable working conditions and mixed standards.

Barth Variable Sharing Plan. This plan seldom is used, but it is of interest because it is another illustration of the many different wage curves developed around the turn of the twentieth century and because of its rather novel formula. Faced with no legal requirements to guarantee base wages, Barth apparently wished to accomplish two things: retain the protection of a variable sharing feature somewhat like the Rowan plan at high outputs, and provide a compromise between the charity of guaranteed base wages and the severity of straight piecework wages for very low outputs.

The wage curve is a **horizontal parabola**, starting from the origin, rising more rapidly than straight piecework through low levels of production, yielding base wages at low task (typical daywork) output, then rising at a slower rate until it eventually falls below the Halsey 50 percent constant sharing line. The wage curve is produced as follows: (1) multiply the total standard time produced during a given period by the actual time taken; (2) take the square root of this product; and (3) multiply this result by the hourly (base) rate.

Since the plan yields base wages at low task efficiency, it obviously should be used with low task time standards as obtained from past performance records. In fact, Barth indicated that "it is meant for shops that still have no scientific rating, or such merely in a crude way, which is still all that the majority of shops have."

Barth variable sharing plan formulas can be developed from the above description. For simplicity, the square root will be indicated here by use of the 0.5 power.

$$W = (S_L N \times TN)^{0.5} \times R = (S_L T)^{0.5} \times NR$$

It is inconvenient to take square roots in routine payroll calculations, and therefore it is desirable to reduce this equation to some function of efficiency so that master **wage and bonus ratio tables** can be prepared. Multiplying by T/T gives:

$$W = \left(\frac{S_L}{T} \times T^2\right)^{0.5} NR = (E_L)^{0.5} TNR \qquad (92)$$

Thus total wages can be determined by multiplying straight time base wages TNR by the square root of the calculated efficiency. Dividing by TNR gives:

$$Wr = E_L{}^{0.5} \qquad (93)$$

Since the labor cost ratio generally equals $Wr \times 1.00/E_n$, or $Wr \times 1.20/E_L$:

$$Cr = E_L{}^{0.5} \times \frac{1.20}{E_L} = \frac{1.20}{E_L{}^{0.5}} \qquad (94)$$

When efficiency ratios E_L equal or exceed 1.00, a variable bonus ratio, represented by equation (95), occurs.

$$Br = Wr - 1.00 = E_L{}^{0.5} - 1.00 \qquad (95)$$

High Piece-Rate Plan. The straight piecework plan, previously described, is based on monetary standards and assumes that normal productivity will yield piecework earnings equivalent to the going base wages. This, in turn, assumes that the monetary piece rate M is determined by first establishing a normal task standard S_n, then multiplying by the base rate R, i.e., $M = S_n R$. Wages are determined as the product of the piece rate and the number of units produced, and therefore are directly proportioned to output.

$$W = S_n RN = \frac{S_n}{T} TNR = E_n TNR$$

and

$$Wr = E_n$$

If $N = 0.00$, indicating no production, then $Wr = 0.00$. If the operator works at normal pace and just meets standards, the standard time produced, $S_n N$, will equal the actual time spent, TN, the efficiency ratio E_n is 1.00, and the wage ratio $Wr = 1.00$, indicating actual earnings equal to base wages. The coefficient of E_n may be assumed to be 1.00 (or $Wr = 1.00 E_n$), and the wage curve therefore has a slope of 1.00. If the operator works at an incentive pace and E_n becomes 1.25, then Wr also becomes 1.25, indicating a proper 25 percent bonus.

In some cases it may be more convenient to level the time studies, or otherwise develop standard time values, in terms of high task performance. Such standards should be tighter than normal task standards so that $S_H = S_n/1.25$. With these tighter standards, a given level of performance can yield the same wages only by using a high hourly rate, $R_H = 1.25R$, so that the **monetary piece rate** M, calculated from high task standards, becomes:

$$M = S_H R_H = 1.25 S_H R \qquad (96)$$

and wages become:

$$W = 1.25 S_H RN = 1.25 E_H \times TNR \qquad (97)$$

giving a wage ratio of:

$$Wr = 1.25 E_H \qquad (98)$$

from which it is seen that the high piece-rate wage curve has a slope of 1.25 in terms of high task efficiencies.

The cost ratio becomes:

$$Cr = Wr \times \frac{1.00}{E_n} = 1.25 E_H \times \frac{1.00}{1.25 E_H} = 1.00, \text{ a constant} \qquad (99)$$

which properly is the same as for straight piecework.

Taylor Differential Piece-Rate Plan. Taylor recognized the fairness of piecework wages, but he was aware that high wages did not necessarily mean high unit costs if corresponding high production were obtained. He placed particular emphasis on improvement of tools and methods for each job, the establishment of a high but fair task, the centralization of control, and the selection and training of the man for the task, in addition to the reward of a generous incentive. To make this type of management most effective, he wished not only to attract the very best men of each trade who would take full advantage of the available facilities, but also to discourage less qualified persons.

With this in mind, he conceived a plan which included not only a generous reward for high producers but also a severe punishment for those who would not produce up to task. Instead of building his reward on top of a basic (straight) piece rate, he deliberately instituted a low piece rate to which he added a 50 percent step bonus at high task.

Taylor used careful methods and time study procedures to set high task performance, then used a high hourly rate ($1.25 \times R$) to yield wages equal to 1.25 (125 percent) of base wages at $E_H = 100$. Above high task output, the wage curve has a slope of 1.25, similar to that in the Gantt task and bonus plan. These wages were to be 50 percent higher than those obtained from the lower differential rate; thus the lower piece-rate wage curve has a slope of 1.25/1.50 or 0.833 (83.3 percent). In this manner Taylor placed great emphasis on meeting specified (task) levels of performance. While Taylor used the term "piece rates," it is probable that the plan was administered with time rather than with monetary standards.

Formulas can be developed for the **Taylor differential piece-rate plan** from the above description as follows. Up to high task:

$$W = 0.833 S_H NR \qquad (100)$$

Dividing by TNR:

$$Wr = 0.833 E_H \qquad (101)$$

Earnings in this range are considerably lower than typical base wages, hence there is no bonus. As with all other plans, the labor cost ratio is $Wr \times 1.00/E_n$ or:

$$Cr = 0.833 E_H \times \frac{1.00}{E_n} = 0.833 E_H \times \frac{1.00}{1.25 E_H}$$

or

$$Cr = 0.6666, \text{ a constant} \qquad (102)$$

At and above high task:

$$W = 1.25S_H NR \tag{103}$$

and

$$Wr = 1.25E_H \tag{104}$$

If only monetary standards were used, typical base wages actually might not be known. But, if standards are expressed in time, the base rate R must be used in calculating wages; hence base wages TNR will be known and the difference between wages earned and base wages will be the bonus, and the bonus ratio becomes:

$$Br = 1.25\,E_H - 1.00 \tag{105}$$

and the cost ratio becomes:

$$Cr = 1.25E_H \times \frac{1.00}{1.25E_H} = 1.00, \text{ a constant} \tag{106}$$

Merrick Differential Piece-Rate Plan. Taylor foresaw the advantage of more than two piece rates. He wrote:

In cases where large and expensive machines are used, such as . . . . steam hammers or rolling mills, in which a large output is dependent upon the severe manual labor as well as the skill of the workman (while the chief cost of production lies in the expense of running the machine rather than in the wages paid), it has been found of great advantage to establish two or three differential rates, offering a higher and higher price per piece or per ton as the maximum possible output is approached.

Merrick realized that employees were by no means divided into only two classes, low and high producers; also that many employees, still struggling for better production, should be encouraged. He avoided Taylor's low rate by starting with basic piece rate, which was used up to 83.3 percent of high task output, i.e., up to normal output. Between normal and high task, a 10 percent step bonus was given, while a 20 percent bonus was applied for output at and above high task. This resulted in three piece rates with two equal bonus steps.

Other divisions of the bonus might be used as well. Lytle suggests **two uneven steps** of 8 and 12 percent to reward the more difficult achievement with a higher bonus. This would approximate the geometric series of bonus increases obtained with the Emerson empiric scale, and it appears a little simpler.

Formulas for the Merrick differential piece-rate plan may be developed, assuming a 25 percent bonus at high task (rather than 20 percent), with an intermediate bonus of 12.5 percent beginning at normal. With the 25 percent bonus, normal task becomes 80 percent (rather than 83.3 percent) of high task, and the curves thus become directly comparable with those of the Taylor plan from which they were derived. Up to normal output where $E_H = 0.80$, basic piece rate is used, the wage curve having a slope of 1.00:

$$W = 1.00S_H NR \tag{107}$$

and

$$Wr = 1.00E_H \tag{108}$$

For earned efficiencies below 0.80, earnings will be less than base wages, and there can be no bonus as such.

The labor cost ratio is $Wr \times 1.00/E_n$, or $Wr \times 1.00/1.25E_H$.

$$Cr = 1.00E_H \times \frac{1.00}{1.25E_H} = 0.80, \text{ a constant} \tag{109}$$

Between normal and high task output, where $E_H = 0.80$ to 1.00:

$$W = 1.125 S_H NR \tag{110}$$

$$Wr = 1.125 E_H \tag{111}$$

Base wages will be earned where $E_H = 1.00/1.125 = 0.8888$, above which:

$$Br = 1.125 E_H - 1.00 \tag{112}$$

Within the efficiency range from 0.80 to 1.00, the labor cost ratio becomes:

$$Cr = 1.125 E_H \times \frac{0.80}{E_H} = 0.90, \text{ a constant} \tag{113}$$

At and above high task output, where $E_H = 1.00$, wage and cost curves are identical with those of high piece rate, or with the Gantt plan:

$$W = 1.25 S_H NR \tag{21}$$

$$Wr = 1.25 E_H \tag{22}$$

$$Br = 0.25 E_H \tag{23}$$

$$Cr = 1.00, \text{ a constant} \tag{24}$$

EFFECT OF GUARANTEED MINIMUM WAGES. By imposing the requirement of a minimum guarantee, the Fair Labor Standards Act of 1938 with subsequent amendments has made illegal, for companies engaged in interstate commerce, the lowest part of all earning curves that go low enough to yield a wage ratio which, when multiplied by the base rate, results in an earned hourly rate that is lower than the current legal minimum. In actual practice, efficiencies seldom are so low that such low portions of the wage curves become applicable. With any plan, it is a simple matter to stay within the law by comparing earned wages from the plan with the legal minimum wages, and paying whichever is the higher. The relatively high base wages in most industries make such comparisons rarely necessary except, perhaps, for the lowest labor grades. However, successive increases have brought the legal minimum closer to the base or guaranteed rates currently used for the lower labor grades in some plants. If, or as, this trend continues, such comparisons will become more frequent. Accordingly, some attempts have been made to design new wage plans which automatically will yield wages that are wholly within the law, i.e., always above the legal minimum. Lytle (Wage Incentive Methods) discusses **accelerating premium** plans, based on parabolic and hyberbolic wage curves, that can be applied over the entire range of efficiency values.

A **general-purpose** wage curve should be applicable to all grades of labor and correspondingly to all hourly rates. Accordingly it must be designed so that actual earnings will be a calculated ratio of any base wage, depending on whatever hourly rate momentarily is in effect for the individual employee. Basic hourly rates necessarily vary between labor grades, and individual or personal rates may vary within a grade. But the legal minimum is a fixed amount and therefore cannot be any fixed ratio of all the different hourly rates from which bonuses may be calculated under a given incentive plan.

Unless otherwise specified by definition, **minimum earnings** from a wage curve will occur at zero productivity, or where $E = 0.00$. If used with a $2.00 base rate, the curve must start with a wage ratio of 0.50 in order to yield a legal minimum of $1.00 per hr. If applied to a base rate of $1.00 per hr., the curve must start at a wage ratio of 1.00, or at the base, to yield the legal minimum. It virtually is impossible, therefore, to design a general incentive wage curve which will always automatically yield minimum earnings exactly equivalent to the legal minimum wages.

It should be possible to design a separate curve for each different base rate. This would require at least one curve for each labor grade, and yet the curve would not apply correctly to any variations in individual hourly rates within the grade. But, even if only properly evaluated base rates were used (this is administratively sound), such a multiplicity of curves hardly could be considered practical.

It might be somewhat more feasible to develop such a wage curve for the lowest hourly rate within a company and apply it to all higher rates in effect. This at least would insure that all calculated earnings would be equal to, or higher than, the legal minimum wages. However, even this curve would be temporary, for it would give the desired results only as long as both the legal rate and the lowest hourly rate either remained unchanged or remained in the same relationship to each other.

RELATIVE PERFORMANCE LEVELS. In analyzing the several wage plans. it has been assumed that a 25 percent bonus, above base wages, should be paid for true **high task** performance. This corresponds with the Taylor piece-rate plan, one of the first incentive plans in America which was based on performance standards established by careful time study procedures. Furthermore, a 25 percent bonus appears to be the most popular concept of an appropriate reward in modern wage incentive practice. Wage curves, like straight piecework, are most widely used and reward the operator in direct proportion to his output. To give wage ratios that are directly proportional to calculated efficiencies, such a curve must start at the origin and rise as a straight line with a constant slope. It is simple and logical to assign an efficiency ratio of 1.25 to represent high task performance corresponding to a wage ratio of 1.25, and the slope of the line thus becomes $1.25/1.25 = 1.00$.

Normal performance is assumed to be the level which would just produce base wages or a wage ratio of 1.00, and therefore, from the above curve, would be represented by an efficiency ratio of 1.00. However, since the incentive pace is the level on which practical agreement most readily can be obtained, it often is preferred to assign an **efficiency index** of 1.00 to high task performance; and in this case, normal performance would be represented by a high task efficiency ratio of $1.00/1.25$, or $E_H = 0.800$.

The concept of **low task** performance refers to the average level of output obtained under typical unmeasured daywork conditions. Under these conditions, rates of output are highly variable, but averages can be obtained from records of past performance. The Halsey 50 percent sharing plan was one of the first incentive plans to be used with loose standards based on such averages, and therefore it is used here for determining an efficiency ratio which may fairly represent average low task performance.

With the 50 percent plan [see equation (42)], it has been shown that a numerical ratio of 1.50 is required to yield the desired wage ratio of 1.25; thus an efficiency ratio of 1.50 from low task standards represents high task performance. An efficiency ratio of 1.00, calculated from such standards, should produce a wage ratio of 1.00 (for base wage earnings); hence low task performance may be represented by a high task efficiency ratio of $1.00/1.50$, or $E_H = 0.667$. If normal task standards were used, low task performance would be represented by a normal task efficiency ratio of $0.667/0.800$, or $E_n = 0.833$. Fig. 20 shows the **calculated relationships** of the three principal recognized levels of performance.

Relative Performance	High Task Efficiency Ratio (E_H)	Normal Task Efficiency Ratio (E_n)	Low Task Efficiency Ratio (E_L)
High task	1.000	1.250	1.50
Normal task	0.800	1.000	1.20
Low task	0.667	0.833	1.00

Fig. 20. Relative efficiencies for wage ratio of 1.25 at high task.

Different Bonus for Incentive Performance. Various wage plans have been designed by engineers with other concepts of appropriate wage ratios for high task performance. For example, in the early 75 percent sharing plan, Bedaux gave a wage ratio of 1.25 for an efficiency ratio of 1.333, which thus represented high task; but, with the more recent adoption of full sharing, the wage ratio has increased to 1.333 for the same performance index. Still other engineers, such as Emerson, considered 1.20 adequate, a value still used by some of the more conservative management consulting firms. While not being entirely consistent in all his illustrations, Lytle generally accepted the 1.20 concept, as in his accelerating bonus plans.

High task is the most reliable point of reference; therefore the identification of normal and low task should be made relative to high task. But **variations in the wage ratios** selected for high task will alter the relative identifications of normal and low task performances. Since the 1.20 concept is quite common, and necessarily was used in a few of the above illustrations, corresponding new identifications of normal and low task performances may be calculated.

Using a straight piece-rate curve of unity slope, a wage ratio of 1.20 requires an efficiency ratio of 1.20, which thus identifies incentive performance in terms of normal task standards, i.e., $E_n = 1.20$ at high task. But, if high task is identified by an efficiency ratio of 1.00, normal performance is identified as 1.00/1.20 or $E_n = 0.833$.

Again using the 50 percent sharing plan to establish the location of low task performance, equation (42) requires a numerical ratio of 1.40 to yield a wage ratio of 1.20. Thus, low task is represented by a high task efficiency ratio of 1.00/1.40, or $E_H = 0.7143$. If normal task standards are used, low task will be represented by normal task efficiency ratio of 0.7143/0.833, or $E_n = 0.8571$. These new relationships are summarized in Fig. 21

Relative Performance	High Task Efficiency Ratio (E_H)	Normal Task Efficiency Ratio (E_n)	Low Task Efficiency Ratio (E_L)
High task	1.000	1.20	1.400
Normal task	0.833	1.000	1.167
Low task	0.714	0.857	1.000

Fig. 21. Relative efficiencies for wage ratio of 1.20 at high task.

From the above calculations it is seen that any other desired wage ratio selected for high task performance would necessitate new index values for mathematically precise identifications of low, normal, and high task performances.

Also it must be remembered that, when an operator just meets a standard, no matter how loose or tight it may be, the calculated efficiency ratio automatically becomes 1.00. Therefore, efficiency ratios, as such, are not reliable indicators of true **relative performance** unless all standards consistently reflect similar performance requirements. Neither are they reliable indicators of **absolute levels of performance** unless the standard level of performance is known.

No method has yet been devised that can establish precisely any specific level of performance. All time standards, no matter how carefully they are determined, are relative to some base which reflects an opinion, an agreement, or a statistically sound summary of observations. Such a base can be defined in arbitrary and usually very general terms or in some cases in statistical terms, and therefore it is subject to some variation and change.

Accordingly, the terms low task, normal task, and high task indicate relatively broad ranges of performance levels. The efficiency ratios, as calculated above, have been determined from specific wage equations and reflect only theoretical, although reasonable and logical, relations. The values have been necessary for purposes of mathematical and graphical consistency in presentation. But, because the calculations have been carried to several decimal places, they may leave a false impression of precision. Furthermore, even if these relative levels could be so precisely identified, the inherent errors of most performance rating (leveling) make it impossible to set standards with equivalent precision. In general, it is safe to assume, however, that average low task performance is somewhere between 60 and 75 percent of high task, and that normal performance is approximately 80 to 85 percent of the high task level which typical well-motivated workers reasonably can be expected to maintain.

Choice of Plan According to the Standards. Although it is impossible to know exactly what performance level a standard may require, nevertheless these three levels are significantly different and can be recognized with good judgment and intuition. Thus, if standards are crudely **estimated** or reflect averages of past daywork performance, they are likely to be in the general low task range and appropriate partial sharing incentive plans should be used.

If standards are determined by careful **time studies** which are leveled to a reasonable concept of normal they are likely to be in the general normal task range. Standard data which have been tested in previous installations where bonuses average close to 25 percent of base wages are likely to give normal standards with the greatest consistency. Any of the plans illustrated with normal task efficiencies may be used, the specific choice being determined by good judgment regarding the consistency of working conditions or the consistency of time study procedures.

Time studies taken of employees already working under good incentive conditions, and given a performance rating index close to unity, are likely to reflect approximately high task performance. More consistent high task standards usually can be obtained from **standard data** which have been developed from such time studies or which have proved to yield average efficiency ratios near 1.00 in previous incentive installations. Standards calculated from mechanically paced equipment, such as capacity outputs of fixed-speed machines or processes, usually can be assumed to be in the high task range, particularly if manual portions of the cycles also are carefully adjusted to require consistently high operator effort. With such standards it will be reasonably safe to select a high sharing or step bonus plan such as any of those illustrated with high task efficiencies. Again, the selection will be influenced by the specific type of work and the particular combination of incentive features desired.

Group Incentives

APPLICATION OF GROUP INCENTIVES.
A wage incentive plan, basically, is a formula by which the wages of one or more workers are related to productivity. A group incentive is any wage incentive plan applied collectively to two or more workers.

A group incentive is likely to be most successful when the several members are engaged in work which has the group characteristics of interdependent relationship between operations, physical proximity, and unity of interest, and particularly where mutual cooperation among the members is essential or desirable.

Group administration is almost unavoidable where the work of one individual cannot be isolated from the work of others. Typical examples include machine crews, maintenance and repair crews, assembly crews on large products, short conveyor lines, etc. Where material flows continuously through a sequence of operations, no operator can produce any more work than is passed to him by the preceding operators. While a separate standard may be determined for each station in order to obtain an equitable "balance," the output of each operator necessarily is the same as that of all others along the line. Thus, whether the rate of flow is determined by the operators themselves or is mechanically paced by a conveyor, group administration is most appropriate.

Many engineers recommend that **individual administration** of incentives be used wherever possible, that is, wherever material is delivered to an operator in relatively large quantities, or wherever the performance of one operator is not immediately dependent upon that of another and the output can be isolated readily for measurement of quantity and quality. Typical examples include individual machine operators, assemblers, etc. But even on these operations there often is a physical proximity due to convenient groupings of similar machines or operations and this, by itself, creates a considerable community of interest, and group incentives can be used. Although many companies still adhere to the tradition of individual incentives (an early precedent of monetary piece rates), others have obtained better over-all results with group administration on all incentive work. Group incentives can be used on any type of measurable work, while individual incentives necessarily are limited to activities which can be isolated.

GROUP LEADERSHIP.
Group incentives require cooperation and leadership. Typically, this leadership must be obtained from a "group leader" to whom certain supervisory responsibilities are delegated but who also serves as a **setup man** or **lead man** and, as such, is a regular member of the group and participates in the group's earnings. As a supervisor, he relieves the departmental foreman of administrative details which he can perform more effectively because of his closer association with the members of his group. Time required for this supervisory work usually is included in the standards by means of a percentage, i.e., a suitable increase in the **allowance factor**; the costs for such work are thereby transferred from burden expense to direct labor.

GROUP SIZE.
A large group requires more leadership ability than a small group. This makes **small groups** preferable. It is desirable to break long

sequences of work into small natural divisions of similar or closely related activities which can be controlled by working leaders.

There are other factors in favor of small groups. The self-elimination of unnecessary members is suggested as one of the principal advantages of group organization. Generally a group is organized with a **standard number** of members, and work is scheduled accordingly. If one member is tardy or temporarily absent, the remaining members will often try to handle all the assigned work without a substitute. This is to their advantage if the total earnings during such periods are distributed among the fewer members. The absence of 1 member from a group of 100 persons could affect the earnings of the others by only 1 percent; but the absence of one from a group of eleven would yield a 10 percent increase in earnings for the remaining ten during the period of such absence.

This effect is shown in Fig. 22, in which the horizontal scale represents the standard size of the group. The vertical scale indicates the **ratio of increased earnings** for the remaining members of the group who maintain full output when 1 member is absent. It is unlikely that 2 men could carry the full load of a 3-man group, even for short periods, or that 3 could carry the load of 4; hence substitutes will be required. However, the smaller the group, the more nearly are the

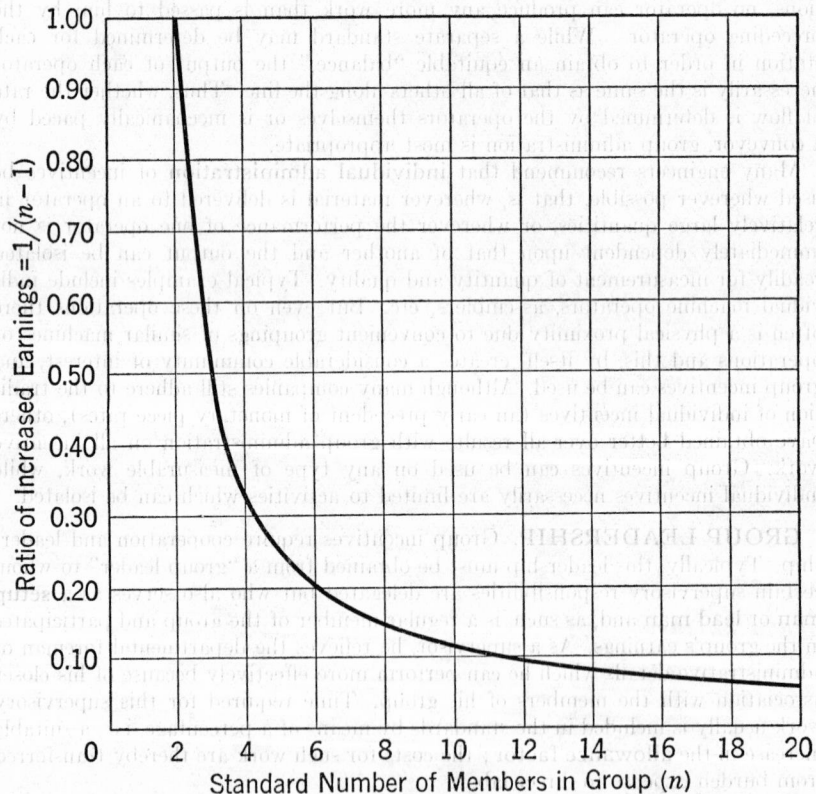

Fig. 22. Ratio of increased earnings for remaining members of group who maintain full output when 1 member is absent.

advantages of individual incentives approached, yet the feature of cooperative teamwork is retained. As the group size increases, it becomes easier for the remaining members to carry the load of an absentee, assuming that his work can be distributed with reasonable equity. But, as the group size approaches 20 or more, the extra reward becomes less significant, and the remaining members are more likely to request a substitute than to make the effort of redistributing the absentee's work. The curve clearly illustrates why groups tend to average less than 20 members, and why at least one company has set a practical limit of 12 persons per group.

GROUP ADMINISTRATION. Group administration with monetary standards usually is called **gang piecework,** while with time standards it usually is called **group bonus;** however, these terms are used somewhat interchangeably. If all members of a group are required to have approximately equal skills (all in the same labor grade), and accordingly have the same guaranteed hourly rate, then monetary piece rates are feasible and group earnings may be divided equally. If unequal hours have been worked, the earnings must be apportioned according to the respective times spent in the group. However, if workers of unequal skills and different hourly rates are in the same group, the piecework earnings must be apportioned according to both the times worked and the hourly rates, i.e., according to the respective straight time earnings. Such apportionment is a laborious payroll routine.

Equitable distribution of group earnings is simplified with the use of time standards. Furthermore, as long as methods are unchanged, time standards can remain fixed regardless of negotiated changes in hourly rates. For these and other reasons, many companies have converted from gang piecework to group bonus.

Group administration tends to distribute, among the members of the group, any inequities due to inaccurate or inconsistent standards. On certain types of work it is impossible to set accurate and consistent standards because of temporary variations in work content; yet, with standards set for **average conditions** and the use of groups, incentives have been applied successfully to activities for which individual incentives would be most inappropriate. For example, group incentives have been applied to machine repair crews, building maintenance gangs, truckers, general materials handlers, elevator operators, crane operators, sweepers, tool makers, and a variety of other service activities. Advantages have been mutual. Operators' earnings have increased significantly to a point comparable with other incentive workers' with similar skills. With the reduction of idleness and unnecessary "busy work," costs have been greatly reduced. Standards not only permit better cost control, but they also provide the basis for intelligent planning of work schedules and manpower requirements.

Whenever standards are based on relatively crude averages, they tend to be liberal, and **partial sharing plans** are most appropriate. It is common therefore to find group incentives applied with partial sharing plans, particularly on such variable activities as those mentioned immediately above. Furthermore, because of the leveling effect of group administration, some time study men become careless in setting group standards, even for standardized repetitive work. When this is suspected, partial sharing plans definitely should be used.

Group administration should not be an excuse for careless time study work. Every effort should be made to set standards with the same accuracy for group application as for individuals. When this is done, the same general rules will apply for the selection of the incentive plan, regardless of whether incentives are

	Individual Incentives	Group Incentives
1. Performance.	Since each operator is "in business for himself," there is strong inducement for high performance. Management can readily determine the relative productivity of each individual. Actual time spent on specific orders is easily determined and standards checked. Limited or "pegged" production is more likely to occur on items with loose standards than in the case of group incentives.	Group incentives tend to have a leveling effect. The superior producer may feel that he is carrying more than his share of the load and therefore reduce his effort. Group pressures may likewise have an upward leveling effect upon the operator who would be satisfied with relatively low individual earnings. Therefore, average group output often is as high as, or higher than, average individual output.
2. Earnings.	Each individual is rewarded according to his own output. Low production on the part of one operator does not affect the earnings of others. Earnings by the day, order, or lot are readily determined.	Earnings are more consistent, since all members of a group share equally in the bonus. Objective records of individual production are often not readily available. Individual hourly rates may be adjusted on the basis of periodic merit ratings by the group leader, individual records for temporary periods, or work-sampling studies.
3. Quality.	Defective work penalizes only the person responsible. If, however, several persons are performing the same operation, it may be difficult to identify the one responsible for poor work. Hence, quality standards may be difficult to enforce and the company may have to absorb the cost of rework.	Defective work penalizes all members of the group. Quality standards are simpler to enforce since it is usually easier to identify a group responsible for defective work than to fix responsibility upon an individual.
4. Morale.	Significant inconsistencies in earnings leading to controversies and lowered morale, may be created.	The incentive group promotes social consciousness among its members, giving each person a sense of "belonging" and of greater security. This is an important psychological advantage and is consistent with typical union philosophy.
5. Cooperation.	There is little inducement for the individual to cooperate with others.	The group reduces the tendency toward unfriendly rivalry and encourages cooperation among its members.

6. Supervision.	The foreman must give detailed supervision and make all individual task assignments. Discrimination or favoritism in work assignments may occur. Management has the complete responsibility for disposing of the ineffective operator.	Routine supervisory functions can be delegated to the group leader, relieving the foreman of these details. Discrimination or favoritism in task assignments is practically eliminated. Self-elimination of excess members tends to reduce the group to the minimum size necessary to carry out assigned work loads. Record-keeping and payroll costs are reduced since productive efficiencies are calculated for only a few groups.
7. Planning.	Centralized production planning and scheduling is more complex and detailed with individual operators or machines than when work can be scheduled on a group basis.	Routing and scheduling routines are simplified with tasks assigned to groups rather than to individuals. Tardiness and short periods of absence cause less disruption to production schedules.
8. Training.	There is little inducement for the regular operator to help train new employees.	Seasoned operators are usually willing to teach new employees the "tricks of the trade" so that they may more quickly assume their proper shares of the work load.
9. Daywork.	The capable operator resists assignment to daywork tasks with resulting loss of bonus.	Nonincentive tasks may be assigned to a group, with payment to be made at the straight time rate. The more capable group members often accept such assignments in order to hold nonincentive time to a minimum.
10. Indirect labor.	It is difficult to provide for the inclusion of setup men or service workers in the production incentive plan.	Groups provide a convenient means for including setup men and service workers in regular productive units, with all members having a common interest. The setup and service men have an incentive to keep machines in good operating condition and supplied with materials, and both will perform direct productive activities rather than remain idle when not occupied with their customary duties.

Fig. 23. Comparison of the principal characteristics of individual and group incentive systems.

to be administered with groups or with individuals. A comparison of the principal characteristics of individual and group incentives as an aid in deciding which type of plan to use is given in Fig. 23.

Learners' Allowances

PROGRESS IN LEARNING. Age is believed to have little effect upon the ability to learn. Some investigators maintain that the general **laws of learning** apply with equal force throughout the age range from 15 to 50. The same rules of training therefore can be applied to all adult learners, and in a particular apprentice system average response can be expected according to a single **general training curve** such as that shown by the broken line in Fig. 24. However, the rate is only relative and the time taken will vary with jobs and with individuals, as shown by the solid line in Fig. 24, which indicates the actual progress in efficiency of one individual.

Often it is assumed that a steady increase in efficiency should be expected from new employees. But, for the average worker, and depending upon the nature of the work, there is a period near the middle of the normal training cycle where improvement practically ceases. Thereafter the balance of **average proficiency** is attained very rapidly.

Where remuneration such as straight piecework is based upon a constant increase in proficiency (which is practically impossible for the average worker to maintain), the loss of employees before they have attained normal proficiency has been a serious problem, particularly with female labor. Legal minimum guarantees have eliminated the most discouraging portions of wage curves which extend to the origin. In those few industries or locations where evaluated base rates are near the legal minimum, this minimum probably is sufficient to hold new employees long enough for them to become reasonably efficient. In many industries, however, typical base rates are considerably higher than the legal requirement.

Since a relatively high guaranteed rate is lacking in incentive, it is frequently desirable to use a wage plan with a curve that yields earnings, between the legal minimum and the evaluated base rate, that are approximately in accordance with the **beginner's rate of progress.** In most situations the legal minimum will be at least equivalent to earnings that would be appropriate for about 40 or 50 percent of high task performance. Above this level several different wage curves will yield very similar earnings, all being sufficiently close to the typical rate of learning for practical application.

Either the (40-60) beginner's plan, or a downward extension of the Halsey 50 percent plan, would be appropriate and simple. Also within the range from 50 to 100 percent of high task efficiency, nearly the same results would be obtained from the slightly more complex Barth plan. All these plans automatically relate the learner's earnings to his output and therefore provide an incentive for rapid progress.

LEARNERS' ALLOWANCES IN GROUPS. With a legal minimum guarantee combined with one of the sharing plans suggested above, the problem of providing adequate earnings is relatively simple, particularly when the new employee can be assigned to individual tasks. A somewhat different problem arises when a new member is introduced into an established group.

A typical general procedure is as follows and, for simplicity, it is assumed that the new member is assigned full time in the group. The group automatically receives credit for whatever output the new member accomplishes. Only a portion of the new member's actual time is charged against the group. This portion will be relatively low at first but gradually increases according to a prescribed schedule until eventually all his time is charged to the group. For the time charged to the group, the new member is paid an **apprentice bonus** according to the group's bonus ratio and his own hourly rate; but, for the remainder of his time, he is paid only his regular hourly rate.

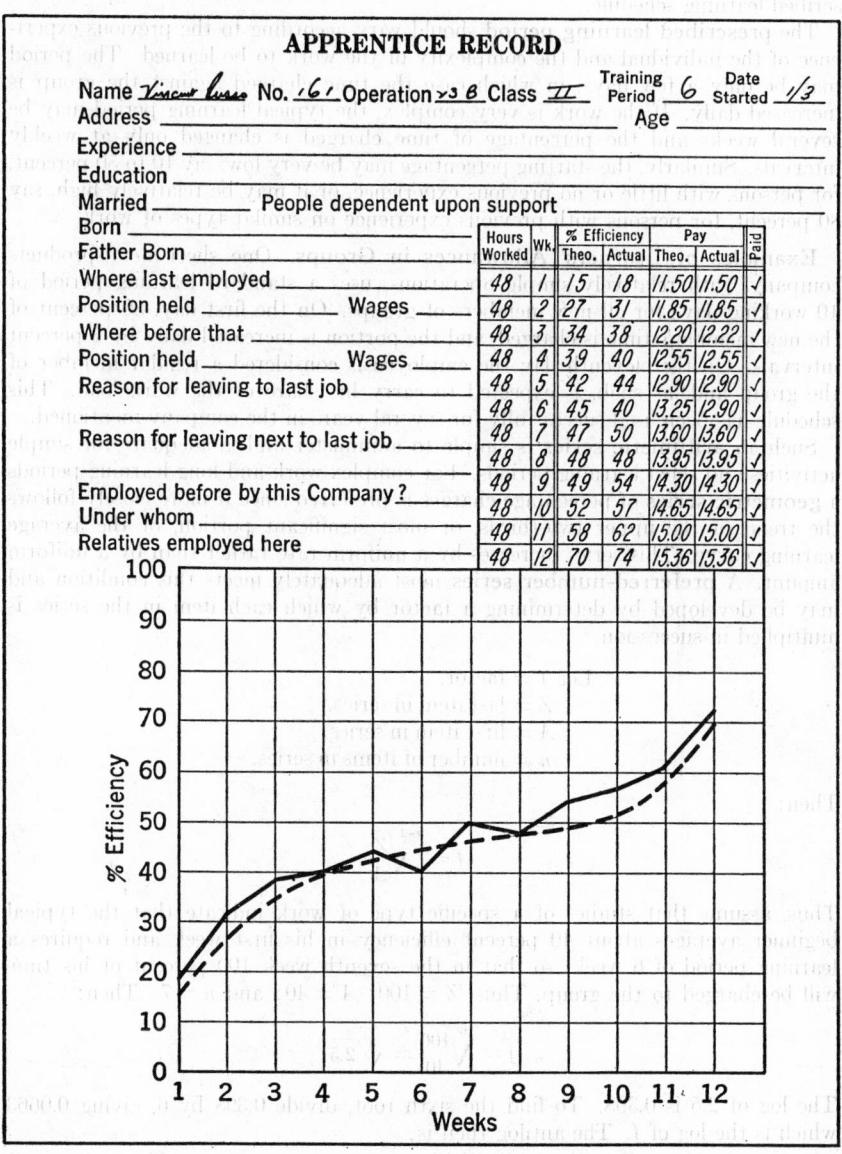

Fig. 24. Apprentice record showing theoretical and actual efficiencies.

Since the group benefits by whatever the new member contributes, he is readily given instruction and help by the older members; and, since he also benefits from the group's bonus ratio, he has an incentive to contribute as much as possible. Furthermore, if the new member has attained suitable proficiency and if the older members agree, he may be classified as a regular member before the expiration of his prescribed learning period so that he can enjoy the group's bonus ratio on all his working hours. This provides an additional inducement to "beat" the prescribed learning schedule.

The **prescribed learning period** should vary according to the previous experience of the individual and the complexity of the work to be learned. The period may be only a few days, in which case the time charged against the group is increased daily. If the work is very complex, the typical learning period may be several weeks and the percentage of time charged is changed only at weekly intervals. Similarly, the starting percentage may be very low, say 10 to 50 percent, for persons with little or no previous experience, or it may be relatively high, say 80 percent, for persons with previous experience on similar types of work.

Examples of Learners' Allowances in Groups. One sheet-metal-products company, with relatively simple operations, uses a standard learning period of 10 working days for all new members of groups. On the first day, 80 percent of the new member's time is charged, and the portion is increased daily by 2 percent intervals. On the eleventh day the employee is considered a regular member of the group and, as such, is expected to carry his share of the work load. This schedule has been used successfully for several years in the company mentioned.

Such an **arithmetic series** is simple to administer and is adequate for simple activities and short learning periods. For complex work and long learning periods a **geometric series** of percentage charges is preferred since it more closely follows the trend of the upper two-thirds, or most significant portion, of the average learning curve. This series increases by a uniform rate rather than by a uniform amount. A **preferred-number series** most adequately meets this condition and may be developed by determining a factor by which each item in the series is multiplied in succession.

> Let f = factor.
> Z = last item in series.
> A = first item in series.
> n = number of items in series.

Then:

$$f = \sqrt[n-1]{\frac{Z}{A}}$$

Thus, assume that studies of a specific type of work indicate that the typical beginner averages about 40 percent efficiency in his first week and requires a learning period of 6 weeks so that in the seventh week 100 percent of his time will be charged to the group. Thus, $Z = 100$; $A = 40$; and $n = 7$. Then:

$$f = \sqrt[6]{\frac{100}{40}} = \sqrt[6]{2.5}$$

The log of 2.5 is 0.398. To find the sixth root, divide 0.398 by 6, giving 0.0663 which is the log of f. The antilog then is:

$$f = 1.165$$

Starting with 40 percent and multiplying successively by 1.165 gives the following series, rounded to the nearest 1.0 percent:

Week Number	Percent of Time Charged	Interval of Increase in Percent
1	40	
2	47	7
3	54	7
4	63	9
5	74	11
6	86	12
7	100	14

The preferred-number series is a useful device in many applications since it tends to reflect natural rates of increases. For example, in addition to the application just illustrated, it frequently is used in such job-evaluation work as setting up consistent base rate structures for successive labor grades and relating the hourly rates to scales of evaluated points for jobs requiring varying degrees of skills. Trainees or apprentices usually are started at hourly rates somewhat lower than the typical base rate for the "trade," and **progressive scales** are needed between the starting and base rates. Such scales often follow a preferred-number series. The increases may be granted according to a definite time schedule, according to formal merit ratings if such a system is in existence in the plant, or according to some combination of these two procedures.

OTHER INCENTIVES FOR APPRENTICES. Certain **nonfinancial incentives,** particularly for apprentices, are: job preference after training, opportunities for specialized training, and advancement as a result of examinations, all of which are nonfinancial. Other **financial incentives** may be used, such as provision of tools and textbooks and special bonuses throughout the program. Some companies allow regular incentive work at certain stages of the program, but this practice is questionable, particularly in short, intensified programs.

Payroll Calculations

TIME RECORDS. Certain records of actual and allowed time are essential in the administration of any payroll system involving wage incentives. The six forms described below provide the essential information from the shop for calculating wages and for allocating labor costs to specific orders, items, or other appropriate accounts.

Entrance-Clock Card. This is a basic record of time worked. A special **time clock** is located near the entrance of the plant or department in which the employee works. The employee punches the time on his card at the clock as he enters and as he leaves. The **time card** contains seven columns, one for each day of the week. The cards are collected daily, and the total time worked on the previous day is computed and recorded for each employee.

Daily Time Sheet. It is usually desirable, and often necessary, for allocation of labor costs to appropriate accounts, to know how an employee's actual working time is distributed to incentive or nonincentive work, to group or individual work, to specific work orders or products, or to special assignments. A simple but usually adequate system involves the use of a daily time sheet made out by the foreman, the departmental time clerk, or by the employee himself. Each different assignment or activity is listed with corresponding starting and stopping times. The **total elapsed hours** on the daily time sheet must agree with those indicated on the entrance time card.

Order and Route Sheet. This is an authorization for work to be performed. On it are shown the issue date, order number, quantity desired, a complete identification of the part to be produced, and the sequence of operations necessary to the production. (See section on Production Control Systems and Procedures.) A complete **time record** is kept for each individual, group, or department, and, when the order is completed, the sheet goes first to the payroll department and then to the accounting department for cost and other record purposes.

Group Summary Sheet. This is used with group incentives for collecting all the actual hours charged, and all the standard hours credited, to each group. A record is prepared for each bonus calculation period. The **actual time charged** is shown by date, clock number of the individual, and his actual hours in the group. The **standard hours allowed** on each order are posted by completion date, order number, the part, and the operation. This sheet provides a complete summary of the group's charges and credits.

Extra Standard Time Allowance. On incentive work, a specific standard time is allowed for performing an operation in a prescribed manner on a standard unit of material. This standard is indicated on the order and route sheet. However, variations often occur. The material may differ from standard specifications or previous operations may not have been done properly, and extra time may be required to produce acceptable units. Special repair or rework tasks may be assigned. Orders may be issued for trial runs or small quantities of special products. Rather than let such work be done on an uncontrolled straight time basis, it is common practice to give the operator or group an extra standard time allowance. If the **extra allowed time slip** is issued to an individual, he submits it to the time clerk along with his other records of work produced. If it is issued to a group, the time is posted to the group summary sheet as additional allowed hours.

Individual Pay Summary Sheet. This sheet provides a convenient place to accumulate the total wages of an individual for a bonus calculation period. On it are posted daily figures for actual hours spent in each group, hours on personal (individual) incentive work, total hours on incentive, and daywork hours on individual nonincentive assignments. Weekly postings are made of total earnings at hourly (base) rate. These are the wages which normally are paid each week, and they include actual hours worked plus 50 percent of overtime hours, all calculated at the regular hourly rate. At the close of the bonus calculation period, totals are found for actual hours on group and individual incentive work. Bonus ratios are determined and **total bonus** earnings computed. Subtracting the legal deductions leaves the **net bonus** to be paid.

Supplementary Incentives

INCENTIVES FOR QUALITY OF PRODUCT. Recognition of superior workmanship on a given operation, by means of higher than ordinary hourly rates, is an old custom; but it is becoming less justified with extreme subdivision of work and better control of tools, materials, and methods. As a consequence of quantity incentives, the present need is rather for an extra check on quality. The **quality** incentive therefore is a secondary measure and usually is applied in addition to a **quantity** incentive. It often is as uneconomical to the company for an operator to overdo a quality standard as to underdo it. But no bonus should be expected to maintain quality without a full program of design, purchase by specification, proper equipment, maintenance of tools, use of gages, and suitable inspection. Nor should promotion, the inevitable hope of superior employees, be ignored.

The simplest plan for **direct control of quality** is to inspect all output and allow quantity credit for only those units which meet quality specifications, but such a simple plan is not possible on every type of production. Where destructive tests are required, 100 percent inspection is impossible and sampling inspection is the only alternative. Sampling has often proved effective and more economical, even where 100 percent inspection is possible. Furthermore, measurable dimensions or attributes seldom meet the ideal specifications. Whether products are fully inspected or sampled, variations are unavoidable and ranges of acceptable variation must be established. (See section on Quality Control for a complete discussion of scientific sampling procedures.)

Accordingly, products may be classified into at least three **areas of quality:**

1. Products which are better than specification requirements and for which a quality bonus may be paid if superior quality is desired.
2. Products which meet specifications within acceptable tolerances.
3. Products with excessive defects which must be discarded, reworked, or sold at subnormal prices, resulting either in extra costs or reduced income, and for which a justifiable penalty may be imposed.

The nature and degree of these areas must be determined according to the emphasis desired, and they must be standardized for measurement and instruction. A possible pattern for **quality bonuses** and **penalties** has already been illustrated in Fig. 1.

Quality Bonus for Office Work. A variation of this pattern has proved effective in a group of **stenographer-typists** working on individual incentives in a large department store where prestige and good will could be affected by the quality of letters sent in reply to customers' complaints or inquiries. While form letters were followed to some extent, many replies required special composition in whole or in part.

After examination of a great many of these letters, a list was made of all the **types of defects** found, including: misspelled words; wrong punctuation; erasures; position of typed material on the sheet; colloquial or slang expressions; untactful comments; over-all neatness; and general tone of the letter. An empiric **point value** was assigned to each type of defect according to its considered importance and ease of elimination. Defect scores were determined for about 300 letters, including some from every typist, from which an **average allowable defect score** was established with a **tolerance range** statistically determined for chance variations.

In administering the plan about 20 letters each week are taken at random intervals from each typist. These are read by the departmental supervisor or the industrial engineer to determine current defect scores. If the typist's score is within the tolerance limit, incentive earnings are calculated from her total output; but, if the defect score exceeds the limit, her entire quantity bonus is canceled for the week. With this plan in effect, and greater use of carefully prepared sample letters as guides, the over-all quality has been significantly improved.

Accordingly, defect scores seldom exceed the limit and normal bonuses are the rule rather than the exception.

Quality Bonus for Production Inspectors. At Real Silk Hosiery Mills a quality bonus plan was installed for **inspectors of finished stockings.** An inspector received neither a bonus nor a penalty for quality when her wrong classifications were equal to 1.7 percent, or the **classification percentage.** This figure was set by careful analysis; it represented a standard which allowed for human deficiencies on this particular work. When the percentage of wrong classifications decreased below 1.7 percent, the inspector received a quality bonus according to a prescribed scale; and when wrong classifications exceeded 1.7 percent, corresponding penalties were imposed. The percent of wrong classifications was obtained from a check by **reinspectors** who were paid a flat salary. Occasionally. super-reinspection was made by the superintendent or his assistants to verify the findings of the reinspectors.

As in the case of the typists, empiric point values were assigned to various types of defects such as holes, seconds, mends, irregulars, pulled threads, mismates, reboards, and redyes, and these defect scores were used in determining the classification percentage.

For each unit of 0.1 percent variation either up or down from the 1.7 percent standard, the inspector's incentive earnings were affected by 0.9 percent. For example, if an inspector had only 1.0 percent of wrong classifications, her quality bonus would be 7×0.9 or 6.3 percent of her regular incentive earnings. Conversely, if she had 3.0 percent of her work wrongly classified (a variation of $3.0 - 1.7$, or 13 units), her penalty would be 13×0.9, or 11.7 percent of her incentive earnings. An important feature of the plan was **posting the results.** The inspectors' names were listed in order of accomplishments with their respective scores, and a red line was drawn at the location of no bonus. The system proved effective, yet it was considered reasonable and fair.

INCENTIVES FOR REDUCING MATERIAL WASTE. Waste-elimination incentives are those applied with a view toward reducing to a minimum the usable-material wastes resulting from manufacturing processes. They are used primarily where **cost of material** constitutes a large portion of total cost, or where the likelihood of much waste amounts to the same thing as in the leather, textile, paint, wood, and food industries. After the most economical processing procedure is established, experience data may be recorded and standards of waste formulated. Seldom is it practical to strive for zero waste, but there is a **most economical percentage of waste** for each case.

The waste incentive plan is simple. It provides a bonus or penalty, related inversely, or nearly so, to the amount of waste per unit of product or per manhour. When effort involved is directly proportional to savings accomplished, the curve plotted for percent of waste and bonus is properly a straight line. The **waste bonus** is usually independent of any quantity bonus and may, or may not, be accompanied by it. Waste bonuses may be applied either to individuals or to groups, and they generally provide bonuses but not penalties. Such plans are simple and automatic, and they do not fail after the novelty wears off, as so often happens with sensational prize campaigns.

Waste Bonus Applications. Waste bonuses have been applied to many different situations. In a **meat-packing house,** an inverse bonus was set up to reduce the carelessness of skinners, according to the percentage of cuts to the number of hides skinned.

An oil refinery applied a similar bonus to **power-plant operation.** At least 10 percent carbon dioxide but no more than 14 percent was desired. Above 14 percent, carbon monoxide appears; this indicates incomplete combustion of fuel. A bonus was paid for maintaining carbon dioxide within the acceptable range, and a penalty, established empirically, was imposed according to the percentage of combustible material remaining in the ash.

Mohawk Carpet Mills applied a waste incentive to **rug weaving** which is of particular interest because the relation of effort to results varies as a parabolic curve rather than as a direct proportion.

Each line on an Axminster rug is "set" on a loom spool. With no waste whatsoever it should be possible to weave a maximum of 125 rugs from one set. Because of inherent loom operations this maximum is difficult to secure. However the standard of 115 rugs was set as a minimum to be woven by the operator. The operator, through careful loom operation in keeping waste to a minimum, could increase the number of perfect rugs woven. It was much more difficult to operate, conserving material, so as to produce the 123rd rug than to produce the 116th rug, which was but one in addition to the standard set. A higher incentive therefore was justifiably paid the operator for the 123rd rug than for the 116th rug. A maximum incentive was paid for the 125th perfect rug.

The materials-saving bonus was determined in dollar amounts which were in line with the "going" hourly rates in effect at the time the plan was installed. The bonus ranged from 4 cents when one additional rug was obtained, up to $2.50 (or 25 cents per rug) when ten additional rugs were produced from each set. The bonus curve closely approximated a **vertical parabola** represented by the equation:

$$\text{Bonus dollars} = 0.04 \times (N - 115)^{1.8}$$

where N is the total number of rugs woven from each set.

In the **lumber industry** economical percentages of waste were established in one company in relation to the amount of lumber cut, and bonuses or penalties were applied for variations from the established standard. In **metalworking industries,** waste-elimination incentives often are based on the number of tons of scrap shipped in relation to the number of tons of raw material used. In a **shoe factory** the bonus for reduction of wasted leather was made relatively greater than the bonus for increased output from the cutters, because it was better to cut 10 pairs of shoes and waste no leather than to cut 15 pairs in the same time but use more leather than required.

Defective Quality and Waste. In some cases a waste-elimination bonus may bear upon the number of **defective units finished** as well as upon the wasting of raw materials. Where no **seconds** are usable, waste and quality problems become identical.

In most kinds of work, defects can be tolerated down to some limit below which the article cannot be accepted. The Shuron Optical Co. met this situation by establishing standards for all three requirements, i.e., **quantity, quality, and shrinkage.** A formula was developed to reflect all three sets of existing conditions:

$$\text{Bonus } \% = \left[\frac{0.6 \text{ production}}{\text{efficiency}} + \frac{\text{quality}}{\text{efficiency}} - \left(\frac{10 - \text{shrinkage}}{\text{efficiency}} \right) \right] - 100$$

This formula provides 0.6 credit for production variations from 60 to 120 percent, and full quality variations from 50 to 100 percent, but also provides debits for shrinkage variations exceeding 10 percent. All variations are empirically scaled in a 4-column 19-row table which allows high quality and low shrinkage to offset loss of production to some extent.

Frequently, products must have finished measurable dimensions or characteristics within certain plus or minus **tolerance limits.** If either limit is exceeded, the product is defective and the credited output is reduced accordingly. Modern statistical techniques have greatly enhanced the feasibility of coordinating quality control with production incentives, particularly where 100 percent inspection is not possible or economical. (See section on Quality Control.) Contrary to some opinions, unmeasured output and straight time wages do not insure high quality. Nor is poor quality a necessary result of incentives; in fact, experience has shown that quality tends to improve with well-integrated programs. Nevertheless, definite specifications and adequate inspection are necessary accompaniments of quantity incentives.

Incentive Plans for Indirect Production

CHARACTERISTICS OF INDIRECT LABOR. Most indirect production jobs are alike in that they are irregular, either as to **conditional** or as to **schedule requirements.** In the former respect they cannot be standardized without considerable expense, and in the latter they may not be standardized merely as a result of neglect. The result either way is an indefiniteness which makes difficult the preparation of intelligent plans or budgets to expedite such work. Excuses for the exemption of such activities from incentives are in themselves evidence of neglect. With an increasing dependence of direct production on such indirect jobs as **maintenance, materials handling, stockroom work,** and similar services, together with an increasing proportion of indirect labor costs to direct costs, much greater attention is being paid to these previously neglected jobs. Most companies at least are setting up **cost ratios** between indirect and direct labor costs beyond which the former may not be allowed to extend. This practice has the danger of discouraging any increase in ratio even if desirable, but it is knowledge gained and, if given some flexibility, may serve as a rough standard.

Some companies have made the mistake of treating too many expense items as **direct ratios.** Under reasonably good management, most overhead accounts have rather definite mathematical relationships with other factors of business. But in most of these accounts there is a considerable portion of fixed costs, and thus in very few cases can this relationship be expressed accurately as a straight ratio of direct labor for all volumes of production. A fixed ratio that is correct for normal output is likely to be in considerable error in subnormal or abnormal periods. It is much better to separate such work into natural units of character, department, etc., but it is still better to develop careful motion-time standards for all true elements of work which can be synthesized into any possible combination, i.e., develop and apply elemental **standard time data.** (See section on Time Study and Work Measurement.) The latter procedure involves both time and expense and may not always be justified, but it is flexible, accurate, and, in the long run, may cost less than other procedures. A rough standard is better than none and, with proper selection of an earning curve, the roughest standards may permit the application of extra-financial incentives with considerable success.

It also is characteristic of much indirect work that effort and effectiveness do not vary directly. For example, a stockroom attendant can double his effectiveness by bringing two packages to the window instead of one, but in doing so he has not increased his effort more than, say, 10 percent. Obviously such an employee should not be given the full savings from increased effectiveness but should be given that share of the savings which is proportional to the effort involved. **Sharing plans** are therefore most suitable for such indirect production. Also they are the safest unless true elements are standardized and carefully synthesized.

CHOICE OF INCENTIVE METHOD. In one of the large electrical companies, plans were made to **extend financial incentives** to a wide variety of jobs not usually covered. As reported by Herbert Bisen, industrial engineer, nine methods were considered. They are listed below in descending order of desirability as they were appraised by the company according to immediacy, effectiveness, administrative cost, and clarity to the worker. For other specific cases this order may not hold. Listed also are the company's suggestions for application.

1. **Plans based on direct measurement of functions performed.** (This is the synthetic task, always most reliable but sometimes considered too expensive.) Possible applications: trucking, layout operators, shipping, storeroom, instructors, janitors, machine setters, and such maintenance work as that of carpenters, painters, pipe fitters, structural-steel workers, sheet-metal workers, laborers, bricklayers, wiremen, millwrights, and window cleaners.
2. **Plans based on records of net results obtained.** Possible applications: general maintenance, machine setters, storeroom, and trucking.
3. **Plans based on reduction of personnel and payment for maintaining schedules.** Possible applications: storeroom, routine maintenance, and shipping.
4. **Plans based on the ratio of indirect to direct hours.** (This is simple, quite common, and relatively effective, but possibly inequitable if volume of output varies over rather wide ranges.) Possible applications: routine maintenance and similar services. (To recognize the presence of some fixed minimum staff, the amount of service required at several different volumes of output should be determined by study and plotted against the respective volumes. Typically the results will show relatively higher ratios for low volumes and lower ratios for high volumes. Accordingly, **flexible ratios** should be established.)
5. **Plans based on placing the indirect personnel into the groups they service.** Possible applications: materials handlers and setup men.
6. **Plans based on paying the indirect personnel either the same, or some fixed percentage of, bonus earned by the direct producers.** (This method permits bonuses but provides little or no control over the size of the service group.) Possible applications: tool crib.
7. **Plans based on evaluation of efficiency.** (Preferably this is the efficiency of small specific groups, but sometimes that of the whole plant.) Possible applications: machine setters, instructors, storeroom, and boiler room.
8. **Plans based on percentage improvement over past performance.** Possible applications: routine maintenance, oilers, instructors, and truckers.
9. **Plans based on estimated allowed time values.** Possible applications: general maintenance and tool room.

APPLICATION TO STORES AND STOCK ROOM. In an installation at the Westinghouse Electric Corp. the standard was set for the work involved in delivering the parts required for one **finished assembly.** With relatively little increase in effort, the employee's effectiveness could be increased greatly by delivering the parts for several assemblies all at one time. The plan used was a variation of the Halsey constant sharing plan represented by the general equation:

$$W = TNR + p(S - T)NR \tag{37}$$

in which the factor 0.10 was used for the term p.

The Real Silk Hosiery Co. used a similar plan for **storeroom attendants.** The 50 percent sharing feature of the Halsey plan was retained, making $p = 0.50$, but in addition a variable deduction factor F_d was introduced to adjust for delivery errors. As applied in the formula, this deduction factor is 1.00 minus a **deduction ratio** for errors as determined from an empiric scale. Furthermore, two bonus "steps" (about 10 percent each) were provided by using three different hourly rates for three corresponding ranges of net **efficiency gains** above task. These rates were R_1 (base rate) for net gains from 0 to 33 percent, R_2 for net gains from 33 to 50 percent, and R_3 for net gains above 50 percent. Combining these features gives a wage equation of:

$$W = TNR + 0.50 \times F_d \, (S - T)NR$$

in which R varies with the calculated efficiency ratios S/T.

APPLICATION TO MATERIALS HANDLING. The usual means of maintaining control of this work is by coordinated planning and scheduling, and by group bonus. Supervision of materials handling often is difficult because of its interdepartmental nature. For this reason all handling is sometimes centralized under a department control of its own. When this is done, it is less difficult to establish uniform standards and to hold everyone responsible for definite performance.

In one example at the Westinghouse Electric Corp., **interdepartmental trucking** was done on standardized routes and the drivers were rewarded in groups for exceeding their task amount of trucking. Task was based on the number of packages handled as reported by a system of delivery stubs. Each of the call stations was assigned a number and provided with a time stamp. The hourly rate used for meeting or exceeding task was about 11 percent above the guaranteed base rate, thereby providing an 11 percent step bonus at task. When the total allowed hours were equal to, or in excess of, the actual hours worked, the allowed hours were multiplied by the higher hourly rate, much as in a high piece-rate (or Gantt) plan. However, as with the stores employees, careful combining of loads could increase the apparent effectiveness more rapidly than the corresponding increase in required effort. Accordingly a **protective feature** (sharing) was introduced into the calculation of total hours allowed:

$$\text{Hours allowed} = T + 0.12(0.066N - T)$$

where T = total actual hours worked by the group in a pay period.
  0.12 = sharing factor, similar to p in equation (37).
  0.066 = average standard hours per package.
  N = number of packages handled in the pay period.

Similar equations were used in determining allowed hours for other trucking activities. For example, in a group using both **flat and hoist trucks,** the allowed hours were related to **delivery times**:

$$\text{Hours allowed} = T + 0.25(0.46N_f + 0.317N_h - T)$$

where 0.25 = appropriate sharing factor p.
  0.46 = standard hours per delivery by flat truck.
  N_f = number of flat-truck deliveries during the pay period.
  0.317 = standard hours per delivery by hoist truck.
  N_h = number of hoist-truck deliveries during the pay period.

These trucking incentives resulted in better coordination of work to maintain full capacity, use of telephones to keep the dispatcher informed, and other manifestations of cooperation. Within a 3-year period the average delivery cost per package was reduced by more than 50 percent.

In a **small sheet-metal plant** with 100 employees, 2 men working as a group take care of degreasing activities as well as trucking and handling of materials and parts in and out of storage areas, between production groups, and through the shipping area. Careful time studies were made and elemental standard time data were developed. For each different type of finished product, all appropriate handling elements are synthesized into a **standard allowed time** per finished unit. The standard handling time for each type of product is multiplied by the number of units of that product shipped, to determine the total allowed hours for the period. A full sharing (100 percent) standard hour plan is used, and bonus is calculated from the average efficiency for a 4-week period. Materials handling costs are significantly less than before this work was placed on incentive, congestion has been relieved, service to the production groups has improved, and the 2 materials handlers earn bonuses comparable with those earned by the regular production groups.

APPLICATION TO MAINTENANCE AND REPAIRS.

An efficient maintenance department is most important to the success of incentives in production departments and can increase production efficiencies throughout the plant. This is evident in continuous-process manufacturing, but it is not always appreciated elsewhere. An incentive for maintenance and repair must encourage elimination of needless repair as well as expedite needed repair. The ideal condition would be for men of this department to spend all their time on preventive work of maintenance, thus eliminating breakdowns altogether. Allotment of definite **area responsibility** to each man is in itself effective and has been known to reduce the volume of breakdown repair by 66 percent and at the same time reduce production delays by 80 percent. Several methods have been used for fixing responsibility.

One practice is to **assign certain individuals to specific machines** and consider them members of the production group. This is practical where production incentives are administered by groups. All that is needed is to determine the amount of maintenance work required (probably from a combination of time studies and past records) and to arrange the share of the group's bonus which the maintenance men shall receive.

Another practice is to centralize control of all maintenance, **establish a cost budget** for the group, and arrange relative shares of the savings.

Still another way is to **fix a route for each individual,** and, if all equipment on that route comes through the month without delays, award a bonus of, say, 25 percent of maintenance time wages. If delays have occurred, deductions proportional to the delay time can be taken from the potential 25 percent. Obviously the nature and newness of the equipment affect the probabilities of delay, and the bonus cannot always be directly proportional to the work or responsibility involved. Adjustments and supervision are necessary. An **itemized schedule** should be developed for inspection and periodic overhaulings of the equipment on the route.

In recent years there has been a growing trend toward greater use of time standards and direct financial incentives for maintenance work. Because of the variable nature of the work, **partial sharing plans** generally are most suitable,

Company	1	2	3	4	5	6	7	8
Industry	Heavy Metal Fabricating	Food	Meat Packing	Steel	Pharmaceutical	Light Metal Fabricating	Chemical Process	Basic Alloys
Number of Employees								
Total	1,100	2,600	1,300	10,376	5,500	750	3,600	1,200
Maintenance (See Note 1)....	125	492	60	2,800	400	35	100	200
When Installed	1945	1933	1951	1934	1950	1946	1948	1941
Labor Union	AFL	CIO-AFL	AFL	CIO	None	None	None	CIO
Maintenance Coverage	80%	98%	50%	96%	98%	90%	95%	100%
Method of application of standards (See Note 2) ...	Checker	Checker	Checker	Checker	Checker	Checker	Analyst	Analyst
Administrative Personnel No. of People Needed ...	11	22	3	67	24	7	11	18
Ratio of Direct Workers	8%	4.5%	5%	2.4%	6%	10%	3.7%	9%
Increase in Output of Workers on Standard	93%	60%	46%	86%	50%	35%	45%	25%
Dollar Savings—Yearly Gross (See Note 3)	$330,000	$900,000	$45,000	$7,200,000	$520,000	$36,000	$135,000	$150,000
Administrative Cost ...	31,650	103,000	15,000	292,000	170,000	30,000	38,000	90,000
Net	$298,350	$797,000	$30,000	$6,908,000	$350,000	$6,000	$97,000	$60,000
Reactions to Plan Management	Very pleased. Extended plan to practically all indirect labor	Likes plan. Resisted union pressure to drop it	Extending plan to cover all maintenance work	Enthusiastic about it	Says incentives are desirable	Likes plan. Extending plan to toolroom	Well pleased. Extending plan	Likes plan. Has applied it to entire plant and office
Union	Cooperative. Wants more coverage	Cooperative	Cooperative	Enthusiastic				

NOTE 1. In plants 1, 6, and 7, the plan also includes toolroom covering 13, 33, and 200 workers, respectively. These workers are not considered in calculation of dollar savings but are included in ratio of administrative personnel to direct workers.
NOTE 2. In checker method (using postset standards), allowed time developed from predetermined standard time data is applied when work is in process or completed. In analyst method (using preset standards), allowed time is applied preferably before the job.
NOTE 3. Gross savings are computed by multiplying number of workers on standard by their increase in output and by their average annual wages.

Fig. 25. Details of maintenance incentive plans in eight companies (based on standards established by time study and standard time data).

although some full sharing plans have been used, particularly where standards are set from elemental standard time data and actual accomplishments are carefully determined.

Performance goals for maintenance work may be established by several different methods. **Estimates** are widely used and may be made either by craft foremen or by a separate staff estimating department. This method is rapid and inexpensive, and the goal is established before the job is started. The estimate offers some basis for scheduling and for comparison with actual performance. Perhaps its strongest feature is the requirement of some prior planning by the foremen, but estimates are inaccurate and inconsistent and accordingly command little respect from the workers. When methods are changed, estimates lag behind in their adjustments to new time requirements for the job. Because estimates are only "guesstimates," their use with incentives is impractical.

Historical records provide information from which averages of actual times taken on previous jobs can be determined. They may be adjusted by arbitrary leveling factors, but there is little basis for knowing what factors to use. Such averages may be useful if similar jobs are repeated, but they are unreliable, since there seldom are accurate records of just what work the previous jobs required. Furthermore, past averages are of little value for new tasks which accordingly must be done on the basis of either actual time charged or pure estimates. Owing to continual variations in maintenance work, as well as the lack of adequate identification, averages of past performance records obviously are impractical for incentive application.

Fig. 25 shows some data on maintenance incentive plans compiled by the Methods Engineering Council (Factory Management and Maintenance, vol. 113). Several observations are pertinent. All eight plants covered in the study use standard data as the bases for their standards. Incentives are applicable to small as well as to large maintenance groups. Properly designed and administered plans can remain successful over long periods. Coverage can be high, being 90 percent or better in six of the eight plants. The ratio of administrative personnel tends to decrease as the number of maintenance workers increases. The ratio of administrative cost to gross annual savings was highest (83 percent for the smallest maintenance group in plant 6). It was 60 percent for plant 8 with 100 percent coverage. In no other plant did this ratio exceed 33 percent, and it was only slightly more than 4 percent for the largest group in plant 4. Thus, despite high installation and administrative costs, work measurement and incentives for maintenance activities offer excellent money-saving possibilities. All managements expressed favorable comments, and, of the five plants where unions were involved, three unions reacted favorably. It should be remembered, however, that a maintenance incentive plan will not substitute for good supervision, train maintenance workers, guarantee the quality of work, or necessarily guarantee good job engineering.

INCENTIVES FOR INSPECTION. Many persons consider inspection work too sacred for financial incentives, but with the spread of mass production many inspection activities have become so standardized and repetitive, in fact so similar to regular production operations, that direct financial incentives are entirely practical. An example has already been cited where incentives were applied successfully to inspectors of women's hosiery. In that case reinspection was an effective device for maintaining control over the quality of the inspectors' work. Reinspection by persons not paid any bonus is a typical pattern for control of routine inspectors who may be paid hourly wages plus bonuses.

In a subsidiary of the Westinghouse Electric Corp., costs appeared to be excessive for the **final inspection of control panels** prior to shipment. Studies were made of the various types of defects which the inspectors were required to find, and an average time was established for locating and correcting each type. The standard time per panel included a basic preparation and testing time related to the size of the panel, plus an additional time for each defect discovered and reported. Efficiencies were calculated as the ratio of standard time allowed to actual time taken. No bonuses were paid; hence the plan, in effect, was measured daywork. As would be expected without bonuses, efficiencies seldom exceeded 100 percent, but the standards provided goals which the inspectors strove to meet, and inspection costs were reduced significantly below those that were common before such goals were used.

In general, routine inspection is a process of **sorting** items into various degrees of acceptability. In its simplest form this consists in removing unacceptable items and of passing those which meet standard specifications. If time standards are based only on the number of items handled, there is little incentive to sort out the defects. If bonuses are determined only from the number of defects found, many acceptable items will be rejected. The problem in setting the inspection standard therefore is one of **determining the proper balance** between the time required to examine and pass a good item, and the time (and effort) involved in deciding that a defect exists and in removing and properly classifying the defective item. With a proper balance, the entire incentive properly is on total production of properly classified items, with no preference for one classification over the other.

This problem became particularly evident in a plant manufacturing **surgical sutures** where high material costs indicated a need to pass all good "strings," yet where it was highly important to remove all defects. Direct time studies were made to determine proper motion patterns and the relative times for good and bad strings. Several months of daily production records also were analyzed, with the standard data approach, to determine the relative effect of variations in string material, diameter, and length. From these two sources of information a complete schedule of standards was developed. For each type and size of string two standards were established, one in hours per 100 good strings passed, the other in hours per 100 defective strings removed. The incentive is a 100 percent standard hour plan applied to individual inspectors. The inspectors' work is **reinspected** on a random basis by the departmental supervisor, who is paid a straight salary. Her work, as well as occasional batches from the regular inspectors, is **super-reinspected,** also on a random basis, by representatives of the quality control department. Average output is more than double that obtained under previous daywork conditions; earnings appropriately are relatively high, resulting in extremely low turnover among the inspectors and a consequent high average level of skill; unit costs are competitively low, yet high quality standards are well maintained. These incentives have been in successful use for several years.

MONETARY BUDGETS AS GROUP STANDARDS. Where it seems impractical to determine tasks in production units, it often is possible to secure a rough equivalent in terms of expense. Actual expense of an operation over a period of several years is used as a guide, and a monetary amount is budgeted which usually is a little under the best previous year. This amount is set up as a "bogie" and used as a group or departmental task. Bonuses are arranged in advance, usually as some percentage of savings relative to the bogie. As this percentage of saving is determined for each group, the individual prorated share of it is increased whenever there is a reduction in the number of members in the group. Obviously such plans are limited to group administration.

There are several difficulties with such arrangements. For example, it is difficult to determine, and correct for, the effects of **technological improvements** or methods changes. During periods of inflation and deflation the value of the dollar changes, and therefore the monetary amount of the budget does not remain a reliable indicator of standard performance. Negotiated changes in wage or salary schedules disturb the intended balance between standard and actual costs. A fixed budget provides a fair standard for only one level of production volume and becomes unfair with any significant change in volume, even if other factors remain constant. Budgets are invariably subjected to periodic reviews, annually or perhaps more often. If the current year's costs are much below the budget, the next year's budget usually will be lowered. This is equivalent to "rate cutting" and tends to discourage future savings.

Budgets, as standards of performance and as a source of bonuses, have been used with considerable success for higher levels of salaried personnel, but they are of doubtful value as incentives for hourly wage earners.

Incentive Plans for Supervisors and Executives

COST-SAVING AND PROFIT-SHARING PLANS. Practically all incentive plans for supervisors and executives are based directly or indirectly on either savings in operating costs or on final over-all profits and occasionally, but rarely, on both. **Cost-saving** plans use measurable or gradable accomplishments out of which a compound task is established, and rewards are derived from operating savings. Usually these savings are shared with the company. **Profit-sharing** plans use profits, if they occur, or specified portions of them, as tasks, and rewards are derived from a fund which is held back from declared profits. Cost-saving plans can reward proportionally to effort, but profit-sharing plans cannot, since profits do not vary directly with human effort. The first type is preferable for all but the highest executives and is even applicable to them, while the second type is suitable only to those who can take a long view and can influence the company in a major way. Between minor foremen and the president, there is a debatable zone, but this zone is not far below the president. Jordan (NACA Bull., vol. 11) suggests that a works manager might well draw one-third of his bonus from a profit-sharing fund and two-thirds from savings.

COST-SAVING PLAN FOR SUPERVISORS. The most direct and simple incentive plan for supervisors is that which uses, as task, a budget of **direct labor plus expense cost** per unit of output and provides percentage rewards for reductions in these costs relative to the budget. The percentage should be suited to the volume so that the bonus for satisfactory results would be around one-fifth to one-fourth of the salary. As in other cases of cost standards, the weakness lies in the inclusive nature of total costs. This weakness might be corrected by using several specific costs. It is even better to establish a compound task based on important measurable factors such as volume, materials waste, and punctualities of deliveries, plus one or more gradable factors such as departmental cooperation and, perhaps, housekeeping. The choice of factors depends upon the emphasis desired, and often the factors are weighted accordingly. **Graded factors** are subject to challenge and seldom should carry more than about 20 percent of the total weight. **Total cost,** although overlapping, sometimes is included as a measurable factor.

PROFIT-SHARING PLAN FOR EXECUTIVES. This type of plan has been used rather widely and has given excellent results in many cases. It consists essentially of the establishment of a **bonus fund** which usually is some pre-arranged portion of final over-all profits remaining after all charges except federal taxes have been deducted from income. Division of the fund among the executives frequently is made arbitrarily, and too often secretly, by the president or by a small committee appointed by him. Grades of participating personnel may be fixed, but **eligibility to grades** is left to someone's judgment of each individual's contribution to, or responsibility for, company success. Payments may be made in cash but are often made in stock. With currently high income-tax rates, there is a growing trend toward **deferred bonus payments,** placed in annuity or pension funds to be available after retirement.

Plantwide Cost-Saving Plans

NUNN-BUSH PLAN. Within recent years several plantwide sharing plans have received considerable publicity. Notable among these are the Nunn-Bush Shoe Co. plan, the Scanlon plan, and the Rucker plan. All these plans are based on the theory that the cost of each function of a business remains more or less permanently at a relatively fixed portion of the income. All have some aspects of cost saving and profit sharing, and the first, in particular, has certain employment guarantees.

The Nunn-Bush plan takes total direct labor costs as approximately 20 percent of factory sales, with minor variations for specific styles. This percentage of sales is credited to a **direct labor fund.** Charged against this fund are regular direct labor wages for both permanent and temporary employees. In general, permanent employees are those having specified lengths of service, and temporary employees are those hired for temporary periods of higher than normal production. At regular intervals, **credit balances** in the direct labor fund are apportioned as bonuses to the permanent employees. Security is promoted by assuring 52 weeks of employment to workers having 5 or more years of service, with lesser amounts guaranteed to employees having less service. Obviously, many other details are involved in the actual administrative procedure.

Several **advantages** may be cited: The cost of direct labor remains at a fixed portion of sales. Employee earnings tend to be correlated automatically with the relative cost of living, whether inflated or deflated. The labor force remains relatively stable, since the permanent employees attempt to handle variations in production volume in order to avoid extra charges to the fund necessitated by employment of any temporary workers. As with any group plan, bonuses are increased by improved performance and consequent reductions in the number of employees needed to produce the required output. In order to provide steady employment for a stable work force, management makes every attempt to hold production schedules at as uniform a level as possible.

SCANLON PLAN. This plan is essentially a plantwide cost-saving plan. Originally it was intended to be applied to all company employees, including top executives and not exclusively to hourly wage earners. Davenport (Fortune, vol. 41) indicates that in some instances, however, its principles have been applied to more restricted categories of employees. For the segment of employees to be covered, this plan involves finding a total normal wage (and salary) cost for the particular company and devising a means for giving the employees anything they can save under this norm. If restricted to direct labor, this plan becomes quite similar in many respects to the Nunn-Bush plan.

Usually the **total normal cost** is established as a percentage of sales. If several lines of products are manufactured, the normal cost percentage reflects a normal "mixture" of products. But the wage (and salary) cost per dollar of sales varies for different products, and the total cost for a given amount of sales for one specific mixture of goods sold may be quite different from the total cost for any other mixture. Accordingly, the normal cost, as a percentage of the sales price, must be found for each different (major) **product classification** so that a proper normal cost can be determined for the particular mixture of products sold during a given period.

The normal cost for the period is credited to a wage and salary account against which have been charged the current wages and salaries of the covered employees. When there is a **credit balance** in this account, usually two-thirds or three-fourths of it is distributed as bonuses, the remainder being withheld as a reserve against potential deficits in future months. Any credit balance remaining at the end of the year is distributed and, of course, any **deficit balance** is absorbed by the company.

The Scanlon plan has been successful in a number of installations. Its success depends upon close employee-management cooperation. An essential feature is the need for, and active encouragement of, employee suggestions for increased efficiency and reduced costs. Suggestions are processed by committees composed of employee as well as employer representatives. The requirement of close cooperation promotes feelings of importance and of belonging to the team, and therefore tends to raise morale and reduce labor turnover.

RUCKER SHARE-OF-PRODUCTION PLAN. This plan is quite similar to the Scanlon plan in most respects. Most installations tend to be restricted to hourly wage earners. Basically this plan relates total annual payrolls to total **value added by manufacture** rather than to sales. From a careful analysis of the company's operating experience, a formula is set up which allocates to the workers a definite proportion of the value added by manufacture. Pohlman (Factory Management and Maintenance, vol. 113) indicates that in several companies the proportion has been close to 40 percent.

As an example, assume that a company has sold $500,000 worth of product during an accounting period and has spent $300,000 on materials, supplies, and allied costs in producing that amount of goods. The difference, $200,000, is value added by manufacture. With a 40 percent proportion, the workers' share is $80,000. If actual wages paid during the period were less than $80,000, the difference is due them as a share-of-production bonus. As in the Scanlon plan, a portion of this difference (typically three-fourths) is distributed, the balance being held in reserve against future deficit periods. Usually the plan is administered by a company-employee (or union) committee, and in several installations the workers' proportion of the value added has been revised at various times with union approval.

Guaranteed Wages or Employment

METHODS FOR PROVIDING SECURITY. Because assurance of a steady income is a primary desire of most employees, the provision of wage or employment guarantees has received increasing attention. The concept involves a shift in emphasis from hourly or daily guarantees to longer periods over which certain income is assured.

Two principal methods have been used for providing a relatively high degree of security to sizable portions, if not all, of the employees. **Guaranteed employment** is an assurance by the employer to the employees of a certain number of hours or weeks of work over a period of time. While this obviously assures income, it does not assure income of a definite amount. In the **Procter and Gamble plan,** for example, all employees with 2 years of service are guaranteed employment for not less than 48 weeks in each calendar year, less time lost by reason of holidays, vacations, disability, voluntary absence, and emergencies. The weekly hours are set by the company and may be cut to 75 percent by the board of directors. Unlimited transfers are permitted between jobs or departments; thus the hourly rates earned by the covered employees are determined by the jobs to which they are assigned.

In contrast, **guaranteed wages** involve an assurance that a certain amount of income will be paid to the employees for some specified period. If the period is 1 year, this becomes **guaranteed annual wages.** A few companies have provided guaranteed annual wages, but most guaranteed-wage plans cover periods of less than 1 year. Latimer (Guaranteed Wages: Report to the President of the Advisory Board) defines a guaranteed-wage plan as any scheme under which an employer guarantees to all or a defined unit or group of his employees a wage or employment for at least 3 months at not less than one-half the regular hours or pay. Using this definition, a total of 196 plans was found.

There are recognized limitations to guaranteed annual wages. Meany, President of the AFL, is quoted as saying (U. S. News and World Report, vol. 35), ". . . it's almost an impossibility under our economic system to have a guaranteed annual wage in certain types of business . . . there are millions of workers with corporations that couldn't possibly make such a guarantee." Latimer indicates that:

1. Wage- or employment-guarantee plans exist in relatively few organizations.
2. Almost all the plans were found in consumers' goods industries, producers' goods industries being almost without such plans.
3. Most of the plans were found in relatively small organizations.
4. Most plans are sufficiently recent that they have not been tested by depression conditions.
5. The firms with such plans were in unusually favorable economic positions.

EFFECT OF GUARANTEED WAGES OR EMPLOYMENT. Broadly speaking, it makes little difference which plan is used, guaranteed employment or wages, as long as **reasonable stability of employment** is assured. In fact, there is little need or real demand for such plans in industries which are little affected by seasonal variations. However, the use of such plans in some companies has directed attention to, and effected significant changes in, policies of marketing and warehousing, so that production schedules which formerly were subject to wide fluctuations have been reduced to relatively uniform levels.

ADVANTAGES AND DISADVANTAGES OF GUARANTEED WAGES OR EMPLOYMENT. Advantages cited for such plans include: greater security for employees; higher employee morale; improved labor relations; employment stabilization; increased incomes and greater purchasing power; improved productivity; greater acceptance by employees of technological changes; eased recruitment problems; and lower training costs. In contrast, some authorities argue that, if guaranteed-wage plans are applied in unfavorable circumstances, they may have such results as: reduced flexibility of competition; reduced investment in production facilities which create jobs; discouragement of new firms; increased unemployment; more serious depressions; inability of new members of the labor force to get jobs; high mortality of small firms; and increased socialization of economic controls. Similarly they point out that many of the advantages attributed to the guarantees would disappear if such plans were usual rather than the exception.

SUPPLEMENTARY UNEMPLOYMENT BENEFITS. Suggestions that wage guarantees be integrated with **unemployment compensation** have been criticized on the grounds that such arrangements would reduce labor mobility, furnish an incentive toward malingering, and encourage the worker to be more hesitant in accepting other work. However, recent labor agreements, notably in the **automotive industry,** reflect a trend in this direction. The application tends to be somewhat limited in either **employee coverage** (frequently based on seniority) or the **length of time** over which payments are guaranteed, or both. The employer contributes a specified rate per labor hour into a fund from which payments are made to employees who are laid off. When the plan is first installed, this fund may be allowed to build up for a specified period, say 1 year, before any unemployment payments are made. When the plan is in operation, the guarantee may expire when the fund is exhausted. When the fund has reached a specified amount equal to, say, 10 weeks' pay for all employees, the employer's contributions may be reduced to a rate only sufficient to maintain the 10-week level. The rate of pay is usually lower than typical earnings while the employee is working, often about 50 percent of the regular wages. Where permitted by state law, company payments may be reduced by the amount received by the employee from state unemployment compensation. These features indicate that the plans are not true guaranteed-annual-wage plans, but are more accurately identified as supplementary unemployment benefit plans.

EXAMPLE OF GUARANTEED ANNUAL WAGE. A notable example of a comprehensive guaranteed-annual-wage plan is the one which has been used for many years at the Hormel Co. meat-packing plant. This plan (the Hormel Annual Wage, Wage Incentive, and Joint Earnings Plans) is a **wage and employment guarantee** administered in addition to, but integrated with, a regular standard hour **wage incentive plan.** Widely fluctuating daily and seasonal receipts of livestock indicated a need for a plan that would encourage the processing of each day's complete receipts, thereby avoiding the expense of feeding and otherwise caring for animals remaining to be processed on the following day. Regular piecework alone had not been sufficiently effective to accomplish this goal.

The wage guarantee covers most of the regular employees, about 80 percent of the total. (Plans for regularizing employment typically exclude certain temporary workers.) Covered employees are assured 52 regular weekly pay checks, each check for 36 to 40 hours, according to the department. When each day's receipts are processed, employees are allowed to go home regardless of the number of hours worked. Within limits, overtime hours required on the heavy days are balanced against the hours off on the light days. These limitations, and the types of agreements under which they apply, are specified in the Fair Labor Standards Act, which also provides that, even under such agreements, the 50 percent overtime premium must be paid for all hours over 12 in 1 day, and for all hours over 56 in 1 week.

Standard hour incentives are paid for actual time on incentive. At regular intervals (originally once a year), if actual hours worked have exceeded the hours already covered by the weekly payments, the employee is paid the difference. The company assumes the responsibility for proper planning. Thus, if more hours have been paid for than worked, the company absorbs the loss; but, with careful planning, this seldom is, or should be, necessary.

A number of interesting results have been noted. The freedom to go home when the day's receipts have been processed has proved a strong incentive. With the regular incentive plan alone, employees occasionally complained that the mechanically paced conveyors moved too rapidly; but, after the "go home" privilege was adopted, they requested that conveyor speeds be increased. Families were assured of uniform weekly incomes, bills were paid more promptly for household necessities, and business in the community generally was improved. Bonuses for extra hours worked were accumulated into significant amounts, and they became available for exceptional family expenses or luxuries. Labor turnover was reduced and morale improved. Output per man hour increased, and unusually heavy receipts on one day seldom required any carry-over to the next day.

Installation and Termination of Incentive Plans

INSTALLING A NEW PLAN. A good incentive plan should benefit employees as well as their employer, but union leaders may be predisposed against incentives and some employees are suspicious of all changes. Hence the leading employees and union representatives must be consulted and satisfied in advance. Sometimes this task is difficult and may require considerable attention. **Printed illustrations** of various earnings may be helpful because money is one of the primary interests of the employee. A **conference** should be held in which employees are allowed to express their views. When large numbers of workers are involved, **department groups** or even operation groups may be consulted separately. There should be no great haste. Influential **leaders** among the employees should be won and should be put on the new plan a few at a time. When convinced of the plan's merits, these leaders will bring their friends to desire the same advantages. By such means, advance opposition usually can be avoided. If the plan will not work with a few, it will not work with many. Failure in properly introducing a new wage incentive plan may forfeit much of the benefit anticipated from expensive job improvement and standardization, whereas if incentives are properly applied, they will help to speed the adoption of such improvements.

DISCARDING INCENTIVE PLANS. It is a well-known truism that employees successfully responding to an incentive plan, and accustomed to high job efficiencies, will immediately drop back to typical low daywork efficiencies when, for any reason, they are deprived of their usual incentive. Companies have been known to promote an incentive plan during a prosperous period, then discard it as soon as orders decrease. Once treated this way, employees will have little enthusiasm for supporting the next production campaign.

FAILURE OF INCENTIVE PLANS. To discard an incentive plan merely because orders decrease would be short-sighted indeed. But there are other factors which contribute, all too commonly, to failures of incentive installations. No incentive plan can remain successful without proper **maintenance** of the standards on which it is based, or without adhering to the **basic principles** of wage incentives. Owing to lack of adequate management support and a consequent lack of qualified industrial engineering personnel, whole structures of standards and administrative procedures have been known to deteriorate so badly as to get completely out of reasonable control. Several conditions have contributed to such deterioration. Inadequate quality control encourages short cuts and invites excessive scrap or rework at unnecessary expense. The payment of average earned rates for nonincentive work, delays, or difficult jobs invites the eventual cancellation of all but the very loose standards and continual loosening of correct standards. Promiscuous allowance of excessive down time merely permits high wages without correspondingly high outputs. Failure to correct standards promptly to correspond with methods changes contributes to the loosening trend.

An incentive plan cannot be allowed to deteriorate indefinitely. Employee or union opposition to appropriate correction may become so great that the only alternative is to discard the incentive plan completely. Such drastic action is certain to have serious repercussions and should be undertaken only as a last resort. It is obviously far better to maintain the incentive program in good operating order.

ELECTRONIC COMPUTERS

CONTENTS

PAGE

Computers for Production

Production engineering 1
Decision to use computers 1
  Untried equipment 2
  Correct applications 2
Cost of computer operation 3
Functions of electronic and electromechanical computers 3
  Control and information abilities 4
Analog vs. digital computers 4
  Comparison of analog and digital computer characteristics (f. 1) 5
  Evaluating the use of computers 4
  Computer speed and accuracy 6
  Computer size 6
  Computer programming 6
    Flow diagram showing interrelation of basic analog computer sections (f. 2) ... 7
  Digital computer elements 8
General-purpose vs. special-purpose computers 8
  Special-purpose analog computers 9
    Analog simulation of unilateral production (f. 3) 10
Economic analogs and production models.... 9
  A production-economic analog 9
  Computer use on inventory control 11

Digital Computer Programming

Basic elements 11
  Diagram of simple stored-program digital computers (f. 4) 12
  Memory element 12
  Arithmetic element 13
  Control element 13
  Input-output elements 13
Operation of the simple computer 13
  Instructions 13
  Execution 14
  The instruction counter 14
  Operating sequences 14
  Store 15
  Transfer 15
Simple programs 15
  Arithmetic programs 15
    Computer response for addition (f. 5) .. 16
    Typical example of coding (f. 6) 16
    Computer response for multiplication (f. 7) 16
  Logical program 16
    Computer response for conditional instruction (f. 8) 17

PAGE

Cyclical program 18
  Elemental decisions made by computer (f. 9) 18
  Flow chart of simple cyclical computer program (f. 10) 19
Systems of instruction 20
  Single- and multiple-address instructions (f. 11) 20

Electronic Data Processing

Inventory control 20
Inventory procedures on computers 21
  Electronic data processing (f. 12) 22
  Process sequence 21
  Computer control of stock room issues 23
  Inventory and accounting control 23
    A comparison of medium-sized general-purpose digital computers (f. 13) 24
  Special-purpose inventory control computer 23
Production control and process planning 25
  Computer loading of machines 25
  Computer shop loading 26
Computer production control procedures ... 26
  Digital computer procedure for production scheduling (f. 14) 27
  Preparation 28
  Scheduling 28
  Analysis 28
  Decision 29
Additional production applications of digital computers 29
  Process control 29
  Linear programming and logistics 30
  Queueing problems 30
  Single-item manufacturing 31

The Automatic Factory

Factory functions of computers 32
  Substitutions for manual and mental functions 32
  Independently automatic machines 34
    A computer incorporating feedback correction with quality control (f. 15) 33
Digital machine control 34
  Systems for programmed positioning by digital controls (f. 16) 35
  Special-purpose digital computers 35
  Systems for programmed machining by digital controls (f. 17) 36

CONTENTS (*Continued*)

	PAGE		PAGE
Computers for existing machine tools	35	trol computer	39
Analog computers on the factory floor	37	Automatic quality control	40
Production of steel bars	37	Automatic quality control computer for discontinuous piece-part production (f. 19)	41
Paper production	38		
Machinability computer	38		
Machinability computer control panel (f. 18)	39	Available computer equipment	44
Production control instruments	38	Commercial data on digital computers (f. 20) 42–43	
Procedure for developing an analog con-			

ELECTRONIC COMPUTERS

Computers for Production

PRODUCTION ENGINEERING. Historically, production management has had an **empirical** basis. Decisions were usually based on the result of trial and error, experimentation, and experience. There was little tendency to investigate various production problems analytically. This is understandable because the simplest production system involves so many variables.

The new trend is for production management to become increasingly **analytical** and to accept the methods and techniques of science, engineering, and mathematics. Because computers make it possible to handle problems involving a great many variables, they are an indispensable aid to modern production management.

The practice of incorporating analytical methods and engineering techniques into production management rather than using empirical methods is sometimes termed "production engineering." Smith (Steps Toward More Creative Production Engineering, ASME) points out that production engineering should have equal stature with product engineering.

A production engineer should not hesitate to take advantage of better analytical tools as they become available. The area of production engineering seems to resist rather than accept the use of mathematical procedures, for there is a tendency to consider attempts to quantify production engineering problems as impractical, unrealistic, and time-consuming. Rather than to take advantage of gains made in other areas of knowledge, trial and error is the practice. Of the many possible analytical tools available to the competent production engineer, one of the most important is the electronic computer. Smith states that when the **variables** in any production system have been identified, and their relationships equated, it is possible to utilize computers for the solution of production engineering problems.

Product engineers make extensive use of computer techniques, and production engineers could learn much by observing the types of problems solved by product engineers, since these are often analogous to production engineering problems.

Electronic computers have proven valuable for studying traffic tie-ups in a busy city. Therefore, there is no reason why they cannot be used for the study of production bottlenecks in a factory.

DECISION TO USE COMPUTERS. The decision to use computers as an aid to production must be based on sound economic grounds. Faulkner (Control Engineering, vol. 3) lists pitfalls that might embarrass a prospective user of electronic data processing equipment, if he decided to use electronic computers without consideration of all the factors necessary to the making of a sound decision.

Faulkner points out that electronic data processing has been pictured in very glowing terms; and the urge to be in front of competitors can override the usual studies that would delineate the borderline cost advantage that may be governing. Installations for publicity purposes may also lead to rude awakenings, since the publicity value is soon nil. Though "armchair engineering" may appear to save time, improper **equipment estimates** may result in increased space requirements. Also, a special type of building may be necessary, and more people than predicted are sometimes needed to handle punch cards and tapes and to maintain the equipment.

There is also the likelihood that early accuracy reports of the installed equipment will indicate that an expensive and unanticipated **balancing operation** is necessary to validate input data. Faulkner cautions that ill-suited equipment, procured after inadequate investigation, can result in early supplementation, premature replacement, or expensive reversal. Insufficient coverage in the original installation will result in the call for more equipment to protect the investment incurred in alterations, engineering, and programming.

Untried Equipment. Much equipment has been bought from the drawing board instead of from the shelf. It is untried, and precious time after delivery must be spent on debugging, modifications, and head scratching, Faulkner says. With proper investigation much of this can be avoided.

Savings that are obtained by comparing the cost under an improved process, which provides additional results, against the cost of obtaining these same results by using old methods are termed **opportunity savings.** This comparison is not valid since the old methods would not have been used to obtain these results.

A favorite criterion in discussing electronic data processing is the number of people or man-hours that an installation saves. However, even in its most conservative form the "how many people" method is faulty, since it overlooks many cost factors on both sides.

Prime among these is the **subsidiary capital investment** factor, usually very large in terms of dollars. This involves the cost of air-conditioned rooms, special typewriters, and unexpected failures. On a five-year (or less) amortization basis, Faulkner points out, these can represent an appreciable annual expense.

Correct Applications. Because of the high-speed nature of the electronic data processing, there may be a tendency to overextend the use of the computer for applications where it is not justified. Juran (Technion Year Book, vol. 13) states that production control uses the principle of identifying those items which represent the longest manufacturing interval or present the greatest production problems, and of concentrating formal planning around these key items so that high executive attention is focused upon them. His universal—"separating the vital from the trivial"—is the generalized form of the concept that in any series of elements to be controlled, there are a selected small fraction, in terms of numbers of elements, which account for a large fraction in terms of effects. It is always necessary to "separate the vital from the trivial" before any analytical control process should be considered, such as the use of computers. The application must be proved to be "vital."

The decision to use automatic data-processing equipment and computers involves many **choices for action,** such as which equipment to use, and how best to use it. Juran points out that one of the choices for action that should not be neglected when making any major decisions is that of making better use of the **existing setup.** It may well be that more efficient use of noncomputer methods would be more practical than use of computers for production control in some cases.

COST OF COMPUTER OPERATION. Forrester (Tool Engineer, vol. 35) shows that one million desk calculator operations, which cost about $30,000, can be completed by an electronic machine for about $30.00.

The equipment now available can operate from 100,000 times to one million times faster than manual methods. However, the pace at which business and industry will make the transition to new data-processing equipment will probably be set by the rate at which new business executives can be trained to have an understanding of the potentialities of the new machines.

The principles of electronic computing machines are easier to understand and learn than are the principles and objectives of the business to which they are applied. Obtaining **trained staff men** who can use the new electronic data-processing machines should be viewed by management as a long-term process, for full use cannot be made of such machines until they are generally understood by many persons in a company. Forrester says that industry must do its part in educating them.

The cost of using electronic data-processing equipment should not be evaluated only in terms of operating expense; its effect on over-all company profit should also be taken into account. Less money will be spent in the future than in the past for information collection, information conversion, and information interpretation.

Ordinarily the cost of preparing computer machine instruction falls in the range of from $1.00 to $10.00 per instruction word. The cost of this planning and computer **program setup** is usually comparable to the cost of the equipment itself.

Forrester further points out that the three categories in which electronic machines can be of benefit to business are:

1. Simple cost reduction wherein present methods are satisfactory but more expensive than necessary.
2. Indirect assistance to management by making information more timely and valuable.
3. The direct use of computing machines as an aid to making management decisions.

The last category, the most challenging, includes the solution of problems in operations research and in linear programming. (See section on Operations Research.)

FUNCTIONS OF ELECTRONIC AND ELECTROMECHANICAL COMPUTERS. Electronic and electromechanical computers (not including desk-type mechanical calculators) can be used in four principal ways to aid production management and control:

1. **Problem Solving.** The use of electronic and electromechanical computers for the purpose of solving problems is familiar to all. Commonly in scientific and engineering applications, there exists a set of formulas which are too tedious or too time-consuming to be solved by conventional methods. These formulas are programmed into the computer, which solves them and gives a numerical answer or produces a graph. Though this is an important area in the use of electronic and electromechanical computers, other less well-known applications are of equal importance.
2. **Control.** For all practical purposes, any physical situation, or process, or event can be described in mathematical terms. A computer can be used to solve the mathematical expression in order to effect the control of a number of variables.

3. **Simulation.** Likewise, a computer can be used to solve equations which describe the function of a system. In this way, a computer can be made to simulate a system or process.

4. **Data Processing.** Another large field of application for digital computers consists of high speed sorting and evaluation of data. Commonly the data is on punched cards, magnetic tape, or magnetic drums. Here, too, a computer can be used for an operation that does not at first appear to be mathematical.

Control and Information Abilities. The term **computer** is so general that several attempts have been made to use other expressions and to redefine the term. Ridenour (Automatic Control) points out that the modern computer is the first machine that can simulate some of the generalized abilities of human beings to perform such operations as controlling dampers, rheostats, and steering wheels. Such control devices have been called computers merely because their main job to date has been computation, but this obscures their broader control applications. Ridenour suggests that the term **information machine** would better distinguish the computers used in control work.

Samuel (IRE Proceedings, vol. 41) emphasizes the fact that a computer is merely an information-processing device. A computer cannot initiate any new information not contained in the original source, although it may transform the original information into a much more usable form. By analogy, a computer may be considered a **mathematical translator,** in the same sense that a literary translator takes information in one language and, without adding or subtracting any basic information, renders this information intelligibly to someone who doesn't understand the original language.

ANALOG VS. DIGITAL COMPUTERS. There are two general computing processes, analog and digital. In an analog machine, **analogy** exists between the operation of the computing device and the type of problem it is intended to solve. Information is supplied to the analog computer in the form of a physical quantity, such as voltage, or current, or the angular rotation of a shaft. The analog computer transforms these input quantities into output quantities in accordance with the **programming** of the computer. If the computer is programmed to simulate a mathematical problem which in turn describes a physical system, the output of the computer is used for control purposes. Thus, if the analog device is to be used for control purposes, the output is used to provide the desired control. **Analog devices,** which include computers, simulators, and differential analyzers, all share the characteristic that the numbers in the problem they handle are represented by corresponding physical or electrical quantities.

In contrast to analog computer elements, the digital device works by **counting.** Fig. 1 (Machine Design, vol. 29) compares analog and digital computers on some of their essential characteristics. For the digital computer, the input data for the problem must be in the form of numbers. It processes the input information in accordance with the rules of arithmetic or logic which it was set up to handle. The output of the digital computer is also in numerical form. In order to operate as it does, by numbers, a digital computer makes use of special **input** and **output** **devices** to translate the input data into a form usable by the computer and in turn to convert the computer operation into a form usable for control and information purposes.

Evaluating the Use of Computers. The production planner or industrial engineer attempting to evaluate the use of computers as a time-saving aid in

Type of Computer	Capacity	Calculation Time	Setup Time Initial	Setup Time Repeat	Accuracy (percent)	Treatment of Nonlinearities
Analog (functional relationships)						
Electric analog (passive element)	Large	Short	Medium	Short to medium	1 to 5	Difficult
Electronic differential analyzer	Medium	Medium	Medium	Short	0.1 to 5	Easier than electric analog
Digital (elementary arithmetic)						
Externally stored program	Limited by internal storage	Long to medium	Long	Very short	Limited only by math involved	Easy if analytic, difficult if arbitrary
Internally stored program	Unlimited	Medium to short	Very long	Very short	Limited only by math involved	Easy

Fig. 1. Comparison of analog and digital computer characteristics.

analyzing his production problems must keep in mind that each type of computer, analog or digital, is best suited to a particular type of application. His specific problems can be handled better on one type of computer than on the other.

McDuff (Machine Design, vol. 29) explains that digital and analog computers differ substantially in their **accuracy, versatility,** and **cost.** These differences arise primarily from the fundamental differences in the two methods of computation.

Computer Speed and Accuracy. Although analog computers are not ordinarily as accurate as digital computers, they may be much faster for some classes of problems than some digital types. Furthermore, analog devices are generally less expensive than digital, but the initial cost for analog machines rises rapidly as greater demand for precision is made. As long as errors from 0.1 to 10 percent can be tolerated, an analog machine will cost considerably less than digital machines.

Digital computers, because they represent input information by integral numbers of electrical pulses, are inherently more accurate than analog machines. If sufficient time permits, a high digital precision can be obtained by increasing the number of significant digits carried in the computation. The digital computer is best in the area of **large-scale computation,** where a high degree of accuracy must be maintained. This is the reason why production problems involving scheduling, inventory control, and data processing are usually handled by digital computers. Computer systems for handling such problems are discussed subsequently in this section.

Digital machines further require **central pulse generating units,** and these must be of a certain minimum size. Consequently, it is not economical to use small digital computers. The economics of computer design places the digital machine in the high-capacity category.

Computer Size. Electronic analog computing machines range in size from desk models that incorporate ten to fifteen amplifiers to large installations that use hundreds of amplifiers. The very large analog installations require considerable associated equipment, such as **patch boards** and **power packs,** and a large staff to maintain them. The small analog machines are somewhat less expensive to run and maintain than are digital computers. For installations of the same general size, the operating costs of analog and digital machines are comparable.

Analog computers are especially well suited for limited accuracy design studies of dynamic systems. Programming (that is, setting up analog machines to translate the input data) is reasonably simple and can be carried out by ordinary production or engineering personnel, who need not be computer specialists. The variables, parameters, and coefficients that are basic to the problem being solved by the computer, as well as the initial conditions, the constants, can be quite easily varied while the problem solution is being obtained on the analog machine. This feature is of particular value in **design** and **system studies** that require many trial solutions to determine the best operating conditions.

Computer Programming. The digital machine programming, that is, introducing the methods of logic and arithmetic by which the input information is handled, usually requires more mathematical skill than does the use of an analog computer. For this reason the programming of a digital computer is often carried out by an experienced **central computing staff.** It is also somewhat more difficult to make changes in the variables of a digital problem when it is in the

INPUT	SERVO COMPUTER	OUTPUT
to a servo computer includes one or more of these elements. The signals are analogs of variables and constants, either in the form of shaft rotations or voltages.	solves equations by analog methods, enabling industrial machines to function at higher orders of automaticity on a mathematical basis.	of a servo computer includes one or more of these elements. The signals are analogs of variables and constants, either in the form of shaft rotations or voltages.

Manual Controls

such as potentiometers, are used for setting scale factors (analog ratios), rates, parameters, and function.

Mathematical Operations

readily performed by servo computers are:

    Addition
    Multiplication
    Differentiation
    Discrimination
    Triangulation
    Subtraction
    Division
    Integration
    Limiting
    Resolution
    Function Generation

(These operations are customarily performed by arrangements of pre-engineered building-block units.)

Control System

of a machine is the usual servo computer output. By means of conventional power servos, valves, regulators, and open-loop actuators, the machine responds to the mathematical function of the control constants and variables originally programmed. In most cases, the computer is physically merely an adjunct to the power servo control system, although functionally the machine depends on the computer function.

Transducers

such as thermocouples, strain gages, differential transformers, synchros, accelerometers and tachometer generators, are used to reveal the status of one or more particular machine functions. This information is used to provide a necessary variable for the control of a mathematically based operation or for feedback purposes.

Building-Block Units

used to formulate servo computers are:

    Summing amplifiers
    Power supplies
    Servo amplifiers
    Phase detectors
    Servo shaft units
    Unit plugs
    Relay units
    Discriminators
    Linear detectors
    Special-purpose units

Indicators and Recording Instruments

are frequently used to display variables and computed functions, either for monitoring purposes or to permit manual control of a machine in accordance with computer solutions. Recorders are used as an aid to economic and statistical analysis.

A Computer Output

frequently represents a function that requires further mathematical operation, in which case it becomes the input signal to another servo computer.

Programmer

stores information concerning the desired mode of operation and changes or sequences the machine process. Timers, counters, magnetic tapes and mechanical programming are used. Program of inputs may be manual, computer or transducer. The inputs may be derived from machine feedback or, in the case of in-line operation, from other machines.

Activation

of these units is usually electro-mechanical, using a rate or positional servo. Electronic activations commonly used for amplifiers and function generators. When the computer is of the electric slide-rule type, manual activation is applicable. Thermal, mechanical and pneumatic modes of computer activation are feasible. Hydraulic activation is not used.

Computer

The output of a servo computer becomes the input to another computer whenever further mathematical operation is required. This is often the case, as most complex equations are solved in parts. Simultaneous equations are solved by setting up a computer for each unknown in explicit form and cross-connecting the computers, so that each computer depends on the other.

Fig. 2. Flow diagram showing interrelation of basic analog computer sections.

process of a solution, even though a partial solution shows that a change in the program would be desirable.

Production problems, such as economic models, control of production machines, and quantity control are typical of those that can be done by analog methods. Some production problems, such as linear programming, operations research, and special product design can be done by either analog or digital methods. Amber and Amber (Electrical Manufacturing, vol. 59) show the interrelation of basic analog computer sections, input, computer, and output, in Fig. 2. As indicated both the input and the output sections may take several forms. Since a control system may actually consist of a number of interconnected computers, the output for one computer may well be the input for the next.

Digital Computer Elements. Digital computers consist of five main components:

1. Input section.
2. Output section.
3. Storage section.
4. Arithmetic unit section.
5. Control unit section.

Information is introduced into the **input section** by means of paper tapes, punched cards, or magnetic tapes. The results of the computation, sometimes called the **readout,** can be obtained from the computer on such media as paper tapes, punched cards, magnetic tapes, cathode ray tube screens or printed on paper by an electric typewriter.

The **storage section** is used to store data and instructions (commonly called the program). The storage of many computers consists of a relatively small, high-speed section with a capacity of from 10,000 to 30,000 numbers or instructions and a relatively large, slow section with a capacity which is essentially unlimited. The high-speed section usually consists of magnetic cores, cathode ray tubes, or acoustical delay lines, while the low-speed, or auxiliary, storage usually consists of magnetic tapes or magnetic drums. The high-speed storage is used in conjunction with the arithmetic units. Programs and large blocks of data are stored in block form in the auxiliary storage and are read in this form into the high-speed storage whenever they are required by the computer.

The **arithmetic unit** consists of the following registers or their equivalents: high-speed storage registers, a multiplier-quotient register, an instruction register, and an accumulator. The high-speed storage registers hold the information involved in current calculations. The multiplier-quotient register contains the multiplier in any multiplication operation and is the register in which the quotient is developed during a division. The instruction register contains directions for the computer operations.

The **accumulator** is an adding register from which the sum or difference of any two numbers can be obtained. It is also used to hold the dividend in division.

GENERAL-PURPOSE VS. SPECIAL-PURPOSE COMPUTERS.

On the basis of computer function—how they are used rather than how they work—all computers can be separated into two main groups, called general-purpose computers and special-purpose computers.

General-purpose computers may be of either analog or digital types. The outstanding characteristics of general-purpose computers are that they are designed to handle a wide variety of problems and that they provide the answer to a problem in graphical or numerical form. The general-purpose computer is usually the concept of the layman when the term "computer" is mentioned. Because general-purpose computers must be flexible to accommodate a wide variety of problems, such computers are necessarily large and complex. General-purpose digital computers are used mainly for solving problems of business, finance, and production. There is increasing use of the so-called **giant brain** digital computers for production, scheduling, and inventory control purposes.

General-purpose analog computers are used mainly for solving problems that involve **differential equations.** For production purposes these would usually involve time-variable dynamic problems, taking into account the interrelations of the variables while the production process is in action. In fact, the ability to solve differential equations is the outstanding characteristic of the general-purpose analog computers, usually called "differential analyzers."

Special-Purpose Analog Computers. Less well known than general-purpose digital computers and the analog differential analyzer computers are special-purpose analog computers, otherwise known as "equation solvers." Special-purpose analog computers include control computers and simulators. **Control computers** are information machines specifically designed to aid in the control of production equipment. An example is the quality control computer which computes the mean ($\overline{X}$) and the standard deviation σ, and also provides the machine mean for feedback control purposes. (See Figs. 15 and 19.)

Simulators are models of systems being studied, such as an economic system, or production scheduling. The electrical model which constitutes the simulation computer does not necessarily physically resemble the system being studied. The similarity exists between the equations which describe the system being studied and the simulation computer equations. An example of a simulator computer is shown in Fig. 3. The use of physical models as an aid to plant layout is familiar to the industrial engineer. Simulators are merely electrical models being used to aid in dynamic rather than static studies.

Production uses of large digital computers are mainly behind the scenes, in the background of the actual production. Special-purpose analog and digital computers are used largely "on the factory floor."

ECONOMIC ANALOGS AND PRODUCTION MODELS. An important application of analog computers as an aid to production is economic analogs and production control models. Smith (IRE Proceedings, vol. 41) discusses the use of electronic analog computers in the solution of economic problems. The large general-purpose analog computer can be used to solve **dynamic unilateral systems.** This can be used for the analysis of a single business, the analysis of an industry, or the study of economy as a whole. As an example, the price of beans might be a function of such factors as the price of cans, the cost of cannery labor, the cost of farm labor, the weather during the previous year, and the interest rate.

Smith points out that large analog computers for solving N equations in N unknowns can be used for **linear static problems,** such as the determination of average production levels in a large number of interrelated industries. This type of analog is relatively inaccurate and is sensitive to the accuracy of the input data.

Small-scale, special-purpose analogs can be built for a large variety of **isolated dynamic problems,** such as the determination of the best ordering rate and the design of the optimum ratio of inventory capacity to production capacity in a proposed small business. The effect of statistical fluctuations can be most easily observed by using an analog with a **random signal generator.**

A Production-Economic Analog. A functional block diagram of a typical production analog of a dynamic unilateral system is shown in Fig. 3 (IRE Proceedings, vol. 41). Smith explains this typical production-economic analog as follows: The analog consists of a set of amplifiers which can be connected either

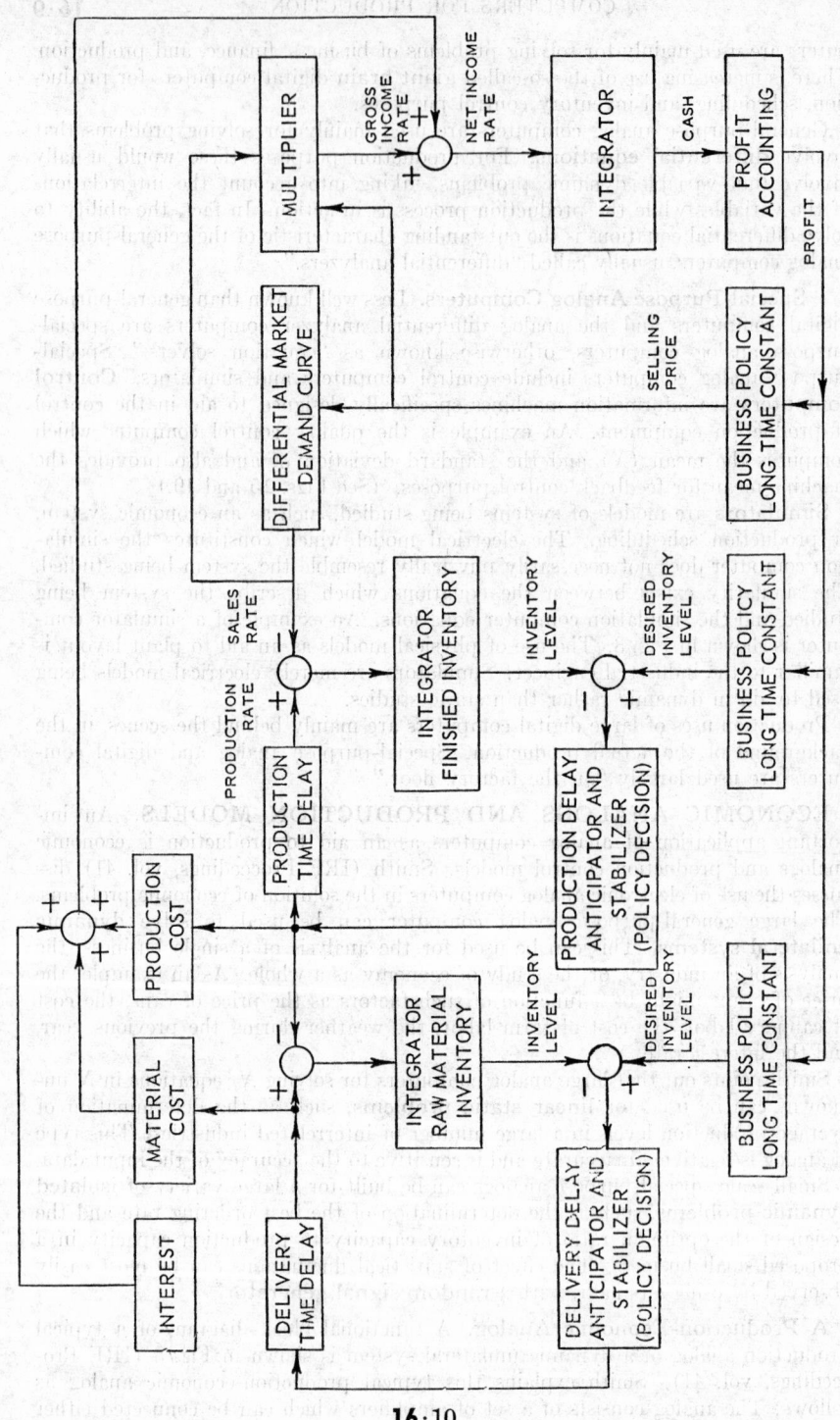

Fig. 3. Analog simulation of unilateral production.

as buffers, nonlinear function generators, integrators, or differentiators, in the same manner as in the solution of servo mechanism problems. In the study of **inventory** and **production rate oscillations,** one input into the system is the desired inventory level, which is determined by business policy. From this is subtracted the actual inventory level, and the error is amplified by the production-scheduling policy decision amplifier.

The output specifies the production rate which, passing through a time delay, is integrated to give the goods component which is added to the inventory level. The price-supply curve is a voltage source with nonlinear internal impedence which drives the demand-price curve, which in turn excites another voltage load with a nonlinear internal impedance. The sales rate and price exist at the terminals of these two units. Sales rate is integrated and subtracted from the inventory quantity. Sales price is multiplied by the rate, integrated, and goes into the profit computer. The production rate is integrated, and subtracts from the raw materials inventory, which causes a deviation between the desired raw materials inventory level and the actual level. This deviation actuates the amplifier representing the ordering of new raw materials. The ordered raw materials are delayed in delivery by an **electronic delay network.** The output of this network is integrated and added to the raw materials inventory.

Computer Use on Inventory Control. Both bilateral and unilateral dynamic analogs show clearly the type of inventory oscillations which are commonly observed by economists. It is easy to determine the effect on **inventory stabilization** of the variations of the different parameters in the analog. As in servo mechanisms, particular attention has to be given to excessive time delays. Wherever possible, a prediction of future trends or the introduction of the phase lead networks which utilize the rates of changes of signals is very desirable. Also, as in servo mechanisms, one must be aware of "too much of a good thing." The improper use of trend predictors or phase lead networks will increase the high response so greatly that high-frequency "noise" (random signals) will be magnified by the system, and the inventory variations become random at a high frequency. Excessive gain due to overzealousness on the part of the manager can result in sinusoidal oscillations at the low resonant frequency characterized by the production delay and the inventory time constant.

The **analog simulator** shows that the purpose of the inventory is twofold: (1) smoothing statistical variations in the sales rate (the set point should be approximately half the capacity from maximum usefulness), and (2) providing stabilization through a high-gain feedback system around a pure production time delay (stabilization can be obtained only with a cascade time constant many times greater than the production delay). The production-scheduling policy and the inventory capacity provide this **stabilizing time constant.** Simon (Econometrica, vol. 20) explains that models and analogs can be used to study production problems, and stresses the similarity between servo mechanism feedback theory and the theory which must be understood in order to handle complex production control problems.

Digital Computer Programming

BASIC ELEMENTS. The most powerful high-speed computer is of no value without **programming,** by which the computer is instructed what to do and how to do it. There cannot be any appreciable understanding of computer operation until the rudiments of computer programming are understood.

Thomas (IRE Proceedings, vol. 41) gives the following explanation of how to program a simplified stored program digital computer:

In order to discuss programming, it is first necessary to describe a typical though simplified computer to which the programs apply. The computer being programmed herein consists of the basic logical elements and a relatively small number of basic instructions. Although the decimal number system is used here, the same principles hold for programming by binary computers, the only difference being in the representation of the numbers.

All stored-program digital computers have four basic elements:

1. The memory, or storage element.
2. The arithmetic element.
3. The control element.
4. The terminal equipment or input-output element.

The relationship of these elements is indicated in Fig. 4 (IRE Proceedings, vol. 41).

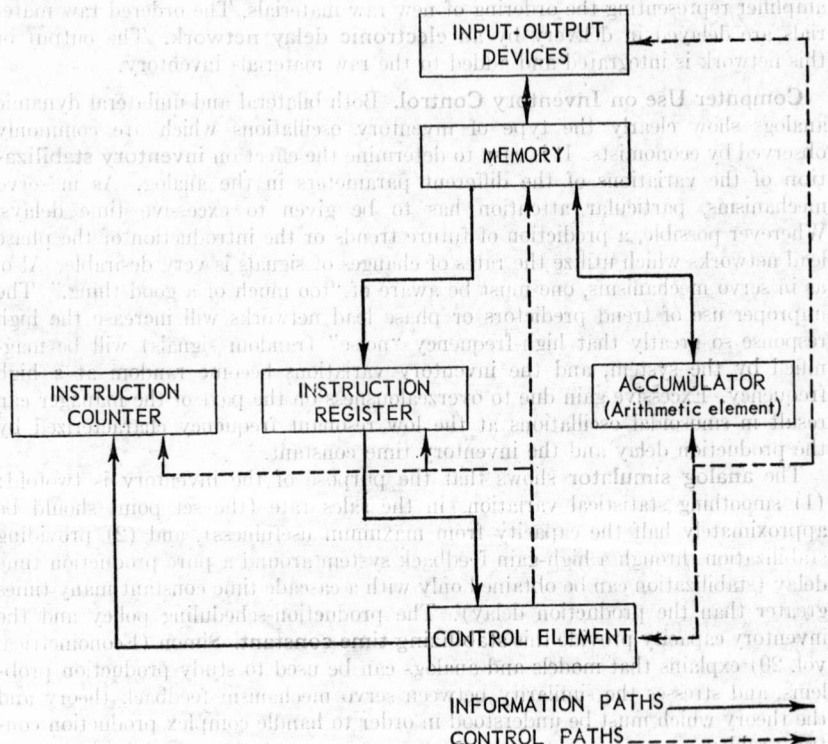

Fig. 4. Diagram of simple stored-program digital computers.

Memory Element. The memory element consists of a number of **storage locations** in which information can be stored and from which this information can be extracted. Information stored in memory remains unchanged until it is replaced by new information. Obtaining information from a memory location does not change its contents. Each of the storage locations which comprise memory is identified by a number, its **address**.

In the computer used herein as an example, memory will consist of 1,000 locations which will be addressed by the numbers 000 through 999. Each location will be capable of storing 5 decimal digits and a sign, which may be either a number or an instruction. Since the **coded form** in which an instruction appears in memory is a number, there is no distinction between a number representing data for calculations and a number representing an instruction.

Arithmetic Element. The arithmetic element of the computer used herein as an example is simply an accumulator with its appropriate information and control paths. The **accumulator** may be likened to a desk calculator. **Addition** of numbers is performed by first entering one of the numbers (the augend) in the accumulator and then giving the command to add, at the same time entering the other number (the addend). After the operation the sum will be retained in the accumulator.

Subtraction is performed in the same manner except that the command to subtract is given. The accumulator has been provided with the necessary logical circuits to attach the correct sign to the difference.

For **multiplication** the multiplier is entered in the accumulator, and the command to multiply is given while the multiplicand is entered. The product, with the correct sign, will be retained in the accumulator, replacing the multiplier. The control circuits provide for the correct sequence of control pulses to the accumulator for each arithmetic operation.

Division is performed by utilizing one of the basic operations described above. Generally, it is a series of subtractions in which the divisor is repeatedly deducted from the dividend.

Control Element. The control element consists of the instruction counter, the instruction register, and various other control circuits. There, counters and switches take each instruction in sequence from the memory and send the proper **command signals** to the various parts of the computer to execute the instructions. Their functions will be made clear in the following description of the operation of the computer.

Input-Output Elements. Input-output elements will not be described for this simple computer, because they differ greatly in different machines, and their basic function of bringing in information to output units is about all that is common to the different computers that have been built. For the computer used as an example, it will be assumed that all necessary instructions and initial data have already been put into memory and that the results, after computation, will be stored in memory.

OPERATION OF THE SIMPLE COMPUTER. In order to follow the sequence of computer operations described below, refer again to Fig. 4, which is a block diagram of the simple computer showing the interconnection of the basic elements.

Instructions. The simple machine has been provided with eight instructions:

Instruction	Operation Code
Add	01
Subtract	02
Multiply	03
Clear and add	04
Store	05
Transfer	06
Transfer if minus	07
Stop	00

An instruction, as stored in memory ready to be executed, has five digits. The first two of these are the **operation code.** The last three, called the **address** part, usually give the address of the memory location which contains the information to be acted upon. Thus the instruction which directs the machine to add the contents of the memory location whose address is 356 would be stored in memory as 01356. The sign on an instruction is immaterial. It should be noted that this instruction in its coded form is a number. It may be acted upon by other instructions to change its meaning. The only thing which identifies an instruction to the computer is that it is brought into the instruction register under control of the instruction counter. This action is described in the following paragraphs.

Fig. 4 shows two information paths from memory, exclusive of the input-output connections. The left path is used to put instructions into the instruction register where they are decoded and executed. The right path, which operates in both directions, is used to send numbers to the arithmetic element and to receive the results of computation. The execution of each instruction takes place in two cycles, an **instruction cycle** and an **execution cycle.** During the instruction cycle the left path is used, and during the execution cycle the right path is used if an arithmetic operation is to be performed.

The operation of the computer during an instruction cycle is the same for all instructions. When the computer is started, the instruction counter contains 000, and the machine automatically performs an instruction cycle. The contents of the instruction counter are acted upon by the control circuits to select the addressed memory location, in this case the location whose address is 000. The contents of this location are put into the instruction register.

Execution. During the execution cycle, which always follows an instruction cycle, switches in the control circuit provide appropriate command signals to the rest of the computer according to the contents of the left two digits, the instruction code. If the instruction is one which calls for a reference to memory, the control circuits select the memory location specified by the address part of the instruction and set up the appropriate information path. On arithmetic instruction—add, subtract, multiply, and clear and add—the accumulator receives the proper sequence of command signals to perform the desired operation. After each execution cycle is completed, except in the cases of the transfer and transfer-if-minus instructions, the instruction counter contents are increased by one. Then another instruction cycle is called for to bring the next instruction into the instruction register.

The Instruction Counter. Thus the machine alternates between instruction cycles and execution cycles, bringing an instruction from memory, executing it, and obtaining the next instruction. The function of the instruction counter should be noted. It is used during the instruction cycle to determine from which memory location an instruction is to be obtained. As mentioned above, on most instructions the contents of this counter are increased by one at the end of each execution cycle. Thus, instructions are normally obtained from **sequential memory locations,** starting with location 000 when the machine is placed in operation. The effect of the transfer and transfer-if-minus instructions on the instruction counter will be described later.

Operating Sequences. The following description of the sequence of events that occur during the execution cycle when the add instruction is executed also applies in most details to the subtract, multiply, and clear and add instructions.

After the add instruction has been brought into the instruction register during the instruction cycle, the control element provides the appropriate control signals to execute the instruction. The contents of the memory location specified by the address part of the add instruction are sent to the accumulator where, on command from the control element, the incoming number is added to the original contents of the accumulator. The sum remains in the accumulator. The execution is now completed; the instruction counter contents are increased by one, and another instruction cycle is executed. After the execution of the subtract or multiply instruction the result is retained in the accumulator. After **multiplication** the product is rounded to five digits. The clear and add instruction first clears the accumulator to 00000, then adds the number from memory, thus bringing the contents of the specified memory location into the accumulator unchanged. None of the instructions described make any change in the contents of memory.

Store. The store instruction is used to return information from the accumulator to memory. The control element, on obtaining the signal from the instruction register to execute the store instruction, conditions the specified memory location to accept information. The original contents of the selected memory location are lost, being replaced by the contents of the accumulator, but the accumulator still retains the information which was stored. The instruction counter is now increased by one and the next instruction is obtained.

Transfer. The execution of the transfer instruction is simple. Upon being signaled to execute the transfer instruction, the control element distributes signals which transfer the last three digits of the instruction in the instruction register to the instruction counter. The instruction counter is not increased by one during the execution of this instruction, and the next instruction is obtained from the memory location specified by the instruction counter contents. Thus, the transfer instruction provides the programmer with the ability to **break the sequence** in which instructions are obtained from memory. For example, if the instruction counter contained 067 and the memory register 067 contained the instruction "transfer to 115," coded as 06115, the next instruction would be obtained from memory location 115 and the program would continue in sequence from there until another transfer instruction was executed.

The transfer-if-minus instruction tests the sign of the contents of the accumulator. If the accumulator contents are negative, the transfer instruction is executed as described above. If the contents of the accumulator are positive or zero, the transfer instruction is not executed; instead the contents of the instruction counter are increased by one, and the next instruction in sequence will be executed. This conditional instruction makes it possible for the programmer to write programs which take different courses of action, depending upon the results of previous computation.

The execution of the stop instruction stops the computer, leaving the contents of all registers and counters unchanged. The address part of this instruction has no effect.

SIMPLE PROGRAMS. In order to demonstrate how digital computers are programmed, a few simple program operations are presented:

Arithmetic Programs. The first program to be discussed **adds** three numbers, a, b, and c, and stores their sum. Let a, b, and c be stored in memory locations 005, 006, and 007. The program (Fig. 5) will add the three numbers and store the result in memory location 008.

Location	Operation	Address Part	Effect
000	clear and add	005	Puts a into the accumulator.
001	add	006	Forms $a + b$ and leaves it in the accumulator.
002	add	007	Forms $a + b + c$ and leaves it in the accumulator.
003	store	008	Stores result, $a + b + c$, in memory location 008.
004	stop	000	Stops the computer.
005	a		⎫
006	b		⎬ Initial data.
007	c		⎭
008	—		Location for storing result.

Fig. 5. Computer response for addition.

If the values $+1436$, -3712, and $+57632$ were assigned to a, b, and c, the coded program would appear in memory as shown in Fig. 6.

Memory Location	Contents
000	$+04005$
001	$+01006$
002	$+01007$
003	$+05008$
004	$+00000$
005	$+01436$
006	-03712
007	$+57632$
008	$+00000$

Fig. 6. Typical example of coding.

After the instructions of the above program have been executed, memory location 008 will contain $+55356$. Notice how the stop instruction stops the computer before any of the numbers to be added can be interpreted as if they were instructions.

The second example (Fig. 7) **evaluates an expression, $ax^2 + bx + c$.** The memory locations whose addresses are 007, 008, 009, and 010 contain a, b, c, and x. The result is to be stored in location 011.

Logical Program. The programmer's ability to write programs which give the computer the power of making simple decisions is provided by the inclusion of **conditional instructions.** The transfer-if-minus instruction incorporated into the computer is such an instruction.

The following program (see Fig. 8) is an example of the use of the transfer-if-minus instruction in **making decisions.** This program examines three numbers, a, b, and c, and determines the largest number of the set. When the machine stops, the largest number will be stored in memory location 016. Note that not all the instructions are executed for any one case. Depending upon which number is the largest, some of the instructions will be skipped.

Location	Operation	Address Part	Effect
000	clear and add	007	Puts a into the accumulator.
001	multiply	010	Accumulator now contains ax.
002	add	008	Accumulator now contains $ax + b$.
003	multiply	010	Accumulator now contains $x(ax + b) = ax^2 + bx$.
004	add	009	Accumulator now contains $ax^2 + bx + c$.
005	store	011	Stores result in memory location 011.
006	stop	000	Stops computer.
007		a	
008		b	
009		c	} Initial data.
010		x	
011		—	Location for storing result.

Fig. 7. Computer response for multiplication.

Location	Operation	Address Part	Effect
000	clear and add	013	Forms $a - b$ in the accumulator.
001	subtract	014	
002	transfer if minus	005	If $a < b$, transfers to 005.
003	clear and add	013	If $a \geqq b$, puts a into the accumulator and executes 006 next.
004	transfer	006	
005	clear and add	014	If $a < b$, puts b into accumulator.
006	store	016	Stores the larger, a or b, in memory location 016.
007	subtract	015	Subtracts c from larger, a or b.
008	transfer if minus	010	If $c > a$ and b, transfers to 010.
009	stop	000	Computer stops here if a or b is the largest with that number stored in memory location 016.
010	clear and add	015	If $c > a$ and b, stores c in memory location 016, replacing a or b.
011	store	016	
012	stop	000	Computer stops here if c is the largest of the set.
013		a	
014		b	} Initial data.
015		c	
016		—	Storage for largest number.

Fig. 8. Computer response for conditional instruction.

The validity of a proposed computer program may always be tested on paper by executing it step by step. The programmer should pretend to be as "dumb" as the computer and try to forget the purpose of each step. By following each instruction to the letter, he may uncover errors in the logic of the program.

Cyclical Program. Much of the versatility of digital computers lies in their ability to have instructions operate on other instructions in a program as if they were numbers. To show this ability, the above program will be expanded into a program to find the largest of a set of 500 numbers (see Fig. 9).

Location	Operation	Address Part	Effect
000	clear and add	017 ⎫	Stores first number in memory location 014.
001	store	014 ⎭	
002	clear and add	(018) ⎫	Subtracts the contents of location 014 from the number currently being tested.
003	subtract	014 ⎭	
004	transfer if minus	007	If number in memory register 014 is larger, transfers to 007.
005	clear and add	(018) ⎫	If current number is larger, stores it in location 014.
006	store	014 ⎭	
007	clear and add	002	Puts the instruction from location 002 into the accumulator.
008	add	015	Adds one to the instruction.
009	store	002 ⎫	Stores the modified instruction in locations 002 and 005.
010	store	005 ⎭	
011	subtract	016 ⎫	If last number has not been compared, transfers back to 002 and checks next number.
012	transfer if minus	002 ⎭	
013	stop	000	Stops computer after last comparison.
014	———		Storage for largest number.
015	+00001		Constant for increasing instructions.
016	+04517		Constant for testing if last number has been compared. It has the same form as the instruction clear and add 517.
017			
.			
.			Initial data (500 numbers to be compared).
.			
.			
516			

NOTE: The parentheses around the address parts of instructions in memory locations 002 and 005 indicate that the address parts will be changed as the program progresses. When the program is put into memory, their address parts will be 018.

Fig. 9. Elemental decisions made by computer.

In the execution of the program shown in Fig. 9 the machine follows the instructions repeatedly after slight modification. A test is required after each comparison to determine whether all numbers have been compared, and the program is sufficiently general to cause the automatic modification of the instructions between each repetition. If a sufficient number of memory registers were available, a program could be written which used each instruction only once, but this would be wasteful of storage registers and would result in considerably more work in the preparation of the program.

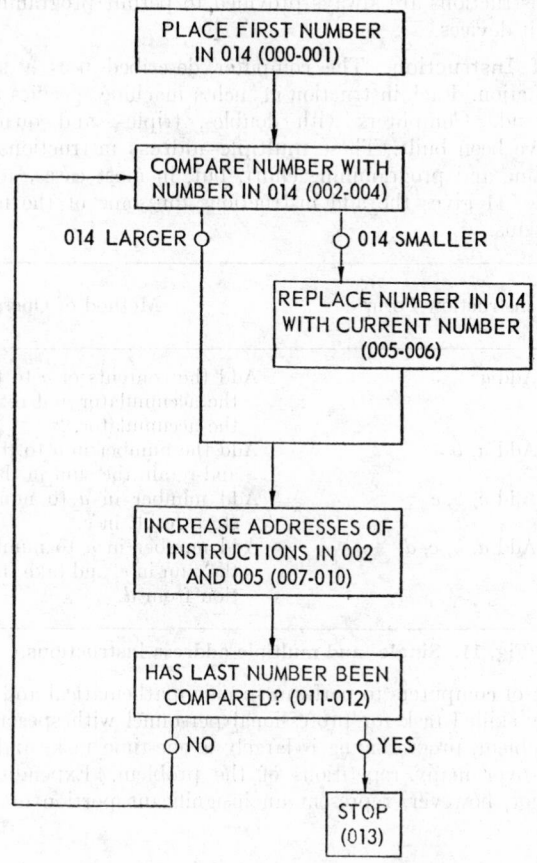

Fig. 10. Flow chart of simple cyclical computer program.

Fig. 10 is a **program flow chart.** Such flow charts show graphically the operation of a program. When complex programs are to be written, a flow chart will assist the programmer in his work.

The foregoing, adapted from Thomas (IRE Proceedings, vol. 41), illustrates such features of digital computer programming as the sequence in which instructions are executed, how this sequence may be broken, and the provisions for modifying instructions by arithmetic processes. The example above shows the use of these features to write a short, powerful program.

The programs used as examples show, of necessity, only the most basic of the programmer's techniques. One programming problem of the first magnitude not mentioned above is **scale factoring**—the problem of keeping the magnitudes of data, intermediate results, and final results within the range of the computer's registers. Computers usually have a number of shifting instructions which multiply or divide the numbers by powers of the radix employed. Another common type of instruction is an instruction which modifies only the address part of a stored instruction. Most, but not all, machines include a divide instruction. A number of instructions are always provided to permit programmed control of the input-output devices.

Systems of Instruction. The computer described uses a **single-address** system of instruction. Each instruction in such a machine specifies the location of only one operand. Computers with double-, triple-, and quadruple-address instructions have been built. These **multiple-address** instructions allow certain economies of time and programming effort, but, in most cases, add to machine complexity. Fig. 11 gives the add instructions for some of the many types of instruction systems.

No. of Addresses	Instruction Form	Method of Operation
1	Add a	Add the contents of a to the contents of the accumulator and retain the sum in the accumulator.
2	Add a, b	Add the number in a to the number in b and retain the sum in the accumulator.
3	Add a, b, c	Add number in a to number in b and store result in c.
4	Add a, b, c, d	Add number in a to number in b, store the sum in c, and take the next instruction from d.

Fig. 11. Single- and multiple-address instructions.

Programming of computers to perform specific mathematical and logical operations is a highly skilled task for professional personnel with specialized training. For a given problem, programming is largely a one-time task, and thus its cost can be spread over many repetitions of the problem. Expenditures for programming do not, however, represent an insignificant portion of the operating costs.

Electronic Data Processing

INVENTORY CONTROL. Lucas (Control Engineering, vol. 2) observes that industrial data processing for automatic production inventory control is a complex problem, in some cases more complex than the engineering and scientific applications of digital computers. It takes considerable study and planning to secure the proper computer system and to program it for an in-plant inventory control job.

Assuming that an industrial firm wants to know what can be done to install an electronic system for handling inventory, Lucas recommends that a system meet the six requirements set forth in the following list.

1. Inventory must be kept at a minimum safe level.
2. An accessible record of all inputs to inventory and of all withdrawals from inventory must be continually available.
3. Printed reports (daily, weekly, or monthly as necessary) must be provided for the production, purchasing, sales, and for the accounting departments.
4. The data-processing system should reduce the load on the clerical staff by reducing the number of people required for strictly routine tasks.
5. There should be enough savings in personnel time so that a new electronic data-processing installation will pay for itself in about five years.
6. The system should be capable of delivering prompt, accurate statistical data as well as solving payroll, sales analysis, and enginering problems.

Inventory Procedures on Computers. Fig. 12 illustrates the "one-pass" method of data processing. Incoming documents are converted into punched paper tape, the operators using Flexowriters. This punched paper tape is read by a **reader.** Another way of getting input information is by means of punched cards on a **card reader.** A master file of information is maintained on several magnetic tape machines. Another magnetic tape unit carries a file of specialized information such as back orders, and a daily record of transactions.

The computer is the hub of electronic systems handling for inventory and production control data. It is programmed to:

1. Maintain balances.
2. Indicate ordering action.
3. Maintain accumulation for reports.
4. Analyze contractural status.
5. Correct the files.
6. Answer queries.
7. Locate acceptable substitutes.
8. Locate best alternate source of supply.
9. Produce daily record and back order record.
10. Process exceptions and back orders.
11. Schedule warehouse load.

The output of the computer is programmed through a card punch by a tabulator from which the answers are typed automatically on a Flexowriter.

Process Sequence. With this industrial automatic production inventory control system, when an issue of a certain item takes place, the following **control sequence** develops:

1. The balance on hand is adjusted down.
2. If this adjustment causes the balance to fall below a minimum level, or an order level, the computer examines the commitment schedule to determine whether a reorder is necessary.
3. If a reorder is indicated, the computer examines the various factors used to compute a stock replacement formula quantity and arrives at a tentative ordering quantity.
4. The computer adjusts this tentative quantity by using stored and analytical factors relating to type of use for the code number, perishability, and projected future usage.
5. Having arrived at a suitable course of action, the computer causes the information to be printed out that the purchasing department should supply in the derived quantity of this code number.
6. Completing its travels through the program for the operating personnel, the computer produces an order-picking or shipping document.
7. The computer records this issue under the account heading, the proper expense distribution.

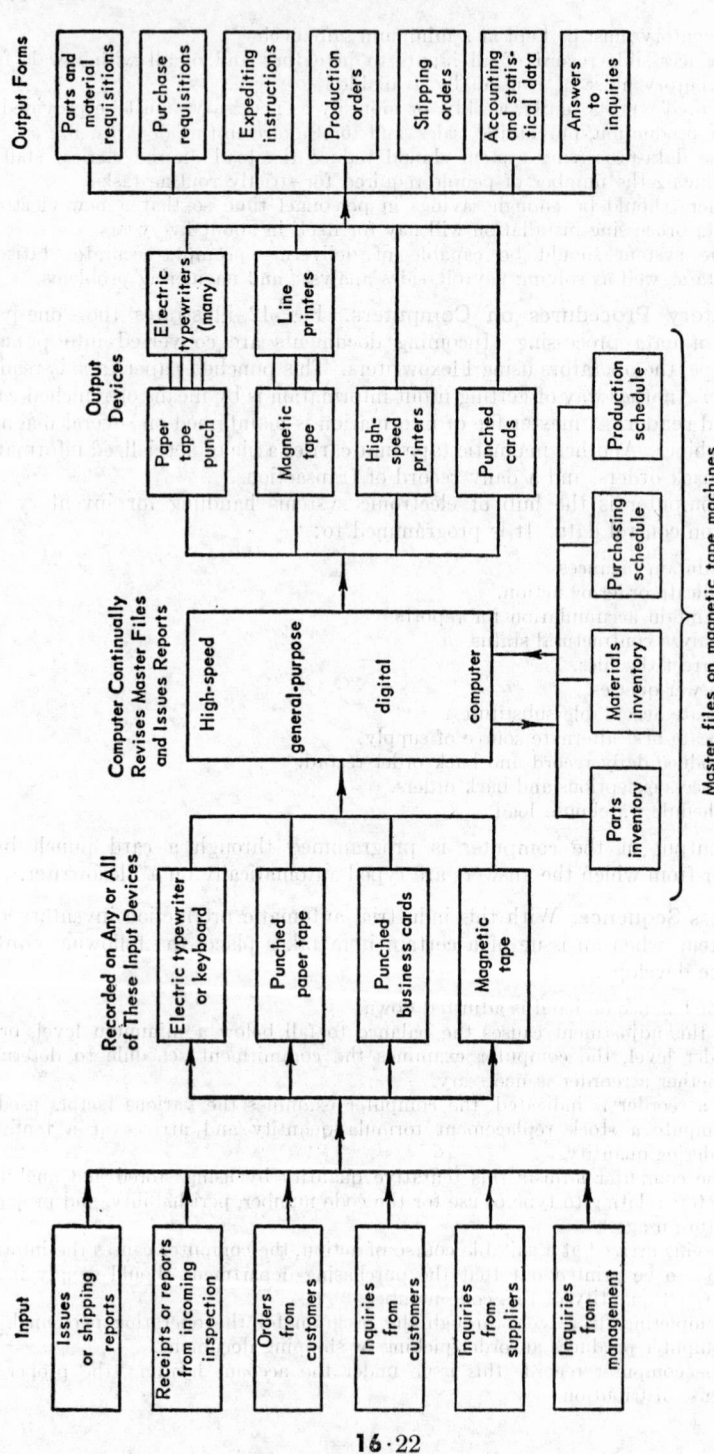

Fig. 12. Electronic data processing.

Input

- Issues or shipping reports
- Receipts or reports from incoming inspection
- Orders from customers
- Inquiries from customers
- Inquiries from suppliers
- Inquiries from management

Recorded on Any or All of These Input Devices

- Electric typewriter or keyboard
- Punched paper tape
- Punched business cards
- Magnetic tape

Computer Continually Revises Master Files and Issues Reports

High-speed general-purpose digital computer

- Parts inventory
- Materials inventory
- Purchasing schedule
- Production schedule

Master files on magnetic tape machines or magnetic drum or cores or punched cards

Output Devices

- Paper tape punch
- Magnetic tape
- High-speed printers
- Punched cards
- Electric typewriters (many)
- Line printers

Output Forms

- Parts and material requisitions
- Purchase requisitions
- Expediting instructions
- Production orders
- Shipping orders
- Accounting and statistical data
- Answers to inquiries

Computer Control of Stock Room Issues. The National Cash Register Electronic Division's applications staff shows how a computer can be used in connection with issues from a manufacturer's stock room. A **punched paper tape** of the daily transactions from the stock room is placed in a high-speed reader, connected to the computer, which then performs the following operations automatically, with no further operator intervention, according to a previously programmed routine:

1. Reads into the computer the paper tape of the daily transactions including stock number, debit account number, credit account number and quantity, and other data as desired.
2. Sorts in order, by stock number and record data, on the magnetic tape master file.
3. Summarizes the quantity by stock number and records it on magnetic tape.
4. Brings inventory record on magnetic tape up to date by subtracting quantity from the balance on hand.
5. At the same time, picks up the unit price and records it on magnetic tape.
6. Prints out an inventory control re-order and critical balance report, including all data on stock number requiring action by management.
7. Compares the new balance with the low limit and prints out all data on stock numbers where the new balance is at or below this low limit.
8. When unit price is known, extends the quantity of each stock number on each requisition.
9. Sorts and summarizes by debit accounts.
10. Sorts and summarizes by credit accounts.
11. Reports out daily inventory cost distribution.

The same system is also used to process punched paper tape obtained daily from the receiving departments, and while doing this, it adjusts the new average price of each item automatically.

Inventory and Accounting Control. An elaborate study of using electronic data-processing and digital-computing equipment for inventory and accounting control of materials and supplies was made by ElectroData Corporation of Pasadena for Southern California Gas Company.

The inventories to be controlled consisted of 13,000 items of which 6,000 were standard supplies with considerable issue and receipt activity. Materials were stock in about 30 warehouses with over 50 percent of dollar value stored in a central warehouse. The **program objectives** were as follows:

1. To supply inventory control personnel with information enabling them to meet the needs of operating personnel in the field at all times.
2. To allow inventory control personnel to minimize the dollar value and obsolescence of inventory maintained which would consume capital.
3. To furnish inventory control personnel with information to govern their requisitions to the purchasing department for replacing inventory.
4. To provide sufficient checks and controls so that accounting personnel may monitor and audit operations for efficiency and integrity.
5. To supply accountants with accurate expense accounts data.

In Fig. 13, Lucas (Control Engineering, vol. 2) compares **medium-sized, general-purpose digital computers** which are suitable for automatic production inventory control.

Special-Purpose Inventory Control Computer. Inventory control is a universal problem in production or distribution. Lessing (Automatic Control) describes a computer run by 10 operators, which is used for the control of a large

Name and Manufacturer	Internal Memory System	Average Access Time (millisec.)	Average Arithmetic Time (millisec.) Add +	Mult. ×	Divide ÷	Word Length	Number of Commands (approximate)
ElectroData Computer ElectroData Corp. Pasadena, Calif.	Magnetic drum, 4,000 words Quick access, 80 words	8.5 0.85 (quick)	2.0	8.5	12.0	42 bits 10 decimal digits and sign	50 Single address
CRC102-A and CRC102-D The National Cash Register Co. —Electronics Division, Hawthorne, Calif.	Magnetic drum, 1,024 words Quick access, 8 words	12.5 1.5	8.0	16.0	32.0	42 bits 9 decimal digits and sign	28 Three address
Bendix G-15A Bendix Computer Division, Los Angeles, Calif.	Magnetic drum, 2,160 words Quick access, 16 words	14.5 0.54	0.54	16.7	16.7	29 bits 7 decimal digits and sign	33 Two address
Readix J. B. Rea Co. Santa Monica, Calif.	Magnetic drum, 4,000 words Quick access, 160 words	9.0 0.4	0.8		20.0	42 bits 10 decimal digits and sign	59 Single address
Alwac III Logistics Research, Inc., Redondo Beach, Calif.	Magnetic drum, 4,096 words Quick access, 160 words	9.0	4.5	21.0	210.0	32 bits 7.5 decimal digits and sign	78 Single address

Fig. 13. A comparison of medium-sized general-purpose digital computers.

inventory of gift and hardware items by a distribution company, filling orders ranging in number from less than 2,000 to more than 15,000 a day, depending on the season. This computer system consists of a magnetic drum memory, a small arithmetic control unit for simple addition and subtraction, and 10 small input units, and it is capable of handling as many as 90,000 tallies a day, replacing 60 tally clerks.

Incoming orders are recorded as magnetized spots on a revolving magnetic drum. Item stock level is imprinted magnetically at the place designating the catalogue number, the magnetized spots being arranged at intervals on magnetic tracks. When a typical order for 10 items is received, the operator taps the order quantity and catalogue number on an input unit keyboard. The machine scans the surface of the magnetic drum, locates the catalogue number, and subtracts the order from the stock total. It takes the machine less than half a second to subtract the amount ordered from one total, add it to another, and return the new totals to the proper place on the magnetic drum. The total supply of any one item appears on an indicator when zero plus the catalogue number of the item is tapped on the input keyboard. The machine can also automatically compute a complete daily stock report on all items in the catalogue, if this is desired. With some modifications in size, in programming, and in type of input and output devices, such a machine could handle many other kinds of inventory problems such as materials scheduling for production.

PRODUCTION CONTROL AND PROCESS PLANNING. Joseph (Production, vol. 38) explains how Northrop Aircraft's Computer Section schedules **machine loads** in accordance with assembly line needs. Prior to use of electronic computer techniques at Northrop, process planning was sometimes little more than a guess, because loading the big machine shop to capacity with completion schedules dovetailed to the needs of the assembly line was a tedious and time-consuming operation.

Computer Loading of Machines. Machine loading is one example of the type of process planning that was turned over to the electronic computers. The decision to turn over the machine loading operation to computers was the result of careful analysis. The production control department began detailing the hours it was expending on the control of machine loading. Based on these data, a **processing analyst** decided that processing the work on tabulating machines would be justified by the saving in hours. The analyst then developed a procedure and made up the special forms necessary.

By means of electronic computer techniques, the production machines can now be "loaded," often in a few hours' time, for even the most complex contracts. In this way an estimated $100,000 is saved annually over manual methods of making machine tool assignments. The electronic computers are used to calculate shop time and to schedule work for every machine in the machine shop. In this way, the machine shop is kept on a tight production schedule.

Contracts are first broken down into individual machine operations having **preassigned time values.** The shop work and machine loads are determined through extension of these time values by the computers. This work was formerly done entirely manually.

Completed machine shop operations, parts accepted as finished, work in process, and open time on machines, all are now tabulated daily and weekly. Using this information, the production control men distribute the shop load to each machine.

Northrop's **data-processing section** operates 65 key punches, 30 tabulating machines, and 4 electronic computers, including a Univac. Machine loading is only one of the many process-planning operations which they perform.

The basis of Northrop's computer production control program is the **time standard** or work-proven increment of time required by a specific machine to complete a specific operation. These time standards are incorporated into a master file of 10,000 punched shop load cards. These master files contain **operation descriptions** of every possible machining job required on parts for Northrop's aircraft and missile projects. Key-punched into each card is the operations code number, the time required on a specific machine, and a setup time.

Machine loading begins when production contracts are broken down into parts requirements. Cards are punched for all operations on all work orders and standards are applied. Tabulators print the cards' information on paper, furnishing an analysis of total machine time and the material requirements. With this information, the contract can be fitted into a long-range schedule.

Computer Shop Loading. A valuable by-product of machine loading is "shop loading" or the spreading of the work evenly over every department.

Work orders in the form of **operations cards** are punched to include such data as:

1. Section, where the part fits into the airplane.
2. Setback, when the part is needed on the line.
3. Affectivity, what planes are affected by the part or group of parts under work order.
4. Plane requirements, the quantity of parts required for one assembly.
5. *M* days, how many manufacturing days are required for an operations order.
6. Part number.
7. Operation, whether milling, grinding, or any other machine tool operation.

A production control man in the shop gets a stack of operations cards each morning. When the cards are handed to a machinist, they become the machinist's **work order.** When the machinist has finished the work specified, he fills out the card, notes the machine number, the hours he worked, and the number of parts that he turned out. At the shift's end, the operations card is routed back to a tabulating section, where it is used to print a **work chart** detailing total work done and the parts completed.

When parts are passed by the inspection department, a **completion card,** which is related to the operations card, is filled out. The card tells how many parts are accepted and total actual hours expended as against standard time allotted. The tabulation tells the planning department what parts must be made up to meet any deficits.

Each day the data-processing section runs tabulations from these various cards to determine all machine shop operations completed, and all parts accepted by the inspectors and judged completed.

Once weekly, total hours by operations are tabulated. Each day for the previous day's operation the machine shop is presented with a **revised listing,** which shows what jobs are still in the shop, how long they will take to complete, and what machines have open time.

COMPUTER PRODUCTION CONTROL PROCEDURES. Canning (Report No. 29, Management Services Research Project, Office of Naval Research, U.C.L.A.) presents the problems incurred in applying electronic digital computers to **job shop scheduling** in production plants. It is Canning's experi-

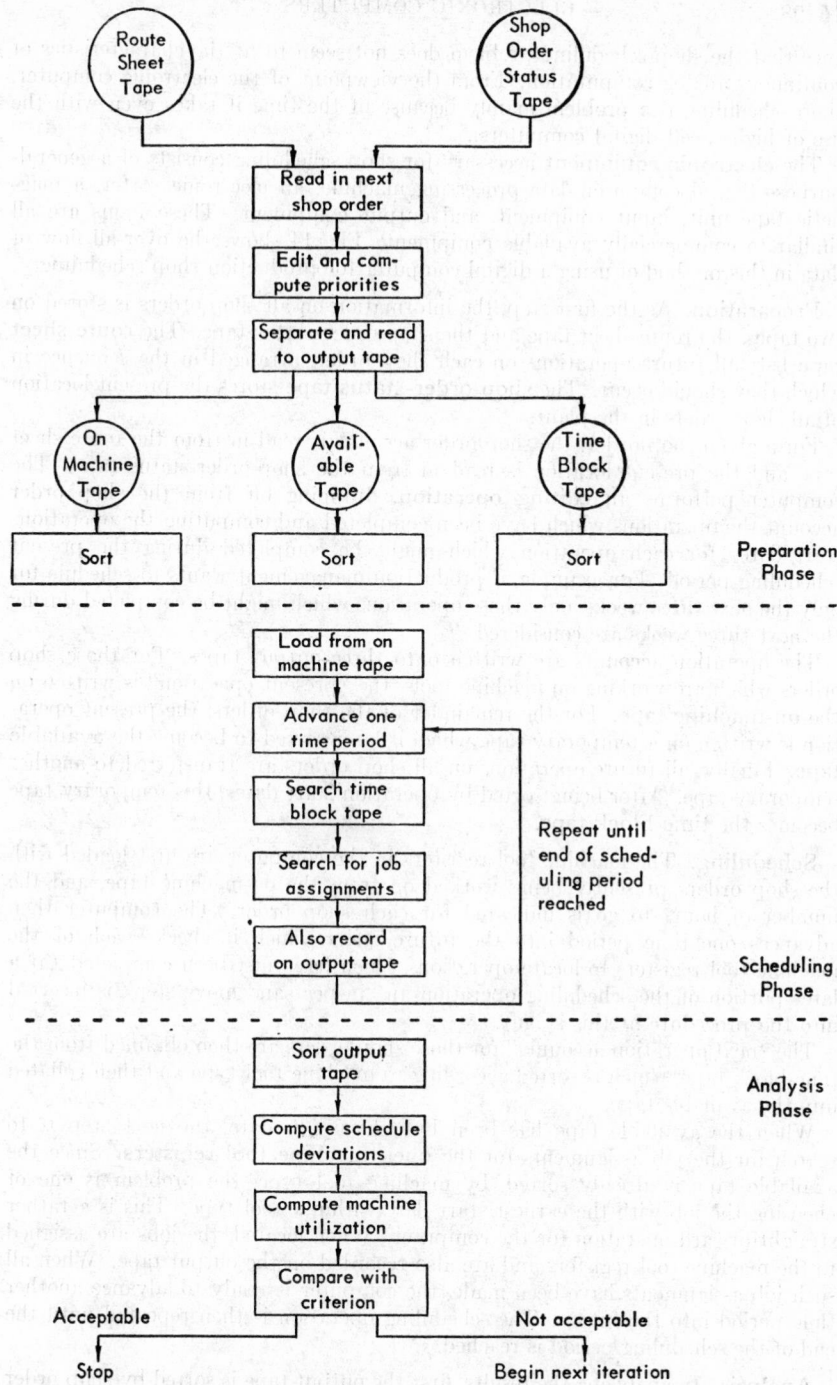

Fig. 14. Digital computer procedure for production scheduling.

ence that the shop-scheduling problem does not seem to fit the characteristics of continuous analog computation. From the viewpoint of the electronic computer, shop scheduling is a problem mainly because of the time it takes even with the use of high-speed digital computers.

The **electronic equipment** necessary for shop scheduling consists of a general-purpose digital computer data-processing machine, an electronic sorter, a magnetic tape unit, input equipment, and output equipment. These items are all similar to commercially available equipment. Fig. 14 shows the over-all flow of data in this method of using a digital computer for production shop scheduling.

Preparation. As the first step, the information on all shop orders is stored on two tapes, the route sheet tape and the shop-order-status tape. The **route sheet tape** lists all future operations on each shop order, arranged in the sequence in which they should occur. The **shop-order-status tape** stores the present location of all shop orders in the plant.

For a given shop order, the shop order account is read in from the route sheet tape and the present location is read in from the shop-order-status tape. The computer performs an **editing operation,** dropping off from the shop order account the operations which have been completed and computing the operations start dates for each operation which might be completed during the present scheduling period. For example, if production management wants to schedule for only the next three weeks, only those operations which might be completed during the next three weeks are considered.

The operation accounts are written onto three output tapes. For those shop orders which are working on machine tools, the "present operation" is written on the **on-machine tape.** For the remainder of the shop orders, the present operation is written on a temporary tape which is later sorted to become the **available tape.** Finally, all future operations on all shop orders are transferred to another temporary tape. After being sorted by operation start dates, this temporary tape becomes the **time-block tape.**

Scheduling. The machine tool registers in the computer are first loaded with the shop orders presently being worked on from the on-machine tape, and the number of hours to go is indicated for each shop order. The computer then advances one time period into the future, after which it checks each of the machine tool registers to locate operations which have just been completed (at a later portion of the scheduling operation an "inspect and move step" is inserted into the procedure at this stage).

The "next operation accounts" for those shop orders are then obtained from the time-block tape, which is sorted according to machine tool type and then collated into the available tape.

When the available tape has been brought up to date, the next step is to search for the job assignments for the **open machine tool registers.** Since the available tape is already sorted, by machine tool type, the problem is one of choosing the job with the earliest start date within a tool type. This is a rather straightforward operation for the computer. When located, the jobs are assigned to the machine tool registers and are also recorded on the output tape. When all such job assignments have been made, the computer is ready to advance another time period into the future. The scheduling operation is then repeated until the end of the scheduling period is reached.

Analysis. In analyzing the results, first the output tape is sorted by shop order serial number and by operation start date. This sorting results in bringing together all the operations on one shop order and in the proper sequence. The computer is then able to compute the **deviations** for each shop order, between the actual progress and the target progress. Machine tool **utilization** can also now be computed.

Decision. Based on the deviation and machine tool utilization figures, a decision can be made as to whether the schedule is acceptable or not, according to the criterion set up by production management. If acceptable, the operation is complete and the output tape results are stored in the route sheet tape. If not acceptable, the process is repeated. This time, however, the operation start dates are recomputed, taking into account the deviations of each of the shop orders.

Quite a large amount of sorting is called for in this process, because it is necessary to organize the data for fast access during the scheduling operation (see Fig. 14). It is, therefore, necessary to provide efficient sorting means when this method is used.

ADDITIONAL PRODUCTION APPLICATIONS OF DIGITAL COMPUTERS. Most production problems are concerned with manufacturing of piece-part products. It would appear that the control of the production of a continuous product, as in an oil refinery or chemical plant, would be much easier. This is not necessarily the case. Computer control of either piece-part production or continuous processes presents difficulties in both cases.

Process Control. James *et al.* (Control Engineering, vol. 3) discuss the prospect of using a computer to control a **continuous process** in a plant, in contradistinction to using a computer to control manufacturing and production operations in a factory. They caution that "you must crawl before you leap." The desirability of computer control for a chemical process is admitted, but at least three important questions must be answered before a specific application can be tried.

1. What are the specifications of a computer suited for industrial process control?
2. Can a computer be tied in with standard industrial instruments?
3. What forms will the industrial information take?

In an attempt to find answers to these broad questions, they undertook a complex **computer control test.** They set up a computer in Philadelphia to provide information every 6 minutes on the following items from a chemical plant located at Niagara Falls:

1. Total raw material transferred to the process.
2. Total production.
3. Production rate in pounds per hour averaged over each half hour.
4. Over-all yield.
5. Yield rate averaged over each half hour.
6. Material balance and accumulated losses around the reactor action.

Results were considered satisfactory although considerable changes were necessary in the computation systems, the long distance communications system, and in the chemical process itself.

Eckman (Control Engineering, vol. 3) cites an example where a pilot project to **optimize** by computer control a sample batch oil hydrogenation process kept 25 graduate students busy for over 2 years studying the kinetics of the reaction, converting these to equations, and then programming the equations into the computer. After all these extensive preliminary operations were finished, intensive work still had to be done to **integrate** the computer into the automatic devices that control the hydrogenator. Eckman cautions that all this work is only the start, for what was learned by the computer control project is leading to the redesign of the chemical process itself, to increase its yield and controllability.

Linear Programming and Logistics. Linear programming deals with problems of maximizing and minimizing that cannot be solved by the ordinary methods of calculus. Problems of the **theory of games** form a special case of linear programming. (See section on Operations Research.)

The theory of linear programming applies to many production problems that involve a great number of variables such as programming, scheduling, and routing. In most applications of linear programming, the computations called for are so extensive that it is impossible to carry them out without the use of automatic computers.

Klein, Williams, and Morgan (Digital Automation) show how linear programming can be used to solve a typical scheduling problem. They consider linear programming to be the technique of finding an optimum solution to problems with many interrelated factors. Mathematically, it is a problem of minimizing a given linear performance equation subject to given linear restrictions among the variables.

They show that various **logistical problems** normally considered insoluble, or at best solved by arbitrary judgment, can be handled by means of linear programming and a digital computer. They cite a simple application of linear programming that comes up in conjunction with the output of three factories and the 5 warehouses which the three factories supply. The factors are at different geographic locations, as are the warehouses. Accordingly, there is a distribution of shipping costs.

Assume it costs $1 per unit to ship from factory *1* to warehouse *3*; it costs $2 to ship from factory *3* to warehouse *5*; it costs $.65 to ship from factory *3* to warehouse *3*; and so on. The factories may ship 2,000 units apiece and the warehouses consume the entire output. The questions involved are: What is the optimal arrangement—the cheapest way for shipping from the various factories to the various warehouses? Shall all the output of factory *1* be shipped to warehouse *1*? And then, if units are still required in warehouse *1*, shall the balance be shipped from factory *3* or from factory *2*? Should the shipments be distributed from each factory evenly among all 5 warehouses? Which schedule and routing give the lowest shipping cost?

It is impractical to handle a problem of this type by means of manual calculus, arithmetical, or algebraic methods. By linear programming via the computer, the problem can be readily analyzed to find the lowest cost method for distributing the shipments. Linear programming also yields a positive quantitative measure of **optimal equipment use** in order to meet any criteria desired and actual performance can be compared with the best that can be obtained.

Queueing Problems. Prince (Product Engineering, vol. 26) discusses the laws governing the formation of "queues" or lines and how they can be shortened. This is of special interest to production men and industrial engineers, because at almost every stage of production, there is a tendency for lines to form. For example, there is a line of fabricated parts awaiting inspection; and parts in process of being manufactured must wait their turn from machine to machine.

To a large extent, production planning is for the purpose of reducing **waiting time** resulting from a line-up of parts waiting for the next operation. Automation reduces the amount of waiting time per part, because the various machines in a production sequence are integrated to work together.

Queueing is based on elements having **random variations.** New members join the tail of the queue at irregular intervals, and members at the head of the queue are taken care of and depart, usually at irregular intervals. Even the length of the queue has no particular fixed value.

Obviously, computers used as an aid to production are themselves subject to delays resulting from queueing. Prince forms the following conclusions from his study of queueing at differential analyzer analog computer installations. These four **computer queueing conclusions** are equally valid in the similar case of parts awaiting their turn at a machine tool in a job-shop manufacturing operation.

1. In a practical computing installation, at least some of the problems will be delayed by waiting in a queue.
2. In the long run, the only way in which the period of delay can be modified is by changing the capacity of the computing installation.
3. If problems associated with scheduled work are not to suffer intolerable delays, the computing installation must not be overloaded with such work.
4. If the capacity of the computing installation is large enough to avoid intolerable delays on scheduled work, there will be an appreciable fraction of the capacity available at random intervals for solving problems not associated with scheduled work.

From this, it would appear that most efficient use is made of a computer as an aid to production when it is specifically scheduled to take on production problems of a certain type as they appear. Problems of a lesser nature can be used as a "fill in" between the time necessary to solve the higher priority system problems. Thus it can be seen how production problems can be solved on computers already in use.

A number of manufacturing firms have computers, used primarily for engineering and scientific purposes. As an introduction to using computers as an aid to production, the production problems should be scheduled into the engineering computers during the slack periods of their use by the engineering department.

Single-Item Manufacturing. In most cases production planning consists of arranging the machines and scheduling in a factory to produce repetitively a large number of identical parts as required. This is not always the case, however.

It is sometimes necessary to manufacture a large number of "single items," each of which must be specifically **custom designed.** While all these items are somewhat similar in nature, no two are exactly alike. In such cases, the design of the parts being manufactured is an intimate part of the production-planning process.

The manufacture of large, high-powered transformers is an example of the single item problem. Middleton (Machine Design, vol. 29) shows how Westinghouse performs in its analytical department the routine calculations necessary for the custom design of high-power electrical equipment. These operations, done on digital computers, are performed in a matter of minutes. Programmed into the digital computer are the known practical ranges of performance, size, and performance characteristics desired, plus the production limitations and manufacturing codes. The computer quickly delivers final working electrical design data. Digital computers have been used to design transformers ranging from 750 to 20,000 kva. Induction motors, with ratings over a range of 200 to 2,000 hp., have also been computer-designed.

In using a digital computer to design a transformer, the computer is programmed to use the same philosophy as that followed by an experienced engineer. Once the input information, such as kva rating, basic impulse level, and temperature rise, has been entered into the computer, it initially selects or assumes certain design parameters necessary to calculate **performance characteristics.** These characteristics are then compared with the specified guarantees to the customer. If the calculated values are not acceptable, the initial assumptions are revised and the process is repeated until a favorable design is produced.

In addition to the obvious saving of designing time by use of a digital computer, it is found that the computer aids in permitting exhaustive **design study** to make certain that performance specifications are being satisfied at minimum manufacturing cost and with no delay. Computers are also used by Westinghouse in **test data analysis** to determine the best relationship of design parameters to performance characteristics of a new line of products.

The Automatic Factory

FACTORY FUNCTIONS OF COMPUTERS. The possibility of using computers to control a completely automatic process or an automatic factory has been the subject of much speculation. Weiner, the founder of cybernetics, says (The Human Use of Human Beings) that as far back as 1940 he was convinced that the automatic factory was on the horizon. The notion of programming in the factory had already become familiar through the work of Taylor and the Gilbreths in time study. The methods of programming factory work were ready to be transferred to computers. Weiner states that this offers considerable difficulty of detail but no great difficulty of principle.

Ridenour (Automatic Control) believes that in a completely automatic process a computer will be used to coordinate the performance of the control point at each stage. The **master control information** will be obtained from automatic product analysis instruments. The **computer memory** will carry the data determining which control points should be corrected and when the product departs from standard. June, Bardis, *et al.* (The Automatic Factory—A Critical Examination), in discussing the use of **central supervisory computers** of the complex electronic type, stress applications pertaining to the automatic factory (piece-part manufacturing industries), not automatic plants, such as chemical plants.

Substitution for Manual and Mental Functions. Two functions are involved in the discussion of manufacturing. One function is manual, such as driving nails and pushing levers; the other is mental, that is, determining what nail to drive and which lever to push. Practically all the progress in making manufacturing more automatic has been in the area of substituting mechanical operations for manual operations or, as it is sometimes phrased, substituting machine power for muscle power. A computer is a device that mechanizes some mental functions, such as those of logic, sequencing, arithmetic, and mathematics.

Until the advent of the automatic computer, little had been accomplished in replacing the human mental function by substituting mechanical brain power. The manual operations of a process must be replaced by some mechanical device before substitution for the mental function of the worker can be made. Another reason why there was little attempt to replace the mental function was that the state of the art of computers which made this possible was not well developed until World War II.

June, Bardis, *et al.* point out that conventional methods of instrumentation, such as those used extensively by chemical plants and oil refineries, supplement rather than replace human mental functions. "Automatic Factory" implies that

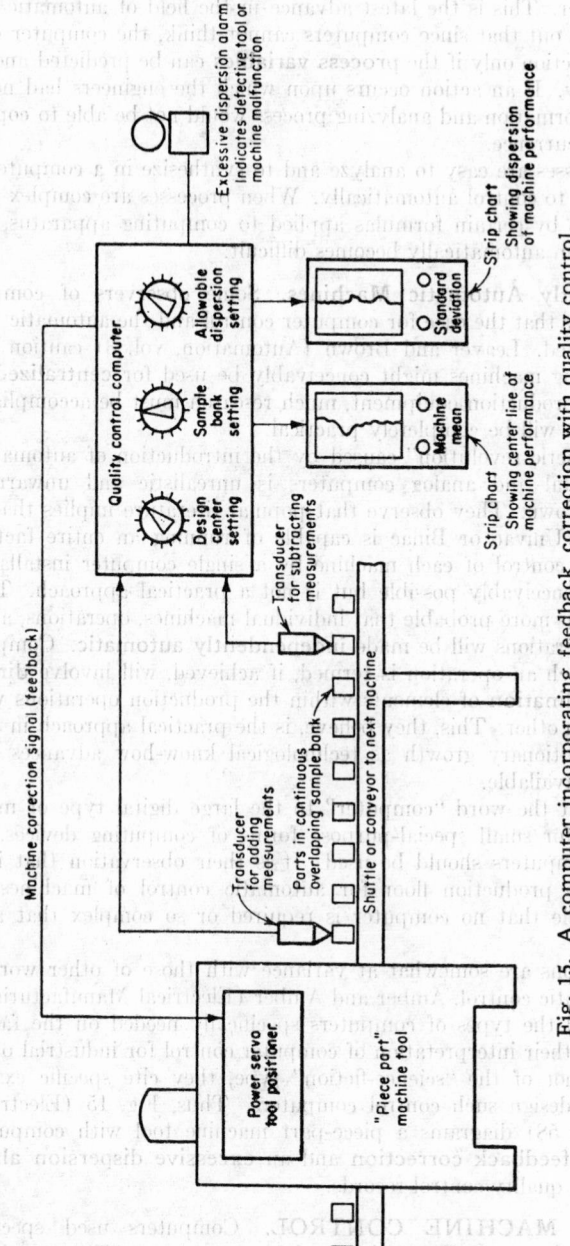

Fig. 15. A computer incorporating feedback correction with quality control.

a large number of mental functions are entirely replaced by means of an automatic computer. This is the latest advance in the field of automatic operations.

It is pointed out that since computers cannot think, the computer can replace the mental function only if the **process variables** can be predicted and expressed mathematically. If an action occurs upon which the engineers had not counted, the pre-set information and analyzing process would not be able to cope with this unexpected occurrence.

When processes are easy to analyze and to synthesize in a computer, they are relatively easy to control automatically. When processes are complex and cannot be represented by certain formulas applied to computing apparatus, the job of controlling them automatically becomes difficult.

Independently Automatic Machines. Some observers of computers and automation say that the case for computer control and the automatic factory has been exaggerated. Leaver and Brown (Automation, vol. 3) caution that, while giant computing machines might conceivably be used for **centralized direction** of a factory's production equipment, much research must be accomplished before the application will be completely practical.

The "cybernetic revolution" caused by the introduction of automatic controls based on digital and analog computers is unrealistic and unwarranted, say Leaver and Brown. They observe that popular literature implies that a type of computer like Univac or Binac is capable of running an entire factory, which means central control of each machine by a single computer installation. This, they feel, is conceivably possible but is not a practical approach. They rather expect that it is more probable that individual machines, operations, and parts of production operations will be made **independently automatic.** Complete "automation," as such an operation is termed, if achieved, will involve **direct decentralized coordination** of elements within the production operations which actually affect each other. This, they believe, is the practical approach in that it provides for evolutionary growth as technological know-how advances and equipment become available.

They restrict the word "computer" to the large digital type of machine and indicate that for small special-purpose forms of computing devices, something other than computers should be used. It is their observation that information needed on the production floor for automatic control of machines is usually either so simple that no computer is required or so complex that a computer is lost.

These opinions are somewhat at variance with those of other workers in the field of automatic control. Amber and Amber (Electrical Manufacturing, vol. 58) have described the types of computers specifically needed on the factory floor. As proof that their interpretation of computer control for industrial operations is realistic and not of the "science-fiction" type, they cite specific examples and show how to design such control computers. Thus, Fig. 15 (Electrical Manufacturing, vol. 58) diagrams a piece-part machine tool with computer control incorporating **feedback correction** and an **excessive dispersion alarm.** Strip charts provide quality control records.

DIGITAL MACHINE CONTROL. Computers used specifically for machine control are usually of the special-purpose type. That is, they are not designed for computations as such, but for control purposes. Of equal importance are digital computers used for machine control. There is no precise line that separates numerical positioning and numerical control systems of the programming type from digital computers. Fig. 16 (Electronics, vol. 30) lists some systems for **programmed positioning** by digital computers. In a sense, any machine control system that receives its information from a tape or magnetic program must use some form of computer to decode the information from the tape to the machine control.

Manufacturer	Data Storage	Notes
Arter Grinding Machine Co.	punched tape	
Farrand Controls Corp.	keyboard input mechanical drum storage	
General Electric Co.	punched cards	Synchros positioned by pins from digital data
Laboratory for Electronics	punched tape	Positioning system for printed circuit boards (under development)
Pratt & Whitney	cards, tape, or keyboard	Resolver-null balance using magnetic pickup
Radio Corp. of America	punched tape	Positioning system for printed circuit boards
Stromberg-Carlson	punched tape or cards	

Fig. 16. Systems for programmed positioning by digital controls.

Special-Purpose Digital Computers. Findlay (Electronics, vol. 30) cites applications of **numerical control,** ranging from complete control of complex operations by punched tape to systems which merely follow an operator's orders in proper sequence. These special-purpose digital systems are mainly methods for moving the work table in one, two, or three, dimensions to cut the desired shape.

In milling machines for aircraft wing members or three-dimensional cams, the complete cutting operation is under control of signals recorded on punched or magnetic tape. In another milling machine, data from blueprints are punched into paper tapes as **control signals** for 5 machine axes and 22 auxiliary machine functions. Additional data are converted into a phase-modulated continuous function. A computer is used to interpolate the curves and linear motions required to connect the discrete point information on the punched tape. The **phase-modulated signals** recorded on the magnetic tape are used to control tool and table motion through an amplidyne servo system.

In the planning section of the system developed by Electronic Control Systems (Stromberg-Carlson), coordinate data are entered from a 10-key adding machine and fed into a storage register along with cutting-speed information; equations for curve type are selected on the control panel. The special-purpose digital computer calculates the **tool path** along the first- and second-degree contours.

Output from the computer consists of a series of pulses recorded on three separate **channels** of the tape recorder. Fig. 17 compares some systems for programmed machining that make use of special-purpose digital computers.

Computers for Existing Machine Tools. Of special interest to industrial engineers are machine computer and control systems that are applicable to existing machine tools, such as lathes, boring mills, contouring mills, and grinders. A **tape control system** which can be used to make standard machine tools automatic, called "Numill," has been developed by North American Aviation, Inc.

Manufacturer	Data Storage	Modulation	Notes
Automation Corp. of America	35-mm magnetic tape	f-m	Machine drive through mechanical differential and synchronous motors
Bendix Aviation Corp.	punched plastic tape	pulse	Special-purpose machine for milling fuel control cams
Bendix Aviation Corp.	magnetic tape	phase	Under development for Martin Aviation Corp.
ECS-Stromberg-Carlson	magnetic tape	pulse	Tool path computed as continuous curve rather than as chordal approximation
Farrand Controls Corp.	punched tape	pulse	
Ferranti, Ltd.	magnetic tape	pulse	Tool path computed as continuous curve rather than as chordal approximation
General Electric Co.	magnetic tape	phase	Program tape recorded from operation by hand or tracer.
Giddings & Lewis	magnetic tape	phase	Based on design developed at M.I.T.
Monarch Lathe Co.	plugboard		Programs up to 5 operations and spindle speeds on lathe
Oerlikon Tool & Arms Co.	Translator for converting from punched tape to phase modulated magnetic tape for GE tape control		

Fig. 17. **Systems for programmed machining by digital controls.**

To use this system, a machinist sets number dials on the **tape reader console** corresponding to the desired part. The tape reader searches and finds the required portion of the magnetic tape which may contain information on how to produce several hundred different parts. Then the operator selects the proper material and cutting tool, such as a drill, from instructions which are flashed on a **display panel.**

The machine automatically drills a series of holes into which the operator inserts and fastens tie screws for holding the material. If additional drilling is required, the display panel indicates the drill size and rev. per min. to be used. When these setup changes are to be made, the required holes are drilled automatically. Subsequent milling operations are achieved in the same way.

The display panel indicates all **setup instructions** to guide the machine operator at each stage of the operation. When these required changes in the spindle speed and cutter type have been carried out by the operator, the machine performs its operations automatically.

The **tape-making** operation begins with engineering drawings. The information from the drawings is set into the general-purpose digital computer. This information consists of:

1. Basic tool or part dimension. The designer expresses his concepts in the simplest possible form, defining part contours as equations which are typical circles or conic sections, or as a series of points through which a curve can be drawn. Hole centers are defined as coordinates.
2. Sequence and type of operations.
3. Machine spindle speeds and cutter sizes. Feed rates are calculated automatically.
4. Type and size of material.

The computer translates this basic data into a series of commands required to produce the part. It calculates the path which must be followed by the center of the cutter to generate the contour specified. The control system translates the digital data from the magnetic tape into machine **positional movement.**

Gordon (Electrical Manufacturing, vol. 54) shows how hybrid **operational-digital techniques** combine the advantages of both analog and programmed digital computation methods for control purposes. By means of standard computer building blocks and techniques it is possible to take advantage of the continous operational nature of analog methods and superimpose on this the advantages of handling data in a discrete form that can be readily processed by means of counters.

Gordon cites small special-purpose control computers, operating on the operational-digital technique, as especially suitable for numerical control of machine tools, computer control for conveyor belt feed, averaging, and precise velocity determinations.

ANALOG COMPUTERS ON THE FACTORY FLOOR. The fact that digital computers can be used as an aid to production is commonly accepted. The fact that analog computers may have an equal role in production is less commonly understood. Bibbero (Automatic Control, vol. 1) insists that the automatic factory of the future is not necessarily destined to be controlled by a digital computer. It is his belief that analog computers will be an integral part of production control. He further points out (Automatic Control, vol. 2) that industry has not made extensive use of analog computers for production because of conservatism, lack of knowledge, and fear of electronics. For some reason, when the average production engineer thinks of using a computer element to substitute for human supervision, he always thinks in terms of the digital computer. This is probably because of the importance of memory and logical circuitry in digital computers. However, the analog computer also possesses memory, even though it is not always thought of in this way. An analog computer cannot store tabulator data as such, but in its function generators it can and does store the same kind of data in **continuous curve form.** The difference is primarily one of accuracy and speed, with the digital computer slower but more accurate, and the analog computer faster but less accurate.

Most analog computers have the required accuracy for production control purposes. The analog approach to control is as capable of achieving over-all supervision functions as is the digital. The approach to be taken depends entirely on the nature of the task at hand. For control purposes, analog techniques are more easily understood than are digital; in most cases, analog computers are far simpler than digital computers for the same job; analog computers evolve naturally from existing servo and machine control systems; and analog accuracy is adequate for most control jobs. Recognizing, however, that the use of digital methods at times has remarkable advantages, users of computers should borrow freely from any art, science, or technique that helps to do the job better, with no prejudice as to the method used.

A typical **computer control system** may therefore contain elements that make use of analog, digital, a.c. or d.c. electrical, or mechanical activation.

Production of Steel Bars. The production of batch products, such as steel bars and pipe, presents unique scheduling problems. In a typical case, either a short pour or an excessive "crop" of a 12-ton ingot can drop the yield of 90-lb. bars by 9 percent. Kuhnel (Computer Handbook) believes that the best way to schedule a rolling operation to minimize waste is to use a **special-purpose analog computer** to determine how best to cut each billet after the ingot is cropped.

As an example of how a special-purpose analog computer can be extended beyond individual machines, Kuhnel discusses the case where a rolling mill manufactures ¾-in.-diameter steel reinforcing bars. Difficulties result from the fact that it is impossible to determine in advance precisely how many pounds of good steel can be obtained from one ingot. The problem is not to determine the size or weight of the bloom after it has been cropped. However, at this stage of the manufacturing process, even if the weight of the cropped bloom is known, time does not permit rescheduling of subsequent operations. The computer, whose **input data** is the size or weight of the steel bloom and also the dimensions of the desired product, can perform the necessary calculations in a matter of seconds. Therefore, such a computer can schedule all the operations in the process in such a manner that there will be virtually no waste of good material.

The first requirement is to determine the net product in the ingot. This is determinable either by weight or by volume. The computer is used to handle the relatively simple arithmetic of how much product is contained in the bloom. Although the problem is essentially digital in nature, the required accuracy does not preclude the use of an analog computer.

Kuhnel also shows how special-purpose computers are used for milling tool operations, cutter control, and **selective assembly** of various thicknesses of electrical steel laminations.

Paper Production. Simple special-purpose analog computers can be used for **process control.** At the Formica plant in Cincinnati the process to be controlled is the impregnation of kraft paper with phenolic resin. As it is impractical to measure the weight of the coating alone, the weight of the uncoated paper is determined, as is the weight of the coated paper. The two-variable computer then subtracts the uncoated weight from the coated weight for absolute magnitude of the coating, and divides one variable by the other to determine the ratio of coating weight to total weight.

Machinability Computer. An example of the "electronic slide rule" type of special-purpose computer is the Carboloy (General Electric) machinability computer. Its control panel is shown in Fig. 18. Computers of this type can be readily devised to handle a wide variety of problems encountered by production planners and industrial engineers.

The machinability computer illustrated is essentially a manually activated special purpose analog computer of the **balanced-bridge equation solver** type. As many as 13 variables concerning machinability and tool characteristics can be set on the dials. The fourteenth dial is then positioned until the microammeter indicates a null condition. The reading on the fourteenth dial represents the mathematical function of all of the other machinability variables.

The computer can also calculate the hp. required for a machining job. It is used as an adjunct to a machine, not as an organic part of the machine control circuit. The computer could be readily redesigned for automatic servo activation of the computer elements, should fully automatic machine control be desired.

Production Control Instruments. Several authorities have developed approxmate formulas for calculating economic lot sizes. Economic purchase lot size determination is discussed in the section on Purchasing, and formulas for economic lot size are discussed in the section on Production Planning and Control. Such formulas can be solved by means of special-purpose analog computers.

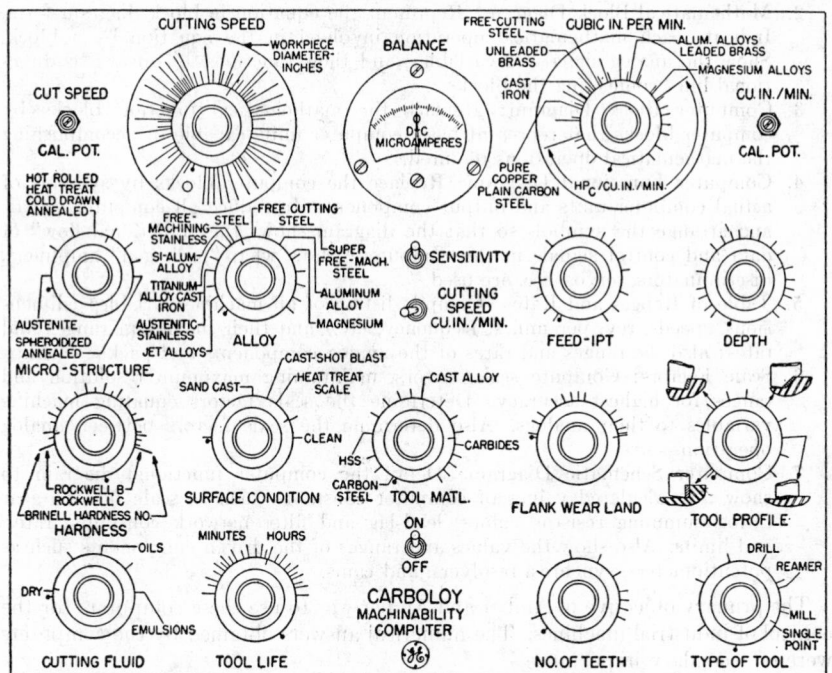

Fig. 18. Machinability computer control panel.

The Tool Engineers Handbook (ASTE) contains numerous formulas for **machine capabilities** and **tooling** which may be facilitated by means of computer solution. The utility of computers for this purpose is indicated by the fact that special slide rules for machine calculations have been created by Barth. A typical special-purpose slide rule of this type can be used to find cutting time of a lathe or boring mill job when the spindle speed, feed, and length of cut are known.

A slide rule is a form of computer, and an electronic computer can be considered to be merely an extension of the slide rule. Many of the formulas used for production control purposes can be handled by means of computers. Of course, it is not always justifiable to use a computer for this purpose. Such formulas are amenable to solution by either digital or analog computers, but are especially suitable for solution by means of simple special-purpose analog computers, sometimes called "electronic slide rules" as shown in Fig. 18.

Procedure for Developing an Analog Control Computer. Calculations for statistical quality control are especially suitable for computer solution. (See the section on Quality Control for the many formulas and equations used in this field.)

Amber and Amber (Electrical Manufacturing, vol. 58) show specifically how to design small special-purpose analog computers to solve for $\overline{X}$, the machine mean, and for σ, the standard deviation.

1. Equation: Write down the computer function in algebraic equation form. Rearrange the terms if necessary to make the equation more compatible to computer solution.

2. Mathematical Block Diagram: Represent the equation in block diagram form. Indicate each mathematical operation involved in the equation by a block. Show the analog signals of variables, and their functions, by means of directional lines connecting the blocks.

3. Computer Block Diagram: Replace the mathematical function blocks by computer blocks that represent basic computer units capable of accomplishing the mathematical operations required.

4. Computer Functional Diagram: Replace the computer blocks by symbols of actual computer units and output components. Introduce all computer signals and arrange the symbols so that the diagram shows the "functional flow" of data and control signals in the computer. Show what "packaged" amplifiers, discriminators, servos, etc. are used.

5. Table of Ranges and Rates: Compile listing of all machine variables (dimensions, speeds, rev. per min.'s, frequency, etc.) and their maximum ranges and rates; also the ranges and rates of the analog components and packaged units.

6. Scale Factors: Compute scale factors, maintaining maximum resolution and ranges for highest accuracy. Determine the scale factors equating machine variables to their analogs. Also determine the scale factors between analog operations.

7. Computer Schematic Diagram: Detail the computer functional diagram to show the calculated values of computer constants, such as scale factors, gear ratios, summing resistor values, lead-lag and filter network constants, rates, and limits. Also show the values and ranges of the driven components such as potentiometers, synchros, resolvers, and cams.

The primary objective of Amber and Amber was to use these computers for the control of industrial machines. The numerical answers obtained by the computers were of secondary importance.

Automatic Quality Control. To detect a drift in machine performance, it is first necessary to determine the average of machine performance, and then to compare this mean (average) to a standard representing the desired performance. The **mean of individual measurements** is used rather than individual measurements themselves because machine performance is characteristically subject to random variations, and individual measurements are not representative of the centerline of machine performance.

Amber and Amber cover the problem of manufacturing operations which are discontinuous in nature, as compared with process operations which are continuous in nature. They hold that the common denominator of all feedback control of piece-part working machines, which is of prime interest to most industrial engineers, is the **machine mean** of piece-part dimensions. Without an adequate technique for developing the machine mean, such as by means of a special-purpose analog computer to perform the averaging operations, feedback control cannot be accomplished. Though averaging separate values is an elementary arithmetic process, computerwise it is much more difficult than solving for definite time integrals.

In addition to the $\overline{X}$ (machine mean) computer, they show how to develop a standard-deviation computer **(sigma computer).** They conclude that feedback control permits closed-loop machines to be built to less exacting tolerances and with greater flexibility than the open-loop machines used for the "Detroit brand" of automation. Such machine **self-control** must be based on the average of machine-mean performance, rather than on each dimensional variation.

For **continuous processes,** the mean and root mean square are determined by continuous integration of the product variable. The mean or root mean square of a **discontinuous variable** is obtained by automatic summation.

Once $\overline{X}$, or a root mean square value of X, is available, the value of sigma is found by a simple **triangulation computer,** which uses either a synchroresolver or the Amber Triangulator Circuit. In this way, a signal of excessive product variation (an indication of machine malfunction) is readily developed.

Fig. 19 shows an "Auto-QC" computer for discontinuous piece-part production. This computer provides machine-mean feedback information so that the power servo on the machine tool can adjust itself as necessary. Also, a feature of this

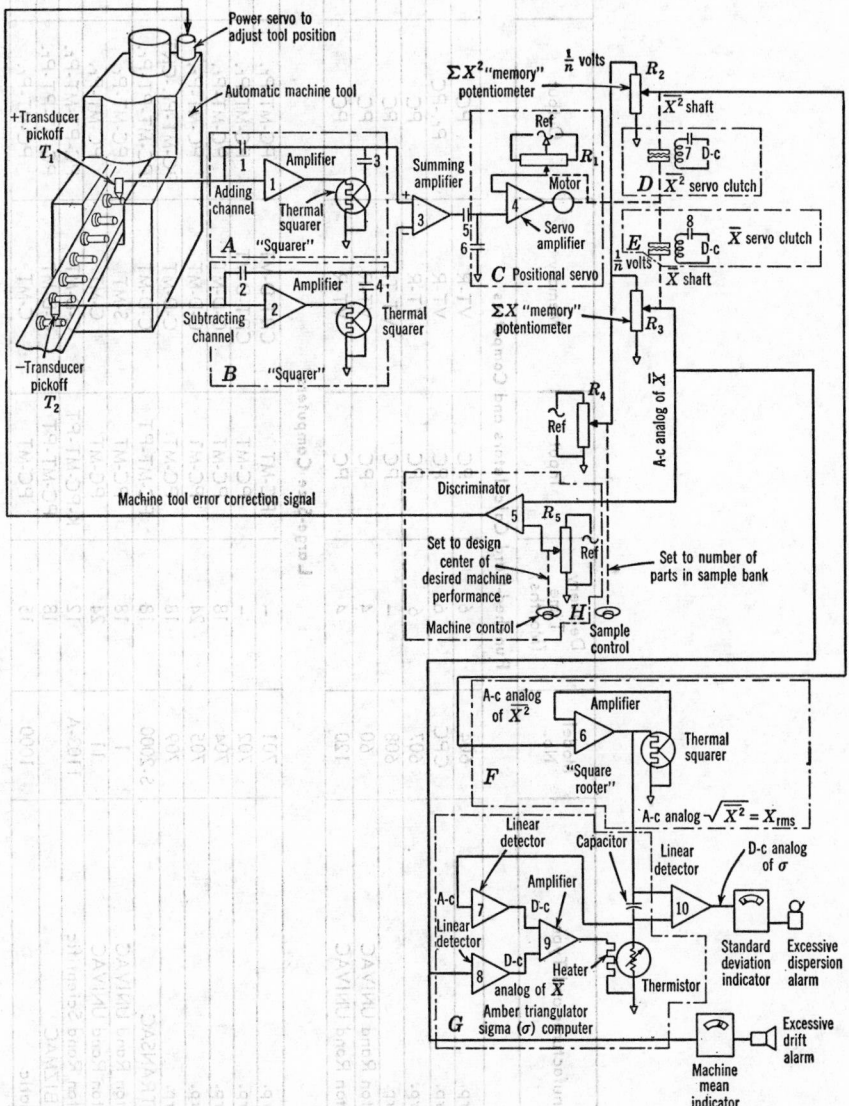

Fig. 19. Automatic quality control computer for discontinuous piece-part production.

Manufacturer and Type	Model No.	Delivery Time (Months)	Input	Memory	Output	KVA Power Required	Area (Sq. ft.)
Punched-Card Calculators and Computers							
IBM Corp.	604	6	PC	VT-R	PC	6.9	20
IBM Corp.	CPC	6	PC	VT-R	Pr.-PC	10	42
IBM Corp.	607	6	PC	VT-R	PC	11	23
IBM Corp.	608	–	PC	VT-Tr.	PC	2.3	25
Remington Rand UNIVAC	60	4	PC	VT-R	PC	10	43
Remington Rand UNIVAC	120	4	PC	VT-R	PC	10	43
Large-Size Computers							
IBM Corp.	701	–	PC-MT	CRT-D-MT	PC-MT-Pr.	99	1,500*
IBM Corp.	702	–	PC-MT	CRT-D-MT	PC-MT-Pr.	92	2,500*
IBM Corp.	704	18	PC-MT	C-D-MT	PC-MT-Pr.	96	1,500*
IBM Corp.	705	24	PC-MT	C-D-MT	PC-MT-Pr.	97	2,500*
IBM Corp.	709	18	PC-MT	C-D-MT	PC-MT-Pr.-CRT	100-150	3,000*
Philco TRANSAC	S-2000	18	PC-MT-PT	C-D-MT	PC-MT-PT-Pr.	1.5	250*
Remington Rand UNIVAC	1	18	PC-MT	S-MT	PC-MT-Pr.	120	2,500*
Remington Rand UNIVAC	11	24	PC-MT	C-MT	PC-MT-Pr.	120	2,500*
Remington Rand Scientific	1103-A	12	K-PC-MT-PT	C-D-MT	PC-PT-MT-PT-Pr.	120	3,000*
R.C.A. BIZMAC		18	PC-MT-PT	C-D-MT	PC-MT-PT-PT-Pr.	100	3,000*
DATAmatic	1000	15	PC-MT	C-MT	PC-MT-Pr.	120	4,500*

Medium-Size General-Purpose Computers

Bendix	G-15A	6	K-PT-MT	D-MT	MT-PT-Pr.	3	5.6
Burroughs ElectroData Datatron	205	5-18	K-PC-MT-PT	D-MT	PC-MT-PT-Pr.	12.7	28
IBM Corp.	650	16	PC-MT	C-D-MT	PC-MT-Pr.	17	37
Laboratory for Electronics	TIM	12	K-PC-PT	C-D	PC-PT-Pr.	4	70
Laboratory for Electronics	DIANA	18	K-PC-PT	C-D	PC-PT-Pr.	52	800
Logistics Research ALWAC	111, 111E	12	K-PC-PT-MT	D-MT	PC-PT-Pr.-MT	8	28
Logistics Research ALWAC	800	12-18	K-PC-PT-MT	D-MT	PC-PT-Pr.-MT	-	-
Marchant MINIAC		6-12	K-PC-PT-MT	D-MT	PC-PT-Pr.-MT	4	28
Monroe Monrobot	VI	12	K-PC-PT-MT	D-MT	PC-PT-Pr.-MT	3	16
National Cash Register	304	24	K-PC-PT-MT	C-MT	PC-MT-PT-Pr.	25	1,600*
Rea Redix		12	K-PC-PT-MT	D-MT	PC-MT-PT-Pr.	5	25
Stewart-Warner		12	K-MC-PT	D	PT-Pr.	.75	25
Underwood ELECOM	125	12	K-PC-PT-MT	D-MT	PC-MT-PT-Pr.	15	1,000*
UNIVAC File Computer	0 and 1	12	K-PC-PT-MT	C-D-MT	PC-MT-PT-Pr.	10	1,000*

Small-Size General-Purpose Computers

Burroughs ElectroData	E101	6	K-PT	D	Pr.	3	17
Royal Precision Librascope	LGP-30	6-12	K-PT	D	PT-Pr.	1.5	8
Underwood ELECOM	50	6-12	K-PC-PT	D	PC-PT-Pr.	2	50*

*Minimum working area. Where exact figures not available, estimates were used.

- Indicates information not available.

PC – Punched Cards.	Tr. – Transistor.	C – Magnetic Core.	K – Keyboard.
PT – Punched Tape.	D – Magnetic Drum.	R – Relays.	CRT – Cathode Ray Tube.
VT – Vacuum Tubes.	MT – Magnetic Tape.	S – Sonic Delay Line.	Pr. – Printer.
			MC – Magnetic Card.

Fig. 20. Commercial data on digital computers.

computer is a **sigma indicator** and an excessive **dispersion alarm** which indicates machine malfunction. A machine-mean indicator reads out the centerline of machine performance, and an excessive drift alarm reports gross machine misadjustment.

The General Electric Pacific thickness gage is used to facilitate quality control computations for yarn measurement. The computer unit incorporates computing, timing, and cycling circuits to indicate both $\bar{X}$, which is the mean of the variable, and $\bar{X}^2$, which is the mean of the square of the variables. From these two dial readings, a technician readily solves for sigma, the standard deviation of the yarn.

AVAILABLE COMPUTER EQUIPMENT. Fig. 20 (Office Automation, Integrated and Electronic Data Processing) lists a number of the larger digital computers suitable for production control purposes. Since new equipment is continually being introduced on the market and new models of existing equipment are constantly being released, it is wise for firms contemplating purchase of computers to keep up to date on recent developments.

RESEARCH AND DEVELOPMENT

CONTENTS

PAGE

Nature of Research and Development

Definition and scope of industrial research.. 1
  Fundamental and directed basic research.. 1
  Applied research 1
  Development work 2
  Operations research 2

The Function of Research in Industry

Objectives of research 2
Product research 3
  Improving existing products 3
  Developing new products 4
  Adapting products to new markets........ 4
  By-product and waste research 5
  Assuring sources of materials.............. 5
Process research 6
  Improving existing processes 6
  Automation of processes 6
  Solving current production problems....... 7
  Reducing production costs 7
Technical assistance to management........ 7
  Furnishing technical information 7
  Exploring diversification opportunites...... 8
  Improving customer relations 8
  Other technical contributions 8

Industrial Research Facilities

Types of research facilities 8
The company-operated research department. 9
  The company research laboratory 9
  Local research divisions 9
  Central research laboratory 10
Independent research facilities 10
  Independent research institutes 10
  Commercial laboratories 11
  Cooperative research with universities..... 11
  University research foundations............ 11
  Trade association research 12
  Technical consultants 12
  Other independent facilities................ 12

Procedures for the Research Program

Initiating the program 13

PAGE

Sources of research ideas 13
  Developing research ideas 14
Requirements in manpower.................. 14
  Qualities for research personnel 14
  The research team 15
  Application of team research 16
  Supplementing the research team 17
Effective use of the research staff............ 17
  Utilization of personnel 17
  Stimulation of personnel.................. 18
  Creative research programs 18
Requirements in equipment 18
  Basic factors in choice of facilities........ 18
  Location of laboratory 18
  Pilot plant facilities 19
  Associated facilities 19
  Capitalization procedures 19
Organization for research 20
  Chart of an idealized research organiza-
    tion (f. 1)............................. 20
  Functional research organization in a
    large oil company (f. 2).............. 21
  A variation of research organization
    (f. 3) 22
Principles of research organization 22
Management control and surveillance........ 22
  Control by planning committee........... 23
  Research costs and accounting 23
Budgeting for research 24
  Factors in budget planning 25
  Standards for guidance 26
  Cost of research as a percent of sales
    by industry (f. 4)..................... 27

Evaluation and Control of Research

Economics of research 27
Criteria for evaluating research 28
  Index of return 28
  Direct and indirect research output........ 29
  Intangible returns 29
  Other criteria 29
Developing successful research 30
Patents 30
Benefits of research 31

RESEARCH AND DEVELOPMENT

Nature of Research and Development

DEFINITION AND SCOPE OF INDUSTRIAL RESEARCH. Research is defined by Webster as "studious inquiry; usually, critical and exhaustive investigation or experimentation having for its aim the revision of accepted conclusions, in the light of newly discovered facts." Research, in this broad sense, is thus applicable to all human affairs and all fields of endeavor. In industry, the term "research" has come to mean scientific investigations, engineering development, pilot plant studies, product and process evaluation, market analysis, and any other formalized study of operations and functions.

In this section, however, the term will be used to mean studious inquiry, accompanied by experimentation, into **technical** and **technical-economic** subjects of interest to industry. Research, by this definition, may deal with present operations or problems of the industry, or it may look to the future and be entirely unrelated to current problems and operations. In all cases, however, the **objective** of industrial research is to further the welfare of the company conducting it.

Fundamental and Directed Basic Research. The term "fundamental research" has different meanings to different people and its promiscuous use leads to much confusion. To the purist, **fundamental research** means scientific inquiry conducted solely out of curiosity with no practical or utilitarian end contemplated or in sight. It is sometimes described as "research for research's sake." Universities, some governmental laboratories, and institutions dedicated to learning conduct such research. Likewise, some companies allow their research personnel to spend part of their time pursuing inquiries into new fields with no objectives defined or contemplated. Moreover, many companies conduct exploratory research into areas where it is believed new knowledge might be uncovered that could lead to industrial values. Such research—called **directed basic research** by some research administrators—contemplates a useful end, even though none is in sight.

Industry spends millions of dollars yearly on exploratory investigations of this nature, and these investigations, while not meeting the purist's definition of fundamental research, are productive of a large portion of the annual increments to scientific knowledge. In this section, the term "fundamental research" will be used in the absolute sense only. When directed basic research is meant, it will be called by that name or by the shortened term "basic research."

Applied Research. The bulk of the research conducted by both industry and government in the United States is applied research. In the broad sense, applied research includes all technical undertakings aimed at **solving problems of practical significance.** By this definition, applied research includes those activities frequently distinguished as development. It also includes that portion of a directed basic investigation that is continued once an end use or a practical value is foreseen.

While applied research aims at solving problems, the problem is not necessarily of a troublesome nature. It may arise from ambition or the desire for progress, as well as from a difficulty. Thus, the problem of finding a new product that can lead to increased corporate prosperity and expansion is solved through applied research, just as a problem in cutting production costs or eliminating a product deficiency is solved.

Development Work. Development work is simply a later phase of applied research. As Furnas (Research in Industry) remarks, "Research in the narrower sense is generally considered to stop when the work outgrows the laboratory workbench. What happens after that is development."

In some laboratories, the term "development" has been dropped altogether, since the broader concept of applied research covers everything implied in the term. The word is useful, however, when one wishes to signify the later stage of applied research, the **adaptation of laboratory proved fact to actual production.** In the development stage, **pilot plants** or **full-scale models** may be used, and problems of production are worked out that are not foreseen or made clear during bench research.

It is possible for development work to be conducted without any immediately preceding laboratory study. Information gained from experience in the operation of a full-scale process or in the use of a product may be the basis for further development of the product or process. Or information gleaned from literature or from the experience of others may show the need for and may suggest developmental studies. Since prior research is not a necessary condition for development works, this is one of the reasons for distinguishing them.

Operations Research. Operations research is a term which has entered the language of science and business since World War II. Like industrial engineering, operations research seeks to isolate the various factors which enter into or influence a **management decision** relating to any phase of operations. It also attempts to measure and weigh the relative importance of each and to find the net result of their interaction so as to provide the executive with a comprehensive picture of the various alternatives open to him and the probable consequences of each (see section on Operations Research).

The extent to which problems of this kind can be solved has certainly been advanced in the past decade through the development of **mathematical concepts** and **electronic computers.** Hence, problems of production, sales, finance, research, administration, distribution, logistics, etc., involving numerous variables can now be analyzed by teams familiar with operations research techniques to provide executives with information on limitations, boundaries, and probabilities which should reduce the margin of error in numerous instances, and assist in decision-making. Both general and special purpose computers of the analog and digital types are discussed in the section on Electronic Computers.

The Function of Research in Industry

OBJECTIVES OF RESEARCH. The goal of all industrial research is to **advance the welfare** of the company conducting it. This may mean anything from helping the company surmount production and competition difficulties, through the development of expansion and diversification opportunities, to improvement of the company's public relations and its prestige in financial circles. Since an industrial enterprise exists to make profit, the finite objective of industrial research is **corporate profit.**

To benefit the welfare of a company, and thus help it make profit, research is used to accomplish various **specific goals.** Some of these are:

1. Improvement of existing products.
2. Development of new products.
3. Improvement of existing production processes.
4. Development of new, more efficient processes.
5. Solution of current production problems.
6. Reduction of production costs.
7. Development of new uses for existing materials, processes, or devices.
8. Adaptation of products to new markets.
9. Improvement of customer and public relations.
10. Exploration of diversification or expansion opportunities.
11. Assurance of sources of materials supply.
12. Assistance to management planning.
13. Abatement of dangers and nuisances and the creation of commercial values from wastes.
14. Assistance in standardization.
15. Development of prestige and acceptance for the company and its products.

These specific goals overlap, of course, and the solution of any one problem may fulfill a number of objectives. Thus, technical research to abate a nuisance and in so doing improve the company's relations with the public may lead to the development of a new by-product, which simultaneously increases the economic efficiency of the basic production process and opens up a new market.

PRODUCT RESEARCH. In a competitive economy, few products can maintain their places in the market without continual change and improvement. So-called **consumer products,** that is, products purchased and used by individuals, must be changed to embrace the latest technological developments or to meet the shifting fads in public taste. New models of **highly fabricated products,** such as automobiles, television sets, refrigerators, and electric ranges, are introduced yearly in the competitive race to win consumer favor. Not even a fountain pen, a lipstick, or a can opener can remain static. Each product offered for sale to the public must incorporate something new, even if it be no more than a change in design or finish. The American public expects change and improvement and will gravitate to those products that exhibit these in the greatest degree in keeping with current concepts of utility, taste, and quality.

Even **basic industrial commodities** are subject to demand for change and improvement. Thus, a steel that is highly acclaimed today may be superseded tomorrow by one that offers, say, improved machinability. Or something as intrinsically unchanging as a pure chemical may have to be packaged and shipped in a new type of convenient container to hold its industrial customers. The pelletizing or briquetting of fine solids may give a product advantage in the market place, or, in the reverse direction, pulverization may be a step toward better acceptance by the buyer. **Industrial machinery,** tools, assemblies, finishes, and miscellaneous supplies are, of course, subject to a demand for improvement hardly less insistent than that for consumer products.

Improving Existing Products. Industrial research provides the means by which companies meet the demand for change and improvement in their products. Although it is difficult or impossible to ascertain how much of the country's research effort is expended on the improvement of products, there is no doubt that this type of research constitutes a substantial portion of the total. A survey (Trends in Industrial Research, NAM) disclosed that 40 percent of 441 companies reported the improvement of existing products as the principal objective. The National Academy of Science and the National Research Council estimate that product improvement may comprise 40 to 90 percent of research programs, with this objective foremost in the consumer goods industries.

Programs of technical research to improve or change products are usually preceded by **market studies** of the characteristics of market demand and by scientifically based predictions as to future trends. Such studies are made by qualified market research departments or organizations. Radical changes in products without adequate market study beforehand can be extremely hazardous.

Developing New Products. The use of research to develop entirely new products seems to be most appealing to industrial firms. New products mean new horizons for enterprise—possibly expansion, progress, and profits beyond anything realized in the past. Often the most successful industrial firms are those that have been able to use research to produce a constant stream of new products. The Minnesota Mining and Manufacturing Company is an excellent example, as are General Electric, Westinghouse, Du Pont, and many of the country's leading chemical and pharmaceutical companies.

In the NAM survey cited, reporting companies rated the development of new products as the most important aim of their research programs. Forty percent stated that the development of new products was their principal objective, the same percentage that stated that product improvement was their principal objective.

A study of 191 companies (Spending for Industrial Research) reveals that 50 percent of research expenditures were directed to the improvement of present products or processes, 42 percent to the development of new products or processes, and 8 percent to unspecified objectives.

Many of the important new products of the past came from fortuitous invention. But modern industry cannot depend on fortuitous invention. A **systematic exploration program** is usually needed to put a company into a position to find new products to manufacture. This means that the company intent upon growth and expansion should conduct considerable basic research in its fields of interest to discover those ideas worthy of more intensive support. The larger corporations with adequate funds are more able to take the risks that are inherent in directed basic research. For this reason, the radically new products that tend to alter an industry usually come from the laboratories of the large corporations. Exceptions to this generality are numerous, of course, and, with contract research coming into greater use, the types of basic investigations needed for new product development are becoming increasingly accessible to small enterprises.

Adapting Products to New Markets. Finding new uses for products is one of the most important functions of research in the **basic materials industries.** This type of research also encompasses the adaptation of the material or product to new markets. To a more limited extent, the finding of new uses and the adaptation of new markets apply to **fabricated products** also. For instance, the development of television for commercial observation and control purposes is a new use for a fabricated product. Or the adaptation of a refrigerator control to air conditioners is a new use for a fabricated assembly. **Processes,** likewise, can be developed or adapted to new uses. An example is the adaptation of a process, say, for the welding of steel to the welding of aluminum.

The terms **use-research** and **utilization-research** are frequently used to designate research of this nature, particularly in the materials industries.

Chemurgy is a special term applied to use-research with agricultural products. Frequently, the boundary line between use-research and research aimed at the development of new products is obscure or nonexistent. Aluminum foil, packaged in a convenient container and sold for kitchen use, is not much different from the aluminum foil used for building insulation. Yet the product is in a new use, and may or may not be considered a new product, depending on the point of view.

Use-research has a decidedly aggressive connotation, and it has been responsible for spectacular gains in corporate growth and profits, particularly since World War II. In essence, the company with a product of uncircumscribed utility considers the possibilities of new uses for the product. It figuratively or actually lists all the **product properties** and then tries to determine how each property might make the product applicable to some field of activity. Once a promising lead is obtained, the prospect is evaluated technically and economically, after which an exhaustive market study is made to determine if the market potential merits further development.

Great imagination, heed to apparently insignificant detail, and breadth of knowledge about science and technology are required to find new uses for products. In the 1930's, when the copper industry was seeking new markets, it did not overlook the fact that minute amounts of copper are found in the ashes from plants. This led to technical research on the role of copper in plant nutrition, and finally to a new market for copper as a supplement in commercial fertilizers. The glass industry, by noting that glass when drawn into fine threads is flexible, has been able to build fabulous new markets for glass out of this observation. Generally speaking, all producers of materials who have experienced growth at a rate greater than that of the economy as a whole have been active in use-research.

The value of a **process patent** to the holder can often be increased by research designed to find new uses for the process. The patent coverage, of course, must be broad enough to include the new use.

By-Product and Waste Research. Industrial wastes represent the fraction of the materials purchased by a company that come to no end use. As such, they can only affect the profit picture negatively. Wastes may be gaseous, liquid, or solid, but whatever their state, they cost money for disposal and may create health hazards, nuisances, and community relations problems. Whenever research can turn a waste into a profit-making, salable product, the gain is double, since the cost of disposal is eliminated. If a commercial product derived from waste merely enables the company to break even in its manufacture, a gain has been scored nevertheless, because a disposal expense has ended.

Frequently, through research a waste is turned into a by-product that becomes a profitable **coproduct** of the operation. Ethylene glycol is an example. Once a waste, it is now a premium antifreeze motor coolant. Many highly integrated chemical and metal-processing operations have been made possible through the finding of commercial values for what were originally waste products.

Assuring Sources of Materials. Without positive action to assure its supplies of raw materials, parts, and assemblies, a company could be at the mercy of its suppliers. For this reason, companies must sometimes engage in research on the **materials** or other **supplies** they use, or on **substitute materials.** Particularly, when a company is dependent upon a foreign source of supply should it use research to protect its interests by developing substitute materials. It is always good business practice to have alternate materials or sources of supply available. **Raw material research** is, of course, a normal phase of the technical activities of large corporations, like the rubber companies, which produce both the raw material and the finished consumer products.

Fabricators of special instruments or machines occasionally require small quantities of unusual alloys having particular properties. They may engage in research on such materials in order to have two or more sources of supply and thus not be dependent on a single source with all the hazards inherent in such a situation.

PROCESS RESEARCH. Like product research, process research may be aimed at improving existing processes or developing new ones. Such research may deal with process **steps** or with the complete **manufacturing method.**

Improving Existing Processes. Improvement or innovation in processes may be desirable either to improve the quality of the product or to reduce production costs. Frequently, process research is aimed at devising an economical method of manufacturing a product that has not been produced commercially before. An example of the latter would be the development of a commercial process for the manufacture of some new chemical or some previously unused metal. Obviously, process research may involve the most difficult of technical problems and may require the highest type of scientific work.

Process improvement probably gets more attention in industry than the **development of new processes.** Because of invested capital, it is desirable to get the highest efficiency from existing processes before considering the development of new ones. But it can be dangerous for a company to be complacent regarding its present processes. A competitor may come along with an innovation that enables him to produce at a much lower cost. For instance, the hand soldering of wire circuits in radio and television sets seemed enduring—hardly subject to change. But printed circuits and dip soldering are now making this method obsolete.

Process research is extremely important in the primary metals and chemical industries. Sometimes the **integration of processes** and the **simultaneous production** of a number of products make feasible operations that could not exist individually. For instance, the simultaneous production of iron ore, sulfur or sulfuric acid, and gold has made the mining and processing of certain pyrite deposits economically possible. Integrated production processes may be expected to become of increasing importance in the extractive industries.

Automation of Processes. Some research administrators and industrial observers believe that process research may increase more rapidly than product research in the future, and, in fact, determine the nature of product research and of products themselves. There is much logic to support this point of view. In the past, ideas for products have been conceived and then the methods have been developed for producing them. The product has determined the nature of the process. But as the availability of labor necessary to maintain the constantly increasing rate of productivity declines, there is need for greater **automation of processes.** Electronic controls and the linkage of production machinery into automatic producing units offer a technical means of solving this problem. Such automation sometimes cannot readily be accomplished without redesigning products to make them amenable to the production scheme. Thus, the processes available, or devisable, force the "rethinking" of products. For instance, printed circuit television and radio sets, previously mentioned, are **rethought products** that are amenable to dip soldering and the automatic assembly of circuit components.

If automation becomes as general in industry as is now predicted, process research will certainly occupy industrial attention for years to come. Atomic energy will also be a great stimulant to this type of industrial investigation, since the use of **atomic radiation** to accomplish industrial goals implies the devising of numerous new production processes. The remark has been made that most research in the past has been "hardware" research, but that most research in the future will be "methods" research.

Solving Current Production Problems. Current production problems frequently have top priority research programs. Their solution is necessary for the immediate welfare of the company. Such problems arise from "bugs" in processes or products, changed standards, changes in the nature of raw materials, and even from such things as changes in the weather. Anything that is hindering production must be taken care of immediately, but such trouble-shooting should not be permitted to interfere with long-range research programs aimed at constructive goals. For this reason, **trouble-shooting units** are sometimes set up in the company's research department for exclusive attention to such problems. This practice prevents interruptions of the personnel engaged in long-range research.

Sometimes a current production problem requires a major effort for its solution. In this case it may be rightfully looked upon as a process or product development problem rather than trouble-shooting.

Reducing Production Costs. Reducing the cost of production is one way of meeting competition, expanding the market base, and making profits. American companies with their mass market and competitive philosophies are always interested in reducing production costs, and much of their process and product research has this as the goal. This long range is a very sound motivation for research as long as it is balanced with research aimed at creating new opportunities. Overemphasis on the lowering of costs, however, at the expense of the development of completely new items for manufacture, may have a limiting effect on the company's growth. No matter how broad the base, markets can become saturated. And even low prices do not move products suffering from **technological obsolescence.**

TECHNICAL ASSISTANCE TO MANAGEMENT. Management has the task of deciding the course the company will take. In a technological economy, decisions are extremely difficult, since no one man or small group of men can have complete understanding of all the technological influences that might affect the business. Management, therefore, turns to the company's research personnel for **evaluation of ideas** and for **technical information** that should be taken into account in its business decisions.

Furnishing Technical Information. Sometimes the technical research laboratory assists management through its reply to informal inquiries or through special reports prepared at the bidding of a planning executive. In large companies, market research groups are maintained as aids in sales and production planning, and specialists in engineering-economics are used for technical-economic studies pertaining to market development, diversification, industrial logistics, and similar subjects. Operations research techniques are also used in some instances. In the operations research approach, teams of scientists and nonscientific specialists work cooperatively to apply scientific techniques to the analysis of factors that affect the company's goals. The object is to find what combination of factors will yield optimum results.

Exploring Diversification Opportunities. A primary function of industrial research is to keep the business growing. Product research, which gives the company more products to sell, and process research, which helps lower the cost and broadens the market base, provide ways for expansion and growth.

Still another function of research is to make the company resistant to fluctuations in the business cycle by providing a **diversity of products.** Diversification of products eases seasonal, as well as cyclical changes, stabilizes earnings, and enables the company to grow without overrunning markets or overrisking capital. Research which has company diversification as an objective seeks to find new ways to exercise existing production talents and facilities in fields of endeavor with good growth potentialities.

Diversification is also accomplished by the **purchase** of other companies or the **merger** of enterprises. But even in these instances the talents of the research departments are called upon for technical appraisal of the undertaking.

Improving Customer Relations. Industrial customers sometimes have difficulty in using a product, and the company making the product may wish to use its research facilities to help the customer solve his problem. An example of such a situation would be a difficulty encountered in the use of a metal electrofinishing process caused by the particular mineral content of local water. The producer of the electrofinishing bath materials may have to solve the difficulty in order to hold the customer.

Machinery producers frequently go to great length to solve the **customers' production problems** in order to get their business. Some industries, whose customers are very small businesses that exist in great numbers (printers, for example), may do most of the **customer's research.**

Other Technical Contributions. Research has still other functions, and it is responsible for numerous unplanned benefits. Research is helpful to companies in the standardization of products and in the development of subsidiary values from the company's technological experience. Research helps the company gain prestige and public good will, and the fact of its existence has sales benefits and also helps the company with financing problems.

Research should never be conducted solely for its publicity or public relations value, and no reputable research man would permit his name to be used for such an end purpose. However, research has come to have a public relations value in the minds of investors and other segments of the population. In its rating of managements, for example, The American Institute of Management includes research as one of the factors to be considered. Certainly, the announcements of research results can have a pronounced influence on security prices. As a result, the presence of a sound research program is generally helpful to corporate financing.

Industrial Research Facilities

TYPES OF RESEARCH FACILITIES. Various methods have been devised whereby industry can derive the benefits of research. A company may operate its own **laboratory** as an integral part of its production plant. Or, if the company is large and has many producing plants, a separate **research division** may be established and operated independently of any of the producing facilities, either as the sole research establishment of the company or supplementary to any number of laboratories attached to individual divisions or plants. Effective research may also be achieved by contracting for its execution in a commercial research laboratory, a nonprofit research institute, or a university research foundation. Grants and fellowships awarded to universities are still other procedures for the conduct of corporate research, particularly suited for basic research. Or a company may join with other companies in its industry to conduct trade research of value to the entire industry. Finally, the company may go to other companies that have extensive research facilities and a mutuality of interests to get research programs executed.

THE COMPANY-OPERATED RESEARCH DEPARTMENT. Although it is not necessary to have a research laboratory to carry on an effective research program, the bulk of industrial research is handled by laboratories maintained and operated by industrial firms. The National Association of Manufacturers found from a survey (Trends in Industrial Research) that 74 percent of companies that have reesarch programs under way maintain their own laboratories.

The Company Research Laboratory. The company research laboratory may be organized as a department of the total operation, with a vice president or research director at its head. The organization of a typical **research and development laboratory** is discussed later in this section. The laboratory may or may not be separated from the **control and testing laboratory.** In the best practice, however, sharp boundaries are placed around the research group even though facilities may be shared.

The **advantages** in company ownership of its research laboratory include:

1. Closeness of liaison with production and management.
2. Intimate control of operations by management and the absolute secrecy made possible in the development of unusually promising ideas.
3. The possibilities for exclusive utilization of the talents of exceptionally able scientists and technologists.
4. Facilities for rapid response to research needs.

The **disadvantages** of a company-owned laboratory are largely related to its cost. There is a certain minimum investment which must be made in technical equipment and scientific personnel to produce sound research results. Some managements feel that it is more profitable to use the physical facilities and staff of contract research organizations than to attempt to build their own research laboratories, which cannot possibly be as diversified in men and equipment. On the other hand, no company, however small, can afford to undertake research unless it has on its own staff a competent scientist or engineer capable of translating the research results to management and helping management put the results to use.

Local Research Divisions. In the large industrial concerns that employ the majority of industrial research personnel, research organization is more complex than in smaller companies. Each operating division or each subsidiary company often has its own research laboratory or department. Divisions or subsidiaries of a large corporation are usually established on a basis of a **class of products or processes.** Thus, an electrical manufacturer may have a lamp division and a motor division, or a synthetic textile company may have a textile unit and a chemical unit.

Laboratories attached to such divisions are normally responsible only for the work that relates to their division's product or processes. This leads to specialization and intensified progress in the specialty, but some possibilities for research may be ignored because they do not fall within the province of any existing division, unless provision is made as well for research for the benefit of the whole company.

Central Research Laboratory. To get around this inherent deficiency in divisional laboratory establishments, central laboratories are maintained by some companies. The central laboratory may be additional to the divisional laboratory or it may do all the research for the company. Sometimes the central laboratory may have the status of a **division** of the company, as for instance the Research Laboratories Division of General Motors or the Research Laboratories Division of the Radio Corporation of America. Or the central laboratory may even be organized as a **separate corporation.** An example is the Bell Telephone Laboratories, Inc., a unit of the Bell Telephone System, which engages in research, development, and engineering for the American Telephone and Telegraph Company and performs development, design, and engineering services for the Western Electric Company, the manufacturing unit of the Bell System.

However constituted, the central laboratory is a mechanism of proven value for the conduct of research. Many profitable research developments come from these laboratories.

INDEPENDENT RESEARCH FACILITIES. One way by which companies can engage in research is to contract for its performance with an outside research organization. Although this practice dates back many years, it has been growing rapidly since the end of World War II. It is sometimes referred to as **sponsoring** or "farming out" research. It is essentially the buying of a **research service,** just as the company buys an advertising service or a printing service. And just as a company goes to specialists in advertising or printing for their services, so it goes to organizations that specialize in contract research when it wishes to buy a research service.

There are good reasons for using contract research. Companies are spared capital costs for laboratories and the expenses of maintaining the facilities and a staff. Details in the management of the research program are obviated. Equipment and personnel sometimes far beyond the ability of the company to provide for itself are available for use as needed in executing the program. Use of contract research enables the company to use all of its research funds for actual execution of research, rather than tying up appropriations in the capital required for buildings and equipment. The **contract research organization** is a "central laboratory" that serves various companies, rather than various divisions or subsidiaries.

Independent research institutes, university research foundations, commercial consulting and research laboratories, and the laboratories of other companies are **sources** for contract research. It is probable that between 50 and 60 percent of American corporations use contract research either continuously or periodically.

Independent Research Institutes. The independent research institutes are all organizations set up for the specific purpose of helping industry solve technological problems. These serve industry on a not-for-profit basis, and a few are backed by endowments. Some have nominal ties with universities, although their operations are usually independent of the university management. Because of the gradual merging of character, it is sometimes difficult to tell where the line of demarcation between independent research institutes and university research foundations can be drawn.

Research institutes conduct **diversified research** and are experienced in many phases of industry and technology. They conduct research in confidence and give the sponsoring company exclusive right to all information, developments, and patents. Research institutes do not normally engage in engineering consultation work, analytical or testing work, or the evaluation and comparison of products for trade purposes.

Commercial Laboratories. Laboratories that operate for profit and do consulting, testing, and research work are commonly grouped under the designation "commercial laboratories." Consulting and testing laboratories are the oldest form of technical assistance to industry. They are outgrowths of private consulting services and the chemist's assaying shop. With the expansion of private laboratories in industry, the types of work referred to consulting and testing laboratories have changed, and the latter have had to adapt their facilities and interests to serve companies that have no research laboratories of their own. Many have evolved into organizations engaging in **research** as much as in **testing, analysis, or consultation.** Some of these laboratories resemble the large research institutes in their handling of broad research programs in many areas of technology. Consulting laboratories are situated in most of the larger industrial centers.

Cooperative Research with Universities. University laboratories can be helpful to companies wishing to conduct research. Particularly is university help useful for the conduct of **directed basic investigations.**

Research arrangements between universities and companies are "cooperative" in that both parties achieve benefits they could not have working alone. Funds made available by a company to a university supplement the regular university research budget. This makes possible an expansion of the university training program, and the supplementary income going to its faculty members enables the university to hold high types of scientific talent on its teaching staff. At the same time, the results of the research are useful to the company financing the work.

Research is placed in universities through **fellowships, grants,** or **contracts.** Fellowships and grants imply the donation of a fixed sum, to be expended, usually as the university sees fit, toward the solution of a technical problem. This may be done as the basis for a master's or doctorate thesis or for a scientific paper, and the actual work may be performed by a faculty member or by graduate students under his supervision. Some 250 colleges and universities offer such research services to industry. Frequently the college or school of engineering of the university, the engineering experiment station, or departments of physics or chemistry provide services that are directly analogous to those performed by the separately organized university foundations. In most instances, faculty members and graduate students conduct the research.

University Research Foundations. A number of universities have established research foundations, where work is done on a contract basis by faculty members or, in some cases, by full-time research personnel having no other duties. In all such cases, the sponsoring company's **rights to discoveries** or **patents** are defined by the agreement and may vary from no rights whatsoever to complete rights of ownership, depending upon the policies of the particular university. University research foundations are very similar to independent research institutes, the chief points of difference being affiliation with a parent university, or a close tie with a university to the extent that faculty members and graduate students may be used on the research staff. Many, however, employ full-time research personnel who have no teaching assignments. There are about 40 institutes and foundations associated with universities that fall into this class. Some are separately incorporated.

The typical university research foundation seeks and negotiates contracts and provides overhead control, financial management, and patent assistance in connection with industrial contracts. Some have separate facilities, while others use the regular university facilities. The distribution of these research organizations throughout the country makes contract research facilities convenient to all industrial firms.

Trade Association Research. Trade association research is a method of solving problems that are common to a whole industry. To obtain the benefits of trade association research, an individual company associates itself with the one or more trade organizations serving its industry.

In addition to trade associations, which have other functions as well as research, **special research associations** or institutes serve some industries. Thus, Bituminous Coal Research, Inc., is an association specially established to serve the research needs of the bituminous coal industry and the railroads and equipment manufacturers that have a stake in bituminous coal. Similarly, Tin Research Institute, Inc., is a special research association serving tin producers.

Associations conduct industrial research and development on **common industry problems** in several ways. Some maintain and operate their own facilities. Many, however, employ the technical and scientific equipment and personnel available at universities, independent research institutes, and commercial laboratories. In some instances, the laboratories of member companies are used. Some employ a combination of facilities.

Altogether, there are some 2,000 trade associations of national and regional scope in the United States. Most were formed for trade or legislative functions, but more and more are embracing technical research in their programs. Some thirty or more maintain their own laboratories.

Research financed by trade associations is usually paid out of the association's **general funds,** although there are instances when special assessment of members is practiced. Committees, set up for the purpose, usually manage the trade association research program.

Trade associations have been very helpful in advancing the technical progress of industries and in protecting them from the onslaughts of competitive technologies. The efforts of associations in advancing the industry can be very fruitful if such efforts are well founded and executed. In some cases, however, industry-wide research is initiated only after a competitive problem has become extremely acute; then it may be too late to realize more than token values from the program.

Technical Consultants. Technical problems not involving great amounts of laboratory work may also be solved through the use of **technical and engineering consultants.** Numerous firms supply advisory and consultation services, and specialists are available in almost all fields of industrial endeavor. Fees are charged for the service, and if actual laboratory or pilot-plant investigation is required, the work is done on a contract basis. The dividing line between a true consultation service and a commercial research laboratory is not sharp, one merging into the other. Many university professors also engage in consultation work in addition to their academic work.

Other Independent Facilities. Some industrial companies with extensive laboratories conduct **contract research** for other companies. Many of the large industrial laboratories got into the contract research business during World War II when their facilities were used to solve technical and engineering problems for the government. Finding such activity profitable, it is only natural that they should extend the same services to noncompetitive industrial companies.

Where applicable, one way to get research done is to let a **potential supplier** who has financial interests in its success do the work. While this works very satisfactorily in many instances, it tends to make the recipient dependent on the supplier.

Procedures for the Research Program

INITIATING THE PROGRAM. The industrial research program may start with the recognition by the company of an existing or potential need. Some typical conditions suggesting the **need for research** are:

1. Lack of growth or too low a growth rate.
2. Diminishing earnings.
3. Competitive difficulties, reduced sales, increased sales resistance.
4. Excessive labor and material costs.
5. Production difficulties, excessive "rejects," lack of uniformity in products, or process failures.
6. Saturated markets, vanishing markets, or the threat of a saturated and vanishing market.
7. High incidence of customer complaint; "bugs" in the product.
8. Waste disposal problems.
9. Lack of sales appeal in the product; product obsolescence in terms of utility or customer taste and fancy.
10. Shrinking prestige of the company.

A **fortuitous idea** conceived by some member of a firm may also be the spark that initiates a program—or even the spark that sets the company out to new accomplishment through the embracing of technical research. Probably most companies originally get into research because of recognition of a need or because of a fortuitous idea. But once a company has learned of the possibilities through research, the process is **self-generating.** Research leads to new ideas and new ideas lead to more research. "Need" can hardly be called a stimulating factor behind the research program of the large, successful corporation of today, unless it be considered primarily as a need for continued growth, new conquests, and increased prosperity. Companies practiced in research have positive motivations, rather than negative.

Sources of Research Ideas. Behind every research project, there must be an idea. The problem is to find ideas. One of the main reasons that companies engage in basic research is to find new information that will suggest ideas.

But ideas do not come from the research staff alone. The entire personnel of most companies is encouraged to submit ideas for research, and substantial rewards may be granted for those that result in savings or profit. **Suggestions** relating to existing products and processes arise from the production, operating, sales, and executive departments. Sales people, coming as they do in contact with the market, are frequently excellent sources of suggestions for product improvement or new products. In one large chemical company, it was found that 50 percent of the ideas offered came from the research and development department; 25 percent came from the sales department; 15 percent from production; and 10 percent from management, market research, and other groups. Of the ideas offered, 65 percent of those from the research and development personnel were accepted and 35 percent of those from nontechnical sources.

Developing Research Ideas. Once the idea has been conceived and brought to attention, it is given preliminary consideration by management. Brief technical and economic studies may be made before management can decide whether to provide funds for future work. If the **preliminary appraisal** is favorable, the proposed project may be reviewed with the production, sales, engineering, and development groups that will eventually be concerned with it. Bringing these groups in before a project is started serves two purposes. It acquaints a wide segment of the company's personnel with the planning, which tends to enlist their support later. It also brings suggestions that may enhance the original idea. Market and economic studies may then be made before the decision is reached to go ahead with the project. This **teamwork** in the planning of a research project contributes heavily to the success of industrial research.

After the decision has been reached and monies have been made available for the project, the research director carries responsibility for execution of the project.

REQUIREMENTS IN MANPOWER. Success in research is dependent upon the people doing it. A good research staff can carry the idea to successful fruition at minimum cost, while an inferior staff will stumble, backtrack, waste time and materials, and perhaps never achieve the objective wanted. Not only must the laboratory workers themselves be properly qualified, but they must be organized in such a way as to bring out their talents, must have a high type of supervision, and must have an ample measure of morale and inspiration. In practically all modern laboratories, team or **group research methods** are used to attack problems. Unless the research staff is organized for and effective in the use of team methods, it has little chance of competing with the research staffs of companies utilizing this technique.

Qualities for Research Personnel. Engstrom and Alexander (Proceedings, Institute of Radio Engineers, vol. 40) have listed the qualities they consider most important in **research workers.** It is probable that their views fairly well typify the views of research management as a whole, even in many cases to the order of presentation. According to them, industry expects its research workers to:

1. Possess originality and, even if in varying degrees, creativeness (inventiveness).
2. Be well trained in the fundamentals of science and continue to improve their knowledge and skills throughout their research careers.
3. Be reliable and of good character.
4. Be energetic and have drive in the conduct of research.
5. Be scientifically inquisitive in the fields assigned and for the objectives established for the research program.
6. Have a practical outlook—a common sense approach to their work.
7. Have wholesome attitudes toward their work and toward the persons with whom they come in contact, and understand and practice cooperation.
8. Make appropriate use of the freedoms of the research environment.
9. Be, insofar as possible, young in mental outlook.

Williams (Proceedings, Eighth Annual Conference on the Administration of Research) sums up the requirements for the research man as follows:

1. Creativeness, or the ability to develop ideas from new associations of information.
2. Scientific integrity, or absolute reliability in the conduct of experiments and the interpretation of results.
3. Cooperativeness, or the ability to get along with others and work harmoniously on the research team.

4. Drive, or the practiced will to get the job done.
5. Knowledge of fundamentals and of research methods.
6. Practicality, including economic sense.
7. Salesmanship, meaning the ability to organize and present ideas so as to communicate to others and to motivate them.

Creativeness or inventiveness is important in the research worker, because the research process is essentially a process of creation or invention. This is an intangible capacity, difficult to measure, and usually evidenced only after the worker has been on the job for some time.

A good **understanding** of scientific and engineering principles is basic. While training is no substitute for inventiveness, in the present state of technology it is a necessary condition for solving problems. Industrial research personnel frequently have advanced university training, and the doctor's degree is commonplace in most laboratories.

Curiosity is a basic trait of the scientist and an important adjunct to the creative spirit. Dissatisfaction with the status quo frequently inspires new ideas, but dissatisfaction per se is no indication of research ability. The research worker should understand that the laboratory exists to promote the earnings of the company and should be able to identify his own motivation with this function. Industry usually strives to promote the research worker's interest in the total activity of the company, as well as his understanding of the part played by his own group.

Previous **experience, scholastic records,** and various **aptitude** and other **psychological tests** are used in singling out competent personnel. **Recommendations** of teachers and previous employers are given weight. **Interviews** with supervisory personnel on the job are helpful in evaluating intangible qualities. Most research administrators feel it is wiser to recruit from many educational institutions, rather than from just a few. Not all men hired meet research requirements, but those who do not succeed in research and development are often prime candidates for jobs that open up in production, sales, or technical service.

The Research Team. The term "team research" is designed to make a distinction between the use of individuals and the use of groups of scientists in the attack on research problems. Practically all industrial research is team research now, and the term is becoming redundant. Except in rare instances, industrial concerns do not assign problems to individuals and let them work on the problems unaided. A description of the team method, or the "group" or "cooperative" method as it is also called, is essentially a description of the universal methodology of industrial research.

Team research is merely the use of specialists to solve the various phases of the problem. Usually a **coordinating body,** composed of the research director and men with broad experience in the fields of science or technology that are applicable, appraises the problem, determines the most promising courses of action, and assigns whatever **specialists** are needed to work on the component parts. As information is developed, it comes back to the coordinating group, which pieces the pattern together and determines how the research in each speciality will affect the over-all problem. On the basis of the developing information, modifications in strategy are made as the work progresses, and unfruitful endeavor is quickly eliminated. Since each scientist in the laboratory is actually working in his field of high proficiency, there is no wasted effort while a man acquaints himself with some science or technology foreign to his training. The **research worker** is, thus, given excellent opportunity to develop and practice his specialty, and he becomes more skilled and valuable to the company with increased experience. Most important, because he devotes all his energies to his specialty, he has a realistic chance to make new contributions to his field—something that would be virtually impossible, merely because of the length of human life, if he had to be well informed in many branches of science and technology. The company, in turn, benefits from the new trails that its staff of specialists are able to blaze.

If a problem involves only one field of science, over-all coordination of the research may be handled by one man, who is responsible to the unit supervisor or the research director. Many commonplace industrial problems fall into this category, and the **coordinator** is frequently a senior scientist working in the laboratory with several specialized assistants.

Application of Team Research. An example of teamwork on an actual problem will illustrate how it operates and how it produces practical solutions to problems quickly and at minimum costs. The following example is a **teamwork case history** of a project conducted at Battelle Institute.

Oil-well drillers in the Permian Basin oil fields of West Texas and New Mexico were having trouble with drill-pipe breakage. New strings of drill pipe would twist off far under the ground, necessitating expensive "fishing" operations and replacement. Drill pipe was costly, and labor and material losses were running into the millions. The American Association of Oilwell Drilling Contractors took the problem to Battelle Institute.

After review of all the known factors, Battelle's coordinating committee sent a metallurgical engineer to the Permian Basin to examine broken drill pipe and talk to men in the field. He began shipping specimens of damaged pipe to the central laboratory in Columbus, Ohio, and in a few weeks metallurgists and metallographers were busy sectioning the specimens, and physicists and experts in materials engineering, aided by corrosion chemists, electrical engineers, and geologists, were evolving a theory to account for the failures. The teams of specialists quickly determined that drill-pipe failure was due to corrosion-fatigue, induced by the peculiar drilling conditions of the area.

With the cause of failure determined, the problem was to find a way to prevent it. Since corrosion-resistant pipe would be too costly, it would be necessary to find ways to reduce or prevent corrosion and fatigue-crack formation without changing the steel. A number of approaches were suggested, and chemists were set to work trying to find chemical inhibitors and develop plastic coatings for pipe interiors; nonferrous metallurgists and electrochemists, in the development of metal-plating processes; mechanical engineers and physicists, in the devising of operating procedures to reduce stress concentrations during drilling; and electrical engineers and nondestructive inspection specialists, in the development of practical field procedures for revealing fatigue cracks before failures occurred.

In the laboratory work, engineers and physicists found that the operating lifetime of pipe specimens could be increased from 10 to 100 times by reducing the bending stresses. A practical field method for reducing bending stresses was worked out by Battelle's mechanical engineers. Chemists and electrochemists, in the meantime, found that the addition of sodium chromate to the drilling fluid would increase pipe life up to four times normal, and that plastic coatings and zinc plating would increase pipe life up to 150 times. Electrical engineers came up with visual and magnetic field methods for detection of fatigue cracks in pipe before breakage, and corrosion specialists showed that pipe life could be doubled by certain cleaning practices.

The final result of the study was a set of drilling practice recommendations. These were made by Battelle within ten months after the project was initiated. They were adopted by drilling contractors, and, a little over a year after the research started, drill-string failure ceased to be a problem in the Permian Basin.

The research program cost the drillers' association $20,000. Despite the fact that many specialists were used, the total time charges of these men did not aggregate appreciably. By old-fashioned research methods, it is doubtful if one man could have even found the cause of the trouble within a lifetime, let alone provide a remedy. Before the Battelle-developed drilling practices were put into effect, individual contractors frequently lost as much as $100,000 on a single drill hole. Gross annual losses ran into millions. In less than one week of normal drilling operation, the entire cost of the research had been recovered by the drilling contractors.

Supplementing the Research Team. It can be seen from this example that a highly **diversified research staff** may be needed for team research, particularly when the problem is complex. Few of the day-by-day research problems encountered by industry require as many different types of specialists as were used in the Battelle drilling study, but it is not uncommon for skills in two or more basic disciplines to be needed, together with training in several highly specialized technologies. To provide the diversity of talents needed for team research, large companies tend to embrace more and more of the sciences and technologies in recruiting staff personnel. Thus, a chemical firm may employ metallurgists, mechanical engineers, and electrical engineers, as well as chemists and chemical engineers, and the technical staff rosters of other firms may be similarly diversified.

Small companies unable to employ a diversified staff of technologists can use **contract research** with outside laboratories to achieve a completely balanced research team. Thus, a company whose research staff is composed entirely of chemists and chemical engineers can take the phases of the problem that deal with, say, electrical engineering, mechanical engineering, or physics, to a commercial laboratory, independent research institute, or university research foundation. **Close liaison** between the company's own staff and the personnel of the engaged laboratory will provide an effective team operation.

There is a limit to how far it is wise for a company laboratory to diversify— even the laboratory of a very large corporation. **Diversity** to the extent of the large research institutes would be impractical, since the normal flow of projects would not be of such a diversified nature as to keep all members of the staff busy. Large corporations also solve inadequacies in the diversity of their staffs by using the services of outside research laboratories. Large companies with expansive laboratories of their own are actually the major clients of organizations like Arthur D. Little, Inc., Armour, Battelle, and Mellon.

EFFECTIVE USE OF THE RESEARCH STAFF. Good research people are hard to find, and since World War II the demand for scientists, technologists, and engineers has exceeded the supply. Because industrial needs for technical people are increasing constantly, while the proportionate numbers of young people entering science have been on the decrease, it seems likely that industry will have difficulty in getting research personnel for some time into the future. This means that the most effective use must be made of the people available, and continuous efforts should be made to streamline research procedures and minimize waste of technical staff time.

Utilization of Personnel. The team research procedure is the greatest forward step that has been made in the effective use of scientific personnel. The sharpening up of team research operations is one way to solve technical manpower problems. Team research operations can be improved through better planning of the research program and by providing the scientist and engineer with adequate technical, secretarial, and clerical aides. The **departmentalizing** of routine testing and analytical work and the use of technically or mechanically inclined workers for manual operations free the scientist and engineer for creative tasks. It is wasteful to permit highly trained technical people to handle personally any of the usual laboratory, clerical, or stenographic tasks, and the practice of providing scientists and engineers with secretarial and clerical help is to be encouraged. Some laboratories are even using professional writers, editors, and artists to **assist technical people** in preparing papers, correspondence, and reports, and where the volume of work is adequate this practice is proving helpful.

Stimulation of Personnel. Various plans are being tried in industrial laboratories to stimulate the **productivity** and **creativity** of research workers. Some of these plans permit the scientist to share financially in the benefits derived from patents. Bonuses are offered for suggestions and ideas that cut costs or help the company improve profits. The merit system of salary raises—that is, the recognition and reward for outstanding service—is used widely with excellent results. Good equipment, good working conditions, a high type of leadership, and opportunity for professional recognition, all contribute to research productivity.

Creative Research Programs. In recent years, research administrators have given much thought to ways for stimulating the creative powers of research people. Research is a creative process, and creativity is a capacity that possibly everyone has to some degree, although few people use more than a small fraction of their latent abilities. Some psychologists doubt, in fact, if the average working scientist or technologist uses more than 10 percent of his latent creativity. This being the case, industrial laboratories might achieve rich rewards if they could but awaken, say, another 5 or 10 percent of creative capacity.

As of now, no assured methods have been devised for unleashing inherent creative powers, but experiments toward this end are being conducted at various laboratories. Some of these take the form of **informal group meetings,** where hypothetical problems are posed merely for letting imaginations run wild. Others involve **management emphasis** on creative approaches and the guarantee that all ideas will be given sympathetic audience. Letting the staff know that the creativity exhibited will be taken into account when salary increases are considered is believed to have been successful in some cases.

The contract research laboratory strives for a high standard of research productivity. Before it signs a contract it ascertains very carefully the probability of success, and, being competitive with other research organizations, it must use every precaution to eliminate wasteful effort and conduct the investigation at the lowest possible cost. Competition, thus, assures that sums invested in contract research will be expended efficiently.

REQUIREMENTS IN EQUIPMENT. High-grade research requires good laboratory facilities and equipment. To prevent lack of facilities from standing in the way of research results, requires both laboratory space and equipment in excess of foreseen basic requirements.

Basic Factors in Choice of Facilities. When new laboratories are constructed, attention should be given both to the comfort and convenience of working arrangements. Consideration should also be given to the changing nature of research requirements and to the possibility of future changes in the company's research policies. For these reasons, a building that provides great flexibility of interior arrangement is desirable.

Location of Laboratory. Research facilities may be located at the main plant or office of the company, or they may be located entirely apart from other company operations. Sometimes close working relations with the production departments may be deemed desirable, but location of the laboratory at the plant increases the likelihood that research men will be distracted by demands for aid on production problems. Usually, the **initial** research laboratory of a company will be located in the production plant; then, as the research organization grows, it moves to its own laboratory building, either close to or removed from the production plant. The recent tendency has been for separation of the laboratory from the manufacturing plant. **Proximity** of the laboratory to a large center of population, and especially to a university offering graduate training in science and engineering, is desirable.

Pilot Plant Facilities. Large open areas may be provided in the building for pilot-plant and other **large-scale experimental operations.** Special laboratories, such as constant-temperature and controlled-humidity rooms, instrumentation and calibration rooms, analytical chemistry laboratories, mechanical testing areas, x-ray and electron diffraction rooms, and dark rooms—dependent on the nature of the company—supplement the module working units. A laboratory is planned to suit the activities of the particular company. This may entail provisions for unusually hazardous operations, heavy floor loads, high head room, or various other special conditions.

Associated Facilities. Libraries are important in industrial research, and a technical library is a necessary part of the industrial research laboratory. **Machine** and **carpentry** shops are frequently needed, and if much chemistry is involved a **glass-blowing shop** is desirable. Supplies are usually issued from a central storeroom.

The equipment of the laboratory will depend upon the nature of the work. In most fields the equipment for applied research will be more costly than equipment for basic research, since large-scale testing, semibench, and pilot-plant facilities will be required. Fritz estimates (Research in Industry, C. C. Furnas, ed.) that the total investment per research worker in building and equipment in a general research laboratory is of the order of $18,000 per research worker. When large-scale testing or pilot-plant facilities are added, an investment of $25,000 per research worker may be exceeded.

Capitalization Procedures. As science becomes more complex, the instruments, apparatus, and equipment also become more complex and costly. Individual companies can plan the **capitalization** and **depreciation** of physical plant without too much difficulty, but, unless the company is exceedingly large, equipment may be a problem. One research investigation may require the temporary use of a piece of equipment costing from $10,000 to $100,000. Yet, there may not be a need for the use of that piece of equipment again for months, or even years. It is thus virtually impossible to depreciate the equipment without inordinate charges against the research investigation requiring it. And the tie-up of capital in equipment that is infrequently used can be disastrous to the company's finances, far outweighing the benefits derived from the research.

For this reason, **purchase requisitions** for any highly specialized and costly equipment should be reviewed critically. Unless there is positive assurance that future use will be great enough to amortize the equipment with reasonable charges against projects, it is much wiser to go outside the laboratory for the specific tests and experiments requiring its use. Commercial laboratories and the large contract research organizations can sometimes provide the needed services at costs less than those resulting from ownership of the equipment by the company. For example, the necessary tests or experiments might be made outside the company laboratory, say, for $2,000 on a piece of equipment that would cost $100,000. One year's ownership of the same piece of equipment alone would cost the company perhaps from $3,000 to $7,000 in interest charges against its bonded indebtedness.

The same consideration of capital tie-up, loss of working capital, amortization problems, and interest charges against funded debt should be given by small companies to the thought of establishing any more than a minimum of facilities for research. With other facilities so highly developed and successful in solving industrial problems, there is no reason for a company to make financial sacrifices in order to carry on research.

ORGANIZATION FOR RESEARCH. A skeleton chart of organization of the research function is shown in Fig. 1. The chart represents an idealized situation and would probably rarely exist in practice. As shown, the chief research executive has vice-presidential status and is directly responsible to the president. Through the presidential office he has contact with production, sales, finance,

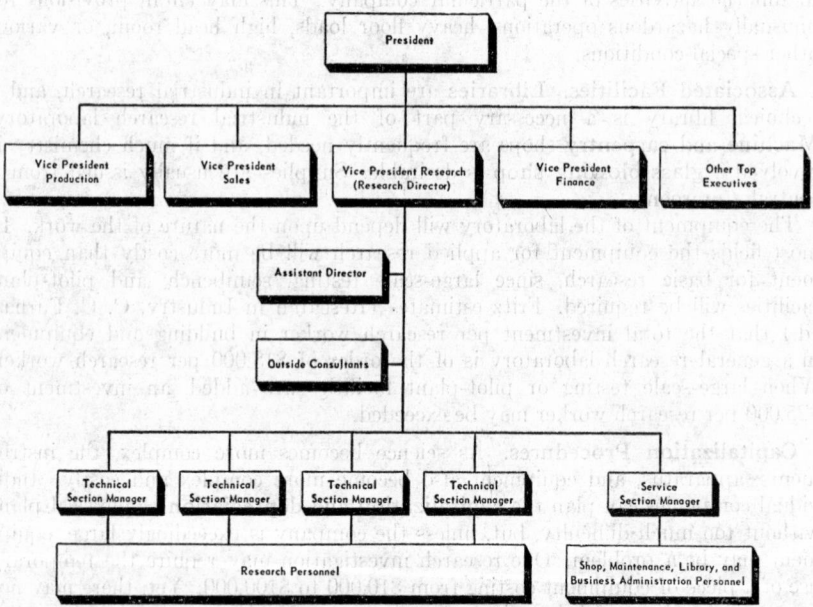

Fig. 1. Chart of an idealized research organization.

and other executive branches of the company. He has **direct executive responsibility** for the technical sections, but at the same time, all details of day-by-day management need not clear through him, but may go to his assistants or to outside consultants. He is also responsible for broad policy in the management of the service and business units that supplement his technical sections.

In this **idealized scheme,** production control, quality control, and other technical operating functions have been deliberately omitted from the responsibility of the research director. In theory, these are functions of production and merely dilute the activities of the research department. Many companies, however, put all laboratories under the executive responsibility of the research director. Practical considerations, including the nature of the company's product, the size of the operation, and the number of research personnel employed, make deviations from this idealized scheme expedient.

Fig. 2 (Applied Research in the United States, NAS-NRC) shows the functional research organization of a large oil company. The director of research, in this case, reports to a vice president in charge of research. Under him are several functional groups representing the major interests of the corporation. Each is administered by an assistant director. There is also an assistant director in charge of business administration. Economic studies, analytical work, and exploratory

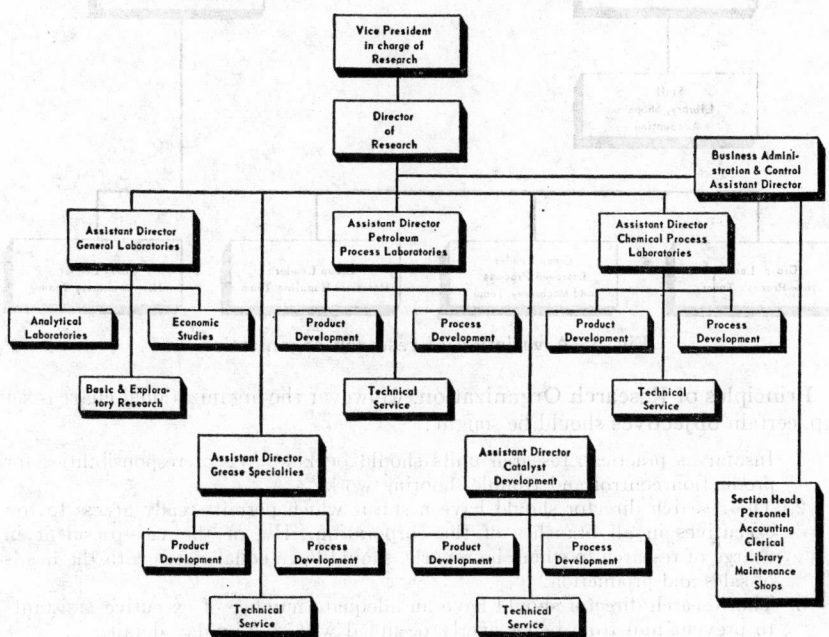

Fig. 2. Functional research organization in a large oil company.

and basic work are done in a "general" laboratory division. Each **functional division**—petroleum processes, chemical processes, grease specialties, and catalyst development—is further broken down into functional **sections,** namely product development, process development, and technical service. Within each of these are found working groups that carry on the actual research and development. Such an organization might employ 500 persons or more.

Fig. 3 (Applied Research in the United States, NAS-NRC) shows another variation of research organization. The company, in this case, is an equipment manufacturing firm. The vice-president, who is also director of engineering and research, has under him a research manager and a manager of administration and services. Individual groups under the research manager may have one or several objectives. For example, one team might have the single objective of developing a new process, while another might have numerous projects aimed at the improvement of the products of the firm. The **manager of administration and services** is responsible for the administrative and clerical staff, library, shops, and service facilities.

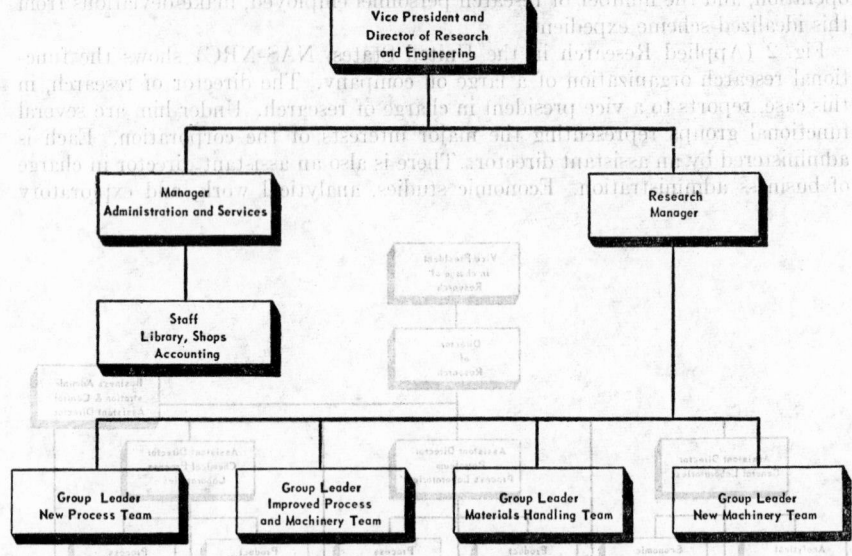

Fig. 3. A variation of research organization.

Principles of Research Organization. However the organizational chart is set up, certain **objectives** should be sought:

1. Insofar as practical, research units should be kept free of responsibilities for production control and trouble-shooting work.
2. The research director should have a status which permits ready access to top executives in all branches of the corporation. He, or the vice-president in charge of research to whom he reports, should have equal status with the heads of sales and production.
3. The research director should have an adequate number of executive assistants to prevent him from being overly occupied with day-by-day details.
4. The research director, after consultation with other executives on proposed research activities, should have absolute authority for the direction and execution of the work, and his policies should have the support of the president.
5. Throughout the laboratory, an informality of communications and working conditions should prevail. This means that the organization should be as loose as possible, consistent with good business practice.
6. Research personnel should be kept free of clerical, maintenance, mechanical, and business administration responsibilities.

MANAGEMENT CONTROL AND SURVEILLANCE. Although it is desirable that the research director have full authority in the execution of projects, it is necessary that research be under scrutiny and control of top management, even, indirectly, of the board of directors. The ultimate aim of research is the welfare of the company, and top management must be certain that it is so directed. No one man is infallible and without proper surveillance it is possible for the research director's policies and program to get out of line with the company's over-all program. Likewise, although the research director has faith in the men heading his technical and service units and does not wish to be pressed by details, he too must maintain control and surveillance to prevent tangential courses from his program and company policy. For these reasons, certain **control practices** are necessary to keep the research laboratory in line, while permitting it maximum freedom.

Control by Planning Committee. The broad planning of the technical program might be made through a committee made up of, say, the president, various vice-presidents, the director of research and assistant directors of research, and perhaps even the heads of major technical units. Through group discussion, moderated by the president, the sales, production, and financial executives can bring problems involving the company's **technological status** to the executives concerned with research. At the same time, technological limits and opportunities, as seen by research personnel, can be conveyed to executives concerned with other phases of corporate operation. From such committee discussion, broad planning policies are resolved. When radical departures from previous programs or things of unusual importance are proposed, the president may even wish to take the matter up with the board of directors.

Once a broad program is put into effect, periodical meetings of the **planning committee** may be desirable. Such meetings inform the executives of the operating divisions of the progress being made and bring forth suggestions for modifications of the program. The interjection of the critical viewpoints of the nontechnical executives tends to keep the program beamed at corporate objectives, and, conversely, expressions of enthusiasm and support back up the program and help to assure the funds for its completion. Final decisions on matters brought up at committee meetings will probably be resolved in separate conferences by the president and research director, but their decisions will rely heavily on the collective judgment of committee members.

The research director also will want to examine the operations of his units periodically. In conference with his assistants and unit heads, he will review the work in progress and evaluate how it is contributing to the over-all program. Costs are important, and there will be numerous occasions when the research director will confer with the technical unit managers and the manager or managers of his business administrative and service units regarding costs.

Research Costs and Accounting. Most companies treat the **operating costs** of their research departments as an expense item. According to National Academy of Sciences and National Research Council (Applied Research in the U. S.), from 60 to 80 percent of the continuing costs in industrial research are in salaries and wages. When engineering and pilot-plant work is the major activity of the laboratory, however, expenditures for salaries and wages may be on the low end of the scale. Administrative costs range up to 10 percent; supplies and expendable equipment run from 5 to 20 percent. Maintenance and depreciation may run about 10 percent. Miscellaneous expenditures, such as travel, telephone, books and periodicals, and consultants' fees, rarely run larger than 12 percent of the amount paid the professional-technical staff. The average annual cost of operating research laboratories per professional scientist or engineer ranges from $10,000 to over $30,000.

Accounting for research costs is relatively uniform and simple in most laboratories. The primary objective is to produce adequate information for management to determine that expenditures are within the budget and are in accordance with approved research programs. The system is normally the simplest that can be devised. **Individual projects** are usually given account numbers and the cost of personnel, time, materials, and supplies are charged to these accounts. **Rate charges** against expensive equipment may be established for its depreciation and individual projects charged for its use on a time-rate basis. Other charges may be lumped as overhead and prorated against individual projects. An accounting system, even though it be a very simple one, is necessary so that management can appraise what the company is getting for its research money and can determine the courses of investigations that are paying off the best returns for the sums expended.

The Accountants' Handbook (Wixon, ed.) states that,

Two methods of accounting for research and development costs are used. The simplest method is to expense such costs immediately without attempting to allocate to projects or even to approximate the total amount of research and development costs. Where this method is used, there can be little control over these costs, but this method may be satisfactory where there is very minor research activity.

The alternative method provides for better control of costs by using cost accounting techniques to assign research and development costs to projects. A **job-costing procedure** is universally used, since the nonrepetitive nature of research does not lend itself to process costing. . . .

Research and development costs are classified on the income statement either as **cost of goods** sold or as an **operating expense.** Under the former, research is regarded as part of, or an adjunct to, the manufacturing function, whereas, under the latter, research and development are usually organized and used as general management staff functions.

In large corporations with central laboratories or research divisions, project costs are commonly charged against the branch of the company for which the work is being done. Thus, a project may be undertaken at the request of a production division of the company, in which case that division will be charged for the cost of the research. If the research laboratory aids the sales department with a technical service problem, the sales department is assessed the cost of the work. When research is conducted for a customer, the customer may be billed for the services rendered, perhaps with a percentage mark-up for depreciation of basic facilities and for profit. As remarked previously, the custom of supplying research services to noncompetitive companies has become quite prevalent since World War II, and many companies with well-organized and staffed laboratories actively solicit research projects from other companies.

BUDGETING FOR RESEARCH. There is no formula for establishing the research budget. References are frequently made to the **percentage of sales** spent for research. While this is an easily computed figure, it actually has little significance. Companies dealing in large bulk materials having only a small gross profit margin obviously cannot and should not spend the same percentage of their sales dollar for research as companies making and selling specialty alloys, tools, machines, chemicals, or other products with high gross profit margins. Furthermore, sales volumes fluctuate, and research cannot be successful if the effort tends to fluctuate with extraneous factors.

Consequently, the research budget is generally established initially to cover the cost of a specific program comprising one or more well-defined objectives. Succeeding budgets are authorized by management depending on the demonstrated ability of the research executive to produce profitable results and the resources of the company available for experimental work.

The Accountants' Handbook (Wixon, ed.) indicates that,

Preparation of the research and development budget begins with the total amount to be allocated by management to the function. The amount of the budget depends on such factors as (1) the scope of the research and development program, (2) research facilities and personnel, and (3) competitive and economic conditions. Another approach to the total appropriation is to adjust research and development costs of prior periods to the expectations of the current year.

Some companies establish research budgets for **specific projects.** Thus, each project must be approved individually, except in cases where a group of small projects may be lumped together for blanket approval. Still another practice is to base the budget primarily on the approved number of personnel, using some evolved ratio based on past experience.

Certain expenses in research are **fixed** or **semifixed.** Good research personnel need experience within a company before their work may be expected to show profitable results, and replacement of the research staff is costly. For these reasons, the salaries for personnel are often regarded as fixed costs in formulating the research budget. Even when it is desirable to reduce research expenditures, companies generally hesitate to release competent personnel. Other fixed costs are requirements in supplies and equipment, depreciation of capital investment in equipment and plant, and laboratory maintenance. The sums of these relatively fixed expenses serve as the first approximation of the final research outlay. Expenditures beyond this point largely indicate how dynamic the research program shall be in terms of addition to staff, increased amounts for equipment and supplies, and outside help.

Factors in Budget Planning. In arriving at the budget for research, management must make many difficult decisions. Management, in effect, must consider what is for the best interests of the owners of the company, namely the stockholders. Expenditures for research mean immediate direct reductions from **reported earnings,** and if excessive, may affect the **dividend rate.** If the research is successful, however, the temporary loss of maximum dividends will be more than made up by higher earnings in the future, with the expectancy of increased dividends and appreciation of the capital value of the stock. If unsuccessful, however, large expenditures for research would be reflected negatively in earnings statements and would lead to depreciation of the stockholders' investments.

Another problem that management must consider is the company's **ability to follow through** and put to use the results from research. It has been estimated that from 10 to 20 dollars must eventually be invested in new capital for every dollar spent in research. A company could conceivably "overresearch" its ability to finance. A slower, sustained pace of progress may be more desirable than one that would put the company in financial straits through too rapid expansion.

Another consideration is that **earnings invested** in research are not available for other purposes. Management must decide whether such sums might be more beneficially used in the expansion of production, sales, or distribution facilities, the retirement of indebtedness, or for other uses affecting profit.

Management must bear in mind that not all research projects yield returns on the investment. It has been a rule of thumb in the past that, in a carefully considered program, only about one out of ten projects may be expected to lead to increased profits. Some research administrators regard this rule as obsolete, in light of new advances being made in the planning of projects, using such tools as operations research. However, unless the most modern planning techniques with mathematical evaluation of the probable effects of the project on profits are used, the expectancy of successful results in terms of profit is still probably of this order of magnitude.

A **proper balance,** thus, must be established between financial risk and probable returns. Placing too low a limit of expenditure on a given research proposal may jeopardize the entire investment before any work is undertaken. On the other hand, it is not good policy to permit expenditures consistently larger than the returns from previous research. (See discussion of Criteria for Evaluating Research below.)

Past experience with research is useful in estimating costs and the probabilities of the success of proposed projects. If the research department has a good record, management is disposed to believe that good performance will be continued.

Conditions outside the company frequently have greater bearing on budgeting decisions than internal considerations. **Economic trends** that are forcing prices and sales down, or the fact that **rival products** are taking over portions of a market, may necessitate action. Lower product costs, better quality, or new products may be called for, and if the company is to stay in business there may be no choice but to increase expenditures for research. A management that finds itself in such an uncompromising position may have failed to budget research adequately in the past to provide for this contingency.

Standards for Guidance. Various attempts have been made to establish standards for the guidance of management in budgeting for research. As pointed out previously, a rule-of-thumb relationship frequently used is the ratio of research costs to the volume of sales. If an individual company's **ratio of research expenditures to sales** is as high as the average of the industry as a whole, the company is supposedly as progressive-minded as the average of its industry. If the ratio is higher, the company is supposedly exhibiting greater aggressiveness, and vice versa.

This ratio probably has some superficial value to management, particularly in evaluating the adequacy of the research budget over the long pull, but it means very little on a year-to-year basis. There is actually no correlation between the sales figure of a product and the amount of research required. Entirely new products require heavy research and development expenditures to overcome the initial difficulties and to establish them on the market. Then, when they are well established and production and sales are increasing, the amount of research on the product may be diminished. Nevertheless, in default of better criteria, the relation between total sales and expenditures for research is of interest.

In Fig. 4 (Bureau of Labor Statistics and Research and Development Board), the cost of research as a percent of sales for several industries is given. It will be noted that the average for all industries is approximately 2 percent. The aircraft industry has the highest ratio at 13 percent (extensive federal subsidy), and petroleum refining, primary and fabricated metals, and "other manufacturing" the lowest, at 0.6 percent.

In all nonmanufacturing industries taken together, the ratio of research to sales or services is 1.7 percent, close to the average for all industries. This over-all ratio for nonmanufacturing organizations reflects primarily the situation in the telecommunications industry, which accounts for most of the research spending by nonmanufacturing firms.

Comparison of these ratios, however, does not necessarily indicate the relative progressiveness of the industries. When material costs are great in reference to the value added by manufacture, the magnitude of gross sales tends to depress the ratio and give a fictional appraisal of research activity. For instance, petroleum refining, with a 0.6 percent ratio, would seem to be relatively weak in research. But when one analyzes the effects of material cost and the magnitude

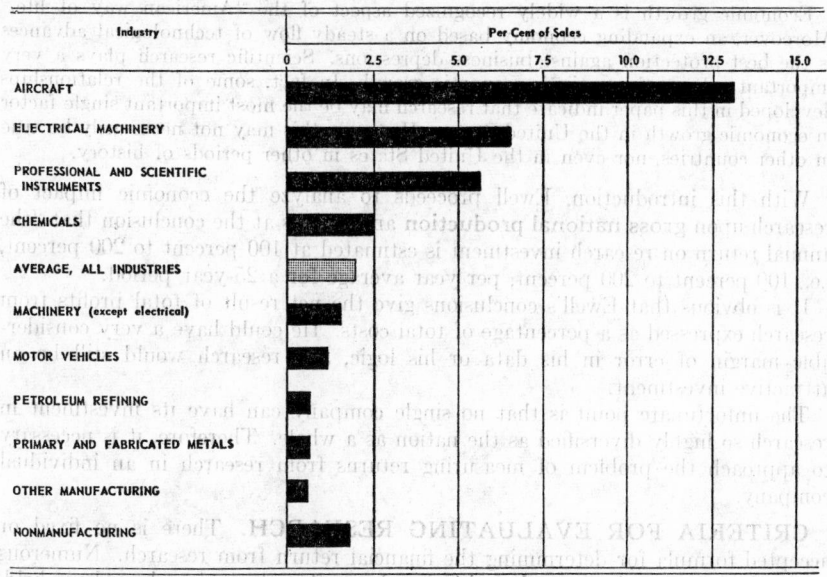

Fig. 4. Cost of research as a percent of sales by industry.

of sales on the depression of the ratio, he finds that the ratio is misleading. Actually, the petroleum industry is among the most progressive of industries in the use of research.

Despite the fallacy of basing research expenditures on volume of sales, the National Association of Manufacturers (Trends in Industrial Research) found from a study of 750 companies that 22 percent used this practice. An additional 12 percent used a percentage of profit as the base for their research budgets. Six percent gave consideration to both sales and profits. The remaining 60 percent used other factors to control the size of the research budget, among them the recognized needs of the company and general business conditions.

Evaluation and Control of Research

ECONOMICS OF RESEARCH. Management has every right to expect profitable returns from its expenditures for research. Yet research executives do not agree on the proper methods for measuring such returns.

When the National Science Foundation was established a few years ago, one of its first studies was directed at this problem. Ewell, who conducted this study, stated in the first two paragraphs of his report (Chemical and Engineering News, vol. 32):

The United States has probably the highest economic growth rate among the highly industrialized countries of the world. The United States is also distinguished by devoting the highest percentage of its national income to research and development. There is a definite correlation between these two facts. Research is a highly creative activity—it produces new products, creates new jobs and new industries, cuts costs of production, and makes a large contribution to our economic growth and our over-all national welfare. Research is the spearhead of economic growth in a modern industrial nation.

Economic growth is a widely recognized aspect of the "American way of life." Moreover, an expanding economy based on a steady flow of technological advances is the best protection against business depressions. Scientific research plays a very important role in the nation's economic growth. In fact, some of the relationships developed in this paper indicate that research may be the most important single factor in economic growth in the United States. However, this may not necessarily be true in other countries, nor even in the United States in other periods of history.

With this introduction, Ewell proceeds to analyze the economic impact of research upon **gross national production** and arrives at the conclusion that "the annual return on research investment is estimated at 100 percent to 200 percent, i.e., 100 percent to 200 percent, per year average for a 25-year period."

It is obvious that Ewell's conclusions give the net result of total profits from research expressed as a percentage of total costs. He could have a very considerable margin of error in his data or his logic, and research would still be an attractive investment.

The unfortunate point is that no single company can have its investment in research so highly diversified as the nation as a whole. Therefore, it is necessary to approach the problem of measuring returns from research in an individual company.

CRITERIA FOR EVALUATING RESEARCH. There is no fixed or accepted formula for determining the financial return from research. Numerous papers have been written on the subject and countless discussions have been held, with no uniform agreement or conclusion emerging.

Abrams (address at the Fourth Conference of the Administration of Research) described the methods used by several companies in attempting to evaluate research results:

1. A large chemical company credits all **sales of new products** to the research department when the latter conceives the idea for the product, works out the process for manufacture, and demonstrates the pilot-plant operation successfully. When any of these functions, however, are provided by another department, the credits to research are reduced.
2. A lumber company has an **arbitrary system** for evaluating research, in which it:
   (a) Credits the research department with an amount equal to four times the research cost when a project results in a successful product or process;
   (b) Credits research with twice the cost when the results have value, but are not reflected directly in sales volume or production costs;
   (c) Gives no credit when research results are wholly unsuccessful.
3. An oil company credits research with all of the **profits of a new product** in the best of the first five years following its introduction. On new processes the **savings** for one year are credited to research, and research receives credit for **royalties** collected on all patents on research developments.

Index of Return. Olsen (Coordination, Control, and Financing of Industrial Research, A. H. Rubenstein, ed.) describes an evaluation system used by the Olin-Mathieson Corp. This system involves the preparation of an estimated **index of return**, which has the approval of the research, the sales, the patent, and the production departments. This estimated index is compared with the actual index each quarter, and progress is closely observed.

Olsen states that one of the important values of this system is that it confronts the research director with a challenge to secure the cooperation of the production and sales departments and demonstrates to the board of directors that a real team effort does exist.

Direct and Indirect Research Output. In analyzing the problem of setting criteria for research and development, Rubenstein (Harvard Business Review, vol. 35) distinguishes between **direct output** of research information, used to evaluate research results, and the **indirect output** of research in economic results, used to control research progress. He then relates the characteristics of the laboratory and the conditions under which it operates, which he calls **design features,** "including, among other things, facilities, communication techniques, operating procedures, organizational location, information sources available, and the number and kind of people in the activity," to the direct and indirect output of the laboratory. There are "three sets of relationships to consider: (1) the effects of design features on economic results; (2) the effects of design features on information output; and (3) the effects of information output on economic results." He concludes that research and development activities can be controlled and evaluated through the establishment of "helpful relationships between design features and economic results by examining (a) the effect of design features on information output; and (b) the effect of information output on economic results."

Intangible Returns. An additional value of research on which reliable data are almost completely lacking is its contribution to new employment. For instance, Armstrong Cork honored more than 100 employees whose inventive genius has been responsible for 1,500 new jobs in that company in a 10-year period.

Crout (address to Cleveland chapter, National Society for Business Budgeting) has noted:

At Battelle, we have had the opportunity of seeing research pay off in various ways.

On the profit side, I can think of a most simple development which involved a total expenditure of some $3,000 in research and patent costs fourteen years ago, and on which the sponsor has realized a net profit of $6,000 to $10,000 per year ever since.

I can also think of a project which began eleven years ago and has involved a total research and development cost of perhaps $5,000,000 in that period. These research costs will be completely amortized this year and the sponsor should earn a clear profit of $2 to $3 million annually for some years hence.

On the other hand, I can think of projects which have resulted in no new product, new process, or new profits. And yet the findings have saved the sponsor untold dollars in revealing technological or economic weaknesses in proposed designs or plans for expansion.

It is thus clear that there is no standard, accepted method for evaluating research. And research sometimes has values which are not reflected in the balance sheet.

Other Criteria. Wilson (address at the Industrial Research Institute) stated that he was not a strong believer in complex accounting systems which sought to separate the costs of each research project. Instead, he said, "I believe in getting a good research director and then letting him produce good results."

Suits (address at the Fourth Conference on the Administration of Research) described the complexities of assigning fair and proper values to research, especially when the contributions of other departments are considered, and said, "This problem has been studied many times in the course of the history of the General Electric Co. laboratory, and I can summarize at once by saying that in our case we have never found an objective and complete solution of the problem of measuring the return from research."

This seems to be typical of the opinion of most people in the profession. The returns from research are so numerous and so complex, and yet they are so interdependent on the contributions of other departments, that it is impossible to segregate the values which belong to research alone. Certainly it is known that those companies with a long and successful experience in research place a high value on it and credit it with the maintenance of their markets.

For example, McNight stated (New York Times, vol. 41) that research had enabled his company to diversify from one to more than 1,000 product items and to realize $25 in sales for every dollar thus expended. In one recent year, the products marketed as a result of research accounted for 85 to 90 percent of the company's $190 million sales volume.

Reynolds (Getting the Most from Research and Engineering) reported that two-thirds of his company's profits in one recent year came from the sale of products nonexistent in 1932. In a period of 22 years, Merck increased its research expenditures by 7,400 percent, expanded its sales 900 percent, and realized an increase of 2,000 percent in profit.

Business Week (no. 1343) stated in a special report on research: "Company after company reports that 50 to 75 percent of its current sales come from products that didn't exist 15 years before."

Yet the problem of measuring the research value precisely and accurately resists solution to date. Perhaps it may be defined as a challenge to the research abilities of research managers applied to their own operations.

DEVELOPING SUCCESSFUL RESEARCH. Outside of superior personnel, planning is probably the most important feature in making research successful and profitable. **Planning** takes into consideration the impact of successful research upon profits, as well as orderly procedures for its execution. The expenditure of money merely to accomplish a technical feat is not enough; there must be assurance that successful research will have adequate effects on profits.

Next to planning, research administrators would probably list **patience** as the corporate quality most likely to influence the results of research positively. Creative work cannot be rushed beyond certain limits, and the company must be willing to wait out the experimentation required to bring results. After the laboratory work has been completed, time is also needed for adaptation of the knowledge obtained to production and for working out the new problems that almost invariably show up. Before the advent of highly organized team research, and before industrial management developed skill in applying the results of research, a generation was usually required between the conception of an idea and its successful application. Today, it is not uncommon for a new major idea to begin to show effects on corporate profits within three to five years after conception. As a rule, however, companies usually think some five to ten years ahead with their research and development. Thus, at the moment, much of the most important research being conducted by the laboratories of America's largest corporations is beamed at the early- to mid-sixties period. The research bearing fruit now is that conceived some five to ten years previously.

PATENTS. Patentable inventions are one of the results of successful research, often coming as the main product or as a by-product of the research program. Most companies follow the practice of obtaining United States patents on all inventions arising from the research they support. Some inventions are also patented in other countries, particularly in those having a potential market. A patent gives the company exclusive right to the invention for 17 years, and may provide a source of income through licensing.

When a substantial demand for a new patented product is displayed, competitors are usually quick to develop alternative products. For this reason, companies in highly competitive industries frequently license their patents to the competition. Since most competitors hold patents also, **cross licensing arrangements** are frequently established. The net result is that money paid out by a company for licenses is offset, at least partially, by income from licenses on its own patents. Patents are thus results from research that give the company leverage in obtaining the licenses of other companies and in avoiding the paying of license fees.

Nearly all large companies have their own **patent departments.** Smaller companies employ law firms specializing in patents. The research director works closely with the patent attorneys and advises them on undertaking patent applications for specific developments. In some companies the patent department follows laboratory work through reports and conferences and undertakes to determine when patent action should be initiated.

BENEFITS OF RESEARCH. It should be clearly understood that the facts, comments, and opinions expressed herein pertain to research as it is practiced in the United States.

In European and other foreign countries, the very term "research" applies to the ivory-tower variety conducted in the academic tradition of a generation ago. Industrial or **applied research,** as we know it, is just being accepted in other nations, and hence is in its infancy in these localities.

It is not a coincidence that research has progressed as it has in this country while remaining as an undeveloped profession elsewhere. There is a definite correlation between the growth of research here and the standard of living of our people. On this point Hoover's Commission (Research and Development in the Department of Defense) says, ". . . the foundation of the greatest sector of human advancement in modern times is basic research. . . ."

Yet it must be recognized that research has developed in our country solely because of its value to managements in increasing corporate profits. And this in turn has come from the intense competition for sales volume, which is so characteristic of, and so unique to, our society. Research, therefore, is a natural resource and a valuable tool of management. But it will be used only so long as incentives exist for managements to do a continuously better job.

OPERATIONS RESEARCH

CONTENTS

PAGE

Nature of Operations Research

Definition 1
Assumptions 1
Objectives 1

The Scientific Approach to Industrial Problems

Scientific method 2
The rationality of nature 2
Business approach 2
Techniques of scientific explanation 3
  Observation 3
  Hypothesis 3
  Model or theory 3
  Prediction 4
Role of operations research 4
Typical projects handled 5

Operations Research Concepts

The model 5
  Types of models 5
  Operations research models 6
  Exact and probabilistic models 6
  Model for setting time standards 7
    Variables in a tape-winding operation ($f.$ 1) 8
The measure of effectiveness 8
  Inconsistent company goals 8
  Explicit and consistent goals 9
  Ultimate and subordinate goals 9
The role of decision-making 10
  Management sets goals and policies 10
The role of experimentation 11
  Experiments for information and prediction 11

Techniques in Operations Research

Techniques facilitate understanding 11
Mathematics in operations research 12
  Role of mathematical techniques 12
  Optimum size of a purchase quantity 13
    Inventory variation in time ($f.$ 2) 13
  Customer turnover in retailing 14
    Schematic diagram of customer group movement ($f.$ 3) 14
  Problems suited for methods of analysis .. 15
Use of theory of probability 16
  Statistical techniques 16
  The binomial distribution 17
  The Poisson distribution 17
  The normal distribution 18
  Other techniques 18

PAGE

The Monte Carlo method 19
Servo theory 20
Linear programming 20
Game theory 21
  Basic concepts of game theory 21
  Choosing a sales budget 22
    Most profitable level of promotion assuming alternate economic levels ($f.$ 4) 24
  Method of approach 24
    Profit expectation under alternative promotion policies and economic levels ($f.$ 5) 24
    Regret compared with best policy in face of resulting economic condition ($f.$ 6) 25
  The minimax technique 25
Queueing theory 25
  Basic characteristics of queueing 26
  Operations research applied to machine servicing 26

Experimental Methods in Operations Research

Design of operations research experiments ... 27
  Measurable experimental results 28
Optimum or maximum response 29
  Problem of maximum net profits 29
    Relations between net profits and two variables ($f.$ 7) 29

Areas of Investigation

Nature of operations research problems 30
Production scheduling in inventory control .. 31
  Examples of production control applications 31
Allocation of resources 32
  Examples of allocation problems 32
Other types of application 33

Comparison with Other Services to Management

Flexible functions of operations research 35
Industrial engineering 36
Quality control 36
Process engineering 36
Market research 37
Accounting 37
Economics 38

Management of Operations Research

Areas for management decision 38

CONTENTS (*Continued*)

	PAGE
Selection of the problem areas	39
Situation for initial research	39
Achieving success in operations research	40
Personnel and organization	40
External operations research group	41
Internal operations research group	42
Operations research groups for specific problems	42
Combination of internal and external groups	43
Place of operations research in organization	43

	PAGE
Access to management	44
Long-term program	44

Evaluation of Operations Research

	PAGE
Basis for sound decisions	45
Contributions from existing data	45
Contributions through new methods	46
Limitations of operations research	46
Executive and research roles	46
Management control of operations research	47

SECTION 18

OPERATIONS RESEARCH

Nature of Operations Research

DEFINITION. The Committee on Operations Research of the National Research Council ("Operations Research with Special Reference to Non-Military Applications") defines Operations Research as ". . . the application of the scientific method to the study of the operations of large complex organizations or activities." The Committee notes that its objective "is to provide top-level administrators with a quantitative basis for decisions that will increase the effectiveness of such organizations in carrying out their basic purposes."

ASSUMPTIONS. This definition of operations research serves as a basis for a characterization of operations research as it has developed to date in American industry. Operations research is, in short, research on the operations of business, civil, or military organizations. Business has for some time recognized the importance and validity of the application of experimental research techniques to the study of equipment, processes, and products. More recently, new methods of psychology have been applied to the study of individuals, their relationships, and the structure of the organization. The **thesis** of operations research is that the operations of business or other organizations exhibit basic patterns of orderly behavior and that the combination of men, equipment, organization, and technology at work toward an economic or social goal is, therefore, a subject for fruitful application of the techniques of experimental research. The subject matter studied is not the equipment used, the capabilities of participants, or the physical properties of the output: It is the combination of these as a **total economic process.** This combination is subjected to analysis by the mental processes and methods which have come to be associated in particular with experimental research, or research in the physical sciences.

OBJECTIVES. There has been a great deal of disagreement concerning the place of operations research in the American industrial scene—disagreement caused by the diverse background of many of the men now engaged in it. We should not on this account lose sight of the rewards available to those who understand and apply it. Operations research is a field of applied research; its objective is intensely practical. From the point of view of operations research, an **operation** is viewed as a set of decisions or strategies, with an outcome associated with each. The objective of operations research is to clarify the relations between the several actions and their outcomes, to indicate the action whose outcome is most nearly consistent with the purposes of the managing executive, and thereby to assist him in choosing his decision or course of action intelligently.

The operations studied in industry may be those of a department, a plant, a division, or a company as a whole. The important point is that, whatever the organizational unit, it is studied as a unit. Where the unit studied is in some sense subsidiary, certain problems arise in the statement of objectives. These problems are noted in the sections below.

The Scientific Approach to Industrial Problems

SCIENTIFIC METHOD. Scientific research differs markedly from the ordinary operation of a business. Further, it has characteristics which distinguish it from such activities as production control or routine engineering; these characteristics give it its power in the particular areas in which it is used. Conant (On Understanding Science) remarks that a man who has been a successful investigator in any field of experimental science approaches a problem in science with a special point of view, even when the problem lies outside his particular area of knowledge. This point of view, independent of the particular facts or techniques in the area, will almost always, in Dr. Conant's opinion, be missed by even the highly educated and intelligent citizen without research experience. The layman will fail to grasp the essentials in a discussion which takes place between scientists, not because of his lack of knowledge or his failure to comprehend the technical jargon, but in large degree because of his fundamental ignorance of what science can accomplish in the course of planning a scientific investigation. This, in essence, is the reason why operations research has been so rewarding and fruitful in areas which normally have not been explored by the scientific method. The core of science or scientific research is not so much a body of fact related to a particular area as it is a method of thinking related to the use of **experiment, conception,** and **hypothesis**—a way of thinking which has been shown to be exceedingly powerful in areas where it is applicable, though by no means the only legitimate one, or the only sound method of approaching any particular industrial problem.

THE RATIONALITY OF NATURE. Whitehead (Science and the Modern World) states that the basic premise underlying the methods of science is a simple and abiding faith in the **rationality of nature,** leading to the belief that all phenomena have related causes. The seeking out of these causes, the exposure of the underlying structure of the phenomena which the scientist can sense, is his task. If phenomena do have a cause, it is the scientist's contention that by hard work and careful investigation, the mechanism or **systematic organization** underlying the observed facts can be ferreted out from the revelations in his experiments.

Another important ingredient of science is its careful examination of observable facts. Facts become the raw material to which the thought processes of scientific research are applied, principally the processes of **induction** and **inverse deduction.** In the former, the scientist reasons from the facts to the mechanism; in the latter, he attempts to set up assumed mechanisms from which he can deduce the equivalent phenomena to check against observed facts. These methods of thought, together with observed information, are used to arrive at an approximation to the underlying system.

BUSINESS APPROACH. It is true, obviously, that all businessmen are used to absorbing and using facts. Modern executives use facts and figures to control their operations, and these are interpreted in the light of the objectives which are maintained in any company. The questions asked of the figures stem from the objectives, and the executive is primarily concerned with the results— only secondarily with causes. In examining figures related to production or financial results, the first figure the normal business executive looks at is net profit. When an executive looks at sales figures, he does it in terms of the success of his sales campaign and its effect on profit. When the scientist looks at figures and facts, however, he seeks in them a clue to the fundamental behavior pattern underlying the figures, the **fundamental system** which produced this particular set or combination of figures and facts. For example, when he studies the same sales figures, he seeks light on the behavior pattern of the customers who produced these figures. Thus, he is often able to improve the sales program and the total business obtained from a given sales area. This difference of approach, in essence, is the basic reason for the success of operations research even in organizations which are normally regarded as well managed.

TECHNIQUES OF SCIENTIFIC EXPLANATION. The process of scientific research through the years might be looked at as the process of solving a great Chinese puzzle. Facts, like pieces in a puzzle, are picked up and fitted together; and as new facts come to light, the original arrangements must frequently be changed in order to accommodate the new assembly of facts. Day by day the fact-finding and experimentation proceed, to yield new raw material for the puzzle-making process. At times the scientist is lucky enough to be able to anticipate in some detail what the character of some piece must be if it is to fit the puzzle form as he currently thinks that form exists. Sometimes he is right, sometimes his experiment fails. Whitehead remarks on the great drama surrounding historic **critical experiments** of this type, as, for example, the announcement at the meeting of the Royal Society of London by the Astronomer Royal of England that the photographic plates of the famous eclipse had verified Einstein's prediction that rays of light are bent as they pass in the neighborhood of the sun. However, while such critical experiments and great discoveries are important steps in scientific progress, they are distinctly milestones along a continuing road, made possible by the cooperative, day-to-day work of scientists who pick away at the experimental pile to produce new facts and to suggest new ways of putting aspects of the great puzzle together.

Observation. The observation of fact is the first and probably the basic step in the scientific process. The process of observation is an essential and continuing process which has been going on steadily since the days of Tycho and the early scientists of the Renaissance. Wilson (An Introduction to Scientific Research) shows the extent to which the attitudes, techniques, and procedures generally classified under "the scientific method" come down to careful attention to detail, particularly in making observations.

Hypothesis. From observation comes hypothesis, and the development of method from the making and establishing of fruitful hypotheses has probably been the greatest strength of scientific research. We make hypotheses every day; when, for example, we find that an electric light will not respond to a pull on the chain. The scientist's hypothesis-making must go beyond this level; it must generate new concepts. Boyle's concept of air as an elastic fluid, Lavoisier's of the role of oxygen in combustion, the concept of the molecular structure of matter —all represent hypotheses, but very different from everyday hypotheses. These concepts lead in turn to the development of theory or models to describe explicitly how the concept works.

Model or Theory. A model, conception, or theory, if it is to hold up, must be valid, efficient, and fruitful. For a model to be **valid,** the facts on which the model is based must be reproducible. A model, or conception, is **efficient** if it reduces the amount of data required to explain observed fact. The explanation of the motion of the planets by the concept of gravity, and the reduction of the bewildering array of available materials to the table of elements, are examples of efficient models or concepts. A concept is **fruitful** if it supplies new insight into the observed facts or suggests new lines of experiment toward understanding these facts. A model, as understood in the physical sciences, should be something beyond a method for obtaining statistical reduction of data.

Prediction. To be valid, a concept or model must predict. Its predictions are tested through experiment. A great deal of testing and theorizing goes on in business every day, and each of us in our daily lives is forced to try things out and come to conclusions. However, techniques of experimentation in the field of scientific research have developed to such a degree beyond everyday testing as to reach an essential difference in kind.

Research experimentation is done, first, to learn facts, and second, to test theories. Experiments in the fact-finding category are aimed at developing the raw material for the creation of hypothesis and theory. One of the great advantages of the conceptual or model-making method of the scientist is the opportunity to use a **critical experiment** to test the validity of a theory by relatively simple and elegant means. If the theory holds up in these critical experiments, then security in accepting conclusions from the theory may be considerably strengthened, where other experimental verification is difficult or unwieldy. The check of the Einstein theory through a critical experiment to test its prediction of a gravitational influence on light was noted above.

In business operations, trials often go on under the names of "tests" or "experiments" which are, in fact, **pilot trials** of working policies. This testing amounts to trying out conceivable operating policies which might be substituted for existing policies on the large scale if pilot trials showed them to be superior. It is important to distinguish such pilot runs from information-gathering or critical theory-testing experiments.

An important strength aspect of scientific research is the **interplay of experiment and theory.** The processes of observation, hypothesizing, and model-building, repeated time and again, are used to arrive at the scientist's best approximation to the system underlying observed fact. The **test of the validity** of this approximation is simple: Does the assumed mechanism or systematic organization act enough like nature? The word "enough" is noteworthy. The scientist knows his analogue to nature will never be perfect; his objective is to make it sufficiently accurate to suit the particular purposes at hand. Newton's mechanics would not have produced an atom bomb, but it is useful in constructing bridges. A satisfactory analogue to nature should be quantitative in order that it can be predictive—the only accepted fundamental test of being physically meaningful.

ROLE OF OPERATIONS RESEARCH. Recent decades have seen a tremendous growth in the intricacy, diversity, and sheer size of business operations. The increasing efficiency of conversion processes, with rising direct labor productivity and reduction in direct labor content of material consumed, has been brought about by the intensive technological research and development implemented by extended investment in physical processing facilities. Size, increased productivity, and specialization have brought their own associated problems. Further, automation has made it necessary for management to be right when equipment is purchased, since the total capital outlay involved is often a sizable percentage of the capital available for fixed investment purposes. Errors here would mean the financial end of the business. Operations research, therefore, was the logical tool to be employed to increase the accuracy of management decisions and to improve management's ability to predict the future.

TYPICAL PROJECTS HANDLED. The work of industrial operations research teams has had wide scope to date. In questions related to **marketing**, teams have helped to determine the most profitable size and use of an advertising budget, to set up means for judging branch sales and expense, and to set up a more profitable price structure. In **production** areas, operations research units have helped set up quality standards for component parts that were consistent with company goals and have designed scheduling and order flow techniques to achieve a desirable balance among production, inventory costs, and layoff of labor. **Distribution** problems tackled include location and capacity of branch plants, warehouses, and distribution points, and the analysis of the operation of transport fleets. Operations research teams have assisted in the design and installation of central data-handling and information systems, and have worked with research and engineering groups in designing experiments, in guiding product development through analysis of anticipated cost and performance, and in running field and production-line test programs to discover causes of product and process failure.

Business organizations have been struggling for many decades with all these, and similar, areas of work of operations research units. Problems in these areas have been, in some cases, made more critical and difficult by the increasing technological and operating complexity of modern business, but the problems are not new. Nor are the basic methods and concepts of operations research new. They go back to the origins of experimental science. What is new is the organized and systematic application of these methods and concepts, which have been supported by business in product and process work since the beginning of the twentieth century, to the study of **operations as an entity,** accepting existing products, skills, and technology, rather than the study of products, equipment, or technology.

Operations Research Concepts

Concepts of fundamental importance to the practice of operations research include:

1. The model.
2. The measure of effectiveness.
3. The role of decision-making.
4. The role of experimentation.

THE MODEL. The most frequently encountered concept in operations research is the notion of the model. This concept is simple enough. It is comparable to the meaning of the term when applied to a model railroad or a model ship. The operations research model is a simplified representation of an operation, containing only those aspects which are of primary importance to the problem under study. This concept has been of great use in facilitating the investigation of operations.

Types of Models. We might cite some familiar types of "models" in other fields. There is the **engineering model**—the model of an aeroplane, for example, which is used for the investigation of aerodynamic properties in a wind tunnel.

It could not take the place of an aeroplane in practical use; it has no seats, it may not even be hollow. It is, however, a satisfactory physical model for studying the flight characteristics of the ship.

Another kind of model with which we are all familiar, although perhaps not in these terms, is the **accounting model.** This is, after all, nothing but a simplified representation on paper in the form of accounts and ledgers of the flow of goods and services through a business enterprise, for the purpose of providing measures of the rate of flow, the values produced, and the performances achieved. It is adequate to these purposes, although it is hardly a complete representation of a business in detail.

Many models are used in physics. Frequently we see photographs or other examples of models of complex molecules. On the other hand, the most powerful models in the field of physics are sets of mathematical equations.

Operations Research Models. The operations research model is a model of an operation. It is usually not physical, although it might be. For example, a model of waiting lines or queueing processes (see below) has been set up using radioactive sources and selective counters to simulate the arrival and servicing of customers under a variety of possible assumptions. The operations research model comes in a variety of forms. The two common characteristics are its explicit and quantitative nature.

A particular operations research model can be described first by the manner of representation used. Most operations research models are **mathematical in form,** being a set of equations relating significant variables in the operation to the outcome. Another type of model frequently used is the **punched-card model,** where components of the operation are represented by individual punched cards and masses of these are manipulated on standard punched card equipment. For example, in a study of a sales distribution problem, each customer, of thousands served by the company, was represented by a punched card containing significant information about his location, type of business, frequency of purchase, and average rate of business. The punched cards representing the customers could then be subjected to assumed promotional treatments, with the effects of the promotions punched into the cards, resulting business calculated, and the punched card model thereby used to test out alternative sales promotion campaigns. Finally, there is the **physical model,** such as that described above.

Exact and Probabilistic Models. Operations research models can also be differentiated as exact or probabilistic models. An **exact model** is used in operations or processes where chance plays a small role, where the effect of a given action will be reasonably closely determined. Exact models can be used, for example, in long-range production scheduling problems in the face of known or committed demand. The exact model is sufficiently accurate, since it can be assumed that over the long run, planned and actual production will coincide reasonably closely, barring a major catastrophe.

Probabilistic models, on the other hand, contain explicit recognition of uncertainty. Probabilistic models are highly useful in the analysis of advertising problems, where the unpredictability of consumers plays a great role. Probabilistic models make extensive use of the highly developed theory of probability which has come to be of such great value in the physical sciences. One customarily thinks of a physicist as dealing with rather exact concepts and highly predictable experiments. Yet physicists faced a problem equivalent to the advertising problem in predicting atomic activity. Methods developed for problems involving mass behavior under random conditions can be applied with great facility and value to operating problems.

The model is a major goal of the operations research analyst. In one sense, the construction of the model, or a faithful representation of the operation, is the scientist's primary job. In the **construction** of the model is contained the development of a theory to explain the observed characteristics of the operation. The remaining task is the interpretation of this theory through the **manipulation** of the model, whether mathematical or physical.

Model for Setting Time Standards. The evaluation of machine operating characteristics for the purpose of setting time standards illustrates the combined use of experimental and a priori information in building a model. In one such case, a model was built which was based in form on the physically known facts related to the strengths of materials used. The actual numerical value of certain constants in the model was derived by comparison of the model with observational data.

The machine being observed is used for winding various types of protective tapes on steel cable. The cable is pulled horizontally through a "taping head," which carries the roll of tape and revolves around the cable. As the "taping head" revolves, the tape is unwound and wrapped around the cable. Metal, rubber, cloth, and paper tapes are used to wrap a wide range of diameters of cable. A number of machines of different designs, purchased at different times, were being used, and time study had failed to yield adequate time standards due to the nature and variability of operators' jobs. Statistical analyses of work records failed to explain the time variations found.

Preliminary investigation indicated that setup time was about the same for all jobs, and the run-speed was set by experience to keep tape breakage down. Investigation indicated tension on the tape was proportional to speed, and tensile strength was proportional to tape width. The time needed to wrap L feet of cable is given by

$$T = T_o + \frac{L}{nl}$$

where T_o is the setup time, n is the number of revolutions per minute the machine makes, and l is the "lay" of the tape, the length of cable covered in one revolution. Fig. 1 shows the geometrical relationship between the width and lay of the tape, the diameter of the cable, and the velocity and tensile strength of the tape.

The amount of tape applied in one revolution is $\sqrt{\pi^2 d^2 + l^2}$. The speed at which the tape moves is $n\sqrt{\pi^2 d^2 + l^2}$. Since the maximum tension the tape will take is proportional to its width, and the actual tension is proportional to the tape speed, the maximum machine speed n is

$$n = \frac{Kw}{\sqrt{\pi^2 d^2 + l^2}}$$

where K is related to the tensile strength of the particular material.

In operating the process, the product specifications give the diameter, d, and lay, l, and the appropriate width, w, is chosen. The required width, as shown in Fig. 1, is

$$w = l \sin \theta = \frac{l \pi d}{\sqrt{\pi^2 d^2 + l^2}}$$

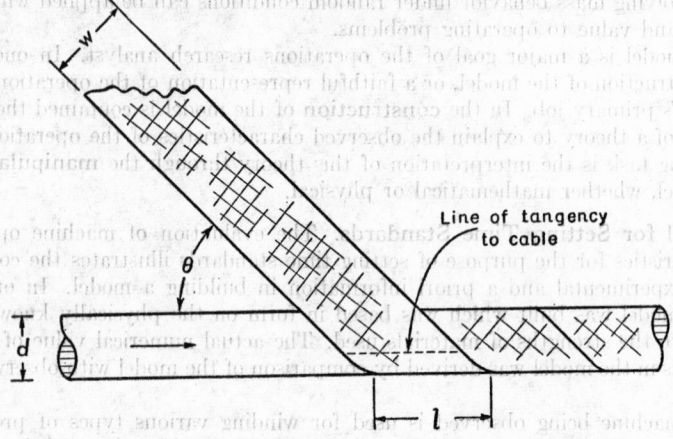

Fig. 1. **Variables in a tape-winding operation.**

and the maximum machine speed is

$$n = \frac{K\pi l d}{\pi^2 d^2 + l^2}$$

The time required to cover a length, L, of cable of diameter d at lay l is given by

$$T = T_o + \frac{L}{Kl}\frac{\pi^2 d^2 + l^2}{\pi l d}$$

This formula was found to predict reported times accurately enough for use in setting standard times. It was applicable to all types of taping machines, and showed that the apparent differences among machines were due to different mixes of product assigned.

THE MEASURE OF EFFECTIVENESS. Fundamental to the concept of the model or theory of operation is the notion of a measure of effectiveness, or an explicit measure of the extent to which an operation is attaining its goal. For example, one common, over-all measure of effectiveness in industrial operations is return on investment. Another one frequently found is net dollar profit. A measure of effectiveness which might be used in a smaller-scale or more detailed operation might be the number of customers serviced per hour, or the ratio of productive to total hours of a machine operation. The ability to construct an explicit measure of effectiveness implies that there exists an **explicit statement of the goal** toward which the operation is directed. Around this measure, and toward this goal, the model is built.

Inconsistent Company Goals. The goal underlying the measure of effectiveness must be self-consistent. Inconsistent goals appear frequently in management discussions, and while they may be useful administrative techniques, they can often be interpreted as danger signs, and frequently lead to management conflicts and frustrations. The ideal example of an inconsistent set of goals was the statement by one executive that his objective was maximum dollar profits with maximum return on investment and with maximum share of the market.

Operations research on **production scheduling** problems has frequently brought to light inconsistencies in company goals. Very often, for example, the object of the production scheduling has been stated as scheduling production to meet sales forecasts, with minimum production costs and minimum inventory investment and without customer service failure. It is apparently not at all obvious that minimizing inventory investment typically requires the use of very expensive production plans resulting in excessive production costs, or that elimination of the chance of inability to meet customer demand requires huge inventories in the face of fluctuating and at least partially unpredictable demand.

Explicit and Consistent Goals. A consistent statement of the fundamental goals of the operation is an essential counterpart of the mathematical logic of the model. The goals may be complex, but they must be explicit and consistent. Just as the model cannot make 2 and 2 add up to 5, so it is impossible to make fundamentally inconsistent objectives consistent and meaningful. A frequent contribution of operations research to management problems is the **forced clarification** of operating goals. Goals which appear inconsistent can often be combined into a unified and consistent goal. For example, in the production scheduling problem, the several goals of customer service, production economy, and investment minimization can often be expressed in terms of costs—the cost of inefficient production, the cost of inability to meet a customer's demand, and the cost of investment in inventory. While the last two costs are primarily policy costs, experience has shown them to be reasonably well determinable. Thus the cost of investment in inventory may be the rate of interest the treasurer wishes to charge to conserve his funds, or perhaps the return on investment which can be earned through alternative uses of the available funds. Hence the three apparently inconsistent goals by the **process of sublimation** can be expressed as a single, unified, and consistent goal of minimizing the total scheduling cost made up of the three components—production, investment, and service costs.

The statement of a complete and wholly consistent goal of company operations must be recognized as an ideal. Business goals are very complex, and to catch the full flavor of the objectives of a complex business operation is difficult in any simple, explicit statement. Many business goals remain, and probably always will remain, at least in part, intangible. These include such objectives as the improvement of employee morale, or contribution to public welfare. Thus, to the extent that **intangibles** enter into the formulation of a company goal, the objective of operations research must be more modest than the construction of a complete model and the measurement of the extent to which the operation is attaining the complete set of goals established for it. Rather, the operations research objective then becomes the clarification of the interdependencies of those aspects of the operation and company goals which are measurable, as a guide, but only a guide, to executive decision.

Ultimate and Subordinate Goals. In many problems in large organizations, the ultimate goal of the organization ("winning the war" in military cases, or possibly "maximum long-run profit" in business cases) is too remote from the particular operating situation studied to be useful. Some subordinate goal must be chosen more directly connected with the operation studied. While this sounds easy, experience shows that choice of these subgoals needs care. Maximum accounting profit vs. investment for a division, minimum cost for a producing department, maximum sales for a sales district, and similar goals can be and have in some cases been found to be inconsistent with broader company goals. An operations research unit has two responsibilities in this connection: first, to choose objectives or effectiveness measures in its work which are, at least to a close approximation, consistent with broader goals; second, to help management analyze subordinate goals and incentives for consistency.

McCloskey and Trefethen (A History of Operations Research) cite an example in which, during World War II, an operations research unit found that for maximum likelihood of destroying submarines, air-borne depth charges should be set to explode at very shallow depths, even though at these depths much of the explosive force of the charge would be dissipated into the air, because an operating study showed that an airplane had a chance of making a kill almost only when the submarine was on or very near the surface. Up to that time, depth charges had been set for much greater depths, to effect maximum transfer of explosive energy into the water. Adjustment in the depth setting was credited by military commands with a fourfold to eightfold improvement in air-borne depth charge effectiveness.

Thornthwaite ("Operations Research In Agriculture," J. of Oper. Res. Soc. of Amer., vol. 1) reports an instructive example of proper choice of measure of effectiveness based on a careful analysis of the problem underlying the stated operating complaints. The problem as originally stated concerned scheduling crews to harvest and process crops, when the exact date of maturity of a given field was uncertain and when harvesting was done over a very short period at a very high rate. The problem was "solved" by eliminating the peak harvest period —by showing how the harvest period could be spread out through the use of an experimentally developed "climatic calendar" showing growth rate of crops as a function of time during the year.

THE ROLE OF DECISION-MAKING. A third concept fundamental to operations research is that of decisions and decision-making. The element common to all true operations research problems is the existence of **alternative courses of action,** with a choice to be made among them. Without the requirement or opportunity for choice among alternative courses of action or alternative decisions, the study of an operation becomes academic or theoretical. Operations research, on the other hand, is applied research. In those problems where there is no decision to be made, or where the choice of decisions is severely limited, research is powerless to help the executive choose a sound course. He has no choice at all. From the point of view of operations research, an operation is viewed as a set of decisions or strategies, with an outcome associated with each. The **objective of operations research** is to clarify the relations between the several actions and the outcome, as expressed by the measure of effectiveness, to indicate the action whose outcome maximizes the measure of effectiveness used, and thereby to assist the executive in choosing his decision or course of action intelligently. In every case, however, the ultimate choice of the course of action lies with the executive.

Management Sets Goals and Policies. The development of an inventory control system illustrates the role of **executive decision.** The analyst's job is to design an efficient control system and to show the relationship among, for example, the average inventory investment, the degree of fluctuation in production level, and the level of customer service provided by the system. The executive must weigh his goals to decide what alternative available under the system best meets these. Perhaps the analyst can help by measuring the cost of production fluctuations and even, perhaps, the cost of service failures. However, to express the system objective completely in terms of cost means a cost must be assigned to inventory, in particular to investment in inventory. This cost, the desired return on investment, characteristically depends very directly on basic financial policies of the company. The executive must set these policies; then the analyst can adjust the control system to work with maximum efficiency under them.

THE ROLE OF EXPERIMENTATION. Another important concept of operations research which bears mention is that of the role of experimentation. Operations research is the application of experimental science to the study of operations. The theory, or model, is generally built up from observed data or experience, although in some cases the model development may depend heavily on a priori or external information. The theory describing the operation must be verifiable experimentally. This means two things: first, verification must be possible—and one of the frequent criticisms made by experimental scientists of many of the social sciences is that many theories and conjectures in the social fields are utterly impossible to verify; second, the theory and observation must check.

Experiments for Information and Prediction. Two kinds of experiments are important in the field of operations research. The first is simply to get information, and sometimes it takes the form of an apparently rather impractical test. For example, in one case the operations analysts directed advertising toward potential customers the company considered not worth promoting, and refrained from promoting customers the company typically sought. The reason for this, as expressed by the operations research group, was simple. There was plenty of evidence indicating what happened when advertising was directed toward those normally promoted, and not toward those normally not promoted. To evaluate the effectiveness of the advertising, therefore, it seemed necessary in this case to find out what happened to those normally promoted when they weren't promoted, and what happened to those normally not promoted when they were. The second type of experiment is the critical type, or the experiment designed to test the validity of conclusions. Again the forms of experimentation used frequently appear to be rather impractical. Sometimes the most sensitive experiment of this type, designed to test the validity of the theory or model, may require the use of a test technique or policy rather different from that which would be used in normal practice. Frequently the results of extreme policies indicate most clearly the adequacy and reliability of the model.

Techniques in Operations Research

TECHNIQUES FACILITATE UNDERSTANDING. The basic method of operations research is the method of applied experimental research, as described above. To facilitate the application of this method to specific problems, a variety of mathematical and experimental techniques may be used. It is important, however, that the **role of mathematical and experimental techniques** be put in its proper perspective: as a tool to facilitate operations research rather than the core of the subject.

In the earlier literature on operations research, considerable emphasis was placed on mathematical techniques, particularly on the use of some of the more complex forms generally unfamiliar to the businessman. From this, at times, sprang the erroneous impression that the principal contribution which operations research might offer was the introduction of these relatively new techniques, which could be grafted onto existing staff functions and services.

Morse (Operations Research for Management) states that

Though the techniques are less important than the understanding, nevertheless it is worthwhile studying the techniques. In fact, it is a sort of "hen or egg" argument as to which comes first, new technique or new understanding. New areas of understanding have always been opened up, in basic sciences, by the perfection of a new research technique, either observational or theoretical. In a new field, such as operations research, the development of research techniques may well appear to be more studied and discussed than is the basic accumulation of understanding; this is chiefly because the understanding is as yet scanty and fragmentary. It is not necessarily an unhealthy development, as long as most workers keep clearly in mind that methodology is but a means to the sought-for understanding .

MATHEMATICS IN OPERATIONS RESEARCH. Mathematics in operations research serves basically as a language in which the findings from investigations can be expressed and the consequences of these investigated. Its advantages lie in the conciseness, rigor, and lack of ambiguity of statement which it permits. As a mathematical argument develops in complexity, short cuts in the form of more sophisticated techniques may be fruitfully introduced. Thus, the methods of integral calculus serve effectively to add up the area under a curve or to convert instantaneous **rate** of change into an estimate of **magnitude** of change after an elapsed time. Operations analogous to these, however, can be done by the relatively "unsophisticated" methods of arithmetic, as they often still are in cases where the problems are excessively complex for known integration techniques. In many problems, particularly problems which are relatively new or in fresh areas, the investigator cannot rely on the existence of suitable well-developed techniques; he must rely on his ability to think broadly, constructively, and creatively in mathematical terms.

Role of Mathematical Techniques. The mathematical equipment essential to operations research work is a sound basic grasp of the concepts of **analysis** and **geometry.** Many reasons may be cited. In particular:

1. Application of more complex or highly developed methods of mathematical or statistical analysis generally requires that we make **restrictive and simplifying assumptions** about the problem being investigated. For example, use even of the methods of integral calculus to determine the area under a curve requires that the curve be defined throughout the interval. Use of many devices of mathematical statistics requires the assumption that the distribution underlying the data conform, e.g., to the normal distribution. Linear programming methods (described below) are based on assumptions that the cost or other objectives and the restrictions on the solutions can be expressed as linear functions of the variables to be chosen. The investigator must have enough of a basic grasp of analysis to understand the logic and assumptions on which such methods are built, to test these assumptions for suitability in the particular circumstances under study, to estimate the influence of possible differences between assumption and fact on conclusions, and to construct suitable arguments or methods of attack where existing procedures do not apply well.

2. Many problems in operations research today require basically a **numerical attack.** The conditions which must be satisfied and the complexity of interaction among variables which may exist may force the investigator into the use of the most basic methods of mathematical analysis. This does not mean that the investigator need know only the methods of arithmetic. Frequently, an appropriate line of attack or analysis using numerical techniques can be found only after clearing up conceptual questions in a "rough cut" using more complex techniques. And enough of an understanding of the more complex methods is required so that the equivalent numerical operations can be defined and correctly carried out.

3. Models in many problems do not exist "ready-made" in the form of specific techniques, but must be constructed, using the basic processes of algebra, geometry, and the calculus.

Optimum Size of a Purchase Quantity. The simple and well-known problem of determining the optimum size of a purchase quantity or manufacturing run illustrates the use of these methods. As the problem is characteristically stated, one would like to determine how many items to buy under the following conditions:

1. Purchasing or manufacturing costs include an amount a for setup or paper work, and an amount b per item purchased.
2. Storage costs, including storage, imputed interest on investment, and obsolescence equal an amount i per unit per unit time.
3. Material is used at the rate of s units per unit time.

If n orders are placed per unit time, the size of an order, x, is given by $x = s/n$. The inventory will vary in time, as shown in Fig. 2, from a maximum of x units

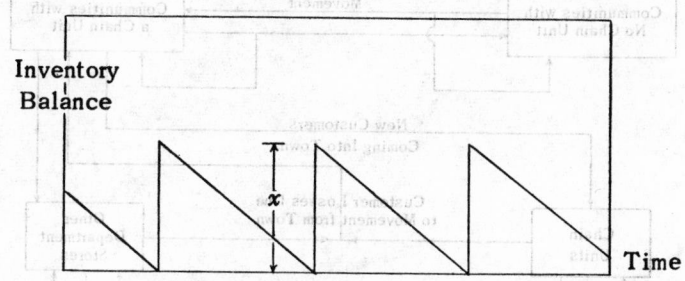

Fig. 2. Inventory variation in time.

when an order is received, to a minimum of no units. The average inventory on hand will be $x/2$ units. The total cost per unit time is given by

$$C = an + bs + ix/2$$
$$= as/x + bs + ix/2$$

The minimum cost order quantity x_0 is the one for which the derivative

$$\frac{dC}{dx} = \frac{-as}{x^2} + \frac{i}{2}$$

equals zero and the second derivative,

$$\frac{d^2C}{dx^2} = \frac{as}{x^3}$$

is positive. These conditions hold when the order quantity is chosen as

$$x_0 = \sqrt{\frac{2as}{i}}$$

This is the familiar "square root" relationship underlying many inventory control systems. The assumptions concerning the types of costs, their relations to the variables x and n, and the degree of uncertainty, e.g., in s, all may be changed radically but the same basic processes of analysis can still be used.

Customer Turnover in Retailing. As another example, a retail department store chain was concerned about its relative position in the communities in which it had stores and about the reasons for turnover in its credit or charge-account customer population. Field surveys indicated a variety of reasons, ranging from movement of families to new cities to dissatisfaction. It was difficult to sort out the influence of different reasons on the growth or decline and turnover in the customer group; and to compare differences in responses from customers and noncustomers in the survey.

A preliminary rough picture of the changes in the customer group was drawn up as shown in Fig. 3:

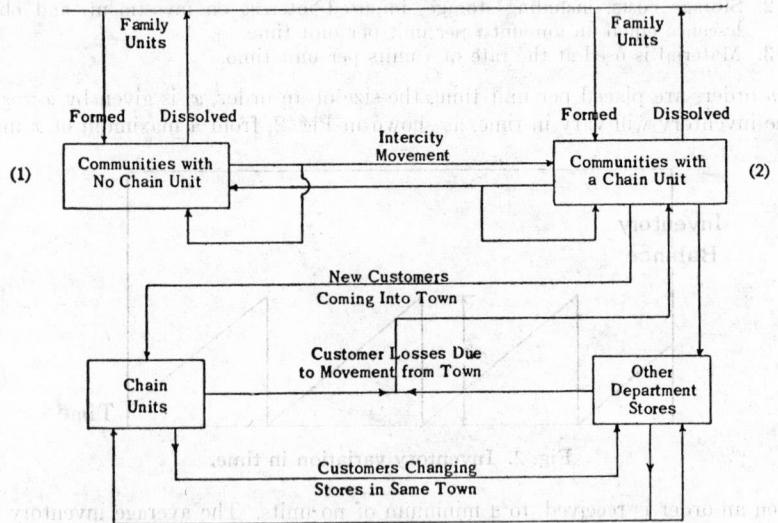

Fig. 3. Schematic diagram of customer group movement.

Under the following very much simplified assumptions, a picture of the chain's **customer population** can be obtained:

1. Fraction of towns surveyed without a chain unit $= n_1$.
2. Fraction of towns surveyed with a chain unit $= n_2$.
3. Total estimated number of customers $= U$; customers in (1) $= n_1 U$; customers in (2) $= n_2 U$.
4. Number of new customers per unit time moving into communities surveyed of type (1) or (2) is given by Uwn_1 and Uwn_2, respectively. The number leaving the state from (1) and (2) is Uvn_1 and Uvn_2.
5. The fraction moving out of (1) to (1) or (2) is given by un_1. The fraction moving per unit time to a new community (1) $= un_1^2/n_1 + n_2$. The fraction moving per unit time to a town (2) $= un_1 n_2/n_1 + n_2$. Similar definitions hold for communities of type (2).
6. The chain customer group at time t equals $A(t)$. The customers of other stores equals $B(t)$.
7. Customers are exchanged among stores as follows:
   a. A fraction k_1 of other store customers change stores per unit time. Of these, a fraction rk_1 move to the local chain unit; a fraction $(1 - r)k_1$ go to some other store.
   b. A fraction k_2 of the chain customers close their charge accounts and move their patronage to some other store per unit time.

8. If a customer in (2) moves, and if he moves to another (2), and if he was previously a customer of the chain, the probability that he will become a customer of the chain at his new location is p_1. If a customer in (2) moves to another (2), and was not a customer of the chain, the probability that he will become a customer of some other store at his new location is p_2.

The total arrivals of customers in communities (2) are given by

$$U\left(\frac{un_1n_2}{n_1+n_2}+\frac{un_2{}^2}{n_1+n_2}+wn_2\right)=U(u+w)n_2$$

The total number of customers in a community of type (2) which has not moved for at least a time t is given by

$$Un_2e^{-(u+v)t}$$

If the rate of acquisition of new customers by the chain units is l_1, and that for other stores in communities surveyed is l_2, and if $A(t)$ is the chain customer group and $B(t)$ the customer group of other stores, and if new customers turn to the chain units and other stores in proportion to their existing size,

$$l_1=A(t)\left[w+\frac{un_2p_1+un_1}{n_1+n_2}\right]+B(t)\frac{un_2}{n_1+n_2}(1-p_2)$$

$$l_2=B(t)\left[w+\frac{un_2p_2+un_1}{n_1+n_2}\right]+A(t)\frac{un_2}{n_1+n_2}(1-p_1)$$

The rate of change of the size of customer groups is expressible as:

$$\frac{dA(t)}{dt}=A(t)\left[w-v-k_2-\frac{un_2(1-p_1)}{n_1+n_2}\right]+B(t)\left[rk_1+\frac{un_2(1-p_2)}{n_1+n_2}\right]$$

$$\frac{dB(t)}{dt}=A(t)\left[k_2+\frac{un_2(1-p_1)}{n_1+n_2}\right]+B(t)\left[w-v-rk_1-\frac{un_2(1-p_2)}{n_1+n_2}\right]$$

This is a set of differential equations of the general form:

$$\frac{dA(t)}{dt}=a_1A(t)+a_2B(t)$$

$$\frac{dB(t)}{dt}=b_1A(t)+b_2B(t)$$

which has a solution of the form:

$$A(t)=K_1e^{m_1t}+K_2e^{m_2t}$$

where

$$2m_1=(a_1+b_2)-\sqrt{(a_1-b_2)^2+4a_2b_1}$$

$$2m_2=(a_1+b_2)+\sqrt{(a_1-b_2)^2+4a_2b_1}$$

The survey data were used to estimate the values of the individual elements or parameters in the system of equations. This very approximate model was then useful in helping to sort out the significance of the survey data.

Problems Suited for Methods of Analysis. Some characteristic general classes of problems for which the methods of analysis are suited include: determination of extremal values, e.g., profits, sales, output, return on investment, as dependent on control variables; determination of effects of continuing differential processes (e.g., customer growth under the influence of promotion); solution of extremum problems where the independent element is not a variable or set of variables but a function (e.g., the optimum rate of production as a function of time in the face of highly seasonal sales).

USE OF THEORY OF PROBABILITY. Probability theory is the most useful single branch of mathematics in operations research. Almost every problem dealt with requires the application of concepts or methods of probability theory or the related field of statistical technique. Measurements of important elements or parameters may be subject to **errors,** even in a presumably purely causal system. Or the system under study may be one in which **chance** plays an important role which it is necessary to recognize clearly.

Probability theory, like most branches of mathematics, received its initial stimulus from very practical problems, questions connected with gambling and the fall of dice. H. C. Levinson (The Science of Chance from Probability to Statistics) sketches briefly the history of the development of probability theory from the two roots of gambling, with which names like Galileo, Pascal, and Fermat are connected, and from the theory of errors of measurements, in which the name of Gauss stands out. Today probability theory is treated from essentially two rather different points of view: as a branch of pure mathematics—of measure theory as pointed out by Cramér (Mathematical Methods of Statistics)—the basic axioms and consequences of which are to be explored and questioned; and as a useful mathematical tool, by experimental scientists, who find that probability theory has a useful correspondence with chance processes in real life.

The axiomatic development of probability theory, as discussed by Feller (Probability Theory and Its Applications), starts with the notion of a sample space and points, left undefined as the notions of "point" and "straight line" in geometry. (These correspond to a situation in which a number of outcomes may result.) The **probability** of a point or differential element of the space is a number or measure assigned to the point or element, in such a way that the sum adds up to unity. As Feller notes, "The probabilities of the various events are numbers of the same nature as distances in geometry or masses in mechanics. The theory assumes they are given but need assume nothing as to their actual numerical value or how they are measured in practice." An **"event"** (or outcome) is a collection of points or elements from the sample space, whose probability is the sum of all the sample points in it.

If the result of the process can be expressed as a number x (i.e., the number of heads in 100 tosses of a coin, or the sales from a customer in some specified period), the probability that x takes on some value x' or less will have a value, $y = F(x')$. The function $F(x)$ is the distribution function of x; $F(-\infty)$ equals zero, and $F(+\infty)$ equals one. The function

$$f(x) = \frac{dF}{dx}$$

is known as the probability density function of x. A number of practically useful distribution and density functions have been discovered, some of which are noted below.

Statistical Techniques. The field of statistical techniques serves as a link between probability theory and the real world. The usefulness of statistical methods is based on the **observations** or **experience** that in spite of short-term fluctuations, long-run sequences of fluctuating or chance results, obtained under uniform circumstances, show remarkable stability on the average. When the probability of an event—a pure number or measure in the theory—is put in correspondence with the long-run or limiting value of the frequency of that event relative to the total number of observations under uniform conditions, useful conclusions are found to result. Statistical techniques, then, are devices for investigating and drawing inferences from statistical data on the basis of their conformance or nonconformance with the idealized models of probability theory.

One of the simplest chance processes occurs when only one of two outcomes is possible, "success" (e.g., the toss of a coin coming up heads) with probability p, and "failure," with probability $1 - p = q$. If repeated trials are independent, the probability of getting, e.g., 2 "successes" followed by 2 "failures" in 4 trials is

$$p \cdot p \cdot q \cdot q = p^2q^2$$

The number of ways in which any given number of successes can be obtained from 4 trials is indicated in the following table, together with the likelihood or probability of each particular outcome:

Number of Successes

4	3	2	1	0
SSSS	SSSF	SSFF	SFFF	FFFF
	SSFS	FSSF	FSFF	
	SFSS	SFSF	FFSF	
	FSSS	FFSS	FFFS	
		FSFS		
		SFFS		
No. of ways........ 1	4	6	4	1
Probability of each.. p^4	p^3q	p^2q^2	pq^3	q^4

The total probability of any number of "successes" in 4 trials is then

$$P(4,4) = p^4$$
$$P(3,4) = 4p^3q$$
$$P(2,4) = 6p^2q^2$$
$$P(1,4) = 4pq^3$$
$$P(0,4) = q^4$$

These are, in fact, the terms in the binomial expansion of $(p + q)^4$.

The Binomial Distribution. More generally, the successive terms in the expansion $(p + q)^n$ give the probability $P(s,n)$ of s successes in n trials. The binomial theorem indicates that these terms are

$$P(s,n) = \frac{n!}{s!(n-s)!} p^s q^{n-s}$$

The sum of the $P(s,n)$ add up to unity, since $(p + q) = 1$.

The formula for $P(s,n)$ defines the **probability density function** for the binomial distribution, one of the most useful and widely encountered. At one extreme, many gambling systems can be analyzed by means of the binomial distribution; at the other extreme, it is applicable to a wide variety of acceptance sampling and quality control systems.

The Poisson Distribution. When the chance, p, of an individual success is very small and the number of trials n, large, the binomial distribution gives rise to the Poisson distribution, as an approximation. If $np = m$, some finite number, the probability of s successes in n trials, $P(s,n)$ can be written as

$$P(s,n) = \frac{n!}{s!(n-s)!} \frac{m^s}{n^s} \left(1 - \frac{m}{n}\right)^{n-s}$$

As n approaches infinity, and p approaches zero, $np = m$, a constant,

$$P(s,n) \to p(s,m) = \frac{m^s}{s!} e^{-m}$$

The terms $p(s,m)$ define the density function for the Poisson distribution.

The Poisson distribution is important, not only as an approximation to the binomial distribution, but in its own right. Where occurrences happen in time (e.g., customers arriving at a ticket window), where these are independent of one another, where the chance of an occurrence in a very short time interval is small and the chance of two or more occurrences effective simultaneously can safely be assumed to be zero, the Poisson distribution arises. If m is the rate of occurrence per unit time, the probability of s occurrences in a time interval of length t is given by

$$p(s,mt) = \frac{(mt)^s}{s!} e^{-mt}$$

The Poisson distribution has been found to arise in such widely diverse circumstances as the number of radioactive particle emissions in a fixed time interval, the number of times a bomb hit is scored in a given small city area, the number of orders placed by a customer in a fixed time interval, or the number of customers arriving at a ticket window in a fixed period of time. (See section on Statistical Methods.)

The Normal Distribution. The normal distribution is the third important probability distribution encountered in operations research work. Indeed, the normal distribution is so pervasive that it underlies much of the more complex statistical method available. It is the limiting case for both the binomial and Poisson distribution. It is, in general, the limiting distribution for sample averages. It is so frequently encountered, in fact, that in using statistical methods, one must check carefully to determine whether there may be an **unstated assumption** that the basic experimental data conform to the normal distribution.

Other Techniques. The statistical methods used in operations research are characteristically the simplest. Methods of plotting observed data, for example, in plotting distribution functions or in making a two-dimensional plot of the relation between two observed sequences, are important, and skill in effectively choosing the measures plotted and the scales may frequently contribute much to seeing one's way into a particular problem. An available supply of various types of graph paper—arithmetic, semilog, logarithmic, circular probability, normal, log-normal paper, etc., in a variety of sizes—is almost an essential in a well-organized operations research unit.

Frequently, parameters to be estimated from observational data can be estimated directly from graphs or plots—probability limits, averages, and other moments, rates of change and other functional parameters. Where closer estimates of parameter values are required, **least squares techniques** can be employed. Lyle (Regression Analysis of Production Costs and Factory Operations) discusses these techniques. The operations research worker should be familiar with the basic methods of mathematical statistics. He should also be sufficiently familiar with the literature of more advanced methods (a) to note an application, and (b) to be able to search available texts reasonably efficiently to find the help he may need.

Some of the more complex methods that will be of use from time to time include tests of significance of differences in means such as the **t-test,** the x^2 **test** for testing how well observed data fit theoretical or a priori distributions, and the **analysis of variance and covariance.** Analysis of variance and covariance methods are designed to help the investigator discern the degree of significance of possible influence of external factors on observed data, and the interaction among external factors or between an external or independent factor and the observed quantities. (See section on Statistical Methods.)

THE MONTE CARLO METHOD. An exceedingly useful analysis method in operations research, closely related to probability theory, is the Monte Carlo method. The use of a probability model to solve problems in mathematics is reasonably old; it was revived by von Neumann, Ulam and others, for problems in nuclear physics of the Atomic Energy Commission during World War II, and given the code name "Monte Carlo." A simple mathematical example might be the following: Suppose we wish to evaluate the definite integral

$$\int_a^b x \, dF(x)$$

but find that it is too complex for our mathematical powers. A directly analogous problem in probability theory is the determination of the mean or expected value of a probability distribution with a distribution function,

$$G(x) = 0 \qquad x \leqq a$$

$$G(x) = \frac{[F(x) - F(a)]}{F(b) - F(a)} \qquad a < x \leqq b$$

$$G(x) = 1 \qquad x \geqq b$$

where the mean is given by

$$E(x) = \int_{-\infty}^{\infty} x \, dG(x) = \int_a^b \frac{x \, dF(x)}{F(b) - F(a)}$$

Using suitable numerical techniques, a series of random values of $\bar{x}$ might be chosen from the distribution defined by $G(x)$. Then the average, $\bar{x}$, of the observed values is an efficient estimate of $E(x)$, and $x[F(b) - F(a)]$ is an estimate of the desired integral.

King (Journal of the Operations Research Society of America, vol. 1) notes two examples of the Monte Carlo method: the determination of π by throwing a needle on a checkerboard and counting the number of times the needle falls across a line; measuring the width of a door using only a two-meter standard with no subdivisions—"The procedure is to walk up to the door blindfolded (i.e., at random) and count the frequency of the different kinds of overlap."

The term "Monte Carlo method" has come to be applied frequently to the use of simulations of gaming methods in operations research. In many problems, an analytic model may be too complex to manipulate. It may be possible, however, to construct a **numerical model,** with tabulated probability distributions, stated basic functional relationships, specified transition probabilities (probability of making a change from one condition to another), and the like. A large number of trials of operating "on paper," with random draws from probability distributions, repeated with functions and distributions adjusted for changes in controllable parameters, can be used to trace out the dependence of outcome on parameter values. The use of **maximizing experimental techniques** together with Monte Carlo methods will be noted below.

SERVO THEORY. A number of particular mathematical techniques have been found useful in operations research, and have received considerable publicity from time to time. One of these is servo theory, a body of concept and mathematical method developed during the past two decades to assist in the analysis and design of automatically or remotely controlled systems. Some concepts of servo theory include feedback, lags or reaction times, the type of control, and the notion of stability.

Feedback is basically the use of information on past behavior of the system to control it in the future. **Lags, or reaction times,** are the times needed for a command from the control system to take effect. The **stability** of a control system is its tendency to some "normal" or desired state, rather than to oscillate or fluctuate wildly in the face of shocks imposed from the outside. The **type of control system**—e.g., whether the system responds to accumulated change (integral control) or to the current rate of change (differential control)—is often very important.

Many control systems can be analyzed intuitively, and adjusted by trial and error. Other kinds are less easy to analyze and much more difficult and expensive to correct. Servo theory makes use of mathematical methods to analyze the behavior of control systems and to show the effect, explicitly, of the concepts described above. **Business organizations** have many control systems. For example, an inventory control system, though not a mechanical device, is subject to many of the same ills as mechanical servos. Analysis of industrial inventory control systems frequently indicates that existing inventory control methods violate sound control concepts, leading to excessive production and capital costs and need for emergency expediting procedures.

LINEAR PROGRAMMING. Linear programming is another field of technique whose business applications have received considerable publicity. The programming problem is the specification of how certain resources or capacities are to be used, subject to stated restrictions on availability and requirements, to maximize or minimize some objective or measure of effectiveness. For example, the problem may be to decide which plants should serve which markets or warehouses, subject to limitations on plant capacities and specification of market requirements. The objective might be to minimize the total freight cost or the total of freight and production costs. In other applications, the objective might be minimum cost of moving empty freight cars or ships from points where more are released than required to points where more material is shipped out than is shipped in.

In principle, the programming problem need not be "linear," although in fact, the great bulk of published material is concerned with linear programming. The term "linear" is derived from the fact that the objective and restrictions can be stated as **linear functions** of the variables to be determined. For example, the general linear programming problem may be stated mathematically as:

Minimization of

$$G(x) = a_1 x_1 + a_2 x_2 + a_3 x_3 + \cdots + a_n x_n$$

subject to the restrictions

$$x_i \geqq 0 \qquad i = 1, 2, \cdots, n$$

$$F_j(x) = b_{j1}x_1 + b_{j2}x_2 + b_{j3}x_3 + \cdots + b_{jn}x_n \geqq c_j$$

$$j = 1, 2, \cdots, m$$

Alternatively, the objective may be to maximize a function $g(x)$ subject to similar linear restrictions.

The basic **limitations** of linear programming are threefold: (1) the assumptions of linearity may be quite unrealistic in particular cases; (2) the use of various stratagems to modify the force of this assumption may lead to unwieldy problems; (3) in many suggested applications, problems which are modest enough in scope may reduce to triviality or be solved by trial and error, while use of linear programming solution techniques on larger problems may require arithmetic or computation capacity well beyond that available even with moderately sizable electronic computer systems. However, as investigation into programming problems continues, progress is being made in the development of adequate and manageable techniques for handling more complex and **nonlinear** problems.

GAME THEORY. Game theory, first discussed by J. von Neumann and O. Morgenstern (The Theory of Games and Economic Behavior) is the analysis of **choice of strategies** in a competitive situation. Problems arising in competitive games, warfare, and business competition are equally open to analysis using this general theory of strategy. Whereas probability theory received early stimulus from problems due to chance in games and gambling, game theory assumes that the chance elements of the contest, and the rules of probability governing them, are understood. The essential problem in game theory is to **choose a strategy** in the face of a conscious antagonist which will in some sense be "optimum."

A basic assumption underlying game theory is that the antagonist is intelligent and equally able to choose a "good" strategy. Part of the objective in choosing a strategy, therefore, is to choose it in such a way that the opponent cannot tell what the complete strategy is, if this can help him; and a "good" strategy is defined by the theory as one which will permit the player to win at least a specified amount—or, alternatively, to lose no more than a specified amount—no matter what the opponent's strategy may be. Three important concepts of the theory flow from this: the "mixed" strategy, the role of bluffing, and the "minimax principle."

Basic Concepts of Game Theory. A **mixed strategy** is one in which some or all of the steps taken are chosen by chance. The purpose of such a strategy is to prevent the opponent from using knowledge he may have, to employ some damaging counterstrategy. For example, in matching pennies, the accepted strategy is to toss the coin—i.e., for both contestants to select heads or tails with equal probability. Von Neumann and Morgenstern show that this is the appropriate strategy to follow—not to keep the game "honest," but to prevent the opponent from guessing the particular choice to be made and taking appropriate counteraction.

The principle of a mixed strategy need not be applied only in repetitive situations. The famous French novelist Gaboriau, in describing the capacities of his detective-hero for assessing the intentions of people, noted his remarkable abilities as a child at a game in which one player held a marble behind his back in one hand, and the other player attempted to choose this hand. The hero was success-ful because of his ability to assess the mental processes of his opponent: the simpleton would leave the marble in the hand in which he first held it; the next higher level of intelligence would shift it to the other hand; the next higher would shift it and shift it back, etc. By correctly assessing the level of intelligence and thus the deception his opponent could choose, the boy was able to determine the number of shifts of hand of the marble and thus choose the correct hand with a high degree of success. If his opponent, no matter how simple, had been aware of the concept of a "mixed strategy" and had used a device for choosing one hand by chance with equal likelihood, Gaboriau's detective would have been helpless—he could have counted only on breaking even.

Bluffing, as the theory indicates, can be viewed as a form of mixed strategy. Its role is not so much to lead the unwary opponent astray in the particular occasion it is used as it is to keep the clever opponent from making use of his knowledge of the bluffer's strategy. Even if the opponent knows—as he should find out—that bluffing is used, he cannot use this knowledge if the bluffing is properly done, since he does not know in any particular case whether a bluff is on or not.

The "good" strategy in game theory is the one based on the **minimax prin-ciple**; that is, the one which makes the player's maximum expected losses a minimum. Employing this principle, game theory leads essentially to a conserva-tive strategy. It has been criticized, on occasion, as being too conservative, as not permitting the strategist to take advantage of opponents' mistakes. The answer is, of course, that one never knows when the "mistake" may be the bluff of a clever opponent.

Game theory to date is still largely a field of pure theory; applications have been very sparse. Only very **limited applications** have been made to, e.g., some simple military combat problems. Limited application is due to the unmanageable complexities that arise in contests more extensive than the "two-man, zero-sum" variety (two opponents, the losses of one equalling the winnings of the other). Some applications have been attempted in cases of planning in the face of uncer-tainty, using the concept of a "game against nature" (i.e., taking "nature" as the opponent with future uncertainty as its strategy). However, the applicability of game theory here, the validity of the concept of "nature" as an intelligent, malignant force, is open to question.

The applicability of the minimax principle to a **business planning problem**, and the influence of a choice of measure of payoff, may be illustrated by the following example.

Choosing a Sales Budget. A food processor distributing to a large number of retail outlets through routemen employs a sizable group of promotional salesmen to visit stores and encourage proper merchandise display, solicit preferred dis-play space, and promote use of point-of-sale advertising. The total direct promotional budget is a sizable part of total cost. The company decides period-ically what level of direct promotion is justified, or, equivalently, how many dealers to call on. About half the dealers are normally called on each quarter.

The problem of picking a **level of promotional activity** became acute during mid-1953. Uncertainty about business prospects in 1954 raised serious doubts about the profitability of a large promotional campaign. A large promotion in 1953 based on anticipated stable conditions barely broke even when conditions softened. The most likely action appeared to be a drastic reduction of promo-tional expense in 1954 as part of a general cost-reduction program. However, before acting, the executive board raised the question with the operations research unit, which had previously studied the company's sales and promotion operations in detail. The use of the model of sales and promotion operations which had been developed led to two results, which are noted by Magee ("The Effect of Promotional Effort on Sales," J. of Oper. Res. Soc. of Amer., vol. 1):

1. The profit resulting from promoting a given fraction, a, of dealers could be expressed as follows:

$$P(a) = \frac{Nv}{2} (1 - b)(1 + 2a - a^2) - Npa - A \tag{1}$$

where $P(a)$ = the expected profit
N = the number of dealers
v = the expected sales from the average dealer when promoted
b = the variable manufacturing and distribution cost
p = the cost of promoting an individual account
A = the fixed overhead

2. By the methods of differential calculus, it can be shown that the profit, $P(a)$, will be maximized when the fraction of dealers promoted, a, is chosen so that

$$a = 1 - \frac{P}{v(1 - b)} \tag{2}$$

Some numerical values are given below to indicate the order of magnitude of the company's operations:

ILLUSTRATIVE NUMERICAL VALUES OF CONSTANTS

N = number of accounts.....................................		100,000
v = expected business from average account..................	$	1,000
b = variable cost of manufacture and distribution............		$0.75/$1.00 sales
p = promotional cost per account...........................	$	125
A = residual or "fixed" cost...............................		$10,000,000

For purposes of illustration, let us assume that the principal effect of economic changes would be on the mean expected business, v. We can imagine and plan for changes in other important parameters as, for example, operating or distribution costs. For simplicity, let us assume, however, that economic changes would be concentrated in changes in v. Economic indices may be used to predict the expected value of v but, as is the case frequently, these indices are of relatively uncertain value in the middle range, and the possible error about the predictions can be large.

Over the coming 12-month period, most of the opinion within the company was that a drop in sales of up to 20 percent was to be looked for. On the other hand, some well-informed opinion based on somewhat different views of economic conditions held that increases in sales were likely, owing to changing consumer habits. The most profitable policy to follow in the event that either extreme conditions or some intermediate possibility resulted could be determined from Eq. (2). Fig. 4 summarizes the most profitable policy under varying economic conditions.

The prevalent view among executives in the company was reasonably pessimistic, leaning toward a substantial drop. Thus the indicated cut of advertising level from 50 percent to 37.5 percent of the accounts—that is, a 25 percent cut— appeared to be the most popular policy and closest to the one ultimately to be adopted. The propriety of this policy would hold, however, only if conditions turned out to be as bad as anticipated.

Relative Economic Level *	Most Profitable Promotional Level (Percent of Dealers Promoted)
80	37.5
100	50.0
120	58.3

* Relative to 1953.

Fig. 4. Most profitable level of promotion assuming alternate economic levels.

Method of Approach. When the question of the appropriate advertising policy to follow in the light of business uncertainties was raised, the existing analysis of the business structure was used to provide guidance. A specific answer was not given, for reasons noted below, but an approach was made which helped at least to clarify the problem and to indicate the stakes involved. The company executives were provided with two tables to help them arrive at their decision.

Fig. 4 showed profit expectations. Eq. (1) was used to compute the expected profit from various levels of promotional effort under the assumption that economic activity fell at various levels. Fig. 5 is a somewhat condensed version of the first table shown to the executives.

	Economic Level			
Promotion Level	80	100	120	Range
37.5	1.30	5.30	9.30	8.00
50.0	1.25	5.70	10.00	8.75
58.3	−0.10	5.50	10.10	10.20

Fig. 5. Profit expectation under alternative promotion policies and economic levels.

Fig. 5 shows, for example, that if the expected level of the economy was 80 percent relative to 1953, profits would be maximized when 37.5 percent of the dealers were promoted, and that if over 58 percent were promoted, some net loss would result. It shows that the company profit depended largely on the level of economic activity, but that it could be significantly influenced by the decision made concerning promotional activity.

The second table shown to the company executives was one showing "regrets" which might be suffered. By regret is meant the loss in profit relative to what might have been, had the company guessed properly about economic conditions. The regret is shown in Fig. 6, corresponding to the profit shown in Fig. 5. For example, the regret in each of the diagonal entries is zero, since these represent the most profitable choice in the face of the indicated level of economic activity. Fig. 5 shows that if the economy is at the 120 percent level, the most profitable policy would be promotion of 58.3 percent of the dealers, yielding a profit of $10.10 million. If promotion were extended to 37.5 percent of the dealers, profits would be $9.3 million, or $0.8 million less. Thus, the regret corresponding to the 37.5 percent level under the 120 percent level of economic conditions is $0.8 million, as shown in Fig. 6. The regret, therefore, measures, in a sense, lost opportunities for profit due to failure to anticipate economic conditions properly.

Promotional Level	Economic Level		
	80	100	120
37.5	0.0	0.4	0.8
50.0	0.1	0.0	0.1
58.3	1.4	0.2	0.0

Fig. 6. Regret compared with best policy in face of resulting economic condition.

The Minimax Technique. One might think of a number of mathematical techniques for choosing the appropriate policy from among these three or some interpolation. For example, if **probabilities** could be assigned to the three levels of economic activity, a level might be chosen which would maximize the expected value of the profit. Lacking this, however, as was in fact the case, some other means must be used. Methods which have been suggested from time to time include the choice of a policy or "strategy" to maximize the minimum profit based on an analogy with the method of **game theory.** In this case, one would be led to choose a promotional level of 37.5 percent, since this would presumably guarantee a profit of at least $1.3 million. On the other hand, one might apply the same **minimax principle** to the table of regret values equally well, leading to the choice of the middle course, or a promotional level of 50 percent. Neither one of these techniques appears quite appropriate for a research or staff decision, however.

The application of the minimax technique, or any similar choice, to either of the two tables in fact implies a judgment concerning matters of policy, willingness to assume risk, and other questions of management decision. For example, the more conservative, or 37.5 percent, level of effort is the one which keeps the company in the best shape in the face of worse conditions, and is the one which tends to minimize the range betwen best and worst results. It is therefore the most conservative, in the sense that it tends to minimize the risk assumed by the company. The second policy might be considered middle-of-the-road and perhaps the policy safest for management to follow, when it it likely to have its actions second-guessed by a board of directors or a strong stockholder group. The third, or most optimistic, policy might be termed reckless, in this example, since there is little to gain relative to the middle policy, and possibly much to lose. However, in some circumstances one may imagine the choice of such a policy.

Something like the minimax concept needs consideration in long-range business planning, such as major promotional planning, capital expansion planning, and the like. Too frequently, plans are drawn up based on some single possibility— the most likely volume of sales, the possible maximum, or the fairly well-assured minimum—without proper consideration of the influence of errors or divergences on profitability.

The methods and concepts of game theory together with the techniques of statistics, such as sequential analysis methods, useful in assessing information and arriving at a course of action in the face of uncertainty, may be generally classed under the heading of **decision theory.**

QUEUEING THEORY. Sometimes referred to as **delay** or **waiting line** theory, queueing theory is a branch of probability theory directed toward the study of the buildup of queues or waiting lines at a servicing facility, as related to the capacity and servicing characteristics of the facility and the statistical characteristics of the demands for service. Some **types of queueing processes** include:

1. The servicing of customers by a change booth in a transit system or at a ticket window.
2. Serving customers in a cafeteria line.
3. Handling calls on a telephone exchange or over a set of trunk lines.
4. Servicing semiautomatic equipment subject to breakdown or stalling, e.g., spindles on a spinning loom or semiautomatic packaging equipment, by servicemen.
5. Serving customers at a counter in a retail store, a library, a tool crib, or a stockroom.
6. Handling shipments on a transportation system with limited facilities.
7. Handling papers in a clerical station or operation, such as processing orders.
8. Setting up a balanced assembly line, where the rates of output of individual stations may be subject to fluctuation due to equipment breakdown or quality rejection.

Basic Characteristics of Queueing. Queueing theory is not a single set of mathematical formulas but an expanding collection of methods and concepts based on a variety of assumptions. Some of the basic characteristics which may vary from problem to problem include:

1. The **size of the group** being serviced, whether it is finite or "infinite," in effect whether it is small enough so that the size of the waiting line influences the rate of demand for new calls.
2. Whether the "customers" or elements requiring service are **"patient"** or not; i.e., whether they will stay in line indefinitely or not.
3. The distribution of holding or **servicing times,** the two most commonly encountered being the constant and exponential servicing time assumptions. (Under the latter, the probability a unit requires service lasting longer than a time t is given by e^{-at}, where $1/a$ is the average service time. A distribution of servicing times approximating this distribution has been encountered in a wide variety of circumstances, such as times to service equipment, length of telephone calls, time for a truck to deliver an order and return, or time for a clerk to wait on a customer, including answering inquiries, at a retail counter. One [not the only] set of physical conditions generating this distribution would be where the amount of time previously spent in service would have no bearing on the amount remaining to be done. It has been remarked that a woman in a comfortable telephone booth is the ideal example of this condition.)
4. The **characteristics of arrivals,** i.e., whether demands for service are generated in a uniform, regular pattern, or at random around some mean rate.
5. The number of servicing units.

Operations Research Applied to Machine Servicing. Many production problems, such as machine servicing problems, can frequently be approached under the following assumptions: The number of units needing service (machines) is N. The number of servicing units (repairmen) is a. The probability that a machine that is running will break down in a time interval Δt is $\lambda \Delta t$. The likelihood that a machine under service will be fixed in a time interval Δt is $\mu \Delta t$. W. Feller (Probability Theory and Its Applications) has shown that the probability that n machines are being serviced or are waiting, $p(n)$, is given by

$$p(n) = \frac{N!}{n!(N-n)!}\left(\frac{\lambda}{\mu}\right)^n p_o \qquad 0 \leq n \leq a$$

$$= \frac{N!}{(N-n)!\,a!\,a^{n-a}}\left(\frac{\lambda}{\mu}\right)^n p_o \qquad a \leq n \leq N$$

From these figures can be calculated a number of operating characteristics of the machine system. For example,

1. The average number of machines in service is

$$N - \sum_{n=o}^{N} np(n)$$

2. The average number of machines waiting for service is

$$\sum_{n=a+1}^{N} (n-a)p(n)$$

3. The average delay in waiting for service is

$$\frac{1}{\mu a} \sum_{n=a+1}^{N} (n-a)p(n)$$

4. The average fraction utilization of repairmen is

$$\frac{1}{a}\left[\sum_{n=o}^{a} np(n) + a \sum_{n=a+1}^{N} p(n)\right]$$

These relationships can be used to determine an **economical balance** between machine capacity and repairmen's time, providing costs or values can be assigned to an hour's time of a repairman or of a machine in operation.

A very important number governing the operation of queues of any kind is the ratio $r/a\mu$ where r is the rate of calls for service, and $a\mu$ is the rate of servicing calls. As this ratio approaches 1, the servicing system will "saturate," that is, the length of the waiting line grows indefinitely long. In some cases, the manager of a servicing function may strive for "efficiency" by cutting out waste time, that is, by trying to pare down the size of the servicing crew until they are busy steadily, leading to a serious deterioration of service. Some "inefficiency" is the price of a queueing process; the amount of lost time vs. the promptness of service is open to choice.

Fry (Probability and Its Engineering Uses) shows that different queueing processes can be treated under a variety of assumptions, and Feller (Probability Theory and Its Applications) shows how they can be considered as one of the general class of time-dependent stochastic processes of wide applicability.

Experimental Methods in Operations Research

Experimental methods and techniques in operations research are of particular importance. An understanding of the purposes and procedures of experimentation is an essential part of the training of an operations research worker.

DESIGN OF OPERATIONS RESEARCH EXPERIMENTS. Two characteristics of operations research experiments stand out as worthy of mention. The first is that these experiments must almost always be conducted in the **framework of existing operations.** The organization cannot be turned upside down, nor can the routine of regular operations be seriously interfered with. Excessive demands for operating people to collect or note down data while working, specifying procedures which may cause loss of pay or mean more difficult operating conditions, even if only temporary, are to be avoided if at all possible.

This does not mean that experimentation is impossible. It simply means that somewhat greater care must be taken and somewhat greater ingenuity exercised to design a meaningful experiment that will fit inside existing operating procedures. In one electronic components assembly plant, an experiment was needed to determine the effect of component tolerance limits on rejects in subsequent operations. It was not practical to follow each item through into a final assembly to see whether the assembly was accepted or rejected, nor was it economically feasible to take down accepted and rejected final assemblies to study the variability of this component's behavior in each group. The research team set up two special inspection stations, supplying the personnel to man these. In one, the accepted components were rescreened and those meeting very fine tolerances were selected out. In the second, rejected components were screened for those falling within a specified performance band well outside normal limits. When enough of each type had been accumulated to meet production needs for several days, each batch was released at different times and the final assembly rejection rate noted. The rejection rates in the test periods plus the average rejection rate under normal tolerances could be interpreted to give three independent observations which could be used to obtain the desired relation. By this technique, with no disruption in production, it was possible to estimate an important function underlying economic production operations.

Measurable Experimental Results. The second characteristic is the amount of **randomness** likely to be encountered in experiments of feasible length, even in well-controlled operations. For this reason, it is important to frame the experimental question in a way which will **maximize the observable effect of the experiment.** In particular, where a proposed change is expected to improve sales, cost, or profit performance by causing some type of intermediate change, an experiment aimed at measuring the direct or intermediate effect is usually more effective. Sometimes, an extreme form of experiment—totally impractical as an operating policy—will yield measurable results. The randomness of operations also makes very precarious the measurement of modest changes by many businessmen's favorite forms of experiment—comparing net results in one period with those in another, or comparing results in one area with those in another. One of the less popular responsibilities of an operations research worker is to review critically the feasibility of hastily proposed tests of this sort which sometimes arise in the enthusiasm of business planning sessions.

The **"black box" effect** (the tendency of operations to improve under an experiment, as a result of greater operating care taken due to the close scrutiny the operation receives) must be guarded against in business experiments. This effect has been seen in military experiments with new equipment, where ultimately valueless devices appeared in first tests to improve operations substantially. It is not uncommon in operating tests of, e.g., new chemical processing methods. It has been seen in operations research experiments, where large improvements in performance wholly unrelated to the content of the experiment were found.

Methods of experimental design associated with **mathematical statistics** are frequently of value and the research worker should be aware of them. These methods, developed originally in connection with agricultural and biological experiments are described by Fisher (The Design of Experiments), by Mann (Analysis and Design of Experiments), and by Cochran and Cox (Experimental Designs). The objective of these methods is to help the experimenter choose the tests to minimize ambiguity in conclusions due to extraneous factors and to test efficiently, in number of tests required, for effects the experimenter is seeking. These methods are only now coming into their own in fields of physical research; their use in business problems has been relatively limited.

OPTIMUM OR MAXIMUM RESPONSE. One relatively new field of experimental program design deserves specific mention—the **experimental exploration of functional relationships** to find optimum or maximum response. These problems arise, for example, when the relationship between the outcome and two or more controlling variables is unknown, but it is desired to find the combination of values of the controlling variables that will maximize the output. For example, in **production planning problems,** we may wish to find the combination of inventory level, rate of response of production, and service level that will minimize total operating cost.

The traditional methods of doing this have been either to change one variable at a time or to make a series of experiments chosen to "map out" the relationship within the limits of the number of experiments made. Under the first, and more common, method, one variable would be changed at a time, to find the value of this variable yielding maximum response at the fixed values of other variables. Then this variable is fixed at the "maximum" value, and some other variable is adjusted. This method will yield a maximum under special circumstances, but, in general, using this method gives the experimenter a high chance of missing the optimum combination of values.

Problem of Maximum Net Profits. For example, suppose the problem were to determine the best combination of intensity of promotion and number of customers promoted to maximize net profits. The **"one variable at a time" method** might call for varying the intensity of promotion to get the right level for the number of customers currently promoted, and then, with intensity fixed, varying the customers promoted. But if the relation between profit and the two variables were represented by the **graphical method,** as in Fig. 7, intensity (x_1) might be chosen as shown and then the number promoted (x_2), with the end result missing the peak. (The curves in the figure represent profit "contours," or lines of equal profit obtainable from various combinations of x_1 and x_2.)

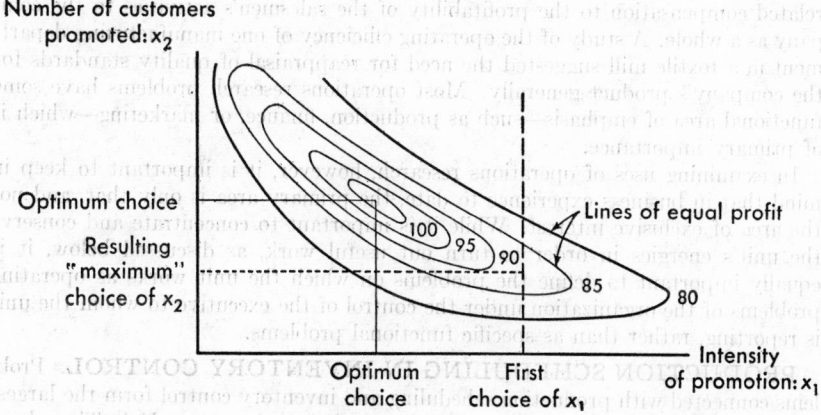

Fig. 7. Relations between net profits and two variables.

The method of running experiments at a variety of selected combinations of values of controlling variables offers less chance of error of this type, but cost limits on the number of tests and the need to run two or more tests at each combination may mean that the resulting information will give only a crude approximation to the maximum profit point.

G. E. P. Box (Biometrics, vol. 10) describes methods for designing efficient test programs in problems of this type. The procedure is one of running a **series of small groups of tests,** with the results of each group of tests evaluated to choose the next group of tests by procedures which Box indicates. Box discusses in detail the difficulties with traditional methods and lays out the basis and procedures for a more effective approach.

The use of Monte Carlo, simulation, or "gaming" methods was mentioned previously in connection with problems where an analytical formulation is not feasible. In many such problems, the objective, after the **simulation model** has been checked for reliability, is to manipulate the model to find the optimum combination of operating conditions. However, since the model is not analytic but is a computing routine, tabled data, or the like, the optimum has to be found by "experiment," by making a series of runs to search for the optimum point. In such problems, Box's methods have proved very valuable in searching for an optimum point.

Areas of Investigation

NATURE OF OPERATIONS RESEARCH PROBLEMS. Many of the problems which operations research units have worked on in business up to now have been company-wide in significance. This has been in part due to the fact that the companies employing them characteristically have well-established staff services such as industrial engineering or market research to help the individual functions of the business. Much of the operations research effort has been concentrated on problems crossing a variety of **functional business areas.** In other cases where the problem itself has not been large, in terms of dollar importance or in its impact across the organization, part of the operations research unit's value has been in its clarification of the relation between the particular operation under study and broader company objectives. In a study of sales force compensation, a sales bonus scheme was set up for salesmen of one division in a way which related compensation to the profitability of the salesmen's activities to the company as a whole. A study of the operating efficiency of one manufacturing department in a textile mill suggested the need for reappraisal of quality standards for the company's product generally. Most operations research problems have some functional area of emphasis—such as production, finance, or marketing—which is of primary importance.

In examining uses of operations research, however, it is important to keep in mind that in business experience to date, the primary area is only that, and not the area of exclusive interest. While it is important to concentrate and conserve the unit's energies in order to turn out useful work, as discussed below, it is equally important to define the problems on which the unit works as operating problems of the organization under the control of the executive to whom the unit is reporting, rather than as specific functional problems.

PRODUCTION SCHEDULING IN INVENTORY CONTROL. Problems connected with production scheduling and inventory control form the largest single group which industrial operations research units have attacked. These have been first to receive the attention of operations research units for a number of reasons. For one thing, problems connected with efficient use of facilities and conservation of capital were critical in many businesses under the pressure of expanding sales during the period when the first operations research studies were being made in business. Second, problems connected with production planning and inventory management exhibit characteristics typical of operations research problems. The interests of a number of functional areas in the business are important: **marketing,** in meeting demand and maintaining customer service; **production,** in maintaining employment stability and keeping costs in line; and **finance,** in conserving the capital resources of the company. These problems characteristically depend on some data which are fairly accurate and determinable, such as operating costs, and other elements which are highly subject to chance fluctuations, such as future sales. The appropriate scheduling policy characteristically depends both on objective elements, such as costs, and on questions of policy, such as the degree of risk the management is willing to assume in making investments and the desired return on investment. Operations research units have contributed to solving these problems, first, by making clear the impact on costs of policy choices open to operating management and, second, by setting up scheduling and control procedures which will effectively translate policy decisions into operations.

Examples of Production Control Applications. 1. A supplier of valves, bearings, and other mechanical components which produced many thousands of items required **sound inventory policies** in the face of violent changes in demand and changing design and style conditions. The company wanted answers to the questions of what to produce, what size and type inventory to maintain, and how rapidly to adjust production operations to changes in the level or mix of demand. A team of physical scientists, with no prior experience in the industry, was able to show that the inventory control procedures had to obey the same fundamental rules as electronic control equipment. Application of methods of servo theory led to development of improved control and reordering methods.

2. A manufacturer of drug products used an operations research group to study means for **reconciling conflicting policies** toward production, sales, and inventory investment. The company's top executives spent many fruitless hours arguing the relative merits of level production, low inventories, and customer satisfaction. Frequently, decisions were made on a precipitous, unsound basis. The operations research group showed how these various factors were interrelated, and provided an explicit basis for arriving at judgments on inventory policy and practical methods for carrying these policies into practice.

3. An operations research team helped a manufacturer of food products get **organized scheduling** for better inventory control. The sales department of this company is responsible for forecasting sales and fixing inventory levels, and thus production rates. The manufacturing organization had only to meet these rates; the sales department was required to back up its sales forecasts by living with the inventories it had established. Finished inventories were set to protect the company against forecast errors, but the manufacturing organization questioned whether these inventories were large enough for economical manufacturing runs too. An operations research team, armed with algebra, some simple statistical methods, and some techniques of servo theory, showed how in fact finished inventory could be cut in half, resulting in a major cut in capital and warehousing costs while still achieving even more stable employment, by (1) relaxing sales department control over finished inventories slightly, and (2) using a simple automatic scheduling method.

ALLOCATION OF RESOURCES. Problems falling into the general classification of "allocation of effort" form another somewhat less well-defined class of applications. This group includes those problems where the resources of the organization are restricted in some way or other, and the objective is to find the best way of using these resources to meet most nearly some stated objective. Linear programming problems, including the allocation of manufacturing facilities serving various warehouses or markets, the allocation of productive facilities among products or between present and future demand, and the use of transport equipment, fall into this class. This group also includes many problems connected with sales compensation, allocation of promotional budgets, and planning of advertising campaigns, where the objective is to make best use of a limited organization or budget in maximizing sales. Military allocation of effort problems include, for example, searching problems as in submarine patrol, allocation of bombing effort, and many problems connected with the deployment of forces among theaters of action.

Examples of Allocation Problems. Examples of some industrial allocation problems include:

1. A specialty products manufacturer serviced a large number of accounts through the use of salesmen. The operations research group recognized that the key to this situation lay in finding a simple but realistic concept of the **way customers behave.** Examination of account records showed that customer behavior could be accurately described as a time-dependent Poisson process—a type of phenomenon found widely in nature, from problems in biology to nuclear physics. This concept yielded the key to establishing precise measures of (1) the efficiency of the salesmen's work and (2) the effect of the promotion in building sales. The most significant outcome was the construction of a new method of directing the promotional salesmen to the appropriate accounts. Careful experiments showed this new method yielded annual increases in sales in the million-dollar bracket, with corresponding increases in net profits.

2. A company with a number of products made at three different locations was concerned about the items to be produced at each location and the points at which the items would be warehoused. Freight costs constituted a substantial part of the delivered cost of the material. The operations research group showed that what appeared to be a complex and involved problem could be broken into a series of rather simple components. Some adaptations of linear programming methods were used to find the **warehousing schedule** which would minimize freight costs. The study is being extended to determine the best distribution of products among manufacturing plants and warehouse locations, to minimize net delivered cost subject to return on investment.

3. An operations research team has helped a transportation company proud of its operating and maintenance efficiency but concerned about its **sales effectiveness.** The team showed, after 3 or 4 months' work on an analysis of the account structure of the company, that the company was not getting its share of the business from major shippers. The selling effort required is of a high-level sort. The salesmen have to understand the customers' needs and sell service and reliability, rather than a product with some tangible advantages. On the basis of the preliminary analysis of the account structure, the team drew up an account classification scheme which indicated the amount of sales attention of various types to be given to accounts of different sizes. The team also set up a control system to get sales effort directed in line with the account classification. An experiment was set up in one terminal area, with two purposes: (1) to measure the effect of sales

effort on various account classes, and (2) to test out the policy for distributing sales effort which was indicated by the preliminary analysis. Though a fairly lengthy experiment was anticipated, two months' experience showed that sales were clearly increased in the test area. Executives of the company commented on the immediate improvement in station morale; and the profits from increased sales in the experiment alone paid the cost of the research.

4. An operations research team designed a simple graphical method for analyzing **distribution questions** of a producer of industrial alcohol. These included such questions as: Which producing plants should serve which markets, in view of production and shipping costs? How would various proposed pricing systems affect the company's competitive position, and in what markets? Where should a new plant be located? How would a proposed change in freight classification affect plant utilization and market position? The method gave the company a quick and accurate way of analyzing a variety of questions of basic business strategy which had hitherto taken up considerable executive time without being resolved.

5. An operations research group set out to determine how the **efforts of missionary salesmen** of an equipment manufacturer might best be directed, and how much missionary sales expense could be justified. For at least fifteen years before this study was begun, the company had used market research and statistical techniques to study these problems. But an operations research team composed of physical chemists and a mathematician, with no previous acquaintance with marketing problems, showed how the existing missionary sales effort could be redirected with greater results, and pointed the way toward an increase in missionary sales effort of over 50 percent. Indeed, the research which showed the way toward improved performance was based in large part on old test data, studied and filed away by the company's statistical research group as being insignificant. In the words of the chief executive of this company, these results were worth literally millions of dollars annually.

6. A manufacturer of chemical products sought a more logical basis for **distributing the advertising budget** among his many products, some of which were growing in use while others were declining. An operations research group showed that his advertising results were related to three simple product characteristics: the market potential, the rate of growth of sales, and the customer loss rate. A mathematical formulation of these three characteristics, each of which could be estimated adequately from existing sales data, provided for the first time a rational basis for distributing advertising and promotional effort.

7. An operations research group demonstrated to a manufacturer in the plastics industry that his **bonus compensation method for salesmen** was in hidden but serious conflict with company objectives. Briefly, the salesmen were being paid most for selling the products of least value to the company. Strange as it may seem, it took an operations research study to point out this inconsistency and to set up the basis on which a sound, consistent compensation plan could be built.

OTHER TYPES OF APPLICATION. Operations research units in the past few years have managed to work on a great variety of business problems. A number of other classifications such as those noted above might be made, including problems in process balancing, problems in the design of data-handling and control systems, and problems in design of operational experiments, to mention a few. The following examples give an indication of the variety of the work which operations research units have been called on to do in particular circumstances.

1. A manufacturer of industrial control equipment wanted an evaluation of a new **method of controlling railroad operations,** as a guide to development. A proposed railway control system was under development which, while costing somewhat more than existing systems, would presumably improve railway operations by increasing the amount of information available to the train operator or engineer. A mathematical model of railroad operations was set up by the operations research group to express the delays suffered by the railway operation as they were affected by the fundamental time characteristics of the control system. This mathematical model, set up in advance of actual construction of the system, showed that improved operation of the control system could not measurably affect the delays suffered by the railroad because of the impact of existing operating rules, and provided a basis for the conclusion that unless operating rules could be changed, the proposed system would not provide any substantial improvement in railroad operation. Development was shifted toward the construction of a system which would provide equivalent service at lower cost.

2. Another operations research team helped a manufacturer of electronic components concerned with the heavy cost of paper work associated with procurement, scheduling, and expediting. Even with these costs, the company was seriously plagued with back orders and parts shortages which held up finished product deliveries. The company makes a wide variety of products, each fairly specialized to a particular end use. Aside from its finished equipment sales, the company does a large spare- and replacement-parts business for both current and former production items. Individual components may be used simultaneously in a variety of finished assemblies. The operations research team found that an **order-explosion** and **base stock inventory control system** could be set up, employing simple statistical methods for extrapolation of component replacement sales (1) for purchasing replenishment stocks, and (2) for controlling product flow through manufacturing operations. The control was also well suited for mechanization, and the operations research team helped the company's systems group define the necessary measurements, review the field of available electronic data-handling systems, and currently program the computer eventually chosen.

3. The federal government and the scheduled air carriers jointly supported a study of the type of **air communications system** best suited to future aviation needs and expected future business load. An operations research team defined the nature of air communications, set up means for measuring communications volumes of various types, and determined the functions of an air communications network and equipment specifications affecting network efficiency. It examined available industry forecasts and analyzed the operational significance of forecasts and possible forecast errors to the communications network. The team dug into equipment and techniques available, as well as operating costs, and finally arrived at a plan for a communications network which is believed to be practical and efficient, and which will handle two to three times the existing communications load, with improved service, below present total cost.

4. A manufacturer of office equipment wanted a method for estimating which companies might be **potential customers** for a radically new type of clerical equipment under development. In a few test cases, the manufacturer had spent several man-years of engineering effort studying the clerical systems of a few potential customers in detail in order to get a reliable estimate of the customers' equipment needs and the probable cost. The manufacturer could easily see that the cost of such sales effort on a routine basis would be prohibitive. The manufacturer wanted some simple measures of the size and complexity of clerical opera-

tions which would be easy to obtain and directly related to equipment needs. An operations research team, through an adaptation of the work of Shannon and Weaver (The Mathematical Theory of Communication) was able to arrive at a basis for estimating the size of clerical operations in terms of five numbers, each of which could be determined fairly readily from available information on the magnitude of inputs, files, and outputs of the clerical operations. These five measures made it possible for the manufacturer to screen out, in a few weeks, those prospects for which the more detailed systems design would be productive.

5. An operations research group was able to set up methods for deriving **time and cost standards** governing large, complex processing operations in a steel cable plant. Conventional industrial engineering methods had failed because of the complexity and variability of the work. The operations research team approached the problem by setting up mathematical functions determined from detailed physical examination of the processes. These functions related the times required to operate the processes to the physical characteristics of the work performed. Together with routine job reports, they enabled the company to set sound and accurate time standards in a few weeks, after many years of failure with conventional methods.

6. A manufacturer of heavy industrial equipment faced a serious problem in setting a **fair incentive wage plan** for servicemen tending several large, semi-automatic pieces of equipment. An operations research team was able to extend the conventional waiting line theory to cover conditions found in these particular operations, thereby providing a basis for a logical incentive plan.

7. One of the better-known chemical companies has set up a small operations research group which up to now has been spending essentially all of its time on problems related to the **application of research findings.** For example, this group has spent a great deal of time working with the research and engineering organizations to help set up pilot plant experiments which will provide maximum information on operating methods for translating research findings into profitable products.

8. In the petroleum field, processes and processing methods have been studied to find out at what points radically **new methods of processing** would pay off most. This work has been useful in directing research toward the study of processes—sometimes not at all obvious ones—where unsuspected bottlenecks were choking off profits.

9. An operations research group helped study a serious **corrosion problem** in paper-making, and has produced significant new findings on the causes and possible cures of this serious problem. This problem may be somewhat outside the normal realm of operations research, being perhaps more a physical than an operating problem, but it illustrates the kinds of problems related to physical research on which an operations research group can work and make significant contributions. This group, composed of a physical chemist, a physicist, and a physicist turned mathematical statistician, has, because of experience in the use of operating data, been able to make a significant contribution in a physical area where careful experimentation is impossible.

Comparison with Other Services to Management

FLEXIBLE FUNCTIONS OF OPERATIONS RESEARCH. Since operations research is one of the newer services to business management, questions concerning the distinction between operations research and other functions, such as industrial engineering, quality control, market research, or accounting, frequently arise. All of these fields have basically very similar objectives: to help business management improve its control over operations and improve operating efficiency. Drawing distinctions between one and another of these fields, therefore, is difficult, in part because the boundaries are indistinct, and in part because drawing distinctions focuses attention on borderline cases where no sharp line can be drawn rather than on the core of the areas considered. It is difficult, analogously, to draw a clear-cut line between the interests of physicists or physical chemists on many particular problems in physical research; it is equally difficult to define separately the interests of the economist, the political scientist, and the sociologist in many problems in the social field. Furthermore, the **functions of an operations research unit** in an organization and the division of responsibilities with other staff units is flexible and will depend on a variety of factors, including company tradition, established interests, and strengths and weaknesses of the several staff units in the company.

The following discussion of operations research and other particular services necessarily deals with each in summary terms. These other services to management have established themselves in business. They have developed methods well suited to their fundamental purposes. Experience indicates that operations research is not competitive with these services, but where other staff activities are well established and flourishing, an operations research unit can make more valuable contributions more quickly, in cooperation with other services.

INDUSTRIAL ENGINEERING. The roots of industrial engineering can be traced to the work of Taylor and others in the scientific investigation of physical labor. Industrial engineering and operations research units have many common interests, both in problems and in the objective of finding numerical solutions or approaches to them. Indeed, today in Great Britain, much of the work done under the name of operations research would be identified in American industry as straightforward industrial engineering. This is presumably due to the relatively limited development of industrial engineering in many British industries, which left a void that the postwar operations research units are helping to fill.

At Ohio State University the work in operations research is conducted by a **multidisciplinary group** which is part of the Department of Industrial Engineering and the Engineering Experiment Station. Many industrial engineers regard incentive wage systems and time study as the core of industrial engineering. This is a far cry from the content and purpose of the industrial engineering curriculum as it is now being taught at progressive universities.

Industrial engineers perhaps have been self-restricting by limiting themselves to emphasis on work measurement, materials handling, and plant layout. The new outlook in industrial engineering, however, is often practically synonymous with the attitudes expressed by those active in operations research.

QUALITY CONTROL. This field is the application of selected statistical techniques to exploit the concept of statistical regularity underlying operating processes. The discovery of the existence of statistical regularity and the resulting definition of the explicit notion of **"statistical control"** represent research achievements of a high order. The power and technical scope of the field is being expanded by similar research into new problem areas. Nevertheless, the core of quality control remains the engineering application of established statistical techniques to exploit the concept of "statistical control."

PROCESS ENGINEERING. The fundamental distinction between operations research and process—mechanical, chemical, etc.—engineering can best be seen by review of the content of operations research. The aim is to study the purposes of the whole operation, the efficiency with which the operation meets these purposes, and the **effect of alternative decisions** on success. Concern with detailed manufacturing or processing methods is incidental. The processes and equipment are usually taken as part of the existing operation rather than as subject matter for study. Interest in specific processing methods and equipment extends only to the manner in which these affect the attainment of the operating goal.

For example, an operations research unit and an engineering group recently worked together on the design of a new railway control system. The job of the operations research unit was to show how to make most effective use of control information of specified completeness and timeliness, and the impact of these on operating cost and safety. The engineering group's problem was to devise hardware for delivering the information quickly and economically. The work of the two groups together showed how far it was worth going in improving hardware to cut down operating inefficiencies. In other cases, the operations research unit may be concerned with the best way of using existing or specified equipment—aircraft, trucks, processing equipment, clerical equipment—rather than with methods for building better equipment.

MARKET RESEARCH. Market research units in business are devoted primarily to gathering, summarizing, and interpreting information describing the market. The **customer universe** may be sampled with some type of questionnaire in order to provide market information, or existing market information (for example, some Government sources) may be analyzed through the use of statistical methods. The objective is to measure, and to gather an impression of, the market. Market research activities provide factual data on the market which can be used as a basis for qualitative judgment, either through examination of the facts directly or by means of statistical analyses of these facts. Highly developed tools, such as sampling and other statistical techniques (see section on Statistical Methods), are used in market research. These tools might be termed "scientific" in the sense that they are carefully designed or highly engineered for the market research field, but the use of such "scientific" or highly developed techniques must be distinguished from the use of the scientific method as physical scientists know it.

Operations research units frequently work on marketing problems. This work, however, tends to be aimed at studying the marketing operation itself rather than the market. The operations research unit would look to the market research section for data describing the market, when this is important to the problem. In addition, most operations research studies of marketing problems are concerned seriously with the interactions among the marketing and other operations of the business. In one case, a market research study of the types and locations of customers for a chemical product was used by the operations research unit, together with data on costs, speed of shipment, etc., in a study of the allocation of salesmen's time to customer accounts. In another case, the characterization of customers' reactions to advertising that came out of an operations research study of methods for smoothing employment stimulated new market research studies to measure newly recognized important customer characteristics.

ACCOUNTING. The traditional and basic **accounting function** is to give stockholders, employees, and the public a consistent and proven record of the flow of assets in a business, as a measure of the stewardship of management. This function influences principles, data collected, and procedures. A second function —**the control function**—is the systematic collection and organization of cost and related control data. These functions, particularly the former, dictate the need for consistency, regularity, and precision in data. On the other hand, consistency and regularity serve little purpose in operations research, and precise data are characteristically not available. Furthermore, consistency in definition, e.g., of costs, is not important, so long as the definitions used are operationally significant in the particular problem.

Despite differences in purpose, and consequent differences in data and people, operations research and accounting units have worked effectively together. Today, the accounting organization is the major agency for **collecting and summarizing operating statistics,** and the operations research units must look to the accounting unit for operating data. Operations research units, in turn, have helped accounting units set up effective **management control reporting systems,** getting the control measures properly defined so as to be significant. Operations research and accounting units have also worked together effectively in designing and organizing a **central data-processing and information-handling unit.**

ECONOMICS. Many of the problems which an operations research unit studies have been studied by economists for some time and in some detail. However, economists—with few exceptions—have been concerned almost exclusively with examination of the consequences or characteristics of highly theoretical models of economic behavior, or with advocacy of large-scale economic policies, or with the description of the economic climate or condition, rather than with the problems of a particular businessman making a particular choice.

Operations research, on the other hand, is both **experimental and applied.** It relies heavily on experimentation as a source of information and a check on conclusions. It is concerned with particular decisions. Its interest is primarily in the internal workings of the organization rather than its economic environment.

Whether operations research will survive as a separate staff function in business or be absorbed into another area, such as an expanded industrial engineering function, remains to be seen. At present, operations research is serving a useful function in those companies with active units, filling the gap between the theoretical disciplines of the social sciences and the engineering functions in business, and carrying over the analytical and experimental methods of the physical sciences into operating fields.

Management of Operations Research

AREAS FOR MANAGEMENT DECISION. Development and management of an operations research unit in business involves decisions and action in three areas:

1. Selection of a place to begin.
2. Selection of personnel to do the work.
3. Establishment of a permanent form and program for the unit.

Experience indicates that there are no pat answers to questions in these areas; they must be answered by each firm with particular reference to its own circumstances and needs. Timing of decisions within these three areas will also vary from company to company. Some companies in the past have begun with selection of the problem area, and have followed this with organization of the group to attack it; others have first found the personnel, then the most likely way for them to begin. Despite the need for reaching decisions on these points with particular reference to the circumstances in each company, certain general conclusions may be drawn from experience in industrial operations research to date.

SELECTION OF THE PROBLEM AREAS. In the past there appear to have been essentially two bases used in the selection of initial problem areas. In some companies the areas selected have been **troublesome** areas in which conventional techniques have failed to provide adequate help, resulting in a desire on the part of the company for additional help and a fresh attack. In other companies, where interest in operations research has stimulated a desire to test out its value without particular reference to an immediately pressing problem area, search has been made for **manageable problems,** where there exists a possibility of testing and evaluating the solutions within a reasonably short period of time.

These have been typically complex problems to which the answers were neither obvious nor trivial, and for which present aids and guides were substantially incomplete. The problems have been in important areas where the investment in knowledge could be expected to pay off manyfold through use in later assignments. A study of retail store operating costs for a company that maintains an extensive retail chain yielded useful measures for control of operating costs and for spotting developing weaknesses in operations of individual units. The resulting knowledge about the operations and associated costs provided part of a significant and far-reaching analysis of chain merchandising policies.

Review of industrial problems where operations research has been successful indicates one characteristic of overwhelming importance, **executive interest and cooperation.** The area and specific question chosen must be one on which the executive wants and is prepared to take action, and where the problem is significant enough to him for him to want assistance and to be willing at least to listen to the research unit's findings. From time to time, one sees an operations research program undertaken with a "specimen" problem, chosen because it is "clear-cut, well defined, and quantitative" rather than because someone is seriously concerned about the problem or dissatisfied with existing conditions. Problems need not be well defined and quantitative—at least at first—to be useful subjects for operations research. On the other hand, it is important that the executive and the team have some common and clear understanding of how the research can lead to decisions, what kinds of decisions can be made, and what limitations are imposed by resources or higher policies, in order to prevent the research unit's work from drifting into "blue sky" or "study" projects.

Situation for Initial Research. Within these general qualifications, the following characteristics are important, particularly in initial work:

1. **Opportunity for decision.**
2. **Possibility of quantitative study and measurement.** The area should be at least in part quantitative and should lend itself to quantitative interpretation and description. At least some aspects of the problem should be measurable, and at least a minimum of data related to the operations should be available. A preliminary study to provide bases for the prediction of the acceptance of fabric styles was quickly dropped in one case because of the inability to construct within a reasonable period an adequate quantitative description of the complexities of fabric, style, pattern, and color.
3. **Chance for experimentation and data collection.** Disruption of operations for special experiments is by no means always necessary, but opportunity for collection of special data is frequently required. In one problem, analysis of accounts receivable extending back over two years yielded the key to a knotty

marketing problem. In another case, an initial study of maintenance problems was found to be uneconomical because of lack of available records showing maintenance and breakdown histories on equipment to be studied. Recommendations were made, however, for the collection of necessary data to provide a basis for investigation at a later time when information of a quantitative nature was available.

4. **Ready evaluation of results.** Neither the analyst nor the most enthusiastic executive can expect operations research activities to be supported on the basis of faith alone. Ready ability to measure effects of changes provides bases for evaluating the research, in order to build up an attitude of mutual confidence. These problems, furthermore, have not been so large in scope as to be utterly indefinite. There should be some aspect which can be tackled readily, an understanding of which would be a contribution to the development of an approach to the whole area under investigation.

The final selection of the specific problem to be studied is best made in cooperation with the research team. Executives have found it useful to map out the area and types of problems in advance; the research group can then comment on those aspects most amenable to study, indicating where the problem can be clearly formulated, and where progress can be expected with reasonable effort. A problem can then be selected which meets the requirements of both the executive (for importance and use) and the research group (for suitability of existing data for quantitative study).

ACHIEVING SUCCESS IN OPERATIONS RESEARCH. Much frustration and dissatisfaction can be avoided if the research team and the executive keep in mind each other's needs. While it is necessary for the research team to arrive at a sufficiently understandable statement of the problem and method of attack to provide the executive with confidence in giving initial support, the executive must also recognize that this activity is research, and part of any research program is typically the **explicit formulation of the problem.** Advance specification of a detailed program, scope, and goals is frequently difficult and usually meaningless.

The executive dealing with an operations research unit will obtain value from it in proportion to the discretion he can use in controlling the group's activities. On one hand, he must recognize that the unit's work is a form of research, and research takes time. Too much insistence on "progress reports" or short-term progress can stifle the group's work. On the other hand, the executive has a responsibility to himself and to the unit to exercise enough control over its activities to be sure first, that its work is practically oriented, and second, that the unit proves its value in the application of its results. Steps in the successful **executive control** of operations research, like any research, are agreement on an initial area of investigation, provision for the group to have access to the data and the people to help formulate the specific problems to be studied, and continued contact to guide and redirect the work along the lines of greatest value as the work develops.

PERSONNEL AND ORGANIZATION. Operations research, as the foregoing discussion indicates, is a technical field. To be used successfully, it requires persons with some experience in, and training for, experimental research. It is not simply applying mathematical techniques to clearly defined business problems; the investigative and experimental aspects are vital. Individuals with the training needed may be obtained from universities or they may be recruited internally, for example, from the physical research laboratory. In either case, it is important to look first to the **experimental research capacities** and **training** of the individuals rather than to their knowledge of the business or business experience in general.

Very successful operations research workers have been drawn from a wide range of fields, from history and law to nuclear physics. They include physicists, chemists, biologists, psychologists, economists, quality control engineers, industrial engineers, and many others. **Diversity in background** and use of the **mixed team** or group with many specialties represented, have been particularly useful in the beginning of operations research as a formal field. This may, however, be traced in large part to the lack of any extensive, well-established "home discipline" rather than to any essential requirement. At present, opportunities for formal academic training in operations research are quite limited. As sources of trained operations research workers, the most fruitful fields currently are probably **physics, physical chemistry,** and **electrical engineering.**

External Operations Research Group. There are basically two sources of operations research personnel available to most reasonably large industrial organizations. The first source is external, and consists of established operations research groups attached to reputable consulting research organizations. These groups, being the principal reservoirs of trained personnel at the present time, provide experienced operations research analysts. Furthermore, there is no fixed commitment if a decision ultimately is made to discontinue the work. The attitudes of reputable groups are not biased by previous positions and contacts, and frequently outsiders have been found to have the stature or prestige required to effect necessary changes in internal attitudes or policies. They bring, moreover, a fresh viewpoint to the operation studied, since they are not steeped in the existing internal experiences and conceptions, and they are less likely to be diverted by pressing but less important day-to-day problems.

The value of **group attack** has been receiving increasing recognition in research fields, particularly in fields of physical research, and it is generally recognized to be of substantial importance in operations research. The group provides, first, the opportunity for exchange of ideas among members of the team, and for resulting stimulation, development, and testing of concepts and approaches. The external consulting groups make available also the time and talents of associated consulting specialists in such fields as marketing, accounting, or industrial engineering—experts who are used to working with the operations research team proper, and who can be brought in when their specific knowledge will contribute to the case under study. Such a team provides an opportunity for the company to purchase part of the time of several experienced persons, obtaining thereby a diversity of experience and training which would otherwise be unobtainable at equivalent cost.

The disadvantages in the use of consulting organizations are the obverse of the advantages. One disadvantage which is frequently mentioned is that of cost; in fact, this is probably considerably less important than it is normally thought. The cost of using a consulting group does not appear to be high relative to the cost of an internal group of equivalent experience, diversity, and training. In comparing the cost of external versus internal analysts, it is important to bear in mind the types of professional people and supporting personnel required, the pay scales currently established for such personnel, and the other overhead costs associated with a group of this type.

Lack of acquaintance with the organization and its operations, while frequently an advantage, can be a disadvantage. The cost of, or investment in, obtaining such acquaintance must be recognized as a definite cost of bringing in external personnel. Another disadvantage which is sometimes mentioned is a possible resentment created by "outsider" investigators dipping into internal operations of the company. This may be a potential disadvantage in some organizations, but it probably can be minimized or eliminated by the integrity and tact with which members of reputable consulting organizations are trained to approach their work. Lack of opportunity for continuous intimate contact with the company may be a more serious disadvantage, but it has the compensating advantage of more time to think undisturbedly, without pressure of day-to-day short-term investigations distracting from more fundamental and ultimately more profitable studies.

Internal Operations Research Group. The establishment of an internal group undoubtedly has advantages in the long run for medium or large-sized corporations. For such companies as can support a professional group with the associated clerical and computing services, an internal group may ultimately be more efficient and less costly, providing an opportunity for closer contact, greater awareness of problems, and deeper acquaintance with management objectives and needs. The short-run disadvantages, however, lie in the difficulty of finding trained and experienced people and the effects of a new operations research activity on the reassignment of existing and valuable people and the hiring of new persons of the calibre required. Another disadvantage is the difficulty in obtaining breadth of experience in an internal group of economically small size. Diversity of experience and training is not an essential to operations research, but it has been found time and again to be extremely valuable.

A variety of internal **organizational forms** have been found useful in different types and sizes of organizations. The simplest is the single unit or group attached at some responsible executive level. At times a unit of one analyst plus clerical help has been productive. Generally, however, two or more technically trained people are needed for the exchange of ideas and to round out the skills of the unit. One might have an experimental bent, while the other might be a strong mathematician. In addition, computing and stenographic help are needed, plus access to major company computing facilities if these exist.

Where a company is highly diversified, it is desirable to have the research unit connected to the direct operating executive level (department or division head). Some diversified companies have followed the policy of fostering a research unit at each operating unit, plus a small coordinating and information exchange group as part of the central staff.

An **operations research unit** may contain from two to twenty analysts (some military groups are substantially larger). Where a commitment in a large group is undesirable or where personnel with the proper training for permanent operations research work are not available, the capacity of the permanent unit has been expanded in some cases by using the permanent members as members of ad hoc teams to study particular problems. The permanent unit acts as a secretariat for the ad hoc groups, the permanent members supply research skills to the group, and the unit serves as a central point for putting together and keeping alive the work of the separate teams, as part of a continuing program.

Operations Research Groups for Specific Problems. Where companies have not been prepared for taking on the commitment immediately of a permanent group of any kind, various compromises have been tried. One is the formation of **ad hoc** teams within the company—teams composed of members drawn from other operating, engineering, and research activities. One well-known company which has experienced rapid growth within the last few years has found the use of such **ad hoc teams** extremely valuable in drawing together the diverse experience throughout the company to focus on a particular problem area. Teams made up of engineers, management personnel, and members of research groups have been organized, for example, to study particular production processes, from specification of raw material to control of finished output, including assignment of workers and work loads, machine settings, control methods, scrap allowances, tolerances, and in-process inventory levels. While such studies may lie in large part outside the framework of a strict definition of research, incorporating as they do relatively little fundamental study of operating problems or investigation of basic concepts, they do serve the useful purpose of operations research in organizing existing data as a basis for improvement of efficiency. The experience of serving in such a group has been found to be of great value in broadening the viewpoint of the members.

To be successful, the members of such teams must be relieved of other administrative responsibilities. It has been found, unfortunately in many cases, that where members are engaged in such team studies only on a part-time basis, and concurrently attempt to carry on normal operating or administrative activities, the work of the team degenerates and frequently collapses. The difficulties of this method of attacking operating problems are fairly obvious. They lie in the problem of finding people of adequate capabilities who can be relieved of existing duties, and in providing continuity in the development of method from one team to the next.

Combination of Internal and External Groups. A second compromise solution has been the use of an outside consulting group to initiate the work and thereafter to provide assistance in getting an internal group organized. This pattern is similar to that frequently followed in the past in physical research. It provides an opportunity for the company to try out operations research before it commits itself permanently and until it grows well out of its initial area, to avoid setting up operations research on a basis restricted to the thinking and problems of the department to which it was first applied. It enables the company to draw on the experience of the outside group for education of its management and analytical personnel. The experience of the outside group can provide guidance and sources for the selection of appropriate personnel.

Once successful results have been obtained in the first two or three assignments undertaken, the organization of an internal group can be commenced, and the use of the external consulting group can be restricted in time to occasional consultation on special problems and extension of the capacity of the internal analytical team in the execution of special studies.

Place of Operations Research in Organization. The organizational position or assignment of the operations research group within the company is a subject which requires some preliminary thought before the group is organized, or before work is undertaken. Operations research analysts have sometimes argued that the operations research group should hold a high position in the company's organization, essentially as a staff group to the chief executive. This argument is based on the need of the operations research group to obtain the viewpoint of the company as a whole and to be aware of the objectives of the top management. This acquaintance with the company viewpoint is required if the objectives of studies are to be consistent with management policies. The same argument holds, unfortunately, for large numbers of groups and services within the organization, all competing for the time of the top executives. It is probably sounder to accept the need for operations research to start modestly, at a lower point within the organization and, as it proves itself, to develop and grow to a more prominent position. This, indeed, has been the common pattern in physical research, where the research group was often first assigned to a rather lowly level within the manufacturing or engineering organizations. The recognition of the importance of physical research accorded by the elevation of the chief research executive to the vice-presidential level is a relatively new development in many, if not most, industrial organizations.

Access to Management. Operations research does have some claim to executive attention, however. In particular, it must be established at or report to some executive level where, within its area of work, it is in a position

1. To talk directly with the part of operating management concerned about problems it may have or the unit may see.
2. To get access to data without generating interdivisional jealousy.
3. To work directly with operating management on the use of results.

Direct contact between people with operating questions and problems and the operations research unit is essential. The unit cannot get its questions second-hand. Often questions are not framed initially in the right terms. Only by give-and-take between the unit and the operating man concerned can the problem be clarified or stated in the right terms for study. If successful, the operations research unit should be given an opportunity to expand the area of its studies as it proves its case, and should not be shut off from or restricted to specific and limited operating areas. Furthermore, the group needs the interest and encouragement of top management if it is to achieve its maximum level of usefulness within the company.

LONG-TERM PROGRAM. If a company undertakes operations research, it should generally do so with the intention of continuing and expanding its use. The investment in knowledge and method, no matter how low the initial cost, is too valuable to be thrown away. The problems first recognized and attacked have, experience has shown, generally not been the most productive problems the group could study. An industrial company should undertake operations research, therefore, with a full recognition of the implications—that when operations research is properly carried out it is not a toy or an idle pastime, and that it is hardly suited to sporadic, offhand use.

Considerations governing choice of problems in the long run are not too different from those governing the initial few problems. Certainly, the **basic criterion** that the question be in an area where management can and will take action of some kind (even if only objecting to higher management) remains important. There is, perhaps, less need to concentrate on problems with an immediate possibility of measurable return, and there is more reason as the unit proves itself to gamble part of the unit's time on some difficult assignments where there is a good chance of inconclusive results.

The **value** of an operations research unit will depend in part on its ability to answer questions raised by management, and in part on its ability to formulate and raise new questions of its own. These questions can be found and properly formulated only if the group has some time to spend on projects of its own which it need not justify. On the other hand, a full diet of such problems could easily turn a unit into a "study" group, adding nothing to the company but volumes in its archives. Specific-application projects (many of which should come out of the longer-range studies) are important to help the group justify its work by directly measurable results, to help it keep its whole program practically oriented by requiring it to take partial responsibility for getting its findings applied, and to keep it in touch with the practical workings of the business. In a long-run program, a balance of about one-third of the group's total effort devoted to **longer-range projects** and two-thirds to **specific-application projects** appears desirable.

The unit must learn to live with and to respect deadlines, as long as these are reasonable and important. Indeed, the operations research unit should welcome a reasonable number of "crash" assignments where a useful answer is needed very promptly. If the unit's work is to lead to satisfactory results on time, it is important that the number of active jobs be kept well under control. There can easily be a tendency to pile up a list of projects with little or no progress made on any. However, enough projects are needed so that work will not bog down if, for example, data cannot be collected for a while, and so that workers can shift from one problem to another for stimulus. A rough working rule sometimes used is **one active project per research man.** This is, of course, rough, but it suggests that a unit of two people would work on two or, at most, three problems.

To meet deadlines and to maintain this schedule of assignments, frequent **joint reviews** by the head of the unit and the executive to whom he reports are needed for jobs in progress and personnel assignments. These reviews can be used very effectively to keep the project load in line with the unit's capacity, to keep the project list fresh, to see that results are obtained, and to keep the unit's personnel in line with needs. Another kind of review which has been found useful is **periodic** (e.g., monthly) **review** of each major project by a review committee composed of operating personnel interested in the project plus one or two technical people from the research unit who are not working on the project. The purpose of the committee is to advise and suggest, to indicate practical and technical difficulties, and to give the individuals working on the project a chance to test ideas as they develop, before any formal report or recommendation is made.

Evaluation of Operations Research

BASIS FOR SOUND DECISIONS. Case histories show that operations research provides a basis for arriving at an **integrated and objective analysis** of operating problems. An integrated, broad view is fundamental to the method, and one characteristic of operations research studies is a tendency toward expansion in viewpoint during the investigation. Objectivity is likewise fundamental to the method, partly because the mathematical force of the model and techniques limits opportunity for biases as a result of personal viewpoints. Moreover, since the method is experimental, the views and biases which may be introduced must check with fact. The end-products of operations research studies are quantitative results. These provide an opportunity for sound estimates in quantitative terms of requirements, objectives, and goals, and the basis for more precise planning and decision-making, leading to more nearly optimal action.

Contributions from Existing Data. The contributions of operations research to **business analysis and planning** have been important and substantial. One of the most valuable of these has been the application of organized thinking to data already existing within a company. Frequently a major operations research contribution has been the location, collection, and ordering of existing data scattered through widely separated branches of the company. In one recent study, an operations research team found fundamentally the same problem cropping up under various guises in a number of different parts of the company. Each division or section had its own point of view toward the problem, and each had data and significant information to contribute. Unfortunately, however, even in this company, well known for its sound and progressive management, failure to recognize the fundamental and pervasive character of this problem and to draw together data existing in diverse parts of the organization had up to then prevented a unified and comprehensive attack upon it.

Contributions Through New Methods. Another contribution has been the introduction of new concepts and methods of analysis. Some of these concepts, such as information theory, control theory, and certain aspects of statistical mechanics, can be carried over from other fields. The physical sciences, and in particular modern physics, have been a very fruitful source of transplanted analytical techniques. The **conscious search** characteristic of scientific research for formalization and generalization of concepts and techniques has led to the development of concepts and methods specific to operations research. The notion of **measure of effectiveness** is simple enough, but the introduction of this concept has often been exceedingly helpful in uncovering and eliminating policy conflicts and inconsistencies in such problems, for example, as production scheduling, or the establishment of incentive compensation plans. The theories of search and of allocation of effort were conscious generalizations of specific military research studies, and the translation of these theories into industrial terms is under way. Within industrial operations research, theories of clerical organization and consumer behavior and inventory control systems illustrate the opportunity for the development of powerful tools for attacking important business problems. The opportunity to explore the effects of alternate decisions, in advance of commitment, through the concept of the model, provides clarification of the interdependencies among variables and the connections between actions and results. This explicit statement of the connection between action and result, together with the quantitative prediction of outcome, is the source of the power of operations research methods in organizing bases for executive action.

LIMITATIONS OF OPERATIONS RESEARCH. Operations research is not a cure-all for every business ill, nor is it a source of automatic decisions. As a quantitative field of analysis, it is limited to the study of tangible, measurable factors; yet many important factors affecting business decisions remain intangible or qualitative. The responsibility rests with the operations research group, therefore, to frame its analysis and statement of conclusions in recognition of this limit. On the other hand, the executive must be prepared to adjust or modify the conclusions drawn from the quantitative analysis to adjust for the impact of qualitative, nonmeasurable factors. The limitation of operations research to quantitative and measurable concepts, however, has often forced successful efforts to find ways and means of measuring factors which had been assumed or presumed to be "intangible" or qualitative.

Executive and Research Roles. The need for decisions and decision-making is by no means removed by operations research. The **research responsibility** is one of analysis: to use existing or experimental factual data to the extent possible; to indicate the assumptions underlying analysis; to indicate the implications of alternative assumptions; to interpret the results of the analysis as they bear on the necessary decisions. The **executive responsibility** remains: to examine the assumptions and evaluate them; to consider factors which may have been neglected, or questions of policy which may have been assumed; to reach, and take responsibility for, decisions.

The distinction between the analytical and executive responsibility was clearly brought out in a recent series of conferences called to implement the results of a long and major operations research investigation. The results of this study were based in part on the assumption that the volume of output of a plant in question could be increased substantially at the existing level of efficiency. The executive responsible for the operation of the plant agreed with this assumption and felt that it could be matched in practice. The official responsible for the ultimate decision, however, expressed the fear that increases in volume would lead to slackening of control and resulting efficiency losses. He decided to follow a more conservative modification of the course of action suggested by the study—a modification based primarily on his estimate of the psychology of the plant personnel as affected by changes in the level of plant operations.

Management Control of Operations Research. The characterization of operations research as an applied science implies certain limitations on its usefulness. Analyses are always incomplete, with results following from successive attacks and successive approximations. Each level of approximation has its own value and limits, but this sequential method of attack and **successive approximation** creates problems in control for the executive in determining whether extension of the study is practical, or whether limitation of the study will smother potentially useful results. The characterization of operations research as scientific, rather than expert, opinion means that while certain advantages may exist in the power and usefulness of results, corresponding disadvantages arise in the time required to achieve useful conclusions—more time than is required for normal engineering analyses.

As an **applied science,** the work is torn between two objectives. As "applied" it strives for practical and useful work; as "science" it seeks increasing understanding of the operation, even when the usefulness of this information is not immediately clear. The executive who plans to support research work of this character must be fairly warned of the duality in application versus research and of the need for restraint in controlling the research or analytical activities. The natural tendency to require that the studies or analyses be "practical" can result in loss of substantial benefits, if enforced too rigidly. Finally, as a form of research, the results of studies of this type are necessarily somewhat speculative. When operations research is purchased, neither the specific program to be followed, the precise questions to be answered. nor the successful achievement of results can be guaranteed. Recognition of this difference between the nature of operations research and that of more conventional engineering methods is essential to the satisfaction of both the controlling executive and the research analyst.

PLANT LAYOUT AND LOCATION

CONTENTS

	PAGE
The factory	1
Classification of manufacturing plants	1
Types of manufacturing which determine plant layouts (f. 1)	2
Definitions of plant layout	1

Plant Layout Functions

Principles of plant layout	2
Place of plant layout in the organization	4
Scope of the plant layout function	4
Specimen functional chart for a plant layout organization (f. 2)	3
Types of plant layout problems	4
Advantages derived from efficient layouts	4

Assembling Data for Plant Layout

Basis of layout	5
Plant layout procedures	6
Flow chart of plant layout procedure for determining plant layout design (f. 3)	8-9
Procure basic data	6
Analysis of production data	7
Production engineering for production line (f. 4)	10
Machinery, auxiliary equipment, and gages required in tooling a production line for one part (f. 5)	11
Analyze and coordinate basic data	7
Typical assembly chart (f. 6)	12
Calculate equipment requirements	12
Select general materials handling plan	13
Building factors related to materials handling	13

Developing the Layout

Sketch plot plan	14
Plot plan of existing buildings. Shaded areas indicate location and size of proposed building additions and extensions (f. 7)	15
Plan general flow pattern	14
Factors affecting the flow pattern	16
Travel charts as an aid in flow analysis	16
Travel chart (f. 8)	16
Influence of processes on plant layout	17
Types of flow patterns	18
Odd-angle layout for passing parts by hand in pairs to successive operations (f. 9)	18

Layout of automobile tire plant and routes of materials (f. 10)	20
Process layout	19
Advantages of process layout	19
Product layout	19
Advantages of product layout	20
Combination of product and process layout	20
Planning for flexibility	21
Check list for determining industrial plant flexibility (f. 11)	22
Plan individual work stations	21
Work-station layout for a No. 3 milling machine (f. 12)	23
Operator cycling or multiple machine operation	24
Old and new layouts showing how machines can be rearranged so that one man can operate more than one machine (f. 13)	24
Number of machines an operator can tend	24
Old and improved machine layouts (f. 14)	25
Machine breakdowns	25
Select specific materials handling equipment	27
Check list of data required for a materials handling project (f. 15)	26

Coordinating the Various Factors

Coordinate individual operations	27
Typical layout planning chart (f. 16)	28-29
Calculate storage space requirements	27
Storage requirements chart (f. 17)	30
Construct flow diagrams for production centers	30
Flow diagram of related groups of operations (f. 18)	31
Line production	30
Subassemblies	32
Automation and plant layout	34
Conversion to automation (f. 19)	33

Developing the Plot Plan

Allocate production centers to areas on plot plan	34
Skeleton floor plan of a machining and assembly plant (f. 20)	36-37
Aisles	35
Columns	35
Plan and locate service areas	35
General office	38
Factory office	38

CONTENTS (*Continued*)

PAGE

Tool cribs and toolrooms 38
Powerhouse 38
Locker rooms, washrooms, and toilets 38
Rest rooms 39
Personnel department 39
Dispensary 39
Cafeterias 39
Other departments 39

Making the Master Layout

Construct master layout 40
Layout boards 40
Scale 40
Templates and models 40
  Plant layout comparison chart. Com-
  parison of most common types of tem-
  plates and models (*f.* 21) 41
  Specimen template sheet for a specific
  milling machine (*f.* 22) 42
Flow lines 43
Reproductions 43
Miscellaneous factors 43
  Plant layout drawing prepared from
  template layout (*f.* 23) 44

Making the Installation

Check final layout 45
  Plant layout check sheet (*f.* 24) 46-47
Get official approvals 48
Install the layout 48

Plant Layout Surveys and Re-Layouts

The re-layout problem 49
Restudy to improve layouts 49
  Conditions to be forbidden in handling
  materials (*f.* 25) 50
Information to assemble in a survey 50
Points to investigate in a detailed study .. 51
Data on buildings and equipment 51
Making new layouts 52

Plant Buildings

Grouping of buildings 52
One-story vs. multistory buildings 52
Factors that determine types 52
Building details 53

Heating and Ventilation

Selection factors 53
Types of systems 54
  Combined or split systems 54
  Central or unit systems 54
  Steam, hot-water, and direct-fluid systems 55
  Gas, oil, or coal-fired systems 55
Selection of a system 56
Fundamentals of design 56
  Design temperatures 56
  Heating season climatic data (*f.* 26) 57
Wind velocity 57
Computation of transmission losses 58
  Thermal conductivities (*k*) and conduct-
  ances (*c*) (*f.* 27) 59
Computation of infiltration losses 60
Ventilation requirements 62
Duct design 62
Pressure losses in ducts 63
  Roughness values for pipe (*f.* 28) 64

PAGE

Friction factor determination 64
  Relation between friction factor and
  Reynolds number (*f.* 29) 65
Noncircular conduits 66
  Friction of air in straight ducts, for
  volumes of 1,000 to 100,000 cu. ft. per
  min. (*f.* 30) 67
Pressure losses in duct fittings 68
Piping design 69
  Steam systems 69
  Hot-water systems 70
Air distribution devices 71
Air heating coils 71
Fans 72
  Selection 72
  Fan efficiency 72
  Performance characteristics 73
  Performance curves of a forward-curved
  blade centrifugal fan (*f.* 31) 73
  Performance curves of a backwardly in-
  clined blade centrifugal fan (*f.* 32) 74
  Fan laws 74
Air filters 75
  Dry filters 75
  Viscous impingement filters 75
  Electronic filters 76
  Air washers 76
Control systems 77

Air Conditioning

Systems 77
Psychrometric data 78
  Thermodynamic properties of moist air
  (standard atmospheric pressure, 29.921
  in. Hg) (*f.* 33) 79-81
Definitions 78
  Psychrometric chart (American Society
  of Heating and Air Conditioning
  Engineers) (*f.* 34) 82
Calculation by table 83
Calculation by chart 86
Computation of cooling loads 86
  Components 86
  Design conditions 87
  Solar load estimates 87
  Heat transmission through glass areas.... 88
  Ventilation and infiltration loads 88
  Occupant loads 88
  Equipment and lighting loads 88
Air conditioning equipment 89
  Unit and central systems 89
  Reciprocating and centrifugal compressors 89
  Direct-expansion and chilled-water systems 89
  Condensing equipment 90
  Heat pumps 90

Plant Lighting

Illumination 91
  Illumination and safety 91
  Effect of good daylight in reducing acci-
  dents (*f.* 35) 91
  Accident reduction by illumination and
  painting 92
  Effectiveness of good lighting in reduc-
  ing accidents (*f.* 36) 92
  Factors of good illumination 92
  Quantity of light 93
  Recommended levels of general illumina-
  tion (*f.* 37) 94

CONTENTS (*Continued*)

PAGE

Daylight lighting 93
Daylight through side windows 93
  Curves of illumination intensity from
    side windows (*f*. 38) 94
Daylight through side and monitor windows 95
  Curves of illumination intensity showing
    effect of monitor windows (*f*. 39) 95
  Daylight distribution in a one-story
    building with different monitor designs (*f*. 40) 96
Artificial lighting 96
General lighting systems 97
  Distribution of light under different
    lighting systems (*f*. 41) 96
Sources of artificial light 97
  Characteristics and applications of the
    three most common light sources (*f*. 42) 97
Fluorescent lighting 97
Mercury vapor lamps 98
Illumination design data for interiors 98
Lumen method of calculation 98
  Diffuse reflection factors (*f*. 43) 99
  Coefficient of utilization (*f*. 44) 100–103
  Room index table for use with Fig. 44
    (*f*. 45) 104–105
Exterior lighting 106

PAGE

Use of Color in Industry

Advantages of lighter colors 106
Color-contrast painting 106
  Walls, floors, aisles 107
  Moving equipment 107
Safety color code 107

Plant Location

Objective 108
Sources of problem 108
Check lists 108
  Comparison chart for recurring costs
    (*f*. 46) 109
Basic factors 110
  Transportation 110
  Labor 111
  Operating expense 112
  Typical water requirements for various
    industries (*f*. 47) 112
  Miscellaneous factors 113
Inducements and concessions 113
  Local government plan 114
Dispersion 115
Site selection 115

Use of Color in Industry

Advantage of better color 106
Color contrast factors 106
Wall, floor, ceiling 107
Moving equipment 107
Safety color code 107

Plant Location

Objective 108
Nature of problem 108
Check lists 108
Consultants, chief for procuring factory (?) 109
Basic factors 110
Transportation 110
Labor 111
Operating expenses 111
Typical water requirements for various industries (T. ..) .. 112
Markets 112
Miscellaneous factors 113
Inducements and concessions 113
Local government phase 114
Decision 115
Key reference 115

Daylight lighting 91
Daylight through side windows 92
Curves of illumination intensity through side windows (T. 33) 94
Daylight through side and monitor windows 95
Curve of illumination intensity showing effect of monitor windows (T. 30) 96
Daylight distribution in a one-story building with different monitor designs (T. 40) 96
Artificial lighting 96
General lighting systems 97
Distribution of light under different lighting systems (T. 1) 96
Sources of artificial light 97
Characteristics and applications of the three most common light sources (T. 45) .. 97
Fluorescent lighting 97
Mercury vapor lamps 98
Illumination design data for interiors .. 98
Lumen method of calculation 99
Diffuse reflection factors (T. 46) .. 99
Coefficient of utilization (T. 48) 100-103
Room index table for use with Fig. 44 (T. 49) 104-105
Exterior lighting 106

PLANT LAYOUT AND LOCATION

THE FACTORY. The term "factory" or, more broadly, "manufacturing plant" means a building or group of buildings together with mechanical equipment, machinery, tools, and the various other physical facilities needed for the production of goods together with the physical, mental, and, in the broader sense, the social well-being of the employees. Briefly, manufacturing implies organization of these physical and human agencies of production using modern machinery together with the principles of division of labor, specialization, standardization, and interchangeability.

CLASSIFICATION OF MANUFACTURING PLANTS. Manufacturing industries may be classified according to the nature of the process performed —continuous process, repetitive process, and intermittent process industries. Generally speaking, a **continuous process** industry is one that is carried on 24 hours per day; a **repetitive process** industry is one where the product is processed in lots; an **intermittent process** industry is one that processes items of product when and as ordered. In the repetitive process industry, the lots may follow each other with such regularity as to create a situation analogous to a continuous process industry, except that production is not of necessity carried on 24 hours per day.

Mallick and Gaudreau (Plant Layout Planning and Practice) have presented this classification very clearly in diagrammatic form as shown in Fig. 1. Owing to plant site, time of construction, caliber of management, nature of process, and many other factors, no two plants have identical layouts, even though their operations may be the same.

DEFINITIONS OF PLANT LAYOUT. Plant layout has been defined by current authors as:

. . . A floor plan for determining and arranging the desired machinery and equipment of a plant, whether established or contemplated, in the one best place, to permit the quickest flow of material at the lowest cost and with the least amount of handling in processing the product, from the receipt of raw material to the shipment of finished products. (Mallick and Gaudreau, Plant Layout Planning and Practice.)

. . . Planning the path each component part of a product is to follow through the plant, coordinating the paths of the various parts so that the manufacturing processes may be carried out in the most practical and economical manner, then preparing a scale drawing, or other representation of the arrangement, and finally seeing that the plan is properly put into effect. (Apple, Plant Layout and Materials Handling.)

. . . (a) placing the right equipment, (b) coupled with the right method, (c) in the right place, (d) to permit the processing of a product unit in the most effective manner, (e) through the shortest possible distance, and (f) in the shortest possible time. (Sansonnetti and Mallick, Factory Management, vol. 103.)

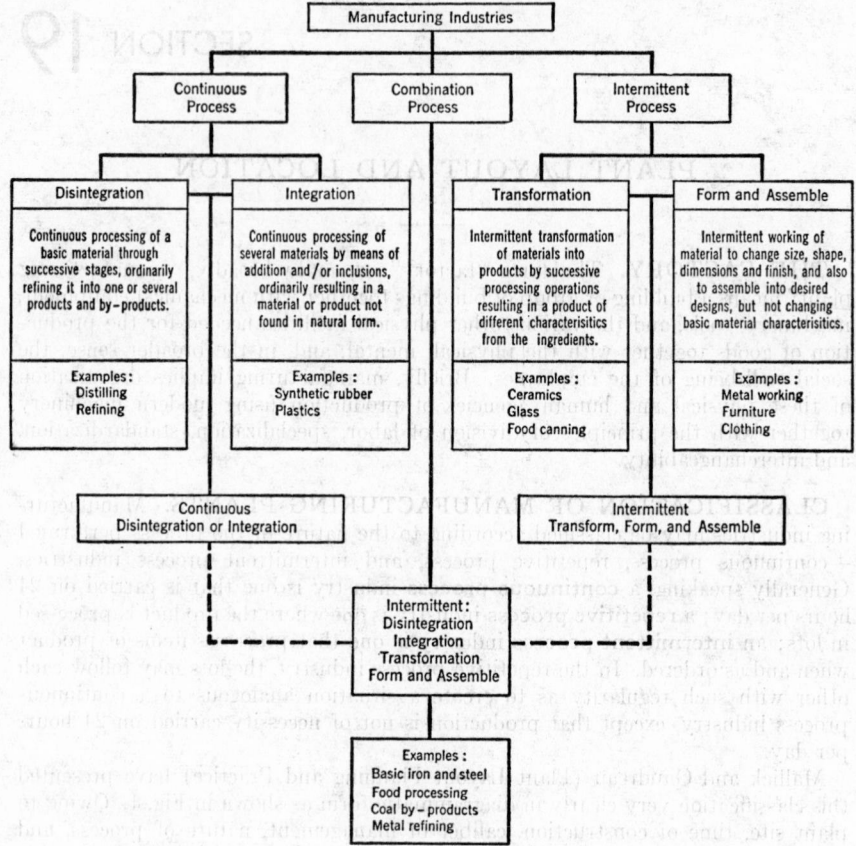

Fig. 1. Types of manufacturing which determine plant layouts.

Plant Layout Functions

PRINCIPLES OF PLANT LAYOUT. Muther (Practical Plant Layout) has stated the following principles to be considered in planning a layout:

1. Principle of over-all **integration.** That layout is best which integrates the men, materials, machinery, supporting activities, and any other relevant factors in a way that results in the best compromise.

2. Principle of **minimum distance** moved. Other things being equal, that layout is best that permits the material to move the minimum distance between operations.

3. Principle of **flow.** Other things being equal, that layout is best that arranges the work area for each operation or process in the same order or sequence that forms, treats, or assembles the materials.

4. Principle of **cubic space.** Economy is obtained by using effectively all available space, both vertical and horizontal.

5. Principle of **satisfaction** and **safety.** Other things being equal, that layout is best which makes work satisfying and safe for workers.

6. Principle of **flexibility.** Other things being equal, that layout is best that can be adjusted and rearranged at minimum cost and inconvenience.

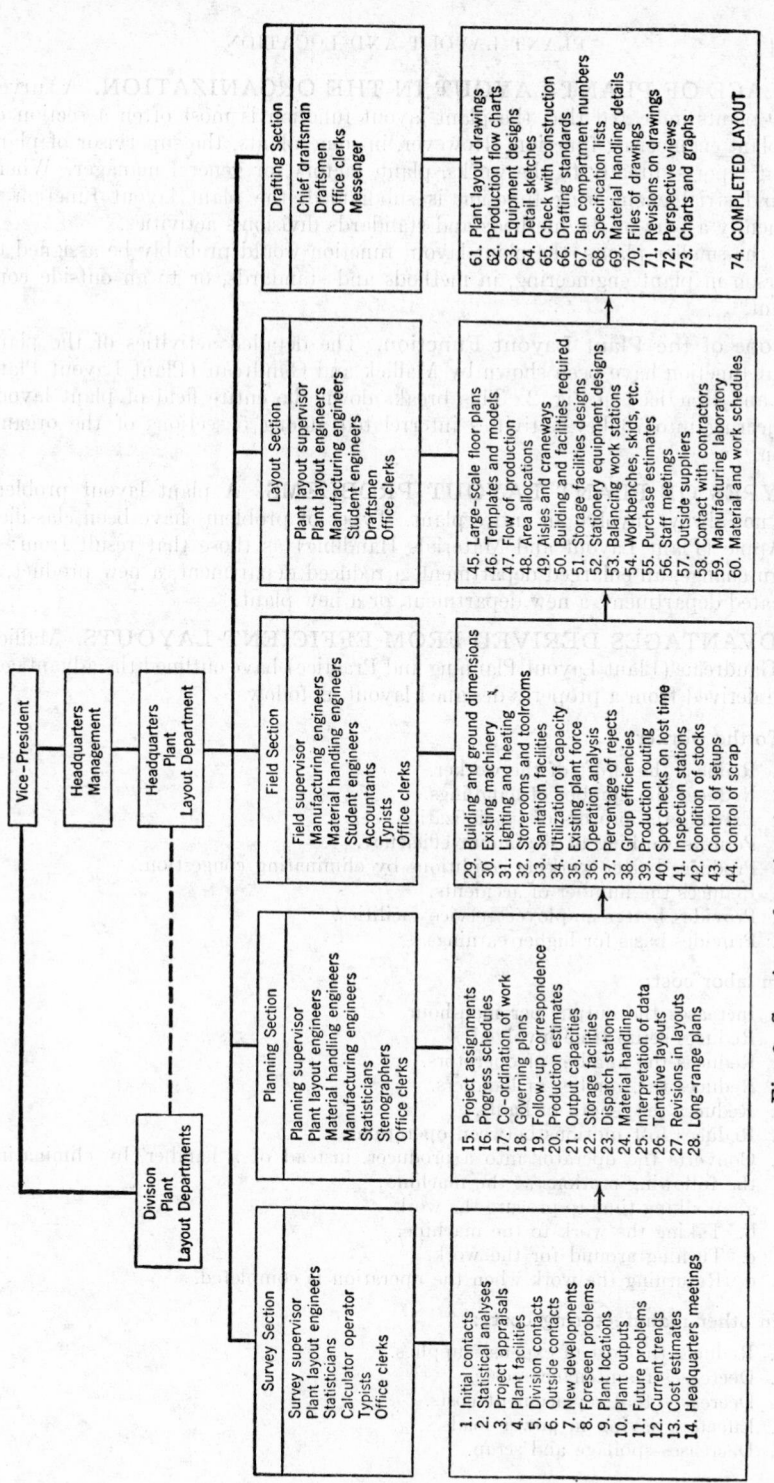

Fig. 2. Specimen functional chart for a plant layout organization.

Survey Section

Survey supervisor
Plant layout engineers
Statisticians
Calculator operator
Typists
Office clerks

1. Initial contacts
2. Statistical analyses
3. Project appraisals
4. Plant facilities
5. Division contacts
6. Outside contacts
7. New developments
8. Foreseen problems
9. Plant locations
10. Plant outputs
11. Future problems
12. Current trends
13. Cost estimates
14. Headquarters meetings

Planning Section

Planning supervisor
Plant layout engineers
Material handling engineers
Manufacturing engineers
Statisticians
Stenographers
Office clerks

15. Project assignments
16. Progress schedules
17. Co-ordination of work
18. Governing plans
19. Follow-up correspondence
20. Production estimates
21. Output capacities
22. Storage facilities
23. Dispatch stations
24. Material handling
25. Interpretation of data
26. Tentative layouts
27. Revisions in layouts
28. Long-range plans

Field Section

Field supervisor
Manufacturing engineers
Material handling engineers
Student engineers
Accountants
Typists
Office clerks

29. Building and ground dimensions
30. Existing machinery
31. Lighting and heating
32. Storerooms and toolrooms
33. Sanitation facilities
34. Utilization of capacity
35. Existing plant force
36. Operation analysis
37. Percentage of rejects
38. Group efficiencies
39. Production routing
40. Spot checks on lost time
41. Inspection stations
42. Condition of stocks
43. Control of setups
44. Control of scrap

Layout Section

Plant layout supervisor
Plant layout engineers
Manufacturing engineers
Student engineers
Draftsmen
Office clerks

45. Large-scale floor plans
46. Templates and models
47. Flow of production
48. Area allocations
49. Aisles and craneways
50. Building and facilities required
51. Storage facilities designs
52. Stationery equipment designs
53. Balancing work stations
54. Workbenches, skids, etc.
55. Purchase estimates
56. Staff meetings
57. Outside suppliers
58. Contact with contractors
59. Manufacturing laboratory
60. Material and work schedules

Drafting Section

Chief draftsman
Draftsmen
Office clerks
Messenger

61. Plant layout drawings
62. Production flow charts
63. Equipment designs
64. Detail sketches
65. Check with construction
66. Drafting standards
67. Bin compartment numbers
68. Specification lists
69. Material handling details
70. Files of drawings
71. Revisions on drawings
72. Perspective views
73. Charts and graphs

74. COMPLETED LAYOUT

Vice-President

Headquarters Management

Headquarters Plant Layout Department

Division Plant Layout Departments

PLACE OF PLANT LAYOUT IN THE ORGANIZATION. A survey of 70 plants indicated that the plant layout function is most often a section of the plant engineering function. However, in some plants, the supervisor of plant layout reports directly to the works, plant, factory, or general manager. Where the industrial engineering function is subdivided, the plant layout function is frequently a part of the methods and standards division's activities.

In the smaller plants, the plant layout function would probably be assigned to a person in plant engineering, in methods and standards, or to an outside consultant.

Scope of the Plant Layout Function. The detailed activities of the plant layout function have been shown by Mallick and Gaudreau (Plant Layout Planning and Practice) in Fig. 2. This breaks down the entire field of plant layout engineering into 73 key activities interrelated among 5 sections of the organization.

TYPES OF PLANT LAYOUT PROBLEMS. A plant layout problem does not always involve an entire plant. Types of problems have been classified by Apple (Plant Layout and Materials Handling) as those that result from: a design change, an enlarged department, a reduced department, a new product, a relocated department, a new department, or a new plant.

ADVANTAGES DERIVED FROM EFFICIENT LAYOUTS. Mallick and Gaudreau (Plant Layout Planning and Practice) have outlined the advantages to be derived from a properly designed layout as follows:

A. **To the worker:**

1. Reduces the effort of the worker.
2. Reduces the number of handlings.
3. Extends the process of specialization.
4. Permits working at maximum efficiency.
5. Produces better working conditions by eliminating congestion.
6. Reduces the number of accidents.
7. Provides better employee service facilities.
8. Provides basis for higher earnings.

B. **In labor cost:**

1. Increases the output per man-hour.
2. Reduces setup time involved.
3. Reduces the number of operators.
4. Reduces the number of handlers.
5. Reduces the length of hauls.
6. Reduces lost motions between operations.
7. Converts the operator into a producer, instead of a handler, by eliminating the following motions at the machine:
   a. Walking time to procure the work.
   b. Taking the work to the machine.
   c. Turning around for the work.
   d. Returning the work when the operation is completed.

C. **In other manufacturing costs:**

1. Reduces the cost of expense supplies.
2. Decreases maintenance costs.
3. Decreases tool replacement costs.
4. Effects a saving in power loads.
5. Decreases spoilage and scrap.

6. Eliminates some of the waste in raw material consumption.
7. Improves the quality of the product by decreasing handling.
8. Provides better cost control.

D. In the manufacturing cycle:

1. Shortens the moves between work centers.
2. Reduces the manufacturing cycle in each department.
3. Reduces the length of travel by the product.
4. Reduces the over-all time of manufacturing the product.

E. In production control:

1. Facilitates receipts, shipments, and delivery.
2. Provides adequate and convenient storage facilities.
3. Permits the maximum possible output.
4. Paces production.
5. Determines production flows.
6. Makes production time predictable.
7. Makes scheduling and dispatching automatic.
8. Sets up production centers.
9. Permits straight-line layout by products for mass production.
10. Permits layout by process for job-lot manufacturing.
11. Moves work in process by most direct lines.
12. Reduces the number of lost or mismatched parts.
13. Reduces the paper work for production control.
14. Reduces the number of stock chasers.
15. Reduces production control expense.

F. In supervision:

1. Tends to ease the burden of supervision.
2. Determines the supervisory control.
3. Reduces the cost of supervision.
4. Reduces the cost of piece counts.
5. Decreases the amount of inspection.

G. In capital investment:

1. Holds permanent investment at a minimum.
2. Adapts plant to present manufacturing methods.
3. Provides for changed methods and future expansion.
4. Keeps the plant from becoming obsolete before it is worn out.
5. Reduces investment in machinery and equipment by:
   a. Increasing the production per machine.
   b. Utilizing idle machine time.
   c. Reducing the number of operations per machine.
6. Maintains a proper balance of departments.
7. Eliminates wasted aisle space.
8. Reduces the floorspace and shop areas required for manufacturing.
9. Reduces the amount of materials handling equipment required.
10. Reduces or eliminates elevator service.
11. Reduces the inventory of work in process and of finished products.

Assembling Data for Plant Layout

BASIS OF LAYOUT. Layout of a plant, both of departments and of machines, should be the expression of a purpose. To this end, the processes through which materials pass, their sequence of flow, the machines and equipment required for the anticipated volume, and the location of the auxiliary departments

—receiving, shipping, toolroom, lavatories, and others—are vital. But the practical and psychological aspects of other factors, the building structure, heating, ventilating, lighting, noise control, etc., must receive thorough consideration.

Although essentials of plant layout are substantially the same for all industries, in application, the results will vary depending upon type of product, size of plant, variety of output, and building limitations imposed. Ideal circumstances exist when an entirely new plant is to be erected, but this is seldom the case. Usually, the layout must be fitted into existing buildings with their inherent limitations. The problem facing the production engineer is usually one of **re-layout** to improve the operating efficiency of manufacturing processes or to provide for making new products.

PLANT LAYOUT PROCEDURES. In attacking a plant layout problem, the general procedure to be followed is as outlined below. Details of each step are amplified in the succeeding discussion, in the order outlined.

1. Procure basic data.
2. Analyze and coordinate basic data.
3. Calculate equipment requirements.
4. Select general materials handling plan.
5. Sketch plot plan.
6. Plan general flow pattern.
7. Plan individual work stations.
8. Select specific materials handling equipment.
9. Coordinate individual operations.
10. Calculate storage space requirements.
11. Construct flow diagrams for production centers.
12. Allocate production centers to areas on plot plan.
13. Plan and locate service areas.
14. Construct master layout.
15. Check final layout.
16. Get official approvals.
17. Install the layout.

A summary of the procedure suggested by Mallick and Gaudreau (Plant Layout Planning and Practice) is shown as Fig. 3. This indicates the sources of data, forms, plans, charts, sketches, drawings, and specifications and the sequence of procedures which may be followed in determining the proper plan to be selected for final design.

PROCURE BASIC DATA. In the development of products and planning for their manufacture, decisions are reached which have an important bearing on the efficiency and cost of manufacturing. **Product designs** should be analyzed by the manufacturing department before final approval, to eliminate features which would prove troublesome in the factory or which would add to the cost. For each part, subassembly, and assembly, there will be prepared an **operation list** indicating operations needed, where performed, their sequence, machines, fixtures, tools used, and other necessary information. This record serves also as a **master route card** for the part or assembly. A summary of similar data for all parts produced, with information of the time required for each operation or process, will aid in determining the amount of machine equipment needed for each department. General factors to be considered are:

1. Volume of production.
2. Maximum capacity of equipment.
3. Hours of work planned.

4. Normal production capacity to be used when scheduling and dispatching work, including allowances for such factors as working arrangements, idle time for setups, and repairs.

A **time analysis** of different operations, in which would be included the necessary time between operations, will supply the over-all manufacturing time. The duration of the manufacturing cycle will be less for parts moving forward a unit at a time than for lots. Some operations require a greater length of time to complete than others, and if parts are handled in lots, congestion may be caused at some points and idleness at others unless work is carefully scheduled and machine capacities provided to meet schedule demands. In the construction and layout of a building, some consideration should be given to the possibility of improved processes or methods being developed and the need for fitting that equipment into the layout satisfactorily.

Analysis of Production Data. Before the layout project can be undertaken, certain basic **production data** are necessary. These items should include:

1. Blueprints of all parts and assemblies in sufficient detail for actual manufacturing.
2. Complete parts list, indicating not only parts to be manufactured but all purchased items as well.
3. Production routings, or operation lists for all parts to be manufactured.

The **process engineer** studies and analyzes the prints. He will then:

1. Plan the operations necessary to process the rough stock into the finished part.
2. Decide on proper sequence of the necessary operations.
3. Select machines and equipment required to perform each operation.
4. Specify or sketch necessary auxiliary equipment such as tools, jigs, and fixtures.
5. Procure production standards, usually in terms of hours per piece, from the time-study records.
6. Write up these data as a production routing or operations list.

Muther (Production-Line Technique) gives a graphical presentation of these preliminary data gathering steps (Fig. 4). Some idea of the complexity of the process engineering step is gained through an examination of his chart (Fig. 5). This chart indicates that to produce one part, the following are necessary:

1. 41 operations.
2. 163 gages.
3. 2 dies.
4. 32 fixtures.
5. 10 tool blocks.
6. 38 cutting tools.
7. 5 arbors.
8. 28 spacers.
9. 38 tools.
10. 13 grinding wheels.
11. 18 special tools.

ANALYZE AND COORDINATE BASIC DATA. After the preceding basic data have been accumulated, it has been found helpful to coordinate it by means of two graphical techniques. These are the assembly chart or graphical parts list (see section on Production Control Systems and Procedures) and the operation process chart (see section on Process Charts).

An **assembly chart** shows in simple graphical form:

1. The parts making up the total assembly.
2. The subassemblies and their components.
3. The order in which parts are assembled.
4. The flow of parts and subassemblies into the assembly.
5. The first concept of the production flow pattern.

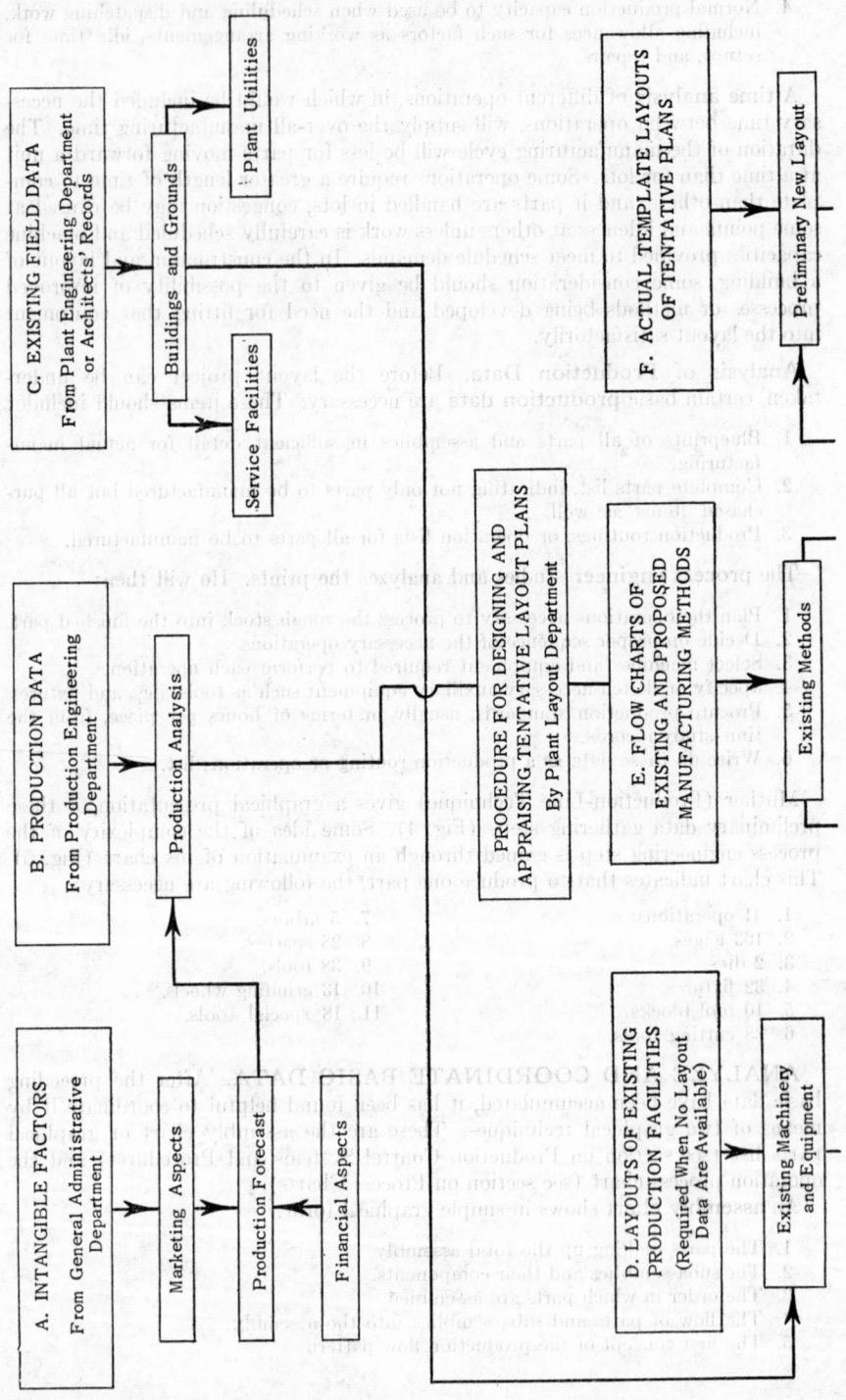

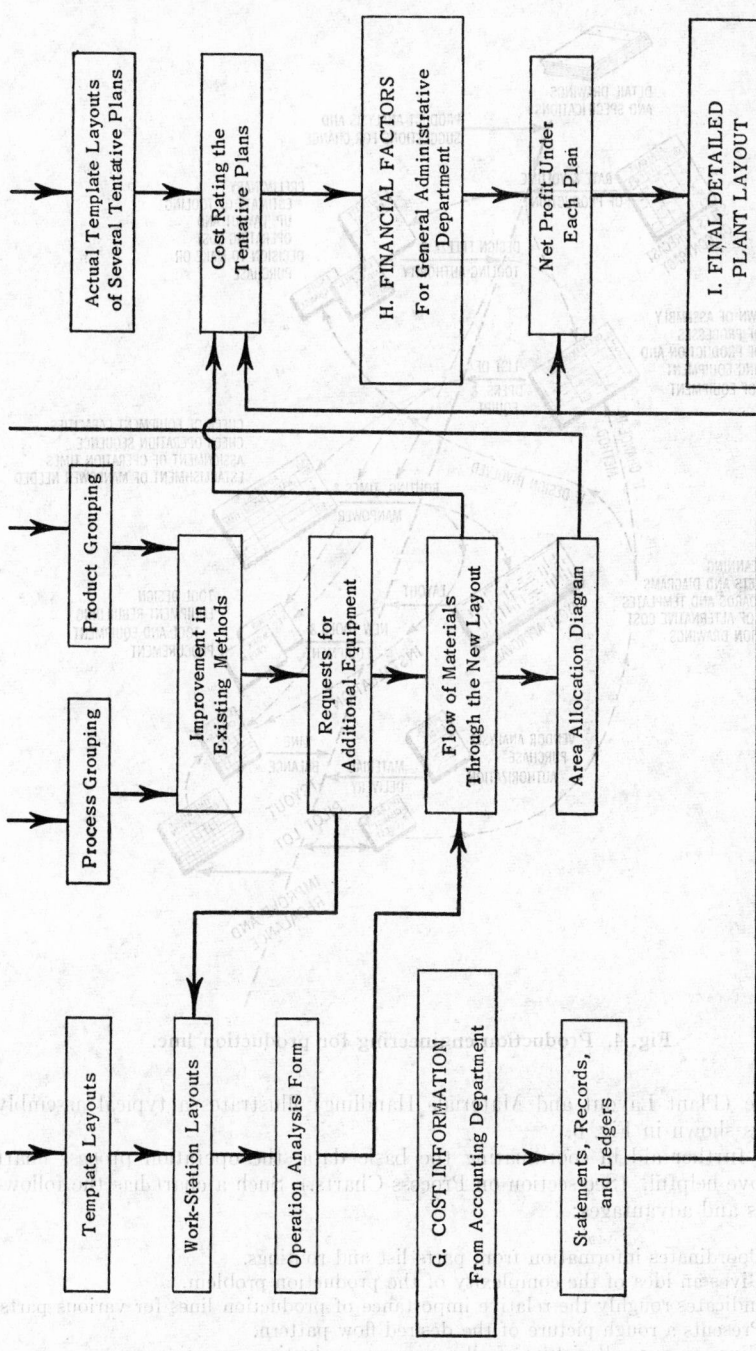

Fig. 3. Flow chart of plant layout procedure for determining plant layout design.

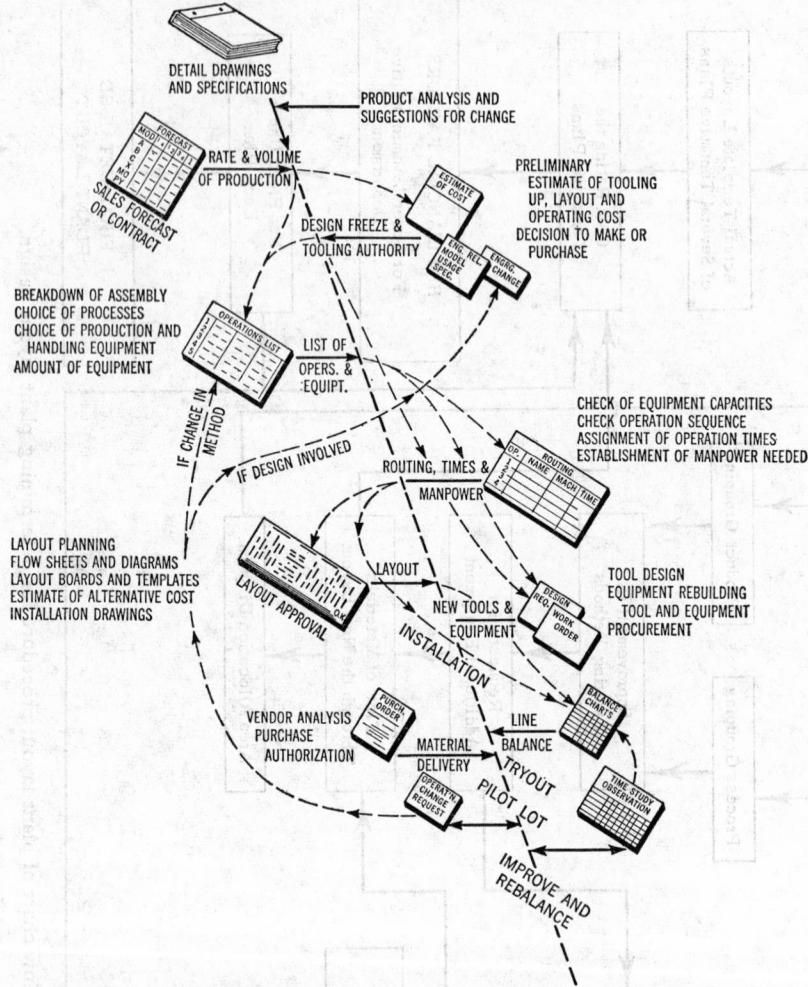

Fig. 4. Production engineering for production line.

Apple (Plant Layout and Materials Handling) illustrates a typical assembly chart as shown in Fig. 6.

As a further aid in coordinating the basic data, the operation process chart can prove helpful. (See section on Process Charts.) Such a chart has the following uses and advantages:

1. Coordinates information from parts list and routings.
2. Gives an idea of the complexity of the production problem.
3. Indicates roughly the relative importance of production lines for various parts.
4. Presents a rough picture of the desired flow pattern.
5. Gives an over-all picture of all necessary production operations.
6. Shows relationships between various parts.

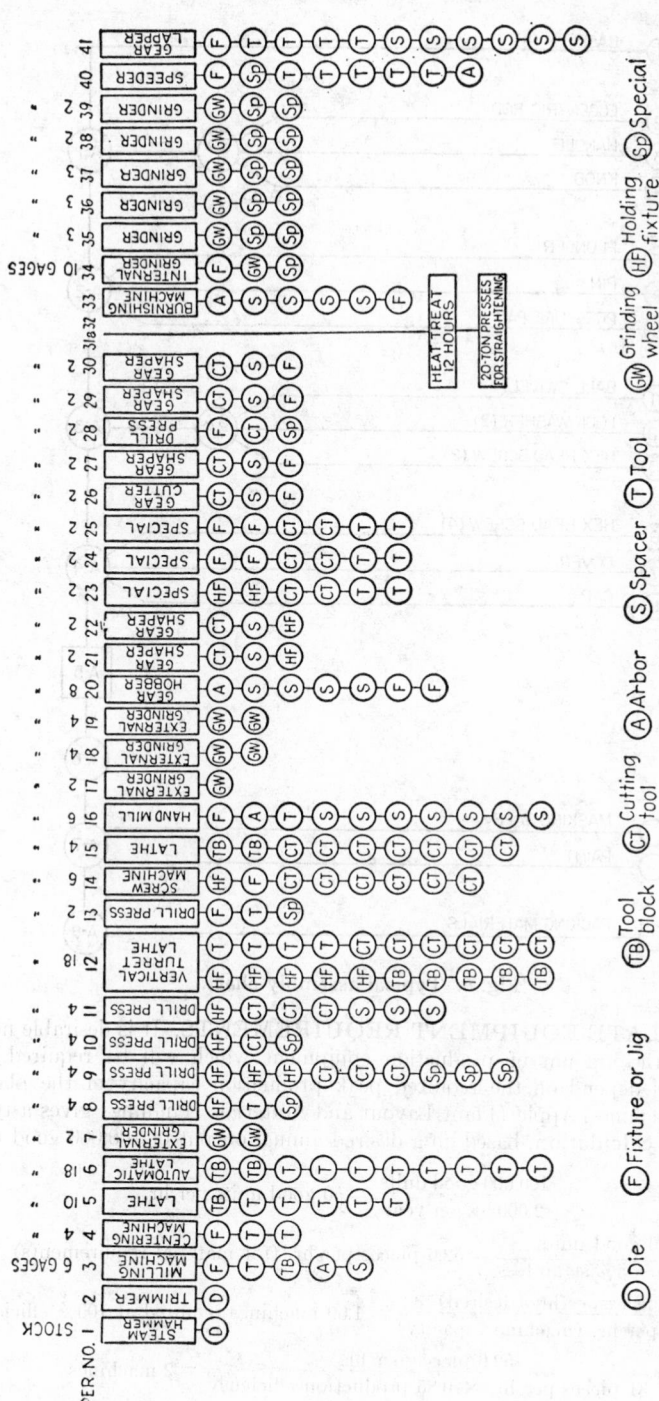

Fig. 5. Machinery, auxiliary equipment, and gages required in tooling a production line for one part.

Automotive Council for War Production

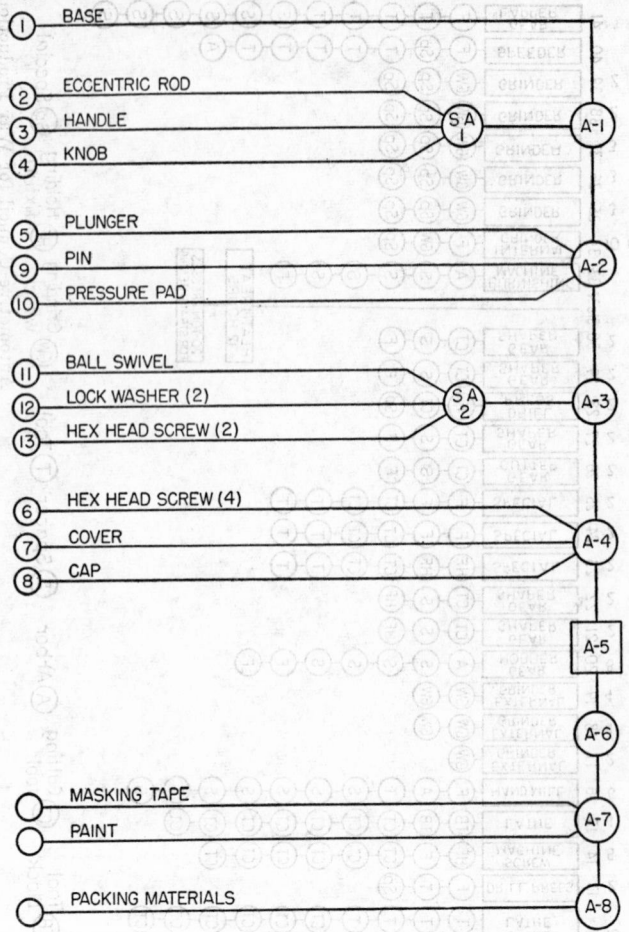

Fig. 6. Typical assembly chart.

CALCULATE EQUIPMENT REQUIREMENTS. It is desirable next to determine the amount of production equipment which will be required. The amount will depend on the required peak production capacity of the plant or group of machines. Apple (Plant Layout and Materials Handling) gives a typical **equipment calculation,** based on a desired annual output of 100,000 good units:

$$\frac{100.000 \text{ good units}}{2{,}000 \text{ hr. per year}} = 50 \text{ good units per hr.}$$

$$\frac{50 \text{ good units}}{100\% - 5\% \text{ scrap loss}} = 52.6 \text{ pieces per hr. (for material requirements)}$$

$$\frac{52.6 \text{ pieces per hr. (desired)}}{31 \text{ pieces per hr. (machine capacity)}} = 1.69 \text{ machines required at } 100\% \text{ efficiency}$$

$$\frac{52.6 \text{ pieces per hr.}}{31 \text{ pieces per hr.} \times 0.85 \text{ production efficiency}} = 2 \text{ machines}$$

Therefore to produce 50 good units per hour, at 85 percent efficiency and with 5 percent scrap, 2 machines will be necessary. This calculation should be made for each production operation. The machine or operation capacity should be determined by time study, estimate, or use of standard data.

SELECT GENERAL MATERIALS HANDLING PLAN. Another preliminary problem is that of deciding upon the general methods to be used in handling materials. Since this activity, on the average, accounts for 25–35 percent of all production costs, it is important that serious consideration be given to this problem.

The Materials Handling Handbook (Bolz and Hagemann, eds.) states that,

When a new product is being planned for manufacture, the time to study the handling problems is in the design stage, before final specifications for materials and manufacturing methods are determined. The same requirement applies when planning a new warehouse or laying out storage areas. The materials handling analyst should be a member of the group making the decisions concerning the new product, its ultimate design, and often, the ultimate layout of the warehouse. Otherwise handling problems will soon arise.

Apple (Plant Layout and Materials Handling) explains that,

By the selection of a general method it is meant that a tentative decision should be made as to whether the plant is to be laid out basically around a system of overhead conveyors, belt and roller conveyors, or industrial trucks, or by some other method or combination of methods. When the basic method is selected the detailed planning of the materials flow through the plant is simplified and the planning of the individual operation methods is considerably aided.

The selection of the materials handling system will depend upon the answers to the following questions (Materials Handling Handbook):

1. What is to be moved?
2. In what will it be moved?
3. Where does the movement take place (origin and destination)?
4. How often does the movement occur?
5. How far does the item move?
6. How fast does the movement take place?
7. Upon what does the movement take place?
8. By whom is the movement carried out?
9. With what equipment is the movement made?

At this point, then, some decision should be made as to the general method or system of handling which will be used. It may be tentative, but at least it will serve as a guide in succeeding steps. (See section on Materials Handling.)

Building Factors Related to Materials Handling. The following is a schedule of building factors related to materials handling:

1. Long, narrow aisles should be widened at intervals to allow two of the largest trucks to pass.
2. Doors and aisles should be wide enough for easy passage of the largest loaded truck.
3. Doors with automatic door openers should have pull-rope switches on both sides, in the path of travel.
4. Loading docks, elevators, aisle ends, and aisle intersections should be of ample width and clearance for right-angle turns of the largest loaded truck.
5. Elevators should be capable of handling the heaviest loaded truck used above the ground floor.

6. Automatic elevator signals and controls minimize truck waiting time and facilitate materials handling.
7. Where ramps are used the grades should be kept to a minimum.
8. Layout of storerooms should be so arranged that columns do not interfere with convenient materials and parts handling.

Developing the Layout

SKETCH PLOT PLAN. The plot plan is a diagrammatic representation of the building outline, showing its location on the property and the location of external transportation facilities. It may show such items as yards, roads, railroad tracks, rivers, tanks, storage areas, fire hydrants, recreation areas, and parking lots.

The plot plan is the key to the actual layout and will determine much of what goes on inside the plant. (See Fig. 7.) The plant should be properly oriented on the property to take advantage of favorable sun, wind, and weather conditions, as well as of the existing or planned transportation facilities. The location of shipping and receiving areas in the plant will depend, of course, on external transportation facilities, whether existing or to be constructed. Therefore, these two facilities should be spotted on the sketch of the plot plan first.

Receiving and shipping departments, adjacent or combined, may be convenient and economical to operate. A shipping department located at one end of a plant and a receiving department located at the other end is often an effective arrangement providing for straight-line flow of work in certain kinds of production. Trackage alongside a plant may suggest unloading near one end and loading near the other. Solutions to the placement of receiving, shipping, and other auxiliary departments are to be found in various examples of layout presented in this section.

PLAN GENERAL FLOW PATTERN. One of the primary objectives of plant layout is to provide an arrangement of equipment which will facilitate the manufacturing process. In an ideal situation, the manufacturing equipment would be laid out to suit the process, and the plant would then be designed around the layout. However, in many cases, a workable flow pattern must be fitted into an existing area and around existing facilities such as elevators, loading docks, and railroad sidings.

According to Mallick and Gaudreau (Plant Layout Planning and Practice), the **flow of material** is the core of plant layout:

In many plant layouts, primary consideration is given to the accommodation of manufacturing processes, and but secondary attention is paid to the requirements of receiving, shipping, and warehousing operations. Needless to state, such layouts are usually found to be unworkable in actual operation because of delays, confusion, "bottlenecks," and excessive rehandling occurring at the receiving and shipping ends of the plant. The flow of materials through the plant is, of course, the core of the entire plant layout. But this core must have both an intake and an outlet at strategic points in order for a smooth internal flow to exist. Since all the material that flows through process and assembly must pass through the receiving and shipping ends of a plant, these two areas require the same close attention in a plant layout as is given the process flow itself.

The over-all purpose of the flow pattern is to plan the movement of the raw materials in as direct a path as possible through the plant. The beginning and ending points of the flow are **deportation facilities,** such as motor truck highways, railroad sidings, and docks or piers on navigable waterways.

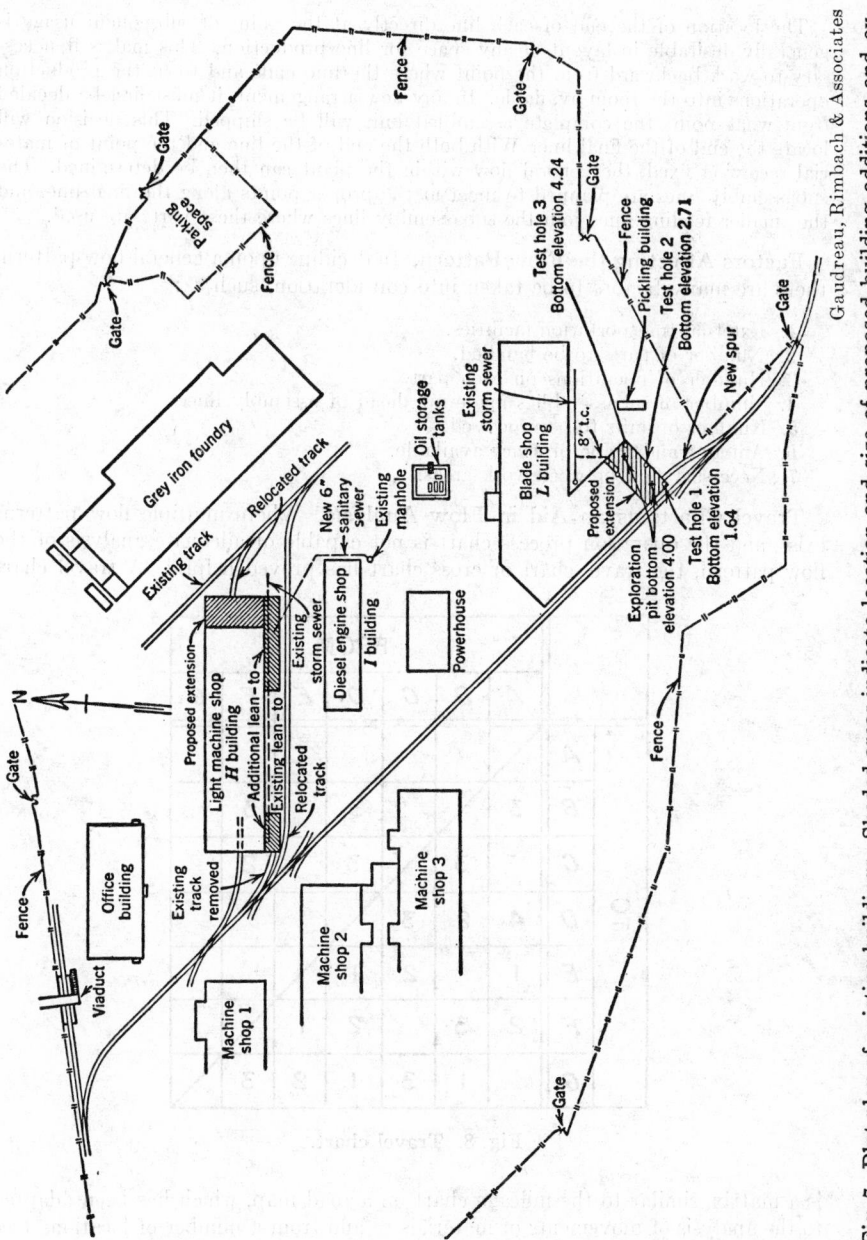

Fig. 7. Plot plan of existing buildings. Shaded areas indicate location and size of proposed building additions and extensions. (Note the three shaded areas appended to the *H* building in the upper center and the proposed extension to the *L* building in the lower center.)

Gaudreau, Rimbach & Associates

Regarding the beginning and ending points of flow lines, Muther (Production-Line Technique) says:

The location of the end of each line directly at the point of subsequent usage is generally desirable in layout of any space for line production. This makes it necessary to work backward from the point where the line ends and to fit the production operations into the room available. In any new arrangement, it must first be decided from what point the complete assembled unit will be shipped. This decision will locate the end of the final line. With both the end of the line and the point of material receiving fixed, the general flow within the plant can then be determined. The subassembly lines are planned to meet at the proper points along the final line, and the smaller feeding lines join the subassembly lines where these parts are used.

Factors Affecting the Flow Pattern. In deciding upon a general flow pattern, there are many factors to be taken into consideration, such as:

1. External transportation facilities.
2. Number of parts to be handled.
3. Number of operations on each part.
4. Number of subassemblies made up ahead of assembly line.
5. Number of units to be processed.
6. Amount and shape of space available.
7. Necessary flow between work areas.

Travel Charts as an Aid in Flow Analysis. Where multiple flow patterns exist, and the operation process chart is not capable of adequate analysis of the flow pattern, the travel chart or cross chart has proved helpful. A travel chart

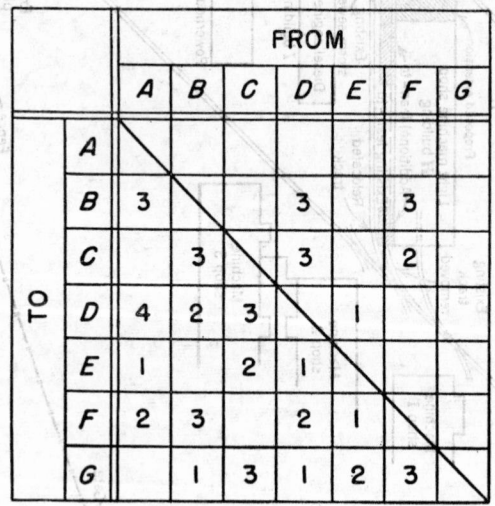

		FROM						
		A	B	C	D	E	F	G
TO	A							
	B	3			3		3	
	C		3		3		2	
	D	4	2	3		1		
	E	1		2	1			
	F	2	3		2	1		
	G		1	3	1	2	3	

Fig. 8. Travel chart.

is a matrix, similar to the mileage chart on a road map, which has been adapted to the analysis of movements of materials to and from a number of locations (see Fig. 8). Numbers in the squares represent number of moves to and from plant areas identified as *A, B, C, D, E, F,* and *G,* as dictated by sequences shown on production routings or operation lists.

By plotting such data, analyzing them, and replotting new arrangements, the optimum **plant area relationships** can be determined. Some uses of the travel chart are to:

1. Analyze material movements.
2. Analyze and plan department locations.
3. Compare layouts.
4. "Measure" layout efficiency.
5. Plan handling procedures and routes.
6. Shorten manufacturing cycles.
7. Reduce work-in-process.
8. Lower labor costs.
9. Aid in visualizing material movement.
10. Show dependency of one area on another.
11. Show relative self-sufficiency of various areas.
12. Show end use of components.
13. Point out inventory control problems.
14. Aid in making economical use of floorspace.
15. Show interrelationship of product lines.
16. Aid in selling the layout.

Influence of Processes on Plant Layout. If a layout is to be the expression of a purpose, it must be built around the process concerned. Processes, then, must be given prime consideration in layout of a plant.

In continuous-process industries such as petroleum refining, where operation follows on operation without interruption, it is apparent that the processes and their sequence by their very nature almost dictate the layout. In interrupted process industries, the relationship of operation to operation is not always clear, nor is it constant. Where a number of different products are manufactured, the sequence of operations is seldom the same for all, so that the relationship of department to department is far from dictated. Yet in many instances individual processes will have definite layout requirements.

On the one hand, processes requiring unusually **heavy floor loads,** due to machines or product, will require a ground- or first-floor layout to prevent excessive building vibration or high construction cost. Heavy punch presses such as are used in the automotive industry are almost invariably located on the ground floor, or in single-story buildings. Tractors, locomotives, large turbines, large pumps, generators, transformers, etc., are built in single-story buildings with ample headroom for cranes.

On the other hand, processes which lend themselves to **gravity materials handling** may make advisable a multistory building with related departments or operations one below the other. Small products, liquids, and powders are easily handled in this manner. A flour mill, for instance, is almost wholly dependent upon gravity feed for downward movement and small material elevators for upward movement, the predominant flow of the material being up and down throughout the processing.

Some meat-packing concerns slaughter on the top floor of a five- or six-story building, driving the animals up a ramp to the slaughter pens, thus using animal energy to get the raw material to a point whence its further flow is by gravity.

However, a multistory building is about 50 percent more costly to build than a single-story building of the same useable floor area. Therefore, the choice is influenced by the initial cost. (See later discussion, Plant Buildings.)

A further influence the process may have on the layout is to **segregate** certain processes or certain departments from the remainder of the plant. Processes which are usually objectionable or dangerous from the standpoint of noise, heat, dust, fumes, vapors, acids, or fire and explosion hazards, which cannot be controlled at their sources, should be placed in separate rooms or separate buildings.

Processes in which **daylight utilization** is important, other factors being equal, should be located in single-story buildings, or on the top floor of a multistory building. Drafting rooms, photographic departments, and general offices are commonly located on a top floor to secure good daylight. Modern lighting techniques in some cases, however, are offsetting this practice.

Types of Flow Patterns. Since every layout problem is different, there is no one best way to lay out a flow pattern. There are, however, several basic types which have come into use, and which can be adapted to many situations.

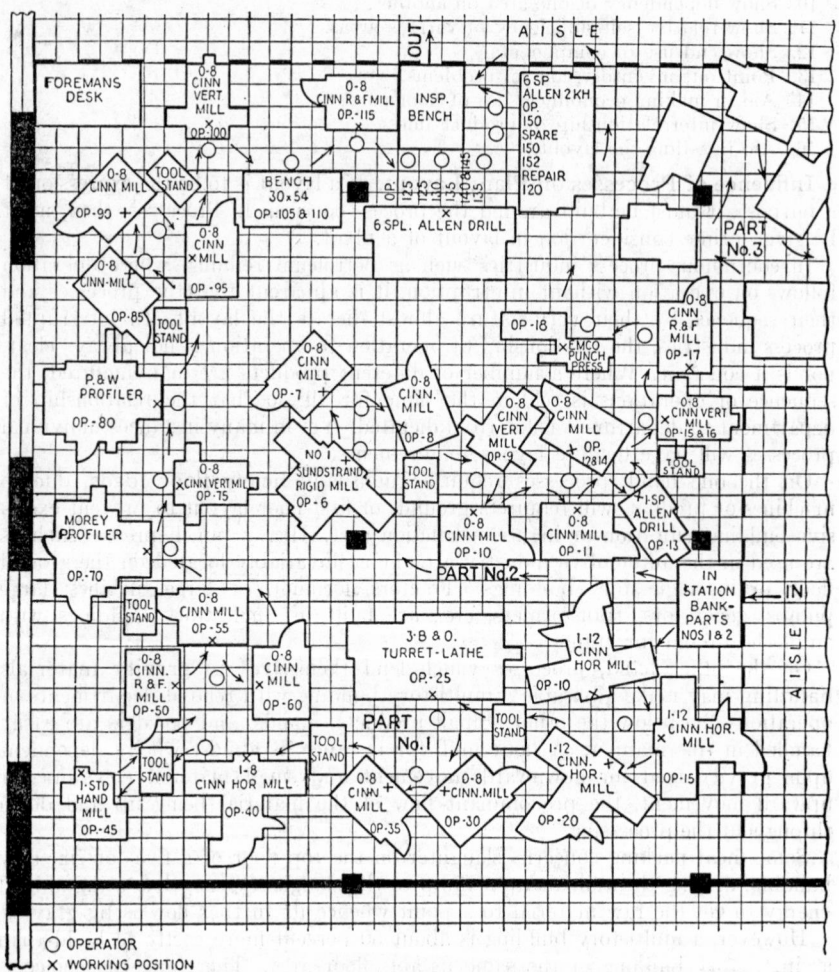

Saginaw Steering Gear Div., General Motors Corp.

Fig. 9. Odd-angle layout for passing parts by hand in pairs to successive operations.

For individual production lines, within the flow pattern, there are four basic types:

1. Straight-line.
2. U-shaped.
3. Circular.
4. Odd-angle.

Muther (Production-Line Technique) illustrates the odd-angle arrangement of equipment in Fig. 9. Such an arrangement on **small-parts machining lines** reduces materials handling and ensures the effectiveness of worker-operating time. However, Muther states that the **straight line** is preferred, unless some of the following conditions hold:

1. The length of the production line makes supervision difficult.
2. The feeding of parts and subassemblies is awkward, and the use of floorspace wasteful.
3. Available space requires a more compact arrangement.
4. The return of empty fixtures is difficult.
5. Certain work stations are common to more than one line or more than one operation in the same line.
6. Connections have to be attached for more than one or two stations.
7. Small parts are more easily handled if regularity is ignored.

An example of a typical flow pattern is shown in Fig. 10.

Process Layout. There are two broad general classes of layout. One is according to the kind of product being made. The other is according to the kind of processes through which products must be passed in the course of manufacture. A process layout is set up where the product is not, and cannot be, standardized, or where the volume of like work produced is low. Such a condition requires flexibility in the sequence of manufacturing, which is readily obtainable with this method of layout.

Advantages of Process Layout. The main **advantages** of the process method of layout are summarized in the following tabulation:

1. Higher degree of machine utilization.
2. Greater flexibility of production process.
3. More efficient supervision due to specialized process.
4. Less interruption in work flow due to machine breakdown.
5. Lower equipment investment due to less duplication.
6. Better control of total manufacturing costs.
7. Higher level of individual operator performance.

Product Layout. A product layout is set up for a standardized product that is to be manufactured in large quantities for a considerable period or indefinitely. Where runs are shorter, but by a few changes in equipment another product may be produced, a product layout is frequently used. In general, product layout is best adapted to mass production industries. The automotive industry is an outstanding example of what may be done in production by "straight-lining." But the principles of straight-lining can be, and have been, applied in many other industries, in either permanent or flexible setups. In product layout of machines, all emphasis is placed on the product. The machines required in the processing of the product are brought together within a department and set up in accordance with the necessary sequence of operations. Since such a line is set up for a certain required production per hour, and the machine for each operation is selected and

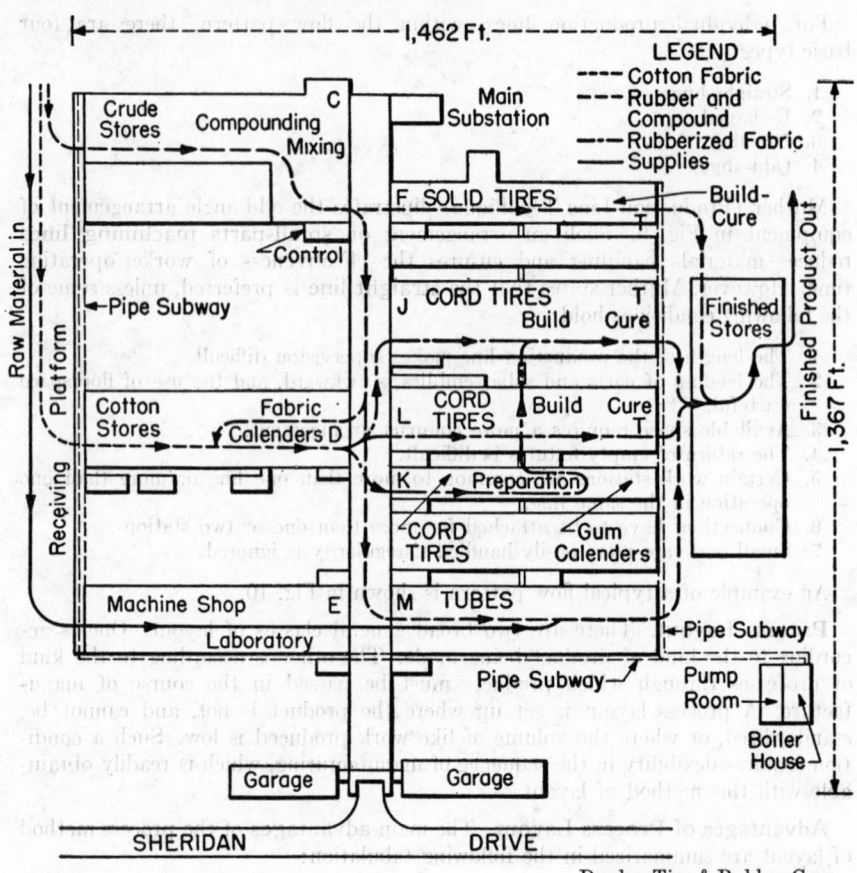

Dunlop Tire & Rubber Corp.

Fig. 10. Layout of automobile tire plant and routes of materials.

geared to a suitable speed with that requirement in mind, the product will flow smoothly along with little delay.

Advantages of Product Layout. Some of the principal advantages to be derived from the product type of layout, as opposed to the advantages of process layout, are:

1. Reduced materials handling cost.
2. Reduced unit production time.
3. Reduced work-in-process.
4. Reduced total floor space required per unit of production.
5. Reduced record-keeping and simpler production control.
6. Reduced total inspection.
7. Higher utilization of unskilled personnel.

Combination of Product and Process Layout. Frequently, the best solution may be obtained by combining the basic features of both product and process layout types. In effect, each process is set up as a unit or department, and these units are arranged into a product layout. This is typical of many "job shops" and semi mass-production situations.

Planning for Flexibility. One of the objectives of plant layout is that the plant should be laid out to maintain flexibility of arrangement and of operation. **Equipment rearrangement** may be necessary to:

1. Alter the process to fit a change in the design of a part.
2. Allow for change in production rate.
3. Permit the addition of a new part or product within the present plant.

Flexibility can be obtained in **existing structures,** by the following means, according to Immer (Layout Planning Techniques):

1. Large unobstructed floor areas.
2. Electrical connections to allow for plugging in machines.
3. Individual motors for machines, permitting machinery to be placed where needed on the factory floor.
4. Mobility of machine units.
5. Portable conveyor units.
6. Extensive use of small tools.
7. Portable jigs and fixtures.

In planning for flexibility in the design of a **new plant,** Immer suggests that the following factors be considered:

1. Extension of production lines.
2. Mezzanines and auxiliary departments.
3. Shape of buildings.
4. Design of plants in manufacturing units.
5. Structural features for expansion.

The check list in Fig. 11 (Modern Industry, vol. 20) serves as a guide in determining layout flexibility.

Plan Individual Work Stations. After the flow pattern has been established, the direction of materials flow through each processing area and each work space can be determined. A check of the flow pattern when planning an individual work station or production center is necessary so that each operation will fit properly into the over-all plan.

Work stations are defined and discussed by Mallick and Gaudreau (Plant Layout Planning and Practice) as follows:

The floor area occupied by the worker and the machine or group of machines which he operates is designated as the workplace, or work station. It constitutes the smallest indivisible space unit on a layout and includes the following amount of floor space:

1. The rectangular space occupied by the length and width of the machine or group of machines operated by one worker, or a group of operators working as one unit, in a given area. This space is expanded to allow for travel of moving parts and for projecting machine parts, such as shafts, levers, pulleys, and doors.
2. Floor space for the machine's own motor or power source when placed on the floor or within the working area.
3. Working space for the operator.
4. Clearance for feeding the work on and off the machine.

MODERN INDUSTRY MANAGEMENT CHECK-UP CHART

Is your plant fast on its feet? Its ability to conform to production changes may be measured by its rating in these essentials:

1. **Movability of Equipment:**
   a. Can machines be mounted on casters, skids for easy transfer to new location?
   Yes.... No....
   b. If vertical or horizontal changes in direction of conveyor lines occur periodically, will portable units help?
   Yes.... No....
   c. Could any operations of large, fixed machines be handled economically by portable tools?
   Yes.... No....

2. **Versatility of Equipment:**
   a. Will machine be called on to perform more than one task?
   Yes.... No....
   b. Can it be equipped with accessories which will expand its utility (such as variable speed drive)?
   Yes.... No....
   c. Is it apt to be handling other materials in addition to those handled now?
   Yes.... No....
   d. If so, will it be unaffected by chemical and physical properties of the new materials?
   Yes.... No....
   e. Is it able to take care of possible increases in production?
   Yes.... No....

3. **Independence of Equipment from Outside Services:**
   a. Does machine have its own motor?
   Yes.... No....
   b. Its own lubrication system?
   Yes.... No....
   c. Its own cooling system?
   Yes.... No....
   d. If its operation involves a critical seeing task, does it have its own supplementary lighting?
   Yes.... No....

4. **Adaptability of Utilities and Services to Any Location in Plant:**
   a. Is there good general lighting in the plant?
   Yes.... No....
   b. Can trolley-duct lighting systems be installed to good advantage?
   Yes.... No....
   c. Would bus ducts enable equipment to be served with power at more locations with less difficulty?
   Yes.... No....
   d. Is piping centralized so that minimum lengths of runs will take care of all locations?
   Yes.... No....

5. **Construction Features:**
   a. Does plant have unobstructed floor areas?
   Yes.... No....
   b. Where areas must be segregated, can demountable walls or light frame structures serve as partitions?
   Yes.... No....
   c. Do plant construction and property permit expansion?
   Yes.... No....
   d. Are floors sufficiently strong to stand weight of whatever machinery may be put on them?
   Yes.... No....

Fig. 11. Check list for determining industrial plant flexibility.

5. Space for the skids, tote pans, racks, conveyor stations, etc., which either contain the work to be processed or receive the work after it has been processed on the machine.

6. Space for whatever tool racks, work benches, and auxiliary equipment each particular machine may need for its operation.

7. Portion of the aisle space or conveyor space immediately adjacent to the operator, the machine or the group of machines he operates.

Fig. 12 shows a typical work station or workplace (Mallick and Gaudreau). The complete work station requires much more space and equipment than the machine itself would indicate. With the use of accurately designed two-dimen-

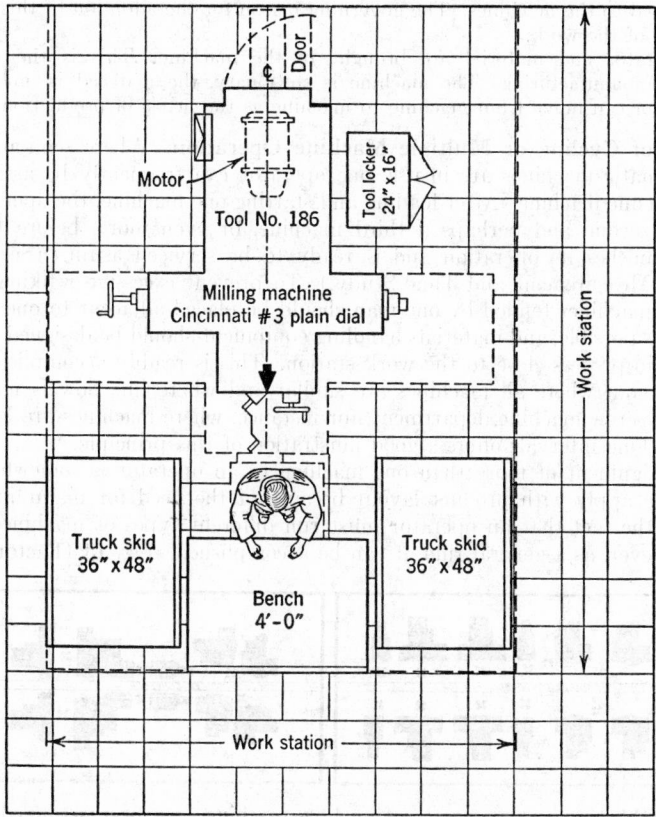

Fig. 12. Work-station layout for a No. 3 milling machine.

sional templates the **clearance area** can be utilized for effective layout. The space in which the operator is standing also serves as clearance for the bench drawer. The tool locker is located adjacent to the machine in a space often overlooked when working with block templates.

Of great importance in effective operation planning are the principles of motion economy. By following these principles in planning equipment layouts the planning engineer may bring about important operating savings, which is a major objective of his activities (see section on Motion and Methods Study).

In planning the work station, men, materials, and machines can be brought together, according to Alford (Principles of Industrial Management) in these ways:

1. By stationing the operator at a given point or machine, and bringing to him the required materials and necessary tools. Continuous operations are an example of this kind of organization. The belt or chain assembly line for an automobile or other product affords an example.

2. By bringing the operator and machines to the material which has been placed in a fixed position in the shop. An example of this method is afforded by the manufacture of very large electric generators, where the machining is done by portable machine tools which are brought to the huge castings instead of the castings being moved to the machines. The governing reason for the adoption of this method is the size of the work.

3. Operator and material are brought to the machine. This is the common method in manufacturing. The machine is stationary, the material is mobile, and the operator can move from machine to machine as the needs of production require.

Operator Cycling or Multiple Machine Operation. Where semi-automatic and automatic machines are in use, one operator can frequently be assigned to more than one machine. After loading and starting one machine, the operator can service a second and perhaps a third machine, or even more, before the first machine finishes its operation and is ready to be serviced again. (See section on Work Measurement and Time Study.) To prevent excessive walking by the operator, machines tended by one man should be placed adjacent to one another as much as possible, and materials handling equipment should be designed to bring the work-in-process close to the work station. This is readily accomplished with process layout where all machines are similar and where line flow is not maintained. A screw machine department, for instance, where machines are loaded at relatively long intervals offers a good illustration of this principle.

The assignment of more than one machine to an operator is somewhat more difficult to apply with product layout because of the need for maintaining line flow and the fact that an operator must run different types of machines. Even here, however, as a general rule, it can be accomplished. Fig. 13 (Factory Man-

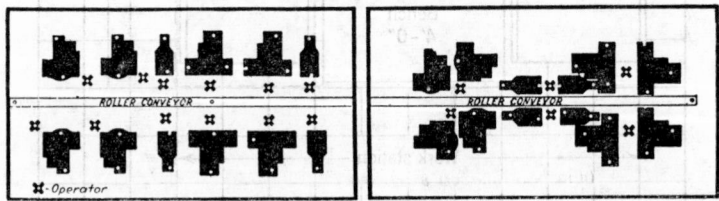

Fig. 13. Old and new layouts showing how machines can be rearranged so that one man can operate more than one machine.

agement and Maintenance) shows an old layout and an improved layout designed to use the operator's time more effectively. While idle machine time may be increased by grouping machines, if properly planned it will be more than compensated for by savings in direct labor. The delays caused by machine idleness, adjustments, breakdowns, or difficulty with the material, are classified as **machine interference.** (See section on Work Measurement and Time Study.)

Number of Machines an Operator Can Tend. The number of machines an operator can tend depends upon the standard time for the operation, the hourly production required from the machine, and the coordination of man and machine time. When machines are to be placed in a group, they should be located as near one another as possible to save walking time and effort of the operator. In a product layout this arrangement depends upon maintaining the line of flow without excessive travel of material. **Line bends** or **loops** often may bring the product back into an area through which it has already passed in the course of operations (see Fig. 14). The improved layout shown in Fig. 14 is designed to lessen walking time and effort in operating and tending several machines.

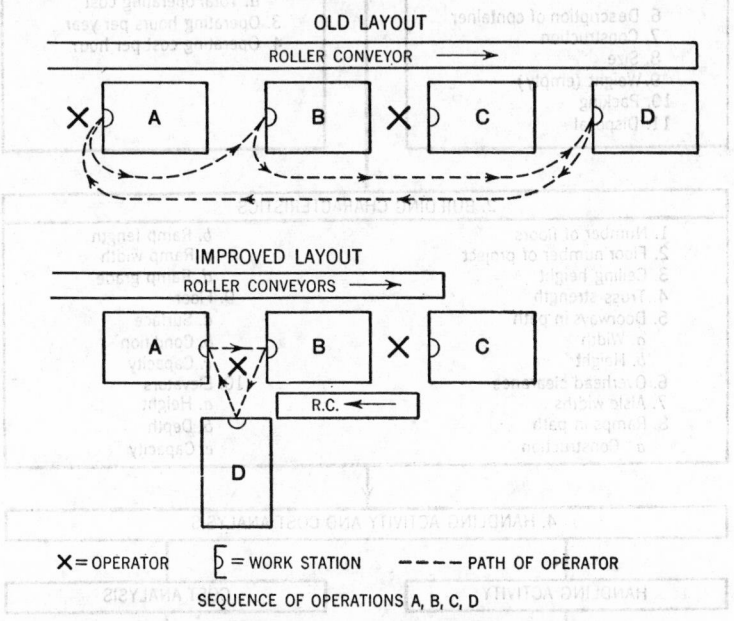

OLD LAYOUT

ROLLER CONVEYOR ⟶

IMPROVED LAYOUT

ROLLER CONVEYORS ⟶

R.C. ⟵

X = OPERATOR   ⊃ = WORK STATION   ---- PATH OF OPERATOR

SEQUENCE OF OPERATIONS A, B, C, D

Fig. 14. Old and improved machine layouts.

Machine Breakdowns. As machine breakdowns are inevitable, provision must be made to keep the maximum amount of the plant working regardless of individual machines which may be out of order. In the process type of layout, operations of subsequent departments are not dependent solely upon flow of work in large volume along a definite production line under any one manufacturing order, nor in successive lots, so a machine breakdown does not cause a general plant stoppage. Since similar machines are grouped together, urgent operations can be shifted readily to another machine.

In the product type of layout a single machine breakdown will stop the entire line. Two provisions can be made to minimize such plant tieups: (1) immediate replacement of the crippled machine, and (2) providing a bank of work ahead of each operator. These procedures require additional investment in capital equipment and work-in-process, respectively. The automobile industry, for the most part, replaces the crippled machine, or sets up a temporary machine through which it shunts the parts while the machine in the line is being repaired. A decision as to which method to use must compare the cost factors of one method against those of the other. If a **work bank** is to be used it should be large enough to keep each operator busy for the length of time taken to make the average

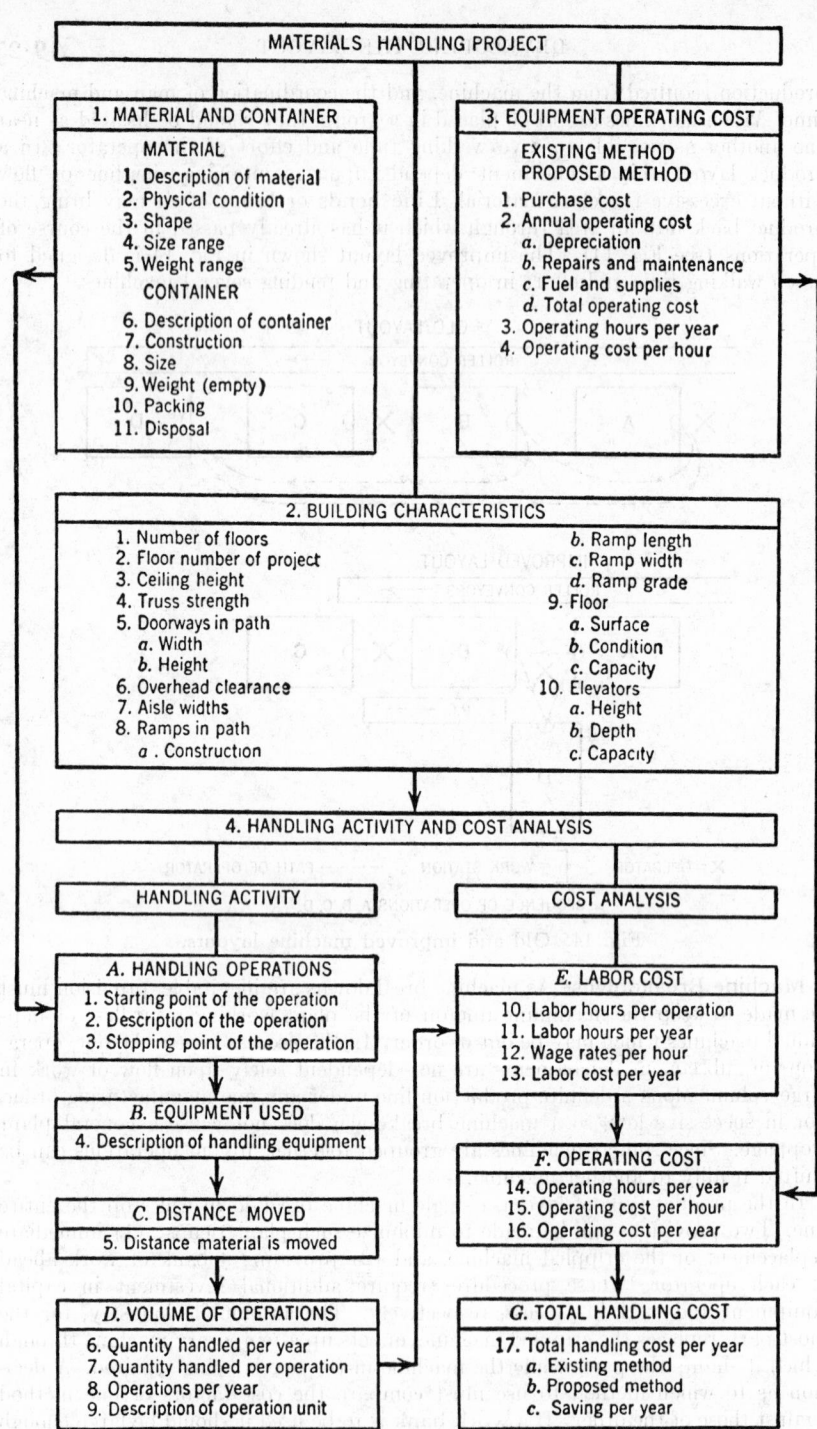

Fig. 15. Check list of data required for a materials handling project.

repair. If the machine is to be replaced, or temporary machines are to be set up, aisle space or crane service must be available.

Maintenance and **machine repair** must also be considered when positioning a machine so that it is completely accessible for normal maintenance and repair. (See section on Plant Maintenance.)

SELECT SPECIFIC MATERIALS HANDLING EQUIPMENT. After the individual work stations have been planned, or possibly as the planning is being done, it is wise to go back to a consideration of materials handling equipment.

As was stated previously, a preliminary consideration must be given to materials handling equipment before the flow pattern is "roughed in." The work stations are then planned on the basis of this general selection of materials handling equipment and the flow pattern.

The primary point to be emphasized here is that materials handling plans should be reviewed at this time in the light of developments in the planning at this stage. Some changes may be made here, but specific decisions as to what materials handling equipment shall be adopted must be made now.

Mallick and Gaudreau (Plant Layout Planning and Practice) give some idea of the complexity of planning for materials handling in Fig. 15. (See also the section on Materials Handling.)

Coordinating the Various Factors

COORDINATE INDIVIDUAL OPERATIONS. Much of the planning work done up to this point can be coordinated by the use of the **layout planning chart.** (See Fig. 16.) This form is an adaptation of the flow-process chart, and combines much of the data from the individual operation plans and the routings. The layout planning chart also serves as a check on work done up to this point and assures that each necessary step in a process has been given proper consideration. This requirement forces the planner to study each step in the process, whether it is a productive or nonproductive step, and serves to show the interrelationship of operations or work stations. (See section on Process Charts.)

CALCULATE STORAGE SPACE REQUIREMENTS. The storage of materials in a plant is a major problem; therefore consideration of this phase of the planning is necessary. Storage space is necessary for raw materials, finished products, and for finished or partly finished materials in process. Size of plant and variety of manufacture influence considerably the degree of centralization of these areas. (See sections on Storeskeeping and Materials Handling.)

Raw materials are usually located close to a receiving track or platform and adjacent to the manufacturing departments which will perform the initial operation on the material. Separate storerooms may be advisable for different classes of raw material, as for paper, steel stocks, tool steel, and supplies. Size of plant, location of departments, available trackage, and character of materials to be stored are determining factors. An outdoor **yard storage** is practical for materials not injured by weather or made more costly to handle or use. Materials light in weight, having special characteristics such as high value, requiring special handling, or used by one department only, may be stored in, and under the control of, the department concerned.

Intermediate storage of parts during the manufacturing process is logically adjacent to or near those departments which require the material. Finished

		LAYOUT	PLANNING
Part No. _____1_____		Part Name ___Powrarm Base___	
Assy. No. _____		Assy. Name _____	
Material ___Aluminum alloy___		Size ___6" x 6" x 5-3/8"___	

ST. NO	F M S I	DESCRIPTION	OPER. NO.	DEPT. NO.	T. S. REG. NO.	TIME PER PC.	PCS. PER HOUR
1		in gondola					
2		to Operation 1					
3		face bottom	1	2		.0167	60
4		to table or roller conveyor					
5		on table					
6		to Operation 2					
7		face top, turn O.D., neck, drill, and ream 5/8" hole	2	2		.042	23.8
8		to roller conveyor					
9		change of carrier					
10		along roller conveyor					
11		on table					
12		to Operation 3					
13		drill 3 bolt holes	3	2		.012	83.4
14		to table					
15		on table					
16		to Operation 4					
17		drill pin hole	4	2		.0042	238.0
18		to table					
19		on table					
20		to Operation 5					
21		drill & ream 3/4" eccentric hole	5	2		.0153	65.4
22		to table					

(F = fabrication; M = move; S = store; I = inspect or count.)

Fig. 16. Typical layout

products are usually stored near shipping departments, convenient for the packing and loading operations.

In many cases, a few simple calculations will solve the major problems in determining storage area requirements. The following illustration is offered by Apple (Plant Layout and Materials Handling):

Assume that production requirements call for the storage of two weeks' supply of a certain casting. Production is at the rate of 50 units per hour, or 4,000 units for two 40-hr. weeks. If one casting is approximately $6 \times 6 \times 6$ in., then 8 castings will require one cubic foot. A $3 \times 5 \times 2\frac{1}{2}$ ft. gondola will hold:

$$3 \text{ ft.} \times 5 \text{ ft.} \times 2\frac{1}{2} \text{ ft.} \times 8 \text{ per cu. ft.} = 300 \text{ units}$$

CHART						SHEET 1 OF 2			
PCS./ASSY. 1 PCS./HR. REQ. _____ PREPARED BY R. J. Waalkes									
ASSY./JOB _____ PROD. HRS./DAY _____ DATE 7/11									
PCS./DAY _____ MODEL M-2									

TOTAL LOAD HRS.	OPER. PER MACH.	TOTAL MAN-POWER	MACHINE OR EQUIPMENT	NO. MACH. REQ'D.	DIST. MOVED	HOW MOVED	TYPE OF CONT'R	REMARKS
							Gon	
					6'	Hand		
	1	1	14" LeBlond engine lathe	1				
					4'	Hand		
			Table & roller conveyor					
					3'	Hand		
	1	3	-3 - Warner & Swasey turret lathes	3				
					3'	Hand		
			Roller conveyor					
					10'	Mech.		
			Table					
					4'	Hand		
	1	1	21" Cleereman drill press	1				
					4'	Hand		
			Table					
					3'	Hand		
	1	1	Delta drill press	1				
					2'	Hand		
			Table					
					2'	Hand		
	2	2	#4 Fosdick 2-spindle drill press	1				
					3'	Hand		

Planning Chart.

Then 4,000 can be contained in:

$$\frac{4,000}{300} = 13\tfrac{1}{3}, \text{ or } 14 \text{ gondolas}$$

If gondolas can be stacked only 3 high, because of the floor-load or ceiling-height limitation, then:

$$\frac{14}{3} = 4\tfrac{2}{3}, \text{ or } 5 \text{ stacks will be required}$$

As each stack requires 15 sq. ft. of floorspace, then 75 sq. ft. of floorspace will be required to store a two-week supply of the castings.

Similar calculations should be made for all parts of considerable size, whether they are raw materials, parts in process, or finished parts. The actual allocation of storage space will be determined by process location. Some storage space for raw materials will be needed at the beginning of the process, some along the fabrication line for parts in process, and some at the end, for finished parts. It may be advisable to construct a chart or tabulation of **storage space requirements** so as to be sure that space is provided. Such a chart is shown in Fig. 17.

STORAGE REQUIREMENTS CHART														
P A R T NO.	QUANTITY NEEDED/WK.			CONTAINERS NEEDED						SPACE REQUIRED			LOCATION		
	RAW	IN PROC.	FIN.	TYPE			NUMBER			RAW	IN PROC.	FIN.	RAW	IN PROC.	FIN.
				RAW	IN PROC	FIN	RAW	IN PROC	FIN						
1	2000	2000	400	GON-DOLA (200)	GON-DOLA (200)	RACK (100)	10	10	4	10x3x5 (150)	10x3x5 (150) AT 5 LOCATIONS	1x6 (24)	A-4	B 4 TO H-4	K-4
														(Bay designations)	

Fig. 17. Storage requirements chart.

CONSTRUCT FLOW DIAGRAMS FOR PRODUCTION CENTERS.

This step is difficult to put in proper chronological order. If it has not already been done (in planning individual operations, or making the layout planning chart) it is necessary at this time to sketch each production center. The sketch or flow diagram should show, to scale, all the machines, stock containers, benches, and other auxiliary equipment necessary to the proper functioning of the particular department or production area.

In making the sketches, attention should be paid to the general flow pattern and the work-station plans developed previously. The flow diagrams may or may not be detailed, but enough information should be included to show fairly accurately the total amount of floor area needed by each production center. It is these flow diagrams (see section on Process Charts) which will later be molded into the final layout around a network of aisles and columns, with the necessary allowances included for service areas. An example of a flow diagram is shown in Fig. 18 (Apple, Plant Layout and Materials Handling).

Line Production. Layout by product and line production are generally considered synonymous phrases, and the application is of interest at this stage. The advantages of product layout have already been cited, but there are **prerequisites** to its use, which are given by Apple (Plant Layout and Materials Handling) as follows:

1. There must be sufficient quantity to justify the product type of machine arrangement.
2. The product must be of such a nature that the operations to be performed on the line can be broken down into units sufficiently small:
   a. To permit each to be learned in a relatively short time by a relatively unskilled operator, thus facilitating the shifting of personnel necessitated when production increases or decreases.
   b. To permit the elements of work to be recombined into time units of about equal length for each operator in the line.

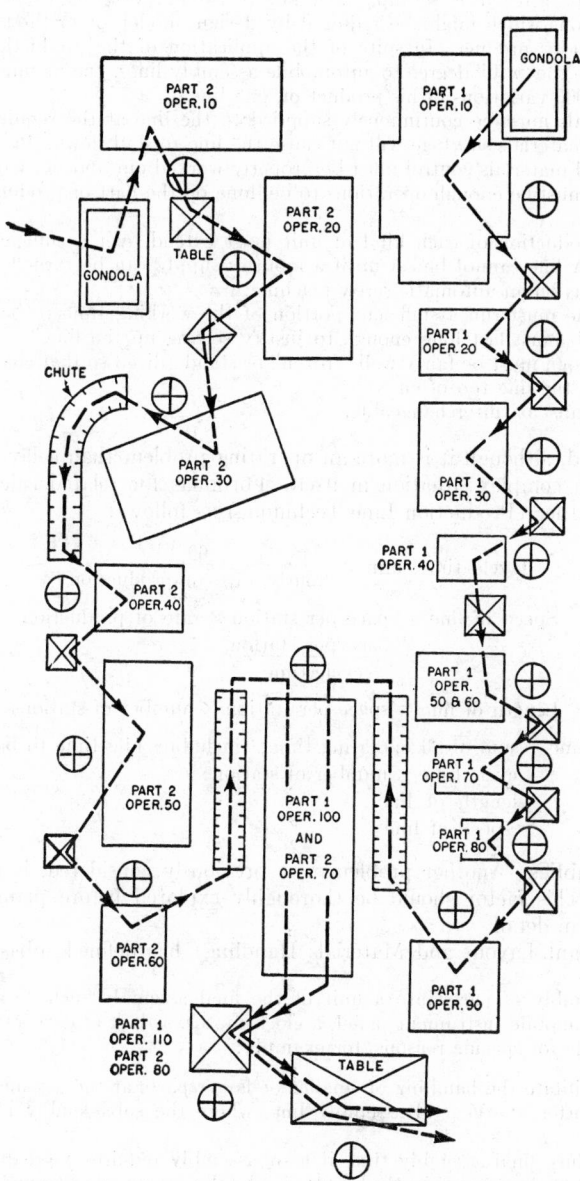

Fig. 18. Flow diagram of related groups of operations.

3. Jigs and fixtures must be used to make sure that each operation is performed in exactly the same manner on each part or assembly.
4. The line, after it is set up, must not be so inflexible as to prevent minor alterations which might be required by design, model, or methods changes on the part or product. In spite of the application of the production-line technique to the "nth" degree to automobile assembly lines, one manufacturer turns out 20,000 variations of his product on one line.
5. Materials must be continuously supplied to the line at the required places so that a materials shortage will not cause the line to shut down. Production control and materials control must be properly worked out and must function well.
6. There must be enough operations to be done on the part or product to warrant the line.
7. The production of each kind of unit must extend over a sufficient period of time. A line cannot be set up if a month's supply can be turned out in a few hours, as on an automatic screw machine.
8. The line must run a sufficient portion of the working time to be economical.
9. The job must last long enough to justify setting up the line.
10. The design must be fairly well "frozen" or standardized so that changes will not disrupt the line too often.
11. Parts must be interchangeable.

Line speed, although it is more an operating problem than a layout planning problem, is a complex situation in itself. Formulas for related calculations are given by Muther (Production Line Technique) as follows:

$$\text{Cycle time, min.} = \frac{60}{\text{hourly rate of production}}$$

$$\text{Speed of line} = \text{space per station} \times \text{rate of production}$$
$$= \frac{\text{space per station}}{\text{cycle time}}$$

$$\text{Length of line} = \text{space per station} \times \text{number of stations}$$

$$\text{Line time} = \text{sum of all operating times (including idle time to balance)}$$
$$= \text{cycle time} \times \text{number of stations}$$
$$= \frac{\text{length of line}}{\text{speed of line}}$$

Subassemblies. Another problem, not previously considered, is that of subassemblies. This factor should be thoroughly explored before planning the assembly area in detail.

Apple (Plant Layout and Materials Handling) has defined subassemblies as:

. . . the assembly of parts into a unit of the final assembly such as a refrigerator door, an automobile instrument panel, a clock motor, a desk drawer, etc. Subassemblies are made for specific reasons, for example:

1. To facilitate the handling of smaller or larger parts at the assembly point.
2. To shorten the general assembly line, where the subassembly requires much space.
3. To reduce final assembly time if a subassembly requires a greater amount of time than can conveniently be fitted into the operations planned for the line.
4. To separate from the line any equipment, the nature of which would interfere with the line.
5. To reduce complications on the line when a part must be machined after it is assembled, and the processing equipment could not well be fitted into the line.

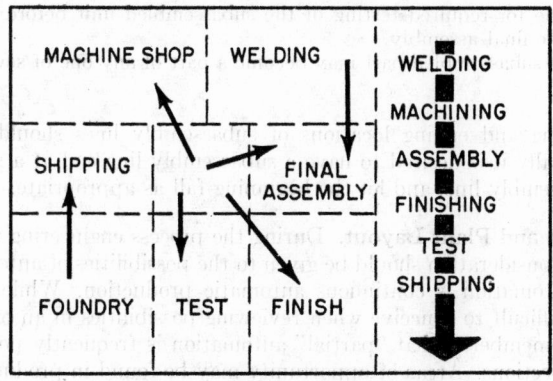

(a) Conventional layout by process

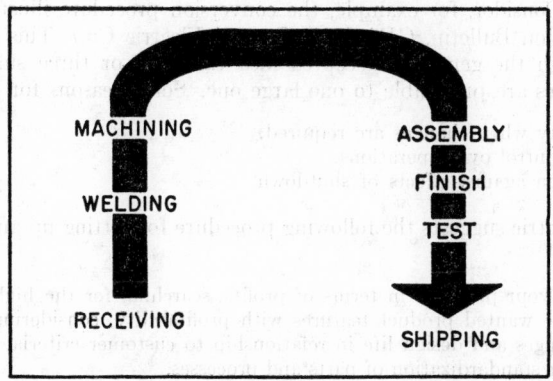

(b) Automatic production flow concept—layout by product

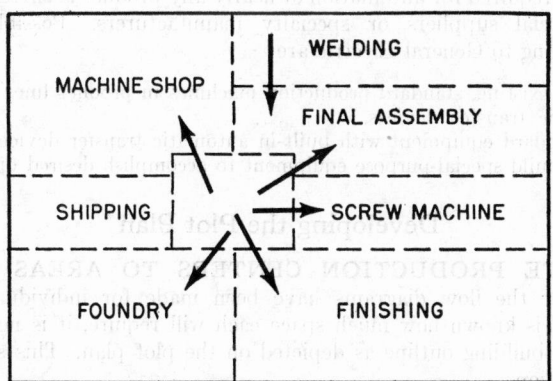

(c) Partial automation by separation of selected processes for automation

General Electric Co.

Fig. 19. Conversion to automation.

6. To provide for required testing of the subassembled unit before it becomes a part of the final assembly.
7. When the subassembled part may become a part of any one of several different products.

The beginning and ending locations of subassembly lines should be planned carefully. Usually it is desired to have a subassembly line end at a specific point on the final assembly line, and let the beginning fall as appropriate.

Automation and Plant Layout. During the process engineering phase of layout planning, consideration should be given to the possibilities of automation. The ultimate in automation is continuous automatic production. While such a concept may be difficult to conceive when reviewing possibilities in an existing plant, it should be remembered that "partial" automation is frequently possible by departments or sections. Areas of opportunity may be found in production, inspection, assembly, testing, and packaging.

The **line-production** (layout-by-product) concept is the first step toward automation. Consider, for example, the conversion procedure illustrated in Fig. 19. (Automation Bulletin. GEA-6405, General Electric Co.) This concept is in agreement with the generally accepted idea that two or three smaller parallel production lines are preferable to one large one. Some reasons for this are:

1. Flexibility when changes are required.
2. Better control over operations.
3. Protection against effects of shutdown.

General Electric suggests the following procedure for setting up an **automation plan**:

1. Analyze your products in terms of profits, searching for the high-profit items.
2. Reconcile wanted product features with profitability, considering possible design changes and design life in relationship to customer criteria.
3. Work for standardization of parts and processes.
4. Compare projected profit and loss estimates of possible alternative plans.

Equipment required for automation of nearly any product is currently available from commercial suppliers or specialty manufacturers. Possible equipment choices according to General Electric are:

1. Arrange existing, standard production machines in product lines and link with automatic transfer devices.
2. Buy standard equipment with built-in automatic transfer devices.
3. Buy or build special-purpose equipment to accomplish desired operations.

Developing the Plot Plan

ALLOCATE PRODUCTION CENTERS TO AREAS ON PLOT PLAN. After the flow diagrams have been made for individual production centers and it is known how much space each will require, it is necessary to fit them into the building outline as depicted on the plot plan. This step is known as area allocation.

Area allocation diagrams are generally made to a smaller scale than that for the layout. The flow diagram, as developed by the assembly chart and operation process chart discussed previously, can also be shown on such a diagram. Mallick and Gaudreau (Plant Layout Planning and Procedure) illustrate such a diagram in Fig. 20, the skeleton floor plan of a machining and assembling plant. This shows building lines, internal partitions, area allocations, and trackage system but not machinery, equipment, or facilities. They indicate that such a diagram is generally used only for reference in analyzing area arrangement and not for plant layout drawings.

Aisles. An important problem at this point is the location of aisles to serve the needs of the plant. Reibel (Industry and Power, vol. 57) has this to say about aisles:

In the average industrial plant, aisles are the highways and byways, the roads on which almost all movement of workers and materials takes place—with the exception, of course, of the work accomplished by conveyors and cranes. Aisles take up a lot of space, sometimes so much that plant efficiency is affected. Therefore, careful consideration of the location and arrangement of aisles is not only advisable but is likely to be profitable as well. On the other hand, carelessness and neglect of aisles may prove to be costly.

Two types of such passageways are found in most plants—main aisles and department aisles. Main aisles, as distinguished from department aisles, are utilized for movement between departments and into or out of a plant. Ordinarily a department will have a main aisle on at least one border line.

In the layout of a new plant one of the first procedures is to locate the main aisles. Once the positions of the main aisles are fixed, they are seldom changed. Moreover, after plant facilities—such as elevators, toilets, locker rooms and washrooms, cafeteria and first aid—are located, they are not easily movable and, of course, they must be installed on aisles or have aisles leading to them. Thus, the placing of aisles is given preference in planning the layout of a new building or plant; that is, main passageways are located first, and then the facilities.

Suggestions for planning aisles are as follows:

1. Locate main aisles first—the larger the plant, the farther apart they can be.
2. Plan at least one main "back-bone" aisle at or near the center of the building, 10 to 20 ft. wide, depending on plant size.
3. Start main aisles at an outside entrance and run them as straight as possible.
4. Use interior aisles of less width for "feeder" purposes, such as movement of personnel, materials, supplies, scrap, service, and fire access.
5. Consider unit-load sizes and truck-turning radii when determining aisle width.
6. Plan for loaded industrial trucks to pass each other, at least in selected spots, along aisles.

Columns. Before too much detailed planning has been done, it is necessary to decide on the column spacing to be used in the plant. The wider the column spacing, the more costly the construction. Columns are commonly placed at intervals ranging from 20 to 60 ft. **Bays** need not be square, so that columns could be placed, for instance, at 40 ft. intervals east and west, and 60 ft. intervals north and south. Actual distances are best determined by consulting building contractors, or architects. After aisles and column locations have been established, **production centers,** as depicted by the area allocation and flow diagrams, can be fitted into the flow pattern on the sketch of the building outline.

PLAN AND LOCATE SERVICE AREAS. While such areas are frequently placed where room is available after planning for manufacturing is done, it is better to keep them in mind during the planning because if they are inconveniently located they may cause excess operating expenditures.

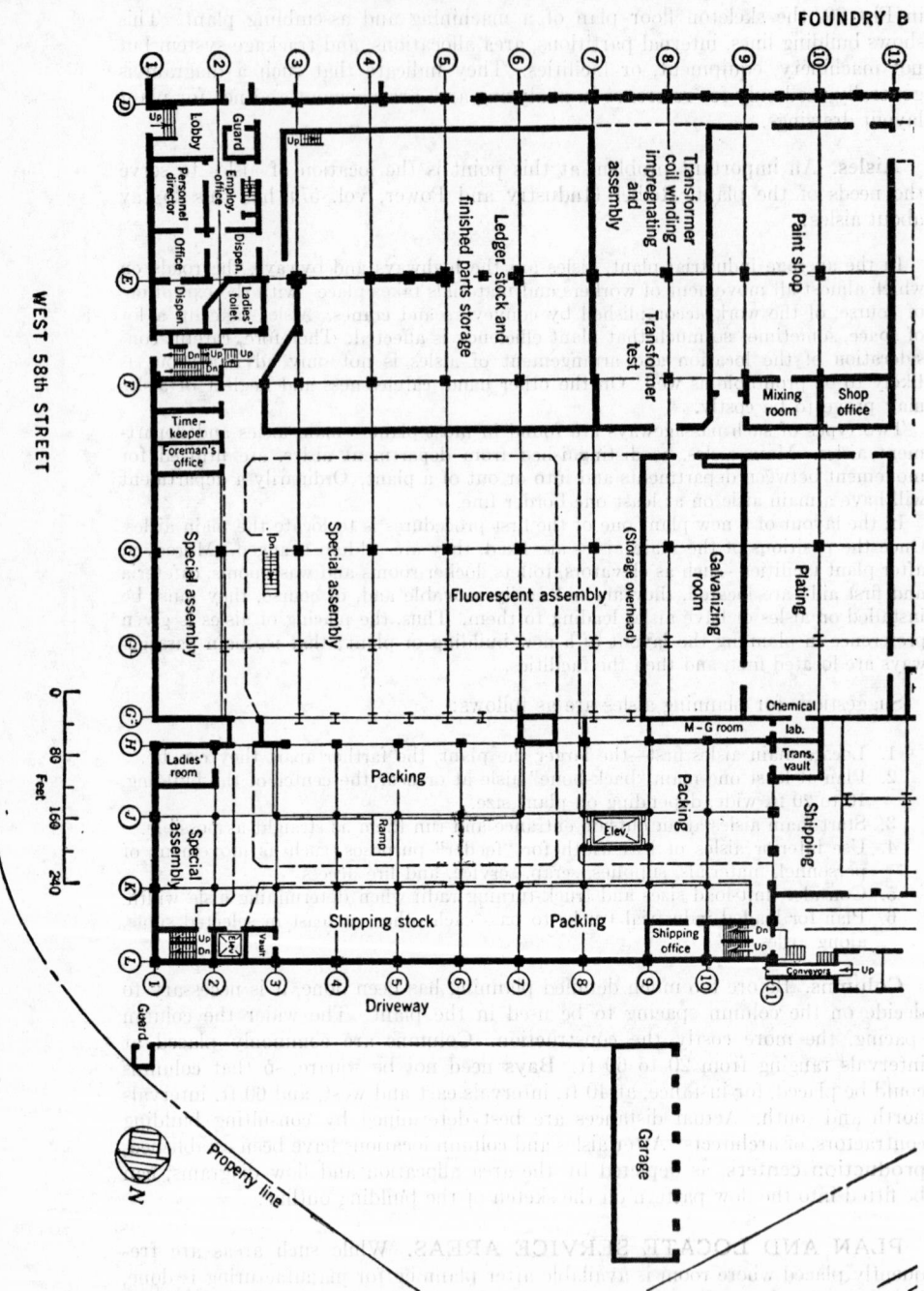

Fig. 20. Skeleton floor plan of

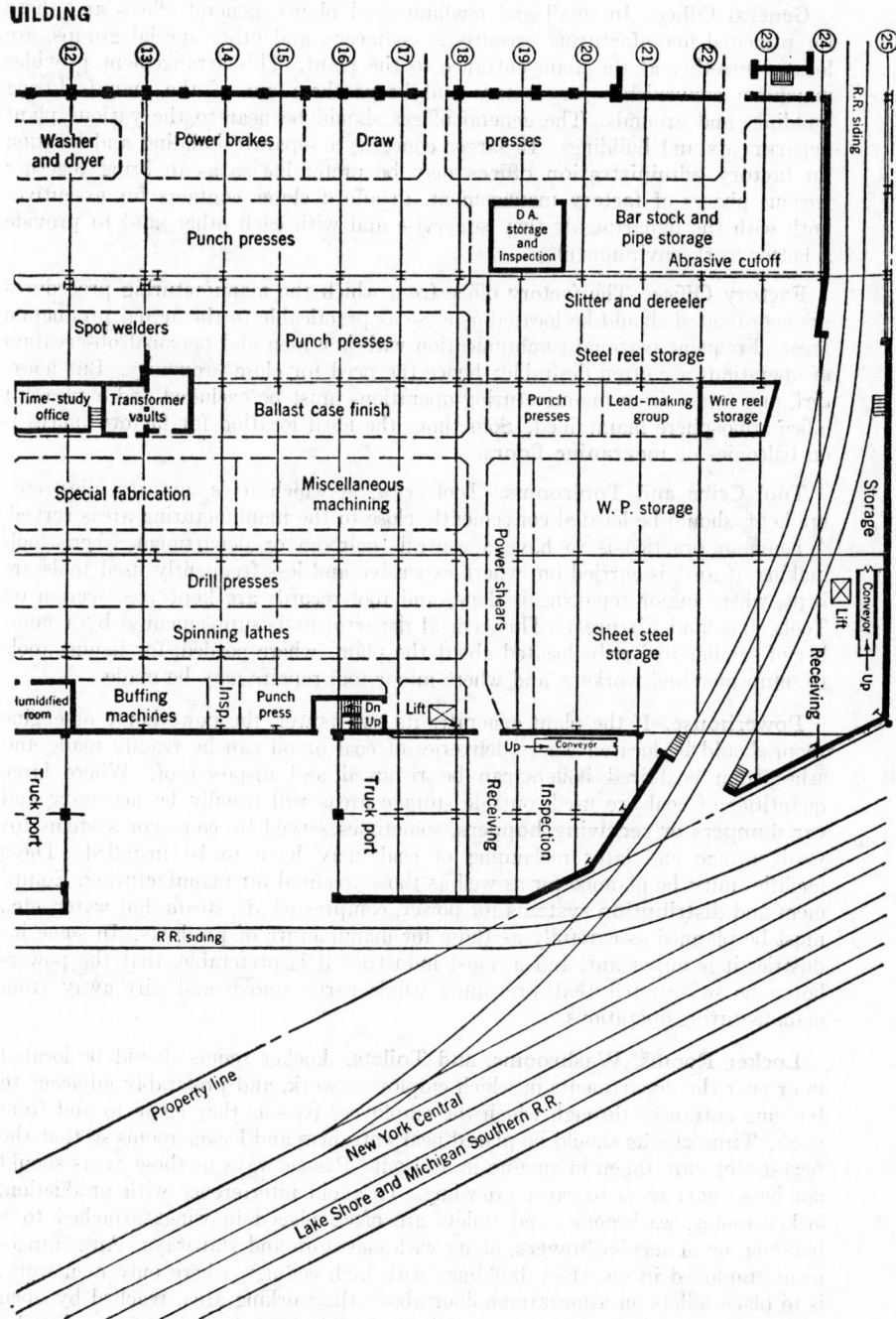

a machining and assembly plant.

Westinghouse Electric Corp.

General Office. In small and medium-sized plants, general offices and those for principal manufacturing executives, engineers, and other special groups, are located together at the main entrance to the plant. This arrangement provides maximum convenience for visitors and keeps them out of the manufacturing buildings and grounds. The general offices should be near to the various plant departments and buildings. In larger concerns a separate building and location for **factory administration offices** may be preferable so as to bring together various phases of factory management, to afford closer contacts for executives both with the departments they supervise and with each other, and to provide a better work environment.

Factory Office. The factory office from which the manufacturing procedures are coordinated should be located as close as practicable to the actual production areas. Frequent personal communication with key men and personal observation of operations are often desirable; hence the need for close proximity. But noise, dirt, and fumes from manufacturing operations must be excluded and a pleasant office atmosphere maintained. Sometimes the ideal location for factory offices is on balconies or **mezzanine floors.**

Tool Cribs and Toolrooms. Tool cribs, in which tools, fixtures, dies, etc., are kept, should be located conveniently close to the manufacturing areas served. A common practice is to have a central toolroom or department where tool-making, if any, is carried on, where expensive and less frequently used tools are kept, where major repairing is done, and tool records are kept (see section on Tools, Jigs, and Fixtures). This central department is supplemented by a number of smaller tool cribs located about the plant, where needed, for issuing tools to setup men and workers, and where minor tool repairs may be made.

Powerhouse. If the plant generates its own power, the powerhouse or engine room should be located where deliveries of coal or oil can be readily made and ashes from coal-fired boilers can be removed and disposed of. Where large quantities of coal are used, outside storage areas will usually be necessary and **car dumpers** or **receiving hoppers,** sometimes served by conveyor systems for yard storage and later reclaiming of coal, may have to be installed. These facilities must be planned for as well as those required for manufacturing. Equipment and **distribution systems** for power, compressed air, steam, hot water, etc., must be planned as carefully as those for manufacture of products. In some industries it is important, and in most industries it is preferable, that the powerhouse be so situated that prevailing winds carry smoke and dirt away from manufacturing operations.

Locker Rooms, Washrooms, and Toilets. Locker rooms should be located in or near the departments in which employees work, and preferably adjacent to building entrances through which the employees pass as they come to and from work. **Time clocks** should be placed near entrances and locker rooms so that the fewest steps are taken in ringing in and out. Passageways in these areas should not be so narrow as to cause crowding. To avoid interference with production, locker rooms, washrooms, and toilets are often placed in wings attached to a building, or in **service towers,** along with elevators and stairways. An arrangement employed in one-story buildings with high ceilings, where only men work, is to place toilets on a mezzanine floor above the working area, reached by open metal stairways. In multistory buildings the placing of washrooms and toilet rooms one above the other on all floors considerably reduces plumbing costs.

Ordinarily it is not desirable to require employees to go from one building to another, or from one floor to another, to reach lockers, washrooms, and toilets. The time lost, the extra supervision required to prevent unnecessary idleness, and the possibility of falls in going up and down stairs from floor to floor entail a considerable and unnecessary loss of work time, especially in the case of women workers.

Where it seems advisable to have one washroom and toilet room serve two floors in a multistory building, it may be placed between floors where the employees need go down or up only half a flight of stairs. In any case, it is well to have service facilities sufficiently **decentralized** to avoid confusion and congestion in their use, especially at quitting time. The separation may be on a basis of departments, and for different groups of employees.

Rest Rooms. Rooms for women employees are preferably located separately from the other service facilities. They should be reasonably accessible, cheerful, provided with good ventilation, and quiet.

Personnel Department. The personnel department is preferably located on the ground floor near the street entrance through which applicants for jobs may enter and leave conveniently. It is not desirable to have them go through the plant to reach the personnel office. Since this department must also have direct contact with the manufacturing departments, keep employee records, and may have hospital and dispensary facilities, it should be located close to the manufacturing area.

Dispensary. The dispensary should be located so that it is convenient to all manufacturing departments and can be reached in a minimum of time in an emergency. It should preferably be near an outside driveway for **ambulance service.** As stated above, the dispensary and the personnel departments are often found adjacent, if not in one department. This arrangement permits the same person or persons to conduct employment procedures, make physical examinations, and attend to first-aid patients.

Cafeterias. Plant restaurants and cafeterias should be centrally located for the convenience of the majority of employees and minimum travel in case of bad weather. Although not profit-making departments, they should contribute to the well-being of the employee, his feeling of satisfaction, and his volume of production. In larger plants table service as well as cafeteria service is provided. As a supplement to central service, **branch cafeterias** may be operated to supply hot foods, sandwiches, fruit, coffee, and milk. Some employees prefer to eat lunch in or near their own departments, and possibly to add only a purchased drink or dessert to a lunch brought from home. **Seating** and **table equipment** may be installed at these points.

Other Departments. As with the departments just mentioned, other miscellaneous departments should be located with regard to the function they perform and their inherent requirements. Drafting and photographic departments, requiring high intensity of lighting, are often given a northern exposure or placed on the top floor where skylights may be used.

As an important factor in labor maintenance, **recreational facilities** for employees should not be overlooked, but they may be located wherever space, convenience, and the nature of the recreation dictate. In large companies, ball fields, basketball courts, bowling alleys, etc., may be company-owned, but smaller companies can better arrange to use commercial or public facilities.

Making the Master Layout

CONSTRUCT MASTER LAYOUT. When the preceding work has progressed step by step through area allocation and the assigning of service areas to their locations on a sketch, the plant layout engineer is ready to construct the master layout. This is the finished project. It represents the work of the plant layout engineer to others, and it should be well done.

Muther (Production-Line Technique) has suggested the following stages in developing the detailed layout with **templates** and **models:**

1. Engineer works up his proposed arrangement by drawings, diagrams, and templates.
2. He places models on the layout plan according to his planned arrangement over the templates. He then invites suggestions from all concerned.
3. Suggested improvements are tried out by moving models or otherwise evaluating the idea.
4. When final arrangement is decided upon, the models are removed and templates fastened securely to undersheet or floor plan for photographing or reproduction.

Layout Boards. The master layout is usually mounted on a backing board. If the project is small, the work can be done on a **drawing board** or drawing table. In the larger plants, special **layout tables** made up of removable sections, about 2 × 4 ft. in size, are used, to permit removal of any section to be studied, worked on, or discussed.

Boards, or sections of the layout, may also be stored or filed in a horizontal position in a rack, with each board pulling out like a drawer.

Sometimes layouts are mounted in a vertical position. They may be placed on walls, stands, or built into **vertical filing racks** of one sort or another. One plant has several sections mounted like window sash, so that each may be lowered into viewing position from a "file" above. Another plant has larger boards, about 7 × 8 ft., sliding on overhead tracks.

Scale. The most common scale in use in industry is ¼ in. equals 1 ft. for the layout itself. Smaller scales (⅛, ¹⁄₁₆, ¹⁄₃₂ in., etc. = 1 ft.) are used for plot plans and preliminary sketches of large areas. Larger scales (⅜ or ½ in. = 1 ft.) are used when smaller areas are being laid out, or when considerable detail must be shown.

Templates and Models. In making the layout, templates are used to represent physical objects. Templates are classified by Apple (Plant Layout and Materials Handling) as follows:

1. Templates:
   a. Rectangular, to maximum length and width of equipment.
   b. Contour (projected shape of the equipment, to scale).
2. Models (three dimensional):
   a. Block.
   b. Contour-base model.
   c. Scale models.
3. Combination of two-dimensional and three-dimensional models.

	Block Template	2-Dimensional Template	3-Dimensional Model	Combination of 2-Dimensional Template and 3-Dimensional Model
Cost	Low first cost. Can be made by inexperienced personnel.	Requires services of a fairly skilled draftsman with a knowledge of machine tools. First cost considerably higher than for block template.	Requires skilled model maker if made special. Cost of models in quantity not appreciably higher than good two-dimensional templates.	Initial cost of this method combines the cost of two-dimensional template and three-dimensional model.
Engineering Value	Very poor. Does not permit good visualization of layout or effective arrangements.	Good. This type of template in the hands of a proficient engineer permits very effective layouts. Does not permit easy interpretation of the layout by nontechnical personnel.	Good. Makes faster development of equipment arrangements for effective layouts. Helps to "sell" the layout.	Best. Combines all the merits of two-dimensional template and three-dimensional model.
Advantages	Can be made quickly at very low cost.	Gives a very accurate layout and reduces time required to make final drawings. Clearly indicates actual floor areas required. Serves as a permanent template when properly made. Greatly reduces possibility of errors as compared to block template.	Aids visualization of layouts by nontechnical personnel. Various arrangements can be made quickly at very low cost. The various schemes can be photographed for comparison studies. Models can be used indefinitely.	Permits highly accurate layouts to be made quickly with complete engineering details. Gives full visualization of layout. Only one set of models necessary to make any number of layouts. Reduces layout and drafting cost.
Disadvantages	Does not provide for accuracy of layout, effective arrangement, or economical utilization of floorspace. Increases drafting time and cost of engineering drawings. Fosters discrepancies and errors. Increases over-all layout cost.	Cost is considerably higher than block templates. Does not provide for ease of perceptibility inherent in models. Requires engineers to carry mentally all planning in the third dimension.	Does not carry the engineering information provided by the two-dimensional template. Does not show machine clearances required for operation or services. Increases drafting time.	Highest initial cost of any method.

Fig. 21. Plant layout comparison chart. Comparison of most common types of templates and models.

Two-dimensional templates of many types are to be found in industry. Some of the more common are:

1   Heavy paper or cardboard, individually cut out.
2. Printed duplicates:
    a. On paper (printed, ozalid, blueprint).
    b. Photographic reproductions, on film stock, and up to ⅛ in. plastic.

Several kinds of two-dimensional templates commercially available are printed on translucent plastic and some are fitted with **permanent magnets.** Layouts are made on metal-surfaced boards, over a **translucent grid,** and a print is made directly from the actual layout, with no drawing necessary.

Three-dimensional scale models are increasingly used because of the realistic touch they add to the layout. Such models are usually easier to interpret and are of great value in explaining the layout to others. Commercial concerns produce a wide variety of both two-dimensional templates and three-dimensional models.

The advantages and disadvantages of templates, models, and combinations have been tabulated by Mallick and Sansonnetti (American Machinist, vol. 90) as shown in Fig. 21.

The American Society of Mechanical Engineers has published a set of standards covering two-dimensional, one-plane templates and three-dimensional models which covers engineering details to be incorporated into the design and production of template and models (ASME Standard for Plant Layout Templates and Models). Among the items covered in the standards are: scale, material, symbols, details of templates and models, finishes, specifications for identification, operator position, and use of color.

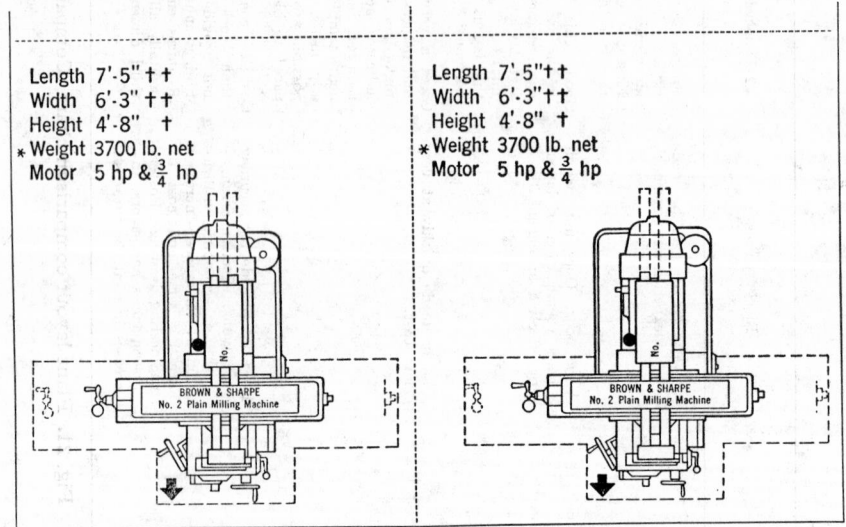

* =Does not include weight of motor, control, or auxiliaries.   † †=Includes clearance allowances.
O=Service riser — air - water - electric - gas or other.   ● =Point of maximum height.
†=Does not include clearance allowances.   ⬇=Operator's normal position.

Fig. 22. Specimen template sheet for a specific milling machine.

Part of a typical **template sheet** to be cut out and mounted on the layout board is shown in Fig. 22 (Mallick and Gaudreau, Plant Layout Planning and Practice). The full sheet contains six identical templates of the same machine. Each template carries a table listing the dimensions and weight of the machine and its motor power requirements. Similar sheets are commercially available.

Templates may be fastened to the layout board with tacks, pins, staples, rubber cement, pressure sensitive tape, etc. Models are often mounted by means of a pin inserted in the bottom of each.

Flow Lines. It is often desirable to draw flow lines on the finished layout to show the path to be followed by the material as it progresses through the plant. Such lines should follow on the drawing as nearly as possible along the same path the part will follow. This is shown in Fig. 19. Flow lines, if accurately drawn, should present a pattern similar to that planned in the flow diagrams developed earlier. The flow lines will show, to some extent, how well the principles of good plant layout have been followed. They are frequently made with narrow, colored, pressure-sensitive tapes.

Carroll W. Boyce (Factory Management and Maintenance, vol. 107) states:

Checking the flow lines for tentative arrangements can be accomplished by actually drawing them in on the tracing. However, after several successive erasures have been made, the base tracing becomes useless for further experimentation. This makes it necessary to relocate all the elements on a new tracing before proceeding.

A simple way to avoid this is to lay out the flow lines with pieces of colored string; distance can be calculated by straightening the string, and multiplying its length by the appropriate scale factor. Colored tapes are somewhat more difficult to work with, but they have higher visibility and are recommended for use when layouts are to be photographed for later reference.

As each arrangement is arrived at, a permanent record can be made by photographing the template layout, or by making a blueprint. If the flow-line strings are filed with these permanent records, a simple method of comparison of the total elemental flow-line distances will be readily available. With these permanent records available, it is always possible to duplicate an earlier tentative arrangement, should this seem desirable for further discussion in the final stage of layout planning.

Where inter-floor operations are encountered, it is necessary to supplement the two-dimensional template layout with front and side elevations. An optional method of accomplishing the same purpose is to mount the template layouts of the individual floors on pieces of fairly substantial fiberboard. These layouts are then placed on a frame, one above another. Analyses may be made by running flow-line string to and from the location of the inter-floor transportation facilities. Alternatively, new inter-floor patterns may be analyzed by drilling small holes in the fiberboard "floor" and passing the string through the holes.

Reproductions. It is often desirable to make copies of the layout for use in the plant by millwrights, plumbers, electricians, and other service men. The more common methods of **producing copies** of the layout board are:

1. Drawing a tracing from which prints can be made.
2. Photographing the layout.
3. Photostating the layout.
4. Making direct prints from the translucent type layouts mentioned earlier.

Miscellaneous Factors. Two other items of interest at this point are the legend on the layout and the use of color. If the layout is to be meaningful to those observing it, certain data should be shown on the drawing or in a **legend.**

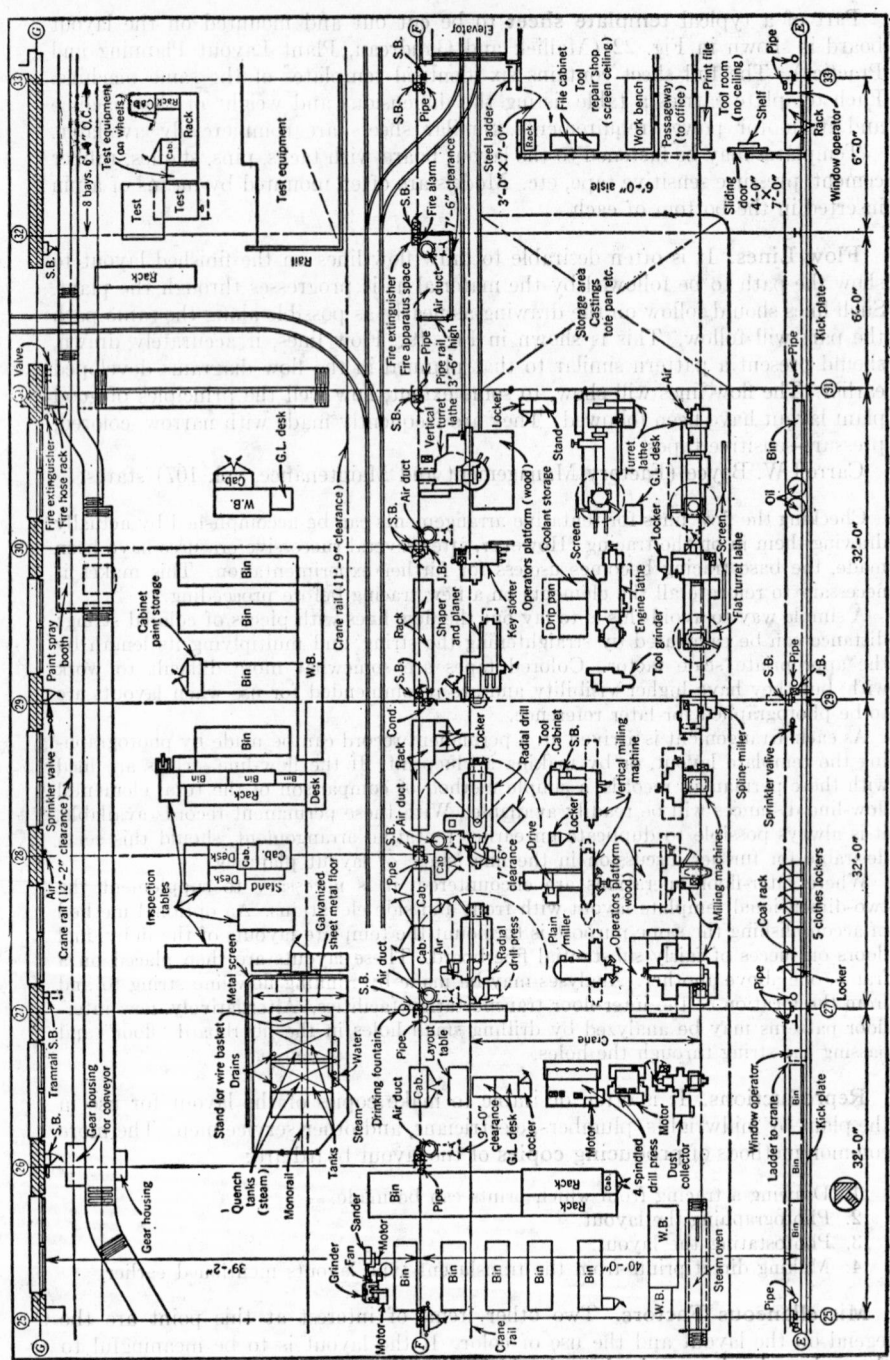

Fig. 23. Plant layout drawing prepared from template layout.

Items suggested by Mallick and Gaudreau (Plant Layout Planning and Practice) are:

1. Title and scale of the drawing.
2. Sketch number.
3. Approval space.
4. Detail notations for use of plant engineer.
5. Construction notations for architects and detail engineers.
6. Notations on heating, lighting, ventilation, and communication facilities.
7. Directional locations and orientation on plant site.
8. Transportation and handling facilities.
9. Overhead obstructions and obstructions below floor levels where foundations or superstructures are necessary.
10. Machine-tool and equipment identification numbers.
11. Column numbers.
12. Service outlets for gas, electricity, water, air, and other utilities.
13. Fire protection and other safety apparatus notes.
14. Signature and date.

Color is useful in emphasizing certain items on the master layout. It is also an aid in "selling" the layout to others. Color may be used to:

1. Indicate certain types of equipment, such as: salmon = production equipment; yellow = materials handling equipment; red = storage equipment.
2. Emphasize flow lines.
3. Differentiate between present and proposed equipment.
4. Indicate equipment used on different parts.

The color can be applied to templates by either making templates out of colored stock or marking on uniform colored templates with crayons or pencils.

An example of a typical **template layout drawing** is shown in Fig. 23 (Mallick and Gaudreau, Plant Layout Planning and Practice).

Making the Installation

CHECK FINAL LAYOUT. As work on the layout progresses, it should be constantly checked to see that detailed attention to one phase of the project is not resulting in an oversight of layout principles in other areas. This checking should be done by the layout engineers themselves, as well as by others interested in the project. Foremen, supervisors, and staff personnel will all have ideas that should be taken into consideration. Besides the production people who will have direct interest in the layout, the following persons are among those to be consulted as the planning progresses:

1. Plant engineer.
2. Safety engineer.
3. Personnel director.
4. Production control supervisor.
5. Materials handling supervisor.
6. Chief industrial engineer.

It must be remembered that it is always easier to "sell" the layout to a person if he has been included in its planning. This procedure will also reduce complaints and criticism after the layout has been put into effect.

Apple (Plant Layout and Materials Handling) gives the check sheet shown in Fig. 24 as an aid in checking the layout.

A. **Materials Handling:**
   1. Are materials received and shipped in unit loads utilizing pallets, gondolas, skids, or racks?
   2. Do incoming materials go directly to the work areas whenever possible?
   3. Are materials handled in one trip or do they have to be handled and rehandled?
   4. Have the processes involving heavy materials been located as near the receiving department as possible?
   5. Do conveyors and materials handling systems run from the receiving department to work areas, to assembly areas, and then to shipping areas?
   6. Does the materials handling system operate for straight-line production with a minimum of back-tracking?
   7. Has gravity been used in materials handling wherever possible?
   8. Can mechanical handling equipment be used within the manufacturing process?
   9. Have all the avoidable manual handling operations been eliminated, and has the total number of handling operations been minimized?
   10. Do subassemblies flow into the assembly line directly?
   11. Is materials handling equipment designed to carry materials in a position so as to conserve space?
   12. Are aisles likely to get "cluttered up" with unused materials and equipment?
   13. Have the conveyors and machines been guarded for the safety of the employees?
   14. Are widely separated work areas connected by suitable conveyor systems?
   15. What provision has been made for auxiliary flow lines in the event of machine or conveyor breakdown?
   16. When finished work is disposed of by one operator can it be readily picked up by the next operator?
   17. What are the sources of possible delays or "bottlenecks"?
   18. Is the flow planned so that inventory checking and inspection can be carried out in the immediate work area?
   19. Are inspection points located at vital and convenient points along the materials handling system?
   20. Has proper storage been allowed for materials-in-process between operations?
   21. Are the containers used to transport materials-in-process designed to speed-up and assist the process?
   22. Are the lift-trucks and motorized equipment kept busy all the time?
   23. Does each materials handling installation fit in as an integral part of the over-all plant system?
   24. Do any of the conveyors "box" anyone in?
   25. Do the materials handling devices bring materials right up to the operator so as to reduce walking?

B. **Production and Production Control:**
   1. Are conditions such that quality of work can be maintained?
   2. Is floor area fully utilized?
   3. Are machines so arranged that their full capacity can be utilized?
   4. Are machines readily accessible for supplying them with materials and for repair and maintenance work?
   5. Can individual operators tend more than one machine?
   6. Are aisles and doorways free of obstacles and clearly marked off for traffic purposes?
   7. Has an approved color scheme been adopted for painting machines and work areas?
   8. Do the machines "block in" anyone, i.e., is enough work space left around the machines for proper operation?
   9. Are machines and equipment located to give maximum motion efficiency during processes?
   10. Are tool cribs located where they will save steps in tool issuing?
   11. Does machine overtravel extend into the aisles or interfere with operator's work space?
   12. Is there room for departmental expansion?
   13. Is the maximum use being made of each piece of equipment?
   14. Are machine cycles balanced?
   15. Can supervisors and foremen easily oversee their entire departments?
   16. Does the arrangement of machines give maximum flexibility?
   17. Has space been allowed for foremen's desks or small booths for production control records, etc.?

Fig. 24. Plant layout check sheet (continued on next page).

18. Have standard machines and equipment been used wherever possible instead of highly specialized machines?
19. Can men smoke on the job? If not, has a smoking area been designated?
20. Can repair and maintenance be performed so as not to interfere with production?
21. Are service controls readily accessible?
22. Can quick exits be made around, over, or under conveyors?
23. What has been done to eliminate noise?
24. Are hazardous operations located in isolated areas?

C. The Building and Its Surroundings:
1. Are floors overloaded?
2. Has space been left for pillars, walls, and supports?
3. Are electrical outlets convenient to the machines so that power lines can be easily connected or disconnected?
4. Are exits, fire doors, and fire escapes adequate and properly located for maximum safety?
5. Have drinking fountains been provided?
6. Is artificial illumination adequate?
7. Has natural light been used to full advantage?
8. Is ventilation adequate in all areas?
9. What provisions are necessary for heating or air conditioning?
10. Are floors level?
11. Have the sources of power been studied as to availability, cost of power. advisability of buying primary or secondary power?
12. Is there danger of smoke or other contamination from nearby plants or industries?
13. Have the plant and process plans been checked by the insurance companies and by the proper local officials?
14. Are the layout and the building itself such as to facilitate good housekeeping and neatness?
15. Are aisles and doors wide enough to accommodate trucks carrying loaded pallets or skids?
16. Whenever possible do doors open and close automatically?
17. Are ramps kept at the lowest possible grade?
18. Can building repairs be made with ease?
19. Are loading and unloading docks covered against weather?
20. Has parking space been provided for the employees?
21. What are the possibilities of natural catastrophe such as earthquake, flood, or tornado?
22. Can fire protection equipment be easily transported to various parts of the plant?

D. Product Design and Engineering:
1. Have the considerations of product vs. process layout been thoroughly weighed?
2. Has the nature of the product been taken into account, i.e., are there any peculiarities of the product that have been overlooked?
3. What will happen to the layout in case of product changes, improvements, and redesigns, etc.?
4. Has criticism been invited from all groups having anything to do with the product?
5. Can new or additional equipment be installed without disrupting the present production?
6. Are specialized machines necessary for turning out the product or will standard machines and equipment serve the purpose with equal economy?
7. Can existing machines be readily retooled to fit new requirements?

E. Service Areas and Employee Comfort:
1. Are service areas easily accessible from all parts of the plant?
2. Are there sufficient washrooms, lockers, drinking fountains, etc., for the convenience of all?
3. Has proper heating, ventilating, and lighting been provided?
4. Are all danger areas clearly marked and guarded?
5. Are there first-aid stations located throughout the plant?
6. Is there proper storage space for inflammable materials?
7. What are the employee recreational facilities?

Fig. 24. (Concluded.)

GET OFFICIAL APPROVALS. After the layout has been completed and checked by all those interested, it must be officially approved by the **plant management** representatives. It is wise to have at least the following persons sign their approval in an appropriate place on the layout:

1. Department foreman.
2. General foreman.
3. Factory manager.
4. Chief industrial engineer.
5. Safety engineer.
6. Plant layout engineer.
7. General manager and/or top executive.

These approvals, as with the consultation mentioned above, assure that the proper persons have seen the layout, studied it, and given approval from their own particular points of view. Each person who has had a part in planning or approving the layout becomes a supporter of the ideas contained therein, when the layout is put into effect.

At the time the layout is approved it will usually be accompanied by supplementary data of many kinds to support the planning and to "sell" the ideas contained in the layout. Apple (Plant Layout and Materials Handling) suggests that the following data should accompany the finished layout:

1. Blueprints or sample parts of the product.
2. Parts list.
3. Layout planning chart.
4. Data on nonproductive activities.
5. Assembly chart.
6. Operation process charts.
7. Estimated costs.
8. Estimated savings.
9. Personnel requirements.

INSTALL THE LAYOUT. The finished plant layout is only the beginning. When it comes to the installation of the layout, **construction drawings** will be necessary if the layout involves a new plant or extensive changes in an existing plant. Detailed plans must be made for the installation of utilities. Many times a pilot line is set up first to test the effectiveness of plans. **Production schedules** in existing areas may have to be halted or altered while changes are being made. This is not always necessary, however. One automobile engine plant expanded its production facilities and assembly line from 50 engines per hour to 85 engines per hour without losing any of its previously planned production. This increase was accomplished by getting everything as nearly set as possible, and then making major transitions during the third shift or on weekends.

The following is suggested by Petzon and Rosenberg (Factory Management and Maintenance, vol. 100) as a means of making changes with a minimum amount of difficulty:

1. Prepare a list of all machines to be moved. This will include machine name and number, and old and new locations.
2. Prepare a schedule for movement of each of the above machines.
3. Issue a move order for movement of machines. This will serve as a work guide to the moving crews.
4. Tag each machine. Include name and number of machine, old and new location, and spaces for inspection, check for all necessary adjustments, and final OK.
5. Keep a progress chart of daily moves until the job is completed.

Plant Layout Surveys and Re-Layouts

THE RE-LAYOUT PROBLEM. While the preceding data on plant layout have been presented from the viewpoint of the planning and design for a new plant, many layout problems are concerned with existing facilities. The detailed procedures to be followed are identical, but a somewhat different approach must be made in attacking the problem of improving an existing layout.

When **inefficient layouts** are suspected, the whole existing situation should be studied. A number of organizational and other reasons for inefficient layouts have been detailed by Shubin and Madeheim (Plant Layout). They point to such factors as a plant site which prevents the proper design of a layout for the production equipment required; use of buildings basically unsuited to the company's layout requirements; layout tasks delegated to unqualified personnel, or layout revisions assigned to department heads or foremen who were in a position to consider only a segment of the total layout; failure of job-shops to adopt adequate line layouts for comparatively standardized phases of their operations; overspecialized layouts and facilities in other types of firms; failure of layout and production facilities to keep pace with technological improvements; failure to adjust for piecemeal product-design changes. They also suggest that ineffective sales-forecasting, production-planning, and plant-maintenance practices may affect a basically efficient plant layout adversely and raise the cost of production.

RESTUDY TO IMPROVE LAYOUTS. Mallick and Gaudreau (Plant Layout Planning and Practice) present, in outline form, some of the operating problems or physical conditions indicative of a possible **need for a re-layout project:**

1. Receiving department:
   a. Congestion of materials.
   b. Complaints of delays at trucking lines.
   c. Recurrent demurrage.
   d. Damage to materials by exposure to the elements.
   e. Necessity for materials handlers to work outside in inclement weather.
   f. Difficult manual handling and rehandling operations.
2. Storerooms:
   a. Congestion of stock storage.
   b. Damage to materials in storage.
   c. Frequent loss of material.
   d. Poor control of inventories.
   e. High ratios of storeroom clerks and materials handlers to productive operators.
   f. Frequent rehandling and restorage of materials before processing.
3. Process departments:
   a. Necessity for skilled operators to handle materials.
   b. Presence of large quantities of materials on the floor, not under production control.
   c. Poor quality of work-in-process.
   d. Complaints from foremen and production supervisors regarding the lack of floorspace while overhead space remains unused.
   e. Excess length of the manufacturing cycle over actual processing time.
   f. Presence of congestion and hazards in narrow or crooked traffic aisles.
   g. Over 15 percent of the total floorspace in the plant taken up by traffic aisles.
   h. Difficulty in the materials handling service to the productive equipment.
   i. Excessive maintenance costs.

Materials Handling Condition	Male Operator	Female Operator
1. Lifting material frequently from floor ..	A point overhead	Chest height
2. Lifting material above knee level when weight exceeds	75 lb.	35 lb.
3. Lifting or moving material with the assistance of	1 helper	1 helper
4. Handling materials constantly for periods longer than	30 min.	30 min.
5. Handling similar materials daily for	Several weeks	Several weeks
6. Moving large quantities or total weight over greater distance than	50 ft.	50 ft.

Fig. 25. Conditions to be forbidden in handling materials.

    j. Necessity for frequent rearrangements of equipment.
    k. Periodic requests for additions to equipment or to the working area.
  4. Productive operators: The existence of any of the excesses in materials handling work performed by productive operators, as tabulated in Fig. 25.
  5. Employee morale:
    a. Complaints from operators regarding:
      (1) Heating.
      (2) Lighting.
      (3) Ventilation.
      (4) Rest rooms.
      (5) Congestion.
      (6) Hazards.
    b. High accident rate.
    c. High labor turnover.
  6. Shipping department:
    a. Delays in shipping even though materials are ready for shipment.
    b. Unsightliness of plant yards.

INFORMATION TO ASSEMBLE IN A SURVEY. After the need for a re-layout has been established by checking the shortcomings of the present layout against the above data, it becomes necessary to make a detailed analysis of the situation. However, before tackling the re-layout problem proper, certain preliminary data should be compiled as a source of information for the analysis and planning of the new layout. According to Mallick and Gaudreau (Plant Layout Planning and Practice), items such as the following should be gathered for study:

  1. Sales volume of each line of products.
  2. Manufacturing labor and expense by control cost accounts.
  3. Net allowed hours and machine loads.
  4. Number of employees on the payroll.
  5. Amount invested in fixed assets and inventories.
  6. Inventory of machine tools and handling equipment.
  7. Organization charts.
  8. Plant layout drawings.
  9. Backlog of unfilled orders.
 10. Past history of production activity.
 11. Quality of product.
 12. Percentage of rejects.
 13. Changes in product designs.

Points to Investigate in a Detailed Study. In making the detailed study of the problem, Mallick and Gaudreau (Plant Layout Planning and Practice) suggest that the following points should not be overlooked. These are intended as a **check list** of major points to be considered, not as a suggestion for a chronological procedure.

1. Study the different types of products to be manufactured.
2. Study the individual designs of these products.
3. Determine the parts or materials that are interchangeable or common.
4. Ascertain the probable life of the separate product designs.
5. Analyze past activity and present loading.
6. Secure projected loading in writing.
7. Break down the projected loading into component parts.
8. Study the feeder-section connections contemplated.
9. Analyze the problems of materials handling and transportation.
10. Review the operation file with the time-study or methods engineer. Ascertain the wage rates, earnings, and operating efficiency of the plant force, overtime, and setups. Secure the responsible supervisor's recommendations.
11. Make a thorough study of the storerooms and stockrooms. Secure full information concerning the present practice of holding stock. Determine the present and contemplated investment in raw materials, work-in-process, and finished stock. Check these figures against the contemplated production loading.
12. Break down the projected loading of component parts into operation elements.
13. Convert the operation elements into operations.
14. Route the operations into their proper sequence.
15. Balance the operations.
16. Align the operations on flow charts.
17. Study the flow charts for bottlenecks, trends in processing, centralization possibilities, facility requirements, and surplus capacities at work stations.
18. Make a comprehensive check of major tools available to determine:
    a. The operating condition of the tools.
    b. The quantity of tools on order, by types.
    c. The contemplated loading of the production equipment.
    d. The types of machine tools to which the planned operations will be dispatched.
    e. The types of small tools, jigs, and fixtures needed.
    f. The drive medium of the machine tools selected.

Data on Buildings and Equipment. In addition to the above operating data on production, Mallick and Gaudreau indicate that data should also be gathered on the buildings and equipment. Items to check are:

1. Prepare machine-tool layout information forms on all machine tools and production equipment.
2. Compile the sizes and shapes of all work benches, racks, and other furniture and fixtures on the existing layout.
3. Check building openings for aisles, entrances, and exits.
4. Prepare a floor plan showing all floor obstructions such as:
    a. Water fountains, switch boxes, lighting panels.
    b. Sprinkler risers, pipelines for gas, water, air, and steam. Drainage facilities, and manholes.
    c. Fire hose reels and extinguishers.
    d. Fire and police boxes.
    e. Industrial and broad-gage trackage.
5. Floor loads and weight of work-in-process. Also allowable loads.
6. Roof construction and overhead clearances.

7. Office facilities.
8. Check the floor plans for the accuracy of building dimensions and locations of aisles, stairways, and elevators.
9. Foundations for machinery.
10. Storerooms, tool cribs, and test facilities.
11. Window arrangement.
12. Location of noisy equipment such as grinders, saws, punch presses, and drop hammers.
13. Conditions of lighting, heating, sanitation, ventilation, and safety.

Making New Layouts. Once the data have been gathered, the analysis made, and the problems identified, the procedure for making the layout is the same as outlined earlier in this section. Obviously, it is seldom that a layout, no matter how good when first planned and put into effect, will remain satisfactory for an indefinitely long period. The tempo of industry is so swift, and the improvements in equipment and procedures which are constantly being developed are so important, that a layout rarely can go without **restudy** perhaps yearly, at least, to check on its adequacy under changing conditions. The result is that progressive companies maintain plant layout men who constantly study the methods of manufacturing products at a higher rate of production and a lower cost, and such studies result in frequent changes in equipment and facilities and consequent re-layout of manufacturing facilities.

Plant Buildings

GROUPING OF BUILDINGS. Past practice has been to lay out buildings corresponding to shapes of such letters as U, H, E, T, L, and F, depending on departmental problems and flow of materials through the plant. All these shapes lend themselves to enlargement, and much can be said for such groupings. More recently, many companies have adopted a solid block shape with all operations on a single floor and under one roof. Nelson (Albert Kahn, Inc.) says: "Multiplicity of buildings increases construction costs due to the number of exterior walls; the intervening courts occupy space which could be used more advantageously for production; and their maintenance is expensive. Heat losses through exterior walls are also greater in a group of buildings."

The main criticism Nelson advances, however, is based on flexibility. "As processes change, as departments shrink and expand, or as new departments are added, the advantages of the single structure become apparent. While this represents a modern viewpoint that must be considered, many engineers regard the question of number of structures as a many-sided question which is debatable."

ONE-STORY VS. MULTISTORY BUILDINGS. The first group of building factors of importance in plant layout is that of the relative advantages of, and the reasons dictating, the types of construction used for a plant—single-story or multistory.

FACTORS THAT DETERMINE TYPES. The factors indicating, and the advantages of, **one-story construction** are:

1. Low cost of ground area.
2. Availability of land for expansion.
3. Less time to erect.
4. Less area lost in sidewalls and columns clearance and for elevators, stairs, approaches to them, etc.
5. High floor loads caused by equipment or product.

6. Greater flexibility in accommodating layout changes.
7. Possible greater efficiency in routing and handling equipment.
8. Supervision easy and effective.
9. Maximum use of daylight and natural ventilation possible.
10. Hazardous and objectionable occupations easily isolated.
11. Lower over-all operating costs.

The factors indicating, and the advantages of, **multistory construction** are:

1. High cost of ground area.
2. Limited area of site.
3. Natural topography of site may permit entrances on different floor levels.
4. Ease of expansion if properly foreseen.
5. Limited need for high floor load.
6. Majority of product and equipment light in weight and of small bulk.
7. Possible better coordination of departments in a vertical plane—handling distances may be reduced and gravity flow utilized.
8. In some locations, less dirt and better lighting and ventilation possible on upper floors.
9. Lower heat loss through roof.

BUILDING DETAILS. The following are notes and comments on current trends in **building design** and **construction:**

1. Tendency toward single-story structures.
2. Increased use of welded frames and structural members.
3. Larger bay sizes—20 × 40 ft. and 30 × 50 ft.—preferably rectangular.
4. Simplified design, to permit flexibility.
5. Preponderance of concrete floors, treated for "dusting."
6. Prefabricated wall and, particularly, interior partition sections, for easy changes.
7. Flat and monitor roofs predominate.
8. Large window areas—much glass block, but with vision strips of clear glass.
9. Ample parking areas, even some private airport facilities.
10. Attention to employee outdoor recreational facilities.
11. Use of pleasantly painted interiors in place of grays, blacks, and whites.
12. Increasing attention to plant exteriors—pleasing building lines and good landscaping.
13. Use of basements primarily for storage, service facilities, and pedestrian traffic from point to point.
14. More attention to factors affecting personnel.
15. Provision for expansion planned into building structures.
16. Ceiling height: 10–15 ft. without heating, ventilating, and materials handling equipment overhead, otherwise 10–18 ft.; or, if determined by product size, maximum height +100 percent.
17. Use of columns to enclose downspouts, conduit, etc.
18. Placement of heating, ventilating, and handling equipment between trusses.
19. Ramps up to 15 percent grade; width determined by maximum load width +2 ft.
20. Use of automatic opening and rubber doors.
21. Docks preferably inside, 50 in. high, with built-in levelers for trucks.
22. Use of balconies for subassembly, light machining, service areas, and storage.

Heating and Ventilation

SELECTION FACTORS. The selection of a heating and ventilation system is an important phase of plant design. Considerable initial investment may be involved in addition to other economic considerations such as operating expenses, maintenance, and repairs.

More attention is now being devoted to the physiological and psychological effects of a **controlled environment** upon workers, and the effects of controlled environment on the quality of products must often be considered. In some instances only a control of temperature is necessary, whereas in others, simultaneous control of temperature, humidity, ventilation, and air cleanliness may be required.

A systematic and logical procedure should be followed in each situation where the design and selection of a heating and ventilating system is involved; the most important items to be considered should be evaluated, and a system should be chosen which will be adequate to provide the degree of control desired without exceeding the economic limitations of initial investment or operation.

TYPES OF SYSTEMS. All heating systems consist of certain basic components when reduced to their most elementary form:

1. **A heat source,** which may be the burning fuel in a boiler or furnace; electric energy; or the earth, water, or air in heat pump systems.
2. **A conveying or distribution system** used to transfer a heating medium from the heat source to the space to be heated, e.g., steam piping, hot water piping, or air ducts.
3. **Heat disseminators** located within the space to be heated, e.g., convectors or radiators in steam and hot water systems, registers and grilles in air systems.

The variations in the actual systems which include these basic components are numerous, and no attempt will be made to describe in detail all possible combinations. Some classifications are important enough, however, to be discussed for purposes of comparison.

Combined or Split Systems. A combined system of heating and ventilation is designed to provide for both the heating requirements and the ventilation requirements by air which is supplied to the building. The entire heating requirements of the building may be supplied by heated air without the use of auxiliary devices such as radiators or convectors, or a part only of the **total heating load** may be supplied by the air-handling system. In any event, sufficient fresh air for ventilation purposes is possible along with a distribution system for air movement throughout the heated space. The distinguishing characteristic of this system is that the temperature of the **supply air** is raised to a level high enough to provide either part or all of the heating requirements.

The **split system** makes use of auxiliary radiation or convection devices to provide for building heat losses and supplies tempered air at approximately room temperature to satisfy ventilation requirements. When ventilation (implying the supply of outdoor air) is not required at times, such as overnight or during periods of low occupancy, operating cost may be reduced by supplying building-heating requirements without the use of the ventilating system.

A similar operational procedure is commonly used with the combined system, making use of dampers to allow for **recirculation** of room air in order to maintain temperatures without providing ventilation.

Central or Unit Systems. A central air-handling system consists of one or more main supply fans with heating coils, filters, heat generation equipment, etc., usually located in a **mechanical equipment room.** A **plenum chamber** is ordinarily provided for supplying air to a system of ductwork which serves the entire area to be heated. Return air ducts, if required, bring recirculated room air back to the equipment room where it is mixed with a supply of fresh outdoor air for ventilation. Individual control of temperature by areas or zones may be accomplished by dampers located in the plenum chamber.

A **unit system** differs from the central system in that the fans, filters, heating coils, and ductwork, including ventilation air supply, are combined in separate units, usually located in or adjacent to the spaces to be heated. Supply and return ductwork may be incorporated with unit systems, but direct discharge of supply air through grilles attached to the housing enclosing the equipment is commonly used. The units may have steam or hot-water heating coils or may be direct-fired by gas or oil. Units of this type range from small unit heaters with no ductwork or ventilation air provisions, to completely self-contained units including filters, ventilation provisions, a mixing chamber with automatically controlled dampers for multiple-zone temperature control, and a complete system of ductwork.

Steam, Hot-Water, and Direct-Fluid Systems. In both central and unit systems, either steam or hot water may be used as a **heat transfer fluid.** Steam systems are commonly designated as high pressure, low pressure, vapor, or vacuum, depending upon the pressure conditions at which the system has been designed to operate. By convention, pressures above 15 lb. per sq. in. gage are considered high, from 0 to 15 lb. per sq. in. gage are termed low; so-called **vapor systems** operate in a range from slightly below to slightly above atmospheric pressure, and **vacuum systems** may operate below atmospheric pressure by using a vacuum-type condensate return pump.

In industrial work, for application with air-handling systems, high-pressure steam in the range of 15 to 150 lb. per sq. in. gage is frequently used, supplied either by a heating boiler or from steam used for process work.

Hot water may be supplied to the air-heating coils of either a central or unit system from a hot-water heating boiler or from a heat exchange supplied with steam. One advantage often given for hot water as the heat transfer medium is the relative ease with which variations in temperature can be achieved in direct proportion to the heating demands. For ventilation systems, however, this advantage is not so important as in the case of a radiator or convector system, since temperature control can easily be accomplished by using mixing dampers in a plenum chamber. Hot-water systems require one or more pumps for circulating the water through the piping system. High-temperature hot-water heating systems (Heating, Ventilating, and Air Conditioning Guide, vol. 34) commonly use single-inlet single-stage centrifugal pumps operating at 1750 rev. per min. and having water-cooled bearings and glands, although mechanical seals are coming into use. Steam systems normally will require a condensate pump for return of condensed steam to a boiler.

Direct gas or oil-fired heat exchangers are normally used in the unit-type system only, there being little application of such equipment to large central systems. This type of system has increased in popularity, partly because of the availability of newer and more flexible equipment and partly because of the ease with which additional capacity may be installed. First-cost considerations are generally favorable, particularly when compared with the expense involved in adding additional boiler capacity or piping required to expand a conventional steam or hot-water system. **Application studies** are important in designing new buildings in order to determine which type of system is better suited to the particular problems involved.

Gas, Oil, or Coal-Fired Systems. For steam generation or hot-water heating, coal, oil, and gas are commonly used as fuels. The prime consideration here is normally one of the cost involved in the heat generation equipment rather than in the applicability of the heating system, since the heat-exchange equipment will usually be quite similar regardless of the fuel used. Availability of fuel, operational costs, and maintenance facilities differ from one application to another; hence no general rule can be established. Storage facilities must be provided for coal and oil, whereas with gas, no storage is required. **Multiple fuel arrangements** are common, using gas when available and oil or coal for stand-by purposes.

In many cases, provision may be made to use waste products for fuel, supplementing the normal supply. Common applications of this are wood-waste, by-product gas, and oil.

The use of the **heat pump** for industrial applications offers advantages in many instances, especially where year-round control of the environment is desired. Where the heat pump can be economically justified, the advantages of using electric energy in conjunction with a low-grade heat source are often quite attractive.

SELECTION OF A SYSTEM. The classifications of systems outlined are only the more general ones into which heating and ventilating systems can be grouped; the designer is afforded many more choices than are noted here. Types of heat exchange elements, air distribution devices, and methods of capacity and temperature control may vary widely. In general, there is no one clearly defined "best" system; there may be several available ways by which the same end result can be achieved. Economic considerations will often be the most important factor in final selection, but individual application studies should be made to determine which type of system offers the most return for the investment required. In order to provide the best system for a specific application, a designer should have a thorough understanding of the fundamentals involved in the design of heating and ventilating systems; he should be familiar with the types of equipment available and should be capable of incorporating a group of individual components into an **integrated system** which will function satisfactorily and require a minimum of maintenance.

FUNDAMENTALS OF DESIGN. The ultimate purpose of any heating system is to maintain specified conditions of air temperature inside a building structure. Since the temperature inside a building will be maintained at a level higher than that of the outdoor air during most of the heating season, heat transfer through the building walls, roof, glass areas, and floor will occur. A heating system must have the capacity to offset this heat loss and maintain the desired level of temperature inside the building.

Heat losses vary with temperature difference between indoor and outdoor air, with outdoor wind velocity, and with the kind of building construction; they are customarily separated into two types: (1) **conduction or transmission losses** through the building structure, and (2) **infiltration losses** resulting from air leakage into or out of the building through cracks around windows, doors, exhaust vents, etc.

Design Temperatures. Although both indoor and outdoor temperatures vary with time, steady-state heat transfer is assumed in calculation of building heat losses. Indoor temperatures to be maintained vary with the type of occupancy, the range for industrial buildings being from approximately 60° F. to 80° F. Outdoor design temperatures are difficult to predict accurately; variations occur with differences in locality and season, and considerable variation in temperature may occur on an hourly basis for any given locality. The designer ordinarily will

State	City	Lowest Temperature on Record (° F.)	Design Temperature Usually Assumed (° F.)	Average Wind Velocity Dec., Jan., Feb. M.P.H.
Alabama	Birmingham	−10	10	8.0
Arizona	Phoenix	16	25	5.4
California	Los Angeles	28	35	6.4
Colorado	Denver	−29	−10	7.5
Connecticut	Hartford	−18	0	8.7
District of Columbia	Washington	−15	0	7.8
Florida	Miami	27	35	10.1
Georgia	Atlanta	− 8	10	11.7
Illinois	Chicago	−23	−10	12.0
Indiana	Indianapolis	−25	−10	11.3
Iowa	Des Moines	−30	−15	10.1
Kansas	Wichita	−22	−10	12.4
Kentucky	Louisville	−20	0	9.8
Louisiana	New Orleans	7	20	8.6
Maine	Portland	−21	−5	10.4
Maryland	Baltimore	− 7	0	8.2
Massachusetts	Boston	−18	0	12.4
Michigan	Detroit	−24	−10	12.0
Minnesota	Minneapolis	−34	−20	11.3
Missouri	St. Louis	−22	0	11.8
Nebraska	Omaha	−32	−10	9.7
New Jersey	Trenton	−14	0	10.9
New York	New York	−14	0	16.8
North Carolina	Raleigh	− 2	10	7.9
North Dakota	Bismarck	−45	−30	9.1
Ohio	Cincinnati	−17	0	8.5
	Cleveland	−17	0	14.7
Oregon	Portland	− 2	10	7.3
Pennsylvania	Philadelphia	−11	0	11.0
	Pittsburgh	−20	0	11.6
South Carolina	Charleston	7	15	10.5
Tennessee	Knoxville	−16	0	7.2
Texas	Dallas	− 3	0	10.6
	Galveston	8	20	11.2
Virginia	Richmond	− 3	15	8.1
Washington	Seattle	3	15	9.8
West Virginia	Parkersburg	−27	−10	7.2
Wisconsin	Milwaukee	−25	−15	12.1

Fig. 26. Heating season climatic data.

make use of United States Weather Bureau data to determine the minimum temperature recorded for a particular locality. Since this minimum temperature may occur infrequently and then only for a limited time, the design temperature is customarily set 10° F. to 15° F. higher. Design temperatures in common use have been tabulated by the American Society of Heating and Air Conditioning Engineers (Heating, Ventilating, and Air Conditioning Guide, vol. 34) as shown in Fig. 26.

Wind Velocity. As with temperatures, the wind velocity to be expected varies hourly as well as with location and season. Both infiltration losses and transmission losses are affected by wind velocity, the effect on the former being more significant. Ordinarily, for average conditions, a 15-m.p.h. wind velocity may be assumed for purposes of transmission loss calculations. This value is also commonly used for estimating infiltration losses, but a more representative value should be used if available (see Fig. 26).

Computation of Transmission Losses. After having selected design temperatures and wind velocities, the designer must determine the over-all coefficients of heat transmission for the structure. Heat transmission occurs by means of convection, radiation, and conduction. The flow of heat from the room air to the surface of a wall is by radiation and convection. In heating and ventilating practice, these effects are not separated but are expressed by a combined **coefficient of convection and radiation,** f_i, the subscript i denoting the inside surface. The magnitude of the coefficient represents the unit rate of heat transfer from the air in the heated space to the inside surface of the building structure, in Btu. per hour per 1 sq. ft. of area normal to the direction of heat flow, per degree Fahrenheit of temperature difference. The temperature difference referred to must be between the air and the surface of the structure in contact with the air, not the over-all temperature difference between the inside and outside air.

The transfer of heat from the outside surface of the structure to the outside air is likewise by a combined process of radiation and convection, designated by an outside coefficient, f_o. The temperature difference which applies to f_o is that existing between the outside surface of the building structure and the outdoor air. From the inside surface of the structure to the outside surface, heat transmission occurs by conduction alone in the case of a single material; if air spaces exist within the structure, convection and radiation effects may also be present.

The designer is concerned with the evaluation of an **over-all coefficient of heat transmission, U,** the unit rate of heat transfer in Btu. per hour per square foot of building surface, per degree of over-all temperature difference between indoor air and outdoor air. Over-all coefficients are affected by the building structural conditions as well as by the inside and outside air velocities.

Over-all coefficients of heat transmission may be calculated for any type of construction by the methods shown below (Heating, Ventilating, and Air Conditioning Guide, vol. 34):

$$U = \frac{1}{\left(\dfrac{1}{f_i}\right) + \left(\dfrac{x}{k}\right) + \left(\dfrac{1}{f_o}\right)}, \text{Btu./(hr.) (sq. ft.) (° F.)} \qquad (1)$$

where k = thermal conductivity of building material (k values are tabulated in Fig. 27 for homogeneous materials, the magnitude representing the rate of heat flow in Btu. per hour, per square foot of area, per degree Fahrenheit temperature difference, per inch of thickness in the direction of heat flow)

x = thickness of building material in inches

In Eq. (1), the terms in the denominator represent resistances to heat flow and are additive; hence,

$$\frac{1}{f_i} = R_i, \text{ the resistance of the inside air film}$$

$$\frac{x}{k} = R_1, \text{ the resistance of the building material}$$

$$\frac{1}{f_o} = R_o, \text{ the resistance of the outside air film}$$

Material	Description	Conductivity k	Conductance c
Air space conductance:			
Ordinary spaces	Vertical, ¾ in. or more in width	–	1.10
Spaces bounded by aluminum foil	Vertical, ¾ in. or more in width	–	0.46
Insulating materials:			
Bats and blankets	Made from mineral or vegetable fiber	0.27	–
Insulating board	Vegetable fiber	0.33	–
Mineral wool	Rock or glass fiber	0.27	–
Interior finishes:			
Gypsum board	⅜ in. thick	–	3.70
Gypsum lath with plaster	⅜-in. lath, ½ with plaster	–	2.40
Metal lath and plaster	¾-in plaster	–	4.40
Plywood	⅜ in. thick	–	2.12
Masonry materials:			
Brick	Common, 4 in. thick	–	1.25
Brick	Face, 4 in. thick	–	2.30
Cement mortar		12.00	–
Hollow clay tile	4 in. thick	–	1.00
Hollow clay tile	6 in. thick	–	0.64
Hollow clay tile	8 in. thick	–	0.60
Concrete	Sand and gravel aggregate	12.00	–
Hollow concrete blocks	Cinder aggregate, 4 in. thick	–	1.00
Hollow concrete blocks	Cinder aggregate, 8 in. thick	–	0.60
Hollow concrete blocks	Cinder aggregate, 12 in. thick	–	0.53
Hollow concrete blocks	Gravel aggregate, 8 in. thick	–	1.00
Hollow concrete blocks	Gravel aggregate, 12 in. thick	–	0.80
Tile and terrazzo	Flooring	12.00	–
Stone		12.50	–
Roofing materials:			
Asbestos shingles		–	6.00
Asphalt shingles		–	6.50
Built-up roofing	Assumed thickness ⅜ in.	–	3.53
Heavy roll roofing		–	6.50
Surface conductances:			
Still air	Ordinary nonreflective materials	–	1.65
Wind velocity— 15 m.p.h.	Ordinary nonreflective materials	–	6.00

Values for k and c are expressed in Btu. per (hr.) (sq. ft.) (degrees F. temperature difference). k values are per 1 in. of thickness, c values are for the thickness stated.

Fig. 27. Thermal conductivities (k) and conductances (c).

The total resistance of heat flow $R_t = R_i + R_1 + R_o$, and

$$U = \frac{1}{R_t}, \text{Btu./(hr.)(sq. ft.)(°F.)} \tag{2}$$

The over-all coefficient for any structure of composite construction may be evaluated by including the resistances of all the terms involved. For many materials which are not homogeneous, a thermal conductance c must be determined. The c term represents the rate of heat flow in Btu. per hour, per square foot of area, per degree Fahrenheit temperature difference for the over-all thickness of the material, i.e., from one surface to the other. Dimensionally, c is equivalent to (k/x); the magnitude of k is constant for a given material, regardless of thickness, since it is based upon the heat transfer per unit of thickness; c values differ for a given material with thickness; hence the thickness must be specified.

For a **composite wall,**

$$U = \frac{1}{\left(\frac{1}{f_i}\right) + \left(\frac{x_1}{k_1}\right) + \left(\frac{x_2}{k_2}\right) + \left(\frac{1}{c_1}\right) + \left(\frac{1}{c_2}\right) + \cdots + \left(\frac{1}{f_o}\right)} \tag{3}$$

Note that the resistance of a material for which a c value is tabulated is expressed as $1/c$, since the magnitude of c depends upon the thickness. In Eq. (3), c_2 might represent the conductance of an air space with dimensions the same as c_1.

Tabulations of **thermal conductivities** and **air space conductances** are shown in Fig. 27. Values of air-space conductances are dependent upon temperature difference, width, height, and orientation and surface characteristics of boundary materials.

After design temperatures have been selected and U values determined for each different type of construction transmission, **heat losses** may then be computed by the relation (Heating, Ventilating and Air Conditioning Guide, vol. 34):

$$H_T = U \times A \times (t_i - t_o) \tag{4}$$

where H_T = transmission heat loss, Btu./hour
      A = net area corresponding to the structure for which U has been determined, square feet
      t_i = inside design air temperature to be maintained, ° F.
      t_o = outside design air temperature, ° F.

The designer must include in his heat loss calculations all surfaces through which heat losses may occur: exterior walls, windows, doors, roof and ceiling areas, floors on the ground or above unheated basement, and partition walls separating heated from unheated space. Temperatures of the ground and adjacent unheated spaces will not be the same as those of the outside air and must therefore be estimated. Over-all coefficients of ground floor slabs will not involve the outside surface conductance f_o. Heat losses through such surfaces may often be insignificant when compared with the total building loss, but an approximate evaluation should be made in order to determine their relative magnitude.

Computation of Infiltration Losses. It is to be emphasized that the determination of heat losses resulting from infiltration is an estimate rather than a precise calculation. The leakage of air into or out of a building is caused by pressure differences existing between the inside and the outside. **Pressure differences** are created by wind velocities, differences in air density due to indoor-outdoor temperature differentials, building height, and relative locations of openings through which air may leak. In attempting to predict infiltration rates, the designer is confronted by a number of variables which will affect the accuracy of his results and over which he may have little control. Differences in quality of construction, variations in wind velocity and direction, and building exposure may make exact determinations extremely unlikely.

Two methods for predicting infiltration losses are commonly used. One is termed the **crack method,** the other the **air-change method.** By either method, an attempt is made to determine the air volume leaking into a building. An assumption is made that an approximately equal volume will leak out. Therefore, the infiltration heat loss is represented by the amount of heat required to heat the inleaking air from the design outside temperature to the indoor temperature. In equation form, then:

$$H_i = Q \times \varrho \times c_p \times (t_i - t_o) \tag{5}$$

where H_i = infiltration heat loss, Btu./hour
   Q = volume of air leaking into the building, cubic feet/hour
   ϱ = air density, pound/cubic feet
   c_p = specific heat at constant pressure for dry air, 0.24 Btu./pound-° F.
   t_i, t_o = design inside and outside air temperatures, ° F.

Conventionally, an air density of 0.075 lb. per cu. ft. is assured, representing "standard" air for heating and ventilating practice at 14.696 psia (lb. per sq. in. absolute) barometric pressure and approximately 70° F.

The crack method is considered to be more accurate than the air-change method for determining the air quantity leaking into a building, provided that reliable data are available for estimating air infiltration rates for the actual windows used. To determine **crack length** to be used, the method recommended is:

1. For 1 wall exposed, use total crack.
2. For 2, 3, or 4 walls exposed, use wall having the most crack or one-half the total, whichever is greater.

Although the available tabular data may not be precisely correct for field conditions, the infiltration losses determined by this method are directly dependent upon the total number of windows installed, which is not true in the air-change method. More accurate data may be obtained from window manufacturers in some instances.

An inherent disadvantage of the crack method lies in the manner in which the designer determines the total linear footage of crack to be used for infiltration estimations. Although the leakage per foot of crack may be determined with reasonable accuracy in many instances, it is difficult to predict the total amount of crack through which air may leak at a given time. Similarly, the data for leakage at doors are to be considered approximate and may be subject to considerable revision for a given application.

The data available for predicting infiltration by the air-change method represent "rule-of-thumb" practice and show considerable variation among different references. Frequently used values range from one-half to three air changes per hour, depending upon the type of building and the exposure. For industrial buildings, however, due to the wide variation in construction details and the number and types of windows used, the conventional approximations should be used with caution.

VENTILATION REQUIREMENTS. Ventilation may be provided for industrial buildings by either **natural means,** making use of wind forces and indoor-outdoor temperature difference, or by a **mechanical system** employing either powered exhaust ventilators, supply fans and ductwork, or a combination of both. A disadvantage encountered with natural ventilation systems is that both the air quantity and distribution are variable with little control of air movement afforded. Positive distribution of specified quantities is more likely if a mechanical system is used.

Due to the many variables involved, there are no precisely defined rules for general ventilation practice; in many instances **state** or **local codes** prescribe minimum requirements which must be met. These requirements are usually stated in terms of the **quantity** of outdoor air required per occupant or the number of air changes required per hour within a given space.

Although insufficient attention is often devoted to it, the problem of satisfactory **ventilating-air distribution** is as important as the quantity required. The designer should provide for adequate control of air movement in all areas which are to be ventilated, with sufficient quantities of fresh air to eliminate or minimize undesirable conditions arising from heat and moisture loads, odors, dust, dirt, toxic gases, vapors, or other air contaminants due to occupants or industrial processes.

Frequently, the heating or cooling-air system can provide adequate amounts of outside air for ventilation, but where severe problems of contamination exist, exhaust hoods or other localized ventilating systems may be required. (See section on Safety and Fire Prevention.) In all instances, the designer must provide a sufficient quantity of outdoor air to replace that which is exhausted.

Consideration should be given to the possibility of using **recirculated air** when possible in order to reduce the amount of heat required by the introduction of outdoor air. Particularly where large air quantities are involved, economy of operation may be effected by recirculating air, using filters for removing dust and dirt particles, absorbents or washer for removing moisture, and activated carbon for removing odors and certain organic gases.

Ventilation rates for industrial buildings are frequently based on a supply of 10 cu. ft. of air per min. for each person in the space, although many exceptions to this rule are encountered. A study should normally be made to determine the **optimum air quantity** required in order to compensate for heat or moisture loads and for the sources of vitiation.

Duct Design. Two commonly used methods of duct design are (1) the velocity-reduction method, and (2) the constant friction-loss method. In the **velocity-reduction** method, an allowable or desirable air velocity is assumed at some point in the duct system, usually at the fan discharge; the remainder of the system is designed for progressively lower velocities in the main section downstream from each branch connection. Velocities throughout the entire duct system are assumed, normally based upon the designer's experience or data which can be obtained from manufacturer's catalogs or data books. Although duct sizes may be determined with ease once the desired air quantity and velocity are known, the velocity-reduction method requires sound judgment and experience in determining optimum velocities in all parts of the system. Furthermore, since pressure losses per foot of duct length vary, the determination of over-all pressure loss may be somewhat tedious.

In the **constant friction-loss** method, a velocity at only one point in the system is assumed, usually at the fan outlet; knowing the air quantity and velocity, a size is determined and the friction loss established. The remainder of the system is then sized to obtain the same unit pressure loss per foot of duct length, regardless of the air quantity involved. This method automatically reduces air velocities as the quantities are reduced; in addition, the total friction loss may be determined by knowing the total length of duct and the unit pressure loss used for design. The effects of elbows, fittings, transition sections, and other resistances must be included and added to the actual length in order to determine a **total equivalent length.**

In systems where ductwork **in parallel** is connected to the same fan, the pressure to be produced by the fan is based upon the branch having the greatest resistance, not the sum of the resistances of the parallel branches. Additive resistances are only those which are **in series** with one another along the flow circuit. If parallel circuits are essentially symmetrical, little balancing is required for a system designed by the constant friction-loss method; for runs which differ appreciably in length, or in numbers and kinds of fittings, considerable **dampering** may be required for flow balancing. Often only the main duct is sized by this method, with branch ducts designed to dissipate the static pressure available at the point of connection to the main duct.

In either method, care should be taken to insure that duct velocities are not excessive from the standpoint of both **noise** and **pressure loss.** Since the pressure loss resulting from friction varies as the square of the velocity, and power consumption of the fan varies directly as the pressure, excessive velocities will lead to high operating costs. On the other hand, the duct size and cost will increase as the allowable velocity decreases for a fixed air quantity. A reasonable compromise should be made, based upon accepted practice and experience. The recommendations of equipment manufacturers should be used as a guide in establishing allowable velocities.

Pressure Losses in Ducts. Vennard (Elementary Fluid Mechanics, 3d ed.) shows how pressure losses resulting from frictional effects may be determined by the Darcy equation:

$$\Delta_P = f \times \frac{L}{D} \times \frac{\gamma V^2}{2g} \tag{6}$$

where Δp = pressure loss, pounds/square foot
f = friction factor, dimensionless
L = length of conduit considered, feet
D = internal diameter of conduit, feet
γ = specific weight of air, pound/cubic foot
V = average velocity, feet/second
g = gravitational acceleration, 32.174 ft./sec.^{2}

Eq. (6) is applicable to all liquids and may be used for gases when **compressibility effects** can be neglected (ordinarily when the loss in pressure does not exceed about 10 percent of the initial pressure).

In heating and ventilating design, certain simplifying assumptions may be made; the fluid handled (air) may be treated as a perfect gas with very little error, compressibility effects may be ignored due to the relatively low pressure losses and velocities encountered, and turbulent flow will normally exist.

Eq. (6) may be used to determine the loss in pressure resulting from friction whether the flow is laminar or turbulent, depending upon the way in which the **friction factor** is evaluated. Since here, only **turbulent flow** need be considered, the friction factor may be expressed as a function of the **Reynolds number** and the **relative roughness** of the conduit. Vennard (Elementary

Fluid Mechanics, 3d ed.) indicates that the Reynolds number may be evaluated as:

$$R_e = \frac{VD\varrho}{\mu} \tag{7}$$

where R_e = Reynolds number, dimensionless
V = average velocity, feet/second
D = internal diameter of conduit, feet
ϱ = air density, pounds/cubic foot, numerically equal to γ
μ = absolute viscosity of the air, pounds/foot-second

A value of $R_e = 2,000$ is ordinarily considered to be the lower limit or **critical value** for turbulent flow, and $R_e = 4,000$ the upper limit for laminar flow. Between 2,000 and 4,000, an **unstable region** exists where flow conditions may be changing from laminar to turbulent, or vice versa.

For air at a temperature of 70° F., a density of 0.075 lb. per cu. ft., and a viscosity of 1.22×10^{-5} lb. per ft.-sec. flowing through a 12-in. diameter duct at an average velocity of 500 ft. per min., the Reynolds number is

$$R_e = \frac{500 \times 1 \times 0.075}{60 \times 1.22 \times 10^{-5}} = 51,300$$

Here, with a relatively low velocity and representative values for viscosity and density, turbulent flow exists. Reynolds numbers of this order of magnitude or higher will be encountered in duct design problems.

The effect of **pipe roughness** is expressed in terms of a ratio, e/D, where e represents the absolute height of the roughness protuberances and D is the pipe or conduit diameter, both expressed in feet. Values of e for pipes of different materials are shown in Fig. 28, adapted from Heating, Ventilating, and Air Conditioning Guide, vol. 34.

Type of Pipe	Absolute Roughness e, feet
Smooth steel or wrought iron	0.000005
Commercial steel or wrought iron	0.00015
Asphalted cast iron	0.0004
Galvanized iron	0.0005
Cast iron	0.00085
Riveted steel	0.003 to 0.03

Fig. 28. Roughness values for pipe.

Friction Factor Determination. Fig. 29, adapted from the ASME Transactions, may be used to determine the friction factor (f) for known values of the Reynolds number and the relative pipe roughness. For example, the pressure loss caused by friction is to be determined for a 10-in. diameter galvanized iron duct 150 ft. in length which conveys 545 cu. ft. of air per min. The air temperature is 80° F., the density is 0.0735 lb. per cu. ft., and the absolute viscosity is 1.25×10^{-5} lb. per ft.-sec.

The solution is obtained as follows:

The air velocity is

$$V = \frac{\phi}{A} = \frac{545 \times 4 \times 144}{\pi \times 10^2} = 1,000 \text{ ft./min.}$$

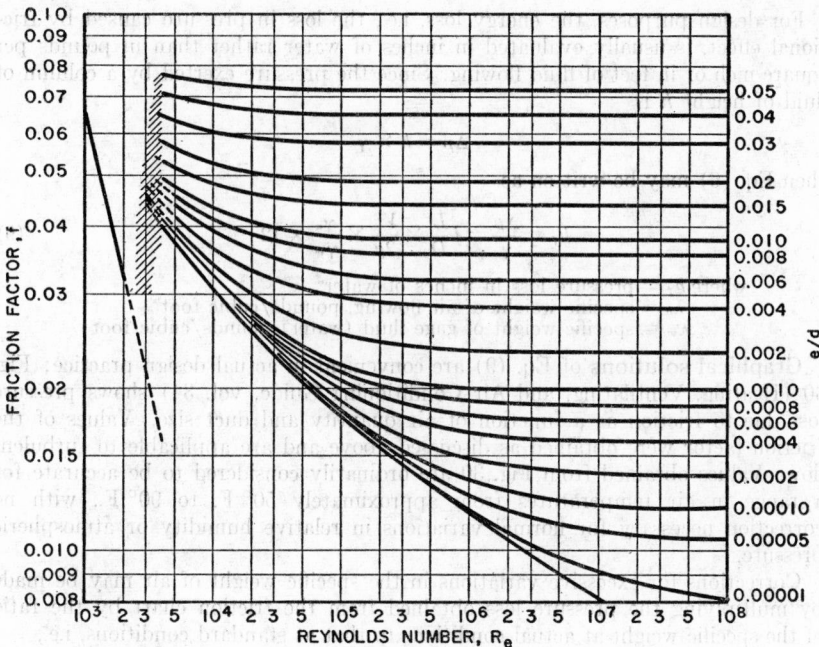

The straight line at left shows values of friction factor for laminar flow.

Fig. 29. Relation between friction factor and Reynolds number.

The Reynolds number is

$$R_e = \frac{1,000 \times 10 \times 0.0735}{60 \times 12 \times 1.25 \times 10^{-5}} = 81,600$$

For a 10-in. diameter galvanized iron pipe,

$$e/D = \frac{0.0005 \times 12}{10} = 0.0006$$

From the friction chart, at $R_e = 81,600$ and $e/D = 0.0006$, $f = 0.021$.

The pressure loss is

$$\Delta_P = f\frac{L}{D}\frac{V^2\gamma}{2g} = 0.021 \times \frac{150 \times 12}{10} \times \left(\frac{1000}{60}\right)^2 \times \frac{0.0735}{64.35} = 1.205 \text{ lb./sq. ft.}$$

or,

$$\frac{1.205}{144} = 0.0084 \text{ lb./sq. in.}$$

Eq. (6) is often expressed as an **energy loss,** foot-pounds per pound of fluid flowing, commonly defined as a loss of head in feet. To obtain this form, Eq. (6) may be rearranged as

$$h_f = \frac{\Delta p}{\gamma} = f\frac{L}{D}\frac{V^2}{2g} \qquad (8)$$

where h_f = energy loss due to friction, foot-pounds per pound of fluid, or head loss in feet of fluid flowing.

For design purposes, the energy loss, i.e., the loss in pressure caused by frictional effect, is usually evaluated in inches of water rather than in pounds per square inch or in feet of fluid flowing. Since the pressure exerted by a column of fluid of height h is

$$\Delta p = h \times \gamma$$

then Eq. (6) may be written as

$$h_f = \frac{\Delta p}{\gamma} = f \frac{L}{D} \times \frac{V^2}{2g} \times \frac{\gamma_a}{\gamma_w} \times 12 \qquad (9)$$

where h_f = pressure loss in inches of water
λ_a = specific weight of air flowing, pounds/cubic foot
λ_w = specific weight of gage fluid (water) pounds/cubic foot

Graphical solutions of Eq. (9) are convenient in actual design practice; Fig. 30 (Heating, Ventilating, and Air Conditioning Guide, vol. 34) shows pressure loss due to friction as a function of air quantity and duct size. Values of the friction factor were obtained as discussed above and are applicable to turbulent flow. Values obtained from Fig. 30 are ordinarily considered to be accurate for a range in air temperatures from approximately 50° F. to 90° F., with no correction necessary for normal variations in relative humidity or atmospheric pressure.

Corrections for excessive variations in the specific weight of air may be made by multiplying the pressure loss obtained from the friction chart by the ratio of the specific weight at actual conditions to that at standard conditions, i.e.,

$$h_{f_a} = h_{f_s} \left(\frac{\gamma_a}{\gamma_s} \right)$$

where the subscript a refers to actual conditions and s to chart or standard conditions. For duct construction other than that upon which the chart is based, the designer may use Eq. (9), evaluating the friction factor as described previously from the data shown in Fig. 28 and Fig. 29.

Noncircular Conduits. The relations already discussed for evaluating pressure losses resulting from friction in ducts apply to conduits of circular cross section. In heating and ventilating practice, ducts of rectangular cross sections are commonly used because of space limitations and ease of fabrication.

In using Eq. (9) or Fig. 30 to predict pressure losses in noncircular conduits, an **equivalent diameter** may be determined. Vennard (Elementary Fluid Mechanics, 3d ed.) defines this by the relation:

$$D_e = 4 \left(\frac{A}{P} \right) \qquad (10)$$

where D_e = diameter of a circular duct "equivalent" to the actual duct, feet
A = cross-sectional area of the actual duct, square feet
P = internal perimeter of the cross section of the actual duct, feet

For example, the diameter of a circular duct which is equivalent in terms of friction loss to a rectangular duct 24 in. wide by 12 in. high is

$$D_e = 4 \left[\frac{2 \times 1}{6} \right] = 1.33 \text{ ft.} = 16 \text{ in.}$$

The use of an equivalent diameter defined by Eq. (10) requires that the average flow velocities be equal in both ducts. For equal cross-sectional areas

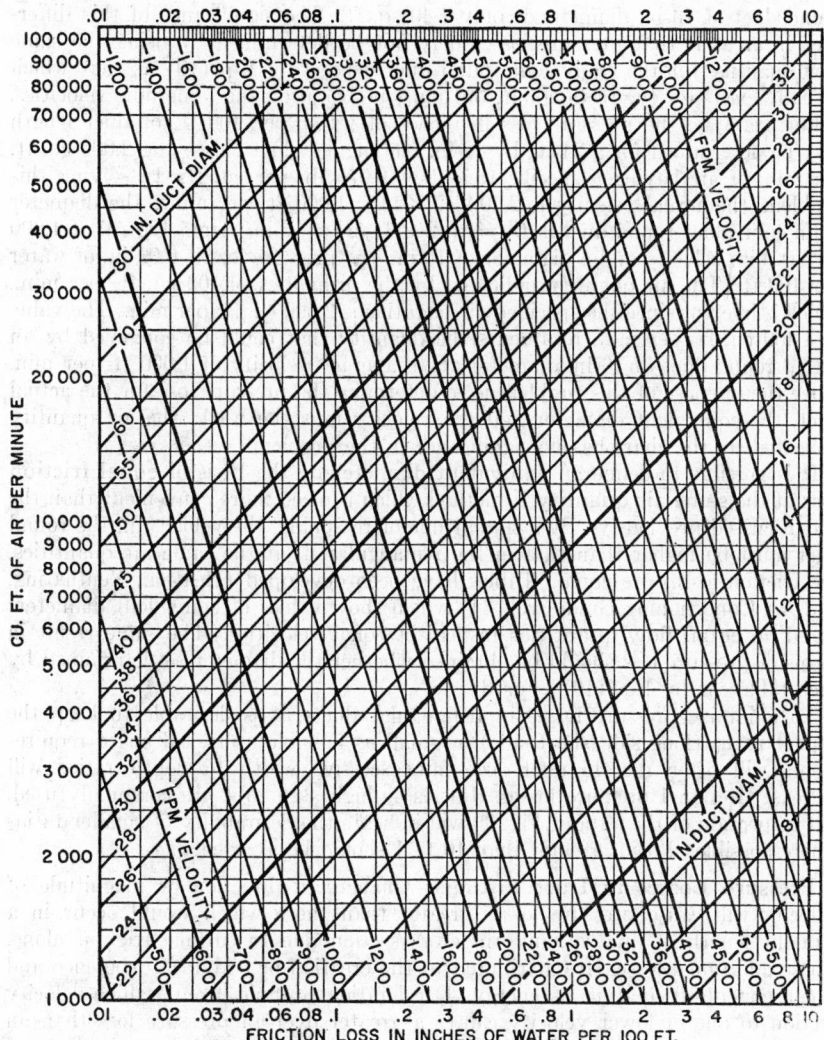

Based on standard air of 0.075 lb. per cu. ft. density flowing through average, clean, round, galvanized metal ducts having approximately 40 joints per 100 ft.

Fig. 30. Friction of air in straight ducts, for volumes of 1,000 to 100,000 cu. ft per min.

and the same quantity of air flow, average velocities in a round and a rectangular duct will be equal, since the average velocity is defined as the flow quantity divided by the area; however, the pressure losses will be lower in the round duct than in the rectangular, assuming equal values of the friction factor. Hence, for equal pressure loss at the same flow velocity, the area of the round duct must be less than that of the rectangular to which it is equivalent. In the example above, the area of the 24-in. by 12-in. duct is 2 sq. ft., while that of the equivalent round duct of 16-in. diameter is only 1.40 sq. ft. The significance of this difference in areas is that pressure losses may not be determined by using the same flow quantity for the equivalent round duct defined by Eq. (10) as that which actually exists for the rectangular, but must be based on the same flow velocities.

For example, the pressure loss in inches of water per 100 ft. of duct length may be determined for a 24-in. by 12-in. rectangular duct conveying 2,000 cu. ft. per min. of air having a specific weight of 0.075 lb. per cu. ft. In solving this problem, the actual velocity is $2,000/(2 \times 1) = 1,000$ ft. per min.; the diameter of an equivalent round duct is $D_e = 4[(2 \times 1)/6] = 16$ in.; from Fig. 30 at 1,000 ft. per min. velocity and a diameter of 16 in., the pressure loss is 0.09 in. of water per 100 ft. The air quantity indicated by the ordinate is 1,400 cu. ft. per min., which is in error since the specified air quantity is 2,000 cu. ft. per min. The value of 1,400 cu. ft. per min. represents the quantity that could be conveyed by an actual round duct of 16-in. diameter at an average velocity of 1,000 ft. per min. Since the purpose of this problem is to determine the pressure loss for the actual duct, the equivalent diameter and the velocity must be used; the air quantity indicated by the chart has no significance in the problem.

It is possible to define an **equivalent diameter** on the basis of **equal friction loss** at the **same air quantity,** a method which is often more convenient than the one discussed previously. By a similar line of reasoning, the velocity in the round duct must be higher than that in the rectangular if, at the same air quantities, the friction losses are equal. Tables have been developed (Heating, Ventilating, and Air Conditioning Guide, vol. 34) which show values of equivalent diameters based on **equal flow quantities** instead of equal velocities. The same result in terms of pressure loss should be obtained whether the diameter as determined by such tables or by Eq. (10) is used.

To minimize pressure losses in rectangular ducts, it is desirable to keep the **aspect ratio** (long side/short side) as small as possible; physical space requirements will often dictate duct size, but excessive width to depth ratios will increase frictional pressure losses. Ratios as high as 6 to 1 are commonly used, but inspection of the data of Fig. 30 will indicate the desirability of smaller ratios where possible. Ratios greater than 10 to 1 should be avoided.

Pressure Losses in Duct Fittings. Changes in direction or magnitude of velocity will cause pressure losses greater than those which would occur in a straight length of duct of uniform cross section due to surface friction alone. These additional losses are attributed to the creation of eddying turbulence and a consequent dissipation of energy. Deceleration of fluid from a high-velocity section to one of lower velocity causes a greater over-all pressure loss than an acceleration section where the flow velocity is increased.

For the purposes of heating and ventilating design, the additional resistance caused by elbows may be treated in either of two ways. In one method, an **equivalent length of straight duct** which would offer the same resistance as the elbow in question is determined, and the total equivalent length of the duct system is considered to be the actual length of straight duct plus the additional allowance for the elbow. In the second method, the dynamic loss is assumed to vary as the square of the average air velocity; therefore, the pressure loss resulting from eddying turbulence is evaluated as a constant times the kinetic energy term or velocity head. Thus, Vennard (Elementary Fluid Mechanics, 3d ed.) gives the equation:

$$\Delta h_d = C\left(\frac{V^2}{2g}\right)$$

where C is a dimensionless constant known as the **dynamic loss coefficient** which must be evaluated for different types of fittings. The Δh_d term may be expressed in any consistent units, but a convenient expression is:

$$\Delta h_d = C \left(\frac{V}{4,005} \right)^2 \tag{11}$$

where Δh_d = dynamic pressure loss, inches of water
V = average velocity, feet/minute

Eq. (11) is based on standard air density of 0.075 lb. per cu. ft. The dynamic loss in an abruptly expanding section may be evaluated as

$$\Delta h_d = C_1 \left(\frac{V_1}{4,005} \right)^2 = C_2 \left(\frac{V_2}{4,005} \right)^2 \tag{12}$$

where V_1 represents the average velocity in the small duct, V_2 the average velocity in the larger duct, feet per minute, and C_1 and C_2 represent loss coefficients.

For gradual expansions, C_r is used as a multiplying factor, representing the ratio of the loss in the gradual expansion to that obtained in an abrupt expansion, dependent upon the included angle between the sides of the duct. The **combined loss coefficient** is obtained by multiplying C_1 or C_2 by C_r, i.e., for gradual expansion:

$$\Delta h_d = C_r C_1 \left(\frac{V_1}{4,005} \right)^2 = C_r C_2 \left(\frac{V_2}{4,005} \right)^2 \tag{13}$$

PIPING DESIGN. In the design of piping systems for **steam** or **hot-water heating**, the basic relations previously discussed for ducts apply for determination of pressure losses. Various modifications of Eq. (6) are used as well as graphical solutions. A brief discussion of some of the more important design considerations for steam and hot-water heating follows.

Steam Systems. The supply and return piping of most low pressure steam-heating systems will be sized for a design pressure loss of $\frac{1}{16}$ lb. per sq. in. gage per 100 ft. of length. There are exceptions to this, depending upon the total length of piping and variations in operating pressures. Generally, for low pressure and vacuum systems, the total pressure loss for the entire system will range from approximately $\frac{1}{8}$ lb. per sq. in. gage to as high as 1 lb. per sq. in.; the pressure drop should not be large enough to cause excessive velocities and, as a general rule, should not exceed one-half the initial gage pressure.

Higher design pressure losses are permissible for systems operating above 15 lbs. per sq. in. gage; the steam supply mains of 30 lbs. per sq. in. gage systems are normally sized for total losses of from 5 to 10 lbs. per sq. in., while 150 lbs. per sq. in. gage systems may have total pressure drops of from 25 to 30 lbs. per sq. in.

On low-pressure systems (up to approximately 15 lbs. per sq. in. gage operating pressure), the supply and return piping are conventionally sized for the same design pressure loss; in the higher pressure systems, however, return lines are sized for design losses ranging from $\frac{1}{2}$ to 1 lb. per sq. in. gage per 100 ft.

Design data for steam systems may be obtained from the Heating, Ventilating, and Air Conditioning Guide and from manufacturers' current literature. Recommended procedures in design vary widely, depending upon the type of systems and the designer's experience. Although basic principles of fluid flow underlie most of the data available for use in designing piping systems, much of the design information reflects the art of engineering practice rather than the science, with consequent variations in recommended procedure.

As in duct systems, the total pressure loss in a **piping circuit** will be dependent upon the actual straight length of pipe plus additional effects resulting from elbows, valves, tees, and other fittings wherein dynamic losses occur. It is conventional in the design of steam piping systems to express the various fittings in terms of an additional length of straight pipe. The total pressure loss is then evaluated on the basis of the specified design pressure drop and the total equivalent length of piping, including the allowance for fittings.

Hot-Water Systems. In forced circulation hot-water heating systems, pressure losses must be evaluated in order to determine the required pressure to be produced by a circulating pump. Pressure losses are dependent upon frictional effects in the piping circuit and additional dynamic losses in fittings and equipment. The **losses in fittings** are ordinarily expressed in terms of 90° elbow equivalents.

Modifications of the basic **friction loss equation** (Eq. 6) are used for hot water heating system design. The relation between flow rate and heat conveying capacity in Btu. per hour is based on an assumption of a 20° F. temperature drop in the heat disseminating unit and a water density of 8.33 lbs. per gal. The Heating, Ventilating, and Air Conditioning Guide, vol. 34, indicates that the amount of heat transferred from the water passing through a heat-exchange device may be expressed as:

$$H = W \times c \times \Delta t \tag{14}$$

where H = heat transferred, Btu./hour
W = flow rate, pounds/hour
c = specific heat of water, 1.0 Btu./pound-°F.
Δt = temperature drop, °F.

Using the values given, the equation may be written as

$$H = G \times 60 \times 8.33 \times 1 \times 20 = 10,000G \text{ (Btu./hr.)} \tag{15}$$

where G = flow rate, gallons per minute; or, expressing the heating capacity in *MBH* (thousands of Btu. per hour),

$$H(MBH) = 10G \tag{16}$$

It should be observed that the friction loss is a function of the actual flow rate, and that the heat-conveying capacity must be corrected for design temperature drops which differ from 20°.

The **total circuit pressure loss** is governed by the total equivalent length of piping in the supply and return mains, including the effects of elbows and other fittings, and the unit pressure loss. As in the case of air flow in ducts, the resistances of parallel circuits are not additive; the longest circuit will generally offer the highest resistance, although excessive numbers of fittings in a shorter circuit may create a greater resistance to flow than that determined for the longer circuit.

For the conventional low pressure hot-water heating system, **supply water temperatures** ordinarily range from 170° F. to perhaps as high as 220° F. at design conditions. Recommended pipe sizes are based on upper and lower limits for both water velocity and friction loss. Generally, velocities ranging from 2 to 4 ft per sec. are considered satisfactory for installations where noise may be a factor. In commercial or industrial installations, particularly where larger pipe sizes will be required, velocities as high as 8 ft. per sec. are not uncommon.

Allowable design friction losses of from 250 to 600 milin. per ft. are frequently recommended, although higher design values are often used in systems for industrial applications.

Reductions in pipe size will result in increased pressure losses and pumping power requirements, but will reduce the cost of pipe and fittings. The designer should determine an **optimum pipe size** based on the recommendations given above for allowable velocities and pressure losses. Performance data supplied by manufacturers' literature may also be used to determine such features as maximum desirable pressure losses for a specified flow rate, piping arrangement, types of hot-water heating specialties, and expansion tanks.

High-temperature hot-water heating systems offer advantages for some types of applications. Water temperatures between 300° F. and 400° F. are in common use. Pressurized systems are required for these elevated temperatures to prevent the water from boiling; steam or inert gases may be used to maintain the desired pressure.

Since water viscosity is reduced at the higher temperatures, the resulting reduction in pipe friction is a definite advantage of high-temperature systems; in addition, flow rates may be reduced due to larger allowable design temperature drops between supply and return water, resulting in the use of smaller pipes. Temperature drops range from 80° F. to 150° F. for supply temperatures of 250° F. to 400° F.

AIR DISTRIBUTION DEVICES. The importance of proper air distribution within an occupied space which is to be heated, cooled, or ventilated should be recognized. Unsatisfactory conditions may result if the problem of air distribution is neglected, even though the temperature and quantity of supply air are satisfactory. An adequately designed heating or air conditioning system should provide for the simultaneous control of air temperature, motion, humidity, and cleanliness within an occupied zone; variations in temperature due to stratification, excessive air motion, or drafts, and objectionable air noise must be avoided, if optimum conditions are to be established.

Manufacturers' data should be used to determine the recommended type, size, and number of outlets for a given application; in some types of installations, particular attention should be paid to recommended outlet velocities for acceptable noise levels.

High-velocity air systems are often used in industrial applications in order to reduce duct sizes. The outlets for such systems usually include a pressure-reduction and round-attenuation chamber in conjunction with a grille or diffuser. Outlets may be located in either the wall or ceiling.

AIR HEATING COILS. Coils used for air heating in present-day practice ordinarily consist of copper tubes with extended surface fins of aluminum or copper. Significant increase in heat transfer effectiveness is accomplished by the use of fins to increase the external surface exposed to the air. Various types of **fin arrangements** are used by the different manufacturers of heating coils, the more common ones being the helically wound ribbon type and the plate type incorporating an offset in the plate surface between tube rows to promote turbulence in the air stream. Methods of bonding fins to tubes also vary; some manufacturers use a mechanical bond, obtained by expanding the tube after the fins are installed; others use a tin-lead alloy solder connection in addition to the mechanical bond. Intimate and permanent contact between tube and fin is important to the maintenance of full heat-transfer capacity of the coil.

Steam and hot water are the most commonly used heating media, although other fluids may be used. Most manufacturers provide both steam-type and water-type coils, which differ primarily in the arrangement of the header connections and the tube circuit details. In steam coils, both a standard single-tube type and a steam distributing tube type are available. The distributing tube coil employs a tube-within-a-tube arrangement to distribute steam uniformly along the entire length of the individual tubes, providing for more uniform air temperatures and minimizing possibility of freezing of condensate under light-load conditions with low temperature air.

For complete information on design features and capacities, reference should be made to manufacturers' current literature.

FANS. For central heating and ventilating systems, centrifugal fans are commonly used to provide air flow. **Propeller fans** are used in some types of unit heaters and often for exhaust applications; **axial-flow fans** are frequently used for exhaust systems requiring ductwork.

Selection. Selection of the proper fan for a given application is important in terms of meeting performance requirements. Fan performance characteristics are commonly presented in the form of tables showing fan speed and horsepower required for a specified air quantity as a function of static pressure.

Fan Efficiency. Fan efficiency may be expressed either on the basis of static pressure or total pressure by means of the following relations:

Fan efficiency is defined as the energy delivered to the air (output) divided by the energy supplied to the shaft (input). In equation form,

$$\eta = \frac{\text{air horsepower}}{\text{input horsepower}}$$

The air horsepower may be expressed as

$$\text{ahp} = \frac{w \times h'}{33,000}$$

where w = air flow rate, pounds/minute
   h' = energy increase of the air, foot-pounds/pound, or as commonly expressed, the head delivered in feet of air
   33,000 = number of foot-pounds/minute equivalent to 1 hp.

Since the flow rate is normally expressed in terms of volume (cubic feet per minute) and the energy increase or head in inches of water the previous equation may be written as

$$\text{ahp} = \frac{(\text{cfm}) \times \gamma a}{33,000} \times \left(\frac{h}{12}\right) \times \frac{\gamma w}{\gamma a}$$

where h = head, inches of water
   γ_a = specific weight of air, pounds/cubic foot
   γw = specific weight of water (gage fluid), pounds/cubic foot

Assuming an average value of 62.3 lb. per cu. ft. for γw, this equation reduces to

$$\text{ahp} = \frac{(\text{cfm}) \times h}{6,356}$$

The horsepower calculated by this equation will be either the **static air horsepower** or the **total air horsepower,** depending on whether h is the static or total head, i.e., pressure.

Using this relation, the fan efficiency is

$$\eta = \frac{(\text{cfm}) \times h}{6{,}356 \times \text{bhp}} \times 100 \text{ (for percent)}$$

where bhp = horsepower input.

Static pressure production is dependent upon centrifugal force resulting from the rotation of the air enclosed in the fan wheel and upon the conversion of the velocity pressure or kinetic energy of the air leaving the wheel. The absolute velocity of the air leaving the impeller is the vector sum of the blade-tip velocity and the velocity of the air relative to the blade. Because of the forward inclination of forward-curved fan blades, the absolute leaving velocity of the air is higher for a given fan size and speed than for the backwardly inclined fan; hence the velocity pressure is greater. The **forward-curved fan** depends more on velocity pressure conversion and less on centrifugal force for pressure production, whereas the converse is true for the **backwardly inclined fan.** As a result, the forward-curved fan will usually run at a lower speed for a given application than that required for the backwardly inclined fan. Also, since the quantity of air delivered is directly proportional to the absolute leaving velocity, the forward-curved fan may be smaller in size for a given air quantity than the backwardly inclined fan.

Performance Characteristics. Typical performance curves for both types of fans are shown in Figs. 31 and 32 (Heating, Ventilating, and Air Conditioning Guide, vol. 34). Values are relative and apply to constant-speed operation. Another characteristic difference due to the blade shape is shown by the **horsepower curves.** The forward-curved blade produces a continually rising curve, indicating an increase in power requirements as the flow capacity increases. The characteristic power curve for the backwardly inclined blade is a self-limiting or **nonoverloading type,** decreasing from a maximum value after the air quantity exceeds a certain percentage of wide-open or free delivery volume. For this

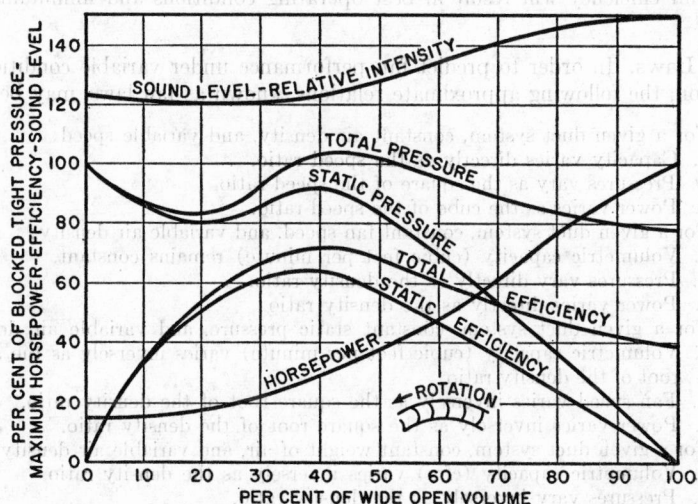

Fig. 31. Performance curves of a forward-curved blade centrifugal fan.

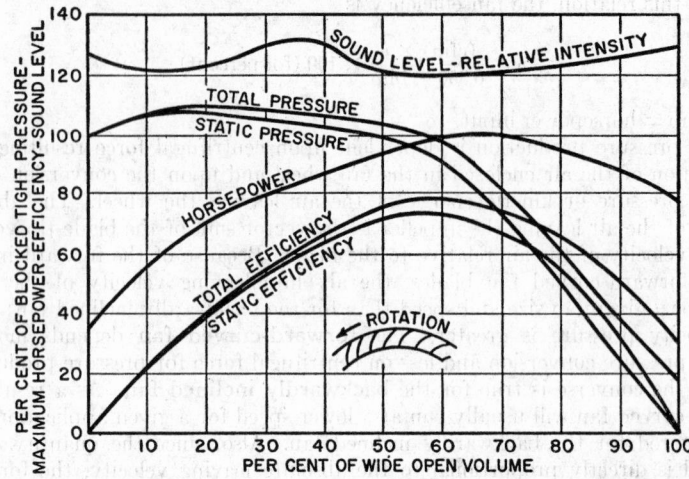

Fig. 32. Performance curves of a backwardly inclined blade centrifugal fan.

reason, operating resistances must be carefully determined and motors accurately sized to prevent overloading when forward-curved fans are used. These performance curves also show the static pressure curve for the backwardly inclined fan to be steeper than that for the forward-curved fan from the maximum efficiency point to wide-open volume, resulting in less variation in the delivered air quantity in the event of a variation in system resistance.

When a fan is selected at or near the top of the static pressure column in the performance tables, the selection will be at or near the maximum efficiency point shown in Figs. 31 and 32. To prevent selection to the left of this point, catalog performance data are usually not shown for this region. Selection at or near maximum efficiency will result in best operating conditions and minimum noise level.

Fan Laws. In order to predict fan performance under variable conditions of operation, the following approximate relations, known as fan laws, may be used.

1. For a given duct system, constant air density, and variable speed:
   a. Capacity varies directly as the speed ratio.
   b. Pressures vary as the square of the speed ratio.
   c. Power varies as the cube of the speed ratio.
2. For a given duct system, constant fan speed, and variable air density:
   a. Volumetric capacity (cubic feet per minute) remains constant.
   b. Pressures vary directly as the density ratio.
   c. Power varies directly as the density ratio.
3. For a given duct system, constant static pressure, and variable air density:
   a. Volumetric capacity (cubic feet per minute) varies inversely as the square root of the density ratio.
   b. Fan speed varies inversely as the square root of the density ratio.
   c. Power varies inversely as the square root of the density ratio.
4. For a given duct system, constant weight of air, and variable air density:
   a. Volumetric capacity (cfm) varies inversely as the density ratio.
   b. Pressures vary inversely as the density ratio.
   c. Fan speed varies inversely as the density ratio.
   d. Power varies inversely as the square of the density.

In general, all performance data for fans are based on standard air density and must be corrected to actual conditions by means of the relations shown above when significant variations in air density occur.

AIR FILTERS. An adequate air filter should be considered an integral part of any modern air-handling system for heating and ventilation. Several kinds of filters are available, ranging from relatively inexpensive throw-away types to large permanent installations such as the moving-curtain and electronic types. The selection of a filter should be governed by the degree of air cleanliness desired and the kind of impurities to be removed as well as by initial cost considerations and maintenance facilities.

Air filters may be classified by principle of operation as dry, viscous impingement, electronic, and air washers. A brief description of each type follows.

Dry Filters. No adhesive material is used to coat the filtering medium in a dry filter; this kind of filter depends upon a **screening action** imposed by very small openings in the filtering medium through which air must pass. The efficiency of dry filters is high but the resistance to air flow may build up quickly due to a build-up of dirt particles which tend to clog the air openings.

Felt cloth, cellulose fibers, spun glass, and other materials are commonly used for filtering media in this kind of filter. The material is usually arranged in deep V-shaped pleats or pockets in order to increase the effective area for air passage. **Filter banks** are formed by assembling groups of individual cells or frames together. Filtering material may be of the cleanable or throw-away type.

The recommendations of various manufacturers may vary somewhat as to capacity, but in general, allowable velocities range from approximately 18 to 35 ft. per min. Capacities are usually expressed in cubic feet of air per minute per filter cell, a representative value being 1,000 cu. ft. per min. for a nominal 2-ft. sq. cell.

It is desirable to install a differential pressure manometer with pressure connections to the upstream and downstream sides of filters of this type to indicate variations in **system resistance** with increase in dirt load. Replacement of filter elements can then be determined on the basis of allowable system resistance.

Viscous Impingement Filters. Viscous filters are manufactured in several styles and may be cleanable or disposable. One type consists of a frame with removable cell. The filtering surface used in this filter consists of strips of screen wire tapered and crimped; the surface of the wire is coated with oil, and filtering action occurs as a result of impingement of dirt particles on the oil-treated surface. Air passages through the filter change direction several times in order to throw dirt particles against the filter surfaces.

Other kinds of media used in viscous filters are glass fiber, steel wool, expanded metal, and knitted wire mesh. In some filters, combinations of the above materials are used with progressively denser packing in the direction of air flow to give greater dust-holding capacity.

Face velocities for filters of this type range from approximately 300 to 500 ft. per min.; a typical cell has a rated capacity of from 720 to 1,200 cu. ft. of air per min. for a nominal 20-in. sq. cell.

Another type of viscous filter is the **automatic self-cleaning unit** consisting of a moving curtain of overlapping panels. Endless chains rotate over a top and bottom sprocket assembly; filter panels are mounted on the chains and overlap to form a multilayer curtain. At one point in the cycle of operation, panels are suspended in a reservoir filled with oil where dirt is removed and the viscous coating on the filtering medium is replenished. Units of this type are commonly used in larger commercial and industrial applications. Design face velocities are ordinarily about 500 ft. per min. with capacities ranging from approximately 3,000 to well over 200,000 cu. ft. per min.

Electronic Filters. Two common types of electronic air filters are (1) **ionizing filters** with ionization wires and electrodes and a series of closely spaced parallel metal plates alternately charged and grounded, and (2) **charged media filters** without an ionizing unit but with an electrostatically charged filtering medium, usually arranged in pleats as for dry filters.

The ionizing filter provides higher efficiency cleaning than does the charged media filter, with resulting increase in cost and complexity. An ionizing filter will provide from 85 percent to 90 percent cleaning efficiency at normal operating conditions compared with approximately 60 percent for the charged media filter. Face velocities vary from about 300 to 500 ft. per min. for the ionizing type and are approximately 35 ft. per min. through the filtering medium of the charged type.

Electronic filters are particularly well suited for applications involving the removal of very small particles from an air stream, such as smoke, pollen, and airborne bacteria. Their use is generally limited to those installations wherein a high degree of air cleaning is mandatory and the additional expense for electronic cleaning can be justified.

A dry-type filter with charged media uses a filtering medium of cellulose paper arranged in 6-ply layers. The paper is treated with a small amount of adhesive material to improve dust arrestment.

Air Washers. Air washers, although widely used in industrial applications, are not used primarily as air-cleaning devices. If the need is for air cleaning only, conventional air filters will probably provide higher cleaning efficiency with lower initial cost and reduced maintenance problems.

Although reasonably effective dust removal may be accomplished in an air washer, its prime function is to provide humidification or dehumidification of the air used for heating, ventilating, or air conditioning purposes. Heat transfer occurs between the water sprays and the air stream, providing moisture addition or removal, depending upon the method of operation and the relative temperature level of air and water.

Air washers consist of a metal casing or chamber equipped with one or more banks of water spray nozzles, a series of air-diffusion plates at the inlet, flooded scrubber plates for dirt removal near the discharge from the chamber, and finally a series of eliminator plates for removal of entrained water droplets from the conditioned discharge air. The bottom of the metal casing is a sump for collecting water from the nozzles and serves as a reservoir for the pump which delivers the water to the nozzles. Make-up water is admitted through a float valve to maintain constant water level in the sump.

Air velocities through the washer ordinarily do not exceed 600 ft. per min. Satisfactory operation of the washer is dependent upon uniform air distribution, intimate contact between air and water, and effective removal of entrained water in the eliminator plates. Operation of the washer, particularly when used for dehumidification, can be seriously affected by clogged nozzles. Regular maintenance is required to remove accumulated dirt from the sump; nozzles should be flushed periodically to insure satisfactory operation.

For **humidification** applications, incoming air must be maintained above 32° F. to prevent freezing of the water; in practice, the air is usually heated to approximately 40° F., and the spray water is heated to the temperature required to provide the necessary humidification. Air leaves the washer in a practically saturated state and may be reheated to provide the desired dry-bulb temperature.

In some cases, air preheating and reheating coils are used without any external supply of heat to the spray water. In such cases, the recirculated spray water tends to approach the wet-bulb temperature of the entering air stream, while the leaving air approaches saturation at the same entering wet-bulb temperature.

Dehumidification may be accomplished when the spray water temperature is below the dew point of the entering air. Various arrangements are possible using externally cooled water, well water, or recirculated water with cooling coils located inside the spray chamber. Air conditions leaving the washer will approach saturation at a lowered dry-bulb temperature, the exact state depending upon the design conditions of the washer and the water temperature.

CONTROL SYSTEMS. The importance of both humidity and temperature control for both manufacturing operations and worker comfort is now recognized by most industries. The main types of control systems may be classified as follows (Heating, Ventilating, and Air Conditioning Guide, vol. 34), according to the primary source of energy:

1. **Self-contained systems,** which combine the measuring system (controller) and the controlled device (valve or damper) in a single unit. The operating power is derived directly from the measuring system, which in turn responds directly to the changes in the process controlled without amplification by auxiliary energy sources.
2. **Pneumatic systems,** which use compressed air as the energy source with a controller regulating air pressure supplied to the controlled device. Systems of this type, ranging from relatively simple to elaborate interrelated applications, are widely used for temperature control in heating and air conditioning work. A source of compressed air is required.
3. **Electric systems,** using either direct-line or low-voltage electricity as the primary energy source. A controller regulates the output to the controlled element either directly or by means of suitable relays. Systems of this type, ranging from simple to complex, are very common for heating and air-conditioning control.
4. **Electronic systems,** which use amplifiers to increase small-scale voltage variations from the measuring element into signals of the strength desired for operation of standard electrically controlled elements. Combination electronic-pneumatic systems are also used.
5. **Hydraulic systems,** which utilize liquids under pressure as an energy source. Pressures used are frequently considerably higher than those employed in pneumatic systems, so such systems are most commonly used where large operating forces are required.

Air Conditioning

SYSTEMS. By popular usage, the term "air conditioning" is often reserved for describing those systems which can provide cooling of the atmosphere within a building structure. Technically, however, air conditioning refers to the **simultaneous control** of air temperature, humidity, motion, distribution, pressure, and purity, including such factors as dust, odors, bacteria, and toxic gases (Heating, Ventilating, and Air Conditioning Guide, vol. 34). A true air-conditioning system must be able to provide control of these factors during both the heating and cooling seasons.

Air-conditioning systems are frequently classified as **comfort** air conditioning, the providing of an atmospheric environment considered desirable for human comfort, and **industrial** air conditioning, the maintenance of an environment for the purposes of manufacture or storage of a product.

In many applications, both end results are achieved, although the emphasis in industrial air conditioning is on product control.

In this portion of the section, consideration will be given to the problem of cooling and dehumidifying air for either purpose; the treatment of heating and ventilation deals primarily with the air-heating phase of environmental control, but it should also be considered applicable to the broad problem of air conditioning.

PSYCHROMETRIC DATA. Problems dealing with air conditioning as related to cooling and dehumidification involve the determination of properties of moist air. **Moist air** may be considered to be a mixture of dry air (the composition of which remains essentially constant for air conditioning processes), and the associated water vapor, which may vary considerably in amount. The amount of water vapor contained in an air-vapor mixture is customarily expressed on a per-pound basis of dry air, i.e., pounds or grains of vapor per pound of dry air. For practical purposes, air and water vapor may be assumed as **perfect gases** at the temperatures and pressures encountered in air conditioning practice. Where precise results are required and deviations from the perfect gas laws must be considered, data such as are shown in Fig. 33 (adapted from Heating, Ventilating, and Air Conditioning Guide, vol. 34) may be used.

If minor inaccuracies due to perfect gas assumptions may be tolerated (which is ordinarily the case), the thermodynamic relations are simplified. According to Dalton's rule for perfect gases, both the air and associated water vapor will occupy the total volume of the mixture, and the mixture pressure will be the sum of the partial pressures of the two components. The temperature of the mixture is considered to be the same as the temperature of the air and the water vapor.

If the amount of water vapor in the air is less than that required for saturation, it may be treated as low-pressure, low-temperature, **superheated** steam. At saturation conditions, the moisture is low-pressure, low-temperature, **saturated** steam. At either condition, the vapor acts very nearly as a perfect gas.

Definitions. The psychrometric terms which are commonly used to describe the thermodynamic state of an air-water vapor mixture are:

1. **Dry-air pressure,** p_a, is that portion of the mixture (i.e., barometric) pressure which is due to the air alone, commonly expressed as pounds per square inch or inches of mercury.
2. **Vapor pressure,** p_v, is that portion of the mixture (i.e., barometric) pressure which is due to the water vapor. The vapor pressure may vary from zero (for dry air) to that required for saturation at a given temperature. For saturation, the vapor pressure is the pressure of saturated steam at the given temperature, pounds per square inch or inches of mercury.
3. **Dry-bulb temperature,** t_d, ° F., is the temperature of the air-vapor mixture as determined by a thermometer or thermocouple which is not affected by water vapor content or heat radiation to or from the surroundings.
4. **Wet-bulb temperature,** t_w, ° F.; for precise purposes, t_w is the temperature of adiabatic saturation, i.e., the temperature at which water can bring air to saturation without heat transfer to or from the surroundings. For most practical purposes, it is the lowest temperature (accurately, the equilibrium temperature) indicated by a thermometer whose bulb is moistened by a wetted wick across which a current of air flows at approximately 1,000 ft. per min

Fahr. Temp. t(°F.)	Humidity Ratio $w_s \times 10^3$	Volume cu. ft./lb. dry air			Enthalpy Btu./lb. dry air			Condensed Water	
		v_a	v_{as}	v_s	h_a	h_{as}	h_s	Enthalpy Btu./lb. h_w	Vap. Press. In. Hg $p_s \times 10^2$
7	1.130	11.756	0.021	11.777	1.681	1.202	2.883	−155.61	5.4022
8	1.189	11.781	0.022	11.803	1.922	1.266	3.188	−155.13	5.6832
9	1.251	11.806	0.024	11.830	2.162	1.332	3.494	−154.65	5.9776
10	1.315	11.831	0.025	11.856	2.402	1.401	3.803	−154.17	6.2858
11	1.383	11.857	0.026	11.883	2.642	1.474	4.116	−153.69	6.6085
12	1.454	11.882	0.028	11.910	2.882	1.550	4.432	−153.21	6.9462
13	1.528	11.907	0.029	11.936	3.123	1.630	4.753	−152.73	7.2997
14	1.606	11.933	0.030	11.963	3.363	1.713	5.076	−152.24	7.6696
15	1.687	11.958	0.032	11.990	3.603	1.800	5.403	−151.76	8.0565
16	1.772	11.983	0.034	12.017	3.843	1.892	5.735	−151.27	8.4612
17	1.861	12.009	0.035	12.044	4.083	1.988	6.071	−150.78	8.8843
18	1.953	12.034	0.038	12.072	4.324	2.088	6.412	−150.29	9.3267
19	2.051	12.059	0.040	12.099	4.564	2.192	6.756	−149.80	9.7889
20	2.152	12.084	0.042	12.126	4.804	2.302	7.106	−149.31	10.272
21	2.258	12.110	0.044	12.154	5.044	2.416	7.460	−148.82	10.777
22	2.369	12.135	0.046	12.181	5.284	2.536	7.820	−148.33	11.305
23	2.485	12.160	0.049	12.209	5.525	2.661	8.186	−147.84	11.856
24	2.606	12.186	0.051	12.237	5.765	2.792	8.557	−147.34	12.431
25	2.733	12.211	0.054	12.265	6.005	2.929	8.934	−146.85	13.032
26	2.865	12.236	0.057	12.293	6.245	3.072	9.317	−146.35	13.659
27	3.003	12.262	0.059	12.321	6.485	3.221	9.706	−145.85	14.313
28	3.147	12.287	0.062	12.349	6.726	3.377	10.103	−145.36	14.966
29	3.297	12.312	0.065	12.377	6.966	3.540	10.506	−144.86	15.709
30	3.454	12.338	0.068	12.406	7.206	3.709	10.915	−144.36	16.452
31	3.617	12.363	0.071	12.434	7.446	3.887	11.333	−143.86	17.227
32	3.788	12.388	0.075	12.463	7.686	4.072	11.758	−143.36	18.035
32*	3.788	12.388	0.075	12.463	7.686	4.072	11.758	0.04	18.037
33	3.944	12.413	0.079	12.492	7.927	4.242	12.169	1.05	18.778
34	4.107	12.438	0.082	12.520	8.167	4.418	12.585	2.06	19.546
35	4.275	12.464	0.085	12.549	8.407	4.601	13.008	3.06	20.342
36	4.450	12.489	0.089	12.578	8.647	4.791	13.438	4.07	21.166
37	4.631	12.514	0.093	12.607	8.887	4.987	13.874	5.07	22.020
t(°F)	$w_s \times 10^3$	v_a	v_{as}	v_s	h_a	h_{as}	h_s	h_w	p_s
38	4.818	12.540	0.097	12.637	9.128	5.191	14.319	6.08	0.22904
39	5.012	12.565	0.101	12.666	9.368	5.403	14.771	7.08	0.23819
40	5.213	12.590	0.105	12.695	9.608	5.662	15.230	8.09	0.24767
41	5.421	12.616	0.109	12.725	9.848	5.849	15.697	9.09	0.25748
42	5.638	12.641	0.114	12.755	10.088	6.084	16.172	10.09	0.26763
43	5.860	12.666	0.119	12.785	10.329	6.328	16.657	11.10	0.27813
44	6.091	12.691	0.124	12.815	10.569	6.580	17.149	12.10	0.28899
45	6.331	12.717	0.129	12.846	10.809	6.841	17.650	13.10	0.30023
46	6.578	12.742	0.134	12.876	11.049	7.112	18.161	14.10	0.31185
47	6.835	12.767	0.140	12.907	11.289	7.391	18.680	15.11	0.32386
48	7.100	12.792	0.146	12.938	11.530	7.681	19.211	16.11	0.33629
49	7.374	12.818	0.151	12.969	11.770	7.981	19.751	17.11	0.34913

Compiled by John A. Goff and S. Gratch.
* Extrapolated to represent metastable equilibrium with undercooled liquid.

Fig. 33. **Thermodynamic properties of moist air (standard atmospheric pressure, 29.921 in. Hg) (continued on next page).**

Fahr. Temp. $t(°F.)$	Humidity Ratio $w_s \times 10^3$	Volume cu. ft./lb. dry air			Enthalpy Btu./lb. dry air			Condensed Water	
		v_a	v_{as}	v_s	h_a	h_{as}	h_s	Enthalpy Btu./lb. h_w	Vap. Press. In. Hg p_s
50	7.658	12.843	0.158	13.001	12.010	8.291	20.301	18.11	0.36240
51	7.952	12.868	0.164	13.032	12.250	8.612	20.862	19.11	0.37611
52	8.256	12.894	0.170	13.064	12.491	8.945	21.436	20.11	0.39028
53	8.569	12.919	0.178	13.097	12.731	9.289	22.020	21.12	0.40492
54	8.894	12.944	0.185	13.129	12.971	9.644	22.615	22.12	0.42004
55	9.229	12.970	0.192	13.162	13.211	10.01	23.22	23.12	0.43565
56	9.575	12.995	0.200	13.195	13.452	10.39	23.84	24.12	0.45176
57	9.934	13.020	0.208	13.228	13.692	10.79	24.48	25.12	0.46840
58	10.30	13.045	0.216	13.261	13.932	11.19	25.12	26.12	0.48558
59	10.69	13.071	0.224	13.295	14.172	11.61	25.78	27.12	0.50330
60	11.08	13.096	0.233	13.329	14.413	12.05	26.46	28.12	0.52159
61	11.49	13.121	0.242	13.363	14.653	12.50	27.15	29.12	0.54047
62	11.91	13.147	0.251	13.398	14.893	12.96	27.85	30.12	0.55994
63	12.35	13.172	0.261	13.443	15.134	13.44	28.57	31.12	0.58002
64	12.80	13.197	0.271	13.468	15.374	13.94	29.31	32.12	0.60073
65	13.26	13.222	0.282	13.504	15.614	14.45	30.06	33.11	0.62209
66	13.74	13.247	0.292	13.539	15.855	14.98	30.83	34.11	0.64411
67	14.24	13.273	0.303	13.576	16.095	15.53	31.62	35.11	0.66681
68	14.75	13.298	0.315	13.613	16.335	16.09	32.42	36.11	0.69019
69	15.28	13.323	0.327	13.650	16.576	16.67	33.25	37.11	0.71430
$t(°F)$	$w_s \times 10^3$	v_a	v_{as}	v_s	h_a	h_{as}	h_s	h_w	p_s
70	1.582	13.348	0.339	13.687	16.816	17.27	34.09	38.11	0.73915
71	1.639	13.373	0.351	13.724	17.056	17.89	34.95	39.11	0.76475
72	1.697	13.398	0.364	13.762	17.297	18.53	35.83	40.11	0.79112
73	1.757	13.424	0.377	13.801	17.537	19.20	36.74	41.11	0.81828
74	1.819	13.449	0.392	13.841	17.778	19.88	37.66	42.10	0.84624
75	1.882	13.474	0.407	13.881	18.018	20.59	38.61	43.10	0.87504
76	1.948	13.499	0.422	13.921	18.259	21.31	39.57	44.10	0.90470
77	2.016	13.525	0.437	13.962	18.499	22.07	40.57	45.10	0.93523
78	2.086	13.550	0.453	14.003	18.740	22.84	41.58	46.10	0.96665
79	2.158	13.575	0.470	14.045	18.980	23.64	42.62	47.10	0.99899
80	2.233	13.601	0.486	14.087	19.221	24.47	43.69	48.10	1.0323
81	2.310	13.626	0.504	14.130	19.461	25.32	44.78	49.09	1.0665
82	2.389	13.651	0.523	14.174	19.702	26.20	45.90	50.09	1.1017
83	2.471	13.676	0.542	14.218	19.942	27.10	47.04	51.09	1.1379
84	2.555	13.702	0.560	14.262	20.183	28.04	48.22	52.09	1.1752
85	2.642	13.727	0.581	14.308	20.423	29.01	49.43	53.09	1.2135
86	2.731	13.752	0.602	14.354	20.663	30.00	50.66	54.08	1.2529
87	2.824	13.777	0.624	14.401	20.904	31.03	51.93	55.08	1.2934
88	2.919	13.803	0.645	14.448	21.144	32.09	53.23	56.08	1.3351
89	3.017	13.828	0.668	14.496	21.385	33.18	54.56	57.08	1.3779
90	3.118	13.853	0.692	14.545	21.625	34.31	55.93	58.08	1.4219
91	3.223	13.879	0.716	14.595	21.865	35.47	57.33	59.07	1.4671
92	3.330	13.904	0.741	14.645	22.106	36.67	58.78	60.07	1.5135
93	3.441	13.929	0.768	14.697	22.346	37.90	60.25	61.07	1.5612
94	3.556	13.954	0.795	14.749	22.587	39.18	61.77	62.07	1.6102

Fig. 33. (Continued on next page.)

Fahr. Temp. $t(°F)$	Humidity Ratio $w_s \times 10^2$	Volume cu. ft./lb. dry air			Enthalpy Btu./lb. dry air			Condensed Water	
		v_a	v_{as}	v_s	h_a	h_{as}	h_s	Enthalpy Btu./lb. h_w	Vap. Press. In. Hg p_s
95	3.673	13.980	0.822	14.802	22.827	40.49	63.32	63.07	1.6606
96	3.795	14.005	0.851	14.856	23.068	41.85	64.92	64.06	1.7123
97	3.920	14.030	0.881	14.911	23.308	43.24	66.55	65.06	1.7654
98	4.049	14.056	0.911	14.967	23.548	44.68	68.23	66.06	1.8199
99	4.182	14.081	0.942	15.023	23.789	46.17	69.96	67.06	1.8759
100	4.319	14.106	0.975	15.081	24.029	47.70	71.73	68.06	1.9353
101	4.460	14.131	1.009	15.140	24.270	49.28	73.55	69.05	1.9923
102	4.606	14.157	1.043	15.200	24.510	50.91	75.42	70.05	2.0528
103	4.756	14.182	1.079	15.261	24.751	52.59	77.34	71.05	2.1149
104	4.911	14.207	1.117	15.324	24.991	54.32	79.31	72.05	2.1786
$t(°F)$	$w_s \times 10$	v_a	v_{as}	v_s	h_a	h_{as}	h_s	h_w	p_s
105	0.5070	14.232	1.155	15.387	25.232	56.11	81.34	73.04	2.2439
106	0.5234	14.258	1.194	15.452	25.472	57.95	83.42	74.04	2.3109
107	0.5404	14.283	1.235	15.518	25.713	59.85	85.56	75.04	2.3797
108	0.5578	14.308	1.278	15.586	25.953	61.80	87.76	76.04	2.4502
109	0.5758	14.333	1.321	15.654	26.194	63.82	90.03	77.04	2.5225
110	0.5944	14.359	1.365	15.724	26.434	65.91	92.34	78.03	2.5966
111	0.6135	14.384	1.412	15.796	26.675	68.05	94.72	79.03	2.6726
112	0.6333	14.409	1.460	15.869	26.915	70.27	97.18	80.03	2.7505
113	0.6536	14.435	1.509	15.944	27.156	72.55	99.71	81.03	2.8304
114	0.6746	14.460	1.560	16.020	27.397	74.91	102.31	82.03	2.9123
115	0.6962	14.485	1.613	16.098	27.637	77.34	104.98	83.02	2.9962
116	0.7185	14.510	1.668	16.178	27.878	79.85	107.73	84.02	3.0821
117	0.7415	14.536	1.723	16.259	28.119	82.43	110.55	85.02	3.1701
118	0.7652	14.561	1.782	16.343	28.359	85.10	113.46	86.02	3.2603
119	0.7897	14.586	1.842	16.428	28.600	87.86	116.46	87.02	3.3527
120	0.8149	14.611	1.905	16.516	28.841	90.70	119.54	88.01	3.4474
121	0.8410	14.637	1.968	16.605	29.082	93.64	122.72	89.01	3.5443
122	0.8678	14.662	2.034	16.696	29.322	96.66	125.98	90.01	3.6436
123	0.8955	14.687	2.103	16.790	29.563	99.79	129.35	91.01	3.7452
124	0.9242	14.712	2.174	16.886	29.804	103.0	132.8	92.01	3.8493
125	0.9537	14.738	2.247	16.985	30.044	106.4	136.4	93.01	3.9558
126	0.9841	14.763	2.323	17.086	30.285	109.8	140.1	94.01	4.0649
127	1.016	14.788	2.401	17.189	30.526	113.4	143.9	95.00	4.1765
128	1.048	14.813	2.482	17.295	30.766	117.0	147.8	96.00	4.2907
129	1.082	14.839	2.565	17.404	31.007	120.8	151.8	97.00	4.4076
130	1.116	14.864	2.652	17.516	31.248	124.7	155.9	98.00	4.5272
131	1.152	14.889	2.742	17.631	31.489	128.8	160.3	99.00	4.6495
132	1.189	14.915	2.834	17.749	31.729	133.0	164.7	100.00	4.7747
133	1.227	14.940	2.930	17.870	31.970	137.3	169.3	101.00	4.9028
134	1.267	14.965	3.029	17.994	32.211	141.8	174.0	102.00	5.0337
135	1.308	14.990	3.132	18.122	32.452	146.4	178.9	103.00	5.1676
136	1.350	15.016	3.237	18.253	32.692	151.2	183.9	104.00	5.3046
137	1.393	15.041	3.348	18.389	32.933	156.1	189.0	105.00	5.4446
138	1.439	15.066	3.462	18.528	33.174	161.2	194.4	106.00	5.5878
139	1.485	15.091	3.580	18.671	33.414	166.5	199.9	107.00	5.7342

Fig. 33. (Concluded.)

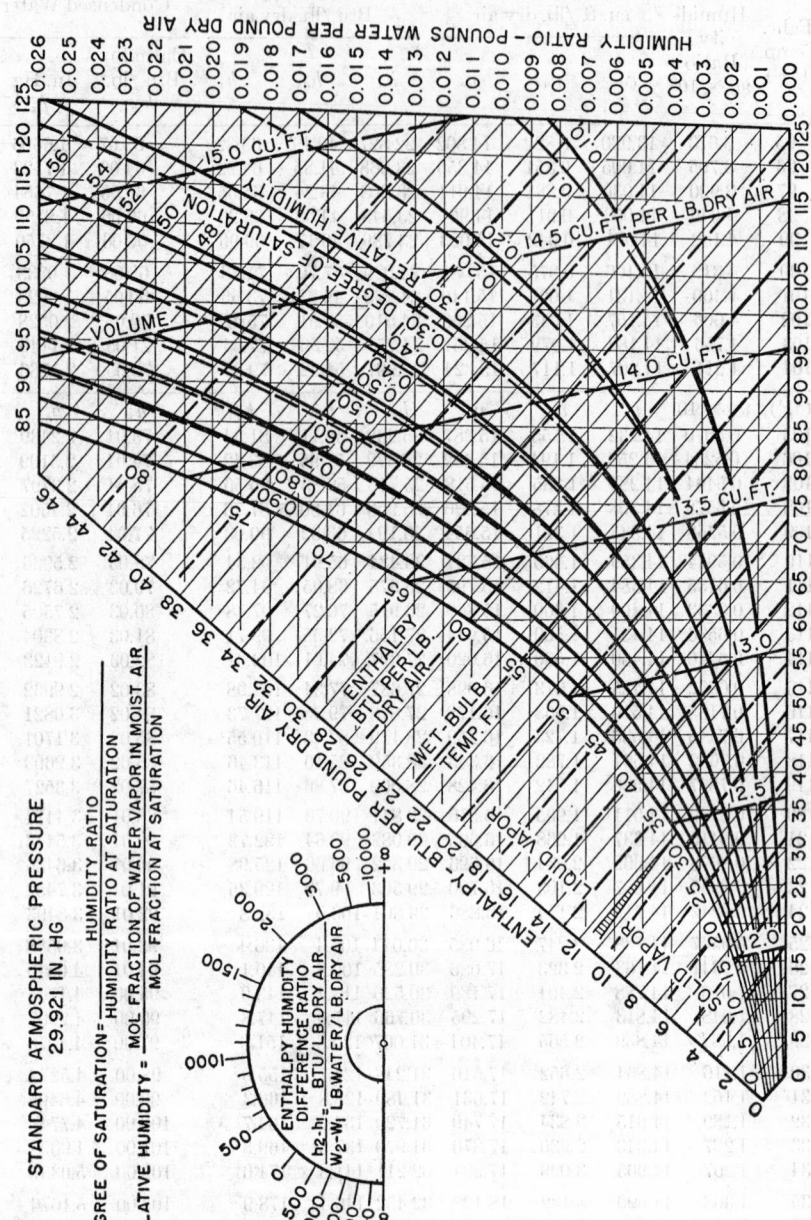

Fig. 34. Psychrometric chart (American Society of Heating and Air Conditioning Engineers).

5. **Dew-point temperature,** t_{dp}, °F.; the dew-point temperature represents the saturation temperature for any given moisture content, i.e., the temperature to which an air-vapor mixture must be cooled before saturation exists and below which condensation will occur.

6. **Humidity ratio,** w_v (commonly termed specific humidity), is the amount of water vapor associated with unit mass (numerically equal to unit weight) of dry air, i.e., the water vapor content of the air expressed in pounds of vapor per pound of dry air. Because of the small magnitudes involved, humidity ratios are frequently expressed in grains of vapor per pound of dry air, where 1 lb. is equivalent to 7,000 grains.

7. **Relative humidity,** Φ, per cent, is ordinarily defined as the ratio of the **actual** vapor pressure in a mixture of air and water vapor to the vapor pressure which would exist if the air were **saturated** with vapor at the same dry-bulb temperature and barometric pressure, i.e., $\Phi = (p_v/p_s) \times 100$, where p_s is the saturation vapor pressure at the specified dry-bulb temperature.

8. **Degree of saturation,** μ, per cent, is the ratio of **actual** moisture content (humidity ratio) to that which would exist if the air were **saturated** at the same dry-bulb temperature and barometric pressure, i.e., $\mu = (w_v/w_s) \times 100$, where w_s is the humidity ratio of saturated air at the specified dry-bulb temperature.

9. **Enthalpy,** h, Btu./lb. of dry air; enthalpy is a mathematically derived property which is useful in the determination of heat transfer quantities in air conditioning problems. In flow processes which do not involve shaft work and in which changes in kinetic and potential energy may be neglected, the heat transfer is equal to the change in enthalpy. The enthalpy is ordinarily expressed per unit mass of dry air, i.e., Btu. per lb. of dry air. The enthalpy of a mixture of air and water vapor is the sum of the dry-air enthalpy and the enthalpy of the water vapor contained in 1 lb. of dry air. In equation form, $h = h_a + w_v h_g$, where h is the mixture enthalpy, Btu. per lb. of dry air; h_a is the enthalpy of 1 lb. of dry air; w_v is the humidity ratio, equal to w_s if the air is saturated; h_g is the enthalpy of saturated steam at the specified dry-bulb temperature.

Tabulations of some of the properties defined above are shown in Fig. 33 for air-vapor mixtures at standard barometric pressure of 29.92 in. of mercury. In the table, the subscript a refers to dry air, the subscript s to saturated air, and the subscript as to the difference between saturation and dry-air values. Since entropy values are not commonly required for air conditioning calculations, this term will not be discussed here.

A graphical representation of the thermodynamic properties of moist air is shown in the abridged **psychrometric chart** (Fig. 34). Frequently, the use of a psychrometric chart is an aid in visualizing air conditioning processes.

Calculation by Table. An example of the use of Figs. 33 and 34 follows; more complete information on psychrometric principles and the use of data such as are shown in these figures appears in the ASHAE (Heating, Ventilating, and Air Conditioning Guide, vol. 34).

The humidity ratio, the degree of saturation, the dew-point temperature, and the enthalpy are to be determined for a mixture of air and water vapor with a dry-bulb temperature of 80° F. and a relative humidity of 50 percent, assuming a barometric pressure of 29.92 in. Hg. The solution may be obtained by the use of the data shown in Fig. 33.

1. Assuming both the air and the associated water vapor may be treated as perfect gases, by Dalton's rule, the volume of the vapor is equal to the volume

of the dry air. From the perfect gas equation of state, for 1 lb. of dry air plus associated vapor, for air:

$$p_a V_a = w_a R_a T_a \tag{17}$$

where p_a = dry air pressure, i.e., the difference between the barometric pressure (p_B) and the vapor pressure (p_v) ordinarily expressed as psia

V_a = volume of air, cubic feet

w_a = mass of air, pounds. (Since psychrometric calculations are based on 1 lb. of dry air, w_a is 1 lb. and V_a is the volume per pound of dry air.)

R_a = gas constant for air, numerically equal to the universal gas constant of 1,545 ft.-lb. per (mol) (degree F. absolute) divided by the molecular weight of dry air, 28.97 lbs per mol. (Hence, $R_a = 1.545/28.97 = 53.34$ ft.-lb./lb.-°R, where °R represents absolute temperature, degrees Rankine, or degrees Fahrenheit absolute.)

T_a = dry-bulb temperature, absolute, i.e., $T_a(°R) = t_{db}(°F.) + 460$, or $T_a = 80 + 460 = 540°R$

Hence, from Eq. (17),

$$V_a = \frac{1 \times R_a T_a}{p_a}, \text{cu. ft.} \tag{18}$$

For the vapor, since it is also considered to be a perfect gas (very closely true for the vapor pressures encountered in air conditioning problems), then

$$p_v V_v = w_v R_v T_v \tag{19}$$

where p_v = vapor pressure, psi

V_v = volume of the vapor, in cubic feet, associated with 1 lb. of dry air, and by Dalton's rule equivalent to V_a and V_m the mixture volume.

w_v = mass of vapor, pound, associated with 1 lb. of dry air; hence w_v is the humidity ratio, pounds of vapor pound of dry air

R_v = gas constant for vapor, 1,545 divided by the molecular weight of water, or $R_v = 1,545/18.016 = 85.76$ ft.-lb./lb.-° R

T_v = vapor temperature, °R, equal to the dry-bulb air temperature T_a

Rearranging Eq. (19),

$$w_v = \frac{p_v V_v}{R_v T_v} \tag{20}$$

where

$$V_v = V_a$$

Thus, substituting from Eq. (18),

$$w_v = \left(\frac{p_v}{R_v T_v}\right) \times \left(\frac{R_a T_a}{p_a}\right) = \frac{53.34}{85.76} \times \frac{p_v}{p_a}$$

or

$$w_v = 0.622 \frac{p_v}{p_a}, \text{lb. vapor/lb. dry air} \tag{21}$$

Since p_a in Eq. (21) is $p_B - p_v$, the **humidity ratio** is seen to be dependent upon the barometric pressure. Eq. (21) may be used to calculate the humidity ratio for any barometric pressure, the results obtained differing for different values of p_B. Note that p_v is the actual vapor pressure, independent of barometric pressure. At saturation, p_v is the saturation pressure (p_s) for steam at the specified dry-bulb temperature; for any condition other than saturation, p_v is the saturation pressure for steam at the dew-point temperature.

For the conditions stated in the example, $\phi = 0.5 = (p_v/p_s)$; from Fig. 33 at 80° F., $p_s = 1.0323$ in. Hg, or, $p_v = 0.5 \times 1.0323 = 0.5162$ in. Hg. From Eq. (21),

$$w_v = 0.622 \times \frac{0.5162}{(29.92 - 0.5162)} = 0.01092 \text{ lb.}_v/\text{lb. of dry air}$$

or $w_v = 7,000 \times 0.01092 = 76.44$ grains/lb.$_{da}$, where w_v is the humidity ratio.

2. The **degree of saturation** may be expressed as $\mu = w_v/w_s$, and from Fig. 33, $w_s \times 10^2 = 2.233$ lb.$_v$/lb.$_{da}$, or $\mu = 0.01092/0.02233 \times 100 = 48.9$ percent.

For any barometric pressure other than 29.92 in. Hg, w_s from Fig. 33 must be corrected. Eq. (21) may be used as follows: Assume that $t_{db} = 80°$ F. and $\phi = 50$ percent, and let $p_B = 28$ in. Hg. Then $p_v = 0.5 \times 1.0323 = 0.5162$ in. Hg (independent of p_B).

$$w_v = 0.622 \times \frac{0.5162}{(28.0 - 0.516)} = 0.01169 \text{ lb.}_v/\text{lb.}_{da}$$

and $\mu = w_v/w_s$, where w_s may be calculated from Eq. (21) as $w_s = 0.622p_s/p_B - p_s)$; from Fig. 33 at 80° F., $p_s = 1.0323$ in. Hg, and

$$w_s = 0.622 \times \frac{1.0323}{28.0 - 1.0323} = 0.0239 \text{ lb.}_v/\text{lb.}_{da}$$

then $\mu = 0.01169/0.0239 = 48.9$ percent.

3. The **dew-point temperature** may be found by interpolating in Fig. 33 to determine the saturation temperature for a vapor pressure p_v of 0.5162 in. Hg. Hence, at $p_v = 0.5162$ in. Hg, $t_{dp} = 59.7°$ F.

4. The **enthalpy** of the mixture may be expressed as

$$h = h_a + w_v h_g \tag{22}$$

where h_a is the enthalpy of 1 lb. of dry air at the specified dry-bulb temperature of 80° F. (h_a is based on a zero datum of 0° F.). The value of h_a may be determined directly from Fig. 33 as 19.221 Btu./lb.$_{da}$ at 80° F. The enthalpy of dry air (a perfect gas) above a datum of 0° F. may also be express as $h_a = c_p t_{db}$; c_p is the specific heat at constant pressure, approximately 0.24 Btu./lb.-° F. for dry air.

In the above equation, w_v is the actual moisture content of the air-vapor mixture (i.e., the humidity ratio) and h_g is the enthalpy of 1 lb. of saturated vapor at the dry-bulb temperature. Thus, $w_v \times h_g$ is the enthalpy of the vapor associated with 1 lb. of dry air. The value of h_g may be determined from conventional tables showing the thermodynamic properties of water and steam, i.e., so-called steam tables. Frequently, however, such data are not complete for the low-temperature vapor dealt with in air conditioning problems. Fig. 33 does not show values of h_g directly but may be used to determine h_g. The column headed h_{as} is actually the product of $w_v h_g$ for saturated air at the indicated dry bulb. If the value shown in the table for h_{as} is divided by the corresponding value of w_s, the result is h_g at any given dry-bulb temperature. Hence, at 80° F., $h_g = h_{as}/w_s = 24.47/0.02233 = 1095.8$ Btu./lb.$_v$; and since w_v in this example has been determined as 0.01092 lb.$_v$/lb.$_{da}$, then $w_v h_g = 0.01092 \times 1095.8 = 11.966$ Btu./lb.$_{da}$.

It will be observed that the same result may be obtained without a separate determination of h_g by multiplying the tabulated value of h_{as} by the degree of saturation μ, i.e., $w_v h_g = \mu h_{as} = 0.489 \times 24.47 = 11.966$ Btu./lb.$_{da}$.

For barometric pressures other than 29.92 in. Hg, h_{as} as listed in the tables should be divided by the table value of w_s and the result multiplied by the actual humidity ratio w_v.

In the example, from the values determined above, $h = 19.221 + 11.966 = 31.187$ Btu./lb.$_{da}$ where h is the enthalpy of a mixture of air and water vapor at 80° F. dry-bulb temperature and 50 percent relative humidity.

Calculation by Chart. The psychrometric chart (Fig. 34) may also be used for a solution to the example. From Fig. 34 at $t_{db} = 80°$ F. and $\phi = 0.50$, the following values are determined:

1. Lines of constant humidity ratio are horizontal lines on Fig. 34; projecting horizontally to the right from the specified conditions, the **humidity ratio** w_v is shown as 0.011 lb.$_v$/lb.$_{da}$, which checks very closely with the calculated value of 0.01092.
2. The **degree of saturation** is slightly below the value of $\mu = 0.50$ in Fig. 34. Lines of constant relative humidity are displaced slightly from lines of constant degree of saturation. In many practical problems, this slight difference is neglected.
3. The **dew-point temperature** may be obtained by projecting horizontally to the left (constant moisture content) until saturation ($\Phi = 100\%$) is reached. The dew point at $\Phi = 100\%$ corresponds with both the wet-bulb and dry-bulb temperatures and may be read on either scale as slightly less than 60° F. (by calculation, t_{dp} was determined as 59.7° F.). Constant wet-bulb lines slope down toward the right and are shown as dashed lines in Fig. 34.
4. Constant enthalpy lines are slightly different from constant wet-bulb temperature lines, as shown by solid lines sloping down to the right in Fig. 34. The assumption that a constant wet-bulb temperature denotes constant enthalpy is frequently used for air conditioning calculations, since the difference is minor. For the conditions stated, the **enthalpy** is approximately 31.2 Btu./lb.$_{da}$ from Fig. 34, corresponding with the calculated value of 31.187.

More precision can be obtained by using a similar chart constructed on a larger scale.

COMPUTATION OF COOLING LOADS. The variables which affect the actual cooling-load requirements for a structure are numerous and are difficult to establish accurately in magnitude. Transmission of heat to the inside of a given structure varies appreciably over a period of time during the day due to the significance of solar effects; furthermore, due to thermal storage effects of the building structure, significant variation may exist between instantaneous rates of heat gain at any given time and the actual internal cooling load at the same time.

It should be recognized that sound judgment must be exercised in problems dealing with building cooling-load calculations. No simple analysis is possible in such problems because of the number of variables which must be considered; results obtained should be regarded as an estimate only, since variations from design conditions will occur. The system selected for cooling purposes should have adequate capacity to meet peak load requirements and must have a control system which will permit satisfactory operation during periods of off-design performance.

Components. By convention, the total cooling load is ordinarily separated into two parts, (1) the sensible load and (2) the latent load. The **sensible load** is that portion of the total cooling load which tends to cause an increase in the dry-bulb temperature of the conditioned space and is occasioned by a temperature difference between conditioned air and adjacent surfaces, outdoor air, or heat-generating equipment such as lights and motors. The **latent load** involves the removal of moisture from a conditioned space in order to maintain specified conditions of humidity. Cooling apparatus must remove water vapor from the air by condensation, thus releasing the latent heat of condensation which must be absorbed by the air conditioning equipment. The **rate of moisture removal** must be equal to the rate of moisture addition to the conditioned space from such sources as people, infiltration of high-moisture content outdoor air, outdoor air brought in for ventilation purposes, and industrial processes.

The most important sources for the **sensible heat load** are:

1. Transmission through walls, roof, glass, partitions, etc., due to temperature difference between the air on opposite sides.
2. Solar radiation effects through glass, wall, and roof areas.
3. Infiltration of high-temperature outdoor air.
4. Introduction of outdoor air for ventilation purposes.
5. Sensible heat liberation from occupants within the conditioned space.
6. Heat liberation from lights, power equipment, processes, etc.

Latent loads may arise from:

1. Moisture contained in the outside air which leaks in by infiltration.
2. Moisture in air introduced for ventilation.
3. Moisture liberation from the occupants.
4. Moisture liberation from industrial processes.

The calculation of the cooling load requires the separate determination of each of the above components.

Design Conditions. For **comfort air conditioning,** a representative condition for the average application is from 76° F. to 80° F. dry-bulb temperature and approximately 50 percent relative humidity. Variation from this is frequent, depending upon the application. Temperatures above 80° F. are not considered desirable from a comfort standpoint, especially for periods of occupancy longer than about 30 min. The optimum design conditions for **industrial air conditioning** vary widely; extensive lists of representative design conditions for many industrial applications have been prepared.

Solar Load Estimates. Practical design tables based on analytical procedures have been developed for the estimation of heat gain from solar effects. Tables are available to determine the **equivalent temperature differential** for estimating heat transfer through walls and roofs exposed to the sun. The effective or equivalent temperature differential accounts for both solar effects and those due to actual indoor-outdoor air temperature difference and is based on the **sol-air temperature** concept. The sol-air temperature is a hypothetical temperature for the outside air which allows for the effects of solar radiation and sky radiation as well as convective heat exchange with outdoor air. Variations in construction, surface character, time of day, temperature, and other factors must be accounted for.

Total sensible heat transmission due to both indoor-outdoor air temperature difference and solar radiation effects may be estimated by the equation

$$H_s = U \times A \times \Delta t \qquad (23)$$

where H_s = sensible heat gain due to solar and convective effects, Btu./hour
  U = over-all coefficient of heat transmission, Btu. (hour) (square foot) (°F)
  A = net area of exposed surface, square feet
  Δt = equivalent temperature differential (°F.) from tables

For walls, the U values may be determined as described in the preceding treatment of heating and ventilation; for roofs, however, other data should be used, including a correction for variations of surface conductance and wind velocity for summer conditions.

Heat Transmission Through Glass Areas. Design data to be used for estimating instantaneous rates of heat gain through glass areas are obtained from tables in which the data are based on solar intensity values for a clear atmosphere and correspond to a nominal August 1 day (Heating, Ventilating, and Air Conditioning Guide, vol. 34). Corrections must be made for heat flow by **convective** and **radiant exchange** at the glass surface, for outdoor dry-bulb temperature, and for shading.

Ventilation and Infiltration Loads. The introduction of outdoor air, whether for ventilation purposes or by infiltration, affects both the sensible and latent cooling loads. Ventilation requirements must be established on the basis of the number of occupants and the application; data for estimating the amount of ventilation air required are available from many sources and vary considerably. Values shown are ordinarily based upon past experience and should always be compared with requirements established by codes to insure that minimum standards are met.

The methods outlined in the preceding treatment of heating and ventilation for estimating infiltration may be used for cooling-load calculations; a wind velocity of 10 mi. per hr. is commonly assumed for summer design conditions.

The sensible and latent loads caused by the introduction of outside air may be calculated by the following equations (Heating, Ventilating, and Air Conditioning Guide, vol. 34):

$$\text{Sensible load, } H_s = Q \times 1.08 \times (t_o - t_i), \text{ Btu./hour} \qquad (24)$$

and

$$\text{Latent load, } H_l = Q \times 4,840 \ (w_{v_o} - w_{v_i}), \text{ Btu./hour} \qquad (25)$$

where Q = rate of entry of outdoor air, cubic feet per minute

t_o = design outdoor dry-bulb temperature, °F.

t_i = design room dry-bulb temperature, °F.

w_{v_o} = specific humidity of outdoor air, pounds of moisture per pound of dry air

w_{v_i} = specific humidity of inside (room) air, pounds of moisture per pound of dry air

The constant 1.08 is obtained from $60 \times 0.075 \times 0.24$, where 0.075 represents "standard" air density, pounds per cubic foot, and 0.24 is the specific heat for dry air, Btu. per (lb.-°F.). A latent heat of condensation of 1,076 Btu. per lb. of moisture is assumed, and for a density of 0.075 pounds per cu. ft., $60 \times 0.075 \times 1,076 = 4,840$.

Occupant Loads. In air conditioning calculations, the rate of sensible and latent heat liberation from occupants must be considered. Activity of the occupants is important in determining the relative proportions of sensible and latent loads as well as the total rate of heat emission per occupant.

Equipment and Lighting Loads. Allowance must be made for heat liberation from lights, motors, processes, etc., within the conditioned space. For industrial applications, equipment and lighting loads may represent a significant portion of the total cooling load. The sensible load due to electric lights may be expressed as

$$H = W \times F_1 \times F_2 \times 3.41 \text{ Btu. per hr.} \tag{26}$$

where W = total wattage
$\quad F_1$ = use factor, to account for the ratio of wattage in use to the total installed
$\quad F_2$ = allowance factor, to care for fluorescent fixtures, ordinarily assumed to be 1.20
$\quad 3.41$ = the heat equivalent in Btu. of 1 watt-hour of electric energy

For electric motors, the horsepower rating must be divided by the motor efficiency if the motor is located within the conditioned space; the ratio of power delivered to the rated power (i.e., the load factor) must be determined and multiplied by 2,544, the heat equivalent in Btu. of 1 hp.-hr.

AIR CONDITIONING EQUIPMENT. There are certain major types of air-conditioning systems and equipment used industrially which should be considered and compared in determining the appropriate design of air conditioning under specific conditions.

Unit and Central Systems. For applications where cooling loads are relatively small, the use of package or unit conditioners has become quite common. Unit conditioners are ordinarily factory assembled and have the advantage of simplicity of installation and operation. Condensing equipment may be air- or water-cooled; service connections are relatively simple to install and for applications where suitable, unit equipment is to be preferred to built-up systems.

For cooling loads of perhaps 10 tons of refrigeration (1 ton of refrigeration = 12,000 Btu. per hr.), or less, **unit equipment** is ordinarily considered more desirable than a **built-up system**. As the size of the load increases, system design usually increases in complexity and built-up systems become more desirable. Obviously, no general rule can be given for selecting one system in preference to another, but advantages of each type must be compared before the best selection for any given application may be made.

Reciprocating and Centrifugal Compressors. In smaller central systems, reciprocating compressors are ordinarily used. In the range of from 10 to 100 tons capacity, single or multiple reciprocating machines with water-cooled condensing equipment are most common.

Although centrifugal machines at one time were not considered for applications where the cooling load was less than 100 tons, machines are now available which may offer advantages well worth considering for the 50 to 100 ton range. In this size range, the initial cost of centrifugal equipment will probably be somewhat higher than the reciprocating, but simplicity of operation, reduced maintenance, and reduced operational noise and vibration may overcome the higher cost.

Capacity control for reduced-load operation can be achieved with cylinder-unloading devices on reciprocating compressors or by the use of multiple machine installations. The provisions for capacity regulation are more complex than for centrifugal machines, however, and the degree of regulation is ordinarily much more limited.

Direct-Expansion and Chilled-Water Systems. Direct-expansion cooling coils, using refrigerant supplied from condensing equipment and returned to the compressor are widely used for both unit systems and built-up systems with reciprocating compressors. Mixing dampers or face-and-by-pass dampers may be used for close regulation of air temperatures.

Chilled-water systems have become more popular due to the introduction of factory-assembled **water chillers** incorporating compressor, condenser, and capacity-control equipment. Installation is frequently simplified appreciably by the use of such equipment, resulting in savings in field installation costs. Coil costs may also be reduced by the use of water-type cooling coils, helping to offset the increased first cost of the package equipment.

Condensing Equipment. Although air-cooled condensers are used on some of the smaller unit air conditioners, water-cooled condensers are common on equipment above approximately one ton in capacity. The increased use of air-conditioning equipment has resulted in regulations governing the use of water; cooling towers or evaporative condensers are now commonly required for installations above perhaps 10 tons capacity. Water consumption is approximately the same for an evaporative condenser as for a condenser-cooling tower combination. Cost comparisons may vary according to size and problems of installation.

Heat Pumps. The growth of interest in the heat pump for both residential and commercial applications has been very rapid. The idea of the heat pump is not new, dating back approximately 100 years, but the successful application for heating and cooling buildings is relatively recent.

The main advantages of the heat pump are that the same items of equipment may be used for cooling during the summer as are used for heating during the winter, and equipment required for direct burning of fuels is eliminated. Many installations, particularly in commercial and industrial applications, are in existence at this time and are performing economically and satisfactorily.

Successful and economical operation of the heat pump is dependent upon the existence of **heat sources** and **sinks** which are satisfactory from the standpoint of temperature, adequate in capacity, and reliable. The principal heat sources (excluding those which may be available as a result of certain industrial processes) are the air, the earth, and water. **Solar energy** will doubtless become an important and practical source of energy for heat pump applications in the future, although it now has only limited auxiliary applications.

Although frequently described as a "reversed" refrigeration cycle, the **heat pump cycle** is thermodynamically identical to a conventional refrigeration cycle. The difference is merely in terms of the desired effect; in the **refrigeration cycle,** the desired effect is the absorption of heat from the air in a room by the refrigerant which boils in an evaporator. The heat equivalent of the compression work along with the heat absorbed in the evaporator is rejected to a sink and wasted, as in a water-cooled condenser.

In the heat pump, however, the heat rejected from the condenser may be used to warm the air inside a building, hence the desired effect. The heat absorption by the refrigerant in the evaporator may be from outdoor air, the earth, or from water. In order to utilize this heat, compression work is required so that the temperature can be raised to the level required for heating the building.

When conditions are suitable, the heat pump offers an attractive possibility for providing for the heating and cooling requirements of a building. Very careful analysis is required, however, to insure that application is practical. **Auxiliary heating** is frequently required and may in some instances make operational costs prohibitive. Reliability of operation as well as of heat sources must be established.

It is important to determine whether some of the inherent advantages of the heat pump are sufficiently desirable and practically obtainable to cause a system of this type to be preferred over a more conventional system.

Plant Lighting

ILLUMINATION. Ease of seeing without eye strain or tiring is fundamental to safe, efficient, economical operation in every factory. Ease of seeing is largely dependent upon good illumination, whether natural or artificial. **Advantages of good illumination** are (Recommended Practice of Industrial Lighting, Illuminating Engineering Society):

1. Greater accuracy of workmanship, resulting in an improved quality of product with less spoilage costs.
2. Increased production and decreased costs.
3. Better utilization of floorspace.
4. More easily maintained cleanliness and neatness in the plant.
5. Greater ease of seeing, especially among older, experienced employees, thus making them more efficient.
6. Less eye strain among employees.
7. Improved morale among employees, resulting in decreased labor turnover.
8. Fewer accidents.

Illumination and Safety. Not the least important among the advantages of good illumination is that of fewer accidents. As a result of extensive statistics collected over a period of many years, it is now generally accepted that poor lighting is the direct cause of 5 percent of all industrial accidents and a contributing cause in at least 20 percent. If improved lighting were to be effective in preventing, say, 15 percent of all industrial accidents, it would amount to tremendous savings in dollars and cents, to say nothing of suffering and misery that would be avoided.

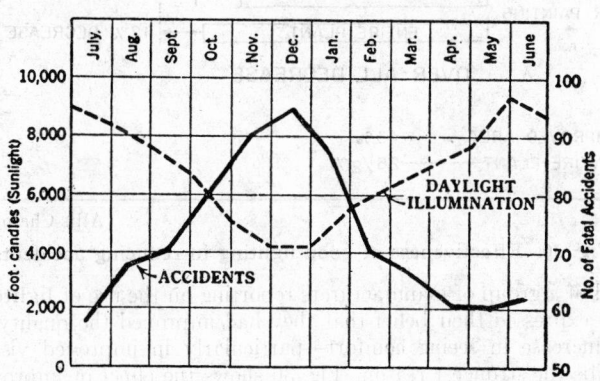

Westinghouse Electric Corp.

Fig. 35. Effect of good daylight in reducing accidents.

That there is a close relationship between industrial accidents and light is shown by Fig. 35, summarizing the results of a study of this subject. **Fatal accidents** definitely show an increase during months of poorer daylight illumination. The poorer illumination comes about because of the reduction in number of daylight hours and the consequent **twilight periods** in the early morning and late afternoon, not because daylight intensities are lower during the middle of the day. The higher frequency of accidents would indicate (1) that a definite relationship does exist between illumination and accidents, and (2) that the level of artificial illumination has not as yet become adequate in supplementing or replacing daylight illumination in many plants, especially in stairways, passageways, and the lesser-used areas.

Accident Reduction by Illumination and Painting. Accident reduction is related directly to production; accidents involve interference with production schedules. In the erection shops of a Milwaukee company, the accident frequency was reduced 43 percent after a new lighting system was installed. A Chicago manufacturer reported that new painting contributed much toward a 73 percent reduction in accident severity rate. Another company reported 75 percent fewer accidents, reduction in the number of rejects, and increases in production in several departments of from 7 percent to 10 percent, brought about by color conditioning, with no change in the lighting system.

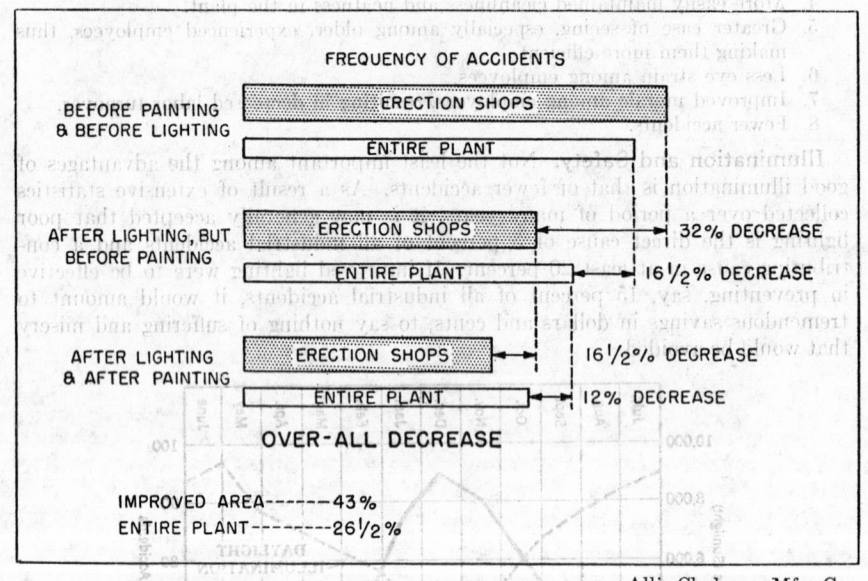

Allis-Chalmers Mfg. Co.

Fig. 36. Effectiveness of good lighting in reducing accidents.

One-third of a group of manufacturers reporting on the use of **lighter colors** in their plants expressed their belief that they had improved the quality of production. The increase in seeing comfort—particularly in improved visibility—was declared to be the strongest reason. Fig. 36 shows the effect of improved lighting and color in the erection shops of one company as compared with the entire plant.

Factors of Good Illumination. Good illumination is made up of more than simply a proper level or quantity of illumination. Proper quality, which includes the color of light, its direction, diffusion, steadiness, and absence of glare, is important as well as proper quantity. Consideration of the many factors involved in good illumination is a complex problem; hence, lighting installations should be designed by competent illuminating engineers.

These factors have been defined and described (Benjamin Electric Mfg. Co.) as follows:

1. **Quantity.** The term "quantity of light" refers to the amount of light which produces the brightness of the task and the surroundings. The minimum quantity of light for seeing efficiently varies greatly with the different kinds of work.
2. **Quality.** The factors involved include amount of glare contrast, diffusion, distribution, direction, color, and brightness. The quality of the light is extremely important because moderate differences are not easily detected. However, the resulting conditions often result in a material loss of seeing efficiency and undue fatigue.
   a. Glare. Any brightness within field of vision which causes discomfort, annoyance, interference with vision, or high fatigue.
   b. Time. The duration of time over which a person is subjected to a glaring condition is a factor. Glare which is not particularly objectionable over short intermittent periods may become extremely trying to a worker over an 8-hr. period.
   c. Contrast.
   d. Shadow.
3. **Diffusion, Shadow, Distribution.** The light source and the type of lighting equipment determine the duration and the amount of diffusion or concentration of light provided. High specular reflecting surfaces require highly diffused light. Difficult-to-see, minute objects may require high concentration of light without regard to its specular quality.
   Distribution refers to the amount of light provided to the various parts of the entire working area. Even distribution permits flexibility and rearrangement of equipment, elimination of dangerous light and dark areas and spotty lighting.
4. **Color.** While variations in the color of light have little or no effect on visual acuity, there are certain operations involving color discrimination where the color of the light is a tremendously important factor.

Quantity of Light. Quantity of light supplied from whatever the source, either natural or artificial, should be determined by the work to be done. In general, the more trying the seeing task and the higher the degree of accuracy or fineness of detail required, the greater should be the illumination. Investigations in field and laboratory have proved that as the illumination on the task is increased, the ease and speed with which the task can be accomplished are increased. These tests have not yet established an upper limit, but the harmful effects of low foot-candle values are well known.

A condensed table of recommended values of general illumination is given in Fig. 37 (General Electric Co.).

DAYLIGHT LIGHTING. Good practice in daylight lighting now requires a minimum intensity of 20 foot-candles on the working plane and a uniform distribution of light. Consequently, window and roof lighting should be designed with this value as a base. It should be noted that the 20 foot-candles is a minimum which should be obtained when the sun is completely hidden and with 6 months' dirt on the windows. In general, single-story industrial buildings should have a window area of at least 30 percent of the floor area. No maximum limit for good seeing has yet been found.

Daylight Through Side Windows. If light comes from the side only, daylight of 10 foot-candles or more will be transmitted into the interior of a normal building for a distance equal to about twice the height of the windows. If light comes from two sides, daylight of 10 foot-candles or more will be transmitted into the

Minimum Foot-Candles in Service
(On Task or 30 in. Above Floor)

Most difficult seeing tasks: finest precision work involving finest detail, poor contrasts, long periods of time (such as extra-fine assembly, precision grading, extra-fine finishing)	100 foot-candles or more
Very difficult seeing tasks: precision work involving fine detail, fair contrasts, long periods of time (such as fine assembly, high-speed work, fine finishing)	100 foot-candles
Difficult and critical seeing tasks: prolonged work involving fine detail, moderate contrasts, long periods of time (such as ordinary bench work and assembly, machine shop work, finishing of medium-to-fine parts, office work)	50 foot-candles
Ordinary seeing tasks: involving moderately fine detail, normal contrasts, intermittent periods of time (such as automatic machine operation, rough grading, garage work areas, switchboards, continuous processes, conference and file rooms)	30 foot-candles
Casual seeing tasks (such as forge and welding shops, stairways, reception rooms, washrooms and other service areas, active storage)	10 foot-candles
Rough seeing tasks (such as hallways, corridors, passageways, inactive storage)	5 foot-candles

Fig. 37. Recommended levels of general illumination.

building from each side for a distance equal to about three times the height of the windows. This fact limits to about 100 ft. the width of buildings dependent upon side windows for illumination. Curves of **daylight intensity distribution** in one-story buildings with sidewall windows are shown in Fig. 38.

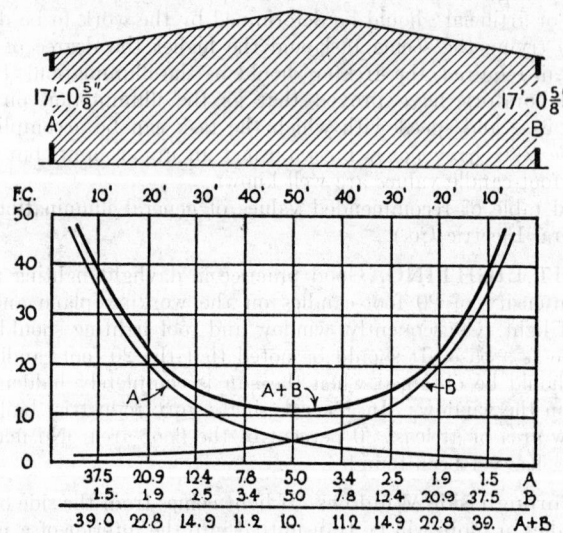

F.C.: Foot-candles

Fig. 38. Curves of illumination intensity from side windows.

Daylight Through Side and Monitor Windows. Monitors with vertical windows provide more light than comes from side windows alone. Monitors with sloping windows are next best. Skylights are least efficient. As a general rule, the best daylighting can be secured through a monitor with vertical windows designed with a monitor width equal to one-half the width of the building. Usually the width of a monitor should not be less than twice the height of its windows. Conversely, the height of a monitor should not be more than half its width

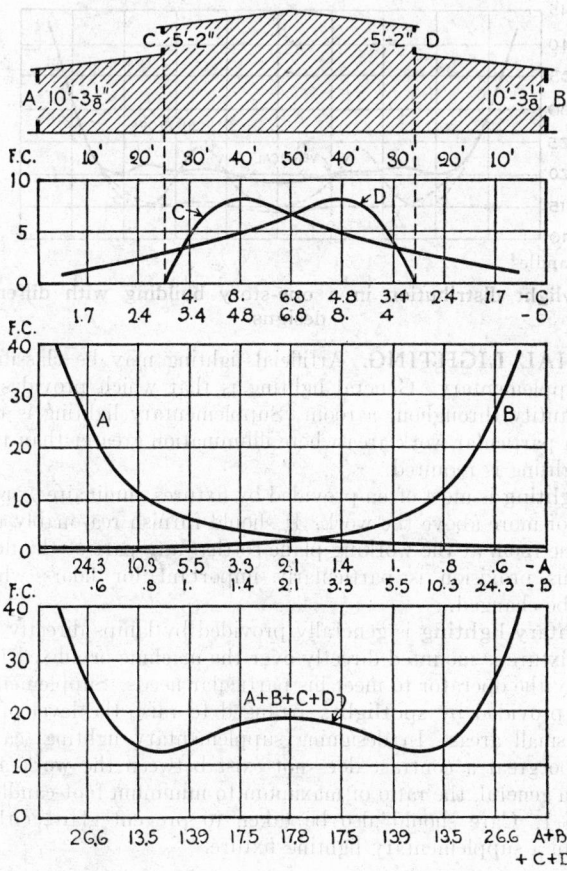

F.C.: Foot-candles

Fig. 39. Curves of illumination intensity showing effect of monitor windows.

Increasing the height of a monitor, whether it be wide or narrow, increases minimum illumination faster than it does maximum and thus helps to secure uniformity. Occasionally, sloping glass in a wide monitor helps to increase daylight at points of minimum illumination. Exceptionally uniform distribution of light can be obtained with a **sawtooth roof** facing north. The height of windows in sawtooth construction should be at least one-third the span. Curves of daylight distribution in a one-story building with two sidewall windows and monitor windows are shown in Fig. 39, and similar curves illustrating the effect of different monitor designs are shown in Fig. 40.

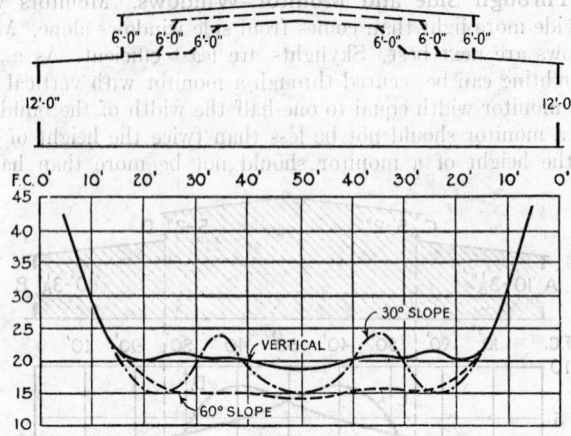

F.C.: Foot-candles

Fig. 40. Daylight distribution in a one-story building with different monitor designs.

ARTIFICIAL LIGHTING. Artificial lighting may be classified as either general or supplementary. General lighting is that which provides the base or minimum quantity throughout a room. Supplementary lighting is that which is provided on a particular work area where illumination greater than that provided by general lighting is required.

General lighting is most often provided by fixtures, luminaires, or grid systems placed 10 ft. or more above the work. It should furnish reasonably uniform light throughout the room at the working plane so that any part of the floor area may be used. This provision is particularly important for floors where machine layouts may be changed.

Supplementary lighting is generally provided by lamps directly at the workplaces. The fixture is mounted directly over the machine or affixed to an arm for adjustment by the operator to meet his particular needs. Supplementary lighting may also be provided by **spotlights** arranged to raise the level of illumination on specified small areas. In designing supplementary lighting, care should be taken that too great a contrast does not exist between the work area and surroundings. In general, the ratio of maximum to minimum foot-candles should not exceed 10 to 1. Care should also be taken to prevent glare, either direct or reflected, from a supplementary lighting fixture.

Classification	Approximate Distribution of Luminaire Output	
	Upward Percent	Downward Percent
Direct	0– 10	90–100
Semi-direct	10– 40	60– 90
General diffuse	40– 60	40– 60
Semi-indirect	60– 90	10– 40
Indirect	90–100	0– 10

Fig. 41. Distribution of light under different lighting systems.

GENERAL LIGHTING SYSTEMS. General lighting systems may be classified into the groups listed in Fig. 41, according to the amount of light distributed up or down from the luminaire.

SOURCES OF ARTIFICIAL LIGHT. Fig. 42 (Benjamin Electric Mfg. Co.) provides a quick picture of the characteristics and applications of the three most common light sources available for industrial lighting. Modern practice is more and more combining the use of these light sources in various arrangements when special lighting problems warrant such combination.

Light Source	Applications	Special Characteristics
Fluorescent	In all classes of plants, at low and medium mounting heights; in large assembly plants at high mounting. Also used for supplementary lighting at benches and machines.	Relatively low brightness, high efficiency, choice of color, lack of heat, offer possibility of increasing illumination without a complete wiring job being necessary. Relatively large number of lamps required to get the desired foot-candle level.
Mercury	At medium to high mounting heights.	Blue-green color combines well with yellow-orange of filament lamps to give a cool appearance. Lowest cost of lighting on over-all basis. Must be shielded more than fluorescent to keep glare within tolerable limits. Higher brightness means higher reflected glare from shiny surfaces.
Incandescent	In all classes of plants, at low, medium, or high mounting heights. Used alone or in combination with mercury. Also used for supplementary lighting.	Smallest investment cost. Easily installed. Flexibility in size, layout, and operation. High brightness of source requires adequate shielding.

Fig. 42. Characteristics and applications of the three most common light sources.

Fluorescent Lighting. Fluorescent lighting is a method of obtaining visible light from fluorescent coatings known as phosphors. The **phosphors** have the property of converting to visible light the short wave length radiant energy of a gaseous discharge. This method is in contrast to incandescent lighting, in which an element is heated to a point where it gives off visible light. The principal drawbacks to the use of fluorescent lights are:

1. First cost, which is higher than for incandescent lamps.
2. Shortened life by repeated starts.
3. Stroboscopic effect from a one-lamp unit may be objectionable if relatively fast movement is to be illuminated.
4. The power factor of a single-lamp unit is approximately 60 percent but can be improved by condensers of appropriate size across the usual type of reactor control. Most modern fluorescent fixtures are of a type of high **power factor,** as high as 90 percent.

Mercury Vapor Lamps. For general illumination, the mercury vapor lamp has often been used for industrial lighting. It is an electric discharge lamp producing spectral lines characteristic of mercury vapor in the yellow-green area, a region of high response for the human eye and thus one of high luminous efficiency. Since mercury vapor light approaches a **monochromatic** light, some objection to its use results. It is commonly used in combination with incandescent lighting, about equal amounts of each being satisfactory to overcome objection to the yellow-green monochromatic light.

By combining the yellow-orange light of filament lamps with yellow-green mercury light in twin-luminaires, a cool, white light is achieved. There is also available a new, color-corrected mercury lamp.

ILLUMINATION DESIGN DATA FOR INTERIORS. The design of any lighting installation is dependent on many factors, among which is the provision of the proper quantity of illumination. This is accomplished by first analyzing the seeing task and its particular illumination requirements. It then becomes possible to select the most desirable type of lighting equipment and mathematically to design the installation.

According to the Illumination Design Data Bulletin (Westinghouse Electric Corp.), the quantity of light for an area may be calculated by two methods:

1. **The lumen method** (developed by Harris-Anderson) which provides average foot-candle values by the use of a relatively simple formula. Each of the factors employed in the formula must be properly evaluated in order to obtain accurate results.
2. **The point-by-point method** which, while more accurate, involves more complex computations. It is ordinarily used only when a relatively few direct-type luminaires are employed and, therefore, it will not be discussed here.

Lumen Method of Calculation. In solving a general lighting problem, six key steps should be taken (Illumination Design Data Bulletin, Westinghouse Electric Corp.):

1. **Determine the required level of illumination.** Handbooks and manuals list the more common seeing tasks and the quantity of illumination needed for each. They usually represent minimum values by good present-day practice, while the ultimate in seeing comfort might be many times in excess of these.

2. **Select the lighting system and luminaires.** Generally, offices are best lighted by a fairly high intensity indirect or semi-indirect system. Manufacturing areas usually employ a direct system. Choice as to just which of the lighting systems and luminaires best suit a given application will depend upon the seeing tasks to be performed and the characteristics of the area to be illuminated. The luminaire chosen should be satisfactory with respect to the following criteria:

   a. It should cause no annoyance from direct glare.
   b. It should minimize reflected glare that might result from polished surfaces present in the working area.
   c. It should provide a sufficient degree of diffusion to avoid shadows too harsh for the nature of the seeing task to be done.
   d. It should provide the necessary illumination on vertical and oblique surfaces.
   e. It should harmonize decoratively and architecturally with its surroundings.

3. **Determine the coefficient of utilization.** This is the ratio of the lumens reaching the working plane to the total lumens generated by the lamps. It is a factor that takes into account the efficiency and distribution of the luminaire, its

mounting height, the room proportions, and the reflection factors of walls and ceiling. (See Fig. 43.)

Color	Average Reflection Factor	Color	Average Reflection Factor
White	.88	Medium	
		Blue-green	.54
Very Light		Yellow	.65
Blue-green	.76	Buff	.63
Cream	.81	Gray	.61
Blue	.65		
Buff	.76	Dark	
Gray	.83	Blue	.08
		Yellow	.50
Light		Brown	.10
Blue-green	.72	Gray	.25
Cream	.79	Green	.07
Blue	.55	Black	.03
Buff	.70		
Gray	.73	Wood Finishes	
		Maple	.42
		Walnut	.16
		Mahogany	.12

Fig. 43. Diffuse reflection factors.

4. **Estimate the maintenance factor.** The in-service foot-candles which will be produced by any lighting installations are determined by a careful analysis of the conditions under which the system will operate. Up to this point in the problem careful consideration has been given to the determination of proper values of illumination, the system and luminaire to be used, the dimensions and architecture of the area, the reflection factors of walls and ceiling, and the resulting coefficient of utilization. All of this effort at accuracy is wasted if a haphazard factor for maintenance is applied to attain the final in-service foot-candle value.

In the operation of any lighting system there are three principal variables which affect the amount of light obtained from the system:

a. Loss in light output of the lamp. The average lumen output throughout the life of a lamp is 10 to 25 percent lower than the initial value. The amount of this depreciation depends on the size and type of lamp.

b. Loss due to accumulated dirt on the reflecting or transmitting surfaces of the luminaire and on the lamps themselves.

c. Loss of reflected light through accumulation of dirt on walls and ceilings. This loss was considered in selecting the coefficient of utilization.

In the accompanying calculations maintenance factors covering lamps and luminaires have been suggested for three conditions:

a. **Good maintenance factor,** where the atmospheric conditions are good, luminaires are cleaned frequently, and lamps are replaced systematically.

b. **Medium maintenance factor,** where less clean atmospheric conditions exist luminaire cleaning is fair, and lamps are replaced only after burnout.

c. **Poor maintenance factor,** where the atmosphere is quite dirty and equipment is poorly maintained.

The designer must exercise careful judgment both as to the existing and anticipated conditions to arrive at a practical maintenance factor.

Luminaire	Ceiling	75%			50%			30%	
	Walls	50%	30%	10%	50%	30%	10%	30%	10%
	Room Index	Coefficient of Utilization							
MF G -.75 M -.65 ↕79 P -.55	J	.37	.31	.27	.36	.31	.27	.31	.27
	I	.45	.41	.38	.45	.40	.37	.40	.37
	H	.49	.45	.42	.49	.45	.42	.45	.42
	G	.53	.49	.46	.53	.49	.46	.48	.46
	F	.56	.53	.49	.55	.52	.49	.51	.49
	E	.61	.58	.55	.60	.57	.55	.56	.55
1 Direct—RLM Dome Reflector	D	.66	.63	.60	.64	.62	.60	.61	.60
	C	.67	.65	.62	.66	.64	.62	.63	.61
MS=1.0×MH	B	.71	.68	.66	.69	.67	.65	.66	.64
	A	.72	.70	.67	.71	.68	.67	.67	.66
MF G -.75 M -.65 ↕70 P -.55	J	.35	.31	.28	.34	.31	.28	.30	.28
	I	.43	.39	.37	.42	.39	.37	.39	.37
	H	.46	.44	.42	.46	.44	.42	.43	.42
	G	.50	.47	.45	.49	.47	.45	.46	.45
	F	.53	.50	.47	.51	.49	.47	.49	.47
	E	.56	.54	.51	.56	.54	.51	.53	.51
2 Direct—RLM Deep Bowl Reflector	D	.61	.58	.56	.59	.57	.56	.56	.56
	C	.62	.60	.57	.61	.58	.57	.58	.56
MS=1.0×MH	B	.64	.62	.61	.63	.61	.60	.60	.59
	A	.65	.63	.61	.64	.62	.61	.61	.60
MF G -.75 M -.60 ↕75 P -.40	J	.43	.40	.39	.42	.40	.39	.40	.38
	I	.51	.50	.49	.50	.49	.48	.49	.46
	H	.55	.54	.53	.54	.53	.52	.53	.52
	G	.59	.58	.57	.58	.56	.55	.56	.55
	F	.61	.60	.58	.59	.58	.58	.58	.57
	E	.64	.63	.62	.63	.62	.61	.61	.60
3 Direct—High Bay, Narrow Spread	D	.68	.65	.64	.66	.65	.64	.64	.63
	C	.69	.67	.65	.67	.66	.64	.64	.64
MS=.6×MH	B	.70	.68	.67	.68	.67	.66	.66	.65
	A	.71	.70	.68	.69	.67	.67	.67	.66
MF G -.75 M -.65 ↕75 P -.50	J	.40	.36	.34	.39	.36	.34	.36	.33
	I	.48	.45	.43	.47	.44	.43	.44	.42
	H	.52	.50	.48	.51	.49	.47	.49	.47
	G	.55	.53	.52	.55	.52	.51	.52	.51
	F	.58	.56	.53	.56	.55	.53	.55	.53
	E	.62	.60	.58	.61	.59	.57	.58	.57
4 Direct—High Bay, Medium or	D	.66	.63	.61	.64	.62	.61	.62	.61
	C	.67	.65	.62	.66	.64	.62	.63	.62
Wide Spread, MS=1.0×MH	B	.69	.67	.66	.67	.65	.64	.65	.64
	A	.70	.68	.67	.69	.67	.65	.66	.64

MF = Maintenance factor (G = good, M = medium, P = poor)
MS = Maximum spacing
MH = Mounting height

Fig. 44. Coefficient of utilization (continued on next page).

5. Calculate number of lamps and luminaires required. The foot-candles, or lumens per square feet reaching the working plane, are equal to the total lumens generated by the lamps, multiplied by the coefficient of utilization and the maintenance factor, and divided by the area of the room in square feet.

$$\text{Foot-candles} = \frac{\text{lumens per lamp} \times \text{number of lamps} \times \text{coefficient of utilization} \times \text{maintenance factor}}{\text{area}}$$

Luminaire	Ceiling	75%			50%			30%	
	Walls	50%	30%	10%	50%	30%	10%	30%	10%
	Room Index	Coefficient of Utilization							
5 MF G-.80 M-.72 P-.65 to 70 — Direct—Heavy Duty, Narrow Spread MS=.5×MH Medium Spread MS=.8×MH	J	.40	.38	.36	.39	.38	.36	.38	.36
	I	.48	.46	.45	.47	.46	.45	.45	.43
	H	.52	.51	.50	.51	.50	.49	.50	.48
	G	.55	.54	.53	.54	.53	.52	.53	.51
	F	.57	.56	.55	.56	.55	.54	.55	.53
	E	.60	.59	.58	.59	.58	.57	.57	.56
	D	.64	.61	.60	.62	.60	.59	.60	.59
	C	.64	.63	.61	.63	.62	.60	.60	.60
	B	.65	.64	.63	.64	.63	.62	.62	.61
	A	.66	.65	.64	.64	.63	.62	.62	.62
6 MF G-.80 M-.72 P-.65 to 70 — Direct—Heavy Duty, Wide Spread, MS=1.1×MH	J	.37	.34	.31	.36	.34	.31	.34	.31
	I	.45	.42	.41	.44	.41	.40	.41	.39
	H	.48	.46	.45	.49	.45	.44	.45	.44
	G	.52	.50	.48	.51	.49	.48	.49	.48
	F	.55	.52	.51	.50	.51	.50	.51	.50
	E	.57	.56	.54	.57	.55	.53	.55	.53
	D	.62	.59	.57	.60	.58	.57	.57	.57
	C	.63	.61	.58	.62	.59	.58	.59	.57
	B	.64	.62	.61	.63	.61	.60	.60	.59
	A	.66	.64	.62	.64	.62	.61	.62	.60
7 MF G-.70 M-.60 P-.45 5 to 58 — Direct—RLM Glassteel Diffuser MS=1.0×MH	J	.27	.23	.20	.26	.23	.20	.22	.20
	I	.34	.30	.28	.33	.29	.27	.29	.27
	H	.37	.34	.31	.36	.33	.31	.32	.30
	G	.40	.37	.34	.39	.36	.34	.35	.33
	F	.42	.39	.37	.40	.38	.36	.37	.36
	E	.46	.43	.41	.45	.42	.40	.41	.40
	D	.49	.47	.44	.48	.46	.44	.44	.43
	C	.51	.49	.46	.49	.47	.46	.46	.44
	B	.53	.51	.49	.51	.49	.48	.48	.47
	A	.54	.53	.51	.53	.51	.49	.49	.48
8 MF G-.60 M-.50 P-.40 to 67 — Direct—RLM Silvered Bowl Diffuser, MS=.8×MH	J	.38	.36	.35	.38	.36	.35	.36	.35
	I	.46	.45	.44	.45	.44	.43	.44	.42
	H	.49	.49	.48	.49	.48	.47	.48	.47
	G	.53	.52	.51	.52	.51	.50	.51	.49
	F	.55	.54	.53	.53	.53	.52	.53	.51
	E	.57	.57	.56	.57	.56	.55	.55	.54
	D	.61	.59	.58	.59	.58	.57	.57	.56
	C	.62	.61	.59	.60	.59	.58	.58	.57
	B	.63	.62	.61	.61	.60	.59	.59	.58
	A	.64	.63	.62	.62	.61	.60	.60	.59

Fig. 44. (Continued on next page.)

$$\text{Number of lamps} = \frac{\text{foot-candles} \times \text{area}}{\text{lumens per lamp} \times \text{coefficient of utilization} \times \text{maintenance factor}}$$

$$\text{Number of luminaires} = \frac{\text{number of lamps}}{\text{lamps per luminaire}}$$

$$\text{Total lumens} = \frac{\text{foot-candles} \times \text{area}}{\text{coefficient of utilization} \times \text{maintenance factor}}$$

$$\text{Area per luminaire} = \frac{\text{lamps per luminaire} \times \text{lumens per lamp} \times \text{coefficient of utilization} \times \text{maintenance factor}}{\text{foot-candles}}$$

Luminaire	Room Index	75%			50%			30%	
	Walls →	50%	30%	10%	50%	30%	10%	30%	10%
		Coefficient of Utilization							
9 Direct—Vapor Tight, Wide Spread, MS=1.0×MH (MF G-.75 M-.65 P-.55, 0/65)	J	.31	.26	.23	.30	.26	.23	.26	.23
	I	.38	.34	.31	.37	.33	.31	.33	.31
	H	.41	.38	.34	.41	.38	.34	.37	.34
	G	.45	.41	.39	.44	.41	.39	.40	.39
	F	.47	.44	.41	.46	.43	.41	.43	.41
	E	.51	.48	.46	.50	.48	.46	.47	.46
	D	.55	.52	.50	.54	.52	.50	.51	.50
	C	.56	.54	.52	.55	.53	.52	.52	.51
	B	.59	.57	.55	.58	.56	.54	.55	.54
	A	.60	.58	.56	.59	.57	.56	.56	.55
10 Direct—Prismatic Lens, Medium Spread, MS=.8×MH (MF G-.70 M-.60 P-.50, 0/53)	J	.25	.22	.20	.24	.22	.20	.22	.20
	I	.31	.28	.26	.29	.28	.26	.28	.26
	H	.34	.31	.29	.32	.31	.29	.30	.28
	G	.36	.33	.32	.34	.33	.31	.32	.30
	F	.38	.35	.34	.36	.34	.33	.34	.32
	E	.40	.39	.38	.39	.37	.36	.37	.35
	D	.43	.41	.40	.42	.40	.39	.39	.38
	C	.45	.43	.42	.44	.41	.40	.40	.40
	B	.48	.45	.44	.47	.43	.42	.42	.41
	A	.50	.47	.46	.48	.46	.45	.45	.44
11 Direct—PAR-38, 150-W Shielded to 45°, Total lamp lumens —1850, MS=.5×MH (MF-.75, 0/62)	J	.52	.49	.47	.51	.49	.47	.48	.47
	I	.55	.53	.51	.54	.52	.51	.51	.50
	H	.57	.55	.53	.56	.54	.53	.53	.53
	G	.58	.57	.55	.57	.56	.55	.55	.54
	F	.59	.58	.57	.58	.57	.56	.56	.56
	E	.61	.60	.59	.60	.59	.58	.58	.57
	D	.63	.62	.61	.61	.61	.60	.60	.59
	C	.64	.64	.63	.63	.63	.62	.62	.61
	B	.65	.65	.64	.64	.64	.63	.63	.62
	A	.66	.66	.65	.65	.65	.64	.64	.63
12 Direct—RLM, 2—40 Watt Lamps MS=1.0×MH (MF G-.65 M-.55 P-.45, 0/79)	J	.38	.32	.28	.37	.32	.28	.31	.28
	I	.47	.42	.39	.46	.41	.38	.40	.37
	H	.51	.47	.44	.50	.47	.43	.46	.43
	G	.55	.51	.48	.54	.51	.47	.50	.47
	F	.58	.54	.51	.57	.53	.51	.52	.50
	E	.63	.60	.57	.62	.59	.56	.58	.55
	D	.68	.64	.61	.66	.64	.61	.63	.60
	C	.70	.67	.63	.68	.65	.64	.64	.62
	B	.73	.70	.68	.71	.68	.67	.67	.66
	A	.74	.72	.70	.72	.70	.68	.69	.67

Fig. 44. (Continued on next page.)

6. **Determine the location of the luminaires.** For general lighting, luminaires are usually located symmetrically in each bay or pair of bays, although this practice is often modified by the position of the previous outlets, the general architecture of the area, the type of luminaire, or the nature and location of the seeing tasks to be performed. Where working positions are fixed, it is sometimes desirable to position the luminaires with reference to the particular areas where high intensities are necessary. In offices or other areas where work is performed throughout the room, a high degree of uniformity is desirable. In such cases the **spacing** from the wall is normally one-half the distance between luminaires. If work areas are next to the walls, one-third the luminaire spacing is customary.

To provide even distribution of illumination for an area it is necessary to observe certain limitations of **spacing-to-mounting-height ratios.** Such values

Luminaire	Ceiling	75%			50%			30%	
	Walls	50%	30%	10%	50%	30%	10%	30%	10%
	Room Index	Coefficient of Utilization							
13 Direct—RLM, 3—40 Watt Lamps MS=1.0×MH MF G .65 M .55 P .45 to 72	J	.34	.29	.25	.33	.29	.25	.28	.25
	I	.42	.38	.35	.41	.37	.34	.37	.34
	H	.46	.42	.39	.44	.42	.39	.41	.39
	G	.50	.46	.43	.48	.45	.41	.44	.41
	F	.53	.49	.46	.51	.47	.44	.47	.44
	E	.57	.54	.51	.56	.52	.50	.52	.50
	D	.61	.58	.55	.59	.56	.54	.56	.54
	C	.63	.60	.57	.61	.58	.56	.58	.56
	B	.66	.64	.61	.64	.60	.59	.60	.59
	A	.67	.65	.62	.66	.62	.61	.62	.60
14 Direct—RLM, 2—85 Watt Lamps MS=1.0×MH MF G .60 M .50 P .45 to 71	J	.33	.28	.25	.33	.28	.25	.28	.25
	I	.41	.37	.34	.40	.36	.33	.36	.33
	H	.45	.41	.38	.44	.41	.38	.40	.38
	G	.48	.45	.42	.48	.45	.42	.43	.42
	F	.51	.48	.45	.50	.47	.45	.46	.45
	E	.55	.53	.50	.55	.52	.50	.51	.50
	D	.60	.57	.54	.58	.56	.54	.55	.54
	C	.61	.59	.56	.60	.57	.56	.57	.55
	B	.64	.62	.60	.62	.60	.59	.60	.58
	A	.65	.63	.61	.64	.62	.60	.61	.60
15 Direct—Dust and Vapor Tight MS=1.0×MH MF G .70 M .65 P .55 to 60	J	.29	.26	.23	.28	.26	.23	.25	.23
	I	.35	.32	.31	.35	.32	.30	.32	.30
	H	.38	.36	.34	.38	.36	.34	.35	.34
	G	.41	.39	.37	.41	.39	.37	.38	.37
	F	.44	.41	.39	.42	.41	.39	.40	.39
	E	.46	.45	.42	.46	.44	.42	.44	.42
	D	.50	.48	.46	.49	.47	.46	.46	.46
	C	.51	.49	.47	.50	.48	.47	.48	.46
	B	.53	.51	.50	.52	.50	.49	.49	.49
	A	.54	.52	.50	.53	.51	.50	.50	.49
16 Direct—3 KW Mercury MS=1.0×MH MF G .70 M .60 P .50 to 80	J	.38	.32	.28	.37	.32	.28	.31	.28
	I	.47	.42	.39	.46	.41	.38	.41	.38
	H	.51	.47	.43	.50	.47	.43	.46	.43
	G	.55	.51	.47	.54	.51	.47	.49	.47
	F	.58	.54	.51	.56	.53	.51	.52	.51
	E	.63	.59	.56	.62	.59	.56	.58	.56
	D	.67	.64	.61	.66	.63	.61	.63	.61
	C	.69	.67	.64	.67	.65	.63	.64	.63
	B	.72	.70	.67	.71	.68	.67	.67	.66
	A	.74	.71	.69	.72	.70	.68	.69	.67

Fig. 44. (Concluded.)

are indicated for certain types of luminaires in the sample Coefficient of Utilization and Room Index tables, Figs. 44 and 45 (Westinghouse Electric Corp.). The spacings shown are maximums, and closer spacings may be necessary in order to obtain the required levels of illumination. Industrial high-bay units and one- or two-lamp fluorescent luminaires, in particular, commonly require closer spacings than those indicated in the table. Where a large number of fluorescent luminaires is to be installed, **continuous-row mounting** has the advantage of simplifying the wiring and reducing the apparent number of sources.

Careful consideration should be given to the **ceiling brightness** which may result when high-wattage lamps are used in luminaires with short suspension hangers. This is especially true with indirect luminaires in low-ceiling areas.

Table columns — Mounting Height Above Floor (Feet): 7, 8, 9, 10, 11, 12, 13, 15, 17, 19, 23, 27

Room Width (Feet)	Room Length (Feet)	7	8	9	10	11	12	13	15	17	19	23	27
		Direct, Semidirect, and General Diffuse Lighting — Mounting Height Above Floor (Feet)										
8	10	H	I	I	J		J						
	12	G	I	I	J	J	J	J					
	14	G	H	I	I	J	J	J					
	16	G	H	I	I	J	J	J					
	18	G	H	I	J	J	J	J	J				
	20	F	H	H	I	J	J	J	J				
	24	F	G	H	I		J	J	J	J			
	30	F	G	H	I	I	J	J	J	J			
	35	F	G	G	H	I	I	J	J	J	J		
	40	E	F	G	H	I	I	J	J	J	J		
	50	E	F	G	H	H	I	I	J	J	J		
10	10	G	H	I	I	J	J	J	J				
	12	G	H	I	I	J	J	J	J				
	14	F	G	H	I	I	J	J	J				
	16	F	G	H	I	I	J	J	J				
	18	F	G	H	I	I	J	J	J				
	20	F	G	G	H	I	I	J	J	J			
	24	F	G	G	H	I	I	J	J	J			
	30	E	F	G	H	H	I	I	J	J	J		
	35	E	F	G	H	H	I	I	J	J	J		
	40	E	F	F	G	H	H	I	I	J	J		
	50	E	F	F	G	H	H	I	I	J	J	J	
	60	E	E	F	G	G	H	I	I	J	J	J	
	70	E	E	F	G	G	H	H	I	I	J	J	
12	12	G	G	H	I	I	J	J	J				
	14	F	G	H	I	I	I	J	J				
	16	F	G	H	I	I	I	J	J				
	18	F	F	G	H	I	I	J	J	J			
	20	F	F	G	H	I	I	J	J	J			
	24	E	F	G	H	H	I	I	J	J			
	30	E	F	F	G	H	H	I	I	J	J		
	35	E	E	F	G	H	H	I	I	J	J		
	40	E	E	F	G	G	H	H	I	J	J		
	50	E	E	F	F	G	G	H	I	I	J	J	
	60	E	E	F	F	G	G	H	I	I	J	J	J
	70	E	E	E	F	F	G	G	H	I	I	J	J
	80	E	E	E	F	F	G	G	H	I	I	J	J
	100	E	E	F	F	F	G	G	H	I	I	J	J
14	14	F	F	G	H	I	I	J	J	J			
	16	E	F	G	H	H	I	I	J	J			
	18	E	F	G	H	H	I	I	J	J			
	20	E	F	F	G	H	I	I	J	J	J		
	24	E	E	F	G	H	H	I	I	J	J		
	30	D	E	F	G	G	H	I	I	J	J		
	35	D	E	F	F	G	H	H	I	J	J	J	
	40	D	E	E	F	G	H	H	I	J	J	J	
	50	D	D	E	F	F	G	H	I	I	J	J	J
	60	D	D	E	F	F	G	G	H	I	I	J	J
	70	D	D	E	E	F	F	G	H	I	I	J	J
	80	D	D	E	E	F	F	G	H	I	I	J	J
	100	D	D	E	E	F	F	F	G	I	I	J	J
16	16	E	F	G	G	H	I	I	J	J	J		
	18	E	F	F	G	H	H	I	J	J	J		
	20	E	F	F	G	H	H	I	I	J	J		
	24	D	E	F	G	G	H	I	I	J	J		
	30	D	E	F	F	G	H	H	I	J	J	J	
	35	D	E	F	F	G	G	H	I	I	J	J	
	40	D	D	E	F	F	G	H	I	I	J	J	J
	50	D	D	E	F	F	G	G	H	I	J	J	J
	60	D	D	E	E	F	G	G	H	I	I	J	J
	70	D	D	E	E	F	F	G	H	I	I	J	J
	80	D	E	E	E	F	F	G	H	H	I	I	J
	100	D	E	E	E	E	F	F	G	H	I	I	J
18	18	E	E	F	G	G	H	H	I	I	J	J	
	20	D	E	F	G	G	H	H	I	I	J	J	
	24	D	E	F	F	G	H	H	I	I	J	J	
	30	D	D	E	F	F	G	H	H	I	J	J	
	35	C	D	E	F	F	G	G	H	I	J	J	
	40	C	D	E	F	F	G	G	H	I	J	J	
	50	C	D	E	E	F	F	G	H	I	I	J	
	60	C	D	E	E	F	F	G	H	I	I	J	
	70	C	C	D	E	E	F	G	G	H	I	J	
	80	C	C	D	E	E	F	F	G	H	I	J	
	100	C	C	D	E	E	F	F	G	H	I	I	
	120	C	C	D	E	E	F	F	G	H	H	I	
Room Width (Feet)	Room Length (Feet)	9	10½	12	13½	15	16½	18	21	24	27	33	39
		Ceiling Height Above Floor — Semi-indirect and Indirect Lighting										

Note: For dimensions greater than those shown in the table, the following procedure can be used: (1) Divide length and width by some common factor which reduces dimensions to values within limits of table;

Fig. 45. Room index table

Room Width (Feet)	Room Length (Feet)	Direct, Semidirect, and General Diffuse Lighting — Mounting Height Above Floor (Feet)												
		7	8	9	10	11	12	13	15	17	19	23	27	33
20	20	D	E	F	F	G	H	H	I	J	J	J		
	24	D	E	F	F	F	G	H	I	I	J	J	J	
	30	C	D	E	F	F	G	G	H	I	I	J	J	J
	35	C	D	E	E	F	G	G	H	I	I	J	J	
	40	C	D	D	E	E	F	F	F	H	I	I	J	J
	50	C	D	E	E	F	F	G	H	I	J	J	J	J
	60	C	D	D	E	E	F	F	G	H	I	J	J	J
	70	C	D	D	E	E	F	F	G	H	I	J	J	J
	80	C	D	D	D	E	E	F	F	G	H	I	J	J
	100	C	D	D	E	E	F	F	F	G	H	I	J	J
	120	C	D	D	E	E	E	F	F	G	H	I	I	J
	140	C	D	D	E	E	E	F	F	G	H	H	I	J
24	24	C	D	E	F	F	G	H	I	I	J	J	J	
	30	C	D	E	E	F	F	G	G	H	I	J	J	J
	35	C	C	D	E	E	F	F	G	H	I	J	J	J
	40	C	C	D	D	E	F	F	G	G	H	I	J	J
	50	C	C	D	E	E	F	F	G	H	I	J	J	J
	60	C	C	D	D	E	F	F	F	G	H	I	J	J
	70	C	C	D	D	E	F	F	F	G	H	I	I	J
	100	C	C	C	D	D	E	F	F	G	H	I	I	
	120	C	C	C	D	D	E	E	F	F	G	H	I	
	140	C	C	C	D	D	D	E	E	F	F	G	H	I
30	30	B	C	D	E	E	F	F	G	H	I	J	J	
	35	B	C	D	D	E	F	F	G	H	I	I	J	J
	40	B	C	C	D	D	E	F	F	G	H	I	I	J
	50	B	C	C	C	D	D	E	F	G	H	I	I	J
	60	B	C	C	C	D	D	E	F	F	G	H	I	J
	70	B	C	C	C	D	D	E	E	F	F	H	I	J
	80	B	C	C	C	C	D	D	E	F	F	H	I	J
	100	B	C	C	C	C	D	D	E	E	F	G	H	I
	120	B	C	C	C	C	D	D	E	E	F	G	H	I
	140	B	C	C	C	D	D	D	E	E	F	G	H	I
35	35	B	C	C	D	D	E	F	G	H	I	I	J	J
	40	B	B	C	C	D	E	E	F	G	H	I	I	J
	50	A	B	C	C	D	D	E	F	F	G	H	I	J
	60	A	B	C	C	C	D	D	E	F	F	H	I	J
	70	A	B	B	C	C	D	D	E	E	F	G	H	J
	80	A	B	B	C	C	C	D	E	E	F	G	H	I
	100	A	B	C	C	C	C	D	D	E	F	G	H	I
	120	A	B	B	C	C	C	D	D	E	E	F	G	I
	140	A	B	C	C	C	D	D	D	E	E	F	G	H
40	40	A	B	C	C	C	D	D	E	F	G	H	I	J
	50	A	B	B	C	C	D	D	E	F	F	G	H	I
	60	A	B	B	C	C	C	D	D	E	F	F	H	I
	70	A	B	B	C	C	C	D	D	E	E	F	H	I
	80	A	B	B	C	C	D	D	D	E	F	G	H	H
	100	A	B	B	C	C	C	C	D	D	E	F	G	H
	120	A	B	B	C	C	C	C	D	D	E	F	G	H
	140	A	B	B	C	C	C	C	D	D	E	F	G	H
50	50	A	A	B	B	C	C	D	D	E	E	F	G	H
	60	A	A	B	B	C	C	D	D	E	F	F	G	I
	70	A	A	B	B	C	C	D	D	E	F	F	G	H
	80	A	A	B	B	C	C	C	D	E	F	G	G	H
	100	A	A	B	B	C	C	C	D	D	E	F	G	G
	120	A	A	B	B	C	C	C	D	D	E	F	G	G
	140	A	A	B	B	C	C	C	D	D	E	E	F	G
	170	A	A	B	B	C	C	C	D	D	E	E	F	G
	200	A	A	B	B	C	C	C	D	D	E	E	F	G
60	60	A	A	A	B	B	C	C	C	D	E	E	F	H
	70	A	A	A	B	B	C	C	D	D	E	F	F	H
	80	A	A	A	A	B	B	C	C	D	E	F	F	H
	100	A	A	A	A	B	B	C	C	D	E	F	F	G
	120	A	A	A	A	B	B	C	C	D	D	E	F	G
	140	A	A	A	A	B	B	C	C	C	D	E	F	F
	170	A	A	A	A	A	B	B	C	C	D	E	F	F
	200	A	A	A	A	B	B	B	C	C	D	E	E	G
80	80	A	A	A	A	B	B	C	C	C	D	E	E	F
	140	A	A	A	A	A	B	B	B	C	C	D	E	F
	200	A	A	A	A	A	A	B	B	C	C	D	E	F
100	100	A	A	A	A	A	B	B	B	C	C	D	E	F
	150	A	A	A	A	A	A	B	B	B	C	C	D	E
	200	A	A	A	A	A	A	A	B	B	C	C	C	E
120	120	A	A	A	A	A	A	A	B	B	B	C	D	E
	160	A	A	A	A	A	A	A	A	B	B	C	C	D
	200	A	A	A	A	A	A	A	A	A	B	C	C	D
Room Width (Feet)	Room Length (Feet)	9	10½	12	13½	15	16½	18	21	24	27	33	39	48
		Ceiling Height Above Floor — Semi-indirect and Indirect Lighting												

(2) Subtract 3 ft. from mounting height (or ceiling height) and divide this dimension by the same factor employed in step 1; (3) add 3 ft. to scaled-down height dimension. Use this value and reduced length and width obtained in step 1 to select Room Index from table.

for use with Fig. 44.

EXTERIOR LIGHTING. Lighting of buildings and grounds at night is used for:

1. Illumination of dark passageways and driveways.
2. Exterior work such as platform loading and rush construction.
3. Protection from prowlers and saboteurs.
4. Advertising.

From the standpoint of protection, the work of the watchman is made easier and detection of an intruder more certain, and, in addition, the intruder is discouraged from trying to enter.

Supply lines to exterior lights should not be unsightly and also should be designed from the standpoint of safety. **Switches** should be available only to authorized persons, or they may be controlled automatically by time switch or photoelectric relays.

Use of Color in Industry

ADVANTAGES OF LIGHTER COLORS. The use of lighter and brighter colors in industry is becoming widespread. It has long been known that the darker colors formerly used on machinery and industrial equipment, and the dirt accumulating on interiors, are not conducive to good seeing. The object of using scientifically selected colors is to bring about clear, three-dimensional seeing instead of the dull, flat effect produced on the eyes by the drab or dark painting of equipment, ceilings, walls, and floors in the majority of present-day offices and factories (Brainerd and Massey, Illuminating Engineering Society). **Three-dimensional seeing** can accomplish three definite tasks:

1. Provide positive visibility with finishes having high reflection factors, by means of adequate contrast in hue.
2. Provide an over-all contrast which is not too harsh to prevent continuous, comfortable seeing.
3. Provide color sensation which is psychologically continuously pleasant and easy to live with.

The cumulative result of having all surfaces of high reflection value is to bring out a marked increase in light utilization. This improvement in many cases can be brought about and maintained to more than double the illumination, with no change of equipment and no increase in wattage of lamps.

COLOR-CONTRAST PAINTING. The following factors form the basis of improvements in illumination in plants and offices (Pittsburgh Color Dynamics, Pittsburgh Plate Glass Co.). **Eye fatigue** is caused by unnecessary travel of the eye over ill-defined areas, tension in holding the eye on work where the surrounding areas are of about the same color, and constant adjusting when changing from light surfaces to dark surfaces. **Focal colors** center the worker's attention on working points. **Receding colors** on surrounding machine parts cause these to drop back and relax the eye. A light green is suitable for most cases, but in certain cases (food or drug plants, etc.) white produces a more sanitary appearance. Double contrast between the work itself and the immediate work area is necessary for more accurate distinction. The **work area color** therefore must give satisfactory contrast with both materials and surrounding machine parts. In addition, cool colors offset the psychological effects of unavoidably high temperatures in workplaces, and warm colors similarly offset the effects of cold workplaces.

Walls, Floors, Aisles. Attention to machine painting must be accompanied by corresponding care regarding walls, columns, partitions, doors, work or tool cabinets, ceilings, roof trusses, overhead cranes or conveyors, piping, factory floors, aisles, and other objects or areas within the employees' field of vision. **Walls, columns,** etc., should have approximately the same general tone of color (not necessarily the same color) as machines and work areas. A light green is good for walls within the employees' vision as they glance up from their work, and brighter colors, such as yellow, for other walls to gain the benefit of simulated sunlight. If work in a department is done on colored materials, the machines and walls should be painted in the complementary color to prevent the image of the work from appearing momentarily in the workers' vision when they look up. When there are numerous roof trusses or wires, pipes, etc., overhead, they should be made to recede into the background by proper painting. If the **ceiling** has little reflection value, a lighter blue can be used to produce the blending effect. For indirect lighting, of course, colors with a high reflecting value are necessary.

Floors should be painted in a light color with good reflectivity. Where good visibility is necessary below as well as above work, as for example in many assembly operations done on the floor, light gray is often used for the floor. **Tops of benches** should be light for bench assembly and related work. Even where it is not necessary to have light floors under and around equipment, it is best to paint the **aisles** light and to band them along each side to form traffic lanes, in a distinctive, bright color, perhaps orange, both to mark them off as traffic limits for the safety of workers at machines, and to keep them clear of materials, finished products, tools, boxes, benches, and other objects. Platforms, ladders, steps, large assembly jigs, and other **operations auxiliaries,** such as in aircraft plants, should be painted a distinctive bright color to mark them off from the surroundings and for safety in use.

Moving Equipment. Industrial trucks, cranes, conveyors, etc., are a source of accident hazards which can be cut down by proper distinctive painting. **Trucks** may be painted yellow all around, including any side projection, because this color has high visibility. **Boxes, racks,** etc., used for moving work from place to place may be painted green to distinguish them from trucks. If the insides of such receptacles are painted in light colors, it is easier to see how much material they contain. **Overhead cranes and crane hooks** painted yellow (sometimes striped in places with black) have high visibility and thus are noticed as they move over areas in which employees are operating. There is less likelihood of accidents from crane operation when this practice is adopted. Colors should preferably be worked into combinations with the aid of expert advice from qualified engineers.

The **paints and enamels** on the market for equipment painting produce a quick-drying surface with a durable and cleanable finish. They are tough and resistant to softening from oil or grease. They have high adhesion qualities and will withstand expansion and contraction caused by temperature changes.

SAFETY COLOR CODE. The intelligent use of color for safety is rapidly being recognized as an important element in the modern plant. Although increased safety is inherent in the treatment of both machinery and walls with proper colors, it should also be used as a direct safety factor. Safety colors for industry have been recognized by leading safety authorities for years simply because they provide an orderly coordinated standard of practice for any plant in any industry. Color enables the workers to memorize all hazards and protective devices; it keeps them alert and prepared for any emergency

In general, the **colors used** are as follows:

1. Yellow—to mark moving objects, and as a warning signal.
2. Yellow and black—to mark stationary objects: posts, stairs, overhead equipment, etc., and stumbling or tripping hazards.
3. Orange—attention to open doors, guards, danger points, etc.
4. Red—fire protection.
5. Blue—out of order (tags) or under repair.
6. Green—first-aid areas or equipment, a safety color.
7. White—marking or guiding traffic; storage areas; sanitation.

Plant Location

OBJECTIVE. The objective of a study to consider the ideal location of a manufacturing facility is primarily one of economics. In fact, Shubin and Madeheim (Plant Layout) consider the **ideal location** as the "one where unit costs of production and distribution are at a minimum and where the prices and volume of sales will bring the maximum profits." Therefore, practically every item in the profit and loss statement is influenced directly or indirectly by the plant location.

Although location decisions are necessarily based on economic factors, the intangible factors must also be brought into focus. Among the **intangible factors** that should be considered are those whose effects are indirect. For instance, no value can be assigned to the cultural life of a community in terms of satisfying the employees. Nor can any value be assigned to a desirable climate as an influence in the recruitment or transfer of key personnel for an operation. These intangibles can spell success or failure of a new operation.

Plant location **studies** should be carried on continuously, according to Alford and Beatty (Principles of Industrial Management), in order to detect shifts in the market, depletion of raw materials, changes in transportation facilities or charges, and development of processes which require a different location.

SOURCES OF PROBLEM. The problem of plant location arises from three basic sources: expansion, decentralization, and diversification. **Expansion** is the most frequent source. Some of the conditions that indicate the need for expansion as cited by Yaseen (Plant Location) are:

1. Obsolescence of present facilities.
2. Restricted facilities and plant sites due to growth.
3. Inability to service customers properly.

Decentralization as an influence in plant location has arisen relatively recently. The need for decentralization arises from several sources, such as the need to meet competition in a shifting or relocated market, restricted facilities and plant sites due to growth, and the need for relocating from an overindustrialized area with its problems involving labor competition, and union activity.

Normally, **diversification** implies the outright purchase of a going company in the same or different area, manufacturing a different product. However, in recent years this situation has changed. An example is that of steel mills manufacturing pipe for the oil producers. They have been forced to manufacture plastic pipe in order to hold the present market. However, since the source of raw material for plastics was in a different location than the source for steel pipe, they located a plant near the source for plastic pipe materials.

CHECK LISTS. In comparing locations, not all the factors will reflect a change in cost. For instance, in comparing one area to another, the raw material cost may not change but its transportation cost may. Therefore, many check lists have been suggested as guides in comparing communities. Yaseen (Plant Location) shows one such comparison chart in Fig. 46. However, these are intended to serve only as a guide and not as yielding a perfect answer in every situa-

Basic Factors	Present Location	City A	City B	City C	City D	City E	City F
Total transportation costs:							
Inbound materials							
Outbound products							
Total	$						
Labor:							
Direct production							
Non-productive							
Total	$						
Plant overhead:							
Rent or carrying costs, excluding taxes							
Additional costs due to inefficient layout, lack of siding, etc.							
Real estate taxes							
Fuel for heating purposes only							
Personal property taxes, etc.							
Total	$						
Utilities:							
Power							
Gas							
Water							
Total	$						
State factors:							
State taxes							
Workmen's compensation							
Insurance							
Total	$						
Miscellaneous:							
Other cost factors inherent or peculiar to your present location(s)							
Total	$						
Grand total	$						

Fig. 46. Comparison chart for recurring costs.

tion. There is no better check list than that made up for a specific operation. In fact, some companies, in setting up a specific check list, weight the various factors in proportion to the influence exerted by that factor.

According to Fish (Manufacturer's Record, vol. 122), Walter Kidde Constructors, Inc., uses a **point system** to rate the desirability of a community for a specific employer. The factors and weights are not arbitrarily established but are directly related to the employer's costs. Fish states that "For example, in the case of one company, it was found that expenses that vary with the plant location amounted to $6.5 million, or 37 percent of the sales dollar. Among these variable costs, total payroll comprised $5.4 million, or 30.7 percent of the sales dollar. Hence, very high point scores are assigned to the labor factor. Small values are assigned to such items as utilities, which comprised only 0.6 percent of the sales dollar. Freight and shipping expense, which comprised 2 percent of the sales dollar, in this instance was given a slightly higher point score. Other variable factors were taxes, which amounted to $150,000, building depreciation, 0.4 percent, and building maintenance, 0.1 percent; insurance, 0.6 percent, and travel of officers, 0.2 percent."

BASIC FACTORS. The basic factors in plant location are primarily those that are subject to change according to the area. They can be classified into four factor groups:

1. Transportation.
2. Labor.
3. Operating expense.
4. Miscellaneous factors.

Each of these factors requires an examination of the tangibles and intangibles involved in order to arrive at a sound decision. So far as possible, the analysis must be objective, without the influence of the personal desires or prejudices of the management group.

DuPont considers 83 **specific factors** in rating a community, among which Fish (Manufacturer's Record, vol. 121) reports the following basic groups:

1. Availability and capability of the labor supply.
2. Attitude of labor.
3. Wage levels.
4. Housing factors.
5. Transportation facilities.
6. Topography, climate, etc.
7. Taxes.
8. Utilities.

DuPont engineers point out that few areas score 100 percent on their rating chart. Some disadvantages can be overcome at low cost; others can be endured. However, they say that the final choice is a compromise governed by the factors which are considered of most importance.

Transportation. In the examination of transportation costs, both the raw material and finished-product freight costs must be included, because the cost to the consumer is the final test of the suitability of a location. Furthermore, in the examination of the freight cost for the raw material, Wood (Fortune, vol. 54) suggests that consideration must be given to the **weight-losing** processes. Obviously, it would not be profitable to ship a raw material any great distance if a large proportion by weight is to be removed in processing. This is true especially if the value of the product is high, an extreme example of which is the refining of gold at the mine.

In calculating transportation costs, the actual figures should be acquired for any given situation because, as Alford and Beatty (Principles of Industrial Management) point out, "transportation costs are not a function of the distance" but depend on specific routes and specific product classifications. They further point out that not the location of raw materials but the economy of the **short haul** and low freight rates are important. They have also established criteria for determining the influence of the location of the raw material and the market on transportation costs. They say that raw material is an influence when:

1. It is bulky or low cost.
2. It is greatly reduced in bulk in the process.
3. It is perishable and the process makes it less so.

The market is an influence when the manufacturing process:

1. Increases the bulk of the product.
2. Renders it more fragile.
3. Makes it susceptible to spoilage.

Other transportation costs which should be determined are the **traveling expenses** of management and sales personnel. The distribution of the market normally influences these costs; however, the transportation facilities available can be influential when a value is placed upon the traveling time of personnel. Some of the intangible considerations in the analysis of transportation include the dependability of the available carriers, the character of the carriers, and the time required to transport the finished product to the market. In addition, the time required to contact or service a customer may be important.

Labor. The common impression regarding labor costs is that a location is desirable because of low wage rates alone. In a limited way this may be true, but it is a shortsighted policy. McManus points out (Iron Age, vol. 176) that the regional differences in labor costs are short-lived because of the unions' continuing pattern of national wage standardization. This theory is supported further by Delaney (Iron Age, vol. 170), who says that a location in a small community offers no advantage as far as wage rates are concerned. He further quotes a company representative whose experience was that "you can't run away from high labor rates."

There are some important noneconomic considerations with respect to the labor factor, such as the **potential labor force available.** According to Wood (Fortune, vol. 54), General Electric attempts to locate their plants in communities where they will absorb less than 10–12 percent of the local labor force. Of course this is not always possible, but it certainly reduces the risk of becoming involved in a tight or competitive labor market. McManus (Iron Age, vol. 176) points out the advantage of locating in communities where there is diversification between industry and commerce. He says that a community with more than half of the labor force in manufacturing does not make the best home for a new plant. Morrison (Manufacturer's Record, vol. 124) reports that Westinghouse selected Raleigh, N. C., for a facility primarily because they did not have to compete for the required segment of the labor force.

Another unmeasurable factor of considerable importance is the **productivity of labor.** The Modern Industry Check Chart (vol. 9) suggests that the employees in highly industrialized areas not only rate relatively low in productivity but are ". . . overindoctrinated with [the] evils of speed-up and technological unemployment." High productivity requires well-trained employees, employee pride, pleasant surroundings, and incentives, in addition to new equipment and methods, and modern plant design. Fish reported (Manufacturer's Record, vol. 122) that one employer selected a site in Georgia to erect a 1.500-employee plant. The employer felt that he could save $1,000,000 per year as a result of the increased productivity of the local labor force.

An important consideration in a community is the **history of labor relations.** This is probably the most difficult of the factors to determine and measure. Obviously, the community leaders and local governmental officials cannot be objective in their comments if they wish to promote the community. Generally, the only reliable sources of information are the newspapers, a study of which is recommended over at least one year. In this examination, evidence of improper and unethical management actions should be noted as well as erratic union behavior because, on occasion, management attitudes have incited labor unrest.

Operating Expense. This factor as an influence in plant location involves the utilities and services required by a factory. Included in the **utilities** are, of course, power, fuel, and water. The variation in utility cost may be as high as 100 percent, depending on the locality, demand, and use (Modern Industry, vol. 9). The accurate determination of these costs requires a contact with the source of the utilities as to rates, demand charges, etc. Along with a specific request for the rate structure, any likely restrictions on use of the service are pertinent. For instance, an area that utilizes hydro-electric power supply may be subject to wide variations in the availability of electricity due to the fluctuating water level.

The **water supply** is a critical item since the industrial consumption of water is so high. First, of course, the quantity of available water must be sufficient to meet peak needs and to compensate for any extended dry spell. Fig. 47 (Yaseen, Plant Location) illustrates the variable nature of water requirements. Then, of course, chemical treatment may be required to compensate for hardness and impurity for use in a specific production process. Finally, the source of the supply must be considered with respect to cost, whether public service or from a well on the site.

Industrial Process	Gallons of Water Required
Produce a ton of bromine	5,000,000
Produce a ton of synthetic rubber	600,000
Produce a ton of aluminum	320,000
Produce a ton of viscose rayon	200,000
Make a ton of steel	65,000
Test an airplane engine	50,000
Generate one kw-h	6,000
Produce a ton of coke from coal	3,600
Refine a barrel of petroleum	770
Brew a barrel of beer	470

Fig. 47. Typical water requirements for various industries.

There are several intangible items in the plant overhead factor that must be evaluated. A community may be lagging in its expansion as far as **public services** are concerned. Therefore, heavy community indebtedness may be necessary, with its attendant tax increases, in order to keep up with the requirements of an expanding population and area. Among the specific services that warrant investigation in this respect are the water supply, sewage facilities, roadbuilding and maintenance program, and school system.

The various **taxes,** such as the property tax, local income tax, and any other state or local tax on a facility, must be determined. Although consideration must be given to any tax concessions granted by the community, these inducements must be examined critically. Hamaker forcefully negates their value (Manufacturer's Record, vol. 123) in that industry will force taxes upward as a result of its increasing demand for public services.

Other items of plant overhead for which cost estimates are required are the **insurance** items. The most obvious of these is the fire insurance. Since fire insurance premiums are a function of the quality of protection and prevention services available, the efficiency of the community fire department exerts a great influence on these premiums. Unemployment and workmen's compensation are items for which costs must be determined. The administration of these insurances influences the premium, as does, of course, the experience rating of the specific plant. Other insurances that may be pertinent involve those specific hazards connected with the production process, for instance, those that involve nuclear energy. Certain of these processes may require more extensive public liability insurance, the costs of which might vary with the area.

Miscellaneous Factors. Most of the miscellaneous factors in plant location cannot be evaluated quantitatively. For instance, the **climate,** unless it influences the production process directly, must be considered on the basis of judgment. It may influence the transfer or the recruiting of personnel.

The **topography** of a community is a consideration in that it may influence the surface water. Along with a surge of rainfall it may, of course, contribute to flooding conditions. In addition, the topography influences the original building construction cost.

An evaluation of the **political climate** of a community is an important factor in plant location. In the examination of the political scene, the political party in control is not pertinent, but rather, any eccentric or erratic policies that are or may be established. These policies may have a decided effect on the potential of a plant. In this respect Clark (Mississippi Economic Council Address) says, "The constant activities of the governmental bodies, in their tendencies to encroach on the prerogatives of businesses, have caused the industrialist to give careful consideration to laws and regulations, both existing and proposed." Obviously, since a new plant contributes more than just a payroll and taxes, the community leaders are going to put their best foot forward. The best defense is an examination of back issues of the local newspapers over a period of time.

More attention is being given to the cultural, social, and educational **community atmosphere.** According to Clark, manufacturers are recognizing the personal desires of key employees regarding these factors, and he points out that, "All the other factors are equal in many communities, therefore, he [the industrialist] selects the town which he and his associates would like to call their home town."

INDUCEMENTS AND CONCESSIONS. Many communities, in an attempt to encourage industrial development, are offering tempting inducements to industry. Alford and Beatty (Principles of Industrial Management) have classified some of them as follows:

1. Offers of a site or existing plant.
2. Subscription to the capital stock.
3. A remission of certain taxes for a specified period of years.

Whether these inducements are effective in their attraction for industry is debatable, according to Slayman, who stated (Labor subcommittee hearings for

Senate Bill No. 2663) that "It is common knowledge . . . . that to a large degree, decisions on where to start or expand a business are dictated by factors over which the community has little control. . . ." He said further that new industry must fit the economic and social pattern of the community, regardless of inducements.

Any inducement or concession offered by a community must be examined from the standpoint of economics and sound judgment as well. Frequently, they are only temporary advantages. Richter (Steel, vol. 134) says with respect to these concessions that you "don't get something for nothing," therefore, that they are not a factor in plant location. He further states that advantages such as favorable freight rates may far outweigh such benefits as free rent or tax remission. In fact, one of the communities that has offered the greatest inducements to industry is York, Pennsylvania. However, none of these inducements are financial. Wecksler points out (Mill and Factory, vol. 52) that among the favorable characteristics of York are a cooperative labor attitude, low taxes, and good transportation. He sums up by saying that industry prefers a community where it is wanted and appreciated.

On the other hand, many examples can be cited where **community development committees** have made notable contributions to the benefit of a prospective plant. The case of a large pipe manufacturer (Manufacturer's Record, vol. 122) who had twice been denied a certificate of necessity for a $3.5 million expansion is an example. Birmingham's Committee of One Hundred represented the manufacturer in an appeal and was awarded the certificate.

Local Government Plan. The purpose of the BAWI (Balance Agriculture With Industry) Plan (Chapter 241, Laws of Mississippi) was to stimulate the industrial development of Mississippi by encouraging the communities to engage in and promote industrial expansion. This unique law permits communities to issue bonds to finance the purchase of land and construction of buildings for a specific manufacturing plant. To qualify under the law, the political subdivision must meet certain standards as to the availability of labor and natural resources and must be approved by the BAWI administering board. The populace must approve of the plan by a two-thirds vote, with a majority voting. The value of the bonds issued for this purpose must not exceed 20 percent of the assessed property valuation of the community.

In negotiating with a specific industry, the community must assure a 10-year supply of raw materials and a labor supply of 150 percent of the specific requirements within a 25-mile radius. A **lease** is established such that the municipality can amortize its bonds in the primary lease, the term of which cannot exceed 25 years. The lease can be renewed at nominal rent up to 99 years. As an additional inducement, newly established plants may be exempted from certain local taxes for a period of 5 yrs. At any rate, they are exempt from all real estate taxes for the life of all leases because the site and buildings are the property of the local government.

According to H. W. Clark, the benefits of BAWI are not granted to industrial enterprises indiscriminately. Rather, the manufacturer must meet these four basic requirements formulated as administrative policies of the BAWI Board:

1. He must have experience in the specific production process.
2. The market must be able to absorb the minimum anticipated production of the proposed plant.
3. The financial strength of the company must be certified and show that the current ratio is 150 percent of the proposed bond issue.

4. The local annual payroll at normal operation should be as a minimum equal to the bond issue. This is a rule-of-thumb guide and therefore need not be specified.

Some of the **advantages** cited for the plan are:

1. Credit of the contracting company is unencumbered because of the lease arrangement.
2. Lease payments are operating expenses and therefore are deductible in income tax.
3. The lease permits use of construction capital for machinery and other accounts, for faster turnover of capital.
4. The company is assured by a general election that they are wanted in the community.

DISPERSION. Although the general dispersion of industry has never been definitely established as a national policy, the federal government and industrial executives have been conscious of the problem in this age of nuclear weapons. In some cases it has influenced the location of specific plants, but generally speaking, industrial areas tend to attract industry. Wood supports this theory (Fortune, vol. 54) in pointing out that 70 percent of the industrial labor force of the country is concentrated in 10 percent of the area. Industry deliberately chose concentration subsequent to World War II, according to Fish (Manufacturer's Record, vol. 123), because it could thus expand at the lowest cost. He points out that any dispersion that will take place will occur in easy stages because the cost of the dispersion effort would be so great.

However, Tagin (New York Times, vol. 45) said that though the atomic bomb has speeded decentralization, the hydrogen bomb has had a sobering effect. He said, "Industrialists now commonly feel that they cannot escape the fall-out of nuclear weapons no matter where they go."

SITE SELECTION. Once a general area is decided upon, the site must be selected. Occasionally the solution to the general area problem leads to a specific site and no alternative is possible. More often, however, the site selection is a problem in itself.

The first decision regarding the site is that of choosing a city, suburban, or country location. On occasion the nature of the process dictates the selection. For instance, in the manufacture of munitions a country location is necessary. On the other hand, for the manufacture of precision instruments, the highly skilled labor supply of the larger city is needed. Ireson points out these general **site conditions** (Factory Planning and Plant Layout) as follows:

Requirements governing the choice of a **country** location are:

1. Large plant site.
2. Objectionable or dangerous production processes.
3. Large volume of relatively pure water.
4. Low property taxes.
5. Protection against sabotage or for a secret process.

Requirements governing the choice of a **suburban** location are:

1. Large plant site close to transportation or population center.
2. Freedom from common city building zoning, and other restrictions
3. High female labor supply.
4. Freedom from high taxes.

Requirements governing choice of **city** location are:

1. High proportion of skilled employees.
2. Rapid transportation and contact with suppliers and customers.
3. Small plant site or multifloor operation.
4. City facilities and utilities.

Aside from these specific factors, there are a few other considerations. One, of course, is the consideration of the employees' tastes, preferences, and habits. In the choice of a country location, Clark (Mississippi Economic Council Address) emphasizes that the cost of a plant site should not exceed the going rate of farm land in that area by more than 50 percent. Any other factors that influence the choice of site location are associated with a specific industry and require, in each case, examination on their own merits.

In the selection of the plant site, some of the major factors that influence the cost of specific **site development** are: provision for railroad siding, drainage facilities, sewage disposal, and suitability of the underlying strata for foundations of buildings.

Regarding the size of the site, Yaseen (Plant Location) suggests that it be not less than five times the area of the plant itself, and further, that it be open on two sides to allow for possible site expansion at a later date.

MANUFACTURING PROCESSES

CONTENTS

PAGE

Definition and scope 1

Casting of Metals

Metals and methods of melting 1
Direct iron casting 1
Gray iron 1
White iron 1
Malleable iron 2
Nodular iron 2
Steel 2
Brass and bronze 2
Aluminum 2
Magnesium 2
Sand casting 2
Procedure for making a mold (f. 1) 3
Patterns 2
Cores 3
Molds 3
Molding machines 4
Machine molding principles (f. 2) 4
Shell molding 4
Schematic of the shell molding process
(f. 3) 6–7
Die casting alloys 5
Types of machines 5
Die-casting alloys 5
Permanent molds 5
Centrifugal castings 5
Centrifugal casting methods (f. 4) 8–9
Miscellaneous casting methods 8

Powder Metallurgy

Basic powder process 10
Methods of producing metal powders 10
Method of manufacture 10
Selection 10
Mixing 10
Pressing 11
Briquetting punch and die for forming
hollow cylindrical parts (f. 5) 11
Sintering 11
Sizing and finishing 11
Hot pressing 11
Types of presses used 11
Tolerances 12
Factors determining the use of powder
metallurgy 12
Design considerations 12
Metal powder applications 12

Forging Processes

Elements of forging 13

PAGE

Smith forging 13
Drop forging 13
Forging operations 13
Sequence of forging operations for a con-
necting rod (f. 6) 14
Types of hammers 14
Gravity-type drop hammer (f. 7) 15
Upset forging 16
Sequence of progressive piercing opera-
tions—radial engine cylinder forgings
(f. 8) 16
Press forging 17
Roll forging 17
Forging rolls making connecting rod
blank (f. 9) 18
Rotary swaging 18
The operation of dies in a swaging ma-
chine (f. 10) 19

Stamping and Forming

Basic processes 19
Types of presses 19
Blanking and shearing 19
Progress of plastic deformation and frac-
ture during a punching operation (f. 11) 20
Bending and forming 20
Method of forming sheet metal using
single die and rubber punch (f. 12) 21
Drawing 21
Drawing operation on single-acting press
(f. 13) 22
Punch and die arrangement for deep
drawing sheet steel (f. 14) 22
Roll forming 23
Sequence of operations in the rolling of a
window screen section (f. 15) 23
Embossing and coining 24
Coining and embossing (f. 16) 24
Metal stretching 24

Welding Processes

Elements of welding 25
Basic types of welded joints and their
positions (f. 17) 25
Arc welding 25
Arc welding with coated electrodes 26
Diagrammatic sketch of arc flame (f. 18) 26
Electrode classification chart (f. 19) 27
Impregnated tape metal arc welding 26
Atomic hydrogen arc welding 26
Atomic hydrogen arc-welding electrode
holder (f. 20) 28

CONTENTS (*Continued*)

PAGE

Inert-gas-shielded metal arc welding 28
Hand-welding torch for inert-gas-shielded
  arc welding (*f.* 21) 29
Submerged arc welding 28
  Submerged arc welding (*f.* 22) 28
Shielded-stud arc welding 29
Unshielded metal electrode arc welding 30
Carbon electrode arc welding 30
Gas welding and cutting 30
  Oxyacetylene gas welding 30
  Air-acetylene welding 31
  Oxyhydrogen welding 31
  Pressure welding 31
  Schematic of pressure gas welding (*f.* 23) 31
  Gas cutting and flame machining 31
  Automatic flame cutting (*f.* 24) 32
Resistance welding 32
  Spot welding 32
  Spot, seam, and projection welding (*f.* 25) 33
  Seam welding 33
  Projection welding 33
  Flash, upset, and percussion butt welding 33
  Sketch of flash, upset, and percussion
    welding processes (*f.* 26) 34
Brazing and soldering 34
Forge welding 34
Thermit welding 35

Assembly Methods

Important factors in assembly 35
Screws and bolts 35
  Standard screw thread forms (*f.* 27) 36
  American standard and special screws
    (*f.* 28) 37
  American standard and special bolts (*f.*
    29) 38
Riveting and staking 37
  Riveting and staking operations (*f.* 30).. 39
  American standard large rivets (*f.* 31) .. 39
Stapling, tacking, and stitching 39
Seaming and curling 39
  Typical seams used in the manufactur-
    ing of light-gage metal containers (*f.* 32) 40
Shrink fits 40
Adhesives 40

Machining Processes

Importance of machining 41
Metal cutting 42
Turning 42
  Lathes 42
  Turret and automatic lathes 42
  Typical turret lathe setup (*f.* 33) 43
Threading 44
  Tap nomenclature (*f.* 34) 44
Shaping and planing 44
  Horizontal push-cut shaper (*f.* 35) 45
Drilling and boring 45
  Drilling, boring, and reaming operations
    (*f.* 36) 46
Milling 47
  Universal milling machine (*f.* 37) 47
Sawing 48
Broaching 48
  Broaching a round hole (*f.* 38) 49
Grinding 49
  Cylindrical grinding (*f.* 39) 50

PAGE

Protective Coatings

Methods of cleaning 50
  Mechanical cleaning methods 50
    Schematic of a blast gun (*f.* 40) 51
  Chemical cleaning methods 51
Coating processes 52
  Organic coatings 52
    Organic coatings (*f.* 41) 53
  Hot dipping 54
Electroplating 54
  Chart of coating characteristics (*f.* 42).. 56
Oxide coatings 55
Metallizing 55
Clad materials 55
Porcelain enameling 55

Extrusion of Metals

Basic extrusion process 57
  Extrusion characteristics 57
  Extrusion pressures and temperatures for
    direct and inverted extrusion (*f.* 43) .. 57
Types of extrusion 57
  Direct or forward extrusion 57
  Direct and inverted extrusion processes
    (*f.* 44) 58
  Inverted or backward extrusion 58
  Impact extrusion 58
  Method of cold-impact extrusion of soft
    metals (*f.* 45) 58

Plastic Molding

Properties of plastics 58
Methods of forming 59
  Compression molding 59
    Compression molding (*f.* 46) 59
  Transfer molding 60
  Injection molding 60
    Operation of plastic injection molding
      machine (*f.* 47) 61
  Casting 61
  Extruding 61
    Method of continuously extruding plastic
      materials (*f.* 48) 62
  Laminating 62
  Vacuum forming and blowing 63
    Vacuum snap-back forming of heated
      thermoplastic sheets (*f.* 49) 63
    Forming heated thermoplastic sheets by
      air pressure in a mold (*f.* 50) 64

Woodworking

Properties and sources of wood 65
Basic woodworking tools 65
  Typical cuts and joints used in wood-
    working (*f.* 51) 65
  Operational speeds and feeds for various
    woodworking machines (*f.* 52) 66
Sawing 66
Turning and boring 67
  Router bit and work piece (*f.* 53) 67
  Hollow chisel mortiser (*f.* 54) 68
Joining 68
  Jointer (*f.* 55) 69
Surfacing and sanding 69
  Planer or single surfacer (*f.* 56) 69
Shaping 70
  Single-spindle shaper (*f.* 57) 70

MANUFACTURING PROCESSES

DEFINITION AND SCOPE. A knowledge of tools, machines, and processes is imperative in working toward the goals of improved production methods and lower manufacturing costs. Manufacturing processes are the primary processes used in the fabrication of engineering materials and must be kept in mind when considering alternative production procedures and attempting to avoid production problems. In order to provide a working knowledge of such processes, a background of the terminologies applied and a description and discussion of the machines and procedures used are given, concentrating particularly in the metal-working and allied industries.

The **selection of a process** for a given operation is influenced by several factors, including the product quality desired, the cost of labor needed, and the number of units to be produced. Although many items can be produced by several methods, there is usually one method that is best for a given set of variables. In the following, each process is defined and described and its major variations presented, with emphasis upon applications of the process and its advantages and limitations. The major financial considerations in selecting inclines and equipment for a manufacturing process are analyzed in the section on Machinery and Equipment Economics.

Casting of Metals

METALS AND METHODS OF MELTING. Casting is the pouring of molten metal into a mold and allowing it to solidify to the shape of the mold cavity. Practically all metals can be cast in this manner since the process is versatile. Among the ferrous metals and alloys which are produced in the greatest tonnage are steel, gray iron, and malleable iron. The nonferrous group includes alloys of tin, copper, aluminum, magnesium, lead, and zinc.

Direct Iron Casting. This is a product of the blast furnace and is seldom used for commercial castings until it is further refined. The castings thus made are known as **pigs** or **pig iron** and normally weigh from 50 to 200 lb.

Gray Iron. Gray iron castings are produced in larger tonnage than most other metals. The raw materials are low in cost, economical to melt, and relatively few castings are lost to scrap.

In pouring gray iron castings, the foundryman must regulate the silicon and carbon contents of the melt and the rate of cooling of the casting, otherwise the desired physical properties will not be obtained. Gray iron is normally melted in a cupola, an air furnace, or an electric furnace.

White Iron. White cast iron can be produced by casting gray iron against a chill or by closely regulating the carbon and silicon content. White iron, melted in a cupola, electric furnace, or an air furnace, is usually made into malleable iron by an annealing process.

Malleable Iron. Malleable iron is made from white cast iron by annealing it at temperatures of from 1,500 to 1,850° F. over a period of several days. These castings have good shock resistance and machinability and find wide use in the railroad, pipe fitting, and agricultural implement industries.

Nodular Iron. Nodular iron is made from gray cast iron by ladle additions of magnesium or cerium alloy. The carbon is in the form of nodules, and the metal exhibits physical characteristics between that of steel and gray iron. Due to its ductility and high strength, nodular iron is an excellent material for many machine parts.

Steel. Steel castings are normally classified as **carbon steels** and **alloy steels.** Medium carbon steels are cast most frequently although the alloy steels are finding increased usage. Although the largest tonnage of steel is melted in the basic open-hearth furnace, it is also melted in large quantities by the acid open-hearth, indirect and direct arc furnaces, crucible furnace, induction furnace, or may be refined in a converter.

Brass and Bronze. Brass is essentially an alloy of copper and zinc while **bronze** is primarily an alloy of copper and tin, although both frequently contain several elements. Brasses, because of their ductility, strength, and corrosion resistance, are cast in large tonnage. They are often alloyed with lead to increase machinability, with zinc to improve fluidity, and with nickel to produce a denser structure. Bronzes are more difficult to machine than brass, but their metallurgical structure makes them ideal for pressure-tight castings. Most brasses and bronzes are melted in induction and crucible furnaces.

Aluminum. Aluminum is approximately one-third as heavy as iron, yet has relatively high strength, excellent corrosion resistance, good electrical conductivity, a low melting point, and good machinability. Aluminum is usually alloyed with one or more of the following: silicon, magnesium, copper, zinc, and iron. Aluminum castings can be cast by almost any method due to its low melting point and are usually melted in induction or crucible type furnaces.

Magnesium. Magnesium, approximately one-fourth as heavy as iron, has excellent machinability. It is often alloyed with aluminum, manganese, zinc, copper, nickel, iron, silicon. Induction and crucible furnaces are most often used in melting magnesium.

SAND CASTING. Most metals can be cast to shape in a sand mold, as represented by Begeman (Manufacturing Processes) in Fig. 1. The molds are easy to prepare and have few limitations as to size and shape of casting to be produced.

Patterns. A pattern is a model of the part to be cast. In sand casting, the sand is packed around the pattern and the pattern is then removed leaving a cavity to be filled with molten metal. Patterns are normally made from wood, metal, mortar, or plastic.

Since metal shrinks when it solidifies, a pattern must have a **shrinkage allowance** to compensate. The shrinkage for various metals is normally taken as: ⅛ in./ft. for cast iron; 3/16 in./ft. for brass; ¼ in./ft. for steel; and 5/32 in./ft. for aluminum and magnesium. In order to remove a pattern from the mold without damaging the mold, the pattern must have **draft** or a taper parallel to the direction in which the pattern is withdrawn. A **finish** allowance, usually about ⅛ in., must be added to all portions of the casting that are to be machined. There are other allowances such as **shake** and **distortion** that an experienced pattern maker provides on the pattern for large castings.

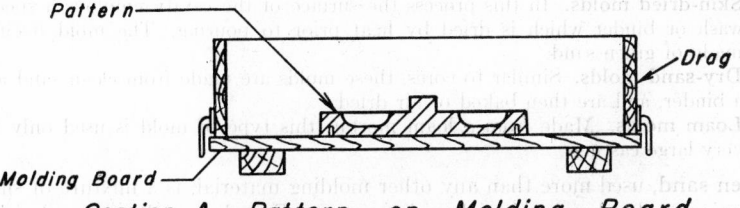

Section A —Pattern on Molding Board. Ready to Ram up Drag.

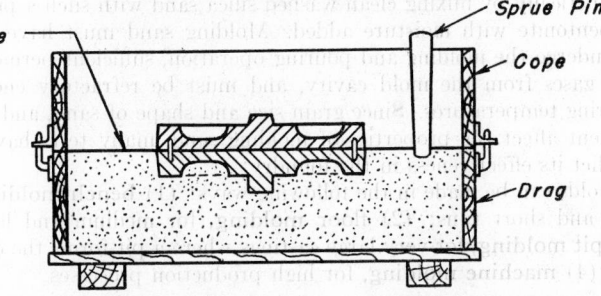

Section B —Drag Rolled over and Pattern Assembled Ready to Ram Cope.

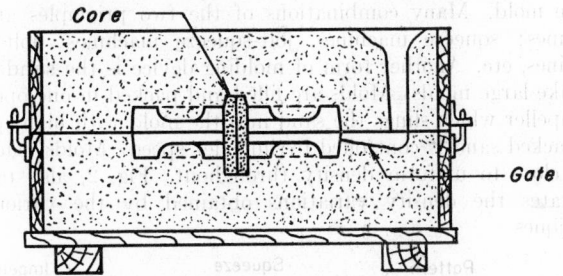

Section C —Mold Complete with Dry Sand Core in Place.

Fig. 1. Procedure for making a mold.

Cores. When a casting is to have a cavity in it, a body of sand known as a core is employed. Cores are generally made of dry sand mixed with a **binder**, such as molasses or linseed oil, and then baked or air dried. They are held in place in a mold by impressions made in sand during the molding operation, or by chaplets. **Chaplets** are small metal supports made from low melting point alloys. Cores must be refractory to withstand the molten metal, but the binding material must burn out or break down after a short interval of time in order that minimum stresses will be set up and the core can be removed easily.

Molds. Molds, classified according to the types of materials used, are:

1. **Green sand molds.** This material, most commonly used, is a damp mixture of sand and clay.

2. **Skin-dried molds.** In this process the surface of the cavity employs a special wash or binder which is dried by heat prior to pouring. The mold itself is made of green sand.
3. **Dry-sand molds.** Similar to cores. these molds are made from clean sand and a binder, and are then baked or air dried.
4. **Loam molds.** Made from a loam mortar, this type of mold is used only for very large castings.

Green sand, used more than any other molding material, is a mixture of silica sand grains, a clay bond material, and moisture. Foundry sands are used either as found in a natural state with the addition of moisture, or they are made synthetically by mixing clean washed silica sand with such a pure clay compound as bentonite with moisture added. Molding sand must have sufficient strength to undergo the molding and pouring operation, sufficient permeability to pass air and gases from the mold cavity, and must be refractory enough to withstand pouring temperatures. Since grain size and shape of sand, and clay and moisture content affect the properties of molding sand, many tests have been devised to predict its effectiveness in the foundry.

Molds can be made in the following ways: (1) **bench molding,** for small castings and short runs; (2) **floor molding,** for medium and large size castings; (3) **pit molding,** for very large castings where a pit forms the drag part of mold; and (4) **machine molding,** for high production processes.

Molding Machines. Molding machines do either or both of two things; shake or squeeze the sand. Shaking or vibrating the sand packs the sand more at the parting plane, whereas squeezing packs the sand greatest at the outside surface of the mold. Many combinations of the two principles are employed in: jolt machines; squeeze machines, jolt-squeeze machines; jolt-squeeze power-draw machines, etc. Another form of molding device is the **sandslinger** which is used to make large molds. Molds are filled and packed in one operation by employing an impeller which slings the sand into the mold with high speed. The density of the packed sand is controlled by impeller speed. Molds made with a sandslinger have close to uniform density throughout. Fig. 2, also taken from Begeman, illustrates the density variations obtained by the various machine molding techniques.

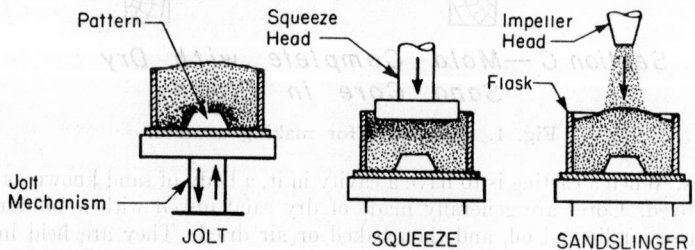

Fig. 2. Machine molding principles.

SHELL MOLDING. In this process a mold is made up of two thin shells outlining the mold cavity, which are clamped or held together with shot or sand for pouring. Castings produced by this method often have a tolerance as small as 0.002 in. A schematic diagram of the process is shown in Fig. 3 (The Borden Co.). The shells are made by dumping a mixture of sand and phenolic resin on a **heated metal pattern** (400–560° F.) that has been sprayed with a **release agent.** A shell forms over the pattern due to the heating of the resin, and any surplus sand-resin material is removed, leaving the shell. This shell is baked or cured for 35–65 seconds at temperatures of 600–1,400° F. and is then removed from the metal pattern. Metals cast by this process include brass, bronze, iron, steel, and the light alloys.

DIE CASTING. The process of die casting refers to castings made by forcing metal under pressure into a metallic cavity or die. The pressures used vary from a few pounds to approximately 50,000 psi and are applied until solidification is complete. The principal advantages of die castings are: rapid operation, excellent surface finish, close tolerances of from 0.002 to 0.001 in., dense structure, and production of thinner sections. The cost of equipment is high, which therefore precludes short-run jobs. Metals commonly die cast include alloys of zinc, aluminum, copper, tin, lead, and magnesium.

Types of Machines. The two fundamental types of die casting machines are the hot-chamber and the cold-chamber machines.

A melting pot is an integral part of the **hot-chamber** machine, and the injection cylinder remains immersed in the molten metal. Inasmuch as the melting pot and injection equipment are subject to very high temperatures, only the lower melting point alloys, which do not have an affinity for iron, are cast in this type of machine. The alloys of zinc, tin, and lead are the most commonly used.

The **cold-chamber** machine is not equipped with a melting pot, but must be furnished with a separate melting furnace. The molten metal is placed in the injection system by hand ladle or mechanical means. Metals that have higher melting temperatures and require greater pressures for sound castings are cast in this machine. If these metals were not heated in a separate pot, the life of the pot and the parts of the injection system would be short. Metals such as alloys of brass, aluminum, and magnesium are cast in the cold-chamber machine.

DIE CASTING ALLOYS. Alloys commonly used in die casting and some of their advantages are:

Alloy	Advantages
Zinc base	High strength, good finish, low casting temperatures, low cost
Aluminum base	Light weight, corrosion resistance
Magnesium base	Light weight, high machinability
Copper base	High strength, corrosion resistance
Lead base	Heavy weight, chemical resistance
Tin base	Corrosion resistance, contact with food or beverages

PERMANENT MOLDS. Permanent molds are made from metal and their life depends on the temperature of the metal being cast. The mold is coated with a wash before each pouring to protect the mold and facilitate the removal of the casting. A permanent mold offers cleaner, smoother, more accurate, gas-free, and shrink-free castings than sand molds. All metals can be cast by this method, but the cost increases rapidly as higher melting point alloys are used.

CENTRIFUGAL CASTINGS. Centrifugal castings are produced by pouring a molten metal into a **rotating mold,** thus utilizing centrifugal force as a means of solidifying the metal in the form of the mold cavity. The centrifugal force insures greater surface detail, a denser and stronger structure, and freedom from impurities, and is used only when the casting is to be machined internally. Metals of all kinds can be cast by this process, depending, of course, on the mold material. There are three types of centrifugal castings.

OVEN

Curing the shells on pattern

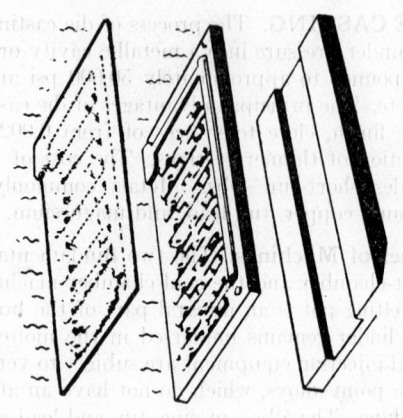

Shell is stripped from pattern

OVEN

Heating the pattern

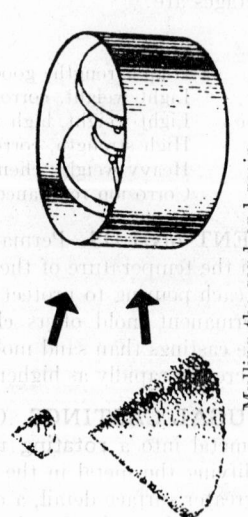

Mulling the sand and resin

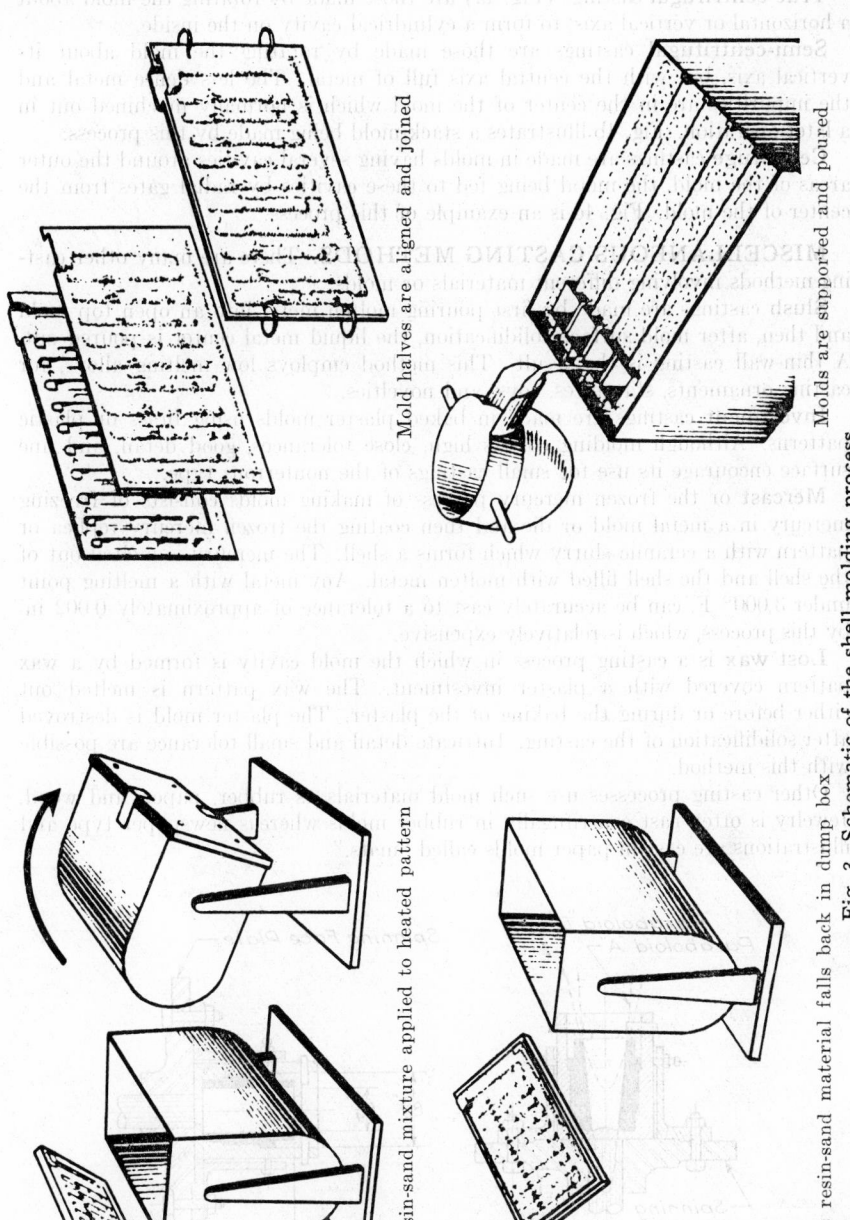

Fig. 3. Schematic of the shell molding process.

Mold halves are aligned and joined

Molds are supported and poured

Resin-sand mixture applied to heated pattern

Excess resin-sand material falls back in dump box

True centrifugal castings (Fig. 4a) are those made by rotating the mold about a horizontal or vertical axis, to form a cylindrical cavity on the inside.

Semi-centrifugal castings are those made by rotating the mold about its vertical axis, but with the central axis full of metal. The less dense metal and the impurities are in the center of the mold which is normally machined out in a later operation. Fig. 4b illustrates a stack mold being made by this process.

Centrifuge castings are made in molds having several cavities around the outer areas of the mold, the metal being fed to these cavities by radial gates from the center of the mold. Fig. 4c is an example of this process.

MISCELLANEOUS CASTING METHODS. There are many other casting methods involving different materials or molds.

Slush castings are made by first pouring molten metal into an open top mold and then, after mold surface solidification, the liquid metal center is poured out. A thin-wall casting is the result. This method employs low melting alloys, for casting ornaments, statuettes, toys, and novelties.

Investment castings are made in baked plaster molds using brass or plastic patterns. Although molding cost is high, close tolerances, good detail, and fine surface encourage its use for small castings of the nonferrous type.

Mercast or the frozen mercury process of making molds consists of freezing mercury in a metal mold or die and then coating the frozen mercury replica or pattern with a ceramic slurry which forms a shell. The mercury is melted out of the shell and the shell filled with molten metal. Any metal with a melting point under 3,000° F. can be accurately cast to a tolerance of approximately 0.002 in. by this process, which is relatively expensive.

Lost wax is a casting process in which the mold cavity is formed by a wax pattern covered with a plaster investment. The wax pattern is melted out either before or during the baking of the plaster. The plaster mold is destroyed after solidification of the casting. Intricate detail and small tolerance are possible with this method.

Other casting processes use such mold materials as rubber, paper, and wood. Jewelry is often cast centrifugally in rubber molds whereas newspaper type and illustrations are cast in paper molds called "mats."

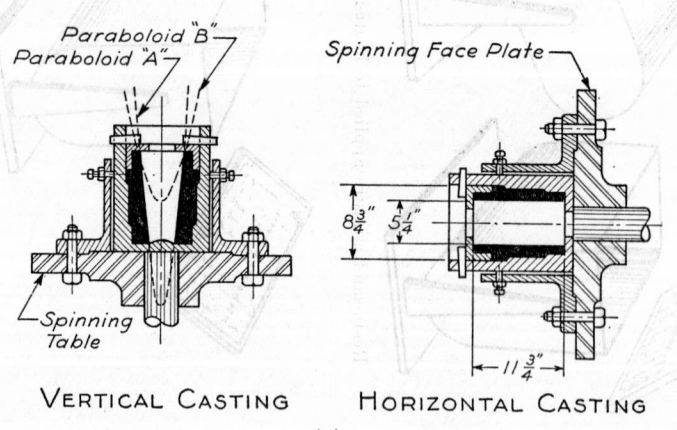

VERTICAL CASTING   HORIZONTAL CASTING

(a)

Fig. 4. Centrifugal casting methods (continued on next page).

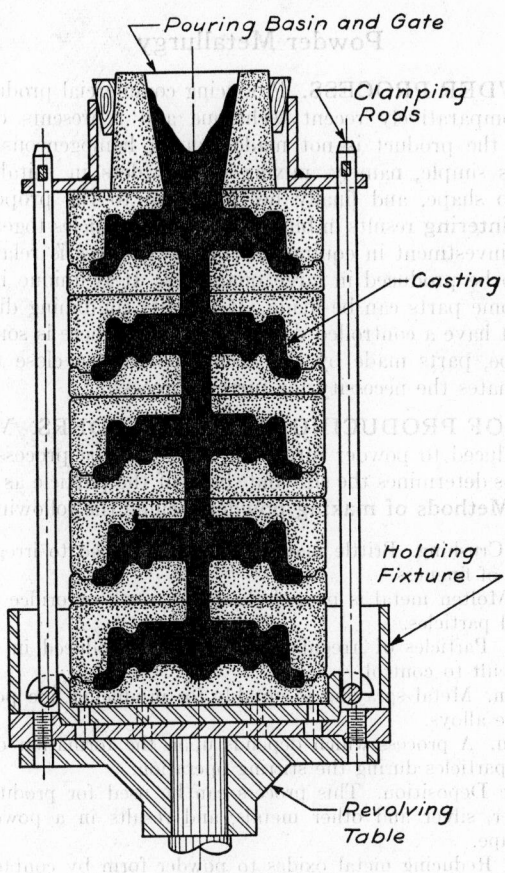

-Pouring Basin and Gate

-Clamping Rods

-Casting

Holding Fixture

Revolving Table

(b) Semicentrifugal casting

Section A-A

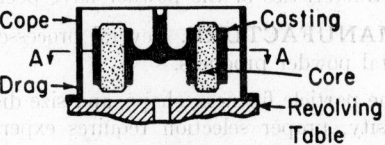

Cope —

A — Drag

Casting

Core

Revolving Table

The American Cast Iron Pipe Co.

(c) Centrifuge casting

Fig. 4. (Concluded.)

Powder Metallurgy

BASIC POWDER PROCESS. Producing commercial products from metal powders is a comparatively recent technique and represents one of the few processes where the product is not made from a homogeneous solid material. The operation is simple, namely, mixing the powders in suitable proportions, pressing them to shape, and finally heating them to the proper temperature. The heating or **sintering** results in binding the solid particles together by molecular forces. The investment in equipment for this process is relatively high and requires parts to be produced in large quantities. It is unique in that it is the only way that some parts can be made. It permits combining different powders for products that have a controlled density. Although there is some limitation as to size and shape, parts made by this technique have a close tolerance which frequently eliminates the necessity for further processing.

METHODS OF PRODUCING METAL POWDERS. Most metals and alloys can be reduced to powder form, but all cannot be processed in the same way. The process determines the size and shape of the particle as well as the cost of the powder. **Methods of making powder** include the following:

1. Milling or Crushing. Brittle materials can be reduced to irregular shapes and any degree of fineness.
2. Shotting. Molten metal is poured through a sieve or orifice resulting largely in spherical particles.
3. Machining. Particles of irregular shape can be produced in this fashion but size is difficult to control.
4. Atomization. Metal spraying is suitable for producing fine powders from low temperature alloys.
5. Granulation. A process which depends upon the formation of oxides on the individual particles during the stirring operation.
6. Electrolytic Deposition. This process can be used for producing powders of iron, copper, silver and other metals, and results in a powder of dendritic particle shape.
7. Reduction. Reducing metal oxides to powder form by contact with a reducing gas is economical for some metals including tungsten, copper, and nickel. Irregularly shaped particles are produced.

Other methods include precipitation, condensation, and various chemical processes.

The **powder characteristics** of flowability and compressibility are dependent upon the shape of the powder particles. Likewise particle size distribution has considerable influence on the apparent density and final porosity of the product. Other properties of metal powders which must be considered in the processing operation include fineness, flowability, and sintering ability. Procedures for testing the important characteristics of the powder have been prepared by ASTM.

METHOD OF MANUFACTURE. Several processes are usually involved in manufacturing metal powder products.

Selection. Since the particle fineness, shape, and size distribution in a powder all influence the density, proper selection requires experience and a thorough knowledge of the process.

Mixing. Mixing or blending of powders is often necessary to obtain desired flowability, and density or particle size distribution. Mixing is also necessary when non-metallics are added. Practically all powders have lubricants (stearic acid, lithium stearate, powdered graphite, etc.) added to reduce wall friction in the dies and to aid in the ejection of the compact.

Pressing. Metal parts are produced from powders by pressing them to shape under high pressure in suitable steel dies as shown in Fig. 5 (Moraine Products Div., General Motors). Because soft particles can be pressed together quite readily, powders that are plastic do not require so high a pressure as the harder

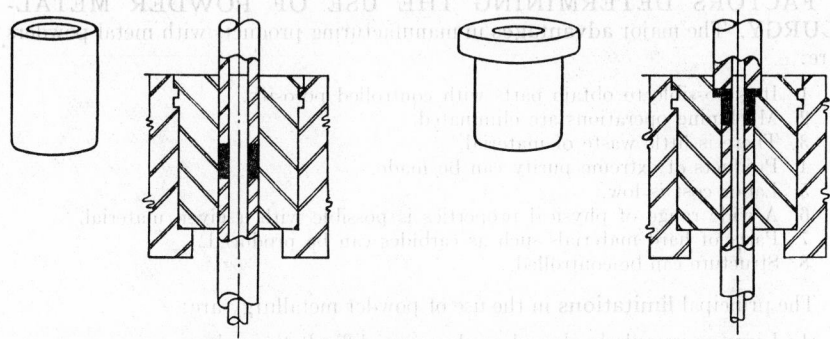

Fig. 5. **Briquetting punch and die for forming hollow cylindrical parts.**

powders to obtain adequate density. Quite obviously the hardness and density increase with pressure up to some optimum pressure above which little change in properties takes place. The product resulting from the pressing operation is known as a **cold or green compact.** In a few cases sufficient strength is obtained by this operation but usually subsequent heating is necessary.

Sintering. Heating a green compact to some elevated temperature below the melting point of the principal powder is known as sintering. This should be done in a reducing atmosphere soon after the compact is made. Both batch and continuous-type furnaces are used in this operation. In all cases, temperature and time should be closely controlled. The application of heat to the compact, at temperatures above the **recrystallization temperature** of the metal, increases the plasticity and mechanical interlocking of the particles, presses them into more intimate contact, and facilitates the bonding of the solid particles by atomic forces.

Sizing and Finishing. Since there is always some size change or distortion after sintering, a sizing or coining operation is often necessary. This provides close tolerance to the part and improves its strength. All pressed metal products can be heat treated, but the best results are obtained with those having dense structures. Increase in strength and density can also be obtained by dipping the sintered parts in molten metal so as to fill up the external pores. Recent developments permit the electroplating of these products.

Hot Pressing. In some cases, pressing and sintering are combined to provide parts with improved strength and hardness. Problems to be met with this procedure include proper atmospheric control, method of applying heat, and selection of suitable dies to resist high temperature, wear, and creep.

TYPES OF PRESSES USED. Many of the conventional mechanical and hydraulic presses can be used for the powdered metal process. Pressures for different powders vary greatly, ranging from 5 to 5,000 tons per sq. in. Pressure of from 1 to 2 tons is sufficient for hot pressing.

TOLERANCES. Tolerances are influenced by the size and shape of the part, and the kind of powder used. Vertical tolerances of ±0.002 in. can be maintained on short parts but as the length is increased a corresponding increase in tolerance must be made. Radial or side-to-side tolerances can be held to ±0.001 to 0.002 in. Slightly closer tolerances can be obtained by sizing.

FACTORS DETERMINING THE USE OF POWDER METAL-LURGY. The major **advantages** in manufacturing products with metal powders are:

1. It is possible to obtain parts with controlled porosity.
2. Machining operations are eliminated.
3. There is little waste of material.
4. Products of extreme purity can be made.
5. Labor cost is low.
6. A wide range of physical properties is possible with a given material.
7. Parts of hard materials such as carbides can be produced.
8. Structure can be controlled.

The principal **limitations** in the use of powder metallurgy are:

1. Large or irregularly shaped products are difficult to produce.
2. Cost of dies and equipment is high.
3. Cost of metal powder is high.
4. A completely dense product is not possible.
5. Some powders present explosion hazards.
6. Some thermal difficulties appear in the sintering operations with low-melting powder.

DESIGN CONSIDERATIONS. For successful operation, dies for metal powder products must be designed and constructed with extreme care. Some of the **die design requirements** are as follows:

1. Punch and die surfaces in contact with the powder must be very smooth as metal powders lack ability to flow readily.
2. The ratio of depth of die to height of finished part should not exceed 3:1 since the density of the compact is greatly affected by the depth of the die.
3. Punch pressures should be applied at both ends of the die if uniform density is required as shown in Fig. 5. An exception to this is in the production of thin parts.
4. If there is appreciable variation in the height of the part, more than one punch should be used to insure uniform density.
5. Holes at angles to the punch cannot be produced and must be machined later.
6. Undercuts such as those involved in threads cannot be formed.
7. Dies should have gradual section changes to eliminate warping during the sintering operation.
8. Dies should be provided with a slight draft to facilitate ejection of product.
9. Inside corners should be filleted to permit better punch design.
10. Outside bevels should be kept as flat as possible to avoid a feather-edge on punch.

METAL POWDER APPLICATIONS. Among the principal uses of powder metallurgy are the following:

Cemented carbides. Tungsten carbide particles are mixed with a binder such as cobalt, pressed to shape, and then sintered at a temperature above the melting point of the matrix metal.

Porous bearings. Copper with tin, graphite, or other metals are used for bearings. After sintering, the bearings are sized and impregnated with oil by a vacuum treatment.

Motor brushes. Copper is added to graphite to provide adequate brush strength; tin or lead may also be used to improve wear resistance.

Magnets. Small magnets can be produced from iron, aluminum, nickel, and cobalt when properly combined in powder form.

Contact parts. Electric-contact parts that are wear resistant, refractory, and have good electrical conductivity can be produced from a variety of metal powders.

Gears and rotors. Accurate small gears and pump rotors of iron can be produced.

Forging Processes

ELEMENTS OF FORGING. In all forging processes metal is heated to some elevated temperature to reduce it to a plastic state. In this condition it can be readily formed by pressure or impact into a predetermined shape. Forging processes may be roughly classified as smith forging, drop forging, upset forging, press forging, roll forging, and rotary swaging.

Hot-working or forging operations are done at temperatures above the work-hardening range of the metal. For steel the temperature must be above the critical range and the work is usually started at temperatures ranging from 2,200 to 2,500° F. For nonferrous metals the temperatures are much lower depending on the alloy composition. The plastic temperature range varies widely for different kinds of metals and alloys.

Forming metals to shape by forging is about the same in the various forging processes. All are commercially proven processes capable of changing raw materials, such as bars and billets, to a predetermined shape. The advantages claimed for these processes include:

1. Decreased porosity of metal.
2. Refinement of coarse grains.
3. Generally improved physical properties.
4. The breaking up and uniform distribution of the impurities in the form of inclusions.
5. Minimum finish allowances necessary.

SMITH FORGING. Smith forging consists of hammering the heated metal between flat dies in a steam hammer. It is similar to hand forging as practiced by a blacksmith in that no impression dies are used and considerable skill is required to shape the metal. The nature of the process is such that close accuracy is not obtained nor can complicated shapes be made. Forging hammers are made in the single or **open frame** type for light work and the **double housing** type for heavier service. The process is used primarily for short-run jobs and repair work which do not warrant the expense of special tooling. Forgings, ranging from a few to over 200,000 lb. are made by smith forging.

DROP FORGING. Drop forgings are produced by shaping the hot plastic metal in **closed impression dies.** Impact blows of the ram, carrying one of the dies, strike the plastic metal held on the base in the other die, compelling it to conform to some planned shape. Both dies are held in perfect alignment. To insure proper flow of the metal during these intermittent blows, the operation is divided into a number of steps. Each step changes the form in a gradual fashion, controlling the flow of the metal until the final shape is attained. The number of steps required varies according to the size and shape of the part, the forging qualities of the metal, and the tolerances required. For products of large or complicated shapes a preliminary shaping operation may be required, using more than one set of dies.

A finished forging will have a thin projection of excess metal extending around it at the parting line. This excess metal is provided to insure complete filling of the dies and is removed in a separate **trimming press** immediately after the forging operation. Small forgings may be trimmed cold. Care must be taken in the trimming operation not to distort the part. The forging is usually held uniformly by the die in the ram and pushed through the trimming edges. Punching operations may also be done while trimming.

Forging Operations. Fig. 6 (Drop Forging Association) illustrates a series of operations performed in the forging of a connecting rod. The raw material is a square billet of steel on which a small projection is prepared, as at *A*. It then goes through a **fullering** operation *B* to reduce the cross-section and the large end is

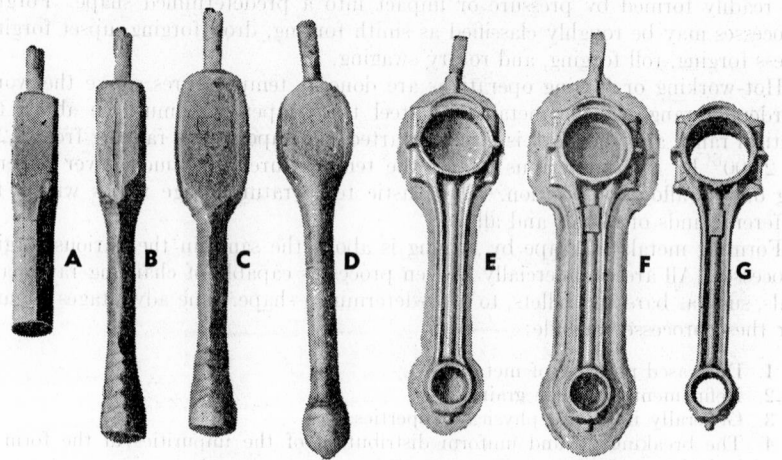

Fig. 6. Sequence of forging operations for a connecting rod.

flattened as at *C*. A second **rolling impression** *D* gathers the stock to proper proportion and the blank then undergoes a **blocking** operation *E* which forms the rod into a definite shape. The final forging operation with the surrounding flash metal is shown at *F*. The flash metal is removed in a **trimmer die** leaving a completed forging *G* ready for subsequent heat treating and machining operations.

Types of Hammers. Two types of drop-forging hammers are used—the **steam hammer** and the **gravity drop hammer**. In the former the hammer is lifted by steam and the force of the blow is controlled by throttling the steam. These hammers work very rapidly and are made in capacities ranging from 500 to 50,000 lb. For a given weight ram, a steam hammer will develop twice the energy at the die that can be obtained from a board or gravity-type hammer.

In a gravity-type hammer the impact pressure is developed by the force of the falling ram and die as it strikes upon the lower fixed die. The **board drop hammer**, illustrated in Fig. 7 (Interstate), is one type which has several hard-

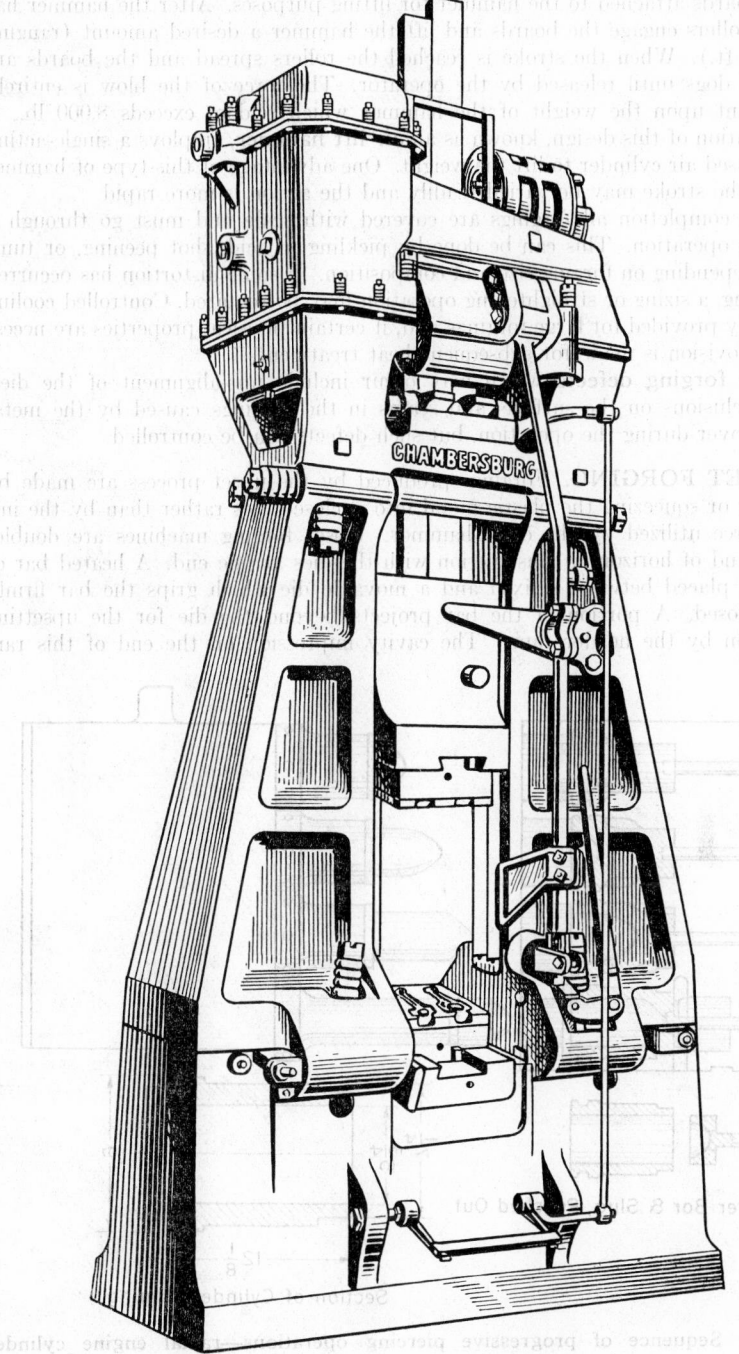

Fig. 7. Gravity-type drop hammer.

wood boards attached to the hammer for lifting purposes. After the hammer has
fallen, rollers engage the boards and lift the hammer a desired amount (ranging
up to 5 ft.). When the stroke is reached the rollers spread and the boards are
held by dogs until released by the operator. The force of the blow is entirely
dependent upon the weight of the hammer which seldom exceeds 8,000 lb. A
modification of this design, known as an **air lift hammer,** employs a single-acting
compressed air cylinder to lift the weight. One advantage of this type of hammer
is that the stroke may be varied readily and the action is more rapid.

Upon completion all forgings are covered with scale and must go through a
cleaning operation. This can be done by pickling in acid, shot peening, or tumbling, depending on forging size and composition. If some distortion has occurred
in forging, a sizing or straightening operation may be required. Controlled cooling
is usually provided for large forgings and, if certain physical properties are necessary, provision is made for subsequent heat treatment.

Drop forging defects which may occur include mis-alignment of the dies,
scale inclusions on the surface, and seams in the forgings caused by the metal
folding over during the operation, but such defects can be controlled.

UPSET FORGING. Forgings produced by the upset process are made by
pressing or squeezing the plastic metal into enclosed dies rather than by the impact force utilized by the drop hammer. Upset forging machines are double-
acting and of horizontal construction with the dies at one end. A heated bar of
stock is placed between a fixed and a movable die which grips the bar firmly
when closed. A portion of the bar projects beyond the die for the upsetting
operation by the header rams. The cavity impression on the end of this ram

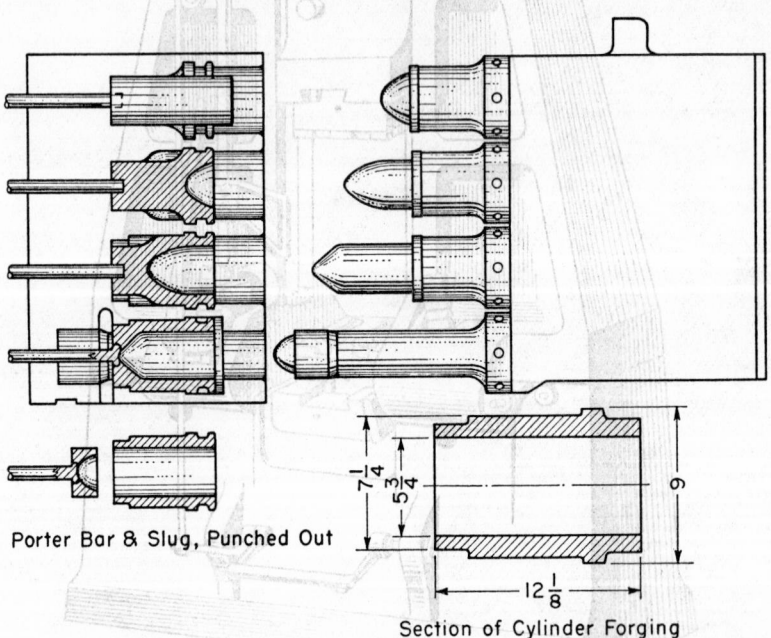

Porter Bar & Slug, Punched Out

Section of Cylinder Forging

Fig. 8. Sequence of progressive piercing operations—radial engine cylinder
forgings.

squeezes the plastic metal until it conforms to the die cavity. For some products the heading operation may be completed in one position, but in most cases the work is progressively placed into different positions in the die. The impressions may be in a punch, gripping die, or both. In most instances these forgings do not require a trimming operation.

Progressive piercing, or internal displacement, is the method frequently employed on upset forging machines for producing parts such as artillery shells and radial engine cylinder forgings. The sequence of operations is shown in Fig. 8, (Ajax Mfg. Co.). Round blanks of a predetermined length for a single cylinder are first heated to forging temperature. To facilitate handling the blank, a porter bar is then pressed into one end. In the following three operations the blank is upset and progressively pierced to a heavy-bottomed cup. In the last operation a tapered-nosed punch expands and stretches the metal into the end of the die, frees the porter bar and punches out the end slug. Large cylinder barrels weighing over 100 lb. can be forged in this manner.

Parts produced by this process vary in weight up to several hundred pounds, The dies are not limited to upsetting; they may also be used for piercing, punching, trimming, or extrusion.

PRESS FORGING. Like the upset forging process, press forging employs a slow squeezing action in deforming the plastic metal as contrasted to the rapid impact blows of the drop hammer. Presses are the vertical type and may be either mechanically or hydraulically operated. The mechanical presses, which are the faster and most commonly used, range in capacities from 500 to 10,000 tons.

Closed impression dies are used for producing press forged products which are finished in one to three steps in most cases. The maximum pressure in these presses is built up at the end of the stroke which forces the metal into shape. Dies are often mounted as separate units, but all of the cavities may be put into a single block. For small forgings individual die units are more convenient. There is some difference in the design of dies for various metals. Copper alloy forgings of brass and bronze can be made with less draft than steel; consequently more complicated shapes can be produced. These alloys flow well in the die and are readily extruded. Most press forgings are symmetrical in shape, having surfaces which are quite smooth and provide a closer tolerance than obtained by a drop hammer. Therefore, presses used for sizing operations in other forging processes are not needed in the press forging process.

ROLL FORGING. Roll forging machines are primarily adapted to reducing and tapering operations on short lengths of bar stock. The rolls on the machine are not completely circular but have from 50 to 75 percent cut away to permit the stock to enter between the rolls. The circular portion of the rolls is grooved according to the shaping to be done, as shown in Fig. 9 (National Machinery Co.). When the rolls are in open position the operator places the heated bar between them, retaining it with tongs. As the rolls rotate, the bar is gripped by the roll grooves and pushed toward the operator. When the rolls open, the bar is pushed back and rolled again or is placed in the next groove for subsequent forming work. By rotating the bar 90° after each roll pass, there is no opportunity for flash to form.

Examples of **roll-forged parts** include axles, blanks for airplane propellers, crowbars, knife blades, chisels, tapered tubing, and ends of leaf springs. In some cases stock is prepared for subsequent forging by other forging operations.

Fig. 9. Forging rolls making connecting rod blank.

Parts made in this fashion have a smooth-finished surface and tolerances equal to other forging processes. The metal is hot-worked thoroughly and has good physical properties. Because of the high cost of the rolls, a large volume of production is necessary to amortize successfully the tooling expense.

ROTARY SWAGING. Rotary swaging is a means of reducing the ends of bars, tubing, or round stock by repeated hammering from rotating dies as they open and close on the work. The head of the machine, shown in Fig. 10, is located at the end of a large hollow spindle through which the work can move. Around the end are rollers which contact the dies when the machine is in operation.

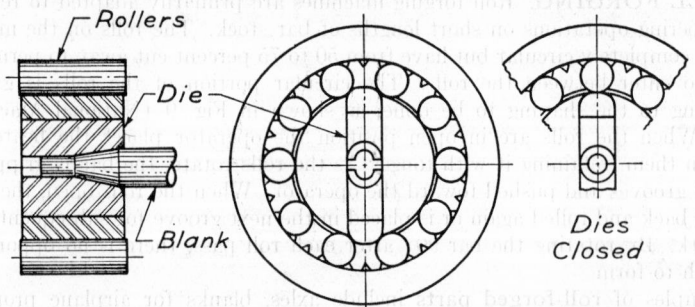

Begeman, Manufacturing Processes

Fig. 10. The operation of dies in a swaging machine.

Centrifugal force opens the dies to permit entry of the work; they then remain open only until the opposite ends are contacted by rollers which force them together again. The rapidity of this pressing or hammering action depends on the rotational speed of the head and the roller spacing.

Most swaging is done on cold metal although it is sometimes used for hot-working when severe reductions are to be made. The effect on the metal is similar to that obtained by other cold-working processes, namely, hardness and strength are increased, grain structure distorted, and a clean smooth surface obtained. Hot-working is necessary on some operations and for some metals, but this results in an appreciable loss in surface finish, tolerance, and physical properties.

Basic operations done by rotary swaging include reducing, pointing, forming, and attaching. The finished product in all cases is round but the size varies. Examples include pointing bars or valve needles, forming axle ends, gear shift levers, golf club shafts and other tubular parts, and the attaching of fittings to ends of steel cables. Capacities range from small machines having a maximum work diameter of 1/16 in. to much larger ones capable of handling stock up to around 6 in. The production rate of these machines is high.

Stamping and Forming

BASIC PROCESSES. Stamping and forming operations are usually cold-working processes involved in the shearing, forming, and stamping of metals in a press. Such machines consist of a frame supporting a bed and a ram, a source of power, and a mechanism to cause the ram to move in a line with and at right angles to the bed. A press must be equipped with punches and dies, designed to perform certain planned operations which are rapid since they are completed with one stroke of the ram.

TYPES OF PRESSES. Of necessity there is a wide variety of presses suited to many types of operations. Classification is usually made according to the manner in which the power is applied, the purpose of the press, or the design features of the frame. For thin sheets of metal there are many **hand operated** presses which are satisfactory for jobbing work. These machines are mostly for general purpose operations such as bending, shearing, seaming, and simple punching. The majority of production presses are **power operated** using various mechanisms such as cranks, eccentrics, screws, gears, knuckle-joints, cams, toggle joints, or hydraulic means to effect the necessary pressure. A large variety of operations can be performed by these presses depending on their design and the type of dies used. Classification according to the **types of press operations** performed is as follows:

1. **Shearing**—blanking, trimming, cutting off, punching, perforating, notching, slitting, shaving, and lancing.
2. **Bending**—angle bending, curling, folding, seaming, and straightening.
3. **Drawing**—cupping, forming tubes, embossing, and reducing.
4. **Squeezing**—coining, sizing, flattening, upsetting, swaging, riveting, and extruding.

BLANKING AND SHEARING. Blanking and shearing are performed on fast operating crank or eccentric presses. As the punch descends upon the metal, the pressure first causes a plastic deformation to take place, as at (b) in Fig. 11, from Begeman, Manufacturing Processes. The metal is stressed in shear, and fractures start on both sides as the deformation progresses. When the ultimate strength of the material is reached the fractures progress and, if the clearance is correct, they meet at the center of the sheet.

Blanking operations usually apply to fairly large areas where the sheet metal is to be cut to a certain shape. Punching holes in metal, notching metal from edges, or perforating are all similar operations, but the metal removed varies. **Trimming** is the removal of "flash" or excess metal from around the edges of a part and is essentially a blanking operation. **Shaving** is similar to trimming but involves the removal of less metal. **Slitting** is making incomplete cuts in a sheet as with a scissors. If a hole is partially punched and one side bent down as in a louver, it is called **lancing**. These operations may all be done on presses of the same type and differ only in the dies that are used.

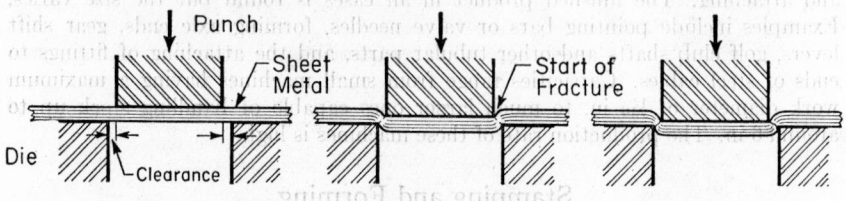

(a) Punch Contacting Metal   (b) Plastic Deformation   (c) Fracture Complete
and Fracture Starting

Fig. 11. Progress of plastic deformation and fracture during a punching operation.

BENDING AND FORMING. Bending and forming may be performed on the same type of equipment as that used for shearing—namely, crank, eccentric, and cam operated presses. In processes involving bending, the metal is stressed in both tension and compression at values below the ultimate strength of the metal. As in a press brake, simple bending implies a straight bend across the sheet of metal. Other bending operations such as curling, seaming, and folding are similar but slightly more involved.

In designing a rectangular bar for bending, one must determine how much metal should be allowed for the bend since the outer fibers are elongated and the inner ones are shortened. During the operation the neutral axis of the bar is moved in toward the compression side which throws more of the fibers in tension. The entire thickness is slightly decreased, with the width being increased on the compression side and narrowed on the other. Correct lengths for bends can be determined by empirical formulas but they are influenced considerably by the physical properties of the metal. Metal which has been bent retains some of its original elasticity and there is some elastic recovery after the punch is removed. This is known as **spring back**. The fibers in compression expand slightly and those in tension contract, the combined action resulting in a slight opening up of the bend. Spring back may be corrected by overbending by an amount such that when the pressure is released the part will return to the required shape.

In the forming and cutting of thin sheet aluminum parts for aircraft manufacture, use of the **Guerin process**, utilizing a thick pad of rubber for the punch, reduces tooling costs. Rubber proves satisfactory in this process because of its similarity to a fluid when properly restrained. Thick pads of rubber are mounted on the ram of the press and confined in a container which extends just below the pads. Appropriate, low-cost dies are placed on the press bed. As the platen moves down and the rubber is confined, the force of the ram is exerted evenly in all directions, resulting in the sheet metal being pressed against the die block, as shown in Fig. 12, also from Begeman. **Forming dies** may be made of Masonite, wood, aluminum, or steel. This process is limited to the cutting of soft aluminum in sheet thickness up to 0.051 in. For bending and forming, the usual limit of thickness is around ³⁄₁₆ in. This process provides simplicity of tooling, use of gang setups on press, and adaptability to various press operations.

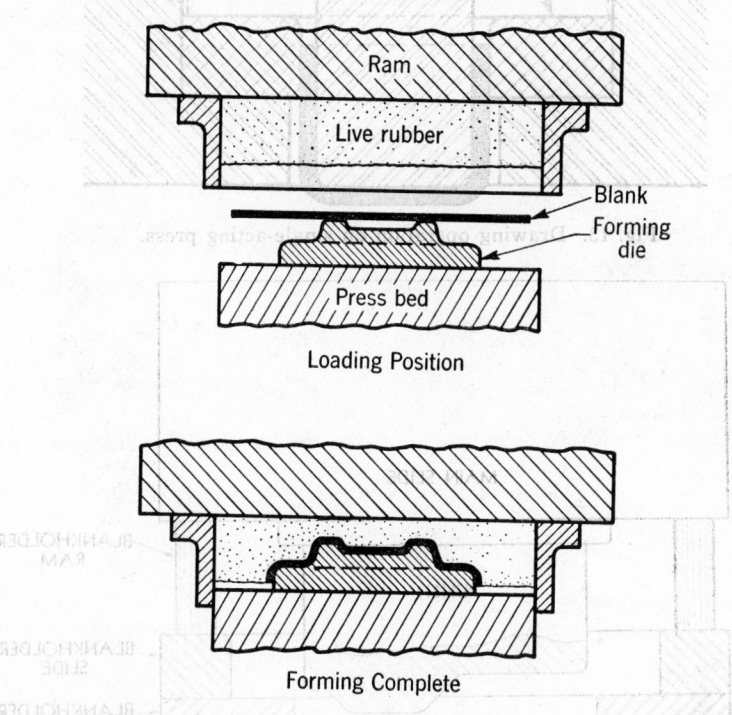

Fig. 12. Method of forming sheet metal using single die and rubber punch.

DRAWING. Drawing is similar to bending or forming except that it requires greater plastic flow in the metal. Stresses are involved which exceed the elastic limit strength of the metal so as to permit the metal to conform to the punch. However, these stresses cannot exceed the ultimate strength without cracks developing. Most drawn parts start with a flat plate of metal. As the punch is forced into the metal, severe tensile stresses are induced in the sheet while it is formed about the punch. At the same time the outer edges of the sheet which have not engaged the punch are in compression and undesirable wrinkles tend to form. In most cases this must be counteracted by a blank-holder or **pressure plate** which holds the flat plate firmly in place.

In simple drawing operations of relatively thick plates, the plate thickness may be sufficient to counteract wrinkling tendencies and the operation may be done in a **single-acting press,** as shown in Fig. 13, from Begeman. Additional draws may be made on the cup-shaped part, each one elongating it and reducing the wall thickness.

Most drawing, involving the shaping of thin metal sheets, requires the use of **double-acting presses** so that the sheet may be held in place as the drawing

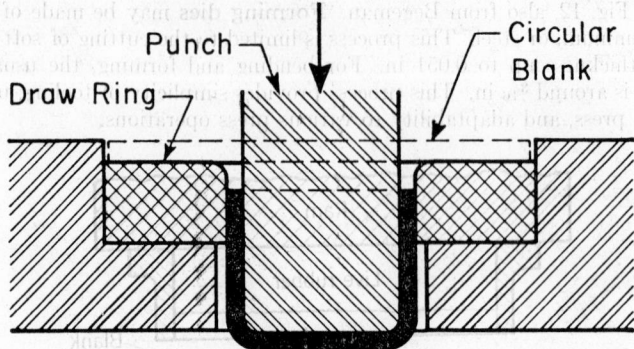

Fig. 13. Drawing operation on single-acting press.

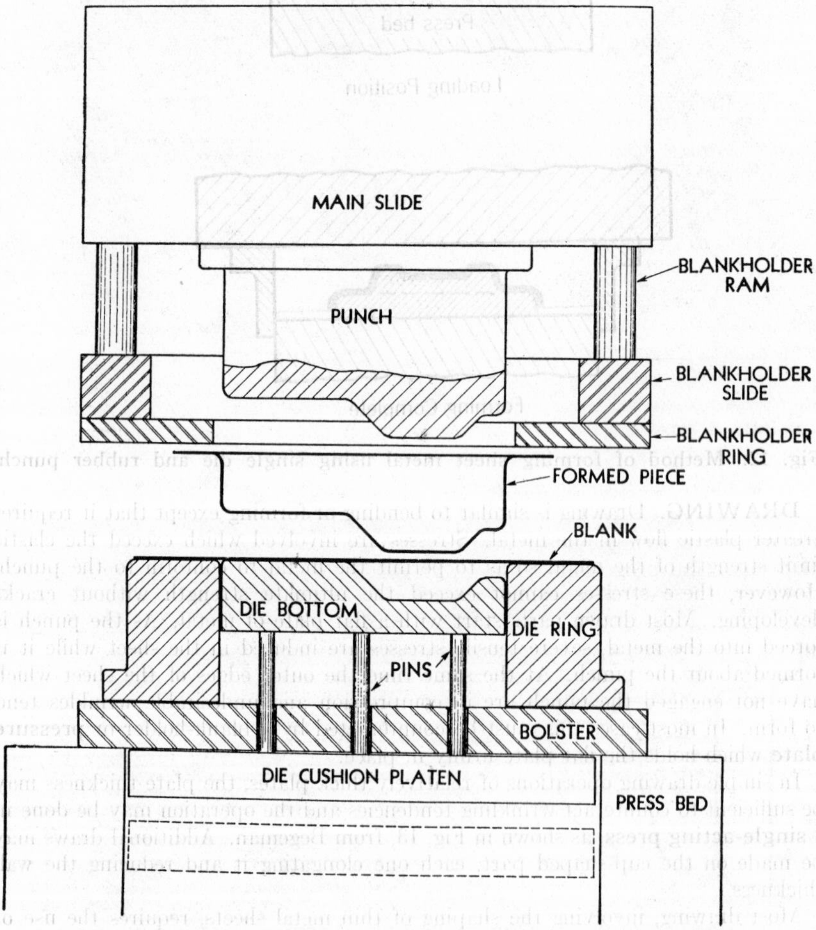

Fig. 14. Punch and die arrangement for deep drawing sheet steel.

progresses. Presses of this type vary considerably in performance but usually two slides are provided, one within the other. One slide moves to the sheet ahead of the other and holds it in place. The motion of the slide is controlled by a toggle or cam mechanism in connection with the crank. Hydraulic presses are also well adapted for drawing because of their relatively slow action, close speed control, and the uniform pressure obtainable during the drawing. Fig. 14 (Hydraulic Press Mfg. Co.), shows the sectional diagram of drawing dies mounted on a hydraulic press. In this case the punch and blank-holder advance together until the blank is reached. As the blank and die are contacted the punch continues its downward movement while the blank-holding ring maintains contact with the blank edges during drawing.

The **Marform process,** employing a rubber punch, may also be used for deep drawing and for the forming of irregularly shaped parts. It combines the features of the Guerin process and the conventional deep drawing process. The confined rubber pad is mounted on the movable slide and, surrounded by the blank holding plate, the punch is below. As the slide descends, the rubber pad contacts the blank and clamps it securely against both the top of the punch and the surrounding plate. As the operation progresses, the blank is formed over the punch and at the same time sufficient pressure is exerted over the unformed section to prevent wrinkles. Any tendency for tearing of the metal, in the drawn part, is materially reduced by the pressure exerted against the metal as the operation progresses. During the drawing operation, the downward movement of the blank holding plate is opposed by pressure pins which can be controlled to exert any pressure.

ROLL FORMING. Cold roll-forming is accomplished by a series of mating rolls in line which progressively form strip metal as it is fed continuously through the machine. The number of **roll stations** required on a machine depends upon the intricacy of the part being formed; for a simple angle two pairs may be used, whereas for a tube some six or more may be required. Most of the roll stations are in a horizontal position although vertical rolls may also be required for guiding, straightening, or assisting in the forming operation. As the products emerge from the machine, other operations such as cutting to length, seam welding, or additional bending may be incorporated.

A sequence of forming operations for a window screen section is shown in Fig. 15 (Yoder Co.). The vertical center or **pass line** is first established so that the number of bends on either side is about the same. Forming usually starts at the center and progresses out to the two edges as the sheet moves through successive roll passes. The amount of bending at any one roll station is limited. If

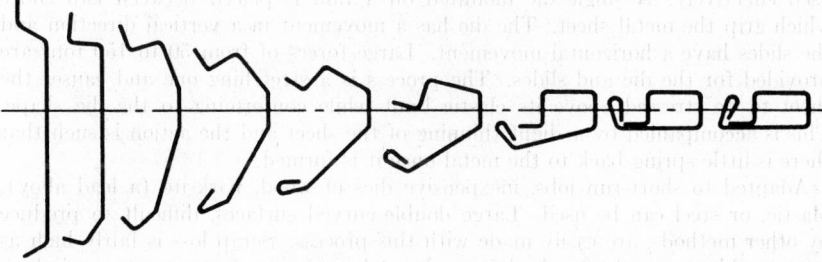

Fig. 15. Sequence of operations in the rolling of a window screen section.

the bending is too great it carries back through the sheet and affects the action at the preceding roll station. Corner bends are limited to a radius of the sheet thickness.

In terms of capacity for working mild steel, standard machines form strips up to 0.156 in. thick by 16 in. wide. Special units have been made for much heavier and wider strip steel. The process is rapid since most machines operate at around 100 ft. per min. It is applicable to the forming of products having sections requiring a uniform thickness of material throughout their entire length. Unless production requirements are high, the cost of the machine and tooling cannot be justified.

EMBOSSING AND COINING. Embossing and coining, illustrated by Begeman (Manufacturing Processes) in Fig. 16, are similar in appearance; yet the action in the metal differs. **Coining** is performed in an enclosed die and the metal flow is restricted in a lateral direction. It is accomplished by an impact or compressive force which causes the metal to flow in the shallow configurations of the blank being coined. Coining operations are restricted to soft metals and alloys.

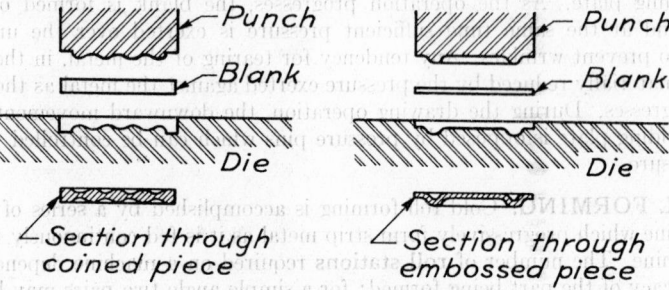

Fig. 16. Coining and embossing.

Embossing is more of a forming or drawing operation. The metal is stretched or formed according to the configuration as in the dies. Both the punch and die have the same configuration so there is little squeezing of the metal to change its thickness. The punch is usually relieved so that it touches the metal only at the place being embossed. The action in making deep configurations is similar to that of drawing and there is often some decrease in metal thickness.

METAL STRETCHING. In the forming of large sheets of thin metal involving symmetrical shapes or double-curve bends, a metal stretch press can be used effectively. A single die mounted on a ram is placed between two slides which grip the metal sheet. The die has a movement in a vertical direction and the slides have a horizontal movement. Large forces of from 50 to 150 tons are provided for the die and slides. The process is a stretching one and causes the sheet to be stressed above its elastic limit while conforming to the die shape. This is accompanied by a slight thinning of the sheet and the action is such that there is little spring-back to the metal once it is formed.

Adapted to short-run jobs, inexpensive dies of wood, Kirksite (a lead alloy), plastic, or steel can be used. Large double-curved surfaces, difficult to produce by other methods, are easily made with this process. Scrap loss is fairly high as considerable material must be left at the ends and sides for trimming and there is a limitation to the shapes that can be formed.

Welding Processes

ELEMENTS OF WELDING. Welding is the fusion or uniting of two pieces of metal by heat or a combination of heat and pressure. This important process has been so highly developed and diversified in recent years that it is now a necessity in every manufacturing plant which uses metal for such purposes as casting repair, building erection and repair, piping, bridge building, fabrication of pressure vessels, sheetmetal, household appliances, automobiles, airframes, and guided missiles. The great variety of welding processes can be divided into two basic groups, electric welding and gas welding. Brazing and soldering differ in that they do not require fusion of the parent metal.

All welding processes are facilitated by the **parent metal preparations**— grinding, machining, wire brushing, sand blasting, or degreasing. Impurities in the weld tend to decrease the joint strength and cause such imperfections as poor penetration, gas pockets, cracks, slag inclusions, excess oxidation, and poor appearance. Soundness and appearance of any weld are also improved by proper "fit up" and **alignment of the parts** prior to, and during, welding. Choice of the

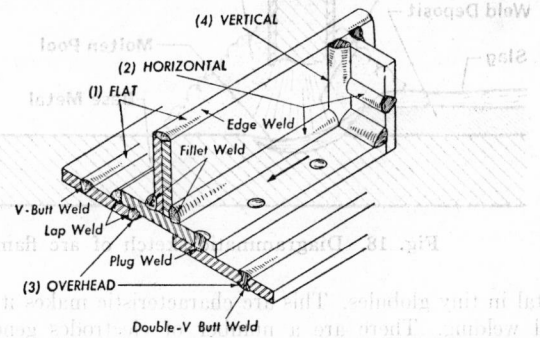

Lincoln Electric Co.

Fig. 17. Basic types of welded joints and their positions.

proper process for the particular welding job is of utmost importance. Information on procedure and welder qualification can be found in the Welding Handbook, published by the American Welding Society. Various codes and specifications for pressure vessels and special processes are also available from the "Codes, Standards and Specifications," American Welding Society. Berard, Waters, and Phelps (Principles of Machine Design) illustrate the principal types of joints used in most welding processes in Fig. 17. The forms may vary slightly according to the thickness of the material, but all can be used for either gas or arc welding.

ARC WELDING. Arc welding is a welding process in which coalescence is obtained by heat produced from an electric arc between the work and the electrode. Contact is first made between the work and electrode to create an electric circuit, and then, by separating the conductors, an arc is formed. The arc attains a temperature of 9,000°–10,000° F. causing the adjacent metal to melt almost instantly.

Arc welding equipment produces either alternating or direct current. Most A.C. machines are simple transformers with output ratings in the neighborhood of 200–300 amp. at 18–25 volts, 60 cycle. Some special purpose A.C. machines have high frequency attachments. D.C. machines are either motor generator sets, gasoline-engine or electric-motor driven, or a.c. rectifiers. These machines are built with capacities up to 600 amp., having an open circuit voltage of 50 to 95 volts. The machines most widely used are rated at 200 amp., with an actual output of from 40 to 250 amp. and a closed circuit voltage of 18 to 25 amp. **Rectifier**-type D.C. welders, readily available, are rapidly gaining wide usage. More recent models provide both A.C. and D.C. output at the option of the operator.

Arc Welding with Coated Electrodes. Williams and Harris (Structural Design in Metals) illustrate the action of the arc using a heavy coated electrode (Fig. 18). In operation, the molten metal from the electrode is forced onto the

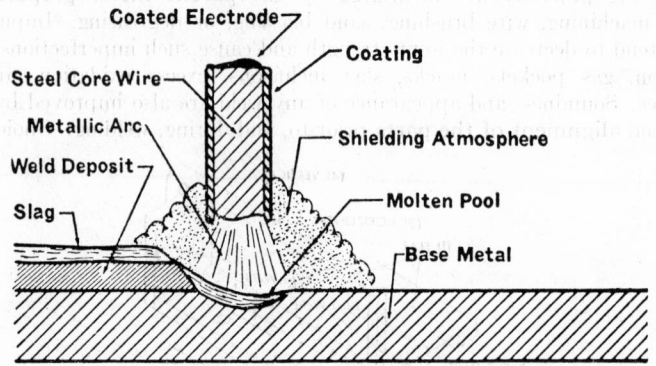

Fig. 18. Diagrammatic sketch of arc flame.

base metal in tiny globules. This arc characteristic makes it possible to perform overhead welding. There are a number of electrodes generally designated as heavy coated. The American Welding Society's tentative specifications for mild steel arc welding electrodes are listed in Fig. 19 (AWS Designation A5.1–48T). Coalescence is produced by the heating effect from the arc between the coated electrode and the work piece. Shielding is obtained from the coating, the electrode being used as filler metal. The heavy coatings stabilize the arc, prevent formation of oxides and nitrides, provide a slag to protect the weld, slow the cooling rate, and perform metallurgical refining operations. This **shielded-metal arc process** is applicable to all metals, providing the proper electrode is used, and is the most widely used of all welding processes.

Impregnated Tape Metal Arc Welding. In this method, an electrode encased in an impregnated tape wrapping is used. Fusion or coalescence is produced in the same manner as in the shielded metal arc process. Because the tape is wrapped around the bare wire just ahead of the arc, an automatic machine is required. Excellent welds are produced by this process.

Atomic Hydrogen Arc Welding. Here, single-phase A.C. current is utilized to produce the arc between two tungsten electrodes. Hydrogen is introduced into the arc through electrode clamps or holders. As the hydrogen enters the arc, the molecules are broken up into atoms which recombine into molecules of hydrogen outside the arc. This reaction is accompanied by the liberation of intense heat,

MILD STEEL ARC-WELDING ELECTRODES

Electrode Classification Number	Type of Coating or Covering	Capable of Producing Satisfactory Welds in Positions Shown*	Type of Current
E45 Series: Minimum Tensile Strength of Deposited Metal in Non-Stress-Relieved Condition 45,000 Psi			
E4510	Sulcoated or	F, V, OH, H	Not specified, but generally D.C., straight polarity (electrode negative)
E4520	Light coated	H-Fillets, F	
E60 Series: Minimum Tensile Strength of Deposited Metal in Non-Stress-Relieved Condition 62,000 Psi or Higher			
E6010	High cellulose sodium	F, V, OH, H	For use with D.C., reversed polarity (electrode positive) only.
E6011	High cellulose potassium	F, V, OH, H	For use with A.C. or D.C., reversed polarity (electrode positive).
E6012	High titania sodium	F, V, OH, H	For use with D.C., straight polarity (electrode negative), or A.C.
E6013	High titania potassium	F, V, OH, H	For use with A.C. or D.C., straight polarity (electrode negative).
E6015	Low hydrogen sodium	F, V, OH, H	For use with D.C., reversed polarity (electrode positive) only.
E6016	Low hydrogen potassium	F, V, OH, H	For use with A.C. or D.C., reversed polarity (electrode positive).
E6020	High iron oxide	H-Fillets, F	For use with D.C., straight polarity (electrode negative), or A.C., for horizontal fillet welds; and D.C., either polarity, or A.C., for flat-position welding.
E6030	High iron oxide	F	For use with D.C., either polarity, or A.C.

* The abbreviations F, H, V, OH, and H-Fillets indicate welding positions (For electrodes ³⁄₁₆ in. and under except in classifications E6015 and E6016, where electrodes ⁵⁄₃₂ in. and under are used):

F—Flat.
H—Horizontal.
H-Fillets—Horizontal fillets.
V—Vertical.
OH—Overhead.

Fig. 19. Electrode classification chart.

attaining a temperature approximating 11,000° F. Fig. 20 shows the electrode holder and the manner in which the hydrogen is supplied to the arc.

This process, whether used automatically or manually, has three distinct **advantages:** the arc temperature is very high, the tool holder can be moved about without extinguishing the arc, and the work and electrode are shielded by an atmosphere of hydrogen. Operating cost is somewhat more than for other

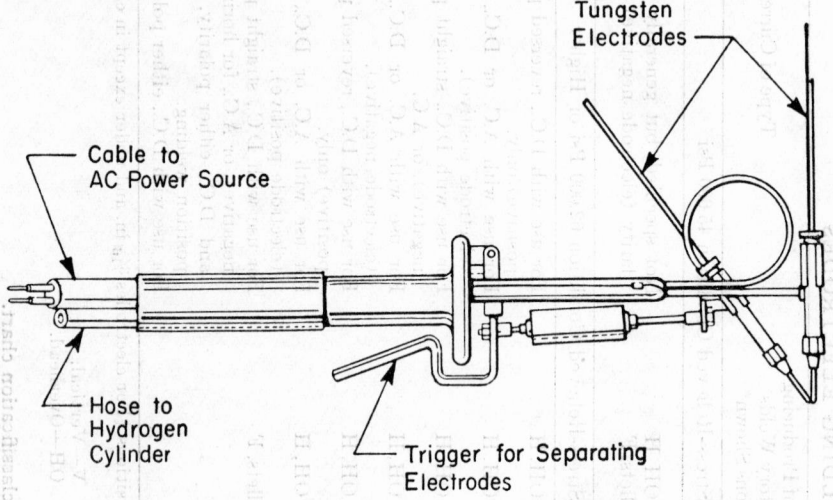

Begeman, Manufacturing Processes

Fig. 20. Atomic hydrogen arc-welding electrode holder.

arc welding processes. The atomic hydrogen process produces metallurgically sound welds in materials such as stainless steel, tool steels, heat resisting alloys, and other alloys normally difficult to weld. **Filler metal** can be added as needed in either bare or fluxed form. Resulting welds are clean, smooth, free from scale, and respond well to heat treatment.

Inert-Gas-Shielded Metal Arc Welding. This is a process in which coalescence is produced by heat from an arc between a metal electrode and the work, which is shielded by an atmosphere of either argon or helium. Filler metal may or may not be used. Tungsten electrodes are generally used because their melting point is high and they are not consumed in the inert atmosphere. Addition of filler metal requires use of a separate welding rod. Automatic or manually operated holders which use a consumable wire electrode are available. Inert-gas-shielded metal arc welding is especially adaptable to welding aluminum, magnesium, beryllium, copper, and stainless steels and is suitable for welding almost all metals without the use of fluxes. The Linde Air Products Co. illustrates a tungsten electrode torch used in this process in Fig. 21.

Submerged Arc Welding. This technique is so named because the metal arc is shielded by a blanket of **granular fusible flux** during welding. The consumable welding electrode is automatically fed through the welding head and into the vee-groove, as shown in Fig. 22 (Linde Air Products Co.). As molten metal is formed in the joint, some of the granular flux is melted. The latter floats on top of the weld and, upon cooling, solidifies into a protective coating over the

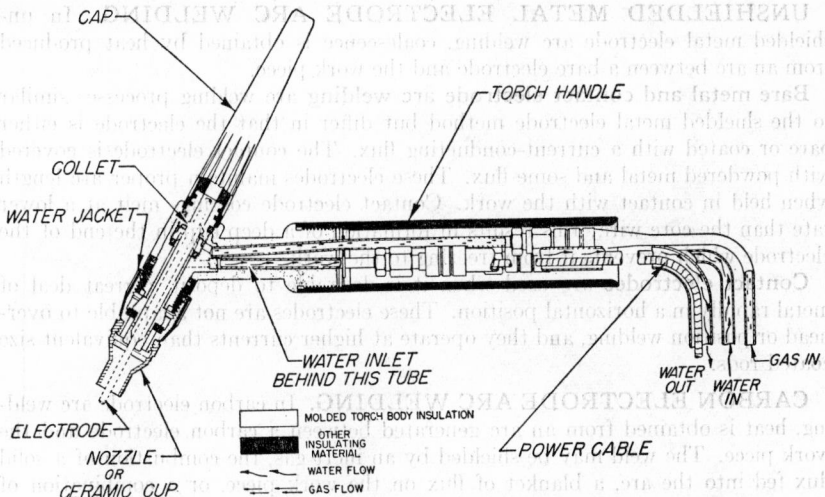

CAP

TORCH HANDLE

COLLET

WATER JACKET

ELECTRODE

NOZZLE
OR
CERAMIC CUP

WATER INLET
BEHIND THIS TUBE

WATER
OUT   WATER
IN

GAS IN

POWER CABLE

MOLDED TORCH BODY INSULATION
OTHER
INSULATING
MATERIAL
WATER FLOW
GAS FLOW

Fig. 21. Hand-welding torch for inert-gas-shielded arc welding.

weld. High welding currents which permit rapid welding speed and metal transfer can be used. This process is used primarily on flat welds where high production and deep penetration are required. While particularly adaptable to low carbon and alloy steels, the process may also be used on many nonferrous materials.

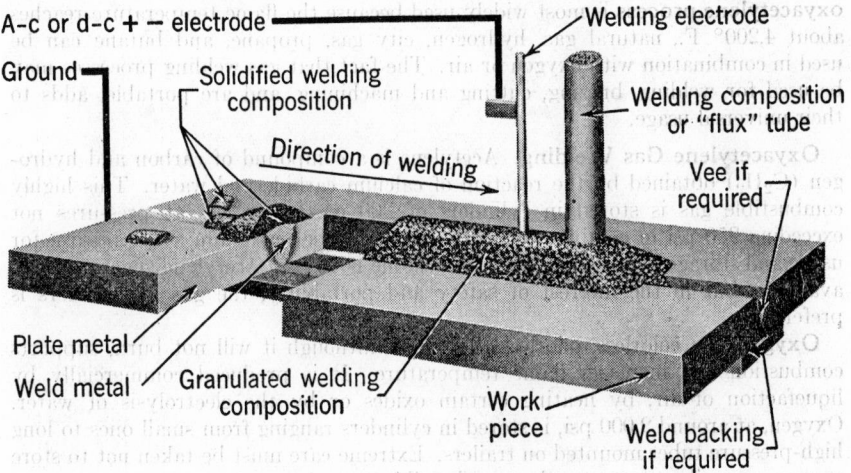

A-c or d-c + − electrode

Welding electrode

Ground

Solidified welding
composition

Welding composition
or "flux" tube

Direction of welding

Vee if
required

Plate metal

Weld metal

Granulated welding
composition

Work
piece

Weld backing
if required

Fig. 22. Submerged arc welding.

Shielded-Stud Arc Welding. This method is used to end-weld metal studs to flat surfaces. It is a D.C. process utilizing a pistol-shaped gun to hold the stud, which in turn, is shielded by a ceramic ferrule. Heat is generated by the arc developed between stud and plate. After heating, pressure is utilized to effect the weld. Such welding is used in shipbuilding and industrial applications involving metal fasteners.

UNSHIELDED METAL ELECTRODE ARC WELDING. In unshielded metal electrode arc welding, coalescence is obtained by heat produced from an arc between a bare electrode and the work piece.

Bare metal and contact electrode arc welding are welding processes similar to the shielded metal electrode method but differ in that the electrode is either bare or coated with a current-conducting flux. The contact electrode is covered with powdered metal and some flux. These electrodes maintain proper arc length when held in contact with the work. Contact electrode coatings melt at a lower rate than the core wire; this results in formation of a deep cup in the end of the electrode which prevents it from freezing to the work.

Contact electrodes are used when it is desirable to deposit a great deal of metal rapidly in a horizontal position. These electrodes are not adaptable to overhead or position welding, and they operate at higher currents than equivalent size coated rods.

CARBON ELECTRODE ARC WELDING. In carbon electrode arc welding, heat is obtained from an arc generated between a carbon electrode and the work piece. The weld may be shielded by an inert gas, the combustion of a solid flux fed into the arc, a blanket of flux on the work piece, or a combination of these. When twin carbon electrodes are used, heating is obtained from the arc produced between the two electrodes. The unit is used manually, much like an oxyacetylene torch. Pressure and filler metal may or may not be used. Steel, galvanized iron, and cast iron are the metals most frequently welded by this process.

GAS WELDING AND CUTTING. Gas welding includes all of the processes in which gases are combined to produce a hot flame. Although the **oxyacetylene process** is most widely used because the flame temperature reaches about 4,200° F., natural gas, hydrogen, city gas, propane, and butane can be used in combination with oxygen or air. The fact that gas welding processes may be used for welding, brazing, cutting and machining, and are portable, adds to their universal usage.

Oxyacetylene Gas Welding. Acetylene is a compound of carbon and hydrogen (C_2H_2) obtained by the reaction of calcium carbide and water. This highly combustible gas is stored in cylinders of 300 cu. ft. or less at pressures not exceeding 250 psi in combination with acetone. The maximum safe pressure for usage and storage of acetylene without acetone is 15 psi. Acetylene generators are available, but in the interest of safety and portability, the gas in cylinders is preferred.

Oxygen is a colorless, odorless gas which, although it will not burn, supports combustion and increases flame temperature. It is produced commercially by liquefaction of air, by heating certain oxides or by the electrolysis of water. Oxygen, at around 2,000 psi, is stored in cylinders ranging from small ones to long high-pressure tubes mounted on trailers. Extreme care must be taken not to store oxygen near oil, grease, or other combustible materials.

The **welding torch** is a device for mixing low pressure gases and delivering them to the welding tip where they are burned. The resulting oxyacetylene flame may, with excess oxygen, be oxidizing; with approximately a one-to-one ratio, be neutral; or, with excess acetylene, be carburizing. The neutral flame is used in most applications. Steel pipe, plate, and sheet are fusion welded with a neutral flame using a steel filler rod without flux. High carbon steel requires a carburizing flame, while brass is best welded with an oxidizing flame.

Oxyacetylene welding has the advantage of being inexpensive, portable, and versatile. Particularly adapted to welding of wrought iron and plain carbon steel, it can also be used for many nonferrous metals, flame hardening, and hard-surfacing of materials.

Air-Acetylene Welding. In this gas welding process, oxygen is replaced with air, and the resulting torch is not unlike a Bunsen burner. Therefore the flame temperature is necessarily low and, as a consequence, the uses are limited to low temperature brazing and soldering operations.

Oxyhydrogen Welding. The oxyhydrogen flame, produced with equipment similar to that used in oxyacetylene welding, operates at about 3,700° F. Larger torch tips are employed and control of the gas mixtures is critical in this process. It is used primarily for welding thin sheets and metals with low melting points, as well as for some brazing. A reducing atmosphere results in good quality welds.

Pressure Welding. Pressure gas welding utilizes an oxyacetylene flame to heat the surfaces to be joined in a butt welding operation. As can be seen in Fig. 23, from Begeman (Manufacturing Processes), the joint ends are heated, the torch is removed, and pressure is applied to produce coalescence. A variation of this

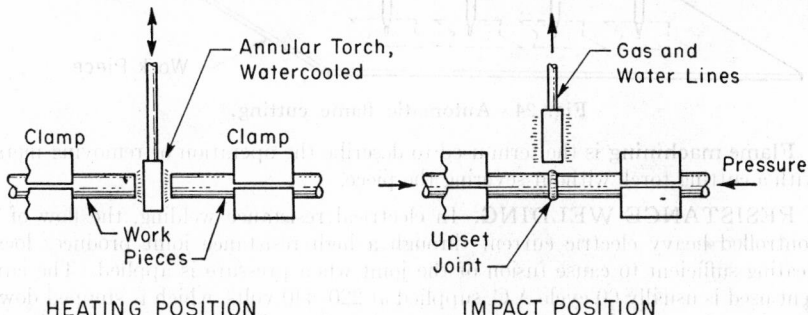

Fig. 23. Schematic of pressure gas welding.

method starts with the abutting areas together while heat is applied, pressure being added when the proper upsetting temperature is reached. Pressures vary from 1,500 psi to 4,000 psi, depending upon the metal to be joined and the size and type of joint.

Pressure welding is useful primarily in the joining of rods, tubes, rails, and pipes. It is employed also in the welding of dissimilar metals, such as high speed steel and carbon steel.

Gas Cutting and Flame Machining. Flame cutting of steel has developed into an important process in the steel fabrication industry. Simple hand or automatic torches with portable accessory equipment make gas cutting an economical process where accuracy is not paramount.

The tip of a cutting torch is so arranged that a number of preheating oxyacetylene flames circle the central passage through which oxygen passes. The steel is first preheated to around 1,800° F.; then a jet of oxygen is directed on it. Instantaneously the steel is burned into an iron oxide slag. Hydrogen, natural gas, or propane can also be used for preheating.

Gas cutting is used either manually or automatically to prepare plate edges, shape large or small parts, scarf rounds, or to cut plate, bar, or sheet. An example of automatic cutting with multiple torches is shown in Fig. 24, also from Begeman. Material up to 30 in. thick can be torch-cut. Cast iron, nonferrous alloys, and high manganese alloys are not readily cut by this process.

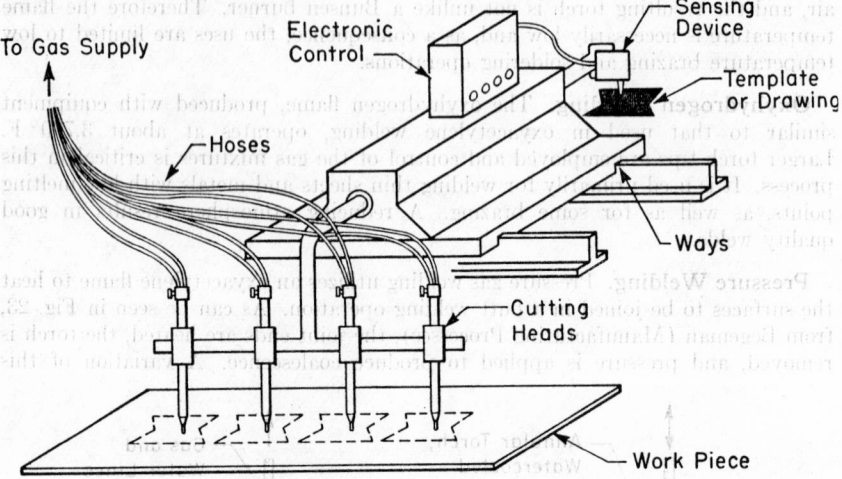

Fig. 24. Automatic flame cutting.

Flame machining is the term used to describe the operation of removing metal with a cutting torch without severing the piece.

RESISTANCE WELDING. In electrical resistance welding, the flow of a controlled heavy electric current through a high resistance joint produces local heating sufficient to cause fusion of the joint when pressure is applied. The current used is usually 60 cycle A.C. supplied at 220/440 volts, which is stepped down in a transformer to a high amperage at 4 to 12 volts for the welding circuit. Direct current, stored energy A.C. damped oscillation, stored energy D.C. surge, or stored energy D.C. may also be used. Proper **electronic devices** are necessary in all applications to control the time and amperage of the current. Pressure can be applied by pneumatic, mechanical, or hydraulic means. This pressure must be coordinated with the flow of current.

Spot Welding. Spot welding is a resistance welding process in which two or more sheets of metal are held between metal electrodes. Berard, Waters, and Phelps (Principles of Machine Design) diagram spot, seam, and projection welding in Fig. 25. The **welding cycle,** controlled electronically, starts with a "squeeze time"—the interval during which pressure is applied with no current passing. Next, while the material is under pressure, current flows during "weld time." So that the weld may solidify, pressure is maintained for a period after the current passes; this is known as "hold time." Where repetitive welds are made, the interval between welds is known as "off time."

Spot welding is the simplest form of resistance welding and most other types are derived from it. It is a production method usually employing stationary machines. The electrodes, however, may be attached with proper cables and made portable. A large variety of machines perform spots in thin sheet (0.001 in.)

or in materials up to ½ in. thick. Multiple spot welders have been developed to make several spots at one time.

Nearly all metals can be fabricated by spot welding. Spot welds are widely used in manufacture of automobiles, refrigerators, metal toys, airframes, and numerous other sheet metal applications.

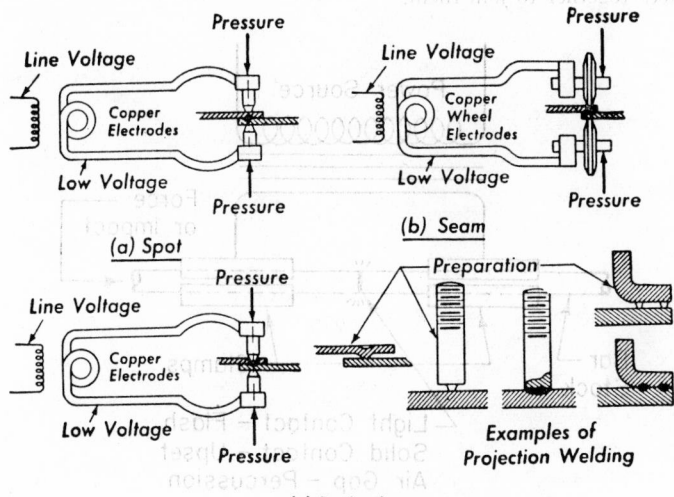

Fig. 25. Spot, seam, and projection welding.

Seam Welding. If the electrodes in a spot welder are replaced with mechanized pressure rollers and current is passed, the resulting welds are called either roll spot welds or seam welds. The flow of current is regulated and synchronized with the movement of the material to produce from 5 to 14 spots per inch. The number and size of spots are determined by the type of material and its thickness. The seam weld, shown in Fig. 25, is so named because the welds overlap and produce a gas- and water-tight joint. Seam welding is an extremely rapid process capable of producing continuous welds at speeds of 200 in. per min. and up. Metal containers, automobile mufflers, stove pipes, refrigerator cabinets, and gasoline tanks are fabricated by this method.

Projection Welding. While seam welding is considered as a series of overlapping spot welds, projection welding might be described as multiple spot welds. One sheet is dimpled or embossed while the second sheet is flat. Both sheets are held under pressure between flat electrodes or platens while current is passed to produce coalescence. The **projection spots** are usually of a diameter equal to the thickness of the sheet and project about 60 percent of the sheet thickness. Practically all metals which are spot weldable may be projection welded.

Flash, Upset, and Percussion Butt Welding. Resistance welded butt joints are usually made by one of these three processes. These methods, illustrated by Begeman (Manufacturing Processes) in Fig. 26, utilize clamps to hold the material while the current passes. Welds are produced with pressure after the plastic temperature has been reached. **Flash welding** is accomplished by bringing the abutting surfaces into light contact, drawing an arc to melt the metal, then applying pressure to forge the joint. **Upset welding** starts with the abutting surfaces in solid contact and depends upon contact resistance to produce heat prior to the application of forging pressure. **Percussion welding** requires that an air gap be present just prior to the discharge of a heavy current which melts the surfaces to be joined. Simultaneously, a percussive or impact blow brings the surfaces together to join them.

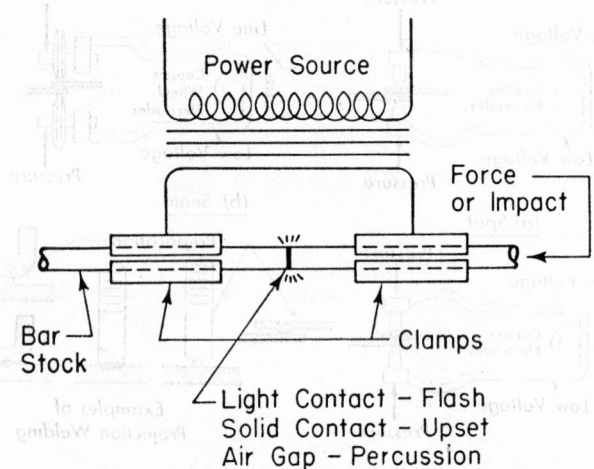

Fig. 26. Sketch of flash, upset, and percussion welding processes.

These processes are all applicable to welding of rods, pipes, tubes, and other butt joints. Flash welding is the most popular and versatile, while percussion welding is particularly adaptable to welding heat-treated parts and dissimilar metals, since penetration is only about 0.01 in.

BRAZING AND SOLDERING. Brazing and soldering are metal joining processes in which nonferrous alloys are used to join either similar or dissimilar metals. The brazing or soldering alloy must melt at a temperature below the melting point of the base metal. To be effective, both processes require clean metal and joints with proper fit. Brazing differs from soldering in that it uses alloys of copper, silver, or aluminum base which melt at temperatures above 800° F. Strength of the joint depends upon the area of overlap into which the filler metal has penetrated by capillary action. Soldering, which utilizes lead and tin base alloys that melt at temperatures from 300 to 700° F., is accomplished with numerous means of heating including irons, furnaces, induction heaters, and hot plates.

Types of brazing are usually defined by the different methods of heating or applying the braze metal: **torch brazing** uses the oxyacetylene or fuel gases and the typical oxyactylene torch; **carbon arc brazing** uses twin carbon electrodes; **furnace brazing** uses gas or electrically heated furnaces; **induction brazing,** the resistance of a part or joint to the passage of electric current; **dip brazing,** a molten metal or a chemical dip furnace; and **flow brazing** involves pouring molten metal into the joint.

FORGE WELDING. Forge welding was the first form of welding and for many centuries the only one in general use. The process consists of heating the metal in a forge to a plastic state and then uniting it by pressure or hammer blows. It is used with low carbon steels and wrought iron. Butt-welded steel pipe is made by a similar technique.

THERMIT WELDING. In thermit welding, coalescence is produced by heating with a superheated liquid. Pressure may or may not be used. The super-heated liquid is obtained by igniting with a magnesium ribbon a thermit mixture of finely divided aluminum and iron oxide. The mixture reacts to produce purified iron or steel at a temperature of approximately 4,500° F. with a slag on top. The pieces to be welded are enclosed in a refractory mold, and, as the superheated metal fills the mold, the weld is produced. Thermit welding is used primarily in the repair of thick sections which would be difficult to weld otherwise.

Assembly Methods

IMPORTANT FACTORS IN ASSEMBLY. Most manufactured products are the result of two or more assembled components. There are many types of assembly methods and devices including machine screws, bolts, self-tapping screws, rivets, glue adhesives, and welding. In order to simplify the selection of the best method of assembly for a product, it is necessary to consider such factors as:

1. Frequency of disassembly and reassembly.
2. Loading on fastener and how applied.
3. Types of material being joined.
4. Purpose of the fastener other than for holding power.
5. Environmental conditions associated with the particular assembly.
6. Ease of making a particular assembly.
7. Improved efficiency of a product, such as the benefits derived by reduced use of rivets on airplane wings.
8. The influence of fastener upon final appearance of a product.

SCREWS AND BOLTS. When machine elements must be disassembled and reassembled, the best means of assembly is usually a **screw fastener.** Various types of threads for fasteners are shown in Fig. 27. Fine threads are used in preference to coarse threads when the part is subjected to vibration, as in automotive and aircraft components. Coarse threads can be produced at a lower cost and assembly is faster. The strength of a screw fastener is based upon the root area of the threads.

Screws are threaded fasteners with heads of various types, illustrated by Berard, Waters, and Phelps (Principles of Machine Design) in Fig. 28. Screws are designed to screw into a threaded hole and not through it. At times, however, screws are used like bolts with a nut to secure an assembly. The term "machine screw" applies to small screws and is often used interchangeably with the term "cap screw."

Set screws are threaded members that are screwed through one part and prevent relative motion with a second part due to a locking action. They are secured with a screw driver or a recessed head wrench.

Self-tapping screws are threaded fasteners which are sufficiently harder than the material into which they are screwed to cut their own threads, and thus eliminate a tapping and, in some cases, a drilling operation. They function best with sheet metal, plastics, and wood materials. **Drive screws** are a special type self-tapping screw.

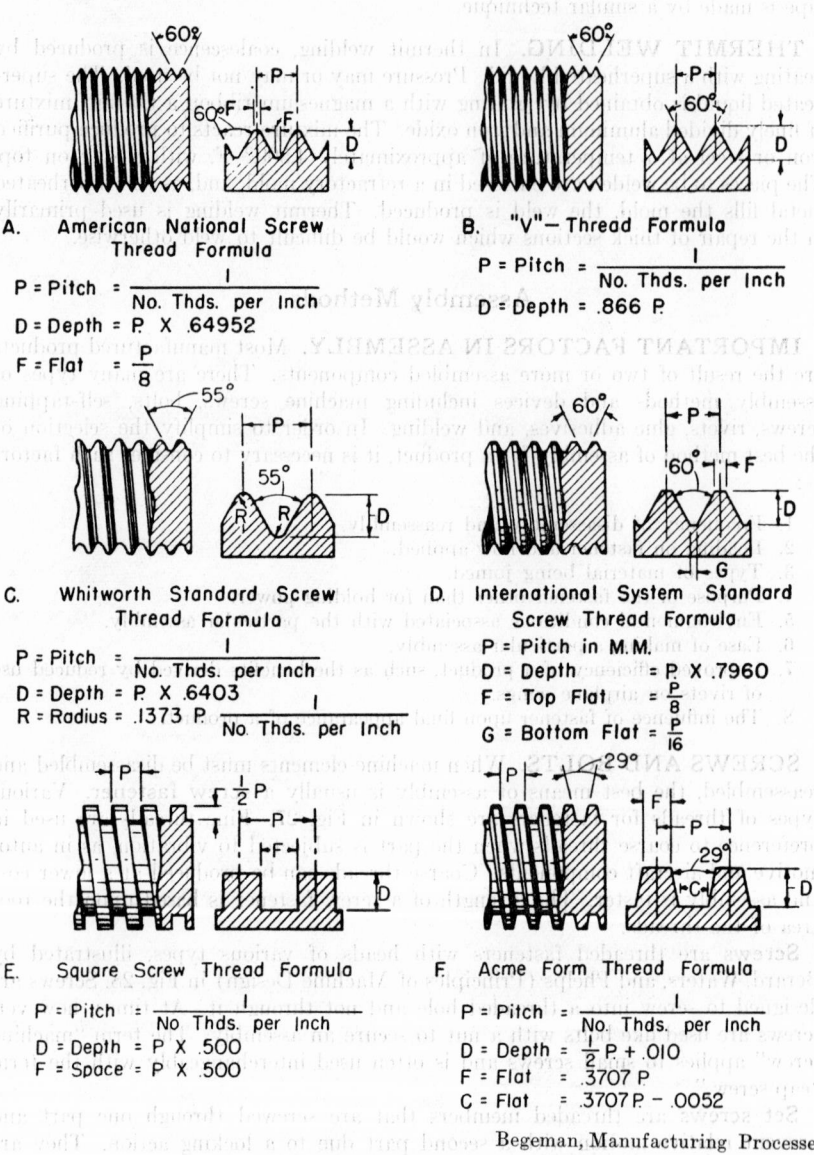

A. American National Screw Thread Formula

P = Pitch = $\dfrac{1}{\text{No. Thds. per Inch}}$

D = Depth = P X .64952

F = Flat = $\dfrac{P}{8}$

B. "V"—Thread Formula

P = Pitch = $\dfrac{1}{\text{No. Thds. per Inch}}$

D = Depth = .866 P.

C. Whitworth Standard Screw Thread Formula

P = Pitch = $\dfrac{1}{\text{No. Thds. per Inch}}$

D = Depth = P X .6403

R = Radius = .1373 P. $\dfrac{1}{\text{No. Thds. per Inch}}$

D. International System Standard Screw Thread Formula

P = Pitch in M.M.

D = Depth = P X .7960

F = Top Flat = $\dfrac{P}{8}$

G = Bottom Flat = $\dfrac{P}{16}$

E. Square Screw Thread Formula

P = Pitch = $\dfrac{1}{\text{No. Thds. per Inch}}$

D = Depth = P X .500

F = Space = P X .500

F. Acme Form Thread Formula

P = Pitch = $\dfrac{1}{\text{No. Thds. per Inch}}$

D = Depth = $\dfrac{1}{2}$ P + .010

F = Flat = .3707 P

C = Flat = .3707 P − .0052

Begeman, Manufacturing Processes

Fig. 27. Standard screw thread forms.

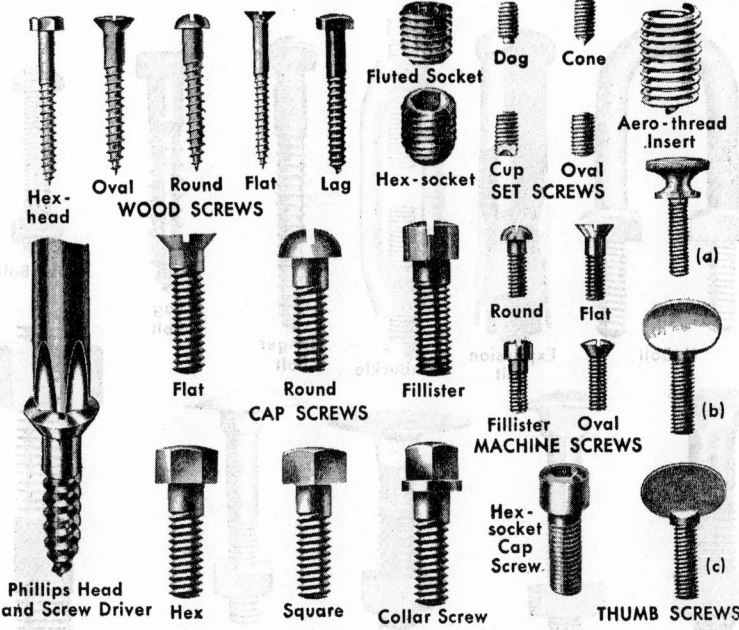

Fig. 28. American standard and special screws.

Bolts are threaded fasteners that are secured with nuts during assembly. Although they vary in length and have different types of heads and finish, most bolts are threaded a length of 1½ to 2 diameters. Various types are machine bolts, carriage bolts, stove bolts, stay bolts, eye bolts, and u-bolts. Berard, Waters, and Phelps (Principles of Machine Design) show American standard and special bolts in Fig. 29.

Studs are threaded on both ends and are used where through bolts are impractical or undesirable. The assembly is made by driving (screwing) the stud in one part, the second part of the assembly being held to the first by a nut. Studs are especially adapted to securing cylinder heads and removable covers.

Nuts are mating parts to bolts and are classified as full, jam, castellated, slotted, or wing nuts, according to function.

Locknuts, speednuts, or threadlocks are used as vibration proof holding devices for screw threads. There are many devices such as cotterkeys, elastic stop nuts, Palnuts, etc., to prevent vibration and other forces from causing parts to unscrew. The use of deformed threads and fiber inserts in a nut are popular methods of making nuts withstand a tendency to unscrew.

Washers are of two types: (1) flat washers, which provide a seat for a bolt, screw head, or nut; and (2) lockwashers, which serve to retard the tendency of a bolt or screw to loosen.

RIVETING AND STAKING. Both riveting and staking are fastening or assembling methods.

Riveting (Fig. 30) is the process of inserting a rivet in a punched or drilled hole; the second head being formed by hand or machine with die, rivet set, or

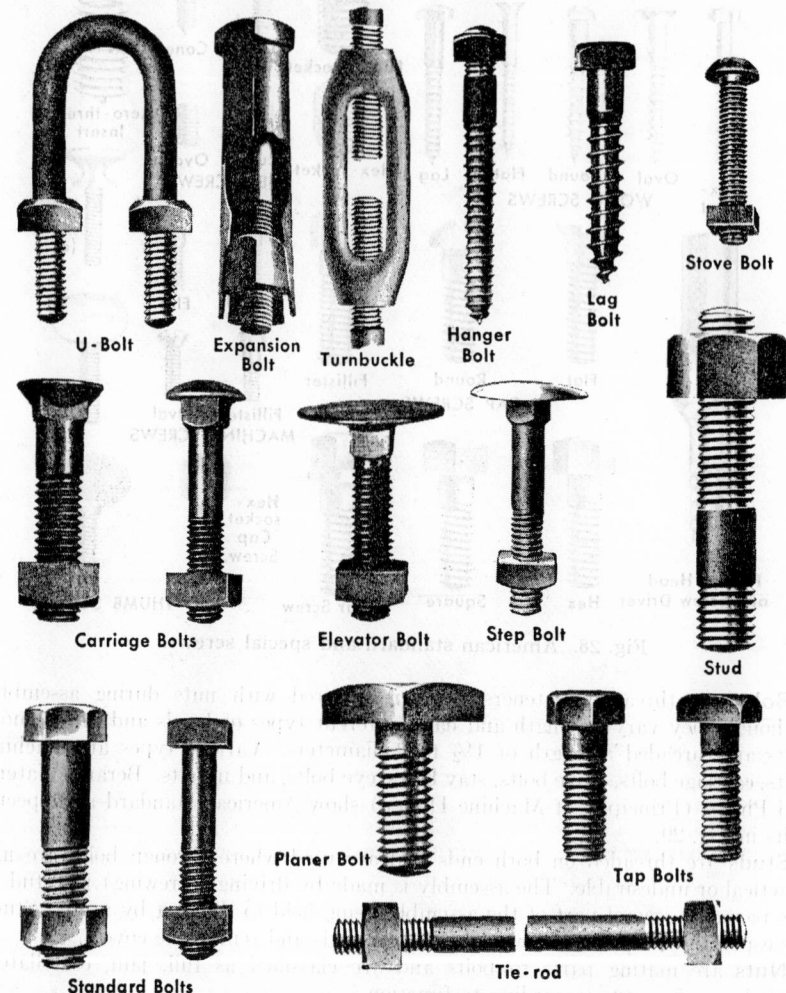

U-Bolt

Expansion Bolt

Turnbuckle

Hanger Bolt

Lag Bolt

Stove Bolt

Carriage Bolts

Elevator Bolt

Step Bolt

Stud

Planer Bolt

Tap Bolts

Standard Bolts

Tie-rod

Fig. 29. American standard and special bolts.

rivet punch. Most rivets are made of wrought iron or soft steel, although for certain applications, rivets may be made from copper or aluminum. Larger rivets are set at elevated temperatures, and small rivets are normally set cold. Berard, Waters, and Phelps (Principles of Machine Design) show various standard types of rivet heads (Fig. 31). These include button, acorn, cone, pan, flat, and round-top rivets.

Staking (Fig. 30) is a similar operation in that the metal of one part of an assembly is upset or peened in such a fashion as to make a tight fit with the second part. Staking is used extensively in the assembly of watch and clock components.

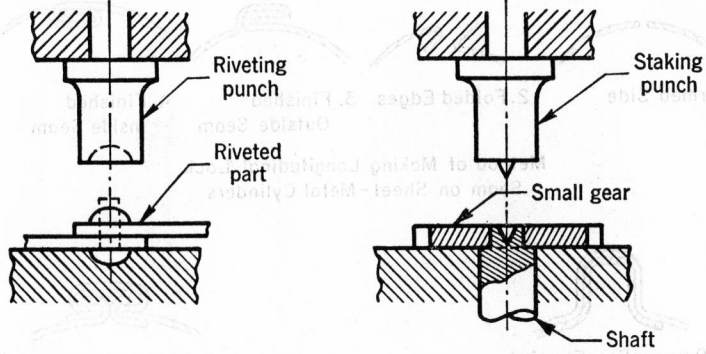

Begeman, Manufacturing Processes

Fig. 30. Riveting and staking operations.

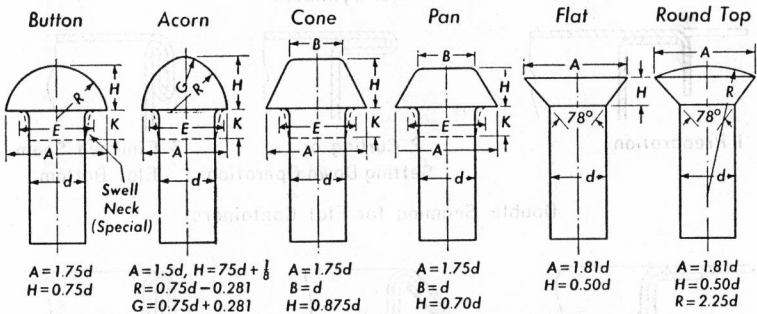

For Swell Necks: E = d + 0.063, K = 0.50d. Not applicable to Flat and Round tops

Fig. 31. American standard large rivets.

STAPLING, TACKING, AND STITCHING. These are methods using various types of wire fasteners for joining materials. **Stapling** is an operation of joining two or more pieces of material by means of a preformed wire staple which is clinched. The familiar stapler used in every office illustrates the principle. Recently, wire stapling has been applied to the joining of two pieces of sheet metal or the fastening of wood, cloth, or paper to a metal sheet. The operation is economical and very rapid up to 400 cycles per min. **Tacking** is similar to stapling except that the staple is not clinched. **Stitching** is similar to stapling except that the staples are not preformed but are made, as they are used, from a spool of wire. Metals over ⅛ in. thick have been successfully penetrated with wire staples.

SEAMING AND CURLING. Sheet metals are joined by these operations. **Seaming,** as illustrated in Fig. 32 (Niagara Tool and Machine Co.), is the process of joining two pieces of sheet metal by bending them in such a way that a permanent assembly is obtained. There are many types of seams that can be made on hand and power seaming presses. The seams may be made pressure tight such as the one shown in Fig. 32 which is used for metal cans. To make the double seam shown, **edge flanging, curling,** and **flattening** operations must be performed. Automatic machines are available for this and other seam operations.

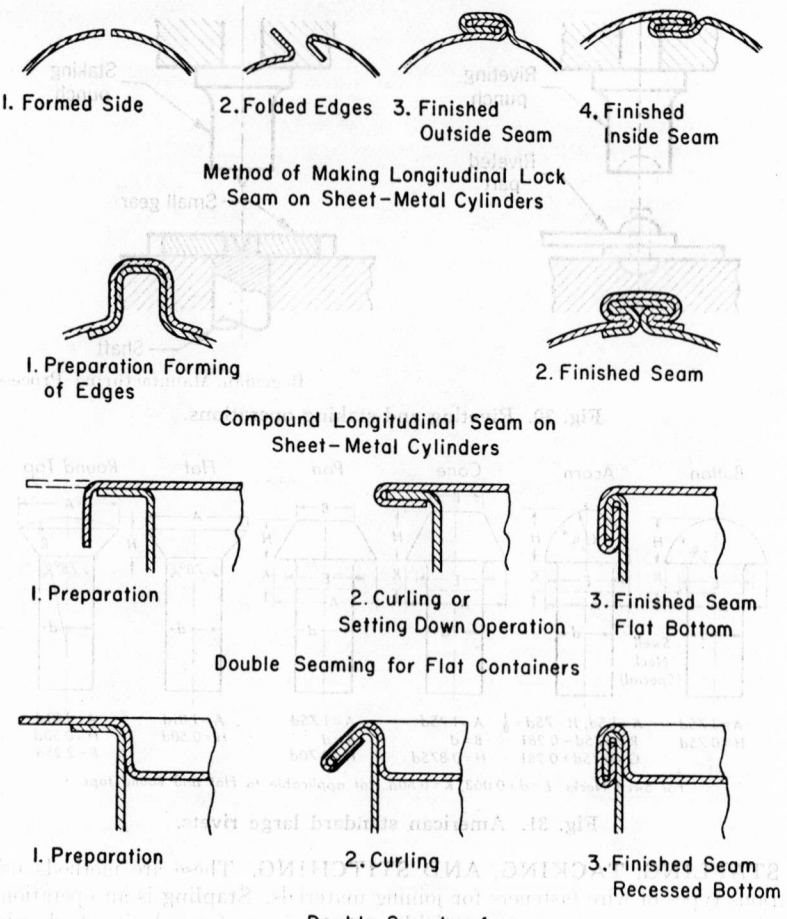

1. Formed Side   2. Folded Edges   3. Finished Outside Seam   4. Finished Inside Seam

Method of Making Longitudinal Lock
Seam on Sheet–Metal Cylinders

1. Preparation Forming of Edges   2. Finished Seam

Compound Longitudinal Seam on
Sheet–Metal Cylinders

1. Preparation   2. Curling or Setting Down Operation   3. Finished Seam Flat Bottom

Double Seaming for Flat Containers

1. Preparation   2. Curling   3. Finished Seam Recessed Bottom

Double Seaming for
Recessed–Bottom Containers

Fig. 32. Typical seams used in the manufacturing of light-gage metal containers.

SHRINK FITS. A shrink fit is made when two parts are assembled by means of a severe interference fit, the interference being eliminated during assembly by dimension changes resulting from heating or cooling the components. Examples are the shrinking of steel rims on cast iron wheels and the shrinking of liners in large bore guns.

ADHESIVES. Adhesives cover a wide field of materials designed to produce joints to hold materials together.

Glue is a product used principally for bonding woods. There are six types of glue; animal, liquid, starch, blood albumin, casein, and synthetic resins.

Adhesives are finding rapid acceptance in the bonding of almost all materials including metals. The term **adherents** applies to the materials to be bonded together. The aircraft and automative industries use "structural-type" adhesives extensively, and other industries are rapidly turning to them. The joints produced by plastic or adhesive bonding are strongest in shear, as in the case of riveted or spot welded construction. The strength compares favorably with other fabrication methods due to the stresses being distributed over the entire bonding area. Adhesives are readily adaptable to mass production, although they do have the disadvantage of not being an instantaneous process. Most adhesives are applied in the liquid or plastic state by brush, roller, spray, or spatula; dry adhesives are applied in stick or powder form. In general, the thinner the adhesive coat, the stronger the joint. After application of the adhesive, the adherents are usually held together until sufficient bond is made; the application of heat is used if necessary to set the adhesive.

The selection of a proper adhesive depends upon the following factors: ability to bond the adherents, resistance to effects of its surroundings, ease of application, expense, appearance of joints, and the possibility of future disassembly of the adherents.

Four general groups of adhesives are used in these applications:

1. **Thermoplastic adhesives.** These adhesives never become permanently hard and can be made ineffective by the application of heat. They have limited use, since their softness, particularly at elevated temperatures, induces joint creep. Examples of this type adhesive are acrylics, cellulose nitrates, oleoresins, and polyvinyl alcohols and acetates.
2. **Thermosetting adhesives.** These adhesives become permanently hard when the cure is complete; however, elevated temperatures do cause some loss in strength. They are the most used when the joint is under a stress, and include such plastics as epoxys, phenolics, alkyds, and formaldehydes.
3. **Elastomeric adhesives.** Although similar to thermoplastic adhesives, these adhesives are less sensitive to temperature. They have relatively low strength unless they are combined with thermoplastic or thermosetting materials. Examples are the natural, reclaim, and synthetic rubbers, and silicones.
4. **Adhesive alloys.** Adhesive alloys are blends made of several basic resins and are designed to exhibit the best characteristics of the components. They usually consist of phenolic blended with such materials as vinyl, neoprene, or polyvinyl butyral.

Several other materials such as the asphalts and shellac are used for general purpose bonding agents as are some of the glues.

Machining Processes

IMPORTANCE OF MACHINING. Machining processes remove metal from a parent body in the form of chips. This is done on a power operated machine tool equipped to hold work and tool in the proper relationship during the cutting operation; its prime function is to change shape, provide proper surface finish and obtain dimensional accuracy. Many different machines and tools are required because of the great variation in size, shape, and accuracy of products to be machined.

Machining can hold closer tolerances than casting, forging, or other similar forming operations. Essentially a finishing operation, it brings a part to some predetermined dimension by turning, shaping, threading, drilling, boring, milling, sawing, broaching, or grinding. Only two motions are used to perform cutting operations: either the tool or the work **reciprocates** (shaping, planing, broaching, etc.) or **rotates** (turning, drilling, milling, etc.). The tool is either fed into the work, as in a planer, or the work moved against the tool, as in a shaper. With these simple relationships available in machine tools, any common type of surface can be formed or generated.

METAL CUTTING. The simplest form of cutting tool is the single-pointed type. (See section on Tools, Jigs, and Fixtures.) When operating in a lathe, the tool is supported rigidly and the work revolves against the edge of the tool. To cut metal efficiently, the cutter tool must be ground with correct angles for the particular metal, and the shearing action requires a keen edge to provide good surface finish.

Machinability is a term which expresses the following cutting properties of a material: length of tool life, power required to make a cut, surface finish, and cost of removing a given amount of metal. Standard cutting tests are not infallible, since machinability is influenced by the coolant, cutting speed, feed, and tool angles.

The forces acting upon cutting tools, the materials used, the life of tools, computations for cutting speeds, and economic factors in tooling are discussed in the section on Tools, Jigs, and Fixtures.

TURNING. Turning is normally done by machines which remove material by rotating the work against a cutter. The lathe, an extremely versatile machine tool, can turn work held between centers, in a chuck, on a face plate, or in a collet. Facing, reaming, boring, drilling, threading, knurling, grinding, and a number of other operations can be performed on a lathe equipped with proper attachments. Lathes vary in size, design, method of drive, arrangement of gears, and purpose.

Lathes. The least complicated of all lathes are called **speed lathes.** As the name implies, they operate at high speeds (600 to 3,000 rpm) and are adaptable to such high-speed operations as woodworking, metal spinning, and polishing. Simple hand tools are used, and light cuts are made.

Engine lathes are the general all-purpose lathes of the metal working industry, differing from speed lathes in that they have controls for spindle speeds and means for feeding the tool. They are more rigid and are equipped with supports and controls for fixed cutting tools. The spindle of these machines may be driven by belts or gears powered by individual motors or line shafts. Engine lathes handle work up to 40 in. in diameter and have beds from 4 to 12 ft. in length.

Bench lathes, as the name suggests, are essentially small engine lathes which are bench-mounted. They are adapted to small work, having a maximum diameter of 9 in. at the face plate, and are often used for precision work.

Toolroom lathes, the most modern of engine lathes, are equipped with all the accessories necessary for toolroom work. These accurate machines have geared heads with a wide range of spindle speeds. Steady rests, quick change gears, feed rods, taper attachments, draw-in collets, and coolant pumps are standard attachments which make them capable of performing precise operations in the fabrication of small tools, test gages, and dies.

Duplicating lathes are machines on which the movement of the tool is controlled by a tracer mechanism which follows a template. The operator need not be skilled, and such products as drive shafts, axles, piston rods, and pump impellers are turned out rapidly and cheaply.

Turret and Automatic Lathes. The development of turret and automatic lathes has made interchangeable manufacture what it is today. Building the skill of the operator into these machines has made it possible to employ unskilled mechanics for production of identical parts in large quantities. The outstanding characteristic of these lathes is that they allow tools for consecutive operations to be set up in proper sequence and remain in readiness for use, as shown by Warner & Swasey Mfg. Co. in Fig. 33.

Horizontal turret lathes are designed for use with bar stock or as chucking machines which hold the work piece in chucks or collets. They may be either ram or saddle type. **Ram machines** allow the turret to slide back and forth on the saddle, which is clamped to the lathe bed. **Saddle units** are arranged so that the saddle moves with the turret. Automatic turret lathes utilize a hydraulic system to manipulate the tools systematically and at predetermined feeds.

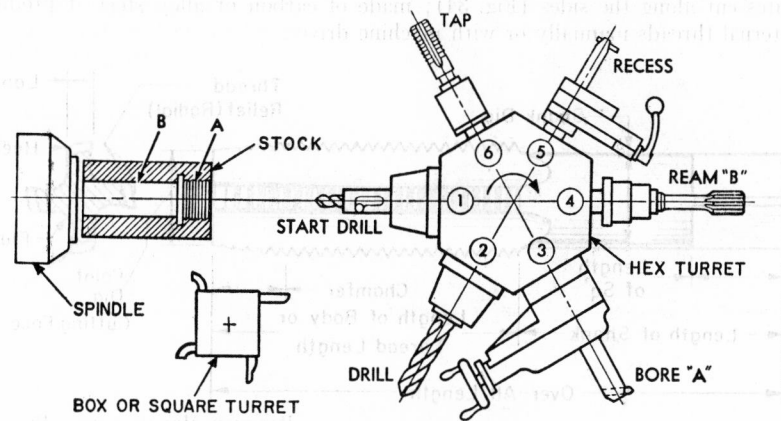

Fig. 33. Typical turret lathe setup.

Vertical turret lathes have the characteristic turret mounted in a vertical position and resemble a horizontal turret unit standing on the headstock end. The spindle is replaced with a table or chuck rotating in the horizontal position. This machine was developed to facilitate the mounting, holding, and machining of heavy parts. **Automatic vertical turret lathes** are units which automatically control the rate and direction of feed, change the spindle speed, and index the turret. Once the cycle of operations is preset, the operator need only load the parts to be machined and unload the finished work.

Automatic vertical multistation lathes are machines in which several spindles operate simultaneously. For example, a six-station machine would have five working spindles and one loading position. The work is held in chucks or fixtures which index under the spindles where separate operations are performed.

Automatic lathes automatically feed the tools to the work and withdraw them after the cycle is complete. Work may be fed to the machine either manually or through a magazine. Lathes of this type can have front, rear, and end tool slides, or, in special cases, they may be equipped with tool slides at angles. Each tool slide has its individual feed and power source.

The **automatic screw machines** are essentially turret lathes designed to use only bar stock. The turret is fed into the work, withdrawn, and indexed to the next position by means of a drum cam located beneath the turret. Stock is clamped in the collet, released at the end of the cycle, and fed against the stock stop automatically by a cam. Boston (Metal Processing) defines a **multiple spindle automatic screw machine** as being "provided with a spindle carrier in which a work spindle is opposite each tool position of the head so that all sets of tools are working simultaneously rather than being brought into play successively." Multiple spindle automatic screw machines are usually spoken of as **multiple spindle automatics.** It should be noted that these machines are no longer limited to the fabrication of screws, but may be used on any number of small parts to be made of bar stock.

THREADING. A screw thread is a ridge of uniform section, in the form of a helix, on the surface of a cylinder. Threads may be external or internal, tapered or straight, and of forms such as square, vee, acme, etc. **Taps** and **dies** are the simplest tools for producing threads. A tap is a tool which resembles a bolt with flutes cut along the sides (Fig. 34); made of carbon or alloy steel, it produces internal threads manually or with machine drives.

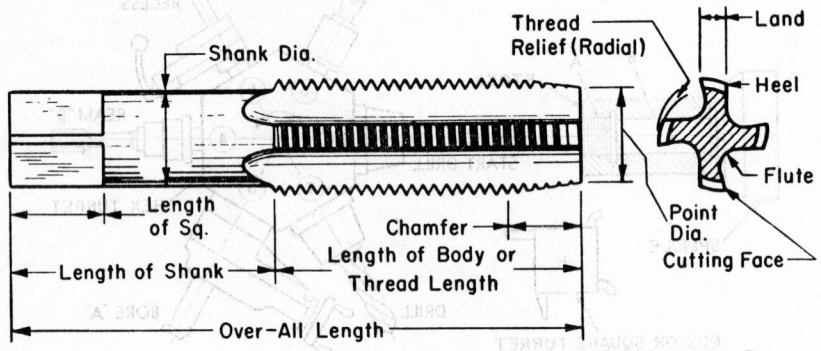

Begeman, Manufacturing Processes

Fig. 34. Tap nomenclature.

External threads are made manually with dies. All forms of threads can be cut on the **engine lathe;** however, the lathe is used only when small quantities or special forms are required. All modern engine lathes are equipped with the necessary gearing and attachments for thread cutting. **Automatic die heads** and **collapsible taps** are commonly used on turret lathes where high production is involved.

Available, in addition, are numerous **automatic tapping** and **threading machines,** which are geared for high production and resemble automatic screw machines. Accurate threads of large size, both external and internal, are sometimes produced on milling machines with standard or hob-type cutters. External threads may also be produced by **rolling** between dies, **die casting,** or **grinding.**

SHAPING AND PLANING. Planers and shapers are used to generate plane surfaces with the use of single-pointed tools. The shaper gives the tool a reciprocating motion and moves the work across the path of the tool, thus producing a plane surface. The planer, which can handle large work, imparts reciprocating motion to the work and feeds the tool across it. Planers and shapers may be driven either hydraulically or mechanically.

Shapers (Fig. 35) are classified by the plane in which the tool-carrying ram moves, either vertical or horizontal, and by the tool action, either push-cut or draw-cut. These basic tools are found in all toolrooms, die shops, and small manufacturing plants because they are fast, flexible, and can cut external and internal keyways, spiral grooves, gear racks, dovetails, T-slots, etc. **Universal shapers** are equipped with table swiveling and tilting arrangements for accurate machining of angles. They vary in size from small bench machines with strokes of 7 or 8 in. to heavy duty models with 36-in. strokes.

Planers can produce plain surfaces which are horizontal, vertical, or at an angle. They are most commonly used for making long straight cuts on thick material. The **double housing planer** is the usual type and is used for routine planer operations. The **open-side planer**, utilizing a single-column tool support, is particularly adapted to handling wide work, while the **pit-type planer** is designed for extremely large work. The latter has a stationary bed, and the tool is moved over the work. **Plate and edge planers** are used in the fabrication of heavy steel plates for pressure vessels and armor plate. They are similar to the pit-type in that the plate is stationary while the carriage, carrying both tool and operator, moves along the work.

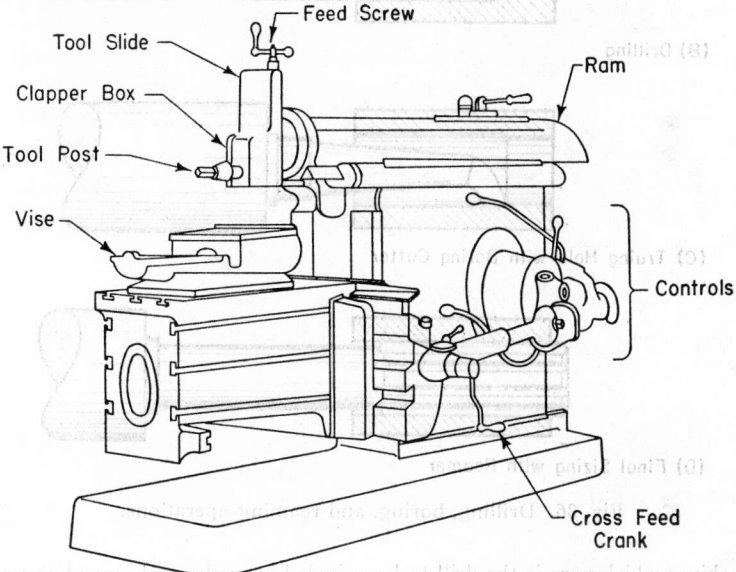

Begeman, Manufacturing Processes

Fig. 35. Horizontal push-cut shaper.

DRILLING AND BORING. Producing a hole in an object by forcing a rotating drill against it is known as **drilling,** while **boring** is the operation of enlarging an existing hole. **Reaming** refers to the finishing of a hole to an accurate size by means of a fluted tool called a reamer, which should never remove more than about 0.015 in. of metal. These three operations, together with **centering** and **countersinking,** are shown schematically in Fig. 36, after Begeman.

Drilling machines may be classified as portable, sensitive, upright, radial, gang, multiple-spindle, and special-purpose. **Portable drills** are compact units, usually electric motor driven, which are hand-operated and carried from job to job. The **sensitive drill,** often referred to as a drill press, consists of an upright standard, a horizontal table, and a vertical spindle. The drill is hand fed into the work through a wheel or lever control. **Upright drills** are similar to sensitive drills, except that they have power feeds and are capable of handling larger work.

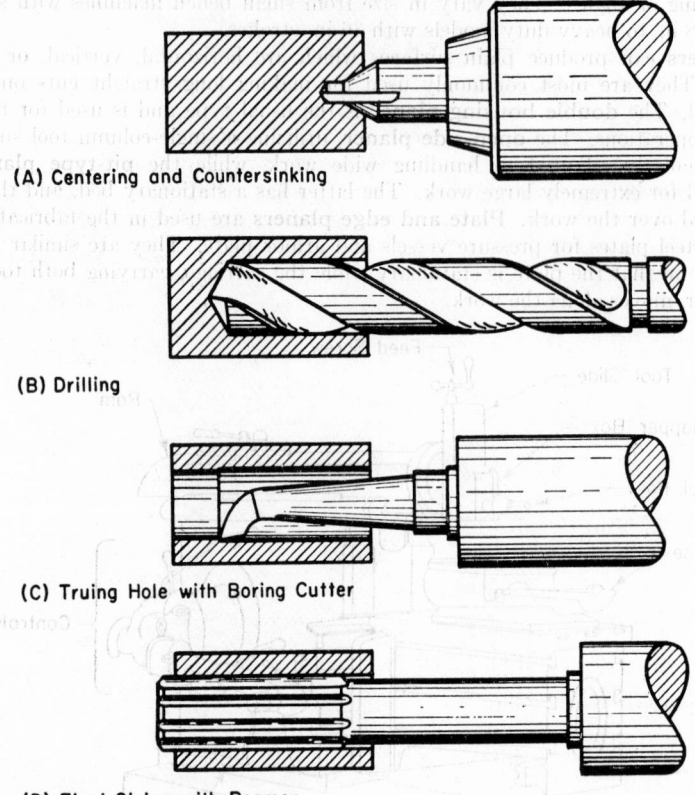

(A) Centering and Countersinking

(B) Drilling

(C) Truing Hole with Boring Cutter

(D) Final Sizing with Reamer

Fig. 36. Drilling, boring, and reaming operations.

Machines which permit the drill to be swiveled at angles and moved accurately from one position to another are known as **universal radial drills.** These units are used for drilling holes in large castings and forgings which are too heavy to move about under the drill spindle. A series of sensitive drills with individual feeds and a common table is referred to as a **gang drill.** This production tool may be set up so that a hole can be drilled, counter-bored, tapped, and spot faced in a series of operations without changing tools.

Multiple-spindle drilling machines were developed for the purpose of drilling several holes simultaneously. They are production machines which, when once set up, drill numerous parts accurately. Multiple-spindle drilling is ordinarily used in the manufacture of interchangeable parts.

Many drilling operations where high production is paramount require the use of special purpose machines. **Automatic-transfer** processing machines have been developed for producing the large number of holes in automobile engine cylinder heads. **Deep-hole drilling** operations, as encountered in the fabrication of rifle barrels, long spindles, and some connecting rods, are done on special machines with long single-fluted drills. The machines automatically retract and re-enter the drills when chips or high resistances are met.

The **jig borer,** designed and constructed for precision work on jigs and fixtures, is similar in appearance to a drill press or a light milling machine and is adaptable to drilling, boring, and end milling.

The **vertical boring mill** is quite similar in appearance to a vertical turret lathe; the horizontal work table revolves while single-point tools execute horizontal facing, vertical turning, or boring. These machines are used in fabrication of large pulleys, flanges, flywheels, and other heavy circular parts. **Horizontal boring machines** drill and enlarge holes by rotating the tool against stationary work pieces. These units are utilized in the same class of work as vertical boring mills.

MILLING. Milling machines remove metal by feeding the work against a rotating multi-blade cutter. The milling cutter, having no motion other than rotation, is circular-shaped. As the work is passed under this cutter, each tooth removes a small amount of metal, resulting in a continuous cut completed in one pass. In addition to cutters of this type, which are supported on an arbor, other cutters may be held in the arbor socket. A few of the many milling cutters available include side milling cutters, metal slitting saws, angle milling cutters, form milling cutters, end mill cutters, T-slot cutters, and inserted tooth cutters. As is evident from this large variety, milling machines perform a great many operations and are considered the most versatile of all machine tools.

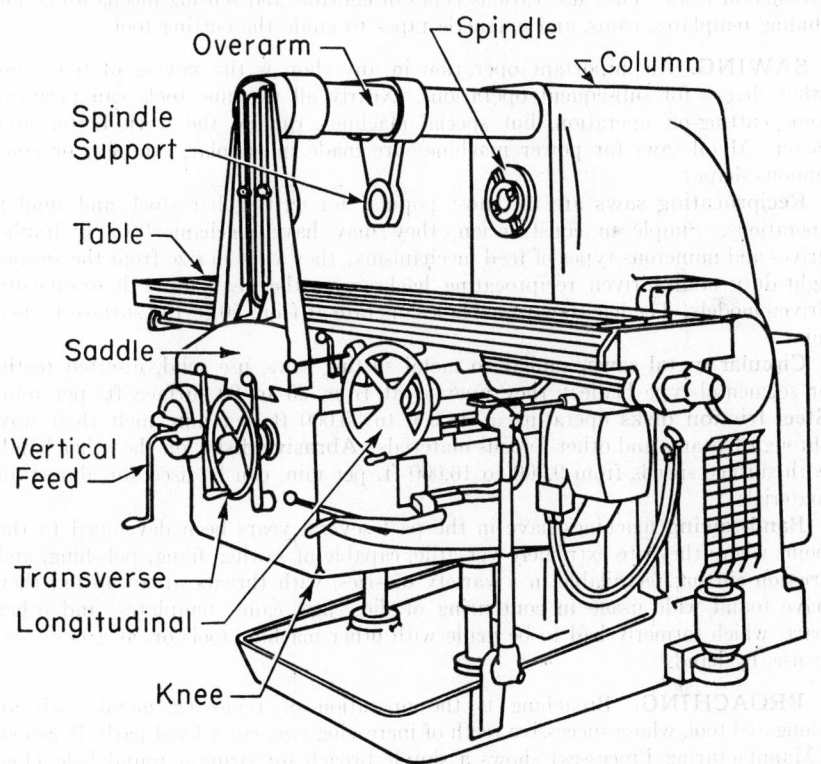

Begeman, Manufacturing Processes

Fig. 37. Universal milling machine.

Milling machines (Fig. 37) are basically of two types, vertical and horizontal. **Vertical millers** have cutters which rotate about a vertical axis, while the **horizontal machines** rotate the cutter about a horizontal axis. The work table may be of the fixed bed type, which has only longitudinal movement, or the column and knee type, which has longitudinal, transverse, and vertical motion. Movement of the table may be controlled manually, mechanically, or hydraulically.

Plain milling machines of the column and knee type are usually equipped with power feeds for all table movements, are of the horizontal type, and may be used for slotting, facing, plain, and form cutting. **Universal millers** are plain milling machines with the added feature of a table swivel which permits cutting of spirals. **Ram-type universal** machines, which can do conventional, horizontal, angular, or vertical milling, have a vertical spindle that moves in and out and can be adjusted to any angle between horizontal and vertical.

Planer-type milling machines resemble a planer and carry the work on a long table having only a longitudinal movement. Machines with multiple spindles and fixed beds are designated as **fixed-bed milling machines** and may be simplex, duplex, or triplex, depending upon the number of spindles used.

Duplicators, die sinkers, profiling machines, and **pantograph machines** are among the many special purpose machines available for duplicating and high-production work. They use various types of controls and sensing mechanisms, including templates, cams, and magnetic tapes to guide the cutting tool.

SAWING. An important operation in any shop is the sawing of bars and other shapes for subsequent operations. Nearly all machine tools can perform some cutting-off operation, but special machines can do the work better and faster. Metal saws for power machines are made in circular, straight, or continuous shapes.

Reciprocating saws are the most popular for cutting bar stock and similar operations. Simple in construction, they may have mechanical or hydraulic drives and numerous types of feed mechanisms; they vary in size from the simple light-duty crank-driven reciprocating hacksaw to the heavy-duty hydraulically driven models. The hacksaw-type blades operate at from 50 to 150 surface ft. per min.

Circular metal saws, similar to metal slitting saws, use solid, inserted teeth, or segmental-type blades; they operate at from 25 to 80 surface ft. per min. **Steel friction disks** operating at 18,000 to 25,000 ft. per min. melt their way through I-beams and other ferrous materials. **Abrasive disks,** on the other hand, with surface speeds from 9,000 to 16,000 ft. per min. can be used for almost all materials.

Band-sawing machines have in the past several years been developed to the point where they are extremely versatile, capable of sawing, filing, polishing, and friction cutting. Available in a variety of sizes, with throats up to 48 in., they have found wide usage in contouring of dies, jigs, cams, templates, and other parts which formerly had to be made with other machine tools or, at greater expense, by hand.

BROACHING. Broaching is the operation of removing metal with an elongated tool, whose successive teeth of increasing size, cut a fixed path. Begeman (Manufacturing Processes) shows a simple broach for sizing a round hole (Fig. 38). Each part is completed by one stroke of the broach, the last teeth performing the finishing and sizing operation. Broaches may be pushed or pulled across the work. The process is equally effective whether the work is held stationary or moved across the broach. Broaches are available for surfacing, keying, slotting, cutting splines (including helical splines), and gear cutting.

The exceptionally high rate of production of broaching machines makes them useful in mass production. Cutting time is a matter of seconds, rapid loading and unloading of fixtures is feasible, and they may be used for either internal or external cuts. Tolerances maintained are suitable for interchangeable manufacture. The limiting factors of broaching machines are the cost of tools, the rigid supports necessary for tools and work, and the fact that the surface to be broached cannot be obstructed.

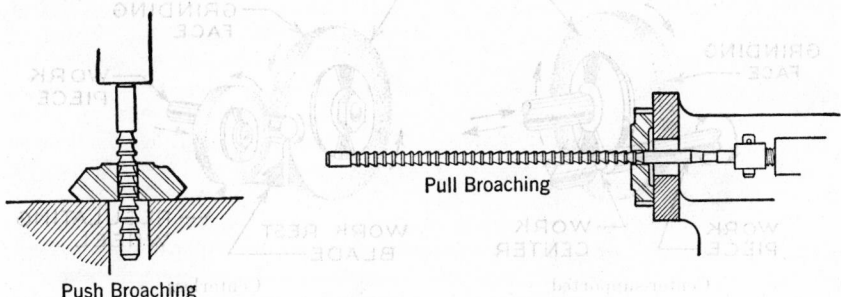

Pull Broaching

Push Broaching

Fig. 38. Broaching a round hole.

GRINDING. Grinding refers to the abrading or wearing away by friction of a material. In metal cutting, grinding is accomplished by forcing the work against a rotating abrasive wheel. The action of the wheel is similar to that of a milling cutter in that it produces minute chips of metal. Grinding is the only method of cutting extremely hard materials. It has the added advantage of producing smooth finishes to accurate dimensions in a short time, and it requires very little pressure, permitting its use on light work which would otherwise spring away. Grinding wheels are made by bonding abrasive materials with ingredients such as clay, shellac, rubber, silicates, and synthetic resins. The size and shape, kind of abrasive, grain size of abrasive particles, grade or strength of the bond, structure of the grain, and the kind of bond material are all factors in the selection of grinding wheels.

Grinding machines are especially designed for cylindrical, internal, surface, and tool grinding, as well as for such special grinding operations as cutting-off, honing, lapping, and superfinishing. **Cylindrical grinders** (Fig. 39) either hold the work between centers or are of the centerless type. In the centerless process, the work is supported by an arrangement of the work rest, a regulating wheel, and the grinding wheel itself. Internal grinding is performed with the work stationary, held in a chuck or by means of rolls.

Rotating or reciprocating tables under vertically or horizontally rotating spindles are utilized in **surface grinding. Tool grinders** are designed to sharpen tools or to grind such tools as drills, milling cutters, or tool bits. Special purpose high-production machines are designed for such jobs as snagging castings, cutting-off, and crankshaft grinding.

Honing, lapping, and **superfinishing** are processes in which surface finish is improved by removal of very minute particles of metal. **Honing** employs abrasive sticks of aluminum oxide or silicon carbide to remove grinding or tool marks left on the internal surface of a cylindrical part. The abrasive cutters are mounted on a mandrel or fixture and given a reciprocating, as well as a rotary motion. The honing action results in a round and straight bore. **Lapping** is done to produce geometrically true surfaces on flat, cylindrical, or spherical objects. The lapping operation requires that the work be in contact with a lap or plate which is softer than the work. Loose abrasive, mixed with oil, grease, or water, and applied between the work and the lapping block, abrades the surface when constantly changing motion is imparted to either the work or the lap.

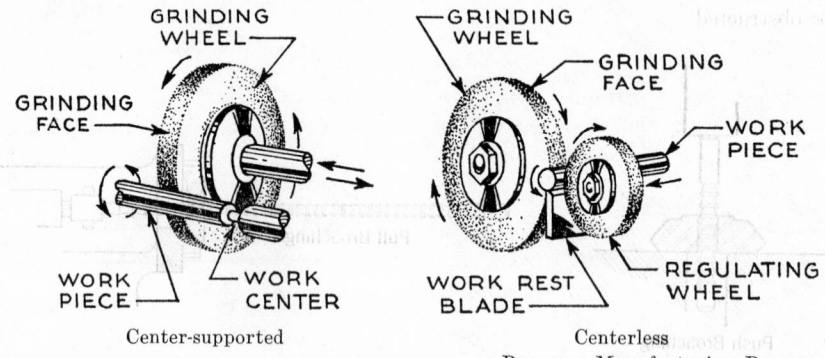

Center-supported   Centerless

Begeman, Manufacturing Processes

Fig. 39. Cylindrical grinding.

Superfinishing is a surface-improving process which removes undesirable fragmentation metal, leaving a base of solid crystalline metal. An abrasive stone, similar to those used in honing, is utilized in finishing round work; oscillated $1/8$–$1/4$ in. over the revolving work piece at about 425 cycles per min., it produces the required finish.

In superfinishing flat work, a rotating cup-shaped abrasive stone is used, with the work resting on a revolving table. The scrubbing action of these systems results in a mirror-like surface on the part. This refinement is a means of reducing wear and seizure problems in bearings.

Protective Coatings

With very few exceptions, any marketable product must be surface finished. Often the primary purpose of a coating or finish is only to increase the appearance and sales value of the item, but coatings must be used on most materials to give permanent resistance to destructive influences. The principal destructive influences are those due to wear, contact with the weather, contact with corrosive atmospheres, and electrolytic decomposition.

METHODS OF CLEANING. Before a metal product can be coated, it is necessary to prepare the surface properly to prevent poor adhesion and appearance. Parts are cleaned by different methods depending upon material, size, and surface peculiarities, but there are three basic ways in which most metal products are cleaned: mechanical, chemical, and electrolytic.

Mechanical Cleaning Methods. Mechanical methods for cleaning include two basic processes: (1) tumbling or blasting, (2) abrasive cleaning or polishing.

Tumbling consists of rotating the parts to be cleaned or finished in a tumbling barrel. These barrels are of various sizes and shapes and usually employ an additional solid material to increase the cleaning action. Such materials as steel or cast iron shot or "stars," aluminum oxide pellets, and abrasive materials are examples of tumbling "abrasives." Often a carrier or lubricant is used as tumbling progresses. In one popular tumbling device for nonferrous materials, a high-velocity stream of water and sand is played against the parts as they tumble. The amount of material loaded in a tumbler is an important factor, since it regulates the intensity of the tumbling action. Tumbling is usually employed only for cleaning purposes, but it can be employed as a means of providing a surface (not a protective finish) which may or may not be coated in a later operation. For example, mirror-type finishes can be produced on small die cast parts by suitable tumbling action.

Sandblasting and shotblasting are accomplished with a "gun," the principle of which is shown in Fig. 40. The air passing through the mixing chamber has high velocity and causes a pressure drop in the chamber. This low pressure draws sand, pellets, or shot into the chamber, from which they pass out the muzzle with air acting as a carrier. The choice of "abrasives" is dependent upon the metal

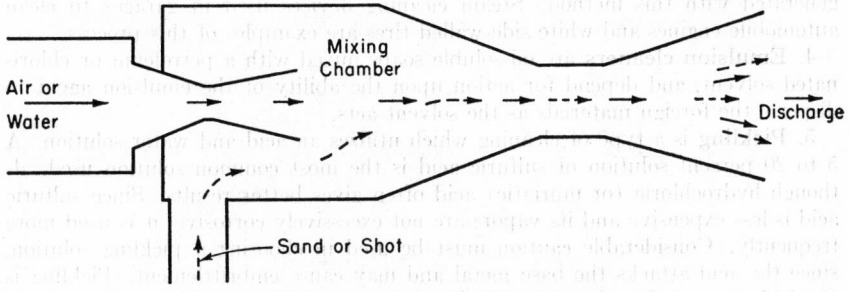

Fig. 40. Schematic of a blast gun.

being blasted and the surface finish required. Often parts which do not have sufficient strength to be tumbled may be blast cleaned. In the case of nonferrous castings, water and oils are sometimes used in the place of air. There are also systems that employ impeller wheels to force the sand or shot against the workpiece. For the most part, blasting is only a cleaning method for metals, but some novel, nonprotective finishes can be produced by the method.

Abrasive belts, wheels, and stones are used extensively in cleaning, polishing, and finishing operations. Coarse abrasive wheels and belts are used for rough cleaning operations, and fine-grained polishing belts and wheels are used to obtain a smoother finish. Mirror-type finishes can be produced by polishing or cleaning with successively finer grit, followed by cloth wheel or belt polishing with a fine abrasive of tripoli or alumina in an oil or grease carrier. Such polishing is called **buffing.** Especially prepared buffing compounds can be used to color some metals a moderate amount during the operation. Buffing offers little in the way of a protective finish, but for corrosion-resistant materials it is usually the final finishing operation.

Chemical Cleaning Methods. For cleaning materials to be coated, chemical methods are the most frequently used. While they do not take off flash or burr, they do remove dirt, grease, most scale and, in a few cases, a very small amount of surface metal. Chemical washing is often employed at elevated temperatures with a mechanical agitation system to improve the cleaning efficiency. Chemical cleaning compounds may be classified as follows:

1. **Petroleum solvents** include gasoline and kerosene and are generally used to remove oils and grease. The action depends upon the material being removed going into solution with the solvent. Stoddard's petroleum solvent is a popular type. Most plants are prevented from using solvents of this type because of the fire hazard.

2. **Chlorinated solvents** include carbon tetrachloride, trichloroethylene, and other chlorinated hydrocarbons. These solvents, slightly more expensive than petroleum solvents, accomplish, in general, about the same results but do not present the fire hazard. The fumes, particularly in vapor degreasing with chlorinated solvents, must be controlled for plant safety, since they are highly toxic.

3. **Alkali cleaners,** composed of approximately 4 to 8 percent of an alkali salt and the remainder water, are the most common cleaning media. Cleaners of this type are usually employed in a tank or with steam. Sodium carbonate (soda ash) is the most popular alkali used. Often a wetting agent is used to increase the efficiency of the cleaner. There is no fire hazard, nor are there toxic fumes generated with this method. Steam cleaning devices used in garages to clean automobile engines and white side-walled tires are examples of this process.

4. **Emulsion cleaners** are oil-soluble soaps mixed with a petroleum or chlorinated solvent, and depend for action upon the ability of the emulsion agent to disperse the foreign materials as the solvent acts.

5. **Pickling** is a type of cleaning which utilizes an acid and water solution. A 5 to 20 percent solution of sulfuric acid is the most common solution used, although hydrochloric (or muriatic) acid often gives better results. Since sulfuric acid is less expensive and its vapors are not excessively corrosive, it is used more frequently. Considerable caution must be used in choosing a pickling solution, since the acid attacks the base metal and may cause embrittlement. Pickling is particularly useful in the removal of scale from steel after rolling or heat treatment.

6. **Electrocleaning or electropolishing** is accomplished by immersing the part to be cleaned in a tank containing an electrolyte. The part being cleaned forms one electrode, and the gas liberated from the metal causes a scrubbing action. Direct current is used. Electropolishing is more nearly the reverse of electroplating, but again, safety precautions are necessary because of the solutions used.

COATING PROCESSES. In general, the coating process is the application of a finite thickness of some material over the metal, or is the transformation of the surface by chemical or electrical means to an oxide of the original metal.

Organic Coatings. Of all the coating processes, organic coatings are the most used. Advantages of this type of coating include ease of application, decorative effect, and protection of the base material from the elements of corrosion, wear, and weathering. Before an organic coating can be applied, the base metal must be clean and, in some cases, special pre-coatings or surface treatment must precede the application of the final coating. For steel, red lead and zinc chromate primers have been very successful as pre-coatings. Although the terms paint, enamel, shellac, lacquer, and varnish no longer can be concisely defined as they once could, they are still the basic trade terms used. Many finishes are a mixture of two or more such products. Fig. 41 indicates the principal differences of the

Vehicle	Thinner	Application	Colors	Drying method	Drying time, hr.	Typical Applications
Paint	Nonvolatile drying oils	Volatile solvent	Brush Spray	All colors	Oxidation	1–24	Structures, light metal, and wood products
Enamel	Resins and drying oils	Mineral spirits	Spray Brush Dip	All colors	Oxidation, evaporation, and plastic change (can be baked)	2–24	Machine tools, metal cabinets, wood products
Lacquer	Cellulose nitrate and synthetic resins	Volatile solvent and plasticizer	Spray Dip Brush	Clear and all colors	Evaporation, (can be heat dried)	¼–2	Automobiles, metal furniture, wood products
Varnish	Resins and drying oils	Volatile solvent	Brush Dip Spray	Clear and stains	Evaporation, oxidation and plastic change	¼–20	Wood products, some cases of top coats on metal finishes
Shellac	Lac resin	Alcohol	Brush Spray	Clear and colors	Evaporation	¼–1	Wood products

Fig. 41. Organic coatings.

predominant organic coatings. Organic coatings are generally applied by brushing, dipping, or spraying the material. Many finishes are now sprayed hot to increase the percent of solids deposited, and to reduce the solvent cost and overspray losses.

Many special finishes can be produced, such as crinkle and luminous coatings. Aluminum paint consists of fine aluminum flakes which are usually used in a varnish-type vehicle.

Hot Dipping. Hot dipping is a process involving the suspension of a metal product in a molten bath of metal that will resist a destructive influence to a greater extent than the original product. The process is simple and relatively inexpensive. The base material must be chemically and physically clean to allow for proper adhesion of the coating. Sheet steel, fences, and outdoor hardware are typical products that are coated by this process (zinc and/or tin alloy coatings).

Zinc coatings are used most extensively for protecting low carbon steel from atmospheric deterioration. They offer a low-cost coating that has reasonable appearance and good wearing properties. An improved appearance, known as the **spangle effect,** can be produced by small additions of tin and aluminum. Zinc baths are usually maintained at about 850° F. Rolls, agitators, and metal brooms are used to remove the excess zinc from the product. Continuous and automatic processes are used for sheet and wire coating. Zinc coatings can also be produced by **spraying** molten zinc on steel, by **sheradizing,** which is the tumbling of the product in zinc dust at elevated temperatures, and by **electroplating.**

Tin coatings are applied extensively to sheet steel to be used for food containers. In fact, tin can manufacturers use approximately 90 percent of the tin produced. Although many tin coatings are now applied by electro-tinning—a process of immersing parts in an electrolyte and passing a current from the electrodes to the work—the hot-dip method is still used considerably. Tin can be applied easily by dipping at temperatures of approximately 600° F. without affecting the base metal. In most cases, the tin coating is approximately 0.0001 in. thick as compared to about 0.00003-in. thicknesses in electro-tinned sheets. Porosity is greater, however, in plated tin coatings, and when used for food, a lacquer seal is necessary.

Parkerizing is a process for making a thin phosphate coating on steel which acts as a base or primer for enamels and paints. In this process the steel is dipped in a solution of manganese di-hydrogen phosphate for about 45 minutes. **Bluing** is a process of dipping steel or iron in a 600° F. molten bath of nitrate of potash (saltpeter) for from 1 to 15 minutes. There are many salts that can be used to color brass and steel by dipping at elevated temperatures, but most of these have limited application and differing degrees of permanence.

ELECTROPLATING. Electroplating is a process in which a direct current is passed between an anode (+) and a cathode (−), the two being immersed in a tank of metallic salt solution called the bath. The metal to be plated is made the cathode, and the material to be deposited is made the anode. When current is applied, the anode transfers some of its mass to the bath and an equal amount of the material is deposited on the cathode which is the part being plated. Although the process is simple in theory, good results are dependent upon careful selection of the bath salts. Concentration, current density, temperature, and metal cleanliness are other important factors. A brighter finish results from a finer crystalline pattern being deposited, a harder finish from higher applied currents, and softer finishes from elevated bath temperatures. The thickness of deposit is controlled by the amount of current flowing; thus, a longer time or a higher current per unit of time will give increased deposits.

Most metals, with the exception of cadmium and zinc, offer protection from corrosion only if they completely cover the base metal. Porosity, except in the case of these two materials, must be closely controlled to keep contaminants from attacking the base metal.

In order to get the best service out of some plated metals, it is necessary to plate on one or more different materials as **"pre-plates"** to the final plating operation. This produces proper ductility, appearance, and corrosion-resistant qualities. For instance, chromium is usually plated over nickel which has been plated over copper; the thickness of the chromium is only about 0.00002 in.

Simonds (Finishing Metal Products) has developed a tabular presentation of the fundamental physical characteristics of the principal coatings deposited by electrolytic action (Fig. 42). Other materials, such as gold, platinum, rhodium, and silver, are also applied by electroplating.

Oxide Coatings. Most coatings of this type enhance the appearance of a product but do little to offer resistance to destructive influences. An exception is the oxide coating on aluminum and magnesium and their alloys. The coloring of metals by immersion, such as parkerizing and bluing, as previously described, are examples.

Anodizing is an oxidation process developed for aluminum. An electrolyte of sulfuric, oxalic, or chromic acid is employed with the part to be anodized as the anode. Since the coating is produced entirely by oxidation and not by plating, the oxide coating is a permanent and integral part of the original base material. Although the coating is hard, it is porous which is an advantage from a decorative standpoint. The oxide coating enables organic coatings and dyes to be successfully applied to the surface of aluminum. Modern aluminum "glasses" and pitchers are examples of this process. Magnesium is anodized in a somewhat similar manner.

Metallizing. Metallizing is the process of spraying molten metal upon other materials by means of a metal spray gun which resembles a paint spray gun. Actually, wire or powder is fed into an oxyacetylene flame, which melts the material to be sprayed, and compressed air forces the molten metal against the surface being coated. Since the bond between the coating and the base metal is purely one of mechanical interlocking, the surface must be properly roughened and cleaned. Metallizing is used to create decorative finishes, to build up worn parts, and for adding materials to the parent metal that might better resist destructive influences. Metals sprayed on in this manner have a density of approximately 80 percent as compared to the same metal in the form of a casting. These coatings are lower in strength but are hard.

Clad Materials. Wulff, et al. (Metallurgy for Engineers) describes clad materials as "Metal sheets, rod, and wire of high strength but inferior corrosion resistance [that] are sometimes laminated (clad) with more corrosion-resistant metals or alloys."

Porcelain Enameling. This term applies to steels that have been heated in contact with an enamel to such an extent that the enamel fuses and reacts with the base metal to form a combination physical and chemical bond. The enamels used in this process are composed of earth elements, such as silicates (glass) and feldspar, along with such fluxes as borax. Various elements can be added to give

Coating	Main Purpose of Application	Commonly Used Thicknesses, Inches	Protective Value	Appearance Initial	Appearance After Exposure	Resistance to Abrasion
Acid zinc	Rust protection	0.0005 -0.001	Excellent	Bluish satin	Dark gray	Poor
Cyanide zinc	Rust protection	0.0005 -0.001	Excellent	Matte white	Dirty gray	Poor
Cyanide copper	A. Base for "oxidized finishes"[1]	0.0001 -0.0003	Poor	Colored and lacquered		Fair
	B. Base for nickel plating[1]	0.0001 -0.0006	[4]	Salmon red[6]	Black to green	Fair
Acid copper	Base for nickel plating	0.0003 -0.0006	[4]	Salmon red[6]	Black to green	Fair
Nickel	A. Appearance and rust resistance directly on steel[2]	0.0003 -0.001	[4]	Matte yellowish white[6]	Dark to brown	Good
	B. On steel over copper plate	0.0003 -0.0008	[4]	Matte yellowish white	Dark to brown	Good
	C. On copper or brass	0.0002 -0.0006	Good	Matte yellowish white	Dark to brown	Good
	D. Directly on zinc	0.0003 -0.0005	Fair	Matte yellowish white	Dark to brown	Good
Chromium	A. Appearance[3]	0.00001-0.00002	[4]	Bluish white—mirror-like[6]	Unchanged	Fair (thin!)
	B. Abrasion resistance	0.001 -0.005	Excellent	Frosty bluish white	Unchanged[5]	Excellent
Cadmium	Rust resistance and appearance	0.0002 -0.0006	Excellent	White lustrous	White	Very poor
Tin	A. Corrosion resistance on copper and brass	0.0003 -0.001	Excellent	Frosty white	Grayish	Very poor
	B. Minimizing piston wear	0.0010	Good	Frosty white	Grayish	Very poor
Brass	Appearance (often colored and lacquered)	0.0001 -0.0003	Poor	Satin yellow to bronze[6]	Black to green	Fair

[1] Sometimes substituted for part of cyanide copper—never direct on steel.
[2] As plated, buffed, or scratch brushed.
[3] Over nickel and nickel plus copper—also rust resistance.
[4] Total coating of copper plus nickel plus chromium on steel should not be less than 0.001 in. thick for outdoor exposure.
[5] Also resistant to oxidation at high temperatures.
[6] Luster is obtained by buffing or analogous mechanical treatment after plating.

Fig. 42. Chart of coating characteristics.

a wide range of colors and surface finish Porcelain enameled steel offers excellent appearance, and resistance to corrosion.

The temperature necessary for porcelain enameling varies with the enamel and the base material, but seldom exceeds 1,600° F. except for high temperature enamels. The primary use is in home appliances, hospital, kitchen, and bathroom products, and in the field of building construction.

Extrusion of Metals

BASIC EXTRUSION PROCESS. Metals are extruded by forcing them through dies in a manner which results in the metal having a cross section of the same shape as the die. Copper, aluminum, and magnesium and their alloys are the materials that extrude most satisfactorily. These materials are extruded at elevated temperatures where plasticity is greatest. Other materials such as zinc and lead and their alloys are extruded both hot and cold. By the use of special presses and erosion-resistant dies, stainless and nickel alloy steel have been extruded at temperatures as high as 2,400° F.

Extrusion Characteristics. Extruded shapes have replaced rolled, forged, and cast shapes in many instances because extrusion dies are low in cost, machining on the section is kept to a minimum, fine surface finishes are obtained, good dimensional accuracy is inherent, and as compared to rolling mill equipment, costs are relatively low. The principal disadvantage of the process is the amount of material that must be thrown away or remelted as a result of the oxidized metal being pulled through the orifice, particularly near the end of each extrusion cycle.

Most presses are horizontal and operate hydraulically. Fig. 43 indicates the approximate temperatures and pressures used to extrude materials by the direct and inverted processes. In most cases the addition of an **alloying material** necessitates a higher extrusion pressure. The speed at which an extrusion is made may vary from 1 to 900 ft. per min., depending upon the metal, the cross section, extrusion temperature, and extrusion pressure.

Material	Extrusion Temperature,° F.	Extrusion Pressures, psi
Aluminum and alloys......................	600– 800	15,000–100,000
Copper and alloys	500– 800	35,000– 90,000
Lead and alloys	450	18,000– 60,000
Magnesium and alloys..................	450– 700	20,000–100,000
Steel	1,700–2,500	120,000
Zinc and alloys	400– 600	40,000–110,000

Fig. 43. Extrusion pressures and temperatures for direct and inverted extrusion.

The variety of shapes that can be extruded are numerous and include such items as rails for a miniature railroad, diving boards, lead drain pipe, and structural shapes.

TYPES OF EXTRUSION. The several basic extrusion processes can be distinguished:

Direct or Forward Extrusion. Fig. 44 illustrates the process of forcing a heated solid block of metal through a die or orifice by means of hydraulic pressure, the product being a continuous length of metal of uniform cross section.

Inverted or Backward Extrusion. Fig. 44 shows a hot or cold process, depending on the material being extruded, in which the die is mounted on a hollow ram which is pushed into the billet instead of the billet being pushed through the die, as in the direct process.

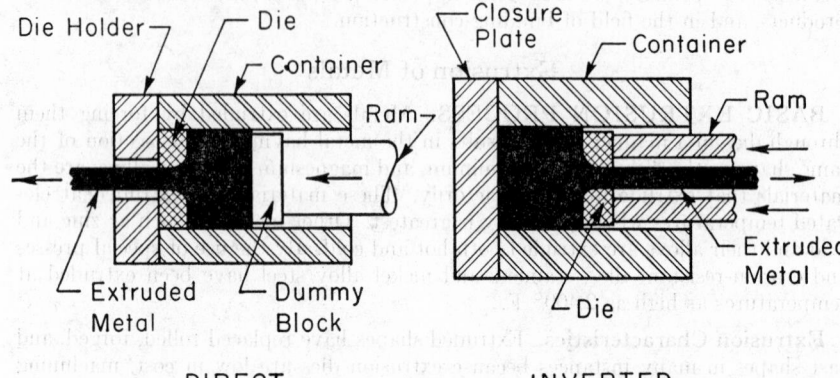

Fig. 44. Direct and inverted extrusion processes.

Impact Extrusion. This method is used primarily in the manufacture of short tubes of soft alloy. Toothpaste, shaving cream, and paint pigment tubes are examples of this process. In this method, thin slugs of metal may be pictured as squirting up around the punch upon impact. Fig. 45 illustrates the Hooker process for extruding small tubes or cartridge cases. In this process, slugs are impact-extruded downward through a die opening.

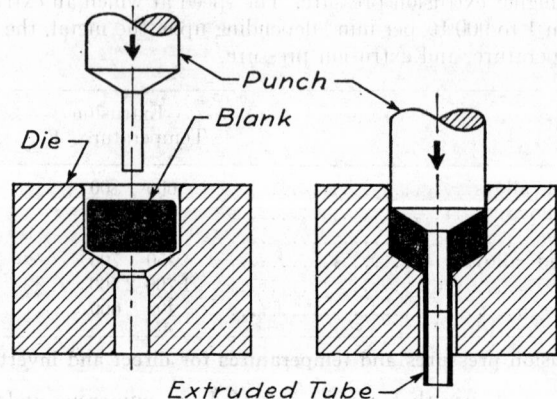

Fig. 45. Method of cold-impact extrusion of soft metals.

Plastic Molding

PROPERTIES OF PLASTICS. Plastics include a large group of synthetic or natural organic materials that become pliable with the application of heat and and are formed to shape by pressure. They are used in place of such other materials as glass, wood, and metals in construction and decoration, for making many articles and coatings; and they are drawn into filaments for weaving. The **raw materials for plastics** include various agricultural products, coal gas, petroleum, limestone, silica, sulphur, and numerous other minerals and organic materials. In the process of manufacture such **additives** are employed as color powders, solvents, lubricants, plasticizers, and filler material. The latter materials are employed to reduce manufacturing cost, minimize shrinkage, improve heat resistance, and impart various other desired properties to the product.

Plastic materials may be classified as thermosetting and thermoplastic. **Thermosetting compounds** are formed to shape by heat and pressure, resulting in products that are permanently hard and not capable of being reprocessed. The material is first softened by heat; then as additional heat and pressure are applied, the product is hardened by a chemical process known as polymerization. **Thermoplastic products** are formed to shape by heat and pressure but do not undergo any chemical change. They remain hard at room temperature, but if heat is applied they are softened and can be reprocessed.

METHODS OF FORMING. Plastic materials can be processed by compression molding, transfer molding, injection molding, casting, extruding, laminating, vacuum forming, and blowing. Although some of the materials can be processed in several ways, many of them are best adapted to one procedure. Of the methods listed above, compression molding is the one most widely used. This method, injection molding, and extruding are illustrated by Begeman (Manufacturing Processes) as shown in Figs. 46, 47, and 48.

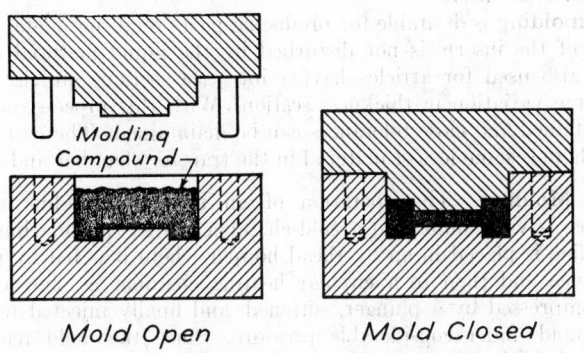

Fig. 46. Compression molding.

Compression Molding. Compression molding, illustrated in Fig. 46, shows the mold in both the open and closed position. This process is used principally for thermosetting plastics such as phenolics, alkyds, melamines, ureas and for material that are molded cold. The **molding cycle of operations** is as follows:

1. Material in the form of powder or special preformed shapes is placed into the mold.
2. The mold is closed while heat and pressure are gradually applied.
3. When the maximum temperature is reached and material becomes fluid, the maximum pressure is applied and maintained as the material hardens.
4. The mold is opened and the formed part is removed.

Thermoplastic materials require that the mold be cooled in order to harden the liquid mass before the part is removed; otherwise, distortion is apt to result.

In compression molding the material is often compressed into small pellets or shapes called **preforms.** Preforms facilitate the loading of molds, prevent the wasting of material, control the weight of the charge, and permit preheating. They are used only in compression and transfer molding; some compounds do not compress readily and the expense is not justified.

A large variety of hydraulic presses, ranging from hand-operated to completely automatic, are available for compression molding. The press is the main functional unit in the operation as it furnishes both pressure and heat for the process. Heat, transferred from heated platens or applied directly to the metal mold, can be applied by steam, electrical resistance, high frequency current, or heated fluids. In most cases the powder or preforms are preheated before entering the mold. Presses for compression molding range in size up to 3,000 tons capacity.

Transfer Molding. Transfer molding is a process of molding thermosetting compounds in a closed mold, but differs from compression molding in that the powder is first placed in a pressure chamber adjacent to the mold cavity. Here it is heated to a liquid state and then injected into the mold under pressure where it is cured and hardened. The mold is closed by the upward movement of a press platen. The operator drops the material into an opening in the center of the transfer chamber plate where it is plasticized. The plunger supplies the necessary pressure and forces the liquid molding material into the mold where it cools and hardens. The cycle differs from compression molding in that the mold is closed before any material enters.

Transfer molding is desirable for producing parts requiring metal inserts since the location of the inserts is not disturbed by the liquid material entering the mold. It is also used for articles having intricate sections and in cases where there is a large variation in thickness section. With this process, more uniform density is obtained and close tolerances can be maintained. The cost of the mold is high and there is some loss of material in the transfer chamber and sprue.

Injection Molding. The operation of an injection molding machine for thermoplastics is very similar to a cold-chamber die casting machine. Material for the machine is placed in an overhead hopper where it is fed by gravity to a metering device and then to a circular heating chamber as shown in Fig. 47. Here it is compressed by a plunger, softened, and finally injected into the relatively cold mold under considerable pressure. Since the mold temperature is maintained below the melting temperature, the molded parts harden rapidly. The mold then opens and the parts are ejected. Most injection presses are fully automatic, the presses having one hydraulic unit for feeding the material to the mold and another for opening and closing the mold.

Some of the **common thermoplastic materials** used in injection molding are cellulose acetate, nylon, polystyrene, methyl methacrylate, and various vinyl resins. The use of thermoplastic materials in injection molding equipment permits a much faster cycle operation than in compression molding since the mold does not have to be alternately heated and cooled. As a rule, the mold is held at a fairly constant temperature by circulating water, permitting a production cycle of several shots per minute. Because of the rapid operation of this machine, fewer die cavities are necessary to maintain equivalent production than by other possible methods. Material loss when using thermoplastic materials is low, as sprues, gates, and defective parts can be reused. A limitation of the process is the high equipment cost and accompanying maintenance and overhead charges.

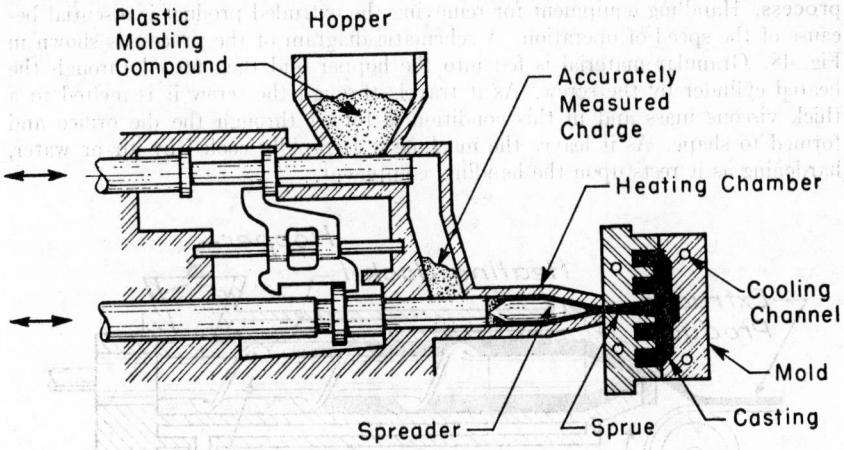

Fig. 47. Operation of plastic injection molding machine.

Casting. The casting of plastics is similar in principle to the casting of metals. Plastic materials are melted, blended with the necessary catalysts and filler materials or hardening agents, and then poured into a conventional mold where they solidify. Both thermosetting and thermoplastic materials can be used in this process although the phenolics (thermosetting) are preferred. Other materials commonly processed by casting include the acrylics, polyesters, ethyl cellulose, and epoxy materials.

As in the casting of metals, **mold construction** necessitates consideration of draft and shrinkage. However, the molds are light in construction and inexpensive to make. Frequently, open molds for short rods and simple shapes are formed by dipping a tapered steel mandrel into molten lead and stripping the shell from the sides of the mandrel after it solidifies. The wall thickness of such molds is from ⅛ to 3/16 in. **Lead split molds,** cast in a die casting machine, are used for more involved shapes having undercut. Molds of a **rubber latex** or an **elastomeric plastic** substance can be used for some materials. The elastic material is applied on the object to be reproduced by dipping or spraying until sufficient thickness is obtained. It is then removed by cutting at a desired parting line and is backed with plaster of Paris to give it rigidity. Molds of **glass** or **plaster of Paris** can also be used. The curing and hardening phase of the process takes place in the mold and varies considerably according to the material used. It is often done in closed ovens under controlled conditions as most materials require heat in the curing process, though a few materials can be cured in open molds.

Advantages of the casting process include low tooling costs, adaptability to short-run jobs, wide range of properties available, and ability to cast large sections and stock shapes. These shapes, in the form of short rods, tubes, and plates, are often used as material for machining operations. Costume jewelry, lenses, clock cases, handles, and drilling jigs are all products of plastic casting, as are large punches and dies used in the aircraft industry for drawing, forming, and stretching operations.

Extruding. The extrusion process is one that is adapted especially to the molding of simple uniform sections as in rods, tubes, film, filaments, and sheets. Most extrusion molding is done in a **screw-type machine** and is a **continuous**

process. Handling equipment for removing the extruded product is essential because of the speed of operation. A schematic diagram of the process is shown in Fig. 48. Granular material is fed into the hopper and then forced through the heated cylinder by the screw. As it travels through the screw it is melted to a thick viscous mass and in this condition is forced through the die orifice and formed to shape. As it leaves the machine it is rapidly cooled by air or water, hardening as it rests upon the handling equipment.

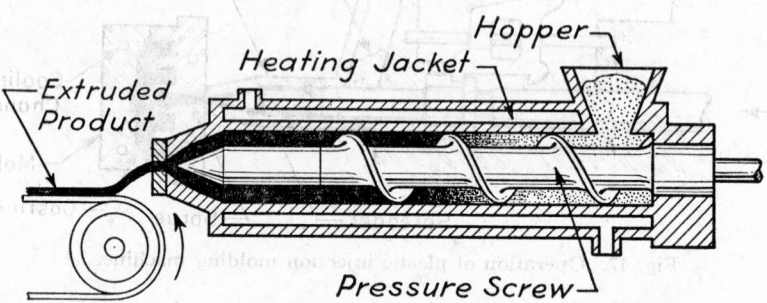

Fig. 48. Method of continuously extruding plastic materials.

The **design of the screw** is important and varies considerably for different materials. Clearance should be small and the depth of screw shallow to permit uniform heating of the material. The rate of flow through the cylinder is controlled by the pitch of the screw. Cylinders are usually heated with oil although steam or electricity can be used. Temperatures vary with the materials being processed and must be closely controlled.

Although both thermosetting and thermoplastic materials are processed in this manner, the thermosetting materials are not well adapted to this process because of the rapidity in which they harden. Products made by extrusion include garden hose, molding sections, conduit, safety glass sheeting, bristles, and filaments for plastic fabrics. Insulation also is now being extruded on wire and cable.

Laminating. Laminated plastics consist of sheets of paper, fabric, asbestos, spun glass, wood veneer, or similar materials which are first impregnated with resin and then combined under heat and pressure to form a solid body. In the manufacture of laminated products, the **resinoid material** (phenolic, melamine, or silicone) is first dissolved by a solvent to convert it into a liquid varnish. Rolls of the fabric, mat, or paper are then passed continuously through a bath of liquid material and from there enter a drying oven where the solvent is removed. This results in a fairly stiff sheet, impregnated with the plastic material, which is accumulated on rolls. To form **laminate sheets** or products these sheets are unwound, cut to shape, and stacked together in sufficient numbers to make up the desired thickness of the product. Each group is assembled between polished steel plates and then stacked in the press between the steam platens.

Hydraulic presses, capable of attaining pressures from 1,000 to 2,500 psi, are used for this work. The heated platens furnish temperatures around 300° F. which are necessary in the **curing operation.** For large products the pressures mentioned above often exceed press capacities. To counteract this limitation, materials have been developed requiring low pressures ranging only from atmospheric to 300 psi. One method of forming is to place the resin impregnated sheets on a half mold, covering it with a flexible sheet. The mold is then placed in a closed steam chamber where it is kept at a predetermined pressure and temperature until curing is complete. Tubes are made by machine-winding strips of the prepared stock around a steel mandrel between heated pressure rolls. The mandrel is then removed and the tube cured in an oven or in a heated metal mold.

Laminated plastics are hard, strong, impact resisting, heat or water resistant, and have desirable properties for numerous electrical applications. These properties depend largely on the sheet material or filler used. **Fabric-base materials** are strong and well adapted for stressed parts such as gears. **Asbestos and Fiberglas** are recommended for heat-resisting and low water-absorption uses. Laminates have good machining characteristics, which add to their value as a product material.

Vacuum Forming and Blowing. While many processes have been devised for forming sheets of thermoplastic material, the common way is by a pressure differential on the two sides as the sheet is heated to a soft pliable condition. Vacuum processes are limited to obtainable pressures below atmospheric pressure which are usually in the magnitude of 10–13 psi. Higher pressures can be obtained by using a positive air pressure. A section of **spherical surface** can be formed by either of these methods without the use of dies. To accomplish this a sheet is clamped to the top surface of a vacuum or pressure chamber and is either blown or vacuum drawn to shape. By avoiding contact with dies, surface marks are eliminated. Some variation in shape can be obtained in the vacuum process by changing the opening shape, but it is best adapted to the production of spherical or dome-shaped parts used in aircraft, display cases, canopies, etc.

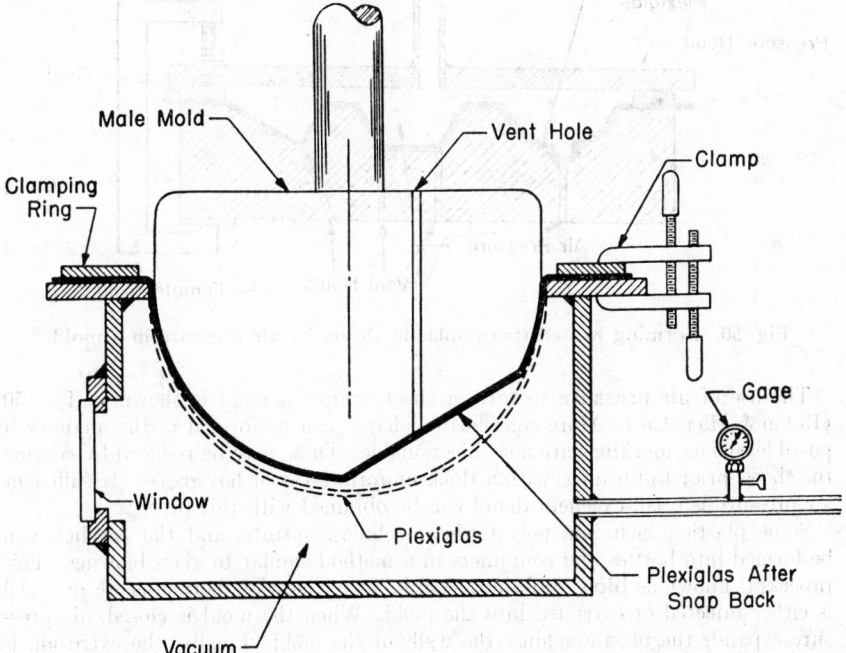

Fig. 49. **Vacuum snap-back forming of heated thermoplastic sheets.**

A similar process known as **vacuum snap-back forming** is shown by Rohm & Haas Co. in Fig. 49. After the sheet is clamped, a vacuum is created in the chamber which causes the sheet to drawn down, as shown by the dotted lines. The male mold is then introduced into the formed sheet, and the vacuum is gradually reduced, causing the sheet to snap back against the mold. Ample draft must be provided on the mold to reduce surface marking to a minimum when the mold is withdrawn. Since a mold form is used in this process, closer tolerances can be maintained than in either vacuum-forming or free-blowing processes. Reverse curves cannot be formed.

A modification of vacuum snap-back forming is known as **ridge-forming.** The same equipment is used, but instead of inserting a form mold, a skeleton frame is used. When the vacuum is released the sheet contacts the ridges of the frame and is held in this position until it is cooled. Articles which can be made in this fashion include such products as large open jars, tank housings, bassinets, etc.

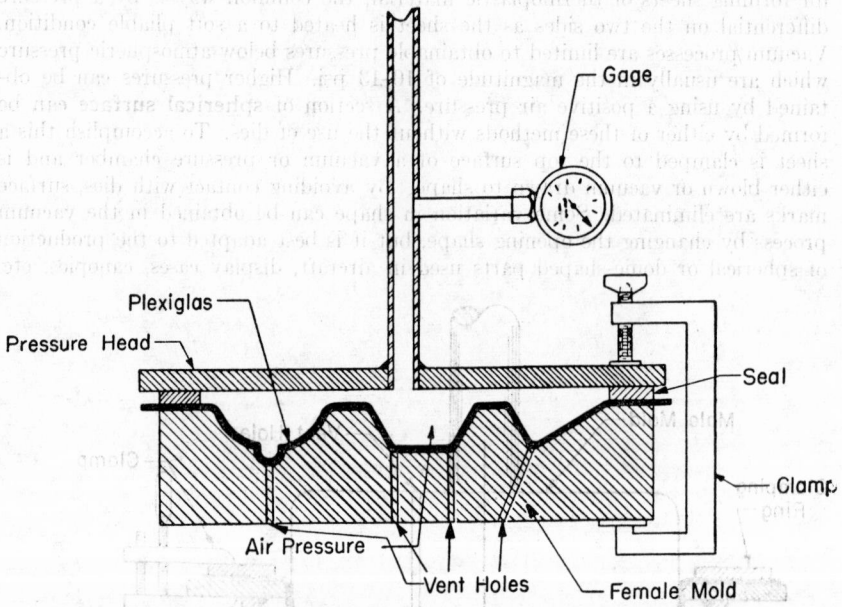

Fig. 50. Forming heated thermoplastic sheets by air pressure in a mold.

The use of **air pressure** to form a sheet against a mold is shown in Fig. 50 (Rohm & Haas Co.). More complicated shapes can be formed in this manner if possible surface markings are not objectionable. These may be reduced by coating the sheet, prior to forming, with a thick uniform layer of hot grease. If sufficient air pressure is used, excellent detail can be obtained with this process.

Some plastics, including polyethylene, cellulose nitrate, and the acrylics, can be formed into bottles and containers in a method similar to glass molding. This process is known as **blow-molding.** A tube or **parison** of thermoplastic material is either injected or extruded into the mold. When the mold is closed, air pressure expands the plastic against the walls of the mold. Finally, the extrusion is cut from the top of the mold and the mold is indexed to the next position where the formed part is air ejected and cooled by water spray. Articles made by blowing include cosmetic containers, floats, ornaments, and hot-water bottles.

Woodworking

PROPERTIES AND SOURCES OF WOOD. Wood, one of our most important building materials, as well as the most popular one used in furniture fabrication, was the first substance ever machined by man. It has a cellular structure and, as a consequence, is relatively light. Strong, yet easily fabricated, it is readily available and low in cost. Lumber is prepared from timber in the sawmill and planing mill by the use of band saws, circular saws, and planing or surfacing machinery. At the mill the moisture content of the wood—which affects not only its weight and stability but also its workability and machinability—is controlled and largely removed.

From finished or semifinished lumber the industrial or wood fabricating plant makes such products as home furnishings. Both **hardwoods** and **softwoods** are used. The hardwoods or deciduous materials include the oaks, mahogany, maple, gum, hickory, walnuts, and ebony, while the soft or coniferous woods are the pines, fir, cypress, redwood, red cedar, etc. Developments in the fields of adhesives have brought about a new group of woods and wood-base materials known as **reconstituted woods**. Wood waste, such as chips and shavings, is treated and bonded together in the form of sheets or panels sometimes known as hardboard. These panels find particular application in the field of home building. As in machining of metals, the hard materials are less workable than the soft ones.

BASIC WOODWORKING TOOLS. Because wood is easily workable, the basic tools are simple; but high production, together with labor saving tech-

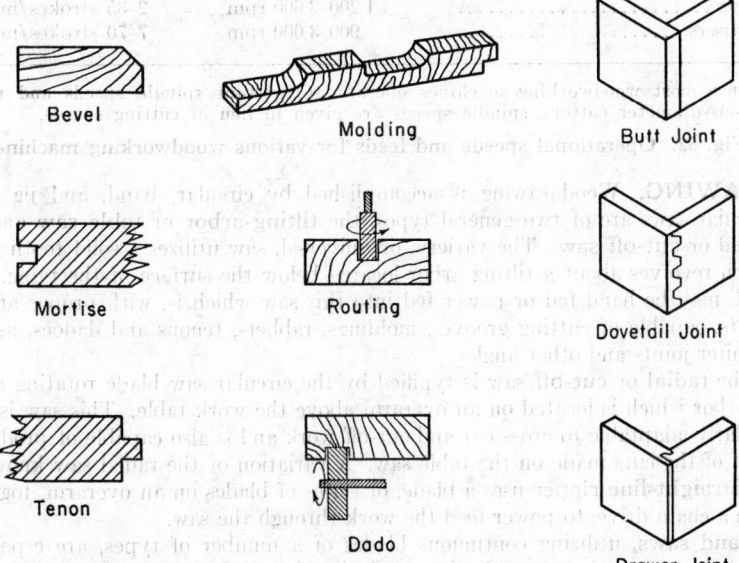

Bevel

Molding

Butt Joint

Mortise

Routing

Dovetail Joint

Tenon

Dado

Drawer Joint

Fig. 51. Typical cuts and joints used in woodworking.

niques, requires multipurpose devices of considerable complexity. A woodwork-ing shop capable of making all types of cuts and joints, including those shown in Fig. 51, and performing finishing operations might contain only the following **fundamental tools:**

1. Circular or table saw for cross-cutting, ripping, dadoing, etc.
2. Shaper or planer for finishing operations.
3. Jointer for joining.
4. Drill press for drilling, routing, mortising, etc.
5. Wood lathe for turning operations.
6. Sander for final finishing.

The production shop uses these same tools or combinations of these for making such products as flooring in one pass by a molding machine.

The cutting speeds and feeds of woodworking machinery are determined by the hardness and moisture content of wood, direction of the grain, and the cutter angle and edge spacing. Most woodworking cutters revolve at a fixed speed, and the amount of material removed is determined by the feed which in turn deter-mines the finish. Spindle speeds and feed ranges are shown in Fig. 52.

Machine	Approx. Range (Spindle Speed)	Range of Feeds
Circular saws 9″ to 20″ diam.	2,000–3,600 rpm	50–300 fpm
Band saws	7,000–9,000 fpm	55–225 fpm
Planers (matchers, molders)....	3,600–7,200 rpm	20–90 fpm
Sanders (drum)	1,200–1,800 rpm	12–36 fpm
Routers	10,000–20,000 rpm and up	Hand and automatic
Tenoners	3,600 rpm	17–60 fpm
Lathe	Up to 4,000 rpm	Hand and automatic
Borers	1,200–3,600 rpm	2–35 strokes/min.
Mortisers	900–3,600 rpm	7–70 strokes/min.

Since most woodworking machines operate at constant spindle speeds and utilize various diameter cutters, spindle speeds are given in lieu of cutting speeds.

Fig. 52. Operational speeds and feeds for various woodworking machines.

SAWING. Wood sawing is accomplished by circular, band, and jig saws. Circular saws are of two general types, the **tilting-arbor** or **table saw** and the **radial** or **cut-off saw.** The variety, or universal, saw utilizes a solid tooth blade which revolves about a tilting arbor located below the surface of the table. The work may be hand fed or power fed into this saw which is, with proper attach-ments, capable of cutting grooves, moldings, rabbets, tenons and dadoes, as well as miter joints and other angles.

The **radial** or **cut-off** saw is typified by the circular saw blade rotating about an arbor which is located on an overarm above the work table. This saw is par-ticularly adaptable to cross-cut and cut-off work and is also capable of producing most of the cuts made on the table saw. A variation of the radial saw known as the **straight-line ripper** uses a blade, or series of blades on an overarm, together with a chain drive, to power feed the work through the saw.

Band saws, utilizing continuous blades of a number of types, are especially adaptable to cutting curved edges and may be used for resawing and certain ripping operations as bevel ripping. These saws have the advantages of being able to cut short radii and produce irregular-shaped and beveled holes. Production machines of this type are equipped with feeding devices, and some that are equipped with multiple blades have attachments—known as **gang saws**—for duplicating parts. One advantage of the band saw is that it produces a small amount of kerf.

The **jig saw** is used for cutting irregular-shaped objects and producing irregular holes by means of a vertically reciprocating blade similar to a hacksaw blade. The use of this tool is limited to light material, which is usually hand fed because it is a light-weight low-power tool.

TURNING AND BORING. The basic turning tool of the woodworking industry is known as the speed lathe, so named because it revolves the work at speeds up to 4,000 rpm. This machine is used for short-run work and pattern-making employing numerous hand tools known as gouges, chisels, and parting tools to produce round parts. As in the turning of metal, the work may be held between centers, on face plates, or in chucks.

Modern mass-production techniques have changed the design of the wood lathe to the point where table legs, bed posts, bowling pins, lamp bases, etc. are produced in a matter of seconds. This change has been accomplished by replacing the chisels and gouges with revolving cutters which are fed into the rotating work piece automatically. The name **automatic shaping lathe** has been assigned to this type machine which, with proper attachments and synchronization, can produce perfect squares, casket corners, and square-contoured legs, as well as "Queen Anne" feet for upholstered furniture.

Veneer cutting is a wood-turning operation in which a thin sheet is rotary cut from a log. These thin sheets are used as fill material, with the grain crossed for additional strength The outside sheets of decorative hardwood are made by huge knives slicing the wood into thin sheets which are subsequently glued to the outside of the laminated pile. **Pole peeling** is another unique wood-turning operation in which a rough telephone pole is taper-cut with a set of cutter heads similar to a large pencil sharpener.

Wood-boring machines are especially adapted to producing, enlarging, or truing holes in wood. This operation can be accomplished on simple drill presses, single spindle borers, or universal spindle, gang-boring machines. **Routing** operations (Fig. 53) are also performed on these machines. In some routing operations, such as the mass production of scrolls upon headboards for beds, a pantograph-type machine is used.

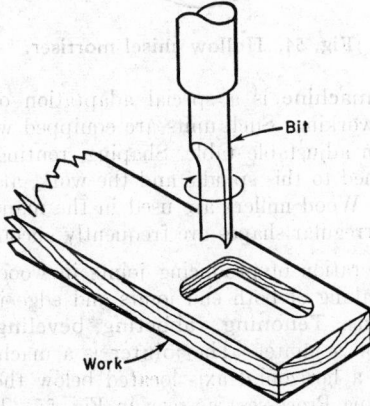

Fig. 53. Router bit and work piece.

All boring-type machines use revolving drill bits or tools especially designed for wood. The drill or boring tool may be fed manually for short-run jobs or automatically for high production. Power feeding mechanisms may be either hydraulic, pneumatic, or mechanical.

Mortising machines produce square holes in wood. They are normally referred to as hollow chisel mortisers (Fig. 54), so named because the hole is produced by a hollow chisel inside of which is a revolving drill. The drill produces a round hole, and the square or shaped chisel follows up to finish the hole. With proper manipulation the mortising tool can produce a square slot, as is used in making a mortise and tenon joint. Mortising machines are either single spindle for job shops or multispindle for production work.

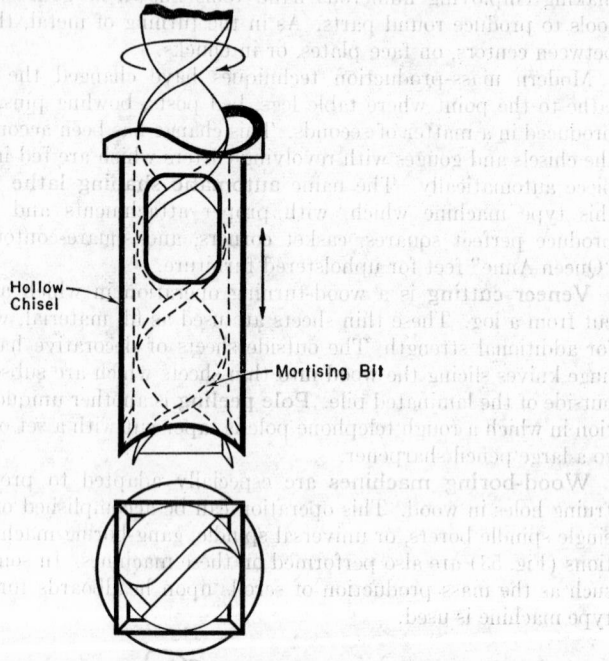

Hollow
Chisel

Mortising Bit

Fig. 54. Hollow chisel mortiser.

The **wood-milling machine** is a special adaptation of the vertical milling machine used in metalworking. Such units are equipped with a vertical rotating spindle located over an adjustable table. Shaping, routing, joining, boring, and drilling tools are attached to this spindle and the work, attached to the table, is fed against the cutter. Wood millers are used in the manufacture of wood patterns where intricate, irregular shapes are frequently encountered.

JOINING. The operation of producing joints in wood is known as joining. Joining includes the making of both end joints and edge joints, as well as some edge-surfacing operations. **Tenoning, rabbeting, beveling, tapering, chamfering,** etc. can be done on a jointer. The **jointer** is a machine with a high-speed cutter revolving about a horizontal axis located below the table, illustrated by Begeman (Manufacturing Processes) as seen in Fig. 55. There are no rollers or pressure feeding mechanisms on the simple jointers; this allows the work to be cut on only one side at a time and is an excellent means of eliminating warp. The jointer, unlike the planer, will produce straight edges but not parallel sides. If parallel surfaces are to be produced, the work should first be jointed, then planed. With proper cutters, shaping operations such as molding and routing can be performed on the jointer.

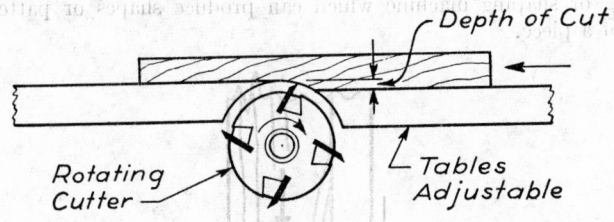

Fig. 55. Jointer.

Such other joining operations as dovetailing, doweling, and fly-cutting may be accomplished on a shaper, drill press, or other special machines designed for the job.

Special machines designed for **tenoning operations** are either single-end or double-end tenoners. When fully equipped, they take stock cut to length and completely finish either, or both, ends for a number of joints. The modern tenoner is equipped with feed chains, pressure beams, cut-off saws, spindle tilting adjustments, cope units, dado attachments, shaping spindles, and a number of other refinements applicable to mass production.

SURFACING AND SANDING. Wood-surfacing machines include planers, sanders, and other tools which perform surface-finishing operations. The planer is most commonly used for finishing flat surfaces that must be parallel. The single **surfacer** or **planer,** also illustrated by Begeman (Fig. 56), has one cutter

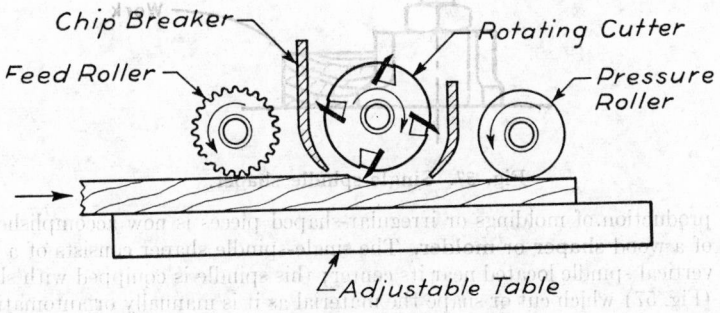

Fig. 56. Planer or single surfacer.

head which rotates about a horizontal axis over the work, finishing one side of the material and producing work to a specified thickness. **Double surfacers or planers,** with cutter heads both above and below the work piece, finish both sides of the work.

Sanding machines include drum, disk, vertical spindle, and belt sanders. All of these are basically described by the name given them. While irregular shapes can be sanded on most of these machines, the belt sander is probably the most versatile in that it can sand flat, curved, or irregular surfaces both on edges and plane surfaces. Belt sanders are used extensively for sanding doors, moldings, table legs, table tops, and numerous other items.

SHAPING. The machining of a pattern on one side of a piece of wood was first known as "sticking." The sticking machine was the forerunner of the modern molding or shaping machine which can produce shapes or patterns on all four sides of a piece.

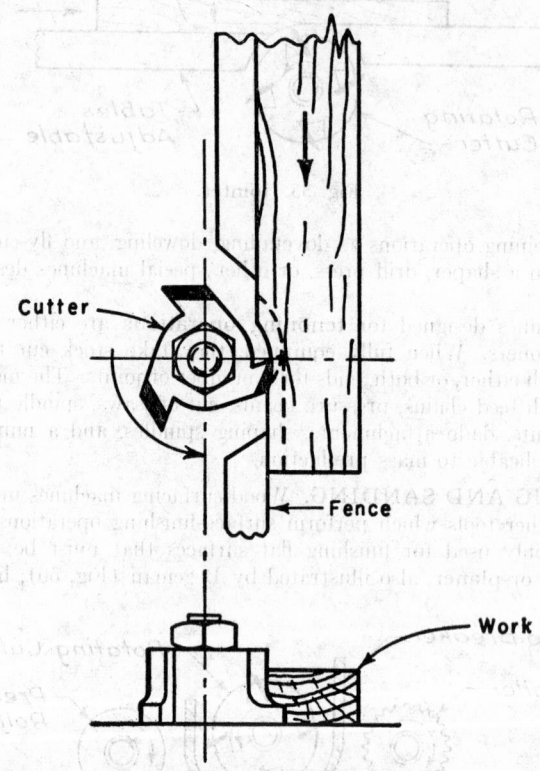

Fig. 57. Single-spindle shaper.

The production of moldings or irregular-shaped pieces is now accomplished by means of a wood **shaper or molder.** The single-spindle shaper consists of a table with a vertical spindle located near its center; this spindle is equipped with shaper knives (Fig. 57) which cut or shape the material as it is manually or automatically fed into the cutter. Some high-production molders have as many as five cutter heads located on both horizontal and vertical spindles. This type is generally used for production runs of straight molding stock.

TOOLS, JIGS, AND FIXTURES

CONTENTS

PAGE

Nature of Tools

Definitions 1
Purpose 1
Types of cutting tools 1

Economic Factors in Tooling

Types of costs 2
Cost relationships 2
  Production costs (f. 1) 3
Cost formulas 3
Nomographic cost determinations 5
  Tool life for minimum cost (f. 2) 5
  Tool life for maximum production rate
  (f. 3) 6
  Optimum cutting speed (f. 4) 7
Feed and economic tool life 7
Feed force and tool wear 7
  The tool force and its components (f. 5) 8
  Evaluation of tool life in terms of the
  area machined (f. 6) 8

Tool Life and Standardization

Factors in tool life 9
  Types of chips 9
Control of tool wear 10
Tool-life tests 10
  Tool-life–cutting-speed relationship in
  turning two forging die steels (A and
  B) (f. 7) 11
Nomographs for tool life and power.. 12
Tool-life determinations 12
  Combined tool-life and power nomo-
  graph (f. 8) 14–15
Tool force determinations 13
Maximum output 16

The Tool Crib

Location 16
Layout of tool crib 17
  Space required for tool cribs 17
Charge-out systems 18
  Single-check system 18
  Double-check system 18
  Triplicate tool-slip system: spring-clip
  boards 18
  Typical tool order made out in triplicate
  (f. 9) 19
  Card record system in triplicate 20
  Tool inventory control card (f. 10) 21

PAGE

Electric machine method 21
Metal plate method 22

Tool Inventories

Control of inventory 22
  Combined purchasing and distribution-
  to-crib records for tools (f. 11) 24–25
  Quantity of each tool to carry 23
Checking the inventory 23

Tool Classification

Identification of tools 23
Numeric systems 26
  Straight numeric system 26
  Classified numeric system 26
   Numerical tool classification key sheet—
   Dewey decimal system (f. 12) 26
  Example of a numeric system 27
Letter systems 28
Mnemonic systems 28
  Application 28
  First stage of mnemonic classification of
  measuring devices (f. 13) 29
Marking symbols on tools 30

Cutting-Tool Standardization

Purpose 30
Standardization committee 30
Standardization results 31

Electro-machining Tooling

The process 31
Applications 32
Advantages 32

Cutting-Tool Materials

Factors in selection 32
Plain-carbon steels 32
  Composition of plain-carbon tool steel
  (f. 14) 33
High-speed steels 33
  High-speed tool steels—composition and
  properties (f. 15) 34
Cast nonferrous alloys 33
  Composition of cast nonferrous alloy tool
  material (f. 16) 35
Sintered carbides 35
  Carbide manufacturers' grade recom-
  mendations (f. 17) 37

CONTENTS (*Continued*)

PAGE

Diamonds 36
Ceramic materials 36

Tool Geometry

Single-point tools 38
   Solid single-point cutting-tool termi-
     nology (*f.* 18) 38
   Tipped single-point cutting-tool termi-
     nology (*f.* 19) 39
   Tool angle nomenclature 38
     Single-point cutting-tool angles (*f.* 20) .. 39
     Single-point tool designation (*f.* 21) 40
   Chip breakers 40
     Typical chip breakers (*f.* 22) 41
Multiple-cutting-edge tools 41
   Drills 41
     Twist drill nomenclature and geometry
     (*f.* 23) 42
   Reamers 42
   Broaches 42
   Milling cutters 43
Tool finishing 44
   Advantages of finish grinding 44

PAGE

Jigs and Fixtures

Principles of locating work piece 45
   Degrees of freedom 45
     Placement of locators (*f.* 24) 45
   Influence of work-piece surface 45
Types of locators 46
   Application of edge or bottom locators
     (*f.* 25) 46
Principles of clamping 47
   Placement of clamps (*f.* 26) 47
   Influence of work piece on clamping 48
Other considerations in design 48
   Chip clearance 48
   Example of drill jig design (*f.* 27) 48
   Foolproof operation 49
   Influence of forces encountered 49
Design check list 49
   Check list of factors in jig and fixture
     design (*f.* 28) 50-51
Economy of jigs and fixtures 49
   Formulas 52
   Debit factors 52
   Credit factors 52
   Economy analysis applications 53

TOOLS, JIGS, AND FIXTURES

Nature of Tools

DEFINITIONS. The small tools commonly used in the mechanical industries are treated in this section from the standpoint of their performance, classification, economics, and design as these pertain to the production engineer. The operating mechanisms frequently referred to as machine tools are taken up in the section on Manufacturing Processes, while gages and gaging equipment are discussed in detail in the section on Inspection. All attention is devoted here to tools used for material removal, with accuracy of reproduction under production conditions as the ultimate goal.

The various devices to be discussed in this section may be defined as follows:

A **tool** is a device or element designed and used for the express purpose of removing material from a work piece under controlled or stable conditions.

A **jig** is a work-supporting, work-holding, and tool-guiding device.

A **fixture** is a work-supporting and work-holding device.

PURPOSE. All persons who would properly apply modern tools, jigs, and fixtures must understand the purposes for which they are created.

Mass production is taken for granted today. But it would be impossible without **interchangeable manufacture,** in which any piece in a given size class may be substituted for any other piece in the same size class, and used in any assembly. Accurate tooling, resulting in such reproducibility of parts, is one of the primary purposes of the tooling effort in modern industry.

A second consideration is the economic factor. Tooling for quantity production is possible only in a **predictable market.** There is always a minimum production volume, below which tooling cannot be justified. The engineer must therefore weigh the economic factors before he decides on a course of action, or grave financial blunders may be made in specifying and designing tooling.

In an era of rising labor costs, a primary purpose of tooling is to relieve the worker of the need for high skill in a variety of operations. Proper tooling permits **specialization of labor** so that less skilled workers may be utilized without jeopardizing the quantity and/or quality of the product.

Modern tooling transfers the needed skill from the worker to the machine and markedly reduces the chance of inadvertent error.

TYPES OF CUTTING TOOLS. Cutting tools may be broken down into three broad classifications:

1. **Single-point tools,** which apply one cutting edge to the item being machined Turning and facing tools are typical tools of this sort.
2. **Multiple-edge tools,** which apply more than one cutting edge to the item being machined. Examples of these tools are broaches, drills, reamers, and milling cutters.

21·1

3. **Nonmechanical, noncontact tools,** which include the following:

Method	Nature of Action	Field of Application
Electro-spark	Thermal	Metal removal, coating, and surface hardening
Electric impulse	Thermal	Same as electro-spark
Anode-mechanical	Thermal and chemical	Metal removal
Electric contact	Thermal	Metal removal
Electro-mechanical	Thermal combined with mechanical action	Metal removal

The development of nonmechanical, noncontact tools has progressed rapidly in both England and Russia. All devices using combinations of electrical, electrolytic, and chemical material removal fall in this category. Most of these are restricted to use on hard materials which are either uneconomical or impossible to machine by other methods.

Economic Factors in Tooling

TYPES OF COSTS. Present-day manufacturing is composed of many functions, each contributing either directly or indirectly to the cost of production. Each cost area is usually scrutinized for economic operation, but until recently very little effort was directed toward the analysis and quantification of the many interrelated functions of manufacturing and the minimizing of cost as a whole. An analysis of production costs, of tooling in particular, reveals the factors which can be varied to decrease costs.

An approach to the consideration of all costs involved in a work situation is given by Gilbert (Machining—Theory and Practice, The American Society of Metals). Gilbert analyzes **single-point tool-cutting costs** as follows:

1. The **idle and loading costs** which represent the noncutting time of normal production. This time may be reduced with the introduction of automatic devices to speed loading and unloading and by giving proper incentive to the operator to perform at a high level of proficiency. In a jobbing shop 40 to 80 percent of the total cycle time may be consumed in idle and loading time.
2. The **cutting costs** represent the time that the tool is actually cutting. On highly repetitive machining operations the cutting time, and in turn cost, may assume a large proportion of the total cycle time. The cutting time may be reduced by increasing the cutting speed.
3. The **tool-changing costs** represent the time necessary to remove, replace, and reset the tool and put the machine back into production. If the operator regrinds his own tools, then this time should be included.
4. The **tool-grinding costs** include depreciation of the original tool cost, and the cost of labor, grinding wheels, and equipment for regrinding the tool.

COST RELATIONSHIPS. The relationships of these costs to each other is shown by Gilbert in Fig. 1, with the given cost and operating information.

The terms used in expressing the cost relationships in Fig. 1 are:

K_1 = Direct labor rate + overhead rate (dollars/min.). Includes depreciation, power, insurance, and maintenance.

K_2 = Tool cost per grind. Includes tool depreciation and regrinding cost (dollars/tool).

L = Length of cut (inches).

D = Diameter of cut (inches).

V = Cutting speed (SFPM).

f = Feed per revolution (inches).

$VT^n = C$, cutting-speed–tool-life relation.

T = Tool life (minutes).

t = Tool-changing time (minutes).

n = Exponent (slope of cutting speed vs. tool life on log-log plot. See Fig. 7).

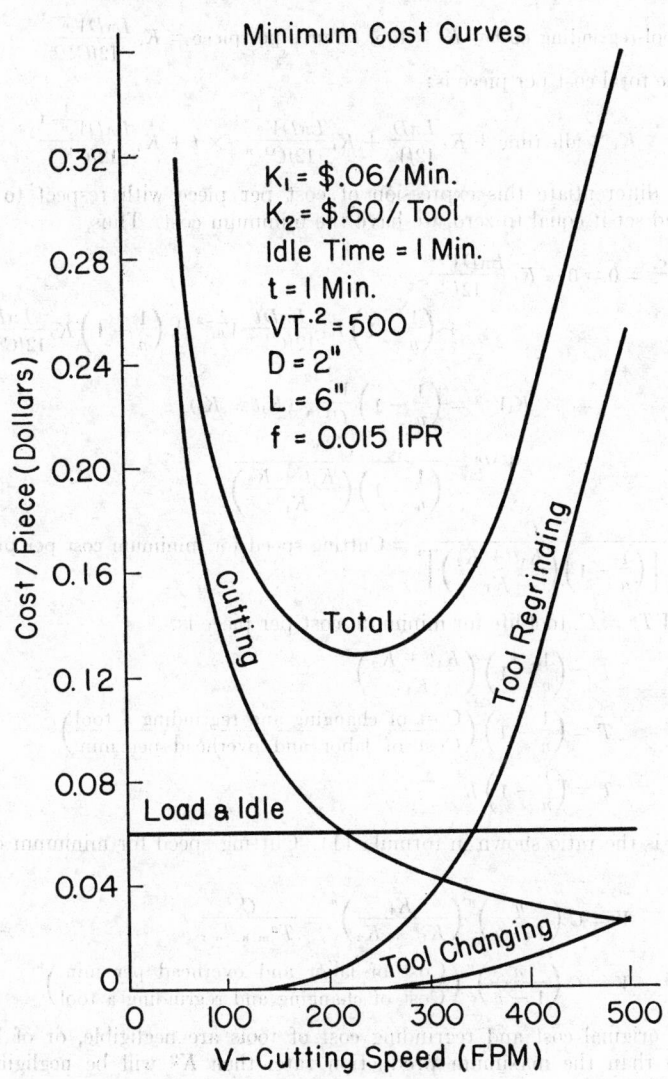

Minimum Cost Curves

K_1 = \$.06/Min.

K_2 = \$.60/Tool

Idle Time = 1 Min.

t = 1 Min.

$VT^{.2}$ = 500

D = 2"

L = 6"

f = 0.015 IPR

Cost / Piece (Dollars)

Cutting

Total

Tool Regrinding

Load & Idle

Tool Changing

V–Cutting Speed (FPM)

Fig. 1. Production costs.

Cost Formulas. Gilbert then established the following expressions:

1. Idle cost per piece = K_1 × idle time per piece.
   (Includes loading, unloading, tool approach, etc.)

2. Cutting cost per piece = K_1 × cutting time per piece = $K_1 \dfrac{L\pi D}{12fV}$

3. Tool-changing cost per piece $= K_1 \times$ tool failures per piece $\times$ tool-changing time, or

$$K_1 \frac{L\pi D V^{\frac{1}{n}-1}}{12fC^{1/n}} \times t$$

4. Tool-regrinding cost $= K_2 \times$ tool failures per piece $= K_2 \frac{L\pi D V^{\frac{1}{n}-1}}{12fC^{1/n}}$

Thus, the total cost per piece is:

$$K_1 \times \text{idle time} + K_1 \frac{L\pi D}{12fV} + K_1 \frac{L\pi D V^{\frac{1}{n}-1}}{12fC^{1/n}} \times t + K_2 \frac{L\pi D V^{\frac{1}{n}-1}}{12fC^{1/n}}$$

If we differentiate this expression of cost per piece with respect to cutting speed and set it equal to zero, we have the minimum cost. Thus,

$$\frac{d/\text{cost/pc.}}{dV} = 0 = 0 - K_1 \frac{L\pi D V^{-2}}{12f}$$

$$+ \left(\frac{1}{n} - 1\right) K_1 \frac{L\pi D t}{12fC^{1/n}} V^{\frac{1}{n}-2} + \left(\frac{1}{n} - 1\right) K_2 \frac{L\pi D}{12fC^{1/n}} V^{\frac{1}{n}-2}$$

$$K_1 V^{-2} = \left(\frac{1}{n} - 1\right) \frac{V^{\frac{1}{n}-2}}{C^{1/n}} (K_1 t + K_2)$$

$$V^{1/n} = \frac{C^{1/n}}{\left(\frac{1}{n} - 1\right)\left(\frac{K_1 t + K_2}{K_1}\right)}$$

$$V = \frac{C}{\left[\left(\frac{1}{n} - 1\right)\left(\frac{K_1 t + K_2}{K_1}\right)\right]^n} = \text{Cutting speed for minimum cost per piece.}$$

Since $VT^n = C$, tool life for minimum cost per piece is:

$$T = \left(\frac{1}{n} - 1\right)\left(\frac{K_1 t + K_2}{K_1}\right) \tag{1}$$

$$T = \left(\frac{1}{n} - 1\right)\left(\frac{\text{Cost of changing and regrinding a tool}}{\text{Cost of labor and overhead per min.}}\right)$$

$$T = \left(\frac{1}{n} - 1\right) R$$

where R is the ratio shown in formula (1). Cutting speed for minimum cost per piece is:

$$V = C \left(\frac{n}{1-n}\right)^n \left(\frac{K_1}{K_1 t + K_2}\right)^n = \frac{C}{T^n_{\text{min. cost}}} \tag{2}$$

$$V = C \left(\frac{n}{1-n}\right)^n \left(\frac{\text{Cost of labor and overhead per min.}}{\text{Cost of changing and regrinding a tool}}\right)^n$$

If the original cost and regrinding cost of tools are negligible, or of less importance than the maximum production rate, then K^2 will be negligible, and formula (1) will be:

$$\text{Tool life} = \left(\frac{1}{n} - 1\right)t = T_{\text{max. prod.}}$$

and

$$\text{Cutting speed} = V = \frac{C}{\left[\left(\frac{1}{n} - 1\right)t\right]^n} = \frac{C}{T^n_{\text{max. prod.}}}$$

Nomographic Cost Determinations. Gilbert further developed the concept of minimum cost and made it more easily used with the nomographs shown in Figs. 2, 3, and 4.

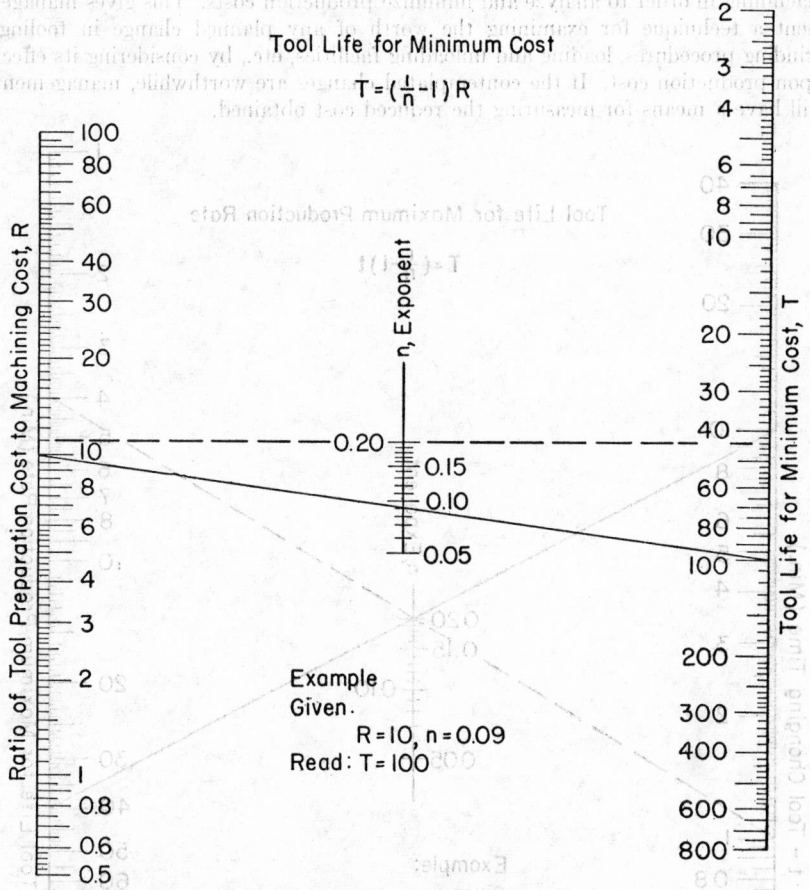

Fig. 2. Tool life for minimum cost.

To illustrate the use of the developed nomographs, the following example may be cited:

Tool Material—Sintered Carbide

$D = 2$ in.
$L = 6$ in.

Work Material—Alloy Steel

$t = 1$ min.

$f = 0.015\,(1\,PR)$
$VT^{0.2} = 500$
$K_1 = \$3.60/\text{hr.} = \$0.06/\text{min.}$
Idle and load time = 1 min.
$K_2 = \$0.60/\text{tool failure}$

The value of $(1/n - 1)$ is 4, and the cost ratio R is 11. From Fig. 2 the tool life for minimum cost is 44 min., and the cutting speed from Fig. 4 is 235 surface ft. per min., which checks with the result shown in Fig. 1. The tool life for maximum production, from Fig. 3, is 4 min. with a cutting speed, from Fig. 4, of 378 surface ft. per min. The higher rate of production would increase the cost per piece to $0.19, as compared to $0.127 minimum cost. This increase in cost would be acceptable in a "crash" program or all-out war effort.

Gilbert's work demonstrates the value of examining all costs pertinent to machining in order to analyze and minimize production costs. This gives management a technique for examining the worth of any planned change in tooling, grinding procedures, loading and unloading facilities, etc., by considering its effect upon production cost. If the contemplated changes are worthwhile, management will have a means for measuring the reduced cost obtained.

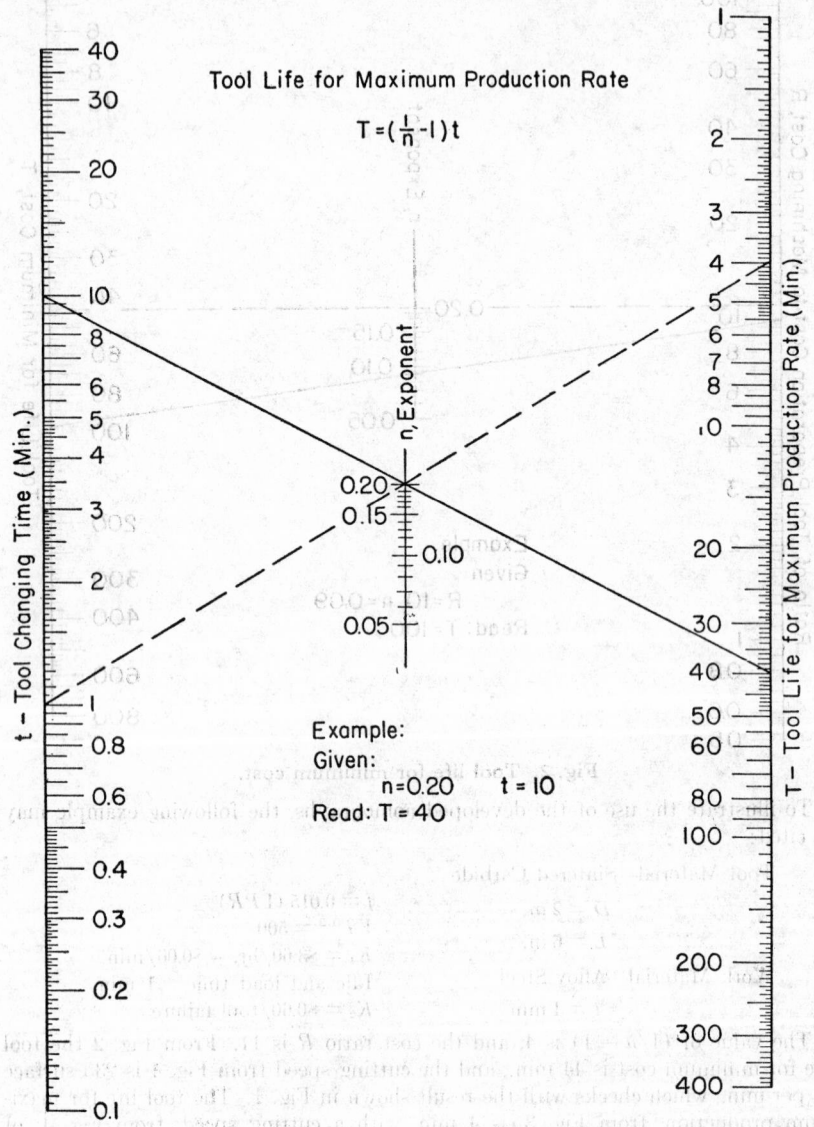

Fig. 3. Tool life for maximum production rate.

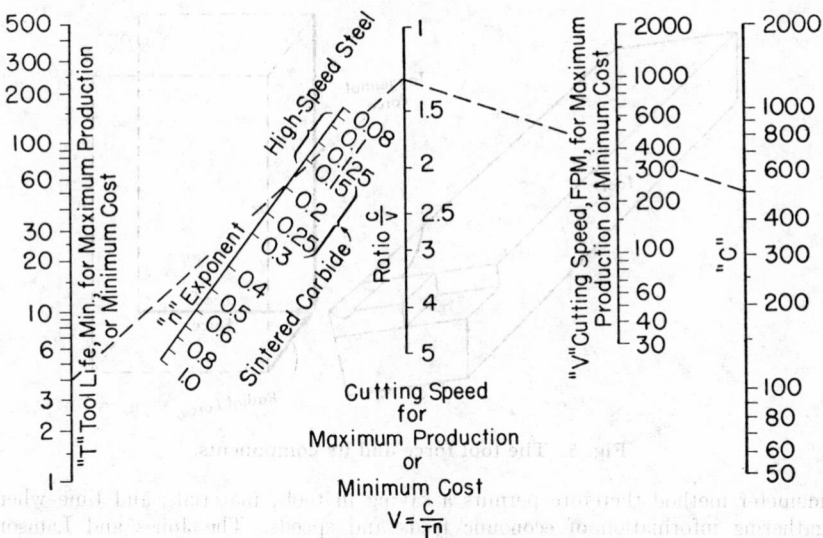

Fig. 4. Optimum cutting speed.

FEED AND ECONOMIC TOOL LIFE. With consideration for the same factors affecting the economic situation in tooling, Skrivan (Czechoslovak Heavy Industry) further subdivides the problem of economic tooling into consideration for power requirements and types of cut, rough or finished. Skrivan found, through experimentation, that in finish-turning the additional limitations of degree of precision and surface finish desired influence the choice of feed and speed chosen. Using the same basic relationships as those utilized by Gilbert, Skrivan found that in a **finishing** operation the most economical machining is obtained if the cutting speed corresponds with the economic tool life, here assumed to be 90 min. When **roughing,** the full power of the machine should be utilized to give the least cost. This should be accomplished by the use of a feed appropriate to the product requirements or specifications. This will result in going well beyond the recommendations given in conventional feed and speed tables, since generally these recommendations are predicated on a uniform tool life rather than over-all cost consideration.

FEED FORCE AND TOOL WEAR. Work performed at the Jones and Lamson Machine Co., reported by Hebert and Fersing (Western Machinery and Steel World, vol. 46) reveals a different approach to the problem of economic selection of feeds and speeds. Fig. 5 represents the **force components** present in a turning operation, namely, **tangential, feed,** and **radial forces.** A **tool dynamometer** was developed that supported the tool and with the addition of three strain gages coupled to a recording oscillograph made possible the continuous measurement of the component forces during cutting. As cutting progressed, the tool wear was reflected as a gradual increase in feed force. If sudden chipping occurred it reflected an erratic pattern, thus making it possible to stop the test immediately rather than continuing until the end of cut. It was found that a 50 percent increase in feed force was the result of a wear land of approximately 0.006 in. This was found to be such an accurate **index of tool wear** that it became unnecessary to become involved in wear land measurements. The dyna-

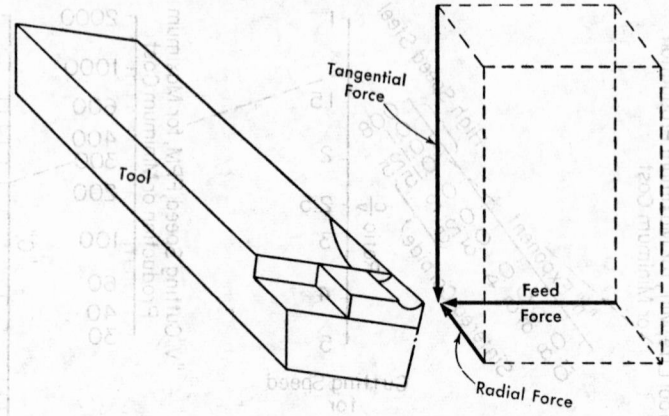

Fig. 5. The tool force and its components.

mometer method therefore permits a saving in tools, materials, and time when gathering information of economic feeds and speeds. The Jones and Lamson research also revealed that by defining tool life in terms of square inches of machined surface for a wear land of 0.006 in. the information was more meaningful on the production floor. They found that the readily accomplished calculation

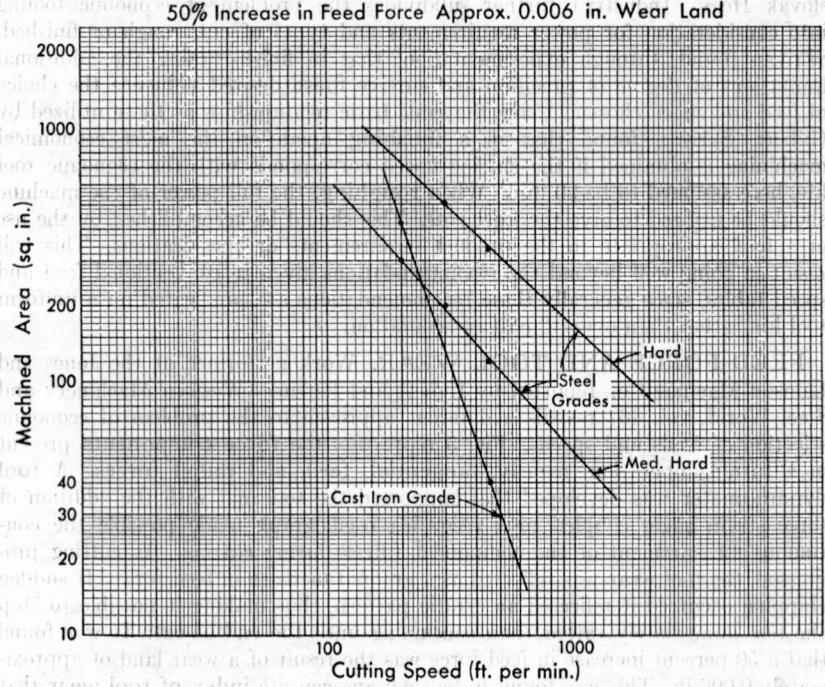

Fig. 6. Evaluation of tool life in terms of the area machined.

of the newly formed diameter times the length of cut times π was easily understood. Fig. 6 is a typical graph of tool life as found by Jones and Lamson Machine Co.

Tool Life and Standardization

FACTORS IN TOOL LIFE. Tool life is generally accepted to mean the time between tool resharpenings or tool replacements. The most common methods of specifying tool life are as follows:

1. The elapsed time of machine operation. The tool may actually be cutting during only a portion of the machine cycle.
2. The actual cutting time, or the time the tool is in contact with the work piece. This is the most common method of defining tool life.
3. The volume of material removed.
4. The number of pieces produced. This is common in shop parlance, but finds very little application in tool life testing.
5. The "Taylor" speed, or equivalent cutting speed. This refers to the cutting speed at which an actual cutting time, usually 60 min., is obtained under a given set of conditions.
6. The relative cutting speed. This refers to the relative tool life against a previous standard such as developed in item 5 above. This is used to rate both tools and materials cut in reference to a base of 100 percent.

Tool failure is manifested in either the tool or the work piece in one of the following ways:

1. **Flank wear** on cutting tool. This occurs on the flank of the tool just below the cutting edge. This is a common method of expressing tool failure.
2. **Cratering** of the cutting tool. This occurs as the result of the chip impingement on the face behind the cutting edge with a resultant hole or crater in the tool face.
3. **Chipping** of the cutting tool. In this case fine pieces of the tool material break out along the cutting edge.
4. **Poor finish** on the work piece. This can be the result of the tool becoming dull, flank wear, or excessive cratering or chipping.
5. **Loss of desired size** as cutting progresses and tool wear increases.
6. **Increased power requirements** because of tool dulling.

Types of Chips. The type of material being cut has a distinct bearing upon the tool life. Machining of metal materials, both ferrous and nonferrous, results in the following types of chips:

Type I—the **segmental chip.** When machining brittle materials like cast iron the chip is sheared from the work piece ahead of the cutting edge, resulting in a fair surface finish, low power requirements, and a reasonable tool life. This type of chip is a discontinuous or powder type of chip. The cutting of ductile materials at a low speed will also result in a Type I chip. However, the resultant surface finish is poor, the power requirements comparatively high, and the tool wear excessive.

Type II—the **continuous chip without a built-up edge.** When machining ductile materials at high speeds there is a deformation of metal ahead of the cutting edge without fracture. This is accompanied by the absence of a deposit of work-piece material on the tip of the tool. This cutting situation results in best surface finish, least power required, and least tool wear. **A chip breaker** is generally necessary to aid breaking up this continuous chip for easier disposal.

Type III—the **continuous chip with a built-up edge on the tool.** This is the most common cutting situation encountered in the machining of metals. The work material adheres to the face of tool immediately behind the cutting edge. This is caused by excessive heat because of friction and extreme pressure. This situation is identified with the cutting of ductile materials at normal speeds. The Type III chip results in poor surface finish on the work piece.

CONTROL OF TOOL WEAR. Niedzwiedzki (American Machinist, vol. 100) points out the need for a more thorough understanding on the part of the average practitioner in regard to chip formation and tool wear. Niedzwiedzki points out that **tool wear** is prompted by the fact that there are never perfectly smooth surfaces in contact in the work-chip-tool cutting situation. As the cut progresses a collision between two meeting peaks may produce either purely mechanical abrasion (when a harder peak cuts off a softer one) or abrasion by minute particles being welded between work and tool. Further movement results in the minute weld breaking at its weaker peak, this in turn causing abrasion and tool wear. Niedzwiedzki gives the following **microwelding factors** that might be considered:

1. High chip pressure.
2. High cutting temperature.
3. Intimacy of metal-to-metal contact.
4. Faculty for forming solid solutions.
5. Long duration of intimate contact.
6. Favorable microstructure.

Antiwelding agents may be introduced in the form of material being cut, tool material, or more usually in the form of chemically active cutting fluids. Thus, by awareness of the causes of tool wear, steps may be taken to minimize their effects.

TOOL-LIFE TESTS. Since many metalworking companies interested in tool economy carry on tests to determine tool life, the American Standards Association Technical Committee 21, through its Sectional Committee B5 on the Standardization of Machine Tools and Machine Tool Elements, has developed a proposed standard of tool-life tests for evaluating the machinability of single-point cutting tools, cutting fluids, or materials cut. Boston (Mech. Eng., vol. 66), chairman of the Sectional Committee, presents data of which the following is a brief summary. The methods covered are those for tools of steel and cast nonferrous alloys, which fail or wear differently from tools with cemented-carbide tips.

1. Single-point tools may be solid or tipped with a small piece of metal-cutting material.
2. Outline of a test must cover the objective—performance rating of tool, material cut, or cutting fluid—method of test, factors and apparatus used, and method of analyzing data and correlating them with actual shop conditions.
3. Merits of a tool, metal cut, or cutting fluid may be based singly or collectively on: tool-life–cutting-speed relationship, surface quality produced, form of chip produced (well-broken-up chips are best), and forces, energy, or power involved.
4. Cutting conditions should be as near as possible to actual conditions, to determine the four factors in item 3. Such conditions may be: light, intermediate, and heavy cuts on abrasive materials or one giving discontinuous chips, as cast iron; the same on steel of several types and structures; tools, cuts, and materials for general purpose work; cuts, tool materials, cutting materials for specific commercial practice.
5. Variable factors involved are the machine tool—type, condition, capacity or size, method of power transmission, speeds, feeds, and tool-mounting and work-holding means; material cut—analysis, structure, hardness, strength; tools—

material composition, physical condition, scale or surface condition, shape and rigidity under continuous and intermittent cutting, as-forged or as-cast or as-rolled (cleaned, pickled, blasted, hot-rolled, or cold-drawn), heat treatment. kind of tip and method of attachment if tip is different from shank and shape of tool point; cutting fluid—class, properties, and methods of manufacture; size of cut (depth and feed) and its shape.

6. Methods of test for cutting-speed–tool-life relationship should involve but one variable at a time, all other factors being kept constant, and a number of standards should be set up to determine this relationship. For tool material tests, for example, the factors to be kept constant are tool shape, depth of cut and feed. setting angle of tool, analysis and heat-treatment of material being machined, and type of cutting fluid (including dry cutting).

Size of cut must be varied—light, intermediate, and heavy—to give specific tests under commercial conditions attending the use of the tool. **Feed** is represented in thousandths of an inch per revolution of work or cutter. Suggested cuts are:

1. 0.005 to 0.010-in. depth of cut and 0.002-in. feed.
2. 0.100-in. depth of cut by 0.0125-in. feed.
3. ⅛-in. depth of cut by 0.020-in. feed.
4. 3/16-in. depth of cut with 0.005-in. or 0.010-in. feed.
5. Maximum of ¼-in. depth of cut with 0.03-in. to 0.05-in. feed.

Cutting speed is measured on the uncut work surface ahead of the tool, and recorded in feet per minute.

Mat'l	Cut	n	Cor V_1	V_{10}	V_{30}	T_{150}	T_{60}
A	Light	0.08	181	152	140	12	
B	Light	0.08	181	152	140	12	
A	Heavy	0.11	84	65.5	59		11.5
B	Heavy	0.11	78	61	54		25

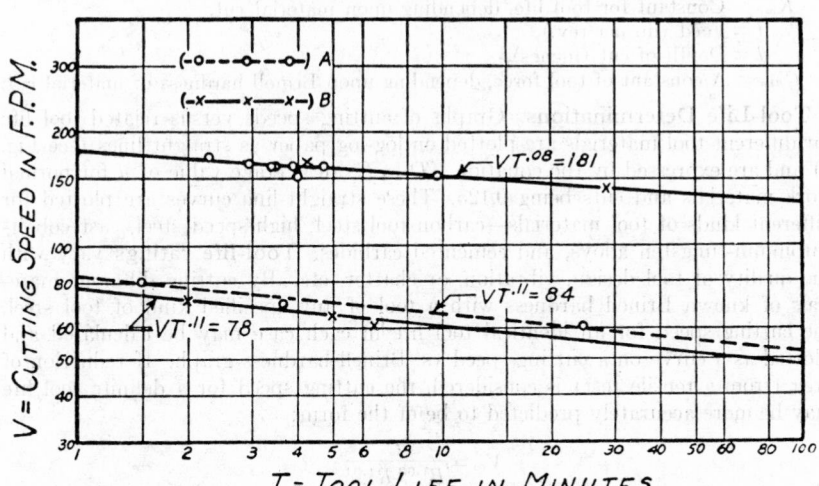

Fig. 7. Tool-life–cutting-speed relationship in turning two forging die steels (*A* and *B*).

The two general methods for obtaining machinability ratings based on tool life are:

1. To obtain tool life when cutting under standardized conditions at a constant cutting speed, as in turning cylindrical test bars.
2. To obtain tool life when cutting at a uniformly increasing or decreasing speed, as in facing on a taper.

The formula for expressing the relation between cutting speed and tool life between grinds for a given tool, material, feed, and depth of cut (method 1, above) is:

$$VT^n = C$$

where V = Cutting speed (ft. per min.).

    T = Tool life or duration of cut between grinds (minutes).

    C = A constant, depending on conditions, representing the cutting speed for a tool life of 1 min.

    n = The slope of the tool-life straight line on log-log paper.

Fig. 7 (ASA, Life Tests of Single-Point Tools) shows the results of cutting-speed–tool-life tests on two die steels, both heat-treated and tempered to give a Brinell hardness of 363. Two cuts were made dry: a light one with a feed of 0.0127 in. and a depth of cut of 0.0125 in., and a heavy one with a feed of 0.0137 in. and depth of cut of 0.100 in.

NOMOGRAPHS FOR TOOL LIFE AND POWER. Nomographs have been developed to include the basic idea of Taylor and Barth slide rules in balancing horsepower against tool life and also to include modern materials and to be applicable on geared-head motor-driven equipment as well as belt-driven tools. They apply to cutting steel with single-point tools (see Fig. 8). Surface finish has not been correlated with the other variables. The variables of machinability included are:

    V = Cutting speed (ft. per min.).

    T = Tool life (minutes).

    K_{tm} = Constant for tool life, depending on tool material.

    K_{mc} = Constant for tool life, depending upon material cut.

    f = Feed (in. per rev.).

    d = Depth of cut (inches).

    C_{Bhn} = A constant of tool force, depending upon Brinell hardness of material cut.

Tool-Life Determinations. Graphs of cutting speeds versus related tool life for different tool materials are plotted on log-log paper as straight lines (see Fig. 7) and are expressed by the equation $VT^n = C$, an average value of n for normal work materials and cuts being 0.125. These straight-line curves are plotted for different kinds of tool materials—carbon tool steel, high-speed steel, cast cobalt-chromium-tungsten alloys, and cemented carbides. **Tool-life ratings** vary with the quality of tool design, vibration, or chatter, etc. By cutting different materials of known Brinell hardness with a tool of any specified kind of tool steel, the cutting speed for an identical tool life in each case may be calculated and plotted as a curve on a cutting-speed vs. Brinell-hardness graph. If reduction of area (from a tensile test) is considered, the cutting speed for a definite tool life may be more accurately predicted to be of the form:

$$V_{60} = \frac{C}{B^{1.63} R^{1.01}}$$

where B is Brinell hardness and R is percent reduction of area (Janitzky, ASM Transactions, vol. 26).

Graphs of cutting speeds versus inches feed or depth—that is, size of cut—for a definite tool life, plotted on log-log paper, are straight lines and are prepared from tests keeping the tool material and the material cut constant. For instance, the equation for a 90-min. tool life is $V_{90} f^{.61} d^{.36} = K$. Doubling depth of cut reduces speed only 22 percent but rate of metal removal is 56 percent more. Doubling feed reduces speed only 34 percent but rate of metal removal is 31 percent more.

Tool shape in the nomograph (Fig. 8) has been corrected to a tool having 8° back rake, 14° side rake, 6° end relief, 6° side relief, 6° end-cutting-edge angle, 15° side-cutting-edge angle, and 3/64-in. nose radius. Increasing nose radius or side-cutting-edge angle may increase tool life or increase cutting speed as much as 50 percent, except perhaps on cemented-carbide tools. A rake angle of 20° to 30° is best for cutting soft, ductile steels; 0° to 10° is best for hard, brittle steels.

The tool-life nomograph, left half of Fig. 8, including "Feed—inches per revolution," was constructed on the basis of

$$VT^{.125} = \frac{K_{tm} K_{mc}}{f^{.61} d^{.36}}$$

All scales are logarithmic, because the functions of the variables are exponential. With 5 variables known in this half of the diagram, the sixth may be found. By pivoting the long dash line on the point where it crosses line C, the effect of changing feed on the velocity of cutting may be checked. As feeds decrease, speeds would go up, but the volume of metal removed would be reduced.

Cutting fluids (the nomograph is based on dry cutting) may increase cutting speed 15 percent to 30 percent in the case of emulsions, 10 percent to 25 percent in the case of oils if long tool life is important.

Tool Force Determinations. Tool forces in the tests showed no appreciable variation among tools of different materials, except that as tools dulled, the tangential force decreased slightly, and at tool failure the force may double. Similarly, in a test conducted at the Consolidated Aircraft Corp., Vultee Field Division, no change in load resulted as surface velocity changed, for speed variations within the test range of 200 and 1,500 ft. per min., under various feed combinations from light to heavy (Brainard, Mech. Eng., vol. 66). A 35 percent allowance was made in the nomograph for tool-dulling and failure and consequent danger of machine-stalling and tool-breaking. Tool force varies with material cut, being higher with plain carbon steels, for which the nomograph is designed, than with free-cutting steels, for which the power requirements will be about 40 percent less. For an average slope of 0.75 for straight-line curves on log-log tangential-force versus Brinell-hardness number charts, the tangential force equation would be $F_t = K(Bhn)^{.75}$.

Feed and depth increase in cuts has practically a direct effect on horsepower or tangential tool force. With tools of the larger radii, the tangential-force equation is $F_t = Cf^{.8} d^{.9}$, showing that it is beneficial to increase feed or depth by reducing cutting speed—the tangential force increasing but the power for removing a unit amount of metal decreasing.

Larger nose radii or **side-cutting angles** have no appreciable effect on tangential tool force but would affect radial and longitudinal tool force. With higher rake angles, tool forces and power are reduced. Rake angles below 14° require more power (Boston and Kraus, Trans. ASME, vol. 58).

Cutting fluids, useful in reducing tool forces, have little effect on tangential force or power at high speeds but may reduce power at low speeds.

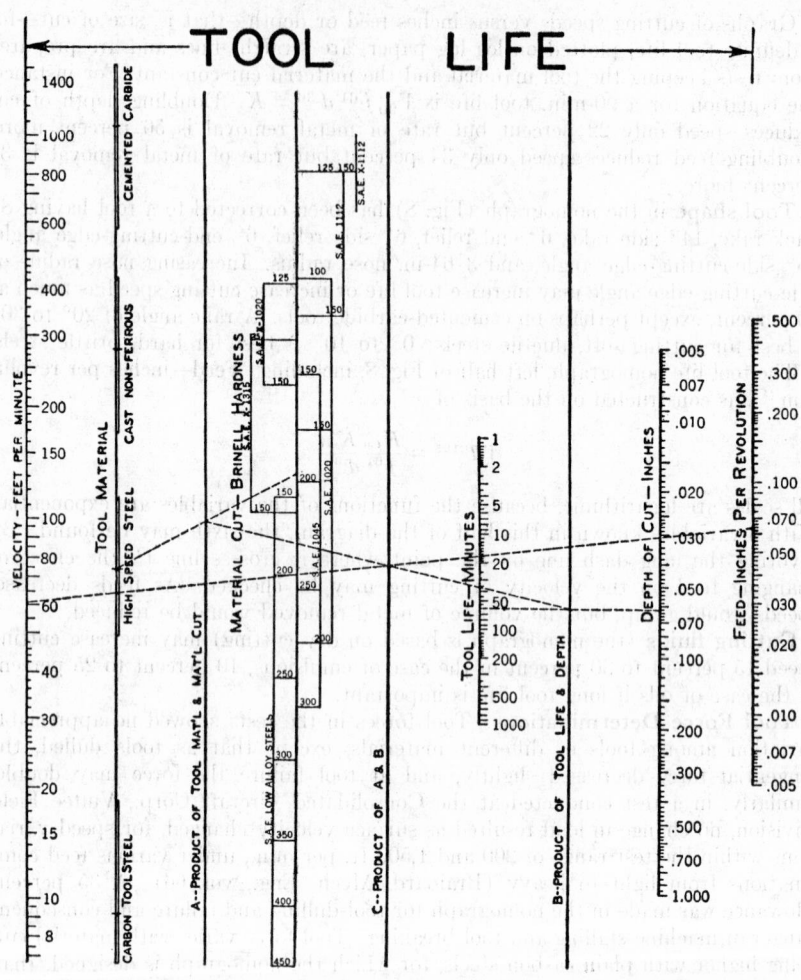

Sample Calculations—Tool Life

Given:
Tool material ....High-speed steel
Material cut ....160 BHN—SAE 1020 steel
Desired tool life ......60 min.
Depth of cut ....0.0625 in.
Feed ....0.0625 in. per rev.

Read from chart:
Velocity = 60.5 ft. per min.

Maximum Output

Given:
Tool material
Material cut
Tool life
Depth of cut
(Deepest cuts most efficient)
Machine efficiency
Motor horsepower
(Use rated horsepower)

(Calculations based on studies of a single-pointed tool under dry cutting.)

Fig. 8. Combined tool-life

POWER

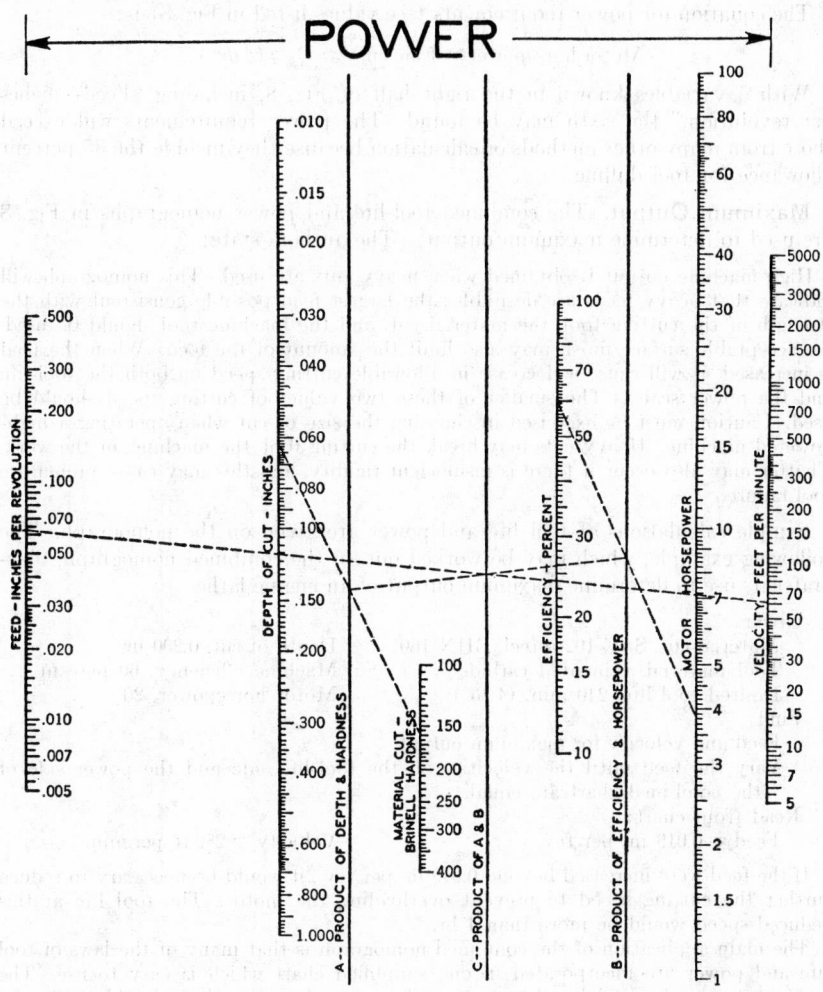

Sample Calculations—Power

Given:
Feed ....0.0625 in. per rev.
Velocity ....60.5 ft. per min.
Depth of cut ....0.0625 in.
Material cut ....160 BHN—SAE 1020 steel
Machine efficiency ....60 percent

Read from chart:
Motor horsepower = 3.75

Maximum Output

The feed should be varied until the velocity on the Tool Life side is equal to the velocity on the Power side. This feed and speed will give the maximum metal removal for the given conditions.

Gilbert and Truckenmiller, Metal Processing Dept., Univ. of Michigan, Mech. Eng., vol. 65.

and power nomograph.

The equation for power requirements (see values listed in Fig. 8) is:

$$\text{Motor horsepower} \times \text{Efficiency} = C_{Bhn}\, f^{.8}\, d^{.9}\, V$$

With 5 variables known in the right half of Fig. 8, including "Feed—inches per revolution," the sixth may be found. The power requirements will exceed those from many other methods of calculation because they include the 35 percent allowance for tool dulling.

Maximum Output. The combined tool-life and power nomographs in Fig. 8 are used to determine maximum outputs. The authors state:

High machine output is obtained when heavy cuts are used. This nomograph will indicate that heavy feeds are desirable; the largest feed possible consistent with the strength of the cutting tool, the material cut, and the machine tool should be used. An acceptable surface finish may also limit the amount of the feed. When the feed is increased, it will cause a decrease in allowable cutting speed on both the tool-life and the power scales. The smaller of these two values of cutting speed should be used. Caution must be exercised in choosing the size of cut when operating a high-powered machine. Heavy cuts may break the cutting tool, the machine, or the work. Chatter may also occur if there is insufficient rigidity, and this may cause premature tool failure.

Sample calculations of tool life and power are given on the nomograph. The following example, which may be worked out on the combined nomograph, illustrates its use to determine maximum output of an engine lathe.

Given:
    Material cut, SAE 1020 steel, BHN 160   Depth of cut, 0.200 in.
    Tool material. cemented carbide   Machine efficiency, 60 percent
    Desired tool life, 240 min. (4 hr.)   Motor horsepower, 20
Find:
    Feed and velocity for maximum output
    Vary the feed until the velocities on the tool-life side and the power side of the combined chart are equal.
Read from chart:
    Feed = 0.019 in. per rev.   Velocity = 280 ft. per min.

If the feed were increased beyond 0.019 in. per rev., it would be necessary to reduce further the cutting speed to prevent overloading the motor. The tool life at this reduced speed would be more than 4 hr.

The main application of the combined nomograph is that many of the laws of tool life and power are incorporated in one simplified chart which is easy to use. The cutting speeds obtained by the nomograph are conservative, but should materially assist in estimating the speeds and feeds for giving higher production rates.

In the "Manual on Cutting of Metals" of the American Society of Mechanical Engineers, extensive data are given on the calculation of cutting speeds and horse-power required for feeds varying from 0.002 to 1/8 in., each for nine depths varying from 1/32 to 1 in. Data from the machining of 35 commonly used steels by seven kinds of tools—four roughing, one finishing, one parting, and one forming—are also included. The information was compiled by research covering a period of five years.

The Tool Crib

LOCATION. There are three general methods in use for tool storage:

1. **Central tool crib** system has a large control crib in which all factory tools are concentrated and from which they are issued.

2. **Subtool-crib** system provides a central, or head, tool crib used more in the capacity of a storeroom than as an issuing tool crib. Each department, under this system, has a tool crib which carries only tools used by that department. When these tool cribs need additional tools, they requisition them from the main tool storeroom.

3. Flexible plan whereby a **movable tool crib** is provided with tools for the entire plant so that, upon signal or upon receipt of tool issue slips, it can go to the department needing tools and make deliveries from its shelves.

Factors in the problem of where and how to store tools are (Christensen, Tool Control):

1. **Size and layout of factory.** Cost of tool distribution from a single central tool crib may be excessive in large factories.

2. **Allocation of space to departments.** One section of a factory is sometimes given over to assembly and testing, while other sections are used for fabrication of parts. Relatively few tools are needed in the former, while the latter may require the use of every kind of tool that the factory owns. Obviously, the cribs should be placed nearest to the departments that use the most tools.

3. **Nature of product.** Some products lend themselves to complete fabrication, assembly, and test in a single department. Many companies have one or more articles of this kind. In cases where a department functions independently of the rest of the factory, it may be advisable to have a tool crib solely for its use.

4. **Methods of operation.** Products manufactured determine methods of operation to follow. In factories where process methods are used, such as textile mills or cement plants, tool requirements are different from those of a highly developed machine shop.

5. **Grade of operators employed.** High-grade operators take pride in good tools and are generally careful in their use. Machine attendants, however, are not always so careful, especially if they are on piecework. As a rule, factories that use piecework have a more complex tool problem than those that operate on day rate.

In general, the location of a tool crib is governed by facilitation in receiving and checking out tools. Tool delivery, however, should not conflict with general transportation activities in the factory. Neither are tool cribs always put where they would be most convenient for the issuing of tools, especially where they would then be set in the middle of some manufacturing area and thus interfere with the flow of work.

Men selected for responsible operation of a tool crib system should be chosen with regard to a knowledge of, and familiarity with, tools, appreciation of responsibilities of the work, and suitable personal characteristics. Preferably they should be men with a good understanding of machine processes. A classification for such personnel is: foremen, tool inspectors, clerk, group attendants, laborers, and possibly apprentices.

LAYOUT OF TOOL CRIB. The layout of a tool crib depends upon the area allotted to it and the shape and relative dimensions of this area. Layouts, consequently, are sometimes expedients, but often can be definitely planned to give the greatest efficiency in tool storing, issuing, receiving back, inspecting, reconditioning, replacing on shelves, and record-keeping.

Space Required for Tool Cribs. General principles which aid in the proper location of space for each class of tools are:

1. The tools should not, as a general rule, be stored over 6 ft. high. The top sections of bins should be left empty in the beginning to take care of additional tools of each class which are sure to accumulate as time goes on.

2. Tool sizes are given in dimension, number, weight, etc. For example, twist drills are made in size increments of 1/64 in. Therefore, a rack for drills should have a space for each 1/64 in. from smallest to largest size carried, provided 1/64-in. increments are used throughout the entire range.
3. Aisle space between bins should be ample for free passage of men through them. Thirty inches for bin aisles and 36 in. for main aisles have been found suitable, but should be the minimum.

It is evident that the space required varies with the number of tools to be handled, as well as the variety of each class of tool. Expenditures for establishing an operating tool crib are classed as overhead, and for this reason should be kept under control. Space assigned should be limited to that which is necessary. At the same time it should be ample to avoid the tendency to overcrowd the crib and thus hamper its effectiveness.

CHARGE-OUT SYSTEMS. It is important to keep records of the issues of tools because of the following factors:

1. Value of tools, which makes it imperative to prevent their loss and secure their return.
2. Need for their use on other jobs to keep production going, thus necessitating prompt replacement in the tool crib, or location in the shop if they have to be recovered for immediate transfer.
3. Keeping tools continually in good condition, by getting them back for prompt inspection and repair.
4. Replacing tools that are lost, broken, or damaged, by placing purchase or manufacturing requisitions at once, especially when replacement requires a long time.
5. Fixing responsibility for the possession and care of the tools to prevent carelessness on the part of workmen.
6. Maintaining a history of use to guide in future purchasing (as to vendor) and in determining tool life, replacement time cycles, and quantities to carry on hand.

There are a number of methods under which tools are charged out, each having features making it of particular use under certain circumstances. These methods are:

1. Single-check system.
2. Double-check system.
3. Triplicate tool-slip systems.
4. Electric machine method.
5. Metal plate method.

Single-Check System. Under the single-check system the worker securing a tool from the tool crib, either in person or by delivery service, gives for it a brass check with his number stamped on it. This check is hung on a hook by the place where the tool is kept, or it can be hung on a board indexing the tools. If the tool is wanted, the toolkeeper knows who took it, but not when or for what job, or whether the check is on the right or wrong hook, or if some other worker used a fellow-worker's check, and there is no record of how many tools the worker may have withdrawn. This plan is used in only the simplest cases.

Double-Check System. The double-check system is similar to the single-check system and has the same characteristics and faults. Its only other feature is that the second check is hung on a hook under the worker's number and there it can be seen how many (but not which) tools he has secured.

Triplicate Tool-Slip System: Spring-Clip Boards. One variety of the triplicate tool-slip system (McCaskey) makes use of spring-clip holders as record compartments, the tool slips being filed under the clips, as stores requisition slips are sometimes handled. When an employee calls or sends for a tool, he fills out a tool order (Fig. 9) in triplicate with one writing, using inexpensive carbon-backed forms—original white, duplicate yellow, triplicate pink. The operator writes in his clock number, date, and tool drawn, and signs his name. The bin number is entered by the crib attendant, and the tool is handed to the workman with the yellow copy which he keeps in a slip-holder on his machine or bench. The white

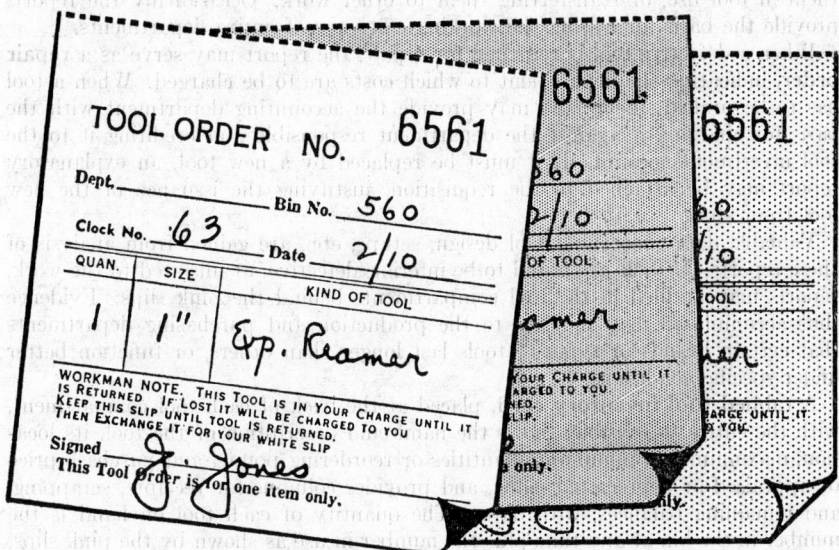

TOOL ORDER No. 6561

Dept._____

Bin No. 560

Clock No. 63

Date 2/10

QUAN.	SIZE	KIND OF TOOL
1	1"	Ep. Reamer

WORKMAN NOTE. THIS TOOL IS IN YOUR CHARGE UNTIL IT IS RETURNED. IF LOST IT WILL BE CHARGED TO YOU KEEP THIS SLIP UNTIL TOOL IS RETURNED. THEN EXCHANGE IT FOR YOUR WHITE SLIP

Signed J. Jones

This Tool Order is for one item only.

Fig. 9. Typical tool order made out in triplicate.

copy acknowledges receipt of the tool and is retained in the employee's compartment under the clip bearing his number. The pink copy is filed in the tool compartment under the clip for that particular tool, in a cabinet that may be closed and locked. Employee's records usually are filed on wall boards giving visibility to the slips of 60 men on each side, so that those accumulating too many tools are identified at a glance. During a rush, the attendant hands out tools and yellow slips rapidly but delays filing slips until the peak is over. This plan speeds up service and permits men to return to work.

The tool crib attendant, under this method, can tell instantly what tools have been issued to each operator, and the exact location of every tool out. When the employee returns a tool he also returns his yellow copy of the tool order. If the tool is in good condition, the tool crib attendant removes the corresponding white slip, matching the serial number which appears on all three copies of each set, and the employee immediately destroys them. His responsibility for that particular tool is ended. Then, or later, the attendant removes the pink copy from the tool record compartment, thus indicating that the tool has been returned, but not destroying the record of the transaction. Pink copies are filed to provide valuable data for purposes described below. The tools need not be replaced in the bins at once, but may be held for further inspection or repair. Thus the accumulation of defective tools in the bins, which may occur under the single-check system, is avoided.

A broken or defective tool is accepted by the tool crib attendant only when accompanied by an **explanatory report** O.K.'d by the foreman of the employee returning it. The report may be made on the employee's yellow copy of the tool order or preferably on a report identifying the cause of the damage. If carelessness or inefficiency of the employee was responsible, a copy may be filed at the back of his compartment. Such breakage may be reduced by warning the small percentage of offending employees against continued carelessness, instructing them in tool use, or transferring them to other work. Occasionally the reports provide the basis for raising the working efficiency of entire departments.

When a defective tool is returned for repair, the report may serve as a **repair order,** indicating the department to which costs are to be charged. When a tool has to be junked, the report may provide the accounting department with the basis for charging it against the department responsible and crediting it to the tool investment account. If it must be replaced by a new tool, an explanatory report may be attached to the requisition, justifying the issuance of the new tool from stock.

Valuable data concerning tool design, setups, etc., are gained from analysis of these reports. If tools are found to be inferior, defective, or unsuited to the work, reports may be filed in the tool compartments behind the pink slips. Evidence thus accumulated may indicate to the production and purchasing departments that certain brands or types of tools last longer than others, or function better under specific conditions.

A **tabbed tool inventory card,** placed at the back of each tool compartment, with the entire top visible, shows the name and description of the tool, its location, maximum and minimum quantities or reordering points, and purchase price or appraised or depreciated value, and provides columns for receipts, scrapping, and remaining balances, with dates. The quantity of each tool on hand is the number in the bin at any time plus the number in use as shown by the pink slips. Control of tool requisitions or purchases and inventory are thus readily carried on.

Tool activity, or the frequency with which tools are issued, is secured by accumulating pink copies of tool orders behind the inventory cards when tools are returned. Once a month the slips for each kind of tool are counted, the number is recorded on the back of the inventory card, and the slips are destroyed. After a few months, this information provides a factual basis for removing obsolete tools and reducing the inventory of slow-moving tools. Inventory reduction in average cribs frequently varies from 35 to 50 percent.

When tools are issued together as a kit, the transaction can be handled on one tool order. The combination is given the equivalent of a tool number, such as Kit or Setup No. 25. The individual tools in the kit are charged against that number by the attendant to maintain the accuracy of the tool records. The employee is given a standard list of tools in the setup for which he is responsible. When an employee requisitions tools from several cribs, his use of tools may be controlled through some one crib to which he is assigned, or through all of them. The former plan is advantageous if the employee leaves and is checked out, since the records of all tool withdrawals are in one place.

Card Record System in Triplicate. Supplanting a brass check plan, the Osborn Manufacturing Co. installed a Kolect-A-Matic tool control system consisting of pockets with celluloid tips mounted on panels which rest vertically in a tray. Records of a permanent nature are placed under the celluloid tip, but temporary records, such as tool loan orders, are merely dropped in the pockets.

Three separate records are kept: a record card with the employee's name, filed by employee number, on which tool loss and breakage are recorded; the tool inventory control card, on which ordering, receiving, and balance-on-hand information is kept (Fig. 10); and the parts cards, on which standard and special tools needed to make the part are listed. The tool inventory control card should always show a balance equal to the quantity of tools loaned, as recorded on slips, plus the number still in the crib.

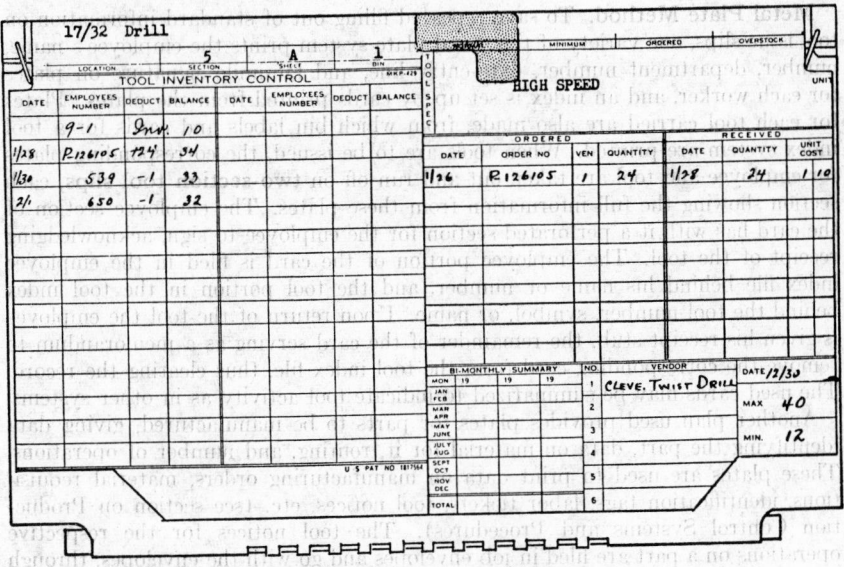

Fig. 10. Tool inventory control card.

In operation, the employee fills out a **tool loan order** in duplicate. The original is filed with his employee name card, the duplicate with the tool inventory control. Upon return of the tool he receives the original. The duplicate is pulled for later recording on a tool usage report.

The employee is responsible for all tools for which signed originals are found in his record pocket. If he should break a tool he shows it to his foreman and receives a broken or **damaged tool report** made out in duplicate. Both copies are turned in with the tool, posted to the employee's name card, and deducted from the tool inventory control. At the end of the month a **broken-tool dis-tribution report** by departments and shifts is prepared for the management. Thus any inefficient departments and careless employees will be shown up by the records.

The part name record is kept in the tool crib as a listing of the standard and special tools, jigs, and fixtures required for making certain parts. When a part is to be made the planning department merely notifies the tool crib and all necessary tools are gathered so that production can proceed without delay.

Electric Machine Method. Under the recording machine plan, when a tool is issued the tool number or symbol, employee number, and date are set up by keys, after which a bar is pressed and the information is printed on a consecutive tape together with two tickets, thus giving legible records. The original ticket is signed by the employee withdrawing the tool, and this ticket is filed under his number in the employees' tool record file. The duplicate is placed in the ticket holder at the bin from which the tool is withdrawn, or it can be posted on a tool issue board or in a file.

When the employee returns the tool, he receives his signed slip. The duplicate slip is used for analysis as in other systems, or, if the tool is damaged, goes into the broken or damaged tool file until the disposition of the tool is determined (The Controller, vol. 11).

Metal Plate Method. To save repeated filling out of standard information on tool issue slips, one variety of the metal plate system prints the employee's name, number, department number, date-entry line, and facsimile signature on plates for each worker, and an index is set up by cards printed from the plates. Plates for each tool carried are also made, from which bin labels and cards for a tool index system are printed. When tools are to be issued, the corresponding plates for employee and tool are taken out and run off on **two-section tool slips,** each section showing the full information from these plates. The employee section of the card has with it a perforated section for the employee to sign, acknowledging receipt of the tool. The employee portion of the card is filed in the employee index file behind his name or number, and the tool portion in the tool index behind the tool number, symbol, or name. Upon return of the tool the employee is given his receipt stub, the remainder of the card serving as a memorandum to remove the corresponding card from the tool index file, thus clearing the record. The used cards may be summarized to indicate tool activity as in other systems.

Another plan used provides plates for parts to be manufactured, giving data identifying the part, data on material for it, routing, and number of operations. These plates are used to print data on manufacturing orders, material requisitions, identification tags, labor tickets, tool notices, etc. (see section on Production Control Systems and Procedures). The tool notices for the respective operations on a part are filed in job envelopes and go with the envelopes, through scheduling and production control, to the successive operating departments, in each of which the work dispatcher (or foreman) removes the tool notice—if tools are needed—for the operations to be performed there and sends them to the tool crib with work order card on which the tools required are listed and detailed. The tools are then charged out and supplied and, after the operation is done, are returned to the crib with a filled-out finished work order for identification. The tools are replaced in storage, the charges and notices are canceled, and the work order is forwarded to the production control department for recording (The Controller, vol. 11).

Tool Inventories

CONTROL OF INVENTORY. The control of the tool inventory involves records which govern procurement, quantities carried, and disbursements to tool cribs from any central tool crib or from the storeroom.

A large Cleveland industrial plant uses the Kardex record illustrated in Fig. 11 to control the procurement and distribution of tools for ten separate tool cribs. The cut-down **requisition form** is 8×5 in. in size. When tools are to be reordered it is filled in and sent to the purchasing department. Upon placement of the order it is returned, the order number is noted in the ordered section of the lower card, the $\frac{1}{4}$-in. signal is set to show the month of order, and the requisition form is filed under the upper card. Carrying permanent information, such as vendors' names, it thus saves considerable time in reordering.

The lower card acts as the **receiving and disbursement record** for the entire stock and shows the balance in both quantity and dollar amount. **Distribution** among the various cribs is shown on the upper card. On both cards the only entries recorded as disbursements are those originating from scrap reports showing that tools are no longer usable. Therefore, the balance on the lower card should always equal the balances of all cribs shown on the upper card. By centralizing the records of all cribs it is possible to effect economies by filling stock shortages in one crib from surpluses in another.

Quantity of Each Tool to Carry. Figures showing the number of individual tools in each group to be kept in the tool crib should be worked out from actual experience as to how many of each are generally used. **Standard tool lists** give valuable aid in this work. After these figures are determined, a study should be made of the most economical ordering units either by purchase or from manufacture within the factory: for example, on $\frac{5}{8}$-in. machine taps, the best manufacturing quantity is about 100 and the most economical purchase unit is one gross or above. However, this quantity is too great to keep in the tool crib, because if the crib is allowed too many tools of any specific item, the tendency is to give out new tools instead of using the old ones until they are worn out. Therefore, any excess of tools should be kept in a separate central tool crib or in the regular storeroom and disbursed to the tool crib as needed to keep its stock to the specified quantity.

CHECKING THE INVENTORY. A complete inventory of every tool and appliance entrusted to the tool crib should be maintained. This inventory should be perpetual in character, additions to the tool-crib stock being promptly entered on it, and lost, broken, or discarded tools removed from it. The number of tools on inventory should at all times correspond with the sum of the number of tools and employees' checks, representing tools, in the tool crib. The inventory should be checked on a regular program by counting tools in the successive sections of the tool crib, in sequence as opportunity offers, the entire tool crib to be covered at intervals of from three to six months.

The methods for keeping a perpetual tool inventory do not differ in principle from those that apply to perpetual inventory of stores (see section on Materials Control and Standardization).

Tool Classification

IDENTIFICATION OF TOOLS. There are five systems under which tools may be identified, but only three of those systems, 1, 2, and 4 below, are in general use:

1. **Straight numeric system** where tools are numbered in sequence in a series, these numbers being put on the tools themselves and on the drawings as well.
2. **Classified numeric system** best represented by the Dewey decimal system.
3. **Straight letter system.**
4. **Mnemonic system** where a combination of letters is suggestive of the tool symbols.
5. **Combinations of letters and numbers.**

There are many varieties of these systems. It is good practice to use the same system also for jigs, fixtures, and gages for uniformity in identifying all tools and devices for any given job.

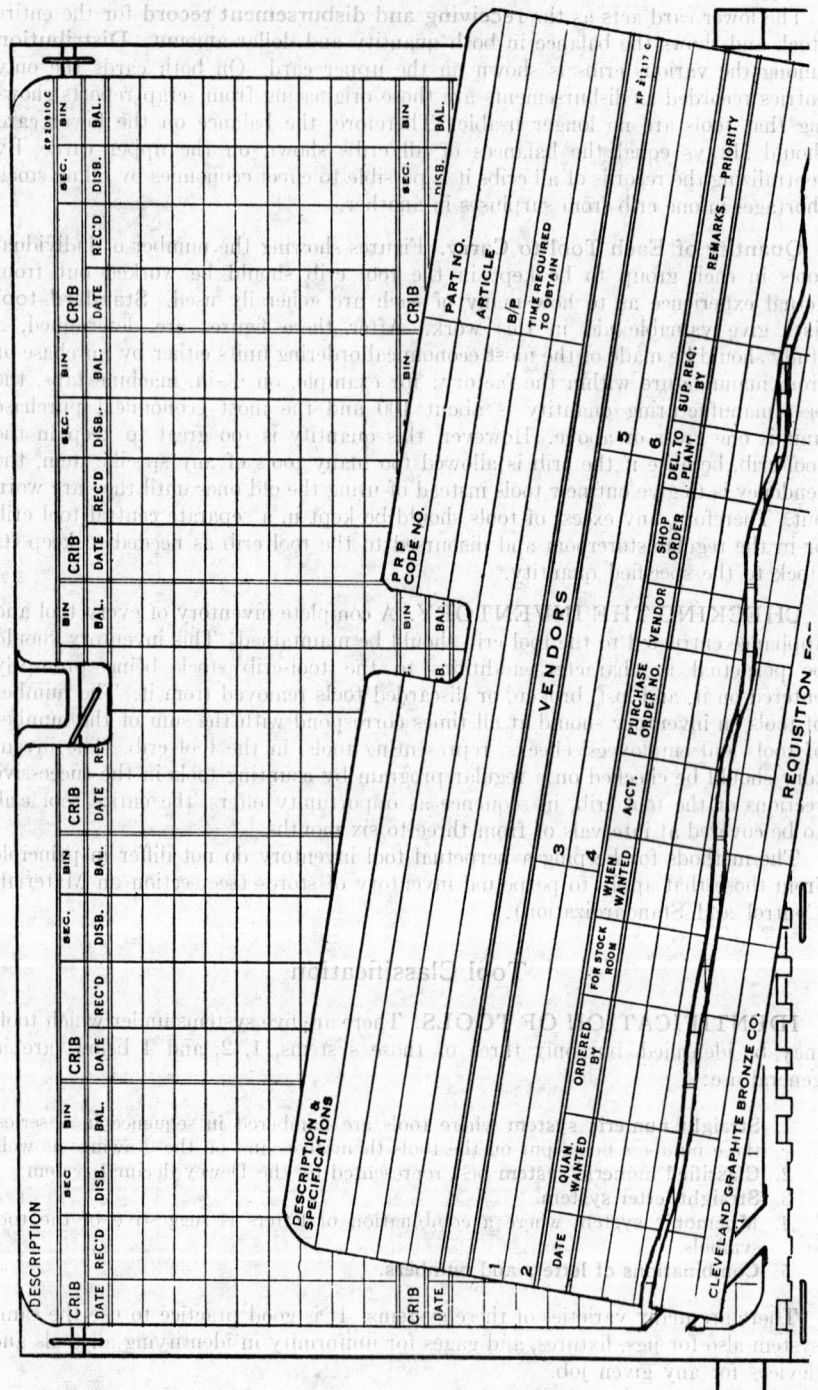

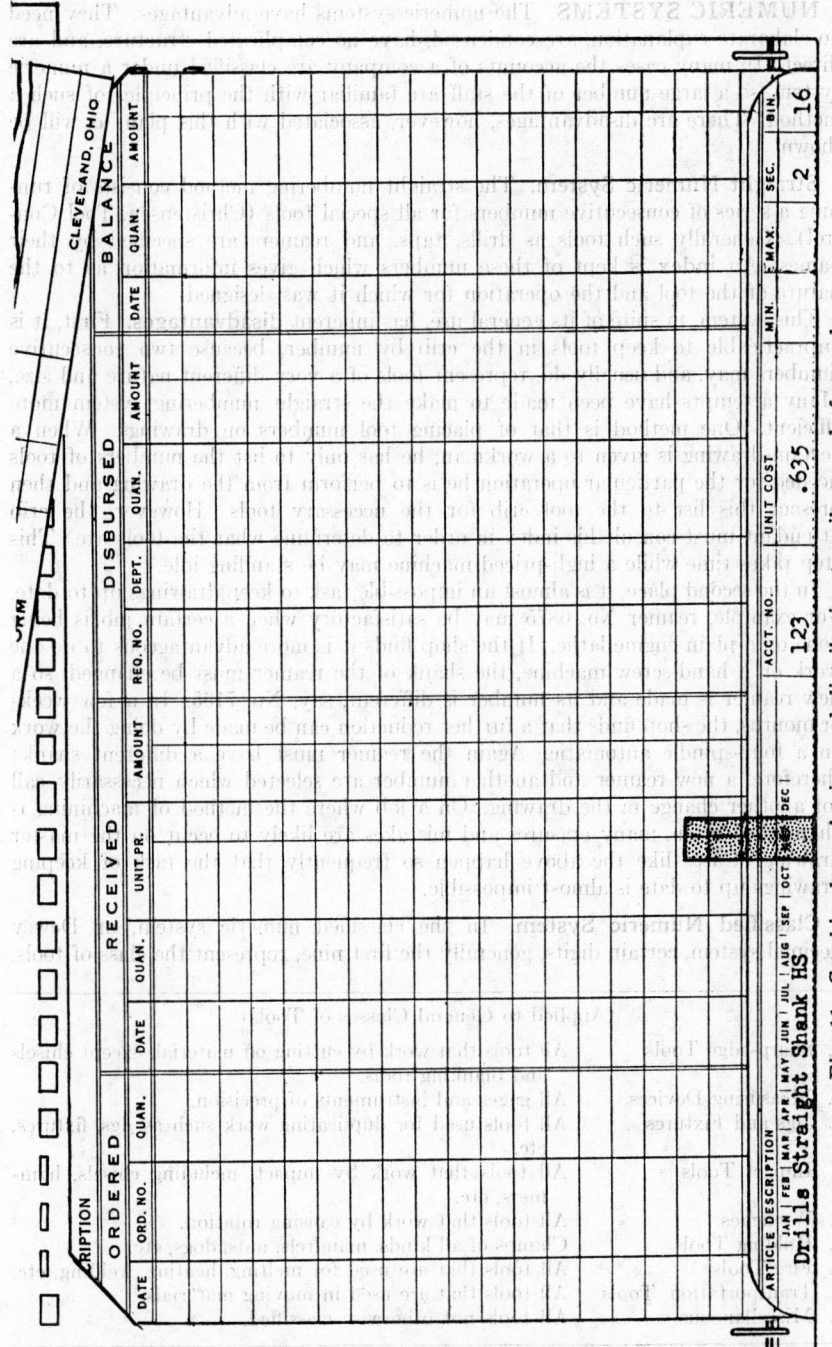

Fig. 11. Combined purchasing and distribution-to-crib records for tools.

NUMERIC SYSTEMS. The numeric systems have advantages. They need no elaborate explanation, are condensed, have no complicated structure, and are direct. In many cases the accounts of a company are classified under a numeric system, so a large number of the staff are familiar with the principles of such a method. There are disadvantages, however, associated with this plan, as will be shown.

Straight Numeric System. The straight numbering method consists of running a series of consecutive numbers for all special tools (Christensen, Tool Control). Generally such tools as drills, taps, and reamers are specified by their names. An **index** is kept of these numbers which gives information as to the nature of the tool and the operation for which it was designed.

This system, in spite of its general use, has inherent **disadvantages.** First, it is impracticable to keep tools in the crib by number, because two consecutive numbers may, and usually do, represent tools of a very different nature and size. Many attempts have been made to make the straight numbering system more efficient. One method is that of placing tool numbers on drawings. When a certain drawing is given to a workman, he has only to list the numbers of tools needed for the particular operation he is to perform from the drawing and then present this list to the tool crib for the necessary tools. However, the crib attendant must consult his index in order to determine what the tools are. This step takes time while a high-priced machine may be standing idle.

In the second place, it is almost an impossible task to keep drawings up to date. For example, reamer No. 6875 may be satisfactory when a certain job is being done on a plain engine lathe. If the shop finds it is more advantageous to do the work on a hand-screw machine, the shank of the reamer must be changed, so a new reamer is made and its number is different, say, No. 7165. In a few weeks or months, the shop finds that a further reduction can be made by doing the work on a four-spindle automatic. Again the reamer must have a different shank; therefore, a new reamer and another number are selected which necessarily call for another change in the drawing. On a job where the method of machining is changed so often, many erasures and mistakes are likely to occur on the master drawing. Cases like the above happen so frequently that the task of keeping drawings up to date is almost impossible.

Classified Numeric System. In the classified numeric system, or Dewey decimal system, certain digits, generally the first nine, represent the class of tools.

(Applied to General Classes of Tools)

1. Sharp-edge Tools	All tools that work by cutting off material, except chisels and blanking tools.
2. Measuring Devices	All gages and instruments of precision.
3. Jigs and Fixtures	All tools used for duplicating work such as jigs, fixtures, etc.
4. Impact Tools	All tools that work by impact, including chisels, hammers, etc.
5. Wrenches	All tools that work by causing rotation.
6. Holding Tools	Clamps of all kinds, mandrels, nuts, dogs, etc.
7. Fire Tools	All tools that are used for melting, heating, welding, etc.
8. Transportation Tools	All tools that are used in moving materials.
9. Miscellaneous	All tools not otherwise classified.

Fig. 12. Numerical tool classification key sheet—Dewey decimal system.

Christensen (Tool Control) gives the numeric key sheet for the system applied to general classes of tools in Fig. 12.

Each group may be subdivided indefinitely. To illustrate, a further division of the sharp-edge tools follows:

1.1 —Drills
1.11 —Twist drills
1.112 —Taper shank twist drills
1.1123 —High-speed twist drills with taper shanks
1.11234—High-speed taper shank twist drills of standard length
1.2 —Taps
1.21 —U. S. Standard taps
1.212 —U. S. Standard taps with machine shanks
1.2123 —U. S. Standard high-speed taps with machine shanks

Simply by continuing to add digits to the key number, it is possible to classify tools to as small a variable difference as is desired. The difficulty is that only ten variables can be provided for in any given division. Clearly this is not sufficient to care for all the classes of tools in many general groups: for example, tools that have cutting edges are drills, taps, reamers, counterborers, countersinks, milling cutters, hack saws, thread-cutting dies, lathe tools, and a great many others.

Another difficulty is in remembering the numbers of tools where they run into seven or eight digits, which would be necessary for a complete classification. If an attempt is made to carry the numbers on the drawings, erasures and mistakes are likely to occur. Many other schemes and combinations of classification may be worked out, but they will all have the same inherent weaknesses.

Example of a Numeric System. A six-digit system of tool classification was found to work satisfactorily in one case. Throughout the plant in both part-designing and tool-designing, the metric system was used. Thus, the tool classification as regards size was based on metric units. The principles of this **six-digit system** were:

Every tool of exactly the same design had the same six-digit number.
The main group was indicated by the first and second digits, of which the first indicated the main class of operation that the tool could perform as follows:

0—Tools for miscellaneous use
1—Circular cutting tools
2—Flat cutting tools
3—Impact tools
4—Tools for making holes
5}
6} —Tools for holding and steadying
7—Tools for threads and gears
8—Tools for grinding and polishing
9—Tools for measuring and checking

The subdivision was indicated by third and fourth digits, of which the fourth indicated the main size in millimeters.
The fifth and sixth digits indicated the consecutive number.
Zero as any digit except the fifth and sixth indicated unclassified or miscellaneous tools.

The fourth digit changed for every 1-, 10-, or 100-mm. main size, depending on class of tools, which meant, for example, that 99 numbers were available for different plain milling cutters (class 156000) within 10-mm. thickness, 99 for different grinding wheels (class 815000) within 100-mm. diameter, and so on. The correct size was given for each subdivision in classification lists.

The main feature of this classification system was that all similar tools within a certain size range of rather close limits had exactly the same four first digits; in other words, these figures told a definite story.

For example, every twist drill with taper shank over 20 mm. but under 30 mm. in diameter had a six-digit number beginning with 4212, these four figures identifying this type of tool without the need for referring to any other record:

> 400000—Tools for making holes
> 420000—Drills
> 421000—Twist drills with taper shank
> 421200—From 20 up to (but exclusive of) 30 mm. in diameter

Another important feature was that this system forced the user actually to classify the tool, not merely to add another decimal or letter as in other systems. A tool number could never be correct with more or less than six digits.

This six-digit number was used all the way through to identify the tool:

1. As the drawing number for every tool that could be conveniently drawn on a standard 8½ × 11-in. sheet.
2. As the number on records of any kind.
3. As the identifying number stamped on each tool.

Tools of the company's own manufacture carried, in addition, an individual "serial" number, so that reference could be made at any time to the order on which any unsatisfactory tool was made, and the material used or the method of manufacturing changed. Tool cribs throughout the plant were arranged according to number. This plan automatically placed similar tools together, thus cutting out a lot of record-keeping, danger of misplacing, etc. The tool classification helped to control the total expenditure for small tools, showing a direct saving of about $50,000, or a decrease of over 20 percent of the total cost of tools, in one year.

LETTER SYSTEMS. Straight letter systems without special features have probably been tried in some cases for tool identification but are not often used because of the trouble involved. They are not so naturally and readily adapted to orderly and logical applications as is the case with numeric systems. For limited uses the straight letter system might give satisfactory service but the superiority of other methods makes the latter far more useful for most applications.

MNEMONIC SYSTEMS. The principle of a mnemonic letter system for tool classification, which should be clearly distinguished from the straight letter system, was stated thus by Gilbreth: "All tools that are alike shall be together, and those that differ by one variable only shall be contiguous." In applying this principle, tools are subdivided into general classes, the arrangement being according to the functions that they perform, taking into consideration where and how work they perform is done. The mnemonic, or memory, factor is introduced by using for each general tool class a letter significant in identifying the class. Thus *A* is the first letter of abrading, *B* for blanking, and *F* (fire) signifies heat and its associated phenomenon light. Tools are thus arranged alphabetically as well as mnemonically.

Application. To classify a tool by the mnemonic method, look first at the general tool class sheet and find the group in which the tool belongs, after which make up a key sheet with subdivisions for that group. To do this, take a sheet of paper and fill in general group symbols at the top, as shown in Fig. 13. Then enter classes of tools in this column, assigning the alphabet letter which corresponds to the first letter in the noun of the tool term. In cases where the name of more than one tool begins with the same letter in any given subdivision, use letters that give the most distinctive sound to the word. Thus, in the subdivision in Fig. 13, letter E was used for end measuring rods. Therefore, it is necessary to assign another letter to electrical instruments, which in this case is K. Letters O and I are omitted because they are likely to be confused with figures.

M—Measuring Devices

All gages and instruments of precision

M	A—		M	N—Indicators
	B—Bevels			P—Protractors
	C—Calipers			Q—Squares
	D—Dividers			R—Rules
	E—End measuring rods			S—Scale weighing
	F—Reference disks			T—Timing device
	G—Gages			U—Plumb bobs
	H—Pressure gages			V—Verniers
	J—			W—
	K—Electrical			X—Heat measuring
	L—Levels			Y—Miscellaneous
	M—Metering			Z—

Fig. 13. First stage of mnemonic classification of measuring devices.

As an example, suppose a 5–5½-in., external, adjustable, limit gage of the caliper type is to be classified. On the group head sheet M, Fig. 13, under G appears the class gages. A gage head sheet is made out and on this sheet, under C, place caliper gages. Next the head sheet for caliper gages MGC is made out. Adding the letter E for external gages gives $MGCE$. On another sheet list the different types of external caliper gages. Letter L is used for limit gages. On the head sheet $MGCEL$ under A enter adjustable gages. This classifies the particular gage in question to its smallest variable. The complete symbol for a 5–5½-in., external, adjustable, limit gage is $MGCELA$ 5–5½ in. The steps are indicated in the accompanying breakdown.

MG	A
	B
	C—Caliper
	D—Depth
MGC	A
	B
	C—Combined external
	D
	E—External
$MGCE$	A
	B—Bar type
	C—Type
	D
	L—Limit

MGCEL A—Adjustable
          B
          C
          D—Double-end

In like manner any tool may be classified. Letter *Z* of each head sheet is left for special tools of that division which cannot be otherwise classified.

MARKING SYMBOLS ON TOOLS. Every tool should be marked plainly in a conspicuous place with its tool symbol in such a manner that the marking will be permanent. Cutting tools designated by size should have tool size added to symbol. Special tools for a particular manufactured part are often stamped with that part number. If the tool is soft, or has a soft spot, the symbol should be stamped with a die. If the tool is hard or delicate, so that it might be injured by stamping, the symbol should be etched. **Electrical etching apparatus** will pay for itself in a short time where much tool marking is done. Size of characters should be large enough to be easily read. One-eighth to one-quarter inch high is satisfactory. Small characters cause loss of time in identifying the tool in the hands of the operator, or when replacing in storage. Characters on cutting tools, such as drills, reamers, counterbores, and the like, should be such that they can be read in any light in an ordinary shop. Figures ordinarily stamped on by manufacturers are difficult to read at the machine. Often a tool must be carried to the light before the symbol can be understood. To accommodate large characters it is usually necessary to grind flats upon shanks of round tools. These flats serve the double purpose of permitting the use of satisfactory characters and also of indicating instantly the location of the tool size. Both features conserve time where it is necessary to verify size of tools prior to use.

Large plants engaged in mass production prefer not to stamp part numbers on small tools because the tools may be used for a number of different parts and confusion would result. Likewise, there would be no definite number to identify the tool. A tool number the same as the tool drawing number is frequently used instead, and the tool is specified by this number on the operation sheet for each part on which it is to be used.

Cutting-Tool Standardization

PURPOSE. Wick (Machinery, vol. 60) reports that a survey at and by the Ford Motor Co. revealed the need for an expansion of their standardization program to the area of cutting tools (see section on Materials Control and Standardization). The purpose of the cutting tool standardization program at the Ford Motor Co., according to Wick, is:

1. To promote uniform performance of tools and to obtain maximum usefulness.
2. To serve as a guide in the establishment of new facilities.
3. To reduce inventory variety, volume, and space requirements. Less variety permits quantity buying with its advantages of lower costs and multiple sources of supply.
4. To promote safety.
5. To increase the availability of tools.
6. To promote interchangeability, thus minimizing downtime in changing the tools on machines.

STANDARDIZATION COMMITTEE. The standardization committee on cutting tools was composed of manufacturing engineers, tool designers, tool engineers, suppliers of cutting tools, and technical men in the field of metal-cutting. The makeup of the committee was given careful consideration to insure the most representative experience in formulating standards for cutting tools. The investigations carried on by the standardization committee resulted not only in standards for the cutting tools themselves but also for the inspection, grinding, and maintenance of these cutting tools. The final choice for a standard is based on over-all economy rather than initial cost of the tool.

STANDARDIZATION RESULTS. Some of the results, cited by Wick, obtained by the Ford Motor Co. in their tool standardization program prove the value of such a program.

Prior to the standardization program seven types of face-milling cutters were purchased, stocked, and used. Now, the same requirements are being met with three types of face-milling cutters. Another example of the value derived from tool standardization is that one cut-off blade is now used on automatics where formerly six had been used. Four styles of single-point, carbide-tipped turning tools, and one style of tool-holder for round, triangular, and square solid-carbide inserts have now been standardized for the majority of turning applications. Very few special turning tools have been necessary since the standards have been developed. Insert-type carbide tools are employed for turning wherever possible, because they are more economical. A standard holder with a solid-carbide triangular insert having six cutting edges, replaces sixteen single-point, carbide-tipped tools. Equally desirable results were obtained with the development of standards for drills, reamers, taps, and counterbores.

Tool grinding practice is another area of the cutting tool standardization program developed to insure uniform performance of tools.

With the grinding of all tools now being done in the tool room, the next phase of the tool standardization program is the recommendation of speeds and feeds and a schedule of tool replacement. Tool geometry, tool material, and tool application are now controlled by the standards developed to date, and with this control the next logical step is predicted tool life based on investigations being carried on at specified feeds and speeds.

Electro-machining Tooling

THE PROCESS. Electro-machining is defined by Livshits and Rassokhin (The Engineer's Digest, vol. 16) as the removal of metal or modification of the structure of the surface layer of the material, which takes place as a result of the **thermal, chemical,** or combined **thermo-chemical** action of an electric current supplied directly to the material and the tool. Thus the need for intermediate stages of conversion of electric current into mechanical, thermal, electromagnetic, and other kinds of energy is eliminated. The basic methods of electro-machining are electric spark, electric impulse, anode-mechanical, electric contact, and electro-mechanical.

Livshits and Rassokhin point out that three **basic conditions** must be fulfilled in order to perform electro-machining:

1. Electric energy must be supplied to the area for machining in the form of an impulse of sufficiently short duration to insure accuracy in the reproduction of the tool shape in the material being worked.
2. The area of the work to which the energy impulse is applied must be sufficiently small to guarantee smooth finish and accurate reproduction of tool size. This is generally accomplished by using roughing and finishing tools.

3. The energy impulses must be supplied directly to the molecular areas of volume of metal to be removed, and with sufficient frequency. This condition insures the continuity of the process and the required performance.

The energy is **supplied** to the surface being machined:

1. By contact between tool and material. This method is carried on in the electro-mechanical method of electro-machining.
2. By electrical discharge over a short arc. This method is the most widely used in electro-machining.
3. By combining contact and short arc. This method starts with contact between tool and work, followed by a break in the contact with an accompanying electrical discharge. This is generally used in a roughing operation.

The **tool material** most generally is brass, which allows that it may be shaped rather easily. Thus, the tool may have intricate, accurate shapes which are reproduced in the item being worked. **Tool erosion** occurs as the process continues at varying rates, depending on rate of metal removal and material being removed. Erosion of the tool necessitates the use of roughing and finishing tools when the accuracy and finish of work piece are critical.

APPLICATIONS. Applications of electro-machining have been reported (Light Metals, vol. 18) that have hitherto been impossible. For instance, machining of curved (noncircular) holes is possible with electro-machining. Electro-machining has also been applied to dies of all description, such as blanking, forging, and extrusion dies. Machining of extremely hard materials such as tungsten carbide is well within the scope of electro-machining.

ADVANTAGES. The advantages accruing from electro-machining are no reduction of hardness in item being machined, accuracy in the order of 0.0002 in. per in., and finish in the order of 10 microinches. An added advantage of electro-machining is the fact that there are no heat checks of any consequence present in tooling prepared in this manner.

Cutting-Tool Materials

FACTORS IN SELECTION. The choice of cutting-tool material is based on material to be cut, cutting temperature, the finish desired, hardness, and toughness. The wide range of production practices, specifications, and engineering materials has imposed severe demands upon present-day cutting tools. To accommodate these many conditions, a wide range of tool materials has been developed. The most commonly encountered cutting-tool materials are:

1. Plain-carbon steels.
2. High-speed steels.
3. Cast nonferrous alloys.
4. Sintered carbides.
5. Diamonds.
6. Ceramics.

PLAIN-CARBON STEELS. In past years, the plain-carbon steels were used extensively as cutting-tool materials. However, the recent events of high-speed continuous production coupled with the need for new product materials and increasingly exacting specifications to be met by the product have relegated plain-carbon steels as a cutting-tool material to a position of lesser importance. The **carbon content** of the plain-carbon steels ranges from 0.70 to 1.20 percent. Also included are small amounts of other alloying materials, such as are shown in Fig. 14. The use of this cutting-tool material is limited by its inability to maintain hardness when cutting temperatures are in excess of 400° F.

Tools of this material will produce satisfactory results because of the hardness and toughness of the tool material whenever the actual cutting time is short. Carbon tool steel is often used for materials such as free-cutting steels and brass. Carbon steel is the least expensive of the tool materials. When tool life or endurance is a prime factor, however, plain-carbon steel is supplanted by more heat- and wear-resistant tool materials. Carbon steel is adapted to light and limited duty on most free-cutting metals.

Tool Material	Percentage of Elements					
	C	Si	Mn	P	S	Fe
Plain-carbon tool steel ...	0.70–1.20	0.30 max.	0.30 max.	0.30 max.	0.30 max.	Balance

Fig. 14. Composition of plain-carbon tool steel.

HIGH-SPEED STEELS. This term is used to describe a wide variety of tool steels which contain alloying elements to improve the cutting properties. The most commonly encountered **alloying elements** found in high-speed steels are tungsten, molybdenum, chromium, vanadium, and cobalt. The most common grade of high-speed steel contains from 0.55 to 0.75 percent of carbon, 18 percent tungsten, 4 percent chromium, and 1 percent vanadium. This form of high-speed steel is referred to as 18–4–1. Molybdenum is sometimes substituted for the tungsten wholly or partially, giving a performance comparable to the 18–4–1 form of high-speed steel. Cobalt is added to high-speed steel to increase the red hardness (hardness at high operating temperatures). The chief advantage is its hardness which is maintained up to a cutting temperature of 1100° F. Its high hardness and toughness make it adaptable to heavy-duty cutting and to interrupted cutting with good tool life on nearly the full range of engineering materials. Boston (Metal Processing) and Du Mond (Engineering Materials Manual) give the compositions of various high-speed tool steels and the recommended usage in Fig. 15.

CAST NONFERROUS ALLOYS. This alloy appears on the market under such trade names as Crobalt, Stellite, Deloro, and ALX, to name but a few. Cast alloy tool materials are composed of cobalt, chromium, tungsten, carbon, and small amounts of iron, nickel, molybdenum, and vanadium. Fig. 16 gives the range of the chemical composition of the family of cast alloy tool materials. Its abrasion resistance is very good, and it is used in machining cast irons and steels. Tool forms are cast to shape from materials melted in an electric furnace. A small **stock allowance** is provided in the casting for grinding to finished shape. The cast alloy tool has a hardness of 58 to 64 (Rockwell C.) as cast. One of the distinct advantages of this alloy over high-speed tool steel is its ability to retain hardness up to 1500° F.

Cast alloy tools are recommended for use in situations calling for heavy feeds and deep cuts at a medium speed. They can withstand some shock and vibration without serious effect on tool life, but generally require more rigidity and no chattering to function at highest efficiency. Cast alloy tools are not recommended for use as pointed tools. A radius is generally required at the point of the tool. The outer surface of this tool material is the hardest and therefore should form the cutting edge of the tool. In redressing the tool, stock should be removed from

Steel Type	Percent Element Composition											Remarks
	C	Si	Mn	P	S	Co	Cr	V	W	Mo	Fe	
1	0.55–0.75	0.32	0.20	0.011	0.009		4.0	1.00	18.0		Balance	General roughing and finishing work on most types of materials.
2	0.66	0.42	0.32	0.029	0.025		4.0	2.00	14.0		Balance	
3	0.75–0.85	0.32	0.32	0.02	0.014		4.0	2.00–3.25	18.0		Balance	
4	0.70	0.25	0.15	0.02	0.02	5.00–8.00	4.0	2.00	13.0		Balance	Tougher. Used with heavier cutting.
5	0.65–0.80	0.15	0.41	0.021	0.008	3.00–5.00	4.0	1.00	18.5		Balance	Rough cutting cast iron and nonferrous alloys.
6	0.70					6.00–9.00	4.0	1.90	18.0	0.18	Balance	
7	0.70					10.0–13.0	4.0	2.00	19.0	0.75	Balance	Great resistance to abrasion. Used on gritty material.
8	0.70–0.85						4.0	0.90–1.50	1.25–2.00	8.00–9.50	Balance	Tungsten saving alternate. Same as 18-4-1.
9	0.70–0.90						4.0	1.50–2.25	1.5	7.50–9.00	Balance	Tungsten saving alternate. Same as 18-4-1.
10	0.70–0.90					4.0	4.0	1.0	1.5	8.0	Balance	Tungsten saving alternate. Same as 18-4-1.
11	0.75–0.90					4.50–5.50	4.0	1.05–1.35	6.00	8.00–9.00	Balance	Tungsten saving alternate. Same as 18-4-1.
12	0.75–0.90						4.0	1.25–2.00	6.00	5.00	Balance	Tungsten saving alternate. Same as 18-4-1.

Fig. 15. High-speed tool steels—composition and properties.

Tool Material	Percent of Elements							
	C	W	Cr	Co	Mo	Fe	V	Ni
Cast nonferrous alloy	1.8–2.15	17–19	30–35	43–48	(Small Quantities)			

Fig. 16. Composition of cast nonferrous alloy tool material.

the ends, not from the sides or top. It is further recommended that the cutting edges be honed at a 45° angle in order to remove any protruding particles that may break out and cause galling at the cutting edge.

SINTERED CARBIDES. This tool material is made up of varying proportions of tungsten, tantalum, and titanium carbides, with a cobalt binder. One of three methods of powder metallurgy (see section on Manufacturing Processes) is used to obtain the tool form:

1. **Cold pressing.** The powders are preshaped on small presses, then presintered, and finally formed and sintered.
2. **Hot pressing.** In this method the powders are compacted and sintered in a single operation.
3. **Extruding.** This method of forming utilizes extrusion as the preshaping operation, then follows the procedure employed in cold pressing.

After sintering, the only method that may be utilized to change the shape of the tool is grinding. The **tungsten carbide** provides high hardness at relatively low cost. The **tantalum carbide** was introduced in sintered carbide tooling to give added resistance to **cratering** that occurs just behind the cutting edge. The addition of tantalum carbide tended to reduce the effect of the chip upon the area immediately behind the cutting edge, thus adding to tool life. In mixed combinations of carbides, **titanium carbide** imparts the same properties to the tool as the tantalum carbide, and at a reduced cost. It also possesses stable high-temperature properties which form the basis of its addition to the sintered carbide tool material. A **double carbide** of two metals, tungsten-titanium carbide, rather than a mixture of two normal carbides, tends to reduce cratering and also provides good corrosion resistance and the ability to produce excellent finish. Generally, cobalt is selected as the **binder** in carbide materials because of its strength and ductility at high temperatures.

The outstanding properties possessed by the sintered carbide tools are retention of hardness at high temperatures and exceptionally high wear resistance. As an example, the temperatures at which tool materials will have the same hardness value, Brinell 600–680 (Engineering Materials Manual), are as follows:

Carbon tool steel .... 650° F.
High-speed steel .... 825° F.
Sintered carbides .... 1550° F.

There has not been a sudden widespread adoption of carbides since the General Electric Co. introduced them to this country in 1928. Machine tools needed substantial revision to make proper use of carbides, and such capital expenditures were not made until World War II. The growth in the use of carbides followed fifteen years of development in the various grades necessary for the many varied cutting conditions encountered. Fig. 17 is a composite of manufacturers' recommended usage based on data prepared by the Carbide Industry Standardization Committee.

DIAMONDS. The hardest known cutting material is the diamond. After being cut and polished to the desired shape it is mounted in an appropriate holder. The diamond as a cutting material exhibits an extremely low coefficient of friction against materials being cut and has an excellent resistance to wear. For these reasons it is recommended for use when cutting extremely hard materials in processes requiring light cuts and a high finish and degree of accuracy. It is also used when cutting abrasive materials such as carbon or many of the plastics. However, the brittleness of the diamond cutting tool tends to limit its applications. An interrupted cut, or sudden impact of any type such as a drop upon the floor, or a hard spot in a material being cut may cause serious chipping of the tool. The high cost of industrial diamonds, coupled with their extreme brittleness, have limited their application to continuous boring or turning under conditions requiring light cuts of high accuracy and finish on abrasive materials.

CERAMIC MATERIALS. This family of cutting-tool materials has not yet been subjected to conclusive testing, but some work has been done which is worthy of consideration. Ceramic cutting material offered on the market is 80 to 95 percent aluminum oxide, the remainder being silicon dioxide. The material is prepared by powder techniques, being compacted and then sintered. The ceramic cutting-tool material is appreciably harder than carbides at the higher temperatures. It also offers excellent resistance to abrasion, making it applicable for use with the extremely abrasive materials. Schmidt, Ham, Phillips, and Wilson (Ceramic and Carbide Tool Performance Tests, part I, ASME) report that ceramic cutting tools demonstrated greater tool life than carbides on certain types of turning operations. This study also indicates the need to operate ceramic tools at high speeds, as high as five times that of carbide, to utilize the tools more fully. The experimental data presented indicates that equal tool life when cutting cast iron was attained with carbide and ceramic tools when the ceramic tools were operating at speeds three times that of the carbides. At low speeds, however, carbide displayed superior performance compared to the ceramic tools. Ceramic tools also suffered rather rapid **initial flank wear** totaling 0.004 in., in the first few seconds, and then a reduced wear rate for a prolonged period. In an effort to avoid this initial rapid wear rate it is recommended that a flat of 0.003 in. be honed at the cutting edge. No crater wear was evidenced in this testing nor was there any **welding of work particles** to the tip of the ceramic tool.

Hook (The Tool Engineer, vol. 37) reports that ceramic tools on like cuts with carbide tools required only 80 percent of the power required by carbides. However, Schmidt and others indicate that the power required by ceramic tools was 95 percent of that required by carbide tools. Hook further reports that rigid support must be given ceramic tools to offset the brittleness of the material.

Schmidt's experimental work was conducted using a ½-in. hexagonal and ¾-in. square clamp-on-type tips. Much more testing must be done before a standard can be established to guide the user of ceramic cutting-tool materials.

Ceramic cutting tools at present are recommended for use on setups offering rigidity of tooling and work, and availability of high feeds and speeds on extremely abrasive materials. Limited applications work has been reported on cuts of an interrupted nature.

	Application	Designation	Adamas	Carboloy	Carmet	Firthite	Kennametal	Talide	Vascoloy Ramet	Wesson	Willey
CHIP REMOVAL											
Cast Iron, Non-ferrous, and Non-metallic materials	Roughing cuts—cast iron and nonferrous materials	C-1	B	44A	CA3	H	K6	C89	2A68	GS	E8
	General purpose—cast iron and nonferrous materials	C-2	A	883	CA4	HA	K6	C91	2A5	GI	E6
	Light finishing—cast iron and nonferrous materials	C-3	AA	905	CA7	HE	K8	C93	2A7	GA	E5
	Precision boring—cast iron and nonferrous materials	C-4	AAA	999	CA8	HF	K8	C93	2A7i	GF	E3
Steel and Steel Alloys	Roughing cuts—steel	C-5	434, DD	78C 78B	CA5, CA51	T-04	KM, K2S	S88	EE	WS	945
	General purpose—steel	C-6	D	78B 78	CA1	TA	K2S	S90	EM	WM	710
	Finishing cuts—steel	C-7	548, C	78	CA2	T-19, T-16	K3H	S92	E	WH	606
	Precision boring—steel	C-8	CC	831	CA6	T-31	K5H	S92	EH	WH	509
WEAR APPLICATION											
	Wear surface—no shock	C-9	A	44A 883	CA4	HA	K8	C89	2A5	GI	E6
	Wear surface—light shock	C-10	B	779 44A	CA3	H	K6	C88	2A68	GS	E8
	Wear surface—heavy shock	C-11	BB	55B 55A	CA10	HC	K1	C8515	2A3	M	E18
IMPACT APPLICATIONS											
	Impact—light	C-12	BB	44A 55A	CA10	DC-2	K1	C8515	2A3	GS	E13
	Impact—medium	C-13	HD-15	55B 55A	CA11	DCX	K18	C8020	AX	M	E18
	Impact—heavy	C-14	HD-25	190	CA20	DC-3	K25	C7525	AY	M	E25

Fig. 17. Carbide manufacturers' grade recommendations.

Notes: 1. This chart presents the manufacturer's independent recommendations for carbides for the uses indicated; it is not intended as a grade comparison chart. It is not an endorsement of any manufacturer's product, nor is it an approved list of sources.
2. Where two grades are shown for a single application, the first is recommended for heavier duty.

Tool Geometry

SINGLE-POINT TOOLS. The single-point tool is used on such machines as lathes, planers, shapers, and boring mills. It is a cutting tool with a single face and one continuous cutting edge which produces the machined surface. The single-point tool is made up in all materials previously discussed in line with the varied operational setups encountered.

Single-point tools are classified according to material, use, and construction. The **material classification** covers plain-carbon steel, high-speed steel, cast non-ferrous alloy, diamond, carbide, and ceramic types. The material has a distinct influence on tool geometry. The **construction classification** consists of two distinct types:

1. **Solid tools,** which have the full section of the cutting end made up of metal-cutting material. The cutting end may be formed by either grinding to shape or by forging to rough shape and then hardening and grinding.
2. **Tipped tools,** which are made up of a small piece of cutting material attached to a shank or holder of noncutting material. This cutting material may be attached by soldering, brazing, welding, or clamping. The **clamp-on cutting edge** has come into use by virtue of being more economical.

The operational requirements imposed make up the **classification of use** of single-point tools. Typical classifications are threading, facing, turning, and boring. This classification by usage also has a direct bearing on the geometry sought in single-point tools.

Terminology generally associated in the metalworking industry with **solid** single-point tools is given in Fig. 18 (American Standard Single-Point Tools and Tool Parts, ASA B 5.22–1950, ASME). Fig. 19 indicates terminology commonly associated with **tipped** single-point cutting tools.

Tool Angle Nomenclature. The angles of tools affect tool life, chip flow, and surface finish of the work. Since tool geometry is an all-important variable in the machining, considerable work has been done to determine desirable characteristics for cutting. Single-point cutting tools used in lathe and shaper work are supported, quite often, in a tool post having a **rocker base** in order to adjust

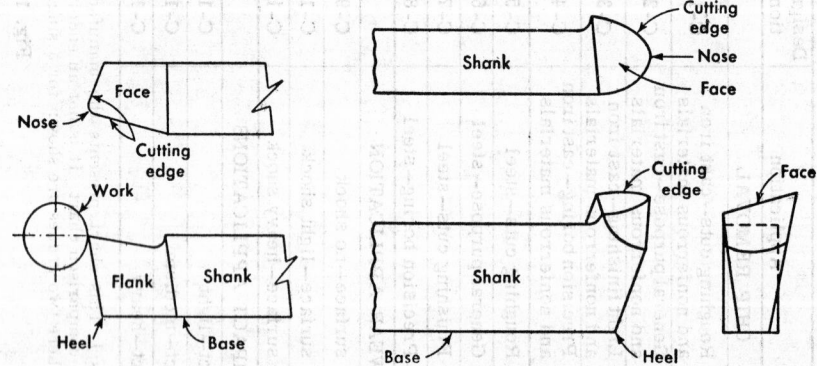

(a) A typical right-cut, straight-shank, single-point ground tool.

(b) A typical right-cut, straight-shank, single-point, raised-face, forged-type tool.

Fig. 18. Solid single-point cutting-tool terminology.

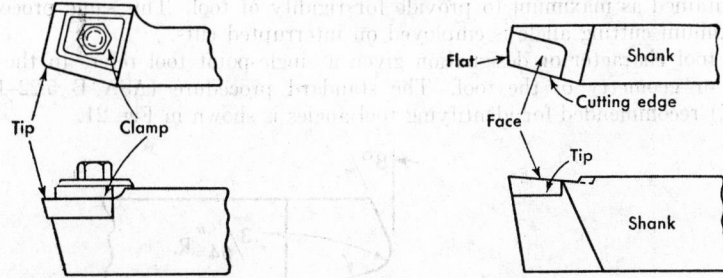

(a) A typical tipped single-point cutting tool clamped to a shank.

(b) A typical tipped single-point cutting tool brazed to a shank.

Fig. 19. Tipped single-point cutting-tool terminology.

for work centerline. When this method of tool-holding is employed it results in presenting the tool to the work at angles other than those ground on the tool. For this reason it is recommended that **fixed-bed** tool posts and holders be employed as supports to single-point cutting tools in order to maintain tool geometry as planned in tool-grinding. The tool angles given consideration in grinding single-point cutting tools to shape are shown in Fig. 20.

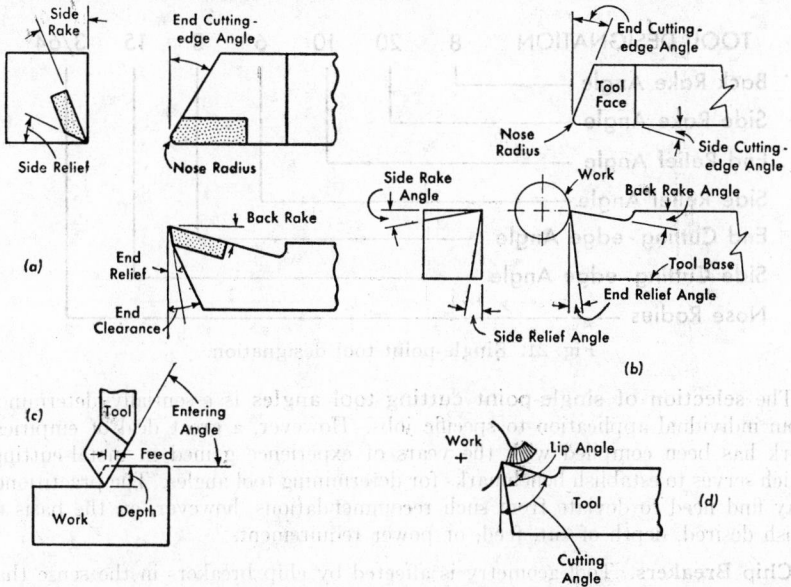

Fig. 20. Single-point cutting-tool angles.

The tool angles and elements associated with tipped tools are shown in Fig. 20(a) while those same tool angles and elements are shown in Fig. 20(b) in conjunction with solid single-point cutting tools. The **working angles**, the **entering angle** and **cutting angle**, are shown in Fig. 20(c) and (d). These working angles have a direct bearing on chatter and surface finish as well as tool life. For instance, when using ceramic tooling it is recommended that the entering angle be kept to a minimum in an effort to reduce breakage due to the impact-loading at the start of cutting. When machining high-strength materials, the cutting angle is maintained as maximum to provide for rigidity of tool. This same procedure of maximum cutting angle is employed on interrupted cuts.

The tool character or designation given a single-point tool refers to the tool angles or geometry of the tool. The standard procedure (ASA B 5.22–1950 ASME) recommended for identifying tool angles is shown in Fig. 21.

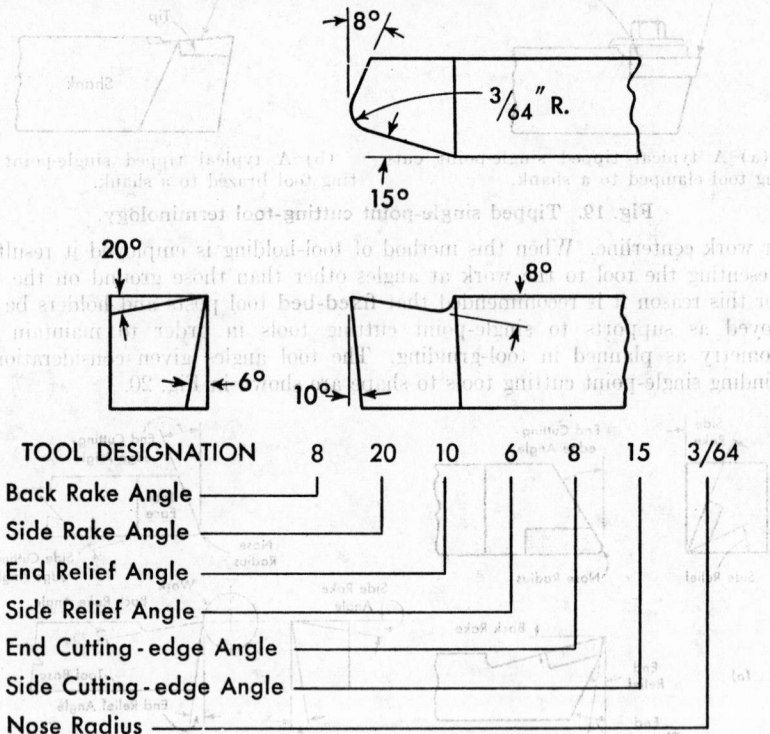

TOOL DESIGNATION	8	20	10	6	8	15	3/64
Back Rake Angle							
Side Rake Angle							
End Relief Angle							
Side Relief Angle							
End Cutting-edge Angle							
Side Cutting-edge Angle							
Nose Radius							

Fig. 21. Single-point tool designation.

The **selection of single-point cutting-tool angles** is essentially determined from individual application to specific jobs. However, a great deal of empirical work has been compiled with the years of experience gained in metal-cutting, which serves to establish benchmarks for determining tool angles. The practitioner may find need to deviate from such recommendations, however, on the basis of finish desired, depth of cut, feed, or power requirements.

Chip Breakers. Tool geometry is affected by chip breakers in the sense that they alter the tool face. Chip breakers are provided in single-point tools when a long continuous chip is encountered in machining. This long continuous type chip presents the dual problem of a hazard to the operator and also the threat of scarring a finished surface if the chip becomes tangled on the work piece. The chip breaker provides a means of breaking the chip as it is sheared from the parent material. The most frequently used type of chip breaker is one provided by grinding a depression or **gullet** in the face of the tool immediately behind the cutting edge. Typical chip breakers utilized in breaking up long continuous-type chips are shown in Fig. 22.

The width and depth of the step or gullet are determined from the depth of cut and feed employed in the cutting operation. The gullet type of chip breaker will employ a width as small as 0.015 in. and a depth of 0.015 in. when the depth of cut is approximately 0.030 in. with a feed of 0.010 in. per rev. A feed rate of 0.030 in. per rev. with a depth of cut of ½ in. would dictate a gullet 0.030 in. wide and 0.030 in. deep. The gullet is located at least 1/32 in. behind the cutting

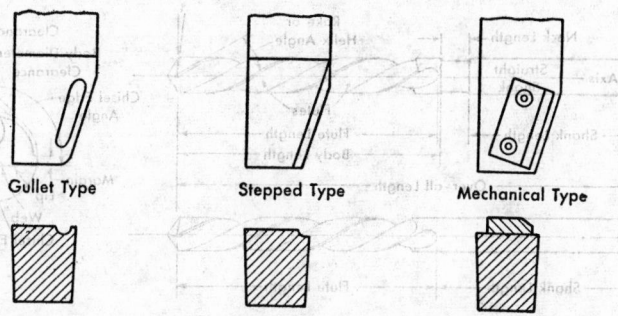

| Gullet Type | Stepped Type | Mechanical Type |

Fig. 22. Typical chip breakers.

edge. On the low feed and depth of cut, the step-type chip breaker would assume the dimensions 0.015 in. deep and 0.060 in. wide. When employing the depth of cut of ½ in. and the feed of 0.030 in. per rev., the step would be 0.030 in. deep and 0.250 in. wide. Some types of ceramic tools employ a raised portion behind the cutting edge that is approximately 0.025 in. high. This chip breaker on ceramic tools is formed at the time of compacting the ceramic material.

MULTIPLE-CUTTING-EDGE TOOLS. The multiple-cutting-edge tools are tools that provide more than a single edge for purposes of metal removal. This family of tools is composed of drills, reamers, counterbores, milling cutters, and broaches. The cutting action, and in turn the tool, is much the same, no matter if the surface machined is acquired by employing a single- or a multiple-edge cutting tool. Multiple-cutting-edge tools are classified into two types in terms of construction. There are **solid-type** and **tipped-type** multiple-edge tools similar to those previously defined under Single-Point Tools.

Drills. Boston (Metal Machining) classifies drills according to use as follows:

1. Twist drill, a helical fluted drill.
2. Farmer drill, a straight fluted drill.
3. Flat drill, with a point ground on the end of flat bars.
4. Core drill, for enlarging a cored, forged, or previously prepared hole.
5. Center drill, used to drill and countersink ends of center mounted work.

The **twist drill** is used most frequently in machine-shop work, while the other types of drills are restricted to a very specialized application.

Twist drills (ASA B 5.12–1950, ASME) are end cutting tools having one or more cutting edges and helical or straight flutes or grooves adjacent thereto for the passage of cuttings or chips. Twist drills are used for originating or enlarging holes. The nomenclature and geometry for twist drills given in the standard are shown in Fig. 23.

The practice of grinding drills without regard to their geometry should be avoided, since it results in nonstandard geometry and, in turn, unpredictable drill

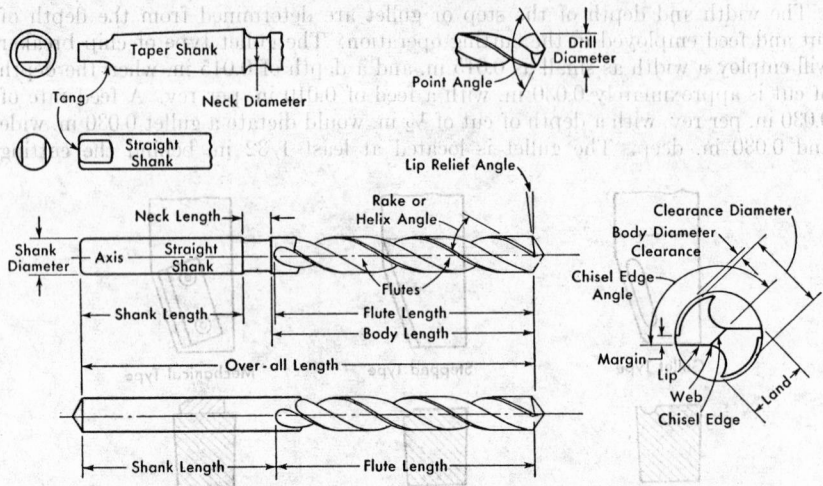

Fig. 23. Twist drill nomenclature and geometry.

performance. Drill grinders have more than proved their worth by accurately supplying ground tools with a predictable tool life.

Reamers. The American Standards Association (B 5.14–1949, ASME) defines reamers as tools used for enlarging, or finishing to size, holes previously formed. Most frequently the hole is formed by drilling or boring, but there are times when a cored hole is reamed.

Reamers are classified according to operation, purpose, and shape as follows:

1. Hand reamers.
2. Taper-shank jobbers' reamers.
3. Chucking or machine reamers.
4. Shell reamers.
5. Center reamers.
6. Taper reamers.
7. Expansion reamers.
8. Adjustable reamers.
9. Special reamers.

Practically all cutting done by reamers (with the exception of the hand reamers, center reamers, taper reamers, and hand expansion reamers) is accomplished by the **chamfer** on the end of the reamer which forms the cutting edges. The longitudinal flutes do little or no cutting in a reaming operation. Reamers are a finishing tool and give best results in terms of surface finish and hole accuracy by limiting the material removed to 0.004 in. to 0.012 in. on the diameter. On rough reaming, such as **rose reaming** of cored holes, 1/16 in. may be removed. However, surface finish and hole accuracy are sacrificed in this type of reaming operation.

Broaches. Broaches are cutting tools for removing material, primarily metal, by means of an elongated bar or holder having teeth of increasing size along its length. The cutting action is accomplished by pushing or pulling the broach past the work piece held rigidly in a fixture. The one exception to these methods of broaching is **continuous surface broaching** where the broach is stationary and the work moves past, held in fixtures attached to platens on an endless chain. The cutting action in broaching is very similar to shaping except that the finished surface is obtained with one stroke when broaching, whereas the shaping operation requires repeated stroking and advance of tool to finish a like surface. For the most part broaches are solid-type tools, but there are a few applications of built-up or section broaches. The solid broaches find the most widespread application. Broaches may be classified as follows:

1. Method of operation—push or pull.
2. Type of operation—internal or external.
3. Type of surface—round, spline, flat, keyway, etc.

Milling Cutters. A milling cutter (American Standard B 5.3–1950, ASME) is a rotary cutting tool provided with one or more cutting elements called teeth, which intermittently engage the work piece and remove material by relative movement of a work piece and cutter. Milling cutters are classified by construction, relief of teeth, purpose or use, method of mounting, and the "hand" of cutter, which are discussed in the following:

1. **Construction.** Milling cutters are often described by using terms which refer to their construction characteristics, such as:

   a. **Solid cutters,** made of one piece of material; e.g., high-speed steel.
   b. **Tipped solid cutters,** similar to solid cutters, except that such materials as cast alloys or carbides are joined to them so as to provide the cutting edges of the teeth.
   c. **Inserted-tooth cutters,** which have mechanically retained solid or hard-alloy-tipped teeth or blades.

2. **Relief of teeth.** Milling cutters may also be described on the basis of one of two methods of providing relief for the cutting edges. These methods determine the manner of resharpening.

   a. **Profile-relieved cutters,** on which the relief is obtained and sharpening done by grinding a narrow land back of the cutting edge. Profile-relieved cutters may produce flat, curved, or irregular surfaces, the latter being called profile-type form cutters.
   b. **Form-relieved cutters,** on which a curved relief back of the cutting edge is produced by a cam-actuated tool or grinding wheel. These cutters are sharpened by grinding the faces of the teeth.

3. **Purpose or use.** Milling cutters are sometimes described by terms which refer to their use or the purpose for which they are made. By way of illustration there are:

   a. **T-slot cutters,** specially used to finish the "head space" of a T-slot.
   b. **Woodruff keyseat cutters,** the purpose of which is the machining of seats of Woodruff keys.
   c. **Gear-milling cutters,** designed to produce properly shaped teeth on a gear.
   d. **Corner-rounding cutters,** intended for rounding the edges of a work piece.
   e. **Single- and multiple-thread milling cutters,** used to produce screw-threads, one thread at a time or a number of threads, respectively.

4. **Method of mounting.** Milling cutters may also be described by their manner of mounting on the milling machine. The three types are:

   a. **Arbor-type cutter,** intended for mounting on a machine arbor and usually driven by a key.
   b. **Shank-type cutter,** having one or more straight or tapered extensions for the purpose of mounting and driving.
   c. **Facing-type cutter,** with provision for mounting directly on the milling machine spindle nose, stub arbor, or adapter.

5. **Hand of cutter.** The terms "right-hand" and "left-hand" are used to describe both rotation and helix of milling cutters.

    a. **Direction of rotation** of any cutter may be referred to as the hand of rotation when viewed toward the end of the spindle as the cutter revolves so as to make a cut. If the rotary motion is counterclockwise, the cutter is operating with a right-hand rotation. If this rotary motion is clockwise, the cutter is operating with a left-hand rotation.

    b. **Hand of helix.** Cutters with teeth in planes parallel to the cutter axis are described as having "straight teeth." Cutters with every other tooth of opposite (right- and left-hand) helix are called "alternate helical tooth cutters." When the helix is in one direction only, cutters are described as being right- or left-hand helix. A cutter viewed from one end, with flutes that twist away in a clockwise direction, has a right-hand helix, while a cutter with flutes that twist away in a counterclockwise direction has a left-hand helix.

TOOL FINISHING. Tests made on grinding at the Norton Co. (Ericson, Mech. Eng., vol. 66) showed that about the same time was required to get a fair edge with regular grinding wheels as was needed to mount the proper finer-grit wheels and obtain the better results with special finish grinding. It is the practice, therefore, to assemble a number of tools to be ground, so that one change of wheel from rough to finish grind will take care of the entire lot. Using regular 46- and 60-grit wheels, a smoothness of 20 to 30 microinches (rms.), as measured by a profilometer, may be obtained on tools of various metals. More skilled tool grinders obtain 8 to 12 microinches (rms.) Fine-grit finish-grinding wheels give 2 to 5 microinches (rms.)

Other factors, besides kind of abrasive and grit size in wheel or honing stick, which affect finish of the tool (Wise, Am. Mach., vol. 85), are strength of bond in the abrasive body, dressing of the wheel, skill and method of the operator, rigidity of setup, and properties of tool material. Use of a grinding coolant is also helpful. Finer finishes are obtained with harder tools and harder wheels. Finishing wheels should be used only for finishing. If used for roughing they wear too fast and overheat the tools.

Advantages of Finish Grinding. In one plant, properly ground reamers $1\frac{1}{2}$ in. in diameter used to machine No. 21 aluminum castings were found to last for two or three days without resharpening, as compared to a half-day before. The reamers thus were resharpened only one-fifth the former number of times, increasing the life of both reamers and grinding wheels, besides saving grinding time, shutting down production only one-fifth as often, and producing a better finish.

In another plant large hobs for cutting large reduction gears were found to be burned back so little under use when properly sharpened that only 0.010 in. had to be ground off, instead of 0.060 in., as formerly required. Time of grinding was cut from 17 hr. down to 5 hr., finishes were better, and cutter life was considerably increased. In the same plant, finish-milling cutters used on work requiring extra-fine finish were able to do the operation in 6 hr. instead of the former 16 hr. because of the keener cutter edges produced by the better grinding methods. Previously, work had to wait until cutters were sharpened, and a cutter would mill only part of a piece before it would have to be removed for grinding; after the proper grinding wheels and procedures were introduced, cutters were ready in advance, one cutter finished the piece without regrinding, and work stoppages were eliminated.

Records of research tests on the improvement of finish grinding practices were kept and it was proved that six definite advantages were obtained.

1. Longer life of cutters because resharpenings were fewer.
2. Fewer grinding wheels used.
3. More production between regrinds. Tests showed from 9 to 300 percent increase.
4. Less power consumption.
5. Better quality of work produced.
6. More uniform cutter teeth.

Jigs and Fixtures

PRINCIPLES OF LOCATING WORK PIECE. Modern manufacturing of interchangeable parts is based on the fact that each part will be produced within an established tolerance range. Jigs and fixtures offer a means of producing interchangeable parts, since it is their function to present the work piece to the tool in a fixed relationship conforming to the tolerance prescribed. The use of jigs and fixtures makes possible the manufacture of interchangeable parts without the need for highly skilled labor. Each jig or fixture is composed of the elements of **locators** and **clamps.**

Degrees of Freedom. Locating elements place the work piece in essentially the same position cycle after cycle. In this sense, the locator provides a reference point from which all sizing or spacing may be accomplished. A free body may have three degrees of freedom of translation and three degrees of freedom of rotation. It is the purpose of locators to restrict these six degrees of freedom in order to give points of reference.

A work piece would lose three degrees of freedom if placed and maintained on the locators lettered (A) shown in Fig. 24.

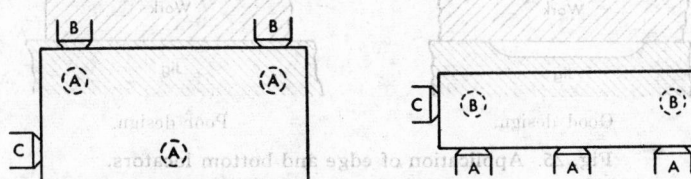

Fig. 24. Placement of locators.

If the work piece is then brought in contact with locators (B), two more degrees of freedom are restricted. The final degree of freedom is lost when the work piece is brought in contact with locator (C). In the example shown in Fig. 24, the **reference surfaces** could be the surface resting on the (A) locators, the surface resting on the (B) locators, or the surface resting on the (C) locator. Thus, the placement of locators, as shown in Fig. 24, insures reproducible location of the work piece each time the surfaces are brought in contact with the locators.

Influence of Work-Piece Surface. The form of the locator selected is influenced to a large degree by the condition of the reference surface. **Finished surfaces** can be located on a plane rather than suspended on points. However, even if a high finish and true surface is available as a reference surface, there is danger of misalignment from minute chip particles or dirt lodging between adjacent planes. **Rough surfaces** are given as few points of contact as deemed necessary for stability of part. Three points form a plane and the introduction of additional points may offer greater stability, but also introduce the risk of unevenness with the plane formed by three points. Identification of reference surfaces must be made prior to the selection of locators, since the condition of the surface is so influential in choosing locators.

TYPES OF LOCATORS. The type of locator selected for application is largely a function of the shape of the work piece and more particularly the shape of the reference surface. Fig. 25 shows various types of edge and bottom locators commonly employed.

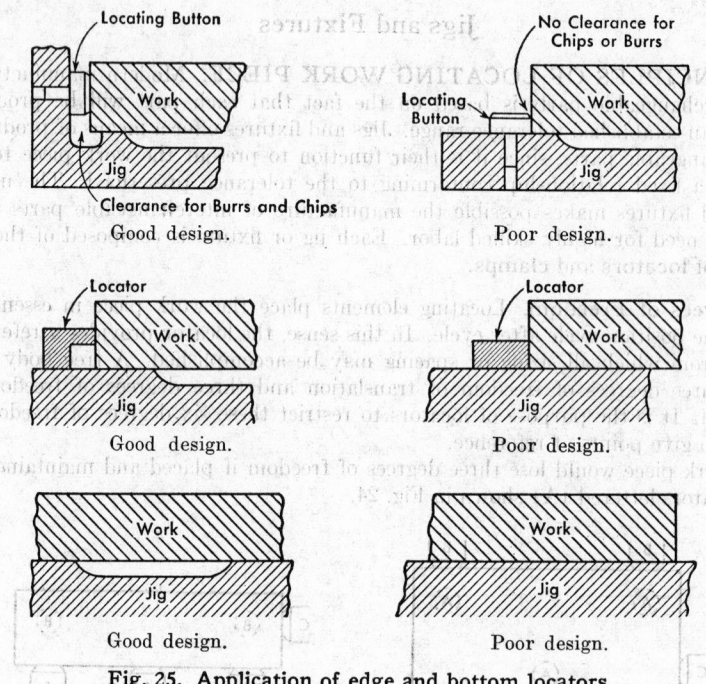

Fig. 25. Application of edge and bottom locators.

Edge locators must provide recognition for the problem of burrs on the work piece and the presence of chips in the jig or fixture as the result of previous cutting operations. Misalignment resulting in spoilage can be the outgrowth of the jig or fixture designer's failing to provide this needed clearance for edge and bottom locators.

Pin locators where holes are used as reference points are widely used. In addition to the allowance both for burrs on the work piece and for the presence of chips or dirt, consideration must be given to placing the work piece over the locating pin.

When situations are encountered where the reference surface is the outside diameter of a cylindrical part, the **V-locator** provides the most desirable means of locating. The 90° angle between faces on the V gives the best cylindrical surface locator. Care must be exercised when using the V-locator to insure that the direction of the force introduced by the tool bisects the included angle of the V-locator. This practice insures positive seating. For instance, the only center of the lateral surface of a cylindrical piece located by a V-locator is the one bisecting the included angle.

On occasion it is necessary to center a piece of other than cylindrical shape. In this situation a **centralizer** or **radial locator** is used to position the work piece in some fixed relationship to the work.

PRINCIPLES OF CLAMPING. The purpose of clamping is twofold. First, it must hold the work piece firmly against the locators provided, and second, it must resist all forces introduced by the operation. **Placement of the clamp** is extremely important in the design of jigs or fixtures. Care must be taken to apply the clamp in an area that is directly opposed by the locators. A poorly placed clamp can cause warping of the work piece or introduce a turning moment that would tend to unseat the work piece. Examples of desirable clamp locations are shown in Fig. 26.

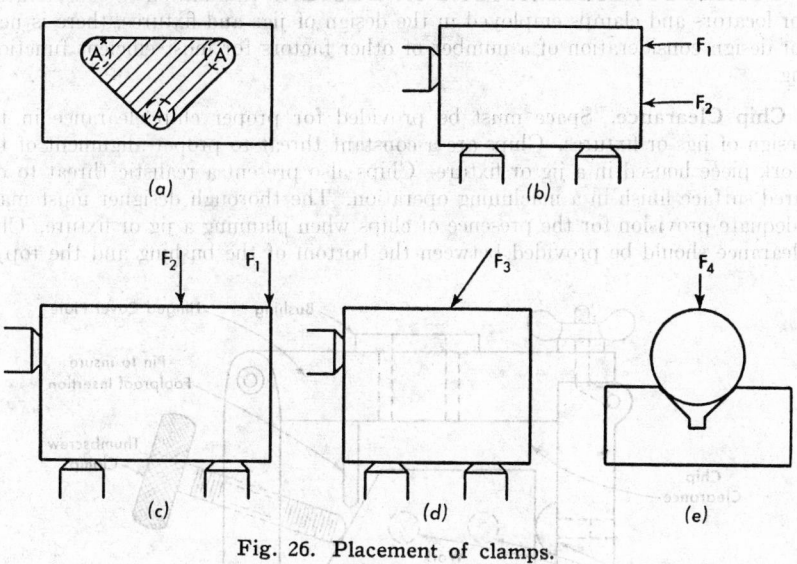

Fig. 26. Placement of clamps.

The shaded area shown in Fig. 26(a) offers the correct site for applications of a vertical clamp. If the clamping force is applied outside this shaded area it would result in either part deformation or a tilting of part away from the base locators. The forces F_1 shown on Fig. 26(b) and (c) would introduce a turning moment, whereas if the clamping forces F_2 were introduced at the points designated the part would be seated firmly on the locators. If a single clamp is used to secure the work piece, its line of action must lie within the extreme points of contact, such as is shown at F_3 in Fig. 26(d). Fig. 26(e) again demonstrates the need for the application of the clamping force F_4 in such a manner so as to insure contact at the locator points. The use of a **single clamp,** such as shown in Fig. 26(d), is not only the most economical, since there is but one clamp to tighten, but also the best method for insuring positive contact on all locators. When employing a clamping system similar to those shown in Fig. 26(b) and (c), the tightening of one side clamp may lift the work piece from the locators on the adjacent side. If the first side clamp is tightened securely the second side clamp may never seat the work piece against the opposing locators.

Influence of Work Piece on Clamping. The work piece, to a large extent, determines the **form, placement,** and **magnitude** of the clamp employed. If, for instance, the entire top surface is machined, a side clamp must exert both a horizontal and vertical force in order to assure a firm holding action. Finished surfaces that must remain free of marks or scratches require a form of clamp that will not mar the finish. Work pieces of a fragile nature limit the magnitude of the clamping force to that which would not deform or warp the part. Rough surfaces permit the use of either **hold-down pins** that dig into the work or **serrated-faced clamps** that give more positive holding action. It is with these considerations for the work piece that the jig and fixture designer must approach the problem of clamping or holding.

OTHER CONSIDERATIONS IN DESIGN. In addition to consideration for locators and clamps employed in the design of jigs and fixtures, there is need for design consideration of a number of other factors for most efficient functioning.

Chip Clearance. Space must be provided for proper chip clearance in the design of jigs or fixtures. Chips are a constant threat to proper alignment of the work piece housed in a jig or fixture. Chips also present a realistic threat to desired surface finish in a machining operation. The thorough designer must make adequate provision for the presence of chips when planning a jig or fixture. Chip clearance should be provided between the bottom of the bushing and the top of

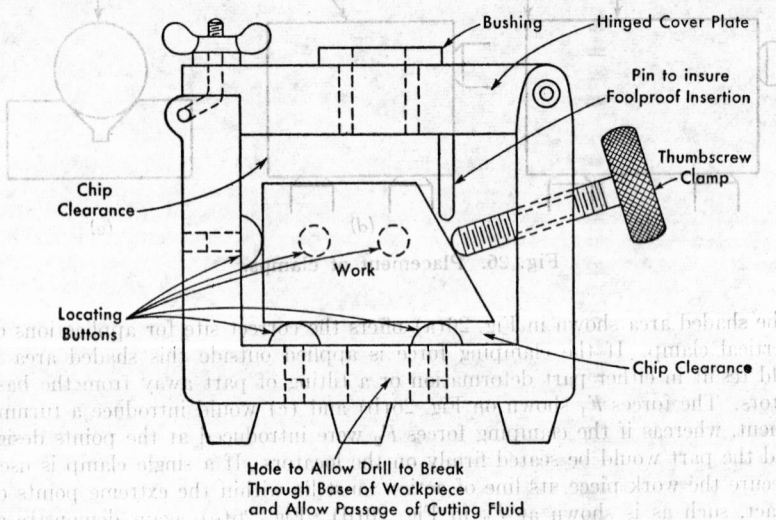

Fig. 27. Example of drill jig design.

the work piece, as shown in Fig. 27. This chip clearance at the top of the work piece keeps the chips from packing up in the drill flutes and marring the surface of the hole drilled. As a rule of thumb, the upper chip clearance is equal to the drill diameter used. The space provided between the base of work piece and the jig by the presence of the base locators, as shown in Fig. 27, reduces the hazard of misalignment of the part as the result of a chip remaining in the jig after cleaning.

Foolproof Operation. The pin shown on the underside of the jig hinged cover plate in Fig. 27 is an example of a device which is used to insure foolproof insertion of a work piece in either a jig or fixture. Should the part be inserted in any other manner than that shown, it would be impossible to close the hinged cover plate. Thus, by warning the operator of improper referencing of the work piece, costly mistakes in part loading can be avoided by the simple consideration for foolproof work-piece insertion in a jig or fixture.

Influence of Forces Encountered. The forces introduced by the drilling setup shown in Fig. 27 would be twofold. There would be an **axial force** downward that would be transmitted through the part to the base locators which would seat the part firmly on the locators. A **torque** introduced by the cutting action of the drill would tend to rotate the part. This force would be transmitted through the part to the side locators since the work piece is held firmly on the locators by the thumbscrew clamp. To insure positive clamping, an additional clamp would be utilized on the front side of the jig shown in Fig. 27. This clamp has not been shown in order to give the reader a clear view of the work piece in the jig.

DESIGN CHECK LIST. A check list for use when designing jigs or fixtures has been prepared by Tilles (American Machinist, vol. 95) as an aid in evaluating designs. This check list (Fig. 28) provides for the orderly analysis of jig and fixture design and avoids the omission of pertinent details.

ECONOMY OF JIGS AND FIXTURES. Roe (Principles of Jig and Fixture Practice, revised in Mech. Eng., vol. 63, originally published in Trans. ASME MSP–51–11) developed a group of simple formulas to be used in determining the economic results from the use of jigs and fixtures. He states that the economy problem involved in any situation centers around one or more of the following questions:

1. How many pieces must be run to pay for a fixture of given estimated cost to show a given estimated saving in direct labor cost per piece? For instance, how low a run will justify a fixture costing $400 to save 3 cents on direct labor cost of each piece?
2. How much may a fixture cost which will show a given estimated unit saving in direct labor cost on a given number of pieces? For instance, how much can be put into a fixture to "break even" on a run of 10,000 pieces, if the fixture can save 3 cents on direct labor cost of each piece?
3. How long will it take a proposed fixture, under given conditions, to pay for itself, carrying its fixed charges while so doing? For instance, how long will it take a fixture costing $400 to pay for itself if it saves 3 cents on direct labor cost per unit, production being at a given rate?

Questions 1, 2, and 3 assume that savings just balance the expense. There is another practical question:

4. What profit will be earned by a fixture of a given cost, for an estimated unit saving in direct labor cost and given output? For instance, what will be the profit on a $200 fixture if it will save in direct labor cost 3 cents a piece on 10,000 pieces?

These questions involve something more than simple arithmetic for an answer. While the credit items for the fixture depend mainly on the number of pieces machined, the debit items involve time and number of setups required, i.e., whether pieces are run off continuously or in a number of runs.

Factor	Definition	Influenced By	Example
Location	Establishing desired relationship between work piece and jig or fixture.	1. Reference points or surfaces.	1. Sight location. 2. V-blocks. 3. Locating pins.
Clamping	Use of a mechanical device to maintain the relationship established above during the operation being performed.	1. Ratio of cost of clamp to cost of operation. 2. Frequency of setup. 3. Clamping force required. 4. Size and condition of work. 5. Convenience of operation.	1. Sliding clamp. 2. Hinge clamp. 3. Cam-actuated clamp. 4. Pneumatic clamp. 5. Vise. 6. Thumbscrew.
Chip control	Minimizing the adverse effects of chip and burr formation on the functioning of the jig or fixture.	1. Type of operation being performed. 2. Form of chip. 3. Material being cut. 4. Use of coolant.	1. Chip clearance. 2. Relief at corners, pockets, or contact areas. 3. Chip slides.
Positioning	Establishing desired relationship between jig or fixture and the cutting tool.	1. Machine tool being used. 2. Tolerance desired. 3. Availability of standard positioning devices. 4. Use of tool guides.	1. Universal tilting table. 2. Box or tumble jigs. 3. Trunnion mounts. 4. Index fixtures. 5. Bushings.

Standardization	Use of standardized components wherever possible.	1. Sizes commercially available. 2. Amount of tooling manufactured. 3. Type of part needed.	1. Bushings. 2. Hand knobs. 3. Locating pins. 4. Crank levers.
Ease of operation	Facility with which the operator is able to use the completed jig or fixture. Minimum requirements of time, effort, dexterity.	1. Positioning. 2. Clamping device selected. 3. Size and shape. 4. Location of manual components.	1. Quick-acting clamps or pneumatic devices where possible. 2. All levers within easy reach. 3. Quick location.
Safety	Absence of hazards in use of jigs or fixtures.	1. Clamping device selected. 2. Chip control. 3. Machine tool being used.	1. No protruding sharp edges. 2. Hands not required to operate jig or fixture while close to cutting tool. 3. Ample clearance for knuckles and fingers.
Cost	Initial investment required to design and build the jig or fixture.	1. Number of parts to be made. 2. Size and shape of part. 3. Tolerances desired. 4. Materials specified.	1. All components as simple as possible. 2. Standard parts used wherever possible. 3. Replaceable parts where subject to wear.

Fig. 28. Check list of factors in jig and fixture design.

Formulas. Roe developed his formulas for jigs and fixtures from general equations for the efficiency of equipment which were formulated by the Materials Handling Division of the American Society of Mechanical Engineers. The original equations provide a basis for the economic analysis of industrial equipment, and for the determination of probable profit on any proposed installation for a given situation and cost of performance. They take into account interest, depreciation, obsolescence, and other items of overhead. They can be used, with modifications and simplifications, for tool equipment. These modifications Roe has made. Certain factors in materials handling formulas are important in installations in that field, but are of less importance in dealing with tools, and may be dropped entirely. Other factors, such as interest rate, taxes, and the like, may be taken as a constant and brought together.

Roe originally presented nine formulas which have since been reduced to four simple and workable forms designated as (1), (2), (3), and (4) by leaving out factors for power cost, unamortized value of equipment displaced (less its scrap value), and savings through increased production, which are small values.

To be of practical value the formulas should be as simple as possible and yet reflect essential conditions, and should be easily applied. Equations (1), (2), (3), and (4) meet this condition for most fixtures. They take into account number of pieces manufactured, saving in unit labor cost, overhead on labor saved, the cost and frequency of setups, interest on investment, taxes, insurance, upkeep, and depreciation.

In using formulas it must be remembered that N is the number of pieces manufactured in a **year**, not per run, except for the case of a single run of less than one year's duration. Roe's symbolization follows:

Let N = Number of pieces manufactured per year

Debit Factors:

A = Yearly percentage allowance for interest on investment. Either original cost or depreciated value of investment may be used.

B = Yearly percentage allowance for such fixed charges as insurance, taxes, etc.

C = Yearly percentage allowance for upkeep.

$1/H$ = Yearly percentage allowance for depreciation and obsolescence on the basis of uniform depreciation, where H is the number of years required for amortization of investment out of earnings.

I = Estimated cost of the equipment or fixture, i.e., cost installed and ready to run, including drafting and tool-room time, material and tool-room overhead, in dollars.

Y = Yearly cost of setups, in dollars. This value should include expense for taking down the apparatus and putting machine into normal condition.

Credit Factors:

S = Yearly total saving in direct cost of labor in dollars
$= Ns$

where s = Savings in unit labor cost.

T = Yearly total savings in labor overhead, in dollars
$= St$

where t = Percentage of overhead on the labor saved

V = Yearly gross operating profit, in excess of fixed charges, in dollars

To "break even," the yearly operating savings equal total fixed charges per year.

$$N = \frac{I\left(A + B + C + \dfrac{1}{H}\right) + Y}{s\,(1 + t)} \tag{1}$$

$$I = \frac{Ns(1 + t) - Y}{A + B + C + \dfrac{1}{H}} \qquad (2)$$

$$V = (Ns)(1 + t) - Y - I\left(A + B + C + \frac{1}{H}\right) \qquad (3)$$

$$H = \frac{I}{Ns(1 + t) - Y - I(A + B + C)} \qquad (4)$$

Items A, B, and C, once settled upon, need change little. If the plant has the practice of requiring new equipment to pay for itself in a definite time H, say 2 years, depreciation $1/H$ may be added to the other carrying charges, making a single percentage factor for the term $(A + B + C + 1/H)$ which can be used until management deems that changed conditions require modification.

Economy Analysis Applications. To illustrate the economy analysis of a fixture using Roe's formulas, eight examples are worked out below. These are adapted from his paper, assuming the following data:

s = Estimated unit saving in direct labor cost	= 3 cents
t = Percentage overhead on labor saved	= 50 percent
Y = Estimated cost of each setup	= $10
A = Interest rate	= 6 percent
B = Fixed charges rate	= 4 percent
C = Upkeep rate	= 10 percent
H = Equipment life, estimated	= 2 years
$1/H$	= 50 percent
$A + B + C + 1/H$	= 70 percent

1. If estimated cost, I, of a fixture is $400, how many pieces must be put through each year, in one run, or lot, per year, to return cost out of earnings in 2 years?

From formula (1),

$$N = \frac{\$400 \times 0.70 + \$10}{\$0.03 \times 1.5} = 6,450 \text{ pieces}$$

That is, if a $400 fixture is to pay for itself in 2 years and carry overhead, with a single run per year, 6,450 pieces must be put through each year.

2. If pieces are put through in 6 runs, or lots, per year, how many pieces must be made per year to return cost out of earnings in 2 years?

Using formula (1),

$$N = \frac{\$400 \times 0.70 + \$60}{\$0.03 \times 1.5} = 7,550 \text{ pieces}$$

Obviously more pieces must be run per year if the number of setups is increased. There is, of course, a breaking point where it pays to have multiple runs, even at a higher production cost per piece, in order to balance production costs and fixed charges on increased inventory.

3. If a fixture is to return its cost in a single run, how large must that run be?

Turning to formula (1), in this case H is unity as the fixture must pay for itself within the year.

$$A + B + C + 1/H = 6\% + 4\% + 10\% + 100\% = 120\%$$

Then

$$N = \frac{\$400 \times 1.20 + \$10}{\$0.03 \times 1.5} = 10,900 \text{ pieces}$$

This analysis shows that a smaller total output is required than when 6,450 pieces are made per year for each of 2 years, or 12,900 in all. This is due to one less setup and carrying overhead for only 1 year instead of 2. It will be noted that this example assumes the full year values for A, B, and C. If the run is short and it is felt this is too drastic, the values can be cut down in the proportion of the actual running time to one year. It is safer, and therefore good practice, to use yearly rates, as the time for complete turnover of money going into the fixture is hard to determine and certainly is longer than the run itself. Cost of short-lived equipment should be extinguished as soon as possible.

4. How much money can be invested in a fixture for a single run of 10,900 pieces at an estimated saving of 3 cents per piece?

From formula (2),

$$I = \frac{10.900 \times (\$0.03 \times 1.5) - \$10}{1.20} = \$400$$

5. How much money can be invested in a fixture that is to produce 7,550 pieces per year in 6 runs, if saving per piece is 3 cents, and if cost of fixture must be returned in 2 years?

From formula (2),

$$I = \frac{7,550 \times (\$0.03 \times 1.5) - \$60}{0.70} = \$400$$

6. In how long a time will a fixture costing $400 pay for itself under the conditions of example 5?

From formula (4),

$$H = \frac{\$400}{7,550 \times (\$0.03 \times 1.5) - \$60 - \$400 \times 0.20} = 2 \text{ years}$$

Example 5 shows that break-even is at a cost of $400.

7. If a fixture to meet the conditions of Example 6 can be made at a cost of $250 instead of $400, what would be the profit?

Using formula (3) for 7,550 pieces per year in 6 runs per year,

$$V = 7,550 \times (\$0.03 \times 1.5) - \$60 - \$250 \times 0.70 = \$105 \text{ per year}$$

For a single run of 10,900 pieces the profit would be,

$$V = 10,900 \times (\$0.03 \times 1.5) - \$10 - \$250 \times 1.20 = \$180.50$$

8. How much money can be put into a fixture for a single run of 2,000 pieces under the conditions of the preceding examples: (a) If fixture will save 3 cents per piece with a setup cost of $10? (b) If fixture will save 5 cents per piece with a setup cost of $15?

From formula (2),

For (a), $$I = \frac{2,000 \times (\$0.03 \times 1.5) - \$10}{1.20} = \$66.66$$

For (b), $$I = \frac{2,000 \times (\$0.05 \times 1.5) - \$15}{1.20} = \$112.50$$

The above examples show how economy formulas help in deciding tooling problems as they arise. They apply not only to jigs and fixtures but also to punches and dies, special tool equipment, and, in fuller forms, to machine tools. (See section on Machinery and Equipment Economics.)

It is recommended that in authorizing expenditures for all fixtures and tools above some established minimum cost, an **estimate** be made of

1. Cost of the fixture.
2. Output of the fixture.
3. Profit or saving from it.

When it is put into operation, the actual results should be checked with these estimates.

Such a procedure will give a check on quality of tool designing. If tool costs are overrunning estimates and output and savings are falling short, the facts will be shown. If tool work is good, the management will know it, and have means for measuring the profit obtained.

MACHINERY AND EQUIPMENT ECONOMICS

CONTENTS

PAGE

Definition and scope 1
Standard versus specially built equipment... 1

Depreciation and Return on Investment

Definition of depreciation 2
Methods of apportionment 2
  Straight line 2
  Sinking fund 3
  Sum of digits 3
  Declining balance 4
False premises in depreciation 5
Return on investment 5
  Accuracy of calculations 6
  Intangible factors 6

Original Equipment Analysis

Retooling for new manufacturing 6
Methods of economic analysis 7
  Differential yield method 8
    Differential yield method (f. 1) 8
  Capitalized cost method 9
    Capitalized cost method (f. 2) 9
  Minimum annual cost method 9
    Minimum annual cost method (f. 3) 9

Replacement Analysis

Machine replacement factors 10
Technical and cost elements 10
  Technical and cost factors in a machine
    replacement check (f. 4) 11
Influence of depreciation 13
Principles of sunk costs 13
Intangible factors 13
Methods of analysis 14
  Minimum annual cost method 14
    Minimum annual cost method for re-
    placement analysis (f. 5) 14

PAGE

MAPI replacement method 15
MAPI chart procedure 16
  Chart for deriving challenger's adverse
    minimum by the MAPI formula (f. 6) 17
  Re-equipment analysis and operational
    comparison (f. 7) 18
Comparison of operating characteristics ... 19
Guides in replacement analysis 20
  Simplified guide for re-equipment (based
    on the MAPI formula) (f. 8) 21

Replacement Policy and Organization

Management obligation 22
  Comparison of increased productivity and
    age of selected machine tools in the
    United States (f. 9) 22
Operation of replacement program 23
Classification of replacements 23
Assignment of responsibility 23
  Responsibilities of departments in selec-
    tion of equipment (f. 10) 24
Methods engineering department plan 25
  Equipment reports and records 25
  Coordination with production control 26
Tool and equipment engineering department
  plan 26
Committee plan of selecting equipment 27
  Standardization committee 27
  Equipment committee 27
  Advantages and disadvantages of commit-
    tee plan 27
Screening procedure plan 28
Replacement programs in action 28
Systematic replacement analysis 30
  Nomogram relating savings per year,
    equipment cost, and number of years to
    pay off an investment plus a given per-
    centage return on investment (f. 11) .. 29

MACHINERY AND EQUIPMENT ECONOMICS

CONTENTS

Page

Definition and Scope
Standard terms, length, both economic

Depreciation and Return on Investment

Original Equipment Analysis

Replacement Analysis

Replacement Policy and Organization

MACHINERY AND EQUIPMENT ECONOMICS

DEFINITION AND SCOPE. Among the factors that must be considered in the selection of machinery and equipment are: (1) suitability for product, (2) demand for product, (3) risk of obsolescence, (4) competitive advantage. (5) technological development, (6) quality of product, (7) interrelationship of available equipment, (8) quality and availability of labor, (9) economics of specific process, (10) cost and source of capital, (11) cost of operation, and (12) cost of possession. The economics of machinery and equipment is based on such factors. Obviously there is some degree of overlapping among them.

These factors can be grouped for specific purposes, however. For instance, the factors cited can be grouped as intangible or tangible. The first eight factors are considered **intangible** because they cannot be evaluated quantitatively. The last four items can be measured or estimated with reasonable accuracy and, therefore, are considered **tangible.** This economic area, then, can be defined as the study of the interrelation of all the tangible factors of capital investment in a commercial or industrial venture.

There are certain influences that must be understood in this area. For instance, depreciation methods should be considered; the influence of the return on investment should be recognized; and, finally, the organization and operation of an equipment program should be examined. These influences, then, in addition to the discussion of specialized techniques in machinery analyses are included in this section.

STANDARD VERSUS SPECIALLY BUILT EQUIPMENT. Volume manufacturing calls for building equipment around product, rather than manufacturing product around equipment. Involved in this concept are the many factors governing the choice between standard and special machines. Included among the factors which enter into the picture are: production rate, volume, man-hours, floor space, depreciation, and degree of adaptability of standard machines. Much thought and planning is required to determine when it is profitable to operate with **adapted standard machinery,** and when to utilize the advantages of **specially built machinery** particularly suited to the production schedule.

Engineering departments should be given a relatively free hand in determining the advisability and costs of special installations. When the product presents unusual situations, it is sound engineering practice to compare, at the outset, the advantages of both special and standard machines. From these findings, intelligent decisions can be made, resulting in fewer difficulties and greater profits.

The concept of adapting standard machines to volume production is outmoded. However, there is no side-stepping the fact that the standard machine costs less when, and if, its application is practical in the setup. Investigation shows, however, that a vast number of jobs could be more profitably handled with specially built equipment, were all cost factors taken into account. In many cases, the use of specialized machinery has resulted in lower initial investment and process costs than the use of standard machinery.

In industry, there is more tendency to adapt unsuited machinery than to utilize equipment that is outdated or worn out, although in the last decade the menace of machinery obsolescence was a major problem. World War II, to a considerable extent, eliminated a very large amount of overage and noncompetitive machinery. An aftermath of the war was, however, the attempted adaptation of carry-over machinery to peacetime uses.

Manufacturers realize that, in competitive market conditions, production, sales, and profit are dependent upon utilizing efficient production methods which will insure proper quality at low unit cost. Transition periods afford the best time to set the house in order, to institute modern techniques, and to install improved equipment.

Adaptation of standard equipment to jobs which do not vary too far from their intended function is sound practice, when not carried to extremes. In any case, the adaptation should accomplish results comparable to those possible with machines specially built for the volume work.

Parts-manufacturing now demands a standard of precision never before required or believed possible. Better tools and dies, and improved methods, as well as larger markets and diversity of products, have expanded the field for special machinery.

Depreciation and Return on Investment

DEFINITION OF DEPRECIATION. There are many controversial definitions offered for the word "depreciation." Likewise for each definition available there is a specific use, because as Grant (Principles of Engineering Economics) points out, the definitions of technical terms are derived from their uses. Therefore, for use in machinery selection and replacement studies, depreciation can be considered as the prepaid expense for the recovery of the capital investment. Grant and Norton (Depreciation) suggest that it be handled as is any **prepaid expense.** This definition does not incorporate any adjustment for changes in the price structure, and further assumes that the life of any piece of equipment can be established accurately. However, since most definitions of depreciation suffer from these same handicaps, this definition can stand.

METHODS OF APPORTIONMENT. The ways of apportioning depreciation most used today are:

1. Straight line.
2. Sinking fund.
3. Sum of digits.
4. Declining balance.

Although the straight-line method is used most widely, the other methods cited will be defined, because each has its advantage. Government policy and business conditions exert a strong influence on the use of the various types and, therefore, it is important that each method be understood.

Straight Line. Grant and Norton (Depreciation) define this method as "the uniform distribution of the cost less salvage value of an asset among the years of its service life." They point out that it is used almost universally except for the public utilities, because of its simplicity and historical experience which contributes to a better understanding of the method. The formula used for the annual allowance for depreciation is:

$$D = \frac{I - S}{N}$$

where D = annual depreciation allowance

I = in-place cost of equipment

S = estimated salvage value at the end of its service life

N = estimated years of service life

The straight-line method is evaluated in the Accountants' Handbook (Wixon and Kell, eds.) as follows: "As shown in numerous surveys, the straight-line method is in very wide use. It is not essentially unreasonable and its simplicity in conception and application commends it to the businessman and accountant. Most of the experience data with respect to the depreciation of particular assets have been collected in terms of straight-line rates. The principal objections to the use of the straight-line method are:

"1. Maintenance work tends to increase in the later years of use of a machine. These increased maintenance costs when added to the constant charge for depreciation result in a higher total cost during the very years when the efficiency of the machine tends to diminish.

"2. The method does not give effect to the extent to which an asset is used. During periods of intensive use depreciation is understated and during periods of less than normal use depreciation is overstated."

Sinking Fund. This method can be defined as the uniform annual charge that must be established so that its total plus its accumulated compound interest (predetermined) will equal the capital to be recovered at some fixed future time. In general, it is not used except by some public utilities. The predetermined interest to be assigned is not related in any way to the return on investment, but rather is an estimate of the market value of money. This method is such that as the **interest rate** approaches zero, the **depreciation rate** approaches a straight line. The disadvantage of this method is the fact that depreciation charges are very light in the early years and grow increasingly heavier. This method, therefore, is contrary to accepted practices in machinery and equipment depreciation.

The formula for its use is:

$$D = (I - S) E$$

where E = the sinking fund factor for any given interest rate for the estimated service life. The other factors are the same as used in the straight-line formula.

Sum of Digits. Meyers (Machinery, vol. 61) considers this depreciation factor as a fraction that varies over the service life of the apparatus. The numerator is the remaining service life and the denominator is the sum of all the digits from one to and including the service life. For instance, the depreciation fraction for the first year on a machine whose service life is 5 years would be 5/15 or 1/3. For the second year this fraction would be 4/15. The major disadvantage of this method is that the depreciation rate changes every year. However, the advantage of this method, as pointed out by Grant and Norton (Depreciation), is that it permits approximately 75 percent depreciation in half of the service life, and is therefore the most liberal of the methods permitted by the Internal Revenue Service at this time.

The formula for this method is:

$$D = \frac{2(N-A)(I-S)}{(N^2+N)}$$

where A is the age of the equipment, D the specific depreciation at that age, and the other factors are the same as previously used.

Declining Balance. This method uses a constant percentage factor that is applied to the depreciated value to determine the annual depreciation charge. This method, which is now permitted by the Internal Revenue Service, depreciates approximately 40 percent of the asset in the first quarter of its service life and two-thirds of the asset in the first half of its life. One of the premises on which this method is based, according to the Accountants' Handbook (Wixon and Kell, eds.), is that "repairs tend to increase as the machine approaches the end of its useful life. Accordingly, depreciation charges should be smaller as the repair charges increase so that the sum of the two charges would be equalized over the life of the asset." The Accountants' Handbook cautions that in considering this method "The tax advantages of the early years must be related to the disadvantages in later years when a relatively lower rate of depreciation will have to be employed."

The major disadvantage of this method is that the asset cannot be completely depreciated, i.e., a **salvage value** must be used. Therefore, the greatest advantage, as pointed out by Meyers (Machinery, vol. 61), can be gained by using this method only when the salvage value is relatively high or when the asset is to be disposed of prior to the end of its service life. The reason is obvious in the examination of the formulas:

$$R = 1 - \sqrt[N]{\frac{S}{I}} \tag{1}$$

where R = the constant for depreciation.

$$D = VR \tag{2}$$

where V = the current depreciated value, and D = the specific depreciation for that value.

$$X = \left(1 - \frac{2}{N}\right)^N \tag{3}$$

where X = ratio of the salvage value to the in-place cost.

The latter formula is derived from the first formula, and can be used to determine the advantage of the declining balance method. Since the 1954 Revenue Code does not permit a declining balance depreciation rate greater than twice the straight-line rate, this formula defines specifically what portion of the asset will not be depreciated at the end of the service life. For instance, 12½ percent of an asset whose life is 25 years will be undepreciated. An asset whose life is 5 years will be approximately 8 percent undepreciated. Therefore, in these cases, if the actual salvage value is greater than 12½ percent or 8 percent respectively, this depreciation method is profitable. However, the code permits the taxpayer to change his depreciation base from declining balance to straight line any time it is to his advantage. In this connection, there seems to be some disagreement among depreciation authorities as to the interpretation of this law (Grant and Norton [Depreciation] and Lasser [Taxes, vol. 32]); therefore, rulings by the

Revenue Service and even the courts may be necessary. Accordingly, this method must be used judiciously.

FALSE PREMISES IN DEPRECIATION. In the selection of any base for depreciation, the current tax laws should be consulted and thoroughly understood. Each of the depreciation methods has its advantages in specific situations and therefore should be selected knowingly. However, the fallacy of the **short pay-off** and **return on investment** theories should be recognized for what they are. The theory that a machinery purchase is justified only if it saves its cost in direct labor in some relatively short period of time, generally tends to work against the replacement of equipment that is costly to operate. The following example is reported in the Production Planbook (American Machinist, vol. 97):

A company near New York City recently purchased six multispindle automatics to do the work formerly done by 16 old machines. Careful analysis showed there was very little labor saving to be made; the new machines required the same number of operators and more frequent setups. But savings in floor space, materials handling, and in cam storage, plus the lesser advantages in direct and indirect labor costs, totalled $90,000 a year against an investment of about $130,000. Yet this replacement would never have been made on the basis of labor saving alone—had been, in fact, delayed for about ten years at what proved to be a loss of $600,000.

RETURN ON INVESTMENT. In every economic choice, the important element is the financial yield or return on investment. However, there is some disagreement among the authorities as to whether a specific charge for the use of capital should be included in the estimate. Rautenstrauch and Villers (The Economics of Industrial Management) are of the opinion that doing so will lead to "errors in judgment." They maintain that in any choice of investment, the investor "will estimate the probable returns on his investment . . . and its use in production as compared to the return he would get if he lent the money to another." They point out that "the fundamental purpose in cost accounting is to account for all the items of cost that are incurred." When borrowed money is used, then the interest payments are proper charges because they are costs of possessing the equipment. However, in other situations, that is not true. Rautenstrauch and Villers believe that including the interest in the annual cost estimate tends to underestimate the potential profit.

Grant (Principles of Engineering Economy) prefers to include interest as a cost because "(it) exists as a business fact; if you borrow money it is necessary to pay interest; if you have money you can get interest for it. Where a choice is to be made between alternatives which involve different money receipts and disbursements at different times, it is . . . essential to consider interest." Bullinger (Engineering Economic Analysis) points out that the return on investment is not included in the later cost accounting but is used strictly for estimating. Ayres (Engineering Economy) prefers to identify the interest charge as contentment return. He defines **contentment return** as ". . . that interest or rate of return value below which an alternative becomes unattractive and at or above which the alternative becomes attractive." In any case, he believes that the contentment return is properly included in the original analysis.

The authorities generally are in agreement, however, in the method of calculating interest costs. Balderston (Management of an Enterprise) points out that when straight-line depreciation is used in any cost estimate ". . . the interest rate should be applied against the average investment over the depreciation period, since the investment in equipment is obviously shrinking during the period of its use." He suggests use of this formula for the **average value** of the investment:

$$A = \frac{1}{2} V \left(\frac{N+1}{N} \right)$$

where A = average value

V = value of equipment when analysis is made

N = number of years over which the equipment is to be depreciated

This formula can be written for use in calculating the average value of interest by substituting the acceptable interest rate for V. The formula then becomes:

$$E = \frac{R(N+1)}{2N}$$

where E = average interest

R = interest rate required for investment

The use of average values for either investment or interest in investment comparisons is discouraged by some authorities. Bullinger (Engineering Economic Analysis) says that the average interest is used on the assumption that capital is borrowed. Then, as the debt is paid off, the interest is gradually reduced, and therefore the interest paid follows the pattern of average interest. Bullinger points out that the financing of a given investment requires a separate analysis and therefore the full interest rate should be used. Further, the use of the full interest rate rather than the average interest tends to act as a conservative influence in economy studies, which is the major objection that Grant expresses. He feels that it "overstates costs" for a given interest rate and therefore is not desirable.

Accuracy of Calculations. Obviously, there are many ways to calculate interest more precisely than through the use of the foregoing formula. The use of the **capital recovery factor** yields a precise value for depreciation and interest combined. However, since an economy study is contingent on the use of other figures which cannot be arrived at precisely, the need for calculating the interest accurately disappears. All estimates are as accurate as the available facts permit, but the results should not be construed to be more reliable than the original data. Obviously, then, those studies that attempt to evaluate small money differences are futile.

Intangible Factors. The intangible factors in any analysis are defined by Ayres (Engineering Economy) as those "matters that defy evaluation in dollars, for inclusion in the arithmetic of the problems of investment choice." He further cites typical factors that cannot be evaluated quantitatively such as safety, company policy, and the availability of funds. Even though these factors cannot be measured, they must be considered in any equipment analysis.

Original Equipment Analysis

RETOOLING FOR NEW MANUFACTURING. Equipping to reorganize the manufacture of an existing product or to begin the making of a new product is not uncommon. The problems are different from those of mere equipment replacement which concern the substituting of new and improved machines for those which are inadequate, inefficient, or obsolete.

Before the factory layout for a new installation can be completely developed the equipment must be selected—kind, capacity, number of units, type or make, size, drive, and other factors. For this purpose, it is necessary to:

1. Obtain drawings or sketches, bills of material and specifications of the product, and then list and analyze the materials and parts required.
2. Establish the volume and rate of production to be considered.
3. Obtain or develop operation sheets for the parts, subassemblies, and final assembly or assemblies.
4. List operations according to the type of equipment on which they will be performed. If machine tools are to be arranged by process, like operations may be grouped to be done on the same machine or group of machines. Where a product layout is planned, it will be necessary to install machines in the sequence in which the required operations must be performed, which often means a duplication of machines.
5. Obtain estimates on the unit times of operations, allowing for the use of jigs and fixtures, acceptable methods of processing, and the introduction of any semi-automatic or automatic machines. Calculate the daily capacities of the kinds and sizes of machines which it is assumed will be installed, and determine the number of machines of each kind required. Where only limited use of a machine is indicated, perhaps the work can be done on a machine already in the plant, or it may be subcontracted. In either case, routing and scheduling of work will be more complicated.
6. Select the types or makes of machines which appear to be most desirable for the installation. Some machines already available in the plant, and not operating at full capacity, may be used. Where it is necessary to buy new machines, duplicate the types and makes already in the plant, if feasible, to secure interchangeability and simplify maintenance and repair-parts problems. The best machines for the purpose, however, regardless of make, should be chosen. Experienced field engineers of manufacturers can give valuable information answering specific questions about their machines.
7. Develop layouts for the proposed installation (see section on Plant Layout and Location); if the equipment has to fit an existing building, the layouts will have to be adjusted to tie in with other machines and departments. Floor loads must be calculated for heavy machines and sometimes such machines may have to be taken out of their desired location and placed on the ground floor where separate foundations can be put in.
8. Investigate the possibility of expanded production, which may change the plans so as to require certain machines with greater capacity, or may call for a modified layout with excess area available for later occupancy.

METHODS OF ECONOMIC ANALYSIS. There are many techniques for determining the **most economical choice** of equipment. Each method has its advantages and each industry has its favorites. Each technique must be selected on the basis of the specific problem at hand. The three techniques that will be presented here are the basic techniques. They can be adapted to fit almost any study. These techniques are: differential yield, capitalized cost, and minimum annual cost. All of these techniques, of course, are based on the fact that an investment is definitely going to be made and the question is, which one is the most profitable.

Whatever technique is used, Grant (Principles of Engineering Economy) suggests a check list be followed to insure that no pertinent factors are omitted. He lists these factors to be checked:

Investment.
Expected economic life in years (or capital recovery period specified by management to be used for economy studies).

Estimated salvage value at end of life.
Annual cost of taxes.
Annual cost of insurance.
Annual cost of material.
Annual cost of direct labor.
Annual cost of indirect labor.
Annual cost of maintenance and repairs.
Annual cost of power.
Annual cost of supplies and lubricants.
Annual cost associated with space occupied by machines.
Other annual indirect costs.

Regardless of the technique used, the analyst should recognize that the type of depreciation method does not influence the comparative results, provided that the same method is used in all the alternatives.

Differential Yield Method. In this technique the selection among several alternate choices is based on the financial return on the increased investment. Therefore, the selection will start with the alternative that requires the least investment, and the increment increase in investment must be justified by an acceptable increment increase in financial return.

As an example, assume there are three machines available for a given process that have the same production rate, and service life of 10 years. Because of differences in tooling arrangements, operator skills, power requirements, etc. their initial cost and operating costs differ. The management will expect a financial return of 10 percent on investment. Obviously a reduction in operating cost is really a measure of operating profit. This analysis requires the tabulation of the alternatives in increasing order of the investment as shown in Fig. 1.

	Machine A	Machine B	Machine C
In-place cost (investment)...............	$16.000	$20,000	$26,000
Average investment	8,800	11,000	14,300
Annual operating cost (excluding return on investment)	6,900	6,450	6,200
Increment increase in average investment		$2,200	$3,300
Increment decrease in operating cost....		450	250
Differential yield (return on extra investment)		20%	8%

Fig. 1. Differential yield method.

Normally, machine A would be selected as requiring the minimum investment. However, with an increase of $4,000 investment, management stands to gain a 20 percent return which exceeds their requirement. Note that if machine B had been disqualified because of a low yield, machine C would have been selected because, for a $10,000 investment increase over machine A, the decrease of costs (increase of profits) would be $700, which yields 13 percent. This fact does not destroy the validity of the original analysis, because machine C compared to B did not qualify in its differential yield. In this analysis, production rate is not significant beyond the fact that each alternative meets the **minimum required production rate.** Any excess production would be evaluated as an intangible element.

Capitalized Cost Method. An analysis of alternatives by this method compares the sums of the capitalized annual cost and the in-place cost. The capitalized cost is calculated by dividing the annual cost by the minimum acceptable financial return. In the use of this technique care must be taken to avoid misinterpreting the figures used. The figures merely measure the magnitude of difference in alternatives and should not be construed as anything else.

For example, using the same figures as in the previous example, the annual cost figures are divided by the average interest, 5.5 percent, to get the capitalized cost values, as shown in Fig. 2.

	Machine A	Machine B	Machine C
In-place cost (investment)............	$ 16.000	$ 20,000	$ 26,000
Capitalized annual costs.............	125.000	117,000	113,000
Total capitalized costs..............	$141,000	$137,000	$139,000

Fig. 2. Capitalized cost method.

Machine B would be selected because its total capitalized cost is the minimum. In this analysis as in the preceding, if machine B were not acceptable, machine C would be selected as being the most economical choice.

The capitalized cost method is used most frequently in public projects rather than in industrial analyses. Bullinger (Engineering Economic Analysis) points out that capitalization implies perpetual replacement. Therefore its one application in industry would be in buildings and structures. One other caution in the use of this technique is emphasized by Grant (Principles of Engineering Economy) who points out that estimators frequently use the market value of money as the interest rate instead of the expected financial return on investment.

Minimum Annual Cost Method. This technique is based on the premise that the least annual cost for a given production rate is the most profitable. Therefore, the choice between alternatives is based strictly on the minimum annual operating cost which includes the expected return on investment.

The same machines cited can be compared to show how this technique is applied (see Fig. 3).

	Machine A	Machine B	Machine C
In-place cost (investment)	$16,000	$20,000	$26,000
Annual operating cost (excluding return on investment)	6,900	6,450	6,200
Required return on investment (average interest)	880	1,100	1,430
Total annual cost	$7,780	$ 7,550	$ 7,630

Fig. 3. Minimum annual cost method.

In this case machine B is again the first choice and C is the second choice. However, note that the money difference is very small. Therefore it would be well to examine the intangible factors more carefully, because machine C may have advantages that cannot be measured but are worth more than the difference in annual cost.

Replacement Analyses

MACHINE REPLACEMENT FACTORS. The manufacturing cost of a product is made up of labor, materials, and overhead. The overhead includes provision for the recovery of the investment in the capital goods and equipment which are used for processing. The two elements of cost—labor and recovery of investment in capital goods—can be considered together, since labor costs are related to productivity of equipment.

It is essential that the analytical techniques for determining methods used in manufacture be up to date. All machines and capital goods equipment are subject to wear and tear, which results from use. This **depreciation** is provided for in each year during the service life of the equipment. **Obsolescence** occurs when a machine is made valueless through the appearance on the market of a new and better machine or a new method. This may occur any time, even a few months after the installation of a new piece of equipment.

No live industry can keep pace with the advance of technology without continuous renewal and transformation of its productive facilities. Existing equipment must be kept on the defensive, compelled always to justify its tenure against the challenge of new and more modern machines. If any piece of existing equipment fails to meet this challenge, it must be displaced, regardless of its age or condition, and regardless of whether it is physically "worn out." A re-equipment policy that fails to give full recognition to obsolescence is bound to lead to poor manufacturing processes and inefficiency. It is not enough to examine one's equipment to see if it is still in usable condition or not. The criterion must be whether it is sufficiently modern to compete with the newest and most productive equipment of its kind now in use.

If new equipment and machines were available free, every company would naturally keep its productive facilities completely modern. However, equipment investment is too high to warrant the discarding of existing facilities every time there is an improvement. Therefore, the installed capacity of industry necessarily lags, on the average, far behind the best that is currently available. The problem is not to eliminate the lag but to hold it to the lowest limits that are economically justifiable. Thus it follows that the primary task of re-equipment policy is a continuous and timely transformation of installed facilities.

TECHNICAL AND COST ELEMENTS. Machines may be replaced according to a definite program or only when some problem in connection with manufacturing arises, such as the amount and quality of work being obtained from existing equipment, or the addition of a new product which necessitates a study of present machining processes and the adequacy and accuracy of the machines in the plant. In any case, it is necessary to develop some plan of investigation. In the main, this plan will be to set up, or adopt, a check list of points on which to evaluate the present and proposed replacement machines from the standpoint of technical suitability and cost-saving features. Also, methods of economic analysis described later are often used.

The points requiring attention fall into two classes, one covering the physical and **technical operating characteristics** of the machines, and the other taking into consideration the cost and **financial factors.** The equipment engineer will concern himself, first, with an investigation as to the technical operating characteristics and limitations of the existing machines, and second, with a survey to see what substitute equipment might be installed and what manufacturing advantages would probably result. He may find no reasons for making a change.

A. Technical Factors

1. Is the present equipment worn out?
2. Is it obsolete?
3. Is it inadequate from the standpoint of:
   a. Range or size of work
   b. Speed of operation
   c. Accuracy or degree of fineness of work
   d. Strength or rigidity for heavier operations
   e. Rate of output
   f. Insufficient power?
4. Has it been made unsuitable by other changes in equipment in the plant, as, for example, the setting up of a product line of manufacture, or the procuring of other machines working to closer tolerances?
5. Can its operations be more readily done if combined with other operations on an automatic machine?
6. Does it lack the controls, special attachments, and safety features of newer kinds of equipment?
7. Will a new machine do not only the present work but also other kinds of work which the present machine cannot handle?
8. Will a new machine replace hand operations or bench work?
9. Will a new machine have special advantages from the standpoint of:
   a. Ease of setup
   b. Convenience of operation
   c. Safety, such as guards, stop buttons, etc.
   d. Reliability in performance?

B. Cost Factors

1. Is the cost of keeping present equipment in repair too high?
2. Will the cost of changing or remodeling it for new work be too great?
3. Will spoiled work be reduced by the greater accuracy of new equipment?
4. Will greater output, or a faster rate of production, be obtained?
5. Will one new machine do the work of two or more existing machines of the same kind?
6. Can machine operatives be substituted for skilled craftsmen, thus lowering labor costs by the change?
7. If several machines are to be replaced, can one operative tend two or more of the new machines?
8. Will the maintenance cost of the new equipment be less than that of the old?
9. Will new equipment save manufacturing space?
10. Will it be conducive to better work and higher output by the worker?
11. Will it smooth out the production curve?
12. Will it provide the basis for better service to the customer?
13. Will the product for which the machine is to be procured continue to be made for a considerable time, and, if it should later be dropped, will the machine fit into other work?
14. How soon must the machine pay for itself to justify its purchase, especially if products may change?
15. How many years of effective service may be expected from the machine?
16. How will the costs of operating the new equipment be charged to the product?
17. Are funds available for the purchase of the equipment or can the investment be specially financed?

Fig. 4. Technical and cost factors in a machine replacement check.

Usually some technical advantages are discovered, especially since machine and equipment manufacturers are continually improving their existing products and bringing out improved models or new basic machinery. Frequently, then, these advantages can be measured in terms of a cost study. While sometimes a cost accountant might make this study, the points are so interconnected with operating factors that it is better for an equipment engineer to make the investigation. Sometimes desired operating advantages are obtained even though no immediate substantial cost saving can be demonstrated. The factors listed in Fig. 4 comprise those which would generally be considered in a check.

Final decisions on making a change rest with some executive who—unless the machine under consideration is of moderate cost and within the normal budget— may have to weigh the question of investment carefully against other needs of the department, requirements of other departments, and the financial situation of the company as a whole. It is not impossible for a condition to exist where the changes cannot be financed readily at the time even though there are assured savings to be obtained by installing new machines.

There are certain technical factors to be surveyed in evaluating substitute or new equipment which might be used or installed and the manufacturing advantages which it might produce, as follows:

1. The fundamentals of equipment **design and performance.**
    a. The influence of product design in terms of shape, size, and proportion.
    b. The effect of cutting tool design and application on product design.
    c. The influence of the type of motion and its control.
2. The fundamentals of equipment **construction and operation.**
    a. The function of various components.
    b. The parts or units that grasp and rotate work piece.
    c. The parts that hold and move the tool.
    d. The units that control the speed and direction of motion.
    e. The selection and application of standard tools.
    f. The working characteristics of the material.
    g. The influence of the type of operations to be performed.
3. The fundamentals of equipment **operating procedures.**
    a. The number of setups for standard operations.
    b. The number of setups requiring use of attachments for special operations.
    c. The methods of performing multiple operations in sequence.
4. The factors influencing **efficient machine production.**
    a. The effect of feed to speed ratios on production.
    b. The effect microstructures of materials being machined have on cutting procedure.
    c. The effect of cutting compounds on production, tool life, and finish.
    d. Power for optimum productivity.
5. The **condition** of equipment as to:
    a. Bearings.
    b. Gearing.
    c. Clutches.
    d. Attachments.
    e. Accessories.
    f. Lubrication system.
    g. Hydraulic system.
    h. Controls.
    i. Rigidity for high speed operations.
    j. Worn-out bearing surfaces.
    k. Number of times machine has been reconditioned.
    l. Nature of repairs rendered.
    m. Time involved in manipulating controls.

INFLUENCE OF DEPRECIATION. Depreciation rates, depreciation reserves, and book values have been important factors in replacement analyses. The depreciation rate is included in any calculations of the analyses. As in the original equipment analysis, the depreciation method used is not so important as the consistency of use. It is obvious that one cannot compare the operating cost of equipment, using the declining-balance method, with the cost of equipment, using the straight-line method.

The **depreciation reserves** indicate whether funds are available for replacement. However, the fact that internal financing is not available does not preclude the advantage of a replacement analysis. A replacement analysis may indicate that the use of borrowed capital is profitable. Therefore, in the analysis two factors are changed. One factor, depreciation, is charged only for that portion of the investment that represents the outright equity of the investor. The other factor, amortization of the loan, is included in the analysis as an annual cost. However, an analysis using borrowed funds tends to magnify the yield on the original investment and likewise magnifies the losses. For instance, if a certain investment can earn 15 percent and one-half of the investment is borrowed money at 5 percent interest, the yield to the speculator will be 25 percent on his equity. On the other hand, if the venture is not successful, the investor can lose his equity to the creditor. Therefore, analyses involving borrowed funds require close examination of the intangibles and the risk.

The **book value** has acted as one of the greatest obstacles to sound replacement analyses. Management frequently dictates the principle that any investment for replacement purposes must not only be profitable in its own right but must also recoup the unamortized value of its predecessor. The theory behind this thinking frequently involves the question of the disposition of the unamortized value. This problem is considered by engineers as one of sunk costs.

PRINCIPLES OF SUNK COSTS. In any replacement analysis, the cost factors to be considered are those that occur in the present and future. Any costs that have occurred in the past are merely of historical value and are not included in the analysis. Ayres (Engineering Economy) then defines sunk costs as "investments in plant, machinery, materials and labor which have been rendered unproductive and irretrievable by changes in conditions." The fact that the money has been spent does not influence any future action and, therefore, is not considered except for its direct influence in future actions. For this situation, Matchett (Iron Age, vol. 176) establishes this rule: "The only costs pertinent in an equipment study are those that would actually be changed by a decision to replace or not to replace." Newhouse of Allis-Chalmers reports (Journal of Engineering Education) on a machine that was developed in order to increase the production of war materiel. Its use displaced twenty lathes and operators, and consequently paid for itself in labor savings alone in three months. Newhouse comments that, "no manufacturer could afford not to build such a machine whether or not he scrapped twenty lathes."

INTANGIBLE FACTORS. In replacement analyses, the factors to be considered are obviously different from those in original equipment analyses. Some examples of factors that cannot be reduced to economic terms will be self-explanatory:

1. The **displacement of employees** by a new process would require analysis from a sociological and humanitarian standpoint.
2. The **introduction of a hazard** by a new process would require study.

These are two examples of intangible factors that cannot be reduced to money values and therefore cannot be included in any replacement analyses. However, their influence is far-reaching and cannot be ignored just because they cannot be measured in terms of economics.

METHODS OF ANALYSIS. The methods used in the replacement analyses are similar to those used in original equipment analyses. One difference in replacement analysis is the necessity for estimating the **remaining service life** and the **present value** of the existing equipment. These estimates must be objective, before any analysis on which they are based can be noted.

Another difference is that there is a readily available standard for comparison, namely, the machine under study. The question always is: "Shall that machine be replaced?" Any alternate replacement is compared against the equipment under study. However, the problem is complicated by (1) the muddled thinking regarding sunk costs, (2) by the practice of short pay-off, and (3) the improper use of replacement analysis techniques. Management must evaluate for itself the factors to be considered and the conditions under which a replacement will be made. Furthermore, management then must accept the success or failure of the replacement on the same terms.

The common types of replacement analyses are (1) minimum annual cost and (2) MAPI (Machinery and Allied Products Institute). The selection of the proper technique depends entirely on the given situation, and each is further discussed.

In the use of replacement analyses, the inclusion of factors that are estimates must be recognized as not producing precise results. Therefore, small differences in alternatives should not be accepted arbitrarily as yielding the best decision.

Minimum Annual Cost Method. This technique is favored in replacement analysis by most authorities, including Grant, Woods and DeGarmo, Bullinger, and Ayres. The basic theory behind this technique is in the selection of the alternative that gives the lowest sum of annual operating cost and annual capital cost.

For **example**, a 5-year-old lathe whose book value is $3,000 is being examined for replacement because the quality of its product is unsatisfactory. Its estimated remaining service life is 3 years, provided it undergoes a minor overhaul which will cost $600. The estimated market value of this lathe is $900. A replacement lathe can be purchased for $8,000 which will have an estimated service life of 12 years. It has some improvements that are valuable, but they must be evaluated as intangibles because the basic function is no different from the existing lathe. For this situation, salvage value of the new equipment is not considered

	Annual Costs (to the nearest dollar)	
	Old Lathe	New Lathe
In-place cost	$1,500	$8,000
Capital cost		
Depreciation	500	667
Average interest	120	520
Operating costs		
Annual maintenance (average over service life).....	50	75
Other (inefficiency, quality, material losses, etc.)....	500	100
Total annual costs	1,170	1,362

Fig. 5. Minimum annual cost method for replacement analysis.

and the yield on investment is expected to be 12 percent. Since the process is not changed, the direct labor cost is not considered as a part of the operating cost because it will be the same in both cases. The solution is shown in Fig. 5.

It appears that the new machine is not a satisfactory replacement because the old machine results in the lowest annual cost. However, the difference in operating costs is so small that the intangibles will bear close scrutiny because they may be worth more than the money difference noted. Furthermore, the decision on this particular choice does not preclude the possibility that there is another lathe available that will meet all the requirements. Therefore, all possibilities should be considered before a final decision is made.

Note that in calculating the annual capital cost for retaining the old lathe, the present market value was used instead of the book value. This calculation is preferred practice by the authorities noted in the discussion of sunk costs.

MAPI Replacement Method. This technique which was developed by George Terborgh (Dynamic Equipment Policy and MAPI Replacement Manual) is the newest technique in replacement analyses. In this research, Terborgh has made a substantial contribution to the field of replacement analysis. Although there is some controversy regarding his method, the primary objection appears to be in the understanding of its use. Norton, however, (American Machinist, Production Planbook, vol. 97) questions ". . . the validity of a method which in effect seems to force the proposed machine into a strait jacket based entirely on a guess as to the service life of the proposed machine."

Some of the advantages of the MAPI formula reported (Production Planbook) are:

It answers the question: "When should it be replaced?"
It provides a means for figuring the cost of not replacing.
It furnishes a good tool for budgeting equipment expenditures.
It makes full allowance for future deterioration and obsolescence to be expected on the new machine.
It is rooted in a firm basis of theory spelled out in complete detail.
The actual mechanics of the calculations are not difficult.
It can be applied to a single machine or a combination of replacement and expansion.

Terborgh makes two basic assumptions (Dynamic Equipment Policy) on which his whole analysis is based. They are:

1. Future potential replacements will always have the same **economic service life** (age at which total annual costs are the minimum) for the specific operation under study.

2. The operating cost of the present potential replacement will increase at a constant rate.

These two assumptions, of course, are applied to a specific piece of equipment on a specific operation.

Grant (Principles of Engineering Economy) points out that the Terborgh analysis implies certain forecasts which are frequently considered intangible. For instance, (1) a prediction is required as to the average yearly increase in operating cost; (2) a prediction is required stating that any replacement can be purchased for the same price at any given future time.

In the MAPI terminology, the machine or equipment which it is proposed to replace is known as the **defender,** while the machine or equipment which is being proposed as a replacement is known as the **challenger.** The **operating inferiority** of a piece of equipment is the amount by which it is operationally inferior to its best alternative. Instead of projecting the future operating costs of the present machines or equipment, the MAPI method projects their future operating inferiorities. The object of equipment replacement becomes simply a matter of securing the lowest obtainable capital cost and operating inferiority or imperfection. By reckoning this minimum combination in terms of the lowest annual averages of the two machines or pieces of equipment being compared, the best one will be that which yields the lowest average. The **adverse minimum** of the defender or challenger is the lowest sum of the time-adjusted average of capital cost and operating inferiority obtainable from a machine.

MAPI Chart Procedure. While the MAPI replacement analysis may be made by means of formulas, it is often done by a chart method which gives an approximate solution of the formulas. In order to determine whether the proposed replacement of a machine or other piece of equipment is advantageous, the adverse minimums of the defender and the challenger are found and compared. The challenger's adverse minimum is determined from the chart (Fig. 6). The defender's adverse minimum is the total of the next-year defender inferiority to the challenger, the prospective loss in defender salvage value during the next year, and one year's interest on the defender's present salvage value. The next-year inferiority of the defender is the total of the challenger's next-year income advantage and operating cost advantage.

Orensteen (Factory Management and Maintenance, vol. 115) indicates that estimates of the following factors are required in using the simplified MAPI replacement analysis:

1. For new equipment: primary service life in years; terminal salvage value at end of primary service life in percent of acquisition cost; interest rate in percent; and installed cost in dollars.
2. For equipment in use and considered for replacement: current salvage value in dollars; next-year salvage value; and next-year operating cost disadvantage of continuing the old machine in use.

He defines **primary service life** as the number of years it is expected the new equipment will be used in the task being considered (much shorter than total service life through all ownership and uses). **Terminal salvage value** usually involves an estimate of what can be expected upon trade-in or disposal at the end of primary service life. Choice of **interest rate** is based on the rate of return on investment that is necessary to justify the risks involved.

In order to discover the challenger's adverse minimum, two items of information are needed: the primary service life of the challenger and its terminal salvage value, as defined above. Using the chart (Fig. 6), the horizontal scale is followed out to the estimated primary service life. Then one reads up vertically to the curve of the estimated terminal salvage ratio, and horizontally across to the percentage reading. The interest rate is added to this percentage, and the total multiplied by the acquisition cost of the challenger. This gives the challenger's adverse minimum. The defender's adverse minimum is reached by adding the salvage value loss, consisting of the present salvage value minus the next-year salvage value, to the next-year operating inferiority and the interest on the present salvage value. If money must be spent to keep the old equipment in use, this expenditure is prorated over the expected life of the renewal, the interest on the renewal investment added, and the total included in the defender's adverse minimum. A comparison then shows whether the challenger or the defender has the lowest adverse minimum.

Orensteen exemplifies the use of the simplified MAPI method with a case in which the challenger costs $18,000, has an estimated primary service life of 13 years, a terminal salvage value of 26 percent, and on which the interest is 10 percent. The percent from the MAPI chart (Fig. 6) is 7.3 percent. Added to the

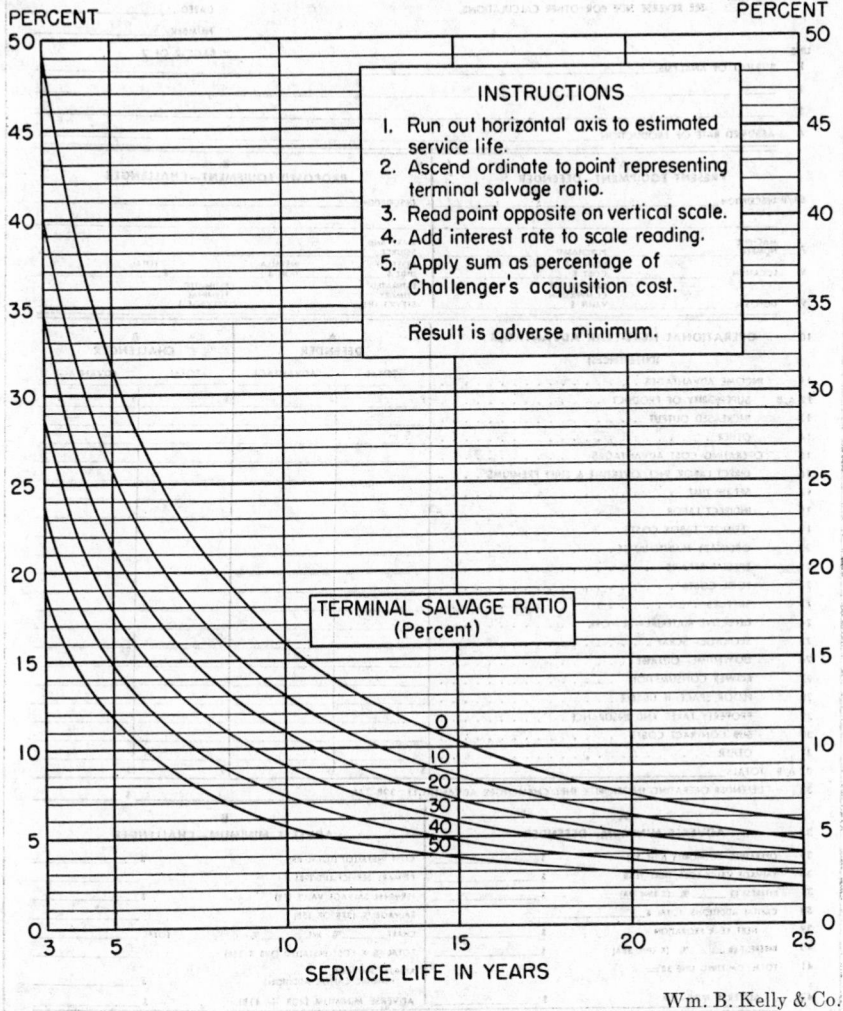

PERCENT

INSTRUCTIONS

1. Run out horizontal axis to estimated service life.
2. Ascend ordinate to point representing terminal salvage ratio.
3. Read point opposite on vertical scale.
4. Add interest rate to scale reading.
5. Apply sum as percentage of Challenger's acquisition cost.

Result is adverse minimum.

TERMINAL SALVAGE RATIO
(Percent)

SERVICE LIFE IN YEARS

Wm. B. Kelly & Co.

Fig. 6. Chart for deriving challenger's adverse minimum by the MAPI formula.

interest rate, this gives a total of 17.3 percent. The challenger's adverse minimum (17.3 percent × $18,000) is then $3,114. The defender is an 11-year-old machine with a current salvage value of $3,000. Its salvage value next year is estimated at $2,700. It will cost $2,800 more to operate the old machine next year than the new one. The interest is 10 percent. The addition of the salvage value loss ($300), the interest on the present salvage value ($300), and the operating cost advantage ($2,800) gives the defender's adverse minimum of $3,400. The chal-

RE-EQUIPMENT ANALYSIS AND OPERATIONAL COMPARISON

WORK SHEET SEE SUMMARIZING REPORT AND RECOMMENDATIONS (PAGE 1 OF 2).
SEE REVERSE SIDE FOR OTHER CALCULATIONS.

DATED _____
NUMBER _____
PAGE 2 OF 2

LINE		
1	SUBJECT OF ANALYSIS	
2		
3		
4	ASSUMED RATE OF PRODUCTION	

	A PRESENT EQUIPMENT—DEFENDER	B PROPOSED EQUIPMENT—CHALLENGER
6A/B DESCRIPTION		DESCRIPTION
7	MACHINE NUMBER _____ DATE PURCHASED _____	MAKE AND SOURCE
8	LOCATION _____ INSTALLED COST $ _____	COST OF UNIT $ _____ INSTALLA-TION $ _____ TOTAL
9	DISPOSAL _____ SALVAGE OR CONVERSION VALUE $ _____	ESTIMATED PRIMARY SERVICE LIFE _____ ESTIMATED TERMINAL SALVAGE, $

10 OPERATIONAL NEXT-YEAR ADVANTAGES (DIFFERENCES)	A DEFENDER		B CHALLENGER	
	TOTAL	ADVANTAGE	TOTAL	ADVANTAGE
11 INCOME ADVANTAGES				
12 A/B SUPERIORITY OF PRODUCT	$	$	$	$
13 INCREASED OUTPUT				
14 OTHER				
15 OPERATING COST ADVANTAGES				
16 DIRECT LABOR, INCL. OVERTIME & SHIFT PREMIUMS . . .				
17 SET-UP TIME				
18 INDIRECT LABOR				
19 "FRINGE" LABOR COSTS				
20 ORDINARY MAINTENANCE				
21 SPECIAL REPAIRS				
22 TOOL COSTS				
23 SUPPLIES				
24 DEFECTIVE MATERIAL—REWORK				
25 SPOILAGE—SCRAP				
26 DOWNTIME—OUTAGE				
27 POWER CONSUMPTION				
28 FLOOR SPACE, IF USABLE				
29 PROPERTY TAXES AND INSURANCE				
30 SUB CONTRACT COSTS				
31 OTHER				
32 A/B TOTALS	$	$	$	$
33 DEFENDER OPERATING INFERIORITY (NET CHALLENGER ADVANTAGE) 32B-32A				$

34 A ADVERSE MINIMUM—DEFENDER		B ADVERSE MINIMUM—CHALLENGER	
35 OPERATING INFERIORITY (LINE 33)	$	COST INSTALLED (TOTAL 8B)	$
36 SALVAGE VALUE LOSS, NEXT YEAR	$	PRIMARY SERVICE LIFE (9B)	
37 INTEREST @ ___ % (X LINE 9A)	$	TERMINAL SALVAGE VALUE (9B)	$
38 CAPITAL ADDITIONS, TOTAL $ ___		SALVAGE % (37B OF 35B)	
39 NEXT YEAR PRORATION	$	CHART ___ % INT. ___ %	TOTAL
40 INTEREST @ ___ % (X LINE 38A)	$	TOTAL % X COST INSTALLED (39B X 35B)	
41 TOTAL, OMITTING LINE 38 =		ANNUAL AVERAGE, PERIODIC CAPITAL ADDITIONS	$
42 ADVERSE MINIMUM	$	ADVERSE MINIMUM (40B + 41B)	$

43 NEXT YEAR GAIN FROM REPLACEMENT (42A MINUS 42B)	$

ANALYSIS BY _____ APPROVED _____

Wm. B. Kelly & Co.

Fig. 7. Re-equipment analysis and operational comparison.

lenger wins out with an adverse minimum of $3,114 and the new machine is indicated.

The Machinery and Allied Products Institute recommends the use of the form shown in Fig. 7 in following the MAPI method. The Institute points out that the advantage in the use of a form is that there is little chance that any important factor will be omitted. However, the use of any form should never be permitted to replace good judgment in any equipment analysis.

Comparison of Operating Characteristics. A number of factors are considered in comparing the operating characteristics of the challenger and the defender and thus arriving at the next-year operating inferiority of the defender, or the old equipment. Lines 11 to 30 of Fig. 7 list the operating features weighed in this way. There is some variation in the features considered in the replacement studies of different companies, but they all pertain to the income and operating cost characteristics of the machines under study.

A new machine may contribute such added income advantages as improvement in the product turned out, possibility of a wider variety of products, greater capacity, and more reliability with less risk of shutdowns. Adequate coverage of savings includes the saving of direct labor and saving through lower maintenance, decreased spoilage of materials, reduced overhead, lower power consumption, reduced toolroom costs, increased convenience and flexibility, etc. Too often these have been considered as "intangibles." However, well-considered estimates, even if conjectural, are almost certain to add up to a more rational result than the usual practice of lumping all the intangibles. The following is a check list suggesting the range and diversity of the factors that may enter into the **next-year operational comparison:**

1. Direct labor saving.
   a. Allowable speeds or feeds of the machines may differ.
   b. Location of controls and indicating devices may cause operating time to differ.
   c. Automatic features may provide multiple operation.
   d. Differences may exist in setup time.
   e. Handling time may be reduced through automatic loading and unloading; through hydraulic or magnetic holding devices; through built-in inspection features.
   f. There may be unequal requirements for the auxiliary labor used for such operations as inspection, stock supply, stock loading, moving and cleaning product.
   g. The effect of the machines on the labor requirements of operations which precede and follow them may vary.

   When computing direct labor saving, a number of items should be added to the operator's hourly rate. These include overtime premiums, production bonus premiums, annual bonus, profit sharing plans, etc. For the purpose of replacement studies, the hourly rate should be multiplied by an appropriate factor reflecting these additions.

2. Supervisory and administrative costs. A reduction in direct labor cost may reduce the necessary supervisory time. Overhead savings, however, should be the subject of specific item-by-item estimates, and, if not definitely known, should be assumed.

3. Maintenance costs.
   a. The present machine may have deteriorated to such a point that its maintenance cost is far above that of the proposed machine. This extra cost must be figured only on the basis of normal maintenance expectancy; rebuilding or renewals are handled as capital additions.

    b. The machines may differ in requirements for routine preventive maintenance, such as: time needed for lubrication, for changing hydraulic oil.

    c. The two machines may carry an equal risk of down time and interruption of production.

  4. Cost of supplies.

    a. The machines may require different cutting tools: hack saw blades vs. band saw blades, or high-speed steel cutters vs. carbides.

    b. They may call for different holding tools, fixtures, and attachments.

    c. They may provide varying replacement times on cutting tools because of rigidity, speeds available, and the method used.

    d. They may demand different qualities and quantities of lubricants and coolants.

  5. Miscellaneous cost items.

    a. Utilities requirements. Different amounts of electricity, gas, or compressed air may be required.

    b. Floor space.

    c. Taxes.

    d. Insurance. The annual cost of fire and casualty insurance should be included.

  6. Quality factors. Improvement of the quality of the product with the proposed machine may show up in two ways:

    a. Reduction in cost. The proposed machine may eliminate or reduce previous secondary operations, or may improve the adaptability of the part to subsequent operations; spoilage may be reduced; inspection may be reduced or eliminated.

    b. Improvement in salability of the product because of its finer quality or finish. Added income from this source should be credited to the proposed equipment.

  7. Capacity factor. Possible increase in capacity of operation would make possible an expansion of output and sales. Any resulting increase in income should be taken into account.

GUIDES IN REPLACEMENT ANALYSIS. Since it is already established that the only costs which can influence a replacement analysis are those costs that will change upon replacement, there are some simple rules suggested by Matchett (Iron Age, vol. 176) for use in the actual analysis.

  1. For equipment in use:

    a. Do consider:

      (1) Operating cost.

      (2) Repair and maintenance cost.

      (3) Down-time cost.

      (4) Salvage value.

      (5) Costs involved in producing fewer or inferior parts.

      (6) Rebuilding or reconditioning costs.

    b. Do not consider:

      (1) Original cost.

      (2) Money already spent on repair or maintenance.

      (3) Unrealistic book value.

  2. For new equipment:

    a. Do consider:

      (1) Initial cost.

      (2) Interest charge on money invested.

      (3) Salvage value at end of useful life.

      (4) Cost advantages of improved product.

      (5) Labor savings.

PRESENT EQUIPMENT OR METHOD	PROPOSED EQUIPMENT OR METHOD
Age: 16 and 18 years	One new automatic rise-and-fall
2 milling machines	milling machine

	PRESENT	PROPOSED
1. How Labor Costs Compare (dollars per year)		
Direct labor (wages, plus incentives and bonuses)	$ 16,200	$ 10,450
Indirect labor (supervision, inspection, helpers, etc.)		
Fringe benefits (vacations, pensions, insurance, profit sharing, etc.)	1,940	1,254
2. How Other Operating Costs Compare (dollars per year)		
Maintenance (only normal service costs)	930	81
Tooling, supplies		
Down time (include value of lost production time)		
Property Taxes and Insurance (if exact figures are not known, figure at 3% of value)	82	673
Others: Scrap	640	220

3. Cost of Using Present Equipment

Its salvage value today	$ 930		
Its estimated salvage value next year	830		
Difference in salvage values		100	
Interest (10%) on today's salvage value		93	
Expense next year for rebuilding, improvements, etc.	$ 2,000		
Next year's cost: (Divide total by additional years of life)		400	(5-year life)
Interest (10%) on total expense for improvements		200	

4. Cost of Using Proposed Equipment

Cost of equipment installed in your plant	$22,430	
First year's interest (10%) on installed cost		2,243
First year's cost of obsolescence (Figure this way):		
a. Estimate equipment life *on this job* Years:	15	
b. Estimate salvage value at end of that life	$ 1,500	
c. Figure salvage value as a percentage of cost installed	6.7%	
d. Use equipment life and salvage percentage to find Chart Value in chart (Fig. 6)	9.3%	
e. Multiply Chart Value times cost installed to get first year's cost of obsolescence		2,086

	PRESENT	PROPOSED
TOTAL COSTS FOR NEXT YEAR	$ 20,585	$ 17,007
GAIN OR LOSS NEXT YEAR FROM REPLACEMENT (difference in total costs)	$3,578 (gain)	

Fig. 8. Simplified guide for re-equipment (based on the MAPI formula).

(6) Primary service life.

(7) Any effect of a change in the firm's tax status.

b. Do not consider:

(1) Any savings not clearly recognizable.

(2) Arbitrary burden or overhead charges.

Matchett (Steel, vol. 136) points out that the final test in any replacement is, "Will this decision put the firm in a more profitable position?" and offers the simplified guide to such an approach shown in Fig. 8.

Replacement Policy and Organization

MANAGEMENT OBLIGATION. The replacement analysis technique is of limited value except when utilized as a tool of a replacement policy. Obviously, it has advantages under all conditions, but its use in connection with a **replacement program** brings order out of the chaos of replacement. The replacement analysis, as a part of an established policy, singles out which equipment to replace first; therefore, the capital investment is always yielding the maximum return.

However, a replacement policy and program must be initiated and supported by top management. Baker of National Gypsum Company points out (AMA Special Report No. 1) that the "establishment of sound administrative policies with regard to capital expenditures is the sole responsibility of top management."

Some of the **advantages to management** in a replacement policy are cited below:

1. The equipment is replaced on a continuous basis, rather than on an expensive emergency basis.
2. The objection to a single large capital expenditure is avoided by many smaller expenditures over a period of time.
3. The use of depreciation reserves continuously reduces the risk of using these reserves as working capital, or for other purposes.
4. The use of the depreciation reserves in capital expenditures yields a higher return than it does as cash or securities.

The Production Planbook (American Machinist, vol. 97) points out forcefully the obligation of management to establish a replacement policy. The inventory of equipment indicates that 55 percent of the nation's machine tools are more than 10 years old. Further, that 10-year period brought machine tools into use which average 40 percent more productivity. Therefore, by considering the direct

Type of Machine Tool	Percent of Increase in Productivity in 10 Years Studied	Percent of Specific Type Over 10 Years Old
Horizontal boring machines	105	63
Vertical boring machines (including vertical turret lathes)	250	64
Broaches	100	50
Saddle-type turret lathes	100	57
Automatic lathes	500	65
Planers	150	79

Fig. 9. Comparison of increased productivity and age of selected machine tools in the United States.

labor cost only, the loss from not replacing this equipment closely approaches one billion dollars per year. This estimate is very conservative because the direct labor was calculated at $1.25 per hour and the other tangible savings in replacement were not included.

Fig. 9 (adapted from 7th Annual American Machinist Inventory of Metalworking Equipment) indicates specific machines that require replacement. In effect this figure emphasizes the dollar savings possible from the productivity increase alone. This figure can be summed up simply by pointing out that replacement of half of the machine tools cited will net a reasonable profit.

The replacement of Terborgh's "mechanical cadavers," then, is the sole responsibility of management, and the replacement analysis will be of insignificant value unless it is a part of an organized replacement policy.

OPERATION OF REPLACEMENT PROGRAM. In evaluating the quality of a replacement program, these questions are suggested by the Machinery and Allied Products Institute (Steel, vol. 136):

1. What equipment can be replaced economically?
2. What does it cost not to make these replacements?
3. What program is available to keep management and production informed on replacement opportunities?

These questions lead to the operation of a replacement program which generally consists of these elements:

1. Classification of replacements by purpose.
2. Assignment of responsibility for replacement analysis.
3. Establishment of a continuing replacement program.

CLASSIFICATION OF REPLACEMENTS. The desirable starting point for any replacement program is in the classification of capital expenditures. Baker (AMA Special Report No. 1) reports that National Gypsum Company considers three categories of significance to them. These replacement expenditures are for continuity of operation, improvement in quality, and reduction in cost.

Sylvania Electric Products, Inc., however, considers its replacement policy as a part of its capital equipment program according to Guest (AMA Special Report No. 1). The company's needs are identified according to the following classifications:

1. New products.
2. Obsolescence.
3. Reduced cost.
4. Increased capacity.
5. Improved profit.
6. Safety.
7. Replacements.

The purpose of these classifications is to permit recognition of the equipment that requires immediate action.

ASSIGNMENT OF RESPONSIBILITY. In the purchase of equipment, whether for replacements or new installations, many departments might be concerned: manufacturing, production control, methods engineering, standardization, quality control, plant engineering, purchasing, the controller, treasurer, safety engineering, and sometimes product engineering. Their responsibilities, from the various standpoints, are listed in Fig. 10. Selection, therefore, should

Department	Nature of Responsibility in the Selection
Product Engineering	Suitability of new equipment for processing parts of the size, shape, etc., which may be designed, and materials which are to be worked on the equipment. Degree of accuracy obtainable on new machines.
Production Control	Suitability, adequacy, and capacity of equipment from standpoint of getting out production. Changes which may be necessary in methods, routings, times, scheduling, etc. Effect on workers—training, wage-rate changes, etc. Relation of new equipment to present equipment from the standpoint of alternate routings, carrying of overloads, etc.
Manufacturing	Adequacy and capacity of new equipment for the work. Relation to present equipment. Convenience, reliability, and safety of operation. Changes which may be necessary in methods. Required training of, and supervision over, workers.
Methods Engineering	Changes in processing which the equipment may introduce. Tooling required for new equipment—jigs, fixtures, dies, small tools, etc.
Standardization	Standardization of materials, parts, etc., which may be made possible by new equipment. Standardization of routine paper-work procedures, or changes in existing standards, which may be brought about. Standardization of processing methods which may be introduced.
Inspection and Quality Control	Nature, amount, and kind of inspection required on work from the new machines. New inspection equipment (electronic gages, etc.) which the installation may make possible. Degree of accuracy obtainable on the equipment.
Plant Engineering	Requirements as to moving in and installing the new equipment (foundations, floor loads, doorway and elevator sizes, etc.). Power requirements. Maintenance and repairs (location for convenience in repairing, stocks of repair parts necessary, etc.).
Purchasing	Securing authorization for the purchase, with proper approval signature. Securing proper specifications for the new equipment. Negotiation of an adequate and legal purchase contract, including any necessary guarantees of performance, provisions for acceptance tests, etc.
Controller	Keeping equipment purchases within the budget, or seeing that proper authorization is secured for buying any special items. Checking the effect of the installation on cost methods and cost data.
Treasurer	Amount of commitment and methods for meeting it. Time when payment must be made to obtain discount.

Fig. 10. Responsibilities of departments in selection of equipment.

undergo the scrutiny of each of these departments at some stage of the procedure so that all the factors relating to the acquisition and use of new or replacement machines receive proper consideration.

Where no special organization is set up to handle equipment problems, as in small plants, initiation of the study and recommendation usually come from the shops—the production control manager, or some executive or member of the firm supervising manufacturing operations. The problems are faced as they arise. There are seldom any planned methods for dealing with questions of equipment in the smaller organizations.

Among the methods used for placing the **responsibility of replacement policy** are:

1. Assignment to the methods engineering or tool engineering group.
2. Assignment to a standardization or equipment committee.
3. Use of a screening procedure.

However, Matchett (Iron Age, vol. 176) points out that even though a responsible group has been created for carrying out the replacement program, key personnel from all divisions must participate if the program is to be effective.

METHODS ENGINEERING DEPARTMENT PLAN. The most advanced and effective way to handle problems of equipment engineering is through either a methods engineering department or a tool engineering department. Either, or both if they exist concurrently, may report to the production department head or the factory manager, or they may form part of the general engineering organization and report to a chief engineer. The responsibility setup to adopt is that which will produce the best results in the particular company. Eventually, in most cases, recommendations must meet with the approval of the factory manager.

Most large and well-organized companies have a methods engineering department. Fewer companies have a tool engineering department, or anything similar. It is therefore more likely that the methods engineering department will be assigned the responsibility for equipment selection.

Under the methods engineering plan, which is often set up to report to the head of production, all factors concerning the effective selection and application of equipment receive proper attention in a department well organized to handle such duties. The work can be carried on as a full-time job of competent engineering specialists who will assume full responsibility for the results as far as their studies and recommendations are concerned. These men should be supplied with all texts and reference works on the technical and equipment phases of their industry, and all magazines dealing with the manufacturing work of the industry or with the equipment which it uses. They should also be encouraged and aided in keeping in touch with professional and technical associations in their field; thus, the company may be intelligently abreast of the times in developments affecting its equipment and operations.

Equipment Reports and Records. Details of the methods of operating an equipment department, studies made, records kept, forms used, recommendation procedures, and other activities vary with the plant and industry, the plans of the management, and the types of the problems faced. In any case, adequate reports should be made, used, indexed, and filed with a statement as to action taken, in order that studies will not be repeated and that information on the equipment is readily available to all departments which may need it. The equipment records can also be kept in this department, and in that case all reports on machine inspection, condition, maintenance, alteration, moving, etc., should likewise clear through it for extraction of necessary notations.

Coordination with Production Control. An important advantage of placing the inactive replacement function under the methods engineering department is that it is a part of the production division; it may therefore either conduct or be closely associated with all **time and motion study work**, and likewise with rate-setting on jobs. Hence, it is thoroughly familiar with equipment in action under operating conditions. It is also concerned with the **tooling of jobs**—including the design, making, and use of all jigs, fixtures, appliances, and small tools required and the extent to which such devices may be profitably utilized. Its surveys cover the methods of processing and the layout of equipment. It is familiar with machine capacities, ranges of work, routing, operations performed, and conditions surrounding the process. Its equipment studies and recommendations, therefore, will fit in with plant operation to the most effective degree, and it will be definitely interested in following up each machine replacement or installation to see that the equipment is used as intended and gives both the operating and cost-saving results planned.

Equipment salesmen should be interviewed in this department. Even at times when no equipment changes are contemplated, it is advisable to keep in touch with equipment manufacturers through their salesmen to get news of machine developments and the way equipment is being efficiently utilized in other plants. The purchasing department's relation to the buying of equipment is usually only commercial, since it is not often possible to have an expert machinery buyer in the purchasing department. At any rate, he would have to be in intimate touch with the whole plant at all times. Usually the technical questions regarding the purchase of equipment are left to the methods engineering department and the shops, and, if the purchase is within the budget and receives the approval of a financial officer, the order will be put through under the standard purchasing procedure.

TOOL AND EQUIPMENT ENGINEERING DEPARTMENT PLAN.

Where a tool and equipment engineering department handles equipment problems, it operates much like a methods engineering department in making studies and determining which machines should be bought. This department sometimes is set up separately, and would usually report to the works or factory manager. Rarely, it might operate under the chief design engineer. Where there is a general engineering department in the company, however, this general department may be broken down into several sections, one of which might be tool and equipment engineering.

The tool and equipment engineering section handles all questions relating to new or replacement equipment, alteration or scrapping of old equipment, determination of the remaining useful life of operating equipment by depreciation calculation and replacement analyses, and application of the equipment to serve regular or special manufacturing needs. Many large companies build a considerable part of their special manufacturing equipment, and in this case the equipment engineering section might not merely plan the installations but also design the equipment, supervise its manufacture, and direct its installation through the completion of the trial run.

It is customary to keep the design, manufacture, and application of dies, jigs, fixtures, and small tools separate from those of large equipment and machines. **Machine equipment** is a fundamental factor involving problems of heavy expenditures. A mistake results in considerable losses. If the wrong machine is selected, installed, run, and found to be a failure, it can be removed; but in normal times the second-hand price is far below original cost, and the freight, installation, and removal charges are not recoverable. Dies, jigs, fixtures, and **small tools,** however, adapt and fit machine tools to manufacturing operations. They are designed for the needs of particular jobs. Methods studies and time and motion studies are used, directly or indirectly, in planning for such equipment. Problems regarding the accessories are related to daily operation—in contrast to problems of major equipment with their large investments and long range aspects.

COMMITTEE PLAN OF SELECTING EQUIPMENT. When a company is of such size that the equipment problem is of major importance, executives must divide their time among many activities of an operating nature, and usually no one man can adequately investigate and decide on the selection of new machinery. At the same time, it may not be considered necessary to set up a department for the purpose. The advisability of integrating the equipment needs of the entire plant is of great enough importance to warrant group action. The solution, therefore, may be to adopt a committee plan of handling the problem, so that the requirements of all departments may be met with due consideration to the demands of the company as a whole, and to insure that all factors concerning any particular installation will be considered.

Standardization Committee. Larger and more extensively organized companies sometimes have a standardization committee, usually reporting to the factory manager, to which equipment matters may be referred. While such committees are concerned largely with standardization of materials and processes, these questions often involve equipment problems, and therefore these studies can be conveniently referred to the committee. **Equipment standardization** is highly desirable from the standpoint of uniformity of equipment, interchangeability of machines in layouts, reduction of stocks or machine repair parts, development of the most efficient use of equipment, taking and using of time studies, training of operators, efficiency of labor, routing of work, preparation of operation and route sheets, machine loading, and dispatching of work. However, as discussed above, many jobs can be more profitably handled with specially built equipment, and the decision to adopt standard machinery or to utilize specially built machinery must be reached by the committee in the light of all of the conditions.

These factors have a significant bearing on the kinds of materials used and the methods of processing, both of which obviously must be standardized as part of any plan of mass or straight-line production.

Equipment Committee. A still further development in larger companies is the establishment of an equipment committee, which concerns itself mainly with investigations of possible new or replacement machines for improved processing, and to which all suggestions of this nature are referred for study. This committee in most cases reports to the factory manager, and its recommendations are usually accepted unless financial reasons prevent their adoption.

Advantages and Disadvantages of Committee Plan. In all these committee plans, the membership represents most if not all departments concerned with the acquisition or use of the equipment. To this extent, the final selection meets the requirements and falls within the limitations of all divisions—operating and financial—having an interest in the problem. A frequent disadvantage, however, is that no members of the committee are specialists in equipment. Many of them are well informed about the technical and operating factors of their industry and plant, but from the standpoint of product rather than efficiency of the machinery and devices used for processing. The work of committees, moreover, is regarded as a side issue apart from regular operation of the plant. The committees meet only when necessary, the members finish their work as quickly as possible because of other obligations, and carry on any outside studies largely in a perfunctory and often inadequate and superficial manner.

SCREENING PROCEDURE PLAN. The first two methods for assignment of replacement responsibility explained above are not in as general use as the third method. The reason is that the screening procedure seems to be the natural occurrence in the development of a company. According to Iron Age (vol. 97), Monroe Calculating Machine Company, Inc., uses this method. Its **normal replacement pattern** is:

1. The foreman recommends a replacement when he feels it is justifiable.
2. The plant superintendent and foreman jointly decide on a specific replacement.
3. The plant manager's approval is the superintendent's authority to originate a purchase order.
4. The vice-president in charge of manufacturing then is the final authority unless the nature is such that the top management would be involved.

However, this procedure is not fixed at Monroe because replacement can be initiated by (1) the production department, (2) any of the engineering departments, (3) the methods or time study department, and (4) the vice-president in charge of manufacturing.

The screening method as used by the National Gypsum Company is reported by Baker (AMA Special Report No. 1) and follows this pattern:

1. The request for replacement is initiated by the plant.
2. It is then screened by the engineering department and production managers.
3. The request is then considered by top management.
4. It can then be approved by the president if the expenditure is less than $5,000 or is of an emergency nature.
5. Otherwise, it is referred to the board of directors for their approval.

Baker points out that the request for replacement is tested at each stage so that the influence of all factors—engineering, production, financial, and sales—can be presented to the board of directors for their consideration.

This method tends to be informal in operation and, therefore, is well adapted for use in smaller companies. The advantage of the method is that the personnel responsible for production respond to deficiencies in process equipment immediately. In fact, John Archer of the Harris Seybold Company (Steel, vol. 136) says, "Watch for equipment that foremen and production men route only secondary work to. If the equipment won't do first grade work, it's a good subject for replacement consideration." Therefore, this pattern is effective and ideal for the small organization.

REPLACEMENT PROGRAMS IN ACTION. The following case studies demonstrate that replacement analysis is not just a theory but a guide to the more efficient use of capital and greater profits.

The Harris Seybold Company manufactures equipment for the graphic arts. Archer and Blosser (Factory Management and Maintenance, vol. 112) report

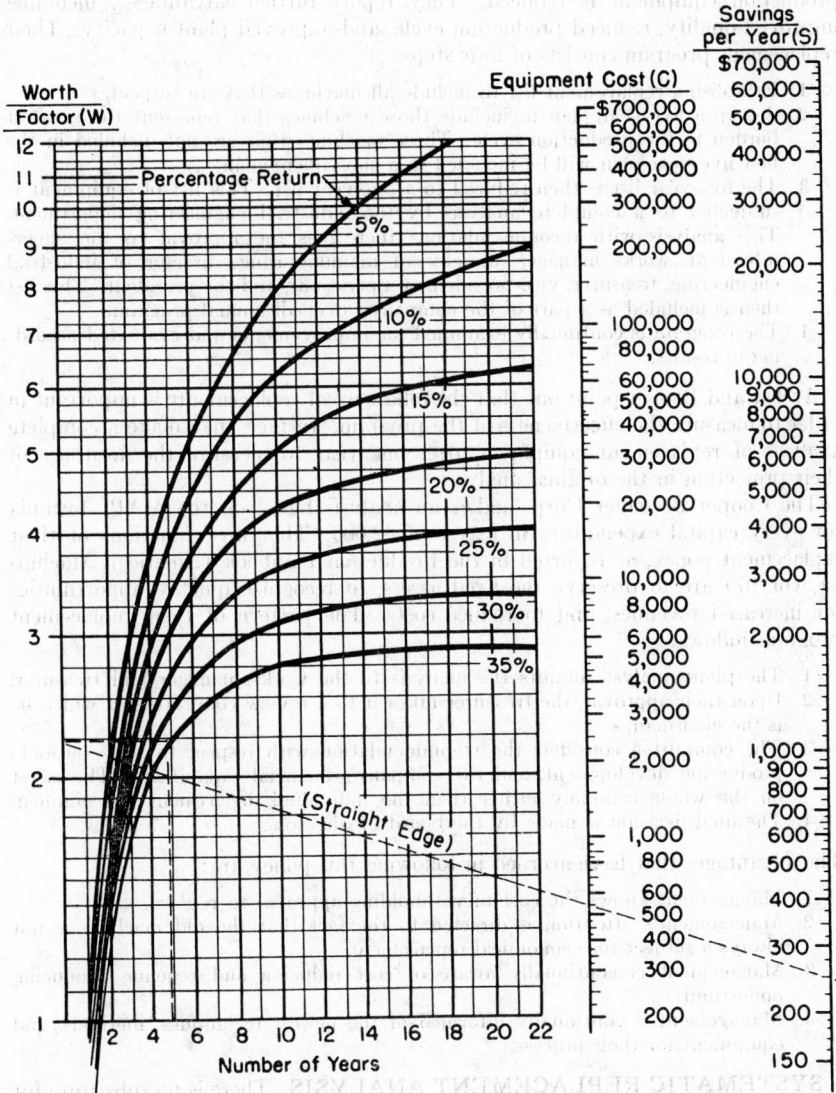

Fig. 11. Nomogram relating savings per year, equipment cost, and number of years to pay off an investment plus a given percentage return on investment.

that, as a result of their program, not only are they recording actual savings of $125,000 annually, but the savings are pyramiding as the average age of the production equipment is reduced. They report further advantages, including improved quality, reduced production cycle, and improved plant capacity. Their replacement program consists of four steps:

1. Establish a replacement list to include all machines that are suspect.
2. Set up a five-year plan to include those machines that represent the greatest burden to the production cycle. Those machines that are not included in the first five-year plan will be included in a subsequent plan.
3. The five-year list is then reduced to a one-year list. This list of equipment is subjected to a complete analysis by the industrial engineering department. This analysis with recommendations then goes for approval to the super-intendent, works manager, director of manufacturing, director of industrial engineering, treasurer, vice-president of operations, and the president. This list then is included as a part of the company's over-all annual program.
4. The program is continually examined for improvements and evaluated according to results.

Archer and Blosser point out that the follow-up of replacements is important in order to measure the effectiveness of the program. In fact, they make a complete analysis of replacement equipment after one year to measure the accuracy of their projection in the original analysis.

The Cooper-Bessemer Corp. makes an analysis based on the MAPI formula for every capital expenditure in excess of $2,000. The three functions of their replacement policy, as reported in the Production Planbook (American Machinist, vol. 97) are to preserve the fixed assets, to recognize quickly opportunities for increased revenues, and to reduce costs. The pattern of their replacement program follows:

1. The plant analyst submits the analysis to the works manager and treasurer.
2. Upon their approval, the treasurer takes it to a review committee of which he is the chairman.
3. The committee considers the recommendation with respect to sales outlook, production development, and the company's financial capabilities. The effect on the whole company rather than the individual department is examined.
4. The final decision is made by the board of directors.

The advantages that have accrued in following this policy are:

1. Management knows the cost of withholding approval to replace.
2. Management's attention is directed to the fact that the old machine is not always a subject for economical replacement.
3. Management is continually aware of cost reducing and revenue producing opportunities.
4. Management is continually informed of the newest techniques, methods, and equipment for their process.

SYSTEMATIC REPLACEMENT ANALYSIS. There is no substitute for systematic analysis before deciding on replacement policies and practices. Partially valid figures can often lead to erroneous conclusions. Every effort must be made to include all valid factors in the analyses.

Much work has been done to provide management with adequate tools to guide their decisions. In Fig. 11, Scheuble (Harvard Business Review, vol. 33) shows a nomogram which can assist in obtaining quick answers in cases where common considerations are accurate enough to guide decisions. (For methods of constructing nomograms, see the section on Charting and Graphic Methods.)

MATERIALS HANDLING

CONTENTS

The Materials Handling Function

	PAGE
Definition	1
Materials handling engineering	1
Basic handling principles	2
Principles of economical materials handling	2
Principles for planning and improving handling methods	3
Principles for planning and layout of facilities	3
Principles for selecting handling equipment	3

Engineering and Economic Factors

Materials handling engineering survey	3
Factors in a handling survey	4
Adequacy of equipment	5

Relationship to Plant Location and Layout

Choice of plant site	5
Building design	6
Floors	6
Structure	7
Multistory design	7
Warehousing and storage	7
Storage layout	8
Typical mail-order warehouse (f. 1)	9
The car-aisle storage principle (f. 2)	10
Types of vacant space (f. 3)	11
Typical storage arrangements (f. 4)	12
Management and control of materials	12

Organization of Materials Handling

Materials handling in the business structure	13
Nature of the products	13
Organization of responsibility	14
Equipment pools	15
Responsibility for training and maintenance	15
Multiplant operations	16

Interorganizational Relationships

Production control	16
In-process handling	17
Traffic and sales	17
Effects of sales	18
Effects of customer requirements	18
Purchasing and materials control	19

Selection of Materials Handling Equipment

Selection of systems and equipment	20
Selection for new plant systems	20

	PAGE
Integration into existing plant systems	20
Fundamental considerations	20
Integration of equipment	21
Equipment classification to assist selection	21
Production materials handling equipment	22
Reliability of equipment	22
Economics of materials handling	22
Computation of handling equipment costs	23
Cost formulas	23
Formulas for computing equipment economies (f. 5)	24
Cost accounting procedure	25
Comparative cost analysis form (f. 6)	26–27

Operation and Maintenance of Equipment

Qualification and training of personnel	27
Fork truck operator's true-false questions and answers (f. 7)	28
Safe handling methods	29
Manual handling techniques	29
Oxygen consumption (c.c. per min.) and relative efficiency for various loads and positions (f. 8)	30
Safety rules for lift trucks	30
Enforcement	30
Maintenance	31
Replacement policy	31

Measurement of Materials Handling Operations

Production control of materials handling	32
Estimating equipment and manpower requirements	32
Incentive basis	33
Cost reduction	34
Standard time data	35

Materials Handling Equipment

Methods of classifying equipment	35
Conveyors	36
Belt conveyors	37
Typical troughed belt conveyor with feeder and tripper and showing idler (f. 9)	37
Belt applications (f. 10)	38
Typical portable belt application (f. 11)	38
Elevating conveyors	39
Bucket elevators (f. 12)	39
Typical tray elevators (f. 13)	40
En masse conveyor-elevator (f. 14)	41
Chain and cable conveyors	42

CONTENTS (*Continued*)

PAGE

Floor-level slat conveyor installation
(f. 15) 42
Foundry car-type chain installation (f.
16) 43
Typical accessories for overhead chain
conveyors (f. 17) 44
Haulage conveyors 45
Pusher-bar elevator (f. 18) 46
Scraper flight conveyor (f. 19) 47
Roller and skate wheel conveyors 47
Typical roller conveyor junctions, spurs,
and switches (f. 20) 48
Typical power to gravity roller switch
(f. 21) 49
Spiral conveyors 50
Spiral conveyor characteristics (f. 22) .. 51
Pneumatic conveyors 50
Fuller solids pump (f. 23) 53
Air-conveyable materials (f. 24) 55
Section through an air-activated gravity
conveyor (f. 25) 56
Vibrating conveyors 56
Electromagnetic vibrating conveyor (f.
26) 57
Mechanical vibrating conveyor (f. 27) .. 57
Cranes, elevators, and hoists 58
Jib cranes 59
Typical jib cranes (f. 28) 59
Gantry cranes 59
Gantry cranes (f. 29) 59
Bridge cranes 60
Traveling overhead bridge cranes (f. 30) 60
Monorail cranes 60
Cableways 60
Loading and unloading towers 61
Mobile cranes 61
Crane operations 61
Elevators 61
Positioning, weighing, and control equipment 62
Transfer tables 62
Feeders 63
Industrial vehicles 63
Fork lift trucks 63
Typical gasoline fork lift truck dimen-
sions in inches (f. 31) 64
Outrigger fork lift truck (f. 32) 65
Traveloader (f. 33) 65
Platform trucks 65
Typical high and low lift platform
trucks (f. 34) 65
Tractors and trailers 66
Tractor-trailer train used with fork
trucks (f. 35) 66

Straddle carriers 67
Straddle carrier (f. 36) 67
Pedestrian-type trucks 67
Powered walkie skid and pallet trucks
(f. 37) 68
Hand trucks 68
Hand skid and pallet trucks (f. 38) 68
Motor vehicles 69
Apron space 69
Apron space required by tractor-trailer
for one maneuver into or out of posi-
tion (measured from outermost vehicle
or other obstruction) (f. 39) 70
Dock height and equipment 70
Typical adjustable truck docks (f. 40) .. 71
Railroad cars 71
Loading methods 71
Platform and siding clearances 72
Normal railroad loading-platform clear-
ances (f. 41) 72
Marine carriers 73
Aircraft 73
Containers and supports 73
Pallets and skids 73
Typical skids (f. 42) 74
Principal parts and commonly used con-
struction features of stringer and block
design pallets (f. 43) 75
Pallet loaders and unloaders 74
Containers 76
Basic types of unit-load containers for
shipping bulk products (f. 44) 76
Racks, shelving, and bins 77
Pallet racks for stacking of uneven loads
(f. 45) 77

Materials Handling Systems

Systems approach 78
Unit handling 78
Typical pallet loading patterns (f. 46) .. 80
Handling bulk materials 79
Basic handling systems 81
Industrial truck systems 81
Conveyor systems 81
Hand-stacked warehouse storage using a
conveyor system (f. 47) 82
Conveyor system serving an automatic
pallet-loader installation (f. 48) 83
Overhead systems 83
Mass production handling systems 84
Job-shop handling systems 85
Materials positioning 86

MATERIALS HANDLING

The Materials Handling Function

DEFINITION. In summing up the broad problem of materials handling, Harrington (Materials Handling Manual) says, "One of the most lucrative areas for cost reduction in the average manufacturing plant is the field of materials handling. Every time a piece of material, a component, or a finished product is handled, it costs money." It is a generally accepted principle that the movement and control of materials "is costly and adds no value" to the product (EITA Handbook of Material Handling). Reductions in the cost of materials handling often approach 100 percent. This high potential return emphasizes the desirability of materials handling cost-reduction programs.

A modification in materials handling philosophy accepts the principle that handling activities contribute **time and place utility** to the value of the product. This concept recognizes the **make-ready** function in manufacturing and the **accessibility** principles in distribution.

The following definitions explain the fundamental terms used in the materials handling field:

Materials handling is the art and science of the moving, packaging, and storing of substances in any form.

Handling equipment consists of all mechanisms or devices used in materials handling.

Bulk material is any loose, granular, or lumpy substance such as wheat, flour, coal, ore, cullet, or gravel.

Package material is any product or material in a confining device or package such as a carton, crate, barrel, sack, or box, including open pans or tubs with bulk materials in them.

An **item** is a product identifiable by its nature, package, label, name, stock number, or other difference from all other products or packages.

A **unit load** is any group of items (as defined above) which is a well-defined unit for handling by machines such as fork lift trucks, skid trucks, straddle trucks, cranes, etc.

A **pallet** is a platform on which unit loads are placed to permit stacking of material, and the movement of material and pallet as a single unit load (Pallets and Palletization, NWPMA).

Palletization is the modern use of pallets to facilitate handling, storage, and shipment of merchandise and goods (Pallets and Palletization).

A **unit** is any individual package, part, assembly, or piece of material handled as an identifiable item.

Air rights or **cube** is the volume capacity of a building in relation to storage or handling operations.

MATERIALS HANDLING ENGINEERING. The field of materials handling is a broad segment of industrial engineering. It includes problems related to plant layout, storage, mechanical equipment design, automation, management,

23·1

motion and time study, cost reduction, transportation and traffic, distribution, packaging, etc. The materials handling engineer must consider the relationship of each project to the business as a whole. His choice of handling methods can affect storage or shipping methods, process sequences, product design, packaging, production or inventory control procedures, and management policies concerning inventory, labor, maintenance, and distribution. Conversely, each of these related areas of business activity can serve as either a limitation or an incentive to a materials handling cost-reduction project.

In every business something is handled. In **process industries** (petroleum, for example), handling is often an integral part of manufacturing, while in **commerce** the handling of documents (insurance, for example) can be a staggering problem.

In **manufacturing**, each part must be handled to and from each machine, or through each manufacturing operation, and must be transported from department to department during the course of production. When a summation is made of the total weight which this expensive handling and rehandling involves, and the weight of manufacturing equipment which must be handled with the materials, some appreciation is gained of the vast importance of adopting the best means of materials handling. Actual case studies showed, for example, that in a pipe foundry, 67 tons of materials were handled for each ton of pipe turned out, and in a plant making agricultural implements, 180 tons of materials were moved for every ton of finished product. A fair average for all industry would probably be at least a 50 to 1 ratio.

In almost any industrial process, the greater part of the **indirect labor** employed is engaged in materials handling. Over any reasonable period, the percent of savings from eliminating indirect labor wherever possible will be relatively great compared with the percent of savings in other costs such as for raw materials, direct labor, fixed charges, and variable charges other than direct labor. Hand labor is the most costly kind of labor to employ in all places where the volume of work or the weights to be handled offer opportunities to use materials handling equipment.

Basic Handling Principles. The basic principles of materials handling that apply most widely are:

1. Needless handling costs money but cannot add value to the product.
2. Handling must be eliminated wherever possible, and, where it is necessary, the work should be done by mechanical means, not by hand labor.
3. Handling should be correlated with operations, inspections, storages, and other handling that comes before or afterward.
4. Handling routine must be made as nearly automatic as possible so that the costs for this work are a minimum.
5. All handling systems should be integrated.
6. Handling equipment, like production equipment, should be replaced wherever greater efficiency can be so obtained.

PRINCIPLES OF ECONOMICAL MATERIALS HANDLING. The General Electric Materials Handling Manual states that, "Modern materials handling methods, by increasing productivity, mean more goods for more people at less cost." Since the only direct effect of materials handling is additional cost of product, "the ultimate in **materials handling efficiency** is obtained by using the principle: The more pieces, pounds, or tons of materials that can be moved in a specific time, the lower will be the handling cost per piece, pound, or ton."

Principles for Planning and Improving Handling Methods.

1. Eliminate moves wherever possible—the best materials handling operation involves the least handling or none at all.
2. Straighten and shorten moves wherever possible.
3. Materials in transit should be moved as close to the next point of use as possible before being halted.
4. Pre-position for the next operation whenever possible before depositing the materials being handled.
5. Combine or eliminate handling operations whenever possible. Use basic motion study principles (see section on Motion and Methods Study).
6. Give consideration to moving the workers rather than the materials, since it is often more economical.

Principles for Planning and Layout of Facilities.

1. The cost of inter- or intra-departmental handling can often be reduced or eliminated by changes in machine layout, or by department relocation, or by mechanical handling devices between operations.
2. Congestion costs money. Allow sufficient aisle and storage space for smooth handling operations.
3. Doors, floors, ceilings, docks, and elevators are a part of the handling equipment of a plant. Plan them to meet the requirements, or design the handling system to overcome their limitations.
4. Build accounting, inventory, and production control procedures onto an efficient handling system. Do not let clerical requirements govern flow or materials handling methods.

Principles for Selecting Handling Equipment.

1. Use conveyor systems for fixed-path continuous or semicontinuous movement of bulk or small unit materials. Portable conveyors may be used for loading, unloading, or semifixed-path movements.
2. Use unit load systems for itinerant or variable path movements. Fork lift trucks are appropriate for short hauls; trailer trains, highway vehicles, etc., for long hauls.
3. Use specialized (pneumatic, hydraulic, etc.) handling systems whenever applicable.

Engineering and Economic Factors

MATERIALS HANDLING ENGINEERING SURVEY. The following outline (Flow Directory) suggests a guide to making a survey of materials handling operations:

Some one individual should be selected to head up the survey project. He can be an engineer who is already employed or he may be a consultant, from the outside, who specializes in surveys of this type. The surveying engineer will begin by plotting a course of action:

1. **Establish the scope.** The first and most important step is to determine the extent to which management is likely to respond to recommended changes.
2. **Determine physical limits.** The next step is to obtain or prepare a floor plan of the building. Fixed limits should be noted on this plan, as they will govern the recommendations.
3. **Anticipate production.** What and how much will be handled? Estimates of production for the next 1 to 3 years should be procured from management.
4. **Select predominating items.** It is not reasonable to expect any one type of handling machinery to suit all demands. In almost every industry, about

80 percent of the materials handling work is expended on about 10 percent of the items or materials. Flow systems should be designed to handle all the major materials with the best suited equipment.

5. **Estimate cost of present handling methods.** An operation sheet or chart should be filled in for the handling of each of the major items selected. This record will show the man-hours expended on each piece or each load unit.

6. **Apply the principles of efficient handling.** With the completed operation sheets and other data, the engineer has a concise picture of his project. Examination of these data will show where the greatest man-hour or dollar savings can be effected and where changes in layout will eliminate some of the handling elements.

7. **Prescribe the system.** The system suggested by the engineer should be tailored to the handling requirements of the proposed production, to the physical features of the plant, and to the investment limits prescribed by the management.

8. **Report on the survey.** The men who must authorize the program of alterations and equipment installation will need to know the amount of expenditures involved, the estimated savings that will result, and the time required to amortize the investment. Presentation of facts and reasons applied in formulating recommendations is best made in a formal report.

FACTORS IN A HANDLING SURVEY. Some detailed points to be covered in an engineering survey are suggested by Hagemann (Materials Handling Division, ASME) as follows:

1. **Factors of Plant and Operating Methods.**
   a. Are the present methods permanent or temporary?
   b. How long will the present buildings remain in service?
   c. Is the general plant layout the best for the requirements?
   d. Will the sequence of operations give the greatest efficiency?
   e. What processes and departments must be tied together?
   f. Are aisles and passageways ample for convenience in handling, speed, safety, and noninterference with production?
   g. Are the floors made of wear-resisting materials? Are they level and smooth? Will they withstand the loads?
   h. Is the building structure strong enough to hold overhead systems and are clearances sufficient for their installation?

2. **Factors of Materials To Be Handled.**
   a. Kind or nature of materials handled.
      (1) Bulk or units?
      (2) Large or small?
      (3) Heavy or light?
      (4) Shape?
      (5) Rough or fragile?
   b. Handled separately or in containers?
   c. Quantities handled.
   d. Continuous or intermittent flow?
   e. Under processing while moving?
   f. Distances over which transported.

3. **Factors Relating to the Handling Equipment.**
   a. Kind or kinds suitable for the job.
   b. Capacity of equipment.
   c. Hours of service.
   d. Size of equipment.
   e. Space required for operation. (For trucks, this factor covers aisles, passageways, elevator-platform sizes, etc.)
   f. Flexibility (according to loads, etc.).
   g. Adaptability to other service.

  h. Power requirements.
  i. Ease of operation.
  j. Speed of operation.
  k. Durability.
  l. Relationship to other handling equipment in use or contemplated.
  m. Auxiliary equipment required or economical to install (loading platforms, etc.).
4. **Dollars-and-Cents Factors.**
  a. Initial cost of equipment.
  b. Cost of installation; cost of rearrangement of and alterations to present equipment, buildings, etc.
  c. Cost of maintenance.
  d. Cost of power.
  e. Rate of depreciation.
  f. Rate of obsolescence.
  g. Probable salvage value.
  h. Cost of labor to operate.
  i. Cost of any necessary auxiliary equipment (such as charging equipment for truck batteries, etc.).
  j. Taxes and insurance.
  k. Interest on investment.
  l. License fees (for highway trucks).
  m. Rent of space (also garage rent for trucks).
  n. Cost of supervision.
  o. Savings that equipment will bring about in direct labor cost.
  p. Savings in labor burden (supervision, etc.).
  q. Increased productivity.
  r. Savings in fixed charges on equipment displaced.
  s. Unamortized value of equipment displaced.

ADEQUACY OF EQUIPMENT. The adequacy of materials handling equipment being used in a particular situation can be checked by evaluating several factors relating to its application. In the case of mobile equipment, cranes, vehicles, and other nonfixed apparatus, the work load can be measured by various work-sampling methods. Conveyor equipment can be evaluated on the basis of occupancy and work sampling. (See section on Work Measurement and Time Study.)

In each case the equipment **work load,** plus suitable **preventive maintenance allowance,** should be compared to the anticipated work load under study to determine the adequacy of existing facilities. This same procedure can be applied synthetically to determine equipment requirements for proposed new installations. Equipment capacities should be compared to unit load and package sizes to determine the size adequacy of existing equipment. Proposed new equipment should be capable of handling a reasonable overload if firm operating forecasts are not available to determine capacity requirements precisely.

Relationship to Plant Location and Layout

CHOICE OF PLANT SITE. Many factors must be considered when choosing a manufacturing plant site or the location for a distribution warehouse, department store, or other industrial or commercial facility. The value of real estate, the availability of labor, community acceptance, the relationship to market and resources, all must be considered. (See section on Plant Layout and Location.) However, in recent years greater recognition has been given to the materials handling aspects of site selection.

The **nature of the product** has a great deal of bearing on the nature of the materials handling problem. It is logical to assume that such heavy industries as steel, aluminum, glass, heavy chemicals, etc., would select locations which would give them a favorable relationship to their source of raw material. They would probably seek water or rail transportation facilities and perhaps, at some future date, cross-country conveyors. On the other hand, industries which depend upon a large volume, low unit value, and rapidly distributed product, would probably seek locations which would be easily accessible to their market. It is unlikely that a brewery, dairy, or newspaper plant would be located very far outside of a large population center.

These **transportation considerations** relate themselves to materials handling in the plant through the nature of unloading or shipping requirements. Plants which use only one type of transportation have far simpler handling problems than those which use several types of carriers. The variations between rail-car and truck docks and the differences in loading and unloading problems have a real bearing on the design of the facility; thus, traffic problems relate not only to the choice of the site, but to the economics of the plant itself.

Real estate values also have a double-barreled effect on site selection. In recent years, the recognition of handling cost reductions which result from single-story construction has tended to move industry into areas of lower real estate values. However, if other factors dictate the choice of high-value real estate and multistory construction, materials handling costs influence the selection of the site and the design of the building. The accessibility of in-town plants to truck and rail traffic is usually more complicated than in a rural installation. The internal handling is also complicated by the vertical travel element.

The selection of **distribution facilities,** such as warehouses and retail outlets, is usually closely related to their position in regard to the market, purchasing policies among the customers, and the inventory policy of the company involved. However, the increasing recognition of the high cost of handling materials in the distribution phases of industry has led to a more careful selection of distribution facility locations. The same problems which are described above for manufacturing plants apply equally well to the choice of sites for distribution facilities.

In cases where outdoor operations are necessary, climate enters into the materials handling picture. Many types of materials handling equipment are considerably less efficient in wet or icy environments.

BUILDING DESIGN. Building design has a considerable effect on the cost of materials handling. In recent years the functional planning of processes has gained momentum. This approach to **facility planning** involves the development of a maximum-efficiency layout with due consideration to equipment, process, and materials handling.

"The handling of materials is such an important operation that the handling system should be laid out at the time the building is first planned, so that the two can be fully integrated." (G.E. Materials Handling Manual.) It can be said that the building should be "wrapped around" the layout.

Floors. Floor load-bearing capacities must be studied. The capacities of floors will determine the advisability of utilizing industrial trucks, floor-supported conveyors, or powered hand trucks. "The breadth, smoothness, and hardness of floors must be considered. Rough, uneven, and soft floors result in additional tractive resistance for all rolling equipment. Where ramps must be used, the grade should be kept as low as possible, since even one percent of upgrade requires twenty pounds additional tractive effort per ton. Grades, similarly, consume more power when a conveyor must lift materials up an incline." (G.E. Materials Handling Manual.)

Wide aisles facilitate rapid handling with lift trucks. However, they cut into total storage and operating space. Actual **aisle space** is a compromise between space cost, cost of handling equipment and labor, and the velocity of the materials handling operation. Physical characteristics of the handling equipment also dictate minimum aisle requirements.

Structure. Low-hanging lighting fixtures, pipes, unit heaters, exposed beams, sprinkler systems, and other obstructions should be minimized when planning warehouse or plant structures. The most desirable arrangement is to install all such accessories above the bottom chord of the roof truss or the bottom flange of the roof beams. This practice results in a uniform unobstructed operating clearance throughout the plant.

Spacing of **supporting columns** may be a limiting factor on the type of handling equipment or the size of unit loads used in an individual installation. "Modern warehouse structures strive for uninterrupted spans of 50 to 60 feet." (Pallets and Palletization, NWPMA.) Wall-mounted jib cranes and craneway tracks should be considered when wall columns and pilasters are designed. Provision for this equipment in the original design can often save the expense of auxiliary structures in the future. Bay widths should be determined with due consideration of craneway operating areas.

The possibility of **overhead conveyor equipment,** monorails, and roof supported hoists should be considered in the design of roof trusses, ceilings, and columns. Anticipation of future conversion from warehousing to manufacturing occasionally dictates the over-design of warehouse structures to permit installation of overhead conveyor equipment. Many large multiple-plant companies follow this practice as an investment in flexibility.

Building details such as doors, loading docks ,elevators, fire walls, toilets, offices, and personnel entrances should be considered in the light of their effect on the handling function. Door sizes, elevator sizes and capacities, and fire wall and service facility locations all tend to be related to the efficiency of plant layout and materials flow and thus should be developed after the definition of the operating requirements.

Multistory Design. Although single-story plants are more in vogue, the use of a multistory plant is more economical in some instances. An outstanding example of this is Swift's packing plant in Chicago, where the raw materials (livestock) walk to the top and are delivered through the processing operation into the shipping department by gravity. Conversely, it would be almost impossible to build modern aircraft or heavy machine tools in a multistory operation because of the bulk and weight of the assembled product and some of its parts. All of these considerations must be examined in the development of a plant building design.

WAREHOUSING AND STORAGE. The U.S. Navy (NAVSANDA Publication No. 166) points out that:

Storage—the actual warehousing of supplies—is not a separate operation; it is a continuation of the receiving operation, a preparation for the shipping or issuing operation. Good storage warehouses supplies with a maximum of material protection, safety to handling personnel and assurance that the supplies may be shipped with the same efficiency, safety, and above all, speed.

The proper protection of materials in storage covers security from pilferage, adequate fire prevention, prevention from damage in handling, preservation, packaging, protection against water flows, protection from infestation of insects and rodents, protection from deterioration by reason of temperature and humidity, proper control of oldest stock out first, correct segregation of hazardous materials, etc.

Meserole (Consulting Engineer, vol. 5) states that "A warehouse is more than just a belly for merchandise." Many services besides static storage and protection must be performed with the goods. Any distributive warehouse must be large enough to:

1. Hold the inventory load, consisting of so many pounds, pieces, or dollars' worth of merchandise arrayed in some pattern and stacked to some height.
2. Provide access to every different item of goods for order-picking by having sufficient aisle length to show a given number of merchandise "fronts" from which goods are selected.

Wherever possible, materials should be stored and handled in **unit loads** by power equipment. When manual handling is necessary, it should be kept to a minimum through the use of conveyors and vehicular equipment.

Storage Layout. Storage layout is influenced by the characteristics of the materials to be stored and the space available to store them. The **commodity factor** includes several characteristics of the materials in storage:

1. **Activity.** Items that move frequently should be stored nearest to the shipping point or point of use to minimize the travel distance. Turnover is a good measure of activity.
2. **Quantity.** Storage depth and over-all space requirements are determined by item quantities in inventory and anticipated deliveries into storage. Accessibility requirements and item quantities determine aisle patterns.
3. **Item characteristics.** Physical characteristics of the products to be stored determine handling characteristics and storage methods. These considerations have direct bearing on storage layout. The most influential characteristics are size, weight, shape, perishability, inflammability, and pilferage vulnerability.

A **storage layout** that is particularly applicable to mail-order warehouses is shown in Fig. 1 (EITA Handbook of Material Handling). The warehouse shown in Fig. 2 (Industrial Series No. 18, U. S. Dept. of Commerce) utilizes the **car aisle** principle, which is another attempt to reduce the number of handlings. According to the EITA Handbook, "Each car aisle now represents a car lot of fast moving goods. The goods move from the receiving platform directly to the assembly line by the following steps:

1. Goods arrive by freight car on pallets or are loaded on pallets on arrival.
2. A fork truck picks up the pallets and sets them, three high, on the roller conveyor.
3. These three-pallet tiers move forward by gravity or by mechanical means to close up the row. This is continued until the row is full and the car lot is all in place.
4. The far ends of rows are on the last aisle of the assembly line, where the goods are picked into orders. The inaccessible top unit loads are lowered into the aisle by the fork trucks.

"The car aisle system eliminates the conventional task of moving goods to and from distant reserves and efficiently utilizes floor space and cubage of the warehouse."

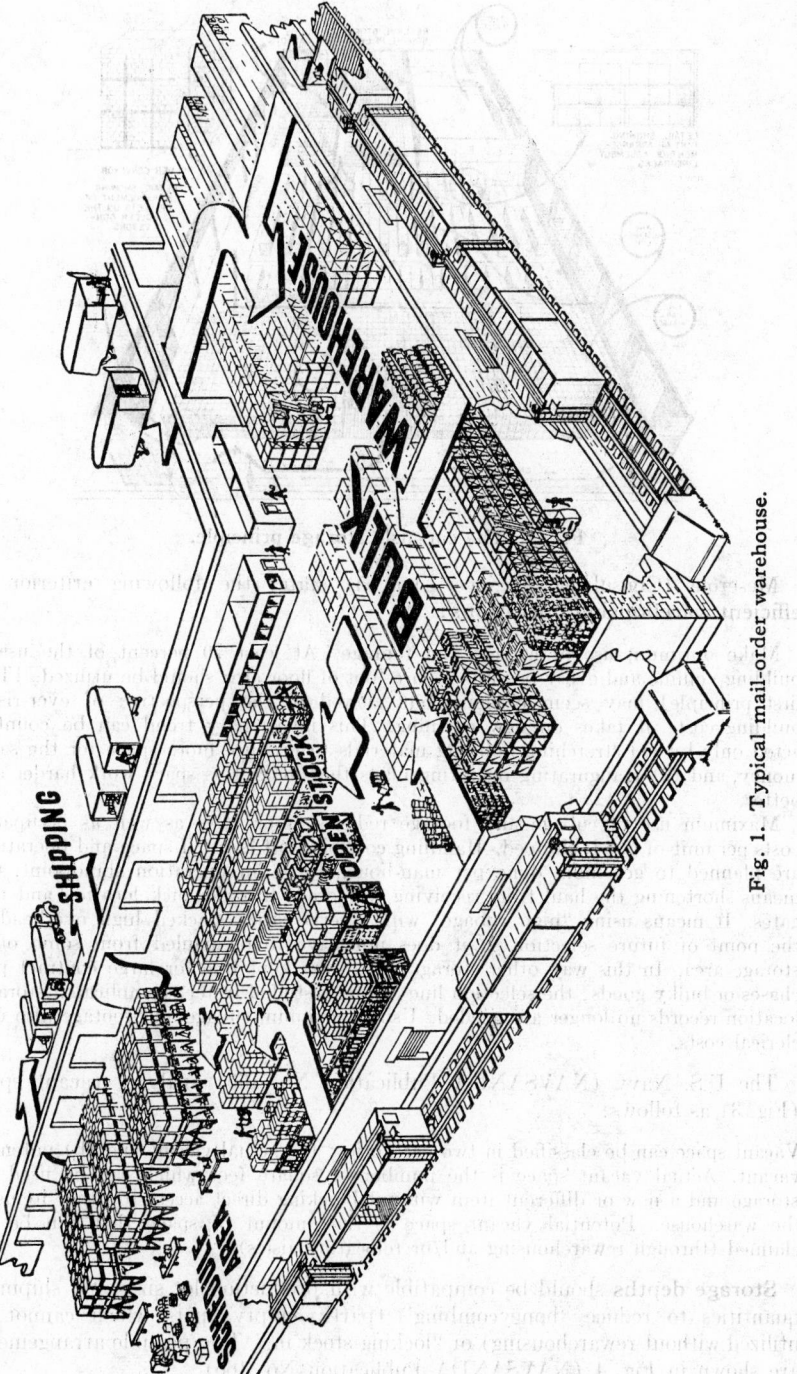

Fig. 1. Typical mail-order warehouse.

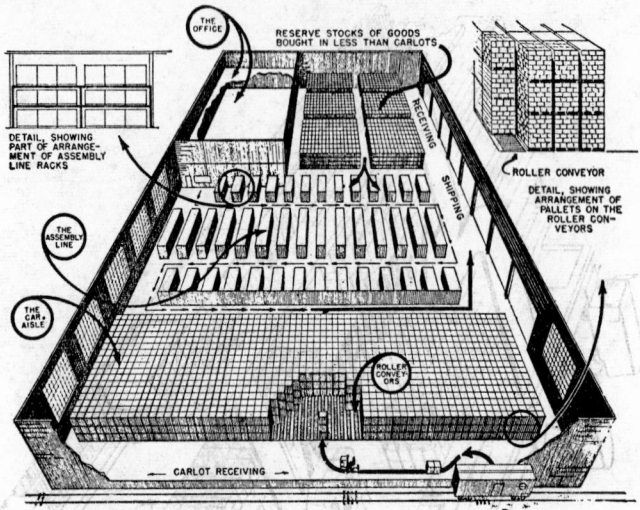

Fig. 2. The car-aisle storage principle.

Meserole (Consulting Engineer, vol. 5) states the following criterion of **efficient warehousing operations:**

Make optimum use of cubage and footage. At least **70** percent of the usable building volume and every possible square foot of floor area should be utilized. [This first principle] may seem obvious, but viewed in the perspective of ever-rising building costs, it takes on new meaning. This inflationary trend can be counteracted only by (1) stretching building materials to produce more space for the same money, and (2) inaugurating operating plans that make this space work harder and better.

Maximum use of cubage and footage reduces labor costs as well as occupancy costs per unit of goods shipped. Handling cost per unit is cut if space and operations are planned to get more done per man-hour. From an operation standpoint, this means shortening the haul from receiving to storage to order-pick location and tailgates. It means using "high cubage" with reserve stock stacked high overhead at the point of future selection so it does not have to be hauled from some other storage area. In this way other storage spaces are kept free for large contract purchases or bulky goods; the selection line can be restuffed faster; complicated storage-location records no longer are needed. Using maximum cubage and footage also cuts clerical costs.

The U.S. Navy (NAVSANDA Publication No. 166) analyzes vacant space (Fig. 3) as follows:

Vacant space can be classified in two categories: (a) actual vacant and (b) potential vacant. Actual vacant space is the number of square feet which can be used for storage and a new or different item without blocking direct access to other items in the warehouse. Potential vacant space is the amount of space that can be reclaimed (through rewarehousing and/or relocating aisles).

Storage depths should be compatible with production lot sizes and shipment quantities to reduce "honeycombing" (partly empty spots which cannot be utilized without rewarehousing) or "locking stock in." Two possible arrangements are shown in Fig. 4 (NAVSANDA Publication No. 166).

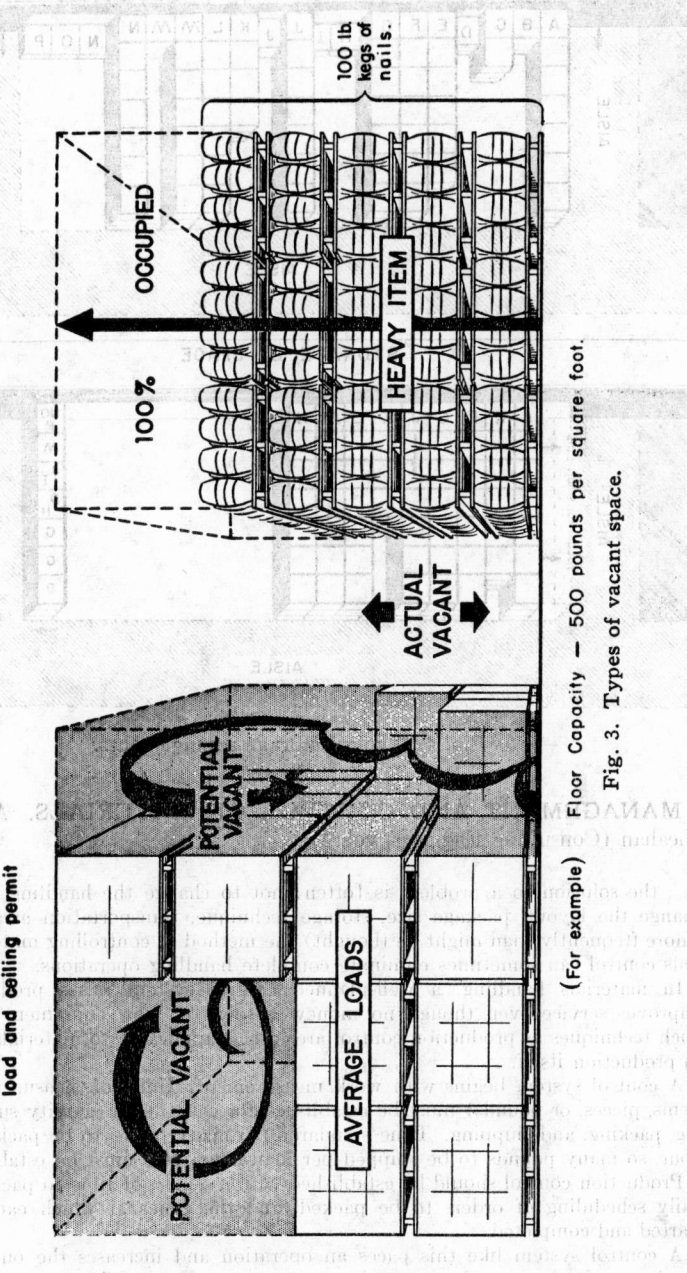

Floor Capacity — 500 pounds per square foot.

Fig. 3. Types of vacant space.

STORAGE BY SEQUENCE

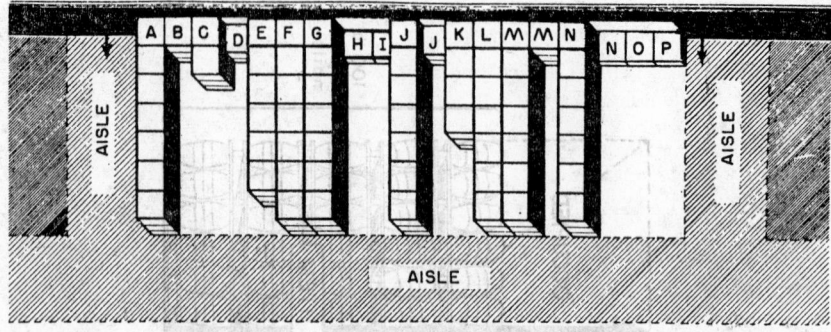

STORAGE BY SPACE

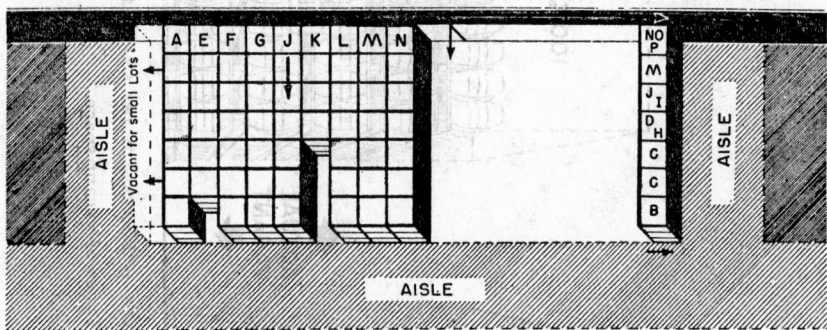

Fig. 4. Typical storage arrangements.

MANAGEMENT AND CONTROL OF MATERIALS. According to Sheahan (Consulting Engineer, vol. 4)

. . . the solution to a problem is [often] not to change the handling alone but to change the layout, package size, storage technique, transportation arrangement, or (more frequently than might be thought) the method of controlling materials. Materials control can sometimes eliminate complete handling operations.

In materials handling, a well-planned control system raises productivity and improves service even though no money is spent on new equipment or facilities. Such techniques as production control are just as applicable to materials handling as to production itself. . . .

A control system begins with work measurement. Units of measure (orders, line items, pieces, or pounds) must be established for each major activity such as receiving, packing, and shipping. Time standards (so many pieces to be packed per manhour, so many pounds to be shipped per man-hour) also must be established.

Production control should be established with a length of time to pack each order, daily scheduling of orders to be packed, and the times at which each should be started and completed.

A control system like this paces an operation and increases the output of each employee. It shortens the processing cycle and makes possible advance determination of the shipping date. . . .

A knowledge of the cost of handling materials (a good cost and standards system) is essential to good management of materials handling operations. The Material Handling Institute (MHI Booklet No. 2) points out that, "Costs of production usually vary directly in proportion to the indirect costs of manufacturing. A large proportion of the indirect costs of a business are associated with materials handling. Materials handling costs break down into the following three sections:

1. The plant location in regard to raw material supply and the marketing of products.
2. Receiving and storage; movement of materials between processing operations; warehousing and shipping of finished product.
3. The extent of handling of material by the operators at the machine or assembly bench."

One of the most apparent segments of this cost might be called warehousing or storage. This would include receiving storage, in process handling and storage, warehousing and shipping.

The Electric Industrial Truck Association lists three important **cost categories** in storage operations, which must be analyzed in order to minimize operating costs and get maximum efficiency (EITA Handbook of Material Handling). These are the storage cost factor, the handling cost factor, and the accounting cost factor. The EITA points out that "Reduction of accounting cost, like handling costs, depends on ease of operation. Action on the following considerations, which are practically standard in unit load systems, should reduce costs:

1. An efficiently designed locating system permits placing goods and filling orders with minimum supervision and checking expense.
2. Goods should be stored in units that simplify storage control and taking inventory.
3. Storage operation can be planned so that merchandise and products can be identified in large groups rather than individual units.
4. Markings should be applied simply and to large units whenever possible."

Organization of Materials Handling

MATERIALS HANDLING IN THE BUSINESS STRUCTURE. The relationship of materials handling to the over-all structure of a business organization is dependent upon the **prime mission** of the company. In recent years management recognition of materials handling as a separate function in both manufacturing and distribution organizations has become more common. However, the relative importance of the warehouse manager in a mail-order or department-store operation as compared to the warehouse manager of a manufacturing concern usually demonstrates the fact that many manufacturing organizations give only secondary consideration to materials handling functions.

NATURE OF THE PRODUCTS. The nature of the products involved in the business also affects the place of the materials handling function in the business structure. Manufacturers of **high-unit-value products** such as machine tools, automobiles, watches, jewelry, and aircraft usually relegate the materials handling function to a staff or secondary line executive in the organization. In the manufacture of **low-unit-value products**, such as lumber, ore, coal, food, containers, and packaging materials, the materials handling function is more often a senior line operation or a function of top management with the support of top-level staff aid. Where bulk items of low unit value are involved, the materials handling cost is often a major element of the total cost of manufacturing the product, whereas in the case of high-unit-value products, materials handling costs are often very minor in their relationship to the total delivered price. Fragility and perishability also increase the cost of materials handling as an element of the total product cost.

ORGANIZATION OF RESPONSIBILITY. The materials handling function can fit into the organization in several ways. It can be considered as a **staff function** involving only the engineering and analysis of materials handling problems. In such cases the materials handling engineer might report to the vice-president in charge of engineering, the chief engineer, the plant engineer, the chief industrial engineer, or the plant or works manager, as he might operate as a staff man in direct liaison at the vice-presidential level. The nature of the product and the attention which management chooses to give to the materials handling function will determine the relationship of the staff materials handling engineer.

Many companies have recognized the materials handling function as a line operation and have created a **separate operating department** responsible for the movement, storage, and control of materials, the design, maintenance, and installation of systems and equipment, and the training of personnel. In this case the head of the materials handling department draws on the firm's engineering staff or outside consultants for technical help as required. He usually reports to top management and integrates the handling program on a company-wide basis. Sheahan (Consulting Engineer, vol. 4) states that "there are four reasons for creating a 'Director of Physical Distribution' at the vice-presidential level, and for giving him full responsibility for materials handling, warehousing, layout, packing, traffic and control of materials:

1. He can command for these functions the top-management attention they deserve.
2. Management can afford to put into this position a high-priced man and gain the benefit of correspondingly high quality performance.
3. These functions become the responsibility of an expert.
4. Coordinated organizationally, these functions are coordinated operationally."

The third common structure for the materials handling organization is to make it a part of the operating management's job. In many plants, materials handling operations are integral with the management and supervisory functions of the **production executives.** In cases where no specific organizational definition is given to materials handling functions, these operating executives draw upon the firm's engineering staff or outside consultants for technical help as required and carry on the materials handling operations as a part of their regular management duties.

Materials handling functions can also be classified as to their organizational relationship to the operation as a whole regardless of how the planning and management responsibility for them is placed in the organization. Many manufacturing departments control materials handling operations which are an integral part of their process. Handling between machines and during processing is and by rights ought to be controlled by the manufacturing department, although the techniques may be developed and improved by the engineering staff. Likewise, service departments, such as storerooms, should control their own internal handling functions within the framework of good operating techniques.

EQUIPMENT POOLS. Many plants have developed the pool-type materials handling organization in order to get maximum utility from automotive equipment, fork trucks, railroad, and tractor-trailer equipment. This pool-type operation can be based upon a variety of management techniques such as:

1. **Routing and scheduling** of vehicular equipment on a predetermined network of trips to create an itinerant transportation system. In this type of operation the production or service departments schedule their work to coordinate with the pickup or delivery schedule of the itinerant vehicular equipment.
2. Assigned **work-center-type** use of vehicular equipment involves the assignment of fork trucks and other machines to specific operating departments. In this case, the daily operation of this equipment comes under the jurisdiction of the department head being serviced, while training, maintenance, technological, and welfare activities are supervised by the head of the transportation pool. This type of operation permits a better distribution of equipment, which can be shared between adjacent departments and aids in the development of uniform techniques and trained personnel.
3. The **dispatching-type vehicular system** can use call boxes, two-way radio, or depot dispatching as a control technique. In this case, vehicular equipment is assigned on a job basis and controlled on a plant-wide level.

Many large plants find that one pool technique is not uniformly applicable to their operation. It is not uncommon to find some departments operating on an assignment basis, with several scheduled tractor-trailer or truck routes running through the plant, and a central dispatching operation controlling a flexible equipment pool.

In conjunction with pool-type operations, the relative merits of departmental storage operations and central, in-process inventory control are often worth considering. Here again, the system must be dictated by the conditions in the field. If tight production control is desirable, a central inventory control and a central dispatching operation for vehicular equipment usually is beneficial and minimizes the possibility for loss of coordination in the production control system.

RESPONSIBILITY FOR TRAINING AND MAINTENANCE. The maintenance of materials handling equipment and the training of personnel in the operation and maintenance of this machinery is another function which can be found in various organizational relationships. The maintenance of fixed equipment, such as conveyors, feeders, hoppers, chutes, piping, and the sundry other plant facilities utilized for handling materials in process and storage, is usually a part of the **plant engineer's** responsibility. In most cases he trains the maintenance personnel, plans and operates any preventive maintenance programs, and initiates the establishment of maintenance cost control and analysis records. (See section on Plant Maintenance.) This latter function is sometimes shared by the staff **materials handling engineer.**

Automotive and mobile equipment, such as fork lift trucks, tractors, trailers, cranes, hand trucks, and handling tools, is sometimes maintained by the plant engineer, but more often, when a pool type operation exists, automotive equipment maintenance becomes a part of the responsibility of the **materials handling department.** (An example of this can be found in the maintenance of delivery truck fleets under the supervision of the **delivery department manager,** who in turn reports to the executive in charge of materials handling.) This arrangement is particularly common where the top-level materials handling executive mentioned above is in control of both the operating and planning of materials handling functions. The advantage of this relationship stems primarily from the enforcement of preventive maintenance techniques through driver training.

MULTIPLANT OPERATIONS. Multiplant operations bring to the materials handling function some additional problems not usually found in the intra-plant handling system. The selection of the carrier for moving materials between plants is directly related to the distance to be traversed, climatic conditions, and the nature of the product.

It can be seen that an inter-plant shipment on a nationwide basis bears very little resemblance to an intra-plant handling system. It is similar to and a part of the traffic operations of the organization involved. On the other hand, multiple-plant operations within the confines of a city or a company-owned compound can be handled on the same basis as intra-plant handling as long as traffic regulations and climatic conditions permit.

Intra-plant operations can often be **controlled by two-way radio.** In inter-plant operations within the range of medium-power radio systems, a radio-dispatched operation is usually highly desirable. The use of radio in long-range operations is not normally economical.

Inter-plant handling often involves the **storage of materials en route,** either in company warehouses or depots or, in some cases, in public warehouses. The same considerations with regard to inventory control, storage techniques, and the storage bank apply here as in the intra-plant operation.

In large corporations where **decentralized management** of the various plants has been accomplished and where inter-plant movement is a factor, it is advantageous to have a central coordination of these inter-plant movements. Each plant manager must of necessity be responsible for the proper scheduling of shipments and their safe handling. However, the "Director of Physical Distribution," suggested by Sheahan, is very suitable to an inter-plant handling function.

In situations where a "mother" plant operates as a center for several feeder plants whose schedules are controlled with relationship to the "mother" plant, this centralized management of materials handling and inventory control can have a very favorable effect upon the over-all scheduling and operation of the system. The decentralization of these functions can result in scheduling malfunctions and confusion if the teamwork between the various plant managers is not perfect.

Interorganizational Relationships

PRODUCTION CONTROL. Production and materials control functions set up production schedules, shipping schedules, and inventory controls over materials. Good communications with these functions are essential to good materials handling. The Material Handling Institute Booklet No. 3 states that

The materials handling activity must know production and shipping schedule plans far enough in advance to schedule its labor and equipment to provide the service required. If such changes in plans represent greater than normal fluctuations, changes in handling methods and facilities may be necessary, or desirable.

Changes in normal inventories of materials should be made known to the materials handling function to plan changes in storage. The materials handling activity should be advised of changes in scheduled receipt of materials. . . .

Materials handling must be in a position to advise production and materials control of its ability to provide service required by a given schedule. That requires knowledge and data of the potential capacity of all segments of the materials handling system. Also, it requires an understanding of the degree of flexibility in the system—changes that can be made and how long it takes to make the changes.

The materials handling function should make known the cost effect of various schedules. It should suggest changes that may effect economies in handling costs.

In-Process Handling. Production control requirements can cause materials handling operations in manufacturing sequences. Whenever two operations, producing parts at unequal speeds, follow one another, a **balancing operation** must take place. In some cases this can be accomplished by multiple machines in one or the other of these operations, but more often it is necessary to create a production bank or surge tank to level off the inequalities in production rates.

Production banks are also necessary for the storage of materials and semifinished parts which must be scheduled into production at a specific place in the sequence. The storage of standard parts for multiple products and the storage of semifinished parts which can be finished into various products can also be classified as a form of production bank.

The handling of materials from one production operation to another or through a production bank to a production or inspection operation with an unequal rate can be costly and unnecessary. Analysis of **scheduling** often indicates the cause of these apparently unnecessary handling operations. Changes in scheduling procedures, routing, or balancing techniques can often eliminate them. (See section on Production Planning and Control.)

Examples of product and facility characteristics which prohibit the simplification of in-process handling procedures can be found in the relationship between a foundry and a machine shop, between a parts fabrication facility and heavy assembly areas, or between steel mills and heavy forging shops. In each of these instances, the production rates and the characteristics of the sequential operations vary considerably and would undoubtedly dictate the use of production bank techniques under the most ideal circumstances.

Some materials handling systems have a favorable effect on minimizing the complexity of production scheduling and control methods by eliminating forms and paperwork procedures. Examples of this simplification might be found in a comparison between the conveyor and trucking systems. When a conveyor is used, no transfer papers are required when moving the product between operations because it travels over a fixed path at a uniform rate of speed and it is rather unlikely to go astray. In contrast, however, a trucking or trailer system is unrestricted in its routing, handles individual units, and can be misdirected. A telephone call between the dispatching and the receiving department can notify the receiver of the beginning of a conveyor run and the quantity to be expected without the necessity of paperwork. Such a procedure would be totally inadequate if a pallet load of material were to be misdirected in a trucking system where no transfer papers were available.

Conveyor storage of materials in process is often adequate as a production bank between operations of unequal rate. If sufficient material can be stored in transit on conveyors, the difference in the rate of the sequential operations can be cushioned by the material on the conveyor. However, the unit-load system, although far more flexible, usually requires the addition of a stacking and unstacking operation to permit its use in a production-bank situation.

TRAFFIC AND SALES. The nature of internal handling is often affected by packaging and shipping requirements. It is possible to **unitize** the product for mechanically loading carriers (Cartwright method). The point at which the unitizing operation occurs in the production sequence can have a major effect upon the handling methods before and after that point. For example, food-packing plants frequently use conveyor handling of individual packages and cartons throughout. They frequently use automatic case-packing machinery and conveyor transportation to an automatic pallet-loader. If the material is to be shipped on pallets or in unit loads, the automatic pallet-loader might prepare unit loads on expendable pallets or loading sheets, or make unit loads suitable for palletless handling. In contrast, if shipments are to be made in bulk with hand stacking in cars and trucks, the practice of running materials directly from production over conveyors into the carrier is frequently attempted. In this case the product is palletized for storage only.

Effects of Sales. The nature of the sale can frequently affect handling practices within the plant. Wholesale houses and mail-order organizations are good examples of shipping operations which require the picking of diverse orders from **multiple-item picking lines.** This type of operation usually results in a very nonstandard shipping practice which limits the use of unitization and in many cases makes conveyor handling difficult. Most of the organizations which have this type of shipping problem unitize their product at the end of the production line, store in bulk, and advance unit loads into the picking line for full-package picking. Many of these organizations also maintain an **open-stock picking line** from which single items can be shipped. In many cases, trailer-train type operations are used in these picking lines. Underfloor or overhead tow systems, electronically controlled tractors, or tractor-trailer equipment are usually applied to pick and deliver the orders to a packing area. In this type of operation, conveyor systems are often used to deliver the packed product to trucks or cars. The irregularity of the package size usually prohibits the use of unit loads, and platform congestion often limits the application of trailer-train systems for loading.

In addition to the nature of the package and the nature of the sale, **rate structures** often affect materials handling practices. Unitization of low-unit-value products for rail or truck shipment frequently results in a prohibitive dunnage and return charge if pallets are used. The shipment of unitized loads of unassembled products for assembly by the purchaser or distributor can, on the other hand, result in a favorable effect on freight rates and frequently overcomes the cost of dunnage and unitizing as well as returning a handling-cost saving.

The **destination** of the product must also be taken into consideration when determining handling methods in the warehouse and shipping department. Merchandise destined for overseas shipment must often be crated and can be handled by different methods from those used for the usual carton-packed domestic shipments. Recent introduction of crate handling attachments for fork lift trucks eliminates the need for skids and pallets in handling and storing many types of crates. Merchandise which is being shipped short distances in intra-city trucks can often be unit-loaded without suffering serious dunnage or pallet return costs. A distant destination would limit this procedure.

Effects of Customer Requirements. In recent years the trend toward customer dictation of delivery schedules and loading methods has increased. In many industries, notably the automobile industry, vendors deliver unitized or specially packed products to the customer's plant on a precisely predetermined schedule. The packaging and shipment of automotive windshield washers is a good example of this practice. This product is shipped in a large compartmented carton with paper legs to permit fork-lift-truck handling and with drop sides to permit production-line unpacking.

Some plants receive products directly into conveyor systems and some unitize the product in the carrier or at the tail gate. In most cases, a packaged product can be shipped either in bulk or unitized to a firm which unloads by conveyor, without making any inroads on their receiving cost. However, when a customer receives material into a unit system, it is often desirable to ship to him in unit loads which are suitable to his operations. Customers sometimes require this type of shipment. As a result, many suppliers are forced to use a multitude of unit-load sizes in their warehousing and shipping operations, in order to satisfy the customer's desire for unit unloading without double-handling the product from their own pallet to that of the customer.

The effect of **scheduled deliveries** on warehousing practices can be very important. The economical run for a product may amount to several months of customer demand. If the customer insists on vendor warehousing and scheduled delivery (and this seems to be a trend), suppliers are forced to build large bulk-storage warehousing facilities. The depths of storage and the height of stacking, as well as pallet size, handling method, and picking operations, will be directly affected by the usual shipment quantity and the frequency of shipments. For example, if a customer requires one carload a day of a particular item, the depth of storage would probably be multiples of carloads, whereas if he required one carload a month, considerable space loss or honeycombing would occur if the storage depth exceeded one carload lot. If the customer was in the habit of receiving a less-than-truckload shipment at regular or frequent intervals, an advance short-lot storage area or picking line would probably be an economical supplement to the bulk storage area.

PURCHASING AND MATERIALS CONTROL. A large segment of in-plant materials handling cost is attributable to the receipt and maintenance of raw material and supply inventories. Traditionally, these functions have been managed by a coalition of production control and purchasing activities.

In recent years a great deal of attention has been given to the **economics of inventory management.** These studies have emphasized the cost and financing of storing and handling raw materials and supplies.

As in the case of other storage operations, item quantities and item characteristics dictate the nature of the storage method. However, in this case, purchasing-price considerations have a major effect on item quantity, often to the exclusion of the effect of item quantity on handling cost. The scheduling activity determines the withdrawal quantities and thus directly affects the order characteristics of every material and supply warehouse.

If the raw material and supply problem is studied in its entirety, with full consideration of quantity-price relationships, inbound shipping charges, inventory dollar lock-up, quantity-storage characteristic relationships, and production-schedule–withdrawal relationships, it may be found that in many cases the **controlling cost factor** is the materials handling expense, and that this has been given the least attention.

The control of materials in storage is traditionally governed by accounting requirements. This relationship is critical in raw materials inventory. As a result, accounting procedures frequently influence handling practices in supply storage operations. It is desirable to apply the principle that materials cost more to handle than paper and to adjust the accounting procedures to suit the most economical materials handling activity.

Selection of Materials Handling Equipment

SELECTION OF SYSTEMS AND EQUIPMENT. The selection of equipment for manufacturing and handling in a new facility or plant modification program is directly related to the **flow of materials** through that facility. The **design of the product** is also a related factor, as pointed out by the Material Handling Institute (MHI Booklet No. 3):

Product design should, so far as compatible with other requirements, consider the relative handling and product protection required by alternative designs.

Handling, packaging, storing, and shipping of a product reveal desirable changes in product design from the viewpoint of handling and protecting it.

Merchandising methods affect the selection of materials handling equipment in that they determine the method and unit of shipment and the nature of the package in which the product is to be distributed. When equipment is selected for existing facilities, floor loading, door dimensions, column spacings, elevator capacities, ceiling heights, and many other installation characteristics must be considered before the particular type of equipment is chosen for the job. Quite frequently, several methods or types of machinery can perform the work required, and facility considerations are the final determining factor in choosing between these various methods.

SELECTION FOR NEW PLANT SYSTEMS. In a new plant it is usually possible to choose the right system for the operation and to develop smooth transition without mechanical interferences or organizational difficulties. If the manufacturing methods are developed on a maximum-efficiency basis, the **integrated materials handling system** will be a natural result. Under the most ideal conditions, the system will be developed before the building design.

INTEGRATION INTO EXISTING PLANT SYSTEMS. Selection of materials handling equipment in any existing application is usually tempered by the nature of the systems already in use in the plant. The linkages between existing facilities and new systems must be seriously considered when selecting new materials handling methods. For example, the cost of converting production from a conveyor system to a unit-load storage and shipping system might seriously affect the economics of the unit-load handling system. In this case an automatic pallet-loader or a central pallet-loading-station setup could probably be worked out to permit smooth transition from one handling method to the other. However, the location of the transition point might also have serious economic implications. If the unit loads were made too early, uneconomical long-haul trucking might result; if too late, high investment in conveyor systems and serious space loss might result. In some cases, the location of a transition point might also be affected by supervision problems and labor relations considerations.

Whenever materials handling methods changes are considered, the relationship of the change to adjacent functions and the over-all facilities must be taken into consideration.

FUNDAMENTAL CONSIDERATIONS. In the selection of the materials handling equipment itself, the fundamental considerations are:

1. Design of the equipment or system, its strength, rigidity, capacity, etc.
2. Method of installation for operating control, ease of adjustment and repair, and provisions for later changes or additions.

3. Methods of operation under normal or abnormal conditions, heavy overloads, or average capacity.
4. Application of power; electric, gasoline, steam, air, and hydraulic sources; flexibility through variable-speed transmission.
5. Application of automatic control devices, such as safety stops, microlevelers on elevators, limit switches on cranes, selectors on conveyors, and the use of electronic controls.
6. Maintenance and repair of equipment, involving its systematic inspection, cleaning, adjustment, lubrication, and repair.
7. Standardization of equipment, to obtain the advantages of duplicate apparatus for interchangeability of units, to have spares available, and to reduce repair parts inventory.

Integration of Equipment. The practice of selecting **materials handling systems** on a functional basis has become more common in recent years. Although from a maintenance viewpoint it would probably be desirable to standardize a plant on one type of materials handling operation such as fork lifts or conveyors, it is quite common to find several of or all the various materials handling equipment classifications in the same plant. The selection of the particular system is usually related to the function it performs in the sequence of operations. For example, in a beverage plant, the bulk materials might be received in tank cars or hopper cars and bulk handled into storage bins or tanks. The glassware or cans might be received in cartons and handled on pallets. The filled bottles would probably be conveyed from the packing line to an automatic pallet loader and lift truck handled into storage, from which they might be placed on a picking line which would permit selection of mixed loads for local delivery trucks. This integration of materials handling equipment into a balanced over-all system is a vital consideration in the selection of equipment. Most manufacturing plants use lift trucks, conveyors, freight elevators, and many other standard items of materials handling equipment. Many of them also have tow lines, cranes, overhead conveyors, slurry systems, and many other engineered handling devices which integrate the standard equipment into an over-all system tailored to the requirements of the facility. Other considerations for selection of equipment include availability of maintenance facilities and safety factors, treated later in this section.

EQUIPMENT CLASSIFICATION TO ASSIST SELECTION. The scope of materials handling engineering information is so broad and complex that most engineers and managers find classification systems helpful in organizing information sources when preparing study programs and plant improvement activities. Useful classification systems are discussed later in this section.

The following, from the G.E. Materials Handling Manual, illustrates the complexities of equipment selection: "Almost every kind of fixed-path handling can be done by the many kinds of conveyors available, among which are gravity, roller, wheel, spiral, live-roller, belt, chute, trolley, chain, floor-chain, apron, pusher-bar, vertical-tray, reciprocating pneumatic, automatic, and portable. Each has its particular advantage and application, and none should be chosen until the other types have been investigated. Conveyors may be selected:

1. Where unit loads are uniform.
2. Where the materials move, or can move, continuously.
3. When rate of movement, unit loads, and location of route are not likely to vary.
4. Where cross traffic can be bypassed by the conveyor."

Vertical movements can be taken care of by the usual freight elevators, dumbwaiters, continuous elevators (vertical conveyors), cranes, and hoists. For example (G. E. Materials Handling Manual), cranes are usually used for:

1. Intermittent movements within a fixed area.
2. Materials which are of variable size or weight.
3. Movement of materials regardless of cross traffic or uniformity of load.

Industrial trucks may be selected:

1. Where materials must be picked up and moved intermittently, over various routes.
2. Where materials are either of mixed size and weight or of uniform size.
3. Where distances are moderate.
4. Where cross traffic exists.
5. When there are suitable running surfaces and clearances.
6. Where the operation is principally handling.
7. Where unit loads are utilizable.

Production Materials Handling Equipment. For the purpose of analyzing production materials handling equipment, in itself a major segment of the materials handling field although not all-inclusive, the following general breakdown has been developed:

1. **Fixed-path** equipment. This includes conveyor equipment of all types, monorail and railroad systems, elevators, skip hoists, piping, duct systems, and various other permanently installed materials handling devices.
2. **Limited-area** equipment. This includes bridge and jib cranes, cable and boom systems, gantry cranes, and various other materials handling devices which are flexible within a permanently restricted area.
3. **Mobile** equipment. Industrial trucks, including fork lift trucks, skid trucks, tractors and trailers, pedestrian power trucks, and other industrial vehicles for indoor use are usually grouped here, as are such yard vehicles as cranes, straddle carriers, side loaders, power shovels, front-end loaders, bulldozers, dump trucks, highway trucks, and other outdoor vehicles.
4. Materials handling **tools** and **storage handling** equipment. This includes hand trucks, hand jacks, casters, dollies, rollers, chain hoists, power pullers, dock plates, pallets, skids, scales, racks, and shelves and bins.

RELIABILITY OF EQUIPMENT. Within each classification or type of materials handling equipment, there are varying degrees of ruggedness of design. A conveyor with a given capacity might be completely adequate in a clean sheltered installation, but might fail if used outdoors or in dusty atmospheres with the same or less load requirement. Likewise, industrial automotive equipment with gasoline power plants might be the best selection in some installations, whereas under other operating conditions, battery electric power might be mandatory.

The reliability of materials handling equipment has a direct bearing on production costs. Selection of equipment with suitable design characteristics to meet the severity of service anticipated in a particular installation is as important as selection of the right type of equipment in the first place. However, reliability cannot be 100-percent designed into the machinery. Even the most rugged installation requires preventive or at least remedial maintenance.

ECONOMICS OF MATERIALS HANDLING. Hall comments (AMHS Address, 1955) that

In the process of converting raw material into useful and marketable goods and placing them in the hands of the ultimate consumer, value has been added by creating form utility, place utility, time utility, and ownership utility. Gathering of the raw material, movement through processing operations and distribution to the consumer create place and time utility by having the raw, in-process, and finished materials at the place where they are needed and at the time they are needed. Processing during manufacture creates form utility; sale to the ultimate consumer creates ownership utility. The economists' conception of materials handling, therefore, is the addition of **place** and **time utility.**

While this statement expresses a much broader concept of the function of materials handling, the older concept that it adds to the cost but not to the value is also valid.

It has been found that the cost of production usually varies in direct proportion to the indirect costs of manufacturing, a large portion of which is the cost of materials handling. Because of this fact, the selection of the correct system must be based on **economic analysis** and **comparison** of systems.

Computation of Handling Equipment Costs. A technique by which to evaluate various handling methods in relation to manual handling costs or to make a comparison between mechanized handling methods is helpful. A basis for estimating the cost of owning and operating industrial trucks of various types and styles is also of value. Reduced to simplest terms, handling costs can be compared in terms of the **man-hours** required to move materials from one location to another. These operations may be repeated many times and with many variations. In every instance, however, **materials handling operations** consist primarily of only picking up, transporting, and depositing or piling loads.

This analysis is, of course, oversimplified, but the method may be applied to various combinations of conveyor (live-roller versus belt-and-gravity combination) and other systems such as the tractor-trailer system, and truck versus rail freight system.

Cost Formulas. The computation of the economies of materials handling equipment can be handled through the use of formulas or the application of accounting principles and standard time data. A good example of the algebraic approach can be found in the formulas of the ASME Materials Handling Division shown in Fig. 5. They show: (1) the expected yearly cost (Y) to maintain the mechanical equipment ready for operation; (2) the maximum justified investment in dollars (Z) which will still earn the required minimum interest to meet all the fixed charges on the equipment under consideration; (3) the expected yearly surplus profit in dollars (V), in excess of required minimum, from the operation of the mechanical equipment under consideration; (4) the expected yearly total net profit in percent (P), including the allowance-percentage (A) on the investment, and (5) the number of years required for complete amortization of investment on equipment studied, out of expected earnings, amounting to the net profit and depreciation and obsolescence allowance (P percent $+ D$ percent). This number of years (H) should be as low as possible. The comparison is made between a labor-saving device $(O°)$, considered as standard (old practice), and a new device (O'). All the symbols if affected by ° refer to the old practice; if affected by ′ they refer to the proposed new installation.

If $O°$ is already installed (and not merely a hypothetical standard of comparison), the results will be influenced by the present value (K) of the equipment to be displaced (which is its unamortized capital value less its resale scrap value)— otherwise, $K = O$ (hypothetical case). A standard year of 300 eight-hr. days or a total of 2400 working hours is assumed.

Factors Entering into Formulas

$X = 100x:$	Percentage of year during which the equipment under consideration (X° and X', respectively) will be or is operated.
$A = 100a:$	Percentage allowance on investment (A° and A').
$B = 100b:$	Percentage allowance to provide for insurance, taxes, etc. (B° and B').
$C = 100c:$	Percentage allowance to provide for upkeep (C° and C').
$D = 100d:$	Percentage allowance for depreciation and obsolescence (D° and D').
$N = 100n:$	Required fixed charges in percentage on investment, or minimum interest to be earned ($N = A + B + C + D$ and $n = a + b + c + d$).
$E = E' - E^\circ:$	Excess yearly cost of power, supplies, and other items which will be consumed (total in dollars).
$S = S^\circ - S':$	Yearly saving (in dollars) in direct cost of labor.
$L = L^\circ - L':$	Yearly labor burden saved (in dollars).
$U = U' - U^\circ:$	Utilized yearly reserve capacity (available for increased production), possible saving in dollars.
$\$I:$	Initial investment in mechanical equipment (I° and I'), its initial cost (installed) in dollars.
$F = Y^\circ = n^\circ \cdot I^\circ:$	Fixed yearly charges in dollars on equipment O°.
$Y = Y' = n' \cdot I':$	Fixed yearly charges in dollars on equipment O'.
$K:$	Present value of equipment to be displaced.
$Z:$	Maximum justified investment in dollars on new device.
$V:$	Expected yearly surplus profit in dollars, in excess of required minimum, from the operation of O'.
$P:$	Expected yearly total net profit in percent (including the allowance A percent on proposed investment).
$H:$	Number of years required for complete amortization of investment on O', out of expected earnings amounting to $(P + D)$ percent: (i.e., net profit and depreciation).

Formulas

The five ASME formulas (with slightly changed notations) are then:

(1) $Y = I' \cdot (A' + B' + C' + D')/100 = I' \cdot n'$
   where $n' = a' + b' + c' + d'$.

(2) $Z = x' \cdot (S + L + U - E)/n' + F/n' - K$
   where $F = n^\circ \cdot I^\circ$.

(3) $V = x' \cdot (S + L + U - E) + F - (Y + a' \cdot K)$.

(4) $P = 100 \cdot v/I' + A'$.

(5) $H = 100/(P + D')$.

Note regarding upkeep: Having in mind that materials handling machinery, even if left idle a large part of the year, will probably require, under most conditions, approximately the same repair through deterioration as though in use, no deduction is made for such lack of use in the estimated cost of upkeep, based on the percentage allowance C'; for greater accuracy it is possible to substitute into the formula which gives Y, instead of C', the value $x' \cdot C'$.

Fig. 5. Formulas for computing equipment economies.

As an example of application of the formulas, assume that handling of miscellaneous materials about a factory which has formerly been done by 4 men receiving $7.00 per day each, allowing 300 days per year, at an annual direct cost of $8,400 = $S°$ can be done by 1 man operating an industrial truck at a direct labor cost of $2,100 = S' per year, thus effecting a saving at the rate of $6,300 = S per year in direct-labor cost.

Assume that also through the greater promptness in moving materials and the more continuous operation of machines there is an increase in earnings, due to increased production, valued at $1,300 = U per year; also that the labor involved, being accounted as nonproductive, carries a fixed charge or burden of 10 percent, so that the yearly labor-burden saved is $630 = L. In actual practice the plant operates 240 days per year or 80 percent (X') of the time. The various factors entering into the formulas are estimated as follows:

$X' = 80$ percent	$E = \$\ 450$	$I' = \$6,600$
$A' = \ 6$ percent	$S = \ 6,300$	$Y = ?$
$B' = \ 4$ percent	$L = \ \ \ 300$	$Z = ?$
$C' = 20$ percent	$U = \ 1,300$	$V = ?$
$D' = 25$ percent	$F = \ 0$	$P = ?$
$N' = 55$ percent	$K = \ 0$	$H = ?$

Solution: Assume that an industrial truck will meet the conditions of the problem and that its cost will be $I' = \$6,600$; then by formula (1) we will find for Y, expressing the yearly cost to maintain the equipment ready for operation, exclusive of labor (fixed charges on investment):

$$Y = \$6,600 \cdot (6 + 4 + 20 + 25)/100 = \$6,600 \times 55 \text{ percent} = \$3,630$$

To see if the investment is justified, we apply formula (2):

$$Z = 80 \text{ percent} \cdot (6,300 + 630 + 1,300 - 450)/0.55 = \$11,316$$

This indicates that equipment costing any sum below $11,316 will earn some profit above interest on investment and maintenance.

To find the profit from operation of the mechanical equipment, we apply formula (3):

$$V = 80 \text{ percent} \cdot (6,300 + 630 + 1,300 - 450) - \$3,630 = \$2,594$$

The total net profit in percent earned upon the investment is found by the formula (4):

$$P \text{ percent} = \$2,594/(\$6,600 + \$396) = 37.1 \text{ percent}$$

This net profit together with depreciation allowed ($P + D'$) will constitute a yearly amortization of 78.23 percent, and formula (5) will give the number of years required for complete amortization:

$$H = 100/(37.1 + 25) = 1.61 \text{ years} = 19 \text{ months}$$

Cost Accounting Procedure. Many firms prefer the accounting approach when analyzing new materials handling equipment or alternatives. This approach is most adaptable in cases where the standard cost system is in effect. In such instances time study data and element costs can be used to synthesize the various alternative operations in order to develop labor and equipment requirements. Standard time data coupled with good cost accounting information will result in an accurate analysis, if properly applied to the problem.

This type of analysis as outlined in Fig. 6 for a comparison of manual, piece-by-piece and unit load, electric industrial truck systems (EITA Handbook of Material Handling), omits a few details such as fringe benefits and the development of labor requirements.

Existing Costs of Manual Handling—Daily

Direct labor ....
Social security taxes ....
Workmen's compensation ....
Hand truck depreciation ....
Packaging cost for tonnage handled, labor and material....
Indirect labor (supervision, personnel services, etc.).......

Total ....

Tons handled per day ....
Cost per ton ....

Industrial Truck Operating Costs—Daily

Investment:
Trucks (including accessory equipment) ....
Pallets, skids, bins, racks, etc.........................
Building improvements (chargeable to capital) ....

Total investment ....

Annual Cost to Replace and Possess

Depreciation:
Trucks and accessories ....
Pallets, skids, etc. ....
Building improvements ....
Taxes ....
Insurance ....

Total annual cost to replace and possess ....

Annual Cost to Operate

Energy (or Fuel) ....
Repairs and maintenance ....
Truck and accessory equipment ....
Labor ....
Material and parts ....
Pallets, skids, racks, etc. ....
Labor ....
Parts ....

Total annual cost to operate ....

Fig. 6. Comparative cost analysis form (continued on next page).

Total annual cost of owning and operating trucks and pallets
Cost per day (divide by number of days worked).........
Direct labor, drivers (daily) ....
Social security taxes (daily) ....
Workmen's compensation (daily) ....
Indirect labor cost (training, supervising, etc.) (daily)....
Packaging cost, including gluing, wiring, strapping, etc.
    (labor and materials) ....

Total daily expense ....

Tons handled per day ....
Total cost per ton ....

Summary—Cost Data

	Manual	Mechanical (Unit Load)
Cost per ton	....
Difference	....

Fig. 6. (Concluded.)

EITA adds that "Savings that result from increased storage space through tiering unit loads should also be included when an anticipated investment in new storage area is avoided by installation of powered-industrial-truck handling."

Operation and Maintenance of Equipment

QUALIFICATION AND TRAINING OF PERSONNEL. Materials handling machinery requires the same degree of preventive maintenance and skill of operation as might be expected of any other industrial machinery of similar complexity. Fixed materials handling equipment normally does not require operators in the usual sense of the word. However, the operating personnel (supervisory) or maintenance staff must give the proper attention to lubrication, bearing and drive inspection, electrical systems, belting, and other components which could suffer damage from overloading, misuse, neglect, lack of lubrication, or other operating hazards.

Fork lift trucks, cranes, and other vehicular equipment normally are under the control of a regularly assigned operator. In most plants these operators are responsible to their supervisors for reporting any equipment defects, and in the case of automotive equipment, they usually are required to see that the vehicle is serviced properly.

Most materials handling equipment can be dangerous if mishandled. This is particularly true of fork lift trucks, cranes, and highway vehicles. It is customary in most plants to have some type of training program and **qualification standards** by which operators are selected. Most labor organizations accept this procedure and manufacturers usually pay a premium rate for qualified operators.

Qualification of operators can include a high degree of **application knowledge** such as warehousing theory for fork lift operators, traffic and dispatching for highway truck drivers, and railroading knowledge for yard locomotive engineers and brakemen. On the other hand, some organizations accept a very rudimentary training program consisting of the viewing of a film on safety and operation and a few hours of supervised operation.

Most fork-lift-truck manufacturers recognize the potential dangers of mishandling and poor operation of fork-lift-truck equipment. The major lift-truck manufacturers issue **training manuals** and, in some cases, provide instruction to

Score	True	False	True or False Questions
6%	☐	☐	1. Fork truck operators shall wipe off their machines when the machine is not operating some time during their working shift.
6%	☐	☐	2. Operators will check gas, oil, and water, at the beginning of each shift.
6%	☐	☐	3. Operators will not have to watch for pedestrians and workers while in motion.
6%	☐	☐	4. Power trucks will not be left unattended with the motor running.
6%	☐	☐	5. Operators must fix immediately any mechanical deficiency.
6%	☐	☐	6. Operators will use "reverse" to stop their machine rather than the brake.
5%	☐	☐	7. The forks or the guard may be used to bump a loaded pallet into position.
6%	☐	☐	8. Fork trucks shall be driven in "reverse" at all times except when stacking, to remove a stack or to enter a boxcar.
6%	☐	☐	9. Bent or damaged loading plates must never be used.
6%	☐	☐	10. Travel in the left-hand side of an aisle whenever possible.
6%	☐	☐	11. Operator must face in the direction in which his machine is operating.
5%	☐	☐	12. Fork truck should never be driven into a boxcar or semi-trailer to get material.
6%	☐	☐	13. It is not permissible for an operator to let his left foot ride the clutch pedal.
6%	☐	☐	14. Operator should pump the foot accelerator while the machine is running.
6%	☐	☐	15. Operator should elevate his load while in motion to and from the stack.
6%	☐	☐	16. Fork trucks should be operated at "full" speed at all times.
6%	☐	☐	17. It is permissible to start, turn, or stop a fork truck immediately.
——% Total			

Answers to True or False Questions

1. True	7. False	13. True
2. True	8. False	14. False
3. False	9. True	15. False
4. True	10. False	16. False
5. False	11. True	17. False
6. False	12. False	

Clark Equipment Co.

Fig. 7. Fork truck operator's true-false questions and answers.

their customers' driver personnel. In most cases, these manufacturers recommend a training program which includes the operation of the machine in its basic functions and practice in **obstacle courses** made up of mazes of pallets standing on edge. These courses usually include some safety training and the rudiments of preventive maintenance. The issuance of an operator's license at the completion of training is recommended. These licenses are usually signed by company representatives and, in some cases, by union officials. Physical standards comparable to those required by state motor vehicle licensing laws are adequate in most cases, although some companies require a check of heart and reflexes. It is quite common to have both a **written** and an **operation test** before permitting qualification. A fork truck operator's questionnaire, recommended by the Clark Equipment Company, includes both multiple-choice and true-or-false questions. Sample true-or-false questions are given in Fig. 7 with the answers below.

SAFE HANDLING METHODS. When studying materials handling methods, the safety aspects must be given consideration, particularly in methods involving manual handling. Better methods should result in fewer accidents as well as lower costs. The N. Y. Dept. of Labor (Bulletin No. 181) states that, "In the whole field of industry, there is no place where safety and efficiency are so intimately associated. The same effort which makes handling of goods less costly also makes it safer."

The National Safety Council (Safe Practices Pamphlet No. 55) lists the following simple **rules to assist in reducing handling hazards.** Others which will apply to the particular work involved should be added.

1. Mark or paint lines on the floor indicating aisles or truck runways.
2. Keep aisles clear of overhanging or projecting obstructions.
3. Provide adequate overhead lighting in aisles.
4. Place large mirrors at blind corners.
5. Keep all runway floors in good repair.
6. In the case of wooden floors, use rubber-tired wheels on hand trucks.
7. Provide knuckle guards on handles of two-wheel trucks.
8. Install glass panels on doors in trucking aisles.
9. Remove defective trucks from service.
10. Train operators in the safe way of doing the work.
11. Avoid overloading or loading too high.
12. Loads should be made secure to prevent falling.
13. Common hand trucks should be pushed, not pulled.
14. Loads on two-wheel hand trucks should be balanced over wheels.
15. Assign heavy tasks to individuals who meet physical requirements of the job.
16. Do not permit anyone to ride trucks.
17. Encourage the use of safety shoes.

Manual Handling Techniques. Nissley advises (Mill & Factory, vol. 57), "If you have to do it manually—carry the load right." He quotes a study by E. N. Bedale (Glasgow University) in making the following summary of the recommended manual handling techniques:

1. The most efficient (i.e., least fatiguing) method for carrying loads of 20 to 50 lb. is the yoke method. This is the method whereby the load is equally distributed and is suspended from two wooden arms of a shoulder yoke.
2. The least efficient method is the hip method. This is the method whereby the load is supported on the hip and held closely to body by one arm.
3. The shoulder method ranks high for most loads as a good way of carrying heavy loads short distances.

4. The comparative efficiency of all the methods of carrying loads may be seen in the accompanying chart (Fig. 8) showing the amount of oxygen consumed (c.c. per min.) when carrying loads from 20 to 50 lb. by eight different methods. Differences of less than 10 percent in oxygen consumption between two methods or weights being carried would make it difficult to draw final conclusions as to the relative efficiency of one method over another.

		Yoke	Bundles	Shoulder	Strap Tray	Tray	Knapsack	Head	Hip
20 Lb. Carried	Efficiency rank	1	3	2	5	4	7	6	8
	Oxygen consumption	400	455	428	473	464	561	527	574
30 Lb. Carried	Efficiency rank	1	2	4	3	3	5	6	7
	Oxygen consumption	440	492	547	522	522	573	575	657
40 Lb. Carried	Efficiency rank	1	2	5	3	6	4	7	8
	Oxygen consumption	486	534	609	604	613	608	626	694
50 Lb. Carried	Efficiency rank	1	4	2	3	5	7	6	8
	Oxygen consumption	516	667	608	656	675	700	692	725

Mill & Factory

Fig. 8. **Oxygen consumption (c.c. per min.) and relative efficiency for various loads and positions.**

Safety Rules for Lift Trucks. Continuous study is being given to specific safety rules for operating fork lift truck equipment. In addition to the usual motor vehicle driving practices which are accepted by most highway traffic enforcement agencies, the American Society of Mechanical Engineers, the National Safety Council, and several other agencies, including most fork-lift-truck manufacturers, have published safety literature on fork-lift-truck operations. The training of personnel in safety procedures requires perseverance, repetition, and follow-up. This is no less true with materials handling personnel than in any other portion of an industrial facility.

Enforcement. Good maintenance and safety records depend upon active cooperation by equipment operating personnel. Education, good labor relations, and careful supervision all contribute to the success of maintenance and safety programs. However, situations often arise that require enforcement of safety regulations. The welfare of personnel and plant equipment is sometimes at stake.

The most successful safety enforcement programs are based upon **safety committees** which include members of both management and labor. In most cases, these committees can only recommend corrective or punitive action. However, in some organizations they operate as a trial court and actually mete out punishment to offenders. Punishments may vary from reprimands or time off to discharge, depending upon the severity of the offense. This type of committee action is based upon a congenial labor-management relationship. Unilateral safety enforcement by management can be successful in some circumstances, but it often leads to difficult grievance problems. For this reason, the committee approach may be favored. The best safety enforcement is based upon preventive action by alert safety committees and avoidance of hazardous situations. (See section on Safety and Fire Prevention.)

MAINTENANCE. A good maintenance program is essential to efficient materials handling practice, plant safety, and the full realization of cost savings. Preventive maintenance should be performed regularly and systematically by qualified mechanics under competent supervision. A complete suitable record of all services done and the date of same should be kept. As the Clark Equipment Co. (Keep 'Em Rolling) points out, "The time and effort required to maintain a Preventive Maintenance program is mandatory to reduce to a minimum the time lost while vehicles are in a repair shop."

Availability of spare parts and an adequate service organization is a vital consideration when selecting materials handling equipment. Few plants have large enough industrial truck fleets or conveyor systems to stock all parts necessary to anticipate breakdowns and operate a preventive maintenance program. (See section on Plant Maintenance.)

Replacement Policy. Obsolescence is expensive—a replacement policy can increase handling savings through application of more advanced equipment and techniques. Rowan (Modern Materials Handling, vol. 10) states the following reasons for replacing materials handling equipment:

1. Wear and tear. Physical deterioration brings existing equipment to the point at which it is no longer economical to operate it. Maintenance is a major cost element in this case.
2. Improved equipment designs. Engineering advances in new equipment permit higher output, lower maintenance charges, easier operation, or some other benefit that makes replacement economically sound.
3. New handling equipment. Equipment not previously available performs the same job as older units with some advantage to the user. Straddle fork trucks, for example, have replaced cantilever types on certain applications because of the ability of straddle models to operate in narrow aisles.
4. Improved handling methods. In well-managed, aggressive companies, methods of handling are under continual study. Proposals range all the way from the simplest idea to complete new handling systems requiring an investment running into thousands of dollars.
5. New production concepts. Innovations in production techniques almost always require some form of mechanized handling.
6. Product redesigns. Model changeovers often require large-scale "retooling" and extensive changes in handling methods. While particularly true of the mass-production industries, it also applies to some extent to shops that are predominantly job-lot, especially as regards containers, packages, and related equipment.
7. Increased plant capacity. Replacement of production equipment generally results in a big boost in output. This is especially true of the metalworking industries, where startling increases in the productive capacity of machine tools have occurred since 1945. If full advantage is to be taken of this increased capacity, the handling system must be revamped accordingly to match the new production pace.
8. Consolidations and relayouts. Handling generally is the major reason for changes in layout and for combining operations previously performed in separate locations. Changing volume as the market expands and shrinks for various product lines demands different kinds of layout and greater or less mechanization.

9. Savings in space. Particularly in warehousing and storage operations, savings in space through better handling methods are among the most important areas of cost reduction.

10. Elimination of heavy physical labor. When manual handling is replaced by powered equipment, savings frequently equal the cost of the installation in less than a year. Even if no savings are involved, the replacement may be justified to reduce operator fatigue or to eliminate a troublesome area in employee relations.

11. Improved production and inventory control. Mechanized handling often reduces work-in-process inventories and simplifies routing and dispatching procedures.

12. Plant expansion. Indicative of the part that materials handling plays in major capital expenditures of this type is the fact that present-day practice is to develop the layout for best possible handling sequence, then erect the building around the layout.

13. Cost reduction. The drive to lower unit production costs often necessitates new equipment. Sometimes this can be done only by decreasing handling costs.

14. Increased safety. Handling is responsible for a high percentage of accidents. New equipment may be installed to eliminate safety hazards.

15. Improved quality. Better handling methods reduce damage to parts and materials. This is an important area for savings in many plants.

Rowan points out further that, "The 1954 Tax Law allows greater freedom in depreciating capital assets than has been permitted at any time during the past 20 years. Depreciation, of course, has no bearing on the profitable life of materials handling equipment. Formulas for evaluating the worth of proposals disregard book value completely. However, as depreciation affects profits and the availability of capital, it is closely related to the operation of a replacement program." (See section on Machinery and Equipment Economics.)

Measurement of Materials Handling Operations

PRODUCTION CONTROL OF MATERIALS HANDLING. B. A. Moski, of Yale and Towne Manufacturing Co., points out that from a production control standpoint, it is essential that materials handling be measured, in order to improve the validity of machine requirements, manpower requirements, manufacturing schedules, and employee productivity standards.

Applications of such techniques of operations research as linear programming underline the importance of measuring materials handling, in order that significant numbers may be assigned to the relevant factors in the equations which must be solved to determine the optimum conditions which are required for maximum profits (see section on Operations Research).

ESTIMATING EQUIPMENT AND MANPOWER REQUIREMENTS. Moski indicates that in all phases of measurement it must be recognized that various techniques may be employed, with varying degrees of accuracy in the final results. Prior to any investment in capital facilities, it is necessary to estimate equipment and manpower requirements, with possible substantial errors in judgment because of the lack of practical experience. With some capital facilities available, it is possible to analyze actual operations in detail, resulting in maximum accuracy in the evaluation of additional equipment and manpower requirements.

In planning a new plant, it is essential to analyze the flow of raw materials, work-in-process, and finished products throughout the plant. (See section on Plant Layout and Location.) Based upon this analysis, minimum requirements of materials handling equipment and manpower may be established. In determining the minimum requirements, however, consideration should be given to the physical problems which may result if minimum requirements are demonstrated in actual practice to be inadequate. The solution of such physical problems generally requires that some provision be made in the floor space originally planned to allow for the introduction of additional equipment and manpower.

After a plant is in operation, and minimum materials handling facilities have been provided, it is relatively simple to determine additional facility requirements with a high degree of accuracy. The techniques of **production time studies, standard time data,** and **work sampling** are well suited to the evaluation of additional equipment and manpower requirements.

Keys to the proper determination of materials handling equipment utilization include standard time data for the equipment in use, and a reasonable approximation of the number and character of materials handling moves involved, related to a given production schedule.

Depending upon the specific type of manufacturing involved, any given production schedule may be evaluated into a certain frequency and character of materials handling **transportations.** The application of standard time data to the transportations will develop standard hours of work for the various types of materials handling equipment employed. Dividing standard hours of work by actual hours of work will develop percent utilization of the equipment.

In the development of standard time data, it is essential to consider the same factors of leveling, base time, personal time, fatigue, incidental delays, and incentive allowances, as are included in the development of standard time data for the more conventional manufacturing operations (see section on Work Measurement and Time Study).

INCENTIVE BASIS. The development of a wage incentive plan for materials handling operations requires full recognition of the problem of adequate control with respect to proper payment for the work which is accomplished. It is particularly necessary to avoid the possible high cost of administration of a highly refined wage incentive plan.

In a typical plant, a number of different buildings, departments, and types of materials handling equipment may be involved with diversified products and constantly changing production schedules. The materials may include raw materials, work-in-process, and finished products. Truckloads of material may be frequently picked up and delivered to manufacturing department areas which are a considerable distance away from the manufacturing department offices, or to locations where supervisors may not normally be readily available.

Under the above conditions, the following basic principles are suggested by Moski, of Yale and Towne, for the installation, administration, and control of a sound **wage incentive plan:**

1. Standard time data should be developed for all materials handling equipment.
2. Allowances for variable factors, over and above base time, should be developed by the time study or work sampling methods. When base time has been developed on the basis of incentive pace, allowances for variable factors must be evaluated.
3. An incentive factor, consistent with individual plant practice, should be added to the base time and allowances to provide incentive opportunity for the employees. An incentive factor of possibly 15 to 25 percent, consistent with other incentive factors which may be in effect in the specific plant, is recommended for consideration.

4. A group incentive plan should be applied, with payments on a weekly basis, to include all materials handling employees. In order to minimize inconsistencies in earnings, and to minimize the cost of administration, a group incentive plan on a weekly basis is preferable in the area of materials handling to an individual incentive plan on a daily basis.
5. Standard hours should be credited to the group on the basis of finished products received from the various manufacturing departments.

Every finished product involves a standard flow of materials and supplies through a plant. Detailed process charts should be prepared to record the standard flow of materials and supplies for representative finished products. The application of standard time data, and allowances for variable factors and the incentive factor, to the process flow charts of representative finished products will develop standard hours per unit of finished product. As finished products are received from the manufacturing departments, the application of this standard will properly compensate the group for all work required to complete the finished product. Under this principle, adequate control of the wage incentive plan, with respect to proper payment for the work which is accomplished, may be ensured. (See section on Wage Plans and Controls.)

COST REDUCTION. Because materials handling is ever-present in the manufacturing function, its cost is a substantial portion of finished product costs. The high cost of materials handling justifies a continuous analysis of the function for cost reduction purposes. (See section on Work Simplification.) In the analysis of materials handling for cost reduction, the following guiding principles should be considered, according to Moski:

1. Although materials handling contributes place and time utility, it does not increase the value of a product, and the entire cost of materials handling must be kept to an absolute minimum.
2. The objective of sound materials handling is the elimination of all handling.
3. The frequency and distance of all handlings should be minimized and the use of manual effort eliminated.
4. The cost of actual travel is generally small in comparison with the cost of unloading, loading, lifting, lowering, and storing materials.
5. Maximum use should be made of gravity and power to replace manual effort, because of the resultant decreased cost.
6. An uninterrupted flow of materials to production centers serves to increase production by minimizing delays in manufacturing operations.
7. Ideal manufacturing consists of each productive operation being performed while the material is progressing to the next operation.

The first step in the cost reduction analysis of materials handling is the preparation of **process charts** for all products. (See section on Process Charts.) Emphasis should be placed upon the frequency of materials handling, the types of containers and transportation-means, as well as the distances involved.

Considerable thought should be devoted to the selection of a possible common denominator, as far as containers and transportation-means are concerned.

Materials handling equipment should be selected with the objective of eliminating materials handling. The nearest approach to this objective may be found in certain chemical process industries, where the materials are fluid and flow through piping and tanks by gravity, supplemented by pumping. In the manufacture of mechanical and electrical products, the best examples of effective materials handling are found in the automotive industry, where subsidiary conveyors feed detail parts and minor assemblies into a main assembly conveyor, and assembly operations are performed as the product passes along.

Whenever possible, a **continuous flow** of materials should be engineered, through the proper selection of conveyors. Where continuous flow is impossible, and intermittent handling is necessary, maximum attention should be given to the proper selection of containers and pallets for handling by industrial lift trucks, which are equipped with a variety of **attachments** which serve to eliminate the use of pallets, leading to a reduction of capital investment for materials handling purposes. In industries where manufacturing operations are of a highly repetitive nature. the application of automation principles is developing **transfer fingers** which move the part from one operation to another in the same machine, or from one machine to another, with the effect of eliminating materials handling as a separate operation within a given span of processing.

STANDARD TIME DATA. The application of time standards to materials handling operations meets with the problem of varying rates of effort, as in all other productive operations. Several systems of **element time data** have been developed for general application to manual and industrial truck operations (Materials Handling Handbook, Bolz and Hagemann, eds.). These element times can be used to synthesize materials handling operations and develop equipment and manpower requirements. In general, they should not be considered adequate for wage incentive programs. Wage incentives and pricing standards should be based upon actual time studies made by competent industrial engineers on experienced operators, working under normal production conditions.

Travel time curves and **conveyor speed data** have been developed for use as materials handling standards. These data are also adequate for equipment and manpower computations, but local conditions frequently reduce their value for setting wage standards.

Materials Handling Equipment

METHODS OF CLASSIFYING EQUIPMENT. Materials handling equipment is generally classified to aid in the organization of information when solving materials handling problems. The complexity of the field has caused the development of several classification systems. In some cases these systems are augmented by decimal coding to facilitate the use of punched-card information handling. The five principal ways in which materials handling equipment is usually classified are as follows:

1. Nature of material handled, such as loose or bulk, pieces or parts, packages, bundles, boxes, barrels.
2. Nature of service performed, such as lifting and transporting.
3. Major fields of industry served, such as mining, manufacturing, transportation, construction.
4. Relative mobility of equipment, such as fixed path, travel in limited area, travel over wide areas.
5. Classes of apparatus, such as cranes, hoists, conveyors, lift trucks.

Materials handling equipment has been divided into **package-handling** and **bulk-handling** equipment. There is a great deal of overlap between these two classifications, since much bulk material is handled in bags, sacks, barrels, or other packages, and in some cases packaged items (or loose material, castings, machine parts, etc.) are handled over belt conveyors and in tubs or hoppers in much the same way as bulk material. Handling systems outside the plant facilities (including highway vehicles, railroads, shipping, aircraft, and other transportation facilities) usually are not restricted to this functional classification except in the case of specially designed applications.

Since materials handling equipment classifications are primarily of value during the selection of machinery for a particular application, **classification by nature of move** is often useful. The materials movement may be:

1. Fixed-path.
2. Flexible-route.
3. Intermittent.
4. Continuous.
5. Long distance.
6. Short-haul.
7. Indoors.
8. Outdoors.
9. Vertical.
10. Horizontal.

Materials handling technology is normally studied according to equipment groupings. However, some work has been done recently in the attempt to divide this subject matter into functional divisions or series of activities. The Materials Handling Handbook (Bolz and Hagemann, eds.) cites six functional divisions as follows:

1. Bulk handling.
2. Unit handling.
3. Industrial packaging.
4. Warehousing.
5. Carrier handling.
6. Handling operation analysis.

Hall (Material Handling Equipment and Containers, AMHS) suggests the following basis for classifying materials handling equipment:

1. **Conveyors.** All types of conveyors including belt, chain, cable, roller, screw, pipeline, and vibrating.
2. **Cranes, elevators, and hoists.** All types of cranes, elevators, and hoists including fixed, traveling, and portable cranes, elevators, cableways, hoists, winches, and auxiliary crane equipment.
3. **Positioning, weight, and control equipment.** Includes manipulators and positioners, upenders and dumpers, fixed and portable positioning tables and platforms, positioning bridges, ramps and transfers, portable transferring and positioning equipment, scales, and handling control equipment.
4. **Industrial vehicles.** Includes powered trucks, hand trucks, industrial tractors and trailers, industrial cars and locomotives, bulk handling vehicles, and other special vehicles.
5. **Motor vehicles.** Includes highway passenger automobiles and buses, motor trucks, tractors, and trailers.
6. **Railway cars.** Includes passenger and baggage cars, box, refrigerator and live-stock cars, flat cars, gondolas, hoppers, tank cars, locomotives, and other special railroad cars.
7. **Marine carriers.** Includes ocean and lake vessels, river and canal boats, barges and lighters, tow boats, small craft, and other miscellaneous floating equipment.
8. **Air transports.** Includes all types of aircraft.
9. **Containers and supports.** Includes pressure vessels, tight containers, entirely enclosed loose containers, open topped containers, platform and coil supports, securements, and auxiliary packaging equipment.

This classification has been followed, in general, in the functional description and analysis of materials handling equipment which follows.

CONVEYORS. According to the Materials Handling Handbook (Bolz and Hagemann, eds.) this classification includes all equipment for transporting material between two fixed points with continuous or intermittent forward movement and continuous drive, whether the equipment is fixed or portable. This definition with some exceptions corresponds closely with that given by the Conveyor Equipment Manufacturers' Association (Conveyor Terms and Definitions).

Belt Conveyors. Harold Medley of the Jeffrey Manufacturing Co. describes a belt conveyor as consisting of a power driven endless belt, with terminal pulleys and idlers or slider beds carrying the loaded and empty strands of the belt (Fig. 9). Its first cost is moderate and its maintenance cost low (barring accident to the belt).

Belt conveyor systems are very economical of power and are used for handling constant and intermittent flows of materials for long or short distances. Harrington points out (Materials Handling Manual) that "they transport goods horizontally or up and down an incline—some are designed to do all three." They can also be used to retrieve grade in gravity systems or to maintain control of the rate of descent of material on declines.

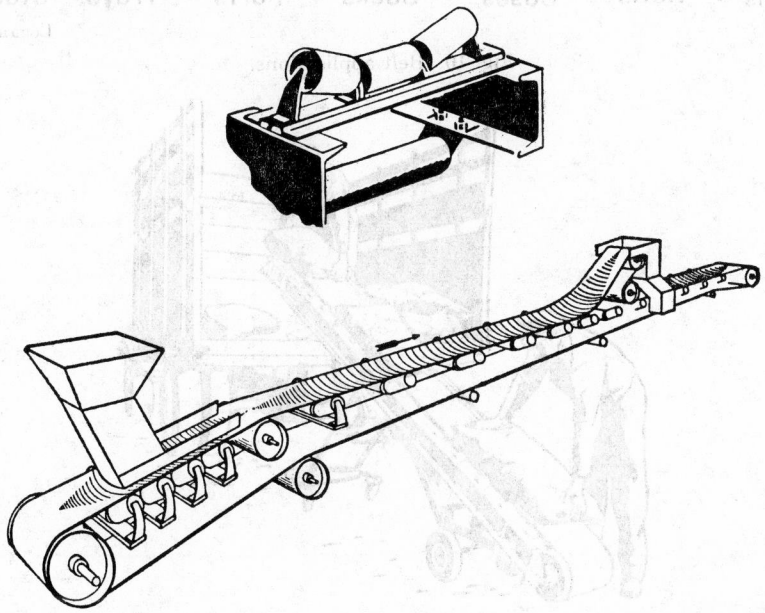

Chain Belt Co.

Fig. 9. Typical troughed belt conveyor with feeder and tripper and showing idler.

Belt conveyors may be either fixed (Fig. 10) or portable (Fig. 11) in nature. Harrington says, "It is in the portable variety that there are a great many belt conveyors that can be adjusted to move goods horizontally or up or down an incline, as is needed. This versatility is an extremely valuable feature. Conveyors of the so-called booster type belong to this group."

Idlers are a series of rollers on which the endless fabric- or rubber-covered belt travels. For light loads up to 50 lb. per sq. ft., a steel or wood trough or slider bed may be substituted for the idlers. Belts are often troughed to reduce spillage in handling bulk materials. Troughing idlers normally are inclined at 20°. Recent developments have put molded-rubber, flexible-shaft troughing rolls on the market. Thinner belts are used and troughing idlers are often inclined to 45° for handling light materials, such as wood chips or grain

While a belt conveyor most frequently discharges at its end, bulk loads can be discharged at points along its length by **trippers** or by **plows.**

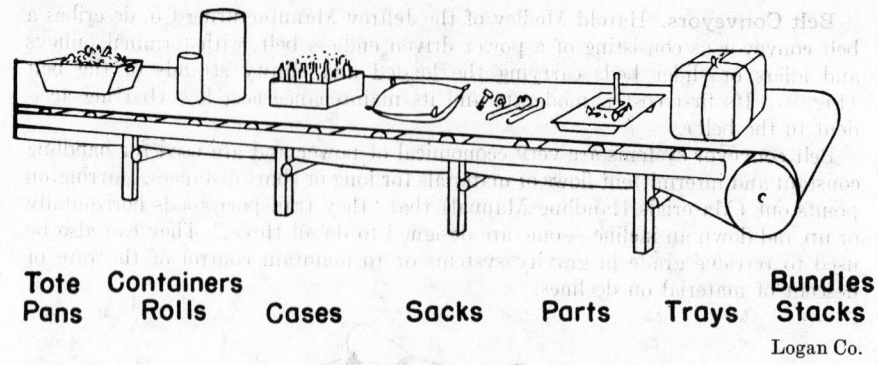

Tote   **Containers**   **Bundles**
Pans   **Rolls**   **Cases**   **Sacks**   **Parts**   **Trays**   **Stacks**

Logan Co.

Fig. 10. Belt applications.

Mathews Conveyer Co.

Fig. 11. Typical portable belt application.

The belt conveyor is highly suited to package handling because of its smooth, noiseless operation, reversibility, and the ease with which packages may be diverted. More efficient at high speeds than any other continuous carrier, its continuous surface adapts it to packages of even the smallest size. In manufacturing operations belt conveyors perform two-way service by carrying loaded boxes of work-in-process on the upper side and returning empty containers on the return side of the belt.

While untreated cotton canvas belting can be used indoors under constant normal humidity conditions, rubber-impregnated belts are installed where humidity varies greatly, and fully rubber-covered belts are required where the conveyor is exposed to the weather. Rubberized belting is not usually used when belts slide in troughs.

The customary angle of inclination is 15° for flat-belt conveyor installations conveying miscellaneous materials up or down. This incline can be increased to

27° by using a rough-surface rubber belt. Cleats fastened to the belting permit handling of packages on even greater inclines.

"The **wire-mesh conveyor** is similar to the belt conveyor except that the moving bed is formed by a continuous belt of wire mesh between two strands of continuous chains. . . . It is used largely in light-weight production on washing, draining, or other operations involving immersion of parts in, or their separation from, liquids. Wire mesh belts are also used without the side chains." (Lamson Conveyor Facts.) Alloy-mesh belt is also used in heat-treating applications where fire is applied through the mesh.

A special form of the belt conveyor is the **"zipper" conveyor.** This conveyor is constructed of a piece of flat conveyor belt upon which are mounted two pieces of rubber with teeth molded in one edge. The connection to the belt is by means of thin pieces of rubber which are sufficiently flexible to act as hinges. When forced together the teeth lock to form a closed joint, with the result that the conveyor becomes the equivalent of a moving pipe.

Closure is effected by two rollers bearing against the bead upon which the teeth are molded. For opening, two similar rollers placed inside the section force the teeth open and swing the sides into open position.

The conveyor is able to negotiate any slope up to and including the vertical and accomplish numerous changes in direction. It is particularly suited to handling materials which are dusty or those which must not be contaminated, and where degradation must be kept to a minimum.

Elevating Conveyors. Medley states that the most widely used means of elevating material in a restricted horizontal distance is the **bucket elevator.** It is made up of buckets mounted on either belt or chains running over terminal wheels. Such elevators are built in a number of types (see Fig. 12).

Centrifugal discharge bucket elevators (Fig. 12a) may be vertical or inclined, with buckets mounted at intervals on a single or double strand of chain or on a

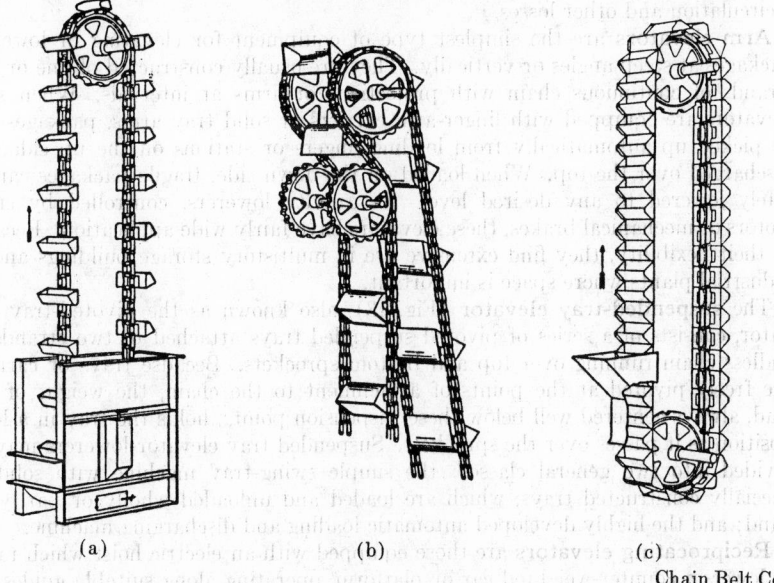

(a)   (b)   (c)

Chain Belt Co.

Fig. 12. Bucket elevators.

belt. This type of elevator is used to handle bulk materials which can be picked up by spaced buckets as they pass under the footwheel and are discharged by centrifugal force as the buckets pass over the head wheel.

Positive discharge elevators (Fig. 12b), which operate at slow speeds, are made up of spaced buckets mounted between two strands of chain. The material is scooped up by the buckets passing under the footwheels and discharged at the head when the buckets are inverted over the discharge opening by means of knuckle wheels. This type is recommended for handling light, fluffy, or sticky materials.

Continuous bucket elevators (Fig. 12c) may be vertical or inclined, with buckets mounted continuously on single or double strands of chain or on a belt. The material is usually fed to the buckets through a loading leg and is discharged over the face of the preceding bucket in passing around the headwheel. These elevators may be used to handle the same kinds of material as the centrifugal type, but are particularly adapted to handling materials that are difficult to pick up or are friable due to the manner in which they are fed to and discharged by the elevator.

Super-capacity elevators are continuous bucket elevators in which the buckets are mounted between two strands of chain and project backward in toward the center of the elevator, thus carrying larger capacities and permitting larger lumps to be handled. They are used for handling friable, heavy, or abrasive materials ranging from fines to heavy lumps.

The **power** required to drive an elevator is an uncertain quantity, largely because all of the load is not discharged at the discharge chute. In the most carefully designed elevators some recirculation takes place. Duplicate elevators handling the same feed will not always require the same power. In view of these uncertainties many designers select an elevator capable of handling the nominal load with the buckets 75 percent full. Fifty percent is then added to the horsepower computed to lift this load. The resulting motor will be adequate to handle recirculation and other losses.

Arm elevators are the simplest type of equipment for elevating or lowering packages at steep angles or vertically. They are usually constructed of one or two strands of continuous chain with projections or arms at intervals. When such elevators are equipped with finger-arm carriers or solid tray arms, packages can be picked up automatically from loading fingers or stations on the up side and discharged over the top. When loaded on the down side, fragile packages can be safely lowered to any desired level. As gravity lowerers, controlled by small motors or mechanical brakes, these elevators have fairly wide application. Because of their flexibility, they find extensive use in multistory storage buildings and in industrial plants where space is important.

The **suspended-tray elevator** (Fig. 13), also known as the pivoted-tray elevator, consists of a series of pivoted suspended trays attached to two strands of endless chain running over top and bottom sprockets. Because trays or carriers are freely pivoted at the points of attachment to the chain, the weight of the load, always centered well below these suspension points, holds the tray in a level position as it passes over the sprockets. Suspended tray elevator-lowerers may be divided into two general classes: the simple swing-tray machine with solid or specially constructed trays, which are loaded and unloaded wholly or partly by hand; and the highly developed automatic loading and discharging machine.

Reciprocating elevators are those equipped with an electric hoist which raises or lowers a counter-weighted car or platform, operating along suitable guides, by means of a chain or cable over a sprocket or sheave. The construction is simpler than that of the continuous-elevator type such as the suspended-tray elevator; hence the cost is less. Such an elevator handles packages, cartons, barrels, boxes, pallets, or trays but is used where great capacity is not required.

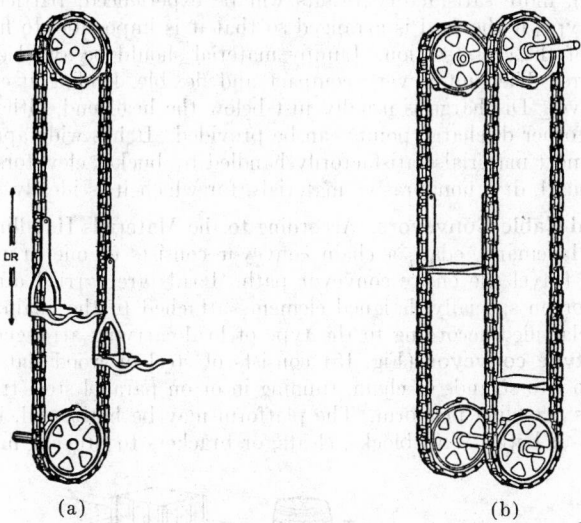

(a)   (b)

Chain Belt Co.

Fig. 13. Typical tray elevators.

The **en masse** conveyor (Fig. 14) is one of the several classifications of elevating conveyors. It consists of a series of flights totally enclosed and capable of conveying on any slope up to and including the vertical. The distinguishing feature is a rectangular casing in which a partition separates the carrying run from the return run. In this casing is carried a single strand of chain on which

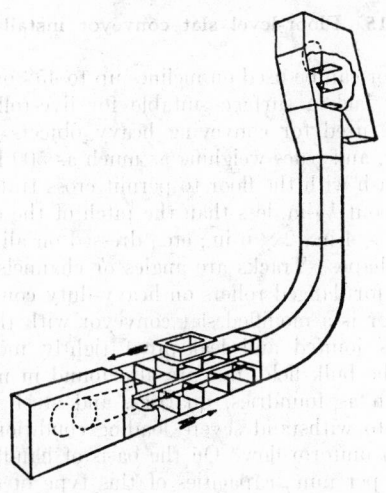

Chain Belt Co

Fig. 14. En masse conveyor-elevator.

the flights are mounted on relatively short spacing. In most types the flights fill the cross section except for working clearance.

Medley says that while conventional flight conveyors are almost always fed, the **en masse** type is an exception, as it is more frequently used as a self-feeder. When used as such, more satisfactory results will be experienced, particularly in the solid flight type, if the feed is arranged so that it is impossible to fill more than 90 percent of the cross section. Lumpy material should be avoided in the case of self-feeders. The unit is very compact and flexible, lending itself to various paths of travel. Discharge is usually just below the head end, although in horizontal units other discharge points can be provided. It has wide application and will handle most materials satisfactorily handled by bucket elevators, in addition to finely ground, dry, nonabrasive materials, for which it is ideally suited.

Chain and Cable Conveyors. According to the Materials Handling Handbook (Bolz and Hagemann, eds.), a chain conveyor consists of one or more **endless chains** that travel the entire conveyor path. Loads are carried directly on the chain links or on specially designed elements attached to the chain. These conveyors are classified according to the type of load-carrying arrangement used.

The **slat-type conveyor** (Fig. 15) consists of steel or wood slats attached at their ends to two strands of chain, running in or on parallel steel tracks to form a continuous traveling platform. The platform may be horizontal, inclined, or a combination of both. With blocks, cleats, or brackets to prevent materials from

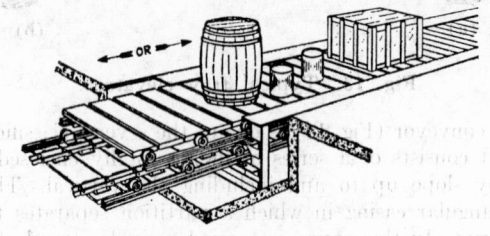

Chain Belt Co.

Fig. 15. Floor-level slat conveyor installation.

shifting, a slat conveyor can be used on inclines up to 45° or more. It is normally used where the loads lack a surface suitable for live-roll conveyors or would damage belting. It is used for conveying heavy objects or packages, such as cartons, boxes, barrels, and bales weighing as much as 500 lb. Slat conveyors are frequently installed flush with the floor to permit cross traffic.

The slat width is about ½-in. less than the pitch of the chain. Wood slats are of commercial sizes, 2×4 in., 2×6 in., etc., dressed on all sides. Steel slats may be flat bars or steel shapes. Tracks are angles or channels for plain rollers and standard rail sections for flanged rollers on heavy-duty conveyors.

The **apron conveyor** is a modified slat conveyor with the "slats" overlapping to form a continuous jointed and leak-proof tightly moving bed. They are primarily known in the bulk field, but are also found in many heavy-duty unit type installations such as foundries, quarries, and steel plants. This type of conveyor is designed to withstand severe loading conditions and high temperatures, and to deliver a uniform flow. On the basis of handling 50 lb. of material per cu. ft., at 100 ft. per min., capacities of this type of equipment vary from 80 tons per hr. for an apron 18 in. wide to 290 tons per hr. for an apron 60 in.

wide. Such conveyors are usually operated at speeds ranging from 60 to 100 ft. per min. and can negotiate inclines up to 25°.

The simplest of the chain types is that consisting of a single strand of chain riding in a steel track and serving as a carrier for the object to be conveyed. This equipment, sometimes referred to as a **drag chain** or **carrier chain conveyor,** is designed to convey light, small, and uniform-size objects such as bottled beverages, bottled milk, and pineapples, and can be designed to carry heavy steel drums and logs. Multiple-strand conveyors are also available. These conveyors can turn 90° corners with most loads. The chain usually is guided in a steel track at turns.

Car-type chain conveyors are used in foundries (Fig. 16) to move flasks from molding to pouring, to shake out empty flasks, etc. Other varieties of pallet conveyors are used in assembly operations where the work is not suited to flat-belt conveyors, and pallets designed for holding specific parts carry them through progressive assembly operations. These conveyors are often intermittent in movement and operations are performed without removing the work from the pallet.

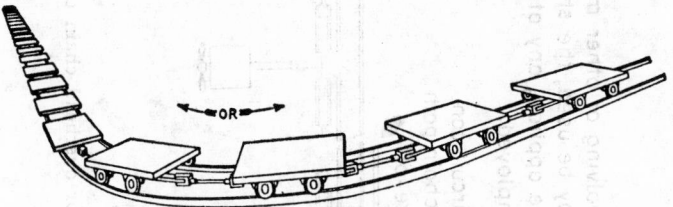

Chain Belt Co.

Fig. 16. Foundry car-type chain installation.

The accomplishments of the carrier attachments are the sole purpose of the chain conveyor system. In many systems the attachments are no more than hooks on which materials are hung for transportation and storage. There are many varieties (Fig. 17), and some producers design and manufacture overhead chain conveyor attachments as their principal business. Most **monorail systems** would be more effective if greater attention were paid to carrier attachment function and design.

Carrier attachments can be pivoted on the chain pins or swivels to create rotary or other motions of the load, thus increasing effectiveness of electroplating baths, cleaning baths, etc.

The monorail chain conveyor is also known as the **trolley conveyor.** It consists of an endless-circuit overhead monorail track beneath which moves an endless chain connected to trolleys at regular intervals. Two-wheel trolleys carry the load by means of hooks, racks, special carriers, etc., and the chain pulls them along. Line of travel may include 90° and 180° bends from the horizontal, and inclines up to 45° from the vertical, depending upon the spacing of trolleys and loads carried. Special installations have been made where the load is also carried vertically as well as horizontally. The most common application for this type of equipment is feeding from subassembly lines to assembly conveyors, or for carrying parts through spraying, plating, baking, painting, and other operations. It is widely used in the automobile and meat-packing industries.

The conveyor also acts as a **storage medium** because if an object is not removed it will recirculate over the system repeatedly until taken off at the point where

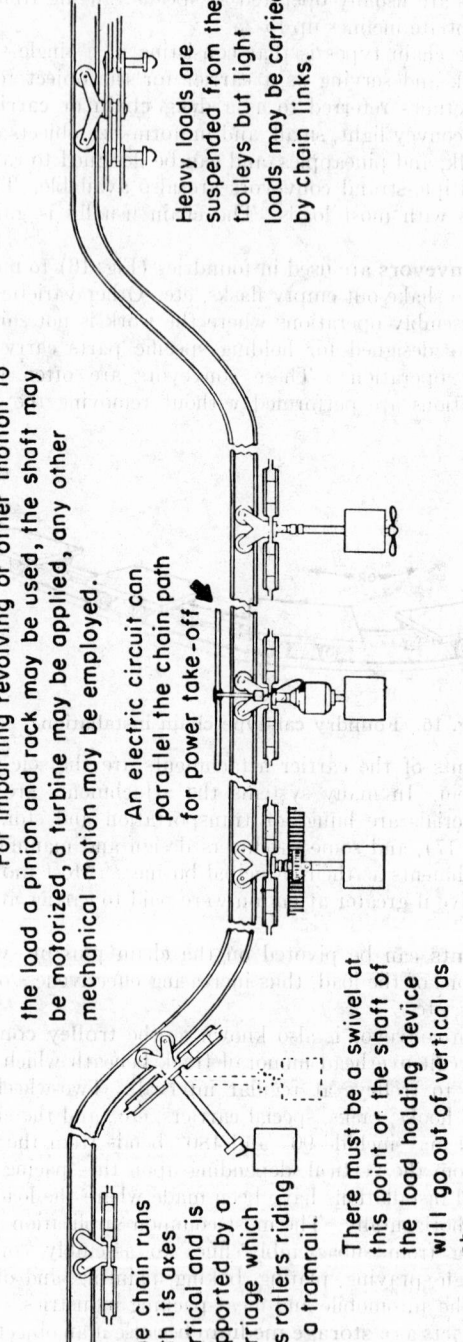

For imparting revolving or other motion to the load a pinion and rack may be used, the shaft may be motorized, a turbine may be applied, any other mechanical motion may be employed.

An electric circuit can parallel the chain path for power take-off.

Heavy loads are suspended from the trolleys but light loads may be carried by chain links.

There must be a swivel at this point or the shaft of the load holding device will go out of vertical as shown.

The chain runs with its axes vertical and is supported by a carriage which has rollers riding on a tramrail.

Mill & Factory

Fig. 17. Typical accessories for overhead chain conveyors.

it is needed. By utilizing the ceiling for transportation, floor space is saved and the vertical or inclined line of travel permits easy unloading at working height.

The 3-in. and 4-in. (I-beam size) chain conveyors are the most common. Horizontal turns are made by means of multiple-roller curves—useful because of low friction resistance and large radii—and by traction wheels. The latter method is best when the conveyor passes through temperatures of 400° or more because of its simple lubrication.

Drives are of the corner-sprocket or the caterpillar type. The former is used except where the corner radius is too large. Drives should be at the point of maximum pull and near a down curve, if any exists, to take chain slack away from the drive. The drives should never be in ovens or spray booths. Radii of vertical dips should be as large as practicable. If the conveyor has more than four horizontal turns, it is necessary to calculate the pull on the chain progressively and to add 5 percent for friction loss at each turn.

In some instances a monorail-type conveyor uses a **cable** in place of the chain to transmit the power. The general principles of operation of the cable type are similar to those with chain. There are some differences in sprocket design and long downhill runs usually must be avoided to prevent "piling up" of the carriers as a result of the lack of rigidity of the cable.

Bulk materials are frequently carried in cars or buckets on **aerial tramways.** In this case the cable is usually a continuously running power system and the carriers are automatically locked onto it at the point where the load is placed in the system and unlocked at the point of delivery. Such a means of transportation is ideally adapted to rugged terrain and is sometimes used to cross cultivated land since the area lost from cultivation is only that occupied by the cable supporting towers.

There are four general classifications of tramways for bulk materials handling. The **monocable tramway** was the earliest development of the group. One endless running rope is used for supporting as well as moving the carrier. It is rarely used now. The **single reversible tramway** uses one track cable and one bucket which is fastened to a continuous traction rope driven by machinery which imparts a reciprocating motion to it. This type of tramway is widely used for disposing of mine waste. In such cases an automatic tripping carriage is used which opens the bucket when the pull on the traction rope is reversed.

The **double reversible tramway** is used for much the same purpose as the single reversible type when larger capacity is required. It is constructed with two track cables of the same diameter, continuous traction rope, two buckets and a drive which produces a reversing motion in the traction rope. The bucket may be automatically dumped as with the single reversible type, but the dumping point is fixed by the spacing of the buckets on the traction ropes. Consequently this type is not so flexible as to dumping point as is the other.

The **continuous bicable tramway** is the type most frequently used for transporting material from one fixed point to another, although it can be arranged for dumping at intermediate points by the use of trip frames. Two stationary track cables are used with single continuous traction ropes to which carriers are fitted by means of grips. The return track rope can be made smaller than the loaded track rope because the carriers return without load.

Haulage Conveyors. According to the Materials Handling Handbook (Bolz and Hagemann, eds.):

The main classifications under the general heading of haulage conveyors are drag conveyors, flight conveyors, and tow conveyors. The first two divisions—those of drag and flight types of conveyors—involve dragging and pushing of material by means of a chain, or chains, traveling against all sorts of variations in materials and products, making use in some cases of flights and in other cases of the surfaces innate in the chains themselves. The chain of the third division—tow conveyors—actually tows materials, packaged or otherwise, placed on trucks, dollies, or cars.

A **floor-type system** frequently used in assembly lines and warehouses consists of a chain or other linkage mounted near or flush with the floor and guided by tracks. Pulling or pushing attachments connect to the unit in motion and, in the case of assembly lines, tracks often guide the wheels supporting the work unit. In most instances these conveyors are timed to pace the assembly or machining operations and maintain continuous motion. In some instances periodic moves are used.

Among the many applications of the **tow conveyor** flexible system is the **order-picking lines** of warehouses. In most cases, a slot is built into the floor and a simple, single strand chain-type conveyor is installed below it. In these cases a warehouse trailer or hand truck is pushed or towed to a point above the slot in the floor and a rod is dropped into a linkage point in the chain below. The truck is then pulled to its destination without further manual effort. An automatic disconnecting device can be installed at the point of delivery.

In some cases the propelling chain is mounted overhead and the trailer is connected by means of tow rods. These systems are useful for delivering orders from the picking area of the warehouse to the shipping dock or for maintaining continuous motion of the order-picking truck while the warehouseman removes merchandise from shelves or pallets to build the order. They can also replace tractor-trailer systems in some instances.

Drag conveyors consist largely of one or more endless propelling mediums, usually chains or cables, which drag materials in a trough, or along a defined path. The materials being carried rest on the chain.

Cross-bar conveyors consist of two strands of chain with cross-bars mounted between the chains at regular intervals and moving above a stationary bed. The cross-bars push the loads, such as packages or boxes, horizontally or up an incline. This type of conveyor is also sometimes known as a booster or pusher-bar elevator (Fig. 18) and is used extensively as a grade retriever in gravity conveyor systems. It is also used for elevating or lowering packages from one floor to another and is

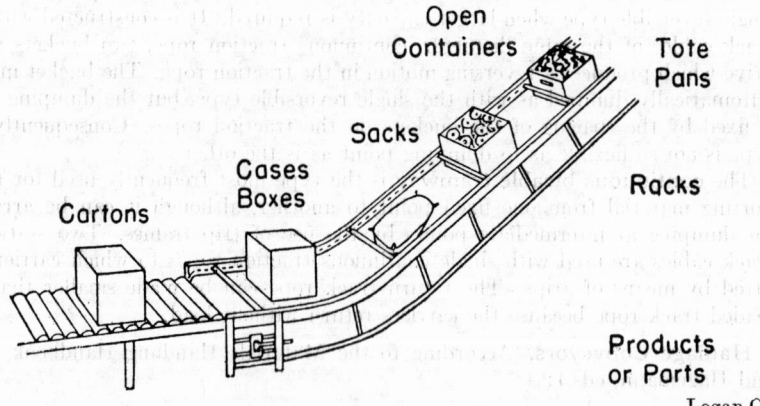

Logan Co.

Fig. 18. Pusher-bar elevator.

suited for a fairly uniform range of packages, or for practically any object of sufficient solidity and shape to slide on a runway at inclines of 30° to 60°. Capacities range from 500 to 1,200 packages per hr. at a chain speed of 60 to 90 ft. per min.

In the **flight conveyor** (Fig. 19) scrapers or flights replace the pusher bars described above and serve to push bulk materials along a stationary trough. For light conveyors a single strand of chain is sometimes used, while two strands are used for heavier units.

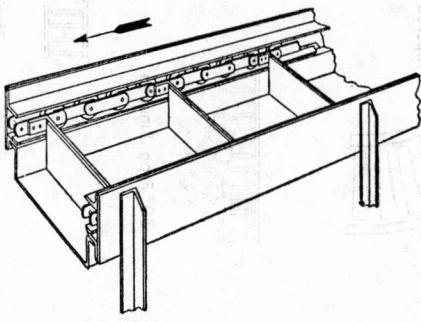

Chain Belt Co.

Fig. 19. Scraper flight conveyor.

The principal advantages of flight conveyors are their ability to negotiate slopes up to 45° and to deliver material at intermediate points. The disadvantages are high power consumption and rapid wear on trough bottoms and sides. This susceptibility to wear makes it unsuitable for use with the more abrasive materials. A lesser disadvantage is the build-up of sticky material on the scrapers when such material is being handled.

The power requirements for flight conveyors are dependent upon the material being handled and the design of the equipment. Calculations should be based upon vendor information.

Roller-flight conveyors differ from the above mainly in that the flights are supported on tracks by rollers, thus reducing power requirements by replacing sliding friction with rolling friction.

Roller and Skate Wheel Conveyors. The skate-wheeled conveyor equipment can be further broken down into standard skate-wheel units and single-rail-type units. Single-rail units are often used in pairs or sets for special handling operations. A gravity conveyor is used in both portable and permanent installations. The supports vary with the requirements. Wheel conveyors are available with steel, aluminum, magnesium, or stainless steel frames; steel, aluminum, and plastic wheels; closed tops; open tops; and in various capacities. The skate wheel conveyor is usually considered most practical for smooth-bottom unit items such as cartons, boxes, trays, and bundles. It is not usually desirable for installations where irregular surfaces might be encountered and is not capable of withstanding much impact or cross loading. It is the least expensive, most easily repaired type of gravity equipment for many package-handling installations. In most cases a grade of 5 in. per 10 ft. of conveyor will give a free flow for smooth, hard-bottomed packages.

A roller conveyor is usually more rugged and versatile than a wheel conveyor. Roller conveyors can be built to carry heavy loads and to withstand severe im-

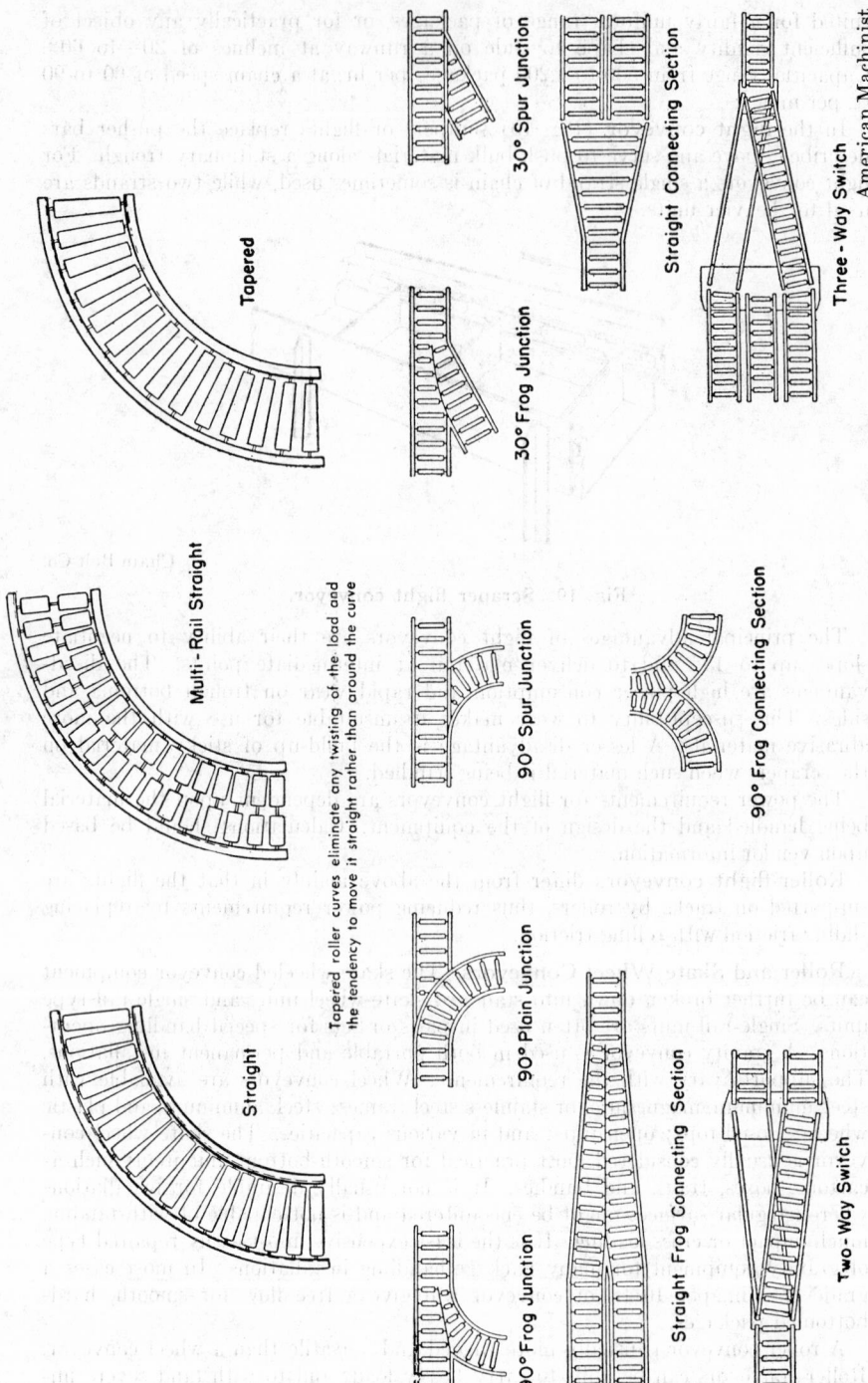

Fig. 20. Typical roller conveyor junctions, spurs, and switches.

American Machinist

pact and cross loading. It is occasionally built in a "V" or "U" troughed form to handle cylindrical objects, such as coils of steel, beer kegs, and ammunition. It is also used to handle items from light-weight packaged materials to heavy castings, molds, and machine parts. In general, the roller conveyor consists of two laterally braced channels with equally spaced holes punched in the webs, and tubular steel rollers supported by antifriction bearings are usually suspended between these channels. As in the case of the skate wheel conveyor, the plane of rolling can be either above or below the frame, depending upon whether the frame is to be used as a guide. Roller conveyors are available in standard widths from 6 in. to 36 in. and on special order can be made almost any width. The size of the roll depends upon the weight of the object to be conveyed and whether or not the roll will be subject to shock from loads dropped on the conveyor.

Roller and wheel conveyors are available in adjustable length designs known as "accordion" and telescopic conveyors. This equipment is commonly used in situations where the work station is changed frequently or where the conveyor must be retracted when not in use to permit cross traffic.

Directional changes are made by switching devices of all types and curved track sections. Fig. 20 shows simple switch designs and curves.

Fig. 21 shows a typical conveyor junction switching between power and gravity equipment. In complex installations, the gravity conveyor is often fed by and delivers to the power conveyor. Switches, junctions, and various other devices utilize gravity where it is available. A power conveyor is often used to elevate or regain height for long gravity runs.

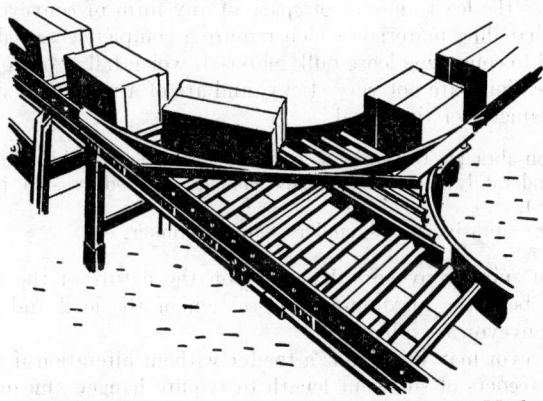

Mathews Conveyer Co.

Fig. 21. Typical power to gravity roller switch.

Live roller conveyors are substantially roller conveyors powered by a belt snubbed against the underside of the carrying rolls. The result is a powered roller conveyor which is ideally suited for automatic accumulation or temporary storage.

The flat-belt type of live roller drive is commonly used when the conveyor is straight, while the round-belt type is used when there are curves in the conveyor. With this type of conveyor the load can be moved up or down grades and can be stopped without undue friction. Roller-chain and sprocket drives are also used to drive the rollers. Loads should have rigid riding surfaces, but need not be of uniform weight. Fragile loads should not be handled on conveyors where storage occurs, because of the danger of breakage due to blocking.

Chutes are a common handling device for both bulk and unit materials. However, they are likely to require more field alteration than any other equipment when used for bulk handling. Material behavior is greatly influenced by size, consistency, and moisture content. In carbon steel chutes the following slope data can be used as a guide for installation:

Dry, unsized material containing the normal percentage of pieces at least
1½ in. in size .... 35°
Clean, dry, sized material with all sizes smaller than 14 mesh removed and
with the largest particles not more than 3 times the size of the smallest... 26°
Dry fines .... 55°
For damp materials, increase these angles 15°.
For stainless steel chutes, these angles may be reduced 5° to 10°.

Flumes are special cases of chutes in which solids mixed with a liquid, generally water, are transported. Since the mixture of solids and water is often the result of a process which controls the percentage of solids, the conveyability may not be ideal. In cases where the weight of the water is less than that of the material to be moved, it is desirable to use a trapezoidal cross section with a narrow bottom to prevent the water from short circuiting the solids.

Spiral Conveyors. According to Medley the spiral conveyor (Fig. 22), often referred to as screw conveyor, consists of a metal helix, usually steel, fastened to a shaft and suspended between suitable bearings in a U-shaped trough or tube.

The spiral conveyor has no return strand or other outside parts and consequently requires the least amount of space of any form of conveyor, and readily lends itself to handling materials which require a completely sealed conveyor. It is best adapted to conveying loose bulk materials which fall in one of the following general classifications, are not very sticky, and are of a maximum size not greater than ¼ the diameter of the spiral.

Class 1. Non-abrasive (bituminous coal, crushed asphalt, pebble lime, etc.).
Class 2. Moderately abrasive (portland cement, crushed gypsum, phosphate rock, etc.).
Class 3. Very abrasive (coke, cinders, cement clinker, etc.).

Capacities of spiral conveyors depend upon the nature of the material to be handled, since both the maximum cross section of the load and the maximum speed of the conveyor are affected.

A spiral conveyor may be used as a **feeder** without alteration if no hangers are required. For feeders of sufficient length to require hangers, means of providing the equivalent of a reduced cross section of load must be used. Two methods are to reduce the pitch or to reduce the diameter at the loading point and for some distance beyond it.

Pneumatic Conveyors. The Conveyor Equipment Manufacturers Association recently completed an excellent study recommending standard nomenclature for all conveyors. The pneumatic conveyor is defined as "a system of tubes, or ducts, through which objects or bulk materials are conveyed in a pressure and/or vacuum system."

Its application is "in any production or warehousing operation that handles granular or other fine bulk materials, which are not sticky or fragile; additionally, for unloading freight cars, ships and barges, and for rehandling bulk material into storage."

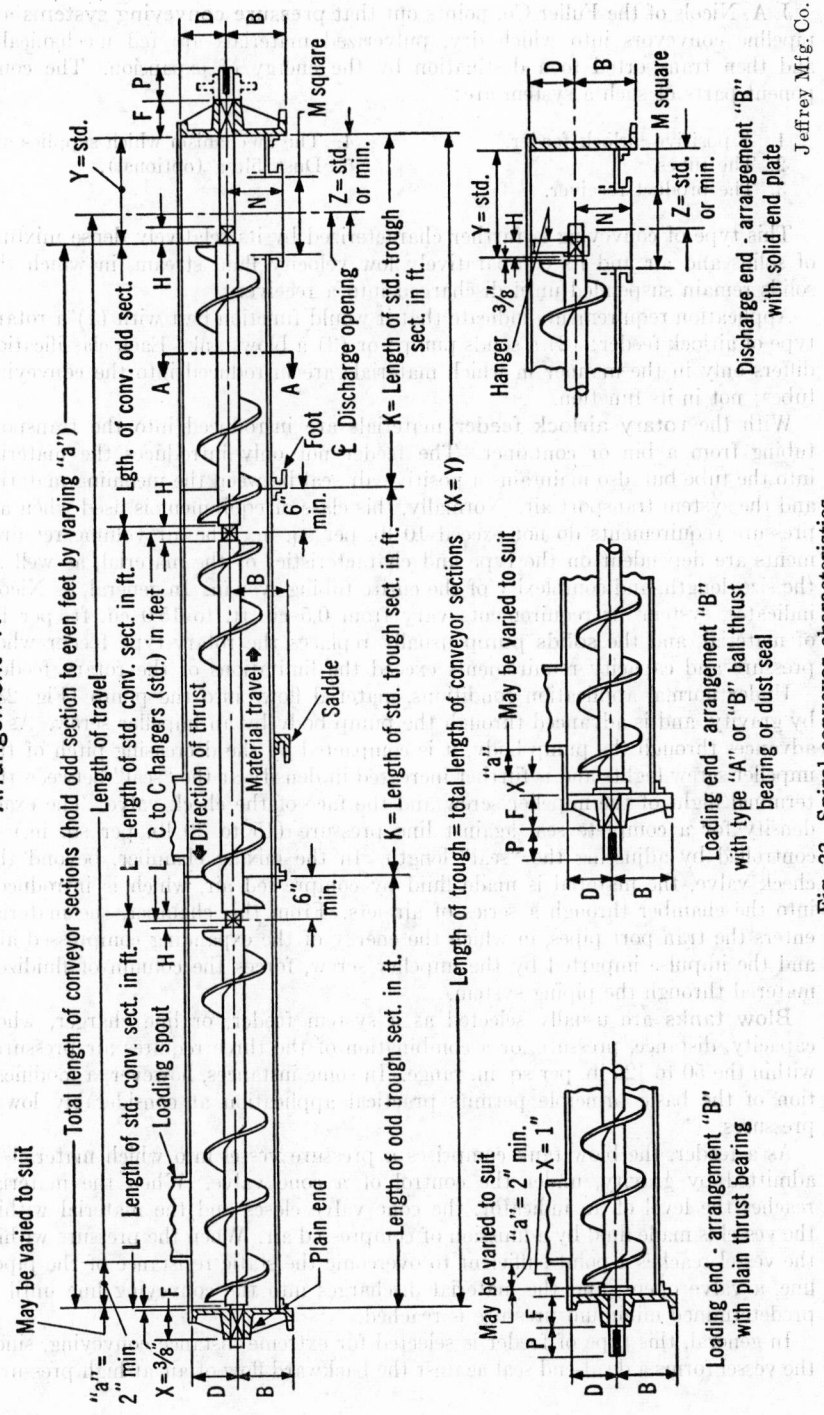

Fig. 22. Spiral conveyor characteristics.

Jeffrey Mfg. Co.

J. A. Nicols of the Fuller Co. points out that **pressure conveying systems** are pipeline conveyors into which dry, pulverized materials are fed mechanically and then transported to a destination by the energy of expansion. The component parts of such a system are:

1. A positive airlock feeder.
2. The tubes.
3. The product receiver.

4. The mechanism which supplies air.
5. Dust filter (optional).

This type of conveying is further characterized by its relatively dense mixture of solids and air and its comparatively low velocity fluid stream, in which the solids remain suspended until discharged into a receiver.

Application requirements indicate that it would function best with (1) a rotary type of airlock feeder; (2) a solids pump; or (3) a blow tank. Each classification differs only in the manner in which materials are introduced into the conveying tubes; not in its function.

With the **rotary airlock feeder** materials are introduced into the transport tubing from a bin or container. The feeder not only introduces the material into the tube but also maintains a positive air seal between the incoming material and the system transport air. Normally, this class of equipment is used when air pressure requirements do not exceed 10 lb. per sq. in. The air volume requirements are dependent on the type and characteristics of the material, as well as the size, length, and complexity of the entire tubing system. In general, as Nicols indicates, system air requirements vary from 0.5 cu. ft. to 15.0 cu. ft. per lb. of material, and the **solids pump** usually replaces the rotary-type feeder when pressure and capacity requirements exceed the limitations of the rotary feeder.

Under normal application conditions, material flows into the pump (Fig. 23) by gravity, and is advanced through the pump body by an impeller screw. As it advances through the pump body, it is compacted by the decreasing pitch of the impeller screw flights and is further increased in density at the "seal" between the terminal flight of the impeller screw and the face of the check valve. The exact density for a complete seal against line pressure (15 to 30 lb. per sq. in.) is controlled by adjusting the "seal" length. In the mixing chamber, beyond the check valve, the material is made fluid by compressed air, which is introduced into the chamber through a series of air jets. From this chamber, the material enters the transport pipes, in which the energy of the expanding compressed air, and the impulse imparted by the impeller screw, forces the column of fluidized material through the piping system.

Blow tanks are usually selected as a system feeder, or line charger, when capacity, distance, pressure, or a combination of the three requires air pressures within the 50 to 125 lb. per sq. in. range. In some instances, however, a modification of the basic principle permits practical application at considerably lower pressures.

As a feeder, the blow tank comprises a pressure vessel into which material is admitted by gravity, under the control of a cone valve. When the material reaches the level of an indicator, the cone valve closes and the material within the vessel is made fluid by admission of compressed air. When the pressure within the vessel reaches a point sufficient to overcome the static resistance of the pipeline, a valve opens, and the material discharges into the conveying line until a predetermined minimum pressure is reached.

In general, this type of feeder is selected for extreme distance conveying, since the vessel forms a dead-end seal against the backward flow of air at high pressure

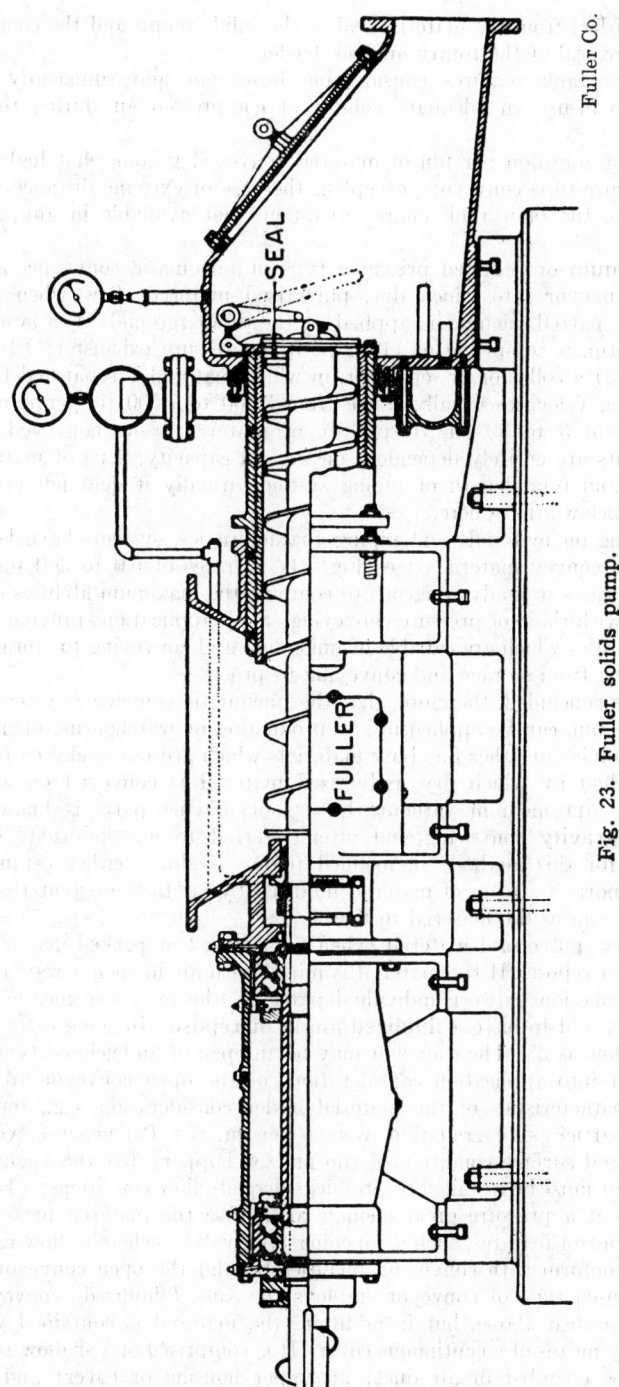

Fig. 23. Fuller solids pump.

Fuller Co.

as distinguished from the material seal of the solids pump and the comparatively low pressure seal of the rotary air lock feeder.

The blow tank requires considerable headroom and sufficiently large air receivers to insure an adequate volume of compressed air during the blowing period.

Power consumption per ton of material conveyed is somewhat higher than in other pressure-type conveyors, except in the case of extreme distance conveying. In this case the blow tank offers advantages not available in any other type of feeder.

The **vacuum** or **reduced pressure** type of pneumatic conveying identifies a pipeline conveyor into which dry, pulverized materials flow when a reduced pressure or partial vacuum is applied at the discharge end. The system, in its simplest form, is comprised of (1) a positive pressure exhauster; (2) a system of tubes; (3) a collector or separator, in which material is separated from air.

Conveying velocities usually range from 3,000 to 7,500 ft. per min., and air volumes from 3 to 30 cu. ft. per lb. of material being conveyed. Pressure requirements are entirely dependent on system capacity, type of material being conveyed, and total length of piping system; usually it does not exceed 5 lb. per sq. in. below atmosphere.

Depending on materials and piping characteristics, systems have been developed which convey materials (see Fig. 24) at rates of 5.0 to 300 tons per hr.

In many cases it is advantageous to combine the maximum abilities of vacuum conveying with those of pressure conveying. Such applications provide in a single system facilities which are capable of unloading and conveying to storage, as well as reclaiming from storage and conveying to process.

It can be concluded, therefore, that the pneumatic conveying system, pressure and/or vacuum, can be applied in any production or warehousing operation that handles granular or other fine bulk materials which are not sticky or fragile.

The method by which dry, pulverized material is conveyed on an inclined porous (to air) medium without the use of moving parts is known as **air-activated gravity** conveying and often referred to as "fluidized" conveying. Normally, for this method, an inclined porous medium, either ceramic tile or fabric, supports a stream of material fluidized by air to the extent that gravitational force causes the material to flow.

Every dry, pulverized material, when not aerated or packed, has a determinable angle of repose. If the material is mixed with air in such a way as to break down the cohesion between individual particles, the mass becomes activated or fluid, and is said to have a **fluidized angle of repose.** In some cases this angle may be as low as 2°. The conveyor may be an open or an enclosed type. Factors which enter into application considerations of the open conveyor are: (1) the physical characteristics of the material under consideration, e.g., temperature, moisture, particle size, gradation, weight per cu. ft.; (2) general over-all configuration and surface condition of silo and/or hopper; (3) the angle at which the conveyor must be installed to produce adequate flow conditions; (4) sufficient air volume at a pressure great enough to fluidize the material mass; and (5) adequate control features, such as openings and valves, whereby flow can be controlled to conform with conveying facilities beyond the open conveyor.

The enclosed type of conveyor employs the same "fluidized" conveying principle as described above, but in addition, the material is contained within the conveyor by means of a continuous cover. It is comprised of a shallow rectangular plenum-type chamber or air duct; an upper housing or cover; and a porous

Material	Solids Pump and Blow Tank	Vacuum or Pressure	Air Activated Conveyor
Alum	✓	✓	✓
Aluminum oxide	✓		✓
Ammonium sulphate	✓	✓	✓
Arsenic oxide	✓	✓	✓
Asbestos dust	✓	✓	✓
Asphalt fillers	✓	✓	✓
Barite	✓	✓	✓
Bauxite	✓	✓	✓
Beet pulp, dried		✓	✓
Bentonite	✓	✓	✓
Bone, steamed		✓	✓
Borax		✓	✓
Brucite			✓
Calcium carbonate	✓	✓	✓
Calcium phosphates	✓	✓	✓
Carbon, activated		✓	✓
Carbon black	✓	✓	✓
Catalysts, petroleum	✓	✓	✓
Cellulose acetate		✓	✓
Cement, portland	✓	✓	✓
Cement raw material	✓	✓	✓
Cereals		✓	✓
Chalk	✓	✓	✓
Chromite		✓	✓
Clays	✓	✓	✓
Coal, pulverized	✓	✓	✓
Coffee beans, green		✓	✓
Coffee solubles		✓	✓
Coke dust	✓	✓	✓
Copper converter dust	✓	✓	✓
Copra		✓	✓
Cornflakes (brewers')		✓	✓
Corn grits		✓	✓
Corn germ		✓	✓
Cottonseed meal	✓	✓	✓
Cryolite		✓	✓
Cyanamid		✓	✓
Detergent powders		✓	✓
Dextrin		✓	✓
Diatomaceous earth		✓	✓
Dicyandiamide	✓	✓	✓
Dolomite		✓	✓
Eggs, dried	✓	✓	✓
Feed ingredients		✓	✓
Feeds, soft		✓	✓
Feldspar	✓	✓	✓
Ferrochrome		✓	✓
Fertilizers	✓	✓	✓
Flaxseed		✓	✓
Flint	✓	✓	✓
Flour		✓	✓
Flour premixes		✓	✓
Flue dusts	✓	✓	✓
Fluorspar		✓	✓
Fly ash	✓	✓	✓
Fuller's earth	✓	✓	✓
Gilsonite	✓	✓	✓
Gluten meal		✓	✓
Grains		✓	✓
Graphite		✓	✓
Gypsum (raw or calcined)	✓	✓	✓
Ilmenite	✓	✓	✓
Iron salts		✓	✓
Lime, hydrated		✓	✓
Lime, pebble		✓	✓
Lime, pulverized	✓	✓	✓
Limestone, pulverized	✓	✓	✓
Litharge		✓	✓
Magnesite		✓	✓
Magnesium oxide		✓	✓
Malt		✓	✓
Manganese dioxide	✓	✓	✓
Milk, dried		✓	✓
Mineral wool	✓	✓	✓
Nylon pellets		✓	✓
Ores, pulverized	✓	✓	✓
Petroleum coke (fluid process)		✓	✓
Phosphate rock, pulverized	✓	✓	✓
Polyethylene		✓	✓
Pyrites	✓	✓	✓
Quartz, pulverized	✓	✓	✓
Resins, synthetic		✓	✓
Rice		✓	✓
Rubber pellets		✓	✓
Salt		✓	✓
Salt cake	✓	✓	✓
Sawdust		✓	✓
Seeds		✓	✓
Semolina		✓	✓
Shells, pulverized		✓	✓
Silica, pulverized	✓	✓	✓
Slag, pulverized	✓	✓	✓
Slate, pulverized	✓	✓	✓
Soap powders		✓	✓
Soda Ash	✓	✓	✓
Sodium bicarbonate		✓	✓
Sodium phosphates	✓	✓	✓
Starches		✓	✓
Sugars, refined		✓	✓
Talc	✓	✓	✓
Titanium dioxide	✓		✓
Wood chips		✓	
Wood flour		✓	✓
Zinc oxide		✓	✓

Fig. 24. Air-conveyable materials.

Fuller Co.

medium of low permeability secured between the lower and upper housing (Fig. 25).

Until recently, the principal uses of this type of conveyor were in the cement industry. Its utility in the handling of other materials, however, is being continually extended to the conveying of such materials as gypsum, soda ash, fly ash, flour, hydrated lime, ground ores, detergents, and soap powders. In this application of the closed-type conveyor, the material is transferred from bulk car to bulk van, each equipped with the open type conveyor.

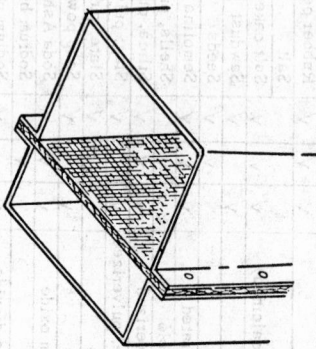

Fuller Co.

Fig. 25. Section through an air-activated gravity conveyor.

Recent developments in chemistry have resulted in the need for corrosion-resistant and clog-proof pipeline systems. This has led to the development of alloy, copper, aluminum, glass, plastic, and lined piping, as well as a great many varieties of corrosion-resistant and clog-proof pumps and valves. For example, the dairy industry, where lactic acid in the milk makes metallic joints difficult to maintain and where, moreover, sanitation laws often require glass piping, is using Pyrex pipe and Teflon joint gaskets to meet these problems.

The increased use of fluids to transport solids in suspension has also resulted in the development of specialized machinery and equipment. Finely divided solids, such as coal, are transported over long distances in this manner.

In some cases **jet streams** and aspirator-type systems are used for short-run hydraulic tranportation of solid products. This is not the most economical application, however.

Although the initial installation for handling solids in a hydraulic system might require a large investment in special pumping equipment and abrasive- or corrosion-resistant piping, the maintenance and operating costs are very low. In addition, the application of gravity to these systems is rather simple and contamination is usually impossible.

The technical data required for the installation of hydraulic equipment are largely empirical and thus should be developed in cooperation with equipment suppliers for each installation.

Vibrating Conveyors. Vibrating conveyors transport any granular material which is not sticky or tacky through the application of strokes which cause the material to hop along the conveyor. The conveyor consists of a flexibly supported trough or tube, and vibration may be induced **electrically** with a balanced electric power unit (Fig. 26), or **mechanically** by an eccentric shaft connected to the deck or trough (Fig. 27). The material, being free to move, does not return with the backward movement of the deck, but falls under the force of gravity until it is intercepted by the next forward and upward stroke. Thus, while in appearance the movement of the material is that of a uniform flowing stream, it is, in reality, a continuous series of rapid, short forward hops which are imperceptible to the eye. This hopping action keeps the material in suspension so that there is no sliding action on the deck surface. Abrasive wear on the deck is therefore negligible, and for this reason, on large tonnages material can be handled most economically. (The Materials Handling Handbook, Bolz and Hagemann, eds.)

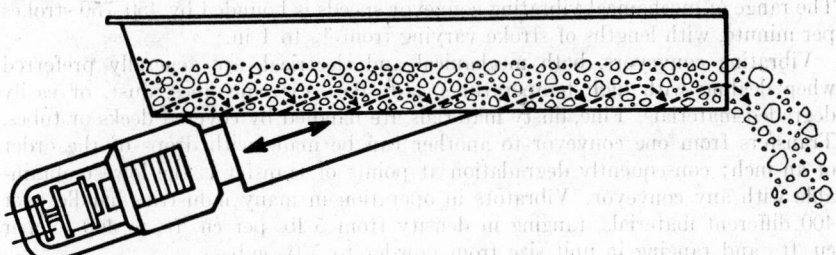

Jeffrey Mfg. Co.

Fig. 26. Electromagnetic vibrating conveyor.

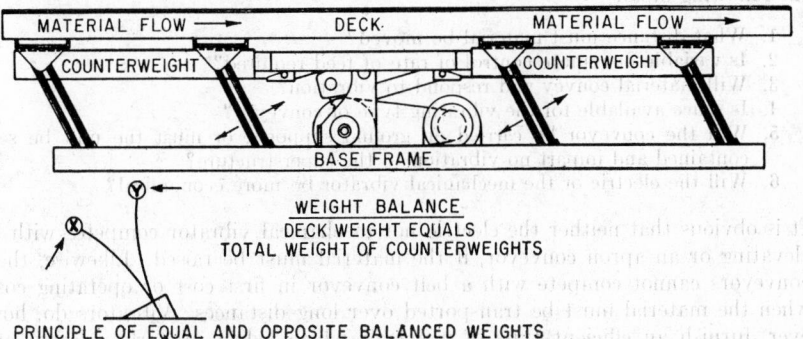

Fig. 27. Mechanical vibrating conveyor.

The feeder trough of vibrating feeders is designed so that it is only long enough to stop the material, at its natural angle of repose, from running off the end of the deck when the feeder is standing idle. The vibrating conveyor may be of any length desired, however, so the angle of repose of the material is not the determining factor. Usually, the vibrating conveyor is designed to handle a fixed rate of material flow. When this rate must be carefully controlled, the electric type may be preferred.

The electric vibrators (Fig. 26) are driven by a motor which is made up of an electromagnet called a stator, an armature which is attracted to the stator when the latter is energized, springs which provide restoring force, to which the armature is attached, and a connection from the springs to the deck. The stator and the springs are attached to a main frame which is several times as heavy as the deck and provides the reaction for the deck. It can be considered the machine's foundation. The length of stroke is adjustable in a given machine from a maximum downward. The maximum allowable stroke depends upon the size and design of the particular unit and falls within the range of $\frac{1}{32}$ to $\frac{1}{8}$ in.

Most **mechanical vibrators** (Fig. 27) are built upon the same principle of spring restoring force as the electrics. The means of producing the stroke is a crank or an eccentric driven from some outside source of power, generally an electric motor. The crank or eccentric shaft is mounted on the base and drives the deck through a connecting rod.

Mechanical vibrating conveyors are either balanced or unbalanced. Where the conveyor can be mounted on a solid foundation, the unbalanced conveyor will prove satisfactory and carry a lower first cost. On the other hand, the more expensive balanced type can frequently be mounted on less substantial supports. The range of mechanical vibrating conveyor speeds is bounded by 450–750 strokes per minute, with lengths of stroke varying from 3/8 to 1 in.

Vibrating conveyors, both mechanical and electrical, are generally preferred when dealing with high temperatures, abrasives, extreme fines, dust, or easily degraded materials. Fine, dusty materials are handled by covered decks or tubes. Transfers from one conveyor to another can be made with drops of the order of an inch; consequently degradation at points of transfer is the lowest obtainable with any conveyor. Vibrators in operation in many industries handle over 400 different materials, ranging in density from 5 lb. per cu. ft. to 400 lb. per cu. ft., and ranging in unit size from powder to 5-ft. cubes.

According to the Materials Handling Handbook (Bolz and Hagemann, eds.), the choice of an electric or mechanical vibrator can be assisted by ascertaining the following facts:

1. What distance must material be moved?
2. Is variable or remote control of rate of feed required?
3. Will material convey and respond to vibration?
4. Is space available for the vibrating type of conveyor?
5. Will the conveyor be carried on ground supports, or must the unit be self-contained and impart no vibration to the superstructure?
6. Will the electric or the mechanical vibrator be more economical?

It is obvious that neither the electric nor mechanical vibrator competes with an elevating or an apron conveyor, if the material must be raised. Likewise, these conveyors cannot compete with a belt conveyor in first cost or operating costs when the material must be transported over long distances. Vibrators do, however, furnish an efficient type of conveyor which, when properly selected and applied, is best and most economical for its purposes.

CRANES, ELEVATORS, AND HOISTS. Hall (Material Handling Equipment and Containers—AMHS) defines this group as "all equipment for moving material having a reversing vertical or lateral movement—drum windup and payoff or reciprocating plunger drive." This definition covers all hoists and elevators with a drum windup and payoff as contrasted to the continuous-drive automatic elevating conveyors which are classed as conveyors. Pneumatic and hydraulic plunger hoists, as well as capstans and winches, are included in the crane, elevator, and hoist grouping.

Cranes are versatile lifting and transporting mechanisms that are made adaptable to a wide variety of jobs by the attachment of an almost infinite number of specially designed grabs. This category of equipment may be subdivided broadly into three groups: fixed cranes, traveling cranes, and portable cranes. The first of these groups is generally associated with limited area handling. The second group is capable of travel along a fixed track, and the last is capable of considerable mobility. **Basic crane designs** include jib cranes, gantry cranes, bridge cranes, cableways, towers, and derricks or boom cranes. Each of these designs may be applied to one or more of the three groups described above. The more important design types are treated below.

Jib Cranes. There are several types of jib cranes. They are generally classified according to the type of construction into the five basic groups of bracket jib, cantilever jib, interlocking jib, pillar jib, and walking jib. Jib cranes may be

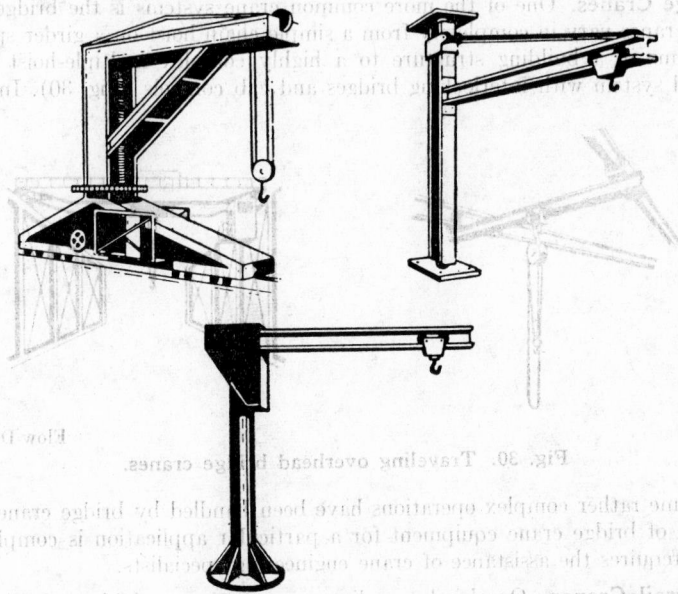

Flow Directory

Fig. 28. Typical jib cranes.

fixed, traveling, or portable and may be used as integral parts of, or as supplements to, many other types of equipment. They range in size from small manual units to loading towers with capacities exceeding 300 tons. The basic design is illustrated in Fig. 28.

Gantry Cranes. Gantry cranes (Fig. 29) are basically bridge cranes which have girders supported at both ends by gantry legs which may be fixed, wheeled to travel on rails, or mounted on casters for portability. They are widely used

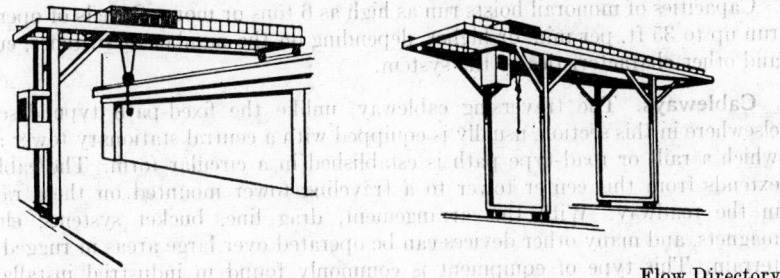

Flow Directory

Fig. 29. Gantry cranes.

outdoors in steel yards, shipyards, etc., or in buildings which will not support a bridge crane structure. There are several variations of the gantry crane. The standard gantry operates on the same principle as the bridge crane. The cantilever type is designed to permit the bridge crane to travel beyond the legs. The semi-gantry is so called because one end of the bridge girders are supported by a building or runway attached to a building and the other by a gantry leg.

Bridge Cranes. One of the more common crane systems is the bridge crane. Bridge cranes vary in complexity from a simple chain hoist on a girder spanning two beams in a building structure to a highly complex multiple-hoist power-operated system with interlocking bridges and cab controls (Fig. 30). In recent

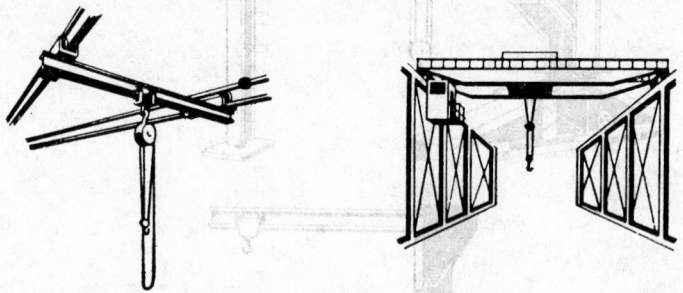

Flow Directory

Fig. 30. Traveling overhead bridge cranes.

years some rather complex operations have been handled by bridge cranes. The selection of bridge crane equipment for a particular application is complex and usually requires the assistance of crane engineering specialists.

Monorail Cranes. Overhead traveling cranes using a rigid track are often called monorail cranes. The monorail, being suspended from the ceiling or other overhead portion of a building, may be installed and used without interfering with operations in the area underneath.

Monorail systems may be floor-operated traveling hoists or can be run by an operator who rides in a cab suspended on trolleys. Practically any kind of power-operated hoist can be used with a monorail system. Slings or skips are often used to handle unit materials, or buckets for bulk loose or wet materials.

Switches and turntables in a monorail system can be manually or electrically operated. Photoelectric cells or indicator pins can be used to actuate the electric mechanisms so that the systems are fully automatic.

Capacities of monorail hoists run as high as 6 tons or more. Speeds of operation run up to 35 ft. per min. or higher, depending on the number of switches, curves, and other characteristics of the system.

Cableways. The traversing cableway, unlike the fixed-path type described elsewhere in this section, usually is equipped with a central stationary tower about which a rail- or road-type path is established in a circular form. The cableway extends from this center tower to a traveling tower mounted on these rails or in the roadway. With this arrangement, drag line, bucket systems, electromagnets, and many other devices can be operated over large areas in rugged open terrain. This type of equipment is commonly found in industrial installations. (Flow Directory.)

Loading and Unloading Towers. Most frequently found in ore and grain ports and rail terminals, these cranes are designed to handle large quantities of materials. They consist of a fixed or revolving tower which may be mounted on gantry legs and which supports a crane structure or hoist mechanism.

Mobile Cranes. Mobile or portable cranes are built in many sizes and capacities. Booms and others of the basic designs referred to above are given broad operating ranges when mounted on a variety of vehicles. The basic types, categorized by their motive power and running gear, include:

1. Crawler-mounted cranes of the track-laying or caterpillar type. They have two parallel continuous crawler or tread belts.
2. Locomotive-mounted cranes, in which the revolving superstructure is mounted on the deck of a railroad car on standard railway trucks, permitting movement on railway trackage.
3. Truck-mounted cranes, which may be operated by a power take-off from the propelling motor or by a separate engine. This type of mounting provides maximum mobility in both speed and distance, with a top speed of approximately 30 miles per hour, permitting highway travel.
4. Wheel-mounted cranes, cranes mounted on a wheeled chassis which may be propelled by the same engine which drives the mechanism on the superstructure. This type is suited for operations that require constant and relatively rapid movement of the crane around the job, such as in a factory or storage yard.

Crane Operations. Yard or plant operations based upon cranes require careful planning. Aisle and bay widths; equipment considerations, such as reach, clearance, and capacity; material weight and placement within bays; material location; and yard or plant operating procedure must be considered, and all have an important bearing on layout. Because the crane is primarily a lifting machine, a major objective of layout is to minimize travel by material location.

Clearance must also be considered in checking a proposed layout. The required vertical height of the boom above the surface must be determined so that the load can be lifted high enough above all surrounding material to be swung to the aisle or roadway. The minimum required boom height is the sum of the height of the surrounding material, the height of the load, the distance from the load to the block, and a clearance height required to permit safe swinging of the load over the surrounding material.

A major advantage of crane storage operations is selectivity. The boom extends over stored materials to pick up the particular items on order without moving or disturbing other materials closer to the crane.

In planning bay layout, lateral **walk-in aisles** must be provided at right angles to the main aisles so "hookers-on" can attach the lifting devices to the loads. These aisles usually can be the clearance spaces between the various stacks, rather than definite aisles. The first step is to establish the required width for the particular crane. The materials to be stored, their bulk, the way they are stored, and the crane dimensions will be the aisle-width criteria.

Elevators. According to the Materials Handling Handbook (Bolz and Hagemann, eds.), a well-planned freight elevator installation in a factory, warehouse, or multistory terminal results in the handling of a greater volume of materials, in lower operating costs, and in higher net earnings. Also, freight elevators can be integrated with almost every method of horizontal materials handling—manual or mechanized—to speed the vertical flow of raw materials and in-process or finished goods.

The following information is developed from data supplied by the Elevator Manufacturers' Association. In all cases the characteristics of the elevators, either passenger or freight, depend on the requirements of the individual installation, which are particularly important in the case of freight elevators because of the wide variation in the weight and bulk of articles to be carried. Where factories produce and handle small articles of considerable weight, the inside dimensions of the elevator platform should be approximately 6 ft. by 6 ft. or larger. When larger articles are to be carried, the platforms may be 8 or 9 ft. in width by 10 to 20 ft. in depth.

In most buildings, a variety of industrial trucks and trailers are used and in many cases must be carried from floor to floor on elevators. Detailed information on the characteristics of such equipment must be obtained before platform dimensions can be determined.

Freight elevator car speeds vary with the height of the buildings and may range from 100 to 300 ft. per min. in industrial buildings and up to 800 ft. per min. in commercial buildings.

The traction-type electric elevator, making use of the friction between grooved traction sheaves and hoisting cables, has proved far safer and more efficient than the drum-type elevator machine and is in general use. Traction elevators of the geared type have a worm and gear combination and are used for car speeds up to 350 ft. per min. For higher speeds the elevator machines are of the gearless traction type with slow-speed motors, so as to eliminate the intermediate gearing and thus permit faster car speeds and provide greater efficiency. Gearless machines provide car speeds up to 1,200 ft. per min. for intensive passenger service in tall buildings. Hydraulic electric elevators have been gaining favor in recent years.

Portable elevators are of great importance in industry for various lifting operations which are intermittent and not in a fixed location. Such units can be used to lift maintenance men to high repair jobs, to stack heavy objects, to lift heavy parts onto machines, to handle dies, and many other diverse jobs.

A **skip hoist** consists of a large steel bucket equipped with flanged wheels, running on vertical or inclined guides of steel channels or T-rail tracks. The bucket is loaded manually or automatically, hoisted up to a discharge position over a storage bin or silo by winch and cable, and automatically dumped. The skip hoist is a unit complete in itself for receiving, elevating, and discharging batches of materials, usually abrasive, corrosive, or containing large, sharp lumps, or when exceptionally high lift is needed. It is used largely for handling coal or ashes and capacities vary up to 250 tons of coal per hr. Size of buckets varies up to 150 cu. ft. and height of lifts ranges up to 160 ft.

POSITIONING, WEIGHING, AND CONTROL EQUIPMENT. This classification includes equipment used for local positioning and transferring, for weighing, and for controlling material movement (Materials Handling Handbook, Bolz and Hagemann, eds.). Among these are such items as manipulators, feeders, up-enders, positioning platforms, and transfers, whether portable or fixed; also all types of scales and weighing equipment; and handling control devices such as float control devices, bin indicators, electrical and mechanical limit controls, and counters.

Transfer Tables. Transfer tables come in various forms. In plants handling heavy steel plate, casters or single-ball transfers are often mounted on rods anchored to the floor so that men can move the plate at a good working height while walking among the supports. A more common transfer system is the ball transfer table which is suitable for most installations where a fairly hard surface is available. However, these ball transfers have a tendency to clog up in dusty operations. Retractable skate wheels or casters are sometimes used and in some instances a simple slide plate will do the work.

Feeders. Various types of production handling systems require sequential delivery of parts into processing machinery. In many instances the part must be oriented when it arrives in the processing station.

This type of delivery is accomplished in many ways. Rotary feeders can unscramble bottle caps, washers, screws, and other parts from a hopper and deliver them in an oriented position down a chute to capping machinery, assembly devices, punch presses, etc. This operation can also be performed by the use of controlled vibration. In most cases vibrating part feeders are constructed with a spiral ramp leading from the bottom of the hopper around the inside surface to a discharge point at the rim. The hopper is then oscillated in a rotary motion which moves the parts up this ramp. By machining grooves and orienting forms into the ramp, the parts can be discharged one at a time in the proper orientation for the next process. It is also possible to place gaging openings in the ramp so that undersized parts will drop through them or oversized parts will be ejected through a branch track. This type of part-feeding mechanism is commonly used for feeding such items as rivets, electrical contacts, screws, and small parts into assembly operations requiring the use of presses or welding machines.

INDUSTRIAL VEHICLES. According to the Materials Handling Handbook this classification covers all types of materials handling vehicles used in industry, excluding motor highway vehicles and public-carrier railroad cars, and includes industrial trucks, rail cars, trailers, tractors, excavating and grading equipment, off-highway carriers and agricultural vehicles used in materials handling.

Fork Lift Trucks. The fork lift truck, with electric, gasoline, diesel or propane gas power plant, is the most important type of **industrial truck** and is probably the best known mobile materials handling device. It is built in a range of capacities from 1,000 to 80,000 lb. The fork lift truck is well suited for combined horizontal and vertical movement of material. The normal industrial range of capacities is from 1,000 to 6,000 lb., measured in the form of a 48-in. homogeneous cube. This load is normally used as a basis for rating lift trucks.

The fork lift truck is usually equipped with tapered steel forks to handle palletized loads, or loads on skids. However, it is possible to equip these trucks with various attachments for specialized applications. Paper roll clamps, carton clamps, cotton, wool, and scrap paper bale clamps, rotators, side shifters, scoops and end dumping devices are typical of the attachments available.

Approximately 90 percent of the fork trucks in use are within the 6,000-lb. capacity range. The standard sizes within this range are 1,000 lb. at 24 in., 2,000 lb. at 24 in., 4,000 lb. at 24 in., and 6,000 lb. at 24 in. These trucks are available with pneumatic tires which permit operation over hard-surfaced areas. Fig. 31 gives the general over-all dimensions, together with turning diagrams for some typical gasoline trucks. (O. S. Carliss, The Yale & Towne Manufacturing Co.)

Fork lift trucks are built in a range of standard over-all heights and maximum fork elevation heights. It is customary to use a lower load capacity for trucks

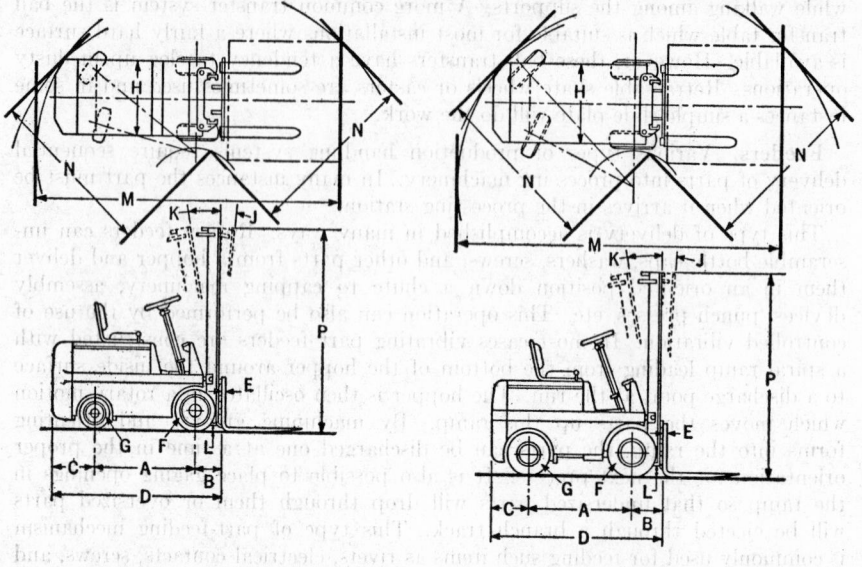

CAPACITY	LOAD CENTER	WHEEL BASE	OVERHANG		OVERALL LENGTH (Less Forks)	FORK THICKNESS	TIRES		OVERALL WIDTH AT FRAME	TILT		UNDER-CLEARANCE AT UPRIGHTS	AISLES (with 48" Cube Load)	
			Front	Rear			Drive	Trail		FORWARD	BACKWARD		Right Angle Turn	Inter-secting
GASOLINE FORK LIFT TRUCKS														
SOLID	–	A	B	C	D	E	F	G	H	J	K	L	M	N
2000	24	39	11¾	16¼	68	1½	17 × 5	13 x3½	38	3	10	3	131	71
4000	24	49	14	19	82	1¾	21 × 6	16¼x5	40	3	10	3	146	77
6000	24	54	15½	23	92½	2	22 × 8	16¼x6	46	3	10	3	158	83
PNEUMATIC	–	A	B	C	D	E	F	G	H	J	K	L	M	N
2000	24	42	14½	16	72½	1½	6:00x9	5:00x8	34	3	10	3	137	72
4000	24	55	18	22	95	1¾	7:50x15	6:50x10	45	3	10	3	158	83
6000	24	70	21	22	113	2	7:50x15 Duals	7:50x10	63	3	10	3¾	187	101

Yale & Towne Mfg. Co.

Fig. 31. Typical gasoline fork lift truck dimensions in inches.

where the load is elevated in excess of 144 in. The amount of reduction in load-carrying capacity for increased height of lift is largely dependent upon the type of truck, the wheel base of the truck, and operating conditions. It is recommended that the manufacturer be consulted on problems involving exceptionally high lifts. Fork trucks are available for high tiering up to 30 ft. Such applications require careful attention to the maintenance of the warehouse area, excellent floors, and extensive driver training.

One modification of the fork truck is equipped with outriggers to stabilize loads. The **outrigger fork truck** is intended for load carrying capacities up to 4,000 lb. It is especially suited for warehousing uniform loads and is designed for operations in a minimum aisle width (Fig. 32). The aisle width for operation of this type of truck varies with the size of the load but is normally between 6 ft. and 7 ft. This truck is advantageous in warehouses or storerooms where selective or rack storage is required.

The outrigger type stacker is particularly useful in multistory warehouses where a low floor load is a factor. Because of small diameter wheels on the outriggers (4 in. to permit the operation with wing type pallets) this type of truck is intended for smooth floors and should not be operated on ramps or dock plates. It is essential that the size of pallet be standardized for the operation of this type of vehicle.

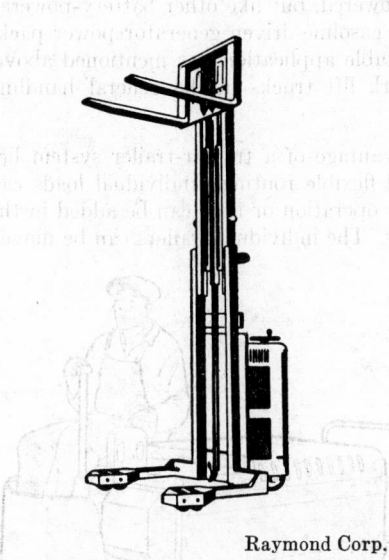

Raymond Corp.

Fig. 32. Outrigger fork lift truck.

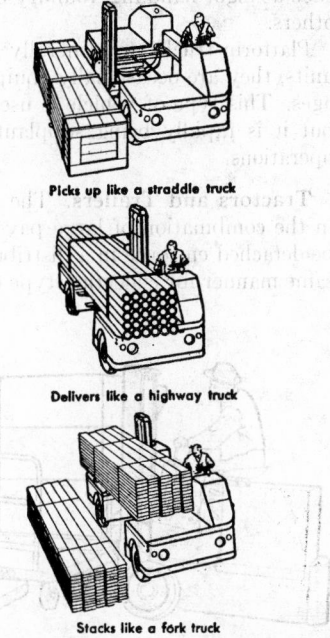

Picks up like a straddle truck

Delivers like a highway truck

Stacks like a fork truck

Baker-Rawling

Fig. 33. Traveloader.

The applications of **retractable forks** have broadened the utility of the fork truck. This device facilitates picking and placing of loads without sacrificing stability in transit. One example of the use of this design is the Traveloader shown in Fig. 33. Loads are picked and placed outboard and carried inboard, thus permitting large wheels and widening the range of the truck to highway travel.

Platform Trucks. Fixed, or low and high lift platform trucks are another important class of **industrial truck** (Fig. 34). Some of these trucks are equipped

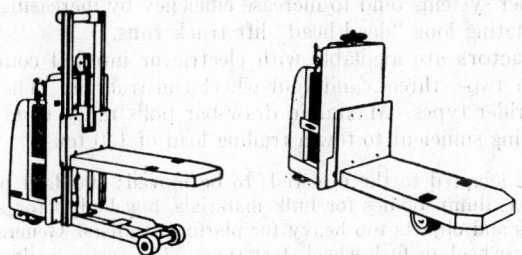

Raymond Corp.

Fig. 34. Typical high and low lift platform trucks.

with four-wheel steer and end control, making them extremely maneuverable. These trucks are widely used in handling skidded material and should be considered when quantities of large area low strength material, such as plaster board, wallboard, or thin sheet stock, are to be handled without palletizing or other dunnage. These trucks are frequently tailor-made for the specific applications such as ingot handling, foundry operations, warp beam handling, rug storage, and others.

Platform trucks are generally battery powered, but like other battery-powered units, they are occasionally equipped with gasoline-driven generator power packages. This type of vehicle is useful in suitable applications, as mentioned above, but it is rapidly being supplanted by fork lift trucks in the general handling operations.

Tractors and Trailers. The prime advantage of a tractor-trailer system lies in the combination of large pay loads and flexible routing. Individual loads can be detached en route in a distribution-type operation or they can be added in the same manner for collection-type operations. The individual trailers can be moved

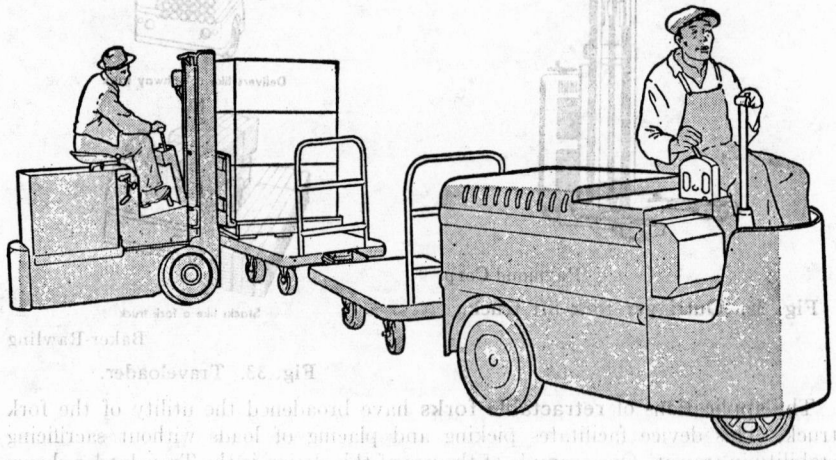

American Machinist

Fig. 35. Tractor-trailer train used with fork trucks.

manually for short distances and in some applications are arranged to permit stacking by fork lift trucks. When used in combination (Fig. 35) fork lift trucks and tractor-trailer systems tend to increase efficiency by increasing loads for long hauls and eliminating long "dead-head" lift truck runs.

Industrial tractors are available with electric or internal combustion power plants and with two-, three-, and four-wheel construction. They are built in pedestrian and rider types. Maximum draw-bar pulls range from 2,000 to 6,000 lb., the latter being sufficient to tow a trailing load of 150 tons.

Trailers can be adapted to the materials to be moved: standard platform trailers for general service, dump bodies for bulk materials, box bodies for small parts and dollies for barrels and objects too heavy for platform trailers. Generally, trailers are of the caster, four-wheel, or fifth-wheel steer types. The caster trailer has good trailing qualities and can be maneuvered close to walls or piles of material. The latter two types also have good trailing qualities and are employed generally for handling extremely heavy loads, for long hauls and for general yard work. On the caster-type of trailer, self-couplers make it possible to couple trailers automatically and more safely than with hand-operated couplers. . . . The number of trailers one tractor can keep in operation is determined by the working conditions—loading time, length of haul, steepness of inclines, weight of load, nature of materials. Under normal conditions, one tractor can keep three sets of trailers in operation—one being loaded, one in transit, and one being unloaded. (G. E. Materials Handling Manual.)

A recent innovation in the field of tractor-trailer operations has been the development of radio and photoelectric call-controlled tractors requiring no operator. These systems are most frequently applicable where the trailer train follows a preplanned repetitive route. A wire is suspended above the path along which the train is expected to travel or is buried in the floor. **Radio control** is exerted through impulses from the wire to the tractor. The photoelectric system follows a line painted on the floor. Installations are particularly useful for long hauls from production to storage, storage to picking, and picking to shippers.

Straddle Carriers. Straddle carriers are four-wheel inverted frame trucks designed to straddle the material to be handled (Fig. 36). The load is often handled on skid-type platforms called "bolsters." Long loads can often be handled without bolsters on recently developed lifting arms. These self-loading vehicles are used extensively to handle long and heavy materials, and are capable of highway travel.

Fig. 36. Straddle carrier.

In recent years the straddle carrier has been applied to more and more diverse materials handling functions. Its ability to load itself with a variety of loads of 8 tons and above, to travel on highways at normal highway truck speeds and distances, and to operate over rough terrain as well as paved areas has made it useful in some widely differing applications. This machine, which was originally designed for handling lumber and long loads, is now frequently used in a wide variety of agricultural and industrial operations. Recent developments in the use of **specialized containers** have made the straddle carrier applicable to handling of bulk materials and unpacked products in large loads. One example is the Mobilvan System for transporting freight, which takes advantage of the most economical aspects of trucking and railroad transportation. This shipping and storage method can be used with either truck or rail transportation, or in combined movements utilizing both. The Mobilvan System is based on the use of a light-weight van 17 ft. long, 8 ft. wide, and 8 ft. high. Automatic locking devices permit the van to be fastened securely to the bed of a railroad flatcar or the body of a flatbed highway truck.

Pedestrian-Type Trucks. When small volumes, short or infrequent hauls, space limitations, and structural restrictions do not warrant or permit rider-type trucks, a pedestrian-controlled powered vehicle, or walkie, is often effective. Walkie models are available for many of the trucks described above, including fork trucks, platform trucks, pallet trucks, tractors, and specialized equipment for specific applications.

Pedestrian fork trucks are built in capacities of 1,000, 1,500, 2,000 and 3,000 lb., all at 24-in. load center. They can be used effectively in narrow aisles and on upper floors where floor loading is an important consideration. Because of their over-all size and weight they will frequently fit into existing freight elevators, permitting the use of a single unit on several floors.

Walkie-type pallet and platform trucks (Fig. 37) are very effective for quick short movements of unit loads. They are intended for horizontal movement over relatively short distances (usually less than 100 ft.). Materials to be handled should be on pallets or skids. Loose parts or bulk materials can be handled in skid or pallet bins. These units travel at normal walk speeds and are usually

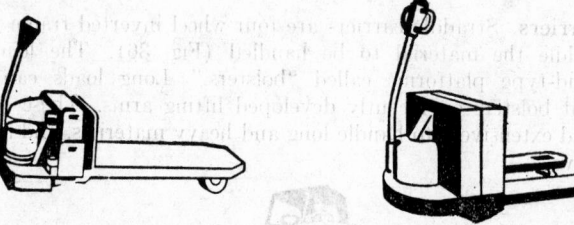

Flow Directory

Fig. 37. **Powered walkie skid and pallet trucks.**

battery powered. Powered hand trucks are manufactured in a variety of fork lengths and widths and usually require chamfered bottom boards on the pallets with a minimum of 8 in. opening in the bottom face to permit the retractable load wheels to pass through to the floor. The steerable drive wheel is controlled from a handle and steered in the same manner as a toy wagon.

Manual hand trucks are built for the same purpose and with very similar characteristics as the powered hand trucks discussed above. They are usually impractical for loads in excess of 4,000 lb., on ramps, for distances over 100 ft., and for highly repetitive moves. These trucks should be considered a warehousing or handling tool rather than a vehicle.

Hand Trucks. Various types of hand trucks are used in manufacturing and warehousing operations (Fig. 38). Four-wheel trucks with a variety of wheel

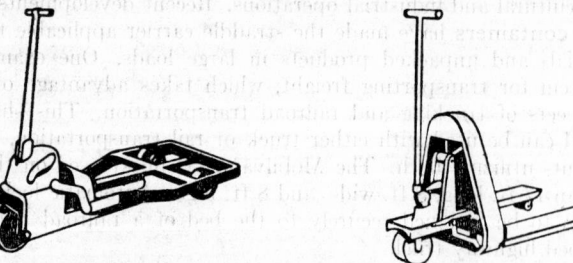

Flow Directory

Fig. 38. **Hand skid and pallet trucks.**

arrangements including castered wheels, fifth-wheel arrangements, double end steering, etc., are available in capacities and sizes to meet almost any requirement. These trucks are used as trailers in tractor-trailer trains, with drag line installations, and for manual shifting and moving functions. The more common sizes have capacities up to about 6,000 lb. In some instances very large units are available.

The common two-wheel warehouse truck is also available in special designs for handling barrels, home appliances, crates, acid carboys, bales, etc. They are made of wood, steel, aluminum, and magnesium, and are equipped with iron, aluminum, rubber, and plastic treads. Few plants are completely independent of these hand trucks. They are very useful as maintenance tools and in some operating departments. However, they are becoming less significant with the development of mechanical handling systems and should be avoided wherever possible because of their small unit load capability.

MOTOR VEHICLES. This classification covers all types of highway passenger and cargo vehicles including trucks, tractors, and trailers whose dimensions and capacities permit use on public highways. Highway transportation is a major factor in modern materials handling techniques. Most products are mechanically handled and the trend toward the mechanical loading of highway vehicles is increasing rapidly. New innovations in unit load systems have made it possible to handle large unit loads of cartons, boxes, bricks, masonry, barrels, drums, paper rolls, and many other containers with lift trucks without the benefit of pallets. One of the major deterrents to unit load handling into highway vehicles has been the cost of returning pallets, the cost of disposable pallets, and the freight charges on the pallets in transit. These new techniques make unit load handling in highway vehicles economical.

There are many types of highway vans, bodies, and trailers. Many special-purpose bodies have been developed for handling bulk materials, machinery, liquids, gases, etc.

The variance between states in **regulations** limiting dimensions of highway vehicles still creates a problem; however, most states have standardized on an 8-ft. over-all width and a 12-ft. 6-in. over-all height. The new high volume semi-trailer van units are, therefore, being standardized at 96-in. outside width, 94-in. inside width, and 91 in. clear at the door frame in both width and height.

These units are particularly adaptable to the new **palletless-handling** techniques known as the Cartwright or Kirkhof systems. In these systems a unit load, which is essentially a "slice" of the van, can be driven straight into the trailer by the fork lift truck and the individual handling of packages is completely eliminated. Since these same unit loads are stackable in storage, this system permits either manual or mechanized loading or unloading.

Another van body modification which has recently become available is a sliding-roof van which permits crane loading of heavy objects into a closed van body for protected shipments. The roof is moved forward or backward by means of a crank. This van is also designed for high volume shipments.

Apron Space. The apron space required to maneuver highway tractor-trailer units into or out of loading positions in one maneuver has been worked out empirically with standard equipment handled by experienced drivers. A high average turning radius has been arbitrarily used to provide a margin for differences in equipment. The apron space required is measured out from the outermost part of any vehicle or other possible obstruction in the area of the maneuver

Fig. 39 (Fruehauf Trailer Co., Modern Docks for Modern Transports) shows dimensions and space requirements for the most efficient maneuvering of motor transports into and out of loading positions. These figures do not constitute a plan in themselves, but are intended to assist in the best utilization of motor transport.

Over-all Length of Tractor-Trailer	Width of Position	Apron Space Required
35 ft.	10 ft.	46 ft.
	12 ft.	43 ft.
	14 ft.	39 ft.
40 ft.	10 ft.	48 ft.
	12 ft.	44 ft.
	14 ft.	42 ft.
45 ft.	10 ft.	57 ft.
	12 ft.	49 ft.
	14 ft.	48 ft.

Fig. 39. Apron space required by tractor-trailer for one maneuver into or out of position (measured from outermost vehicle or other obstruction).

Margins for driver error, congestion, storage or parking of equipment are not included. At least the minimum apron space should be allowed. It should be kept clear for the approach and maneuvering of transport units. The apron space recommended is based on one maneuver. In locations where the proper space is not available, trailers can be "jockeyed" into position. This, however, is a time-consuming process for transport operators.

Dock Height and Equipment. According to Modern Docks for Modern Transports (Fruehauf Trailer Co.):

A troublesome factor in loading and unloading is the inherent variation in loading level (distance from pavement to floor level) of motor transport equipment. This distance averages 51 inches for heavy equipment but varies within a 6-inch range depending on model, tire size, and load. Due to spring compression a trailer, when heavily loaded, may be 3 inches lower than when it is running empty. If such a trailer is to be completely unloaded at one dock, this complete variation will occur during the unloading operation. Also, one model trailer may be equipped with any one of a number of tire sizes, depending on the load it is required to carry. This factor can cause a variation of as much as 3 inches in loading level. Dock heights of from 44 to 50 inches are in general use.

In general, 48 to 54 inches is most satisfactory for heavy-duty units, while slightly lower docks are more convenient for lighter equipment.

If the dock and trailer-bed levels are not equal, it is usually more satisfactory to have the dock level lower than the trailer-bed. This will permit opening and closing of trailer doors while in loading position. Except in rare cases, a slight difference in level between trailer and dock is of no great concern, although a large difference is often a handicap.

In order to cope with this problem, many companies have found it necessary to install adjustable truck docks or truck-leveling devices (Fig. 40). This equipment is hydraulically or mechanically operated and consists of a hinged steel ramp which can be adjusted to suit the vehicular equipment in question.

Where carriers and shippers or receivers maintain a close relationship, the choice of trailer and the design of the dock can be adjusted for the mutual needs so that **standard bridge plates** are adequate. These bridge plates will accommodate several inches of variation and are usually installed with a span of several

Flow Directory

Fig. 40. Typical adjustable truck docks.

inches between the bumper plate of the trailer and the sill of the truck dock. Bridge plates are available in steel, aluminum, and magnesium, with lugs for handling them by fork lift trucks and, in some cases, with retractable wheels and levers for easy manual handling.

Doors and stalls are usually arranged to allow 12 ft. per truck. As position width increases, the "apron" space required for maneuvering will decrease. Standard trailers vary in height up to 12½ feet. Consequently, it is recommended that 14-foot clearance be provided at docks or in yards, driveways, doors, stalls and interior roadways. Special transportation conditions such as delivery of large machinery may require greater clearance but, in general, 14 feet provides a satisfactory margin. (Modern Docks for Modern Transports, Fruehauf.)

RAILROAD CARS. This classification covers all standard and narrow-gage public carrier railroad rolling stock used on the country's railroad system. It does not include narrow-gage industrial rail cars used in interplant operations nor the industrial tractors or locomotives used for motive power, which are included under industrial vehicles. It includes such cars as passenger and baggage cars, box, refrigerator and livestock cars, flatcars, gondolas, hoppers, tank cars, locomotives, and other specially designed railroad cars.

Railroads are among the oldest and most basic materials handling devices. As mechanized handling methods have developed, the basic freight cars gradually have been modified to meet special purposes and to accommodate new handling methods. As with trucks, many special-purpose freight cars are in use such as tank cars for handling fuels and other inflammable liquids, glass-lined tank cars for corrosive material, pressure tank cars for gases, hopper cars, covered hopper cars for contaminable or dusty materials, gondola cars, refrigerator cars, automobile cars, flatcars, well-hole cars, well-pocket cars, flat depressed cars, and many single-purpose units. The **boxcar**, however, is still the basic unit of railroad handling. Boxcars vary in size from 40 ft. to 50 ft. 6 in. inside length and from 8 ft. 6 in. to 9 ft. 4 in. inside width. The door widths vary from a low of 5 ft. 6 in. for single doors to a high of 15 ft. in some double-door cars. This lack of standardization has disadvantages when attempting mechanized loading and unloading of freight cars.

Loading Methods. Developments in blocking and segregating boxcar loads have resulted in improved techniques of damage prevention in freight shipments. The Freight Container Bureau of the Association of American Railroads has developed a system known as the **Conbur brace.** This system requires a minimum of equipment and is intended to be a flexible low-cost blocking system for mixed loads, pool cars, and drop shipments. One of the newer shipping methods being studied by the railroads is a five-compartment unit load freight car. This freight carrier is 45 ft. 6 in. long and 10 ft. 4 in. wide. The carrier's five compartments are the width of a highway trailer. They are designed to accommodate two pallets wide and two pallets deep. The two opposite overhead doors to each compartment work on the same track, so only one can be opened at a time. The car has a capacity of 100,000 lb.

In addition to the important loading and unloading economies, the **five-compartment car** provides for fast turn-around time, protection for shipments, and segregation of shipments. This segregation is of particular importance to LCL (less than carload) shippers. It eliminates the necessity of opening sealed cars to remove a portion of the contents. (Modern Materials Handling, vol. 10.)

Along with the Mobilvan System discussed previously, another development in the combination use of railroad and truck transport—the Pick-a-back System —has been gaining momentum. In this method standard highway trailers are loaded by the shipper and delivered to the freight yard where they are driven or hoisted onto specially equipped flatcars, two trailers per car.

Platform and Siding Clearances. The application of railroad operations to industrial facilities involves a knowledge of the standard restrictions and dimensions which apply to railroads, clearances, and equipment. Fig. 41 shows the normal clearances which might be expected at loading platforms and sidings.

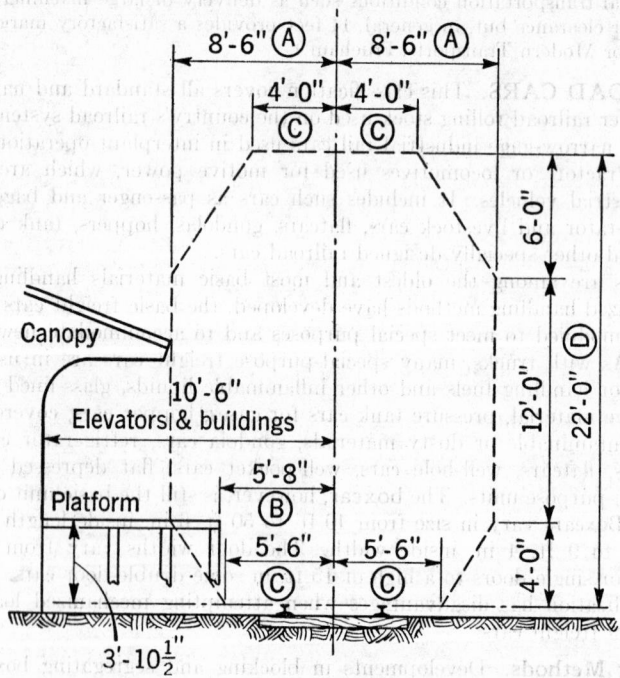

Fig. 41. Normal railroad loading-platform clearances.

Clearances are for straight track A and B. Some railroads require an 8-ft. 6-in. minimum. C—In some states, this clearance must be increased. D—One western railroad requires 24-ft. 6-in. vertical clearance above top of ties. Nominal clearances are required as a matter of safety between locomotives and cars, and structures near tracks. These are averages for **straight-track**—some companies and states require more as noted. The clearances are based on standard 4-ft. 6-in. track gage.

Allowances must be made on **curves,** due to the increase in effective width of equipment. The increase inside curves depends on the distance between truck centers, and the increase outside curves depends on length beyond trucks. Tilt of equipment toward inside of curve, due to banking of rails, must be included as well as any slewing action caused by tire wear and other lateral play. As a rule, the front of a locomotive will govern effective width for a foot above the top of the rail and the rear of the cab for the remainder of the height. For preliminary calculations of clearance outside curves, it will usually be ample to allow 1 in. per degree of curve plus 2 in. for all curves. For inside clearance, a general allowance of 1½ in. in addition to the middle ordinate distance for a 45-ft. chord will be sufficient.

In cases involving new construction, a sketch of clearances should be submitted to the railroad for approval. Some railroads permit special clearances when tracks enter coal tipples and buildings. Railroad company engineers can be contacted for requirements.

MARINE CARRIERS. This classification covers all water-borne vessels, including ocean, lake, river, and canal boats, barges and lighters, tow boats, small craft, and other miscellaneous marine equipment used in the handling of materials.

AIRCRAFT. This classification covers all types of aircraft, including passenger and cargo airplanes, rotary-wing aircraft, gliders, and lighter-than-air airships.

CONTAINERS AND SUPPORTS. Containers may be defined (Materials Handling Handbook, Bolz and Hagemann, eds.) as carriers formed to retain a quantity of an item for movement between processes, into or out of storage, or in transit from a point of manufacture through to a point of ultimate disposal. A wide variety of standard and custom-made containers are available, designed to carry in-process and finished parts, assemblies, or products through all phases of the manufacturing cycle, including shipment of the end product. This classification covers all types of pressure, tight, loose, and open-top containers; also platform and coil supports, and all types of securements such as strapping, cinches, bulkheads, dunnage, etc.

Pallets and Skids. Among the most widely used platform supports are skids and pallets of which there are many varieties. **Skids** (Fig. 42) are platforms made of wood or metal with enough underclearance to admit the platform of a platform lift truck. They can, of course, also be handled by fork trucks.

Skid bins permit handling heavy loads of small parts by platform lift truck or fork lift truck. Some are designed for tiering. The corrugated steel skid bins usually have sling eyes for crane handling. Sectional sided bins provide adjustable capacity and easier access to the contents in the bottom. **Skid racks** hold stacked loads of parts and offer better accessibility than bins.

Pallets are elevated platforms with lower underclearance than skids. Single-faced pallets are simple wood platforms on runners. High stacking or tiering of single-faced pallets may be feasible if the top of the load can withstand the concentrated forces imposed by the runners. Double-faced wooden pallets are the most widely used. The lower face often provides clearance for the wheels of a hand pallet truck. When pallets admit forks on all four sides, they are known as four-way pallets. When they can be entered from all four corners as well, they are called eight-way pallets. Two-way double-faced pallets have the largest load-bearing area on the lower face. This is the principal advantage of the two-way double-faced pallet. Double wing-type stevedore pallets provide for bar slings or spreaders to hoist unit loads by ship tackle or pier cranes. Plywood can be used to make pallets light and strong.

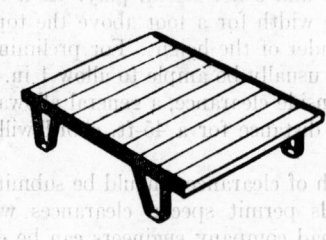
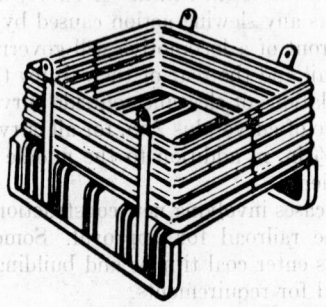

General Electric Co.

Fig. 42. Typical skids.

Steel pallets are used to withstand hard usage such as occurs in the metal-fabricating industries. Several types are available. Steel wire mesh pallets are light in weight, but the bearing area is comparatively small. In some applications the fact that they do not absorb odors is important. They are also used where drainage of liquids is a factor. Aluminum pallets combine strength and lightness, and usually avoid the corrosion problem.

Expendable paper pallets were developed to solve the problem of the expense for returning pallets accompanying shipments. Moisture resistant paper pallets withstand static loads up to 18,000 lb. Prescribed stacking patterns must be followed. Another type paper pallet rests on three runners consisting of square, diagonally braced paper tubes. Expendable pallets may also be made of wood or metal. One type is of wire-bound wood construction.

Pallet racks or "picture frame" pallets with collapsible superstructures are often used for handling and storing irregularly shaped or easily crushed merchandise. They are made in a wide variety of designs. Pallet bins are often collapsible to facilitate return.

The National Wood Pallet Manufacturers Association has established standard nomenclature and a conventional dimensioning system which is generally accepted in industry today (Fig. 43).

Pallet Loaders and Unloaders. Pallet loaders are capable of unitizing cartons and bagged goods in a variety of patterns. Most of the automatic pallet-loading equipment on the market today is capable, through an electronic programming device, of handling many different pallet patterns through a single machine. The pattern can be changed by an operator or by a predetermined schedule.

The **pallet-loading machine** consists of a pallet-feeding device into which a lift truck places a stack of empty pallets; a pattern-forming device which places the cartons or bags in the proper arrangement for the pattern; a tier-loading mechanism which places the tiers one upon the other and lowers the pallet to accommodate the next tier; and a conveyor removal system for delivering the loaded pallet into a conveyor system or to a fork lift truck pickup point. Some of the automatic pallet-loading machines contain electrical programming systems for automatically forming one or more patterns.

A **semi-automatic pallet loader** consists of a ball table or power-operated pattern table upon which a man forms the tier pattern. Each tier is then automatically loaded onto the pallet in the same manner as in the automatic machine. Semi-automatic bag palletizers handle 600 to 1,200 bags per hour, while automatic pallet-loading equipment handles 1,500 to 1,800 cartons or cases per hour, and semi-automatic carton- and case-palletizing machinery falls somewhere in between, depending upon the weight and size of the package.

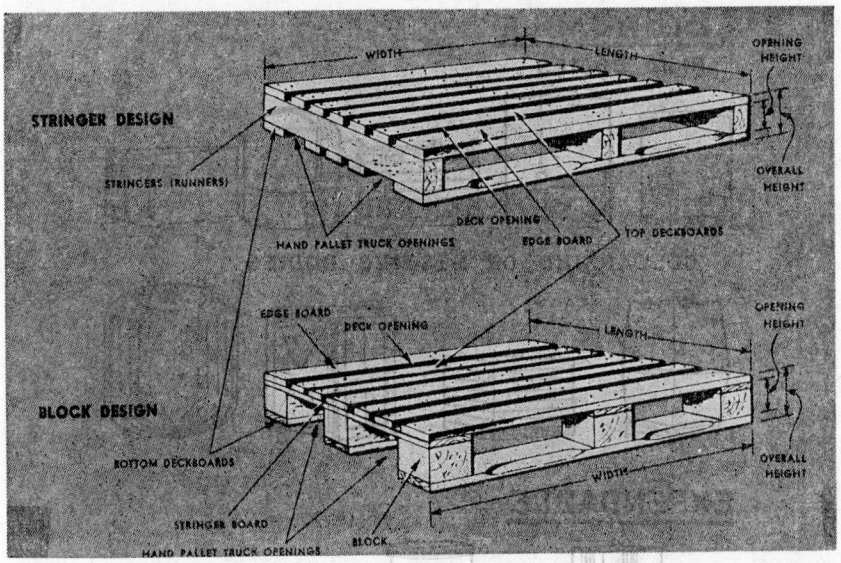

Fig. 43. Principal parts and commonly used construction features of stringer and block design pallets.

The **pallet-feeding** mechanism may be used as an independent unit. This device can eliminate a great deal of the manpower and complexity in high-speed manual pallet-loading operations. This machine feeds a pallet onto a conveyor leading to the loader on demand.

Automatic **pallet unloaders** reverse the process. A pallet load of cartons or cases is placed in the machine and the machine unloads it, aligns the packages, and feeds them onto a conveyor. This unit is particularly helpful in food packing and bottling plants for delivering empty glass or cans in cartons or cases to the filling line. Another device which is available inverts the cartons and unloads the bottles for delivery to the filler.

The recent trend toward the development of palletless unit-load handling methods has resulted in the development of modified automatic pallet-loading machines capable of building unit loads without pallets. These machines can be used with carton clamp and other palletless handling lift-truck attachments.

They have the same general characteristics as pallet loaders, with the exception that no pallet-feeding device is necessary.

The question of the economic justification of unitizing or pallet-loading equipment depends upon the economics of the particular installation. The annual cost of the pallet loader or unitizer, the amortization of the conveyor system and any specialized handling equipment, and the other fixed and variable charges attributable to the automatic operation must be balanced against the labor cost recovered by the investment. In most cases a high rate of production is a prerequisite to economical use of this type of equipment.

Containers. In addition to cartons, barrels, drums, and pallets, this classification includes a variety of large containers for unit-load shipment of packages, parts, and bulk materials. Basic types as illustrated by Dean and Norton (Mechanical Engineering, vol. 78) are shown in Fig. 44. The development of the

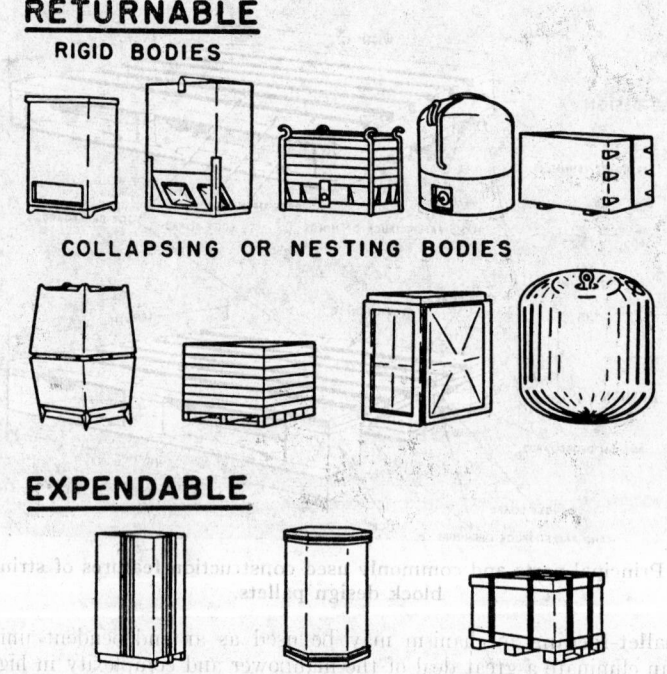

Fig. 44. Basic types of unit-load containers for shipping bulk products.

collapsible bag handling method is probably one of the more advanced unit bulk handling techniques. This new technique permits shipment of bulk products in boxcars or open gondola cars in units of up to 400 cu. ft. In most cases these bags are handled into and out of the cars with cranes or by fork lift trucks with crane attachments. The containers are stored on the ground and are placed on steel frame supports with standard, flexible-type, bin valves and squeezing devices to convert them into a service hopper to feed the material directly into the manufacturing process. The bag, usually made of neoprene, is collapsed for the return trip to the supplier. This method is particularly adaptable for such hard-to-handle materials as lamp black.

Racks, Shelving, and Bins. In many instances, storage operations require furnishings which permit high cube utilization with short lots while maintaining selectivity. Pallet racks, shelving, bins, stackable bins, and tubs fall into this category.

Fig. 45 shows a typical example of a pallet rack in which short lots of various-shaped items are stored. Pallet racks are simply shelves for pallets which make it possible to remove the unit load at the bottom of the stack without disturbing those above it. They are used for irregularly shaped loads, short lots, and picking lines.

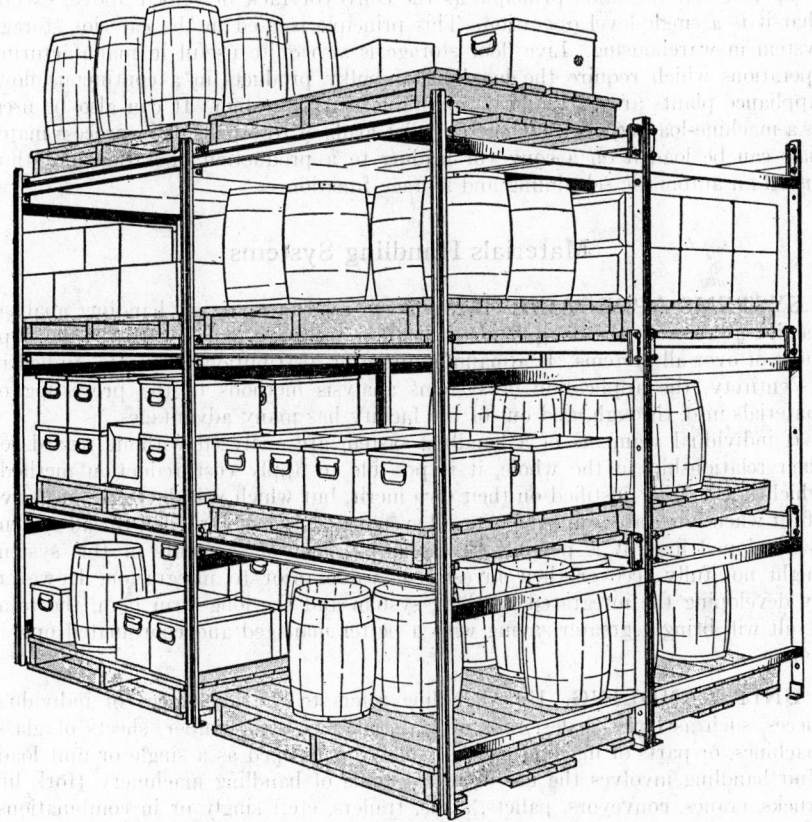

Fig. 45. Pallet racks for stacking of uneven loads.

When open-stock items must be handled, storage furniture is usually required. Large quantities of such items can be handled in stackable pallet boxes from which single pieces can be withdrawn through an opening at the end even when other boxes are stacked on top. Smaller quantities are often handled in bin boxes of similar design. Small quantities are often stored in permanent shelf units, drawers, or rotary bins. There are many types of specialized racks such as barrel racks, reel racks, etc.

A new product which is finding acceptance is a conveyor rack. A series of roller or skate wheel conveyors are placed one above the other in side by side stacks

5 or 10 ft. or more in length. These units slope slightly from the input to the output end. They are quite useful for accumulating packages or tote pans into unit loads at a sorting station and for maintaining a first-in, first-out process inventory between operations. The box or tote pan is placed in the proper slot (conveyor) on its arrival at the storage point and it takes its place in an automatically scheduled moving storage for delivery to the next operation. This system can be very useful as a scheduling device for job machine shops and other diverse operations.

The **live floor** storage system is another method which is gaining acceptance. It operates on the same principle as the conveyor rack described above, except that it is a single-level operation. This principle is used in the car slot storage system in warehousing. Live floor storage is also quite useful in manufacturing operations which require the handling of bulky products in a continuous flow. Appliance plants are particularly adaptable to this system. It can also be used as a machine-loading device whereby pallet loads of tote pans or in-process materials can be loaded on a conveyor leading to a production operation and thus install an automatic scheduling and storage function.

Materials Handling Systems

SYSTEMS APPROACH. The modern trend in materials handling analysis has led away from the equipment application approach and toward the development of over-all systems. If a manufacturing or distribution facility is studied in its entirety, the application of systems analysis methods to the processing of materials into, through, and out of the facility has many advantages.

If individual segments of a handling system are analyzed without regard for their relationship to the whole, it is possible to apply cost reduction methods which can be fully justified on their own merit, but which will develop a negative effect when integrated into the over-all system. Conversely, if the over-all system is developed first, it is possible that establishment of segments of this system might not fully recover their investment value prior to integration. However, by developing the integrated handling system and the long-term plan, the total result will bring a greater saving with a better managed and coordinated operation.

UNIT HANDLING. Unit handling refers to the movement of individual pieces, such as boxes, bales, rolls of material, pieces of lumber, sheets of glass, machines, or parts of machines, either singly or grouped as a single or unit load. Unit handling involves the use of many kinds of handling machinery (fork lift trucks, cranes, conveyors, pallets, skids, trailers, etc.) singly or in combinations. These are organized into systems with each unit or type of equipment operating in integrated sequences under coordinated control through specific management procedures.

As defined earlier, a **unit load** is any group of individual items which is a well-defined unit for handling by means of machines such as fork lift trucks, skid trucks, straddle trucks, cranes, etc. Not only products, packages, and parts, but bulk materials as well, may be unitized under many circumstances. According to the Materials Handling Handbook (Bolz and Hagemann, eds.):

The unit-load principle has been accepted in industry as a means for accomplishing difficult handlings and storage by mechanical methods at considerable cost savings. Bins are designed for holding quantities of like parts or to contain different kinds of bulk materials. Portable racks and easily handled small in-process containers provide flexible transportation. Frequently, product demand does not warrant the development of expensive containers or the installation of racks. In most instances, unitized containers are being used in in-plant or interplant handling to replace the heavy types of containers. The product itself may constitute the means to handle such unit loads, especially in the handling and storage of such items as brick, ceramic products, and corrugated board.

Generally speaking, unit-load systems are more flexible and require less investment than any other approach to materials handling cost reduction. The unit load system usually can be applied in any size organization with some degree of success. It is particularly applicable to operations where nonrepetitive handling sequences are found or where a variety of products and materials are handled. It can, however, be applied in highly repetitive large volume operations with considerable success. Many types of specialized apparatus and attachments have been developed for use in such operations.

In general, the unit-load system is based upon pallets and skids. Fig. 46 shows some typical **pallet patterns** for cartons.

In recent years, the development of **palletless** handling has made it possible to eliminate pallets and skids. Carton clamps, loading-sheet attachments, and griptine forks have increased the capabilities of unit-load operations without changing their basic nature, through the elimination of the cost of purchasing and handling pallets and skids.

In storage areas unit loads are arranged to permit direct access to every item. The items are usually grouped according to storage quantity in order to maintain a uniform storage depth and straight aisles with the elimination of "honeycombing." Identification and location of items in storage is usually based upon a grid locator system. Storage in unit loads provides for good housekeeping and simplified inventory control. The choice of unit-load size and aisle pattern governs the space efficiency.

HANDLING BULK MATERIALS. Bulk handling systems are usually considered to be those systems which ignore the identity of the individual particles, chunks, pieces, or items which are handled. These systems handle a flow of material on a continuous or unit-load basis and assume similarity, homogeneity, or interchangeability of the components of the material being handled. Bulk materials can be handled by various types of conveyors, power shovels, scoops, cranes, drag lines, and construction equipment. More recently, fork lift trucks have been used to handle bulk materials through the use of unit-load bulk handling containers. Front-end loaders and scoop attachments on fork lift trucks have become quite common for bulk handling operations. These machines are well adapted to construction, factory yard operations, loading and handling of loose bulk materials, rubble handling, snow removal, and many other odd jobs. They have also become popular in the bulk loading and unloading of freight cars.

In recent years highway trucks, railroad cars, and ships have become more accommodating to the materials handling characteristics of the products they are moving. Special truck bodies and freight cars have been developed for handling bulk materials with rapid loading and unloading operations. The common practice of drop-bottom unloading and overhead loading of highway vehicles and freight cars has resulted in the more widespread use of hopper cars and hopper-type trailers for handling bulky materials.

Bulk materials by their very nature are shapeless and are often confined in storage and transit by containers of one form or another. These containers

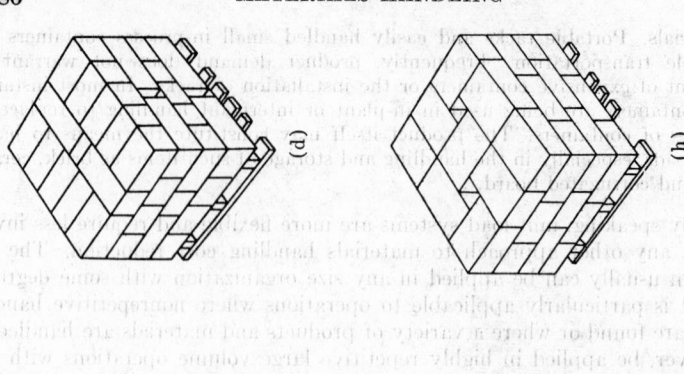

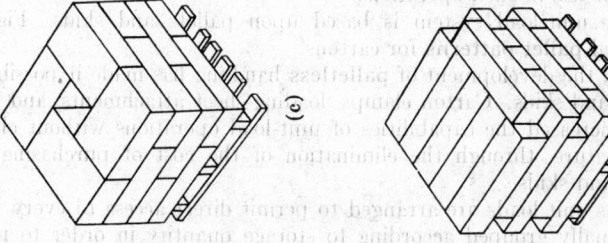

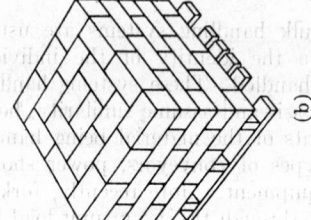

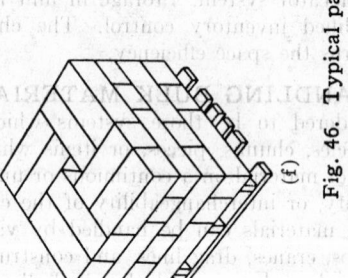

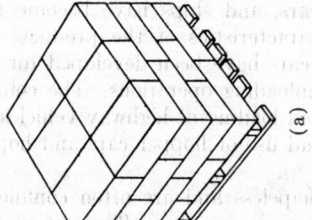

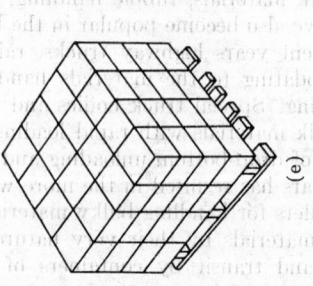

Fig. 46. Typical pallet loading patterns.

include sacks, tubs, rubber tanks, storage bins, hoppers, pallet bins, skid boxes, barrels, and many other containers. Once the bulk material is thus confined, the handling problem is no different than in the case of any unit load.

BASIC HANDLING SYSTEMS. Handling systems are as varied in their make-up as are the operations to which they may be applied. Different plants in the same industry will often use different systems. Differences in plant layout, process, volume of production, receiving procedure, and in other factors from one operation to another may call for variations in the handling system. The systems defined below, however, are basic and will often be found as components of an integrated plant materials handling system. The equipment used in them is described elsewhere in this section.

Industrial Truck Systems. According to the General Electric Materials Handling Manual, the **tractor-trailer system** is a haulage system. Loading and unloading are done by cranes, hoists, platform lift, or fork trucks.

This system is economical for hauling large quantities of material for distances over 300 feet. The per-ton cost for handling material in this way is very low, because one tractor can move many loaded trailers in one haul.

Platform trucks and skids constitute another system. The high-lift platform truck tiers skid loads, whereas the low-lift truck only lifts the load a few inches, high enough to move it from one place to another. Both trucks pick up, transport, and set down skid-loaded materials without manual rehandling. The fact that the fulcrum of the platform is up forward enables this truck to carry very heavy loads.

The principle of the **fork truck and pallet system** is the same as that of the lift truck and skid system. The forks require less clearance than the elevating platform of the lift truck, making it possible to have pallets shallower than skids, which saves space in tiering. **Double-faced** pallets make possible wider load distribution, another space-saving feature.

The powered hand truck may be used with the **skid or pallet** in another system. The powered hand truck is designed to move either a pallet load or a skid load from one place to another. Recent models can also stack. The powered hand truck is ideally used in moving material when the weight or total volume of the material is too small to justify larger equipment, and often supplements the larger equipment. Its light weight and small size are of advantage when floor load capacity is small and space is confined.

Conveyor Systems. Conveyors and conveyor systems are commonly found in operations where bulk materials or items of uniform size and shape are handled over the same path repeatedly or for long periods of time. Generally speaking, an intermittent operation involving a variety of material is a questionable situation for the use of conveyor equipment. The lack of flexibility in a permanent conveyor installation can hamper cost reduction efforts in job shop or miscellaneous handling operations.

Conveyor systems in general are more adaptable to mass movement than the unit system. When the conditions are right, the application of control devices, programming systems, and careful layout can often reduce the time and manpower used in materials handling to a negligible quantity. Conveyors become uneconomical when they must be loaded and unloaded frequently or when complicated installations must be changed frequently. It must be remembered, however, that the art and science of materials handling engineering requires careful application engineering and economic study. Each system must be tailor-made to the situation in which it must operate and no basic principles or rules of thumb will apply all of the time.

Applications of conveyor systems to unit handling are found in storage operations. Hand stacking in storage of packaged materials cannot be economically operated at greater than 7 ft. of stack height. Portable conveyors can increase this height, but a disproportionate increase in manpower may be required to accomplish it. In most conveyor- and hand-stack warehousing operations (Fig. 47), the conveyor system is a fixed or semi-fixed installation, so that in order to achieve the optimum balance between manual handling and space loss, a conveyor **grid** is usually set up. This arrangement causes inflexibility which makes it difficult to rotate stocks and "make space."

Mathews Conveyer Co.

Fig. 47. Hand-stacked warehouse storage using a conveyor system.

Conveyors are very useful in the warehousing operation of plants that produce large volumes of items in reasonably long runs. In the H. J. Heinz Pittsburgh plant (Factory Management, vol. 113), for example, several packaging lines feed into four main-line power conveyors controlled by a central panel. These lines in turn feed into a battery of pallet loaders in a warehouse several hundred feet from the production operation. The control system schedules the lines so that the pallet-loader operator receives full unit-load quantities in his machines. The loaded pallet is then delivered by conveyor and automatic pallet elevator to the floor on which it is to be stored, where it is received on a holding conveyor. From this point it is picked up by a fork lift truck and placed in storage. It is removed from storage and delivered into the truck or car by fork lift truck when it is shipped. Another system is shown in Fig. 48.

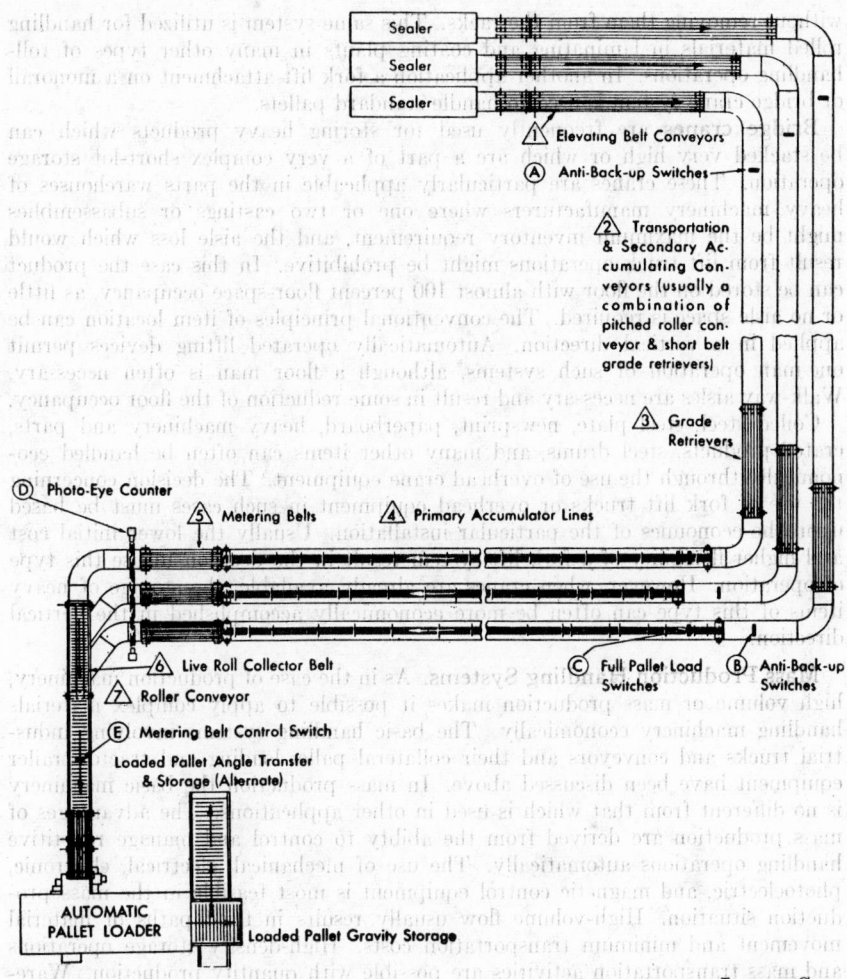

Lamson Corp.

Fig. 48. Conveyor system serving an automatic pallet-loader installation.

Overhead Systems. In some cases overhead cranes and monorail equipment are used in operations where floor-space utilization for processing or storage make the use of fork lift trucks undesirable, and where travel distances and paths can be reasonably restricted. In these cases special considerations have resulted in the use of overhead equipment. For example, most rug-cutting and -storing operations use monorail systems from which racks are suspended. These racks support several broadloom rolls in a horizontal position, one above the other. Many of these racks are mounted side by side with the rails running perpendicular to the aisle or cutting floor. The customary procedure is to deliver the unit by truck to a position parallel to the rack upon which it is to be hung, remove the crate from the roll, then lift the carpet into the rack with a fork lift truck or portable crane. In the case of cutting operations, the carpets can be unrolled without removing them from the racks. This same system is utilized for handling rolled materials in laminating and coating plants in many other types of roll-handling operations. In another application a fork lift attachment on a monorail or bridge crane system is used to handle standard pallets.

Bridge cranes are frequently used for storing heavy products which can be stacked very high or which are a part of a very complex short-lot storage operation. These cranes are particularly applicable in the parts warehouses of heavy machinery manufacturers where one or two castings or subassemblies might be the maximum inventory requirement, and the aisle loss which would result from lift truck operations might be prohibitive. In this case the product can be stored on the floor with almost 100 percent floor-space occupancy, as little or no aisle space is required. The conventional principles of item location can be applied in a vertical direction. Automatically operated lifting devices permit one-man operation of such systems, although a floor man is often necessary. Walk-way aisles are necessary and result in some reduction of the floor occupancy.

Coiled steel, steel plate, newsprint, paperboard, heavy machinery and parts, crated products, steel drums, and many other items can often be handled economically through the use of overhead crane equipment. The decision concerning the use of fork lift trucks or overhead equipment in such cases must be based upon the economics of the particular installation. Usually the lower initial cost and higher flexibility of a fork lift system result in the decision to use this type of operation. However, when cranes are already available, the storage of heavy items of this type can often be more economically accomplished in the vertical direction.

Mass Production Handling Systems. As in the case of production machinery, high volume or mass production makes it possible to apply complex materials handling machinery economically. The basic handling systems involving industrial trucks and conveyors and their collateral pallet-loading and tractor-trailer equipment have been discussed above. In mass production the basic machinery is no different from that which is used in other applications. The advantages of mass production are derived from the ability to control and manage repetitive handling operations automatically. The use of mechanical, electrical, electronic, photoelectric, and magnetic control equipment is most feasible in the mass production situation. High-volume flow usually results in fixed paths of material movement and minimum transportation costs. High-density storage operations and mass transportation activities are possible with quantity production. Warehouses can be laid out with storage depths keyed to full truck or full car shipments to minimize "honeycombing" and aisle loss. Automatic pallet loaders and unloaders show their capabilities to best advantage in mass production situations.

A typical mass production **unit-handling system** can be found in the manufacture of appliances (Westinghouse, Columbus, Ohio). In this case, major components are delivered to the conveyor-mounted assembly line from subassembly and fabricating shops by various types of conveyor. Small components are delivered to the feeder lines and main line work stations in various types of unit loads. The final work station delivers a complete, tested, and packed appliance to a collecting conveyor. Fork lift trucks with special carton-handling attachments may stack the packed appliances in a storage area at this point. The appliances may proceed via an automatic elevator to an overhead long-distance conveyor for transportation to the warehouse, where they are stored with the same type of lift truck equipment. Appliances are stacked 20 to 25 ft. high in deep storage blocks with a minimum of aisle loss. Shipments are usually in truck or carload quantities and the product is handled from storage to the carrier with the specially equipped lift trucks.

This integrated system demonstrates the value of mass production techniques in simplifying complex operations. Some of the components are handled to the main assembly line by overhead chain conveyor, some by unit loads. The assembly line moves on slat conveyor and the finished product is on roller and belt conveyor. Warehousing is based upon industrial truck methods. **Electrical contacts** for in-motion process testing are similar to standard trolley conductor techniques. The timing and synchronizing of the various components of this system are the result of careful planning, good management, and effective design. Mass production permits the optimum in integrated handling techniques.

A mass production **bulk handling system** is typified by the coal-burning power plant at the mouth of a mine. In this instance mining machinery develops the product (lump coal) and loaders deliver it to belt conveyor equipment in the mine. It is automatically handled through cleaning and sizing operations and delivered by conveyor boom to the stockpile. When required for fueling the boilers, the coal is collected by power shovels or conveyor-type loaders. It is conveyed to pulverizing machinery and blown into the boiler. This system has a multiple of variations and can be found at many utility power installations. The uniformity and high volume of the product handled gives it mass production characteristics. Automatic controls are very precise at the boiler end of the system and more coarse at the mine end of the system. The stockpile adjusts the variations between the control level of each.

Job-Shop Handling Systems. The conventional concept of a job shop involves metal-working operations on a one- or two-unit basis. However, many semiproduction operations also fall in this category. The manufacture of machine tools, heavy aircraft, glass tableware, pottery, furniture, and many other everyday items is based upon job-shop-type operations. In this case an order may run from one hour to one month, but it is seldom long enough to justify large investment for automatic materials handling operations. The **unit-load system** and portable conveyors or "packaged" sectional conveyor units are usually applied in these cases.

A large portion of the production often involves a very few of the items produced. Therefore, by establishing handling systems suitable to several similar products which permit the application of identical handling techniques, part of the facility can approach the efficiencies of mass production.

The remaining items must gain their handling efficiency from judicious application of such flexible equipment as fork lift trucks, unit-load handling and storage devices, portable and adjustable conveyors, and good job-shop-production control. In some cases, efficient in-process inventory management can build up handling quantities to a level approaching small-run mass production. Thus, handling efficiency in job shops is more dependent upon good management than on good equipment applications.

A glass container manufacturing plant (Lamb Glass Co., Mt. Vernon, Ohio) is a good example of job-shop techniques on a high production basis. In this case the quantities are large and the diversity is great. High-speed machines produce large quantities in a very short running time. The handling of **batch material** and the flow of molten glass from the tank through the feeders into the molds is an automatic process requiring good control and a minimum of labor. Each machine produces several items simultaneously. Their physical characteristics are similar enough to permit fully automatic handling from the mold into the lehr. Up to this point the job-shop characteristic of the operation has had no effect on the handling system.

At the selection end of the lehr, a segregation process reduces the item quantities to a typical small-lot job-shop operation. In this case quantities are insufficient to permit automatic pallet-loading operation. Conventional fork lift truck and pallet-handling functions provide efficient and flexible handling unhampered by the diversity of the items. The major effect of diversity is found in the relatively high aisle loss that short storage lots develop in the warehouse. The need for good location and inventory control becomes evident in this warehousing operation.

Integrated handling is equally applicable to job-shop operations as it is to mass production. However, automatic control becomes less practical and the effectiveness of the handling system is more dependent on good management.

Bulk handling operations at a job-shop level are typified by the handling of carbon black in the preparation of wire insulation (Rome Cable Co., Rome, New York). In this instance the product is very dirty and difficult to handle and a bulk handling system is highly desirable. The material can be delivered in bags or in bulk. It is handled in bag or container units to a feed hopper which delivers it to the mixing equipment via **screw feeders**. Since several colors are manufactured in this same mixing equipment, the carbon black is not continually handled and conforms well to the definition of a job-shop operation. New developments in this field include large **neoprene bladders** equipped with bin valves. These units can perform the function of transportation container, storage container, and feed hopper, thus eliminating the dirt and handling loss problem.

In general, job-shop-type bulk handling operations incorporate several types of handling equipment into an integrated system. As in the case of job-shop unit-handling systems, management is more critical than in mass production applications.

MATERIALS POSITIONING. Materials positioning is that phase of materials handling activities which accomplishes the "make-ready" and "put-away" segment of the production cycle. All conventional materials handling equipment can be applied to this activity in some cases. More often, however, specialized equipment is designed to perform this function.

The economic capability of mass production to absorb high capital investment and recover rapidly is more apparent in the positioning field than in any other segment of materials handling activities. An example of this is the typical automotive engine block **transfer machine.** In this case a high-precision, intermittently moving conveyor is interlocked with a group of automatic machines to perform a sequence of manufacturing operations. This type of handling equipment more closely resembles a machine tool than a conveyor. Its operating cycle is precisely controlled and interlocked with the operating cycle of the longest operation in the machine group. Careful operation balance must be developed and precise installation of equipment is a necessity.

The blocks are usually delivered from the foundry on a conveyor which feeds them directly to the transfer machine. The operator orients the casting and locks it in place on the conveyor. The balance of the operations are performed automatically, and the block is usually ejected into another conveyor at the output end of the machine group.

Cartridge feeds have been developed to deliver raw material into various types of production machinery. Vibrating feeders are utilized to deliver assembly components, rivets, screws, etc., at a prearranged rate. Fork lift trucks, conventional conveyors, cranes, and other common handling devices are also used as positioning equipment. This field has a broad area of overlap with the tool engineering function. It is a very critical factor in mass production cost control.

Many of the basic principles used in mass production positioning activities are applicable in job shops. Feeders, transfer conveyors, turntables, lift trucks, and conveyors can all be used for short-run production with the proper application of tooling to accommodate different items and different production rates. The major difference between the job-shop positioning problem and the mass-production positioning problem is the conflict between a greater need for flexibility and a shorter run to amortize the cost.

An example of job-shop positioning techniques can be found in the **feeding devices** applied to centerless grinders. In this case the work trough and escapement must be modified to suit the particular part, but the principle of operation is basic to the machine. **Vibrating hopper feeders** with a multiple of bowls to handle different parts in assembly operations also demonstrate this principle. Here again the critical factor in the economic application of job-shop positioning machinery is in the management function.

PLANT MAINTENANCE

CONTENTS

PAGE

Purpose of maintenance 1
Work of the maintenance department 1
The plant engineer 1
   Functions of plant engineering (f. 1) ... 2
Importance of preplanned maintenance 1

Maintenance Department Organization

Need for organization 3
Size of maintenance force 3
Ratio of maintenance forces to plant forces 4
   Percentage of maintenance workers to
   total plant force (f. 2) 5
Ratio of maintenance expense to value of
   equipment 6
Selection of equipment: effect of equipment
   design 6
Control of maintenance work 6
Form of organization 7
   Structure of a maintenance organization
   (f. 3) 7
Assignments of work to crafts 7
Maintenance working hours 8

Maintenance System

Assignment of work 8
Origin of work orders 8
Form of work orders 9
   Maintenance work order (f. 4) 10
   Maintenance order routine (f. 5) 11
   Combined job order and time ticket
   (f. 6) 12
Material requisitions 9
Planning maintenance work 12
Scheduling maintenance work 13
   Mechanisms for scheduling work 14
Scheduling of inspection work 14
   Equipment index of an inspection sys-
   tem (f. 7) 15
Tickler file 16
Daily planning and scheduling procedure ... 16
   Daily work program 17
   Daily force report 18
Reports on construction 18
Filing completed job orders 18

Equipment Records

Kinds of records 18
   Equipment record card (f. 8) 19
Combined equipment data and maintenance
   cost records 21
   Plant engineer's equipment record (f. 9) 21

PAGE

Equipment record of maintenance ex-
   penditures (f. 10) 21
Motor truck maintenance records 24
   Motor vehicle maintenance master rec-
   ord, work sheet, and summary (f. 11).22–23
Records of miscellaneous equipment 24

Job Standards and Wage Incentives

Job analysis and standards 14
   Results from maintenance work meas-
   urement program (f. 12) 25
Establishing proper work methods 26
   Illustration of standard practice in-
   structions (f. 13) 26
Maintenance force productivity 27
Maintenance work measurement 27
Bases for incentives 28
Introducing wage incentives 28
Typical incentive plan 28
Maintenance training program 28

Preventive Maintenance

Design of machinery and equipment 29
Inspection for maintenance 30
Instructions for inspection 31
Timing inspections 31
   Periods for inspection of buildings and
   equipment 32
   Schedule of routine maintenance inspec-
   tion in a plant (f. 14) 32

Long-Term Planning

Development of the program 33
Planning reduces peak loads 33
   Schedule for making heavy repairs (f. 15) 34
Economic maintenance cycles 34
Operating committees 35
Maintenance in continuous-process industries 35
   Determining size of crew 38
Maintenance work during shutdowns 38
   Schedule arrangement for maintenance
   overhauling in a continuous-process
   plant (f. 16) 36–37

Tools, Equipment, and Materials

Providing tools and equipment 38
Time- and labor-saving devices 39
Storage and issue of tools and equipment ... 40
Storage and issue of materials and supplies 40
   Stores record system 41
   The maintenance storeroom 41

CONTENTS (*Continued*)

PAGE

Maintenance Methods

Best practices 42
Buildings 42
Elevators 42
Heating and ventilating equipment 43
Air-conditioning systems 43
Scheduled maintenance of lighting equipment 43
Sanitary facilities 43
Drinking water supply 44
Fire protection equipment 44
Production equipment 44
Power and heating plants 45
Compressed-air equipment 45
Pipelines 45
Yards, grounds, and walks 45
Hydraulic system maintenance 45

Lubrication of Equipment

Responsibility for lubrication 46
Lubricating devices 46
Selection of lubricants 46
Frequency of lubrication 47
Methods employed 47
Disposing of used oil 48

Good Housekeeping

Order, neatness, and cleanliness 48
A good housekeeping committee 48
Methods for organizing the work 49
Inspections and follow-up 49
Advantages of good housekeeping 49
Check list for maintaining an orderly plant 50

Maintenance Budgets

Maintenance expense allocation 53
Budget procedures 54
Change of maintenance cost level 55

Nuclear Plant Engineering and Maintenance

Objective 55
Ventilation and air cleaning 56
Maximum permissible air concentrations .. 56

PAGE

Comparison of toxic substances in air (concentration in mg./cu. met.) (f. 17) 57
Air supply and exhaust design 56
Exhaust outlets and ventilation rates for nonradioactive industrial dusts (f. 18) 58
Radiochemical laboratory ventilation 58
Plan of modular radiochemical laboratory units (f. 19) 59–60
Radiochemical glove box (f. 20) 61
Section through work cell of radiation analytical facilities (f. 21) 62
Methods of air cleaning 62
Suggested minimum particle size groups for different collectors (f. 22) 63
Operational characteristics of air-cleaning equipment (f. 23) 64–65
Radioactive waste disposal 66
Sources of radioactive wastes 66
Quantities of fission products derived from 1 ton of U^{225} (150 days' irradiation, 30 days' cooling) (f. 24) 66
Types of waste treatment and disposal ... 67
Ideal method for handling chemical processing waste (f. 25) 68
Ground disposal 67
Flow pattern for disposal of liquid waste (f. 26) 69
Sea disposal 69
Air disposal 70
Low-level disposal 70
Formulating a waste disposal program 71
Shielding 71
Biological effects of ionizing radiation ... 72
Alpha and beta particle shielding 72
Photon particle shielding 72
Material and personnel contamination and decontamination 73
Surface contamination 73
Maximum permissible surface contamination (MPSC) 78
Personnel decontamination 78
Equipment and floor decontamination 78
Surface decontamination methods in civil defense (f. 27) 74–75
Methods of checking for contamination .. 79
Typical radiation survey meters (f. 28) ..76–77
Economics of radiation protection 79
Annual whole-body gamma exposures above 1 roentgen at the Hanford works (f. 29) 79

PLANT MAINTENANCE

PURPOSE OF MAINTENANCE. The task of maintenance is to keep buildings and grounds, service equipment, and production machinery in satisfactory condition, according to standards set by management. The work assigned to the maintenance department usually includes removals and installations of equipment. In cases where new construction and alterations are added to maintenance duties, care should be taken to keep separate records, because such work on either buildings or equipment is beyond the limits of maintenance and becomes capital expenditure.

WORK OF THE MAINTENANCE DEPARTMENT. In small plants, maintenance activities are combined with the work of other departments, such as the engineering department, the production department, or plant engineering. In large plants the work is organized separately, with an executive in charge who reports directly to a works manager or plant superintendent. A term commonly used to designate the maintenance function in its broad sense is **plant engineering**; this term is used extensively in this section.

THE PLANT ENGINEER. A plant engineer's range of work is indicated in Fig. 1. Under modern conditions, continuous introduction of improved service equipment, new operating methods, and machinery add continuously to the tasks of maintenance. Selection of manufacturing equipment is primarily the concern of production engineering, but the plant engineer will often be consulted about installation, power and service requirements, and specifications affecting maintenance. (See section on Machinery and Equipment Economics.) Minimum maintenance costs require sound engineering all the way from the proper selection and arrangement of equipment to the development of efficient tools and methods in maintenance work. With such a broad field to cover, the plant engineer needs wide technical knowledge and must also be a good executive. In large multi-plant organizations, each plant usually has its own plant engineer. The production engineering will often be done at headquarters where general plans of operation and the investment program are formulated, usually under a company officer responsible for all operations.

IMPORTANCE OF PREPLANNED MAINTENANCE. The trend toward the modern practice of organizing maintenance work to prevent interruptions of operations is the outgrowth of several factors:

1. **Increased mechanization,** while decreasing direct labor costs per output unit, has required at least a portion of the gain to be spent on maintenance of the equipment. Maintenance work has grown to the point where costs of labor and material warrant more detailed study and control. It has been found uneconomical to retain large maintenance staffs for emergencies which planning and systematized inspection can avoid.
2. **Close management of production,** with minimum stocks between operations or direct flow from one machine to the next, has made interruptions to produc-

1. Building Construction and Maintenance

a. Masonry—foundations, walls, permanent partitions, plastering, tiling
b. Steel work—columns, beams, stairways, windows, fire-escapes
c. Floors—concrete, plank, wood block, mastic, steel plate, or gratings
d. Service mains—water, gas, steam, compressed air, oil, piping for solutions used in production
e. Heating, ventilating, air conditioning —piping, ducts, radiators
f. Carpentry and wood construction
g. Painting
h. Plumbing
i. Roofing and tinning. cleaning
j. General building upkeep—hardware, glazing
k. Minor construction. (In large plants, sometimes major construction is carried on.)
l. Inspection of construction done by outside contractors

2. Mechanical Equipment Maintenance

a. Steam power equipment
b. Steam-heating, ventilating, and air-conditioning equipment
c. Millwright work—shafting, pulleys, drives, equipment installation, moving, set-up, alignment, removal
d. Compressed air equipment
e. Heat-treating and furnace equipment
f. Machine and operating equipment installation and repairs
g. Lubrication of machinery and equipment
h. Sheet-metal and welding work for maintenance or special construction
i. Materials handling equipment
j. Storeroom equipment setup
k. In some cases, factory layout—at any rate carrying out relayout plans
l. Mechanical meters, gages, recording devices and instruments

3. Electrical Equipment Maintenance

a. Electrical power plant equipment, transformers, etc.
b. Wiring, conduits, switch boxes, cutouts, power outlets
c. Electric lighting
d. Motors—rewinding, commutator repairs, etc.
e. Alarm, signaling, call, and communication systems

3. Electrical Equipment Maintenance (Cont'd)

f. Private telephone systems
g. Electrical equipment, tools, furnaces, etc.
h. Lightning protection devices
i. Electronic control
j. Electric meters, and instruments, gages, recording devices
k. Battery charging

4. Plant Safety, Fire and Theft Protection, and Other Services

a. Safety guards and all safety installations
b. Floor marking in plant, road marking, and walkways outdoors
c. Warning signs
d. Railroad and roadway crossing protection
e. Watchmen's service—fire, burglary, etc. (Plant protection in wartime was placed under works manager or other executive.)
f. Fire-fighting equipment—yard hydrants, sprinkler systems, trucks, ladders, axes and other tools, hose, lanterns, pails, extinguishers
g. Janitor services and general cleanliness
h. General plant housekeeping and clean-up

5. Yard and Ground Maintenance

a. Railroad tracks, switches, trestles, etc.
b. Roadways, walkways, paving, concreting
c. Tunnels and conduits
d. Sheds and other yard structures
e. Outdoor crane structures
f. Poles for cables, wiring, etc.
g. Fences
h. Outdoor signs
i. Rigging
j. General yard layout
k. Outdoor storage areas and facilities
l. Landscaping and gardening—lawns, trees, shrubbery
m. Parking facilities
n. Yard drainage
o. General yard cleanliness and good housekeeping
p. Collection and disposal of refuse, rubbish. ashes. etc.
q. Snow removal, road sanding

In all cases this work includes maintenance inspections, and adjustments, repairs, replacements, and the operation of shops for various kinds of work.

Fig. 1. Functions of plant engineering.

tion more costly. Even where workers are paid on an output basis, regulations often prescribe payment for waiting time when workers are held on the job waiting for work. Lost profits from production stoppage frequently exceed the cost of idle labor.

3. **Failure to deliver on time,** with serious consequences and possible loss of business, may result from interruptions to operations.
4. **Correction of defective conditions** not only decreases cost of repairs but maintains performance efficiency of machinery as to quantity and quality.
5. **Service expenses** for steam, electricity, air, water, etc., are often reduced by continuous maintenance.
6. **Specialization of maintenance work,** within reasonable limits, results in increased reliability of work done and lower over-all cost.
7. **Planning of maintenance operations** will insure that needed spare parts are on hand in stores without excessive accumulation of obsolescent material.

The principal objective of maintenance is, therefore, to anticipate and prevent interruptions in operation and keep equipment in condition for high-efficiency performance.

Maintenance Department Organization

NEED FOR ORGANIZATION. To achieve the above objective at reasonable cost, a certain amount of formal organization is essential. The following condition is frequently encountered:

In a new plant, once construction is completed, there is a period during which maintenance work is limited to minor routine matters and various adjustments. Unless the plant engineer has had previous experience in similar production, no clear pattern of maintenance work will stand out, and work arrangements will tend to settle on the basis of meeting each need or emergency as it arises. After operations have been carried on in this manner for some time, the impact of wide daily variety will give the impression that the range of work and variations in conditions are beyond the possibility of standardization and planning.

This impression, however, has been found by engineers versed in organizing maintenance work to be largely illusory. It is true that the kinds of tasks occurring are highly variable from day to day. Hence, the organization must be kept flexible. No ready-made system can be imposed on the individual plant because development of methods and procedure is a gradual process to be adapted to particular requirements. Despite great variation of detail, however, certain **general principles** can be outlined, relating to:

1. Size and control of working maintenance force.
2. Planning of work on long-term basis.
3. Daily issuance of work orders.
4. Standard practice instructions.
5. Storing of spare parts and tools used for repairs.
6. Inspection methods and schedules.
7. Maintenance records.

These factors of successful maintenance are discussed subsequently.

SIZE OF MAINTENANCE FORCE. A primary requisite for adequate maintenance is sufficient men—but not an excessive number—of each craft to meet the demands under peak loads. It is unwise to budget too closely, but in the interest of plant discipline as well as economy, excessive personnel should be avoided. Where peak loads can be foreseen but the nature of the jobs prevents spreading work over a suitably long period, **temporary shifting** of men from production to maintenance may remove the need for carrying a large maintenance crew. Where maintenance work has not been set up on an organization basis, past history is an unreliable guide; frequently, unnecessarily large crews have been retained. On the other hand, an aging plant may require an increase in the crew to avoid the danger of undermaintenance.

A satisfactory solution of the problem requires a **man-hour rating of the work and an annual program of jobs,** as discussed later under planning of maintenance activities. Many jobs recur only at long intervals; hence the accumulation of adequate data may take a year or more. As an initial guide in setting up the maintenance force, a general over-all ratio to determine the proper number of workers may help, but such a ratio must be used with caution.

In budgeting, it is important to specify what personnel belong to maintenance. With increasing use of automated equipment, **roving mechanics** are assigned to keep machinery in adjustment for output within specified tolerances. Such personnel customarily report to operating management and are classed as production personnel, not maintenance.

RATIO OF MAINTENANCE FORCES TO PLANT FORCES. The percentages of maintenance workers to total plant force for various types of plants, ranging from fabric and metalworking plants to an oil refinery and an atomic energy gaseous diffusion plant, are shown by G. I. Ross in Fig. 2.

As equipment units become larger, heavier and more intricate, the proportion of maintenance workers increases, but the claim is made that, in a given type of manufacturing, approximately equal ratios are found in well-managed plants. Where the ratio is heavier than normal for the particular type of industry, the figures suggest there may be faulty organization, inadequate supervision or inspection, lack of a maintenance order system and records, or inadequate budgetary control.

Automation reduces the amount of maintenance work per unit of product output. In one automated plant, about 12 times as many workers would have been needed with the techniques used in 1934, including 150–200 maintenance personnel, compared with the actual current 30.

A breakdown by **crafts** is useful in adjusting the maintenance force to the annual level of activity. Comparisons between plants, even when the product is similar, should be made with caution.

For example, in judging groups K and M in Fig. 2, where the pattern is fairly constant, managements prescribe varying degrees of **cleanliness** and **plant protection.** A food concern welcoming many visitors may have a modernistic building in a landscaped setting, with the advertising value justifying somewhat large expenditures for groundsmen, floor-polishers, painters, and other workers, far beyond any reasonable necessities of manufacturing. **Location** has a bearing. Northern plants with yards, sidings, and roadways have heavier snow removal expense. Plants in open areas have added yard expenses for the parking and protection of employees' cars.

Mechanical crafts items are so peculiar to each plant that general ratios must be used warily. For example, in garment-making one machinist may readily manage current adjustments of machines used by total force of 200, sending machines out to a service shop for major repairs, provided spare machines are available. A large garment factory, however, with its own repair shop, would show a higher maintenance ratio.

The general conclusion is that where the plant engineer has reliable data from closely comparable plants with which he is familiar, such existing satisfactory

Classification of Work	4 Fabric-working Plants	5 Metal-working Plants—Light Assembly	10 Metal-working Plants—Small Products	12 Metal-working Plants—Medium to Heavy	Average 27 Metal-working Plants	Oil Refinery†	Atomic Energy Gaseous Diffusion Plant‡
A. Maintenance supervision and clerical	0.15	0.30	0.48	0.41	0.44	1.0	5.27
B. Belt repairmen, oilers, millwrights	.29	.50	.75	1.27	.96	2.1	13.87*
C. Welders, heat-treaters, ironworkers	.02	.15	.17	.14	.16	6.3	*
D. Masons, plumbers, pipefitters, tinsmiths	.12	.20	.71	.68	.66	0.9	*
E. Electricians, motor winders	.10	.50	.64	.58	.60	3.1	3.74
F. Machinists and all machine fixers	.46	.30	.98	1.63	1.22	0.3	.88
G. Carpenter on maintenance work, pattern-maker on maintenance work	.10	.35	.48	.39	.43	0.9	.57
H. Painters, glaziers	.04	-	.16	.12	.13	-	.31
I. Truck repairmen	.03	-	.01	.12	.06	2.0	.38
J. Instrument men							4.32
K. Janitors, porters, sweepers	1.10	1.31	.80	1.64	1.20	1.6	3.21
L. Watchmen, roundsmen, plant policemen	.31	.66	.63	.71	.66	1.1	2.75
M. Yardmen, clean-up men, general maintenance laborers, miscellaneous	.24	.35	.66	.54	.59	6.3	.76
Total	2.96	4.62	6.47	8.23	7.11	25.6	36.06

Total plant force includes all personnel in manufacturing activities, but excludes nonmanufacturing, such as audit, sales, general accounting, advertising, and billing.
* The percentage for B includes the percentages for C and D as well, since these are not separately classified.
† Data furnished by Emerson Engineers.
‡ Data furnished by F. Lauxterman.

Fig. 2. Percentage of maintenance workers to total plant force.

maintenance personnel ratios can be of assistance in establishing the proper size of maintenance crews.

RATIO OF MAINTENANCE EXPENSE TO VALUE OF EQUIPMENT. In some instances, ratios of expense of maintenance labor and material to the value of equipment in the plant may appear more satisfactory. One influence in their favor is that, in budgetary control and expense allocation, the same base can be used as for the calculation of depreciation. As a means of comparison between plants, the investment ratio is open to the same objections as the plant-force ratio. Size and age of units, intensity of use, and design of equipment may justify widely differing ratios on two machines with identical functions. Yet, in practice, similar well-managed plants often show closely similar amounts in the annual percentage of investment represented by the amount spent on maintenance. Where a satisfactory maintenance expense ratio can be established, it can be useful in adjusting craft personnel to changes in the amount of equipment to be maintained, and in allowing for maintenance expense in estimating the operating cost of new acquisitions.

For example, the Emerson Engineers state:

Our experience is that the annual cost of labor and material in maintenance of modern oil refineries, with well-planned maintenance programs, tends to run between 5½% and 6½% of total plant cost, excluding land. Various parts of the plants, however, show widely different ratios, as indicated by a few samples from refineries with stabilized maintenance:

Equipment or Service	Percentage of Total Original Cost
Crude storage	4.7
Steam system and lines	5.0
Electric light and power	4.0
Gas plant	5.7
Sewers and drains	12.1
Lines and connections	3.5
Fire protection	5.0
Maintenance shops	10.0
Staff houses	6.2

Labor and material components vary widely, but the plant total is about evenly divided, with materials and supplies at least as important as labor.

SELECTION OF EQUIPMENT: EFFECT OF EQUIPMENT DESIGN. Both frequency and amount of upkeep work hinge to a large extent on the relation of design to maintenance load imposed. Basic ruggedness of construction, balance of moving parts, and accessibility for repairs are all stressed in the theory of design, but differing ideas of machine builders on first cost and operating efficiency complicate the choice of equipment; new alloys, synthetics, closer specifications of materials and tolerances, and improved elements of construction bring about improved designs and lengthened periods of operation. The plant engineer must keep posted on developments and sources of supply, since selection of equipment is the first step in maintenance. Visiting sales engineers are valuable sources of information, but can take up excessive time; the consensus is that the plant engineer should arrange with the purchasing agent to be notified when the visiting salesman may have interesting information and decide then whether to see him.

CONTROL OF MAINTENANCE WORK. The original status of maintenance work was that operators did their own oiling, belt fixing, and even tool-

making. Vestiges of this practice still persist. The **basic requirement of func-
tionalized maintenance** is prompt skilled attention to machinery when requested
by operators, as well as periodic attention to minimize the need for requests.
Separation of the maintenance function does not mean that operators should
know nothing about equipment, but that the emphasis should be on the common
objective of perfect operating conditions and prompt report by operators of even
suspected defective conditions. Since responsibility is placed on the maintenance
department, however, all such work should be done at its direction. Operators
assigned to repair work should report in such instances to the designated maintenance man.

FORM OF ORGANIZATION. Fig. 3 shows a representative organization
for maintenance work where plant investment and volume of upkeep and changes
warrant a permanent plant engineer. When the plant engineer has to spend
much time on alteration and installation work, the addition of a master mechanic
is advisable to relieve the engineer of routine supervision and instructions. Where
changes are infrequent or plans are made outside, the two positions may be consolidated. In smaller plants, craft foremen may be omitted. Where the work is
mostly of a routine nature, a dispatcher may be unnecessary and job control may

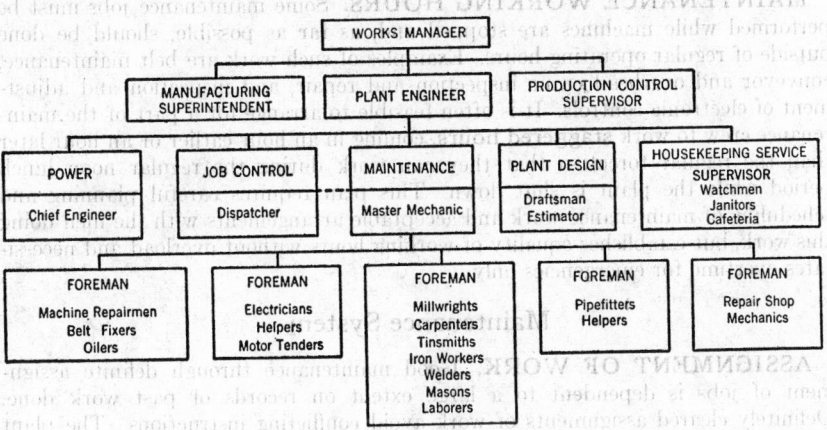

Fig. 3. Structure of a maintenance organization.

be made the joint function of master mechanic and cost clerk. This form of
organization is arranged to use any craftsman anywhere in the plant; it permits
full utilization of manpower, at the discretion of the centralized planning section.
Organization of separate crews, limited to a department, is undesirable. It
leads to overmanning and, by limiting disposal of men, slows up dealing with
emergencies or peak loads. However, organization by crafts for the whole plant
does not prevent localized routine daily assignments. Such assignments are made
when efficiency dictates, but authority remains with the master mechanic to
borrow men from any postponable routine for more urgent work.

ASSIGNMENTS OF WORK TO CRAFTS. Formulation of instructions
for doing maintenance work, as described later in this section, will permit economy of work assignments. Too rigid separation of work among crafts is to be
avoided in favor of consolidating work. Splitting up a job among crafts may be
avoided by giving adequate instructions. Thus, on conveyor maintenance, the

largest part of the work falls within the millwright class. If the millwrights are instructed also on visual inspection of motors, they can make the frequent external inspection of motors along with the regular complete conveyor inspection. Electricians then will make the more complete inspection with instruments at longer intervals.

The common practice of **assigning a territory or group of machines to one man** to inspect and adjust simplifies maintenance supervision. An inherent danger is that the work load may change and become either more or less than a fair day's work. Such assignments, therefore, should be subject to periodic review. For example, in a large textile plant with 15–20 print machines and auxiliaries, the plant engineer may assign a mechanic to the printroom area with the general responsibility of seeing to all equipment including steam lines, valves, gaskets, motors, bearings, etc. The assignment assumes 90 percent of machines running. Should the department be operated at half-capacity, the assignment might be adjusted by borrowing the mechanic for other work in other departments or by assigning special overhaul and alteration work within the printroom. In any case, for completion of maintenance payroll accounting records, it is advisable to issue work tickets to each man for each day's work, as will be explained subsequently.

MAINTENANCE WORKING HOURS. Some maintenance jobs must be performed while machines are stopped and, as far as possible, should be done outside of regular operating hours. Examples of such work are belt maintenance, conveyor and overhead crane inspection and repair, and inspection and adjustment of electronic controls. It is often feasible to arrange for a part of the maintenance crew to work **staggered hours,** coming in an hour earlier or an hour later than the regular force, so that they can work during the regular noon lunch period while the plant is shut down. This plan requires careful planning and scheduling of maintenance work and acceptable arrangements with the men doing this work, but establishes equality of working hours without overload and necessitates overtime for emergencies only.

Maintenance System

ASSIGNMENT OF WORK. Good maintenance through definite assignment of jobs is dependent to a large extent on records of past work done. Definitely cleared assignments of work avoid conflicting instructions. The plant engineer's office should assign jobs to each man or gang (see Planning Maintenance Work). The record of each job done is the basis of maintenance control. Hence, the cardinal rule is that no maintenance work should be done without a written job order or work ticket. Except in sudden emergency, the issue of a job order should precede assignment of the job to a man. In case of emergency, men may be sent to the job by verbal instruction, but a covering order should be issued promptly, with notice to persons affected by removal of maintenance men from jobs they are already on and the stopping of routine jobs. Where a maintenance man is detached for a routine assignment, he may be exempted from his daily assignment schedule but should turn in daily time tickets and remain subject to call for emergency work.

ORIGIN OF WORK ORDERS. Work orders may originate from:

1. Prescribed regular inspection routine and maintenance requirements uncovered by inspection.
2. Operating department requests for maintenance or repair work.
3. Changes initiated by management, production, or engineering departments.

To avoid conflicting claims and promises, all work should be cleared and scheduled by a single authority, who will be the plant engineer or his delegate. The general rule is that requests from departments should clear through this central point. Exception may be made where the maintenance man has a standing assignment on the upkeep of a group of machines and the request is for minor adjustment only.

FORM OF WORK ORDERS. Maintenance work orders may be either of a specific type involving one project or of a blanket type for repeated and more routine maintenance jobs. A typical maintenance work order for specific work is shown in Fig. 4 (Planning, Controlling, and Accounting for Maintenance, NACA Accounting Practice Report No. 2). Such forms provide space for a brief description of the work requested, the person requesting the work, an estimate of the time it will require, an estimate of the cost, the location and number of the equipment to be worked on, the date wanted, date completed, order number, approval space, and similar data which varies from company to company.

Not only does the work order initiate work requests, but, after being given a priority rating, it is used for appropriate scheduling of maintenance work, serves as a form on which project costs can be collected, and provides a running record of the status of maintenance in process. When the job is completed, it becomes the basic record from which maintenance costs on each item of equipment can be developed and supplies the financial data needed for formal accounting, planning, and control reports.

A maintenance job order routine for major, minor, and emergency jobs is shown in Fig. 5.

Fig. 6 shows a form designed for use where work often requires several men in the crew. It is a combination work order and time ticket. The form also shows suggested items to be checked before issuing the order:

1. Is equipment available and safe for maintenance men?
2. Is needed material on hand in the storeroom?
3. What tools are to be used?
4. Are sketches or drawings to be given out with the job?
5. Is there any deadline for completion?

Forms sometimes have the order on the face and time entries on the back. This practice is not recommended. Shop copies are often folded to keep the face clean, and the back becomes soiled. Moreover, subsequent reference, checking, etc., is simpler with data all on the face. Two copies usually are made, a white carbon being kept at the order desk and a buff original going out on the job. If the organization is large, with many orders, and triplicates are needed, the form can be made to fit the billing-type register.

In most cases, **written instructions on job orders** will and should be quite brief. More elaborate instructions will usually be covered by a standard practice procedure or a memorandum to the master mechanic. The space provided on Fig. 6 has proved ample for all regular work. Note that equipment and location designations avoid the need for explaining further on the order where the job is. Material requisitions are made to match. They are attached to the job order and further diminish the need for explanations on the job order. Materials carried in stores should be coded for convenience of identification and withdrawal.

MATERIAL REQUISITIONS. A material requisition form should be made out as a receipt for all withdrawals of items from stores. (See section on Storeskeeping.) In most cases, the exact requirements for a maintenance job can

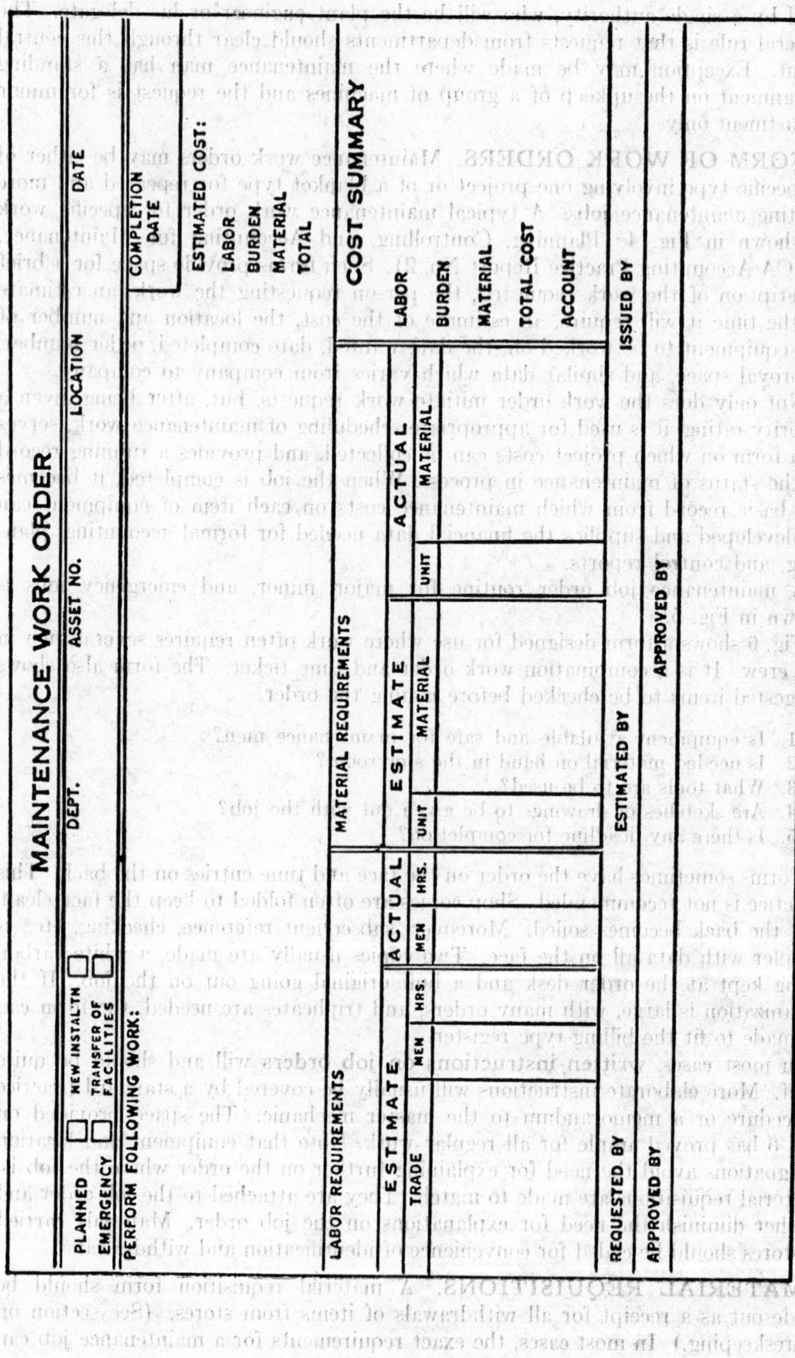

MAINTENANCE WORK ORDER

PLANNED ☐   NEW INSTALL'N ☐
EMERGENCY ☐   TRANSFER OF FACILITIES ☐

DEPT.   ASSET NO.   LOCATION   DATE   COMPLETION DATE

ESTIMATED COST:
LABOR
BURDEN
MATERIAL
TOTAL

PERFORM FOLLOWING WORK:

COST SUMMARY
LABOR
BURDEN
MATERIAL
TOTAL COST
ACCOUNT

LABOR REQUIREMENTS

ESTIMATE			ACTUAL	
TRADE	MEN	HRS.	MEN	HRS.

MATERIAL REQUIREMENTS

ESTIMATE		ACTUAL	
UNIT	MATERIAL	UNIT	MATERIAL

REQUESTED BY
APPROVED BY
ESTIMATED BY
APPROVED BY
ISSUED BY

Fig. 4. Maintenance work order.

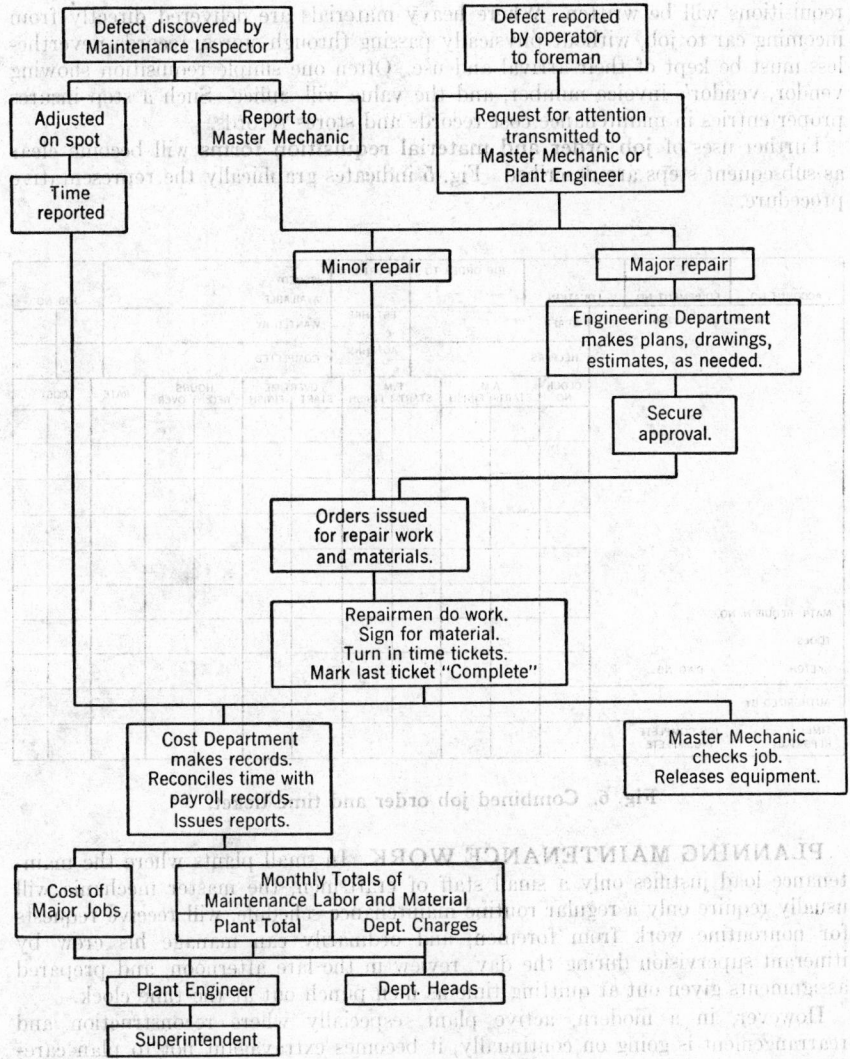

Fig. 5. **Maintenance order routine.**

be predetermined, but provision must be made for items for which need is disclosed only after dismantling the equipment. For this reason the master mechanic or inspector should be provided with a requisition book.

The blanks should have spaces for entry of account number and equipment number to be charged with the material. Requisitions are often numbered serially. Two copies usually are sufficient, the original being issued to the worker with the job order and the carbon being retained for office use. Authority to issue materials requisitions for repairs and renewals will ordinarily be vested in the master mechanic or inspector. On major alteration and installation work, the plant engineer will authorize the preparation of a bill of materials from which the requisitions will be written. Where heavy materials are delivered directly from incoming car to job, without physically passing through stores, records nevertheless must be kept of their arrival and use. Often one simple requisition showing vendor, vendor's invoice number, and the value will suffice. Such a step insures proper entries in maintenance cost records and stores records.

Further uses of **job order and material requisition forms** will become clear as subsequent steps are described. Fig. 5 indicates graphically the representative procedure.

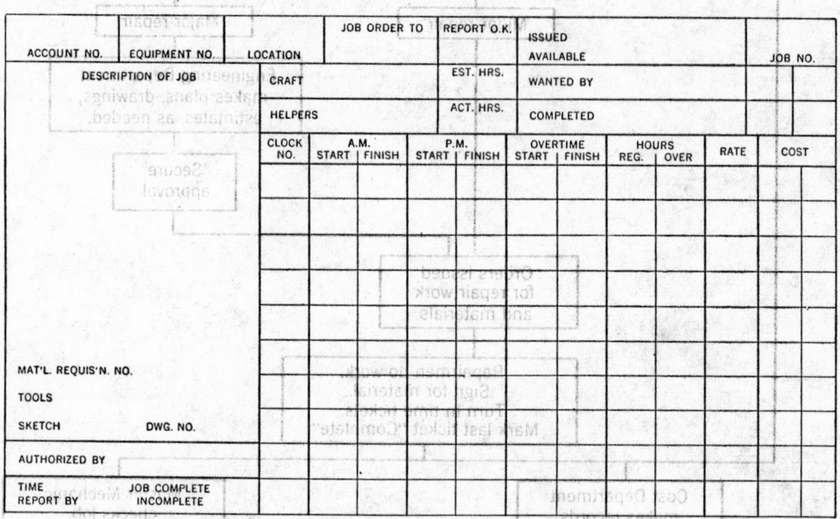

ACCOUNT NO.	EQUIPMENT NO.	LOCATION	JOB ORDER TO	REPORT O.K.	ISSUED						JOB NO.

DESCRIPTION OF JOB	CRAFT	EST. HRS.	WANTED BY
	HELPERS	ACT. HRS.	COMPLETED

Fig. 6. Combined job order and time ticket.

PLANNING MAINTENANCE WORK. In small plants where the maintenance load justifies only a small staff of craftsmen, the master mechanic will usually require only a regular routine maintenance schedule, will receive requests for nonroutine work from foremen, and ordinarily can manage his crew by itinerant supervision during the day, review in the late afternoon, and prepared assignments given out at quitting time as men punch out at the time clock.

However, in a modern, active plant, especially where reconstruction and rearrangement is going on continually, it becomes extravagant not to plan carefully. To promote economy, there must be orderly **disposition of maintenance manpower** to fit current requests and routine needs. While the plant engineer is generally responsible for plant condition and maintenance procedure, it is often advisable to relieve him and his master mechanic of duties pertaining to the daily routine of work assignments. Such duties may be delegated to an assistant, who will function as job order clerk or maintenance dispatcher. He will be responsible for all maintenance records of work done and schedules of work to be done, for checking material requirements, and for finding out whether these materials are on hand in stores. If any necessary materials are not carried, he must put through purchase requisitions for them. He will actually issue orders and requisitions, securing approvals as specified, and report to the plant engineer as to the relation between personnel available and work ahead.

To facilitate orderly procedure, appropriate routines are needed, as follows:

1. **Approval** of the plant engineer may be required when estimated cost of labor and material exceeds a given maximum, usually about $25. The plant engineer may set a detailed policy covering classes of expenditure he desires to follow up personally, or equipment slated for early replacement. On major alterations or acquisitions, approval of expenditures and appropriation of funds by the superintendent or other plant executive may be specified. The limit for jobs done without executive approval commonly ranges from expenditures of $250 to $500, or about 5 percent of monthly budget.

2. An **equipment record** is vital, to show the maintenance history of each important piece of equipment. This record will be described in later paragraphs.

3. A **schedule of work ahead** is required. This schedule will be made up of three classes of work: (1) jobs which can be definitely planned well ahead, such as inspections and routine jobs, (2) jobs which may vary with conditions but nevertheless must be fitted in at approximate times, and (3) jobs which must be done as emergencies arise. To fit in the latter jobs, flexibility in the master schedule is necessary.

4. A **tickler file** in which work orders and data on forthcoming jobs to be done can be filed according to the date on which such jobs must be planned and scheduled.

5. A **daily work program,** made out from the schedule of work ahead, and fitting in emergency jobs for which orders or requests have just been received.

6. A **daily force report** showing the disposition of the maintenance men according to the kind and location of jobs to which they have been assigned for the particular day.

7. An **estimate of man-hours** must be made up for jobs but is a difficult undertaking. Much help can be gained by keeping a file of completed jobs for reference. On work with repetitive elements, standards, as explained later, can be gradually established.

8. A system of **long-term planning,** or annual planning, can be adopted to build up a stabilized maintenance force, and a well-balanced maintenance program can be established, as indicated in a subsequent part of this section.

SCHEDULING MAINTENANCE WORK. The scheduling of maintenance work involves two steps—the **master planning** of jobs whose time of performance can be reasonably closely predicted in advance, and the **daily adjustment of this master plan** by fitting in all request or emergency jobs which have just come up and which may necessitate realignment of the already scheduled jobs, to meet the current situation as to immediately required work and the force and equipment available to do it.

While a **tickler file** is convenient for assembling the work orders and data for forthcoming jobs and bringing them to attention in advance of the necessary starting date, it does not schedule these jobs according to the hours of work involved as compared with the labor time available, and the specific time at which they should be undertaken. For these latter purposes either a **schedule-of-work board** or a **Gantt chart** is of greatest use.

Routine inspection—except for longer jobs on heavy equipment or on building structures—perhaps may more conveniently be handled through a tickler file or **visible record system** (see later under Equipment Records) from which job orders, if necessary, could be written or the time schedule developed and put on the daily work program sheet. From this work sheet, the total load on the maintenance department can be built up to the labor hours available, and the men finally assigned. Maintenance jobs are often short and usually isolated, in contrast to production jobs. Scheduling, therefore, is more immediate and must be more flexible than in production. Nevertheless, the jobs must be carefully scheduled to make the best use of the men's time and must be performed on schedule —or at once, in emergency—to avoid interruptions to production or plant shutdowns. When a flanged connection in a main steam line broke in a large plant operating on a 24-hr. schedule and employing thousands of workers, shutting off the power and heat and closing the plant down for several hours, schedules of maintenance work were, of course, forgotten for the time being.

Mechanisms for Scheduling Work. To control maintenance work on jobs other than short routine operations which would take too much time and be too costly to post on work boards, some kind of board such as is used to schedule production is useful. Down the left-hand side of the board a list of the departments or equipment requiring maintenance work can be posted. Across the top of the board a date scale (Saturdays and Sundays included) can be entered. If the board is of the pocket, groove insert, spring clip, or a similar type, work order forms, or an identification card or slip, can be put on the board opposite the department or equipment to be worked on and under the date when the job is to be done. If the work will require several days, a series of copies of the order or identification cards can be posted under the respective dates.

Obviously, the job order number, name or number of equipment and class and kind of work to be done would be shown on the job order or identification slip. As jobs are done, the slips can be removed, any required data entered, and the slips filed for posting to permanent records. A nail or peg put at the end of each date period across the top of the board provides a means for hanging an **indicator string** down over the board to be moved along daily to the close of the previous day. Any tickets to the left of the string show work behind, those to the right show work ahead. By having the department or equipment names on cards (unless there is always work at such places), the listing down the left side of the system can be kept flexible and the list may be kept shortened. The date entries also may be on strips or cards so that the board may be reposted when the last few days currently showing are approached.

An alternative plan is to use a **Gantt chart,** which is essentially the above method recorded on paper. (See sections on Production Planning and Control and Production Control Systems and Procedures.)

SCHEDULING OF INSPECTION WORK. For regular inspection and adjustment or merely minor repair of building structures, building services, fire protection and safety devices, and manufacturing equipment, the systems just discussed are not necessary. A tickler file system, or the visible index systems of the hinged, center panel post, vertical card, or insert types, are well adapted to such short-cycle, repetitive jobs. The advantages of these more flexible systems are the absence of expensive posting time and "pencil work," ease of making quick changes, high degree of flexibility, ease of locating data, and graphic control features.

A form of equipment index used for the scheduling, control, and recording of inspection work in maintenance is illustrated in Fig. 7. Williamson (Maint. Eng., vol. 89) describes this system as it has been used in the Carborundum Co. It consists of visible index cards for each piece of equipment. At the top of the card the data on the equipment are entered. Below this section is an area ruled off into 52 spaces for weeks of the year, and down the left of the area are spaces to enter the years. The squares are for checking the performance of maintenance inspection as to weeks when the work was done. If the inspection card is marked O.K., a check mark is entered in the proper square. If any repairs are made, a serial

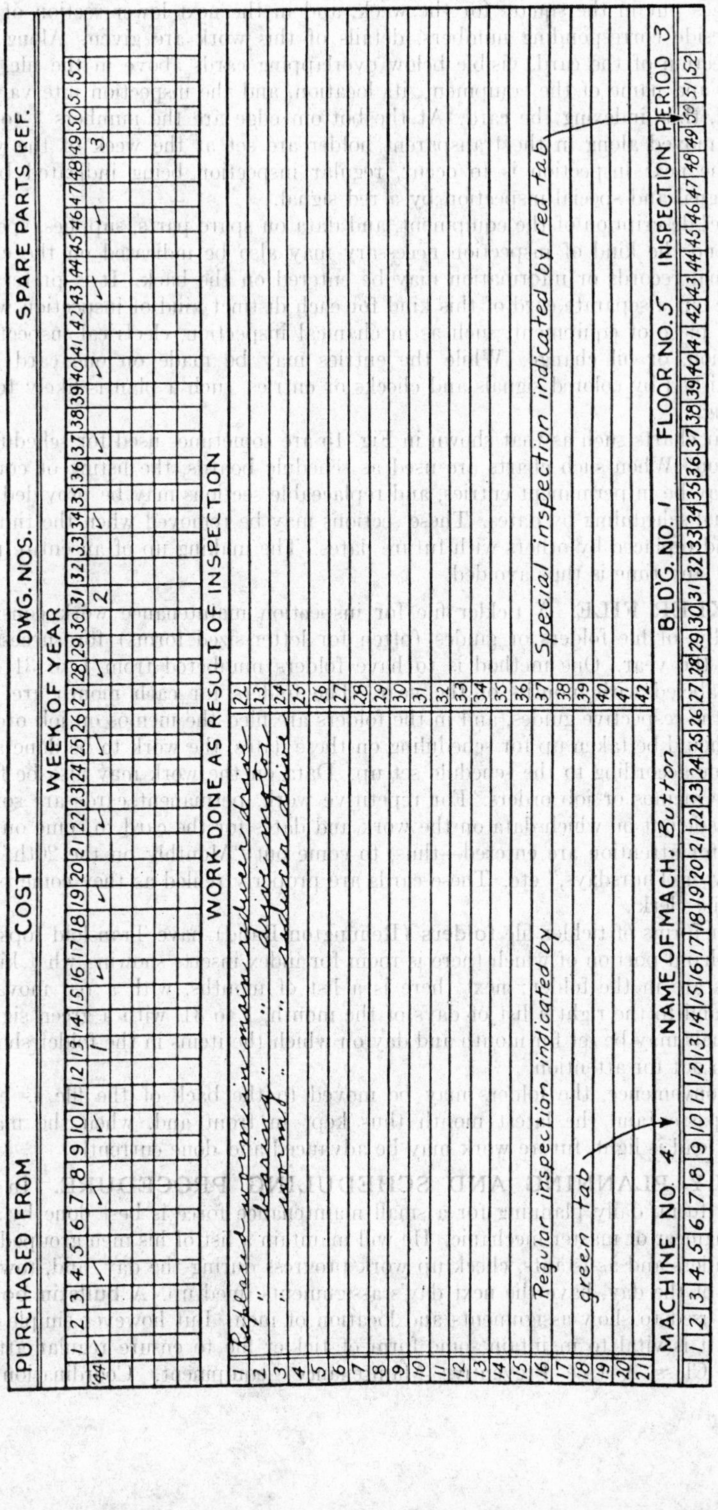

PURCHASED FROM	COST	WEEK OF YEAR	DWG. NOS.	SPARE PARTS REF.

WORK DONE AS RESULT OF INSPECTION

1 Replaced up main sphere drive
2   "   "   "   bearing
3   "   "   "   normal
4
5
...
42

Special inspection indicated by red tab

Regular inspection indicated by green tab

MACHINE NO. 4	NAME OF MACH. Button	BLDG. NO. 1	FLOOR NO. 5	INSPECTION PERIOD 3

Fig. 7. Equipment index of an inspection system.

number is put in the square for the week, and in the next lower section of the card, beside corresponding numbers, details of this work are given. Along the lower section of the card, visible below overlapping cards above in the file, the number and name of the equipment, its location, and the inspection interval are inserted, thus indexing the card. At the bottom edge are the numbers 1 to 52. Signals moved along in the transparent holder are set at the week of the year when the next inspection is to occur, regular inspection being indicated by a green signal and special inspection by a red signal.

A brief description of the equipment, and data on spare parts, supplies, special items, and the kind of inspection necessary may also be indicated on the card. Additional records or information may be entered on the back. It is preferable to make out a separate card of this kind for each distinct kind of inspection work on each piece of equipment, such as mechanical inspection, electrical inspection, lubrication, or oil change. While the entries may be made on one card and distinguished by colored signals and checks or entries, such a plan is likely to be confusing.

Repair charts such as that shown in Fig. 15 are sometimes used for scheduling inspection. When such charts are used as schedule boards, the listing of equipment may be in permanent entries, and replaceable sections may be provided for the actual scheduling by dates. These sections may be removed when the time is past, and replaced by others with future dates. The making up of an entire new chart at any time is thus avoided.

TICKLER FILE. A tickler file for inspection maintenance work consists, essentially, of file folders or guides (often for letter-sized forms) for successive days of the year. One method is to have folders numbered from 1 to 31 and guides labeled with months of the year. The folders for each month are put behind the respective guides, and in the folders are filed the memos on job orders which should be taken up for scheduling on these dates, the work to be done at a later time according to the schedule set up. Data on the work may also be filed with the memos or job orders. For repetitive work, permanent cards are sometimes made out on which data on the work and dates for the card to come out of the file for attention are entered—thus, to come out "Monthly on the 20th," or "Weekly on Thursdays," etc. These cards are properly refiled as they come back to the file clerk.

Newer forms of tickler file **folders** (Remington Rand) have Transloid tops, in the left-hand portion of which there is room for index inserts showing what kinds of items are in the folder; next there is a list of months, with a red movable signal; and to the right a list of days of the month, 1 to 31, with a green signal. The signals may be set for month and day on which the items in the folder should be taken out for attention.

For convenience, the folders may be moved to the back of the file as each month passes and the latest month thus kept in front and, when the maintenance load is light, future work may be advanced and done currently.

DAILY PLANNING AND SCHEDULING PROCEDURE. In its simplest form, daily planning for a small maintenance force is best done by the plant engineer or master mechanic. He will maintain a list of his men grouped by craft leaders and assistants, check up work progress during the day, and, toward the end of the day, have the next day's assignments lined up. A **bulletin board** is often used to show assignments and location of men. But however simple the system, it is vital to maintain some form of tickler file to ensure regular attention to Class A (see Preventive Maintenance) equipment. Coordination of maintenance work is improved by planning each day for all assignments to be made on the following day. Objection is sometimes made that emergencies will make such a plan unworkable. Actually, frequent emergencies indicate either undermaintenance or poor control. Some emergencies will always occur, but they can be reduced to between 10 and 20 percent of the total jobs. The daily work plan shows the location and jobs of each crew and makes it easier to get emergency help with the least possible disruption. Cooperation of department heads decreases last minute requests.

The usual practice is that **forenoons are used by supervisors to acquaint themselves with the status of all work** in progress and current operating conditions. Any maintenance requests from operating departments for work the next day should be on the dispatcher's desk by noon; any received after a deadline, which may be 2 P.M., are considered emergency orders, with a count kept of all emergency orders and their origin. Meanwhile, the **dispatcher** will have checked the tickler file for routine work due and the status of various crafts as to work ahead. If there is a shortage or excess of immediate jobs for any craft, he will notify the master mechanic of the situation for his consideration while on the tour of inspection. Any conferences on the immediate program with the plant engineer, department heads, or chief executive may be arranged around the lunch hour. A regular **daily planning conference** should be an inviolable routine, with 2:30 or 3 P.M. a suitable hour. Its purpose is to make complete plans for the following day, which is usually done by the master mechanic and dispatcher. The dispatcher's function is to outline the job program and priorities, and release only jobs on which all items are available. The master mechanic will govern the assignments of men as best suited to the nature of the work. Assignment can be aided by using the list of craft leaders with their regular helpers, followed by lists of men used for general work, marking assigned jobs against men to prevent duplicating or missing assignments. A full day's work should be assigned to each man. Job orders may be prepared ahead, but are issued at this time, any time allowances shown being checked by the master mechanic. When the work is well organized, assignments and issue of orders for a crew of 50 men can be done in less than an hour. In very large plants the procedure may be modified, the dispatcher having separate sessions in turn with the millwright foreman, electrical foreman, and yard foreman.

Job tickets for the next day may be distributed to craft leaders before quitting time as they come in to the tool crib to turn in tools. Hence, job orders should be at the tool crib not later than 15 min. before quitting time. This method saves time and avoids the confusion of organizing crews each morning. It is also useful to notify the crib attendant about tools and materials needed, with requisitions accompanying job orders, so that he may have the tools and materials ready for the jobs. Any minor adjustments needed in the morning may be readily handled by always having some postponable work in the daily schedule.

Daily Work Program. Where work takes maintenance crews over scattered buildings and floors, the master mechanic will need a daily **reference sheet.** Operating foremen and the superintendent may wish notices of equipment under repair. To meet such needs, after work assignments are made, a list of jobs slated for the next day may be made up. This list may be made up on a mimeographed blank giving the names of craft leaders, the jobs on which they have been assigned, and where these jobs are located—equipment numbers, building floors, and bay numbers. Carbon copies can be made for the plant engineer, superintendent, tool crib attendant, and dispatcher. This plan also aids in locating men when wanted.

Daily Force Report. Job tickets will be returned after they are checked by foreman or inspector, and will show the time taken. They will require reconcilement with clock time cards, a check which is usually made by the cost clerk or payroll clerk. Originals may be used for cost and payroll records. The clerk can pick up the corresponding batch of duplicates kept by the dispatcher and mark on them the time actually used (omitting start and stop times) and labor charges, then return the batch of duplicates to the dispatcher for use in maintenance records. A **summarized daily maintenance payroll** may be prepared by the cost clerk and sent to the plant engineer for signature and forwarding to the works manager. This payroll sheet serves as a constant check on the number of maintenance personnel. Job order numbers will identify the work being done on jobs for which appropriations have been made, so that any such expenditures can be shown separately to account for any temporary increase over normal.

REPORTS ON CONSTRUCTION. The customary practice on new construction is to engage outside contractors, but the plant engineer may be responsible for seeing that the plans are carried out, and may exercise the function of the architect's supervision and check progress against schedule. **Plant alterations** may have to be carried out in stages to minimize interruptions to production. Such work is difficult to contract, and if the plant has the nucleus of a construction crew, it may be preferable to have the plant engineer handle the whole job. Where the engineer is responsible for construction cost, the representative practice is for him to report periodically on the percentage of the job physically completed and the actual labor cost to date against estimate, with a report on material cost to date indicating any substantial materials charged but not used. If the work is planned and scheduled and materials are allotted, a check of progress against due dates may provide all the control needed.

FILING COMPLETED JOB ORDERS. Records of work done are often required for future reference and play an important part in control. Many jobs will be completed on one ticket. Where several tickets are issued, a simple suspense file may hold the tickets until the last one comes in, showing that the job has been checked off as complete. The tickets may then be stapled together. Before filing them, entries should be made on the equipment record (described in succeeding paragraphs) showing the date, total labor cost, total material cost, and other important notations. A suggested method of filing job and material tickets is by equipment number, because a search for information will most frequently relate to a particular piece of equipment. Where information on craft activity is wanted, the best source will be a file of the daily work programs.

Equipment Records

KINDS OF RECORDS. There are two main kinds of equipment records. One is kept for the purpose of recording data on the equipment itself—name, number or symbol, date of purchase, cost installed, maker and model, location in plant, changes or additions, current condition, perhaps a calculation or estimate of current value, and record of final disposal. Such a record forms the basis of efficient maintenance work and should be kept in the plant engineer's office, where current entries can be made when the equipment is altered, repaired, moved, or disposed of. The record forms a **history of the machine** and a basis for certain production planning.

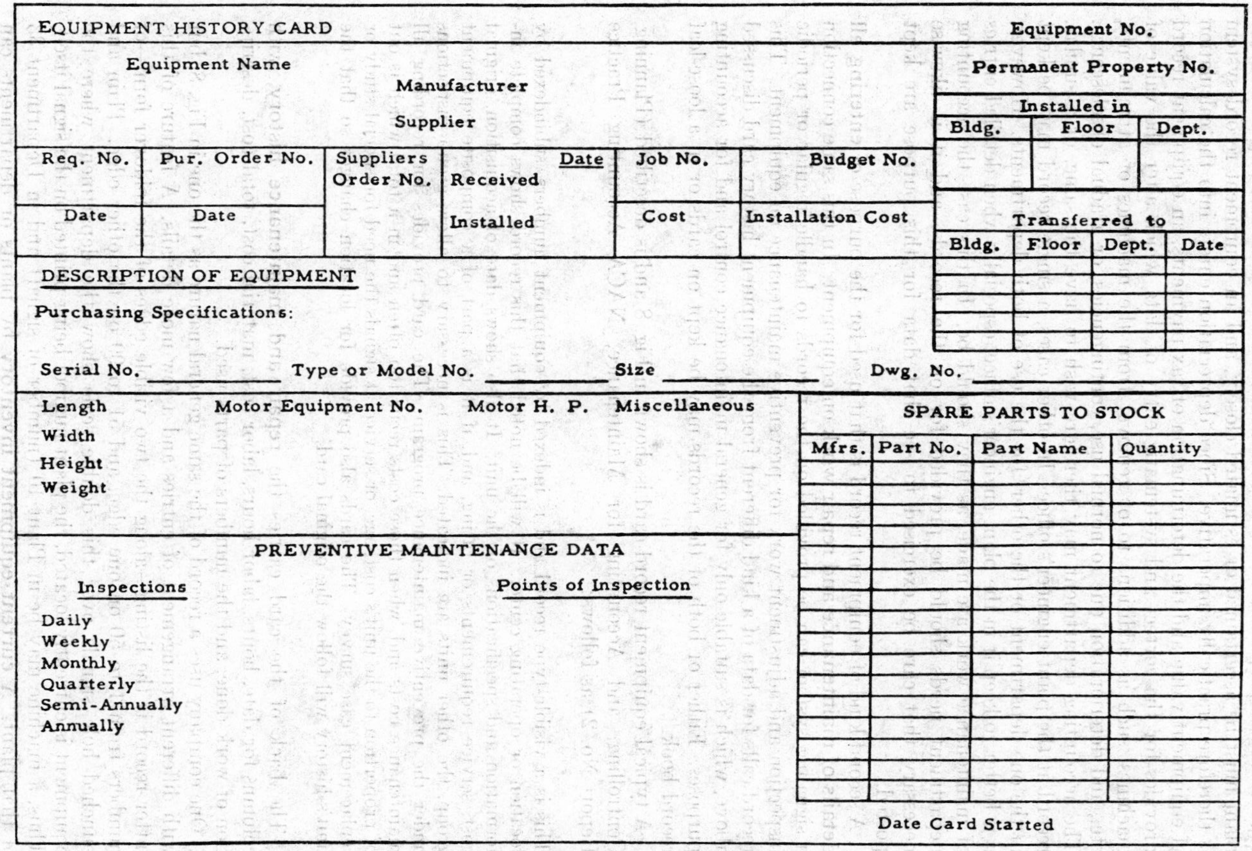

EQUIPMENT HISTORY CARD

Equipment No.

Equipment Name

Permanent Property No.

Manufacturer

Supplier

Installed in

	Bldg.	Floor	Dept.

Req. No.	Pur. Order No.	Suppliers Order No.	Date	Received	Installed
Date					

Transferred to

	Bldg.	Floor	Dept.	Date

	Job No.	Budget No.
Date	Cost	Installation Cost

SPARE PARTS TO STOCK

Mfrs.	Part No.	Part Name	Quantity

DESCRIPTION OF EQUIPMENT

Purchasing Specifications:

Dwg. No.

Serial No.   Type or Model No.   Size

Motor Equipment No.   Motor H. P.   Miscellaneous

Length
Width
Height
Weight

PREVENTIVE MAINTENANCE DATA

Points of Inspection

Inspections

Daily
Weekly
Monthly
Quarterly
Semi-Annually
Annually

Date Card Started

Fig. 8. Equipment record card.

Another use of such a record is for **accounting purposes.** In making financial reports and in preparing tax returns, the amount and value of equipment in the plant must be ascertained or estimated closely, and an equipment record system is therefore practically imperative. Since depreciation enters into the calculation of equipment value and the determination of tax payments, an equipment record provides for the correct and systematic entry of data which alter the value of machines, such as additions to or removal from the machines of attachments, etc., and deterioration due to normal use, contingencies, or gradual obsolescence. The accounting department may therefore wish to have the same, or a similar, record at the plant engineer's office. In other cases, a single record may be kept in the one department or the other, for the use of both departments. However, it is better to keep it in the plant engineer's office, especially when detailed entries of maintenance work are made, as they should be. In this case the accounting department needs should be provided for on the records, and it is likewise necessary that care be exercised to see that data for this purpose are kept posted.

A second kind of equipment record is that used for the purpose of **entering all details of maintenance and repair work** on equipment. In this same connection a signaling system can be provided on the records to handle regular or periodic inspection and adjustment work for preventive maintenance on equipment. This record calls for data of a kind different from the equipment history card discussed above, which is suitable only for general maintenance control and for accounting purposes. Either or both of the records may be kept on cards or in a loose-leaf record book.

A typical equipment record card is shown in Fig. 8 and is described (Planning, Controlling, and Accounting for Maintenance, NACA Accounting Practice Report No. 2) as follows:

This is a visible-type record and is indexed by equipment numbers, subindexed by location or operating center. It will be noted that this record shows complete information and specifications of the unit. It also shows date of acquisition, original cost, service requirements or rating, and, if it is a part of a composite equipment group, the other units are indicated. This is necessary to allow group inspections under the preventive maintenance program. The card provides for recording all maintenance costs and, when those costs recur too often and in a total which is out of proportion to the unit's cost, age, or service. it signals the need for special study or replacement case survey. The cards also provide for location changes so that the unit's history will follow the original card.

The back of the card carries the **repair and maintenance history,** with columns for date, hours, labor hours, labor cost, material cost, total cost, description of work done, and the numbers of parts used.

One company uses a record of the same general nature as the one in Fig. 8, but with different arrangement of entries and a few more details. A feature of this latter record is the listing—along the two visible edges of the foldover form—of numbers from 1 to 50 on one edge, and 51 to 99 on the other edge. Plain and punched hole signals over this double scale show the department where the equipment is currently located, the plant number being printed on the signal itself. Thus, a machine may be in Plant 10 (number of signal) and in Department 33 of that plant. A **current equipment inventory** by plants or departments can thus be quickly taken. The inventory-type or historical record, useful in part for certain accounting data, is the simplest form to keep. The complete physical inventory is described in the section on Materials Control and Standardization.

COMBINED EQUIPMENT DATA AND MAINTENANCE COST RECORDS. Fig. 9 shows a type of card on which general information may be entered for quick reference. The design of a card for universal use throughout a plant is difficult and such a card should have a blank space for special entries. Unusual cases may be handled on the 5 x 8-in. card shown in Fig. 9 by entering information on a blank 4 x 6-in. card and stapling it to the regular card, of which only the top and right-hand side will then be used.

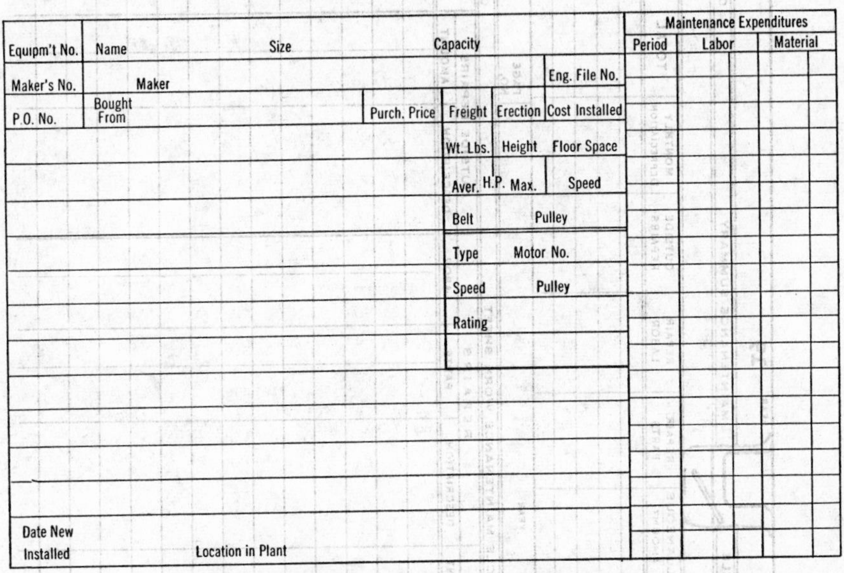

Equipm't No.	Name	Size		Capacity				Maintenance Expenditures		
								Period	Labor	Material
Maker's No.	Maker						Eng. File No.			
P.O. No.	Bought From			Purch. Price	Freight	Erection	Cost Installed			
					Wt. Lbs.	Height	Floor Space			
					Aver. H.P. Max.		Speed			
					Belt		Pulley			
					Type		Motor No.			
					Speed		Pulley			
					Rating					
Date New Installed		Location in Plant								

Fig. 9. Plant engineer's equipment record.

A suggested **method of supervising maintenance cost** is to use two files. The plant engineer or master mechanic will have the equipment card file. The maintenance dispatcher will have a job order file, in which each piece of equipment or plant unit has a tab card, as shown in Fig. 10. As jobs are completed, entries are made on this card and job tickets are filed behind it. Expenditures may be totaled annually, quarterly, or at shorter intervals, and the total transferred to the equipment card file, at which time the plant engineer may review the record.

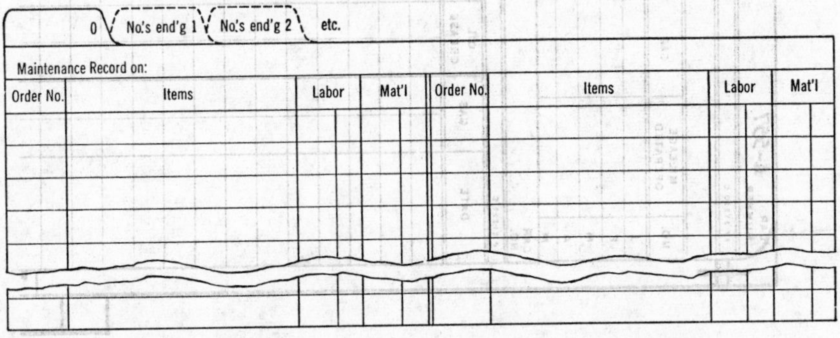

0 No.'s end'g 1 No.'s end'g 2 etc.							
Maintenance Record on:							
Order No.	Items	Labor	Mat'l	Order No.	Items	Labor	Mat'l

Fig. 10. Equipment record of maintenance expenditures.

MAINTENANCE SUMMARY

CAR NUMBER A-557 MAKE Chrysler YEAR 19 CAT. NO. 1-8926

MOTOR VEHICLE

NO.	MILEAGE OPERATED	GAS	OIL GREASE	TIRES	MISCELLANEOUS REF.	MISCELLANEOUS AMOUNT	REPAIR PARTS	REPAIR LABOR	OUTSIDE REPAIRS	MONTHLY DEPRECIATION	TOTAL	CENTS PER MILE
J												
F												
M												
A												
M												

MOTOR VEHICLE MAINTENANCE WORK SHEET

CAR NO. _____ MAKE _____ YEAR _____ PAGE NO. _____ CAT. NO. _____

DATE	GAS	OIL GREASE	TIRES	MISCELLANEOUS DESCRIPTION	MISCELLANEOUS AMOUNT	REPAIRS DESCRIPTION	REPAIRS PARTS	REPAIRS LABOR	OUTSIDE REPAIRS DESCRIPTION	OUTSIDE REPAIRS AMOUNT	TOTAL

Fig. 10. Equipment record of maintenance expenditures.

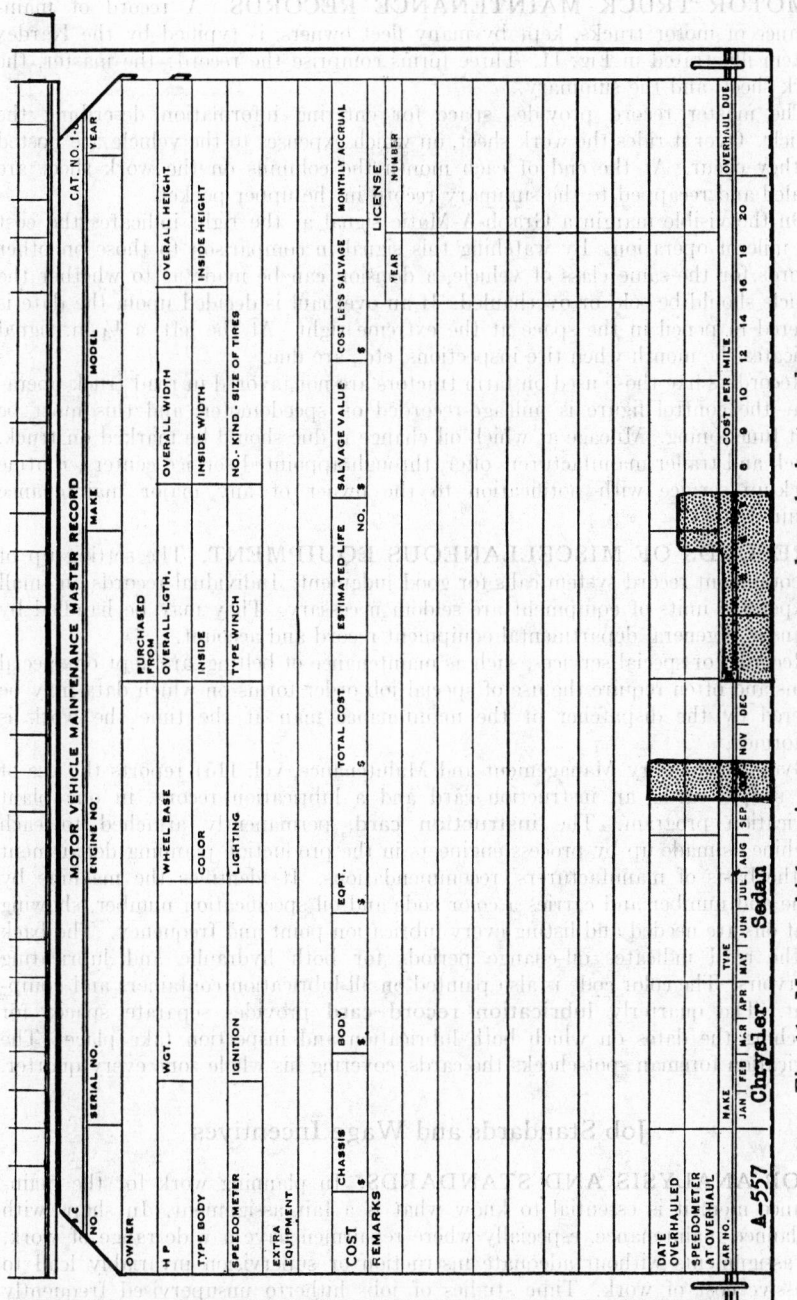

Fig. 11. Motor vehicle maintenance master record, work sheet, and summary.

MOTOR TRUCK MAINTENANCE RECORDS. A record of maintenance of motor trucks, kept by many fleet owners, is typified by the Kardex system illustrated in Fig. 11. Three forms comprise the record: the master, the work sheet, and the summary.

The master record provides space for entering information describing the vehicle. Over it rides the work sheet, on which expenses to the vehicle are posted as they occur. At the end of each month the columns on the work sheet are totaled and recapped to the summary record in the upper pocket.

On the visible margin a Graph-A-Matic signal at the right indicates the cost per mile of operation. By watching this signal in comparison to those on other records for the same class of vehicle, a decision can be made as to whether the vehicle should be sold or overhauled. If an overhaul is decided upon, the date is entered in pencil in the space at the extreme right. At the left, a ¼-in. signal indicates the month when tire inspections, etc., are due.

Recorders like those used on farm tractors are not favored in road truck operation—the control figure is mileage-recorded on speedometer, and this must be kept functioning. Mileage at which oil change is due should be marked on truck. Truck and trailer manufacturers offer, through appointed service centers, routine check-up service with notification to the owner of any major maintenance required.

RECORDS OF MISCELLANEOUS EQUIPMENT. The setting up of an equipment record system calls for good judgment. Individual records on small inexpensive units of equipment are seldom necessary. They may be handled by means of a general departmental equipment record and account.

Records for special services, such as maintenance of belting, are kept on special forms and often require the use of special job order forms on which data may be entered by the dispatcher or the maintenance man at the time the work is performed.

Gydesen (Factory Management and Maintenance, vol. 115) reports the use of two simple cards, an instruction card and a lubrication record, in one plant lubrication program. The **instruction card,** permanently attached to each machine, is made up by process engineers in the production planning department on the basis of manufacturers' recommendations. It identifies the machine by name and number and carries a color code and oil specification number, showing what oils are needed and listing every lubrication point and frequency. The back of the card indicates oil-change periods for both hydraulic and lubricating reservoirs. The color code is also painted on all lubrication containers and equipment. The quarterly **lubrication record card** provides separate spaces for punching the dates on which both lubrication and inspection take place. The lubrication foreman spot-checks the cards, covering his whole zone every quarter.

Job Standards and Wage Incentives

JOB ANALYSIS AND STANDARDS. In planning work for the maintenance men, it is essential to know what is a fair assignment. In shops with unplanned maintenance, especially where repairmen have a wide range of work, job assignments without adequate instruction or supervision invariably lead to excessive cost of work. Time studies of jobs hitherto unsupervised frequently yield a development of new work methods or improved tools which alone produce decided improvement. When, in addition, a **standard time is set up for performance,** still greater savings can be attained. The measurement of maintenance work in a large plant with a wide range of equipment necessarily requires many months of sustained effort, but can be very rewarding. (See section on Work Measurement and Time Study.) Fig. 12 shows the progress achieved by a completely guided program of maintenance improvement. A minor part of the increase in tons production per maintenance man-day came because of increased

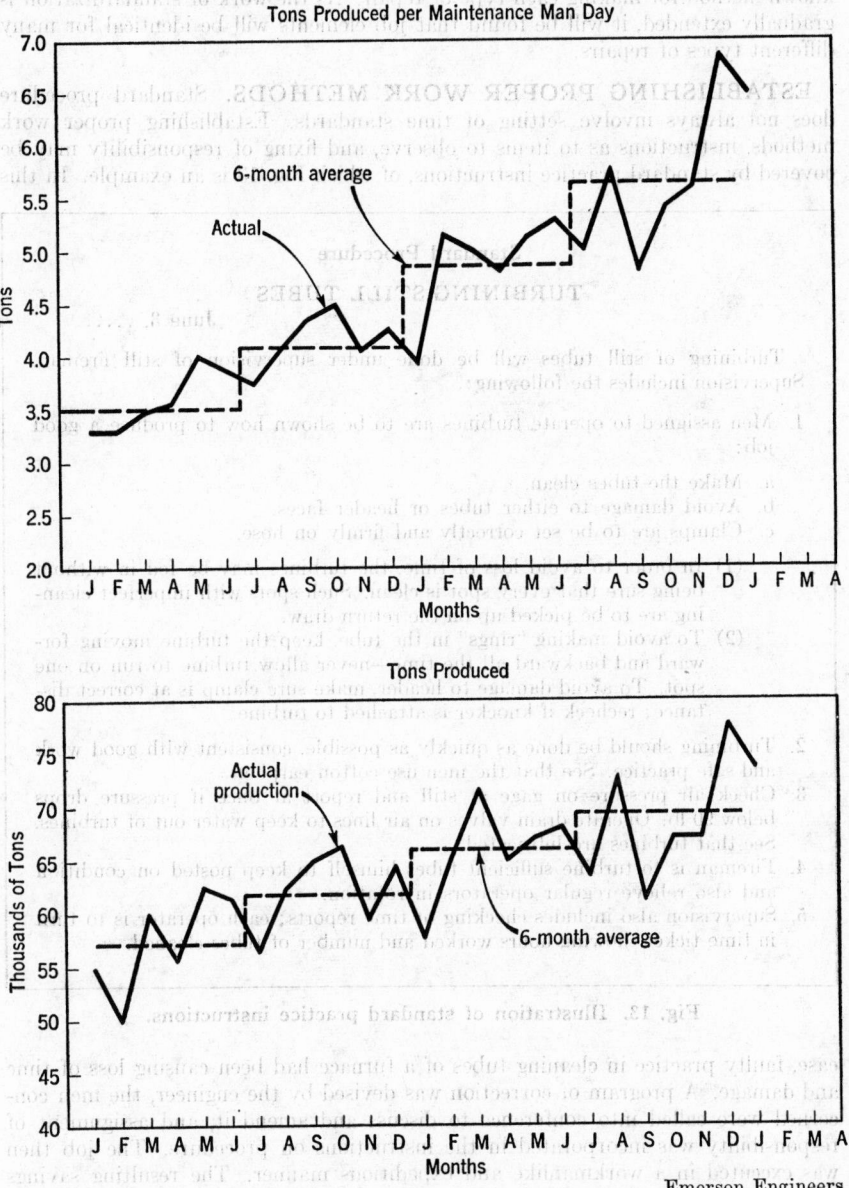

Emerson Engineers

Fig. 12. Results from maintenance work measurement program.

tonnage. By far the larger part of the gain resulted from a 25 percent numerical decrease in maintenance payroll. The total tangible dollar saving over a period of eighteen months was a million-dollar figure.

In every plant there are many repair jobs of a repeat nature. It is these jobs that should first be standardized. Job analyses should be made, to set the best-known method for making each type of repair. As the work of standardization is gradually extended, it will be found that job elements will be identical for many different types of repairs.

ESTABLISHING PROPER WORK METHODS. Standard procedure does not always involve setting of time standards. Establishing proper work methods, instructions as to items to observe, and fixing of responsibility may be covered by standard practice instructions, of which Fig. 13 is an example. In this

---

Standard Procedure

TURBINING STILL TUBES

June 3, ...

Turbining of still tubes will be done under supervision of still fireman. Supervision includes the following:

1. Men assigned to operate turbines are to be shown how to produce a good job:

    a. Make the tubes clean.
    b. Avoid damage to either tubes or header faces.
    c. Clamps are to be set correctly and firmly on hose.

    (1) In order to avoid loss of time, the turbines may be fed in without being sure that every spot is clean. Such spots with imperfect cleaning are to be picked up on the return draw.
    (2) To avoid making "rings" in the tube, keep the turbine moving forward and backward all the time—never allow turbine to run on one spot. To avoid damage to header, make sure clamp is at correct distance; recheck if knocker is attached to turbine.

2. Turbining should be done as quickly as possible, consistent with good work and safe practice. See that the men use cotton earplugs.
3. Check air pressure on gage at still and report at once if pressure drops below 90 lb. Operate drain valves on air lines to keep water out of turbines. See that turbines are lubricated.
4. Fireman is to turbine sufficient tubes himself to keep posted on condition and also relieve regular operators in rotation.
5. Supervision also includes checking of time reports; each operator is to turn in time ticket showing hours worked and number of tubes cleaned.

Fig. 13. Illustration of standard practice instructions.

case, faulty practice in cleaning tubes of a furnace had been causing loss of time and damage. A program of correction was devised by the engineer, the men concerned were called into conference to discuss and amend it, and assignment of responsibility was incorporated in the instructions on procedure. The job then was executed in a workmanlike and expeditious manner. The resulting savings were considerable in man-hours and, more important, in reducing refinery down time without engaging new hazardous "green" help. As another example of this kind, the experience is cited of a company with several thousand motors operated by magnetic controls. To avoid trouble with poor connections, rigid instructions were issued on soldered joints:

Wires must be cleaned bright, joint-soldered hot and joint-cooled with damp rag to set solder before moving it in any way that might cause loosening or high resistance.

Instructions of this type, although general in application, enumerate specifically how the work is to be performed and the points needing special attention. Hence the instructions are readily enforced and contribute much to reduce maintenance trouble and cost.

Where maintenance studies indicate plant deficiencies, they should be made the subject of a report to management. For example, improvements were made on the periodic cleaning of a large steam boiler, but maintenance reports on the steam system revealed poor blowdown practice, with priming and boiler compound carried over into the steam system. The appropriate cure was complete elimination of the job by treatment of water before feeding to the boiler.

MAINTENANCE FORCE PRODUCTIVITY. Where production workers are paid on some form of incentive basis, the same reasoning which dictated this step, and also the desirability of equal treatment of all workers, leads to the consideration of incentives for maintenance workers.

The objection is often made that maintenance work is not sufficiently standardized, but experience shows that, over an annual period, the largest part of such work is repetitive and therefore lends itself to method study and time study. The standards may not be so precise as in continuous production, but can be set up with a workable degree of accuracy. As to special jobs, in any case they should be studied in advance and methods and times should be outlined in connection with the planning of the work. Such estimates can be used as temporary standards.

This represents a fair summary of competent opinion. Although there is wide disparity of opinion on the advisability of incentives, there is general agreement that maintenance work can be measured in terms of standard labor hours and with a margin of error of less than 10 percent and in some cases to an average plant accuracy better than 5 percent—which is closer than many production work standards. It is generally agreed that measurement and reporting will of themselves, properly administered, raise productivity to a high level, and it is frequently contended that the further gain from introducing incentives is not sufficient to repay the added administrative expense, plus accuracy demands and possible friction when bonus earnings are unsatisfactory. (See section on Wage Plans and Controls for factors which must be considered when incentive systems are installed.)

MAINTENANCE WORK MEASUREMENT. Heritage (Factory Management and Maintenance, vol. 113) lists three methods of setting standards for maintenance work:

1. By estimate, on jobs over a set amount, and with the collaboration of the craft foreman concerned or by a central maintenance planning office.
2. From collected or charted historical records of job types.
3. By standard time data.

Heritage reports that du Pont uses the measurement method in plants ranging from 50 to 1,000 maintenance personnel, and generally uses an analyst to preplan jobs. Dow Chemical Co. (Factory Management and Maintenance, vol. 113) reports satisfactory use of historical standards for measured work without incentive.

There is also evidence based on a survey of eight companies by Methods Engineering Council (Factory Management and Maintenance, vol. 113). All report favorably on operation with maintenance incentives for several years. The coverage of jobs by standards is high, rating, with one exception, 80–100 percent. In all cases a financial gain is shown after charging administrative expense. Administrative personnel averages 7 percent of maintenance force. Unions have generally accepted the plans, some with enthusiasm, in one case after protest.

In recent years there has been increased use of **work sampling** to determine maintenance worker productivity. This method basically uses a variety of routes through the plant and a random circulation by a trained observer and time-study man to take random studies daily and tabulate rating. The method has stood the test of experience and, wisely used, has been successful. (See section on Work Measurement and Time Study.)

BASES FOR INCENTIVES. Incentive systems have been used for many types of maintenance work, applied on the basis of various techniques, the most satisfactory of which is the ratio of actual to standard times. The section on Wage Plans and Controls discusses various individual and group incentive systems applicable to maintenance work.

INTRODUCING WAGE INCENTIVES. When starting an incentive wage system, extreme care should be taken to have a complete understanding with the maintenance force as to future modifications. The incentive idea should be promoted as recognition by the management of the importance of good maintenance and as encouragement of cooperation, attentiveness, and careful workmanship, and not to stimulate speed. The prevailing method is to handle the incentive on a group basis, either departmentally or for the entire maintenance force, with foremen participating, and to calculate and pay the incentive for regular pay periods.

The character of maintenance work is such that it is particularly important first to achieve **reasonable standardization of methods and procedures** before attempting to introduce incentives. Stable and orderly management is a prime requisite.

TYPICAL INCENTIVE PLAN. One company which installed an incentive plan describes its operation thus:

Twenty percent of our total force is used to maintain plants, mines, and facilities. We attempt to observe three fundamentals: (1) Use production equipment of most suitable material and design. (2) Take care of this equipment. (3) When repairs must be made, make them efficiently. The company has taken the position that there can be standards on repair work. Time values based on time studies have been worked into formulas and tables for such operations as laying a pipeline, welding a piece of machinery, painting a building, relining a blast furnace. Men are informed of the allowed time for each operation and paid in proportion to the time saved over allowance. On jobs that have repeated themselves since the advent of incentives, the time has been reduced 40 percent; repair cost per unit of mill production shows a substantial reduction. We stress the fact that it is costly to slight repairs, and we check constantly. We feel that our equipment is in good shape.

MAINTENANCE TRAINING PROGRAM. Small companies may hire craftsmen (millwrights, plumbers, carpenters, etc.) on the basis of getting experienced help as needed from the general labor market. The plant engineer with a large maintenance force usually prefers to develop his own force. Unskilled or semiskilled labor is recruited within the plant on a gradual-promotion method. Likely candidates are encouraged to apply for vacancies on the maintenance staff as they may occur. Such personnel serves an in-plant formal or informal apprenticeship to train for a specific craft such as electrician, pipe fitter, or welder, working for perhaps two years as helper and attending suitable night courses at trade schools to acquire any necessary certification as a rated mechanic. This style of training provides advancement incentive to general plant employees. Selection is under the eye of the master mechanic, who gets to know promising plant men. Training is directed to meet specific plant needs with knowledge gained of peculiar plant requirements.

Automation maintenance requires a more formal training program to meet increased technical requirements. According to L. E. Clover, of General Electric, the maintenance crew in an automated plant will be confronted with many new devices which are critical components of the process, such as photoelectric tubes, X-ray equipment, speed variators, automatic welding equipment, machines controlled by magnetic tape, punched cards, or tape, and miscellaneous monitoring and measuring devices. These items will be used with various combinations of electric, hydraulic, and pneumatic power drives, and mechanical linkages.

Experience has shown that the general run of maintenance electricians and mechanics are not able to locate trouble and take corrective action quickly enough to keep automated equipment running. In addition a whole new setup may be required to handle calibration and repair of instruments—vitally important where quality control is part of the process.

The obvious solution is a training program. In one General Electric plant, for example, to cope with increasing electronic problems, an in-plant educational program is given, using the services of instructors from a nearby technical institute. Other in-plant training programs cover the field of general productive maintenance, using films and lectures, and aided by representatives of equipment manufacturers who have a wide background in their own specialties and can pass on knowledge and procedural methods gained from firsthand experience in many plants with their own equipment.

Preventive Maintenance

DESIGN OF MACHINERY AND EQUIPMENT. The source of maintenance work is a failure to withstand wear, abuse, or attrition. Successful design balances added first cost against savings in maintenance and also provides for economical labor and material cost of replacement parts.

For example, the modern heavy-duty truck tire was promoted in the 1920's by a two-year detailed record of fleet maintenance by the Swiss federal postal service, to compare operating and repair costs on the then standard solid rubber tire versus a new pneumatic tire for truck use. The modern machine tool has automatic chip collection and guards to protect the ways from chip damage. Roller chains on agricultural machinery have been replaced by rubber V-belts. Freight car hotboxes caused use of roller bearings. Tanks and dye-becks made of stainless steel permit rapid cleaning with negligible risk of contamination. Boiler tube maintenance is much reduced by water purification.

Design should primarily aim at construction which will minimize deterioration. Next in importance is design for servicing by the repair man. If lubrication is not automatic, service fittings should be easily reached. Parts subject to wear should be renewable with minimum demounting. The plant engineer in selecting new equipment should fully investigate the attendant maintenance problems to be expected under his prevailing working conditions.

The ideal of **preventive maintenance** is to make renewals before the failure of equipment and remedy minor defects before they cause the need for major repairs. The major sources of physical deterioration are:

1. Impact.
2. Vibration.
3. Corrosion.
4. Erosion.
5. Abuse.

Impact may be essential (e.g., picker-stick to propel the shuttle in a loom), in which case design should provide for shock-absorbing elements and also design to require the minimum impact (e.g., shuttle and lay designed for minimum friction).

Vibration can often be eliminated by design. It may be possible to put mass in stationary parts and lightness and strength in moving parts. Or design may achieve dynamic balance. Where necessary, separate foundations (heavy presses) are provided. Mathematical design of cams can often smooth out motions to diminish jar. Bearings with very close tolerances have shown great improvement in diminished wear caused by impact and vibration.

Corrosion may be prevented or delayed by using more resistant material, by applying a protective coating, by correcting a corrosive environment, or by introducing a sacrifice element. Among the metals, stainless steel, red and yellow brass, and arsenical copper are often suitable for preventing corrosion. The various chrome-nickel iron alloys have differing properties for varying applications. Glass-lined smoke stacks are made to prolong life. Where first cost prohibits the use of special material, protection against corrosion may be achieved by suitable paint, lacquer, asphalt, waterproofing, or bituminous coating; steel parts may be protected by galvanizing, parkerizing, sherardizing, or bonderizing. Iron pipe subject to electrolytic corrosion may be protected by a thin coating of concrete. Where corrosion is due to abnormal environment, appropriate protection may lie in attention to the conditions. Thus, de-aeration of boiler feed water will help prevent oxidation. The **sacrifice element** technique ranges from passing corrosive water over finely divided iron with subsequent filtration, to more elaborate systems of electrolytic anodes.

Erosion may be controlled through the proper proportioning of velocity and area factors, and by careful selection of materials. For example, rubber tubing may have greater resistance to abrasion of sharp particles than hardened steel. Similarly, nylon may stand erosion better under some conditions (in certain bearing applications) than metal.

Abuse is a problem of supervision. Constant training in the proper use of equipment is one method by which damaging treatment of apparatus can be reduced. But stern measures against violators of known rules may be necessary in cases of repeated negligence or wilful destruction.

INSPECTION FOR MAINTENANCE. Successful preventive maintenance depends in large degree upon an adequate inspection program. The ideal of preventive maintenance is to remedy minor defects before they cause the need for major repairs and to make renewals before the failure of equipment. Maintenance inspection is the means of translating the ideal into practice. A good inspection program will cover the whole field of plant and equipment, detect defects, and report when renewals and replacements must be made. For inspection guidance, equipment may be classified as follows:

Class A. Outage costly in widespread interruptions to production, emergency expense, and high mechanical cost.

Class B. Outage primarily a matter of high mechanical expense.

Class C. Low-cost machinery with no direct tie-in to general production schedule.

On Class A and B equipment, preventive maintenance concentrates on avoiding unscheduled shut-down. Regular inspection reports and records condition. **Wear-tolerance points** are established. Sufficient scheduled outage is provided for both inspection and minor and major repair. On Class C equipment, ordinary good maintenance procedure is used and equipment runs till condition requires overhaul work.

In large plants there may be a **maintenance inspection foreman,** reporting directly to the plant engineer. In smaller plants the plant engineer may lay out inspection schedules and assign inspection jobs to the various crafts. Items to be considered in organizing inspection are:

1. Detailed instruction as to construction elements which are to be inspected, measurements required, and tolerance or service limits.
2. Timing of inspections, as to frequency and coordination with maintenance operations.
3. Assignment of inspection work to appropriate men.
4. Provision for inspection records and a follow-up system.

INSTRUCTIONS FOR INSPECTION. Both general and specific kinds of instructions may be used. The general program will fix plant policy on the various kinds of inspections to be made; what defects to look for in bearings, gears, motors, control panels, and other elements of construction; when and how to report renewal requirements; other inspection rules developed from plant experience.

Where there is a wide range of equipment, the above procedures may be formulated into a book of inspection rules, with alternate kinds of inspection of similar equipment, each under a separate rule number. Reference to rule number will simplify the issue of specific directions as to work required on a given inspection job.

TIMING INSPECTIONS. The objective of timing is to space inspections as far apart as possible to reduce cost but stay within safe limits of time during which defects ordinarily do not develop to the point of needing attention. Many inspections can be dovetailed into maintenance work, as when equipment is opened for cleaning or taken apart for adjustment and repair. Periods of accessibility and convenience are often a factor. Thus, general heating equipment may have a thorough check in early spring to list all work to be done in summer while it will be out of use.

Some companies distinguish between **visual or external inspection** and **testing or checking.** Thus, a main steam line might be visually inspected weekly for absence of leaks and outward tightness of insulation, and annually checked with instruments to determine insulation efficiency. Motors may be inspected monthly for cleanliness, commutator condition, and normal heat rise, but more thoroughly checked with ammeter and megameter every 3 to 6 months, depending on severity of service.

Initial frequency of inspection will be determined by judgment and general experience with the kind of equipment in use. Inspection and maintenance records will show when the frequency should be changed.

Periods for Inspection of Buildings and Equipment. In general, timetables like that given below (Williamson) will help to determine the frequency of inspections:

Buildings or groups of buildings should be listed separately in the file, and inspection periods set for intervals of from 6 months to 1 year, depending upon climate, age, foundations, and equipment housed. Inspection of building proper should cover in detail foundations, walls, columns, girders, building joints, etc.

Roofs should be listed separately in file, and inspection periods should be set from 6 months to 1 year, depending on climate, age, and construction.

Floors should be carried in separate groupings in file by buildings or groups of buildings and inspected, depending upon their use, in periods ranging from 3 months to 2 years.

Paint should be checked at stated intervals, 6 months or more, taking into consideration protection, light reflecting capacity, and cleanliness.

Electrical power transmission equipment should be inspected in periods of 3 months or less to insure dependability.

Power-control equipment should be listed separately or in groups or territories and inspected according to use, in periods ranging from 4 to 12 weeks.

Heating equipment and low-pressure steam lines should be covered by thorough inspections every month.

High-pressure steam equipment should receive attention in semi-monthly or weekly periods.

Protection equipment, such as sprinkler lines, fire apparatus, and accessory equipment, should be checked over thoroughly in intervals of from 3 to 6 months. Some portions, however, require inspection more frequently, as daily or weekly.

Fixtures, such as elevators, require not less than weekly inspections, covering both mechanical and electrical equipment.

Continuously	Monthly	Quarterly	Semiannually

1. All Construction
2. Completed Jobs
3. Yards
4. Drinking Fountains
5. Piping
  a. Air
  b. Water
  c. Hydraulic
  d. Gas
  e. Oil
  f. Steam
6. Electric Wiring
7. Ladders
8. Electric Signs
9. Roofs
10. Fire Doors
11. General Safety
	1. Cranes
	2. Jibs
	3. Elevators
	4. Dumbwaiters
	5. Conveyors
	6. Special Lifting Devices
	7. Chain Blocks
	8. Hoists
	  a. Electric
	  b. Air
	9. Crane Runways
	10. Trolley Wires
	11. Slings
	  a. Chain
	  b. Wire Rope
	  c. Manila Rope
	12. Switchboards
	  a. No. 1 Pwr. Hse.
	  b. No. 2 Pwr. Hse.
	  c. MF Substa.
	13. Tunnels
	14. Melting Pots
	15. Ovens
	16. Furnaces
		1. Test Floors
		2. Cable Tunnels
		3. Sewers
		4. Gasoline Tanks
		5. Benzol Tanks
		6. Floor Loadings
		
		Monthly
		(Cont'd)
		
		17. Enameling Towers
		18. Kitchen Equip.
		19. Elec. Welders
		20. Portable Elec. Grinders
		21. Lead Covered Power Cables
		22. Power Transformers
		23. Maintenance Dept.
		  a. Mach. Tools
		  b. Storerooms
		  c. General
			1. Outdoor Substation
			2. Pole Lines
			3. Outdoor Power Lines
			4. Buildings
			5. Fences
			6. Bridges
			7. Walks
			8. Driveway
			9. Fire-Escapes
			10. Stacks
			11. Manholes
			12. Safety Belts
			
			Note: This does not include Fire-Fighting Apparatus and Systems (being covered by another Department)

Weekly 1. Pressure Tanks 2. Shop (Regulations Committee) 3. Ventilating, ZX-1 4. Exhausters, E & I 5. Blowers, H-1			

Fig. 14. Schedule of routine maintenance inspection in a plant.

Materials handling equipment, such as hoists (air and electric), must be covered by weekly inspections. Process materials handling equipment should be inspected in semi-monthly periods, depending upon usage.

Transmission equipment, such as line shafting, should be covered by monthly inspections, with alignment checked at least every 3 months. Other heavily loaded transmission equipment should be inspected weekly.

Equipment such as machine frames, rolls, foundations, and bases should be thoroughly inspected for flaws and checked for alignment in periods ranging from 2 to 6 months.

Oil-well bearing or any oil-reservoir equipment should have oil removed, equipment flushed with kerosene, and clean oil put in in periods ranging from 3 months to a year, depending upon service. Practice of replenishing oil supply as it becomes low is unsound.

Drinking water systems should be inspected every day; likewise **toilets** and **washbowls,** the latter sometimes twice a day.

The schedule of routine inspection used in one plant is shown in Fig. 14.

Panel controls should be inspected and cleaned every 3 weeks, according to one manufacturer with over 5,000 motors on magnetic controls. Inspection includes seeing that boxes are tight and that any open knockout holes are plugged. Panels are placed at maximum convenient height to minimize fouling by oil haze. **Electronic controls** require daily attention.

Long-Term Planning

DEVELOPMENT OF THE PROGRAM. The principal function of long-term planning is to provide a basis for a stabilized maintenance force and to arrange major jobs so that peak loads do not develop into emergencies.

Where standards or good experience data are available, the most desirable procedure is to assemble a schedule of equipment and buildings and compile a **man-hour summary of normal maintenance work** required by each craft, separating craftsman hours and helper hours in each. In addition, experience and plant policy should permit an estimate of installation work, alteration, and removal work. Total estimated man-hours divided by expected normal annual work-hours per man will give the minimum average force. This number of workers is then translated into a minimum skeleton crew which, because of practical minimums in certain crafts, will probably be somewhat over the figure estimated for the force as a whole.

The next step is to consider **emergency work and definitely known peak loads.** The first item envisages work imposed on the maintenance crew by storms, heavy snowfall, freezing of lines, power failures, and the like. Even when all reasonable precautions have been taken and disasters provided against, extra patrolling, repair, and inspection must be expected. The second item of known peak loads consists of such work as overhauling of major pieces of equipment, outside painting and roof work done in good weather, plant shutdown for changes in production setup, and, in a large plant, considerable yard maintenance on trackage, water, and other service lines, etc.

PLANNING REDUCES PEAK LOADS. Usually it will be found that by planning ahead, **peak loads can be considerably reduced,** both by preparation and by improved organization of the job itself, as illustrated by Fig. 15. If the most advantageous arrangement still imposes too great a load to complete in the desired time, the plant operating personnel should be considered as a possible source from which to secure the added manpower. Where a shutdown will be of long duration, this source should be drawn upon in any case to reduce the shutdown time.

DEPARTMENT & EQUIPMENT	CYCLE	JAN				FEB				MAR					APR				MAY				JUNE					JULY				AUG				
		5	12	19	26	2	9	16	23	2	9	16	23	30	6	13	20	27	4	11	18	25	1	8	15	22	29	6	13	20	27	3	10	17	24	31
Department "A"																																				
Boiler #1	8 Weeks	•								•								•																		
2	" "		•								•								•																	
3	" "						•						•											•												
4	" "	•								•								•																		
5	" "		•								•								•																	
6	" "						•						•											•												
Department "B"																																				
Pumping Unit #1506	20 Weeks							•																						•						
1507	" "		•																							•										
1508	" "								•																						•					
1509	" "																																	•		
Department "C"																																				
Furnace #20	12 Weeks										•															•										
21	" "									•											•															
22	" "							•												•																
23	" "						•										•																			
24	" "				•										•																					
25	" "			•										•																						
Department "D"																																				
Generating Unit 101	15 Weeks					•														•																
102	" "				•														•																	
103	" "							•													•															
104	" "								•									•																		
105	" "								•									•																		
106	" "													•												•										
107	" "													•												•										

Fig. 15. Schedule for making heavy repairs.

Other methods of insuring an adequate force, without having idle men or excessive overtime work, are:

1. Adding maintenance department facilities to carry on repair work in the plant instead of sending out to service shops. A pipefitter may repair valves, salvage fittings, and make nipples. An electrician may inspect and recondition motors.
2. Carrying maintenance craftsmen on the payroll in an operating capacity, with an understanding as to alternate maintenance work which they may do.
3. Listing men who can be borrowed or engaged on call, either from friendly contractors or service shops, from among former employees, or through application lists, etc.

One important feature is to make up **an annual program** so that men have the satisfaction of being continually and usefully employed. Otherwise, men are temporarily laid off and may be lost, with a lowering of group morale, or they are allowed to loaf, which is bad for discipline in the plant, or the foreman digs up some unnecessary work, which is regarded as "inefficient and wasteful."

ECONOMIC MAINTENANCE CYCLES. Scheduling of heavy repairs may be done with the aid of a graphic or Gantt-type chart. Chamberlain (Mill & Fact., vol. 19) provides the example in Fig. 15, with the following explanation:

Certain classes of repairs should be scheduled in definite cycles to obtain the best results. Great care and good judgment must be used to determine the economical cycle for major overhauls, but once this cycle has been accomplished, a very important step has been taken toward securing superior maintenance at reasonable cost.

Locomotive and truck mileage, tonnage of mill output, or units delivered from production lines are still used to determine when to schedule such maintenance as lubrication. However, where use is consistently steady, it has been found advantageous to put inspections on a **calendar date basis.** This tends to produce an even maintenance work load.

The **main principle** of establishing the maintenance cycle is to determine the point of maximum economy as well as the point at which hazards develop. Such points can be determined only by a study of the performance efficiency as to quantity, quality, percentage of rejects, operations from machines, etc., the increasing frequency of adjustments and minor repairs, and the approach of the time when the serious failures may be expected. Detailed study of the cycle, causes of failure, and cost of major overhauls may lead to the use of improved construction elements, changes in operating practice, more specific inspection practice, and—by increasing the frequency of minor replacements—lengthening of the major cycle.

For example, in an oil refinery, the on-stream time may be limited by pending still-tube failure through erosion. Substitution of alloy steel tubes at critical points may extend tube life, and heat-exchanger fouling may become the limit. A better design of heat exchanger may further extend on-stream time till diminished heat transfer in still tubes requires shutdown for cleaning.

From the above discussion it is clear that a maintenance program is not static, but should be in continual process of improvement. An annual review is a useful guide in directing efforts to steps promising the best results.

OPERATING COMMITTEES. In the case of many maintenance problems, the joint concern of engineering and production departments in good upkeep leads some companies to appoint a standing committee whose duty it is to consider desired improvements and make recommendations. Such committees are useful in fostering mutual understanding and cooperation. They function most effectively when called upon to discuss definite problems, preferably with a tentative but not final proposal ready to be discussed. The usual members will be the works manager, plant engineer, superintendent, and production control supervisors, with foremen asked to attend when concerned with the proposal under consideration.

MAINTENANCE IN CONTINUOUS-PROCESS INDUSTRIES. Special considerations enter into the planning and management of maintenance in plants which necessarily are in continuous 24-hr. operation, such as blast furnaces, coke ovens, cement plants, and oil refineries, where operation may continue for months without interruption:

1. Much of the maintenance work can be done only while the plant is shut down
2. Shutdown usually puts an expensive sequence of equipment out of revenue-producing activity.
3. The plant often has tight commitments on material deliveries and on shipments, so emergency shutdowns are commercially objectionable.
4. Emergency shutdowns are a great strain on the personnel and lead to unsafe methods of operation; besides, they are more expensive than planned shutdowns.
5. Efficient disposition of the maintenance force is difficult at best. Emergency conditions may demand complete disregard of cost.

These reasons make it especially desirable to plan the entire maintenance program on a **long-term basis.** Every piece of equipment should be scheduled for inspection and overhaul within safe limits of uninterrupted service. Standard methods for the overhaul should be developed, together with a careful estimate of man-hours required for the complete handling of the repair work,

A.M. 0 1 2 3 4 5 6 7 8 Noon 5 0 5 8 Noon 5

No. 1 Still — 1, 2, 3

No. 2 Still — 4, 5, 6

Transfer Lines — 7

Separator — 8, 9, 10, 12, 13, 16

Low Pressure Tower — 11, 14, 15, 17

High Pressure Tower — 18, 19, 20, 21

Exchangers Sched. A — 22, 23, 24, 25

Exchangers Sched. B — 26, 27, 28, 29, 30, 31, 32, 33

Pumps Schedule C — 34, 35, 36, 37, 38, 39

Compressor — 40, 41, 42

SHIFT MEN

Shift Foremen — General Supervision All Inspection Work and Inspection Records — Shutting down →

Still Foremen — General Supervision All Turbining and Equipment Cleaning — Shutting down →

1st Helper — 2, 16, 41, 8-12-20

2nd Helper

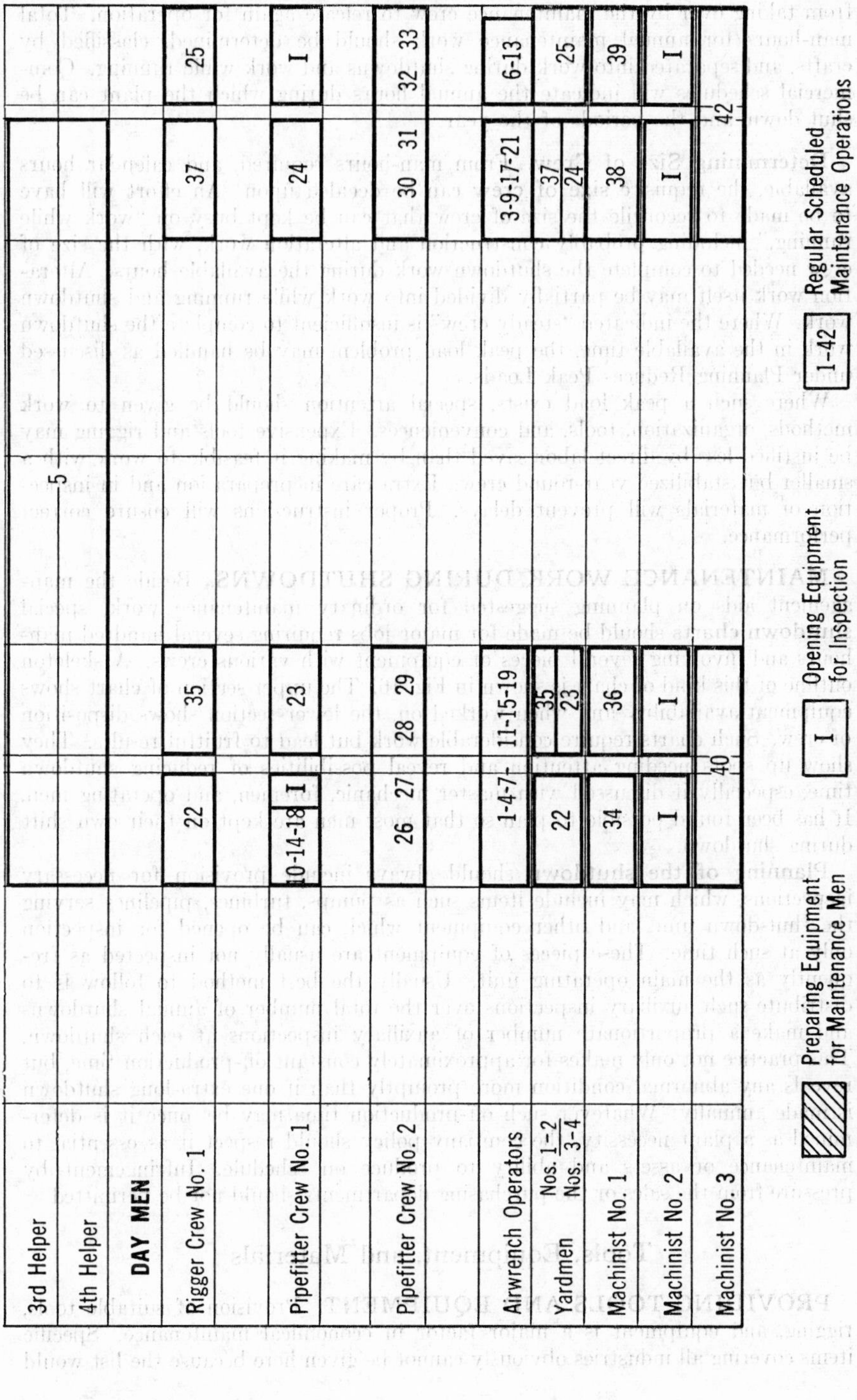

Craft / Crew				
3rd Helper				
4th Helper		5		
DAY MEN				
Rigger Crew No. 1	22	35	37	25
Pipefitter Crew No. 1	10-14-18 I	23	24	I
Pipefitter Crew No. 2	26 27	28 29	30 31	32 33
Airwrench Operators	1-4-7 11-15-19		3-9-17-21	6-13
Yardmen Nos. 1-2	22	35	37	25
Yardmen Nos. 3-4		23	24	
Machinist No. 1	34	36	38	39
Machinist No. 2	I	I	I	I
Machinist No. 3		40	42	

Legend:

▨ Preparing Equipment for Maintenance Men

I Opening Equipment for Inspection

1-42 Regular Scheduled Maintenance Operations

Fig. 16. Schedule arrangement for maintenance overhauling in a continuous-process plant.

from taking over by the maintenance crew to release again for operation. Total man-hours for annual maintenance work should be determined, classified by crafts, and separated into work during shutdowns and work while running. Commercial schedules will indicate the annual hours during which the plant can be shut down, and the periods of the year.

Determining Size of Crew. From man-hours required, and calendar hours available, the requisite **size of crew** can be decided upon. An effort will have to be made to reconcile the size of crew that can be kept busy on "work while running," including probably construction and alteration work, with the size of crew needed to complete the shutdown work during the available hours. Alteration work itself may be partially divided into work while running and shutdown work. Where the indicated "steady crew" is insufficient to complete the shutdown work in the available time, the peak load problem may be handled as discussed under Planning Reduces Peak Loads.

Where such a peak load exists, special attention should be given to work methods, organization, tools, and conveniences. Expensive tools and rigging may be justified less by direct labor saved than by making it feasible to work with a smaller but stabilized year-round crew. Extra care in preparation and in inspection of materials will prevent delays. Proper instructions will ensure correct performance.

MAINTENANCE WORK DURING SHUTDOWNS. Beside the management aids on planning suggested for ordinary maintenance work, special **shutdown charts** should be made for major jobs requiring several hundred man-hours and involving several pieces of equipment with various crews. A skeleton outline of this kind of chart is shown in Fig. 16. The upper section of chart shows equipment availability and when worked on, the lower section shows disposition of crew. Such charts require considerable work but lead to fruitful results. They show up spots needing attention and reveal possibilities of reducing shutdown time, especially if discussed with master mechanic, foremen, and operating men. It has been found possible to plan so that most men are kept on their own shift during shutdown.

Planning of the shutdown should always include provision for necessary inspections, which may include items such as pumps, turbines, pipelines serving the shut-down unit, and other equipment which can be opened for inspection only at such time. These pieces of equipment are usually not inspected as frequently as the main operating unit. Usually the best method to follow is to distribute such auxiliary inspections over the total number of annual shutdowns and make a proportionate number of auxiliary inspections at each shutdown. This practice not only makes for approximately constant off-production time, but reveals any abnormal condition more promptly than if one extra-long shutdown is made annually. Whatever such off-production time may be, once it is determined as a plant necessity, the company policy should respect it as essential to maintenance of assets and ability to produce on schedule. Infringement by pressure from the sales or the purchasing departments should not be permitted.

Tools, Equipment, and Materials

PROVIDING TOOLS AND EQUIPMENT. Provision of suitable tools, rigging, and equipment is a major factor in economical maintenance. Specific items covering all industries obviously cannot be given here because the list would be too extensive and many devices are specialized, but a general outline may be suggested:

Job studies should be made using the general principles of time and motion analysis, but with more attention to the motions than to attempting an impractical degree of accuracy of time. Reduction in the preparation and make-ready time involving such equipment is a fruitful source of savings. Such simple steps as setting aside and tagging ropes, planking, hose, etc., used repeatedly for certain jobs save preparation time and considerable material expense. Preferred jobs on the study list will be those of the kind causing the largest maintenance expense, or peak load jobs, or jobs where the plant engineer and master mechanic request a study to straighten out instructions to men and improve maintenance procedure. The first thought should be given to reducing the frequency of the job; the minimum remaining annual expense will indicate the justifiable expenditure on tools. Reduction of down time may be more important than saving of labor. A survey of all the work of one craft may be made with a view to reducing man-hours to within the capacity of the given crew.

TIME- AND LABOR-SAVING DEVICES. The following are the commoner kinds of work and the labor-saving devices which may be used on each:

Painting is customarily done with suitable paint-spraying equipment, using extensions for high parts of walls to avoid scaffolding. On outside walls, a running track is often put in during construction, from which to suspend painters' and cleaners' scaffolds. (See also Ladders.) Power-driven wire brushes are used for preparing surfaces.

Cleaning work can often be lightened by use of suitable hot sprays or of dipping tanks with cleaning compounds. On large floor areas, hand mopping is being replaced by power scrubbing machines. Industrial-type vacuum cleaners are essential where dust is a handicap. Good housekeeping practices simplify cleaning work.

Roof and tower work requires hoisting of materials and tools. The permanent installation of simple davits will save rigging. A portable power-winch reduces the manpower needed for hoisting and the waiting time of the crew aloft.

Portable power tools, such as chipping hammers, riveters, drills, and wrenches find wide application. The plant system of compressed air and electric lines should provide ample tapping facilities to avoid the need for extreme lengths of hose and cable.

Opening and closing of equipment, such as cylinder heads, manholes, headers, and turbines, may be expedited by the use of power wrenches. The latest types of pneumatic impact wrenches will handle the heaviest bolting work in one-quarter the time of handwork and with fewer men in the bolting crew.

Welding work usually requires both gas- and arc-welding portable units and a good supply of screens. A supply of different kinds of welding rod should be kept; building up worn parts is a great time and cost saver. Care must be taken to avoid destruction of metal at the point of the weld. Be certain the composition is known and matched to the composition of the welding rod.

Moving or lifting heavy equipment in an area unserviced by a crane is facilitated by a rail or ring above the equipment, to which a chain hoist can be attached, or by the use of a portable crane. Where a tractor is available, it can be used to tilt the machine, insert ski-shaped steel bars between machine and floor, and pull the machine to place. Devices are now available which help to put heavy machines on rollers for moving.

Alignment of machines, shafting, etc., calls for levels, transits, and indicators adapted to needs. Tolerance and feeler gages should be provided to control allowable play.

Belt repair requires a special room or crib arranged for belt storage, a repair bench and tools, clamps and scales according to kinds and amount of belting in use.

Kinds of ladders used are worth special study to minimize the work of moving them and to provide safe working conditions for one-man jobs. Rolling step-ladders are available which are self-locking when stepped on. A modification of the lift truck can travel to the job and swing an elevated platform in a wide radius to reach overhead equipment.

Fluorescent lighting maintenance cost derives more from labor than from tube cost when tubes are replaced singly. Modern practice is to schedule complete renewal of a large area at one time, followed by only minor renewals of excep-tionally damaged tubes. Cleaning is done by a 2-man crew with special washing equipment.

Electric trucks are parked daily at charging stations. These must be kept clean and preserved for exclusive use.

Emergency repairs for reducing down time of equipment such as furnaces or kilns may call for blowers, wooden sandals, inhalators, and special clothing to permit work under otherwise intolerable conditions.

The safety committee should be encouraged to keep posted on current prac-tices and should be informed of all contemplated improvements or changes so that safe practices and safety guards or other precautions may be properly planned and instituted before operation under the new methods is started.

STORAGE AND ISSUE OF TOOLS AND EQUIPMENT. The regula-tions governing maintenance tools must be as meticulously observed as those for tools and equipment used in production, because a large inventory is often involved. Usually the maintenance department has its own tool crib and issues and takes care of its own tool equipment under a system similar to that for production tool cribs. The tool crib must be kept locked, and only the regular attendants, or possibly the responsible head of the off-shift maintenance crew, should have keys and be allowed to enter. Others must call at the window for withdrawals of equipment, or the equipment, like heavy or bulky issues of mate-rials, may be delivered to the job.

A tool record is necessary to keep track of all implements used in maintenance. While the men will have regular tool kits, whenever they need special tools for a job they should fill out a requisition or deposit tool checks for the item. The tool is charged out by either a double check method or the McCaskey Register method, whereby the tool is charged to the workman under his name or number and also is recorded as out at its regular storage place or under its class designa-tion (and perhaps its number) in a file system. These charges are canceled when the tool is returned in proper condition. If all right, it is replaced in its location. If dulled, it is sharpened and replaced. When worn or damaged, it is repaired under a repair order or tag, if possible, or if beyond repair is scrapped and a replacement secured if necessary. Tools damaged through a worker's inexcusable carelessness often are charged against him. New tools or equipment should be inspected and approved before being placed in the tool crib. (See sec-tion on Tools, Jigs, and Fixtures.)

STORAGE AND ISSUE OF MATERIALS AND SUPPLIES. The usual arrangement is for the maintenance department to have its own storeroom, although in a small plant the production storeroom may handle maintenance stores as well. Separation is better in medium-sized and large plants. The items are thus available in a central place and at all hours for withdrawal by the maintenance man.

Materials control follows the same procedure as for production materials, and may be under the general supervision of the materials control department. Stores-keeping procedures, likewise, are the same as in the case of production items, and may be supervised, in general, by the chief storeskeeper. Actual direction and handling of the work, however, will be taken care of in the maintenance department.

Stores Record System. The stores record system should follow the same general principles, stores grouping methods, and postings as prevail for regular stores. Usually a simple record of receipts, withdrawals, and balances of each item, and each size of item where varieties are kept, is sufficient. An order point should be established for each item regularly carried, and when the quantity falls to this point, a purchase requisition should be filed with the purchasing department for replenishment. For items carried in the regular storeroom, however, replenishments can be made from regular stores with greater convenience and without affecting the operation of the central stores control. A requisition on the regular storeroom in each case will suffice, and the transfer will be recorded on the records of both departments.

All incoming materials and supplies should be regularly inspected in a place set aside for the purpose, and reports of quantity, kind, and condition should be made out.

Items of materials and supplies which are not stocked must be obtained on purchase requisitions placed with the purchasing department, just as in the case of production activities. Those left over from miscellaneous jobs are carried on unclassified stores lists.

Materials for maintenance work should be issued only upon duly authorized requisitions posted to the records and then used for cost purposes. Inventory control should be as strict as for regular production stores.

The Maintenance Storeroom. The maintenance storeroom is under the control of a storeskeeper and, to avoid keeping men waiting, an attendant must always be on hand during working hours. At starting and quitting time, a relief man is needed to help, since the heaviest withdrawals often occur then. Also, the storeskeeper needs a substitute during lunch hour. A junior clerk is often put on the stores records and may help with the issuing. Sometimes a maintenance helper may be picked for a tour of duty in stores and to learn storeskeeping.

In the storeroom orderly arrangement is essential. Layout should follow the rules for good storing. Items carried in quantity should have separate bins. Those stored in limited amounts can be separated by bin dividers, or merely by placing them in boxes side by side on the shelves. The most frequently used items should be near the issue window, less used items farther back. Heavy or bulky items belong in lower bins or on the floor. Bar stock can be kept on racks in line with the issue window or a small sliding door, for convenience in delivery to the workmen.

The storeroom should be kept locked at all times, no one should be admitted without due authorization, and pass keys should be issued only to the regular storeskeepers and perhaps to the responsible head of the maintenance work carried on during shutdown hours, so that essential needs may be served should an emergency arise.

Maintenance Methods

BEST PRACTICES. While among different manufacturing plants there is less standardization of maintenance methods than of production methods, because of the absence of design standards and the varied, intermittent, and short-duration nature of maintenance jobs, nevertheless there are best practices in rather wide use. It is advisable, therefore, to plan the procedures and operations along the lines of the most improved and efficient practices of representative companies doing the same kinds of work under much the same circumstances. At the same time, the plant engineer should see that his organization has access to the latest ways of performing maintenance work as they are described in articles in leading industrial magazines and in pamphlets or instruction sheets gotten out by many of the manufacturers of maintenance materials and equipment. Exchange of ideas with other plants is to be recommended because the information given and received is not of a competitive nature. Good maintenance is a means of eliminating waste, an undertaking in which all plants can well afford to cooperate.

The discussion which follows must necessarily be limited to cover only the essential factors in the maintenance of buildings and equipment and cannot be given in great detail because it includes all kinds of industries operating under all sorts of conditions, and highly specific data would essentially work down to the practices of individual plants, on which there might be some logical disagreement. The information is grouped by classes of maintenance work.

BUILDINGS. Maintenance of buildings calls for a variety of work and is best considered by parts. **Outside walls** should be inspected for cracks and openings around windows, and for disintegration of mortar joints. Necessary repairs may be effected by using cement mortar for pointing open joints, and possibly a mastic calking compound about windows. **Outside painting** of steel work, wood, sheet metal, steel sash, etc., is usually required every 2 or 3 years. **Windows** should be washed at least twice a year, once in the fall when broken panes should be repaired, defective putty replaced, and any necessary painting done.

A roof manufacturer is best qualified to repair the usual **tar and gravel and built-up roof,** having made the felts and possessing a thorough knowledge of roofs. He also has the equipment. If the roof is protected by a surety bond, the roofer responsible should in all cases be called. Heat of summer, frost action of winter months, and damage caused by severe storms, vibration, atmospheric gases, or moisture may cause leaks, flashing may deteriorate, and joints of gutters open up. The **roof drainage system** requires protection against clogging with debris; screens, gratings, and traps need periodic cleaning.

Foundations and footings need to be checked for settlement and imperviousness to water. The condition and safety of the building above is dependent upon them. **Floors** are of many kinds, each calling for different care. Concrete floors are repaired by patching, wood floors by replacement, and mastic floors by filling cracks or applying heat to close cracks. Prevention of accidents and facilitation of industrial truck traffic are aided by floor maintenance.

ELEVATORS. Various kinds of elevator maintenance are offered by manufacturers. The simplest covers an ordinary examination with a resulting report to the owner on condition of apparatus. The next variety of service is examination at regular intervals, including lubrication of apparatus and adjustment of parts. Another service provides these same features and in addition the replacing, without additional charge, of small items, such as carbon and copper contacts, springs, washers, etc. A complete service covers regular examination, cleaning, lubricating, adjusting, furnishing of all parts required, making repairs, and including new ropes which may be needed during the life of the contract. This service is at a fixed cost, and assures continuous operation and safety. Emergency service is available day or night. The American Standard Safety Code for Elevators gives complete information covering construction, inspection, maintenance, and operation.

Where a large number of elevators is to be maintained, it has been found feasible to select trainees from among the elevator operators and teach them the various elements of maintenance of motors, hoisting gear, signal wiring, safety devices, and cable inspection and replacement.

HEATING AND VENTILATING EQUIPMENT. Periodic inspections should disclose any operating deficiencies in piping systems, radiators, valves, and traps. Minor and necessary repairs may be made as needed, but others may be postponed until the summer months, when the entire system can be given attention and made ready for the next heating season. Parts of ventilating equipment, such as fans, motors, pumps, etc., may need daily attention; other parts require inspection and adjustment less frequently. Humidifiers in use should be checked daily.

AIR-CONDITIONING SYSTEMS. Special problems of maintenance are generally centered in the cooling towers and spray rooms. This equipment is particularly subject to corrosion; all metal work should be rust-proofed with extreme care and precautions taken against flaking off of paint. Inspection is not always easy, and maintenance should be completed ahead of peak season with equipment in condition to run through the hot season without dismantling. Where make-up water is added, or where water picks up dust in the washer, adequate bleeding and flushing of recirculated water should be provided to ensure low concentration of solids and flush out sludge.

Shutdown for the winter and exposure to low temperatures are causes of deterioration in water towers.

Duct-work, when properly installed without irregular protrusions to catch dust, tends to be self-cleaning, with any dirt and dust picked up in the return caught by the filters. Filter inspection and renewals should be put on a schedule determined by individual experience according to season. Contact filters will remove most dust and dirt. When requirements are exceptional, electrostatic equipment may be required. This is expensive to install but not to operate.

SCHEDULED MAINTENANCE OF LIGHTING EQUIPMENT. Regularly scheduled maintenance of lighting equipment brings about economies in the use of materials, longer life of fixtures, and better illumination. Dirt on lamps and reflecting surfaces reduces illumination 30 to 50 percent, and in many cases alters light distribution.

SANITARY FACILITIES. Maintenance of **toilets and plumbing fixtures** generally consists of proper janitor service and attention during the day. Matrons on duty in women's rest rooms will report to the proper maintenance department any fixtures out of order, and a posted bulletin in all toilets should contain the phone number of the department to be notified. Periodic inspection will be made by the maintenance department. A cleaning department will thoroughly clean all fixtures every night and check the mechanical functioning of all faucets and equipment. **Floors of toilet rooms** should be scrubbed at these times. Locker rooms should be cleaned daily and scrubbed weekly, or oftener, as required. **Supplies** of towels, soap, and toilet paper should be replenished each day, containers being provided for soiled towels. Attractiveness and upkeep of sanitary facilities influences employees to treat them properly, minimizes repairs, and promotes sanitary habits and conduct.

Where employees bring lunches, insistence on deposit of all scraps and paper in closed **metal containers,** prompt clean-up of the lunchroom, and incineration of trash will prevent vermin nuisance.

Drinking Water Supply. Fountains should be of impervious, vitreous material, with jets of nonoxidizing material. A daily or semi-daily cleaning should be thorough, not only of the fixtures but also of the area immediately adjacent. **Vending machines** to dispense beverages and packaged items are in wide use, commonly installed by a vending machine operator who services the machines. The service operator is trained to know and remedy commonly occurring defects and in case of major trouble reports the condition for the district supervisor to send a special mechanic or replacement unit. Part of the machines' revenue sometimes reverts to shop recreation or welfare committee, and the machines thus retain the good will of employees.

FIRE PROTECTION EQUIPMENT. **Fire extinguishers,** most of which depend upon their effectiveness in the generation of CO_2 gas, should be recharged immediately after use, and at least once a year. Any damaged or frozen extinguishers should be reconditioned by the maker. Unlined linen **hose** deteriorates when left wet. It should be hung vertically after use or test, to drain and dry out. **Fire buckets** must be kept filled. Addition of calcium chloride, 5 lb. for each gallon of water, will protect it from freezing down to 10° below zero. **Sprinkler systems** must be protected from freezing, and heads kept free from corrosion, paint, or dust deposits. **Water supply** should be checked as to quantity and proper working of pumps and equipment. **Dry-pipe systems** must be checked for leakage of valves which may cause ice to form in pipes and prevent their functioning when needed, if the proper air pressure has not been maintained.

Yard hydrants may freeze due to leakage or poor drainage. They may be thawed out by using steam or hot water with unslaked lime added. Hydrants should be flushed and oiled about twice a year. **Fire doors and fire windows** should be inspected to see that they work freely and smoothly and that all automatic devices are in order. Materials and equipment must not be so piled against them as to hinder proper closing.

PRODUCTION EQUIPMENT. Each plant develops its own policy on maintenance of productive equipment. The common task of maintenance is the installation of machinery, aligning it and securing it to a foundation, connecting to it the power supply, and finally testing it and delivering it to the operator ready to run. Where the vendor sends a demonstrator to get the new machine into operation, the master mechanic should check over the instruction book and the machine, discuss the maintenance procedure with the demonstrator, and file a report on items to inspect or service and the intervals at which such work should be done.

Other common duties include:

1. **Checking of equipment** as to foundation, alignment, bearings, vibration, clearances, proper functioning of control devices, and safe condition.
2. **Replacing** of worn bearings, bushings, packing, gaskets.

3. Replacing or **repairing** worn parts; regrinding knives, rollers, wear-plates, etc.
4. **Inspection** of general condition with reports on work to be done and cost estimates as required.

The need for and extent of a machine shop for repairs will depend on the relation between quantity of work and cost of tools, availability of outside service shops, the nature of work, the occurrence of emergencies, and the number of mechanics on the permanent maintenance staff.

POWER AND HEATING PLANTS. The power plant crew may do some maintenance work, but good practice has the stationary engineer report to the plant engineer on all equipment to ensure a complete program of maintenance in the power house and throughout the manufacturing plant. The use of chemicals in **water treatment** may cause foaming and carryover of solids; appropriate inspections of turbines, traps, heating coils, etc., should be scheduled and any accumulations removed; kerosene injection while running, or as a wash when dismantled, will soften deposits on turbine blades and aid in cleaning. Extreme care should be used in **cleaning boiler tubes** with pneumatic turbines; scaling occurs much faster on a turbined tube than on new ones, but careful cleaning will increase tube life. A check on the maintenance costs of the entire steam plant may indicate the advisability of installing a water-softening plant.

COMPRESSED-AIR EQUIPMENT. The compressed-air system is peculiarly susceptible to abuse and overloading and is affected by the humidity of intake air. Receivers and lines should have **traps** to discharge accumulated moisture. Where drain pots are used, they should be blown out daily or oftener. **Outside air lines** may freeze in cold weather if moisture is not removed from compressed air prior to circulation. Expansion of air in actuating air tools results in a sharp temperature drop which may cause freezing if the air is not dry. Besides periodic overhauling of the compressor, a frequent check on demand is advisable. Installation of an **auxiliary receiver** near points of surge demand may obviate the need for enlarging the line or compressor capacity.

PIPELINES. Continuous inspection of pipelines will keep maintenance work at a minimum. New lines should be closely watched, especially after temperaure changes, to check the functioning of expansion joints, swings, and bends. Lines buried in the ground should be checked for electrolysis by earth removal to expose short sample sections. The fifth year after installation should usually be soon enough for the first inspection, but local experience dictates the frequency of testing. **Exposed steam lines** should be insulated to the degree dictated by possible economy from reduced heat radiation and insulation kept in weatherproof condition.

YARDS, GROUNDS, AND WALKS. These require continued attention to keep in safe, neat condition. Walks, runways, outdoor platforms, and stairs require the same treatment as floors.

HYDRAULIC SYSTEM MAINTENANCE. Hobson (Industrial Lubrication Practice) gives details of hydraulic system construction and maintenance and indicates some principal points to watch:

Overheating Oil: Plugged cooler or lack of cooling water, defective pump, internal leakage, air leakage into suction, excessive discharge pressure, wrong or insufficient oil, or plain overload.
Loss of Pressure: Valve trouble, leaks, worn or defective pump, or wrong oil.
Erratic Action: Dirt in system, leaks, or wrong oil. It is necessary to use correct oil and to determine proper inspection and oil-change routine.

Lubrication of Equipment

RESPONSIBILITY FOR LUBRICATION. It is good practice to make the plant engineer responsible for all lubrication throughout the plant, with authority to specify lubricants and frequency of attention, all lubrication work being done by his maintenance men. The objective should be beyond mere avoidance of trouble. Engineering attention to the mechanisms of lubrication, power transmission losses, cost of oils and greases, cleanliness, etc., has often yielded remarkable reductions of overhead expense. Consideration should be given to:

1. Selection of lubricating mechanism.
2. Selection of lubricants.
3. Systematic lubrication at prescribed frequency.
4. Control of oil consumption.

LUBRICATING DEVICES. If **hand oiling** is used at all, open oil holes should not be permitted; with spring-cap oil cups, oil of the proper body, and oilers provided with press-button oil cans to control dispensing, even hand oiling can provide good lubrication without running oil to waste, making greasy floors and unsightly machines, and fouling products.

Where the **simpler feed devices,** such as wick feed and bottle oilers, are used, consideration should be given to the more modern automatic varieties of such equipment, by means of which oil is continuously fed in excess, but recovered, filtered, and fed back into the system with make-up allowance. These newer models are not only better lubricators, but also may reduce oil consumption to one-half that of the older methods.

Where **severe service** requires a constant stream of lubricant delivered by continuous pumping, the system should provide against failure, either by automatic alarm or automatic cut-in of an independent secondary source.

Where fully automatic recirculating lubrication of a machine is not economical, a centralized feeder system may be used. A metering device allows the correct volume of lubricant to be fed to each bearing in a group from one central injection point through tubing and metering mechanisms. This reduces service time and, more important, ensures that bearings inaccessible for hand work are not neglected.

SELECTION OF LUBRICANTS. Selection of lubricants is often a highly technical matter, but the following general rules are useful:

Hand oiling. If bearing conditions are such that oil is wasted, grease cups are indicated. A slight excess of grease prevents dust and grit from entering the bearing. If waste is not abnormal, heavy-bodied oil may be used, preferably compounded oil —mineral oil with about 5 percent to 15 percent fixed oil, such as acidless tallow oil, added.

Drop-feed. If specific pressure in bearing is high, a compounded oil is preferred. Straight mineral oil is satisfactory for moderate or low pressure.

Ring oiling. Since there is constant flooding, and oil is agitated, no compounded oil should be used, as the fixed oil content would cause gumming. Straight mineral oil is to be used.

Splash oiling. Oil should be light in body.

Circulation oiling. Since oil is constantly circulating, it must be adapted to temperatures reached and to withstand exposure to oxidation. It should be suitable for filtering and re-use.

In general, machinery builders' and lubrication equipment makers' recommendations should be followed. To avoid the nuisance and waste of stocking several oils of almost identical properties, a **survey of oil requirements should be made.** Suitable selection of oils to carry in stores can then be made, with steps between specifications small enough so that requirements for any case can be fairly closely matched by one of the oils stocked. Oil stores can then be managed on a regular maximum-minimum stores and purchase system, and ordered in economical quantities.

One company reports reduction by this method to 4 grades of oil stocked, instead of 14 grades accumulated by unsupervised specifications; through this study the use of high-priced oil was also reduced.

Exceptionally severe service may require a combination of a special lubricating system and a special lubricant. **Conveyors moving through baking ovens,** with temperatures so high that they destroy oils, have been successfully lubricated by the following method: After the conveyor emerges from the oven, at a point where the conveyor has cooled off sufficiently (to about 400° F.) an air-operated spray lubricator is used to apply colloidal graphite suspended in carbon tetrachloride, with a small amount of light oil and kerosene added to retard evaporation. The coating of graphite left on the moving parts provides adequate lubrication to last for several hours, the spray being applied for at least one complete revolution of the chain at a time.

FREQUENCY OF LUBRICATION. Frequency of attention is governed by the type of oiling device and by severity of service. In **ring, bath, and splash methods of oiling,** the governing factor is that oil is subject to deterioration, regardless of activity. In 6 months or less, most oils form a jellylike sludge or a sediment. The prescribed treatment is to drain the oil completely, flush out the bearing with kerosene, and refill with fresh oil. Hand oiling may be required daily on high-speed work, weekly on low-speed shafting, etc. **Automatic systems,** whether gravity or force-feed, should have at least daily inspection of reservoir levels.

It is often practical to assign the care of lubrication to an electrician or to millwright helpers, as part of their inspection routine. Especially where machinery is divided into territories for maintenance men, consolidation of lubrication with maintenance makes for more intelligent care of equipment.

METHODS EMPLOYED. Control of oil consumption begins with proper storage and distributing facilities. Oil refiners go to great trouble to provide pure products. The stores department should arrange all **oil drums in a central storage room** and equip them with suitable tapping facilities to avoid either contamination or waste. The prevailing practice in shops is to provide the oiler with a pushcart of lock-up type, in which to carry suitable oil cans plainly marked with the type of oil contained, and kerosene for flushing bearings and cleaning tools. A **fire extinguisher** may be carried in clips outside the cart, available at all times. Oil may be drawn from the storeroom on requisitions. The method of charging to the operating departments should be based on the territory assigned. That is, **consumption should be measured** only for large groups as a whole, the charges being divided pro rata according to the number and size of units in each department.

Where the amount of oil consumed warrants, standards may be set for the **oil budget** of the oilers. A distinction should be made between devices such as bath and ring oiling, where renewal is made on a time basis, and automatic or bottle oiling, where consumption is proportionate to activity. In the latter case, plant man-hours may furnish the best gage of expected oil consumption.

DISPOSING OF USED OIL. The method used for the disposition of dumped old oil depends on the quantity. Where the volume justifies the use of equipment, the oil may be reclaimed by appropriate treatment, separation, and filtering. Unusable waste oil should not be dumped in the sewer, unless proper oil traps are built into sewage lines. Where oil-burning equipment is in use, the best method of disposing of unusable lubricating oil is to dump it in a small covered steel tank with a false bottom and an overflow to a fuel oil tank. Sediment collecting on the false bottom is removed periodically and burned in an incinerator, with unreclaimable greasy rags. **Oily waste and rags** are serious fire hazards and should be collected and cleaned or destroyed as soon as possible. They are subject to spontaneous combustion.

Good Housekeeping

ORDER, NEATNESS, AND CLEANLINESS. Good workmanship, high production, sound personnel relations, and final quality of product are so definitely dependent on order, neatness, and cleanliness in the plant that the production engineer finds himself a leading crusader for good housekeeping. While department foremen are supposed to instruct and supervise their workers in keeping departments and workplaces orderly, neat, and clean, there are many factors which require more attention and service than can be given in the normal course of shop operation. Some equipment and certain facilities are not in direct personal use by individual workers and therefore no one is directly responsible for their care. The accompanying check list includes most such items, with an indication of the procedure to follow to bring about proper conditions.

In some cases—toilets and washrooms, drinking fountains, safety equipment, etc.—periodic inspection and minor attention may be already in effect. There are likewise scheduled times for cleaning of floors, washing of windows, cleaning and check-up of lighting systems, in many plants. Some of the work is done by janitors who may report to an operating supervisor in the regular line organization. But the plant engineering department, by the very nature of its duties, is called upon to maintain so many of the plant facilities that much of the actual housekeeping work comes under its regular operations. If there is a possibility that the plant engineer can take over the whole responsibility and handle it more successfully than any other available executive, the work should be made a part of his regular assignment.

A GOOD HOUSEKEEPING COMMITTEE. So much depends upon the backing of management and the authority needed in such efforts, there are so many chances of friction between operating department heads, production engineers, and plant engineers on the matters of local order and cleanliness, and the workers so often do not spontaneously respond to good housekeeping instructions, that frequently the best way to handle the undertaking is to set up for the purpose some permanent, and perhaps rotative, committee composed of representatives of all groups, including operating departments, production control, plant engineering, the office, and top management. The work of such a committee is most successfully carried on under plans similar to those followed in suggestion systems. It is very necessary to have the committee consist only of enthusiastic, live, tactful, persistent, patient, forward-looking, and realistic men, with certain leadership qualities. "Die-hards" and those satisfied to run in ruts dampen the interest and kill the effort.

METHODS FOR ORGANIZING THE WORK. The good housekeeping drive must be ably planned, advertised widely on bulletin boards, in plant papers, and perhaps by circulars or cards in payroll envelopes. It should begin by the issuing of explanatory sheets indicating what to do to clean up the departments and set them in order. A short period of time should then be allowed for each department to set its house in order. Then the committee should make a full inspection, perhaps awarding two or three prizes to the departments which —considering their limitations and the nature of the work they have done— show the best results, all limitations taken into account.

INSPECTIONS AND FOLLOW-UP. After this, the inspections should be periodic, announced in advance, and followed by published reports or announcements, to keep the laggards in line. Awards then can be made over periods, say every quarter. The plant manager must periodically see to it that the committee stays live, that its activities are backed up by proper enforcement to get non-cooperative foremen or workers into line. It seems that once a year a special campaign should be run prior to one of the inspection periods. Memorandums to the foremen and supervisors will keep them informed of matters which have escaped their attention. The committee must be prepared whenever necessary to work out detailed plans for correcting bad conditions and for regularly maintaining cleanliness and order in spots which give particular trouble. It should therefore have access to all the technical facilities in the plant, but as far as possible should see that all the work done is in and by the departments where the wrong conditions exist. Otherwise the responsibility will be passed on to the good housekeeping committee or the maintenance department, when the latter's job may be one of upkeep and repairs rather than order and cleanliness in manufacturing operations.

Key slogans in any such work are:

"A place for everything and everything in its place."
"A clean and orderly plant is a safe plant; a safe plant keeps orderly and clean."

Other crisp, printed slogans can be easily developed (perhaps with awards to suggestions) in any plant where good housekeeping is made a regular part of plant operation.

ADVANTAGES OF GOOD HOUSEKEEPING. Among the important advantages of good housekeeping are:

1. Production rate increased because of the orderly, businesslike condition of departments, removal of obstacles to production, etc.
2. Production control made easier. Materials and parts do not get lost or mixed. Speed of removal of work and less banking of rough or processed materials are corollaries of good order. It is easier and quicker to check operations and get data for records.
3. Inspection work takes on a high character. Quality control of work follows order and cleanliness control of conditions.
4. Materials and parts conserved and salvaged. All unused materials or parts, spoiled work, scrap, etc., are removed to proper places.
5. Time saved. Search for tools, work, etc., eliminated. Workers have more room to operate freely. No time lost in clean-ups to get space in which to work.
6. Floor areas are cleared for production instead of being littered with rubbish or crowded with unnecessary banks of work.
7. Maintenance and repair work facilitated. Repairmen can get at machines, do not have to clean them of dirt and grease, have room in which to do the work.

8. Safety protection made more certain. Elimination of crowded quarters makes machine operation safer. Clear, clean floors cut down stumbling and tripping, and slipping on greasy or oily spots. Clear traffic aisles reduce collisions of trucks, running into workers, knocking over piled materials, etc.

9. Fire protection improved. Fire hazards and spontaneous combustion are removed. Areas are cleared for quick exit, and for room to get at and fight any fires. Carelessness with matches is avoided.

10. Cleaning costs reduced. Janitors can do their work faster and better. It is cheaper to keep dirt down than to remove long-time accumulations.

11. Morale is heightened. Workers used to decent conditions at home become more interested in the plant when cleanliness and order are enforced.

There are no disadvantages in cleanliness and orderliness. No arguments can be advanced against a program of this kind which cannot be disproved by any executive or production engineer who has put methods of plant good housekeeping into operation. Neither merit nor profit attaches to being dirty or disorderly, and no excuse exists for the toleration of such conditions. If they exist, they are a direct reflection on the character of the plant management.

CHECK LIST FOR MAINTAINING AN ORDERLY PLANT. The points upon which continued orderliness and neatness in the plant are maintained may be summarized according to the following typical check list. Modifications may be made to fit the list to the needs of any particular plant.

Walls, Windows, Ceilings.

1. Walls should not be used for storage of materials, such as pipe, small fittings, wire, cord or string, wiping rags, etc.

2. Unnecessary bulletin boards, production boards, work order or time ticket clips, charts, pictures, etc., should be taken down. Notices and information should go on bulletin boards, not on the wall proper.

3. In places where dusty or dirty operations are done, the walls should be cleaned several times a year. Vacuum cleaning is preferable to brushing.

4. Shop as well as office walls in many cases should be painted when cleaning no longer removes the dirt, or when illumination and work visibility can thus be improved.

5. Storage of items along the ceiling is unsightly and dangerous. Ceilings, like walls, should be cleaned, and painted when badly soiled. Better work illumination results.

Aisles, Exits, Stairways.

1. Traffic lines painted along aisles will keep them clear of work banks, as well as prevent accidents by marking off the work areas.

2. Exits and surroundings should be kept clean of all banks of work so that traffic of trucks and workers will not be impeded.

3. Doors get dirty from contact with trucks, clothing, and hands. They should be washed occasionally and frequently touched up, at least, with paint.

4. Stairways must be kept clear of all materials, equipment, rubbish and dirt. They need daily cleaning. If corners are painted white, they will be kept free from papers, dirt, tobacco juice, chewing gum, and other unsightliness.

Floors.

1. Oil, waste material, paint, dirt, and other accumulations under machines can be caught in pans or on sheet metal, scrap fabric, or paper which can be regularly removed and replaced. Oil-soaked floors cause accidents and are added fire risks.

2. Painted lines will mark off machine and work areas to prevent cluttering and congesting them with materials.

Toilets, Washrooms, Locker Rooms, Showers.

1. Daily cleanings and rubbish removal are imperative to good housekeeping. Floors should be washed. Frequent painting is of definite aid in good sanitation.

2. Rubbish cans, receptacles for used paper towels, neat racks for wet towels and cloth, and other facilities aid in cleanliness.

3. Daily use of inoffensive disinfectants keeps such rooms germ- and vermin-free.

4. Good light and ventilation add to the cleanliness.

5. Soap dispensers are cleaner and more economical than soap cakes.

Drinking Fountains, Beverage Dispensers.

1. Drinking fountains should be washed daily.

2. Signs should be put up, if necessary, to discourage use of the fountains as depositories for chewing gum, or as cuspidors.

3. Dispensers of bottled or bulk beverages should be replenished regularly and kept clean. If the beverage is in bulk form, the unit should be washed off with hot water periodically.

4. For bottled items, receptacles should be provided for empties and caps. Otherwise they will be thrown around the floor.

Manufacturing Equipment.

1. Dirt and oil accumulations should be removed from machines daily, in most cases, sometimes several times a day, if the work must be kept clean.

2. Painting is necessary on many kinds of equipment, not only for reasons of preservation and good illumination but also to keep the factory clean.

3. Chips from metalworking, cuttings from fabrics, and other collections should be dumped directly into containers, if possible, rather than brushed off to the floor.

4. Tools, gages, etc., should not be left on machines when work is completed. Finished or unfinished parts should be kept in receptacles, not stored on machines.

5. If the machines have highly burnished or plated parts, these should be cleaned occasionally with suitable polishes.

6. Work tables on textile and other machines should be cleaned and waxed periodically with proper polishes.

General Equipment.

1. Tables needed for manufacturing operations should be kept free from collections of finished or unfinished parts, scrap, tools, rubbish, etc. They also require periodic cleaning and polishing.

2. Racks for work should not have clothing, rags, equipment, or odds and ends hung on them.

3. Benches often accumulate all kinds of tools and accessory items used in the department, spare parts, bolts and nuts, odds and ends of material, etc., as well as rags, papers, and old records, bottles, and all sorts of rubbish. If a worker thus "keeps the pig in the parlor," his work and his methods will be similarly affected. This area of good housekeeping is the place where it is often hardest to bring about improvements, for the employee obviously must have some place to keep certain personal belongings. Examples of order and cleanliness in benches, and pointed propaganda, will cure much of the trouble and release considerable accumulations of materials and even tools and instruments.

4. Cabinets, like benches, collect all sorts of items which do not belong in them. Signs on the cabinets marked something like this, "This cabinet is for .... only. Please keep it in order," and occasional inspection get rid of the junk and reserve the space for proper use.

Safety Installations.

Besides regular inspection for service and to see whether they are in use, safety installations need attention for condition and cleanliness. Guards draped with rags, and other cluttering and uncleanliness of safety devices discourage their use.

Fire Protection.

1. Fire-fighting equipment should be kept clear of all materials, work in process, boxes and packing cases, unused machinery, or any other obstacles to immediate access. Hand extinguishers, fire pails, axes, fire hose, lanterns, etc., should be kept neat and in order, immediately available in proper places, as well as undergoing periodic inspection for condition.

2. All such items should be cleaned and kept polished or painted. City fire departments find that preparedness is increased by the well-known meticulous care used to keep equipment clean, bright, polished, and painted. The term "shipshape" for cleanliness and orderliness typifies the importance attached to such factors as preparedness measures in naval and marine services.

Unused Manufacturing Equipment, Tools, Etc.

1. All equipment which is obsolete or worn out should at least be removed from the manufacturing floor, and stored in a central place, marked with an identification tag stating its name, number, make, department used in, date and reason of removal, intended disposal, and perhaps its estimated value. The removal record should be noted on the equipment card, so that the machine can be replaced in use if needed later. If the equipment is of no further use, it should be sold or broken up for scrap. Such a plan enables departments to be kept in better order and to gain more floor area for rearrangement of processes. Also, the departments can be more easily kept clean. Equipment should never be stored within the department, in passageways, under stairs, or in odd spots where there happens to be vacant space.

2. Broken, worn, and obsolete tools should not be allowed to collect in or around workplaces, where they are in the way and indicate lack of order. They should be removed for repair or scrapping.

Salvage Items.

1. Paper which can be re-used should be collected in regular containers provided for the purpose. Scrap paper, if possible kept sorted at point of origin, can be put into other containers and collected.

2. Boxes, crates, cartons, and other packing containers which can be re-used should be promptly collected and removed to storage in a reclaiming department. The rubbish trucks can make the collections and deliveries.

3. Used rags and waste may be reclaimed by washing and should be removed promptly for this purpose because they constitute fire hazards.

4. Discarded materials and spoiled work should be taken over by the salvage department daily to keep operating departments free from disorder, and also to control and account for the causes and costs of these losses. Spoiled work should have a release from the foreman or inspector.

Scrap Removal.

Regular scrap items, such as chips, borings, or other waste materials from operations can be collected, if possible, in boxes or pans right at points of origin, or can be periodically cleaned up and taken to a department receptacle. The different items should be kept separated, particularly different kinds of metals. Where such items as borings can be used in the company foundry, strict discipline on use of proper containers to send scrap to the foundry properly segregated has produced savings in the six-figure range annually.

Rubbish and Garbage Removal.

Floor sweepings consisting only of dirt, miscellaneous rubbish such as small quantities of sawdust, rags too soiled to reclaim, odds and ends of twisted or broken nails or other small items, and soiled paper and cartons should be collected in waste cans instead of accumulating under machines or benches or in some corner. If employees eat their lunches in the departments or buy candy, sandwiches, etc., from traveling vendors, the refuse should at once be deposited in cans to prevent attracting vermin.

These cans should be emptied into traveling trash bins twice daily. The cans should be kept clean and in good condition. Periodically they should be washed and repainted.

Storage Areas.

1. In operating departments, white lines painted on floors will keep work banks in proper places at machines.

2. Marking off floor areas in storerooms for items which must be kept on the floor, likewise will keep these items within proper boundaries and be conducive to orderly piling and regular contour of storage piles.

3. Proper storage layout, with like items together, and regular stacking on shelves will facilitate locating and issuing stores, making physical checks, adding new stock, etc.

4. Orderly storage, with everything neatly in its place, will avoid loss of materials, reordering items already on order, ordering when stocks are already high, etc.

Plant Yard.

1. If for no other reason than the resulting advertising value and public good will, plant yards visible from railroads, highways, and nearby manufacturing or residential areas should be kept neat, orderly, and free from trash, rubbish, and dumps. Even piles of coal, sand, clay, and other bulk materials can be kept trimmed, with the contents all within allotted areas. Yard storage areas, therefore, should be given as much attention as inside areas.

2. Tracks, walks, and roadways must be kept free from obstacles, rubbish, and growths of weeds and coarse grass. The limits should be neatly marked. Traffic and clearance lines also are often effective and are good safety precautions.

3. Outsides of buildings should be kept repaired, painted, if necessary, and clean. The effects of such attention and yard cleanliness are reflected in the higher production and better morale of workers. Company orderliness adds prestige to employees in the plant.

General Cleanliness and Order.

1. Aside from isolated attention to separate factors, there are general matters of order and cleanliness which require attention. In offices, accumulations of unnecessary or unused papers and other items should be thrown out, or stored in proper cabinets or files. Scraps should be thrown into waste baskets, not on the floor.

2. In shop and headquarters offices, mats are sometimes needed to remove dirt from the shoes of men who come in from the yard, foundries, etc.

3. Where smoking and tobacco chewing are permitted, cuspidors should be provided. Small rubber or linoleum mats will catch the "near misses." Regular cleaning is imperative.

4. All bulletin boards should be kept in good trim. When notices get old, they should be removed. It is better to have separate boards for permanent notices, or to put such items into employee manuals. Current notices on other boards will then be read. Posting should be neatly prepared and squared with the edges of the board. Prompt removal of past events keeps the board orderly and up to date.

5. Items of cleanliness and order relating to window cleaning, lighting-fixture cleaning, and schedules for the care of toilets, washrooms, locker rooms, drinking fountains, etc., are covered under the paragraphs of this section dealing with Maintenance Methods.

Maintenance Budgets

MAINTENANCE EXPENSE ALLOCATION. According to S. D. Leidesdorf & Co., any cost system should provide allowance for the cost of plant maintenance. While it is feasible to make a plant-wide maintenance charge to general overhead, this may not yield equitable product costs. Maintenance costs are generally calculated on a **department** basis. Even if the plant is a continuous-process or single-product type (cement—pig iron—wallboard), it will facilitate cost control if maintenance expense is classified by convenient **production centers** or by **activities** (motors, pumps, instruments, etc.). Hence the budget formulation requires a somewhat detailed estimate of the requirements for the various items of capital equipment maintenance.

Maintenance budgets are best established at the time when other plant expense standards are determined. In any case, a complete plant labor schedule, coded for accounts chargeable, will clearly define which is maintenance labor and which is departmental indirect labor. This procedure will avoid confusion in payroll accounting. Similarly, general review of the material requisition classification will distinguish between maintenance materials and departmental supplies.

There are many instances where the maintenance function is of such continuous nature that it may be made into an operating department function with supervision by the operating foreman. For example, a loom fixer in a weave shed, besides maintaining looms, also makes machine changes for new patterns, and is usually classified as weave-room indirect labor reporting to operating management. A setup man on automatic metalworking will do minor maintenance work and is charged as departmental indirect labor. By contrast a toolman working in a crib on reconditioning returned general-service tools may be classed as a routine maintenance man.

BUDGET PROCEDURES. Commonly used methods of **budget compilation** are:

1. Labor cost of a maintenance force acceptable to the plant engineer to fulfill his responsibility is estimated on an over-all plant basis. This budget is set up on a craft payroll basis to perform work within the times when machinery is not working, with allowances for overtime and holiday pay. Check whether outside contractors or borrowed operating labor are frequently required to hold the regular maintenance force to a minimum. Provide for such extras in the maintenance budget.

2. Labor cost is estimated on basis of past records, with consideration of wage-levels index.

3. Past records of total maintenance charges, if available by department, are reviewed with consideration of the proposed maintenance level, restoring deferred maintenance or making reductions after major renewals.

4. Materials costs may be estimated as a ratio of labor cost determined by past local experience. On an over-all basis, this ratio tends to be stable within a plant unless there is a policy change involving increase or decrease of repairs by outside contractors. Materials costs, exclusive of major renewals and reconstruction, are usually at least as much as the total maintenance payroll, but will vary with company policy as to outside contracting.

5. Where major maintenance and overhaul is done during plant shutdown, the budget is frequently divided into two separate portions: (a) regular continuous maintenance, and (b) periodic major overhaul. To avoid misleading variance statements and stabilize reported costs, item (b) may be treated as a monthly fixed charge to departments and credited to an overhaul reserve account. Actual overhaul expenses are charged to the overhaul reserve account, with offsetting credits to maintenance or other accounts.

6. The maintenance department itself is run under budget control, earning credits from materials and labor and overhead charged to operating, building, power, or other service units. The maintenance department overhead usually consists of allowances for supervision and payroll charges, stockroom, miscellaneous shop tools and service material, and nonchargeable shop time. Time charged to jobs will be on the basis of actual time at a uniform maintenance rate which covers labor and overhead. The plant engineer or master mechanic

receives a monthly statement of earned charges (including standard overhead) compared with the budget.

The overhead is usually charged at an hourly rate per man-hour, whereas material and repair parts are charged on a basis of priced requisitions. In the interest of prompt monthly cost statements, all maintenance work tickets should be cleared up daily and reconciled with the payroll, and filed by chargeable department ready for prompt end-of-month summary. General supplies are frequently charged to maintenance overhead as invoices are passed. This method bypasses inventory accounting of miscellaneous service material and makes it unnecessary to price minor requisitions. However, in cases of special accumulation of reserve stock of parts, it is advisable to create an inventory account for such reserve.

Special parts and purchases for specific jobs are charged via job tickets or requisitions to departments and may also be entered on the individual machine's maintenance record.

One company describes its fairly typical maintenance budgeting process in the following terms (Planning, Controlling, and Accounting for Maintenance, NACA Accounting Practice Report No. 2):

Each year the works manager, through his staff and with the assistance of the financial office, prepares a budget of forecasted maintenance costs. The compilation consists of both predictable and nonpredictable maintenance costs. Predictable items include such jobs as oiling, lubricating, painting, cleaning, replacing light fixtures, routine inspections, filling fire-fighting equipment—and, on a larger scale, roof repairs, replacing steel bands on dryers, retubing boilers and condensers, replacing conveyor parts, maintenance of planned capital installations. Nonpredictable items embrace emergency repairs, maintenance caused by a normal wear and tear, maintenance caused by process changes and alterations and unforeseen effects of floods or weather abnormalities.

The budget allowance for the usual maintenance of reoccurring predictable items is based on a combination of past experience, engineering studies of particular wear and tear and indicated obsolescence, and historical cost data. The allowance for the semimajor and major predictable items is based on detailed studies and estimates of the individual jobs to be done.

Unpredictable maintenance costs cannot be forecast to the same degree as the predictable maintenance costs. However, past experience indicates that unforeseen incidents will occur, and a realistic contingency amount is budgeted to cover these costs.

CHANGE OF MAINTENANCE COST LEVEL. Factory's Cost Index, published monthly in Factory Management and Maintenance, shows the monthly changes of cost of upkeep and repair on buildings and equipment. Details given of the many material and labor component items are taken from the Bureau of Labor Statistics. If a company has special requirements, the data is used to construct an **adapted cost index.**

Caution should be exercised in using this index for forecasting; trends may change direction without warning. The index can be used in reviewing variations in current maintenance costs to gage how much variation may be due to price changes. It may also be considered in establishing budgets on the basis of past experience, making corrections for changes in price level.

Nuclear Plant Engineering and Maintenance

OBJECTIVE. Nuclear engineering and its many problems are no longer an enigma to engineers, scientists, or managers of plants. The widespread use of isotopes and the many new applications for various forms of nuclear energy in industry make its presence commonplace. But the powerful destructive forces ever present, the high cost per unit handled, and the grave danger of injury to personnel make it imperative for the plant engineer and other maintenance personnel to have an understanding of the special problems involved. Further, they must know what precautions to take, and when to take them.

The following treatment of ventilation and air conditioning, radioactive waste disposal, and shielding will be helpful in achieving an initial grasp of the problem. The coverage on contamination and decontamination highlights the dangers to personnel, and emphasizes the need for care wherever radioactive materials are used.

VENTILATION AND AIR CLEANING. Airborne radioactive gases and particulate matter today arise in the following general areas:

1. **Mining, refining** (including isotope separation), and **production of radioactive metals and powders.**
2. **Reactor operation.** If air cooling is used for the reactor shield or slugs, the air coolant will become radioactive through thermal neutron bombardment. Slug rupture is possible, that is, the sealed reactor fuel may rupture its cover, spilling out highly radioactive fission products. These materials must be prevented as much as possible from reaching the atmosphere.
3. **Processing of slugs.** In recovering the unused fuel in reactor slugs, the rather elaborate chemical procedures used at present lead to air contamination unless controlled.
4. **Processing of wastes.** Most waste concentration processes, such as evaporation, or adsorption by ion exchange, give rise to radioactive air contaminants.
5. **Research and pilot plant laboratories.** Laboratories may bring about radioactive air contamination, usually on a smaller scale than 1–4. But air concentrations, unless controlled, may be higher due to the experimental nature of the work.

Maximum Permissible Air Concentrations. McCullough, et al. (Peaceful Uses of Atomic Energy, vol. 13) give a comparison between the maximum permissible air concentrations (MPAC) for radioactive and nonradioactive substances in Fig. 17. Because the MPAC is greatly decreased if there is an added hazard due to radiation, ventilation and air cleaning assume even greater importance than is attached to them in normal industrial health practice. Processes that one would not ordinarily consider as causing airborne contamination have to be thoroughly checked because of the very low MPAC for radioisotopes. In fact, it is axiomatic when working with **unsealed radioisotopes** to assume that there will be airborne contamination, until it is definitely proved otherwise.

The **nonoccupational** MPAC are taken to be one-tenth ($\frac{1}{10}$) of occupational concentration values. Furthermore, because of the present uncertainties in air cleaning methods, plus the fact that no sense of the human body is stimulated by radiation, the efficiency of collection must be checked by taking **air samples.** For particulate matter, the electrostatic precipitator modified for air sampling has been found to be very effective, but bulky in practice. Air sampling by collection on filter paper, usually Whatman 41 or, more recently, millipore filters, have resulted in less bulky equipment. The U.S.A.E.C. states in the Handbook on Air Cleaning (Friedlander, *et al.*) that for particle size distribution as well as total dust count, the modified cascade impactor is suited for the particle size range 100–0.2 microns. The oscillating thermal precipitator is suited for the particle size range greater than 0.001 microns.

Air Supply and Exhaust Design. The problem of general ventilation versus local ventilation that is common in the field of industrial hygiene normally does

Substance	Tolerance†	"Fatal Dose"‡	Ratio Fatal to Tolerance
	Chemical Poisons		
Chlorine	2.9 ¶	290§	100
Arsine	0.16¶	800§	5000
Beryllium	1.5×10^{-5}	?	?
	*Radioactive Poisons**		
U^{288} (insol.)	1690×10^{-9}	1690×10^{-5}	10,000
Pu^{289}	32×10^{-9}	32×10^{-5}	10,000
Sr^{90}	1.3×10^{-9}	1.3×10^{-5}	10,000

* It should be remembered that industrial poisons are usually in many-ton quantities, whereas radioactive poisons are in 100-kg. quantities.

† "Tolerance" for chemical poisons is defined as the maximum tolerable level for 8 hours per day exposure. In the case of radioactive poisons tolerance is the maximum level which can be tolerated every day for 8 hours equivalent to 0.043 rem per day.

‡ "Fatal Dose" in the case of chemical poisons is defined as the "rapidly fatal" dose when the given concentration in air is inhaled for 30 minutes to 1 hour. In the case of radioactive material this means about 50 percent survival if the dose is acquired quite rapidly, for example, over a minute or perhaps during an 8-hour day. This is equivalent to about 400 rem.††

¶ Adopted at meeting of the American Conference of Governmental and Industrial Hygienists in Atlantic City, N. J., in April 1951.

§ Industrial Hygiene and Toxicology, Frank H. Patty, Editor, Interscience Publishers, Inc., 1949.

** Maximum Permissible Amounts of Radioisotopes in the Human Body and Maximum Permissible Concentrations in Air and Water, Handbook 52, National Bureau of Standards, March 20, 1953.

†† The Effects of Atomic Weapons, U. S. Government Printing Office, Revised September, 1950.

Fig. 17. Comparison of toxic substances in air* (concentration in mg./cu. met.).

not exist when working with radioisotopes. The MPAC are so low that a **combination of general and local ventilation** is almost mandatory. In a room with two hoods, for example, the general air flow would be designed so that it would come from clean areas into the room with hood and then exhaust through hood. By the maintenance of such **air-flow-pattern control,** air contamination, even if it should happen outside the hood, is carried not into the clean areas but out the hood exhaust.

Air supply for the exhaust would normally come from clean areas such as corridors or administrative offices, but local exhaust velocities required with radioisotopes usually dictate air supply make-up from **perforated ceiling pans** or **outlet panels.** The air supply should have a low intake velocity so that no air currents are created in the room. The **maximum inlet air velocities** that have been recommended (ASA Code F 9) for various inlet heights are:

120 ft. per min. for inlets less than 8 ft. above floor.
250 ft. per min. for inlets 8–12 ft. above floor.
500 ft. per min. for inlets 12–18 ft. above floor.
1,000 ft. per min. for inlets more than 18 ft. above floor.

The local exhaust velocity (or control velocity) depends on the process as outlined above. In nuclear engineering practice, practically no information exists on this point except for chemical hoods. In the case of **streamlined chemical hoods,** studies at Oak Ridge National Laboratory (ORNL) indicate that a face velocity of 50 linear ft. per min. is sufficient, but the ordinary **nonstreamlined hood** requires 100–150 linear ft. per min. Grinding, buffing, and polishing of radioactive materials will increase greatly with the increase of nuclear power. Fig. 18, adapted from Brandt (Industrial Health Engineering), summarizes the recommendations for average to heavy nonradioactive industrial dusts requiring a transport velocity of 4,500 ft. per min. for different types of equipment. There must be additional velocity if radioisotopes are used in any of the processes. Design velocities should be checked for safety in practice by one of the air-sampling methods.

Type of Equipment	Wheel or Belt Dimension (inches)	Hood Exhaust Outlet Diameter in Inches					
		3	4	5	6	7	8
		Exhaust Ventilation Rate in Cubic Feet per Minute per Outlet					
		220	390	610	880	1200	1560
Grinding and cut-off wheels { Diameter		<9	9–16	19–24	24–30	30–36	—
{ Width		1½	2	4	5	6	
Buffing and polishing wheels { Diameter		—	—	16–19	—	—	—
{ Width		—	—	4	—	—	—
Horizontal single-spindle discs	Diameter	<12	12–19	19–30	30–36	—	—
Horizontal double-spindle discs	Diameter	—	—	<19	19–25 / 30–53 (2 outlets)	25–30	53–72 (4 outlets)
Vertical single-spindle discs (not covered)	Diameter	—	<20 (2 outlets)	—	30–53 (4 outlets)	53–72 (5 outlets)	—
Vertical single-spindle discs (more than half covered)	Diameter	—	20–30 (2 outlets)	—	30–53 (2 outlets)	—	53–72 (2 outlets)
Belts and straps	Width	<3	5–7	9–11	—	—	—

Fig. 18. Exhaust outlets and ventilation rates for nonradioactive industrial dusts.

If at all feasible, the so-called **enclosing hoods** are recommended for radioisotope work. Examples of this type of hood are the laboratory chemical hood, the glove box, and, for example, a lathe with stock of uranium being machined totally enclosed by lucite except for air inlet holes.

In industrial hygiene practice, three other general hood types—rectangular or round hoods, slot hoods, and canopy hoods—are available to choose from. If any of these types are used, air contamination is probable; but on the other hand, they may be useful with radioisotopes with a relatively high MPAC, e.g., natural uranium. Air samples should, of course, be taken to check this point, especially where continuous exposures will result.

Radiochemical Laboratory Ventilation. The design of the radiochemical laboratories at Argonne is an excellent example of a well-ventilated laboratory with both **general** and **local** ventilation. This laboratory was designed on the modular principle with 200–300 sq. ft. per module. Fig. 19 (Proceedings of Conference on Laboratory Design for Handling Radioactive Materials, BRAB Conference Report No. 3, National Academy of Sciences) gives a plan and elevation view of two 10 x 24-ft. units with offices. The labs are air-conditioned, but with all hoods in operation make-up air from corridor and office space must be pro-

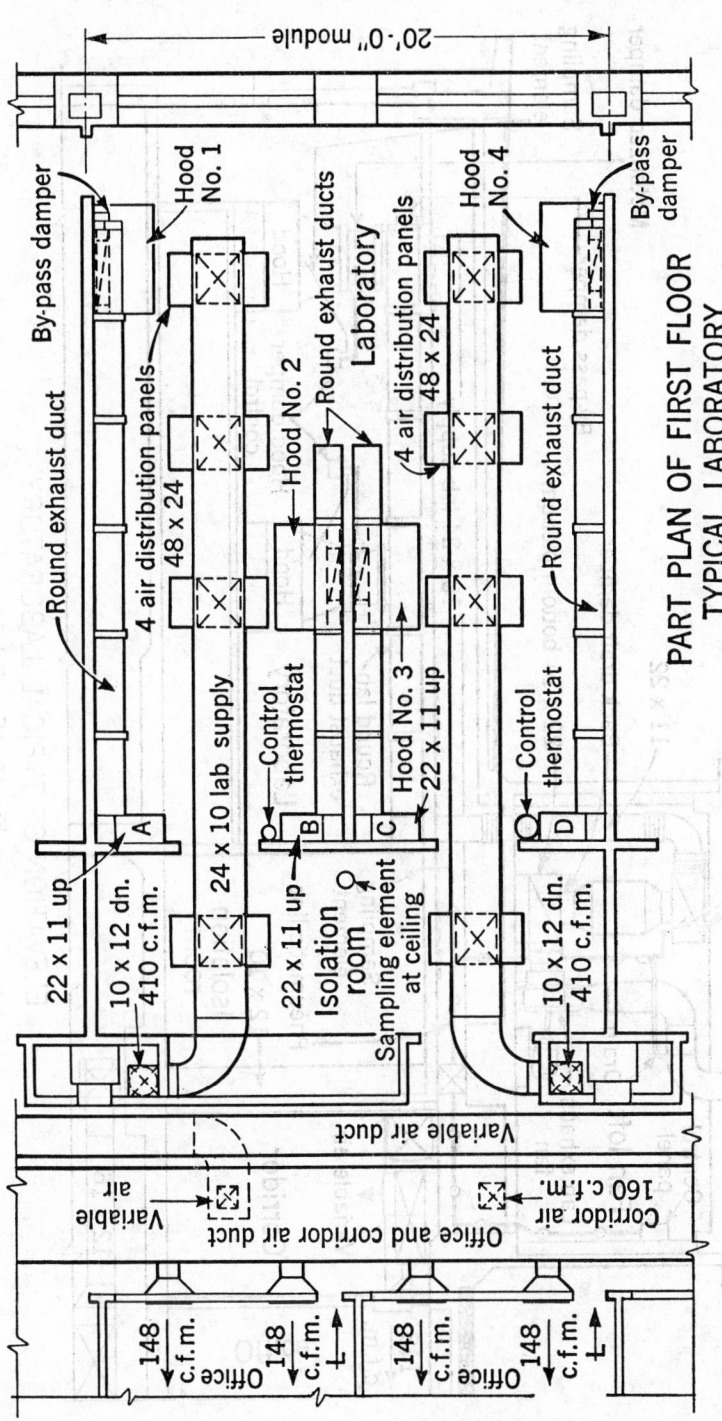

Fig. 19. Plan of modular radiochemical laboratory units (continued on next page).

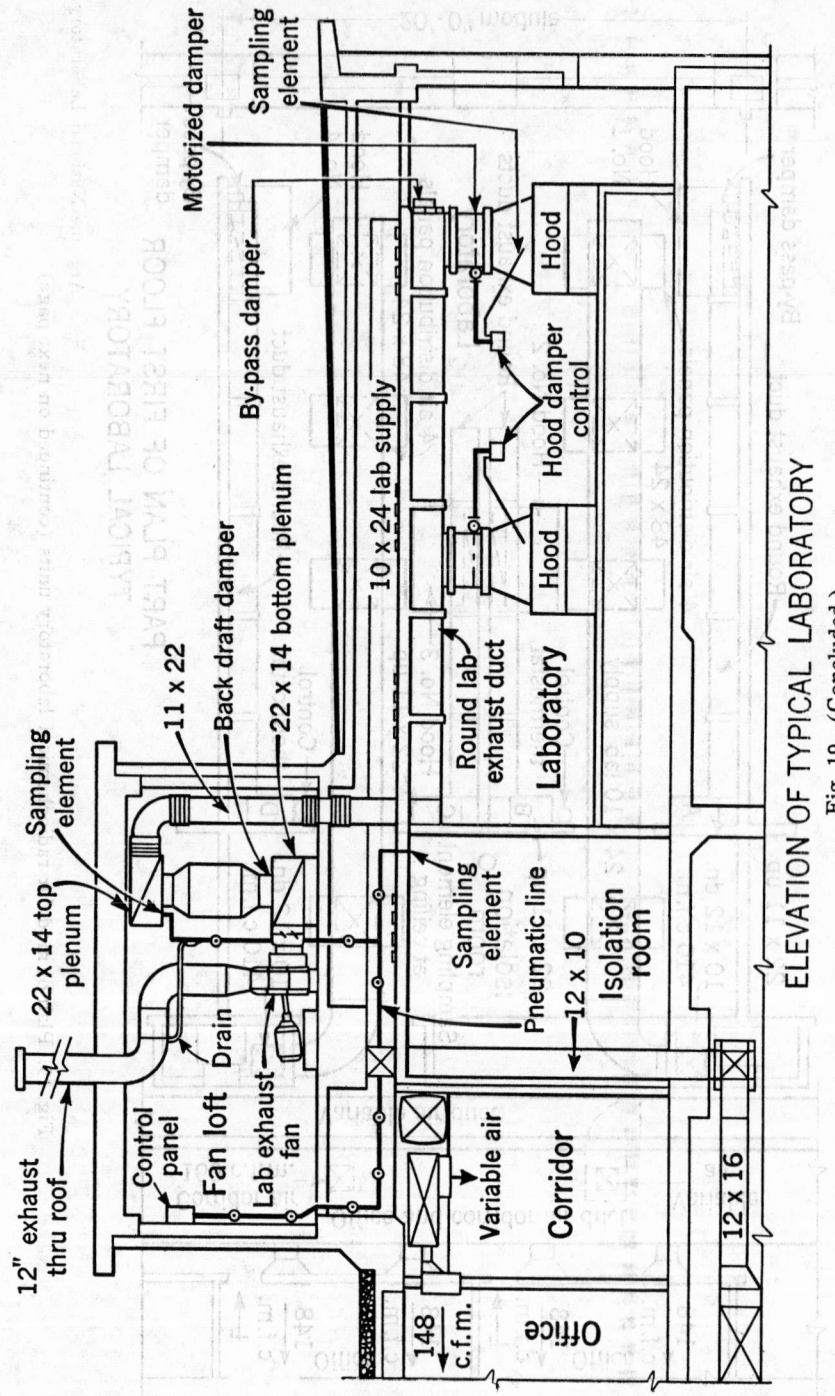

ELEVATION OF TYPICAL LABORATORY

Fig. 19. (Concluded.)

vided. These hoods are of the controlled-face-velocity type. The **sampling element** senses the air velocity and then transmits this information to the hood damper control, which in turn controls the damper motor. This unit can be set to give 100 plus or minus 20 ft. per min., regardless of hood opening. There is normally a prefilter at the hood, and a final high-efficiency filter (CC—6) is next to the fan in the fan loft.

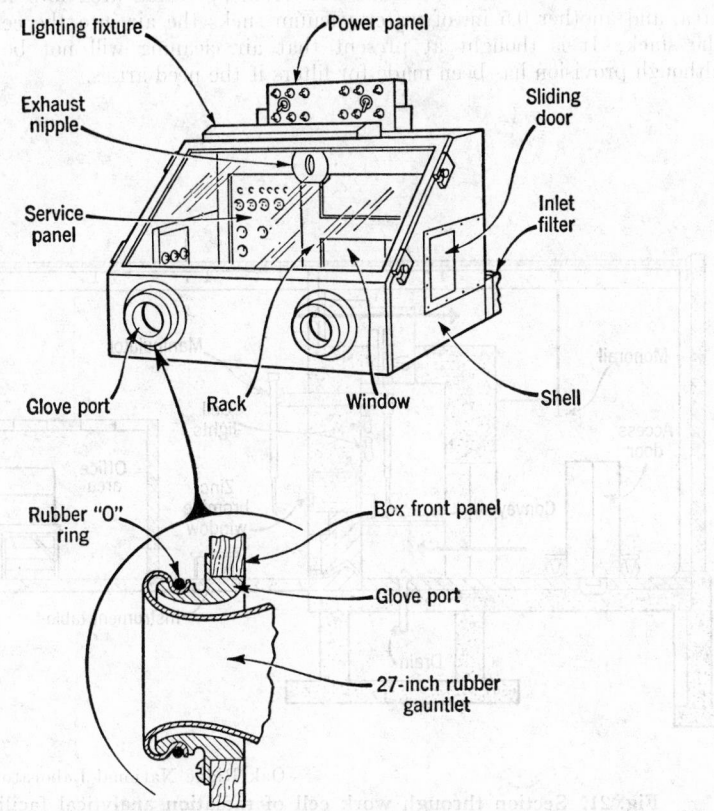

Fig. 20. Radiochemical glove box.

Because of the low expense, especially in maintaining and conditioning the air supply, **glove boxes** have found considerable favor in radiochemistry work, especially at the University of California Radiation Laboratory, where their design has been extended to cover many difficult radiochemistry problems. A modified form of glove box has been used in the radium-dial-painting industry for years. The Berkeley-type glove box is totally enclosed, with an optional air flow of 5–10 cu. ft. per min. Fig. 20 (Chemical Processing and Equipment, TID 5276) is an example of a glove box; such closed boxes have been perfected so that almost all chemical manipulations can be performed in them.

A different approach to similar problems is followed in the design of the new radiation analytical facilities at Oak Ridge National Laboratory. This facility has been designed for gram quantities of highly radioactive materials (mainly used reactor fuels). In Fig. 21, the elevation view is shown. The biological shield is 3-ft.-thick concrete, standard concrete for **analytical cells** and high-density—i.e., barite ($BaSO_4$)-aggregate—concrete for the **storage cells.** This shield has been designed to give a dose of 1 mrep per hr. on the outside surface. The area on the left, the maintenance and cell area, is completely isolated from the right-hand or operating area except for air flow. A pressure differential of 0.5 in. of water vacuum maintains air flow from operating area into maintenance area, and another 0.5 in. of water vacuum sucks the air into the cells and out the stack. It is thought at present that air cleaning will not be necessary, although provision has been made for filters if the need arises.

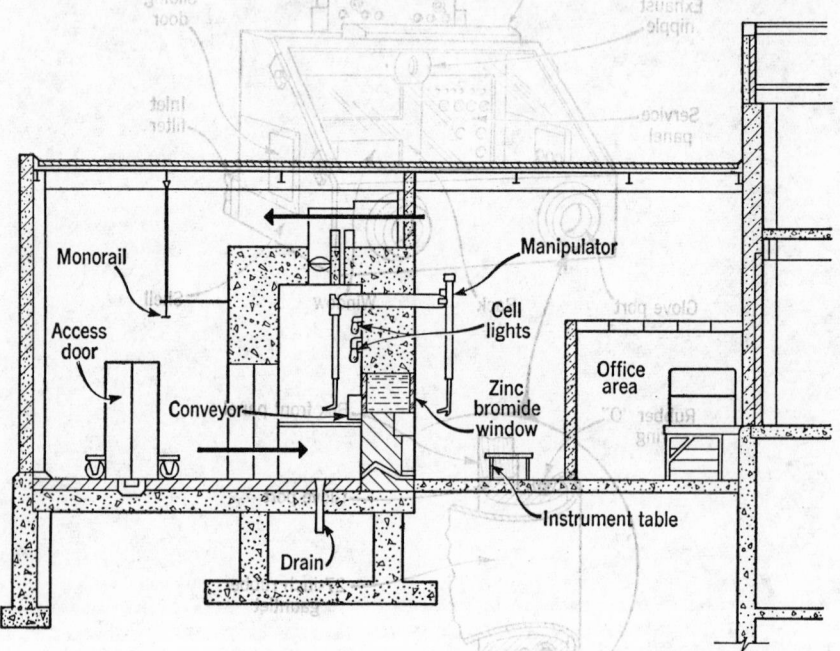

Oak Ridge National Laboratory LR 1075
Fig. 21. Section through work cell of radiation analytical facilities.

Methods of Air Cleaning. For purposes of air cleaning, the following break-down of air contaminants according to their physical properties is made: dusts, fumes, mists, gases, vapors, and smoke. The ASA definitions of these contaminants are:

Dusts: Solid particles generated by handling, crushing, grinding, rapid impact, detonation and decrepitation of organic or inorganic materials such as rock, ore, metal, coal, wood, grain, etc. Dusts do not tend to flocculate except under electro-static forces; they do not diffuse in air but settle under the influence of gravity.

Fumes: Solid particles generated by condensation from the gaseous state, generally after volatilization from molten metals, etc., and often accompanied by a chemical reaction such as oxidation. Fumes flocculate and sometimes coalesce.

Mists: Suspended liquid droplets generated by condensation from the gaseous to the liquid state or by breaking up a liquid into a dispersed state, such as by splashing, foaming, and atomizing.

Gases: Normally formless fluids which occupy the space of enclosure and which can be changed to the liquid or solid state only by the combined effect of increased pressure and decreased temperature. Gases diffuse.

Vapors: The gaseous form of substances which are normally in the solid or liquid state and which can be changed to these states either by increasing the pressure or decreasing the temperature alone. Vapors diffuse.

Smoke: Carbon or soot particles less than 0.1 micron in size which result from the incomplete combustion of carbonaceous materials such as coal, oil, tar, and tobacco.

In choosing a method of air cleaning, ideally, one should know the **physical and chemical characteristics** of the air contaminant. Unfortunately, not very often is much thought given to determining the exact nature of the air contaminant at the pilot-plant stage, so that the choice of air-cleaning equipment is left generally to guesswork and past experience of the engineer in the final design.

Air cleaning involves two distinct steps: **conditioning of particulate matter** for precipitation, and **precipitation.** In some cases these two steps are combined in one step, as, for example, in scrubbers.

The procedure to follow in choosing air-cleaning equipment should be as follows:

1. Determine particle size range, and whether particulate matter is gas, liquid, or solid.
2. Determine transport velocity and volume flow rate of air.
3. Determine radioisotope(s) present in effluent.

Normally, the larger-sized particulate matter (100–200 microns) can be removed by a **settling chamber.** These are designed on the basis of gravity removal in an enlarged chamber where the velocity is decreased and the large particles follow Stokes's law in settling out. In Fig. 22, Brandt (Industrial Health Engineering) suggests certain types of collectors for the various particle size ranges.

Type of Collector	Minimum Particle Size (microns)
Settling chamber	100–200
Inertial collector	50–200
Centrifugal collector	
Cyclone—large diameter	40–60
Cyclone—small diameter	20–30
Fan type	15–30
Filter	0.5–2.0
Wet collector	1.0–2.0
Electrostatic precipitator	0.001–1.0

Fig. 22. **Suggested minimum particle size groups for different collectors.**

Gases, mists, and soluble particulate matter are most easily removed by wet fiber filters. These units are normally followed by a high-efficiency dry-collection method. In practice, it may be necessary to heat the effluents because of the possibility of plugging the dry filters.

In Fig. 23, Silverman summarizes the characteristics of present air-cleaning equipment as employed in the U. S. atomic energy program.

Type of Equipment	Particle Size Range (mass median microns)	Percent Efficiency for Size in Col. 2	Velocity (ft./min.)	Pressure Loss (in. of water)	Approximate Cost (cfm)	Current Application in U.S. Atomic Energy Program
Simple settling chambers	>50	60 to 80	25 to 75	0.2 to .5	$0.05	Rarely used.
Cyclones, large diameter	>5	40 to 85	2,000 to 3,500 (entry)	0.5 to 2.5	$0.10 to $0.25	Precleaners in mining, ore handling, and machining operations.
Cyclones, small diameter	>5	40 to 95	2,500 to 3,500 (entry)	2 to 4.5	$0.25 to $0.50	Same as above.
Mechanical centrifugal collectors	>5	20 to 85	2,500 to 4,000	–	$0.20 to $0.35	Same as large cyclone application.
Baffle chambers	>5	10 to 40	1,000 to 1,500	0.5 to 1.0	$0.05	Incorporated in chip traps for metal-turning.
Spray washers	>5	20 to 40	200 to 500	0.1 to 0.2	$0.10 to $0.20	Rarely used, occasionally as cooling for hot gases.
Wet filters	Gases and 0.1 to 25 μ mists	90 to 99	100	1 to 5	$0.09 to $0.10	Used on laboratory hoods and chemical-separation operations.
Packed towers	Gases and soluble particles 5 μ	90	200 to 500	1 to 10	$0.40 to $0.80	Gas absorption and precleaning for acid mists.
Cyclone scrubber	>5	40 to 85	2,000 to 3,500 (entry)	1 to 5	$0.25 to $0.40	Pyrophoric materials in machining and casting operations, mining, and ore handling. Roughing for incinerators.
Inertial scrubbers, power-driven	8 to 10	90 to 95	–	3 to 5 hp. per 1,000 cfm	$0.15 to $0.25	Pyrophoric materials in machining and casting operations, mining, and ore handling

Venturi scrubber	>1	99 for H_2SO_4 mist. SiO_2, oil smoke, etc. 60 to 70	12,000 to 24,000 at throat	6 to 30	\$0.50 to \$3.00	Incorporated in air-cleaning train of incinerators.
Viscous air-conditioning filters	10 to 25	70 to 85	300 to 500	0.03 to 0.15	\$0.004 to \$.006	General ventilation air.
Dry spun-glass filters	5	85 to 90	30 to 35	0.1 to 0.3	\$0.02 to \$0.04	General ventilation air. Precleaning from chemical and metallurgical hoods.
Packed beds of graded fibers, 1 to 20 μ 40 in. deep	<1	99.90 to 99.99	20	10 to 30	\$1.00 to \$5.00	Dissolver off gas cleaning.
High-efficiency cellulose-asbestos filters	<1	99.95 to 99.98	5 through media 250 at face	1.0 to 2.0	\$0.04 to \$0.06	Final cleaning for hoods, glove boxes, reactor air, and incinerators.
All-glass web filters	<1	99.95 to 99.99	5 through media 250 at face	1.0 to 2.0	\$0.07 to \$0.10	Final cleaning for hoods, glove boxes, reactor air, and incinerators.
Conventional fabric filters	>1	90 to 99.9	3 to 5	5 to 7	\$0.30 to \$1.00	Dust and fumes in feed materials production.
Reverse-jet fabric filters	>1	90 to 99.9	15 to 50	2 to 5	\$0.50 to \$1.00	Dust and fumes in feed materials production.
Single-stage electrostatic precipitator	<1	90 to 99 90–95 on metallurgical fumes	200 to 400	0.25 to 0.75	\$0.50 to \$2.00	Final cleanup for chemical and metallurgical hoods. Uranium machining.
Two-stage electrostatic precipitator	<1 to 5	85 to 99	200 to 400	0.25 to 0.50	\$0.25 to \$0.50	Not widely used for decontamination.

Peaceful Uses of Atomic Energy, vol. 9

Fig. 23. Operational characteristics of air-cleaning equipment.

RADIOACTIVE WASTE DISPOSAL. There are two approaches to radioactive waste disposal: concentration and containment, and dispersal into environment. Most high-level, highly radiotoxic waste is concentrated and stored in large underground tanks today. For **true containment** these wastes must be stored for approximately 600 years. The life of the present tanks is estimated at between 50 and 75 years; therefore, they are a long way from representing true containment.

Dispersal into the environment is practiced on a limited scale for low- and intermediate-level wastes almost universally today. Dispersal is normally not outright dispersal, but controlled dispersal. The increase in radioactivity caused by this dispersal into the environment is continuously monitored, and if the radioactivity increases above certain maximum permissible limits, dispersal is stopped.

Sources of Radioactive Wastes. Radioactive wastes arise in the following general areas:

1. Processing of uranium into feed materials and reactor fuel slugs or elements.
2. Reactor coolants.
3. Chemical processing of reactor fuel slugs.
4. Radioactive laundry wastes.
5. Pilot plants, research labs, and hospitals.

A tentative **waste classification** into high-, intermediate-, and low-level wastes has been made on the basis of activity and dose rate. High-level wastes require extensive shielding for handling, and their activity might be as high as 100 curies per liter, while the low-level wastes are 10^{-6} to 10^{-7} curies per liter. Obviously this is a very loose classification. Normally, wastes that are stored or contained because they cannot be diluted sufficiently for dispersal are termed **high-level wastes,** while **low-level wastes** are those that are readily processed for dispersal. Limited dispersal on an experimental basis is being attempted for the intermediate-level wastes.

The greatest amounts of radioactive wastes today arise from the method of processing reactor fuel slugs. Gueckauf (Peaceful Uses of Atomic Energy, vol. 9)

Group	Element	Kg.
0	Kr + Xe	128
1	Rb	15
	Cs	118
2	Sr	42
	Ba	43
3	Rare earths + Y	317
4	Zr	125
5	Nb	5
6	Mo	92
	Te	16
7	Tc	29
	I	7
8	Ru, Rh, Pd	61

Peaceful Uses of Atomic Energy, vol. 9

Fig. 24. Quantities of fission products derived from 1 ton of U^{225} (150 days' irradiation, 30 days' cooling).

gives the fission products (F.P.) produced during the fission process, listed by chemical group, in Fig. 24. The two most important isotopes from the point of view of radiotoxicity and half-life are **strontium-90** and **cesium-137**. It has been estimated that high-level wastes with these two isotopes present will remain highly active for 1,000 years.

Types of Waste Treatment and Disposal. The chemical method of processing is solvent extraction, with the uranium and plutonium coming out in the organic phase and most of the fission products remaining in the aqueous phase, usually a nitrate solution. Because of the large liquid volume of the aqueous fission-product phase, several methods of reducing the volume and concentrating the fission products have been tried. At costs estimated between $0.14 and $0.71 per gallon, **evaporation** is used extensively on this liquid, while **coprecipitation** and **ion exchange** are two methods used to separate out certain fission products. Types of waste disposal are: tank storage, evaporation, land burial, and sea burial. Gueckauf (Peaceful Uses of Atomic Energy, vol. 9) indicates in flow-diagram form (Fig. 25) the ideal method for handling chemical-processing waste. Unfortunately, all the steps on this flow-diagram have not been developed to the point where they are economically feasible as yet.

In engineering specialties in an advanced state of development, it is common to go from general theory to practical applications, while the opposite is true for new engineering arts. The latter is the present situation with respect to radio-active-waste disposal except for the low-level wastes, and therefore, some of the practices at sites where the solution to this problem has been evolving will be discussed.

Ground Disposal. The Clinton Laboratories, now Oak Ridge National Laboratory (ORNL), were formed in 1943 to serve as a pilot plant for Pu production, which later was located at Hanford, Washington. Varied radioactive wastes have been handled in this laboratory since that time. The radioactive wastes are of the following two types:

1. Metal waste: compounds of uranium collected and stored for recovery.
2. Radiochemical waste: fission products and various chemical byproducts from production and developmental processes.

Fig. 26 gives the flow pattern for most of the liquid waste at ORNL.

Only radiochemical waste is dispersed at present in ORNL, amounting to 50,000 gal. per wk. New facilities, and most of the old, are equipped with special drains that connect to a building collection tank which is provided with a level recorder, sampling device, and agitator. This tank discharges to a surge tank, which is used to even out the flow to the evaporator. The water vapor from the evaporator passes through a centrifugal or cyclone-type separator for entrainment removal and then through a manifold to four parallel tube condensers. The condensate is monitored by a **conductivity probe** to check for radioisotope entrainment in the distillate. If this occurs, the evaporator's liquid level and steam pressure are reduced. The radioactive residue or sludge is fed by gravity to the underground storage tanks. Characteristics of the ORNL evaporator are:

$$\frac{300 \text{ gal. of water}}{\text{hr.}} \text{ at atmospheric pressure.}$$

Decontaminator Factor (DF) $= \dfrac{\text{Influent activity}}{\text{Effluent activity}} = 2.94 \times 10^3$ (the effluent in this case is the distillate).

Volume Reduction $= \dfrac{\text{in}}{\text{out}} = \dfrac{60}{1}$

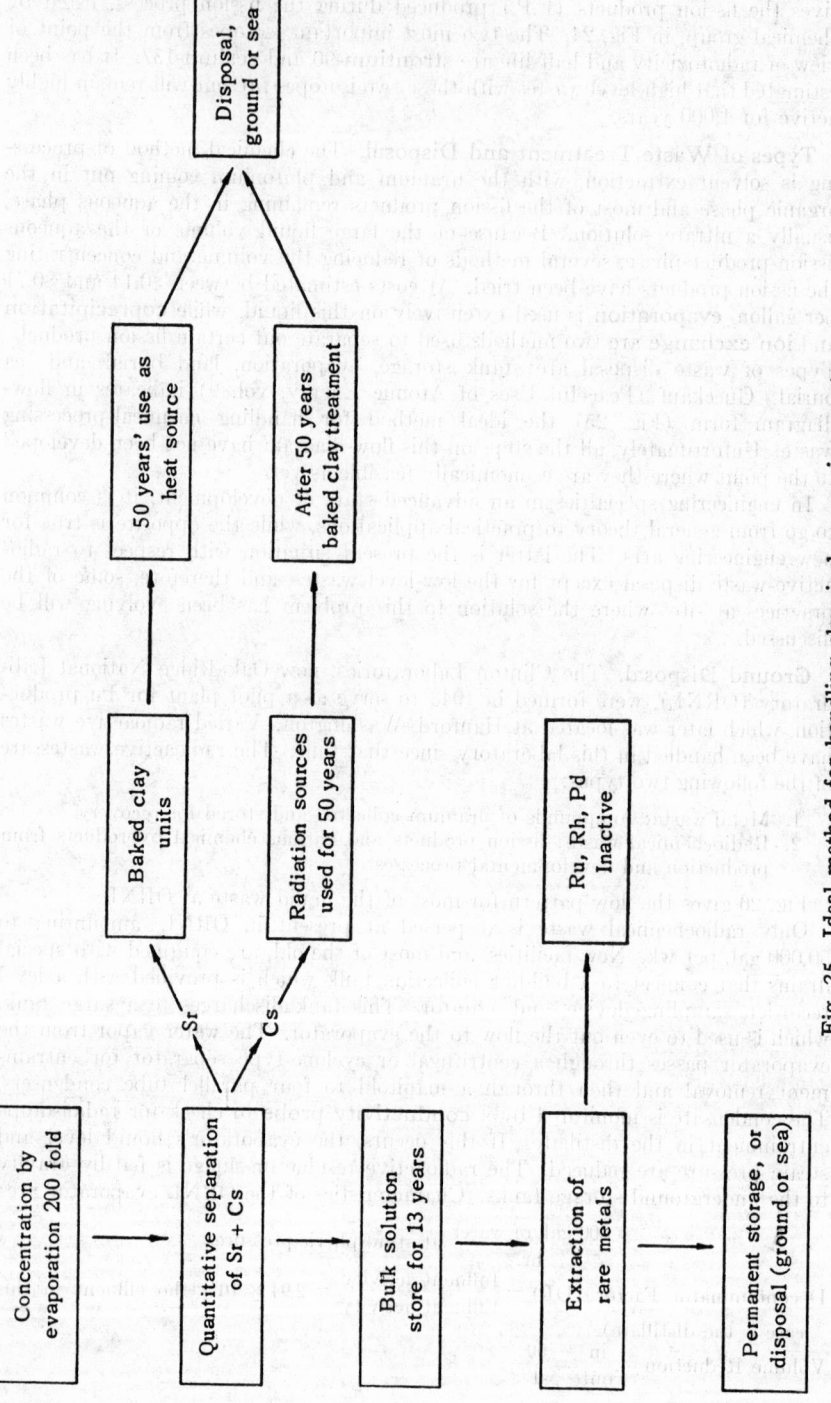

Fig. 25. Ideal method for handling chemical processing waste.

The distillate goes to the settling basin, White Oak Creek, and finally the Clinch River, and has contributed 0.224 curies per wk. to the creek.

Because of the high cost of the tank storage, an alternate to this method of storage was sought in **terrestrial pits** or **open ground pits** dug in soil with a suitable liner and covering. Intermediate-level liquid wastes, 1/300 to 1/30 curies per gal., are disposed of in these pits. High level wastes and metal wastes are still stored in **steel-lined concrete tanks.** Solid radioactive wastes are **buried** in the Conasauga **shale formation.**

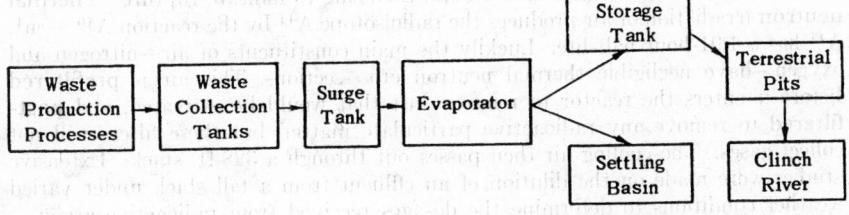

Oak Ridge National Laboratory

Fig. 26. Flow pattern for disposal of liquid waste.

These pits have been dug on the weathered soil covering Conasauga shale which is 1,500 ft. thick in this locality. The ground water table varies from 0 to 35 ft. in depth. Sampling wells indicated that ruthenium and nonradioactive nitrate ions travel approximately 1 ft. per day in the weathered clay and shale. None of the other radioisotopes were found at the nearest sampling well after three years. For the soil and shale to take up most cations, the pH must be in the range 10–14; therefore, the chemical wastes have to be pretreated before disposal. Asphalt was used to line the pits. The very low cost as compared with tank containment makes this method very attractive but risky at present.

Sea Disposal. At the Windscale Works, in England on the Irish Sea, tests have been run to determine the feasibility of disposing of radioactive wastes into the sea. England, with a relatively high population density, cannot afford to tie up land indefinitely for waste disposal and has turned to the sea to help solve this problem. Tests with **fluorescein dye** to determine the fate of material dumped into the ocean were first run. Next, **tracer amounts** of radiochemical wastes were dumped. The results of these studies have helped determine maximum permissible limits on the discharge rates from the Windscale Works.

It was projected that the effluent was to amount to 79–106 gal. per day, with a low concentration of fission products, uranium, plutonium, and small quantities of stable chemical wastes. A pipeline was laid out into the Irish Sea and the effluent was discharged over a period of 2–3 hours immediately after high water. Tests indicated that the effluent would be dispersed by:

1. Dilution with large volumes of water.
2. A process of eddy diffusion.
3. Removal from the general area by a mixture of eddy diffusion and nontidal currents.

On the basis of information obtained from the dye studies and the recommendations of the International Commission on Radiological Protection on internal and external exposure limits, the estimated maximum permissible discharges to the sea were developed. The limiting factors at the Windscale Works are the edible fish and seaweed which concentrate the diluted effluent.

Air Disposal. At the present stage of technological development, disposal of waste into the air is probably the least desirable of the three methods of dispersal, but still there are many instances where radioactivity becomes airborne. The Brookhaven National Laboratory Research Reactor, a natural-uranium, graphite-moderate, 30-megawatt reactor, illustrates air cooling and disposal.

The heat generated in the uranium slugs passes out to the circulating air through a helium jacket provided around each slug to indicate rupture. **Thermal neutron** irradiation of air produces the radioisotope A^{41} by the reaction $A^{40} + {}_0n^1$. A^{41} has a 1.91-hour half-life. Luckily the main constituents of air—nitrogen and oxygen—have negligible thermal neutron cross-sections. This air is **prefiltered** before it enters the reactor to remove dust that would be activated, and **post-filtered** to remove any radioactive particulate matter, but these filters will not collect gases. The cooling air then passes out through a 328-ft. stack. Extensive studies were made on the dilution of an effluent from a tall stack under varied weather conditions to determine the dosages received from radioactive argon.

From these studies, formulas were obtained which are of engineering significance for estimating ground dose prior to installation of a stack which is to disperse a radioactive effluent, including the following data (Singer, BNL 292):

Inversion: Negligible vertical diffusion.
Lapse: Vertical and lateral diffusion,
$Q = 694$ mc. per sec.; **30-megawatt power level.**
Distance: 2,040 ft.
Dose: 0.26 mc. per wk.

Brookhaven also packages its solid and liquid wastes into 55-gal. drums. Liquid waste is incorporated into cement to form a protective annulus of concrete 2–8 in. thick inside of which the solid waste is packed and covered over with contaminated concrete. These drums are buried at sea in 7,500 ft. of water and 150 miles from shore. Gemmel (Paper before American Industrial Hygiene Assoc. Meeting, 1956) reports that in 1955, 600 curies were disposed in this manner at a cost of $20.00 per drum (excluding overhead costs).

Low-Level Disposal. While the above methods cover dispersal of relatively large amounts of radioactive material, hospitals and research laboratories also dispose of "hot" waste, usually on a nonperiodic basis. Hospitals treating patients with therapeutic doses of iodine-131 (I-131) and phosphorus-32 (P-32) have the problem of disposal of radioactive urine.

From considerations of safety to sanitation workers and sewage-plant personnel, **maximum permissible disposal rates** for I-131 and P-32 have been formulated. For example, if a 500-bed hospital has two patients, one with 4 millicuries (mc) of P-32 and the other with 10 millicuries of I-131, the amount M excreted is:

$$M\ (\text{I-131}) = 1.5 \text{ mc.}$$
$$\underline{M\ (\text{P-32}) = 0.24 \text{ mc.}}$$
$$1.74 \text{ mc.}$$

which is below the 2–8-mc. night maximum permissible disposal in a single event. For greater rates of disposal, a **constant drip bottle** which spreads the discharge over a longer period of time must be used.

Carbon-14 (C-14) is another isotope that has been singled out for specific recommendations (Recommendations for the Disposal of Carbon-14 Wastes, NBS Hb 53):

Isotope Dilution: C-14 may be disposed of in any manner provided it is intimately mixed with stable carbon in the same chemical form in a ratio that never exceeds 1 microcuric (μc.) C-14 for every 10 grams of stable carbon.

Sewer Disposal: less than $\dfrac{1 \text{ mc.}}{100 \text{ gal. of sewage}}$ based on sewer flow within one's own institution.

Incineration: Maximum concentration must not exceed 5 μc. per gram of carbon.

Atmospheric Dilution: $C^{14}O_2$ can be discharged from a hood with a linear air flow of 50 ft. per min. at a rate not to exceed 100 μc. per hr. per sq. ft. of air intake area.

Garbage: Less than 1 μc. per lb. of garbage available to disposer within his own institution.

Burial: Under at least 4 ft. of well-compacted earth (maximum permissible concentration of C-14 in biological materials shall not exceed 5 μc. per gram; maximum permissible amount of C-14 in chemical compounds mixed with 1 cu. ft. of soil shall not exceed 10 mc.)

Research laboratories using other radioisotopes in amounts that do not warrant special drains have to formulate their own policy in conjunction with the Radiological Safety Branch, Division of Civilian Application, U.S.A.E.C.

Radioactive wastes dumped into the **public sewage systems** may be concentrated to a certain extent in the various conventional water treatment processes; therefore, it is the responsibility of institutions availing themselves of this disposal method to check periodically the sewage treatment plant in their area to determine if the reconcentrations are becoming in any way hazardous. Disposal service is available commercially and also from ORNL.

Formulating a Waste Disposal Program. On the basis of the solutions to the problem of radioactive waste disposal that have been tried and found, at least for the present, satisfactory, the following general procedures for formulating a waste disposal program may be stated:

1. Estimate level of "hot" waste to be disposed.
2. Determine its physical and chemical character.
3. Determine methods available for disposal in the given area.
4. If by containment, **estimate life of container,** which should be approximately 15-20 half-lives for permanent containment; if by dispersal, **estimate maximum disposal rate,** computed from dose to be received by the persons living in environment.

One method of permanent waste disposal consists of incorporating certain cations, usually strontium-90 and cesium-137, onto clay and firing the clay to give a supposedly leach-proof mass. A proposed commercial-scale permanent waste-disposal setup of this kind has been designed. It is hoped that radioactive wastes will become economically valuable, as happened to the petroleum industry wastes of 20–30 years ago, so that their disposal will no longer be a necessity.

SHIELDING. When sunlight strikes the body it can cause discoloration in the skin. This arises from the fact that energy is absorbed by the skin, thereby initiating chemical changes. Similarly, with ionizing radiation, if the wave length of external ionizing radiation is right, it can also cause this discoloration; but in many cases external ionizing radiation is able to penetrate farther into the body before it is absorbed. Energy that is absorbed by the body from ionizing radiation may upset body processes or trigger a body reaction.

Biological Effects of Ionizing Radiation. The energy effects of ionizing radiation have been enumerated by the International Commission on Radiological Protection (National Bureau of Standards Handbook 47) as:

1. Superficial injuries.
2. General effects on the body, particularly the blood and blood-forming organs, e.g., production of anemias and leukemias.
3. The induction of malignant tumors.
4. Other deleterious effects, including cataract, obesity, impaired fertility, and reduction of life span.
5. Genetic effects.

Based on the experience and experimentation of the last 50 years with ionizing radiation, it has been deduced that **thresholds** exist for the first four effects, but it has been theorized that no threshold exists in man for the genetic effects, considering the results of experimentation on lower animals.

The so-called **biological shield** reduces the intensity from ionizing radiation to maximum permissible external exposure limits or below. Photons (γ-ray, X-ray), beta particles (positive and negative), alpha particles, and neutrons are the four most important **sources of ionizing radiation.** These particles may come from sealed sources, from reactors, or from particle accelerators (X-ray machine, cyclotron, etc.).

Alpha and Beta Particle Shielding. Alpha (α) particles present no shielding problem because they are easily stopped by soft tissue, air, or paper. Beta (β) particles arise in the nucleus of unstable isotopes or radioisotopes; but high-speed electrons are also produced as secondary particles, by the other forms of ionizing radiation, and in the electron-particle accelerator or **betatron.** A 1-mev alpha particle travels 0.56 cm. in air while, in contrast, a 1-mev beta particle travels about 310 cm. in air. However, the distance beta particles travel is usually so short, in a solid medium, that the procedure in beta shielding is to determine what this maximum range is. This value is normally so small that for structural reasons alone the shielding is thicker. For beta particles above 0.1 mev, Bremsstrahlung or **braking radiation** increases as an absorption process. In passing near atoms in the absorber, the high-speed beta particles are slowed down, emitting electromagnetic radiation (X-rays) proportional to their decrease in kinetic energy. This process is identical with the method of X-ray production in a commercial X-ray tube. It is important in shielding large quantities of beta emitters of greater than 0.1 mev to shield these X-rays.

Photon Particle Shielding. The field of **X-ray shields** has been intensively studied for many years because of its importance in the use of the X-ray machine. Tables for shielding requirements for fluoroscopic, radiographic, dental, fluorographic, and therapeutic X-ray installations (National Bureau of Standards, Handbook 60) greatly simplify X-ray shielding.

In tranversing matter, photons as **gamma (γ)-rays** are attenuated by the three predominant processes of photoelectric absorption, Compton scattering, and pair production. These three coefficients have been tabulated for elements H_2, Be, C, N_2, O_2, Na, Al, Fe, Cu, Sn, W, Pb, U, for air, and for ordinary concrete (G. White, National Bureau of Standards Report 1003). Because certain source geometries are very common, nomograms have been made up which facilitate shielding such sources.

Unfortunately, **neutron shielding** has not reached as advanced a stage of analytic development as photon shielding. Maximum permissible limit lists for different neutron energies have been made up, since neutrons of different energies interact with matter with different efficiencies. Photons and charged particles interact predominantly with electrons outside the nucleus of an atom, while the neutron easily penetrates the electron cloud surrounding the nucleus and reacts, if at all, with the nucleons in it. Three types of interaction with atomic nuclei predominate: capture, elastic scatter, and inelastic scatter.

Capture by atomic nuclei predominates at thermal neutron energies (0.025 ev). Following capture, the excited nuclei decay by emitting a charged particle in the case of B^{10} and Li^6, for example, but it is more likely to be a photon; inelastic scattering also gives rise to a photon. Formulas have been developed for the design of adequate shielding.

MATERIAL AND PERSONNEL CONTAMINATION AND DE-CONTAMINATION. In working with radioactive materials in the open, some air contamination is a certainty. The same statement can also be made regarding surface contamination, although two schools of thought exist as to the relative importance of surface contamination.

Surface Contamination. This is important because the contaminant may:

1. Enter the body by ingestion.
2. Cause high dust concentration and therefore enter the body via breathing.
3. Interfere with research experiments or industrial processes.
4. Cause the expenditure of much time and money in surface decontamination.
5. Give a dose of radiation to the body from external deposition on the skin.

As opposed to air contamination, where the mechanism of entry and deposition in the body can be postulated, and analytically derived maximum permissible air concentrations formulated, it is much more difficult to postulate how surface contamination becomes a health hazard. In fact, it probably differs from individual to individual, depending on such variables as smoking or eating on the job and personal hygiene habits. Therefore, two rather divergent schools of thought, which may be called "A" and "B," have arisen on the importance of surface contamination. Both schools have been conditioned somewhat by environment and circumstances. The "A" school got its start during the war, when a conservative attitude was adopted at the very beginning because of the lack of knowledge of the hazard. Therefore surfaces were kept clean so that **smear** or **swipe tests** on walls, floors, and benches were kept below 100 counts per min. This work was predominantly of a research nature, and the limits were not difficult to live with. The "B" school inherited a situation where production rather than research was foremost in the minds of supervisors. The plants were mainly processing natural uranium, where surface contamination was not considered initially, and to impose "A" school standards would have required a considerable monetary expenditure. In an attempt to determine the exact extent of the hazard under actual operating conditions, surface contamination and bioassay surveys were made in plants which had been using radium for years (Eisenbud *et al.*, Nucleonics, vol. 12). In the case of one plant, smears running as high as 1.25×10^3 times the highest permissible smear value of 2,000 disintegrations per minute per 100 sq. cm. normally allowed were found. The **bioassay method** for the radium plants is a breath Radon test which has a maximum permissible limit of 1 micromicrocurie ($\mu\mu$c.) per liter. This was exceeded by one person in one plant, one person in a second, and three persons in a third plant. On the whole, there did not appear to be very good

Surface	Method	Advantages	Disadvantages
Paint	Water	Most practical method for gross decontamination from a distance. Contamination reduced by approximately 50 percent.	Protection needed from contaminated spray. Runoff must be controlled. Water under high pressure should not be used on a surface covered with contaminated dust.
	Steam (with detergent if available)	Most practical method for decontaminating large horizontal, vertical, and overhead surfaces. Contamination reduced by approximately 90 percent.	Same as for water.
	Soapless detergents	Where effective, reduces activity to safe level in 1 or 2 applications.	Mild action.
	Complexing agents: oxalates, carbonates, citrates	Holds contamination in solution. Contamination on unweathered surfaces reduced by approximately 75 percent in 4 min. Easily stored, nontoxic, noncorrosive.	Requires application from 5 to 30 minutes for effectiveness. Has little penetrating power; hence of small value on weathered surfaces.
	Organic solvents	Quick dissolving action makes solvents useful on vertical and overhead surfaces.	Toxic and flammable. Requires good ventilation and fire precautions.
	Caustics	Minimum contact with contaminated surface. Contamination reduced almost 100 percent.	Applicable only on horizontal surfaces. Personnel hazard. Not to be used on aluminum or magnesium.
	Abrasion (wet sandblasting)	Complete removal of surface and contamination. Feasible for large-scale operations.	Contaminated sand spread over large area. Method too harsh for many surfaces.
Metal	Water	Contamination reduced by approximately 50 percent.	Same as for painted surfaces.
	Detergents	Removal of oil or grease films.	Do.

		Do.
Organic solvents	Stripping of grease.	Difficult to keep in place on any but horizontal surfaces. Limited value on weathered or porous surfaces.
Complexing agents: oxalates, carbonates, citrates.	Holds contamination in solution.	Do.
Inorganic acids	Fast, complete decontamination.	Good ventilation required; acid fumes toxic to personnel. Possibility of excessive corrosion. Acid mixture cannot be safely heated.
Acid mixtures	Action of weak acid. Reduces contamination of unweathered surfaces.	Same as for inorganic acids.
Abrasion (buffers, grinders)	Useful for detailed cleaning.	Follow-up procedure required to pick up powdered contamination.
Abrasion (wet sandblasting)	Same as for painted surfaces.	Same as for painted surfaces.
Concrete — Abrasion (vacuum blasting)	Direct removal of contaminated dust.	Contamination of equipment.
Vacuum cleaning	Same as for vacuum blasting on concrete.	Same as for vacuum blasting on concrete.
Flame cleaning	Only method of trapping contamination on surface.	Slow and painstaking. Fire and airborne-radiation hazard is great.
Brick — Same as for concrete	Same as for concrete.	Same as for concrete.
Asphalt — Abrasion	No direct contact with surface; contamination may be reduced to safe level.	Residual contamination fixed into asphalt. If road is subject to further contamination, may require recovering.
Wood — Flame cleaning	Same as for flame cleaning on concrete.	Same as for flame cleaning on concrete.

Radiological Contamination in Civil Defense, FCDA, TM-11-6

Fig. 27. Surface decontamination methods in civil defense.

Instrument	Radiation detected	Description	Ranges[1]	Remarks
Lauritsen electroscope	Beta, gamma	Quartz fiber electroscope.	Single range, nominal maximum: 1 r./hr.	Incomplete saturation gives nonlinear response and requires specialized calibration. May be equipped with 0.0002-in. window for alpha detection and used with alpha (e.g., 0.002-in. paper) and beta (e.g., 3-mm. Al) shields for almost all necessary small laboratory surveys.
L-W (Landsverk-Wollan) survey meter	Do	Improved quartz fiber electroscope; 100-cu.-cm. ion chamber; timing circuit flash illuminates microscope scale indicating limits of preselected time interval. Sliding metal screen to eliminate beta radiation.	Dual range, nominal maxima: 100 mr./hr., 1 r./hr.	Rugged; holds calibration well. Relatively slow but otherwise convenient and versatile. Satisfactorily free from wavelength dependence.
Victoreen survey meter	Gamma	Compact chamber and amplifier circuit. Wide variety of ranges available on special order.	Single range, nominal maximum: 200 mr./hr.	Readily adaptable to operating chamber on a long probe, providing distance protection for the operator.
Portable Geiger-Müller counters	Beta, gamma	Audible signal and/or counting rate meter. Numerous commercial forms available.	Multiple range, nominal maximum: 80,000 c./m.	For rapid radiation detection. Normally improper for quantitative work. Each type should be tested for temperature and failure at high counting rates.

Instrument	Radiation	Description	Range	Remarks
Poppy	Alpha	Audible signal and counting rate meter.	3 ranges, nominal maximum: 7,500 c./m.	Normally used as qualitative audible indicator. Detects minimum of about 150 d/m.
C. P. meter	Beta, gamma	Chamber 3-in. diam. by 6-in. long of Bakelite with detachable end cap for beta-gamma discrimination. Simple electrometer circuit.	3 ranges, nominal maxima: 50, 500, 5,000 mr./hr.	Weighs 4 pounds, easily set to zero in radiation field. Excellent general purpose instrument for radiation field or surface contamination measurements.
Juno	Alpha, beta, gamma	Ion chamber similar to Zeuto. Has built-in shields controlled from handle to discriminate between alpha, beta, and gamma. Simple electrometer circuit.	3 ranges, nominal maxima: 50, 500, 5,000 mr./hr.	Combines many of the advantages of the C. P., Zeuto, and Zeus.
Zeus	Beta, gamma (alpha)	"Shoe box" type with 1 to 2 liter ion chamber, with wire-mesh window. Thin screen slides in to eliminate alpha radiation and thick plastic screen further discriminates between beta and gamma rays. Amplifier has favorable time constant.	4 scales up to 25, 100, 500 mr./hr., 2.5 r./hr.	Rugged and reliable general purpose instrument. Not entirely free from wavelength dependence, but this is not a critical defect.
Zeuto	Beta (alpha)	Similar to Zeus circuit, but with feedback to increase sensitivity. Designed for alpha measurements, but suitable for beta radiation.	2 scales up to 4 mrep./hr., up to 40 mrep./hr.	High sensitivity and fair stability. Good for surface contamination measurements and can be applied to C^{14} and S^{25} contamination.

[1] For beta-gamma instruments, the gamma rays are quoted. Calibrations for beta radiation may depend on the energy of the particles and the geometrical distributions of the source.

Safe Handling of Radioactive Isotopes, National Bureau of Standards, Handbook 42

Fig. 28. Typical radiation survey meters.

correlation between surface concentration and air concentration. But values in the range 7 to 20 have been reported for the ratio

$$p = \frac{\text{dpm. per sq. cm. of surface}}{\text{dpm. per cu. met. of air}}$$

In the survey of uranium plants, smears ranged up to 20 times the maximum permissible of 2,000 dpm. per 100 sq. cm., but the bioassay method of urinalysis indicated no high uranium excretions. It was therefore recommended that surface monitoring be de-emphasized and more reliance placed in **air** and **bioassay monitoring** for health hazard control. On the basis of these studies, higher surface contamination in controlled areas for natural uranium would appear to be justified.

Maximum Permissible Surface Contamination (MPSC). It would seem then that the maximum permissible air concentration (MPAC) values may be extended to give the maximum permissible surface concentration (MPSC) by multiplying the MPAC in dpm. per cu. met. by 7 to give the MPSC in dpm. per sq. cm. of surface area. But this is a risky procedure, especially for the more radiotoxic elements. It may also be that, if one starts from the very beginning controlling surface contamination, air and bioassay methods would be less of a necessity. Because of the uncertainties involved, the above formula might be used in a controlled area where clothing change and body monitoring are required before leaving the area, and a more conservative approach used in uncontrolled areas.

The National Bureau of Standards (Handbook 48) gives the MPSC as:

1. Skin and surface contamination for Group I and Group II radioisotopes, 1 milliroentgen per hour (mr. per hr.) above any 2 sq. in. (corresponds approximately to 1000 counts per min. with a GM counter with an area of 2 sq. in.).
2. Skin and surface contamination for Group III radioisotopes, less than 0.1 mrep per hr. (less than 100 counts per min.).

Personnel Decontamination. The first defense against personnel contamination is the use of protective clothing: coveralls, caps, work shoes (or shoe coverings), and gloves. These would normally be used in a controlled area. For certain jobs in uncontrolled areas they should also be used.

In the case of actual skin contamination, Chemical Processing and Equipment (TID 5276) recommends the following **decontamination solutions:**

1. A solution of 0.3 M citric acid, 0.5 M hydrochloric acid, and 0.1 percent Aerosol.
2. A solution of 1 percent detergent, 5 percent versene, and a trace of phenolphthalein for color.
3. In showers: ordinary bath soap followed by tincture of green soap.

Equipment and Floor Decontamination. Chemical Processing and Equipment (TID 5276) indicates that in case of contamination of asphalt floors covered by a heavy coat of wax, the wax can be removed with strong detergents by scrubbing. Tools may be decontaminated with dilute nitric acid, 10 percent solution of sodium citrate or ammonium bifluoride, or versene, and if these chemical means fail, electrolytically or by blasting.

Fig. 27 summarizes the various surface decontamination methods, with the advantages and disadvantages of each, for such large scale decontamination as might be encountered in nuclear warfare or reactor runaway.

Methods of Checking for Contamination. In research laboratories where surface or air contamination may range over the whole spectrum of radioactive nuclides and no contamination can be tolerated, a **windowless flow counter** with scaler is ideally suited for checking for contamination and requires very little maintenance. For identification of radioisotopes, differential pulse-height counting by **scintillation** or **proportional counter** may be used. A tabulation of health physics instruments for area and personnel monitoring is given in Fig. 28. The only truly effective control of an industrial radiation hazard is on-the-spot checking for ionizing radiation which instruments of this type afford.

Economics of Radiation Protection. In the industrial application of nuclear energy, there will be very little room for radiation protection luxury. Right now an ultracautious attitude is taken, and with good reason. As familiarity with ionizing radiation grows, there will be demands, as there are in the uranium processing industry now, for raising the **maximum permissible limits.** In many cases such demands will be justified on the basis of practical experience, as the limits are, in a number of cases, nothing but educated guesses; but that will be the time to guard against the pendulum's swinging too far in the other direction. As a case in point, Parker cites the experience at the Hanford works. Up to 1950, work was planned so as to reduce exposure as far as possible, but since 1950 a planned relaxation to operate to a maximum permissible exposure limit of 3 roentgens per year has been in effect. The sharp increase in whole-body exposures after 1950 (Fig. 29) indicates that the relaxation was a success.

Year	Number of Cases *				
	$>1\,r$	$>2\,r$	$>3\,r$	$>4\,r$	$>5\,r$
1944	0	0	0	0	0
1945	8	1	0	0	0
1946	8	2	0	0	0
1947	13	2	1	1	1 (6.1 r)
1948	10	2	0	0	0
1949	4	0	0	0	0
1950	3	0	0	0	0
1951	23	0	0	0	0
1952	179	22	1	0	0
1953	323	42	4	0	0
1954	372	68	16	3	1 (14.4 r)

Peaceful Uses of Atomic Energy, vol. 13

* Number of cases in any column for a given year includes all the cases in the columns to the right for that year. For example, the 42 cases $>2\,r$ in 1953 include the 4 cases which were $>3\,r$. Figures in parentheses give the highest individual total in the years in which this exceeded 5 r.

Fig. 29. Annual whole-body gamma exposures above 1 roentgen at the Hanford works.

This will probably be the course of radiation protection in general, but it will take good judgment to control such relaxation. Economics will play a large role in determining the extent or degree of relaxation needed to make nuclear energy competitive. The figures of McAdams (Idaho Falls Health Physics Conference

Abstracts) for the Hanford Operation are illuminating. Radiation protection represented 3 percent of total operating cost. Radiation monitoring represented 46 percent of the radiation protection cost, exposure records were 23 percent, regional survey 6 percent, laboratory analytical work 9 percent, instrumentation (maintenance and repair) 5 percent, meterology 2 percent, and miscellaneous costs 9 percent.

Approximately 4 percent of the total operating force at Hanford is engaged in radiation protection work with about one **health physics surveyor** per 60 persons. Manov (Peaceful Uses of Atomic Energy, vol. 13) estimates that the U. S. AEC is spending approximately $100 per yr. per man on radiation protection.

SAFETY AND FIRE PREVENTION

CONTENTS

PAGE

Prevention of Accidents

Economic aspects 1
  One year's fatal accidents in the United
    States (f. 1).......................... 1
Management responsibility 1

Safety Organization and Planning

Safety organization 2
  Safety program activities and organiza-
    tion relationships (f. 2).............. 4–5
  Safety director and safety department.... 2
  Safety committees 3
Ten basic steps in planning for accident
  prevention 5
Developing the plan 6
  The safety director 6
  Analysis of accident records.............. 7
  Plant inspections 8
  Eliminating hazards 8
  Communication with employees........... 8
  Training programs........................ 8
    Warning tag (red) attached to equip-
    ment ordered out of service (f. 3).... 10

Maintaining Interest in Safety

Keeping the safety program active.......... 10
Awards and exhibits 11
Classes for instruction 11
Meetings 11
Safety rules 12

Engineering Factors in Safety

Mechanical 12
  Belts 13
  Rotating equipment 13
  Hydraulic equipment 13
Electrical 13
Chemical 14
Materials handling 14
  Overhead traveling cranes 15
  Hoisting apparatus 15
  Conveyors 15
  Trucks and tractors 15
Grinding, buffing, and polishing............ 16
Exhaust systems 16
  Hoods 17
    Minimum control velocities (f. 4)..... 18
  Construction of ducts 18
  Fire safety 18
  Air supply and cleaning 19

Hand tools 19
Woodworking machinery 19
Welding 20
  Gas welding and cutting 20
  Arc welding 21
  Resistance welding 22
Maintenance and plant housekeeping 23
  Building maintenance 23
  Tool cribs and storerooms............... 24
  Awards for plant housekeeping........... 25
Safety inspections 25
  Schedule of inspections 25
  Inspections to eliminate special hazards.. 26
  Safety inspectors 26
Purchasing safe equipment................. 26
  Unsuspected hazards in purchased items.. 27
  Safeguards on new equipment........... 27

Study and Analysis of Accidents

Accident investigation 28
  Purposes of investigation 28
  Making the investigation 28
Investigation procedures 29
  Preliminary investigation 29
  Intermediate investigation 29
  Formal investigation 29
  Follow-up by the safety department...... 32
Analyzing causes of accidents 32
  Standard form for employer's first
    report of injury, suitable for accident
    analysis (f. 5).........................30–31
  Classifying data 32
  Accident analysis chart (f. 6) 33

Maintaining Accident Records and Reports

Records of injuries 34
Reports 34
  Form for monthly summary of injuries
    (f. 7).................................34–35
Nondisabling accidents 35

Fire Prevention

Fire and panic 36
Danger of familiarity with ordinary hazards. 36
Classification of hazards 37
  Smoking 37
  Housekeeping 37
  Heating and electrical equipment......... 37
  Open flames 38
  Spontaneous ignition 38
  Lightning 38

CONTENTS (*Continued*)

	PAGE
Explosive atmospheres	38
Fire-safety organization	38
Fire brigade	39
Fire drills	39
Fire protection equipment	39
Detection	40
Sprinklers	40
Fire extinguishers	41
Building fire safety into a plant	41

Civil Defense Measures

	PAGE
Organization	42
Evacuation plans	43
Shelter areas	43
Bomb-proof facilities	44
Dispersal	44
Casualty care	45
Damage control and repair of facilities	45

SAFETY AND FIRE PREVENTION

Prevention of Accidents

ECONOMIC ASPECTS. Occupational accidents in 1955 resulted in a loss of production time equivalent to 235,000,000 man-days. Of this total, 45,000,000 man-days were lost by those actually injured, and 190,000,000 man-days were lost by their fellow workers in helping the injured, in repairing damage caused by accidents, and in slowdowns resulting from loss of efficiency by those witnessing serious accidents. For each of the approximately 60,000,000 workers in the United States this is an average of almost 4 days per year, and is in addition to all other causes of lost time.

The heavy toll of **fatal accidents** throughout the United States is further reflected in data issued by the National Safety Council (Accident Facts) for the year 1956 and summarized in Fig. 1. The total cost of all **industrial accidents**

Kind of Accident	Total Number of Persons Killed
Occupational	14,300, of which all were workers
Home	28,000, of which approximately 6,300 were workers
Motor vehicle	40,000, of which approximately 19,400 were workers
Public (except motor vehicle)	16,000, of which approximately 6,300 were workers

Fig. 1. One year's fatal accidents in the United States.

in 1956 was roughly $3,750,000,000 or about $60 per worker including wage loss, medical expense, and overhead costs of insurance, property damage, and the so-called overhead costs of occupational accidents.

Although millions of workers manage to stay on the job after an accident, and minor injury, their efficiency is temporarily and sometimes permanently impaired. Tens of millions of workers must take time to get the necessary first-aid treatment for minor preventable injuries. These and other direct losses continue to drain away productive effort, particularly under a continuous-flow or closely coordinated production system. An accident may slow up the production of one plant, and delay of that product may prevent a customer plant from operating at full speed, and so on, until a single accident may have widespread effects.

The importance of safety training and safety engineering as a means of accident prevention should require no more forceful demonstration than is given by these figures. The safety consciousness and will of the employee to aid in preventing accidents rests first and foremost on the management, executives, and supervisors directing production. It is axiomatic, moreover, that "the safe plant is an efficient plant; the efficient plant is a safe plant."

MANAGEMENT RESPONSIBILITY. The forty-eight states, the several territories, and the Federal Government have placed **legal responsibility** on employers for the safe operation of their establishments. Although these laws vary, they are founded in part on the premise that management provides the working environment and, through its organization, controls the behavior of its employees. The so-called employers' liability and workmen's compensation laws have placed **financial responsibility** on management as well. As a result, managers now have a visible, direct, and monetary objective as well as a humanitarian or intangible reason for promoting safety.

Top management in any plant must first be convinced of the value of a safety program, and that management itself must play a continuous, active part in implementing the program. Executives are often convinced of the necessity of an organized effort to prevent accidents to workers but are uncertain of the best methods for conducting such a program. The basic **safety program elements** to be kept in mind are stated by H. W. Heinrich (Industrial Accident Prevention—A Scientific Approach) to be:

1. Creating and maintaining an interest in safety.
2. Fact finding through periodic inspection of plant and equipment.
3. Finding remedies for unsafe practices and mechanical hazards.

Safety Organization and Planning

SAFETY ORGANIZATION. A safety organization may be set up in several ways to suit the size and need of the plant. T. O. Armstrong, in Industrial Safety (Blake, ed.), discusses three basic **organization types:**

1. Safety work carried on wholly through the **line organization.** Usually found in small organizations where the safety director's work is assigned to a line executive as an additional duty. The chief advantage is that it places responsibility for safety directly on each operating head as part of the production function. Its weakness lies in the fact that supervisory personnel may be occupied with other pressing production problems. Care must be taken to provide those responsible for safety with adequate additional time and facilities.
2. Safety work directed by a full-time **safety director** reporting to a major executive. This type of organization is used mostly by large companies, and the safety director may have one or more assistants or subordinates.
3. Safety work carried on primarily by **committees** set up for the purpose. This type is usually found in companies too small to justify the use of a full-time safety director; it may show the weaknesses inherent in committee-type organization.

Frequently, combinations of types 2 and 3 are effective. The National Safety Council (Accident Prevention Manual) shows (in Fig. 2) the safety program activities and usual organizational relationships where safety work is carried on as a staff function through the line organization with the safety supervisor.

Safety Director and Safety Department. The safety man, whether called safety engineer, safety inspector, or safety director, is the representative of management in accident prevention activities carried on in the plant. The chief operating executive, however, should attend as many safety meetings as possible and take an active part in the entire program. When this practice is not possible, one of his assistants should be delegated to perform this duty.

The safety director's actual **position in the plant organization** varies with the general organization of the individual plant. A recent survey made by the American Society of Safety Engineers (Accident Prevention Manual, National Safety

Council) shows that, of the safety directors in American industry, 44.3 percent report directly to a member of top management, 11.7 percent report to the factory, production, or works manager, and 44 percent report to the industrial relations manager. The survey also states that the frequency rate and severity rate are appreciably lower in plants where the safety director reports to top management.

It is now generally accepted that practically every phase of an employee's life has a bearing on accident prevention. For this reason the safety director is often placed under the jurisdiction of the industrial relations department, and also because this department usually includes the medical and other functions with which the safety director must be in contact. In any event, the safety director must occupy a position of such rank that the channel to all departments is available to him.

While final responsibility for safety rests entirely with the "line," and foremen are recognized as the key men in safety, some plants have developed a completely organized department whose members spend 100 percent of their time on safety. This method is more effective in some cases, since it gives management a definite place where **responsibility for accident prevention** can be focused. The department must have authority granted by top management to cover such important matters as shutting down dangerous jobs, designation of the type of safety device which must be used, and, at least, parallel authority on many items of methods, personnel, training, and compensation policy that affect safety. Administration of any necessary discipline must be left to foremen and supervisors, but that part of the workers' activities bearing on safety is the province of the safety man. The safety man must be continuously in the factory and thoroughly familiar with the hazards present and the methods of correcting them.

A safety department should have a reasonably **central location,** near the dispensary if possible, and with sufficient space available to provide for group meetings. Facilities must be available for storing and displaying samples of safety equipment, posters, safe-practice references, equipment catalogs, and for the necessary records, files, and charts of the department.

Safety Committees. A safety committee or group of plant committees is subject to the usual problems of committee operation. (See section on Plant Organization.) These committees require executive initiative, control, and support to be effective. No hard-pressed manager may assume that his accident prevention problems are solved by activating a committee and assigning responsibility for safety to it. The carefully established committee, however, can promote interest and participation in the safety effort, and through group study and recommendation it can strengthen the judgment of the executive. Important at all times, but particularly at the outset, is a **written statement** of:

1. The scope, or mission, of the committee activity.
2. The extent of committee authority, including budgeted funds, if any.
3. The procedure as to time and frequency of meetings, attendance requirements, agenda, records to be kept, and reports to be submitted.

Committee size should be kept small for effective work but large enough to include the breadth of knowledge and experience involved in the plant's operation. In the larger plants these two objectives often are obtained by forming one committee on the executive level and one or more committees at the departmental or shop level. Coordination of the committee activities, encouragement of their effectiveness, and provision of assistance in their studies are leading functions of the safety director. The need for this specialized activity is the reason for the combination of the committee type and safety director type of organization frequently found in the medium- or large-size industrial plant.

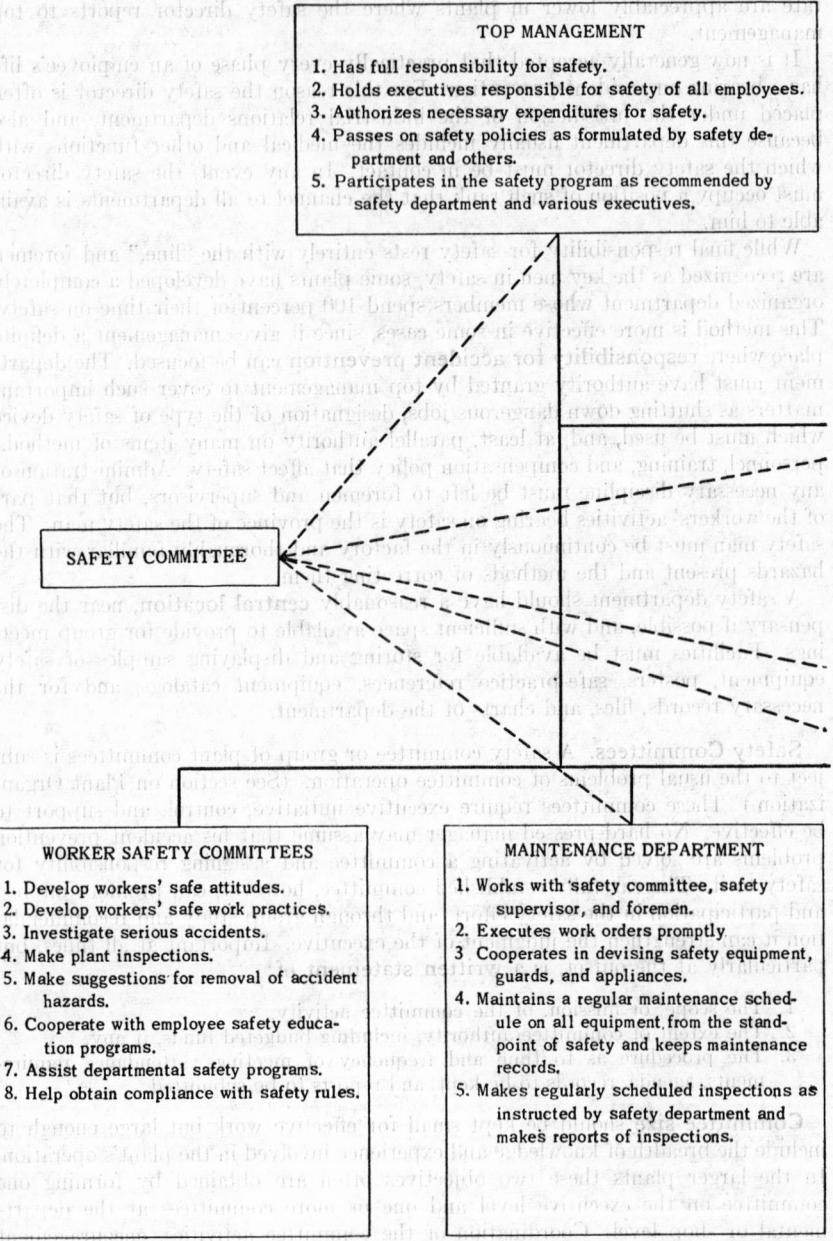

TOP MANAGEMENT

1. Has full responsibility for safety.
2. Holds executives responsible for safety of all employees.
3. Authorizes necessary expenditures for safety.
4. Passes on safety policies as formulated by safety department and others.
5. Participates in the safety program as recommended by safety department and various executives.

SAFETY COMMITTEE

WORKER SAFETY COMMITTEES

1. Develop workers' safe attitudes.
2. Develop workers' safe work practices.
3. Investigate serious accidents.
4. Make plant inspections.
5. Make suggestions for removal of accident hazards.
6. Cooperate with employee safety education programs.
7. Assist departmental safety programs.
8. Help obtain compliance with safety rules.

MAINTENANCE DEPARTMENT

1. Works with safety committee, safety supervisor, and foremen.
2. Executes work orders promptly.
3. Cooperates in devising safety equipment, guards, and appliances.
4. Maintains a regular maintenance schedule on all equipment from the standpoint of safety and keeps maintenance records.
5. Makes regularly scheduled inspections as instructed by safety department and makes reports of inspections.

Fig. 2. Safety program activities

TEN BASIC STEPS IN PLANNING FOR ACCIDENT PREVENTION.

Many plans, some of them far reaching, have been formulated for the prevention of accidents. Regardless of the size of the company and the kind of work in which it is engaged, all useful plans are based on fundamental principles which start with ten simple, basic steps that are necessary to create any **program to prevent accidents.** These steps are usually undertaken in the following order:

1. **Obtain cooperation of plant manager.** The manager must do his part in helping to "put safety on the map."
2. **Obtain cooperation of superintendent.** The superintendent must make safety an integral part of the operating organization.
3. **Appoint safety director.** One man must be designated to direct the safety program.

SAFETY SUPERVISOR

1. Serves in a staff capacity without line authority.
2. Coordinates safety activities.
3. Keeps and analyzes accident records.
4. Conducts educational activities for supervisors at all levels.
5. Conducts activities for stimulating and maintaining interest of employees.
6. Develops employee safety education programs.
7. Serves on safety committee, usually as secretary.
8. Supervises and appraises accident investigations.
9. Plans and directs a regular program of safety inspections.
10. Checks for compliance with applicable safety laws and codes.
11. Issues regular reports showing safety performance and accident trends.

FOREMEN

1. Inspect for compliance with safe work practices and safety rules.
2. Train men to work safely.
3. Responsible for safety of their crews.
4. Responsible for a safe workplace, good housekeeping, proper light and ventilation, safe piling; also, enforce wearing of protective clothing and equipment.
5. Responsible for obtaining prompt first aid to injured.
6. Report and investigate all accidents and correct causes.
7. Serve on safety committee.
8. Hold crew safety meetings.
9. Discuss safety with individual employees.

EMPLOYEE

1. Works in accordance with accepted safe practices.
2. Reports unsafe conditions and practices.
3. Observes safety rules and regulations.
4. Serves on safety committees.
5. Makes safety suggestions.
6. Does not undertake jobs he does not understand.

and organization relationships.

4. **Analyze accident records.** After his appointment, the safety director should analyze the accident reports for the past year or two to learn, if possible, the how, who, where, when, and why of each accident.

5. **Hold meeting of operating executives.** All foremen, superintendents, and operating heads should then be summoned to a general meeting presided over by the manager or general superintendent.

6. **Make inspection of operations.** Following this meeting each foreman should make a complete inspection of his department.

7. **Start mechanical safeguarding.** The safeguarding program should then be developed and carried out, making sure that the most serious conditions are corrected first.

8. **Make general announcement.** Then, and not until then, should the workers be acquainted with the accident prevention plan.

9. **Organize educational work.** Formulate a program to maintain interest and supply information on safety to management, foremen, and workers. Consider appointing workers on plant safety committees.

10. **Consider engineering revision.** Consider methods for improving machinery, equipment, and processes to eliminate hazards and increase production efficiency.

DEVELOPING THE PLAN. Safety must start at the top. First, the **manager** must do his part, and his part is to "put safety on the map"; make it a necessary part of the process of production; get back of it and keep back of it so actively that every foreman and worker will know what the company proposes to do to make the plant safe. Any safety organization without an enthusiastic manager back of it is bound to fail. The manager must convince his men by action, in the form of mechanical guards, good lighting, etc., that he is doing his full part before he can expect his men to take safety seriously or give any genuine cooperation. It is especially important that the manager bring his superintendents and foremen to believe in safety just as they believe in production, and to give it their wholehearted and intelligent cooperation. This backing can be brought about by demanding from the organization exactly the same degree of attention to safety as to production, by frequent conferences, and by placing before the foremen the experiences of other companies which have done successful accident prevention work.

What applies to the manager applies equally well to the **superintendent**; he must be the field marshal in the safety campaign, and by his own faith and enthusiasm he must win for it the respect and support of his foremen. If he treats it as a side issue, his foremen will treat it likewise. It must be made a vital part of the operating department. The superintendent should keep in close touch with the safety director and acquaint himself with every important feature of the safety program so he will be able to aid in discussion and implementation of the safety program.

Plans should be made to permit both manager and superintendent to have as systematic and active a **follow-up contact with subordinates** on safety as is established for cost or production performance.

The Safety Director. One man must be responsible for the safety work in every plant, regardless of its size or the type of safety organization used. It may be advisable or necessary for the manager himself to carry this responsibility, or he may delegate it to an assistant whose duties and qualifications will determine whether he should be known as safety engineer, safety director, safety inspector, or some equally significant title. (For the sake of uniformity, he is referred to here as the safety director.)

The National Safety Council (Accident Prevention Manual) lists the following **responsibilities** for the head safety man, regardless of whether he is a line executive or head of a separate department:

1. Exercise complete responsibility for formulating and administering the safety program.
2. Act in an advisory capacity on all matters pertaining to safety for the guidance of management and all departments.
3. Submit periodic reports to management on the working of the program (monthly, weekly, daily).
4. Maintain the accident record system.
5. Supervise or assist the training director on matters of safety training.
6. Coordinate with medical department on proper placement of employees.
7. Inspect the plant personally.
8. Contact outside agencies professionally to insure that the plant has the latest safety information.
9. Insure that applicable federal, state, or local laws are obeyed, and that insurance company recommendations are carried out.
10. Secure help from government agencies or insurance companies on safety problems.

In addition to a knowledge of safety, the successful safety director must have nearly every **personal qualification** that is to be found in successful men in all walks of life. He should have vision, initiative, persistence, judgment, diplomacy, leadership, and, above all, sympathy. To be worthy of the title "engineer" he should have had a technical training or its equivalent in actual experience. Such **professional qualification** is unquestionably required in large organizations or where difficult technical problems arise.

An important feature of accident prevention work is that the safety director should know the men he is working for and with, because much of his success will depend upon the manner of his contact and his dealing with the men. The accident prevention work which is most constructive and most lasting is often accomplished by getting other men to do the work. Sometimes this participation is brought about by suggestion, perhaps by a direct request or as a personal favor, and again by an order from the manager or superintendent. Whatever the means, the result will be that the man who does the work is interested to a greater degree than he would be otherwise, and feels a personal responsibility for his share of the work. If handled tactfully, this technique will work with the plant engineering department and the plant executives, as well as with the workers.

Analysis of Accident Records. It is assumed in this discussion that no safety work has been attempted in the company other than the safeguarding required by an insurance company or the state factory inspector. In accepting his position, the safety director will have satisfied himself that the management is sincere in its desire to prevent accidents and that it proposes to follow every reasonable and practicable plan for securing the cooperation of its employees in safety work. The first step which he should take after his appointment is to start an analysis of the company's accident reports for the past two or more years. While making these analyses of accident records, the safety director should take advantage of every opportunity to establish personal and close relations with the superintendent, foremen, and other plant executives. Doing so may prevent unpleasant misunderstandings later on.

In many instances it is found that records have been kept with insufficient information to **identify causes.** So far as possible, the new safety director should search out this information by inquiry and interview. A knowledge of causes is essential to accident prevention. Using the procedures suggested in this section will result in a systematic treatment.

Plant Inspections. When an industrial plant embarks on a new or intensified safety program, a thorough plant inspection is desirable. The environment of the work force must be known; the entire operation must be considered, and indirect production as well as direct production facilities and methods must be observed and evaluated. Management may assist the safety director in this inspection by utilizing the services of fire and casualty insurance company inspectors, state industrial commission inspectors, or industrial consultants (firms or individuals).

A consulting inspector will submit an **independent report.** The safety director, however, should accompany the consultant, if employed, and the foreman of each department on the inspection. The foreman should make the inspection and file the **departmental report.** The safety director's duty is simply to help by suggesting ideas to the foreman, by making sure that the most important things are not overlooked, and by encouraging the foreman to correct any of the conditions within his control.

The safety director should not be overly concerned if the foremen fail to note all the unsafe conditions that should be corrected. If none of the serious conditions is overlooked, many of the lesser items can be "caught" at later dates.

Provision should also be made for **systematic reinspection** of all plant departments and the plant as a whole. The safety director, the line supervision, maintenance men, and department safety committees all should be brought into the activity of safety inspection on a systematic basis. This subject is more fully discussed in a subsequent section.

Eliminating Hazards. After all inspection reports are turned in, the safety director should help the superintendent to determine just which **safety recommendations** made by the foremen and consultant should be carried out and in what order. Many recommendations should be referred back to the foremen from whom they originated, with orders to "go ahead." Others may have to be referred to the master mechanic or to some other person or department for necessary action. The few recommendations which seem impracticable, or on which favorable action cannot be taken at once, should be discussed either at another meeting of all foremen or with the individual foremen by whom they were submitted.

Carrying out this part of the program satisfactorily will not only eliminate the majority of the accident hazards which are within the control of the management, but it will also impress upon the minds of the workers the fact that the company is sincere in promoting safety and willing to do its full part toward that end.

Communication with Employees. Safety is not obtained by management decision or even by management instruction. Safety develops through the teamwork of management, plant engineers, supervisors, and workers. To effect this desirable teamwork, management must use all the best techniques known in the communication skills. Once the company has made a definite start in its correction of unsafe conditions, then, and not until then, an effort should be made to secure the full cooperation of the work force. The worker needs visible evidence that management is not merely emphatic, but truly sincere, in its desire for safety.

The first step is to acquaint the supervisory force and then the workers with the fact that the company is starting an **organized effort to prevent accidents.**

In doing so, management should emphasize its position: that it will do everything in its power to make dangerous conditions safe; that it expects workers to do everything in their power to perform their work safely; and that it intends to do its best to inform workers how to do their work safely and under no circumstances require or permit work to be done in an unsafe manner or with unsafe conditions.

These facts may be communicated to the workers through personal letters from the management, through announcements posted on the bulletin boards, through the plant publication, at departmental meetings, or at a general mass meeting. Such a step is necessary to give publicity to the plan and to arouse enthusiasm for carrying it out. Without the cooperation of the workers, the plan will fail.

Training Programs. In all but a few plants the actual training of the worker in performance of his job is done by the foreman or some more experienced worker. Although many trades require apprenticeships, the above is still true and the training in safe working methods received by the new employee may be slighted, or non-existent, depending upon the individual foreman or leader. Pressures are strong and constant for training to achieve satisfactory quantity and quality of work. The objective of a safety training program is to improve the ability of foremen and leaders in the training of new workers in safe performance in all aspects of the job.

There are many facets of **supervisory safety training.** A training director, if present in the organization, should be responsible for the over-all program, but should coordinate closely with the safety director for training in safety. The safety director must make certain that the foremen learn the principles of effective **job-instruction** and their application.

Through careful **safety analysis of jobs,** plans can be developed whereby workers can be instructed to do their jobs in the safe way. This requires:

1. Getting the worker's attention to safety.
2. Telling the worker in the language of the "shop" what the hazards are.
3. Demonstrating the proper, safe procedure.
4. Observing the worker on the job.
5. Correcting his procedure until safety habits are formed.
6. Following up to be certain that familiarity does not breed laxity.

Besides the foreman's verbal and manual training, other methods may be used. On production cards, tally sheets, or time cards for jobs, a short, concise **safety message** may be included. For example, on a press job where there is a definite hazard of operation, there may be written or printed on the card, "Job must not run unless guard is in place," or, "Use safety pliers on this job," or, "This job must not turn over, it is rated for start and stop." On portable tools such as grinders, either air or electric, **name plates** should be fastened to the machine indicating such information as, "Do not use wheel larger than 4 in. in diameter," or, "Goggles must be worn while using this tool." Again, where automatic-push-button control devices are used for series operation, a sign should read, "All buttons must be open while working this job unless otherwise authorized by your foreman." A collection of safety information placed directly in front of the worker at the time he is to use the device is more effective than a book of rules, or a previous warning on the bulletin board or verbally by the foreman.

The promotion of such safe practices throughout the entire organization develops safe thinking for future accident prevention. The use of **red danger tags** on machines shut down for the correction of some accident hazard has proved valuable in many instances. To place a tag reading "Danger" or "Do Not Use," as in Fig. 3, on any device or machine arouses inquisitiveness among the employees, and even the foremen from other departments, who usually stop to look at the tag to discover why the machine or device is not in operation. The plan also has a much-desired effect on the production departments, which urge the repair division to get the machine back into service. Since the machine has originally been shut down by the safety department, the advertising feature is obvious.

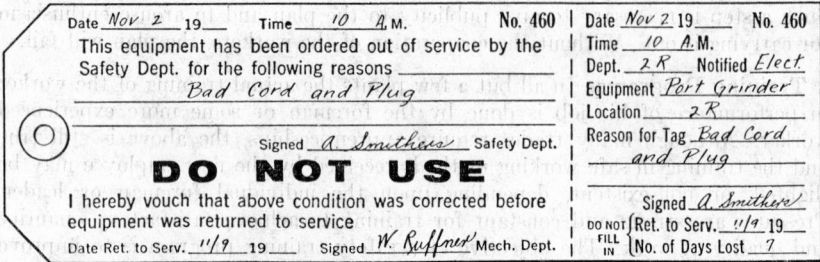

Fig. 3. Warning tag (red) attached to equipment ordered out of service.

In addition, the safety director provides the specialized safety know-how concerning materials, machines, and methods that enables the foreman to be sure that his instruction is "safe." Over an extended period the safety director supplies new **safety information** to the foremen or consults with them on methods of improving the safety consciousness of the workers. As indicated in the Catalog of Occupational Safety Services (National Safety Council), supplying the foremen with interesting, novel ways of reemphasizing established safe-practice at shop safety meetings is an important part of a continuing training program.

Maintaining Interest in Safety

KEEPING THE SAFETY PROGRAM ACTIVE. There are many ways in which the safety movement may be kept actively before employees. Posters, bulletin boards, banners, etc., are of definite value, but they are not new devices and their use must be carefully controlled to keep them effective. Action posters describing current events, together with a safety message in the same area of display, bring about a keen interest in both, but they must be changed frequently or they will be passed by unnoticed. Pictures of well-known workers who have accident-free records or devices which have saved employees from injury, should be displayed on well-lighted and conspicuous bulletin boards.

Congratulatory messages from management when an excellent safety record has been accomplished will never go unnoticed by workmen. Personal letters mailed to new employees stressing the value of safety are often an important aid to training. These letters should preferably originate in the executive office, so that workers will be made to feel that the "big boss" is vitally interested in the safety and welfare of his employees.

Plant publications and house organs can perform an important service in selling safety to their readers. Photographs of well-known "buddies" with their remarks about safety, particularly if they have been personally involved in accidents, attract much attention. Publication, through this medium, of records of progress in safety in various departments, together with suitable remarks from company officials, brings about a spirit of cooperation. Since most of these publications find their way into the homes, the messages may be read and reemphasized many times.

Awards and Exhibits. A company in Philadelphia having an excellent safety record used a novel method of maintaining interest in its safety program. Once a month a **prize drawing** was made in each department where no lost-time accidents had occurred. Each employee placed a check stub, upon which his shop number appeared, in a box during the week when such a drawing was to be made. At a specified time, usually at the close of one shift and the beginning of the next, workers assembled in their own departments. The safety engineer, in each case, picked at random one of the group who drew the numbers. The prize was a radio, and great enthusiasm was demonstrated in each of these drawings. After a department had worked for 6 months without a lost-time accident, a special prize drawing was held, at which time a higher-priced radio was given, or another article of corresponding value. **Grand prizes** were given at the end of a year. Keen competition in accident prevention developed out of this plan. Other systems of publicity have been used, including large charts portraying horse races, airplane engagements, thermometers, etc., to keep up a continued spirit of healthy accident prevention work.

Cash awards, medals, etc., are sometimes given for valuable safety suggestions, good safety records, and outstanding work done by individual employees. Many valuable ideas for progress in safety, and in production as well, have resulted from these suggestion systems.

An effective way of obtaining the interest and cooperation of employees is to make a **well-prepared exhibit** of tools, goggles, safety shoes, etc., which have actually been damaged in service as protective devices. Smashed safety pliers, broken goggles, damaged safety shoes are always helpful in cases where those who must be "shown" are concerned. Each article definitely becomes an object lesson to employees, many of whom may have rebelled when requested to use such protective devices. While it is not good psychologically to lean too far toward the gruesome side of the instruction, effective results have been obtained by such expedients as, in one case, carrying around a generous handful of hair torn from a girl's head by a machine accident. Together with the fact that a generous part of the root end of the hair was black while the balance was of a decidedly blonde hue, the effect was particularly good in deciding for a few doubting feminine machine operators that a safety cap should be worn at all times by women doing shop work.

Classes for Instruction. There are courses in safety engineering, and for training industrial supervisors in safety, which are well worth the time and attention of foremen, leaders, and safety inspectors to assist in building up a strong organization to attack accident problems. With such basic training, a well-defined program can be set up to fit the various individual needs. When a well-regulated program has been designed to fit in with the safety department's or safety director's plans, a high degree of cooperation with all departments should result.

Meetings. More and more, management will find that meetings involving plant matters in general should include the safety director. Committees considering new methods, the use of new materials, production setups, purchase of new machinery, and other problems should realize that nearly every phase of their proposed plans has items which require the consideration of safety. Factory layout departments considering the setting up of new manufacturing facilities or the relayout of present floor areas need to consider the hazards in storage of material, handling and storage of work in process, plant transportation, materials on the floor in traffic aisles, dangerous turns in aisles, and many other details which sometimes are planned without thought of safety. **Die and tool design** may bring about many hazards which do not always show up on the drawing board, and a safety director who is continually looking for such hazards can many times suggest changes for clearance areas in dies, the use of dial feeds, chutes, and automatic feeds which not only produce a safer tool to work with but also permit in most instances an increase in production. A slightly higher first cost which reduces costly accidents and increases production is certainly money well spent.

SAFETY RULES. To set up a standard group of safety rules for plant practice is obviously a difficult matter in consideration of the wideness of the field of industry, but it can be done if suitable information is obtained. Rules established by companies engaged in similar work may be studied to good advantage. This valuable exchange of safety ideas and contacts made through local and national organizations, together with the data made available by casualty insurance companies and state labor departments, will be found to be a continued source of vital and up-to-date information.

Safety rules cannot bring about a reduction in accidents unless provision is made for **enforcement.** Enforcement, however, is not entirely a matter of discipline. One of the first steps toward rule observance is that all supervisors must become familiar with the rules and follow them continually. Their good example can do much to influence the workers. If they disregard the requirements, the workers will feel privileged to do likewise. The best weapon of enforcement is patience and perseverance rather than threats, insults, and discharge slips. Some workers, however, will resist even the best efforts of the foremen and safety advisers, and stern warnings should be given for such deliberate violations. If, after a short layoff for a willful violation of an important rule, the worker persists in such disobedience of safety rules, a long layoff or discharge is in most cases required. When labor groups or unions represent employees, these groups should be consulted and an agreement made upon methods of enforcement to be used when the occasion arises. Continual offenders always become involved in accidents if their tendencies are not corrected.

Engineering Factors in Safety

MECHANICAL. Any safety department, safety director or other executive specifically responsible for safety should obtain, have available, and become familiar with the published **safety standards** relating to the types of equipment present in the plant. Among the several agencies publishing valuable safety standards are:

1. American Standards Association (ASA).
2. National Board of Fire Underwriters.
3. National Safety Council.
4. Association of Casualty and Surety Companies.
5. National Fire Protection Association (NFPA).
6. Bureau of Mines, U.S. Department of the Interior.
7. National Bureau of Standards, U. S. Department of Commerce.

Only in comparatively recent years have machine-tool builders included adequate provisions for safety in their design. Proper guarding before that time, for the most part, was left to the customer, since lack of uniformity in state regulations often meant special guards to meet the respective requirements. The user, however, in every case must carefully check each item, from the mechanical transmission of power to the machine up to the point of operation, on through each step in the process to the delivery of a finished or partly finished part. **Mechanical power transmission apparatus** includes all shafting, belting, pulleys, gears, starting and stopping devices, and other moving parts of such machinery. Reliable starting and stopping equipment must be provided for the safe and efficient operation of power transmission apparatus. These devices, together with their auxiliaries, include belt shifters, belt shippers, poles and perches, clutches, and remote control apparatus.

Belts. Many accidents have been caused by belts. The National Safety Council (Accident Prevention Manual) recommends that all V-belts, round belts, and rope drives be enclosed and that all belts with metal lacings or fastenings be guarded. In addition, any belt traveling in excess of 250 ft. per min. and less than 7 ft. from the floor level should be guarded to a minimum distance of 7 ft. above the working area. These recommendations must of course be considered in the light of many other factors, such as load, strength, tension, and the proximity of workmen to the belt. In general, it is best to enclose all belts where possible. The construction of the **belt guard** must be carefully considered, using expanded metal, perforated or solid sheet metal, or wire mesh on a frame of angle iron secured to the floor or the machine. The construction of the guards should be such that they can be easily removed by maintenance men only. Access doors or hinged sections should be provided for making adjustments to the moving parts, and, where possible, lubricating points should be provided with an extension through the guard so that it need not be removed or opened for oiling during operation of the machine.

Rotating Equipment. Mechanical guarding of shaft couplings, collars, keys, setscrews, pulleys, gears and sprockets, and chains will do much to prevent injury to workers. The same care should be used in making guards for such moving elements as is taken for belts and any other moving parts. **Standard practices** should be set up calling for the use of revolving collars of the cylindrical type, without projecting screws and bolts, and setscrews set flush with or countersunk beneath the surface of the metal part in which they are inserted. Pulleys, gears, sprockets, and chains which are 6 ft. or less from the floor or working platform, or are exposed to contact, should be guarded, and the guards should provide complete safety in case chains, etc., should break while in motion. The more intricate guarding of the machine tool itself, or of processing equipment such as emery wheels, belt sanders, power presses, conveyors, portable power tools, should be considered separately and more intensively, since it usually becomes the hazard nearest to the operator.

Hydraulic Equipment. Equipment which depends on high pressure for power must necessarily receive careful study when designed, and piping, cylinders, and other devices should have an adequate factor of safety to protect the operators and any others near such equipment. Even small units, where processing operations require hole punchers, riveters, jig clamps, etc., should have guards over the operating cylinders and other vital parts, since a small blowout will emit a fine stream of liquid at such a high pressure as to do considerable damage if it strikes the human body.

ELECTRICAL. Generators, power lines, wiring, transformers, etc., should be constructed and installed with the highest standard of safety. All manufacturers of such apparatus recognize this important factor, and the installation and maintenance of such equipment should follow the rules and codes set up by electrical engineering or standards associations. The **smaller tools and electrical devices,** portable drills, grinders, welding transformers, heating devices, etc., because of the large amount of handling they receive, cause many accidents. A constant check of such equipment by competent electricians should be a strictly enforced requirement. Electric shocks of as low as 110 volts, caused by faulty wiring, careless handling, incomplete repair, etc., may sometimes cause serious or fatal accidents. Because of the increasing use of portable electrical tools, workers must be taught to take proper precautions with low voltage as well as high voltage. The replacement of **attachment plugs** on small tools and receptacles throughout the plant in accordance with the new Standard for Attachment Plugs and Receptacle (American Standards Association, C73) will not only provide for the automatic grounding of electrical devices, but will also prevent the accidental connection of a tool to improper voltage.

Common **outlet boxes and panels** seen in most factories do not seem to be much of a hazard until, by careful check, it is often found that workmen use these places as receptacles for lunches, tools, etc. A short circuit from such a source may result in bad burns and possibly more severe consequences if the eyes are involved. Here again is an opportunity for the safety department to discover hazards and, through the proper departments, eliminate them.

CHEMICAL. Caustics are used in many industries. Because their use is frequently incidental to other operations, many employers and workers give little consideration to the dangers involved. Acids and alkalis in concentrated form, and sometimes even in milder forms, may cause injury in four different ways:

1. Burning, from direct contact with skin or eyes, or indirectly through clothing.
2. Fume poisoning or suffocation. Some chemical fumes are poisonous if inhaled, while others tend to exclude oxygen. If they are in sufficient concentration in the atmosphere, this atmosphere may fail to sustain life.
3. Poisoning when taken internally.
4. Fires or explosions resulting from their improper handling and storage.

Proper **protective clothing and devices**—rubber and neoprene gloves, boots, wooden clogs, rubber aprons, tight-fitting goggles preferably with rubber face pads, face shields, and acid-proof hoods—are essential.

Chemical burns caused by workers' tripping or slipping while handling containers may often be avoided if floors are kept in good repair and free from grease or oil. Good lighting is also an aid in prevention of such accidents. High-grade respirators, of a proper type furnished to suit the kind of hazard to which the worker is exposed, must be available for protection against fumes. A very high standard of safety instruction is required in all chemical plants where large assortments of chemicals are used, and a rigid system of orderliness, on the part of both the worker and the plant, is essential to reduce the frequency of accidents from this dangerous source. Many chemicals give rise to dermatitis, especially if the employee is allergic to the substances.

MATERIALS HANDLING. Handling materials causes a large percentage of the compensable accidents in industry. Many companies have found it advantageous to study the work of handling materials by hand as thoroughly as time studies are taken on other operations.

In **handling materials by hand,** sometimes a slight change from the usual method of grasping a piece, carrying it, and setting it down will bring about greater safety as well as greater efficiency. Many workers are injured because they do not know the safe method of lifting. Back strains and hernia are likely to develop if workers bend at the waist when leaning over to pick up a heavy or oddly shaped object. Hand protection, such as hand leathers and gloves that will resist rough usage, will often reduce injuries from rough or sharp materials. The large variety of "homemade" devices or specially designed tools has helped to improve handling methods as well as to eliminate accidents. Tote boxes, hand trucks to carry gas cylinders, adjustable die trucks for die setters, hand trucks for handling sacks, barrels, boxes, etc., and many other devices are supplied primarily to assist workers to accomplish their tasks safely and without strain and fatigue.

Overhead Traveling Cranes. Too many hazards are involved to be fully discussed here, but precautions to observe on the operating floor below the cranes merit attention, such as avoiding overhanging loads, and observing the warnings of the crane operator and the floor men, who should be trained in safe practices. Complete periodic inspection of cranes and hoists should be rigidly enforced. Special safety meetings should be held for crane men and truck and tractor operators.

Hoisting Apparatus. Equipment purchased from a reputable maker, including devices such as block and fall, chain hoists, air hoists, jib cranes, portable floor cranes, crabs and winches is usually designed with safety in mind. All these devices are as safe as the operator who handles them and men with rigging and handling experience should always operate such equipment These employees should be taught the **safe limits** of the apparatus, because there is a general tendency to overload such equipment on account of its flexibility in difficult places.

Conveyors. Serious hazards are involved with conveyors unless proper precautions are observed. No adjustments or repairs of any kind, including oiling, should be made while a conveyor is in motion, unless the oiler does not come within dangerous proximity to moving parts. Many accidents have been caused by starting conveyors without first giving warning to men who might be making repairs or adjustment or oiling the machinery. A **lock** or **warning sign** should be provided for repair men to block the control until everyone is clear. Control devices should be installed at frequent intervals in all power-driven conveyors for stopping the conveyor in case of an accident or other emergency. A safe-footing rubber matting or other anti-slip floor surface should be provided at the loading and discharging stations, and any material which might be spilled from conveyors should be removed immediately. The speed should be such that a worker will have ample time to place material in position without losing his balance, and material being moved should not project over the side of the conveyor or be likely to fall. Many types of conveyors are used: gravity, chute, roller, belt, chain, etc., all of which must be carefully studied when installed to provide the proper safety for workers and for those passing by. Bridges should be provided where it is necessary to cross over conveyors, and overhead conveyors should have inclines to take them up over aisles or passageways to clear any traffic beneath. Guard rails, toe-boards at floor openings, and complete housing of the power drives are likewise necessary. Since the conveyor is a moving device and usually in the open, near workers, every precaution must be taken to insure its safe operation.

Trucks and Tractors. Electric or gasoline-driven trucks and tractors, because they traverse or cross aisles, passageways, roadways, elevator approaches, etc., at many points in a plant, present particular accident hazards. Floors must be kept in good condition and aisles must be properly marked off and kept free of materials to prevent injury to truck drivers and to employees working beside the aisles. Operators of trucks and tractors must be taught not to exceed a stated **safe speed limit.** Entrances to tunnels, crossovers, sharp turns and corners should be clearly marked with warning signs, and warning gongs or horns should be sounded by the operator at such places. The truck itself, of course, should be kept in good mechanical condition, brakes checked, switching devices, etc., maintained in proper repair, and a suitable and very substantial guard provided on the operator's platform to protect his legs. The truck must be considered from most angles practically as an automobile, and the condition of the truck, the responsibility of the operator, and existing traffic conditions are comparable with highway transportation requirements except for the need for a higher degree of safety consciousness incident to the very close manipulation required in the plant.

GRINDING, BUFFING, AND POLISHING. Grinding wheel is a term often used in referring to all rotating devices used for grinding or polishing. **Abrasive wheels** are solid wheels made of abrasive particles held together by natural mineral or artificial bonds. **Grindstones** are flat, circular stones made from natural sandstone, the cutting material of which is oxide of silicon, or quartz, as it is commonly called. **Polishing and buffing wheels** are sometimes made of wood and faced with paper or leather to which emery or some other suitable abrasive is glued, or are wheels made of canvas, sheepskin, felt, or paper with a polishing medium of rouge, tripoli, crocus, etc.

Special instructions or regulations covering the use of such wheels have been formulated by and are available from, grinding-wheel manufacturers, state labor departments, the National Safety Council, and other sources. In general, all surrounding conditions should be carefully studied to make the use of such equipment safe. Operators should always wear suitable **goggles and shields** to protect their eyes. Dust generated by dry abrasives is a health hazard and should be removed at the point of origin by an efficient exhaust system.

Whenever a wheel breaks, a careful check should be made to determine the cause of the break. Inspection should also be made to make sure that the hood has not been damaged or the spindle and flanges sprung out of true or out of balance.

Work should not be forced against a cold wheel, but applied gradually, giving the wheel an opportunity to warm and thereby minimizing the danger of breakage. This precaution applies to starting work in the morning in cold rooms and to new wheels which have been stored in a cold place. Great care should be taken to avoid striking the wheel a side blow, as when grinding castings suspended on chain blocks. Grinding on the flat sides of straight wheels is often hazardous and should not be allowed when the sides of the wheel are appreciably worn or when any considerable or sudden pressure is brought to bear against the sides.

Only competent men should mount, inspect, and care for grinding wheels and, preferably, specific men should be assigned to do all this work.

EXHAUST SYSTEMS. Dusts, gases, vapors, and fumes generated by industrial equipment and processes constitute special classes of hazards. In addition, high temperature, high humidity, or a combination of these contribute, through worker distraction, to accidents and loss of production. Control of the workers' atmosphere for health, safety, and comfort is accomplished by exhaust systems and complementary ventilation with clean uncontaminated air. The safety director and plant engineer should be familiar with any city, state, or federal laws applying to **air-borne contaminants,** either as released by processes in the plant or exhausted from the plant into the community. Simple exhausting of contaminated air from the interior of the plant is often inadequate:

1. It must not be harmful or hazardous to other areas of the plant or to neighboring property holders.
2. It must be exhausted in a manner to prevent its being redrawn into the plant by natural or forced ventilation.

The hazards of undesirable air contaminants may be controlled by different methods such as the following:

1. Installing automatic or enclosed machinery.
2. Using wet processes.
3. Isolating the process or machine that creates the condition in a separate room or building.
4. Providing and requiring exposed workers to wear respiratory protective equipment.
5. Ventilating naturally and diffusing—dispersing.
6. Mechanical exhausting, possibly combined with filtering, washing, scrubbing, or chemical adsorbing systems.

It is desirable to eliminate air pollution at its sources, if possible. Where the elimination at the source is not economical, practical, or possible, control by one of the steps above becomes necessary. (See section on Plant Maintenance.)

Where it is not possible to remove the source of contamination, and mechanical exhaust systems are being considered, a **check of local laws and fire insurance company requirements** (National Board of Fire Underwriters Standards) should first be made. A system of collection and exhaust ducts with essential hoods or collectors, blowers or ejectors, and filtration devices may then be designed to meet the particular needs of the plant. In general, **local exhaust systems** are preferable to general exhaust systems because the dispersion of the contaminant is better controlled. Only the most general principles of design are given here.

Hoods. The purpose of hoods, according to C. N. Davies (Dust Is Dangerous) is not to reduce concentrations of dusts, etc., below some minimum, but rather to draw enough air to **entrain** all particles or gases to reduce the source of contamination. It is well established that a hood cannot "reach out" effectively to accomplish this, therefore it is necessary to bring the hood as close to the working area as possible without interference to the worker. The effectiveness of a hood depends on the **capture velocity** at the point of contamination; it must be sufficiently high to prevent the general dispersion of the dust or gas. Brandt (Heating and Ventilating, vol. 42) recommends the minimum control velocities shown in Fig. 4.

The capture velocity is primarily a function of the mass flow of air, not the velocity in the duct or hood. For example, at a distance of twice the diameter from the suction end of a round unflanged duct the air velocity drops to less than 2 percent of duct velocity. Providing a **flange** at the suction end of a duct will increase the effectiveness of the duct through better air-flow control. Additional **baffles** should be placed so that there is no possibility of the worker affecting the desired air flow.

Hood installation requires consideration of the work position in relation to the air flow. The hood should be so located that there is no chance of the contaminant entering the worker's breathing zone. If a worker is required to bend over open tanks containing volatile and toxic materials, he should be provided with a suitable filtering respirator.

Conditions of Generation, Dispersion, or Release of Contaminant	Minimum Control Velocity (ft. per min.)	Examples of Processes or Operations
Released with no significant velocity or into relatively quiet air	100	Evaporation or escape of vapors, gases, or fumes from open vessels; degreasing, pickling, or plating
Released with low initial velocity or into moderately quiet air	100–200	Spray paint booths, cabinets, and rooms; intermittent dumping of dry materials into containers; welding
Released with considerable velocity or into zone of rapid air movement	200–500	Some spray painting in small booths and with high pressure; active barrel or container filling: conveyor loading
Released with high velocity or into zone of very rapid air movement	500–2,000	Grinding; abrasive blasting; surfacing operations on rock

Minimum air velocities recommended for the capture of dusts, fumes, smokes, mists, gases, and vapors released at various types of operations.

Fig. 4. Minimum control velocities.

Construction of Ducts. The **air velocity** in all parts of a duct must be maintained above certain minimum values to prevent the contaminant from settling out. Generally, speeds up to 2,000 ft. per min. are recommended for fumes; 4,000 ft. per min. for average industrial dusts; 5,000 ft. per min. and up for heavy dusts. The ducting should not have sharp changes in direction, shape, or cross-section area.

The **cross-section area** of any main duct should equal the sum of all branch areas. Some local codes require an excess of 20 percent in the main duct for possible future additions. A circular cross section is preferred with narrow, rectangular shapes least desirable. All laps should be made in the direction of air flow. Materials of construction include riveted or welded sheets of plain or galvanized steel, aluminum, stainless steel, copper, plastics or plastic- and rubber-lined metals. The choice of materials requires consideration of strength, first cost, operating costs due to maintenance, and replacement cost entailed by corrosive conditions.

Fire Safety. Wherever ducts pass through fire walls an automatic closing damper should be provided. If the system is to carry flammable gases or explosive dusts, the entire system should be grounded. If there are any gaps in the system, such as at joints, the parts should be connected with a **grounding strap** preferably made of copper. Under certain conditions it may be advisable to install an inert-gas or dry-powder fire-control system concurrently with the ducting. Also, if one system is to handle more than one type of contaminant, it must be made certain that the mixing of these contaminants in the main duct will not lead to a dangerous condition. It is advisable to submit detail plans of any duct system to the fire insurance company for appraisal.

Air Supply and Cleaning. All air supply containing vapors, fumes, and dusts that is exhausted must be replaced by fresh air. Fresh air, sometimes filtered, heated, or cooled, can be supplied either to the general work area or in the immediate vicinity of a contamination source. General area ventilation may disturb the collecting ability of hoods if there are several in the same area.

The selection of an **air cleaner** depends on the nature of the contaminant, its concentration, and the total volume of air handled. Heavy dusts generally are separated in centrifugal or cyclone separators; and lighter, fine-grain dusts in cloth or fibrous filters or electrostatic precipitators. Fumes and smokes behave as extremely fine dust particles and are controlled by precipitators, wet collectors, and cloth or fibrous filters. Gases and vapors may be removed by absorption, adsorption, combustion, or condensation.

Two general types of fans are available: the **axial flow,** which will move large volumes of air against low static pressures; and the **centrifugal flow,** which can be designed to move large volumes against medium or high static pressures. The fan and motor should be selected only after calculation of the total duty, cubic feet per minute, and static pressure of the exhaust system and any filtration equipment.

HAND TOOLS. Statistics show that hand tools cause a large portion of the injuries in industry. Mishandling hand tools, neglecting to keep them in proper condition, and leaving them in dangerous places are frequent causes of accidents. It is of prime importance, in the effort to prevent accidents, cut tool costs, and maintain a high rate of production, that only the best materials be used for making hand tools. Chisels, punches, drifts, etc., made from poor stock soon become dull, and their heads mushroomed and cracked. Hence, only tools made from the most suitable grades of tool steel should be employed: not necessarily the special expensive brands of alloy steels, but proper grades for the various purposes. Probably the greatest contribution to the reduction of accidents from hand tools comes from **proper maintenance.** Tools with cracked handles, mushroomed heads, improper tempering, etc., should be promptly removed from service and repaired, as a start in eliminating accidents from such sources.

WOODWORKING MACHINERY. The variety of operations performed on woodworking machines, the high speed and sharpness of the cutting tools, and the comparatively light weight of the wood being worked on combine to produce high accident rates on such equipment. The range of uses of certain woodworking machines makes satisfactory guarding particularly difficult and increases the temptation of workers to operate without guards. The natural course, particularly where the volume of work is not large, is to save in first cost of equipment by performing many different operations on one machine. Actually, frequent changes in machine setup are so costly in wasted time and in poor work that true economy usually lies in **providing enough machines to limit the operations on each to closely similar work.** It is possible, for instance, to avoid grooving (dadoing) on circular saws or to avoid using two tools that are operated by the same control, as an auger and a grinder on the same spindle. An absolute fundamental for safety in all such combinations is to arrange the drive so that only one tool can be operated at a time.

The high speed at which woodworking machines are operated often causes excessive vibration unless the machines are properly designed and well made, and unless bearings are properly maintained and tools correctly set.

It is important to enclose completely all belts, pulleys, clutches, gears, sprockets, spindles, and reciprocating parts and to provide practical (and where possible, automatic) **safeguards** for the point of operation of all woodworking machines. No class of machines, with the possible exception of power presses, presents such difficult safeguarding problems. There are many protective devices on the market for use on various woodworking machines, each of which, however, has certain limitations. Careful study should be given to all operations performed on every machine, and a type of guard selected or made that will be practical and effective for each. It is best to secure the cooperation of the operator and his foreman, for not only does a good operator "know his machine," but, once he and his supervisor put their minds to it, they are likely to contribute just the ideas needed. Homemade guards, if well designed and well constructed, are satisfactory, but, if the chief objective is to get something cheap, they are likely to prove unduly expensive in the long run through failure to prevent accidents. A guard that gives a false sense of security may actually be worse than no guard at all.

Machines can best be guarded by the manufacturer. In the purchase of new machinery, specifications should call for guards on all driving parts, as well as for the point of operation. Guards should perform specific functions or meet definite requirements.

WELDING. The nature of the safety measures required for welding depends on the kind of welding equipment used. **Gas welding** includes the particular hazards of handling and using materials capable of explosion. **Electric arc** and **resistance welding** have the particular hazards of electric shock and radiation, harmful not only to the eyes but also to the unprotected body. All types of welding have the hazards attendant to high temperatures: severe burns, fume inhalation, and property damage by fire.

Gas Welding and Cutting. These processes include the use of oxygen and acetylene, oxygen and hydrogen, and other combinations of oxygen with some suitable fuel gas, which present hazards (Safety in Electric and Gas Welding and Cutting Operations, American Standard Z49.1, American Welding Society). Acetylene with oxygen gives a much higher temperature than the other combustible gases, and for this reason it is generally employed for gas welding. Many hazards are present in the manufacture and use of acetylene, and extreme care must be exercised at all times. The use of homemade generators has caused many accidents. Such equipment should be procured from reliable makers who furnish instructions for safe operation. These instructions should be posted where they will be seen and followed.

Most of the gas used for welding and cutting is purchased in **cylinders.** These cylinders should be manufactured and filled in accordance with I.C.C. specifications and regulations and should be properly marked. They should never be handled with a magnet, and a suitable cradle should be provided if they are moved by crane. Careful handling at all times is essential. Knocks, falls, and rough handling are likely to damage the cylinder, valves, or fuse plugs and cause leakage. Since acetylene gas at pressures above 15 lb. per sq. in. is dangerous, it is absorbed in acetone in the pressure cylinders. Acetylene cylinders, therefore, should be set on end for several hours before use to give free vapor opportunity to collect at the top. Oxygen cylinders should have the same careful handling, and no grease or oil should be used on any of the fittings. Oil and grease in the presence of oxygen under pressure may ignite violently and cause serious accidents. All built-in lines to be used for oxygen must therefore be degreased carefully before use.

Regulators, gages, hose and hose connections, and torches should be kept in perfect condition at all times and rigid inspection enforced for their careful handling. Suitable clothing and, particularly, adequate eye protection are essential for welders, and the proper shade of lenses for goggles and hoods will afford ample protection from the light rays. Such equipment should be of high quality, even if the cost is higher. Aprons, shoes, gloves, etc., are required for complete protection. It is important that the operators of such equipment be fully qualified by adequate training and be given all safety precautions to avoid accidents from this type of welding (Safe Practice for Installation and Operation of Oxy-Acetylene Welding and Cutting Equipment, International Acetylene Association).

Arc Welding. This is a fusion welding process in which the welding heat is obtained from an electric arc formed between an electrode and the base metal, the heat of the arc being approximately 6,000° F. The welding voltage in most cases is low, but it can become a serious hazard, particularly in locations which are damp and wet. The usual precautions should be taken against coming in contact with live conductors by the use of insulated equipment and personal protective equipment. Where welding current is used for arc welding, and the operator is required to work in a metal-enclosed space, **protective relays** should be installed on the circuit so that the operator will not be exposed to an open-circuit voltage of more than 50 volts.

The fact that low voltages are employed should not cause negligence on the part of the operator. Fatal injuries have occurred when persons contacted the frames of welding machines energized by short circuits. Frames of all portable electric welding machines operated from electric power circuits should be effectively grounded.

The electric arc produces **high intensity of ultraviolet and infrared rays** which have a harmful effect on the eyes and skin under continued and repeated exposure. The effect of exposure of the skin to the direct rays of the electric arc is very similar to sunburn. It may be very uncomfortable and even painful but causes no permanent injury. Ultraviolet rays do not usually cause permanent injury to the eyes unless by continued and repeated exposure, but temporary effects may be quite painful. Even short exposures have caused painful results and disability. Infrared rays are the heat rays of the spectrum. They do not cause permanent injury to the eyes except from excessive exposure.

It is necessary, therefore, to provide full protection at all times in the presence of the arc, both while the operator is engaged in actual welding and while he is observing welding operations. Both the operator and his assistant must use a **protective hand shield** or **helmet** which protects the skin of the face and neck, and which is also equipped with a suitable filter glass (shades 6 to 14) that will provide adequate eye protection. In the selection of **filter glass** it is necessary to depend on laboratory tests, as the transmission of ultraviolet and infrared radiation cannot be determined by visual inspection. Depth of color does not necessarily indicate removal of the invisible radiation which may be injurious to the eyes. Reliable dealers are able to supply filter glasses which have been shown by tests to conform to requirements of the American Standard Safety Code for the Protection of Heads, Eyes, and Respiratory Organs of Industrial Workers.

During arc welding operations, certain **gases, fumes, and dusts** are evolved by the heat of the arc, depending on the type of welding rods used, the base metal being welded, and whether or not the base metal is coated with such material as oil, tar, salt, paint, lead, zinc. Some of the gases are believed to include oxide of nitrogen, ozone, carbon dioxide, carbon monoxide, sulfur dioxide, and phosgene. Some of the metallic and mineral substances that may be found in the fumes and dust include iron, zinc, lead, copper, manganese, selenium, silica, arsenic, titanium, and flourine. Poisoning due to the presence of some of these substances in the fumes has been reported although evidence based on actual cases is rare.

One of the principal health hazards presented by electric welding is **lead poisoning.** If painted or lead-coated materials are cut or welded, the lead volatilizes and may be breathed, causing lead poisoning. Also "zinc chills" may result from breathing fumes when welding zinc, brass, bronze, or galvanized metal.

It is difficult to obtain definite data concerning the effects of various gases, fumes, and dusts generated in electric welding operations; consequently, it is usually necessary to make sure that employees do not breathe them. Where welding is carried on outdoors, or in large, well-ventilated shops, and nontoxic materials are involved, experience shows that welding operators suffer no harmful effects. But in other cases the hazard must be minimized by providing **efficient ventilation and exhaust systems.** Where harmful concentrations of gases, fumes, and dusts are generated, it is preferable to provide local exhaust systems to remove such substances at their point of origin, particularly where welding is done in confined areas such as small rooms, welding booths, tanks, boilers. In many cases where welding operations are permanently located, the entire booth may be ventilated by an exhaust system such as is used for spray coating booths, or an adequate exhaust pipe may be provided, connected to a central duct system. Portable exhaust systems are also available for this purpose.

Where, because of the intermittent nature of the work or for other good reasons, it is impossible for gases, fumes, and dusts to be kept below their toxic limits by means of general ventilation or by local exhaust systems, welding operators should be required to wear **special respiratory protective equipment** approved for such purposes by the U. S. Bureau of Mines. Supplied-air respirators, such as air-line respirators, hose masks with or without blowers, or self-contained oxygen-breathing apparatus, are recommended for use in confined areas and other locations where high concentrations of toxic substances are encountered.

The present safe practice is to **ventilate all welding operations** which are carried on in relatively small enclosed or restricted space, as in tanks, boilers, pressure vessels, compartments and holds of vessels, because of the possibility of an accumulation of toxic and explosive gases, and the possibility of an oxygen deficiency. Where there is any question, tests should be made to determine the presence of toxic and explosive gases, and, if such gases are found in harmful concentrations, the area should be thoroughly cleaned and ventilated and again tested before permitting welders to enter. Artificial ventilation may be necessary. Safety lamps and other instruments are available for tests for oxygen deficiency.

Resistance Welding. This is a metal-fabricating process in which the fusion temperature is generated at the joint by the resistance to the flow of electric current. When the welding temperature has been reached, the electric circuit is opened and mechanical pressure is applied to complete the weld. The three fundamental factors of resistance welding, therefore, are current, time, and pressure, each of which must be accurately controlled.

The principal **hazards in the operation of resistance welding** equipment include lack of point of operation guards, flying hot metallic particles, handling materials, unauthorized adjustments and repairs, and possible electrical shock. The hazards involved vary greatly with the type of equipment being used, and the kind of work being performed. It is suggested that a careful job analysis be made of the operations on each welding machine to determine the safeguards and personal protective equipment that will be most appropriate for each job.

On many kinds of resistance welders, particularly automatic and semi-automatic equipment, serious **point-of-operation hazards** exist similar to point-of-operation hazards on punch and forming presses. The possibility of finger amputation requires the installation of guards or devices that will enclose the point of operation or otherwise make it impossible for the operator to reach into the danger zone. In most cases welding machine operators should use some form of face and eye protection to guard against flying hot metallic particles. Goggles with clear lenses and side shields provide effective protection for most resistance welding; however, goggles with filter lenses (shades 1 to 5) may be necessary on some special operations. Face shields to protect the face and neck from hot sparks are desirable and should preferably be of fire-resistant material.

The hazard of **flying sparks** can also be eliminated by installing a shield guard at the point of operation. Such guards should preferably be of transparent material such as safety glass or cellulose acetate. Where such guards are not used, it is good practice to erect some type of shield to prevent injury to other employees who may be passing the machine.

On many operations, leather or canvas gloves and aprons are desirable for preventing burns from hot sparks and avoiding cuts and scratches. In addition, some operators wear leather sleeves primarily to avoid burning their clothing and also to guard against small skin burns. Woolen outer clothing is preferable to cotton as protection against burns.

MAINTENANCE AND PLANT HOUSEKEEPING. The millwright and maintenance-of-equipment department should keep all machinery in first-class operating condition, but many times the safe condition of equipment is forgotten or at least put in second place. It is the job of the safety department and management to bring forcefully to the attention of such departments the necessity of keeping all equipment in a safe condition, but the matter cannot be left entirely to their care without the added precaution of a definite check by a group of their own personnel, or by plant safety committee members or the safety department itself. In a well-formulated **plan of plant housekeeping** such a program should accomplish three objectives: (1) elimination of accident and fire hazards; (2) conservation of space, time, material, and effort; and (3) improvement of employee morale. (See section on Plant Maintenance.)

Statistics show that a high proportion of industrial accidents are directly traceable to falls, falling objects, and mishandling materials, and that such accidents are often a direct result of disorder in the plant. Therefore, the problem of industrial housekeeping is a major one, and in the interests of safety, morale, and efficiency it requires careful consideration.

Good housekeeping has often been summarized by the phrase "A place for everything and everything in its place." If management fails to provide the "place," the employee finds adherence to this principle impossible. Providing the "place" should be carried out in its broadest sense. The start of a good program is an analysis of physical plant facilities and a determination of the adequacy of existing equipment, such as shelves, bins, storage rooms, work places.

Building Maintenance. Stairways should be kept clear of all materials and should be properly illuminated. Accidents resulting from tripping and falling are more likely to occur in these locations than on level surfaces. To comply with fire regulations, as well as good safety procedure, handrails of suitable height should be provided.

Aisles and passageways should be kept clear at all times for the safety of pedestrian traffic and trucks. Materials should not be permitted to project into aisles, and the latter should be clearly marked off, either by painted lines, inlaid tile, or other method.

Floors should be kept free from holes, uneven boards, and obstructions, especially where the floors form parts of aisles or walking places. Materials used in floors should be considered from the safety standpoint in the erection of new buildings or in repair of old structures. Small objects, such as scraps of metal, nails, tools, should not be allowed to lie on the floors or in passageways. Oil, grease, chips, and other sources of hazards which could be the cause of slipping or falling should be promptly removed.

All unnecessary hangings and trappings on walls should be removed. Windows should be in good working order, panes clean, and those cracked or broken replaced. Ceilings should be inspected for loose plaster, and skylights kept clean and in good order.

Inadequately illuminated work places are breeding grounds for bad housekeeping. All workbenches, aisleways, and stairways should be suitably lighted and free from shadows. Night lights should be provided throughout departments so that watchmen will not be exposed to tripping and falling accidents. Exit lights should be placed at all emergency doors and exits. The location of fire-fighting apparatus should also be suitably illuminated.

Waste cans with self-closing covers should be provided to hold cotton waste in each machine department. Two cans should be at each location, one for clean, and the other for soiled, waste.

Proper operation and maintenance of **elevator equipment** are essential factors in a good housekeeping program. Storage of any kind of material in elevators should be prohibited, and floors should be kept clear of debris. Elevators which do not stop level with factory floors create a tripping hazard. Elevators should be equipped with interlocking devices which will prevent them from leaving landings while gates are open. Serious accidents have resulted from employees opening hoistway doors, expecting to find elevators at floor level, and falling down the shaft as a result.

Tool Cribs and Storerooms. Convenient and well-maintained tool cribs are important. Small hand tools and implements should not be permitted to lie about where they may be the cause of slipping or tripping accidents. Special tool houses or rooms for picks, shovels, trowels, and similar implements for excavation and construction work may be provided. Some companies provide tool drawers and shelves for both outside and inside jobs. When these storage places are located conveniently, employees will use them, and the temptation to leave equipment around at workplaces where it would cause accidents, or be lost, is greatly reduced.

Improper piling or **storage of materials** is a major evidence of poor housekeeping. Only enough materials should be in the operating departments to keep production going. Raw materials should be brought in from the storeroom as needs arise, and in no greater quantity than is necessary. A minimum of material in the operating departments—just sufficient to keep an even flow of production—promotes both efficiency and safety.

In the storage of bulky objects, such as rods, pipe, lumber, many companies provide specially designed racks or guards to prevent the material from shifting and falling or rolling into aisles or places where men may be working. Small-sized material is usually put on shelves or in bins.

Awards for Plant Housekeeping. Many companies have found the promotion of a competitive spirit among employees an important factor in the good housekeeping program. Sometimes tangible awards or recognitions are given to individuals and departments for good housekeeping as an adjunct to awards for good safety records.

SAFETY INSPECTIONS. Safety inspections are one of the principal means of locating accident causes. They assist in determining what safeguarding is necessary to eliminate or otherwise remove hazards before accidents and personal injuries occur. Prompt safeguarding of hazards is one of the best methods for management to demonstrate to employees its interest and sincerity in accident prevention work. Inspections, however, should not be limited to unsafe physical conditions but should include unsafe practices. One company recommends that for each inspection made for unsafe conditions three should be made for unsafe practices.

At the same time it should be remembered that safety inspections are not made primarily to find out how many things are wrong, but rather to determine if everything is satisfactory. The whole purpose should be one of helpfulness in correcting conditions to bring the plant up to accepted and approved standards and make a safer and more helpful place in which to work, one where the working environment is such that operations can be conducted economically, efficiently, and safely.

Schedule of Inspections. It is best to plan regular inspections to be made on schedule at definite periods, so that safety conditions are maintained at a high standard throughout the plant. Surveys should include all **means of egress** from the building. All exits, fire towers, fire escapes, halls, fire alarm systems, emergency lighting systems, and places seldom used should be thoroughly inspected to determine their adequacy and readiness for emergency use.

Another kind of periodic inspection is that **required by state and local laws.** These regulations include the inspection at regular intervals of elevators, boilers, unfired pressure vessels, and other special hazards. Such equipment, however, is not usually inspected by plant employees but often by outside inspectors, perhaps from casualty insurance companies, because of the special training necessary to qualify for this type of work. It is necessary, however, to follow a prearranged schedule of inspections as required by law.

Chains, cables, ropes, and other equipment subject to severe strain in handling heavy materials should be inspected at regular intervals, and a careful record kept of each inspection. Some state regulations require such inspections and records. This type of equipment should be stenciled or otherwise marked for ease of identification. Some companies require that all portable electric tools and extension cords be sent to the electrical department, say, between the first and tenth of each month. The electrical department inspects the tools, makes necessary repairs, and attaches a colored tag to the tool or cord showing the month the equipment was last inspected. A different colored tag is used for each month. Any tool or cord found without the proper tag is sent to the electrical department at once.

Other types of equipment, such as **cranes, hoists, presses, ladders, and power trucks,** require periodic inspection. Any equipment used in the field also requires frequent and periodic inspections. Such inspections should be ordered by the proper plant executives, and the safety director should prepare a working schedule so that the correct intervals of inspection can be maintained.

Along with scheduled inspections, a careful survey should be made as to the **adequacy and safety of equipment in the plant.** Recommendations should be made for replacement of defective and obsolete equipment, as well as for the purchase of any additional equipment that may be necessary. Such recommendations should be followed up until the changes are completed. As new processes and products are added to the manufacturing system, inspections may show that new accident or fire hazards may be introduced that require individual treatment; for example, special extinguishing devices.

One of the common kinds of inspections is that made at **intermittent intervals,** as the need arises, including unannounced inspections of particular departments, pieces of equipment, or small work areas. Such inspections made by the safety department tend to keep the supervisory staff alert to find and correct unsafe conditions before they are spotted by the safety inspector.

Inspections To Eliminate Special Hazards. The need for intermittent inspections is frequently indicated by accident tabulations and analysis. Should the analysis show an unusual number of accidents for a particular department or location, or an increase in certain kinds of injuries, special inspections should be made to determine the reasons for the increase and what must be done to remove the hazards.

In preparing for an inspection, it is advisable to **analyze all accidents for the past several years** so that special attention can be given those conditions and those locations known to be accident producers. Where accurate accident statistics are kept, such data are usually available in monthly and annual reports. Wherever an accident has occurred, it may take place again unless the unsafe condition is corrected. Experience gained in correcting a hazard at one location will be helpful in safeguarding similar conditions in other locations. Inspections should not be confined to those places where serious injuries have occurred. Even no-injury accidents and near-accidents often point to causes of possible future injuries.

Wherever there is a **suspected health hazard,** a special inspection should be made to determine the extent of the hazard and what precaution or mechanical safeguarding is necessary to provide and maintain safe conditions. These inspections usually require air sampling for the presence of toxic fumes, gases, and dust, testing of materials for toxic properties, or the testing of ventilation and exhaust systems for efficiency of operation.

Safety Inspectors. The number of safety inspectors in any plant depends a great deal on the size of the plant and the kind of industry. Large plants with well-organized accident-prevention programs usually employ a staff of full-time inspectors who work directly under the safety supervisor. Large plants may also have a number of specially designated employees who spend part of their time on inspections. Also, there are usually employee inspection committees which assist in this kind of work.

Plants too small to employ a full-time safety director and assistant inspectors depend on inspections made by maintenance men and supervisors. Frequently an employee carries out the duties of a safety director on a part-time basis and makes periodic inspections. Many plants depend entirely on **inspection service** supplied by casualty insurance inspectors and also state factory inspectors. More frequent inspections, however, are usually necessary than are provided by these agencies.

PURCHASING SAFE EQUIPMENT. Cooperation between the safety director and the purchasing agent is important. The purchasing agent is not concerned with the educational and enforcement activities of safety, but with its engineering activities. It is his duty to purchase the various items of machinery, tools, equipment, and materials used in the establishment, and it is his responsibility—at least in part, and often to a considerable degree—to see that safety receives adequate attention in all purchases.

For this purpose he should be familiar with the workplaces and processes as well as the hazards of plant departments. He will want to know where and why accidents are happening and whether or not machinery, tools, or materials are at fault. He will not undertake to purchase any article until he has a thorough knowledge of its strength and work efficiency, and whether it can be used by the workers with the highest possible degree of safety.

Unsuspected Hazards in Purchased Items. It is surprising to find that many items have a more important bearing upon safety than would be at first suspected. Particular attention should be given to the purchase of all personal protective equipment, all equipment provided for the movement of suspended loads or for the movement and storage of materials, all miscellaneous substances and fluids used for processing which might constitute or increase a fire or health hazard, and similar items. But investigation also will show that **unsuspected hazards** may lie in very ordinary items, such as the commonest kinds of hand tools, tool racks, cleaning rags, the types of paint to be applied to shop walls and machinery, reflectors, and even bill files. Characteristics such as maximum load strength, long life without deterioration, sharp, rough, or pointed surfaces or edges, the need for frequent adjustment, ease of maintenance, effect of fatigue upon the employees, and hazards to the workers' health are among the many factors requiring attention.

The following are a few examples of hazards attending purchased items that were thought to be safe. Because a small hammer had been improperly annealed, a man's eye was lost when a piece of metal from its head flew 20 ft. and struck him as he sat before his own well-guarded machine. Goggles supplied to one group of workers were found to have such imperfections in the lenses that they caused eye strain and headache, which led to fatigue and accidents. The toes of a laborer were crushed when the safety shoe he was wearing had an inferior cap and collapsed under a weight that should have been supported easily by a well-made shoe.

Safeguards on New Equipment. When an order for equipment is about to be placed, the purchasing agent who cooperates with the safety director will not consider any machine that has been only partly guarded by the manufacturer and that therefore will have to be fitted with makeshift safeguards after it has been installed. He will also be particularly careful to see that any purchased machine complies fully with the safety regulations of the state in which it is to be operated, for safety requirements vary widely in different states. The safety man will assist in every way to make tests on new equipment, and, in fact, periodic checks on regular equipment, to assure the highest degree of safety by making certain that the best equipment available is being utilized. Many times it will be discovered that **special safety equipment** such as safety pliers, tongs, tweezers, stands for holding portable tools, spark curtains, are not readily available on the market, and much time may be lost by having them made specially by outside firms. By close contact between safety department and mechanical departments, many such devices can be made in the plant in a few hours, thus removing the hazard and in many cases maintaining production which otherwise would be at a standstill. All safety equipment and, in fact, all machinery to which safety equipment has been attached at the suggestion of the safety director should be carefully tested by, or in the presence of, the safety director and the mechanical division before it is released for production. Where **portable tools** (pliers, tweezers, etc.) are provided, they should be systematically followed up by the safety man to check on their performance from the standpoint of safety.

Study and Analysis of Accidents

ACCIDENT INVESTIGATION. Accident investigation is of prime importance. Its purpose should be definitely to develop better means for carrying on an accident prevention program. Otherwise, as fast as one accident hazard is detected and removed, another hazard may develop and eventually result in an accident of even greater proportions.

In most organizations an investigation of some kind is made of each accident resulting in death or injury to an employee. However, accidents which might have caused death or personal injury, but which by a stroke of luck did not harm anyone, often are unreported, or when they are reported are rarely investigated. Members of the National Safety Council, who make a practice of investigating all accidents, claim there is no more justification for assuming that a noninjury accident will not hurt anyone if it happens again than there is in drawing the same conclusion regarding an accident involving personal injury or death. They operate on the theory that there may be another "horse" and therefore a real necessity for "locking the barn."

Purposes of Investigation. The principal purposes of an accident investigation are:

1. To ascertain the cause or causes so that measures may be taken to prevent similar accidents. These measures may include mechanical improvements, better supervision, instruction of workmen, and sometimes discipline of the person found guilty.
2. To secure publicity among the workmen and their supervisors for the particular hazard, and for accident prevention in general by directing attention to the accident, its causes and results.
3. To ascertain facts bearing on legal liability. Investigations for this purpose only, however, will not always suffice for future accident prevention purposes. But an investigation for preventive purposes may disclose facts that are important in determining liability. In this discussion the investigation is considered from the standpoint of safety, not liability.

Making the Investigation. Depending on the importance of the accident and other conditions, the investigation may be made by one or more of the following persons or groups:

1. The foreman.
2. The safety engineer or inspector.
3. The workmen's safety committee.
4. The general safety committee.
5. A court of inquiry, board of inquiry, or jury.
6. In accidents involving special features it is often advantageous to call in an engineer from the insurance company or appropriate government agency to assist.

Each investigation should be made as soon after the accident as possible. A delay of even a few hours may permit important evidence to be destroyed or removed, intentionally or unintentionally. The results of the inquiry should also be made known quickly, as their publicity value in the safety education of workmen and supervisors is greatly increased by promptness.

Fairness is an absolute essential. The value of the investigation is largely destroyed if there is any suspicion that its purpose or result is to "whitewash" anyone or to "pass the buck." A "verdict" which places the blame on the workman, especially on the man who was injured, is likely to be scoffed at unless the personnel of the committee or jury arriving at the decision includes a generous proportion of fellow workmen having good standing among their associates. Perhaps even more important is the attitude of the safety department or other company representatives in making the inquiry. No one should be assigned to this work unless he has earned a reputation for fairness and is tactful in gathering the evidence. No browbeating of witnesses, either in private inquiry or in public, should be tolerated.

An accident causing death or some serious injury should obviously be investigated, but the near-accident that might have caused death or serious injury is equally important from the safety standpoint. Any **epidemic of accidental injuries** demands immediate special study. A particle of emery in the eye, or a scratch from handling sheet metal, may be a very simple case. The immediate cause is obvious, and the loss of time may not exceed a few minutes, but, if cases of this or any other kind occur frequently in the plant or in any one department, an investigation should be made to determine the underlying causes.

INVESTIGATION PROCEDURES. One company's procedure in the investigation of accidents covers such questions as: What happened? Why did it happen? How can a similar occurrence be prevented?

Four important steps are taken immediately after the accident occurs:

1. The safety department makes an immediate preliminary investigation at the scene of the accident to get all the facts.
2. Later, as an intermediate step, the job is analyzed carefully.
3. A formal investigation is made by a committee composed of the manager or his assistant, an employee, an observer, and the safety engineer, whose duty it is to assemble all the facts and place responsibility.
4. Recommendations are later made by the safety department to prevent recurrence of the accident.

Preliminary Investigation.

1. The first-aid records are consulted to determine: what happened, what the employee was doing, where he was working.
2. The safety engineer goes to the scene of the accident, questions all the workers in the area, takes pictures of all conditions.
3. The injured man is interviewed at once, if his condition permits, to get his story before he has a chance to change it.

Intermediate Investigation.

1. The injured man is again questioned to detect any change in his story.
2. A detailed study of the work methods of men on similar jobs and of similar equipment is made.
3. A study of the experience of other companies in similar cases is also made.
4 An investigation is made of the safety appliances in use.
5. The safety records of the injured man and his foreman are checked.

Formal Investigation.

1. A meeting is held in the main office to establish in the mind of the employee that management is interested.
2. The investigating group is composed of the general superintendent, employee representative, and a foreman in the same line of work, chosen by the safety man. The safety man assumes the chairmanship, questions the witnesses, and then presents the evidence.

Employer

1. Name of Employer
2. Office address: _____ (No. and Street) _____ (City or Town and Postal Zone Number) _____ (State)
3. Insured by Liberty Mutual Insurance Company
4. Give nature of business (or article manufactured)

Time and Place

5. (a) Location of plant or place where accident occurred _____ Department _____ State if employer's premises
   (b) If injured in a mine, did accident occur on surface, underground, shaft, drift or mill
6. Date of injury _____ 19___ Day of week _____ A.M. _____ P.M. Hour of day _____ A.M. _____ P.M.
7. Date disability began _____ 19___ 8. Was injured paid in full for this day?
9. When did you or foreman first know of injury
10. Name of foreman

Injured Person

11. Name of Injured _____ (First Name) _____ (Middle Initial) _____ (Last Name) _____ (Social Sec. No.)
12. Address: No. and St. _____ City or Town _____ State
13. Check (√) Married ___, Single ___, Widowed ___, Widower ___, Divorced ___; Male ___, Female ___; White ___, Colored
14. Nationality _____ Citizen of _____ Speak English
15. Age _____ Did you have on file employment certificate or permit
16. (a) Occupation when injured _____ (b) Was this his or her regular occupation
    (If not, state in what department or branch of work regularly employed)
17. (a) How long employed by you _____ (b) Piece or time worker _____ (c) Wages per hour $
18. (a) No. hours worked per day _____ (b) Wages per day $
    (c) No. days worked per week _____ (d) Average weekly earnings $
    (e) If board, lodging, fuel, or other advantages were furnished in addition to wages, give estimated value per day, week, or month

	19. Machine, tool, or thing causing injury _____ 20. Kind of power (hand, foot, electrical, steam, etc.) _____ 21. Part of machine on which accident occurred _____
	22. (a) Was safety appliance or regulation provided _____ (b) Was it in use at time _____
	23. Was accident caused by injured's failure to use or observe safety appliance or regulation _____
Cause of Injury	24. Describe fully how accident occurred, and state what employee was doing when injured _____
	25. Names and addresses of witnesses _____
	26. Nature and location of injury (describe fully exact location of amputations or fractures, right or left) _____
Nature of Injury	27. Probable length of disability _____ 28. Has injured returned to work _____
	If so, date and hour _____ At what wage $ _____
	29. At what occupation _____
	30. (a) Name and address of physician _____
	(b) Name and address of hospital _____
Fatal Cases	31. Has injured died _____ If so, give date of death _____
Date of this report _____	Firm name _____
	Signed by _____ Official Title _____

Fig. 5. Standard form for employer's first report of injury, suitable for accident analysis.

Follow-up by the Safety Department.

1. Reports of the investigation are sent to the heads of similar departments.
2. Suggestions to correct similar conditions in other departments are submitted.
3. The report, in general, is publicized.
4. Related operations to detect similar hazards that may result in an accident are studied.
5. The accident is used as a subject for discussion in foremen's meetings.
6. A special bulletin is published each month listing all accidents.
7. A tickler system is used to follow up recommendations and see that they have been put into effect.
8. An exchange of accident experiences is carried on with similar industries.

ANALYZING CAUSES OF ACCIDENTS. The data necessary for analysis should include as a minimum:

1. Date of accident.
2. Name of injured.
3. Specific occupation of injured.
4. Nature of injury.
5. Details of accident.
6. Identity of hazard.
7. Preventive action taken.

Standard **injury report forms** well suited to accident and analysis are exemplified in Fig. 5 (prepared by Liberty Mutual Insurance Company as recommended by the International Association of Industrial Accident Boards and Commissions) and may be made available by the Workmen's Compensation insurance carrier.

Classifying Data. There has always been confusion in the terminology used in reporting and analyzing accidents. Listed under "causes" are slips and falls, burns, slivers, punch presses, and other miscellaneous designations. These terms are used without regard for their correct meaning. Such misuse of words greatly reduces the value of accident records and causes confusion in prevention work. Detailed information on the plan and forms recommended for the purpose of collecting and analyzing accidental injuries to industrial employees should be in possession of the safety director.

The American Standards Association's American Recommended Practice for Compiling Industrial Accident Causes (Standard Z16.2) provides a means for uniformly describing and **coding the factors in accidents.** If, for example, a man working on a woodworking saw had his hand caught in the blade because he ignored the rule of using a "pusher," the accident would be described as follows:

1. Agency part (substance most closely related to accident)—Saw, circular, cut-off—Code 00427.
2. Unsafe mechanical condition—None—Code YY.
3. Type of accident—Caught in—Code 2.
4. Unsafe act—Using hands instead of tool—Code 32.
5. Unsafe personal factor—Willful disregard of instructions—Code 00.

The use of this standard will organize the recording of data for its most effective application. Experience has shown that collection and tabulation of accident information in this manner are very helpful in aiding management to determine causes, types of accidents, and hazardous locations for proper corrective measures.

The National Safety Council's Accident Analysis Chart (Fig. 6) has been designed for the **smaller company having fewer total accidents.** All injuries, including those requiring only first aid, should be recorded.

Fig. 6. Accident analysis chart.

Maintaining Accident Records and Reports

RECORDS OF INJURIES. Successful accident prevention by an employer in behalf of his employees requires a good system of recording accidental injuries. No modern executive would expect profits without adequate records of production, costs, and sales. Accident records serve a similar purpose for safety.

REPORTS. A report should be submitted to management at least once each month. Certain items are a "must" on such reports, other items may be included from time to time, or special emphasis may be given to a section of the report where a weakness in accident prevention work is noted. The **essential report items** are:

1. **Frequency rate (number of disabling injuries per million man-hours worked).** The use of the term "disabling injuries" is preferred to "lost-time" injuries. A disabling injury is defined by the American Standards Association (American Standard Method of Recording and Measuring Work Injury Experience Standard Z16.1) as "a work injury which results in death, permanent total disability, permanent partial disability, or temporary total disability."

Monthly Summary

Company _____ Plant _____

Period	No. of Non-Dis-abling Injuries	No. of Man-Hours Worked	Avg. No. of Em-ployees	Deaths & Perm. Total Curr.	Deaths & Perm. Total Adj.	Perm. Partial Curr.	Perm. Partial Adj.	Tempo-rary Total Curr.	Tempo-rary Total Adj.	Total	This Period	Same Period Last Year
				NUMBER OF DISABLING INJURIES							FREQUENCY RATE	
Jan.												
Feb.												
Cum.												
Mar.												
Cum.												
Apr.												
Cum.												
May												
Cum.												
June												
Cum.												
July												
Cum.												
Aug.												
Cum.												
Sept.												
Cum.												
Oct.												
Cum.												
Nov.												
Cum.												
Dec.												
YEAR												

Fig. 7. Form for monthly

2. **Severity rate (number of man-days lost per 1,000,000 man-hours worked).** Prior to 1956 this was based on 1,000 man-hours worked. The number of man-days lost is to be computed in accordance with the same standard (American Standards Association).
3. **Total time lost** or charged for major injuries.
4. **Costs of accidents;** direct cost and indirect cost.

Since the information of such a report is the basis for management evaluation, **comparisons** should be presented wherever practicable. It is possible to show trends by comparing current performance with (a) last month; (b) same month of previous year; (c) a six- or twelve-month total; (d) performance of similar industries as reported by National Safety Council or by U. S. Bureau of Labor Statistics. Further comparisons can be made between similar departments or plants of the company. The National Safety Council's **monthly summary of injuries form** (Fig. 7) summarizes the necessary information for ease of comparison.

NONDISABLING ACCIDENTS. As pointed out earlier, records of non-disabling accidents, even if only first aid is required, may be maintained. A report

of Injuries, 19——

_____ Department _____

TIME CHARGES						SEVERITY RATE		COST	
Deaths & Perm. Total		Permanent Partial		Temporary Total		Total	This Period	Same Period Last Year	This Period	Same Period Last Year
Curr.	Adj.	Curr.	Adj.	Curr.	Adj.				

summary of injuries.

showing trends involving this type of accident is often of value. The small company or small department may not have sufficient "experience" to indicate its true safety performance if measured by disabling accidents alone. The type of accident, the agency, and the cause of "disabling" accidents correlate highly with the type, agency, and causes of those which are nondisabling. Where possible, the monthly and annual reports should summarize and compare the frequency of nondisabling accidents between departments and plants both currently and for prior periods. Agency, accident type, and cause also should be compared.

Finally, when a department or plant has achieved a good safety record, it becomes desirable to report the number of **accident-free days** and the number of **man-hours since the last disabling accident.** The du Pont Company, which has set many safety records, now places considerable emphasis on preventing off-the-job injuries involving loss of working time. Records are kept, reports are submitted, and competition helps keep workers safety-conscious both on and off the plant site.

Fire Prevention

FIRE AND PANIC. The control of possible fire losses and prevention of injuries in industry as a result of fires can be expressed in four fundamental principles:

1. Arrange and maintain the physical condition of the plant to prevent or minimize the possibility of fires.
2. Provide for the prompt detection and extinguishing of fires. All but a very few fires begin in a small, easily extinguished manner.
3. Provide means for confining any fire to as small an area as possible.
4. Provide and maintain personnel exit facilities that will be safe either in fire or panic.

The safety director and plant engineer should become familiar with the provisions of local fire laws and building codes and enlist the service and advice of the fire insurance carrier. Other agencies able to render valuable assistance are the National Fire Protection Association, National Board of Fire Underwriters, and The Engineering Division of Associated Factory Mutual Insurance Companies.

DANGER OF FAMILIARITY WITH ORDINARY HAZARDS. The common or ordinary hazards are the presence of **combustible solids, flammable liquids,** and **electrical equipment,** which are present in everyone's everyday life. In small quantities and in normal use their presence and behavior are accepted by most people. It is in the unusual circumstances of a concentration of large quantities of these materials and equipment and the machinery, power, and temperatures of industry that familiar substances behave in unfamiliar manner. For adequate fire prevention it is essential that the process of fire itself be understood along with the more common fire hazards.

Fire depends on oxygen (usually from air), fuel, and heat. Without all these three elements fire will not occur. Heat is essential not only to ignite the fuel but also to maintain its temperature above kindling. If any one of the three basic elements is removed, a fire will die out. In ordinary circumstances, the three are kept separated or under control; in time, their continuing normal behavior encourages an unwarranted disregard of their fundamental hazards. A combination of congested materials, a careless match, a hot spark, or overheated electrical equipment—and suddenly a fire has started which, unless quickly discovered and extinguished, may rage out of control.

CLASSIFICATION OF HAZARDS. The special hazards of particular industries are beyond the scope of this section. Many of these special hazards are the subject of standards established by industrial associations or by fire protection associations. The eight **most common fire hazards** in industry, generally, are:

1. Smoking (and matches).
2. Poor housekeeping.
3. Defective heating equipment.
4. Electric equipment and wiring.

5. Open flames.
6. Spontaneous ignition.
7. Lightning.
8. Explosive atmospheres.

Smoking. Smoking, together with the unsafe disposal of matches, pipe embers, cigar and cigarette butts, is the major cause of all fires in the United States. It may be necessary to exclude all matches, automatic lighters, and smoking equipment from particularly hazardous areas, even an entire plant. In other operations, it is wise to make an **analysis of the plant** to determine those areas where smoking and the use of matches would be particularly hazardous and those in which smoking might be permitted. Smoking has become such a widespread habit that its absolute prohibition requires continual reminder and rigorous enforcement. In instances where large areas must be designated as **NO SMOKING**, thought should be given to the possibility of providing and maintaining a small area or room where it may be permitted with safety.

Housekeeping. Proper storage of materials and removal of waste materials are important in prevention of fires. Large quantities of combustible materials should be stored with consideration for limiting the spread of a possible fire. Small quantities should be stored in **covered metal bins** or cans. Rubbish of all kinds should be removed daily, if possible, and while awaiting disposal should be confined in covered metal bins or some fire-safe sprinklered structure. Combustible waste and rubbish should be burned in a furnace or incinerator or in such manner as to prevent the spread of fire by flying sparks. Provision also should be made for the elimination or prompt removal of **drippings of flammable oils, greases, and fluids.** Exhaust ducts should be kept clean of any accumulation of combustible dusts or condensed flammable vapors.

Heating and Electrical Equipment. Overheated surfaces and defective heating equipment have caused many serious fires. Shafting and overheated bearings, friction between belts and wood structures, all have contributed to fire losses. All **high-temperature equipment** should be insulated or isolated from combustible material. Long-term heating of wood or fiberboard structures gradually lowers their ignition temperature to the danger point. It should be remembered that stove and furnace flues can ignite combustible structures by overheating alone and may leak explosive gases into the plant if in bad repair.

Electrical equipment should be installed and maintained according to the National Electrical Code (National Fire Protection Association). Common hazards of electric equipment in bad condition are:

1. Short-circuit spark ignition of gases, vapors, or combustible dusts.
2. Overload or high resistance heating of defective wiring in contact with combustible material.
3. Electric motors, inadequately protected against "stall" conditions, consequently developing temperatures sufficient to ignite their insulation.

In addition to these, the hazards of poor housekeeping and overheated surfaces often are present in the use of electric heating equipment.

Open Flames. The use of open flames, welding or burning torches, blow-torches, and the like should be preceded by careful preparation of the area in which they are to be used. Combustibles or flammable materials should be removed or protected by metal shields or by asbestos, glass fabric, or flame-proofed canvas blankets. Whenever an area cannot be completely protected by removal of combustibles or by their shielding or blanketing, a **fire guard** should be present with appropriate fire extinguishers at hand before open flames are used.

Spontaneous Ignition. Spontaneous ignition of combustible materials results from a process of slow oxidation with insufficient ventilation to remove the resulting heat. The consequent temperature rise causes fire when ignition temperature is reached. This process is accelerated by the presence of moisture, decomposing organic materials, chemical reactions, and any external heating. Control involves: better housekeeping, storage of large quantities in a well-ventilated, cool, dry area, small quantities in covered metal containers.

Lightning. Fires started by lightning in the United States caused an estimated $37,000,000 loss in 1954. There is greater hazard from thunderstorms in certain areas of the country than others owing to the frequency of such storms, but no area is entirely free of hazard. Protection of property depends on the provision of an adequate **conductor path** from above the property to the "electrical ground." "Lightning rods," collectors, down connectors, and grounding method must everywhere create a path of less electrical resistance to the "stroke" than that through any other part of the property. Adequate grounding is sometimes difficult, particularly in shallow soils containing little moisture. According to the National Fire Protection Association (Code for Protection Against Lightning), steel-frame or reinforced-concrete structures can provide adequate protection if overhead collectors are bonded to the metal frame or reinforcing, if the metal-to-metal contact is continuous, and if an adequate grounding connection is made.

Explosive Atmospheres. Explosive atmospheres are those in which combustible dusts or flammable vapors or gases are present in the air in such proportions that ignition at any point is carried throughout the entire volume at an accelerating rate with excess heat generation. The U. S. Department of Agriculture (Technical Bulletin 490) lists a large number of explosive dusts. For either dusts or gases there are **limiting concentrations in air** below which and above which explosion does not occur. The generally accepted lower explosive limits of dusts range from 0.015 oz. per cu. ft. for light dusts to 0.5 oz. per cu. ft. for heavy dusts. Vapors and gases have a much wider range of explosive proportions. Concentrations in air, as low as 0.5 per cent by volume, are listed as lower limits. Generally, an increase in temperature depresses the lower explosive limit.

Control of processes to minimize generation of dusts or liberation of gases and vapors is seldom completely effective in itself. **Ignition prevention** and adequate **ventilation-exhaust systems** are frequently needed to reduce the explosion hazard. In particularly hazardous circumstances, it is also wise to limit the extent of damage of a possible explosion by isolating the process and/or housing it in **explosion-vented rooms** or buildings.

FIRE-SAFETY ORGANIZATION. Some one person in the plant organization should be responsible for the fire safety of plant and personnel. In the small plant, this responsibility may be retained by the plant manager or one of his first-line assistants. It may be a combined responsibility with that for accident prevention or an activity assigned the master mechanic or plant engineer.

In larger plants, a full-time position is indicated, the individual reporting directly to the manager, plant engineer, or other top executive.

Fire Brigade. The organization of a fire brigade, full-time, stand-by, or a combination, depends on: the size of the plant, whether compact or dispersed; the type of production—nature of fire hazards; and the availability and amount of help which can be expected from a public fire department. The **plant fire chief** should have his authority clearly defined. He should have access to management to advise on fire safety and should be consulted prior to major equipment changes or new construction. The fire chief should be consulted in the selection, location, and installation of all fire-warning and fire control equipment. These arrangements are essential to his proper organization and training of a fire brigade.

Members of the fire brigade should be selected and trained with the following in mind: all must be able to take training, be able-bodied, and be available for instant fire-duty. Shift operation of the plant requires trained men available on each shift. The **brigade training program** must be purposeful and regular. The National Fire Protection Association (Industrial Fire Brigade Training Manual) advises that the course should be prepared to meet the needs of the plant: i.e., its special hazards and its equipment for fire control. Drills and classroom instruction should be given on company time if at all possible, and continuing purposeful training should be given each member at least twice a month. Much help in training can be secured from outside agencies such as state fire schools, state fire marshals, and the plant's fire insurance carrier.

Fire Drills. Fire drills should be part of the training both of fire brigade members and of the other plant personnel. It is not essential that all drills of the fire brigade be accompanied by an **evacuation drill** of plant personnel, but the latter should not be ignored. Drills by the fire brigade should be thorough and should closely approximate actual fire conditions. Over a period of time, the men should become familiar with the interior arrangement of all buildings, basements, attics, and storage rooms and the location of stairways, exits, and the like. The men should have actual practice with laying hose, making hydrant connections, and carrying and moving hose lines under pressure. All members of the brigade should understand the application of various types of extinguishers on different types of fires and have practice in their use. At the conclusion of a drill, all equipment should be returned to its designated location in readiness for use or stand-by equipment should be substituted.

Management should anticipate the possibility of a fire emergency and evacuation of personnel. All areas of the plant should be studied to determine a **safe exit route for all personnel.** All operations and processes that could constitute hazards if unattended should be located, studied, and provided for by shutdown plans or procedures. In larger plants, room captains, floor chiefs, and searchers should be appointed. The evacuation plan for the plant as a whole and for each building should be published and explained to all employees. Then, and only then, should a simulated fire drill and evacuation be attempted.

FIRE PROTECTION EQUIPMENT. The selection and placement of fire-fighting equipment should be undertaken jointly with the local fire department and the fire insurance company. The two reasons for this procedure are:

1. Technical factors which depend on the particular industry are involved in the selection and placement of equipment.
2. Insurance rates are based not only on the hazard but also on the protection available.

Therefore specialized advice should be sought in the selection and placement of all fire-fighting equipment. Undoubtedly, the most recommended fire protection method is the provision of a fixed system of **automatic sprinklers** with an adequate and reliable source of water. This recommendation, however, does not exclude the provision of numerous other facilities needed for special hazards. **Portable fire extinguishers** of appropriate types and sizes should be readily available in all plant areas, as should hose reels and fire hydrants connected to the water mains.

Detection. The primary requirement in all fire extinguishment and control, however, is early detection of the fire. "Control and extinguish while still small" should be the primary aim. Detection by personnel should be followed immediately by notice to the plant fire chief by telephone or by some manually operated **alarm system.** The fire chief may then take steps to dispatch the fire brigade and/or call the municipal fire department. In addition to detection by personnel, detection can be made **automatic** by several approved devices and systems. Most of such systems depend on electric signals transmitted from the detector device to the fire chief's office and are supplied by more than one source of current. A wide variety of detectors have been approved by Underwriters Laboratories, Inc., and Factory Mutual Laboratories. Most detectors are **thermostatic** and are actuated by temperature rise, rate of rise, or fixed temperature. The thermostatic devices may be located in any part of the plant and may be used in conjunction with automatic sprinkler systems, sounding an alarm shortly before or at the time the sprinklers go into action. For certain applications, **smoke detectors** actuated by a photoelectric cell also are available. The detecting devices should be so located as to be most sensitive to possible fires and yet free of false-alarm possibilities or damage by plant operations.

Sprinklers. Fixed sprinkler systems may be of four types: the wet-pipe, the dry-pipe, the pre-action (normally dry-pipe), and the deluge systems. Where freezing conditions are not present, the **wet-pipe system** may have considerable advantage in quickness of operation and possibly in first cost. Damage to valuable merchandise by leaks sometimes dictates the use of another system. In the **dry-pipe system,** air pressure is maintained in the piping system. A sudden drop in pressure occurs when a fusible link in a sprinkler head operates, the drop in pressure actuates the valve to the water header allowing water to flow throughout the system, to the open sprinkler, and thence to the fire. A disadvantage is the delay between action of the sprinkler head and arrival of water through the system. The **pre-action system** normally gives an earlier warning, floods the system, and delays opening the sprinkler head until a further temperature rise occurs. This may be desirable if personnel are present and able to control a small fire with portable extinguishers. A **deluge system** is also "dry-pipe" but with open sprinklers. The purpose is to wet down at once an entire area in which a fire may originate. A quick-opening valve between the system and the water supply may be manually operated but usually is controlled by a thermostatic fire detector.

In addition to water systems, there are a number of **chemical and inert-gas fixed and automatic systems** for use with special hazards. These systems are of particular value in areas where flammable fluids and chemicals preclude the use of water. It should be remembered that all automatic systems must be in near-perfect condition to give the protection intended. Regular inspection, testing, and maintenance are absolutely essential.

Fire mains and **hydrants** with standard 2½-in. fire hose connections should be installed outside of the plant buildings and in the plant yard. Generally, such hydrants should be located so that two hose lines, neither over 250 ft., can reach every part of the building interior. If at all possible, the yard mains should be separate from the main supplying the standpipe and sprinkler system of the plant. Inside the plant, provision should be made for 1-in. or 1½-in. hose lines connected to the standpipe or sprinkler mains. All hose reels, reel carts, and "ever-ready" reels should carry hose of the same size and type with uniform standard couplings. All hoses, outdoor or indoor, should be carefully drained, dried, and replaced after every use. Even if not used, all hoses should be inspected and tested annually under full pressure.

Fire Extinguishers. To control and extinguish the small fire, there is available a variety of portable and semiportable extinguishers. Each of the three types of fires requires somewhat different extinguishers:

1. Type A fires, combustible materials; water, water sprays, soda-acid, and foam extinguishers.
2. Type B fires, flammable liquids, greases, etc., where a blanketing effect is needed; foam, carbon dioxide, vaporizing liquid, and dry chemical extinguishers.
3. Type C fires, flame in "live" electrical equipment; carbon dioxide, vaporizing liquid, and dry chemical extinguishers.

Access to the extinguishers should be possible at all times, and the location of all units should be vividly marked. The extinguishers should be distributed around the plant in areas according to the type of hazard that exists. The presence in the area of flammable liquids or electrical equipment indicates that units for type B or type C fires only should be provided. Each extinguisher should be **marked** for the type of fire on which it is to be used and **periodically tested** to insure that it is fully charged and in good working order. All workers should be instructed in the proper use of extinguishers and the hazards of using them improperly.

BUILDING FIRE SAFETY INTO A PLANT. Building fire safety into a plant is never an easy task. A great deal of technical knowledge must be applied to the arrangement of the plant, its facilities, and its type of construction. Consideration must be given to the fire hazards of production processes and production materials; the possibilities of segregating high-hazard conditions to protect them more completely or limit damage in event of fire. **Fire-wall partitions** should be used to limit the area extent of a possible fire. Automatic devices should close any openings through such walls, doorways, conveyor-ways, or ventilating ducts in the event of fire on either side of the wall. It should be recognized that plant building construction may be a very important factor in achieving over-all fire safety, but under some circumstances the building may be no more than a furnace if large quantities of combustible or flammable materials are present with inadequate protection or extinguishing means.

In discussing a disastrous fire at a plant where six men lost their lives and the company suffered a direct loss of $55,000,000, the National Fire Protection Association Quarterly (1953) describes the fire as follows and gives an analysis of the interrelated causes for the fire and the heavy loss resulting:

The Livonia, Michigan, General Motors fire was started by sparks from an oxy-acetylene cutting torch operated by a contractor's welding crew. Fire started in an overhead conveyor drip-pan, 10 ft. 8 in. above the floor. The pan was sheet-metal 2 ft. wide and approximately 120 ft. long with a 2-inch lip on either side. It extended beneath a long monorail conveyor which dipped down sufficiently at a dip-tank to immerse metal parts in a 97.7 degree F. flash point rust-inhibiting liquid. The drip pan contained a layer of flammable liquid drippings, probably less than ¼ inch deep.

The fire, when discovered, was immediately attacked with two carbon-dioxide extinguishers from a ladder belonging to the welding crew. The fire was about to be extinguished when the extinguishers were emptied and flames spread the length of the drip pan. Other carbon-dioxide and chemical extinguishers were brought within a few minutes. A 1½-inch hose line also was put in use. However, due to the location of the fire overhead about all that could be accomplished was to prevent fire from extending into the dip tank. The oily condensate on the steel roof members in a nearby heat treatment area ignited, adding heat to the roof deck.

Soon hot tar and asphalt were flowing through cracks between strips in the heat-warped roof deck and igniting. The fire then spread laterally behind the increasing area of melted tar that oozed through the roof. Fires broke out on machinery, in flammable liquid containers and on the wood floor.

The Michigan State Fire Marshal believes that there was a delay of 15 to 20 minutes in notifying the Livonia Fire Department. A spokesman for General Motors fixes this elapsed time as six minutes.

The causes are presented approximately in descending order of importance:

1. An undivided fire area of 1,502,500 square feet (34.5 acres) in which absence of fire walls and roof vents denied access for fire fighting and prevented localization of heat and smoke.
2. Inadequate sprinkler protection (only 20 percent of the total area protected— no sprinklers where the fire started).
3. Incompletely engineered process. Fire protection for the dip tank did not protect the drip pan. Due to the process oily deposits had a tendency to accumulate and increase the fire hazard of the several heat treating areas, yet this condition does not appear to have received engineering attention.
4. Unprotected steel construction, in particular the thin steel (roof) deck that did not offer sufficient insulation between banking heat and the built-up roof covering to prevent asphalt from melting and dripping through joints of the heat-warped deck. Steel trusses collapsed in a matter of minutes.
5. Use of oxy-acetylene torch under unsafe conditions.
6. Lack of an effective private fire brigade.
7. Delayed fire department notification.

Civil Defense Measures

ORGANIZATION. The purposes of a civil defense organization in an industrial plant are:

1. In peacetime or in advance of an actual emergency to anticipate the problems of the emergency. To recommend and assist in providing facilities and personnel trained suitably to meet the emergency. To establish a liaison with the community civil defense organization.
. In time of emergency to:
   a. Safeguard the lives of the workers.
   b. Limit the damage to the buildings and machinery of the plant.
   c. Protect personnel from the demoralizing effects of enemy actions and foster a sense of security and confidence.
   d. Maintain production at highest possible rate at the time of impending attack (Alert), and reduce interruptions due to damage to a minimum.

It is essential that competent individuals be assigned the responsibility of accomplishing these objectives. A framework of authority and responsibility for various phases of the program should be established at the outset. A **civil defense officer** should be responsible for all civil defense activities of the entire plant. He should be responsible for the civil defense administration and training of the organization and the coordination of the plant civil defense activities with those of the community. As far as possible, existing service departments and functional personnel should be utilized for related civil defense responsibilities.

Most plants have peacetime plant protection, fire-brigade, first-aid, maintenance, and custodial sections. The personnel of these and similar sections form the nucleus of the **emergency organization.** They continue to serve in normal capacities until or unless emergencies arise. Well-planned training permits them to cope with disaster emergencies without extensive adjustments.

In general, the executive of the company who is responsible for developing the civil defense plan and for training of C.D. personnel should also be responsible for operation of the organization in time of emergency. **Key assistants** should be assigned to the Defense Officer, and, since most factories may expect, during war time, to operate at night as well as in the day, **deputies** should be appointed for each to serve during absence or disability of their superior. The several **defense functions** to be provided for in a medium- or large-size factory are:

1. Safety, shelter and evacuation.
2. Communications, warnings, alarms.
3. Fire fighting.
4. Rescue and damage control.
5. Health and medical (first aid) facilities.
6. Detection and decontamination (atomic, biological, and chemical measures).
7. Essential plant utilities and services.
8. Other functions indicated by special conditions.

EVACUATION PLANS. One function of the national, state, and local civil defense centers is to give early warning of an impending air attack. The factory must provide facilities and personnel that assure certain receipt of all warnings and prompt notification of the plant Defense Officer or his deputy. When time permits, key personnel should then be notified to take preliminary action. However, no time may be lost in notifying all plant personnel when an active alarm is received. Alarm bells, horns, or sirens should be installed to permit operation from both the Control Post and the point where an alarm is received from the outside source.

A **take-cover alarm** should send all personnel to previously prepared posts. For most personnel this means a prompt but orderly departure from their work area to a protected shelter area. A few key people, wardens, fire-watchers, and the like, should go to other posts where they can perform their special function.

Shelter Areas. It is important that shelter areas be provided in advance of the actual emergency. A survey of existing facilities should be made to determine the extent and location of suitable shelter with little or no structural change. With such unventilated shelters, the maximum occupancy diminishes as the time of expected occupancy increases. Prentiss (Civil Defense in Modern War) indicates that an unventilated shelter with inside dimensions of 10 x 10 x 8 ft. high has a maximum occupancy of 5 people for a period of up to 3 hr., but of only 4 people for a period of from 3 to 6 hr. He also recommends that the cubic footage required per occupant in such unventilated shelters be increased with greater maximum occupancy. Thus, the shelter 10 x 10 x 8 ft. high provides 160 cu. ft. per person for a maximum occupancy of 5 people up to 3 hr., while a shelter 50 x 20 x 15 ft. high provides 366 cu. ft. per person for a maximum occupancy of 41 people up to 3 hr.

Unless independent power supply is provided for operation of ventilation equipment, it must be assumed that most shelter areas will be unventilated, since main power lines throughout the plant will be disconnected.

Should additional shelters be needed to accommodate the entire working force of a single shift, a survey should be made of available land, preferably on or adjacent to the plant site, where additional shelters may be constructed. **Underground shelters**, each for 50 persons and separated by 25 to 30 ft., can be constructed to hold 1,000 persons per acre.

With sufficient shelter provided for, steps must be taken to assure that the space will not be used for other purposes and hence not be available at the time of emergency. A **plan of movement** from working area to shelter area must be established for all personnel, as groups or individuals. The location of the proper shelter and the route to follow in an alarm must be known by every individual. Furthermore, plans should be made for the eventuality of an alarm at a time when many workers are not in their work area, as at lunch time or at a change of shifts.

Bomb-Proof Facilities. Shelters may be indoors, may be part of an existing building or structure, or may be specially constructed areas in or beneath the plant buildings. Three principal requirements govern the **suitability** of **shelter** areas. They are:

1. Strength to resist the collapsing force of all but direct bomb hits.
2. Strength to withstand collapsing overhead structures or machinery.
3. Freedom from any unusual fire or chemical hazards.

The entrances and exits of shelter areas also must be relatively free of the above hazards, and alternate exits should always be available.

Outdoor shelters may be constructed; they should be detached and at a safe distance from structures or buildings which might be demolished in an air raid. Depending on soil and drainage conditions, they may be wholly above ground, wholly beneath the surface, or partly above, partly beneath. Where hills, ravines, or other surface features permit and the subsurface is neither too wet nor rocky, tunnels and galleries may be the most economical form of shelter.

For the few people who should remain on duty during a raid (fire-watchers, etc.), small **two-man shelter posts** should be constructed. Concrete or masonry walls 12 in. thick, and protected from blast debris by sand bags, are recommended. For two men a space 3 ft. x 7 ft. x 7 ft. high should be provided. In all but the smallest plants, two or more fire-watch stations should be provided, allowing approximately two such stations for each 1,000 employees or one station per 40,000 sq. ft. of building area, whichever number is larger.

In addition to providing shelter for personnel, certain critical production facilities may be given some degree of protection by barricades of reinforced concrete or sand bags, or both.

DISPERSAL. The effect of a direct hit by high-explosive bombs is beyond the protective abilities of most defense measures. Limitation of damage and of injuries is possible, and generally is the most effective measure to apply. The **dispersion principle** is a fundamental part of damage limitation. It should be applied to the location of plants, to the individual buildings of the plant, and to the layout of the plant equipment as well.

Wherever possible, **critical equipment** and operations should be housed in separate buildings with splinter-proof walls. Where closely integrated equipment and operations must be housed in the same large building, they should be separated by splinter-proof partitions, fire walls, or barricades.

Defense services such as rescue squads, fire squads, and decontamination personnel also should be dispersed and, with their equipment, should be located in two or more shelter posts.

CASUALTY CARE. After an air raid, when the "all clear" signal is received rescue and first-aid services must be immediately available. Most factories maintain medical dispensaries or first-aid stations in peace time. These may form the nucleus of an **emergency casualty station,** but provision should be made in advance for an alternate or additional station in a well-protected area. All such stations should be equipped with at least the minimum first-aid supplies. **Decontamination facilities** should be available for all personnel and may be provided in conjunction with the main dispensary or at certain of the shower, wash, or locker rooms of the plant. It is desirable that decontamination of the uninjured not interfere in any way with treatment or decontamination of those who may have been injured. Lastly, provision should be made for the prompt removal and transportation of seriously injured employees to a hospital. Coordination with the community C.D. hospital and ambulance services should be arranged for in advance.

DAMAGE CONTROL AND REPAIR OF FACILITIES. One of the major damages to the industrial plant in the event of an air attack is the spread of fire. Since blast effects may have disrupted the established water lines and power sources, quick action with portable equipment is essential. At the same time **equipment repair crews** should make every effort for emergency repair of water lines and pumping equipment. The peace-time fire brigade and plant engineering forces should be instructed in their responsibilities for mutual action in such an emergency.

Adequate peace-time facilities for fire fighting probably would be inadequate in time of war. Each plant might have to rely entirely on its own forces and equipment without help from the local city department. For this reason, each industrial plant may find it necessary to provide its own large-volume water tank or reservoir and one or more heavy-duty pumping engines.

In order to effect repairs to damaged plant facilities as rapidly as possible, a supply of spare parts is essential. The variety and extent of inventory to be maintained will vary with each factory, but may be approximated by a careful study conducted by the plant engineer and maintenance forces. The organization for actual **repair work** should be an expansion of the existing maintenance and erection forces. Many production workers have the skills required for such work and with experienced supervision rapidly fit into a repair force. Round-the-clock operation by two-shift organization should be possible and should be attempted.

ACKNOWLEDGMENTS

In the preparation of the PRODUCTION HANDBOOK reference has been made to virtually the entire literature of industrial production and related fields. The editor of the Handbook, fully recognizing the value and significance to the field of the contributions made by the authors and publishers of these works, wishes to give special acknowledgment to the following publications which have been cited or quoted in the Second Edition of the PRODUCTION HANDBOOK:

Accident Facts. Chicago: Statistical Division, National Safety Council.

Accident Prevention Manual. 3d ed. Chicago: National Safety Council, 1955.

Advanced Management

ALFORD, L. P., and BEATTY, H. R. *Principles of Industrial Management.* Rev. ed. New York: The Ronald Press Co., 1951.

American Machinist

American Railway Engineering Association Bulletin

ARONSON, M. H. (ed.). *The Computer Handbook.* Pittsburgh: Instruments Publishing Co., Inc., 1955.

ASME Transactions

Automatic Control

Automatic Control. Scientific American, Inc. New York: Simon & Schuster, Inc., 1956.

Automation

AYRES, E. D. *Engineering Economy.* Columbus, Ohio: University Bookstore, Ohio State University, 1947.

BALDERSTON, C. C., *et al.* (eds.). *Management of an Enterprise.* 2d ed. Englewood Cliffs, N. J.: Prentice-Hall, Inc., 1949.

BARNARD, C. I. *Organization and Management.* Cambridge, Mass.: Harvard University Press, 1948.

BARNARD, C. I. *The Functions of the Executive.* Cambridge, Mass.: Harvard University Press, 1938.

BARNES, R. M. *Motion and Time Study.* 3d ed. New York: John Wiley & Sons, Inc., 1949.

BARNES, R. M. *Work Sampling.* New York: John Wiley & Sons, Inc., 1957.

BEGEMAN, M. L. *Manufacturing Processes.* 4th ed. New York: John Wiley & Sons, Inc., 1957.

Biometrics

Biometrika

BLAKE, R. P. (ed.). *Industrial Safety.* 2d ed. Englewood Cliffs, N. J.: Prentice-Hall, Inc., 1953.

BOLZ, H. A., and HAGEMANN, G. E. (eds.). *Materials Handling Handbook.* New York: The Ronald Press Co., 1958.

BOND, HORATIO, and KIMBALL, W. Y. *Industrial Fire Brigades Training Manual.* Boston: The National Fire Protection Association, 1954.

BOSTON, O. W. *Metal Processing.* 2d ed. New York: John Wiley & Sons, Inc., 1951.

BRANDT, A. D. *Industrial Health Engineering.* New York: John Wiley & Sons, Inc., 1947.

BROWN, ALVIN. *Organization of Industry.* Englewood Cliffs, N J.: Prentice-Hall. Inc., 1947.

BULLINGER, C. E. *Engineering Economic Analysis.* 2d ed. New York: McGraw-Hill Book Co., Inc., 1950.

Business Week

CANNING, R. G. *Electronic Data Processing for Business and Industry.* New York: John Wiley & Sons, Inc., 1956.

CANNING, R. G. *Electronic Scheduling Machine Requirements.* Management Sciences Research Project, Office of Naval Research. Los Angeles, Calif.: University of California.

CARROLL, PHIL. *Timestudy for Cost Control.* 3d ed. New York: McGraw-Hill Book Co., Inc., 1954.

Catalog of Occupational Safety Services. Chicago: National Safety Council.

Chemical and Engineering News

Chemical Engineering

Chemical Processing and Equipment. United States Atomic Energy Commission. New York: McGraw-Hill Book Co., Inc., 1955.

COCHRAN, W. G., and COX, G. M. *Experimental Designs.* New York: John Wiley & Sons, Inc., 1950.

CONANT, J. B. *On Understanding Science.* New Haven, Conn.: Yale University Press, 1947.

Consulting Engineer

Control Engineering

CRAMÉR, HARALD. *Mathematical Methods of Statistics.* Princeton, N. J.: Princeton University Press, 1946.

Czechoslovak Heavy Industry

DAVIS, C. N. *Rust Is Dangerous.* London: Faber & Faber, Ltd., 1945.

DEARBORN, D. C., *et al.* (eds.). *Spending for Industrial Research.* Cambridge, Mass.: Harvard University Press, 1951.

DIXON, W. J., and MASSEY, F. J. *Introduction to Statistical Analysis.* New York: McGraw-Hill Book Co., Inc., 1951.

DORIS, LILLIAN (ed.) *Corporate Treasurer's and Controller's Handbook.* Englewood Cliffs, N. J.: Prentice-Hall, Inc., 1950.

DU MOND, T. C. *Engineering Materials Manual.* New York: Reinhold Publishing Corp., 1951.

Dun's Review and Modern Industry

Econometrica

EISENHART, CHURCHILL, HASTAY, M. W., and WALLIS, W. A. (eds.). *Selected Techniques of Statistical Analysis for Scientific and Industrial Research and Production and Management Engineering.* New York: McGraw-Hill Book Co., Inc., 1947.

Electrical Manufacturing

Electronics

Engineer's Digest, The

Factory Management and Maintenance

FAYOL, HENRI. *General and Industrial Management.* New York: Pitman Publishing Corp., 1949.

FELLER, WILLIAM. *An Introduction to Probability Theory and Its Applications.* Vol. 1. New York: John Wiley & Sons, Inc., 1950.

FISHER, R. A. *The Design of Experiments.* New York: Hafner Publishing Co., Inc., 1951.

FISHER, R. A., and YATES, FRANK. *Statistical Tables for Biological, Agricultural, and Medical Research.* 4th ed. Edinburgh: Oliver & Boyd, Ltd., 1953.

Flow

Flow Directory

FLOYD, W. E., and WELFORD, A. T. (eds.). *Symposium on Fatigue.* London: H. K. Lewis & Co., Ltd., 1953.

Fortune

FRIEDMANN, GEORGES. *Industrial Society: The Emergence of the Human Problems of Automation.* Glencoe, Ill.: Free Press, 1955.

FRY, T. C. *Probability and Its Engineering Uses*. Princeton, N. J.: D. Van Nostrand Co., Inc., 1928.

FURNAS, C. C. (ed.). *Research in Industry, Its Organization and Management*. Princeton, N. J.: D. Van Nostrand Co., Inc., 1948.

GILBRETH, F. B. *Primer of Scientific Management*. Princeton, N. J.: D. Van Nostrand Co., Inc., 1912.

GILBRETH, F. B., and GILBRETH, L. E. *Applied Motion Study, A Collection of Papers on the Efficient Method to Industrial Preparedness*. New York: The Macmillan Co., 1917.

GOMBERG, WILLIAM. *A Trade Union Analysis of Time Study*. 2d ed. Englewood Cliffs, N. J.: Prentice-Hall, Inc., 1956.

GRANT, E. L. *Principles of Engineering Economy*. 3d ed. New York: The Ronald Press Co., 1950.

GRANT, E. L., and NORTON, P. T., JR. *Depreciation*. Rev. printing. New York: The Ronald Press Co., 1955.

Handbook of Material Handling with Industrial Trucks. Philadelphia: Electric Industrial Truck Association, 1950.

HARRINGTON, C. C. (ed.). *Materials Handling Manual*. Philadelphia: Chilton Co., 1952.

Harvard Business Review

Heating, Ventilating, and Air Conditioning Guide. Vol. 34. New York: American Society of Heating and Air Conditioning Engineers, Inc., 1956.

HEINRICH, H. W. *Industrial Accident Prevention, A Scientific Approach*. New York: McGraw-Hill Book Co., Inc., 1950.

HOBSON, P. D. *Industrial Lubrication Practice*. New York: Industrial Press, 1955.

HOLDEN, P. E., FISH, L. S., and SMITH, H. L. *Top-Management Organization and Control; A Research Study of the Management Policies and Practices of Thirty-One Leading Industrial Corporations*. New York: McGraw-Hill Book Co., Inc., 1951.

HOMANS, G. C., *et al.* (eds.). *Fatigue of Workers; Its Relation to Industrial Production*. New York: Reinhold Publishing Corp., 1941.

HOXIE, ROBERT. *Scientific Labor and Management*. New York: Appleton-Century-Crofts, Inc., 1915.

Industrial Management Society Bulletin

Industrial Quality Control

Industry and Power

Instruments and Automation

IRE Transactions

Iron Age

Journal of Engineering Education

Journal of Industrial Engineering

Journal of the Operations Research Society of America

JUNE, S. A., *et al.* (eds.). *The Automatic Factory*. Pittsburgh: Instruments Publishing Co., Inc., 1955.

JURAN, J. M. (ed.). *Quality-Control Handbook*. New York: McGraw-Hill Book Co., Inc., 1951.

KLEIN, M. L., WILLIAMS, F. K., and MORGAN, H. C. *Digital Automation*. Pittsburgh: Instruments Publishing Co., Inc., 1957.

KNOWLES, A. S., and THOMSON, R. D. *Industrial Management*. New York: The Macmillan Co., 1944.

KOEPKE, C. A. *Plant Production Control*. 2d ed. New York: John Wiley & Sons, Inc., 1949.

KOOPMANS, T. C. *Activity Analysis of Production and Allocation*. New York: John Wiley & Sons, Inc., 1951.

LEHOCZKY, P. N. *Alignment Charts: Their Construction and Use*. Columbus, Ohio: The Ohio State University Engineering Experiment Station, 1947.

Laboratory Design for Handling Radioactive Materials. Building Research Advisory Board. Washington, D. C.: National Research Council—National Academy of Sciences, 1952.

LANG, THEODORE (ed.). *Cost Accountants' Handbook.* New York: The Ronald Press Co., 1944.

LATIMER, M. W. *Guaranteed Wages; Report to the President of the Advisory Board.* Washington, D. C.: United States Government Printing Office, 1947.

LEVINSON, H. C. *The Science of Chance; from Probability to Statistics.* New York: Rinehart & Co., Inc., 1950.

LICHTNER, W. O. *Time Study and Job Analysis.* New York: The Ronald Press Co., Inc., 1921.

Light Metals

LUCKIESH, MATTHEW. *Light, Vision, and Seeing.* Princeton, N. J.: D. Van Nostrand Co., Inc., 1944.

LYLE, PHILIP. *Regression Analysis of Production Costs and Factory Operations.* 2d ed. Edinburgh: Oliver & Boyd, Ltd., 1946.

LYTLE, C. W. *Job Evaluation Methods.* 2d ed. New York: The Ronald Press Co., 1954.

LYTLE, C. W. *Wage Incentive Methods.* Rev. ed. New York: The Ronald Press Co., 1942.

Machine Design

Machinery

MACNIECE, E. H. *Production Forecasting, Planning and Control.* New York: John Wiley & Sons, Inc., 1951.

Management Science

MANN, H. B. *Analysis and Design of Experiments; Analysis of Variance and Analysis of Variance Designs.* New York: Dover Publications, Inc., 1949.

Manufacturer's Record

MAYNARD, H. B., STEGEMERTEN, G. J., *et al. Methods-Time Measurement.* New York: McGraw-Hill Book Co., Inc., 1948.

McCORMICK, C. P. *The Power of People.* New York: Harper & Bros., 1949.

Mechanical Engineering

MEES, C. E., and LEERMAKERS, J. A. *The Organization of Industrial Scientific Research.* 2d ed. New York: McGraw-Hill Book Co., Inc., 1950.

MELNITSKY, BENJAMIN. *Management of Industrial Inventory.* Philadelphia: Chilton Co., 1954.

MICHELSON, L. C. *Industrial Inspection Methods.* Rev. ed. New York: Harper & Bros., 1950.

Mill and Factory

Modern Materials Handling

MOLINA, E. E. *Poisson's Exponential Binomial Limit.* Princeton, N. J.: D. Van Nostrand Co., Inc., 1942.

MOONEY, J. D. *Principles of Organization.* Rev. ed. New York: Harper & Bros., 1947.

MOORE, F. G. *Production Control.* New York: McGraw-Hill Book Co., Inc., 1951.

MORROW, R. L. *Motion Economy and Work Measurement.* New York: The Ronald Press Co., 1957.

MUNDEL, MARVIN. *Motion and Time Study, Principles and Practice.* 2d ed. Englewood Cliffs, N. J.: Prentice-Hall, Inc., 1955.

MUTHER, RICHARD. *Practical Plant Layout.* New York: McGraw-Hill Book Co., Inc., 1955.

MUTHER, RICHARD. *Production-Line Technique.* New York: McGraw-Hill Book Co., Inc., 1944.

N.A.A. Bulletin (Formerly *N.A.C.A. Bulletin*)

NADLER, GERALD. *Motion and Time Study.* New York: McGraw-Hill Book Co., Inc., 1955.

National Bureau of Standards Handbook 42, Safe Handling of Radioactive Isotopes. Washington, D. C.: National Bureau of Standards, 1949.

National Fire Protection Association Quarterly

NIEBEL, B. W. *Motion and Time Study.* Homewood, Ill.: Richard D. Irwin, Inc., 1955.

NORTHRUP, R. B. *Handling Material Accidents, Their Cause and Prevention.* New York: New York State Department of Labor, 1933.

Operations Research with Special Reference to Non-Military Applications. Committee on Operations Research. Washington, D. C.: National Research Council—National Academy of Sciences, 1951.

Pallets and Palletization. Washington, D. C.: National Wooden Pallet Manufacturers Association, 1954.

PEARSON, E. S., and HARTLEY, H. O. (eds.). *Biometrika Tables for Statisticians.* Vol. 1. London: Cambridge University Press, 1954.

Personnel

Planning, Controlling and Accounting for Maintenance. New York: National Association of Accountants, 1956.

PRENTISS, A. M. *Civil Defense in Modern War.* New York: McGraw-Hill Book Co., Inc., 1951.

PRESGRAVE, RALPH. *The Dynamics of Time Study.* Toronto: The University of Toronto Press, 1944.

Product Engineering

Production

Public Administration Review

Purchasing

RAUTENSTRAUCH, WALTER, and VILLERS, RAYMOND. *The Economics of Industrial Management.* New York: Funk & Wagnalls Co., 1949.

RITCHIE, W. E. *Production and Inventory Control.* New York: The Ronald Press Co., 1951.

RUBENSTEIN, A. H. (ed.). *Coordination, Control, and Financing of Industrial Research.* New York: King's Crown Press, 1955.

RYAN, T. A. *Work and Effort.* New York: The Ronald Press Co., 1947.

SCHMID, C. F. *Handbook of Graphic Presentation.* New York: The Ronald Press Co., 1954.

Scientific Monthly, The

SHANNON, C. E., and WEAVER, WARREN. *The Mathematical Theory of Communication.* Urbana, Ill.: University of Illinois Press, 1949.

SHARPIE, R. H., et al. (eds.). *Proceedings of the International Conference on the Peaceful Uses of Atomic Energy.* 16 vols. New York: United Nations, 1956.

SHAW, A. G. *The Purpose and Practice of Motion Study.* London: Harlequin Press Co., Ltd., 1952.

SHELDON, OLIVER. *The Philosophy of Management.* London: Sir Isaac Pitman & Sons, Ltd., 1923.

SHUBIN, J. A., and MADEHEIM, HUXLEY. *Plant Layout; Developing and Improving Manufacturing Plants.* Englewood Cliffs, N. J.: Prentice-Hall, Inc., 1951.

SHUMARD, F. W. *A Primer of Time Study.* New York: McGraw-Hill Book Co., Inc., 1940.

SIMONDS, H. R., and BREGMAN, ADOLPH. *Finishing Metal Products.* 2d ed. New York: McGraw-Hill Book Co., Inc., 1946.

SPEAR, M. E. *Charting Statistics.* New York: McGraw-Hill Book Co., Inc., 1952.

SPECTHRIE, S. W. *Industrial Accounting.* Englewood Cliffs, N. J.: Prentice-Hall, Inc., 1942.

SPRIEGEL, W. R., and LANSBURGH, R. H. *Industrial Management.* 5th ed. New York: John Wiley & Sons, Inc., 1955.

STANIAR, WILLIAM. *Plant Engineering Handbook.* New York: McGraw-Hill Book Co., Inc., 1950.

Steel

SYLVESTER, L. A. (ed.). *The Handbook of Advanced Time-Motion Study.* New York: Funk & Wagnalls Co., 1950.

Taxes—The Tax Magazine

Tech Engineering News

TERBORGH, GEORGE. *Dynamic Equipment Policy.* New York: McGraw-Hill Book Co., Inc., 1949.

TERBORGH, GEORGE. *MAPI Replacement Manual.* Washington, D. C.: Machinery and Allied Products Institute, 1950.

THOMPSON, J. E. *Inspection, Organization and Methods.* New York: McGraw-Hill Book Co., Inc., 1950.

Time and Motion Study

Tool Engineer

TREFETHEN, F. N., and McCLOSKEY, J. F. *Operations Research for Management.* New York: Oxford University Press, 1955.

Trends in Industrial Research and Patent Practices. New York: National Association of Manufacturers, 1948.

U.S. News and World Report

VERNON, H. M. *Industrial Fatigue and Efficiency.* New York: E. P. Dutton & Co., Inc., 1921.

VON NEUMANN, JOHN, and MORGENSTERN, OSKAR. *Theory of Games and Economic Behavior.* Rev. ed. Princeton, N. J.: Princeton University Press, 1955.

VORIS, WILLIAM. *Production Control; Text and Cases.* Homewood, Ill.: Richard D. Irwin, Inc., 1956.

WALKER, C. R., and GUEST, R. H. *The Man on the Assembly Line.* Cambridge, Mass.: Harvard University Press, 1952.

Welding Handbook. New York: The American Welding Society, 1950.

Western Machinery and Steel World

WESTING, J. H., and FINE, I. V. *Industrial Purchasing.* New York: John Wiley & Sons, Inc., 1955.

WHITEHEAD, A. N. *Science and the Modern World.* Baltimore: Penguin Books, Inc., 1938.

WIENER, NORBERT. *The Human Use of Human Beings.* New York: Houghton Mifflin Co., 1954.

WILLIAMS, CLYDE (ed.). *Proceedings—8th Annual Conference on the Administration of Research.* New York: New York University Press, 1955.

WILSON, E. B., JR. *An Introduction to Scientific Research.* New York: McGraw-Hill Book Co., Inc., 1952.

WILSON, F. W. (ed.). *Tool Engineers Handbook.* New York: McGraw-Hill Book Co., Inc., 1949.

WIXON, RUFUS (ed.). *Accountants' Handbook.* 4th ed. New York: The Ronald Press Co., 1956.

WULFF, JOHN, TAYLOR, H. F., and SHALER, A. J. *Metallurgy for Engineers; Casting, Welding, and Working.* New York: John Wiley & Sons, Inc., 1952.

YASEEN, L. C. *Plant Location.* New York: American Research Council, 1956.

ZALEZNIK, ABRAHAM. *Worker Satisfaction and Development.* Cambridge, Mass.: Harvard University Press, 1956.

Acknowledgment is also made for the use of materials from bulletins, reports, transactions, and standards published by each of the following professional, governmental, and commercial organizations:

AMERICAN INSTITUTE OF ELECTRICAL ENGINEERS (AIEE)
AMERICAN INSTITUTE OF INDUSTRIAL ENGINEERS (AIIE)
AMERICAN MANAGEMENT ASSOCIATION (AMA)
AMERICAN MATERIAL HANDLING SOCIETY (AMHS)
AMERICAN RESEARCH COUNCIL
AMERICAN SOCIETY OF MECHANICAL ENGINEERS (ASME)
AMERICAN SOCIETY OF METALS (ASM)
AMERICAN SOCIETY FOR TESTING MATERIALS (ASTM)

AMERICAN STANDARDS ASSOCIATION, INC. (ASA)
AMERICAN WELDING SOCIETY (AWS)
ASSOCIATION OF AMERICAN RAILROADS
ATOMIC ENERGY COMMISSION (AEC)
AUTOMOBILE MANUFACTURERS ASSOCIATION
ILLUMINATING ENGINEERING SOCIETY
INDUSTRIAL HEALTH RESEARCH BOARD
INDUSTRIAL MANAGEMENT SOCIETY
INDUSTRIAL TRUCK ASSOCIATION (ITA, formerly Electric Industrial Truck Association)
INSTITUTE OF MANAGEMENT SCIENCES
INSTITUTE OF RADIO ENGINEERS (IRE)
MACHINERY AND ALLIED PRODUCTS INSTITUTE (MAPI)
MATERIAL HANDLING INSTITUTE, THE (MHI)
NATIONAL ACADEMY OF SCIENCES–NATIONAL RESEARCH COUNCIL (NAS–NRC)
NATIONAL ASSOCIATION OF ACCOUNTANTS (N.A.A., formerly National Association of Cost Accountants)
NATIONAL ASSOCIATION OF MANUFACTURERS (NAM)
NATIONAL BUREAU OF STANDARDS (NBS)
NATIONAL FIRE PROTECTION ASSOCIATION (NFPA)
NATIONAL INDUSTRIAL CONFERENCE BOARD (NICB)
NATIONAL SAFETY COUNCIL (NSC)
NATIONAL TOOL BUILDERS ASSOCIATION
NATIONAL WOODEN PALLET MANUFACTURERS ASSOCIATION (NWPMA)
NUCLEAR ENERGY AND SCIENCE CONGRESS
PRESIDENT'S ECONOMIC ADVISORY BOARD
SOCIETY FOR THE ADVANCEMENT OF MANAGEMENT (SAM)
U.S. ARMY ORDNANCE CORPS
U.S. DEPARTMENT OF COMMERCE
U.S. DEPARTMENT OF DEFENSE
U.S. DEPARTMENT OF LABOR
U.S. NAVY BUREAU OF SUPPLIES AND ACCOUNTS
U.S. NAVY OFFICE OF NAVAL RESEARCH

AMERICAN STANDARDS ASSOCIATION, INC. (ASA)
AMERICAN WELDING SOCIETY (AWS)
ASSOCIATION OF AMERICAN RAILROADS
(AMERICAN RAILWAY ENGINEERING? AREA)
AUTOMOTIVE MANUFACTURERS ASSOCIATION
ILLUMINATING ENGINEERING SOCIETY
INDUSTRIAL DIAMOND RESEARCH BOARD
INDUSTRIAL MANAGEMENT SOCIETY
INDUSTRIAL TRUCK ASSOCIATION, (ITA, formerly Electric Industrial Truck Association)
INSTITUTE OF MAKERS OF EXPLOSIVES
INSTRUMENT SOCIETY OF AMERICA (ISA)
MACHINERY AND ALLIED PRODUCTS INSTITUTE (MAPI)
MILITARY HANDBOOK 17, MIL-HDBK
NATIONAL ACADEMY OF SCIENCES-NATIONAL RESEARCH COUNCIL (NAS-NRC)
NATIONAL ASSOCIATION OF ACCOUNTANTS (N.A.A., formerly National Association of Cost Accountants)
NATIONAL ASSOCIATION OF MANUFACTURERS (NAM)
NATIONAL BUREAU OF STANDARDS (NBS)
NATIONAL FIRE PROTECTION ASSOCIATION (NFPA)
NATIONAL LUBRICATING GREASE INSTITUTE (NLGI)
NATIONAL SAFETY COUNCIL (NSC)
NATIONAL TOOL BUILDERS ASSOCIATION
NATIONAL TOOL, DIE AND PRECISION MACHINING ASSOCIATION (NTDPMA)
PORTLAND CEMENT ASSOCIATION
PNEUMATIC EQUIPMENT ADVISORY BOARD
SOCIETY FOR THE ADVANCEMENT OF MANAGEMENT (SAM)
U.S. ARMY ORDNANCE CORPS
U.S. DEPARTMENT OF COMMERCE
U.S. DEPARTMENT OF DEFENSE
U.S. DEPARTMENT OF LABOR
U.S. NAVY BUREAU OF SUPPLIES AND ACCOUNTS
U.S. NAVY OFFICE OF NAVAL RESEARCH

INDEX

(Boldface numbers, followed by a dot, refer to sections; lightface numbers following are the pages of the section.)

A

A-B-C Control Method, For materials control, 4.31–32
  Inventory analysis, 4.31
  Quantity of reserve stock, 4.31
Abrasives
  Disks for sawing machines, 20.48
  Used to clean or finish metal, 20.51
Acceptance
  By attribute inspection, 8.53
  By variables inspection, 8.65
Accidents (See also "Safety")
  Accident prevention manual (National Safety Council), 25.7
  Analyzing causes of, 25.32–34
  Due to poor lighting, 12.111–12
  Seasonal pattern, 12.111–12
Accomplishment, Standard units of, 13.13
Accounting
  Department
    Invoices handled by, 5.65–67
    Receiving reports sent to, 4.47
  Job-costing procedures, research projects in, 17.24
  Materials issue and stores credit slips, 4.51–52
  Operations research and, 18.37–38
  Purchase orders contain accounting information, 5.56
  Research and development costs, 17.24
  Return on investment, 22.5–6
  Standard cost system, 4.22
Accuracy
  Motion-time standard data, 12.69–70
  Rating and leveling methods, 12.36
  Standard time data, 12.59–60
  Statistical sampling, 12.8
Activity Plateau, Standards and, 15.10
Adhesives, 20.40–41
  Adherents, 20.40–41
  Alloys, 20.41
  Elastomeric, 20.41
  Glue, 20.40
  Thermoplastic, 20.41
  Thermosetting, 20.41
Administration, Definition, 1.3
Advertising Budget
  Allocation problems and, 18.33
  Distribution of, 18.33
Aerial Tramways, Types of, 23.45
Agents, Purchasing, 5.11–12
  Assistant, 5.12
Air-Acetylene Welding, 20.31
Air-Activated Gravity Conveyors, 23.54–56
Air Communications System, Operations research and, 18.34
Air Conditioning
  Cooling loads, computation of, 19.86–89
    Components, 19.86–88
      Latent load, 19.87
      Sensible load, 19.86–87
    Design conditions, 19.87
    Equipment and lighting loads, 19.88–89

Air Conditioning (*Continued*)
  Cooling loads, computation of (*Continued*)
    Heat transmission through glass areas, 19.88
    Occupant loads, 19.88
    Solar load estimates, 19.87–88
    Ventilation and infiltration loads, 19.88
  Equipment, 19.89–91
    Condensing equipment, 19.90
    Direct-expansion and chilled-water systems, 19.89–90
    Heat pumps, 19.90–91
    Reciprocating and centrifugal compressors, 19.89
    Unit and central systems, 19.89
  Psychrometric data, 19.78–86
    Calculation by chart, 19.86
    Calculation by table, 19.83–86
    Definitions, 19.78, 19.83
    Thermodynamic properties of moist air, 19.79–81, 19.82, 19.83
  Systems, 19.77–78
    Maintenance methods, 24.43
Air-Conveyable Materials, 23.55
Air Distribution Devices, Heating and ventilation, 19.71
Air Filters, Heating and ventilation
  Air washers, 19.76–77
  Dry filters, 19.75
  Electronic filters, 19.76
  Viscous impingement filters, 19.75–76
Air Gages, 7.43, 7.44
  Circuit, flow type, 7.43
  Typical setups, 7.44
Air Heating Coils, Heating and ventilation, 19.71–72
Air Rights, Of a building, 23.1
Air Transports, Materials handling equipment, 23.36, 23.73
Air Washers, Heating and ventilation, 19.76–77
Aisles
  Car-aisle storage principle, 23.8, 23.10
  Color contrast painting, 19.107
  In storerooms, 6.10, 6.12
    Types of, 6.12
  In warehouses to permit handling materials, 23.6–7
  Location of, 19.35
Alignment Charts, 12.62 (See also "Nomographic Charts")
Alkali Cleaners, For cleaning metal, 20.52
Allocation Method
  Of materials control, 4.18–23
  Procedure, 4.19
  Record form, 4.19–21
Allocation Problems, Examples, 18.32–33
Allowance
  Definition of, 7.24
  Finish, 20.2
  In inspection, 7.2
  Shrinkage, 20.2
Allowances
  Apprentice (See "Learners' Allowances")

1

Allowances (*Continued*)
For an incentive operation, **12·75**
Spoilage and stock, **3·3**
Types, **15·50**
Wage incentive administration and, **15·14**
Work measurement and time study, **12·40-45**
Delay, avoidable and unavoidable, **12·40-41**, **12·44-45**
Determination of, **12·42**
Fatigue, **12·41**
Interruption studies, **12·40**, **12·42-45**
Computation of allowance, **12·44-45**
Data obtained, **12·42-44**
Observation and analysis sheet, **12·43**
Summary sheet, **12·44**
Personal and delay, **12·41**
Spoilage and rework, **12·41**
Training, **12·41**
Alloys
Adhesive, **20·41**
Die casting, **20·5**
Aluminum
Methods of melting, **20·2**
Protective coatings for, **20·55**
American Gage Design Standards, **7·22**
Amplifying Systems, Gages and measuring instruments, **7·40-43**
Analog Computers (See "Computers")
Analyses
Of work (See "Work, Analysis of")
Operations analysis, **12·1-12**
Original equipment analysis, **22·6-9**
Capitalized cost method, **22·9**
Differential yield method, **22·8**
Methods of, **22·7-9**
Minimum annual cost method, **22·9**
Retooling for new manufacturing, **22·6-7**
Replacement, **22·10-22**
Storeskeeping
Circle charting, **6·8**
Queueing theory, **6·8**
Sequence analysis, **6·8**
Variance and covariance, **18·19**
Analyst, Time study, **12·21**
Angle of Repose, Of dry, pulverized material, **23·54**
Anodizing Process, **20·55**
Appliances
Material inventory policies, **4·5**
Production control, **3·10-11**
Apprentice Allowances (See "Learners' Allowances")
Apprentices, Financial and nonfinancial incentives for, **15·80-83**
Apron Conveyors, **23·42-43**
Apron Space, Truck terminals, **23·69-70**
Arc Welding, **20·25-29**
Atomic hydrogen, **20·26-28**
Carbon electrode arc welding, **20·30**
Electrode classification chart, **20·27**
Impregnated tape metal, **20·26**
Inert-gas-shielded metal, **20·28**, **20·29**
Shielded-stud, **20·29-30**
Submerged, **20·28-29**
Unshielded metal electrode, **20·30**
With coated electrodes, **20·26**
Area Allocation (See "Plant Layout")
Arithmetic Mean, Measures of central value and, **9·9-10**
Arm Elevators, For conveying packages, **23·40**
Arm Motions, **12·77-79**, **12·80**
Normal working area for, **13·35**
Army Ordnance Standard, Gage tolerance tables, **7·32-33**, **7·34-35**

Artificial Lighting, **19·96-98**
Sources of, **19·97-98**
Fluorescent lighting, **19·97**
Mercury vapor lamps, **19·98**
Asbestos, Laminated plastics, **20·63**
Assembly Methods, **20·35-41**
Adhesives, **20·40-41**
Alloys, **20·41**
Elastomeric, **20·41**
Glue, **20·40**
Thermoplastic, **20·41**
Thermosetting, **20·41**
Comparison of average times, **9·33-34**
Important factors in, **20·35**
Riveting and staking, **20·37-39**
Screws and bolts, **20·35-37**
American standard and special bolts, **20·38**
American standard and special screws, **20·37**
Standard screw thread forms, **20·36**
Seaming and curling, **20·39-40**
Shrink fit, **20·40**
Stapling, tacking, and stitching, **20·39**
Typical seams used in the manufacturing of light-gage metal containers, **20·40**
Assembly Operations
Application of punched-card system to, **3·56-61**
Assembly order master form, **3·80**
Charts, **3·19**
Showing sequence of operations, **3·19**
Line setting ticket, **3·76**, **3·78**
Simultaneous operations and, **2·23**, **2·25**
Subassembly order system, **3·83**
Written standard procedure, **13·48**
Assignment, Work, **12·88-94**
Automatic presses, **12·88-91**
Automatic screw machines, **12·91-94**
Atomic Radiation, Process research and, **17·7**
Attention Time and Interference, **12·86**
Audit, Of quality control, **8·11**
Auditing, Invoices, **5·67**
Authority
Acceptance of, **1·5**
Aspects of, **1·5**
Formal, **1·5**
Functional, **1·5**
Personal, **1·5**
Definition, **1·5**
Delegated, **1·5**
Direct, **1·5**
Levels of, **1·7-8**
Cross relationships and, **1·23-24**
Line of, **1·7**
Line organization and, **1·10-11**
Principle of, **1·6**
Automatic Data Processing, **3·70-72**
Electronic computers, **3·70-72**
Loading and scheduling, **3·71-72**
Sales estimates, **3·70**
Automatic Factory, Computer functions and, **16·32-34**
Automatic Gages, **7·44-48**
Final acceptance inspection, **7·47**, **7·48**
In-process control, **7·45-46**
Post-process control, **7·46-48**
Automatic Machines, Time studies of operation of, **12·81-87**
Automation
Conversion to, **19·33**
Effective initiation and use of, **14·7**
Motion and methods study aided in the development of, **13·2**
Plant layout and, **19·33**, **19·34**
Process research, **17·6-7**